SCHOLARSHIPS, FELLOWSHIPS AND LOANS

ISSN 1058-5699

SCHOLARSHIPS, FELLOWSHIPS AND LOANS

A GUIDE TO EDUCATION-RELATED FINANCIAL AID PROGRAMS FOR STUDENTS AND PROFESSIONALS

Volume Three

Sponsors and Their Scholarships: U–Z and Indexes

Thirty-Fourth Edition

GALE
CENGAGE Learning

Farmington Hills, Mich • San Francisco • New York • Waterville, Maine
Meriden, Conn • Mason, Ohio • Chicago

Scholarships, Fellowships and Loans, 34th Edition

Project Editor: Bohdan Romaniuk

Editorial Support Services: Wayne Fong

Composition and Electronic Prepress: Gary Leach

Manufacturing: Rita Wimberley

© 2017 Gale, Cengage Learning

ALL RIGHTS RESERVED. No part of this work covered by the copyright herein may be reproduced or distributed in any form or by any means, except as permitted by U.S. copyright law, without the prior written permission of the copyright owner.

This publication is a creative work fully protected by all applicable copyright laws, as well as by misappropriation, trade secret, unfair competition, and other applicable laws. The authors and editors of this work have added value to the underlying factual material herein through one or more of the following: unique and original selection, coordination, expression, arrangement, and classification of the information.

For product information and technology assistance, contact us at
Gale Customer Support, 1-800-877-4253.
For permission to use material from this text or product, submit all requests online at www.cengage.com/permissions.
Further permissions questions can be emailed to
permissionrequest@cengage.com

While every effort has been made to ensure the reliability of the information presented in this publication, Gale, a part of Cengage Learning,does not guarantee the accuracy of the data contained herein. Gale accepts no payment for listing; and inclusion in the publication of any organization, agency, institution, publication, service, or individual does not imply endorsement of the editors or publisher. Errors brought to the attention of the publisher, and verified to the satisfaction of the publisher, will be corrected in future editions.

EDITORIAL DATA PRIVACY POLICY: Does this product contain information about you as an individual? If so, for more information about our editorial data privacy policies, please see our Privacy Statement at www.gale.cengage.com.

Gale
27500 Drake Rd.
Farmington Hills, MI, 48331-3535

ISBN-13: 978-1-4103-1886-2 (3 vol. set)
ISBN-13: 978-1-4103-1887-9 (vol. 1)
ISBN-13: 978-1-4103-1888-6 (vol. 2)
ISBN-13: 978-1-4103-1889-3 (vol. 3)

ISSN 1058-5699

This title is also available as an e-book.
ISBN-13: 978-1-4103-1902-9
Contact your Gale sales representative for ordering information.

Printed in the United States of America
1 2 3 4 5   20 19 18 17 16

Contents

Volume 1

Highlights	vii
Introduction	ix
User's Guide	xiii
Federal Programs	xvii
AmeriCorps	xix
State Higher Education Agencies	xxi
Abbreviations	xxv
Sponsors and Their Scholarships: A-H	1

Volume 2

Highlights	vii
Introduction	ix
User's Guide	xiii
Federal Programs	xvii
AmeriCorps	xix
State Higher Education Agencies	xxi
Abbreviations	xxv
Sponsors and Their Scholarships: I-T	693

Volume 3

Highlights	vii
Introduction	ix
User's Guide	xiii
Federal Programs	xvii
AmeriCorps	xix
State Higher Education Agencies	xxi
Abbreviations	xxv
Sponsors and Their Scholarships: U-Z	1337
Field of Study Index	1469
Legal Residence Index	1571
Place of Study Index	1647
Special Recipient Index	1721
Sponsor and Scholarship Index	1745

Highlights

This edition of *Scholarships, Fellowships and Loans (SFL)* provides access to nearly 8,000 sources of education-related financial aid for students and professionals at all levels. *SFL*'s scope ranges from undergraduate and vocational/technical education through post-doctoral and professional studies. Students and others interested in education funding will find comprehensive information on a variety of programs in all educational areas, including:

- Architecture
- Area and Ethnic Studies
- Art
- Business
- Communications
- Computer Science
- Education
- Engineering
- Health Science
- Humanities
- Industrial Arts
- Language
- Law
- Literature
- Liberal Arts
- Library Science
- Life Science
- Medicine
- Mathematics
- Performing Arts
- Philosophy
- Physical Sciences
- Social Sciences
- Theology and Religion

SFL Provides Detailed Information on Awards

SFL provides all the information students need to complete their financial aid search. Entries include: administering organization name and address; purpose of award; qualifications and restrictions; selection criteria; award amount and number of awards granted; application details and deadlines; detailed contact information.

Additionally, look for the section on federal financial aid following the User's Guide for a quick summary of programs sponsored by the U.S. government, as well as information on the AmeriCorps program. There is also a section that lists higher education agencies by state.

Five Indexes Allow Quick and Easy Access to Awards

Whether you are a high school student looking for basic undergraduate financial aid, a scientist investigating research grants, or a professional attempting to finance additional career training, SFL aids your search by providing access to awards through the following indexes:

Field of Study Index categorizes awards by very specific subject fields.

Legal Resident Index targets awards restricted to applicants from specific geographic locations.

Place of Study Index provides a handy guide to awards granted for study within specific states, provinces, or countries.

Special Recipient Index lists awards that are reserved for candidates who qualify by virtue of their gender, organizational affiliation, minority or ethnic background.

Sponsor and Scholarship Index provides a complete alphabetical listing of all awards and their administering organizations.

Catchwords

SFL includes catchwords of the organization on each corresponding page, to aid the user in finding a particular entry.

Introduction

As we make our way through difficult economic times, there is a growing need for a more highly-trained and educated work force. From political discussions and debates to reports from future-oriented think tanks and other groups, there is agreement that postsecondary education is a key to success. Yet how are students and their families to afford the already high (and constantly rising) cost of higher education? Searching for financial aid can be very tedious and difficult, even though hundreds of millions of dollars in aid reportedly go unclaimed every year.

Scholarships, Fellowships and Loans (SFL), the most comprehensive single directory of education-related financial aid available, can save you time, effort, and money by helping you to focus your search within the largest pool of awards and avoid pursuing aid for which you do not qualify. In most cases, the detailed descriptions contain enough information to allow you to decide if a particular scholarship is right for you to begin the application process. *SFL* lists nearly 8,000 major awards available to U.S. and Canadian students for study throughout the world. Included are:

- scholarships, fellowships, and grants, which do not require repayment;
- loans, which require repayment either monetarily or through service;
- scholarship loans, which are scholarships that become loans if the recipient does not comply with the award's terms;
- internships and work study programs, which provide training, work experience, and (usually) monetary compensation; and
- awards and prizes that recognize excellence in a particular field.

Also included are other forms of assistance offered by associations, corporations, religious groups, fraternal organizations, foundations, and other private organizations and companies. *SFL* includes a broad representation of government-funded awards at the national and state levels, as well as a representative sampling of lesser-known and more narrowly focused awards, such as those of a strictly local nature or programs sponsored by small organizations. Financial aid programs administered and funded by individual colleges or universities are not included in *SFL*. Both need- and merit-based awards are included. Competition-based awards and prizes are included when they offer funds that support study or research and are intended to encourage further educational or professional growth.

Students of All Types Can Benefit

Traditional students as well as those returning to school, non-degree learners, those in need of retraining, and established professionals can use the funding sources listed in *SFL* for formal and non-formal programs of study at all levels:

- high school
- vocational
- undergraduate
- graduate
- postgraduate
- doctorate
- postdoctorate
- professional development

Content and Arrangement

Scholarships, Fellowships and Loans is organized into a main section containing descriptive listings of award programs and their administering organizations, and five indexes.

The main section, Sponsors and Their Scholarships, is arranged alphabetically by name of administering organization. Entries for each organization's awards appear immediately following the entry on the organization. Each entry contains detailed contact and descriptive information, often providing users with all the information they need to make a decision about applying.

INTRODUCTION

The indexes provide a variety of specific access points to the information contained within the organization and award listings, allowing users to easily identify awards of interest.

Practical Tips on How to Find Financial Aid

While there are many education-related financial aid programs for students of all types and study levels, the competition for available funds is steadily increasing. You will improve the likelihood of meeting your financial aid goals if you:

- carefully assess your particular needs and preferences;
- consider any special circumstances or conditions that might qualify you for aid; and
- carefully research available aid programs.

The following pages list some general guidelines for making your way through the search and application process.

Start Your Search Early

Any search for financial aid is likely to be more successful if you begin early. If you allow enough time to complete all of the necessary steps, you will be more likely to identify a wide variety of awards for which you qualify with plenty of time to meet their application deadlines. This can increase your chances of obtaining aid.

Some experts recommend that you start this process up to two years before you think you will need financial assistance. While you will probably be able to obtain some support if you allow less time, you might overlook some important opportunities.

Some awards are given on a first-come, first-served basis, and if you do not file your application early enough, the aid will already be distributed. In many cases, if your application is late you will not be considered, even if you have met all of the other criteria.

An early start will also allow you to identify organizations that offer scholarships to members or participants, such as student or professional associations, in time to establish membership or otherwise meet their qualifying criteria.

Assess Your Needs and Goals

The intended recipients for financial aid programs and the purposes for which awards are established can vary greatly. Some programs are open to almost anyone, while others are restricted to very specific categories of recipients. The majority of awards fall somewhere in between. Your first step in seeking financial aid is to establish your basic qualifications as a potential recipient. The following are some general questions to ask yourself to help define your educational and financial needs and goals:

- What kinds of colleges or universities interest me?
- What careers or fields of study interest me?
- Do I plan to earn a degree?
- Am I only interested in financial aid that is a gift, or will I consider a loan or work study?
- In what parts of the country am I willing to live and study?

Leave No Stone Unturned

After you have defined your goals, the next step is to identify any special factors that might make you eligible for aid programs offered only to a restricted group. Examine this area carefully, and remember that even minor or unlikely connections may be worth checking. The most common qualifications and restrictions involve:

- citizenship
- community involvement or volunteer work
- creative or professional accomplishment
- employer
- financial need
- gender
- merit or academic achievement
- military or veteran status
- organization membership (such as a union, association, or fraternal group)
- place of residence
- race or ethnic group
- religious affiliation

With many awards, you may be eligible if your spouse, parents, or guardians meet certain criteria by status or affiliations. You should be aware of your parents' affiliations even if you don't live with one (or both) of them, or if they are deceased. And given enough lead time, it may be possible for you (or your parents) to join a particular organization, or establish necessary residence, in time for you to be eligible for certain funds.

Contact Financial Aid Offices

Most colleges, universities, and other educational institutions offer their own financial aid programs. Their financial aid offices may also have information on privately sponsored awards that are specifically designated for students at those institutions. Contact their respective financial aid offices to request applications and details for all of the aid programs they sponsor and/or administer.

Use SFL to Identify Awards Sponsored by Private Organizations and Corporations

Scholarships, Fellowships and Loans (SFL) is the most comprehensive single source of information on major education-related financial aid programs sponsored and administered by private organizations and companies for use by students and professionals. Using *SFL* as a starting point, you can quickly compile a substantial list of financial aid programs for which you may qualify by following these simple steps:

- Compile an initial list of awards offered in your field of study.
- If you have already chosen your field of study, look in the Field of Study Index to find listings of awards grouped by more precise disciplines (such as Accounting or Journalism). If you choose this approach, your initial list is likely to be shorter but more focused. Eliminate awards that cannot be used at your chosen level of study or that do not meet your financial needs. Are you an undergraduate only interested in scholarships? Are you a graduate student willing to participate in an internship or take out a loan? Consult the User's Guide to determine which of the study level categories and award types apply to your particular situation. Both indexes clearly note the study levels at which awards may be used. The Field of Study Index also lists the type of financial aid provided.
- Eliminate awards by citizenship, residence, and other restrictions (minority status, ethnic background, gender, organizational affiliation) that make you ineligible.
- If your list is based on the Field of Study Index, you will need to look under the section for qualifications in each descriptive listing to see what requirements apply.
- Read the descriptive listings for each of the award programs left on your list. The descriptive listings should contain all the information you need to decide if you qualify and should apply for each of the awards on your list.

Expand Your List of Possibilities

If you are willing to take the initiative and do a little extra digging, you should be able to add to your list of institution-related and privately sponsored programs. In most cases, the best possibilities fall into these two areas:

Government Agencies and Programs. The Sponsors and Their Scholarships main section includes a broad representation of award programs sponsored by federal and state governments. Since these listings are not meant to be exhaustive, you should be able to identify additional programs by contacting the government agencies responsible for education-related financial aid programs listed here. On the federal level, contact the U.S. Department of Education at 400 Maryland Ave., SW, Washington, DC 20202, or on their website at http://www.ed.gov, for up-to-date information on U.S. Government award programs. For a broad overview of federal financial aid, consult the Federal Programs section. Similarly, you may contact your state department of education for details on what is offered in your particular state. Please see the State Higher Education Agencies section for state-by-state listings.

Local Sources of Awards. A surprisingly large number of financial aid programs are sponsored by small and/or local organizations. *SFL* contains a representative sampling of such programs to encourage you to seek similar programs in your own geographic area. High school guidance counselors are often aware of local programs as well, and they can usually tell you how to get in touch with the sponsoring or administering organizations. Local newspapers are also rich sources of information on financial aid programs.

Allow Enough Time for the Application Process

The amount of time needed to complete the application process for individual awards will vary, so you should pay close attention to application deadlines. Some awards carry application deadlines that require you to apply a year or more before your studies will begin. In general, allow plenty of time to:

- Write for official applications. You may not be considered for some awards unless you apply with the correct forms.
- Read all instructions carefully.
- Take note of application deadlines.
- Accurately and completely file all required supporting material, such as essays, school transcripts, and financial records. If you fail to answer certain questions, you may be disqualified even if you are a worthy candidate.
- Give references enough time to submit their recommendations. Teachers in particular get many requests for letters of recommendation and should be given as much advance notice as possible.

Make Sure You Qualify

Finally, don't needlessly submerge yourself in paperwork. If you find you don't qualify for a particular award, don't apply for it. Instead, use your time and energy to find and apply for more likely sources of aid.

Available in Electronic Format

Scholarships, Fellowships and Loans is also available online as part of the Gale Directory Library and the Gale Virual Reference Library. For more information, call 1-800-877-GALE.

Comments and Suggestions Welcome

We welcome reader suggestions regarding new and previously unlisted organizations and awards. Please send your suggestions to:

Scholarships, Fellowships and Loans
Gale, Cengage Learning
27500 Drake Rd.
Farmington Hills, MI 48331-3535
Phone: (248) 699-4253
Toll-free: 800-347-4253
Fax: (248) 699-8070
Email: Bob.Romaniuk@cengage.com

User's Guide

Scholarships, Fellowships and Loans is comprised of a main section containing descriptive listings on award programs and their administering organizations, and five indexes that aid users in identifying relevant information. Each of these sections is described in detail below.

Sponsors and Their Scholarships

SFL contains two types of descriptive listings:

- brief entries on the organizations that sponsor or administer specific award programs
- descriptive entries on the award programs themselves

Entries are arranged alphabetically by administering organization; awards administered by each organization follow that organization's listings. Entries contain detailed contact and descriptive information. Users are strongly encouraged to read the descriptions carefully and pay particular attention to the various eligibility requirements before applying for awards.

The following sample organization and award entries illustrate the kind of information that is or might be included in these entries. Each item of information is preceded by a number, and is explained in the paragraph with the same number on the following pages.

Sample Entry

▌1▐ 3445
▌2▐ Microscopy Society of America
▌3▐ 4 Barlows Landing Rd., Ste. 8 Woods Hole, MA 02543
▌4▐ *Ph:* (508) 563-1155
▌5▐ *Fax:* (508) 563-1211
▌6▐ *Free:* 800-538-3672
▌7▐ *E-mail:* businessofficemsa.microscopy.com
▌8▐ *URL:* http://www.msa.microscopy.com
▌9▐ 3446
▌10▐ MSA Presidential Student Awards
▌11▐ *(Graduate, Undergraduate/*
▌12▐ *Award*

  ▌13▐ Purpose: To recognize outstanding original research by students. ▌14▐ Focus: Biological Clinical Sciences—Microscopy, Physical Sciences—Microscopy. ▌15▐ Qualif.: Candidate may be of any nationality, but must be enrolled at a recognized college or university in the United States at the time of the MSA annual meeting. ▌16▐ Criteria: Selection is done based on the applicant's career objectives, academic record, and financial need. ▌17▐ Funds Avail.: Registration and round-trip travel to the MSA annual meeting, plus a stipend to defray lodging and other expenses. ▌18▐ Duration: Annual. ▌19▐ Number awarded: 5. ▌20▐ To Apply: Write to MSA for application form and guidelines. ▌21▐ Deadline: March 15. ▌22▐ Remarks: Established in 1979. ▌23▐ Contact: Alternate phone number: 800-538-EMSA.

Descriptions of Numbered Elements

▌1▐ **Organization Entry Number.** Administering organizations are listed alphabetically. Each entry is followed by an alphabetical listing of its awards. All entries (organization and award) are numbered in a single sequence. These numbers are used as references in the indexes.

▌2▐ **Organization Name.** The name of the organization administering the awards that follow.

▌3▐ **Mailing Address.** The organization's permanent mailing address is listed when known; in some cases an award address is given.

▌4▐ **Telephone Number.** The general telephone number for the administering organization. Phone numbers pertaining to specific awards are listed under "Contact" in the award description.

▌5▐ **Fax Number.** The facsimile number for the administering organization. Fax numbers pertaining to specific awards are included under "Contact" in the award description.

▌6▐ **Toll-free Number.** The toll-free number for the administering organization. Toll-free numbers pertaining to specific awards are included under "Contact" in the award description.

▌7▐ **E-mail Address.** The electronic mail address for the administering organization. Electronic mail addresses pertaining to specific awards are included under "Contact" in the award description.

▌8▐ **URL.** The web address for the administering organization.

▌9▐ **Award Entry Number.** Awards are listed alphabetically following the entry for their administering organizations. All entries (organization and award) are numbered in a single sequence. These numbers are used as references in the indexes.

▌10▐ **Award Name.** Names of awards are always listed. Organization titles or acronyms have been added to generic

Scholarships, Fellowships and Loans, 34th Ed.

award names (for example, MSA Undergraduate Scholarships, Canadian Council Fiction Writing Grant, etc.) to avoid confusion.

❚11❚ Study Level. The level of study for which the award may be used. One or more of the following terms will be listed:

- All: not restricted to a particular level.
- High School: study at the secondary level.
- Vocational: study leading to postsecondary awards, certificates, or diplomas requiring less than two years of study.
- 2 Year: study leading to a bachelor's degree within two years
- 4 Year: study leading to a bachelor's degree within four years
- Undergraduate: study immediately beyond the secondary level, including associate, colleges and universities, junior colleges, technical institutes leading to a bachelor's degree, and vocational technical schools.
- Graduate: study leading to an M.A., M.S., LL.B., LL.M., and other intermediate degrees.
- Master's: study leading specifically to a master's degree, such as a M.A., M.S., or M.B.A.
- Postgraduate: study beyond the graduate level not specifically leading to a degree.
- Doctorate: study leading to a Ph.D., Ed.D., Sc.D., M.D., D.D.S., D.O., J.D., and other terminal degrees.
- Postdoctorate: study beyond the doctorate level; includes awards intended for professional development when candidates must hold a doctoral degree to qualify.
- Professional Development: career development not necessarily restricted by study.

❚12❚ Award Type. The type or category of award. One or more of the following terms will be listed:

- Award: generally includes aid given in recognition and support of excellence, including awards given through music and arts competitions. Non-monetary awards and awards given strictly for recognition are not included.
- Fellowship: awards granted for graduate- or postgraduate-level research or education that do not require repayment.
- Grant: includes support for research, travel, and creative, experimental, or innovative projects.
- Internship: training and work experience programs. Internships that do not include compensation of some type are not included.
- Loan: aid that must be repaid either monetarily or through service. Some loans are interest-free, others are not.
- Prize: funds awarded as the result of a competition or contest. Prizes that are not intended to be used for study or to support professional development are not included.
- Scholarships: support for formal educational programs that does not require repayment.
- Scholarship Loan: a scholarship that becomes a loan if the recipient does not comply with the terms.
- Work Study: combined study and work program for which payment is received.
- Other: anything that does not fit the other categories, such as a travel award.

❚13❚ Purpose. The purpose for which the award is granted is listed here when known.

❚14❚ Focus. The field(s) of study that the recipient must be pursuing.

❚15❚ Qualif. Information regarding applicant eligibility. Some examples of qualification requirements include the following: academic record, citizenship, financial need, organizational affiliation, minority or ethnic background, residency, and gender.

❚16❚ Criteria Information concerning selection criteria.

❚17❚ Funds Avail. The award dollar amounts are included here along with other relevant funding information, such as the time period covered by the award, a breakdown of expenses covered (e.g., stipends, tuition and fees, travel and living allowances, equipment funds, etc.), the amount awarded to the institution, loan repayment schedules, service-in-return-for-funding agreements, and other obligations.

❚18❚ Duration. Frequency of the award.

❚19❚ Number awarded. Typical number of awards distributed.

❚20❚ To Apply. Application guidelines, requirements, and other information.

❚21❚ Deadline. Application due dates, notification dates (the date when the applicant will be notified of receipt or denial of award), disbursement dates, and other relevant dates.

❚22❚ Remarks. Any additional information concerning the award.

❚23❚ Contact. When contact information differs from that given for the administering organization, relevant addresses, telephone and fax numbers, and names of specific contact persons are listed here. When the address is that of the administering organization, the entry number for the organization is provided.

Indexes

Field of Study Index classifies awards by one or more of 450 specific subject categories, allowing users to easily target their search by specific area of study. Citations are arranged alphabetically under all appropriate subject terms. Each citation is followed by the study level and award type, which appear in parentheses and can be used to narrow the search even further.

Legal Residence Index lists awards that are restricted by the applicant's residence of legal record. Award citations are arranged alphabetically by country and subarranged by region, state or province (for U.S. and Canada). Each citation is followed by the study level and award type, which appear in parentheses and can be used to eliminate inappropriate awards.

Place of Study Index lists awards that carry restrictions on where study can take place. Award citations are arranged alphabetically under the following geographic headings:

- United States
- United States—by Region
- United States—by State
- Canada
- Canada—by Province
- International
- International—by Region
- International—by Country

Each citation is followed by the study level and award type, which appear in parentheses.

Special Recipient Index lists awards that carry restrictions or special qualifying factors relating to applicant affiliation. This index allows users to quickly identify awards relating to the following categories:

- African American
- Asian American
- Association Membership
- Disabled
- Employer Affiliation
- Ethnic Group Membership
- Fraternal Organization Membership
- Hispanic American
- Military
- Minority
- Native American
- Religious Affiliation
- Union Affiliation
- Veteran

Awards are listed under all appropriate headings. Each citation includes information on study level and award type, which appear in parentheses and can be used to further narrow the search. Users interested in awards restricted to particular minorities should also look under the general Minorities heading, which lists awards targeted for minorities but not restricted to any particular minority group.

Sponsor and Scholarship Index lists, in a single alphabetic sequence, all of the administering organizations, awards, and acronyms included in *SFL*.

Federal Programs

Federal aid for college students is available through a variety of programs administered by the U.S. Department of Education. Most colleges and universities participate in federal programs, but there are exceptions. Contact a school's financial aid office to find out if it is a participating institution. If it participates, the student works with financial aid counselors to determine how much aid can be obtained.

Aid for students comes in three forms: grants (gifts to the student), loans (which must be repaid), and work-study jobs (a job for the student while enrolled in which his/her pay is applied to his school account). These types of aid are further explained below. More information can be found at http://www.ed.gov.

Grants

Pell Grants are intended to provide funds for any undergraduate student (who does not already have a degree) who wishes to attend college regardless of family financial background. They are available through the financial aid office at the school. The maximum Pell Grant award for the 2016-2017 award year (July 1, 2016 to June 30, 2017) is $5,815.

Federal Supplemental Educational Opportunity Grants (FSEOG) are intended for students with exceptional financial need, these grants are typically for smaller amounts (between $100 and $4,000) than Pell Grants. They are available on a limited basis.

Loans

Student loans are available a variety of ways. Loans may not be taken out for more than the cost of attendance at the school, which is determined by the financial aid administrator. Grants and other forms of aid are taken into consideration when determining the amount a student will be allowed to borrow. Loan amounts may be reduced if a student receives other forms of aid. Loans are divided into two types, subsidized and unsubsidized:

Subsidized loans: the federal government pays the interest on the loan until after schooling is complete.

Unsubsidized loans: the student incurs the interest charges while in school, but payment of the charges may be deferred until schooling is complete. The advantage of unsubsidized loans is that there are usually fewer restrictions against obtaining them. Amounts available through these programs vary depending on academic level. The total debt a student or a student's parents may accumulate for that student is $31,000 for a dependent undergraduate student, $57,500 for an independent undergraduate student (with a limit of $23,000 in subsidized loans), and $138,500 for a graduate or professional student (with a limit of $65,500 in subsidized loans) or $224,000 for health professionals.

Available Funding Programs Direct Loan Program

These low-interest loans bypass lending institutions such as banks. They are a direct arrangement between the government and the student (administered by the school). There are four repayment options for the Direct Loan program: the Income Contingent Repayment Plan, the Extended Repayment Plan, the Graduated Repayment Plan, and the Standard Repayment Plan.

Direct subsidized loans may be taken out for a maximum of $3,500 by incoming freshmen, $4,500 for sophomores, and $5,500 for juniors and seniors. The amounts for independent undergraduate students range from $9,500 to $12,500 per year for direct loans. Independent students face some restrictions on the amount of subsidized funds they can receive from the program. At least half of the funds borrowed through the Direct Loan program by independent students must come from unsubsidized loans. Graduate students may borrow up to $20,500 directly in unsubsidized loans.

Direct PLUS Loans Direct PLUS loans are federal loans that graduate or professional degree students and parents of dependent undergraduate students can use to help pay education expenses. The U.S. Department of Education makes Direct PLUS loans to eligible borrowers through schools participating in the program. The Maximum amount to be borrowed is the cost of attending the shool minus other forms of aid already obtained. For 2016-2017 the fixed rate for a Direct PLUS loan is 6.31%.

FEDERAL PROGRAMS

With the Direct PLUS loan, students or parents fill out a Direct PLUS Loan Application, available at the school's financial aid office. The funds are disbursed to the school. Students and parents may choose from three repayment plans: Standard, Extended, or Graduated.

Perkins Loan Program The Perkins Loan program allows students who have unusual financial need to borrow funds not otherwise available from other loan or grant programs. Up to $5,500 is available to undergraduates each year (up to $8,000 for graduate students). These loans have a fixed interest rate of 5%. Perkins Loans must be repaid within ten years.

Federal Work-Study Program Work-study is an arrangement that allows students to work on campus while they are enrolled to help pay their expenses. The federal government pays the majority of the student's wages, although the department where the student works also contributes. The employment must be relevant to the student's field of study and only so much time per semester may be devoted to the job. If the student earns the amount of aid prior to the end of the semester, work is terminated for the duration of the award period.

Other Considerations

Application: Applying for federal student aid is free. All federal aid is obtained by first completing a Free Application for Federal Student Aid (FAFSA). After the application is submitted, it will be processed by the Department of Education. The student then receives a Student Aid Report (SAR), which contains a figure for Expected Family Contribution. This is the amount that the student should plan on providing from non-federal sources in order to attend school.

Dependency: If a student is eligible for independent status, more money may be available in the form of loans. The interest rates and the programs for repayment, however, are the same. Independent status provides more financial aid for students who do not have the benefit of parental financial contributions.

Deadline: FAFSA deadlines are set by federal and state agencies, as well as individual schools, and vary widely. Applicants are encouraged to apply as soon as possible after January 1 of the year they plan to enroll, but no earlier.

Special Circumstances: The financial aid counselor at the school will often listen to extenuating circumstances such as unexpected medical expenses, private education expenses for other family members, or recent unemployment when evaluating requests for assistance.

Contact Information for Federal Financial Aid Programs

Call (800)433-3243 to have questions answered; (319) 337-5665 to find out if your application has been processed; (800) 730-8913 (TTY) if you are hearing impaired; (800) 647-8733 to report fraud, waste, or abuse of federal student aid funds; or visit http://www.ed.gov for application forms, guidelines, and general information.

AmeriCorps

President Clinton launched this volunteer community service program in September 1993 through the *National and Community Service Trust Act*, aimed at helping college-bound young people pay for their education while serving their communities. AmeriCorps volunteers receive minimum wage, health benefits, and a grant toward college for up to two years.

Funds for the program are distributed by the federal government in the form of grants to qualifying organizations and community groups with the goal of achieving direct results in addressing the nation's critical education, human services, public safety, and environmental needs at the community level. The program provides meaningful opportunities for Americans to serve their country in organized efforts, fostering citizen responsibility, building community, and providing educational opportunities for those who make a substantial commitment to service.

The AmeriCorps programs are run by not-for-profit organizations or partnerships, institutions of higher learning, local governments, school or police districts, states, Native American tribes, and federal agencies. Examples of participating programs include Habitat for Humanity, the American Red Cross, Boys and Girls Clubs, and local community centers and places of worship. Volunteers have nearly 1,000 different groups from which to choose. The AmeriCorps Pledge: "I will get things done for America to make our people safer, smarter, and healthier. I will bring Americans together to strengthen our communities. Faced with apathy, I will take action. Faced with conflict, I will seek a common ground. Faced with adversity, I will persevere. I will carry this commitment with me this year and beyond. I am an AmeriCorps Member and I am going to get things done."

Eligibility and Selection for Service in AmeriCorps

Citizens and legal resident aliens who are 17 years of age or older are eligible to serve in AmeriCorps before, during, or after post-secondary education. In general, participants must be high school graduates or agree to achieve their GED prior to receiving education awards. Individual programs select service participants on a nondiscriminatory and nonpolitical basis. There are national and state-wide recruiting information systems and a national pool of potential service volunteers.

Term of Service

One full-time term of service is a minimum of 1,700 hours over the course of one year or less; or a part-time term, which can range from 300 hours to 900 hours. Short-term service (such as a summer program) provides eligibility for reduced part-time status.

Compensation

You will receive a modest living allowance, health insurance, student loan deferment, and training. After you complete your term of service, you will receive an education award to help pay for your education. Serve part-time and you will receive a portion of the full amount. The amount is tied to the maximum amount of the U.S. Department of Education's Pell Grant. Prior to fiscal year 2010, the amount of an education award had remained the same since the AmeriCorps program began. Effective fiscal year 2017, which began October 1, 2016, the award is $5,815 for a year of full-time service, and is pro-rated for part-time service.

How Can I Use an Award?

These awards may be used to repay qualified existing or future student loans, to pay all or part of the cost of attending a qualified institute of higher education (including some vocational programs), or to pay expenses while participating in an approved school-to-work program. Awards must be used within seven years of completion of service.

Contact

Individuals interested in participating in AmeriCorps national service programs should apply directly. For basic program information, individuals can call the AmeriCorps Information Hotline at 1-800-942-2677 or visit their Web site at http://www.nationalservice.gov/programs/americorps.

State Higher Education Agencies

The following is an alphabetic state-by-state listing of agencies located in the United States. Many of these agencies administer special federal award programs, as well as state-specific awards, such as the Tuition Incentive Program (TIP) offered by the state of Michigan for low-income students to receive free tuition at community colleges. Financial aid seekers should contact the agency in their home state for more information.

ALABAMA

Alabama Comm. on Higher Education
100 N. Union St.
P.O. Box 302000
Montgomery, AL 36104
(334)242-1998
http://www.ache.state.al.us

ALASKA

Alaska Comm. on Postsecondary Education
P.O. Box 110505
Juneau, AK 99811-0505
(907)465-2962
http://acpe.alaska.gov

ARIZONA

Arizona Comm. for Postsecondary Education
2020 N. Central Ave.,
Ste. 650
Phoenix, AZ 85004-4503
(602)258-2435
http://highered.az.gov

ARKANSAS

Arkansas Dept. of Higher Education
423 Main St., Ste. 400
Little Rock, AR 72201
(501)371-2000
http://www.adhe.edu

CALIFORNIA

California Student Aid Comm.
PO Box 419026
Rancho Cordova, CA 95741-9026
(888)224-7268
http://www.csac.ca.gov

COLORADO

Colorado Dept. of Higher Education
1560 Broadway, Ste. 1600
Denver, CO 80202
(303)862-3001
http://highered.colorado.gov

CONNECTICUT

Connecticut Dept. of Higher Education
61 Woodland St.
Hartford, CT 06105-2326
(860)947-1800
http://www.ctdhe.org

DELAWARE

Delaware Dept. of Higher Education Scholarship/incentive Loan Program
The Townsend Building
401 Federal St.
Dover, DE 19901
(302)735-4000
http://www.doe.k12.de.us/Page/316

DISTRICT OF COLUMBIA

District of Columbia Office of the State Superintendent of Education
810 1st St., NE, 9th Fl.
Washington, DC 20002
(202)727-6436
http://osse.dc.gov

FLORIDA

Office of Student Financial Assistance
Dept. of Education
325 W. Gaines St.
Turlington Bldg., Ste. 1514
Tallahassee, FL 32399-0400
(800)366-3475
http://www.floridastudentfinancialaid.org

GEORGIA

Georgia Student Finance Comm.
2082 E. Exchange Pl.
Tucker, GA 30084
(800)436-7442
http://gsfc.georgia.gov

HAWAII

Hawaii Board of Regents
2444 Dole St.,
Bachman Hall, Rm. 209
Honolulu, HI 96822
(808)956-8213
http://www.hawaii.edu/offices/bor/

IDAHO

Idaho State Board of Education
PO Box 83720
Boise, ID 83720-0037
(208)334-2270
http://www.boardofed.idaho.gov

ILLINOIS

Illinois Student Assistance Comm.
1755 Lake Cook Rd.
Deerfield, IL 60015-5209
(800)899-4722
http://www.isac.org

INDIANA

Indiana Comm. for Higher Education
101 W. Ohio St., Ste. 300
Indianapolis, IN 46204-4206

STATE HIGHER EDUCATION AGENCIES

(888)528-4719
http://www.in.gov/che

IOWA

Iowa College Student Aid Comm.
430 E. Grand Ave., Fl. 3
Des Moines, IA 50309-1920
(877)272-4456
http://www.iowacollegeaid.gov

KANSAS

Kansas Board of Regents
1000 SW Jackson St., Ste. 520
Topeka, KS 66612-1368
(785)296-3421
http://www.kansasregents.org

KENTUCKY

Kentucky Higher Education Assistance Authority
100 Airport Rd.
Frankfort, KY 40602-0798
(800)928-8926
http://www.kheaa.com

LOUISIANA

Louisiana Office of Student Financial Assistance
602 N. Fifth St.
Baton Rouge, LA 70802
(225)219-1012
http://www.osfa.state.la.us

MAINE

Finance Authority of Maine (FAME)
5 Community Dr.
P.O. Box 949
Augusta, ME 04332-0949
(207)623-3263
http://www.famemaine.com

MARYLAND

Maryland Higher Education Comm.
6 N. Liberty St.
Baltimore, MD 21201
(410)767-3301
http://www.mhec.state.md.us

MASSACHUSETTS

Massachusetts Dept. of Higher Education
One Ashburton Pl., Rm. 1401
Boston, MA 02108-1696

(617)994-6950
http://www.mass.edu

MICHIGAN

Michigan Higher Education Student Loan Authority
Student Scholarships and Grants
P.O. Box 30462
Lansing, MI 48909-7962
(888)447-2687
http://www.michigan.gov/mistudentaid

MINNESOTA

Minnesota Office of Higher Education
1450 Energy Park Dr., Ste. 350
St. Paul, MN 55108-5227
(651)642-0567
http://www.ohe.state.mn.us/index.cfm

MISSISSIPPI

Mississippi Institutions of Higher Learning
3825 Ridgewood Rd.
Jackson, MS 39211
(601)432-6198
http://www.ihl.state.ms.us

MISSOURI

Missouri Dept. of Higher Education
205 Jefferson St.
P.O.Box 1469
Jefferson City, MO 65102-1469
(573)751-2361
http://www.dhe.mo.gov/

MONTANA

Montana Board of Regents
Office of Commissioner of Higher Education
Montana University System
2500 Broadway St.
PO Box 203201
Helena, MT 59620-3201
(406)444-6570
http://www.mus.edu

NEBRASKA

Nebraska Coordinating Comm. for Postsecondary Education
P.O. Box 95005
Lincoln, NE 68509-5005
(402)471-2847
http://ccpe.nebraska.gov

NEVADA

Nevada Department of Education
700 E. Fifth St.
Carson City, NV 89701
(775)687-9200
http://www.doe.nv.gov

(Southern Office)
9890 S. Maryland Pkwy., 2nd Fl.
Las Vegas, NV 89183
(702)486-6458

NEW HAMPSHIRE

New Hampshire Higher Education Comm.
101 Pleasant St.
Concord, NH 03301-3494
(603)271-3494
http://www.state.nh.us/postsecondary

NEW JERSEY

Higher Education Student Assistance Authority
P.O. Box 545
Trenton, NJ 08625-0545
(800)792-8670
http://www.hesaa.org

NEW MEXICO

New Mexico Higher Education Dept.
2048 Galisteo St.
Santa Fe, NM 87505-2100
(505)476-8400
http://www.hed.state.nm.us

NEW YORK

New York State Higher Education Svcs. Corp.
99 Washington Ave.
Albany, NY 12255
(888)697-4372
http://www.hesc.ny.gov

NORTH CAROLINA

North Carolina State Education Assistance Authority
PO Box 14103
Research Triangle Park, NC 27709

STATE HIGHER EDUCATION AGENCIES

(919)549-8614
http://www.ncseaa.edu

NORTH DAKOTA

North Dakota University System
North Dakota Student Financial Assistance Program
10th Fl., State Capitol
600 E. Boulevard Ave., Dept. 215
Bismarck, ND 58505-0230
(701)328-2960
http://www.ndus.edu

OHIO

Ohio Department of Higher Education
25 S. Front St.
Columbus, OH 43215
(614)466-6000
http://www.ohiohighered.org

OKLAHOMA

Oklahoma State Regents for Higher Education
Oklahoma Guaranteed Loan Program
655 Research Pkwy.
Suite 200
Oklahoma City, OK 73104
(405)225-9100
http://www.okhighered.org

OREGON

Oregon Student Access Comm.
1500 Valley River Dr., Ste. 100
Eugene, OR 97401
(541)687-7400
http://www.osac.state.or.us

PENNSYLVANIA

Pennsylvania Higher Education Assistance Agency
1200 N. 7th St.
Harrisburg, PA 17102-1444
(800)692-7392
http://www.pheaa.org

RHODE ISLAND

Rhode Island Higher Education Assistance Authority
560 Jefferson Blvd., Ste. 100
Warwick, RI 02886-1304

(401)736-1100
http://www.riheaa.org

SOUTH CAROLINA

South Carolina Comm. on Higher Education
1122 Lady St., Ste. 300
Columbia, SC 29201
(803)737-2260
http://www.che.sc.gov/

SOUTH DAKOTA

South Dakota Board of Regents
306 E. Capitol Ave., Ste. 200
Pierre, SD 57501
(605)773-3455
http://www.sdbor.edu/

TENNESSEE

Tennessee Higher Education Comm.
Parkway Towers
404 James Robertson Pkwy., Ste. 1900
Nashville, TN 37243-0830
(615)741-3605
https://www.tn.gov/thec

TEXAS

Texas Higher Education Coordinating Board
1200 E. Anderson Ln.
Austin, TX 78752
(512)427-6101
http://www.thecb.state.tx.us

UTAH

Utah State Board of Regents
Board of Regents Building, The Gateway
60 South 400 West
Salt Lake City, UT 84101-1284
(800)418-8757
http://higheredutah.org

VERMONT

Vermont Student Assistance Corp.
10 E. Allen St.
P.O. Box 2000

Winooski, VT 05404
(800)642-3177
http://www.services.vsac.org/wps/wcm/connect/vsac/VSAC

VIRGINIA

State Council of Higher Education for Virginia
James Monroe Bldg.
101 N. 14th St., 10th Fl.
Richmond, VA 23219
(804)225-2600
http://www.schev.edu

WASHINGTON

Washington Student Achievement Council
917 Lakeridge Way
Olympia, WA 98502
(360)753-7800
http://www.wsac.wa.gov

WEST VIRGINIA

West Virginia Higher Education Policy Comm.
1018 Kanawha Blvd., E., Ste. 700
Charleston, WV 25301
(304)558-2101
http://www.hepc.wvnet.edu

WISCONSIN

Wisconsin Higher Education Aids Board
131 W. Wilson St., Ste. 902
P.O. Box 7885
Madison, WI 53707-7885
(608)267-2206
http://heab.state.wi.us

WYOMING

Wyoming Community College Comm.
2300 Capitol Ave., 5th Fl., Ste. B
Cheyenne, WY 82002
(307)777-7763
http://www.communitycolleges.wy.edu

Abbreviations

U.S. State Abbreviations

AK	Alaska
AL	Alabama
AR	Arkansas
AZ	Arizona
CA	California
CO	Colorado
CT	Connecticut
DC	District of Columbia
DE	Delaware
FL	Florida
GA	Georgia
GU	Guam
HI	Hawaii
IA	Iowa
ID	Idaho
IL	Illinois
IN	Indiana
KS	Kansas
KY	Kentucky
LA	Louisiana
MA	Massachusetts
MD	Maryland
ME	Maine
MI	Michigan
MN	Minnesota
MO	Missouri
MS	Mississippi
MT	Montana
NC	North Carolina
ND	North Dakota
NE	Nebraska
NH	New Hampshire
NJ	New Jersey
NM	New Mexico
NV	Nevada
NY	New York
OH	Ohio
OK	Oklahoma
OR	Oregon
PA	Pennsylvania
PR	Puerto Rico
RI	Rhode Island
SC	South Carolina
SD	South Dakota
TN	Tennessee
TX	Texas
UT	Utah
VA	Virginia
VI	Virgin Islands
VT	Vermont
WA	Washington
WI	Wisconsin
WV	West Virginia
WY	Wyoming

Canadian Province Abbreviations

AB	Alberta
BC	British Columbia
MB	Manitoba
NB	New Brunswick
NL	Newfoundland and Labrador
NS	Nova Scotia
NT	Northwest Territories
ON	Ontario
PE	Prince Edward Island
QC	Quebec
SK	Saskatchewan
YT	Yukon Territory

Other Abbreviations

ACT	American College Testing Program
B.A.	Bachelor of Arts
B.Arch.	Bachelor of Architecture
B.F.A.	Bachelor of Fine Arts
B.S.	Bachelor of Science
B.Sc.	Bachelor of Science
CSS	College Scholarship Service
D.D.S.	Doctor of Dental Science/Surgery
D.O.	Doctor of Osteopathy
D.Sc.	Doctor of Science
D.S.W.	Doctor of Social Work
D.V.M.	Doctor of Veterinary Medicine
D.V.M.S.	Doctor of Veterinary Medicine and Surgery
D.V.S.	Doctor of Veterinary Science
FAFSA	Free Application for Federal Student Aid
FWS	Federal Work Study
GED	General Education Development Certificate
GPA	Grade Point Average
GRE	Graduate Record Examination
J.D.	Doctor of Jurisprudence
LL.B.	Bachelor of Law
LL.M.	Master of Law
LSAT	Law School Admission Test
M.A.	Master of Arts
M.Arch.	Master of Architecture
M.B.A.	Master of Business Administration
M.D.	Doctor of Medicine
M.Div.	Master of Divinity
M.F.A.	Master of Fine Arts
MIA	Missing in Action
M.L.S.	Master of Library Science
M.N.	Master of Nursing
M.S.	Master of Science
M.S.W.	Master of Social Work
O.D.	Doctor of Optometry
Pharm.D.	Doctor of Pharmacy
Ph.D.	Doctor of Philosophy
POW	Prisoner of War
PSAT	Preliminary Scholastic Aptitude Test
ROTC	Reserve Officers Training Corps
SAR	Student Aid Report
SAT	Scholastic Aptitude Test
Sc.D.	Doctor of Science
TDD	Telephone Device for the Deaf
Th.d.	Doctor of Theology
U.N.	United Nations
U.S.	United States

Sponsors and Their Scholarships

9821 ■ UAF Community and Technical College
604 Barnette St.
Fairbanks, AK 99701
Ph: (907)455-2800
Free: 877-882-8827
URL: www.ctc.uaf.edu

9822 ■ William C. Leary Memorial Emergency Services Scholarships *(Undergraduate/Scholarship)*

Purpose: To encourage students to pursue their career in emergency service program. **Focus:** Emergency and disaster services. **Qualif.:** Applicants must be students at the UAF-CTC enrolled in emergency service program. **Criteria:** Selection of applicants will be based on the decision of the scholarship committee.

Funds Avail.: No specific amount. **Duration:** Annual. **To Apply:** Scholarship applications are available at uaonline.alaska.edu (to access the scholarship application, you must choose "Login to secure area" if they have a UA ID or apply for admission for the new students). **Deadline:** February 15.

9823 ■ UAF Community and Technical College Culinary Arts Scholarships *(Undergraduate/Scholarship)*

Purpose: To provide support for deserving students intending to pursue their study in culinary arts. **Focus:** Culinary arts. **Qualif.:** Applicants must be students enrolled at UAF-CTC and intending to pursue a career in culinary arts in Alaska. **Criteria:** Applicants will be selected based on their application requirements.

Funds Avail.: No specific amount. **Duration:** Annual. **To Apply:** Applicants are advised to contact the Culinary Arts for further information about the application requirements and procedure. **Deadline:** February 15.

9824 ■ Morris K. Udall Foundation
130 S Scott Ave.
Tucson, AZ 85701-1922
Ph: (520)901-8500
Fax: (520)670-5530
URL: www.udall.gov

9825 ■ Morris K. Udall Scholarships *(Undergraduate/Scholarship)*

Purpose: To provide students the innovative ideas, professional advice, job and internship opportunities that will help them grow educationally. **Focus:** Environmental technology; Native American studies. **Qualif.:** Applicants must be students who have demonstrated commitment to a career related to the environment; or must be Native American or Alaska Native students who have demonstrated commitment to a career related to tribal public policy or Native health care; must be sophomores or junior level college students; must have a college GPA of at least 3.0 or the equivalent; and must be U.S citizens, U.S nationals or U.S permanent residents. **Criteria:** Recipients will be selected based on the following criteria: (1) demonstrated commitment to environmental or natural resources, tribal public policy, or Native American health care; (2) course of study and proposed career; (3) leadership, character, desire to make a difference, and general well roundedness.

Funds Avail.: Up to $7,000. **Duration:** Annual. **To Apply:** Applicants must complete and sign Udall Scholarship Application and submit along with an 800-word essay (signed and dated), a current official college transcript and transcripts for other colleges attended, and three letters of recommendation. **Deadline:** March 2.

9826 ■ The Ulman Cancer Fund for Young Adults
921 E Fort Ave., Ste. 325
Baltimore, MD 21230
Ph: (410)964-0202
Free: 888-393-FUND
E-mail: info@ulmanfund.org
URL: ulmanfund.org

9827 ■ Board of Young Adult Advisors Scholarships *(Graduate/Scholarship)*

Purpose: To recognize Baltimore, MD, or Washington, DC, area residents who have battled cancer or selflessly supported a parent or sibling through their cancer experience. **Focus:** Health sciences; Medicine. **Qualif.:** Applicants must be patients or with parents or siblings diagnose with cancer disease in a graduate level degree; or those who are seeking a professional attainment ages 15 to 39 during their own diagnosis/treatment or during the diagnosis/treatment of their parent or sibling. **Criteria:** Selection will be based on the committee's criteria.

Funds Avail.: No specific amount. **To Apply:** Applicants must submit a complete online application form together with letter of recommendation, an essay, and physician verification form. **Deadline:** March 1.

9828 ■ Olivia M. Marquart Scholarships *(Graduate, Master's, Doctorate/Scholarship)*

Purpose: To support young adults who are either cancer survivors or currently undergoing treatment. **Focus:** Health

Awards are arranged alphabetically below their administering organizations

sciences; Medicine. **Qualif.:** Applicants must be patients, cancer survivor or with parents or siblings diagnose with cancer disease; must be ages 15 to 39 during their own diagnosis/treatment or during the diagnosis/treatment of their parent or sibling; must be U.S. citizens attending college or university in the United States; must be residents of Pennsylvania pursuing a college degree, masters or Ph.D. in education. **Criteria:** Selection will be based on the committee's criteria.

Funds Avail.: No specific amount. **Duration:** Annual. **To Apply:** Applicants must submit a complete online application form together with letter of recommendation, an essay, and physician verification form. **Deadline:** March 1.

9829 ■ Marilyn Yetso Memorial Scholarships (Graduate/Scholarship)

Purpose: To support the financial needs of college students who have lost a parent to cancer or have a parent with cancer. **Focus:** Health sciences; Medicine. **Qualif.:** Applicants must be college students who have lost a parent to cancer or have a parent with cancer ages 15 to 39 during his/her own diagnosis/treatment or during the diagnosis/treatment of his/her parent or sibling; must be residents of Baltimore/Washington metro area. **Criteria:** Selection will be based on the committee's criteria.

Funds Avail.: $2,500. **To Apply:** Applicants must submit a complete online application form together with letter of recommendation, an essay and physician verification form or death certificate as applicable. **Deadline:** March 1.

9830 ■ Unitarian Universalist Association (UUA)
24 Farnsworth St.
Boston, MA 02210-1262
Ph: (617)742-2100
Fax: (617)367-3237
E-mail: info@uua.org
URL: www.uua.org
Facebook: www.facebook.com/TheUUA
Twitter: twitter.com/uua

9831 ■ Martha and Robert Atherton Ministerial Scholarships (Master's/Scholarship)

Purpose: To provide financial assistance to promising ministerial students in pursuing their education. **Focus:** Religion. **Qualif.:** Applicants must be students in the second or third year of seminary; and citizens of the United States or Canada. **Criteria:** Priority is given to students who have demonstrated outstanding ministerial ability secondarily to students with the greatest financial need, especially persons of color.

Funds Avail.: No specific amount. **Duration:** Annual. **To Apply:** Applicants must apply for financial aid to be automatically considered for scholarships with no additional material is required, except where noted. **Deadline:** April 15. **Remarks:** Established in 1997.

9832 ■ Olympia Brown and Max Kapp Awards (Master's/Scholarship)

Purpose: To support the education of a student in a Masters of Divinity degree program. **Focus:** Religion. **Qualif.:** Applicants must be students enrolled full-time or at least half time in a Masters of Divinity degree program leading to fellowship as Unitarian Universalist (UU) ministers; and citizens of the United States or Canada. **Criteria:** Priority will be given to students who have demonstrated outstanding ministerial ability secondarily to students with the greatest financial need, especially persons of color. Entries will be evaluated by an outside reader.

Funds Avail.: $2,500. **Duration:** Annual. **Number Awarded:** 1. **To Apply:** Applicants must apply for financial aid to be automatically considered for scholarships. In addition, applicants must submit a winning paper, sermon, or other special project on some aspect of Universalism. **Deadline:** April 15.

9833 ■ Children of Unitarian Universalist Ministers College Scholarships (Undergraduate/Scholarship)

Purpose: To provide educational support to the children of Unitarian Universalist Ministers. **Focus:** General studies/Field of study not specified. **Qualif.:** Applicants must be college undergraduates and dependents of a Unitarian Universalist Minister. **Criteria:** Priority is given to applicants with family income not exceeding $50,000.

Funds Avail.: No specific amount. **Duration:** Annual. **To Apply:** Applicants must complete the online Application process and submit a proof of college enrollment to the UUA Office of Church Staff Finances. **Deadline:** October 15. **Contact:** Richard Nugent; Fax: 617-742-2875; Email: rnugent@uua.org.

9834 ■ Pauly D'Orlando Memorial Art Scholarships (Graduate, Undergraduate/Scholarship)

Purpose: To support Unitarian Universalist students with their educational pursuit. **Focus:** Art. **Qualif.:** Applicants must be Unitarian Universalist graduate or undergraduate students pursuing a career in fine arts, except those who are performing arts majors. **Criteria:** Selection is based on active relationship with Unitarian Universalism, financial need, and enrollment in an accredited institution.

Duration: Annual. **Number Awarded:** Varies. **To Apply:** Applicants must submit a completed application form along with the supporting documentation. **Deadline:** February 15.

9835 ■ David Eaton Scholarships (Master's/Scholarship)

Purpose: To support the education of students enrolled in a Masters of Dignity degree program. **Focus:** Religion. **Qualif.:** Applicants must be students enrolled full-time or at least half time in a Masters of Divinity degree program leading to fellowship as Unitarian Universalist (UU) ministers; citizens of the United States or Canada; and, women from a historically marginalized group who share the same vision as David Eaton. **Criteria:** Priority is given to students that have demonstrated outstanding ministerial ability secondarily to students with the greatest financial need, especially persons of color.

Funds Avail.: No specific amount. **Duration:** Annual. **To Apply:** Applicants must apply for financial aid to be automatically considered for scholarships with no additional materials required, except where noted. **Deadline:** April 15.

9836 ■ David Pohl Scholarships (Master's/Scholarship)

Purpose: To support the intellectual, spiritual, and professional development of individuals studying for the Unitarian Universalist ministry. **Focus:** Religion. **Qualif.:** Applicants must be students enrolled full-time or at least half time in a Masters of Divinity degree program leading to fellowship as Unitarian Universalist (UU) ministers; and citizen of the United States or Canada. **Criteria:** Priority is given to

Awards are arranged alphabetically below their administering organizations

students that have demonstrated outstanding ministerial ability secondarily to students with the greatest financial need, especially persons of color.
Funds Avail.: No specific amount. **Duration:** Annual. **To Apply:** Applicants must apply for financial aid to be automatically considered for scholarships with no additional material is required, except when noted. **Deadline:** April 15.

9837 ■ Roy H. Pollack Scholarships *(Graduate, Master's/Scholarship)*

Purpose: To support the education of students in a Master of Dignity degree program through financial assistance. **Focus:** Religion. **Qualif.:** Applicants must be second or third-year students having strong academic records and promising candidates for the Unitarian Universalist ministry; must enrolled full-time or at least half time in a Masters of Dignity degree program. They must be citizens of the United States or Canada. **Criteria:** Priority is given to students who have demonstrated outstanding ministerial ability secondarily to students with the greatest financial need, especially persons of color.
Funds Avail.: No specific amount. **Duration:** Annual. **To Apply:** Applicants must apply for financial aid to be automatically considered for scholarships with no additional material is required, except where noted. **Deadline:** April 15. **Remarks:** Established in 1998.

9838 ■ Alice Southworth Schulman, Class of 1954, Simmons Scholarships for Unitarian Universalist Women *(Undergraduate/Scholarship)*

Purpose: To provide educational support to Unitarian Universalist students. **Focus:** General studies/Field of study not specified. **Qualif.:** Applicants must be Unitarian Universalist Women members attending Simmons College in Boston. **Criteria:** UUA will validate all applicants.
Funds Avail.: No specific amount. **Duration:** Annual. **Number Awarded:** 2. **To Apply:** Applicants must apply and submit the Information Profile for Endowed Scholarships through the Office of Student Financial Services at Simmons College. **Contact:** campaign@uua.org.

9839 ■ Joseph Sumner Smith Scholarships *(Undergraduate/Scholarship)*

Purpose: To support the education of a Unitarian Universalist (UU) student. **Focus:** General studies/Field of study not specified. **Qualif.:** Applicants must be Unitarian Universalist students attending Harvard University. **Criteria:** Priority is given to students who will pursue the ministry after graduation.
Funds Avail.: $250 - $1,000. **Duration:** Annual. **To Apply:** Applicants must contact the Scholarship Administrator of the UU Funding Program for the application process. **Deadline:** July 31. **Contact:** Scholarship Administrator, PO Box 3011149 Jamaica Plain MA02130; Phone: 617-971-9600; Email: uufp@uua.org.

9840 ■ Marion Barr Stanfield Art Scholarships *(Graduate, Undergraduate/Scholarship)*

Purpose: To support Unitarian Universalist students with their educational pursuit. **Focus:** Art. **Qualif.:** Applicants must be Unitarian Universalist graduate or undergraduate students pursuing a career in fine arts, except those who are performing arts majors. **Criteria:** Selection is based on active relationship with Unitarian Universalism, financial need, and enrollment in an accredited institution.
Funds Avail.: Varies. **Duration:** Annual. **Number Awarded:** Varies. **To Apply:** Applicants must submit a completed application form along with the supporting documentation. **Deadline:** February 15.

9841 ■ Otto M. Stanfield Law Scholarships *(Graduate/Scholarship)*

Purpose: To support student's education entering law school at graduate level. **Focus:** Law. **Qualif.:** Applicants must be Unitarian Universalist students who are about to enter or already in law school, except those pre-law students or Political Science majors. **Criteria:** Selection is based on active relationship with Unitarian Universalism, financial need, and enrollment in an accredited institution.
Funds Avail.: No specific amount. **Duration:** Annual. **To Apply:** Applicants must submit a completed application form along with the supporting documentation.

9842 ■ Rev. Chuck and Nancy Thomas Scholarships *(Professional development/Scholarship)*

Purpose: To support the education of a student in a Masters of Divinity degree program leading to fellowship as a Unitarian Universalist (UU) minister. **Focus:** Religion. **Qualif.:** Applicants must be first-year students showing an outstanding commitment to Unitarian Universalism as lay leaders before preparing for ordained ministry; and must be citizens of the United States or Canada. **Criteria:** Priority is given to students that have demonstrated outstanding ministerial ability secondarily to students with the greatest financial need, especially persons of color.
Funds Avail.: No specific amount. **Duration:** Annual. **Number Awarded:** 1. **To Apply:** Applicants must submit two letters of recommendation letters; two to three pages essay and a recent resume. **Deadline:** March 25. **Contact:** cspiegel@uua.org.

9843 ■ Von Ogden Vogt Scholarships *(Master's/Scholarship)*

Purpose: To support the intellectual, spiritual, and professional development of future Unitarian Universalist ministers. **Focus:** Religion. **Qualif.:** Applicants must be students enrolled full-time or at least half time in a Masters of Divinity degree program leading to fellowship as Unitarian Universalist (UU) ministers; attending Meadville Lombard Theological School; and citizens of the United States or Canada. **Criteria:** Priority is given to students who have demonstrated outstanding ministerial ability secondarily to students with the greatest financial need, especially persons of color.
Funds Avail.: No specific amount. **Duration:** Annual. **To Apply:** Applicants must apply for financial aid to be automatically considered for scholarships with no additional material is required, except where noted. **Deadline:** April 15. **Remarks:** Established in 2001.

9844 ■ United Engineering Foundation (UEF)
1650 Market St., Ste. 1200
Philadelphia, PA 19103
URL: www.uefoundation.org

9845 ■ United Engineering Foundation Grants *(All/Grant)*

Purpose: To support engineering and education for the advancement of engineering arts and sciences. **Focus:** Engineering. **Qualif.:** Any non-profit organization, individual and group is eligible for the grant. **Criteria:** The UEF Grants Committee will prioritize the proposals and forward prioritized proposals to the UEF Board of Trustees. Preference will be given to proposals demonstrating U.S. based organizations having 501(c)(3) status, established deadlines and with page limitation.

Funds Avail.: No specific amount. **To Apply:** Applicants must submit a detailed proposal and a two-page concept paper in PDF format. **Deadline:** June 1. **Contact:** Submit completed application to davidlbelden@cs.com.

9846 ■ United Food and Commercial Workers International Union (UFCW)
1775 K St. NW
Washington, DC 20006
URL: www.ufcw.org
Facebook: www.facebook.com/ufcwinternational
LinkedIn: www.linkedin.com/company/ufcw

9847 ■ UFCW Local Union Scholarships
(Undergraduate/Scholarship)

Purpose: To aid UFCW local community members in their educational pursuit. **Focus:** General studies/Field of study not specified. **Qualif.:** Applicants must be UFCW members in their respective localities. **Criteria:** Selection is based on scholastic achievements, community involvement and on submitted essay.

Funds Avail.: No specific amount. **Duration:** Annual. **To Apply:** Applicants may visit the program website or verify the scholarship at their local union offices.

9848 ■ United Methodist Church General Board of Higher Education and Ministry (GBHEM)
1001 19th Ave. S
Nashville, TN 37212-2130
Ph: (615)340-7400
URL: www.gbhem.org

9849 ■ Rosalie Bentzinger Scholarships *(Doctorate/Scholarship)*

Purpose: To assist students from various backgrounds working towards various higher education degrees. **Focus:** Religion. **Qualif.:** Applicants must be ordained deacons pursuing a PhD in Christian Education, enrolled in a University Senate approved Seminary; must have a 3-year membership in the UMC; must have a GPA of 3.0+. **Criteria:** Selection will be based on the committee's criteria.

Funds Avail.: $5,000. **Duration:** Annual. **To Apply:** Applicants must visit the website for the online application process. All required supporting documents like transcripts with grade, letter of reference, essay, signed pledged form must be submitted. **Deadline:** March 1. **Contact:** umscholar@gbhem.org; 615-340-7344.

9850 ■ The Bishop James C. Baker Award
(Doctorate/Scholarship)

Purpose: To assist campus ministers who have been in campus ministry for at least 3 years, and pursuing advanced training: doctorate degree, certification, or independent study. **Focus:** General studies/Field of study not specified. **Qualif.:** Applicants must be current United Methodist Campus Ministers who have been in campus ministry for at least three years; must have received an MDIV degree or equivalent; must be pursuing advanced training: doctorate degree, certification or independent study; must have a GPA of 3.0+; must be committed to remain in campus ministry. **Criteria:** Selection will be based on the committee's criteria.

Funds Avail.: $2,000-$5,000. **Duration:** Annual. **To Apply:** Applicants must visit the website for the online application process. All required supporting documents like transcripts with grade, letter of reference, essay, signed pledged form must be submitted.

9851 ■ Esther Edwards Graduate Scholarships
(Doctorate, Professional development/Scholarship)

Purpose: To assist students from various backgrounds working towards various higher education degrees. **Focus:** General studies/Field of study not specified. **Qualif.:** Applicants must be female administrators or faculty members working for a United Methodist related institution pursuing a PhD in higher education administration; must have a GPA of 3.0+. **Criteria:** Selection will be based on the committee's criteria.

Funds Avail.: $5,000. **Duration:** Annual. **To Apply:** Applicants must visit the website for the online application process. All required supporting documents like transcripts with grade, letter of reference, essay, signed pledged form must be submitted. **Deadline:** March 1. **Contact:** umscholar@gbhem.org; 615-340-7344.

9852 ■ HANA Scholarships *(Undergraduate, Graduate, Doctorate/Scholarship)*

Purpose: To assist students from various backgrounds working towards various higher education degrees. **Focus:** General studies/Field of study not specified. **Qualif.:** Applicants must be born of Hispanic, Asian, Native American or Pacific Island parentage; must be junior or senior level undergraduates or graduate/doctoral students; must be full and active members of the UMC for at least three years; must have a GPA of 2.85+; must have plans to prepare for leadership in the UMC in their HANA (Hispanic, Asian, Native American or Pacific Island) community. **Criteria:** Selection will be based on the committee's criteria.

Funds Avail.: $1,000-$3,000. **To Apply:** Applicants must visit the website for the online application process. All required supporting documents like transcripts with grade, letter of reference, essay, signed pledged form must be submitted. **Deadline:** March 1.

9853 ■ Miriam Hoffman Scholarships *(Undergraduate, Graduate/Scholarship)*

Purpose: To assist students from various backgrounds working towards various higher education degrees. **Focus:** Music. **Qualif.:** Applicants must be undergraduate or graduate students; must be pursuing a vocational career in music education or music ministry. **Criteria:** Selection will be based on the committee's criteria.

Funds Avail.: $500-$1,000. **To Apply:** Applicants must visit the website for the online application process. All required supporting documents like transcripts with grade, letter of reference, essay, signed pledged form must be submitted. **Deadline:** March 1.

9854 ■ Journey Toward Ordained Ministry Scholarships *(Undergraduate, Graduate/Scholarship)*

Purpose: To assist students from various backgrounds working towards various higher education degrees. **Focus:** Religion. **Qualif.:** Applicants must: be pursuing ordained

Awards are arranged alphabetically below their administering organizations

ministry at either the undergraduate or graduate level; be racial/ethnic minorities aged 30 or under; be members of UMC for two years; be attending a UM related institution; have a GPA of 2.85+ for undergraduate and 3.0+ for graduate. **Criteria:** Selection will be based on the committee's criteria.

Funds Avail.: $5,000. **Duration:** Annual. **To Apply:** Applicants must visit the website for the online application process. All required supporting documents like transcripts with grade, letter of reference, essay, signed pledged form must be submitted. **Deadline:** March 1. **Contact:** umscholar@gbhem.org; 615-340-7344.

9855 ■ Elvina Jane Owen Awards *(Graduate, Undergraduate/Scholarship)*

Purpose: To assist students from various backgrounds working towards various higher education degrees. **Focus:** Education. **Qualif.:** Students must be majoring in education. First preference to students in the Jonestown District of the Western Pennsylvania Annual Conference enrolled at Allegheny College. Second preference to graduate students from Western Pennsylvania Annual Conference; must have a GPA of 2.85+. **Criteria:** Selection will be based on the committee's criteria.

Funds Avail.: $500-$1,000. **Duration:** Annual. **To Apply:** Applicants must visit the website for the online application process. All required supporting documents like transcripts with grade, letter of reference, essay, signed pledged form must be submitted. **Deadline:** March 1. **Contact:** umscholar@gbhem.org; 615-340-7344.

9856 ■ United Methodist General Scholarships *(Undergraduate, Graduate/Scholarship)*

Purpose: To provide financial support to those students who are pursuing their educational goals. **Focus:** General studies/Field of study not specified. **Qualif.:** Applicants must be undergraduate, graduate, or doctoral students; must be full active members of the UMC for at least one year; have a minimum GPA of 2.5+; must be attending any accredited institution within the US. **Criteria:** Selection will be based on the committee's criteria.

Funds Avail.: $500-$1,000 for undergraduate; $1,000-$2,000 for graduate students. **To Apply:** Applicants must visit the website for the online application process. All required supporting documents like transcripts with grade, letter of reference, essay, signed pledged form must be submitted.

9857 ■ United Methodist Youth Organization
1908 Grand Ave.
Nashville, TN 37212
Ph: (615)340-7079
Free: 877-899-2780
E-mail: youngpeople@gbod.org
URL: www.gbod.org/youngpeople

9858 ■ Richard S. Smith Scholarships *(Undergraduate/Scholarship)*

Purpose: To support students in pursuing their church-related career. **Focus:** Religion. **Qualif.:** Applicants must be graduating high school seniors entering first year of undergraduate study; must be racial-ethnic minorities; must have a minimum GPA of 2.5, active membership in UMC; must be U.S. citizens or permanent residents; must be admitted to a full-time degree program in an accredited college/university pursuing a "church-related" career. **Criteria:** Selection is based on the submitted application.

Funds Avail.: $1,000. **Duration:** One year. **To Apply:** Applicants must submit a completed application form. **Deadline:** March 1.

9859 ■ United Mitochondrial Disease Foundation (UMDF)
8085 Saltsburg Rd., Ste. 201
Pittsburgh, PA 15239-1977
Ph: (412)793-8077
Fax: (412)793-6477
Free: 888-317-8633
E-mail: info@umdf.org
URL: www.umdf.org
Facebook: www.facebook.com/United-Mitochondrial-Disease-Foundation-202570833099467
Twitter: twitter.com/UMDF

9860 ■ UMDF Clinical Research Fellowship Training Awards *(Professional development/Fellowship)*

Purpose: To support the training of physician scientists who plan to practice clinical management of patients with mitochondrial disorders and to conduct clinically oriented research in the field of mitochondrial medicine. **Focus:** Health sciences. **Qualif.:** Applicants must hold a Doctor of Medicine or equivalent degree and have completed an ACGME or Canadian LMCC accredited residency program by the date of grant funding. **Criteria:** Selection will be based on the committee's criteria. Preference will be given to applicants who intend to remain in the US or Canada after completing training.

Funds Avail.: No specific amount. **To Apply:** Applicants must download the Statement of Intent form available at the website. Fill out the preceding form and then save it as a normal Word document. Use only the NIH biographical sketch format, maximum of four pages. Completed Statement of Intent and all NIH biographical sketches must be submitted through email for applicants and mentors as one document. In addition, applicants must also send a signed hard copy to Jean Bassett. **Deadline:** October 31.

9861 ■ United Negro College Fund (UNCF)
1805 7th St. NW
Washington, DC 20001
Free: 800-331-2244
URL: www.uncf.org

9862 ■ UNCF/Merck Graduate Science Research Dissertation Fellowships *(Graduate/Fellowship)*

Purpose: To help graduate students complete coursework, conduct research, and prepare the dissertation required for a doctoral degree in the biomedically relevant life or physical sciences and engineering. **Focus:** Engineering; Life sciences; Physical sciences. **Qualif.:** Candidates must be African-American; must be citizens or permanent residents of the United States; must be enrolled full-time in a PhD or equivalent doctoral degree program majoring in a life science, physical science or engineering; must be engaged in and within 1-3 years of completing dissertation research; and must successfully complete all qualifying exams. **Criteria:** A UNCF/Merck Selection Committee consisting of educators, scientists and engineers will select the awardees based on academic ability, record of accomplishment, and

Awards are arranged alphabetically below their administering organizations

the soundness of the proposed doctoral research plan. **Funds Avail.:** Up to 53,500. **Duration:** Annual. **Number Awarded:** At least 12. **To Apply:** Applicants may contact the UNCF or the Merck Company Foundation for the application process and other information.

9863 ■ UNCF/Merck Postdoctoral Science Research Fellowships *(Postdoctorate/Fellowship)*

Purpose: To support post-graduate students to obtain postdoctoral training and to prepare for a career in biomedical research. **Focus:** Engineering; Life sciences; Physical sciences. **Qualif.:** Applicants must be African-Americans; must be citizens or permanent residents of the United States; must be PhD or equivalent doctoral degree recipients in a life or physical science by the end of the current academic year; must be appointed as new or continuing postdoctoral fellows at an academic or on-academic research institution in the USA (private industrial laboratories are excluded). **Criteria:** A UNCF/Merck Selection Committee consisting of educators and scientists will select the award winners based on ability, record of accomplishment, and the soundness of the proposed postdoctoral research. **Funds Avail.:** Up to $92,000. **Duration:** Annual. **Number Awarded:** At least 10. **To Apply:** Applicants may contact the UNCF or the Merck Company Foundation for the application process and other information.

9864 ■ United Parent Support for Down Syndrome
Hartford Plz.
1070 S Roselle Rd.
Schaumburg, IL 60193
Ph: (847)895-2100
URL: www.upsfordowns.org

9865 ■ Katie MacDonald Memorial Scholarships *(Graduate, Undergraduate/Scholarship)*

Purpose: To provide financial assistance to those individuals with Down syndrome who are pursuing their education. **Focus:** Disabilities. **Qualif.:** Applicants must be U.S. citizens; must be individuals with Down syndrome or siblings of individuals with Down syndrome pursuing full or part-time educational or job training opportunities beyond high school or must be pursuing junior college, undergraduate or graduate degrees in disability related fields. **Criteria:** Selection will be based on demonstrated accomplishments; obstacles overcome; leadership and community involvement; life goals. **Funds Avail.:** $2,500 each. **Number Awarded:** 4. **To Apply:** Applicants must submit a completed application form; essay/personal statement; two recommendation letters; additional documentation (transcripts, extra-curricular activities, etc). Two copies of the application packet should be submitted. **Deadline:** June 1. **Contact:** Beth Barrett, Scholarship Committee Chairman; Email: embarrett@upsfordowns.org.

9866 ■ Eric Martinez Memorial Scholarships *(Graduate, Undergraduate/Scholarship)*

Purpose: To provide financial assistance to individuals or siblings affected by down syndrome pursuing their education. **Focus:** General studies/Field of study not specified. **Qualif.:** Applicants must be U.S. citizens; must be individuals with Down syndrome or siblings of individuals with Down syndrome pursuing full or part-time educational or job training opportunities beyond high school or must be pursuing junior college, undergraduate or graduate degrees. **Criteria:** Selection will be based on demonstrated accomplishments; obstacles overcome; leadership and community involvement; life goals. **Funds Avail.:** $2,500 each. **Number Awarded:** 2. **To Apply:** Applicants must submit a completed application form; essay/personal statement; two recommendation letters; additional documentation (transcripts, extra-curricular activities, etc). Two copies of the application packet should be submitted. **Deadline:** June 1. **Contact:** Beth Barrett, Scholarship Committee Chairman; Email: embarrett@upsfordowns.org.

9867 ■ United South and Eastern Tribes, Inc. (USET)
711 Stewarts Ferry Pke.
Nashville, TN 37214
Ph: (615)872-7900
Fax: (615)872-7417
URL: www.usetinc.org
Facebook: www.facebook.com/United-South-and-Eastern-Tribes-Inc-545683215479419
Twitter: twitter.com/usetinc

9868 ■ United South and Eastern Tribes Scholarship Fund *(Undergraduate/Scholarship)*

Purpose: To provide financial assistance to Indian students in the USET service area. **Focus:** General studies/Field of study not specified. **Qualif.:** Applicants must be Indian students who are enrolled members of one of twenty-six USET member tribes. **Criteria:** Applicants will be judged based on demonstrated need for financial assistance, satisfactory scholastic standing and current enrollment or acceptance in a post-secondary educational institution. **Funds Avail.:** $500. **Duration:** Annual. **To Apply:** Applicants must submit the complete application form, three (3) letters of recommendation, verification of tribal enrollment in a USET Tribe. **Deadline:** April 30.

9869 ■ U.S. Air Force ROTC
60 W Maxwell Blvd.
Maxwell AFB, AL 36112-5917
Fax: (334)953-6167
Free: 866-423-7682
E-mail: csp@maxwell.af.mil
URL: www.afrotc.com
Facebook: www.facebook.com/pages/USAF-ROTC/290671271043043
Twitter: www.twitter.com/usafrotc

9870 ■ Hispanic Serving Institution Scholarships (HSIS) *(Undergraduate/Scholarship)*

Purpose: To meet officer production requirements and enhance enrollment at HSIs. **Focus:** General studies/Field of study not specified. **Qualif.:** Applicants must be students enrolled as HSIs (Hispanic Serving Institution), including those schools which host an Air force ROTC detachment and those which are crosstowns of another school that hosts a detachment. **Criteria:** Applicants do not have to meet a selection board for this scholarship. **Funds Avail.:** Varies. **Duration:** Annual; 2-3 years. **To Apply:** Applicants may start the application process for the

Awards are arranged alphabetically below their administering organizations

scholarship program by contacting the Air Force ROTC detachment at the school that they wish to attend.

9871 ■ Historically Black College or University Scholarships (HBCUS) *(Undergraduate/Scholarship)*

Purpose: To meet officer production requirements and enhance enrollment at HBCUs. **Focus:** General studies/Field of study not specified. **Qualif.:** Applicants must be enrolled at an HBCU (Historically Black College or University), including those schools which host an Air Force ROTC detachment and those which are crosstowns of another school that hosts a detachment. **Criteria:** Applicants do not have to meet a selection board.

Funds Avail.: Varies. **Duration:** Annual; 2-3 years. **To Apply:** Applications for the HBCU Scholarship are processed and approved at the detachment level. Applicant must contact the detachment serving the school, and the school will work to nominate the applicant for the appropriate scholarship program. Applications are accepted at any time each year.

9872 ■ U.S. Air Force ROTC Express Scholarships *(Undergraduate/Scholarship)*

Purpose: To provide financial assistance for college students enrolled in specific fields. **Focus:** Aeronautics; Aerospace sciences; Atmospheric science; Engineering. **Qualif.:** Applicants must be United States citizens by the end of the projected term of activation; must pass the Air Force Officer Qualifying Test; must pass the Air Force ROTC Physical Fitness Test; must have at least a 2.5 cumulative college grade point average; must pass a physical examination and be certified; must not be a contracted scholarship recipient; and must meet the age, moral and other scholarship eligibility requirements for Air force ROTC. **Criteria:** The Express Scholarship program is operated on a fully qualified basis - those who meet the qualifications are awarded the scholarship and do not meet a scholarship selection board.

Funds Avail.: $18,000. **To Apply:** Applications for the Express Scholarship are processed and approved at the detachment level. Applicant must contact the detachment serving the school that he/she wishes to attend and the school will work to nominate the student for the appropriate scholarship program.

9873 ■ U.S. Air Force ROTC High School Scholarships *(Undergraduate/Scholarship)*

Purpose: To provide financial assistance to high school seniors. **Focus:** General studies/Field of study not specified. **Qualif.:** Applicants must: be United States citizens or able to obtain citizenship by the last day of the first term of the freshman year for 4-year offers, or the first term of the sophomore year for 3-year offers; be high school graduates or have an equivalent certificate; be 17-31 years old prior to scholarship activation; and, not be enrolled full-time at a college or a university except for joint high school college programs. **Criteria:** Selection will be based on leadership and work experience; extracurricular activities; results from the personal interview; questionnaire results; and academic scores.

Funds Avail.: No specific amount. **Duration:** Annual; Up to three and four years. **Number Awarded:** Varies. **To Apply:** Applicants must submit their application online and include the following forms: Counselor Certification, Personal Statement, Physical Fitness Assessment, and resume. they must have their high school transcripts with raised seal or signature as well as their SAT or ACT scores. **Deadline:** December 1.

9874 ■ U.S. Air Force ROTC In-College Scholarships *(Undergraduate/Scholarship)*

Purpose: To provide scholarships to college freshmen and sophomores in any major. **Focus:** General studies/Field of study not specified. **Qualif.:** Applicants must: be United States citizens by the end of the projected term of activation; pass the Air Force Officer Qualifying Test; meet the Air Force ROTC weight and body fat standards; pass the Air Force ROTC Physical Fitness Test; have at least a 2.5 cumulative college grade point average; pass the physical examination; not be contracted scholarship recipients; and, meet the age, moral and other scholarship eligibility requirements for Air force ROTC. Additionally, they must be college freshmen and sophomores in any major. **Criteria:** Selection will be based on academic performance.

Funds Avail.: Amount varies. **Duration:** Up to 3 years. **To Apply:** Applicants must fill out the application request form online. **Deadline:** December 1.

9875 ■ United States Army (U.S. Army) - Center of Miltary History (CMH)
102 4th Ave., Bldg. 35
Fort McNair
Washington, DC 20319-5060
Ph: (202)685-2393
Fax: (202)685-2077
URL: www.history.army.mil/index.html

9876 ■ CMH Dissertation Fellowships *(Graduate/Fellowship)*

Purpose: To support scholarly research and writing among qualified civilian graduate students preparing dissertations in the history of warfare. **Focus:** History, Military. **Qualif.:** Applicants must be civilian citizens of the United States unaffiliated with the U.S. government; that is, they must not be military personnel, not in federal service as civilian employees, and not under contract to the U.S. government. **Criteria:** The Center of Military History conducts its evaluation of applicants on the basis of academic achievement, faculty recommendations, demonstrated writing ability, and the nature and location of the proposed research.

Funds Avail.: $10,000. **Duration:** Annual. **Number Awarded:** 3. **To Apply:** Applicants must submit the following to the Dissertation Fellowship Committee: official transcripts from all undergraduate and graduate schools attended; proposed plan of research; letter of recommendation from their academic director that includes a statement approving the dissertation topic; two other letters of recommendation from individuals who can attest to their qualifications for the fellowship; and writing sample of approximately 25 pages. **Deadline:** January 15. **Contact:** Executive Secretary, Dissertation Fellowship Committee, at the above address.

9877 ■ U.S. Army Health Care
2040 Babcock Rd., Ste. 406
San Antonio, TX 78229
Ph: (210)945-2303
URL: www.goarmy.com

9878 ■ Army Health Professions Scholarships Program *(Professional development/Scholarship)*

Purpose: To help students fulfill their dreams of becoming a doctor, dentist, veterinarian, clinical psychologist, or

Awards are arranged alphabetically below their administering organizations

optometrist. **Focus:** Dentistry; Medicine; Ophthalmology; Optometry; Psychology; Veterinary science and medicine. **Qualif.:** Applicants must be 18 to 36 years of age; must have a GPA of 3.2 or higher; and must be mentally, morally and physically able to serve. **Criteria:** Selection will be based on the Board's criteria.

Funds Avail.: Amount varies. **Number Awarded:** Varies. **To Apply:** Applicants must apply through a Health Care Recruiter. **Contact:** Send e-mail to SFC Cherie K. Kirk at cherie.k.kirk.mil@mail.mil.

9879 ■ United States Army Warrant Officers Association (USAWOA)
462 Herndon Pky., Ste. 207
Herndon, VA 20170-5235
Ph: (703)742-7727
Fax: (703)742-7728
Free: 800-587-2962
URL: www.usawoa.org

9880 ■ USAWOASF/Grantham University On-Line Scholarships *(Graduate, Undergraduate/Scholarship)*

Purpose: To support the education of the relatives and/or dependents of USAWOA members. **Focus:** General studies/Field of study not specified. **Qualif.:** Applicants should be association regular members in good standing, their spouses and their children (natural and adopted) and stepchildren (seniors in high school or above). All must have a cumulative GPA of 3.0 or higher on a 4.0 scale. **Criteria:** Selection will be based on the committee's criteria.

Funds Avail.: No specific amount. **Duration:** Annual. **To Apply:** Application form is available on the website. Applicants must submit a complete application packet consisting of: the application form (typewritten format); an essay (800-100 words, include word count) on educational goals; special circumstances which may affect the applicants' school attendance; list of extracurricular activities; a recommendation letter (from instructor, faculty advisor, etc.); National Test Scores, SAT, ACT, etc.; and a 4x6 photograph (view head and shoulders). **Deadline:** May 1. **Contact:** USAWOA Scholarship Foundation at usawoasf@verizon.net.

9881 ■ USAWOASF Regular Scholarships *(Undergraduate/Scholarship)*

Purpose: To support the education of the relatives and/or dependents of USAWOA members. **Focus:** General studies/Field of study not specified. **Qualif.:** Applicants must be spouses, children (natural and adopted), grandchildren and dependent stepchildren, under the age of 23 years (seniors in high school or above); of members in good standing in the USAWOA; and must be in their senior year of high school (or higher) and plan to attend, or continue their education, in an accredited American college/university, vocational technical institution on a full time basis. All must have a cumulative GPA of 3.0 or higher on a 4.0 scale. The school must be a degree or certificate granting institution. **Criteria:** Selection will be based on the committee's criteria.

Funds Avail.: No specific amount. **Duration:** Annual. **To Apply:** Application form is available on the website. Applicants must submit a complete application packet consisting of: the application form (typewritten format); an essay (800-100 words, include word count) on educational goals; special circumstances which may affect the applicants' school attendance; list of extracurricular activities; a recommendation letter (from instructor, faculty advisor, etc.); National Test Scores, SAT, ACT, etc.; and a 4x6 photograph (view head and shoulders). **Deadline:** May 1.

9882 ■ United States Association for Energy Economics (USAEE)
28790 Chagrin Blvd., Ste. 350
Cleveland, OH 44122-4642
Ph: (216)464-2785
Fax: (216)464-2768
E-mail: usaee@usaee.org
URL: www.usaee.org
Facebook: www.facebook.com/pages/The-United-States-Association-for-Energy-Economics-USAEE/295906107166472
LinkedIn: www.linkedin.com/groups/1631487/profile
Twitter: twitter.com/USEnergyEcon

9883 ■ Calgary USAEE/IAEE North American Conference Registration Fee Scholarships *(Undergraduate/Scholarship)*

Purpose: To offset the conference registration costs for students. **Focus:** Energy-related areas. **Qualif.:** Applicants must be full-time students or students who have completed their degrees within the past six months; and must be members of IAEE in good standing. **Criteria:** Awards will be awarded on a rolling basis.

Funds Avail.: $300. **To Apply:** Applicants must submit a personal letter as well as a letter from their advisor or another faculty member familiar with their research. Personal letter must include the following information: 1) meets all the required qualifications; 2) describes the energy interests and future accomplishments by attending the conference; and, 3) provides name and contact information of a faculty member. Advisor's letter should describe the applicant's research interests, nature of the academic program and progress, and recommendation for the award. **Deadline:** September 13. **Contact:** Dave Williams, USAEE Executive Director; usaee@usaee.org.

9884 ■ Dennis J. O'Brien USAEE/IAEE Best Student Paper Award *(Undergraduate/Award)*

Purpose: To help and encourage students to present their papers in the conference. **Focus:** Energy-related areas. **Qualif.:** Applicants must be full-time students or have completed a degree within the past 12 months. Applicants must also be members of IAEE in good standing. **Criteria:** Recipients will be selected based on the submitted papers.

Funds Avail.: Varies. **Number Awarded:** Varies. **To Apply:** Applicants must submit an abstract; a qualification letter with photocopy of student ID; and advisor's letter or letter from a faculty member confirming that the applicant's paper meets the qualifications. Papers must be original. Only papers co-authored by students will be given consideration. **Contact:** Dave Williams, USAEE Executive Director at usaee@usaee.org.

9885 ■ U.S. Capitol Historical Society (USCHS)
200 Maryland Ave. NE
Washington, DC 20002
Fax: (202)544-8244
Free: 800-887-9318
URL: www.uschs.org

Awards are arranged alphabetically below their administering organizations

Facebook: www.facebook.com/US-Capitol-Historical
-Society-53092472345/timeline/
Twitter: www.twitter.com/capitolhistory

9886 ■ United States Capitol Historical Society Fellowships *(Graduate/Fellowship)*

Purpose: To provide financial support to scholars researching important topics in the art and architectural history of the United States Capitol Complex. **Focus:** Art history; History, American; Museum science; United States studies. **Qualif.:** Applicant must be a graduate student enrolled in a degree program in art or architectural history, American history, American studies, museum studies, or decorative arts, and scholars with a proven record of research and publication. **Criteria:** Applications are judged based on the qualifications of the applicant, the significance of the topic, the degree of need for the proposed research, the feasibility of the research plan, and the likelihood that the research will lead to publication.

Funds Avail.: $2,500 per month, up to $30,000 for a full year. **Duration:** One month and a maximum of one year. **To Apply:** Applicant must submit a curriculum vitae; transcripts of graduate work; two supporting letters; dates for which the fellowship is requested, with estimated time period for each phase of the proposed research; list of expected sources of income during the proposed period; and research proposal (maximum 5 pages). Submit materials by regular mail to Dr. Donald Kennon, or by fax, or email to Dr. Barbara Wolanin. **Deadline:** March 15. **Contact:** Dr. Barbara Wolanin, 202-228-4602, bwolanin@aoc.gov.

9887 ■ United States Department of Agriculture Animal and Plant Health Inspection Service (USDA APHIS)
USDA, APHIS, Biotechnology Permit Services
4700 River Rd., Unit 91
Riverdale, MD 20737
Ph: (301)851-2046
Free: 877-770-5990
URL: www.aphis.usda.gov

9888 ■ Saul T. Wilson, Jr. Scholarships *(Graduate, Undergraduate/Scholarship)*

Purpose: To provide financial assistance to those students who are in a veterinary medicine and biomedical sciences. **Focus:** Biomedical sciences; Veterinary science and medicine. **Qualif.:** Applicants must be U.S. citizens enrolled in an accredited college or university within the United States as full-time students in good academic standing; must be undergraduate students who have completed at least two years (60 semester or 90 quarter hours) of a four-year pre-veterinary medicine or other biomedical science curriculum or graduate students who have completed not more than one year (18 semester or 27 quarter hours) of study in veterinary medicine; must be willing to work for the agency during school breaks (both summer and holiday periods). **Criteria:** Applicants are evaluated based on academic achievement.

Funds Avail.: Up to $5,000 for undergraduate studies; Up to $10,000 for graduate studies. **Duration:** Annual. **To Apply:** Applicants must submit a resume, transcript for all completed college work to date, proof of current enrollment on a full-time basis and/or, if applicable, a letter of acceptance to veterinary school, and a copy of DD-214.

9889 ■ U.S. Department of Commerce - National Oceanic and Atmospheric Administration (NOAA)
1401 Constitution Ave. NW, Rm. 5128
Washington, DC 20230
Ph: (202)482-6128
E-mail: noaa.staff.directory@noaa.gov
URL: www.noaa.gov

9890 ■ John A. Knauss Marine Policy Fellowship *(Graduate/Fellowship)*

Purpose: To provide educational experience to students who have interest in marine/ocean/Great Lakes resources and in the national policy decisions affecting those resources. **Focus:** Water resources. **Qualif.:** Applicants must be graduate students with hosts in the legislative branch, executive branch or appropriate associations/institutions located in the Washington, DC area. **Criteria:** Recipients will be selected based on submitted materials.

Funds Avail.: Amount varies. **Duration:** Annual. **To Apply:** Applicants must submit curriculum vitae, a personal education and career goals statement, two letters of recommendation, copy of all official undergraduate and graduate transcripts, listing of classes and career plan(s). **Remarks:** Established in 1979.

9891 ■ NOAA EPP Undergraduate Scholarships (USP) *(Undergraduate/Scholarship)*

Purpose: To increase the number of undergraduate and graduate students who undertake target areas integral to NOAA's mission; to train students in NOAA-related sciences. **Focus:** Atmospheric science; Oceanography. **Qualif.:** Applicants must be U.S. citizens currently enrolled or accepted as full-time 2nd year students in a four-year academic program or a 3rd year students in a five-year program in a discipline related to NOAA's programs and mission at an accredited minority serving institution (college or university within the United States or U.S. territories); must earn and maintain a minimum 3.2 grade point average on a 4.0 scale. **Criteria:** Selection will be based on evaluation of relevant course work; education plan and statement of career interest; academic recommendations or endorsements; additional relevant experience related to diversity of education.

Funds Avail.: No specific amount. **Duration:** Annual. **To Apply:** Applicants must submit a completed application form; two essays; official college transcripts; two academic references from a faculty member. **Contact:** NOAA/Office of Education, at the above address or e-mail to studentscholarshipprograms@noaa.gov.

9892 ■ NOAA Graduate Sciences Scholarships *(Graduate/Scholarship)*

Purpose: To provide financial assistance to graduate students pursuing a degree in atmospheric and oceanic-related sciences. **Focus:** Atmospheric science; Oceanography. **Qualif.:** Applicants must be U.S. citizens; enrolled as either full-time students and graduating in the spring term, or as full-time students in a graduate program at an accredited college or university within the United States or U.S. territories; must have earned a 3.0 minimum GPA on a 4.0 scale in all completed undergraduate and graduate courses each semester or quarter; must have a graduate level major in a discipline related to atmospheric and oceanic sciences; progressed in coursework such as required coursework and assignments for targeted position that must be completed within two years for a Master's degree and four years for a PhD. **Criteria:** Selection will be based on academic records; statement of career interests and goals; compatibility of the applicant's background with the interests of NOAA.

Funds Avail.: No specific amount. **Duration:** Annual. **To Apply:** Applicants must submit a completed application form; essay on, "How Your Course of Study will Benefit or Complement NOAA's Mission"; statement of the applicant's academic and career goals; letter of acceptance to an accredited graduate school/university; official college transcripts; three references from individuals who know the student in a professional capacity; list of current and planned courses.

9893 ■ U.S. Department of Education - Office of Postsecondary Education

1900 K St. NW
Washington, DC 20006
Ph: (202)502-7750
Fax: (202)401-0689
Free: 800-USA-LEAR
E-mail: customerservice@inet.ed.gov
URL: www.ed.gov
Facebook: www.facebook.com/SecretaryArneDuncan
Twitter: www.twitter.com/usedgov

9894 ■ Jacob K. Javits Fellowships Program
(Master's, Doctorate/Fellowship)

Purpose: To provide fellowships to students of superior academic ability to undertake study at the Doctoral and Master of Fine Arts level in selected fields of arts, humanities, and social sciences. **Focus:** Arts; Humanities; Social sciences. **Qualif.:** Applicants must be individuals who at the time of application: will be entering a doctoral program in the current academic year and/or who, at the time of application, have not yet completed their first full year of study in the doctoral program for which they are seeking support; will be entering a Master of Fine Arts program in the current academic year where the master's is the terminal highest degree awarded in the selected field of study. Applicants must be US citizens or nationals, permanent residents of the US, or citizens of any one of the freely associated States. **Criteria:** Selection will be based on demonstrated achievement, financial need and exceptional promise.

Funds Avail.: No specific amount. **To Apply:** The free application for Federal Student Aid (FAFSA) is required as part of the application for a Javits fellowship in order to complete the financial need calculation. Applicants may obtain a copy of FAFSA online or from their institution's financial aid office. Applicants are encouraged to submit their FAFSA electronically. **Deadline:** September 30. **Contact:** Carmen Gordon, U.S. Department of Education, OPE, Student Service, 1990 K St. NW, 1th Fl., Washington, DC 20006-8524; Email: ope_javits_program@ed.gov; Phone: 202-502-7542; Fax: 202-502-7859.

9895 ■ U.S. Department of Education - Office of Special Education and Rehabilitative Services - National Institute on Disability and Rehabilitation Research (NIDRR)

400 Maryland Ave. SW, MS 2700
Washington, DC 20202
Fax: (202)245-7323
E-mail: nidrr-mailbox@ed.gov

URL: www2.ed.gov/about/offices/list/osers/nidrr/index.html

9896 ■ Mary Switzer Research Fellowships - Distinguished Fellowships *(Doctorate/Fellowship)*

Purpose: To support qualified individuals to engage in scientific research relating to the rehabilitation of individuals with disabilities. **Focus:** Disabilities; Rehabilitation, Physical/Psychological. **Qualif.:** Applicants must be individuals with a doctorate, other terminal degree or comparable academic qualifications who have seven or more years of research experience in subject areas, methods or techniques directly relevant to rehabilitation research. **Criteria:** All applications are subjected to a competitive peer review process that is dictated by federal regulation.

Funds Avail.: $75,000. **Duration:** Annual. **To Apply:** The most current application information is available from Grants.gov. Alternatively, applicants may download an application package online. **Deadline:** May 15. **Contact:** Marlene Spencer, U.S. Department of Education, OSERS, National Institute on disability and Rehabilitation Research, 550 12th St. SW, RM. 5133, Washington, DC 20202-2700; Email: marlene.spencer@ed.gov; Phone: 202-245-7532.

9897 ■ Mary Switzer Research Fellowships - Merit Fellowships *(Professional development/Fellowship)*

Purpose: To support qualified individuals to engage in scientific research relating to the rehabilitation of individuals with disabilities. **Focus:** Disabilities; Rehabilitation, Physical/Psychological. **Qualif.:** Applicants must be individuals with advanced professional training or research experience in an independent study in appropriate areas that are directly pertinent to disability and rehabilitation, but who are in earlier stages of their research career, with less than the required seven years experience, or who do not have a doctorate. **Criteria:** Selection will be based on the committee's criteria.

Funds Avail.: $75,000. **To Apply:** The most current application information is available from Grants.gov. Alternatively, applicants may download an application package online. **Contact:** Marlene Spencer, U.S. Department of Education, OSERS, National Institute on disability and Rehabilitation Research, 550 12th St. SW, RM. 5133, Washington, DC 20202-2700; Email: marlene.spencer@ed.gov; Phone: 202-245-7532.

9898 ■ U.S. Department of Energy - Fermi National Accelerator Laboratory

PO Box 500
Batavia, IL 60510-5011
Ph: (630)840-3000
Fax: (630)840-4343
E-mail: fermilab@fnal.gov
URL: www.fnal.gov

9899 ■ Fermilab Internships for Physics Majors
(Undergraduate/Internship)

Purpose: To familiarize students with opportunities at the frontiers of scientific research in particle physics. **Focus:** Physics. **Qualif.:** Applicants must be undergraduate foreign students, major in physics and attending U.S. or non-U.S. universities. Applicants must provide evidence of identity and eligibility to work in the U.S. and must have medical insurance while at Fermilab. **Criteria:** Selection will be based on the committee's criteria.

Awards are arranged alphabetically below their administering organizations

Funds Avail.: No specific amount. Duration: Annual. To Apply: Applicants may contact the Center for application process and other information. Deadline: February 8. Contact: internship@fnal.gov.

9900 ■ Fermilab Science Undergraduate Laboratory Internship (Undergraduate/Internship)

Purpose: To offer outstanding students a chance to work with Fermilab scientists or engineers on a project within the context of laboratory research. Focus: Engineering; Physics. Qualif.: Applicants must be at least 18 years of age, permanent residents or U.S. citizens currently enrolled as full-time undergraduate physics or engineering major, at least one year as matriculating undergraduate students with minimum cumulative Grade Point Average (GPA) of 3.0 on a 4.0 scale and must have high school diplomas or certificate of General Education Development. All applicants must provide evidence of identity and eligibility to work in the U.S. Criteria: Selection will be based on the committees' criteria.

Funds Avail.: No specific amount. To Apply: Applicants must have the following requirements: must complete entrance and exit surveys; must make a poster presentation to mentors and peers; must submit a one-page peer review of another SULI Intern's poster or oral presentation and; must submit an abstract and a 1500-3000 word research project report in the required format. Deadline: January 8.

9901 ■ Fermilab Summer Internships in Science and Technology (Undergraduate/Internship)

Purpose: To offer outstanding students a chance to work with Fermilab scientists or engineers on a project within the context of laboratory research. Focus: Engineering; Physics. Qualif.: Applicants must be undergraduate college students currently enrolled in four-year U.S. colleges or universities, major in Physics, Engineering (mechanical, electrical and computer), Materials Science, Mathematics and Computer Science and must be members of underrepresented group (Black, Hispanic, Native, American and women). All applicants must provide evidence of identity and eligibility to work in the U.S. Criteria: Selection will be based on the committees' criteria.

Funds Avail.: No specific amount. Number Awarded: 12. To Apply: Applicants may contact the Center for application process and other information. Deadline: January 31. Contact: sist@fnal.gov.

9902 ■ Physics of Accelerators and Related Technology for International Students (Undergraduate/Internship)

Purpose: To offer students a chance to work with Fermilab scientists and engineers regarding on the scientific research in physics and technology of particle accelerators. Focus: Engineering; Physics. Qualif.: Applicants must be at least 18 years of age, students of university in a country in Europe, majoring in Physics or Engineering and fluent in English. Applicants must be at least one full year at the university at the moment of applying and must have a minimum of 4.0 Grade Point Average (in 2-5 grading system). Criteria: Specialization in Accelerator Physics and Technology is preferred.

Funds Avail.: No specific amount. To Apply: Applicants must submit the following requirements: application form; university course list with grades; letter of recommendation and; essay. Deadline: January 11. Contact: parti@fnal.gov.

9903 ■ Lee Teng Undergraduate Fellowships in Accelerator Science and Engineering (Undergraduate/Fellowship)

Purpose: To support and promote the exciting and challenging world of particle accelerator physics and technology to the students. Focus: Physics. Qualif.: Applicants must be sophomores or junior students who are currently, legally enrolled full time at US universities, regardless of their nationality. Applicants must provide identification, as well as evidence of citizenship or visa status. Criteria: Selection will be based on the committees' criteria.

Funds Avail.: No specific amount. Duration: Annual. To Apply: Applicants may contact the Center for application process and other information. Deadline: February 8. Contact: leetenginternship@fnal.gov.

9904 ■ U.S. Department of Energy - Lawrence Livermore National Laboratory (LLNL)
7000 East Ave.
Livermore, CA 94550-9234
Ph: (925)422-1100
Fax: (925)422-1370
URL: www.llnl.gov

9905 ■ Lawrence Livermore National Laboratory Fellowships (Doctorate/Fellowship)

Purpose: To support PhD student to broaden their education, continue their training, and participate in leading-edge scientific research. Focus: Clinical laboratory sciences. Qualif.: Applicants must either be in the process of completing their PhD (within one year and employment may not start until PhD requirements have been verified), or have received their PhD degree within five years of being hired as a Lawrence Fellow. Criteria: Selection is based on the submitted application materials.

Funds Avail.: No specific amount. Duration: Three years. To Apply: Applicants must complete the online application. Contact: fellowship@aps.org.

9906 ■ U.S. Department of Energy - Oak Ridge National Laboratory (ORNL)
200 Administration Rd.
Oak Ridge, TN 37831
Ph: (865)576-0885
Fax: (865)576-1665
Free: 800-382-6938
E-mail: maysgt@ornl.gov
URL: www.ornl.gov

9907 ■ Alston S. Householder Fellowships (Doctorate/Fellowship)

Purpose: To support outstanding students who conduct exceptional and innovative research in mathematics, statistics and scientific computing. Focus: Mathematics and mathematical sciences. Qualif.: Applicants must be recipients of an earned doctorate in Applied Mathematics, Statistics, Computational Science or related field and, with rare exceptions, must be no more than four years beyond the doctorate. Applicants should not have previously served more than one postdoctoral appointment and must have a strong background and expertise in more than one area of particular relevance to the ORNL's computational and mathematics program. Criteria: Selection will be based on the committees' criteria.

Awards are arranged alphabetically below their administering organizations

Funds Avail.: No specific amount. **Duration:** Annual. **To Apply:** Applicants must submit the following requirements: a proven academic record of high quality research with clear potential to perform cutting edge, high-impact and innovative research in applied mathematics, statistics and/or computational science; a rigorous statement of research, that provides the significance of the applicants' current research as well as the technical background of the applicants' proposed research at ORNL and; three letters of reference, describing the applicants distinct contributions to their field of research. **Deadline:** November 31. **Contact:** Clayton Webster, webstercg@ornl.gov.

9908 ■ Liane B. Russell Fellowships (Postdoctorate/Fellowship)

Purpose: To provide financial support to outstanding students who proved exceptional talents in terms of conducting a highest quality and impact research in the field of science and engineering. **Focus:** Engineering; Science. **Qualif.:** Applicants must have received their doctoral degrees before their start dates and can have no more than 36 months of post-PhD research experience at the date of application submission. Fellowship is open to all fields of science and engineering. **Criteria:** Selection will be based on the committees' criteria.

Number Awarded: No specific amount. **To Apply:** Applicants may contact the Center for application process and other information. **Contact:** Lauren Wurth, wurthla@ornl.gov.

9909 ■ Clifford G. Shull Fellowships (Postdoctorate/Fellowship)

Purpose: To support outstanding students to become the new scientists who will continue the path to excellence while substantially contributing to ORNL and U.S. Department of Energy missions and goals. **Focus:** Biology; Chemistry; Engineering; Physics; Science. **Qualif.:** Applicants must be Ph.D. students in condensed matter physics, chemistry, materials science and engineering, biology or related field. Previous experience in neutron or X-ray scattering is highly desired; however, outstanding candidates possessing related expertise are also encouraged to apply. Applicants must have received their doctoral degree before his or her start date and can be no more than three years beyond receiving their doctoral degree. **Criteria:** Selection will be based on the committees' criteria.

Funds Avail.: No specific amount. **To Apply:** Applicants may contact the Center for application process and other information. **Contact:** Steve Cherry, cherrysj@ornl.gov.

9910 ■ Alvin M. Weinberg Fellowships (Doctorate/Fellowship)

Purpose: To support future researchers who have an interest in energy and energy-related science and technology challenges. **Focus:** Biology; Energy-related areas; Engineering, Nuclear; Physics; Science. **Qualif.:** Applicants must have received their doctoral degrees and can be no more than three years beyond receiving their doctoral degrees at the date of application submission. Applicants should not have previously held more than one postdoctoral appointment. **Criteria:** Selection will be based on the committees' criteria.

Funds Avail.: No specific amount. **Duration:** Quarterly. **To Apply:** Applicants may contact the Center for application process and other information. **Remarks:** Established in 2009. **Contact:** Channa Palmer, palmerck@ornl.gov.

9911 ■ U.S. Department of Energy - Office of Science
1000 Independence Ave. SW
Washington, DC 20585
Ph: (202)586-5430
Fax: (202)586-4120
E-mail: sc.science@science.doe.gov
URL: science.energy.gov
Twitter: twitter.com/doescience

9912 ■ Office of Science Graduate Fellowships (Graduate/Fellowship)

Purpose: To support outstanding students to pursue graduate training in basic research in areas of physics, non-medical biology; chemistry, mathematics, engineering, computer and computational sciences, and environmental sciences relevant to the Office of Science. **Focus:** Science. **Qualif.:** Applicants must be US citizens and either a first or second year graduate student, or an undergraduate senior at the time of applying, and must be pursuing or plan to pursue graduate study and research in areas relevant to the science programs supported by the DOE Office of Science. **Criteria:** Selection will be based on the committee's criteria.

Funds Avail.: No specific amount. **To Apply:** In addition to meeting the eligibility requirements, applicants must provide the following: a completed online application with all relevant fields answered, including three essays; an academic transcript for every institution listed by the applicants on the application; General Record Examination (GRE) scores for the General Test and a Subject Test. GRE scores are not required but strongly encouraged; three letters of recommendation from individuals that can speak to the applicants' abilities and potential.

9913 ■ U.S. Department of Health and Human Services - Agency for Healthcare Research and Quality (AHRQ)
540 Gaither Rd., Ste. 2000
Rockville, MD 20850
Ph: (301)427-1364
Free: 800-358-9295
E-mail: info@ahrq.gov
URL: www.ahrq.gov

9914 ■ Health Services Research Dissertation Awards (Doctorate/Award)

Purpose: To support students in developing their career and research skills regarding health services. **Focus:** Health care services. **Qualif.:** Applicants must be in a doctoral level of study, working with their host institutions. **Criteria:** Selection will be based on the committee's criteria.

Funds Avail.: No specific amount. **Duration:** Annual. **To Apply:** Applicants must visit the Grants.gov website for the online application process and other required materials.

9915 ■ Mentored Clinical Scientist Development Awards (Doctorate/Award)

Purpose: To support the development of outstanding clinician research scientists who are committed to a career in health services research. **Focus:** Health care services. **Qualif.:** Applicants must have a clinical doctoral degree; must identify a mentor with extensive research experience; must be willing to spend a minimum of 75 percent of full-

Awards are arranged alphabetically below their administering organizations

time professional effort conducting research and developing a research career during the award period. **Criteria:** Selection will be based on the committee's criteria.

Funds Avail.: No specific amount. **Duration:** Annual. **To Apply:** Applicants must visit the Grants.gov website for the online application process and other required materials.

9916 ■ U.S. Department of Health and Human Services - Centers for Disease Control and Prevention (CDC)
1600 Clifton Rd.
Atlanta, GA 30329-4027
Free: 800-232-4636
URL: www.cdc.gov
Facebook: www.facebook.com/CDC
Twitter: www.twitter.com/CDCgov

9917 ■ CDC Presidential Management Fellows Program *(Graduate/Fellowship)*
Purpose: To attract outstanding graduates from different academic discipline who are committed to excellence in leadership and management of public policies and programs. **Focus:** Management. **Qualif.:** Applicants must be recent graduates with a MA, JD or PhD degree; must be U.S. citizens or permanent residents. **Criteria:** Selection will be based on the committee's criteria.

Funds Avail.: No specific amount. **Duration:** Two years. **To Apply:** Applicants must be nominated by their schools. After their nomination, applicants will take an assessment at the nearest Office of Personnel Management, Presidential Management Fellows (OPM PMF).

9918 ■ CDC Preventive Medicine Residency and Fellowships *(Other/Fellowship)*
Purpose: To provide hands-on experiences in public health agencies at the federal, state and local levels. **Focus:** Medicine. **Qualif.:** Applicants must commit to a one or two-year full-time training period (depending on the program); be willing to relocate throughout the duration of the training; meet the professional and licensing requirements for hiring by the U.S. government according to the U.S. Office of Personnel Management; be U.S. citizens or permanent residents; have trained in the Epidemic Intelligence Service (EIS) program or have comparable applied epidemiology experience; have completed at least 12 months of ACGME-accredited postgraduate clinical training involving at least 11 months of direct patient care; have a current, full and unrestricted medical license from a U.S. licensing jurisdiction; have a Master of Public Health or equivalent accredited degree, per ACGME requirement. **Criteria:** Selection will be based on the committees' criteria.

Funds Avail.: No specific amount. **To Apply:** Applicants must visit the website for the online application and must submit the following supporting documents: three letters of recommendation; a copy of certificated or letters from sponsoring institutions verifying completion of ACGME-accredited postgraduate clinical training; official transcripts for all degrees earned since high school; proof of a current, full and unrestricted license to practice their qualifying clinical specialty in a US licensing jurisdiction. Submit supporting documents via mail or courier that provides tracking services to PMR/F. **Deadline:** September 15.

9919 ■ CDC Public Health Informatics Fellowships *(Professional development, Master's, Graduate/Fellowship)*
Purpose: To provide training and experience in applying computer and information science and technology to real public health problems. **Focus:** Computer and information sciences. **Qualif.:** Applicants must meet both the educational and professional requirements; must have a doctoral or masteral degree; willing to commit a two-year, full-time program; be willing to be relocated in Atlanta, GA. Qualifying degree must be from an accredited academic institution in one of the following: public health, medicine, healthcare, health-services research, computer science, information systems, statistics, epidemiology, public health informatics or related discipline. Documented one-year experience for doctoral level candidates and three-year experience for master's level candidates is required in one of the following fields: public health informatics, health informatics or related field, information systems, information science, computer science and information technology. Additionally, documented one-year experience for doctoral level candidates and three-year experience for master's level candidates is required in one of the following areas: Public health, related healthcare profession (medicine, nursing, veterinary medicine, dentistry, allied health professions). **Criteria:** Selection will be based on the committee's criteria.

Funds Avail.: No specific amount. **To Apply:** Applicants must visit the website for the online application; must submit three letters of recommendation, one letter must be from a faculty member or supervisor and official transcripts for all degrees earned must be mailed as one package.

9920 ■ National Center for Health Statistics Postdoctoral Research Awards *(Postdoctorate/Fellowship)*
Purpose: To provide information to develop programs and policies that will improve the health of the American people. **Focus:** General studies/Field of study not specified. **Qualif.:** Applicants must be citizens of the United States or legal permanent residents with a work authorization. Applicants are responsible for obtaining the necessary authorization. Permanent residency status does not qualify as citizenship; must have held doctorates for less than three years or are in the process of receiving doctorate degrees at the time of application; must hold the PhD or other earned research degree recognized by the United States as equivalent to the PhD; must present acceptable evidences of having completed all the formal academic requirements for the degree before appointment; must have demonstrated ability for creative research; applicant's training and research experiences may be in any appropriate discipline or combination required for the proposed research. **Criteria:** Proposals will be evaluated with respect to the following criteria: project's relevance to NCHS's mission and contribution to the field; strength of the approach, design and methodology; feasibility of the project; applicant's personal and professional qualification.

Funds Avail.: No specific amount. **Duration:** Annual. **To Apply:** Applicants must submit curriculum vitae, official transcripts of all graduate and undergraduate credits, three reference letters and statement of research interest. **Deadline:** July 31. **Contact:** Luigia Franks, Program Specialist, Centers for Disease Control and Prevention, National Center for Health Statistics; Email: lfranks@cdc.gov.

9921 ■ Steven M. Teutsch Prevention Effectiveness Fellowships *(Doctorate/Fellowship)*
Purpose: To establish a cadre of quantitative policy analysts at CDC whose work provides information for health policy decision-makers regarding allocation and use of resources to maximize health impact. **Focus:** Economics; Engineering, Industrial; Health sciences; Health services administration; Operations research. **Qualif.:** Applicants

must hold a doctoral degree in economics or applied economics, decision sciences, health services research or related health sciences, industrial engineering or operations research, public policy or policy analysis or related quantitatively-oriented field; non-US citizens must be legal permanent residents or eligible for J-1 status. **Criteria:** Selection will be based on the committee's criteria.

Funds Avail.: No specific amount. **To Apply:** Applicants must visit the website for the online application; must submit three signed letters of recommendation, signed letter from the Department Chair and official transcripts for degrees earned. Supporting documents can be e-mailed; however, original documents are required prior to final selection.

9922 ■ U.S. Department of Health and Human Services - Health Resources and Services Administration (HRSA)
5600 Fishers Ln.
Rockville, MD 20852-1750
Ph: (301)443-2216
Fax: (301)443-1246
Free: 888-ASK-HRSA
E-mail: ask@hrsa.gov
URL: www.hrsa.gov

9923 ■ HRSA Scholarships for Disadvantaged Students *(Undergraduate/Scholarship)*

Purpose: To provide scholarships for full-time, financially needy students from disadvantaged backgrounds who are enrolled in health professions and nursing programs. **Focus:** Health sciences; Medicine; Mental health; Nursing; Public health. **Qualif.:** Applicant must be: U.S. citizens or lawful permanent residents of the United States, the Commonwealth of Puerto Rico, the Northern Mariana Islands, the Virgin Islands, Guam, American Samoa or the Trust Territory of the Pacific Islands, the Republic of Palau, the Republic of the Marshall Islands or the Federated States of Micronesia; full-time students with financial need from disadvantaged backgrounds, enrolled in health professions and nursing programs. **Criteria:** Applications that pass the initial HRSA eligibility screening will be reviewed and rated by a panel based on the program elements and review criteria. The review criteria are designed to enable the review panel to assess the quality of a proposed project and determine the likelihood of its success. The criteria are closely related to each other and are considered as a whole in judging the overall quality of an application.

Funds Avail.: No specific amount. **Duration:** Annual. **To Apply:** Applicants must complete the online application and must submit all required supporting documentation.

9924 ■ NURSE Corps Scholarship Program *(Professional development/Scholarship)*

Purpose: To provide scholarships to nursing students in exchange for a minimum two year full-time service commitment (or part-time equivalent), at an eligible health care facility with a critical shortage of nurses. **Focus:** Nursing. **Qualif.:** Applicants must be: U.S. citizens or nationals (permanent residents are not eligible) enrolled or accepted for enrollment as full-time or part-time students in an accredited school of nursing in a professional registered nurse program; free from any federal judgment liens; and, free from existing service commitments. Their classes will begin no later than September 30, and must they not be delinquents on a federal debt. **Criteria:** Preference will be given to qualified applicants with the greatest financial need who are enrolled full-time in an undergraduate nursing program.

Funds Avail.: $1,330 monthly stipend. **Duration:** Annual. **To Apply:** Application consists of: an online application, required supporting documentation, and if applicable, additional supporting documentation. **Deadline:** May 5.

9925 ■ U.S. Department of Health and Human Services - National Heart, Lung, and Blood Institute (NHLBI)
NIH Bldg. 31, Rm. 5A48, MSC 2486
31 Center Dr.
Bethesda, MD 20892
Ph: (301)592-8573
Fax: (301)592-8563
E-mail: nhlbiinfo@nhlbi.nih.gov
URL: www.nhlbi.nih.gov
Facebook: www.facebook.com/NHLBI
Twitter: twitter.com/nih_nhlbi

9926 ■ Ruth L. Kirschstein NRSA Individual Pre-Doctoral Fellowships *(Doctorate/Fellowship)*

Purpose: To provide financial assistance to students from underrepresented racial and ethnic groups pursuing biomedical and behavioral sciences. **Focus:** Behavioral sciences; Biomedical sciences. **Qualif.:** Applicants must be U.S. citizens or permanent residents; must have a baccalaureate degree and currently enrolled in an eligible doctoral program; must be individuals with disabilities or from underrepresented racial and ethnic groups or from disadvantaged backgrounds pursuing advanced degrees in biomedical and behavioral sciences. **Criteria:** Selection will be based on evaluation of submitted documents and specific criteria.

Funds Avail.: No specific amount. **Number Awarded:** Varies. **To Apply:** Applicants must submit the application materials electronically using the SF 424 Research and Related (R&R) forms and the SF 424 (R&R) Individual Fellowship Application Guide. **Deadline:** April 13, August 13, December 13.

9927 ■ U.S. Department of Health and Human Services - National Institutes of Health - National Library of Medicine (NLM)
8600 Rockville Pike
Bethesda, MD 20894
Ph: (301)594-5983
Fax: (301)402-1384
Free: 888-346-3656
URL: www.nlm.nih.gov

9928 ■ NLM Associate Fellowships *(Postgraduate/Fellowship)*

Purpose: To provide a broad foundation in health sciences information services, and to prepare librarians for future leadership roles in health sciences libraries and in health services research. **Focus:** Health sciences. **Qualif.:** Applicants must be U.S. and Canadian library and information science professionals, as well as graduate students completing their master's degrees. **Criteria:** Selection shall be based on the aforementioned applicants' qualifications and compliance with the application details.

Funds Avail.: Amount varies. **Duration:** Annual. **Number**

Awards are arranged alphabetically below their administering organizations

Awarded: Up to 5. **To Apply:** All applicants must submit an application form, a structured resume, two narrative statements, three references, and an official transcript for each degree earned. Be sure to carefully follow the instructions provided for each form to ensure that all required information is submitted. Only complete applications will be considered. **Deadline:** January 27. **Remarks:** Established in 1957. **Contact:** ORISE; 1299 Bethel Valley Road, MC-100-36, Oak Ridge, TN, 37830-0117; Phone: (865) 576-9975; Fax: (865) 574-2846; nlm.associate.fellowship@orau.org.

9929 ■ U.S. Department of Health and Human Services - U.S. Public Health Service - National Institutes of Health (NIH)
9000 Rockville Pike
Bethesda, MD 20892
Ph: (301)496-4000
E-mail: nihinfo@od.nih.gov
URL: www.nih.gov
Facebook: www.facebook.com/nih.gov
Twitter: twitter.com/nih

9930 ■ National Institute of Health Undergraduate Scholarship Program (NIH UGSP) *(Undergraduate/Scholarship)*

Purpose: To aid students from disadvantaged backgrounds who are committed to careers in biomedical, behavioral, and social science health-related research. **Focus:** Behavioral sciences; Biomedical research; Social sciences. **Qualif.:** Applicants must be U.S. citizens or permanent residents enrolled or accepted for enrollment as full-time students at an accredited four-year undergraduate institution in the United States. They must also have an undergraduate GPA of 3.3 or higher on a 4.0 scale or be within the top five of their class. **Criteria:** Selection will be based on students' commitment in pursuing a career in biomedical, behavioral or social science health-related research, as well as exceptional financial need.

Funds Avail.: $20,000. **Duration:** Annual; up to four years. **To Apply:** Applicants may apply online at ugsp.nih.gov; and must provide the following forms: 1) application checklist; 2) application form; 3) undergraduate institution certification form; and 4) four copies of recommendation forms. **Deadline:** March 9.

9931 ■ U.S. Environmental Protection Agency (EPA)
Ariel Rios Bldg.
1200 Pennsylvania Ave.
Washington, DC 20460
Ph: (202)272-0167
Fax: (202)260-4997
Free: 800-775-5037
E-mail: r3public@epa.gov
URL: www.epa.gov

9932 ■ EPA Science to Achieve Results Fellowships (STAR) *(Graduate/Fellowship)*

Purpose: To encourage students to obtain advanced degrees and pursue careers in an environmental field. **Focus:** Environmental science. **Qualif.:** Students must attend a fully accredited U.S. college or university for their graduate studies; must be U.S. citizens or legal residents. **Criteria:** Selection will be based on evaluation of the submitted requirements and specific criteria.

Funds Avail.: Up to $42,000. **Duration:** Annual. **To Apply:** Applicants must submit a completed application for Federal Assistance form; Standard Form; EPA Key Contacts Form; personal statement; proposal description; background information; and letters of recommendation. Applications must be submitted either via electronic mail or through paper submissions. **Deadline:** November 27. **Contact:** U.S. Environmental Protection Agency, at the above address.

9933 ■ Greater Research Opportunities (GRO) Undergraduate Fellowships *(Undergraduate/Fellowship)*

Purpose: To provide financial assistance to bachelor-level students in environmental fields of study. **Focus:** Environmental science. **Qualif.:** Students must attend a fully accredited U.S. college or university for their last two years of undergraduate studies; must be U.S. citizens or legal residents; must have at least a "B" average overall at the time of application and during the tenure of the fellowship. **Criteria:** Selection will be based on evaluation of submitted requirements and specific criteria.

Funds Avail.: Up to $20,700 per year of academic support plus $8,600 for internship support. **Duration:** up to $19,700 per academic year of support and $9,500 of support for a three-month summer internship. **Number Awarded:** 40. **To Apply:** Applicants must submit a completed application for Federal Assistance form; Standard Form; EPA Key Contacts Form; personal statement; proposal description; background information; and letters of recommendation. Applications must be submitted via electronic mail or through paper submissions. **Deadline:** December 12. **Contact:** Todd Peterson for electronic submissions at peterson.todd@epa.gov.

9934 ■ U.S. Environmental Protection Agency - National Exposure Research Laboratory (NERL)
MC D305-01
Research Triangle Park, NC 27711
Ph: (919)541-2106
Fax: (919)541-0445
URL: www.epa.gov/nerl

9935 ■ NERL Postdoctoral Research Program *(Postdoctorate, Advanced Professional, Professional development/Fellowship)*

Purpose: To provide scientific leadership, understanding, and tools necessary to quantify exposure for humans and ecosystems. **Focus:** Ecology; Remote sensing. **Qualif.:** Candidates must be U.S. citizens or permanent residents; must be scientists interested in conducting high priority research in areas such as: atmospheric modeling; watershed/hydrological modeling; genomics; geospatial and statistical analyses; human exposure modeling; informatics; and remote sensing. Only in the absence of qualified U.S. citizens will permanent residents be considered, and permanent resident applicants must be seeking citizenship as outlined in 8 U.S.C. 1324b(a)(3)(B). **Criteria:** Selection of candidates will be based on the aforementioned qualifications and compliance with the application details.

Funds Avail.: No specific amount. **Duration:** Periodic. **Number Awarded:** Varies. **To Apply:** Candidates must submit the following: up-to-date curriculum vitae; letter of

Awards are arranged alphabetically below their administering organizations

U.S. ENVIRONMENTAL PROTECTION AGENCY

recommendation from their senior research advisors or comparable officials (this may be emailed with their application or separately, whichever the advisors prefer); cover letter indicating positions/project descriptions and locations of interest, their email address, U.S. citizenship status, and how the candidates learned of the program; form DD-214, if claiming veteran's preference. Please take note that applications sent via email must be submitted in a format readable by the office, such as MS Word, portable document format (PDF), rich text format (RTF), or plain text. Use of any format the office cannot read may invalidate the candidates' application. Online applications from journal websites will not be accepted. Please include "NERL Post-Doctoral Program" in the email subject line. **Contact:** Candidates may email their respective application materials to ordpostdocapps@epa.gov.

9936 ■ U.S. Environmental Protection Agency - National Health and Environmental Effects Research Laboratory (NHEERL)
109 T.W. Alexander Dr., MC B305-01
Research Triangle Park, NC 27709
Ph: (919)541-2282
Fax: (919)541-4324
E-mail: zenick.hal@epa.gov
URL: www.epa.gov/nheerl/

9937 ■ NHEERL Postdoctoral Research Program
(Postdoctorate, Advanced Professional, Professional development/Fellowship)

Purpose: To support research that may contribute to the protection of human health and the environment. **Focus:** General studies/Field of study not specified. **Qualif.:** Candidates must be U.S. citizens or permanent residents; must be scientists interested in conducting high priority research that contributes to protecting human health and the environment. Only in the absence of qualified U.S. citizens will permanent residents be considered, and permanent resident applicants must be seeking citizenship as outlined in 8 U.S.C. 1324b(a)(3)(B). **Criteria:** Selection of candidates will be based on the aforementioned qualifications and compliance with the application details.

Funds Avail.: No specific amount. **Number Awarded:** Varies. **To Apply:** Candidates must submit the following: up-to-date curriculum vitae; letter of recommendation from their senior research advisors or comparable officials (this may be emailed with their application or separately, whichever the advisors prefer); cover letter indicating positions/project descriptions and locations of interest, their email address, U.S. citizenship status, and how the candidates learned of the program; form DD-214, if claiming veteran's preference. Please take note that applications sent via email must be submitted in a format readable by the office, such as MS Word, portable document format (PDF), rich text format (RTF), or plain text. Use of any format the office cannot read may invalidate the candidates' application. Online applications from journal websites will not be accepted. Please include "NHEERL Post-Doctoral Program" in the email subject line. **Contact:** Candidates may email their respective application materials to ordpostdocapps@epa.gov.

9938 ■ U.S. Environmental Protection Agency - National Risk Management Research Laboratory (NRMRL)
26 Martin Luther King Blvd.
Cincinnati, OH 45268
Ph: (513)569-7900
URL: www2.epa.gov/aboutepa/national-risk-management-research-laboratory-nrmrl

9939 ■ NRMRL Postdoctoral Research Program
(Postdoctorate, Advanced Professional, Professional development/Fellowship)

Purpose: To aid aspiring postdoctoral researchers in conducting significant studies on risk management research. **Focus:** Risk management. **Qualif.:** Candidates must be U.S. citizens or permanent residents. Only in the absence of qualified U.S. citizens will permanent residents be considered, and permanent resident applicants must be seeking citizenship as outlined in 8 U.S.C. 1324b(a)(3)(B). **Criteria:** Selection of candidates will be based on the aforementioned qualifications and compliance with the application details.

Funds Avail.: No specific amount. **Duration:** Periodic. **Number Awarded:** Varies. **To Apply:** Candidates must submit the following: up-to-date curriculum vitae; letter of recommendation from their senior research advisors or comparable officials (this may be emailed with their application or separately, whichever the advisors prefer); cover letter indicating positions/project descriptions and locations of interest, their email address, U.S. citizenship status, and how the candidates learned of the program; form DD-214, if claiming veteran's preference. Please take note that applications sent via email must be submitted in a format readable by the office, such as MS Word, portable document format (PDF), rich text format (RTF), or plain text. Use of any format the office cannot read may invalidate the candidates' application. Online applications from journal websites will not be accepted. Please include "NRMRL Post-Doctoral Program" in the email subject line. **Contact:** Candidates may email their respective application materials to ordpostdocapps@epa.gov.

9940 ■ U.S. Environmental Protection Agency - Office of Research and Development - National Center for Computational Toxicology (NCCT)
109 T.W. Alexander Dr., MD-B-205-01
Research Triangle Park, NC 27711
Ph: (919)541-4219
URL: www2.epa.gov/aboutepa/about-national-center-computational-toxicology-ncct
Facebook: www.facebook.com/EPA
Twitter: twitter.com/Baker_IDI

9941 ■ NCCT Postdoctoral Research Program
(Postdoctorate, Advanced Professional, Professional development/Fellowship)

Purpose: To aid the next generation of exceptionally qualified scientists with outstanding talent and credentials by encouraging them to fill EPA postdoctoral positions. **Focus:** Medical research; Toxicology. **Qualif.:** Candidates must be U.S. citizens or permanent residents; must be postdoctoral professionals with diverse expertise in computational and experimental laboratory research. Only in the absence of qualified U.S. citizens will permanent residents be considered, and permanent resident applicants must be seeking citizenship as outlined in 8 U.S.C. 1324b(a)(3)(B). **Criteria:** Selection of candidates will be based on the aforementioned qualifications and compliance with the application details.

Funds Avail.: No specific amount. **Number Awarded:** Varies. **To Apply:** Candidates must submit the following: up-

Awards are arranged alphabetically below their administering organizations

to-date curriculum vitae; letter of recommendation from their senior research advisors or comparable officials (this may be emailed with their application or separately, whichever the advisors prefer); cover letter indicating positions/project descriptions and locations of interest, their email address, U.S. citizenship status, and how the candidates learned of the program; form DD-214, if claiming veteran's preference. Please take note that applications sent via email must be submitted in a format readable by the office, such as MS Word, portable document format (PDF), rich text format (RTF), or plain text. Use of any format the office cannot read may invalidate the candidates' application. Online applications from journal websites will not be accepted. Please include "NCCT Post-Doctoral Program" in the email subject line. **Contact:** Candidates may email their respective application materials to ordpostdocapps@epa.gov.

9942 ■ U.S. Environmental Protection Agency - Office of Research and Development - National Center for Environmental Assessment (NCEA)
Two Potomac Yard
2733 Crystal Dr.
Arlington, VA 22202
Ph: (703)347-8600
URL: www.epa.gov/aboutepa/about-national-center-environmental-assessment-ncea

9943 ■ NCEA Postdoctoral Research Program *(Postdoctorate, Advanced Professional, Professional development/Fellowship)*

Purpose: To provide federal research experience to up-and-coming environmental scientists. **Focus:** Conservation of natural resources; Risk management. **Qualif.:** Candidates must be U.S. citizens or permanent residents; must be scientists interested in learning more about the application of toxicological, epidemiological and environmental research to support the development of human health and environmental risk assessments and science policies related to risk assessment. Only in the absence of qualified U.S. citizens will permanent residents be considered, and permanent resident applicants must be seeking citizenship as outlined in 8 U.S.C. 1324b(a)(3)(B). **Criteria:** Selection of candidates will be based on the aforementioned qualifications and compliance with the application details.

Funds Avail.: No specific amount. **Duration:** Up to three years. **Number Awarded:** Varies. **To Apply:** Candidates must submit the following: up-to-date curriculum vitae; letter of recommendation from their senior research advisors or comparable officials (this may be emailed with their application or separately, whichever the advisors prefer); cover letter indicating positions/project descriptions and locations of interest, their email address, U.S. citizenship status, and how the candidates learned of the program; form DD-214, if claiming veteran's preference. Please take note that applications sent via email must be submitted in a format readable by the office, such as MS Word, portable document format (PDF), rich text format (RTF), or plain text. Use of any format the office cannot read may invalidate the candidates' application. Online applications from journal websites will not be accepted. Please include "NCEA Post-Doctoral Program" in the email subject line. **Contact:** Candidates may email their respective application materials to ordpostdocapps@epa.gov.

9944 ■ United States Geospatial Intelligence Foundation (USGIF)
2325 Dulles Corner Blvd., Ste. 450
Herndon, VA 20171
Fax: (703)793-9069
Free: 888-698-7443
E-mail: info@usgif.org
URL: usgif.org

9945 ■ United States Geospatial Intelligence Foundation Graduate Scholarships *(Graduate/Scholarship)*

Purpose: To help further the geospatial tradecraft. To assist promising students interested in the geospatial sciences. **Focus:** Geosciences. **Qualif.:** Applicants must be graduate students interested in geospatial sciences. **Criteria:** Recipients are selected based on academic standing, financial need and quality of the applicant's essay.

Funds Avail.: No specific amount. **To Apply:** Applicants must complete the application form. Applicants must submit an essay describing their understanding of the geospatial intelligence tradecraft, future goals and how they relate to geospatial tradecraft, their understanding of the variety of careers and opportunities available within the geospatial intelligence tradecraft and their motivation for pursuing this field. Applicants must submit two letters of recommendation. **Deadline:** April 22. **Contact:** scholarships@usgif.org.

9946 ■ United States Geospatial Intelligence Foundation High School Scholarships *(Undergraduate/Scholarship)*

Purpose: To help further the geospatial tradecraft. To assist promising students interested in the geospatial sciences. **Focus:** Geosciences. **Qualif.:** Applicants must be senior high school students interested in geospatial sciences. **Criteria:** Recipients are selected based on academic standing, financial need and quality of the applicant's essay.

Funds Avail.: No specific amount. **To Apply:** Applicants must complete the application form. Applicants must submit an essay describing their understanding of the geospatial intelligence tradecraft, future goals and how they relate to geospatial tradecraft, their understanding of the variety of careers and opportunities available within the geospatial intelligence tradecraft and their motivation for pursuing this field. Applicants must submit two letters of recommendation. **Deadline:** April 22. **Contact:** scholarships@usgif.org.

9947 ■ United States Geospatial Intelligence Foundation Undergraduate Scholarships *(Undergraduate/Scholarship)*

Purpose: To help further the geospatial tradecraft; to assist promising students interested in the geospatial sciences. **Focus:** Geosciences. **Qualif.:** Applicants must be undergraduate students interested in geospatial sciences. **Criteria:** Recipients are selected based on academic standing, financial need and quality of the applicant's essay.

Funds Avail.: No specific amount. **To Apply:** Applicants must complete the application form. Applicants must submit an essay describing their understanding of the geospatial intelligence tradecraft, future goals and how they relate to geospatial tradecraft, their understanding of the variety of careers and opportunities available within the geospatial intelligence tradecraft and their motivation for pursuing this field. Applicants must submit two letters of recommenda-

Awards are arranged alphabetically below their administering organizations

tion. **Deadline:** April 22. **Contact:** scholarships@usgif.org.

9948 ■ U.S. Global Leadership Coalition
1129 20th St., NW Ste. 600
Washington, DC 20036
Ph: (202)689-8911
Fax: (202)689-8910
E-mail: info@usglc.org
URL: www.usglc.org

9949 ■ USGLC Internships - Communications
(Undergraduate, Doctorate/Internship)

Purpose: To help individuals in their career development by means of providing on-job training for them to make their marks on foreign policy. **Focus:** Communications; International affairs and relations. **Qualif.:** Applicants must be juniors, seniors, graduate students, and recent graduates who are able to commit at least 20 hours/week in the Communications Department of USGLC. **Criteria:** Selection of interns will be based on the Communications Department's criteria.

Funds Avail.: No specific amount. **To Apply:** Interested applicants must send their resume and cover letter. **Deadline:** July 15 (fall term); October 21 (spring term); March 24 (summer term). **Contact:** Send application materials to Emily at intern@usglc.org.

9950 ■ USGLC Internships - Government Relations
(Undergraduate, Graduate/Internship)

Purpose: To help individuals in their career development by means of providing on-job training for them to make their marks on foreign policy. **Focus:** Government; International affairs and relations. **Qualif.:** Applicants must be juniors and seniors, graduate students, and recent graduate students who are able to commit at least 20 hours/week in the Government Relations Department of USGLC. **Criteria:** Selection of interns will be based on the Government Relations Department's criteria.

Funds Avail.: No specific amount. **To Apply:** Interested applicants must send their resume and cover letter. **Deadline:** July 15 (fall term); October 21 (spring term); March 24 (summer term). **Contact:** Send applications to Emily at intern@usglc.org.

9951 ■ USGLC Internships - Outreach *(Undergraduate, Graduate/Internship)*

Purpose: To help individuals in their career development by means of providing on-job training for them to make their marks on foreign policy. **Focus:** International affairs and relations; Leadership, Institutional and community. **Qualif.:** Applicants must be juniors and seniors, graduate students, and recent graduates who are able to commit at least 20 hours/week in the Outreach Department of USGLC. **Criteria:** Selection of interns will be based on the Outreach Department's criteria.

Funds Avail.: No specific amount. **To Apply:** Interested applicants must send their resume and cover letter. **Deadline:** July 15 (fall term); October 21 (spring term); March 24 (summer term). **Contact:** Send applications to Emily at intern@usglc.org.

9952 ■ USGLC Internships - Policy *(Undergraduate, Graduate/Internship)*

Purpose: To assist individuals by providing them trainings and career developments for them to make their marks on foreign policy. **Focus:** Government; International affairs and relations. **Qualif.:** Applicants must be juniors and seniors, graduate students, and recent graduates who are able to commit at least 20 hours/week in the Policy Department of USGLC. **Criteria:** Selection of interns will be based on the Policy Department's criteria.

Funds Avail.: No specific amount. **To Apply:** Interested applicants must send their resume and cover letter. **Deadline:** July 15 (fall term); October 21 (spring term); March 24 (summer term). **Contact:** Send applications to Emily at interns@usglc.org.

9953 ■ United States Golf Association (USGA)
PO Box 708
Far Hills, NJ 07931
Ph: (908)234-2300
Fax: (908)234-1883
E-mail: usga@usga.org
URL: www.usga.org

9954 ■ USGA/Chevron STEM Scholarship Program
(Undergraduate/Scholarship)

Purpose: To support students seeking their respective careers in STEM courses. **Focus:** Engineering; Mathematics and mathematical sciences; Science; Technology. **Qualif.:** Applicants must be planning to attend an accredited four-year college or university as full-time students with a focus in STEM-related courses. Applicants must also possess a demonstrated interest in golf, which may include: school team and tournament participation, involvement in a First Tee chapter, and family or other golf-related extracurricular activities. **Criteria:** Recipients will be selected based on academic performance and involvement in extracurricular activities.

Funds Avail.: $5,000 to $10,000. **Duration:** up to three years. **To Apply:** Applicants may visit the website to verify the application process and other pieces of information.

9955 ■ United States Hunter Jumper Association (USHJA)
3870 Cigar Ln.
Lexington, KY 40511-8931
Ph: (859)225-6700
Fax: (859)258-9033
E-mail: membership@ushja.org
URL: www.ushja.org
Facebook: www.facebook.com/USHJA
Twitter: twitter.com/ushja

9956 ■ USHJA General Scholarships
(Undergraduate/Scholarship)

Purpose: To provide financial support to those students who are in need. **Focus:** General studies/Field of study not specified. **Qualif.:** Applicants must be graduating high school seniors or current undergraduate students who are pursuing postsecondary studies. **Criteria:** Selection will be based on academic achievement, financial need, extracurricular activities, community service, involvement with American Saddlebred horses and recommendations.

Funds Avail.: No specific amount. **To Apply:** Applicants must check the available website for the required materials. **Contact:** Christina Vaughn, Phone: 859-225-6714.

9957 ■ United States Judo Federation (USJF)
PO Box 338
Ontario, OR 97914

Awards are arranged alphabetically below their administering organizations

Ph: (541)889-8753
Fax: (541)889-5836
URL: www.usjf.com

9958 ■ George C. Balch Scholarships *(Graduate, Undergraduate/Scholarship)*

Purpose: To provide financial assistance to judo students. **Focus:** Education. **Qualif.:** Applicants must be judo students who are high school seniors or graduate students pursuing a college degree in Education. **Criteria:** Applicants will be judged based on academic records.

Funds Avail.: $1,000. **Duration:** Annual; 4 years. **To Apply:** Applicants must submit a filled-out application form; personal statement and a letter of recommendation. **Deadline:** July 31.

9959 ■ Dr. Joseph Fitzsimmons Scholarships *(Doctorate/Scholarship)*

Purpose: To help physicians offset their medical school fees while studying Judo. **Focus:** Medicine. **Qualif.:** Applicants must be registered physicians who are in their 1st or 2nd year of medical school; must be USJF members for three consecutive years; must be yudansha and members of USJF charter club at the time of application. **Criteria:** Scholarship will be given to applicants who best meet the criteria.

Funds Avail.: No specific amount. **To Apply:** Applicants must submit a filled-out application form which can be obtained online; and must send a copy of their acceptance letter from the medical school.

9960 ■ Keiko Fukuda Scholarships *(Undergraduate/Scholarship)*

Purpose: To encourage female judoka to continue their formal education and to further their training in judo. **Focus:** General studies/Field of study not specified. **Qualif.:** Applicants must be female judoka and must be U.S. citizens. Applicants with post-secondary education must have at least a "B" average. **Criteria:** Award will be based on 1) outstanding contribution to the development of judo on a local, yudanshakai, or national level; 2) good competition records (shiai or kata); 3) good moral character and social conduct; and 4) dedication to judo.

Funds Avail.: $400 - $500. **Duration:** Annual. **To Apply:** Applicants must submit a completed application form.

9961 ■ Tamo Kitaura Scholarships *(Other/Scholarship)*

Purpose: To provide financial assistance to USJF referees. **Focus:** General studies/Field of study not specified. **Qualif.:** Applicants must be USJF referees who have reached a degree of technical proficiency; must show an interest in developing themselves through testing and certification. **Criteria:** Recipients will be selected based on submitted application materials.

Funds Avail.: No specific amount. **To Apply:** Applicants must complete the application form which can be obtained online.

9962 ■ Ben Palacio Scholarships *(Undergraduate/Scholarship)*

Purpose: To financially assist students who wish to continue their judo education. **Focus:** General studies/Field of study not specified. **Qualif.:** Applicants must have plans to enroll in the City College of San Francisco. **Criteria:** Recipients will be selected based on submitted application materials.

Funds Avail.: No specific amount. **To Apply:** Applicants must contact the Board of Trustees for further information.

9963 ■ U.S. Medical Supplies
3901A Commerce Park Dr.
Raleigh, NC 27610
Fax: (919)231-4217
Free: 800-790-4792
URL: www.usmedicalsupplies.com

9964 ■ U.S. Medical Supplies' Medical Professionals of Tomorrow Scholarships *(Undergraduate, Graduate/Scholarship)*

Purpose: To support individuals in their medical education. **Focus:** Education, Medical. **Qualif.:** Applicants must be enrolled in an accredited two-year, four-year school, or a graduate program in the United States; must be enrolled full-time in an educational program that is related to a medical field; must be legal residents of the United States. **Criteria:** Recipients will be selected based on submitted materials.

Funds Avail.: First place - $3,500; second - $1,000; third place - $500. **Duration:** Annual. **Number Awarded:** 3. **To Apply:** Applicants must complete the online application form.

9965 ■ United States Naval Research Laboratory
4555 Overlook Ave. SW
Washington, DC 20375
Ph: (202)767-3200
Fax: (202)265-8504
E-mail: webmaster@nrl.navy.mil
URL: www.nrl.navy.mil

9966 ■ NRL-ASEE Postdoctoral Fellowships *(Postdoctorate/Fellowship)*

Purpose: To increase the involvement of scientists and engineers from academia and industry to scientific and technical areas of interest and relevance to the Navy. **Focus:** Architecture, Naval; Naval art and science. **Qualif.:** Applicants must be U.S. citizens or legal permanent residents and have received the PhD, ScD, or other research doctoral degree recognized in U.S. academic circles as equivalent to the PhD within seven years of the date of application. **Criteria:** Selection is based on the technical quality and relevance of the proposed research, recommendations by the Navy laboratories or centers, academic qualifications, reference reports, and availability of funds.

Funds Avail.: No specific amount. **Duration:** Annual. **Number Awarded:** Varies. **To Apply:** Applicants are required to register online to apply. Applicants must prepare a 5-10 page research proposal suitable for the research facility. Official transcripts for each level (undergraduate, graduate, doctoral) must be sent to ASEE projects office.

9967 ■ U.S. Pan Asian American Chamber of Commerce (USPAACC)
1329 18th St. NW
Washington, DC 20036
Ph: (202)296-5221

Awards are arranged alphabetically below their administering organizations

Fax: (202)296-5225
Free: 800-696-7818
E-mail: info@uspaacc.com
URL: uspaacc.com

9968 ■ USPAACC Ampcus Hallmark Scholarships (Undergraduate/Scholarship)

Purpose: To support high school seniors nationwide for their post-secondary education. **Focus:** General studies/Field of study not specified. **Qualif.:** Applicants must be at least 16 years of age at the time of application; must be high school seniors; must be of Asian Pacific Island heritage; must be citizens or permanent residents of the United States; must be beginning full-time study at an accredited post-secondary educational institution in the United States; must be able to attend the current CelebrAsian Procurement Conference. **Criteria:** Selection will be based on the applicants' academic achievement of 3.3 GPA or higher, leadership in extracurricular activities, involvement in community service and financial need.
Funds Avail.: $2,500-$5,000. **Duration:** Annual. **To Apply:** Applicants may download an application form at the website and must attach a 2x2 high resolution headshot photo. **Deadline:** March 13.

9969 ■ USPAACC Denny's Hungry for Education Scholarship (Undergraduate/Scholarship)

Purpose: To support students by giving them higher educational opportunities in order to learn and succeed. **Focus:** General studies/Field of study not specified. **Qualif.:** Applicants must be high school seniors who are citizens or permanent residents of the United States; must have a 3.3 GPA or higher. **Criteria:** Selection will be based on the committee's criteria.
Funds Avail.: $2,500. **To Apply:** Students' parent or legal guardian must sign an Affidavit of Eligibility and Assignment of Rights; must provide a 300-word essay on how Denny's can impact childhood hunger in their communities.

9970 ■ United States Society on Dams (USSD)
1616 17th St., Ste. 483
Denver, CO 80202-1277
Ph: (303)628-5430
Fax: (303)628-5431
URL: www.ussdams.org

9971 ■ United States Society on Dams Scholarships (Graduate, Undergraduate/Scholarship)

Purpose: To help students pursue their education. **Focus:** Construction. **Qualif.:** Applicants must be student members whose graduate-level research studies have a potential for developing practical solutions to design and construction problems and other dam-related issues and must be U.S. citizens. **Criteria:** Recipients will be selected based on submitted application.
Funds Avail.: $1,000 - $10,000. **Duration:** Annual. **Number Awarded:** Varies. **To Apply:** Applicants must submit a completed application form. **Deadline:** February 20. **Contact:** United States Society on Dams at the above address.

9972 ■ United States Tennis Association Foundation
70 W Red Oak Ln.
White Plains, NY 10604-3602

Ph: (914)696-7223
Fax: (914)697-2307
E-mail: foundation@usta.com
URL: www.ustafoundation.com

9973 ■ Marian Wood Baird Scholarships (Undergraduate/Scholarship)

Purpose: To provide scholarships to deserving young individuals who have participated in the United States Tennis Association. **Focus:** General studies/Field of study not specified. **Qualif.:** Applicants must be high school seniors who have excelled academically, demonstrated achievements in leadership and participated extensively in an organized community tennis program (such as USTA School Tennis, USTA National Junior Tennis League (NJTL), USTA Team Tennis or USTA High Performance or other such qualified programs as determined by the Scholarship Committee). They must also: demonstrate sportsmanship on and off the court; demonstrate academic achievement (3.0 minimum GPA); perform community/volunteer service; participate in organized youth tennis program such as National Junior Tennis and Learning; and, demonstrate financial need. **Criteria:** Selection will be based on the aforesaid qualifications.
Funds Avail.: Total of $15,000 for 4 years. **Duration:** Annual; Up to 4 years. **To Apply:** Interested applicants are requested to provide the following additional information; which is to be uploaded directly to students application (by logging onto their USTA Foundation Scholarship account): letters of recommendation; one from a teacher/guidance counselor or mentor; one from a tennis coach; federal tax returns and/or FAFSA; and, recent photo (.jpg format, no larger than 2 MB). **Deadline:** February 26. **Remarks:** The scholarship is named in honor of the late Marian Wood Baird, who had been recognized by the USTA for over 40 years of volunteer service.

9974 ■ Dwight F. Davis Memorial Scholarships (Undergraduate/Scholarship)

Purpose: To provide scholarships to qualified high school seniors. **Focus:** General studies/Field of study not specified. **Qualif.:** Applicants must be high school seniors who have performed with distinction and actively participated in extracurricular activities, community service and an organized tennis program. They must also: demonstrate sportsmanship on and off the court; demonstrate academic achievement (3.0 minimum GPA); perform community/volunteer service; participate in organized youth tennis program such as National Junior Tennis and Learning; and, demonstrate financial need. **Criteria:** Selection will be based on the aforesaid qualifications.
Funds Avail.: $10,000 ($2,500 per annum). **Duration:** Annual; Up to 4 years. **Number Awarded:** 2 (1 male; 1 female). **To Apply:** Interested applicants are requested to provide the following additional information; which is to be uploaded directly to students application (by logging onto their USTA Foundation Scholarship account): letters of recommendation; one from a teacher/guidance counselor or mentor; one from a tennis coach; federal tax returns and/or FAFSA; and, recent photo (.jpg format, no larger than 2 MB). **Deadline:** February 26. **Remarks:** The scholarship is named in honor of Dwight Filey Davis, who became president of the U.S. Lawn Tennis Association in 1923.

9975 ■ Eve Kraft Education and College Scholarships (Undergraduate/Scholarship)

Purpose: To provide scholarships to qualified high school seniors. **Focus:** General studies/Field of study not speci-

Awards are arranged alphabetically below their administering organizations

fied. **Qualif.:** Applicants must be high school seniors who have excelled academically, demonstrated community service, played tennis in an organized program and who reside in an economically disadvantaged community. They must also: demonstrate sportsmanship on and off the court; demonstrate academic achievement (3.0 minimum GPA); perform community/volunteer service; participate in organized youth tennis program such as National Junior Tennis and Learning; and, demonstrate financial need. **Criteria:** Selection will be based on the aforesaid qualifications. **Funds Avail.:** $2,500 each. **Duration:** Annual. **Number Awarded:** 2 (one male and one female). **To Apply:** Interested applicants are requested to provide the following additional information; which is to be uploaded directly to students application (by logging onto their USTA Foundation Scholarship account): letters of recommendation; one from a teacher/guidance counselor or mentor; one from a tennis coach; federal tax returns and/or FAFSA; and, recent photo (.jpg format, no larger than 2 MB). **Deadline:** February 26. **Remarks:** The scholarship is named in memory of Eve Kraft of Princeton, New Jersey, a tennis pioneer who introduced thousands of young people to the game of tennis, particularly in disadvantaged communities.

9976 ■ Dwight Mosley Scholarships *(Undergraduate/Scholarship)*

Purpose: To provide scholarship to high school seniors of ethnically diverse heritage. **Focus:** General studies/Field of study not specified. **Qualif.:** Applicants must be high school seniors of ethnically diverse heritage who have excelled academically and participated extensively in an organized community tennis program. They must also: demonstrate sportsmanship on and off the court; demonstrate academic achievement (3.0 minimum GPA); perform community/volunteer service; participate in organized youth tennis program such as National Junior Tennis and Learning; and, demonstrate financial need. **Criteria:** Selection will be based on the aforesaid qualifications. **Funds Avail.:** $10,000 ($2,500 per annum). **Duration:** Annual; Up to 4 years. **Number Awarded:** 2 (1 male; 1 female). **To Apply:** Interested applicants are requested to provide the following additional information; which is to be uploaded directly to students application (by logging onto their USTA Foundation Scholarship account): letters of recommendation; one from a teacher/guidance counselor or mentor; one from a tennis coach; federal tax returns and/or FAFSA; and, recent photo (.jpg format, no larger than 2 MB). **Deadline:** February 26. **Remarks:** The scholarship was named in memory of Dwight A. Mosley, the first African American elected to the USTA Board of Directors.

9977 ■ USTA Serves College Education Scholarships *(Undergraduate/Scholarship)*

Purpose: To support high school seniors who have excelled academically, demonstrated community service and participated in an organized tennis program. **Focus:** General studies/Field of study not specified. **Qualif.:** Applicants must be high school senior students entering a two- or four-year college or university. **Criteria:** Selection will be based on the committee's criteria. **Funds Avail.:** $8,000 ($2,000 per annum). **Duration:** Annual; Up to 4 years. **To Apply:** Applicants may contact the Foundation for further information.

9978 ■ USTA Serves College Textbook Scholarship *(Undergraduate/Scholarship)*

Purpose: To assist students in purchasing textbooks or supplies. **Focus:** General studies/Field of study not speci-

fied. **Qualif.:** Applicants must be high school senior students who are entering a two- or four-year college or university program. **Criteria:** Selection will be based on the committee's criteria.

Funds Avail.: $1,000. **Duration:** Annual. **To Apply:** Applicants may contact the Foundation for further information.

9979 ■ U.S.-Ukraine Foundation (USUF)
1660 L St. NW, Ste. 1000
Washington, DC 20036-5634
Ph: (202)524-6555
Fax: (202)280-1989
E-mail: info@usukraine.org
URL: www.usukraine.org

9980 ■ Mychajlo Dmytrenko Fine Arts Foundation Scholarships *(Undergraduate/Scholarship)*

Purpose: To support the education of Art students from the Academy of Fine Arts in Kyiv. **Focus:** Art. **Qualif.:** Applicants must be art students at the academy of Fine Arts in Kyiv. **Criteria:** Selection is based on criteria.

Funds Avail.: No specific amount. **Duration:** Annual. **To Apply:** Applicants must submit a completed application form. **Remarks:** Established in 2000. **Contact:** 1425 La Perla Long Beach CA 90815 USA and look for Mark Dmytrenko, President or call at Phone: 877-813-4591; Fax: 562-986-5770; Email: foundation@dmytrenko.org.

9981 ■ European College of Liberal Arts Scholarships *(Undergraduate/Scholarship)*

Purpose: To offer full scholarships on a need-blind basis. **Focus:** General studies/Field of study not specified. **Qualif.:** Applicants must study German while attending ECLA; must have earned 30 credit hours in a full year program and 8 credits in the summer program; should be between ages 18-24 with the right background and interests, proficient academic performance and good values. **Criteria:** Preference will be given to those students who meet the criteria.

Funds Avail.: No specific amount. **To Apply:** Applicants must check the available website for more information. **Contact:** Dick Shriver; Email: at rhsusa@yahoo.com.

9982 ■ USA/USA-Ukramerazha Scholarships *(Undergraduate/Scholarship)*

Purpose: To provide financial support to talented high school students in Ukraine. **Focus:** General studies/Field of study not specified. **Qualif.:** Applicants must be talented high school students in Ukraine heading to preparatory schools and colleges in the U.S., Canada or the United Kingdom. **Criteria:** Preference will be given to those students who meet the criteria.

Funds Avail.: No specific amount. **To Apply:** Applicants must check the available website for more information. **Contact:** U.S.-Ukraine Foundation, at the above address.

9983 ■ U.S. Ukraine Foundation (USUF)
1660 L St. NW, Ste. 1000
Washington, DC 20036-5634
Ph: (202)524-6555
Fax: (202)280-1989
E-mail: info@usukraine.org
URL: www.usukraine.org
Facebook: www.facebook.com/usukraine

Awards are arranged alphabetically below their administering organizations

LinkedIn: www.linkedin.com/company/us-ukraine
-foundation
Twitter: twitter.com/usukraine

9984 ■ Kovaluk Scholarship Fund *(Undergraduate/Scholarship)*

Purpose: To help deserving students from the village of Zabolotivci to continue their education on a university level. **Focus:** Education; Human rights. **Qualif.:** Applicants must be students from the village of Zabolotivci. **Criteria:** Selection will be based on the committees' criteria.

Funds Avail.: No specific amount. **To Apply:** Applicants may contact the Association for application process and other information. **Remarks:** Established in 2000.

9985 ■ United Student Aid Funds Inc.
PO Box 6028
Indianapolis, IN 46206-6028
Free: 888-272-5543
E-mail: lender-relations-in@navient.com
URL: www.usafunds.org
Facebook: www.facebook.com/usafunds
LinkedIn: www.linkedin.com/company/usa-funds
Twitter: www.twitter.com/usafundsorg

9986 ■ USA Funds Access to Education Scholarships *(Graduate, Undergraduate/Scholarship)*

Purpose: To help students from low- to moderate-income households pay college costs. **Focus:** General studies/Field of study not specified. **Qualif.:** Applicants must be qualified full-time or half-time undergraduates and full-time graduate and professional students. They must be enrolled or plan to enroll in course work at accredited two- or four-year colleges, universities or vocational/technical schools beginning with the fall term through Feb. 1 of the current year. **Criteria:** Selection shall be based on the aforementioned qualifications and compliance with the application details.

Funds Avail.: $1,500 each. **Number Awarded:** Varies. **To Apply:** Applicants may visit the website to verify the application process and other pieces of information. **Deadline:** February 15. **Contact:** United Student Aid Funds, at the above address, or Email: www.usafunds.org/scholarship.

9987 ■ UnitedAg
54 Corporate Pk.
Irvine, CA 92606-5105
Ph: (949)975-1424
Fax: (949)975-1573
Free: 800-223-4590
URL: www.unitedag.org
Facebook: www.facebook.com/UnitedAgOrg
Twitter: twitter.com/UnitedAgOrg

9988 ■ UnitedAg Scholarship Program *(Undergraduate/Scholarship)*

Purpose: To provide financial assistance to students who wish to pursue their education. **Focus:** General studies/Field of study not specified. **Qualif.:** Applicants must: be affiliated with UnitedAg, either as children or grandchildren of members or employees of members (if UABT affiliated, applicants must be participants of the UnitedAg Health Plan); be presently enrolled at an accredited college or university; and have a minimum of 2.5 GPA. **Criteria:** Recipients will be selected based on submitted application materials.

Funds Avail.: Up to $75,000. **Duration:** Annual. **To Apply:** Applicants submit an application form; resume; three letters of recommendation; transcript of records; and financial statement (optional). Applicants must also submit a two-page, double-spaced essay based on the given topic. **Deadline:** February 29. **Contact:** Scholarship Coordinator; Phone: 800-223-4590; Email: membership@unitedag.org.

9989 ■ Unites States Institute of Peace (USIP)
2301 Constitution Ave.
Washington, DC 20037
Ph: (202)457-1700
Fax: (202)429-6063
URL: www.usip.org
Facebook: www.facebook.com/usinstituteofpeace
LinkedIn: www.linkedin.com/company/united-states
-institute-of-peace
Twitter: twitter.com/USIP

9990 ■ Jennings Randolph Peace Scholarship Dissertation Program *(Doctorate/Scholarship)*

Purpose: To support research from top academics in a variety of fields that contribute to a wider understanding of how to manage conflict and build sustainable peace effectively. **Focus:** Peace studies. **Qualif.:** Applicants must be citizens of any country; must be enrolled in recognized doctoral programs in accredited universities in the United States. **Criteria:** Recipients will be selected based on project significance; project design; implementation; potential as a peace scholar.

Funds Avail.: No specific amount. **Duration:** Annual. **To Apply:** Applicants must complete the application form and submit a proposed project.

9991 ■ United States Institute of Peace Jennings Randolph Senior Fellowship Program *(Advanced Professional/Fellowship)*

Purpose: To support targeted research, analysis and writing that is more closely integrated with the work of the Institute. **Focus:** Peace studies. **Qualif.:** Applicants must be citizens of any country. Non-US citizens without permanent resident status must obtain a J-1 exchange visitor visa to participate in the Fellowship Program. J-1 status requires recipients to reside in their home country for two years. **Criteria:** Recipients will be selected based on: overall project significance; project design; implementation; track record and reputation; potential as fellows.

Funds Avail.: No specific amount. **Duration:** Annual. **To Apply:** Applicants must complete and submit the application form together with their proposed project.

9992 ■ Université de Montréal - Centre de Recherches Mathematiques (CRM)
Pavillon Andre-Aisenstadt
2920 Chemin de la tour, Rm. 5357
Montreal, QC, Canada H3T 1J4
Ph: (514)343-7501
Fax: (514)343-2254
E-mail: CRM@CRM.UMontreal.CA
URL: www.crm.umontreal.ca

Awards are arranged alphabetically below their administering organizations

Facebook: www.facebook.com/
Centrederecherchesmathematiques?fref=ts

9993 ■ CRM-ISM Postdoctoral Fellowships
(Postdoctorate/Fellowship)

Purpose: To support promising researchers who have recently obtained or are expected to obtain a PhD in the mathematical science. **Focus:** Mathematics and mathematical sciences. **Qualif.:** Applicants must have obtained a PhD within three years. **Criteria:** Selection is based on merit. Preference will be given to applicants who are not currently registered at one of the ISM member universities. **Funds Avail.:** 40,000 Canadian Dollars per year. **Duration:** Annual; two years. **To Apply:** Applicants must complete the application online. In addition, applicants must submit a curriculum vitae in PDF format; research project (PDF format); and the names of 2-5 people who will write the letters of recommendation in support of the application. **Deadline:** December 11.

9994 ■ Universités Canada
1710-350 Albert St.
Ottawa, ON, Canada K1R 1B1
Ph: (613)563-1236
Fax: (613)563-9745
E-mail: info@univcan.ca
URL: www.univcan.ca
Facebook: www.facebook.com/univcanada
Twitter: twitter.com/univcan

9995 ■ Vale Manitoba Operations Scholarships
(Undergraduate/Scholarship, Internship)

Purpose: To promote mining industry related fields of study, attracting students in the region to pursue careers in mining as part of the Northern Employment Strategy which supports initiatives to "grow our own". **Focus:** General studies/Field of study not specified. **Qualif.:** Applicants must be: residing in Manitoba and living in a community that is North of the 52 parallel; entering the first year or already enrolled in a first bachelor degree or first diploma program on a full-time basis; and, available to accept a summer internship at Vale Manitoba Operations. **Criteria:** Selection will be based on the committee's criteria. **Funds Avail.:** 5,000 Canadian Dollars (Bachelor degree program); 2,500 500 Canadian Dollars (Diploma program). **Duration:** Annual; Tenable for up to five (5) consecutive years for the bachelor degree and three (3) consecutive years for the diploma program. **Number Awarded:** 1. **To Apply:** Application procedures are through online and paper. Further information regarding the application process can be verified at the website. **Deadline:** June 1.

9996 ■ Universities Space Research Association (USRA)
7178 Columbia Gateway Dr.
Columbia, MD 21046
Ph: (410)730-2656
E-mail: info@usra.edu
URL: www.usra.edu
Facebook: www.facebook.com/USRAedu
LinkedIn: www.linkedin.com/company/usra
Twitter: twitter.com/USRAedu

9997 ■ Thomas R. McGetchin Memorial Scholarship Awards *(Undergraduate/Scholarship)*

Purpose: To support students who have shown a career interest in science or engineering with an emphasis on space research or space science education. **Focus:** Aerospace sciences; Engineering; Science; Space and planetary sciences. **Qualif.:** Applicants must be full-time undergraduate students attending a four-year accredited college or university that offers courses leading to a degree in science or engineering; must be within two years of earning a B.S. in a field of science and engineering, including life science and science education by the time the award is received. **Criteria:** Selection will be based on the following criteria: demonstrated or expressed interest in space research and/or space science education; student essay, both in its reflection of students interest and its writing quality; letters of recommendation; academic standing (minimum required cumulative GPA of 3.50); as needed, school and community activities may be used to distinguish otherwise equally qualified candidates.

Funds Avail.: $4,000. **Duration:** Annual. **To Apply:** Applicants must complete the online application form. A completed application must include the following: a completed application form; two letters of recommendation with at least one from a teacher or school official at the college level; an official college transcript showing two or more years of college credits including GPA; a one page (maximum of 500 words) statement stating the applicants' qualification and educational career goals in the field of space research or space science education. **Deadline:** August 12; August 19 - Letters of Recommendation.

9998 ■ John R. Sevier Memorial Scholarship Award *(Undergraduate/Scholarship)*

Purpose: To support students who have shown a career interest in science or engineering with an emphasis on space research or space science education. **Focus:** Aerospace sciences; Engineering; Science; Space and planetary sciences. **Qualif.:** Applicants must be full-time undergraduate students attending a four-year accredited college or university that offers courses leading to a degree in science or engineering; must be within two years of earning a B.S. in a field of science and engineering, including life science and science education by the time the award is received. **Criteria:** Selection will be based on the following criteria: demonstrated or expressed interest in space research and/or space science education; student essay, both in its reflection of students interest and its writing quality; letters of recommendation; academic standing (minimum required cumulative GPA of 3.50); as needed, school and community activities may be used to distinguish otherwise equally qualified candidates.

Funds Avail.: $4,000. **To Apply:** Applicants must complete the online application form. A completed application must include the following: a completed application form; two letters of recommendation with at least one from a teacher or school official at the college level; an official college transcript showing two or more years of college credits including GPA; a one page (maximum of 500 words) statement stating the applicants' qualification and educational career goals in the field of space research or space science education. **Deadline:** August 12; August 19 - Letters of Recommendation.

9999 ■ Frederick A. Tarantino Memorial Scholarship Award *(Undergraduate/Scholarship)*

Purpose: To support students who have shown a career interest in science or engineering with an emphasis on space research or space science education. **Focus:** Aerospace sciences; Engineering; Science; Space and planetary sciences. **Qualif.:** Applicants must be full-time undergraduate students attending a four-year accredited college or

Awards are arranged alphabetically below their administering organizations

university that offers courses leading to a degree in science or engineering; must be within two years of earning a B.S. in a field of science and engineering, including life science and science education by the time the award is received. **Criteria:** Selection will be based on the following criteria: demonstrated or expressed interest in space research and/or space science education; student essay, both in its reflection of students interest and its writing quality; letters of recommendation; academic standing (minimum required cumulative GPA of 3.50); as needed, school and community activities may be used to distinguish otherwise equally qualified candidates.

Funds Avail.: $4,000. **Duration:** Annual. **To Apply:** Applicants must complete the online application form. A completed application must include the following: a completed application form; two letters of recommendation with at least one from a teacher or school official at the college level; an official college transcript showing two or more years of college credits including GPA; a one page (maximum of 500 words) statement stating the applicants' qualification and educational career goals in the field of space research or space science education. **Deadline:** August 12; August 19 - Letters of recommendation.

10000 ■ James B. Willett Educational Memorial Scholarship Award (Undergraduate/Scholarship)

Purpose: To support students who have shown a career interest in science or engineering with an emphasis on space research or space science education. **Focus:** Aerospace sciences; Engineering; Science; Space and planetary sciences. **Qualif.:** Applicants must be full-time undergraduate students attending a four-year accredited college or university that offers courses leading to a degree in science or engineering; must be within two years of earning a B.S. in a field of science and engineering, including life science and science education by the time the award is received. **Criteria:** Selection will be based on the following criteria: demonstrated or expressed interest in space research and/or space science education; student essay, both in its reflection of students interest and its writing quality; letters of recommendation; academic standing (minimum required cumulative GPA of 3.50); as needed, school and community activities may be used to distinguish otherwise equally qualified candidates.

Funds Avail.: $4,000. **Duration:** Annual. **To Apply:** Applicants must complete the online application form. A completed application must include the following: a completed application form; two letters of recommendation with at least one from a teacher or school official at the college level; an official college transcript showing two or more years of college credits including GPA; a one page (maximum of 500 words) statement stating the applicants' qualification and educational career goals in the field of space research or space science education. **Deadline:** August 12; August 19 - Letters of recommendation.

10001 ■ University of Alabama at Birmingham School of Public Health - Lister Hill Center for Health Policy
Ryals Public Health Bldg.
1665 University Blvd.
Birmingham, AL 35294-0022
Ph: (205)975-9007
URL: www.soph.uab.edu/listerhill

10002 ■ UAB Health Policy Fellowship (Graduate, Master's, Doctorate/Scholarship)

Purpose: To assist in the transfer of health policy and health services research skills to the policy making setting, and to provide graduate students with a unique opportunity to learn about the political system through direct exposure to public or private sector roles in health policy development. **Focus:** Health services administration; Public health. **Qualif.:** Applicants must be students from any masters or doctoral program at UAB who have: a demonstrated interest in health policy; an interest in learning more about health policy through direct experience; and the skills to make a contribution in the organization in which they will serve. Applicants should be within twelve months of completing all the requirements for their degree.

Funds Avail.: up to $28,800. **Duration:** Annual. **Number Awarded:** 2. **Deadline:** February 18.

10003 ■ University of Alaska
Butrovich Bldg., Ste. 206
910 Yukon Drive
Fairbanks, AK 99775-5340
Ph: (907)450-8100
Fax: (907)450-8101
E-mail: syserve@alaska.edu
URL: www.alaska.edu/opa

10004 ■ Alaska Aerospace Development Corporation Scholarships (Undergraduate/Scholarship)

Purpose: To provide financial support to deserving students in Alaska who want to pursue an education in any campus of the University of Alaska. **Focus:** Business; Engineering; Mathematics and mathematical sciences; Physics; Technical communications. **Qualif.:** Applicants must be freshmen majoring in mathematics, physics, engineering, business, or a technical science field such as computer science who have graduated from the Kodiak Island Borough School District; must be full-time students attending at any of the UA campus (whether at Fairbanks, at Anchorage, or at Southeast), and enrolled in 14 credits and in good academic standing. **Criteria:** Applicants will be selected based on their academic standing and application documents.

Funds Avail.: No specific amount. **Duration:** Annual. **To Apply:** Applicants should submit a written statement verifying that they have not been convicted of a crime other than a minor traffic violation. They must complete and submit the application form available at the website together with a personal essay, two letters of recommendation, and current transcripts. **Deadline:** February 15.

10005 ■ Alaska Native Medical Center Auxiliary Scholarships (Undergraduate/Scholarship)

Purpose: To provide financial support to deserving students in Alaska who want to pursue an education in any campus of the University of Alaska. **Focus:** General studies/Field of study not specified. **Qualif.:** Applicants must: have graduated from a rural Alaska high school that is off the highway system in Alaska; be full-time students and in good academic standing with a minimum cumulative GPA of 2.5; and, be attending at any of the UA campus (whether at Fairbanks, at Anchorage, or at Southeast). **Criteria:** Preference will be given to Alaska Natives and/or individuals of Native American descent.

Funds Avail.: No specific amount. **Duration:** Annual. **To**

Awards are arranged alphabetically below their administering organizations

Apply: Applicants must complete and submit the application form available at the website. Applicants must also submit a personal essay, two letters of recommendation, and current transcripts. **Deadline:** February 15.

10006 ■ Alaska Press Club Scholarships
(Undergraduate/Scholarship)

Purpose: To provide financial support to deserving students in Alaska who want to pursue an education in any campus of the University of Alaska. **Focus:** Journalism. **Qualif.:** Applicants must be junior, senior or graduate journalism students at any of the UA campus (whether at Fairbanks, at Anchorage, or at Southeast) with a minimum GPA of 2.0. **Criteria:** Preference will be given to applicants from Rural Alaska communities.

Funds Avail.: No specific amount. **Duration:** Annual. **To Apply:** Applicants must complete and submit the application form available at the website. They must also submit a personal essay, two letters of recommendation, and current transcripts. **Deadline:** February 15.

10007 ■ Mike Ardaw Scholarships *(Undergraduate/Scholarship)*

Purpose: To provide support to deserving students in Alaska who want to pursue an education in any campus of the University of Alaska. **Focus:** Education; Engineering; Science. **Qualif.:** Applicants must be full-time students attending at any of the UA campus (whether at Fairbanks, at Anchorage, or at Southeast) and have a minimum GPA of 2.5. **Criteria:** Preference will be given to students studying science, education or engineering and to students who have been Alaska residents for at least one year and are from the Navy Lake area.

Funds Avail.: No specific amount. **Duration:** Annual. **To Apply:** Applicants must: complete the application forms available at the website; must attach a personal essay, two letters of recommendation, and current transcripts. Applicants must also submit a paragraph describing their connection to and love for the Nacy Lake area. **Deadline:** February 15.

10008 ■ Lawrence Bayer Business Administration Scholarships *(Undergraduate/Scholarship)*

Purpose: To provide financial support to deserving students in Alaska who want to pursue an education in any campus of the University of Alaska. **Focus:** Business administration. **Qualif.:** Applicants must be full-time students attending at any of the UA campus (whether at Fairbanks, at Anchorage, or at Southeast) and have a minimum GPA of 3.0. They must also be business administration majors active in clubs and/or sports. **Criteria:** Preference will be given to applicants with financial need.

Funds Avail.: No specific amount. **Duration:** Annual. **To Apply:** Applicants must complete the application forms available at the website; must attach a personal essay, two letters of recommendation, and current transcripts. Applicants must also submit a list of clubs and/or sports in which they are active participants. **Deadline:** February 15. **Contact:** UA Foundation, at the above address.

10009 ■ Charles E. Behlke Engineering Memorial Scholarships *(Undergraduate/Scholarship)*

Purpose: To provide financial support to deserving students in Alaska who want to pursue an education in any campus of the University of Alaska. **Focus:** Engineering. **Qualif.:** Applicants must be: full-time students entering their sophomore, junior, or senior year; attending at any of the UA campus (whether at Fairbanks, at Anchorage, or at Southeast); and, engineering majors who are in good academic standing with a minimum GPA of 2.5. **Criteria:** Selection will be based on applicants' academic standing and application requirements.

Funds Avail.: No specific amount. **Duration:** Annual. **To Apply:** Applicants must complete the application forms available at the website; must attach a personal essay, two letters of recommendation, and current transcripts. **Deadline:** February 15. **Contact:** UA Foundation, at the above address.

10010 ■ Bolick Foreign Student Scholarships
(Undergraduate/Scholarship)

Purpose: To provide financial support to deserving students in Alaska who want to pursue an education in any campus of the University of Alaska. **Focus:** General studies/Field of study not specified. **Qualif.:** Applicants must be full-time students attending at any of the UA campus (whether at Fairbanks, at Anchorage, or at Southeast) who are also holding exclusive citizenship in another country. **Criteria:** Preference will be given to Swedish citizens.

Funds Avail.: No specific amount. **Duration:** Annual. **To Apply:** Applicants must complete the application forms available at the website; must attach a personal essay, two letters of recommendation, and current transcripts. **Deadline:** February 15. **Contact:** UA Foundation, at the above address.

10011 ■ Dr. Betty J. Boyd-Beu and Edwin G. Beu, Jr. Scholarships *(Undergraduate/Scholarship)*

Purpose: To provide financial assistance for tuition and other educational expenses to non-traditional students who are seeking degree completion or retraining at the University of Alaska in Anchorage. **Focus:** General studies/Field of study not specified. **Qualif.:** Applicants must be non-traditional students and have graduated from high school who want or will attend at University of Alaska in Anchorage. They must have worked prior to enrolling or returning to college, thus re-entering college to complete a degree or enrolling to retrain for another position in the workplace, and be in good academic standing with a minimum cumulative GPA of 3.0. Furthermore, they must be formally admitted to a degree seeking program, and enrolled in the semester(s) for which the award is made. **Criteria:** Selection will be based on the applicants' academic performance and application documents.

Funds Avail.: No specific amount. **Duration:** Annual. **To Apply:** Applicants must visit the website for the UA Online Scholarship Application process. **Deadline:** February 15. **Contact:** UA Foundation, at the above address.

10012 ■ Bunnell Scholarships *(Undergraduate/Scholarship)*

Purpose: To provide financial support to deserving students in Alaska who want to pursue an education in any campus of the University of Alaska. **Focus:** General studies/Field of study not specified. **Qualif.:** Applicants must be full-time students attending at any of the UA campus (whether at Fairbanks, at Anchorage, or at Southeast), and have a minimum GPA of 3.2. **Criteria:** Preference will be given to applicants who graduated from an Alaska high school and have lived in Alaska for 3 or more years.

Funds Avail.: No specific amount. **Duration:** Annual. **To**

Awards are arranged alphabetically below their administering organizations

Apply: Applicants must submit an additional paragraph describing how they emulate the ideals of persistence, vision, self sacrifice, concern for others and love of the North. They must complete the application forms available at the website; must attach a personal essay, two letters of recommendation, and current transcripts. **Deadline:** February 15. **Contact:** UA Foundation, at the above address.

10013 ▪ Loyal D. Burkett Memorial Scholarships
(Undergraduate/Scholarship)

Purpose: To provide financial support to deserving students in Alaska who want to pursue an education in any campus of the University of Alaska. **Focus:** General studies/Field of study not specified. **Qualif.:** Applicants must be full-time students attending at any of the UA campus, in good academic standing, and demonstrate motivation, academic and leadership potential. **Criteria:** Applicants will be selected based on the submitted application and academic standing.

Funds Avail.: No specific amount. **Duration:** Annual. **To Apply:** Applicants must complete the application forms available at the website; must attach a personal essay, two letters of recommendation, and current transcripts. **Deadline:** February 15. **Contact:** UA Foundation, at the above address.

10014 ▪ Lyle Carlson Wildlife Management Scholarships
(Undergraduate/Scholarship)

Purpose: To provide financial support to deserving students in Alaska who want to pursue an education in any campus of the University of Alaska. **Focus:** Wildlife conservation, management, and science. **Qualif.:** Applicants must be full-time students attending at any of the UA campus (whether at Fairbanks, at Anchorage, or at Southeast) and majoring in wildlife management, wildlife biology or another closely related major. They must have a minimum GPA of 3.0. **Criteria:** Selection will be based on the applicants' academic standing.

Funds Avail.: No specific amount. **Duration:** Annual. **To Apply:** Applicants must complete the application forms available at the website; must attach a personal essay, two letters of recommendation, and current transcripts. **Deadline:** February 15. **Contact:** UA Foundation, at the above address.

10015 ▪ Mable B. Crawford Memorial Scholarships
(Undergraduate/Scholarship)

Purpose: To provide financial support to deserving students in Alaska who want to pursue an education in any campus of the University of Alaska. **Focus:** Accounting; Business; Economics; Law. **Qualif.:** Applicants must be full-time students attending at any of the UA campus (whether at Fairbanks, at Anchorage, or at Southeast) who have been residents of Alaska for at least two years. **Criteria:** Scholarships will be awarded on the basis of both scholastic ability and need. Preference will be given to applicants majoring in accounting, economics, law or business.

Funds Avail.: No specific amount. **Duration:** Annual. **To Apply:** Applicants must complete the application form available at the website; must attach a personal essay, two letters of recommendation, and current transcripts. **Deadline:** February 15. **Contact:** UA Foundation, at the above address.

10016 ▪ Patricia Hughes Eastaugh Teaching Scholarship
(Undergraduate/Scholarship)

Purpose: To provide financial support to deserving students in Alaska who want to pursue an education in any campus of the University of Alaska. **Focus:** Teaching. **Qualif.:** Applicants must be first-time incoming freshman students enrolled in a baccalaureate degree program at any of the UA campus (whether at Fairbanks, at Anchorage, or at Southeast). They must have the intent to become elementary or secondary school teachers in Alaska and be enrolled in academic programs leading toward that end. Lastly, they must be Alaska residents and graduates of a public or private school in Alaska. **Criteria:** Preference will be given to students who shows a desire to teach and are in the top 25% of their class.

Funds Avail.: No specific amount. **Duration:** Annual. **To Apply:** Applicants must complete and submit the application form available at the website together with two letters of recommendation, and current transcripts. Applicants must also attach an additional statement of 1,000 words or less entitled "Why I Want to become a Teacher of Children in Alaska." Applicants should also briefly express their opinion of Alaska's educational system(s) and their thoughts on changes they would embrace therein. **Deadline:** February 15. **Contact:** UA Foundation, at the above address.

10017 ▪ Excellence in Geographic Information Systems Scholarships
(Undergraduate/Scholarship)

Purpose: To provide financial support to deserving students in Alaska who want to pursue an education in any campus of the University of Alaska. **Focus:** Geography. **Qualif.:** Applicants must be full-time students attending at any of the UA campus (whether at Fairbanks, at Anchorage, or at Southeast) with a minimum overall cumulative GPA of 2.88 or a major GPA of 3.2. They must have declared interest in Geographic Information Systems or Mapping Science and be engaged in a directed or undirected project or class involving Geographic Information Systems during the award period. **Criteria:** Applicants will be selected based on their academic standings.

Funds Avail.: No specific amount. **Duration:** Annual. **To Apply:** Applicants must complete the application form available at the website; must attach a personal essay, two letters of recommendation, and current transcripts. **Deadline:** February 15. **Contact:** UA Foundation, at the above address.

10018 ▪ Lydia Fohn-Hansen/Lola Hill Memorial Scholarships
(Undergraduate, Graduate/Scholarship)

Purpose: To provide financial support to deserving students in Alaska who want to pursue an education in any campus of the University of Alaska. **Focus:** Consumer affairs; Family planning. **Qualif.:** Applicants must be full-time undergraduate or graduate students attending at any of the UA campus (whether at Fairbanks, at Anchorage, or at Southeast) who are majoring in Family and Consumer Sciences or a related field. They must have a minimum GPA of 3.0 and must be a resident of Alaska. **Criteria:** Selection will be based on the applicants' academic performance.

Funds Avail.: No specific amount. **Duration:** Annual. **To Apply:** Applicants must complete the application forms available at the website; must attach a personal essay, two letters of recommendation, and current transcripts. **Deadline:** February 15. **Contact:** UA Foundation, at the above address.

10019 ▪ Johnny & Sarah Frank Scholarships
(Undergraduate/Scholarship)

Purpose: To provide financial support to deserving students in Alaska who want to pursue an education in any

Awards are arranged alphabetically below their administering organizations

campus of the University of Alaska. **Focus:** General studies/Field of study not specified. **Qualif.:** Applicants must: be of Gwich in Athabaskan descents; be full-time students attending at any of the UA campus (whether at Fairbanks, at Anchorage, or at Southeast); have a minimum 2.5 GPA; and, enroll for at least six credit hours. **Criteria:** Preference will be given to students from Arctic Village or Venetie and students from Ft. Yukon, Chalkyitsik, Birch Creek, Circle, Beaver or Eagle.

Funds Avail.: No specific amount. **Duration:** Annual. **To Apply:** Applicants must complete the application forms available at the website; must attach a personal essay, two letters of recommendation, and current transcripts. **Deadline:** February 15. **Contact:** UA Foundation, at the above address.

10020 ■ Charles F. Gould Endowment Scholarships *(Undergraduate/Scholarship)*

Purpose: To provide financial support to deserving students in Alaska who want to pursue an education in any campus of the University of Alaska. **Focus:** General studies/Field of study not specified. **Qualif.:** Applicants full-time students attending at any of the UA campus (whether at Fairbanks, at Anchorage, or at Southeast), preferably Eskimos, with a minimum GPA of 2.0. **Criteria:** Applicants will be selected based on their academic standing.

Funds Avail.: No specific amount. **Duration:** Annual. **To Apply:** Applicants must complete the application forms available at the website; must attach a personal essay, two letters of recommendation, and their current transcripts. **Deadline:** February 15. **Contact:** UA Foundation, at the above address.

10021 ■ Patty Hamilton Early Childhood Development Scholarships *(Undergraduate/Scholarship)*

Purpose: To provide financial support to deserving students in Alaska who want to pursue an education in any campus of the University of Alaska. **Focus:** Education, Early childhood. **Qualif.:** Applicants must be Alaska residents who are full-time students attending at any of the UA campus (whether at Fairbanks, at Anchorage, or at Southeast) and entering their junior or senior year majoring in early childhood development/education. **Criteria:** Preference will be given to students who are working with or volunteering for young children.

Funds Avail.: No specific amount. **Duration:** Annual. **To Apply:** Applicants must complete the application forms available at the website; must attach a personal essay, two letters of recommendation, and current transcripts. They must also submit a paragraph describing his/her experience working with or volunteering with young children. **Deadline:** February 15. **Contact:** UA Foundation, at the above address.

10022 ■ John Henderson Endowment Scholarships *(Undergraduate/Scholarship)*

Purpose: To provide support to deserving students in Alaska who want to pursue an education in any campus of the University of Alaska. **Focus:** General studies/Field of study not specified. **Qualif.:** Applicants must be full-time students attending at any of the UA campus (whether at Fairbanks, at Anchorage, or at Southeast). **Criteria:** Applicants will be selected based on their application requirements.

Funds Avail.: No specific amount. **Duration:** Annual. **To Apply:** Applicants must complete the application forms available at the website; must attach a personal essay, two letters of recommendation, and current transcripts. **Deadline:** February 15. **Contact:** UA Foundation, at the above address.

10023 ■ Donald Wills Jacobs Scholarships *(Undergraduate/Scholarship)*

Purpose: To provide financial support to deserving students in Alaska who want to pursue an education in any campus of the University of Alaska. **Focus:** Art. **Qualif.:** Applicants must be full-time junior or senior students enrolled in a Bachelor of Fine Arts program at any of the UA campus (whether at Fairbanks, at Anchorage, or at Southeast). **Criteria:** Applicants will be selected based on their academic performance and application documents.

Funds Avail.: No specific amount. **Duration:** Annual. **To Apply:** Applicants must complete the application forms available at the website. They must also attach a personal essay, two letters of recommendation, and current transcripts. **Deadline:** February 15. **Contact:** UA Foundation, at the above address.

10024 ■ Iver and Cora Knapstad Scholarships *(Undergraduate/Scholarship)*

Purpose: To provide financial support to deserving students in Alaska who want to pursue an education in any campus of the University of Alaska. **Focus:** General studies/Field of study not specified. **Qualif.:** Applicants must be full-time students attending at any of the UA campus (whether at Fairbanks, at Anchorage, or at Southeast). **Criteria:** Applicants will be selected based on their academic standing.

Funds Avail.: No specific amount. **Duration:** Annual. **To Apply:** Applicants must complete and submit the application form available at the website. They must also attach a personal essay, two letters of recommendation, and current transcripts. **Deadline:** February 15. **Contact:** UA Foundation, at the above address.

10025 ■ Robert W. Korn Scholarships *(Undergraduate/Scholarship)*

Purpose: To provide financial support to deserving students in Alaska who want to pursue an education in any campus of the University of Alaska. **Focus:** General studies/Field of study not specified. **Qualif.:** Applicants must be graduates of Cordova Alaska High School with a minimum of 2.0 average and planning to attend at any of the UA campus (whether at Fairbanks, at Anchorage, or at Southeast). **Criteria:** Selection will be based on the applicants' academic standing.

Funds Avail.: No specific amount. **Duration:** Annual. **To Apply:** Applicants must complete and submit the application form available at the website. Applicants must also attach a personal essay, two letters of recommendation, and current transcripts. **Deadline:** February 15. **Contact:** UA Foundation, at the above address.

10026 ■ Austin E. Lathrop Scholarships *(Undergraduate/Scholarship)*

Purpose: To provide financial support to deserving students in Alaska who want to pursue an education in any campus of the University of Alaska. **Focus:** General studies/Field of study not specified. **Qualif.:** Applicants must be full-time students attending at any of the UA campus (whether at Fairbanks, at Anchorage, or at Southeast). **Criteria:** Preference will be given to students

Awards are arranged alphabetically below their administering organizations

who show a need for financial assistance.

Funds Avail.: No specific amount. **Duration:** Annual. **To Apply:** Applicants must complete and submit the application form available at the website. Applicants must also attach a personal essay, two letters of recommendation, and current transcripts. **Deadline:** February 15. **Contact:** UA Foundation, at the above address.

10027 ■ Franklin M. Leach Scholarships
(Undergraduate/Scholarship)

Purpose: To provide financial support to deserving students in Alaska who want to pursue an education in any campus of the University of Alaska. **Focus:** General studies/Field of study not specified. **Qualif.:** Applicants must be full-time students attending at any of the UA campus (whether at Fairbanks, at Anchorage, or at Southeast). **Criteria:** Selection will be based on the applicants' academic standing.

Funds Avail.: No specific amount. **Duration:** Annual. **To Apply:** Applicants must complete and submit the application form available at the website. They must also attach a personal essay, two letters of recommendation, and current transcripts. **Deadline:** February 15. **Contact:** UA Foundation, at the above address.

10028 ■ Dave McCloud Aviation Memorial Scholarships *(Undergraduate/Scholarship)*

Purpose: To provide financial support to deserving students in Alaska who want to pursue an education in any campus of the University of Alaska. **Focus:** General studies/Field of study not specified. **Qualif.:** Applicants must be full-time students attending at any of the UA campus (whether at Fairbanks, at Anchorage, or at Southeast), and seeking a degree in Aviation. The must have a minimum cumulative GPA of 2.0 and be residents of Alaska. **Criteria:** Preference will be given to students who are affiliated with the military.

Funds Avail.: No specific amount. **Duration:** Annual. **To Apply:** Applicants must complete and submit the application form available at the website. Applicants must also attach a personal essay, two letters of recommendation, and current transcripts. **Deadline:** February 15. **Remarks:** UA Foundation, at the above address.

10029 ■ Richard Mellon Scholarships
(Undergraduate/Scholarship)

Purpose: To support deserving students in Alaska who want to pursue an education in any campus of the University of Alaska. **Focus:** General studies/Field of study not specified. **Qualif.:** Applicants must be full-time students attending at any of the UA campus (whether at Fairbanks, at Anchorage, or at Southeast). **Criteria:** Preference will be given to students who demonstrate a need for financial assistance.

Funds Avail.: No specific amount. **Duration:** Annual. **To Apply:** Applicants must complete and submit the application form available at the website. They must also submit a personal essay, two letters of recommendation, and current transcripts. **Deadline:** February 15. **Contact:** UA Foundation, at the above address.

10030 ■ Molly Ann Mishler Memorial Scholarships
(Undergraduate/Scholarship)

Purpose: To provide financial assistance for tuition and other educational expenses to students who are admitted into the Early Childhood Development or Elementary Education Program. **Focus:** Education, Early childhood. **Qualif.:** Applicants must: demonstrate motivation, academic and leadership potential; have a good academic standing with a minimum cumulative GPA of 2.0; be formally admitted to a degree-seeking program at any of the UA campus (whether at Fairbanks, at Anchorage, or at Southeast); have a plan to enroll at least part-time (6 credits) at any of the UA campus mentioned above; be U.S. citizens, non-U.S. citizens, Alaska residents, or out-of-state resident enrolled in the semester(s) for which the award is offered; and, be enrolled in at least three credits for Early Childhood Development courses. **Criteria:** Preference will be given to applicants formally admitted into the Early Childhood Development program.

Funds Avail.: No specific amount. **Duration:** Annual. **To Apply:** Applicants must complete the MSC scholarship application form; must attach a list of activities/community service in which they have participated; must attach a resume of their work experience they have held over the past four years; must attach a personal essay (not more than 500 words); must have two letters of recommendation and transcripts. Application documents must be submitted to Molly Ann Mishler Memorial Scholarships, Matanuska-Susitna College, Student Services. **Deadline:** February 15. **Contact:** UA Foundation, at the above address.

10031 ■ Andrew Nerland Scholarships
(Undergraduate/Scholarship)

Purpose: To provide financial support to deserving students in Alaska who want to pursue an education in any campus of the University of Alaska. **Focus:** General studies/Field of study not specified. **Qualif.:** Applicants must be full-time students at any of the UA campus (whether at Fairbanks, at Anchorage, or at Southeast). **Criteria:** Preference will be given to students who demonstrate a need for financial assistance.

Funds Avail.: No specific amount. **Duration:** Annual. **To Apply:** Applicants must complete and submit the application form available at the website. They must also submit a personal essay, two letters of recommendation, and current transcripts. **Deadline:** February 15. **Contact:** UA Foundation, at the above address.

10032 ■ Maureen E. Nolan-Cahill Memorial Scholarships *(Undergraduate/Scholarship)*

Purpose: To provide financial support to deserving students in Alaska who want to pursue an education in any campus of the University of Alaska. **Focus:** Science. **Qualif.:** Applicants must be female students majoring in science with a GPA of at least 3.0, and attending at any of the UA campus (whether at Fairbanks, at Anchorage, or at Southeast). **Criteria:** Preference will be given first to applicants who are residents of Southern Alaska and next to graduates of Alaska high schools.

Funds Avail.: No specific amount. **Duration:** Annual. **To Apply:** Applicants must complete and submit the application form available at the website. Applicants must also submit a personal essay, two letters of recommendation, and current transcripts. **Deadline:** February 15. **Contact:** UA Foundation, at the above address.

10033 ■ Don and Jan O'Dowd/SAA Statewide Scholarships *(Undergraduate/Scholarship)*

Purpose: To provide financial support to deserving students in Alaska who want to pursue an education in any campus of the University of Alaska. **Focus:** General studies/Field of study not specified. **Qualif.:** Applicants

Awards are arranged alphabetically below their administering organizations

must be full-time incoming freshmen students attending at any of the UA campus (whether at Fairbanks, at Anchorage, or at Southeast) with a minimum GPA of 3.0, and Alaska residents and graduates of an Alaska high school. **Criteria:** Applicants will be selected based on their academic standing.

Funds Avail.: No specific amount. **Duration:** Annual. **To Apply:** Applicants must complete and submit the application form available at the website. They must also submit a personal essay, two letters of recommendation, and current transcripts. **Deadline:** February 15. **Contact:** UA Foundation, at the above address.

10034 ■ Alvin G. Ott Fish and Wildlife Scholarships *(Undergraduate/Scholarship)*

Purpose: To provide financial support to deserving students in Alaska who want to pursue an education in any campus of the University of Alaska. **Focus:** General studies/Field of study not specified. **Qualif.:** Applicants must be full-time students attending at any of the UA campus (whether at Fairbanks, at Anchorage, or at Southeast), with a minimum GPA of 3.0 and majoring in a field related to fish and wildlife. **Criteria:** Applicants will be selected based on their academic standing.

Funds Avail.: No specific amount. **Duration:** Annual. **To Apply:** Applicants must complete and submit the application form available at the website. They must also submit a personal essay, two letters of recommendation, and current transcripts. **Deadline:** February 15. **Contact:** UA Foundation, at the above address.

10035 ■ Pt. Lay Memorial Scholarships *(Undergraduate/Scholarship)*

Purpose: To provide support to deserving students in Alaska who want to pursue an education in any campus of the University of Alaska. **Focus:** General studies/Field of study not specified. **Qualif.:** Applicants must be: full-time undergraduate students attending at any of the UA campus (whether at Fairbanks, at Anchorage, or at Southeast); residents or former residents of Pt. Lay, Alaska; Alaska residents of one quarter or more Native ancestry who resides north of the Arctic Circle; and, be Alaska residents of one quarter or more Native ancestry. **Criteria:** Selection will be based on the committee's criteria.

Funds Avail.: No specific amount. **Duration:** Annual. **To Apply:** Applicants must complete and submit the application form available at the website. They must also submit a personal essay, two letters of recommendation, and current transcripts. **Deadline:** February 15. **Contact:** UA Foundation, at the above address.

10036 ■ A.D. Al and Maxine Robertson Memorial Scholarship *(Undergraduate/Scholarship)*

Purpose: To provide financial support to deserving students in Alaska who want to pursue an education in any campus of the University of Alaska. **Focus:** General studies/Field of study not specified. **Qualif.:** Applicants must: be full-time students and members of the graduating class of Ketchikan High School in the year the scholarship is awarded; have a minimum GPA of 2.5; and, will attend at any of the UA campus (whether at Fairbanks, at Anchorage, or at Southeast). **Criteria:** Selection of applicants will be based on their academic standing and application documents.

Funds Avail.: No specific amount. **Duration:** Annual. **To Apply:** Applicants must complete and submit the application form available at the website. They must also submit a personal essay, two letters of recommendation, and current transcripts. **Deadline:** February 15. **Contact:** UA Foundation, at the above address.

10037 ■ Clair Shirey Scholarships *(Undergraduate/Scholarship)*

Purpose: To provide financial support to deserving students in Alaska who want to pursue an education in any campus of the University of Alaska. **Focus:** Classical studies. **Qualif.:** Applicants must be Music majors at any of the UA campus (whether at Fairbanks, at Anchorage, or at Southeast) with a demonstrated interest or emphasis in classical/liturgical organ. **Criteria:** Preference will be given to students who are residents of the following geographical areas: Anchorage Archdiocese, Alaska and the Pacific Northwest.

Funds Avail.: No specific amount. **Duration:** Annual. **To Apply:** Applicants must complete and submit the application form available at the website. They must also submit a personal essay describing their interest or emphasis in classical/liturgical organ, two letters of recommendation, and current transcripts. **Deadline:** February 15. **Contact:** UA Foundation, at the above address.

10038 ■ Ward Sims Memorial Scholarships *(Undergraduate/Scholarship)*

Purpose: To provide financial support to deserving students in Alaska who want to pursue an education in any campus of the University of Alaska. **Focus:** Journalism. **Qualif.:** Applicants must be full-time junior or senior students at any of the UA campus (whether at Fairbanks, at Anchorage, or at Southeast), and enrolled in the Journalism program with a minimum GPA of 2.0. **Criteria:** Applicants will be selected based on their academic performance and submitted applications.

Funds Avail.: No specific amount. **Duration:** Annual. **To Apply:** Applicants must complete and submit the application form available at the website. They must also submit a personal essay, two letters of recommendation, and current transcripts. **Deadline:** February 15. **Contact:** UA Foundation, at the above address.

10039 ■ Snodgrass Scholarships *(Undergraduate/Scholarship)*

Purpose: To provide financial assistance for educational purposes to part-time students majoring in Applied Studies at the Matanuska-Susitna College. **Focus:** Accounting; Business administration; Computer and information sciences; Engineering, Architectural; Fires and fire prevention; Heating, air conditioning, and refrigeration; Telecommunications systems. **Qualif.:** Applicants must be full-time students attending at any of the UA campus (whether at Fairbanks, at Anchorage, or at Southeast). **Criteria:** Applicants will be selected based on their academic achievements and scholarship committee's criteria.

Funds Avail.: No specific amount. **Duration:** Annual. **To Apply:** Applicants must complete the MSC scholarship application and attach a resume showing their work experience; must compose an essay of 500 words or less describing their educational and career goals and how they plan to attain them; must have two letters of recommendation, written within the last two years. Application form and other supporting documents must be sent to Snodgrass Scholarships, Matanuska-Susitna College, Student Service. **Deadline:** February 15. **Contact:** UA Foundation, at the above address.

Awards are arranged alphabetically below their administering organizations

UNIVERSITY OF ALASKA

10040 ■ Sourdough Reunion Memorial Endowment Scholarships *(Undergraduate/Scholarship)*

Purpose: To provide financial support to deserving students in Alaska who want to pursue an education in any campus of the University of Alaska. **Focus:** General studies/Field of study not specified. **Qualif.:** Applicants must be full-time students entering their junior or senior years at any of the UA campus (whether at Fairbanks, at Anchorage, or at Southeast) with a minimum GPA of 3.0, and residents of Alaska or the Yukon Territory. They must have graduated from a high school in Alaska or the Yukon Territory. **Criteria:** Selection will be based on academic performance and submitted application materials.

Funds Avail.: No specific amount. **Duration:** Annual. **To Apply:** Applicants must complete and submit the application form available at the website. They must also submit a personal essay, two letters of recommendation, and current transcripts. **Deadline:** February 15. **Contact:** UA Foundation, at the above address.

10041 ■ Umialik Scholarships *(Undergraduate/Scholarship)*

Purpose: To provide financial support to deserving students in Alaska who want to pursue an education in any campus of the University of Alaska. **Focus:** General studies/Field of study not specified. **Qualif.:** Applicants must be full-time students attending at any of the UA campus (whether at Fairbanks, at Anchorage, or at Southeast) who are also in good academic standing. **Criteria:** Preference will be given to Alaska Natives.

Funds Avail.: No specific amount. **Duration:** Annual. **To Apply:** Applicants must complete and submit the application form available at the website. They must also submit a personal essay, two letters of recommendation, and current transcripts. **Deadline:** February 15. **Contact:** UA Foundation, at the above address.

10042 ■ University of Alaska Scholars Program *(Undergraduate/Scholarship)*

Purpose: To provide incentives for Alaska's middle and high school students intending to achieve academic excellence. **Focus:** General studies/Field of study not specified. **Qualif.:** Applicants must: be US citizens or aliens lawfully admitted for permanent residence in the United States; have successfully earned a high school diploma from a qualified Alaska high school; be admitted into a certificate or degree program; be enrolled as full-time, undergraduate students for the first fall semester following the graduation date of the class with which the applicants are designated and continuously thereafter; and, participate in or attend any mandatory orientation or program as may be required by the campus. **Criteria:** Selection of recipients will be based on their academic standing at the end of their junior year.

Funds Avail.: $12,000. **Duration:** Annual; Up to 4 years. **Number Awarded:** Varies. **To Apply:** Applicants may contact the UA Scholars Program for application process. **Deadline:** May 1.

10043 ■ William S. Wilson Memorial Scholarships *(Undergraduate/Scholarship)*

Purpose: To provide financial support to deserving students in Alaska who want to pursue an education in any campus of the University of Alaska. **Focus:** Science. **Qualif.:** Applicants must be full-time students majoring in Science at any of the UA campus (whether at Fairbanks, at Anchorage, or at Southeast). **Criteria:** Preference will be given to undergraduate students, but graduate students will be considered.

Funds Avail.: No specific amount. **Duration:** Annual. **To Apply:** Applicants must complete and submit the application form available at the website. They must also submit a personal essay describing their research interest and/or evidence of research potential, two letters of recommendation, and current transcripts. **Deadline:** February 15. **Contact:** UA Foundation, at the above address.

10044 ■ Guy A. Woodings Scholarships *(Undergraduate/Scholarship)*

Purpose: To provide financial support to deserving students in Alaska who want to pursue an education in any campus of the University of Alaska. **Focus:** Natural resources. **Qualif.:** Applicants must be full-time students attending at any of the UA campus (whether at Fairbanks, at Anchorage, or at Southeast) majoring in Natural Resource Management with a 3.1 GPA, and have been enrolled at least 2 years pursuing a 4-year degree. **Criteria:** Preference will be given to students pursuing a degree in Natural Resource Management with an emphasis on planning and land use and those who have performed community service.

Funds Avail.: No specific amount. **Duration:** Annual. **To Apply:** Applicants must complete and submit the application form available at the website. Applicants must also submit an essay discussing how they envision the growth and development of the state over the next five years and what part they envision themselves playing in that growth and development. **Deadline:** February 15.

10045 ■ Ralph Yetka Memorial Scholarships *(Undergraduate/Scholarship)*

Purpose: To provide financial support to deserving students in Alaska who want to pursue an education in any campus of the University of Alaska. **Focus:** Computer and information sciences; Education, Elementary; Education, Secondary; Engineering. **Qualif.:** Applicants must be full-time students and graduates of Ketchikan or Revilla High School who are attending at any of the UA campus (whether at Fairbanks, at Anchorage, or at Southeast), with a minimum GPA of 2.5 and majoring in engineering, elementary or secondary education, computer science or aviation. **Criteria:** Applicants will be selected based on their application materials and academic standing.

Funds Avail.: No specific amount. **Duration:** Annual. **To Apply:** Applicants must complete and submit the application form available at the website. They must also submit a personal essay, two letters of recommendation, and current transcripts. **Deadline:** February 15.

10046 ■ Joan C. Yoder Memorial Nursing Scholarships *(Undergraduate/Scholarship)*

Purpose: To provide financial support to deserving students in Alaska who want to pursue an education in any campus of the University of Alaska. **Focus:** Nursing. **Qualif.:** Applicants must be full-time students majoring in nursing who have completed one clinical nursing course and is in good academic standing. They must be attending at any of the UA campus (whether at Fairbanks, at Anchorage, or at Southeast). **Criteria:** Selection of applicants will be based on their academic standing and application materials.

Funds Avail.: No specific amount. **Duration:** Annual. **To**

Awards are arranged alphabetically below their administering organizations

Apply: Applicants must complete and submit the application form available at the website. They must also submit a personal essay, two letters of recommendation, and current transcripts. **Deadline:** February 15.

10047 ■ Yukon Delta Fisheries Development Association Scholarships *(Undergraduate, Graduate/Scholarship)*

Purpose: To provide financial support to deserving students in Alaska who want to pursue an education in any campus of the University of Alaska. **Focus:** Nursing. **Qualif.:** Applicants must be undergraduate or graduate students from Alakanuk, Emmonak, Grayling, Kotlik, Mountain Village, Nunam Iqua, Pitka's Point, St. Mary's, Pilot Station, Marshall, Russian Mission, Holy Cross, Anvik and Shageluk who are at any of the UA campus (whether at Fairbanks, at Anchorage, or at Southeast). They must demonstrate a subsistence and/or commercial fishing relationship to the lower Yukon Delta region and maintain a minimum cumulative GPA of 2.5 or higher. **Criteria:** Applicants will be selected based on their application materials and academic standing.

Funds Avail.: No specific amount. **Duration:** Annual. **To Apply:** Applicants must complete and submit the application form available at the website. They must also submit a personal essay, two letters of recommendation, current transcripts, and a letter from their city or tribal council stating their relationship to the area. **Deadline:** February 15. **Contact:** UA Foundation, at the above address.

10048 ■ University of Alaska Anchorage
3211 Providence Dr.
Anchorage, AK 99508-4614
Ph: (907)786-1800
URL: www.uaa.alaska.edu

10049 ■ Elaine Atwood Scholarship *(Undergraduate/Scholarship)*

Purpose: To provide financial assistance to University of Alaska Anchorage students who are formally admitted into the Journalism and Public Communications degree seeking program. **Focus:** Journalism; Public affairs. **Qualif.:** Applicants must be: in good academic standing with a minimum cumulative grade point average of 3.0; formally admitted into a Journalism and Public Communications degree-seeking program at the University of Alaska Anchorage; planning to enroll full-time (twelve (12) credits) at the University of Alaska Anchorage; and, Alaska residents who will pursue a career in Alaska. **Criteria:** Selection of applicants will be based on their demonstrated motivation, talent, academic, and leadership potential.

Funds Avail.: $5,000. **Duration:** Annual. **Number Awarded:** 2. **To Apply:** Applicants must make sure that they meet all of the aforementioned qualifications before proceeding to apply online through UAOnline and completing the scholarship application.

10050 ■ Dr. Jon Baker Memorial Scholarship *(Graduate, Undergraduate/Scholarship)*

Purpose: To offer financial assistance for tuition and other educational expenses to full-time University of Alaska Anchorage students who are admitted into a degree-seeking program, with preference will be given to students majoring in Psychology. **Focus:** Psychology. **Qualif.:** Applicants must be: in good academic standing with a minimum cumulative grade point average of 2.0 for undergraduate and 3.0 for graduate; formally admitted into an undergraduate, graduate, certificate, and/or vocational degree-seeking program at the University of Alaska Anchorage; and, incoming or continuing students at the University. They may be U.S. citizens, non-U.S. citizens, Alaska residents, or out-of-state residents. **Criteria:** Selection of applicants will be based on their demonstrated motivation, talent, academic, and leadership potential. Preference will be given to students who are formally admitted to the Psychology program.

Funds Avail.: $500. **Duration:** Annual. **To Apply:** Applicants must make sure that they meet all of the aforementioned qualifications before proceeding to apply online through UAOnline and completing the scholarship application.

10051 ■ UAA Michael Baring-Gould Memorial Scholarship *(Graduate, Undergraduate/Scholarship)*

Purpose: To provide financial assistance for tuition and other educational expenses to full-time students who are formally admitted to an undergraduate social sciences program or enrolled in an interdisciplinary masters program which includes sociology as one of the disciplines. **Focus:** Social sciences; Sociology. **Qualif.:** Applicants must be in good academic standing with a minimum cumulative grade point average of 2.5 for undergraduate and 3.0 for graduate and formally admitted into an undergraduate Social Sciences major (e.g. Sociology, Psychology, Political Science, Justice, Social Work, Anthropology, etc.) or an Interdisciplinary Masters degree-seeking program that includes sociology as one of the disciplines. Undergraduate applicants must have completed at least thirty (30) credits. Applicants must also have completed at least six (6) credits prior to the semester of the award at the University of Alaska Anchorage, and planning to enroll full time (twelve (12) credits for undergraduate and nine (9) credits for graduate). Lastly, they must demonstrate involvement in a project or area of study which reflects a commitment to social justice, peace, equality, and/or empowerment of minorities. Such involvement may include, but is not restricted to, any of the following: community or campus organizing (e.g. leading or forming a campus or community organization); public education or advocacy (e.g. leading or coordinating a special project, conference, educational campaign, or public policy effort); and/or, research (e.g. working on an independent project or with a faculty member or community group). **Criteria:** Selection of applicants will be based on their demonstrated motivation, talent, academic, and leadership potential.

Funds Avail.: $500. **Duration:** Annual. **To Apply:** Applicants must make sure that they meet all of the aforementioned qualifications before proceeding to apply online through UAOnline and completing the scholarship application. Afterwards, they submit two letters of recommendation and an essay (250 words) describing the students' involvement in a project or area of study which reflects a commitment to social justice, peace, equality, and/or empowerment of minorities. **Contact:** UAA Office of Student Financial Assistance, Michael Baring-Gould Scholarship, PO Box 141608, Anchorage, AK 99514-1608.

10052 ■ Mark A. Beltz Scholarship *(Graduate, Undergraduate/Scholarship)*

Purpose: To offer financial assistance for tuition and other educational expenses to students who are in financial need and have declared majors for an undergraduate, graduate, or a vocational program in any of the following fields: Political Science, Economics, Business Administration, Business

Awards are arranged alphabetically below their administering organizations

UNIVERSITY OF ALASKA ANCHORAGE

and Corporate Law, and Science and Technology. **Focus:** Business administration; Economics; Political science; Science technologies. **Qualif.:** Applicants must demonstrate motivation, academic and leadership potential; must be in good academic standing with a minimum cumulative GPA of 2.0 for undergraduates and 3.0 for graduates; must be formally admitted to a political science, economics, business administration, business and corporate law, or science and technology undergraduate, graduate, certificate, and/or vocational degree-seeking program at the University of Alaska Anchorage; must plan on enrolling at least half-time (6 credits) at the University of Alaska Anchorage; may be an incoming or continuing student at the University of Alaska Anchorage; may be U.S. citizens, non-U.S. citizens, Alaska residents, or out-of-state residents. **Criteria:** Selection of applicants will be based on their demonstrated motivation, talent, academic, and leadership potential. Preference will be given to: Alaska residents; applicants who demonstrate financial need; and, applicants who intend to pursue a career in Alaska.

Funds Avail.: No specific amount. **Duration:** Annual. **To Apply:** Applicants must make sure that they meet all of the aforementioned qualifications before proceeding to apply online through UAOnline and completing the scholarship application.

10053 ■ Pat Brakke Political Science Scholarship
(Undergraduate/Scholarship)

Purpose: To offer financial assistance for tuition and other educational expenses to a full-time student majoring in Political Science. **Focus:** Political science. **Qualif.:** Applicants must be: in good academic standing with a minimum cumulative grade point average of 3.0; formally admitted into the Political Science degree-seeking program at the University of Alaska Anchorage; and, incoming or continuing students planning to enroll at least full-time (twelve (12) credits) at the University. They may be U.S. citizens, non-U.S. citizens, Alaska residents, or out-of-state residents. **Criteria:** Selection of applicants will be based on their demonstrated motivation, talent, academic, and leadership potential.

Funds Avail.: $500. **Duration:** Annual. **To Apply:** Applicants must make sure that they meet all of the aforementioned qualifications before proceeding to apply online through UAOnline and completing the scholarship application.

10054 ■ Emi Chance for Aspiring Artists Scholarship *(Undergraduate/Scholarship)*

Purpose: To offer financial assistance for tuition and other related educational expenses to full-time students attending the University of Alaska Anchorage who have declared a major in Art (for Drawing and/or Painting) who have Junior class standing. **Focus:** Art. **Qualif.:** Applicants must be: full-time students (twelve credits) at the University of Alaska Anchorage; in good academic standing with a minimum cumulative grade point average of 3.0; formally admitted into an Art degree-seeking program at the University of Alaska Anchorage; Drawing and/or Painting majors with Junior class standing; and, enrolled in the semester for which the award is made. They may be U.S. citizens, non-U.S. citizens, Alaska residents, or out-of-state residents and must have demonstrated a commitment to their community. **Criteria:** Selection of applicants will be based on their demonstrated motivation, talent, academic, and leadership potential.

Funds Avail.: $500. **Duration:** Annual. **To Apply:** Applicants must submit one drawing and/or painting with application. They must make sure that they meet all of the aforementioned qualifications before proceeding to apply online through UAOnline and completing the scholarship application. **Contact:** UAA Office of Student Financial Assistance, EMI Chance Memorial Scholarships, PO Box 141608, AK 99514-1608.

10055 ■ Edward Rollin Clinton Memorial for Music
(Undergraduate/Scholarship)

Purpose: To offer financial assistance for tuition and other educational expenses to full-time students who are formally admitted into a Music degree-seeking program at the University of Alaska Anchorage. **Focus:** Music. **Qualif.:** Applicants must be: in good academic standing with a minimum cumulative grade point average of 3.0; formally admitted into a Music degree-seeking program at the University of Alaska Anchorage; and, planning to enroll at least full-time (twelve (12) credits) at the University of Alaska Anchorage. **Criteria:** Preference will be given to the following: (1) entering freshmen planning to study piano; (2) upper division students studying piano; (3) freshman planning to study any instrument; (4) upper division students studying any instrument; and, (5) students who demonstrate financial need.

Funds Avail.: No specific amount. **Duration:** Annual. **To Apply:** Applicants must make sure that they meet all of the aforementioned qualifications before proceeding to apply online through UAOnline and completing the scholarship application. Afterwards, they must submit a compact disc recording which must include a minimum of five minutes of music from two (2) contrasting selections from the standard classical repertoire. Please include a table of contents with recording. Supplemental information must be mailed (or dropped off) to the UAA Office of Student Financial Assistance by the deadline (not postmarked by the deadline). Please submit info in a sealed envelope ATTN: Edward Rollin Clinton Scholarship. **Contact:** UAA Office of Student Financial Assistance; Address: PO Box 141608, Anchorage, AK 99514.

10056 ■ UAA Governor William A. Egan Scholarship
(Undergraduate/Scholarship)

Purpose: To provide financial assistance to students who are formally admitted to a political science or history degree-seeking program at the University of Alaska Anchorage. **Focus:** History; Political science. **Qualif.:** Applicants must demonstrate motivation, academic and leadership potential; must demonstrate a commitment to their community; must be in good academic standing with a minimum cumulative GPA of 2.0; must be formally admitted to a political science or history degree-seeking program at the University of Alaska Anchorage; must plan to enroll full-time (12 credits) at the University of Alaska Anchorage; must be incoming or continuing students at the University of Alaska Anchorage; must be U.S citizens, non-U.S citizens, Alaska residents, out-of-state residents; must be enrolled in the semester for which the award is made. **Criteria:** Preference will be given to applicants who are Alaska residents and have shown a potential for public service.

Funds Avail.: No specific amount. **Duration:** Annual. **To Apply:** Applicants must complete the electronic scholarship application available online. **Contact:** Ivy Spohnholz at 907-786-1944 or anias2@uaa.alaska.edu.

10057 ■ Michael D. Ford Memorial Scholarship
(Graduate, Undergraduate/Scholarship)

Purpose: To provide a scholarship as a memorial to Michael D. Ford as a way to encourage Alaskan students

Awards are arranged alphabetically below their administering organizations

to enter the field of business. **Focus:** Business. **Qualif.:** Applicants must be: in good academic standing with a minimum cumulative grade point average of 3.0; formally admitted into a Business degree-seeking program at the University of Alaska Anchorage; planning to enroll full-time (twelve (12) credits for undergraduate and nine (9) credits for graduate); and, able to demonstrate financial need. They must have been born in Alaska and be current Alaska residents. **Criteria:** Selection of applicants will be based on their demonstrated motivation, talent, academic, and leadership potential. Preference will be given to minority students who need financial assistance.

Funds Avail.: $1,000. **Duration:** Annual. **To Apply:** Applicants must make sure that they meet all of the aforementioned qualifications before proceeding to apply online through UAOnline and completing the scholarship application.

10058 ■ Jan and Glenn Fredericks Scholarship
(Graduate, Undergraduate/Scholarship)

Purpose: To offer financial assistance for tuition and other educational expenses to full-time students who are formally admitted into a Business degree-seeking program at the University of Alaska Anchorage with preference to those that are Alaska Native ethnicity. **Focus:** Business. **Qualif.:** Applicants must demonstrate motivation, academic and leadership potential; must be in good academic standing with a minimum cumulative GPA of 2.0 for undergraduates and 3.0 for graduates; must be formally admitted to a business degree-seeking program at the UAA by the start of the semester; must plan on enrolling full-time (12 credits for undergraduate and nine credits for graduate) at the UAA by the start of the semester of the award; must have at least a junior, senior, or graduate class-standing by the start of the semester of the award; may be U.S. citizens, non-U.S. citizens, Alaska residents, or out-of-state residents. **Criteria:** Selection of applicants will be based on their demonstrated motivation, talent, academic, and leadership potential. Preference will be given to students who are of Alaskan ethnicity.

Funds Avail.: No specific amount. **Duration:** Annual. **To Apply:** Applicants must make sure that they meet all of the aforementioned qualifications before proceeding to apply online through UAOnline and completing the scholarship application.

10059 ■ Ardell French Memorial Scholarship
(Undergraduate/Scholarship)

Purpose: To offer financial assistance for tuition and other educational expenses to full-time students who are formally admitted into a Chemistry degree-seeking program at the University of Alaska Anchorage. **Focus:** Chemistry. **Qualif.:** Applicants must be: in good academic standing with a minimum cumulative grade point average of 2.0; formally admitted into an undergraduate Chemistry degree-seeking program at the University of Alaska Anchorage; planning to enroll full-time (twelve (12) credits) at the University of Alaska Anchorage; and, enrolled in the semester for which the award is made. They may be U.S. citizens, non-U.S. citizens, Alaska residents, or out-of-state residents and have had at least a Sophomore class standing. **Criteria:** Preference will be given to applicants: who demonstrate financial need; and, from Alaska.

Funds Avail.: $500. **Duration:** Annual. **To Apply:** Applicants must make sure that they meet all of the aforementioned qualifications before proceeding to apply online through UAOnline and completing the scholarship application.

10060 ■ Benjamin A. Gilman International Scholarship *(Undergraduate/Scholarship)*

Purpose: To diversify the kinds of students who study and intern abroad and the countries and regions where they go. **Focus:** Engineering; General studies/Field of study not specified; Science. **Qualif.:** Applicants must be U.S. citizen undergraduate students who are receiving Federal Pell Grant funding at a 2-year or 4-year college or university to participate in study abroad programs worldwide. They must be: receiving a Federal Pell Grant or provide proof that they will be receiving a Pell Grant at the time of application or during the term of their study abroad; applying to or have been accepted into a study abroad program eligible for credit by the student's accredited institution of higher education in the U.S; studying abroad for at least 4 weeks in one country; studying abroad in any country except Cuba or a country on the State Department's current travel warning list; and, studying in the fall, spring, or academic year terms including winter inter-sessions. **Criteria:** Selection criteria are based on the Gilman Scholarship Program goals that may differ from other scholarship programs. Award recipients are selected using the following criteria: (1) Diversity of Applicants; (2) Statement of Purpose Essay; (3) Follow-on Project Proposal Essay; (4) Academic Progress and Performance;(5) Fields of Study; (6) Country of Destination; (7) U.S. Institution and State Distribution; (8) Length of Study; (9) Lack Previous Undergraduate Study Abroad Experience.

Funds Avail.: Amount varies. **Duration:** Annual. **To Apply:** Applicants must submit a completed application form with other requirements or supporting documents. **Deadline:** October 6 (spring and summer semester); March 3 (fall semester).

10061 ■ Ken Gray Endowment Scholarship
(Undergraduate/Scholarship)

Purpose: To offer financial assistance for tuition and other educational expenses to full-time junior or senior students who are formally admitted into a Bachelor of Arts or Bachelor of Fine Arts degree-seeking program in the area of sculpture and/or performance art as it relates to the visual art field at the University of Alaska Anchorage. **Focus:** Performing arts; Sculpture. **Qualif.:** Applicants must be: in good academic standing with a minimum cumulative grade point average of 3.0; formally admitted into a Bachelor of Art or Bachelor of Fine Art degree-seeking program in the area of sculpture and/or performance art as it relates to the visual art field at the University of Alaska Anchorage; planning to enroll full-time (twelve (12) credits) at the University of Alaska Anchorage; and, enrolled in the semester for which the award is made. They may be U.S. citizens, non-U.S. citizens, Alaska residents, or out-of-state residents. **Criteria:** Selection of applicants will be based on their demonstrated motivation, talent, academic, and leadership potential.

Funds Avail.: No specific amount. **Duration:** Annual. **To Apply:** Applicants must make sure that they meet all of the aforementioned qualifications before proceeding to apply online through UAOnline and completing the scholarship application. Afterwards, they can submit the following required supplemental information: work portfolio consisting of 20 slides (slides can be digital); three (3) letters of reference from practitioners in the sculptural area and/or UAA faculty; and, a two-page artist's statement reflecting the criteria for selection. **Contact:** UAA Office of Student Financial Assistance, Ken Gray Scholarships, PO Box 141608, Anchorage, AK 99514-1608.

Awards are arranged alphabetically below their administering organizations

10062 ■ Muriel Hannah Scholarships in Art
(Undergraduate, Graduate/Scholarship)

Purpose: To offer financial assistance for tuition and other educational expenses to full-time students who are formally admitted into a degree-seeking program at the University of Alaska Anchorage and who have a demonstrated talent in art. **Focus:** Art. **Qualif.:** Applicants must be: incoming or continuing students at the University of Alaska Anchorage and in good academic standing with a minimum cumulative grade point average of 2.0 for undergraduate and 3.0 for graduate; formally admitted into an undergraduate, graduate, certificate, and/or vocational degree-seeking program at the University of Alaska Anchorage; planning to enroll full-time (twelve (12) credits for undergraduate and nine (9) credits for graduate) at the University of Alaska Anchorage; able to demonstrate a talent in art; and, enrolled in the semester for which the award is made. **Criteria:** Selection of applicants will be based on their demonstrated motivation, talent, academic, and leadership potential.. Preference will be given to students of one-quarter or more Alaska Native ethnicity.

Funds Avail.: $500. **Duration:** Annual. **To Apply:** Applicants must make sure that they meet all of the aforementioned qualifications before proceeding to apply online through UAOnline and completing the scholarship application. Afterwards, they should provide ten (10) slides of artwork to demonstrate their talent in art. **Contact:** UAA Office of Student Financial Assistance, PO Box 141608, Anchorage, AK 99514-1608.

10063 ■ Lenore and George Hedla Accounting Scholarship *(Undergraduate/Scholarship)*

Purpose: To offer financial assistance for tuition and other related educational expenses to University of Alaska Anchorage students who are enrolled full-time or part-time with a declared major in Accounting. **Focus:** Accounting. **Qualif.:** Applicants must be: in good academic standing with a minimum cumulative grade point average of 2.0; formally admitted into an undergraduate Accounting degree-seeking program; planning to enroll at least full-time or half-time; and, enrolled in the semester for which the award is made. They may be U.S. citizens, non-U.S. citizens, Alaska residents, or out-of-state residents. **Criteria:** Selection of applicants will be based on their demonstrated motivation, talent, academic, and leadership potential.

Funds Avail.: $1,000. **Duration:** Annual. **To Apply:** Applicants must make sure that they meet all of the aforementioned qualifications before proceeding to apply online through UAOnline and completing the scholarship application.

10064 ■ Chris L. Kleinke Scholarship *(Graduate/Scholarship)*

Purpose: To provide a monetary award to an outstanding student in the UAA Master of Science in Clinical Psychology program. **Focus:** Psychology. **Qualif.:** Applicants must be: in good academic standing with a minimum cumulative grade point average of 3.0; formally admitted into the Master's Program in Clinical Psychology degree-seeking program at the University of Alaska Anchorage; and, incoming or continuing students at the University planning to enroll full-time (nine (9) credits of graduate course work). They may be U.S. citizens, non-U.S. citizens, Alaska residents, or out-of-state residents. **Criteria:** Selection of applicants will be based on their demonstrated motivation, talent, academic, and leadership potential. Preference will be given to students who have completed at least one year in the Master of Science in Clinical Psychology program. Applicants will be judged by the UAA Clinical Training Committee by the following criteria: (1) Academic performance in the MS in Clinical Psychology program as measured by current UAA graduate GPA, and undergraduate GPA in Psychology courses (not necessarily from UAA); (2) Potential for success in the field of clinical psychology as measured by clinical community, and/or research experience and letters of recommendation from a professional in the field; (3) The strength of personal statement detailing the applicants' plans for a future career in psychology.

Funds Avail.: $500. **Duration:** Annual. **To Apply:** Applicants must make sure that they meet all of the aforementioned qualifications before proceeding to apply online through UAOnline and completing the scholarship application. Afterwards, they must provide two (2) letters of recommendation from Professors and/or Professionals in the Clinical Psychology field. **Contact:** UAA Office of Student Financial Assistance, Chris L. Kleinke Scholarship, PO Box 141608, Anchorage AK 99514-1608.

10065 ■ Kris Knudson Memorial Scholarship
(Graduate, Undergraduate/Scholarship)

Purpose: To offer financial assistance for tuition and other educational expenses to full-time students who are formally admitted into a degree-seeking program in the area of biochemistry, immunology, or microbiology at the University of Alaska Anchorage. **Focus:** Biochemistry; Immunology; Microbiology. **Qualif.:** Applicants must be: formally admitted into an undergraduate or graduate degree-seeking program in the area of biochemistry, immunology, or microbiology at the University of Alaska Anchorage; in good academic standing with a minimum cumulative grade point average of 3.0; involved in a research project within the area of biochemistry, immunology, or microbiology; and, enrolled in the semester for which the award is made. They may be U.S. citizens, non-U.S. citizens, Alaska residents, or out-of-state residents. Those undergraduate applicants must have completed at least fifteen (15) credits in chemistry, biological sciences, and/or natural sciences. Graduate applicants must have earned a baccalaureate degree and completed at least fifteen (15) credits undergraduate in chemistry, biological science, and/or natural sciences. **Criteria:** Selection of applicants will be based on their demonstrated motivation, talent, academic, and leadership potential.

Funds Avail.: $1,000 (Undergraduate); $1,500 (Graduate). **Duration:** Annual. **To Apply:** Applicants must make sure that they meet all of the aforementioned qualifications before proceeding to apply online through UAOnline and completing the scholarship application. Afterwards, they must submit a brief essay (250 word max) describing their involvement in a research project related to biochemistry, immunology, or microbiology (such should be done via online).

10066 ■ Arlene Kuhner Memorial Scholarship
(Undergraduate/Scholarship)

Purpose: To offer financial assistance in the name of Dr. Arlene Kuhner for tuition and other related educational expenses to University of Alaska Anchorage students who have a declared major in English. **Focus:** Education, English as a second language. **Qualif.:** Applicants must be: in good academic standing with at least a cumulative GPA of 3.0; and, students attending the University of Alaska Anchorage with a declared major in English. They must take a minimum of six credits per semester. In the event

Awards are arranged alphabetically below their administering organizations

that two or more students are equally qualified for the scholarship, the scholarship will be awarded to the student with the most financial need. **Criteria:** Preference will be given to students who have been in residence at UAA for at least a year.

Funds Avail.: $500. **Duration:** Annual. **Number Awarded:** 1. **To Apply:** Applicants must make sure that they meet all of the aforementioned qualifications before proceeding to apply online through UAOnline and completing the scholarship application.

10067 ■ Diane Olsen Memorial Scholarship
(Undergraduate/Scholarship)

Purpose: To offer financial assistance to junior and senior students at UAA to help them pay for tuition and other related expenses. **Focus:** Economics. **Qualif.:** Applicants must be economics students or have a demonstrated interest in economics by the completion of at least 12 credits in economic courses. They must be: in good academic standing with a minimum cumulative grade point average of 2.75. **Criteria:** Selection of applicants will be based on their demonstrated motivation, talent, academic, and leadership potential. Preference will be given to non-traditional students.

Funds Avail.: $500. **Duration:** Annual. **To Apply:** Applicants must make sure that they meet all of the aforementioned qualifications before proceeding to apply online through UAOnline and completing the scholarship application.

10068 ■ Pignalberi Public Policy Scholarship
(Graduate/Scholarship)

Purpose: To provide financial assistance for tuition and other educational expenses to students enrolled in a graduate degree program in the UAA College of Business and Public Policy. **Focus:** Business; Public service. **Qualif.:** Applicants must be: in good academic standing with a minimum cumulative grade point average of 3.0; full-time graduate students (9 credits per semester) formally admitted to the College of Business and Public Policy; Alaskan residents with the intent to stay and be involved in local business and/or politics; and incoming or continuing student at the University of Alaska Anchorage. **Criteria:** Selection of applicants will be based on their demonstrated motivation, talent, academic, and leadership potential. Preference will be given to students who demonstrate financial need.

Funds Avail.: $500. **Duration:** Annual. **To Apply:** Applicants must make sure that they meet all of the aforementioned qualifications before proceeding to apply online through UAOnline and completing the scholarship application. Afterwards, they must submit a brief essay (250 words) answering the question: "In your opinion, what is the most important political issue in Alaska today?"

10069 ■ April Relyea Scholarship *(Graduate, Undergraduate/Scholarship)*

Purpose: To offer financial assistance for tuition and other educational expenses to students who are formally admitted into a degree-seeking program at the University of Alaska Anchorage and who have intent to explore human-nature relationships through writing or other creative expression. **Focus:** Human relations. **Qualif.:** Applicants must be: in good academic standing with a minimum cumulative grade point average of 2.0 for undergraduate and 3.0 for graduate; formally admitted into an undergraduate, graduate, certificate, and/or vocational degree-seeking program at the University of Alaska Anchorage; and, planning to enroll at least half-time (six (6) credits for undergraduate students, five (5) credits for graduate students) at the University of Alaska Anchorage. They may be U.S. citizens, non-U.S. citizens, Alaska residents, or out-of-state residents. **Criteria:** Preference will be given to students with an intent to produce work for the Student Showcase and students with a demonstrated interest in writing nature books for children.

Funds Avail.: $500. **Duration:** Annual. **To Apply:** Applicants must make sure that they meet all of the aforementioned qualifications before proceeding to apply online through UAOnline and completing the scholarship application. Afterwards, they must submit an essay about their interest in human-nature relationships and how they intend to pursue that interest at UAA. **Contact:** UAA Office of Student Financial Assistance, April Relyea Scholarship; Address: PO Box 141608, Anchorage, AK 99514.

10070 ■ Brown Schoenheit Memorial Scholarship
(Undergraduate/Scholarship)

Purpose: To offer financial assistance for tuition and other educational expenses to students who are formally admitted into a Music degree-seeking program at the University of Alaska Anchorage. **Focus:** Music. **Qualif.:** Applicants must be: in good academic standing with a minimum cumulative GPA of 2.0; formally admitted to a music degree-seeking program at the University of Alaska Anchorage by the start of the semester for which the award is to be made; Music majors with emphasis in an orchestral instrument; and, planning to enroll at least half-time (6 credits) at the University of Alaska Anchorage for the semester in which the award is made. They may be incoming or continuing students at the University of Alaska Anchorage, and U.S. citizens, non-U.S. citizens, Alaska residents, or out-of-state residents. **Criteria:** Selection of applicants will be based on their demonstrated motivation, talent, academic, and leadership potential. Preference will be given to flute students and to applicants who intend to pursue a career in Alaska upon graduating.

Funds Avail.: $500. **Duration:** Annual. **To Apply:** Applicants must make sure that they meet all of the aforementioned qualifications before proceeding to apply online through UAOnline and completing the scholarship application.

10071 ■ Eveline Schuster Memorial Award/Scholarship *(Graduate, Undergraduate/Scholarship)*

Purpose: To offer financial assistance to cover a student-designated sociology project to be conducted while the student is enrolled at UAA, as well as to encourage creative thinking and excellence in sociology. **Focus:** Sociology. **Qualif.:** Applicants must be: in good academic standing with an overall 3.0 GPA and a Sociology GPA of 3.3 or better; formally admitted into a Sociology degree-seeking program or Interdisciplinary Masters degree-seeking program with Sociology as one of the disciplines, at the University of Alaska Anchorage; planning to enroll full-time (12 credits for undergraduate, 9 credits for graduates). They may be U.S. citizens, non-U.S. citizens, Alaska residents, or out-of-state residents and have: a minimum Junior class standing; and, been enrolled in at least six (6) credits prior to the semester the award is granted. **Criteria:** Selection of applicants will be based on their demonstrated motivation, talent, academic, and leadership potential.

Funds Avail.: $500. **Duration:** Annual. **To Apply:** Applicants must make sure that they meet all of the aforementioned qualifications before proceeding to apply online

Awards are arranged alphabetically below their administering organizations

through UAOnline and completing the scholarship application. Afterwards, they must submit: a cover letter indicating if they are applying for the scholarship or for project funding; two (2) letters of recommendation; and, a project budget and statement indicating the project intent. **Contact:** UAA Office of Student Financial Assistance, Eveline Schuster Scholarship, PO Box 141608, Anchorage AK 99514.

10072 ■ Lillian Smith Scholarship for Teaching Students *(Graduate, Undergraduate/Scholarship)*

Purpose: To provide financial assistance to students at UAA who are studying to become teachers. **Focus:** Education. **Qualif.:** Applicants must be: full-time students attending UAA (12 credits for undergrad, 9 credits for graduate); in good academic standing with a minimum cumulative grade point average of 2.0 for undergraduate and 3.0 for graduate; and, fully admitted to an Education degree-seeking program. They may be U.S. citizens, non-U.S. citizens, Alaskan residents, or out-of-state residents. **Criteria:** Selection of applicants will be based on their demonstrated motivation, talent, academic, and leadership potential. Preference will be given to students who demonstrate financial need.

Funds Avail.: $500. **Duration:** Annual. **To Apply:** Applicants must make sure that they meet all of the aforementioned qualifications before proceeding to apply online through UAOnline and completing the scholarship application.

10073 ■ Sheri Stears Education Scholarship *(Undergraduate/Scholarship)*

Purpose: To provide financial assistance for tuition and other educational expenses to students admitted to pre-service teacher education programs at UAA. **Focus:** Education. **Qualif.:** Applicants must be in good academic standing with a minimum cumulative GPA of 3.0; must be involved in extracurricular activities; must be formally admitted to the College of Education pursuing an undergraduate education degree at the UAA; must plan on enrolling at least half-time (6 credits) at the UAA; may be incoming or continuing students at the UAA; may be U.S. citizens, non-U.S. citizens, Alaska residents, or out-of-state residents. **Criteria:** Selection of applicants will be based on their demonstrated motivation, talent, academic, and leadership potential. Preference will be given to: (1) Applicants who are Alaska residents; (2) Applicants who demonstrate financial need; (3) Applicants who address best how they see themselves advancing education in Alaska; (4) Undergraduate applicants.

Funds Avail.: $2,500. **Duration:** Annual. **Number Awarded:** 1. **To Apply:** Applicants must make sure that they meet all of the aforementioned qualifications before proceeding to apply online through UAOnline and completing the scholarship application. Afterwards, they must submit an essay responding to these questions: (1) How do you see yourself further advancing education in Alaska?; (2) How do your extracurricular activities enhance your educational experience?; Applicants must complete the electronic scholarship application available online.

10074 ■ Sturgulewski Family Scholarship *(Graduate, Undergraduate/Scholarship)*

Purpose: To offer financial assistance for tuition and other educational expenses to full-time students who are formally admitted into Journalism, Engineering, Nursing or an Education degree-seeking program at the University of Alaska Anchorage. **Focus:** Education; Engineering; Journalism. **Qualif.:** Applicants must be: in good academic standing with a minimum cumulative grade point average of 2.0 for undergraduate and 3.0 for graduate; formally admitted into a Journalism, Engineering, or Education undergraduate, graduate, certificate, and/or vocational degree-seeking program at the University of Alaska Anchorage; planning to enroll full-time (twelve (12) credits for undergraduate and nine (9) credits for graduate) at the University of Alaska Anchorage; and, incoming or continuing students at the University of Alaska Anchorage. They may be U.S. citizens, non-U.S. citizens, Alaska residents, or out-of-state residents. **Criteria:** Selection of applicants will be based on their demonstrated motivation, talent, academic, and leadership potential.

Funds Avail.: $500. **Duration:** Annual. **To Apply:** Applicants must make sure that they meet all of the aforementioned qualifications before proceeding to apply online through UAOnline and completing the scholarship application.

10075 ■ UAA Accounting Club Scholarship *(Undergraduate/Scholarship)*

Purpose: To offer financial assistance for tuition and other related educational expenses to University of Alaska Anchorage students with a declared major in Accounting, as well as to encourage non-traditional students to pursue academic endeavors. **Focus:** Accounting. **Qualif.:** Applicants must be: in good academic standing with a minimum cumulative grade point average of 3.0; formally admitted into an undergraduate Accounting degree-seeking program at the University of Alaska Anchorage; and, planning to enroll at least three-fourth time (nine (9) credits). They should: demonstrate an involvement in extra-curricular activities, with specific involvement in the UAA Accounting Club; and, have junior or senior standing and have completed a 300-level Accounting course or be enrolled in a 300-level Accounting course during the semester of the award. **Criteria:** Selection of applicants will be based on their demonstrated motivation, talent, academic, and leadership potential. Preference will be given to applicants demonstrating financial need and to non-traditional students.

Funds Avail.: $500. **Duration:** Annual. **To Apply:** Applicants must make sure that they meet all of the aforementioned qualifications before proceeding to apply online through UAOnline and completing the scholarship application.

10076 ■ UAA Alaska Kidney Foundation Scholarship *(Graduate, Undergraduate/Scholarship)*

Purpose: To provide scholarships in the name of the Alaska Kidney Foundation to prepare new nurses to provide safe and effective care to individuals experiencing chronic kidney disease in Alaska. **Focus:** Nursing. **Qualif.:** Applicants must be: residents of Alaska for three years prior to the start of the semester the award is given; formally admitted to a nursing degree program that leads to RN licensure; and, planning to enroll at least part-time (six credits). They must have completed one clinical nursing course by the start of the semester the award is given, unless new students. Applicants who have successfully completed a clinical nursing course must have a minimum cumulative GPA of 2.5 and nursing course minimum cumulative GPA of 2.0. Applicants who are new students beginning clinical studies and have not completed a clinical nursing course must have a minimum cumulative GPA of 2.8. **Criteria:** Selection of applicants will be based on their demonstrated motivation, talent, academic, and leadership potential.

Awards are arranged alphabetically below their administering organizations

Preference will be given to applicants who write an essay that: (1) Reflects a career plan that includes working with a clientele that could result in working with individuals with chronic or acute kidney disease or with clients at risk for the development of chronic renal disease; (2) Reflects a plan to remain to practice in Alaska.

Funds Avail.: $1,000. **Duration:** Annual. **To Apply:** Applicants must make sure that they meet all of the aforementioned qualifications before proceeding to apply online through UAOnline and completing the scholarship application. Afterwards, they must submit a brief essay (250 words max) describing the following: (1) A career plan that includes working with a clientele that could result in working with individuals with chronic or acute kidney disease or with clients at risk for the development of chronic renal disease; (2) A plan to remain in practice in Alaska. Applicants must complete the electronic scholarship application available online.

10077 ■ UAA Alumni Association Scholarship *(Undergraduate/Scholarship)*

Purpose: To provide financial assistance to students who want to pursue their education at UAA. **Focus:** General studies/Field of study not specified. **Qualif.:** Applicants must be: in good academic standing with a minimum cumulative grade point average of 2.0; formally admitted into a degree or certificate seeking program within one of the following UAA schools/colleges: College of Business and Public Policy, College of Arts and Sciences, College of Health and Social Welfare, Community & Technical College, College of Engineering, and the College of Education; and, enrolled full-time (12 credits for undergraduate, 9 credits for graduate). They may be U.S citizens, non-U.S citizens, Alaska residents, or out-of-state residents. **Criteria:** Selection of applicants will be based on their demonstrated motivation, talent, academic, and leadership potential. Preference will be given to students who are Alaska high school graduates.

Funds Avail.: $1,000 each. **Duration:** Annual. **Number Awarded:** 6. **To Apply:** Applicants must make sure that they meet all of the aforementioned qualifications before proceeding to apply online through UAOnline and completing the scholarship application.

10078 ■ UAA College of Business and Public Policy Scholarships *(Graduate, Undergraduate/Scholarship)*

Purpose: To offer financial assistance for tuition and other educational expenses to full-time students who are formally admitted into a degree-seeking program within the College of Business and Public Policy at the University of Alaska Anchorage. **Focus:** Business; Public service. **Qualif.:** Applicants must be: in good academic standing with a minimum cumulative grade point average of 2.0 for undergraduate and 3.0 for graduate; formally admitted into an undergraduate, graduate, certificate, and/or vocational degree-seeking program within the College of Business and Public Policy; and, full-time (twelve (12) credits for undergraduate and nine (9) credits for graduate); They may be U.S. citizens, non-U.S. citizens, Alaska residents, or out-of-state residents. **Criteria:** Selection of applicants will be based on their demonstrated motivation, talent, academic, and leadership potential.

Funds Avail.: No specific amount. **Duration:** Annual. **To Apply:** Applicants must make sure that they meet all of the aforementioned qualifications before proceeding to apply online through UAOnline and completing the scholarship application.

10079 ■ UAA Friends of the Performing Arts Scholarship *(Undergraduate/Scholarship)*

Purpose: To offer financial assistance for tuition and other education related expenses to a full-time University of Alaska Anchorage student who has shown a proven interest in the Performing Arts. **Focus:** Performing arts. **Qualif.:** Applicants must be: in good academic standing with a minimum cumulative grade point average of 2.0; formally admitted into an undergraduate Performing Arts (Theatre, Music, etc.) degree-seeking program at the University of Alaska Anchorage; planning to enroll full-time (twelve (12) credits) at the University of Alaska Anchorage; incoming or continuing students at the University of Alaska Anchorage; and, enrolled in the semester for which the award is made. They may be U.S. citizens, non-U.S. citizens, Alaska residents, or out-of-state residents. They must also show a proven interest in the Performing Arts. **Criteria:** Selection of applicants will be based on their demonstrated motivation, talent, academic, and leadership potential.

Funds Avail.: $500. **Duration:** Annual. **To Apply:** Applicants must make sure that they meet all of the aforementioned qualifications before proceeding to apply online through UAOnline and completing the scholarship application. Afterwards, they must submit a 1-2 minute recording of a performance. Supplemental information must be mailed (or dropped off) to the UAA Office of Student Financial Assistance by the deadline (not postmarked by the deadline). Please submit info in a sealed envelope ATTN: Friends of the Performing Arts Scholarship. **Contact:** UAA Office of Student Financial Assistance, Friends of the Performing Arts Scholarship, PO Box 141608, Anchorage AK 99514.

10080 ■ UAA GCI, Inc. Scholarship *(Undergraduate/Scholarship)*

Purpose: To offer financial assistance for tuition and other educational expenses to full-time students who are formally admitted into a Journalism and Public Communications degree-seeking program at the University of Alaska Anchorage and who are in financial need. **Focus:** Journalism; Public affairs. **Qualif.:** Applicants must be: in good academic standing with a minimum cumulative grade point average of 3.0; formally admitted into a Journalism and Public Communications degree-seeking program at the University of Alaska Anchorage; planning to enroll full-time (twelve (12) credits) at the University of Alaska Anchorage; able to demonstrate financial need; and, enrolled in the semester for which the award is made. **Criteria:** Selection of applicants will be based on their demonstrated motivation, talent, academic, and leadership potential.

Funds Avail.: $500. **Duration:** Annual. **To Apply:** Applicants must make sure that they meet all of the aforementioned qualifications before proceeding to apply online through UAOnline and completing the scholarship application.

10081 ■ UAA Kimura Scholarship Fund for Illustration *(Undergraduate/Scholarship)*

Purpose: To offer financial assistance for tuition and other related educational expenses to full-time students at the University of Alaska Anchorage with a declared major in Art or Journalism and Public Communications. **Focus:** Illustrators and illustrations. **Qualif.:** Applicants must be: full time students (12 credits per semester) attending the University of Alaska Anchorage with a declared major in Art OR with a declared major in Journalism and Public Communication with an emphasis in illustration; in their Junior year and have completed at least nine credits in studio photography

Awards are arranged alphabetically below their administering organizations

classes at the 200 level or above; and, in good academic standing with at least a 3.0 GPA. **Criteria:** Selection will be based on the aforesaid qualifications and compliance with the application process.

Funds Avail.: $500. **Duration:** Annual. **To Apply:** Applicants must make sure that they meet all of the aforementioned qualifications before proceeding to apply online through UAOnline and completing the scholarship application. Afterwards, they must submit proof of their illustration(s). Illustrations do no have to be the original work. Digital images of the illustration(s) copied to a CD is preferred. **Contact:** UAA Office of Student Financial Assistance, Kimura Scholarships; Address: PO Box 141608, Anchorage, AK 99514.

10082 ■ UAA Kimura Scholarship Fund for Photography *(Undergraduate/Scholarship)*

Purpose: To offer financial assistance for tuition and other related educational expenses to full-time students at the University of Alaska Anchorage with a declared major in Art or Journalism and Public Communications. **Focus:** Art; Journalism; Photography. **Qualif.:** Applicants must be: full time students (12 credits per semester) attending the University of Alaska Anchorage with a declared major in Art OR with a declared major in Journalism and Public Communication with an emphasis in photography; in their Junior year and have completed at least nine credits in studio photography classes at the 200 level or above; and, in good academic standing with at least a 3.0 GPA. **Criteria:** Selection will be based on the aforesaid qualifications and compliance with the application process.

Funds Avail.: $500. **Duration:** Annual. **To Apply:** Applicants must make sure that they meet all of the aforementioned qualifications before proceeding to apply online through UAOnline and completing the scholarship application. Afterwards, they must submit proof of their photography work (no more than 5 photographs please). **Contact:** UAA Office of Student Financial Assistance, Kimura Scholarships; Address: PO Box 141608, Anchorage, AK 99514.

10083 ■ UAA Quanterra Scholarship *(Graduate/Scholarship)*

Purpose: To provide financial assistance to students who are formally admitted to an engineering or science degree-seeking program at the University of Alaska Anchorage. **Focus:** Engineering; Science. **Qualif.:** Applicants must be Alaska natives planning to obtain a Master's or Doctoral degree. **Criteria:** Selection will be based on the scholarship committee's criteria.

Funds Avail.: No specific amount. **Duration:** Annual. **To Apply:** Applicants must complete the online scholarship application process and must provide all required materials.

10084 ■ UAA RRANN Program Scholarships *(Undergraduate/Scholarship)*

Purpose: To provide financial assistance for tuition and other educational expenses to students currently enrolled in a nursing degree program through the Recruitment and Retention of Alaska Natives into Nursing (RRANN Program) at the University of Alaska Anchorage. **Focus:** Nursing. **Qualif.:** Applicants must be: in good academic standing with a minimum cumulative grade point average of 2.0; formally admitted into a degree program within the School of Nursing through the RRANN program; Alaskan residents; and, enrolled in the semester for which the award is to be in effect. **Criteria:** Selection of applicants will be based on their demonstrated motivation, talent, academic, and leadership potential. Preference will be given to Alaska Natives or American Indian students.

Funds Avail.: $500. **Duration:** Annual. **To Apply:** Applicants must make sure that they meet all of the aforementioned qualifications before proceeding to apply online through UAOnline and completing the scholarship application.

10085 ■ Wells Fargo Career Scholarship *(Undergraduate/Scholarship)*

Purpose: To provide financial assistance for tuition and other educational expenses to students who are interested in a career with Wells Fargo. **Focus:** Accounting; Business; Economics; Finance; Management. **Qualif.:** Applicants must be: in good academic standing with a minimum cumulative grade point average of 3.0; interested in a career with Wells Fargo; junior or senior students attending the University of Alaska Anchorage; enrolled full-time (12 credits) during the semester of the award; and, admitted into an undergraduate degree program within the College of Business and Public Policy. **Criteria:** Selection of applicants will be based on their demonstrated motivation, talent, academic, and leadership potential. Preference will be given to candidates in Business Management, Finance, Economics, or Accounting majors or minors, as well as to candidates who have completed accounting, economics, and finance courses.

Funds Avail.: No specific amount. **Duration:** Annual. **To Apply:** Applicants must make sure that they meet all of the aforementioned qualifications before proceeding to apply online through UAOnline and completing the scholarship application. Afterwards, they must submit a brief essay (250 words max) explaining: "why they would like a career in the banking industry."

10086 ■ Melissa J. Wolf Scholarship *(Undergraduate/Scholarship)*

Purpose: To offer financial assistance for tuition and other educational expenses to full-time students who are formally admitted into an Accounting degree-seeking program at the University of Alaska Anchorage. **Focus:** Accounting. **Qualif.:** Applicants must be: in good academic standing with a minimum cumulative grade point average of 2.0; formally admitted into an Accounting degree-seeking program at the University of Alaska Anchorage; planning to enroll full-time (twelve (12) credits); and, enrolled in the semester for which the award is made. They may be U.S. citizens, non-U.S. citizens, Alaska residents, or out-of-state residents. **Criteria:** Selection of applicants will be based on their demonstrated motivation, talent, academic, and leadership potential. Preference will be given to students who demonstrate a financial need.

Funds Avail.: No specific amount. **Duration:** Annual. **To Apply:** Applicants must make sure that they meet all of the aforementioned qualifications before proceeding to apply online through UAOnline and completing the scholarship application.

10087 ■ University of Alaska Anchorage - Matanuska-Susitna College
8295 E College Dr.
Palmer, AK 99645
Ph: (907)745-9774
Fax: (907)745-9711

Awards are arranged alphabetically below their administering organizations

E-mail: info@matsu.alaska.edu
URL: matsu.alaska.edu
Facebook: www.facebook.com/MSCDragons

10088 ■ Bill and Nell Biggs Scholarships
(Undergraduate/Scholarship)

Purpose: To provide financial support to deserving students in Alaska who want to pursue an education in any campus of the University of Alaska. **Focus:** Accounting; Business administration; Engineering; Mathematics and mathematical sciences; Science. **Qualif.:** Applicants must be graduates of Juneau-Douglas High School or Juneau residents who have completed a high school equivalency program. They must also going to attend at any of the UA campus (whether at Fairbanks, at Anchorage, or at Southeast). **Criteria:** Preference will be given to applicants majoring in accounting, business administration, engineering, science and mathematics, related science subjects or foreign languages areas such as Spanish, German or French.

Funds Avail.: No specific amount. **Duration:** Annual. **To Apply:** Applicants must complete the application forms available at the website; must attach a personal essay, two letters of recommendation, and current transcripts. **Deadline:** February 15. **Contact:** UA Foundation, at the above address.

10089 ■ Matanuska-Susitna College Regent's Scholarships *(Undergraduate/Scholarship)*

Purpose: To provide support to deserving students in Alaska who want to pursue an education in any campus of the University of Alaska. **Focus:** General studies/Field of study not specified. **Qualif.:** Applicants must be junior, senior or graduate students in good academic standing whose application reflects demonstrated commitment and involvement in leadership and civic or professional service activities and recognized academic achievement. **Criteria:** Applicants will be selected based on their academic standing and application documents.

Funds Avail.: $5,000. **Duration:** Annual. **To Apply:** Applicants must complete and submit the application form available at the website. Applicants must also submit a personal essay, two letters of recommendation, and current transcripts. **Deadline:** February 15.

10090 ■ Pat and Cliff Rogers Nursing Scholarships
(Undergraduate/Scholarship)

Purpose: To provide financial support to deserving students in Alaska who want to pursue an education in any campus of the University of Alaska. **Focus:** General studies/Field of study not specified. **Qualif.:** Applicants must be full-time students in their junior or senior year of a nursing program at any of the UA campus (whether at Fairbanks, at Anchorage, or at Southeast). **Criteria:** Applicants will be selected based on their application requirements.

Funds Avail.: No specific amount. **Duration:** Annual. **To Apply:** Applicants must complete and submit the application form available at the website. They must also submit a personal essay, two letters of recommendation, and current transcripts. **Deadline:** February 15. **Contact:** UA Foundation, at the above address.

10091 ■ Dr. Orrin Rongstad Wildlife Scholarship
(Undergraduate/Scholarship)

Purpose: To provide financial support to deserving students in Alaska who want to pursue an education in any campus of the University of Alaska. **Focus:** Wildlife conservation, management, and science. **Qualif.:** Applicants must be full-time students majoring in wildlife management at any of the UA campus (whether at Fairbanks, at Anchorage, or at Southeast), and be in good academic standing. **Criteria:** Applicants will be selected based on their academic standing and application documents.

Funds Avail.: No specific amount. **Duration:** Annual. **To Apply:** Applicants must complete and submit the application form available at the website. They must also submit a personal essay, two letters of recommendation, and current transcripts. **Deadline:** February 15. **Contact:** UA Foundation, at the above address.

10092 ■ Russian/Central Asian Student Scholarships *(Undergraduate/Scholarship)*

Purpose: To provide support to deserving students in Alaska who want to pursue an education in any campus of the University of Alaska. **Focus:** Wildlife conservation, management, and science. **Qualif.:** Applicants must be residents of Russia, Central Asia or the former Soviet Union, Kazakhstan, Uzbekistan, Turkmenistan, or Kyrgyzstan. **Criteria:** Preference will be given to residents of the Russian Far East.

Funds Avail.: $500. **Duration:** Annual. **To Apply:** Applicants must complete and submit the application form available at the website. Applicants must also submit a personal essay, two letters of recommendation, and current transcripts. **Deadline:** February 15.

10093 ■ University of Alaska Fairbanks
505 S Chandalar Dr.
Fairbanks, AK 99775
Ph: (907)474-7034
Fax: (907)474-6994
Free: 877-474-7390
E-mail: admissions@uaf.edu
URL: www.uaf.edu
Facebook: www.facebook.com/uafairbanks
Twitter: twitter.com/uafairbanks

10094 ■ UAF College of Liberal Arts - Anchorage Daily News Journalism Awards *(Undergraduate/Scholarship)*

Purpose: To provide financial assistance students who are formally admitted to the journalism degree-seeking program at the University of Alaska Fairbanks. **Focus:** Journalism. **Qualif.:** Applicants must demonstrate motivation, academic and leadership potential; must be in good academic standing with a minimum cumulative GPA of 2.0; must be formally admitted to a journalism degree-seeking program at the University of Alaska Fairbanks; may be incoming or continuing students at the University of Alaska Fairbanks; must be enrolled in the semester for which the award is made. **Criteria:** Preference will be given to Alaska Native students.

Funds Avail.: No specific amount. **Duration:** Annual. **To Apply:** Applicants must complete the electronic scholarship application available online.

10095 ■ University of Alaska Fairbanks Alumni Association (UAFAA)
201 Constitution Hall
Fairbanks, AK 99775

Ph: (907)474-7081
Fax: (907)474-6712
Free: 800-770-2586
E-mail: uaf-alumni@alaska.edu
URL: www.uaf.edu/alumni
Facebook: www.facebook.com/uafalum

10096 ■ Jim Doogan Memorial Scholarships
(Undergraduate/Scholarship)

Purpose: To support students in their pursuit of higher education. **Focus:** General studies/Field of study not specified. **Qualif.:** Applicants must be sophomore students or above. **Criteria:** Selection shall be based on the aforementioned qualifications and compliance with the application details.

Funds Avail.: No specific amount. **Duration:** Annual. **To Apply:** Applicants may visit the program website for other details regarding application process.

10097 ■ Fairbanks Chapter Legacy Scholarships
(Undergraduate/Scholarship)

Purpose: To support students in their educational pursuits. **Focus:** General studies/Field of study not specified. **Qualif.:** Applicants must be UAF sophomore students, or above, with a 3.5 GPA or above who are relatives of active, dues-paying members. **Criteria:** Selection shall be based on the aforementioned qualifications and compliance with the application details.

Funds Avail.: No specific amount. **Duration:** Annual. **To Apply:** Applicants may visit the program website for other details regarding application process.

10098 ■ Jay Hammond Memorial Scholarships
(Undergraduate/Scholarship)

Purpose: To support students who exhibit leadership and desire to make a difference in Alaska. **Focus:** General studies/Field of study not specified. **Qualif.:** Applicants must be students at the University of Alaska Fairbanks. **Criteria:** Selection shall be based on the aforementioned qualifications and compliance with the application details.

Funds Avail.: No specific amount. **Duration:** Annual. **To Apply:** Applicants may visit the program website for other details regarding application process.

10099 ■ Audrey Loftus Memorial Scholarships
(Undergraduate/Scholarship)

Purpose: To support students with their educational pursuit. **Focus:** General studies/Field of study not specified. **Qualif.:** Applicants must be freshmen or transfer students with demonstrated experience in and future commitment to extracurricular/ community activities, and have a GPA of 3.0 and above. **Criteria:** Selection is based on leadership skills and potentiality.

Funds Avail.: No specific amount. **Duration:** Annual. **To Apply:** Applicants may visit the program website for other details regarding application process.

10100 ■ UAF Alumni Association Scholarships
(Undergraduate/Scholarship)

Purpose: To support the education of a dependent of an alumni. **Focus:** General studies/Field of study not specified. **Qualif.:** Applicants must be undergraduate sophomores, juniors and seniors who are dependents of active alumni association members, and have a GPA of 2.5-3.5 range. **Criteria:** Selection shall be based on the aforementioned qualifications and compliance with the application details.

Funds Avail.: No specific amount. **Duration:** Annual. **To Apply:** Applicants may visit the program website for other details regarding application process.

10101 ■ University at Albany, State University of New York - Center for Women in Government and Civil Society
Draper 302
135 Western Ave.
Albany, NY 12222
Ph: (518)442-3900
Fax: (518)442-3877
E-mail: cwgcs@albany.edu
URL: www.albany.edu/womeningov
Facebook: www.facebook.com/womeningov

10102 ■ Fellowship on Women & Public Policy
(Graduate/Fellowship)

Purpose: To maximize the skills and contributions of women to achieve excellence in public service. **Focus:** Government; Public administration; Women's studies. **Qualif.:** Applicants must be graduate students at any accredited college or university in New York State; have completed 12 graduate credits before applying with degree completion scheduled after fellowships; and must have demonstrated interest in studies, research, employment or voluntary activities designed to improve the status of women and underrepresented populations; obtain a minimum 3.0 overall GPA; and, three years of work/internship experience. **Criteria:** Recipients will be selected based on result of the interview. Preference will be given to those applicants who are bright and motivated women who have demonstrated an interest in public policy and issues of underrepresented populations.

Funds Avail.: $10,000. **Duration:** Annual. **To Apply:** Application components include: online application wherein applicants must upload their resume and essay; and, official copies of transcripts to be mailed or sent at the given contact. **Remarks:** Established in 1984.

10103 ■ University Aviation Association (UAA)
2415 Moore's Mill Rd., Ste. 265-216
Auburn, AL 36830
Ph: (334)528-0300
E-mail: uaamail@uaa.aero
URL: www.imis100us1.com/UAA
Facebook: www.facebook.com/
  universityaviationassociation
Twitter: twitter.com/UAAdotAERO

10104 ■ Joseph Frasca Excellence in Aviation Scholarships *(Undergraduate/Scholarship)*

Purpose: To encourage students to reach the highest level of achievement in the field of aviation. **Focus:** Aviation. **Qualif.:** Applicants must have a minimum of 3.0 GPA; must have Federal Aviation Administration certification in either aviation maintenance or flight; a member of at least one Aviation organization; and juniors or seniors currently enrolled in a UAA member institution. **Criteria:** Preference is given to applicants with demonstrated interest or experience in aviation simulation; aircraft restoration; aerobatics;

Awards are arranged alphabetically below their administering organizations

with work experience in aviation; with work experience while in school; and exhibits financial need.

Funds Avail.: $2,000. **Number Awarded:** 2. **To Apply:** Applicants must submit five copies of completed application form; a brief essay; transcript; FAA certificates; one letter of reference; documents about financial status and other supporting documents. **Deadline:** April 7. **Contact:** Dr. David NewMyer, Southern Illinois University Carbondale, College of Applied Sciences and Arts, 1365 Douglas Dr., MC 6623, Carbondale, IL 62901; Phone:618-453-8898; Email: dnewmyer@aviation.siu.edu.

10105 ■ Eugene S. Kropf Scholarships
(Undergraduate/Scholarship)

Purpose: To encourage careers in aviation and other related fields through educational assistance. **Focus:** Aviation. **Qualif.:** Applicants must be U.S. citizens; enrolled in or planning to pursue two- or four-year degrees in the field of aviation; must be officially enrolled in a UAA member institution; and have a 3.0 GPA or above on a 4.0 scale. **Criteria:** Awards are given based on academic merit and character.

Funds Avail.: $500. **To Apply:** Applicants must submit application form; proof of enrollment; transcript; an essay (250 words typewritten, double-spaced) on "How Can I Improve Aviation Education". **Deadline:** June 15. **Contact:** Prof. Kevin R. Kuhlmann, Metropolitan State College of Denver, Campus Box 30, PO Box 173362, Denver, CO 80217-3362.

10106 ■ Paul A. Whelan Aviation Scholarships
(Undergraduate, Graduate/Scholarship)

Purpose: To promote educational pursuits in the field of aviation or space-related fields through financial assistance. **Focus:** Aviation. **Qualif.:** Applicants must be U.S. citizens; sophomore, junior, senior or graduate students; enrolled in a UAA member institution; must have 2.5 overall GPA and 3.0 in Aviation; and must demonstrate a love of aviation, leadership and extracurricular involvement/community involvement. **Criteria:** Priority is given to applicants who have an FAA certification as a pilot or mechanic; formerly or currently in military service via active duty, ROTC, the Air National Guard or Reserves while in school; and member of an aviation-related association or professional group such as the UAA.

Funds Avail.: $2,000. **Number Awarded:** 1. **To Apply:** Applicants must submit original copies and five copies of application form; official transcript; and recommendation letter from the institution. **Deadline:** May 15. **Remarks:** Established in memory of Paul A. Whelan, an aviation educator. **Contact:** Dr. David A. NewMyer, Chair, University Aviation Association Scholarship Committee, Southern Illinois University Carbondale, 1365 Douglas Drive, ASA Carbondale, IL 62901-6623.

10107 ■ University of California, Berkeley - Institute of Governmental Studies (IGS)
109 Moses Hall
Berkeley, CA 94720-2371
Ph: (510)642-1473
Fax: (510)642-3020
E-mail: igs@berkeley.edu
URL: igs.berkeley.edu
Facebook: www.facebook.com/pages/Institute-of
 -Governmental-Studies/214903035270497
Twitter: twitter.com/BerkeleyIGS

10108 ■ IGS John Gardner Fellowship
(Undergraduate/Fellowship)

Purpose: To encourage U.C. Berkeley's and Stanford's best students to pursue a career in public service. **Focus:** Public service. **Qualif.:** Applicant must be a senior graduating from the University of California, Berkeley; must be a United States citizen. **Criteria:** Applicants are evaluated based on the following criteria: (1) Demonstrated commitment to public service; (2) Record of academic accomplishment; (3) Maturity, personal integrity, and sense of responsibility; (4) Creativity, energy, and initiative; (5) Leadership potential: the ability to inspire others to action.

Funds Avail.: $30,000 each. **Duration:** Annual. **Number Awarded:** 6. **To Apply:** Applicant must submit one copy of the complete application form (available online); must have a formal resume; must have an official academic transcript; must have three letters of recommendation, at least one of which must be from a faculty member who is familiar with the applicant's university level work. **Deadline:** March 2.

10109 ■ University of California Institute for Mexico and the United States
University of California
3324 Olmsted Hall
Riverside, CA 92521-0147
Ph: (951)827-3519
Fax: (951)827-3856
E-mail: ucmexus@ucr.edu
URL: ucmexus.ucr.edu

10110 ■ UC MEXUS-CICESE Graduate Student Short-Term Research and Training Program
(Master's, Doctorate, Postdoctorate/Grant)

Purpose: To accomplish specific laboratory, library or field research or to support short-term stays for graduate student research and training. **Focus:** Latin American studies. **Qualif.:** Applicants must be University of California graduate students enrolled in a Master's or Doctoral level program who are in good standing. **Criteria:** Applicants will be selected based on submitted proposal. Such should demonstrate clarity, quality and feasibility.

Funds Avail.: $1,700 per month. **Duration:** Annual. **To Apply:** Applicants must complete the application form; must submit a cover page, project plan, detailed budget, curriculum vitae, UC faculty sponsor's abbreviated curriculum vitae, letter of support, Mexican academic host's letter of invitation and curriculum vitae, letter of acceptance and two sets of the proposal. **Deadline:** October 30. **Contact:** Wendy DeBoer, PhD, at 951-827-7339 or wendyd@ ucr.edu; Alvaro Armenta, PhD, at aarmenta@cicese.mx.

10111 ■ UC MEXUS Grants for Dissertation Research *(Graduate/Grant)*

Purpose: To support dissertation research or MFA final projects by University of California graduate students. **Focus:** Latin American studies. **Qualif.:** Applicants must be University of California graduate students in good standing or Mexican nationals currently enrolled in UC Mexico-related graduate programs. **Criteria:** Recipients will be selected based on submitted proposal.

Funds Avail.: Up to $12,000. **Duration:** Annual; Up to two years. **To Apply:** Applicants must submit a proposal. Such should include an application cover sheet, project institutional approval sheet, project plan, bibliography, budget

Awards are arranged alphabetically below their administering organizations

request, abbreviated curriculum vitae, letters of intent to participate, attachments and support letters. **Deadline:** September 14.

10112 ■ University of California, Riverside - Bourns College of Engineering - Center for Environmental Research and Technology (CE-CERT)
1084 Columbia Ave.
Riverside, CA 92507
Ph: (951)781-5730
Fax: (951)781-5790
E-mail: certinfo@cert.ucr.edu
URL: www.cert.ucr.edu

10113 ■ Ford Motor Company Scholarship
(Undergraduate/Scholarship)

Purpose: To encourage and aid undergraduate students in pursuit of careers in engineering. **Focus:** Engineering. **Qualif.:** Applicant must be a full-time undergraduate student at the University of California, Riverside, currently pursuing a B.S. degree, and have maintained at least a 3.0 grade point average. Candidates should have, or plan to have, a working relationship with CE-CERT. **Criteria:** Judgment criteria include the applicant's academic record, recommendations from faculty, promise in developing a successful career in a field of engineering, and financial need.

Funds Avail.: $5,000. **Duration:** Annual. **To Apply:** Application information and form is available online. **Deadline:** May 29.

10114 ■ University of California, Riverside - Institute for Mexico and the United States
3324 Olmsted Hall
Riverside, CA 92521
Ph: (951)827-3519
Fax: (951)827-3856
E-mail: ucmexus@ucr.edu
URL: www.ucmexus.ucr.edu

10115 ■ UC MEXUS-CICESE Short-term Research & Training Program *(Graduate/Award, Grant)*

Purpose: To accomplish laboratory, library or field research or to undertake specialized training. **Focus:** General studies/Field of study not specified. **Qualif.:** Applicants must be enrolled for the duration of the stay in a master's or doctoral level program at the University of California. CICESE applicants must be enrolled for the duration of the stay in a master's or doctoral level program at CICESE. All applicants must be have been continuously enrolled in their graduate program for at least one academic year by the time the proposed stay begins and be considered in good standing within their program. **Criteria:** Selection will be based on the submitted application materials.

Funds Avail.: $1,700 per month. **To Apply:** CICESE graduate students may apply only for residencies at a UC campus and must be hosted by eligible UC faculty or researchers. UC graduate students may apply only for residencies at CICESE and must be hosted by a faculty members or researcher who holds a full-time academic/research appointment in CICESE. The following items are required to constitute a complete application package: UC MEXUS-CICESE Graduate Student Training Application Form; Curriculum vitae of graduate student applicants; Letter from the applicants' current faculty advisor; Letter of intent from the faculty host; Project plan written in English or Spanish. Each item must be submitted electronically by email in PDF format prior to the application deadline. **Deadline:** March 31. **Contact:** Application materials must be submitted to veronica.sandoval@ucr.edu; Wendy DeBoer, PhD, Director of Academic Programs at wendyd@ucr.edu.

10116 ■ UC MEXUS-CONACYT Collaborative Grants
(Professional development/Grant)

Purpose: To provide seed funding to teams of UC and Mexican researchers with beginning projects in basic and applied collaborative research, instructional development, and public service and education projects that apply research to public issues. **Focus:** General studies/Field of study not specified. **Qualif.:** Applicants must be investigators from a UC campus and from a Mexican institution of higher education and/or research center that is part of the Registro Nacional de Instituciones y Empresas Cientificas y Tecnologicas (RENIECYT). **Criteria:** Selection will be based on the submitted proposals.

Funds Avail.: $25,000. **Duration:** Up to 18 months. **To Apply:** Proposals must be jointly submitted by eligible UC and Mexican collaborators using the online application site. All proposals must include a complete original set of the following items: Application Cover Sheet; Project Co-Principal Investigator/Institutional Approval Sheet, University of California; Project Co-Principal Investigator/Institutional Approval Sheet, Mexican Institution; Budget Request; Abbreviated Curriculum Vitae; Letters of intent to participate; Project Plan (maximum 10 pages); Bibliography; Attachments. Applicants must retain a copy of all application materials submitted. A complete proposal packet with two hard copies (original plus one copy) of all the information must be received by UC MEXUS within 10 days of the electronic submission deadline. **Deadline:** March 7.

10117 ■ UC MEXUS-CONACYT Doctoral Fellowships
(Doctorate/Fellowship)

Purpose: To provide non-resident tuition, fees, a stipend and support towards health insurance. **Focus:** Architecture; Biological and clinical sciences; Earth sciences; Engineering; Environmental science; Humanities; Law; Physical sciences; Social sciences; Urban affairs/design/planning. **Qualif.:** Applicants must be Mexican students doing their doctoral studies at any one of the ten University of California campuses. Students may pursue doctoral studies in most of the academic disciplines, with the exception of the arts. Eligible areas of study include the following: Architecture; Biological Sciences; Earth Sciences; Engineering; Environmental Studies; Humanities; Law; Physical Sciences; Social Sciences; Urban Planning. **Criteria:** Selection will be based on the submitted application materials.

Duration: Up to 5 years of funding. **To Apply:** Applicants must apply for admission to UC programs of study. Once students have applied for admission to a UC program, all applicants are required to complete and submit the "UC MEXUS Formato de Solicitante" to UC MEXUS, indicating to which UC Campuses they are applying. Students must apply for a doctoral fellowship directly with CONACYT. All students must have a provisional letter of acceptance from a UC program in order to submit an application to CONACYT. **Deadline:** April 15. **Contact:** Maestra Marcela Cruz Caballero at CONACYT, mcruzca@conacyt.mx.

Awards are arranged alphabetically below their administering organizations

10118 ■ UC MEXUS-CONACYT Postdoctoral Research Fellowships *(Postdoctorate/Fellowship)*

Purpose: To advance academic scholarship by emerging Mexican researchers and UC scientists and scholars in the early stages of their careers, after obtaining their PhD. **Focus:** General studies/Field of study not specified. **Qualif.:** Applicants must earn their PhD by April of the current year. Mexican citizens who have earned their doctorate from an institution other than the University of California may apply only for residencies at a UC campus and must be hosted by eligible UC faculty or researchers. UC doctoral graduates may apply only for residencies at Mexican research institutions and must be hosted by a Mexican faculty member or researcher who holds a full-time academic/research appointment in a Mexican institution of higher education and/or research. **Criteria:** Each proposal will be reviewed, evaluated, and rated by a committee of faculty members and/or teachers from Mexican and UC institutions representing expertise in relevant topics. In addition to such standard review criteria as clarity, quality, and feasibility of the proposal, UC MEXUS will assign importance to the significant of the proposed activities for the students' academic advancement and training and quality of supervision from UC or Mexican faculty and researchers.

Funds Avail.: No specific amount. **Duration:** Annual. **To Apply:** Proposal packet must include hard copies of all files uploaded to the electronic submission site. The following items are required as part of the proposal packet, for both the online submission and the two hard copies sent to UC MEXUS: online application cover sheet; curriculum vitae of applicants; abbreviated curriculum vitae of faculty host; letter of intent from the faculty host; project plan; timeline; official letter of invitation; if applicable, official evidence that the postdoctoral candidate belongs to the Sistema Nacional de Investigadores of Mexico with the applicants' registration number, and/or official letter from the applicants' home institution indicating that they hold a full-time appointment and will be released for the time requested; certification of completion of the PhD degree. Two letters of reference must be uploaded and sent separately. **Deadline:** March 7. **Contact:** Dr. Wendy DeBoer, Director of Academic Program; Phone: 951-827-7339; Email: wendy.deboer@ucr.edu.

10119 ■ UC MEXUS Dissertation Research Grants *(Graduate/Grant)*

Purpose: To support a dissertation research or MFA final projects by UC graduate students. **Focus:** Latin American studies. **Qualif.:** Applicants must be California graduate students in good standing, or Mexican nationals currently enrolled in UC graduate programs, including UC MEXUS-CONACYT Doctoral Fellows. **Criteria:** Selection will be based on the submitted proposal. Each proposal will be reviewed, evaluated, and rated by a committee of UC and Mexican scientists and scholars representing expertise in relevant academic disciplines and topics in the physical, natural and social science, humanities, and arts. Preference will be given to projects that hold significant promise for the advance of science or scholarship in areas of interest to UC MEXUS.

Funds Avail.: $12,000. **Duration:** Up to 2 years. **To Apply:** Applicants must submit a proposal using the online application site. The following items are required to complete the application: Application Cover Sheet; Project Institutional Approval Sheet; Project Plan (maximum 5 pages); Bibliography; Budget Request; Abbreviated Curriculum Vitae; Letters of intent to participate; Attachments; Support letters. Applicants must retain a copy of all application materials submitted. Within 10 days following the online application deadline, send two hard copies (original plus one copy) of a complete application set with all required materials. **Deadline:** September 14. **Contact:** Andrea Kaus, PhD, Director of Research Programs; Phone: 951-827-3519; Email: andrea.kaus@ucr.edu.

10120 ■ UC MEXUS Scholars in Residence Program - Graduate *(Graduate/Scholarship)*

Purpose: To offer an academic residency program for scholars at critical junctures in their academic careers. **Focus:** Arts. **Qualif.:** Applicants must be graduate students in the write-up phase of their dissertations, master's thesis, or final phase of production for a Master of Fine Arts. Student fellows are expected to interact with UCR faculty and students, and also with other visiting researchers at UC MEXUS. **Criteria:** Selection will be based on the submitted application materials.

Funds Avail.: Up to $4,000. **Duration:** Up to 1 year appointments. **To Apply:** Applications require a short prospectus (no more than 3 pages) indicating what the fellows hopes to accomplish with respect to their career development during the residency, how they expects to interact with the UCR campus community, and what the specific end products will be. Include a current curriculum vita and request three letters of recommendation to be sent independently to the Director of Academic Programs. Fellows must provide proof health insurance prior to beginning their residency. **Contact:** Wendy DeBoer, PhD, Director of Academic Programs; Phone: 951-827-7339; Email: wendy.deboer@ucr.edu.

10121 ■ UC MEXUS Scholars in Residence Program - Recent University Graduates *(Postgraduate/Scholarship)*

Purpose: To provide an opportunity for individuals to establish themselves and broaden the research or activities initiated in the last phase of their graduate career or to expand on activities begun as postgraduates. **Focus:** General studies/Field of study not specified. **Qualif.:** Applicants must be researchers, artists, or scholars within 5 years of receiving their graduate degree (PhD, MA, MS or MFA). **Criteria:** Selection will be based on the submitted application materials.

Funds Avail.: $4,000. **Duration:** Up to 1 year appointments. **To Apply:** Applications require a short prospectus (no more than 3 pages) indicating what the fellows hopes to accomplish with respect to their career development during the residency, how they expects to interact with the UCR campus community, and what the specific end products will be. Include a current curriculum vita and request three letters of recommendation to be sent independently to the Director of Academic Programs. Fellows must provide proof health insurance prior to beginning their residency. **Contact:** Wendy DeBoer, PhD, Director of Academic Programs; Phone: 951-827-7339; Email: wendy.deboer@ucr.edu.

10122 ■ UC MEXUS Scholars in Residence Program - Visiting Faculty *(Professional development/Scholarship)*

Purpose: To provide an opportunity for individuals to reflect and dedicate themselves to a specific project and collaborate with UCR faculty. **Focus:** General studies/Field of study not specified. **Qualif.:** Applicants must be visiting faculty researchers or artists. **Criteria:** Selection will be based on the submitted application materials.

Awards are arranged alphabetically below their administering organizations

Funds Avail.: $4,000. **Duration:** Short-term visits of 1-3 quarters. **To Apply:** Applications require a short prospectus (no more than 3 pages) indicating what the fellows hopes to accomplish with respect to their career development during the residency, how they expects to interact with the UCR campus community, and what the specific end products will be. Include a current curriculum vita and request three letters of recommendation to be sent independently to the Director of Academic Programs. Fellows must provide proof health insurance prior to beginning their residency. **Contact:** Wendy DeBoer, PhD, Director of Academic Programs; Phone: 951-827-7339; Email: wendy.deboer@ucr.edu.

10123 ■ UC MEXUS Small Grants for UC Faculty
(Graduate/Grant)

Purpose: To assist the activities of individuals in all disciplines as related to academic exchange, research training, and scholarly development in areas of interest to UC MEXUS. **Focus:** Latin American studies. **Qualif.:** Applicants must be University of California graduate students enrolled in a masters or doctoral level program and in good academic standing, or Mexican nationals currently enrolled in UC graduate programs, including UC MEXUS-CONACYT Doctoral Fellows. **Criteria:** Selection will be based on the submitted proposals. Proposals will be reviewed by an internal committee and award decisions made by the director of UC MEXUS. In addition to such standard review criteria as clarity, quality, and feasibility of the proposal, UC MEXUS will assign importance to the significance of the proposed activities for the students' academic advancement and training and quality of supervision from UC or Mexican faculty and researchers.

Funds Avail.: $1,500. **Duration:** Monthly. **To Apply:** Applicants must submit a completed application form, available at the website, together with the following required attachments: a project plan; a detailed budget curriculum vitae; for projects that will take place in Mexico, a copy of the letter of invitation from a Mexican faculty member or researchers. **Contact:** Adrea Kaus, PhD, Director of Grants Programs; Phone: 951-827-3586; Email: andrea.kaus@ucr.edu.

10124 ■ UC MEXUS Small Grants for UC Postdocs
(Postdoctorate/Grant)

Purpose: To support students or researchers for their activities in all disciplines as related to academic exchange, research training, and scholarly development in areas of interest to UC MEXUS. **Focus:** Latin American studies. **Qualif.:** Applicants must be University of California graduate students enrolled in a masters or doctoral level program and in good academic standing. University of California postdoctoral researchers may apply, provided they hold a UC postdoctoral position during the entire time period of the proposed activities. Graduate students and postdoctoral researchers in Mexico may consider applying to the UC MEXUS-CONACYT programs for which they are eligible. Mexican nationals currently enrolled in UC graduate programs, including UC MEXUS-CONACYT Doctoral Fellows, may apply to the small grants competition. **Criteria:** Proposals will be reviewed by an internal committee and award decisions made by the director of UC MEXUS. In addition to such standard review criteria as clarity, quality, and feasibility of the proposal, UC MEXUS will assign importance to the significant of the proposed activities for the students' academic advancement and training quality from the UC or Mexican faculty and researchers. Reviews are based on the proposed project or activity only and the thematic fit UC MEXUS goals, independent of the nationality of the applicants.

Funds Avail.: $1,500. **Duration:** Monthly. **To Apply:** Applicants must submit a completed application form, available at the website, and must include the following required attachments: a project plan; a detailed budget; curriculum vitae; for projects that will take place in Mexico, a copy of the letter of invitation from a Mexican faculty member or researcher. A signature of the students' UC faculty sponsor is required and academic standing in a graduate program or postdoctoral position must be certified by the chair of the applicants' department. **Contact:** Andrea Kaus, PhD, Director of Grants Programs; Phone: 951-827-3586; Email: andrea.kaus@ucr.edu.

10125 ■ UC MEXUS Small Grants for UC Students
(Graduate, Postdoctorate/Grant)

Purpose: To assist the activities of individuals in all disciplines as related to academic exchange, research training, and scholarly development in areas of interest to UC MEXUS. **Focus:** Latin American studies. **Qualif.:** Applicants must be University of California graduate students enrolled in a masters or doctoral level program and in good academic standing. University of California postdoctoral research may apply, provided they hold a UC postdoctoral position during the entire time period of the proposed activities. **Criteria:** Proposals will be reviewed by an internal committee and award decisions made by the director of UC MEXUS. In addition to such standard review criteria as clarity, quality, and feasibility of the proposal, UC MEXUS will assign importance to the significant of the proposed activities for the students' academic advancement and training and quality of supervision from UC or Mexican faculty and researchers.

Funds Avail.: $1,500. **Duration:** Monthly; for a 6 month period. **To Apply:** Applicants must submit a completed application form, available at the website, and must include the following required attachments: a project plan; a detailed budget; curriculum vitae; for projects that will take place in Mexico, a copy of the letter of invitation from a Mexican faculty member or researcher. **Contact:** Andrea Kaus, PhD, Director of Grants Programs; Phone: 951-827-3586; Email: andrea.kaus@ucr.edu.

10126 ■ University of California, Santa Barbara - Institute for Social, Behavioral, and Economic Research - Center for Nanotechnology in Society (CNS)
2201 N Hall
Santa Barbara, CA 93106-2150
Ph: (805)893-3350
Fax: (805)893-7995
E-mail: harthorn@cns.ucsb.edu
URL: www.cns.ucsb.edu

10127 ■ CNS-UCSB Graduate Fellowships for Science and Engineering *(Postdoctorate/Fellowship)*

Purpose: To support outstanding graduate students who want to pursue research in science and engineering. **Focus:** Biology; Chemistry; Physics; Technology. **Qualif.:** Applicants must be science or engineering PhD students (U.S. citizens or permanent residents) who are currently enrolled and in good standing in a relevant graduate program at UCSB. Terminal masters students are not eligible. **Criteria:** Selection will be based on the committees' criteria.

Awards are arranged alphabetically below their administering organizations

Funds Avail.: $17,500. **Duration:** Annual. **To Apply:** Applicants must submit the following application requirements: application cover sheet; statement of interest relevant to CNS-UCSB; Curriculum Vitae; unofficial transcript and; recommendation from the applicants' current advisor (must be sent from advisors' email address). **Deadline:** June 12. **Contact:** Bonnie A. Molitor; University of California Santa Barbara, Center for Nanotechnology in Society, No. 2317 Girvetz Hall, Santa Barbara California, United States, 93106-2150; 805-893-5929; bonnie_molitor@cns.ucsb.edu.

10128 ■ University of Colorado at Boulder - Natural Hazards Center

1440 15th St.
Boulder, CO 80309
Ph: (303)492-6818
Fax: (303)492-2151
E-mail: hazctr@colorado.edu
URL: www.colorado.edu/hazards

10129 ■ Mary Fran Myers Scholarships *(Professional development, Undergraduate/Scholarship)*

Purpose: To support individual commitment to disaster research. **Focus:** Emergency and disaster services. **Qualif.:** Applicants must be researchers, students, practitioners in disaster management. **Criteria:** Priority is given to applicants with financial need.

Funds Avail.: No specific amount. **Duration:** Annual. **To Apply:** Applicant must send four copies of the application form. **Deadline:** April 1. **Contact:** Lori Peek, 970-491-6777, lori.peek@colostate.edu.

10130 ■ University Film and Video Association (UFVA)

3800 Barham Blvd.
Los Angeles, CA 90068
Free: 866-647-8382
E-mail: ufvahome@gmail.com
URL: www.ufva.org
Facebook: www.facebook.com/ufvaconnection
Twitter: twitter.com/UFVAConnection

10131 ■ Carole Fielding Student Grant *(Undergraduate, Graduate/Grant)*

Purpose: To support the education aspect of students in the film and video discipline. **Focus:** Filmmaking; Video. **Qualif.:** Applicant must be a student (undergraduate/graduate) at the time the application is made. A faculty member who is an active member of the University Film & Video Association or staff at a UFVA member institution must sponsor the applicant. **Criteria:** Selection will be based on the committee's criteria.

Funds Avail.: $1,000. **Duration:** Annual. **To Apply:** Applicant must submit the following: one-page description of the project that includes a statement of purpose, an indication of the resources available to complete the work, and a summary of the proposed production or research project; one page resume of the applicant, including information on past film/video/new media work, and/or publications; a statement by the sponsoring UFVA Member, assessing the feasibility of the project and indicating his or her willingness to serve as faculty supervisor or consultant; a one-page budget, clearly indicating what portion of the total project will be supported by the grant. Additional following documents include: narrative (a copy of the script for 30 minutes); documentary (a short treatment for 45 minutes); and experimental/animation/New Media (a treatment or script, and/or a storyboard). **Deadline:** December 15. **Contact:** Laura Vazquez at lvazquez@niu.edu.

10132 ■ University of Florida - Center for Latin American Studies

319 Grinter Hall
Gainesville, FL 32611-5530
Ph: (352)392-0375
Fax: (352)392-7682
E-mail: pjw@latam.ufl.edu
URL: www.latam.ufl.edu

10133 ■ UF Center for Latin American Studies FLAS Summer Fellowships *(Master's, Graduate, Undergraduate/Award, Fellowship)*

Purpose: To support individuals who participate or willing to participate in an intensive study program of a less-commonly-taught Latin American Language. **Focus:** Foreign languages; Latin American studies. **Qualif.:** Applicants must be US citizens or permanent residents who are currently enrolled at the University of Florida as full-time undergraduate or graduate students; must have at least intermediate proficiency in their selected language of study for undergraduate students. Non-University of Florida graduate students with citizenship or permanent residency who are planning to attend the University of Florida Language and Culture Program in Rio de Janeiro are also eligible. **Criteria:** Selection will be based on the committees' criteria.

Funds Avail.: No specific amount. **To Apply:** Applicants must submit the following requirements: completed FLAS Summer Fellowship application; two pages statement of purpose describing how the study of the less commonly-taught language will benefit the applicants' program of study and career; two letters of recommendation accompanied by Release form, one should be from the graduate students' adviser; official academic transcripts; budget with information on program fees (not required for UF language and Culture Program in Rio de Janeiro) and; determination of financial need - FLAS Fellowship form or copy of most recent FAFSA form (if submitted to UF for Financial Aid). **Deadline:** March 7. **Contact:** Jocelyn Peskin, Assistant Director for Administration.

10134 ■ University of Florida College of Liberal Arts and Sciences - Center for Women's Studies and Gender Research

200 Ustler Hall
Gainesville, FL 32611
Ph: (352)392-3365
Fax: (352)392-4873
E-mail: page7@ufl.edu
URL: www.wst.ufl.edu

10135 ■ O. Ruth McQuown Scholarship - Graduate Award for Current Students *(Graduate/Scholarship)*

Purpose: To provide educational support to outstanding students enrolled in the College of Liberal Arts and Sciences at the University of Florida. **Focus:** Humanities; Interdisciplinary studies; Social sciences; Women's studies.

Awards are arranged alphabetically below their administering organizations

Qualif.: Applicants must be graduate students who have completed at least one semester of graduate work in the College of Liberal Arts and Sciences. **Criteria:** Scholarships will be awarded on a competitive basis in the fields of Humanities, Social Sciences, Individual Interdisciplinary Studies and Women's Studies.

Funds Avail.: $300 - $10,000. **To Apply:** Application form can be downloaded at the website. All applications, including two letters of recommendation and an essay paper must be submitted by the deadline. **Deadline:** February 22. **Contact:** Arlene Williams at arlenew@ufl.edu.

10136 ■ University of Hawaii at Manoa
2500 Campus Rd.
Honolulu, HI 96822
Ph: (808)956-8111
Free: 800-956-8975
E-mail: uhmanoa.admissions@hawaii.edu
URL: www.manoa.hawaii.edu
Facebook: www.facebook.com/uhmanoa
Twitter: www.twitter.com/uhmanoa

10137 ■ National Security Education Program - David L. Boren Fellowships *(Graduate/Fellowship)*

Purpose: To provide support for outstanding U.S. graduate students intending to pursue a career in language study. **Focus:** Foreign languages. **Qualif.:** Applicants must be U.S graduate students who want to pursue their area of specialization in language study. **Criteria:** Selection of applicants will be based on their application requirements.

Funds Avail.: $30,000. **To Apply:** Applicants are advised to contact Dr. Chizuko Allen for applications and information.

10138 ■ UH Manoa Starr Foundation Graduate Fellowships in Asian Studies *(Graduate/Grant)*

Purpose: To support continuing graduate students for such activities as field study, summer language study or research/conference travel. **Focus:** Foreign languages; General studies/Field of study not specified. **Qualif.:** Applicants must be full-time Asian Studies M.A. students who do not hold FLAS awards. **Criteria:** Selection will be based on the application requirements.

Funds Avail.: $15,000. **Number Awarded:** 2. **To Apply:** Applicants are advised to contact the Fellowship Coordinator of School of Pacific and Asian Studies of University of Hawai'i at Manoa for further information and application materials. **Deadline:** February 21.

10139 ■ University of Hawaii at Manoa East-West Center Graduate Fellowships *(Graduate, Postdoctorate/Fellowship)*

Purpose: To provide support for qualified individuals intending to participate in the educational and research programs at the EWC. **Focus:** General studies/Field of study not specified. **Qualif.:** Applicant must be a citizen and legal resident of an Asian or Pacific country, or the United States; must be interested in participating in the educational and research programs at EWC while pursuing a master's or doctoral degree at the University of Hawaii. **Criteria:** Preference is given to those in a master's degree program.

Funds Avail.: No specific amount. **Duration:** Annual. **To Apply:** Application must be made to the Center's in-country program representative. **Deadline:** November 1.

10140 ■ University of Hawaii at Manoa Graduate Assistantship Awards *(Graduate/Award)*

Purpose: To assist graduate students with their education. **Focus:** Teaching. **Qualif.:** Applicant must have a strong background in Asian Studies; must have a high scholastic record; must be admitted as a graduate student; must have a high level of English proficiency; must carry at least 6 units of credit each semester and maintain a minimum of 3.0 GPA. **Criteria:** Selection will be based on the academic standing of the applicant.

Funds Avail.: No specific amount. **To Apply:** Applicant must submit a letter of application, resume, and names, addresses and telephone numbers of three references. **Deadline:** March 3.

10141 ■ University of Hawaii at Manoa Graduate Student Organization Travel Funds *(Graduate/Grant)*

Purpose: To provide assistance to UH graduate students making scholarly or artistic presentations at conferences and professional meetings on the mainland and elsewhere. **Focus:** General studies/Field of study not specified. **Qualif.:** Applicant must be a classified graduate student. **Criteria:** Selection of applicant will be based on their application requirements.

Funds Avail.: No specific amount. **Number Awarded:** 3. **To Apply:** Applicant may contact the GSO for the application forms and more detailed information on the amount of stipends. **Deadline:** January 1; June 1; September 1. **Contact:** GSO at 808-956-8776/8018/4832, Hemenway Hall 212.

10142 ■ University of Hawaii at Manoa Japan Travel Bureau Scholarships *(Graduate, Undergraduate/Scholarship)*

Purpose: To promote understanding between peoples and nations of the world through higher education. **Focus:** Cross-cultural studies; International affairs and relations. **Qualif.:** Candidates must be full-time classified UHM graduate students or upper class undergraduates interested in international relations or cross-cultural studies and have demonstrated high scholastic achievement. **Criteria:** Candidates will be selected based on their academic standing.

Funds Avail.: $2,000. **Duration:** Annual. **Number Awarded:** 1. **To Apply:** Information and application materials may be obtained from the SPAS Office of Student Academic Services, 315 Moore Hall. **Deadline:** February 21.

10143 ■ University of Louisville Alumni Association
University Club and Alumni Ctr.
200 E Brandeis Ave.
Louisville, KY 40208
Ph: (502)852-6186
Fax: (502)852-6920
Free: 800-813-8635
URL: www.uoflalumni.org/s/1157/site2014/start.aspx
Facebook: www.facebook.com/UofLAlumniAssociation
Twitter: twitter.com/uoflalum

10144 ■ Beth K. Fields Scholarships *(Undergraduate/Scholarship)*

Purpose: To support students in their educational pursuit. **Focus:** General studies/Field of study not specified. **Qua-

Awards are arranged alphabetically below their administering organizations

lif.: Applicants must: be at least 25 years of age; provide support for at least one dependent; have a minimum of 12 semester hours college credit; have a cumulative GPA of 3.0; and, be full-time students at the university for the semester in which the scholarship is awarded. **Criteria:** Applications will be reviewed by the Scholarship Committee of the Board of Directors. Selection shall be based on the aforementioned qualifications and compliance with the application details.

Funds Avail.: Amount varies. **Duration:** Annual. **To Apply:** Applicants must submit a completed application form together with their resume or list of school, community and civic activities; one-page essay explaining their interest in the award and why they should receive the scholarship; and two letters of recommendation from a professor or teacher, while the other may be from their respective employers, community leaders, friends or relatives. **Deadline:** March 15. **Contact:** Rachel Kirk, Student Financial Aid Office: Phone: 502-852-8379; Email: rachel.kirk@louisville.edu.

10145 ■ Raymond A. Kent-Navy V-12/ROTC Scholarships *(Undergraduate/Scholarship)*

Purpose: To support direct descendants of an individuals who served in the Navy V-12 program or the Naval ROTC program at UofL. **Focus:** General studies/Field of study not specified. **Qualif.:** Applicant must be a direct descendant of an individual who served the Navy V-12 program or the Naval ROTC program. Applicant must have a 3.0 GPA. **Criteria:** Applications will be reviewed by the Scholarship Committee of the Board of Directors.

Funds Avail.: No specific amount. **To Apply:** Applicants must submit a completed application form together with a copy of official transcripts; a (300-word) essay; and two letters of recommendation. **Deadline:** March 30.

10146 ■ Kentucky Alumni Club Scholarships - Frankfort/Capital Region Alumni Club *(Undergraduate/Scholarship)*

Purpose: To support students in their educational pursuits. **Focus:** General studies/Field of study not specified. **Qualif.:** Applicants must be residents in the state of Kentucky (specifically in Anderson, Franklin, Henry, Owen, Mercer, Shelby and Spencer counties) pursuing a degree at the University of Louisville, and must maintain a GPA of 3.0. **Criteria:** Students will be selected on the basis of financial need.

Funds Avail.: Amount varies. **Duration:** Annual. **Number Awarded:** Varies. **To Apply:** Applicants must complete the application with an essay; official copies of transcripts; test scores; and two letters of recommendation (one from a teacher) submitted to the Scholarship Committee. **Deadline:** March 15. **Contact:** Rachel Kirk, Student Financial Aid Office: Phone: 502-852-8379; Email: rachel.kirk@louisville.edu.

10147 ■ Kentucky Alumni Club Scholarships - Lexington/Central Kentucky Alumni Club *(Undergraduate/Scholarship)*

Purpose: To support students in their educational pursuits. **Focus:** General studies/Field of study not specified. **Qualif.:** Applicants must: be students pursuing a degree at University of Louisville; have 3.0 GPA; and, residents in the state of Kentucky specifically in Fayette, Jessamine, Woodford, Clark, Bourbon, Scott, Harrison and Madison counties. **Criteria:** Students will be selected on the basis of financial need.

Funds Avail.: No specific amount. **Duration:** Annual. **Number Awarded:** Varies. **To Apply:** Applicants must complete the application with an essay; official copies of transcripts; test scores; and two letters of recommendation (one from a teacher). **Deadline:** March 15. **Contact:** Rachel Kirk, Student Financial Aid Office: Phone: 502-852-8379; Email: rachel.kirk@louisville.edu.

10148 ■ Kentucky Alumni Club Scholarships - Somerset/Lake Cumberland Area Alumni Club *(Undergraduate/Scholarship)*

Purpose: To support students in their educational pursuits. **Focus:** General studies/Field of study not specified. **Qualif.:** Applicants must be students from Adair, Casey, Clinton, Cumberland, Laurel, McCreary, Pulaski, Rockcastle, Rusell, and Wayne counties pursuing a degree at the University of Louisville who meet the minimum admission requirements. They must also have a cumulative GPA of 3.5 or higher on a 4.0 scale and an ACT score of 24 or better. **Criteria:** Selection shall be based on the aforementioned qualifications and compliance with the application details.

Funds Avail.: Amount varies. **Duration:** Annual. **Number Awarded:** Varies. **To Apply:** Applicants must complete the application with an essay; official copies of transcripts; test scores; and two letters of recommendation, one of which must come from a teacher. **Deadline:** March 15. **Contact:** Rachel Kirk, Student Financial Aid Office: Phone: 502-852-8379; Email: rachel.kirk@louisville.edu.

10149 ■ Covington-Cincinnati/Northern Kentucky Alumni Club - Dane Wagge Scholarships *(Undergraduate/Scholarship)*

Purpose: To provide financial assistance to students in Northern Kentucky/Greater Cincinnati area. **Focus:** General studies/Field of study not specified. **Qualif.:** Applicants must residents in the state of Kentucky (specifically in Boone, Kenton, Campbelle, Grant, Carroll, Pendleton and Gallatin counties) or in Hamilton County in Ohio, and must have a cumulative GPA of 3.0 and an ACT/SAT equivalent of 20 or above. **Criteria:** Selection shall be based on the aforementioned qualifications and compliance with the application details.

Funds Avail.: Amount varies. **Duration:** Annual. **Number Awarded:** Varies. **To Apply:** Applicants must complete the application with an essay; official copies of transcripts; test scores; must include a letter of recommendation from either a high school administrative staff or any high school teaching staff. **Deadline:** March 15. **Contact:** Rachel Kirk, Student Financial Aid Office: Phone: 502-852-8379; Email: rachel.kirk@louisville.edu.

10150 ■ Rodney Williams Legacy Scholarships *(Undergraduate/Scholarship)*

Purpose: To support the children and grandchildren of UofL alumni. **Focus:** General studies/Field of study not specified. **Qualif.:** Applicant must be related to a UofL graduate; incoming freshman or transfer student; have a 3.0 GPA; and must be a full-time student for the semester. **Criteria:** Selection is based on the submitted applications.

Funds Avail.: No specific amount. **Duration:** Up to four years. **To Apply:** Applicants must submit a completed application form together with a copy of an official transcript of records; resume or list of school, community and civic activities; a (300-word) essay; and two letters of recommendation. **Deadline:** March 15.

Awards are arranged alphabetically below their administering organizations

UNIVERSITY OF MARYLAND AT COLLEGE PARK

10151 ■ University of Maryland at College Park - Journalism Center on Children and Families (JCCF)
Knight Hall, Rm. 1100
College Park, MD 20742
Ph: (301)405-8808
E-mail: julie@journalismcenter.org
URL: www.journalismcenter.org

10152 ■ JCCF Equal Voice Journalism Scholarship
(Professional development/Scholarship)

Purpose: To recognize outstanding individuals who helped to increase public's understanding of poverty in the United States. **Focus:** Journalism. **Qualif.:** Applicants must be individuals in the field of journalism who have the urge to enlighten citizens of the United States in the issues that can affect their lives through the use of media. **Criteria:** Selection will be based on the committees' criteria.

Funds Avail.: No specific amount. **To Apply:** Applicants may contact the Center for application process and other information.

10153 ■ University of Massachusetts Dartmouth - College of Arts and Sciences - Center for Policy Analysis
285 Old Westport Rd.
North Dartmouth, MA 02747
Ph: (508)990-9660
Fax: (508)999-8374
URL: www.umassd.edu/cas/centers/cfpa

10154 ■ Philip H. Melanson Memorial Scholarships
(Undergraduate, Graduate/Scholarship)

Purpose: To provide financial assistance to undergraduate and graduate students who are enrolled at UMass Dartmouth and maintain an active interest in public policy. **Focus:** Social sciences. **Qualif.:** Students must: be enrolled full-time or part-time at UMass Dartmouth; be currently enrolled in undergraduate or graduate classes in Public Policy, conducting research for the Center for Public Analysis, or participating in a Public Policy Internship; have an overall GPA of 3.0 or higher for undergraduate students, 3.2 GPA or higher for graduate students and newly matriculating graduate students; demonstrate an active interest in extra-curricular activities that involve public policy, public service or community service. **Criteria:** Preference will be given to students who are declared Minors or Majors in Public Policy and students who have matriculated into the Master of Public Policy program.

Funds Avail.: $500 - $1,000. **Duration:** Annual. **To Apply:** Applicants must submit the scholarship application form to the Director of the Center for Public Analysis together with students' current transcript and two page letter of interest highlighting the students' public policy involvement and related achievements and explaining any financial need or hardship that should be taken into account by the award committee. **Deadline:** November 1. **Remarks:** Established in 2006.

10155 ■ University of Memphis
101 Wilder Tower
Memphis, TN 38152-3520
Ph: (901)678-2911
URL: www.memphis.edu

10156 ■ Tillie B. Alperin Scholarship *(Undergraduate/Scholarship)*

Purpose: To support the education of female law students at the University of Memphis. **Focus:** Law. **Qualif.:** Applicants must be female law students who have successfully completed their first year with a B average; have demonstrated a commitment to the legal profession; and demonstrate financial need. **Criteria:** Selection will be based on academic performance, leadership, character, personal achievements and financial need. Preference will be given to applicants who have overcome significant obstacles in pursuit of their education.

Funds Avail.: No specific amount. **Duration:** Annual. **To Apply:** Applicants must complete the online scholarship application form along with a personal statement; resume; scholarship statement; and recommendation letters. Applicants must also complete the FAFSA Form. **Remarks:** The scholarship is named in honor of the late Tillie Blen Alperin, a 1935 graduate of the old University of Memphis Law School and one of the first women to practice law in Tennessee.

10157 ■ Claude T. Coffman Memorial Scholarships *(Undergraduate/Scholarship)*

Purpose: To support the education of law students at the University of Memphis. **Focus:** Law. **Qualif.:** Applicants must be admitted at the University of Memphis Cecil C. Humphreys School of Law. **Criteria:** Selection will be based on academic merit and financial need.

Funds Avail.: No specific amount. **Duration:** Annual. **To Apply:** Applicants must complete the online scholarship application form along with a personal statement, resume, scholarship statement and recommendation letters. Applicants must also complete the FAFSA Form. **Remarks:** The scholarship is named in honor of the late Professor and former interim Dean of the Cecil C. Humphreys School of Law.

10158 ■ C. Cleveland Drennon, Jr. Memorial Scholarships *(Undergraduate/Scholarship)*

Purpose: To support the education of law students at the University of Memphis. **Focus:** Law. **Qualif.:** Applicants must be admitted as full-time students at the University of Memphis Cecil C. Humphreys School of Law. **Criteria:** Selection will be based on academic merit and financial need. Special consideration will be given to student-athlete graduates of The University of Memphis or Vanderbilt University.

Funds Avail.: No specific amount. **Duration:** Annual. **To Apply:** Applicants must complete the online scholarship application form along with a personal statement, resume, scholarship statement and recommendation letters. Applicants must also complete the FAFSA Form. **Remarks:** The scholarship is funded by Humphrey E. Folk, Jr. and the Drennon family and friends.

10159 ■ Evans and Petree Law Firm Scholarship *(Undergraduate/Scholarship)*

Purpose: To support the education of African American law students at the University of Memphis. **Focus:** Law. **Qualif.:** Applicants must be African American law students at the University of Memphis School of Law. **Criteria:** Selection will be based academic performance, leadership, character, personal achievements, and financial need. Preference will be given to returning African American students with financial need.

Awards are arranged alphabetically below their administering organizations

Funds Avail.: No specific amount. **Duration:** Annual. **To Apply:** Applicants must complete the online scholarship application form along with the personal statement, resume, scholarship statement and recommendation letters. Applicants must also complete the FAFSA Form.

10160 ■ Federal Court Bench and Bar Scholarships
(Undergraduate/Scholarship)

Purpose: To support economically disadvantaged law students from the Middle District of Tennessee. **Focus:** Law. **Qualif.:** Applicants must: be economically disadvantaged law students from the Middle District of Tennessee in good academic standing at the law school or the most recent school attended; have demonstrated financial need; and must have graduated from a high school in, or resided for the previous three years as a non-full time student in one of the following Tennessee Counties: Cannon, Cheatham, Clay, Cumberland, Davidson, DeKalb, Dickson, Fentress, Giles, Hickman, Houston, Humphreys, Jackson, Lawrence, Lewis, Macon, Marshall, Maury, Montgomery, Overton, Pickett, Putnam, Robertson, Rutherford, Smith, Stewart, Sumner, Trousdale, Wayne, White, Williamson, or Wilson. **Criteria:** Recipients will be selected based on financial need.

Funds Avail.: No specific amount. **Duration:** Annual. **To Apply:** Applicants must complete the online scholarship application form along with a personal statement, resume, scholarship statement and recommendation letters. Applicants must also complete the FAFSA Form.

10161 ■ Wilford Hayes Gowen Scholarship Fund
(Undergraduate/Scholarship)

Purpose: To support the education of law students at the University of Memphis. **Focus:** Law. **Qualif.:** Applicants must be second or third year law students enrolled at the University of Memphis School of Law. **Criteria:** Selection will be based on academic performance, financial need and personal determination.

Funds Avail.: No specific amount. **Duration:** Annual. **To Apply:** Applicants must complete the online scholarship application form along with a personal statement; resume; scholarship statement; and recommendation letters. Applicants must also complete the FAFSA Form. **Remarks:** The scholarship was established in memory of Wilford Hayes Gowen, through the Community Foundation of Western North Carolina, in memory of Wilford Hayes Gowen.

10162 ■ Herbert Herff Presidential Law Scholarships
(Undergraduate/Scholarship)

Purpose: To support students who have demonstrated high academic or professional achievement and who show potential for an outstanding law career. **Focus:** Law. **Qualif.:** Applicants must: be admitted at the University of Memphis Cecil C. Humphreys School of Law as first year law students; have demonstrated high academic or professional achievement; and, show potential for an outstanding law career. **Criteria:** Selection will be based on academic merit and financial need.

Funds Avail.: No specific amount. **Duration:** Annual. **To Apply:** Applicants must complete the online scholarship application form along with a personal statement; resume; scholarship statement; and recommendation letters. Applicants must also complete the FAFSA Form.

10163 ■ Robert and Elaine Hoffman Memorial Scholarships
(Undergraduate/Scholarship)

Purpose: To support the education of law students at the University of Memphis. **Focus:** Law. **Qualif.:** Applicants must be admitted at the University of Memphis Cecil C. Humphreys School of Law as first year law students. **Criteria:** Selection will be based on academic merit and financial need.

Funds Avail.: No specific amount. **Duration:** Annual. **To Apply:** Applicants must complete the online scholarship application form along with a personal statement; resume; scholarship statement; and recommendation letters. Applicants must also complete the FAFSA Form. **Remarks:** The scholarship is named in honor of the late Chancellor Robert Hoffmann and his sister Elaine.

10164 ■ Kathryn Hookanson Law Fellowship
(Undergraduate/Scholarship)

Purpose: To support the education of female law students at the University of Memphis. **Focus:** Law. **Qualif.:** Applicants must be student at the University of Memphis School of Law. **Criteria:** Preference may be given to female students and those in financial need.

Funds Avail.: No specific amount. **Duration:** Annual. **To Apply:** Applicants must complete the online scholarship application form along with a personal statement; resume; scholarship statement; and recommendation letters. Applicants must also complete the FAFSA Form.

10165 ■ John C. "Jack" Hough Memorial Law Scholarship
(Undergraduate/Scholarship)

Purpose: To support the education of law students at the University of Memphis. **Focus:** Law. **Qualif.:** Applicants must be second or third year law students who demonstrate financial need and are working as volunteers or in a law school externship in the office of the Shelby County Public Defender. **Criteria:** Selection will be based on academic performance, leadership, character, personal achievements and financial need. Preference will be given to applicants who express an interest in a career in government service as a public defender or prosecutor, or in the field of criminal law.

Funds Avail.: No specific amount. **Duration:** Annual. **To Apply:** Applicants must complete the online scholarship application form along with a personal statement; resume; scholarship statement; and recommendation letters. Applicants must also complete the FAFSA Form. **Remarks:** The scholarship is named in honor of the late John C. "Jack" Hough, a former member of the Shelby County Public Defender's Office.

10166 ■ Cecil C. Humphreys Law Fellowships
(Undergraduate/Fellowship, Internship)

Purpose: To support students who have demonstrated outstanding academic performance, leadership, good citizenship, and scholarly achievements. **Focus:** Law. **Qualif.:** Applicants must be second or third year students. Those who will be selected as Fellows are required to work 15 hours per week as research assistants to faculty members. **Criteria:** Selection will be based on demonstrated outstanding academic performance, leadership, good citizenship and scholarly achievements.

Funds Avail.: No specific amount. **Duration:** Annual. **To Apply:** Applicants must complete the online scholarship application form along with a personal statement; resume; scholarship statement; and recommendation letters. Applicants must also complete the FAFSA Form.

10167 ■ Judge William B. Leffler Scholarships
(Undergraduate/Scholarship)

Purpose: To support student who have demonstrated both academic merit and financial need. **Focus:** Law. **Qualif.:**

Awards are arranged alphabetically below their administering organizations

Applicants must be admitted at the University of Memphis Cecil C. Humphreys School of Law as first year law students. **Criteria:** Selection will be based on academic merit and financial need.

Funds Avail.: No specific amount. **Duration:** Annual. **To Apply:** Applicants must complete the online scholarship application form along with the personal statement; resume; scholarship statement; and recommendation letters. Applicants must also complete the FAFSA Form. **Remarks:** The scholarship is funded through the Leffler family, the donations of friends, and proceeds from the annual bankruptcy law seminar in Judge Leffler's memory.

10168 ■ H. H. McKnight Memorial Scholarships
(Undergraduate/Scholarship)

Purpose: To support veterans of the United States Armed Forces with financial need and who are interested in pursuing a career in criminal law. **Focus:** Law. **Qualif.:** Applicants must be veterans of the United States Armed Forces interested in pursuing a career in criminal law. **Criteria:** Selection will be based on academic merit and financial need. Final selection is made by the donor committee.

Funds Avail.: No specific amount. **Duration:** Annual. **To Apply:** Applicants must complete the online scholarship application form along with a personal statement; resume; scholarship statement; and recommendation letters. Applicants must also complete the FAFSA Form.

10169 ■ Memphis Access and Diversity Scholarships
(Undergraduate/Scholarship)

Purpose: To support the education of law students at the University of Memphis. **Focus:** Law. **Qualif.:** Applicants must be Tennessee residents enrolled at the University of Memphis School of Law. **Criteria:** Selection will be based on academic merit and financial need.

Funds Avail.: No specific amount. **Duration:** Annual. **To Apply:** Students interested in being considered for Memphis Access and Diversity Scholarships need to complete the Tiger Scholarship Manager application. They will be asked to complete a 250 word essay on how they will contribute to Diversity at the University of Memphis School of Law. **Deadline:** February 26.

10170 ■ Sam A. Myar Jr. Law Scholarship
(Undergraduate/Scholarship)

Purpose: To support the education of law students at the University of Memphis. **Focus:** Law. **Qualif.:** Applicants must be the Editors-in-Chief and Managing Editors of the University of Memphis Law Review. **Criteria:** Selection will be based academic performance, leadership, character, personal achievements and financial need.

Funds Avail.: No specific amount. **Duration:** Annual. **To Apply:** Applicants must complete the online scholarship application form along with a personal statement; resume; scholarship statement; and recommendation letters. Applicants must also complete the FAFSA Form. **Remarks:** Established in 1960.

10171 ■ Donald and Susie Polden Dean's Scholarships
(Undergraduate/Scholarship)

Purpose: To support deserving law students who have demonstrated a commitment to community or public service or who express their desire to serve their community during or following law school. **Focus:** Law. **Qualif.:** Applicants must be first year law students committed to community or public service and express a desire to serve the community during or following law school. **Criteria:** Recipients will be selected based on academic merit and financial need. Preference will be given to minority students.

Funds Avail.: No specific amount. **Duration:** Annual. **To Apply:** Applicants must complete the online scholarship application form along with a personal statement; resume; scholarship statement; and recommendation letters. Applicants must also complete the FAFSA Form.

10172 ■ Ratner and Sugarmon Scholarship
(Undergraduate/Scholarship)

Purpose: To support the education of law students at the University of Memphis. **Focus:** Law. **Qualif.:** Applicants must be second or third year law students. **Criteria:** Scholarship will be given to students who best exemplify a commitment to the needs of the underrepresented in society.

Funds Avail.: No specific amount. **Duration:** Annual. **To Apply:** Applicants must complete the online scholarship application form along with a personal statement; resume; scholarship statement; and recommendation letters. Applicants must also complete the FAFSA Form.

10173 ■ Joseph Henry Shepherd Scholarship
(Undergraduate/Scholarship)

Purpose: To support the education of law students at the University of Memphis. **Focus:** Law. **Qualif.:** Applicants must be admitted at the University of Memphis Cecil C. Humphreys School of Law. They must be returning 2nd and 3rd year law students. **Criteria:** Selection is based on academic performance and financial need.

Funds Avail.: No specific amount. **Duration:** Annual. **To Apply:** Applicants must complete the online scholarship application form along with a personal statement; resume; scholarship statement; and recommendation letters. Applicants must also complete the FAFSA Form. **Remarks:** The scholarship is made possible by an endowment fund established by Dorothy S. Shepherd.

10174 ■ Amy E. Spain Memorial Scholarships
(Undergraduate/Scholarship)

Purpose: To support law students who have demonstrated academic merit, a commitment to community/professional service, and personal industriousness. **Focus:** Law. **Qualif.:** Applicants must be first year law students with demonstrated academic merit. **Criteria:** Recipients will be selected based on academic merit; commitment to community/professional service; and personal industriousness.

Funds Avail.: No specific amount. **Duration:** Annual. **To Apply:** Applicants must complete the online scholarship application form along with a personal statement; resume; scholarship statement; and recommendation letters. Applicants must also complete the FAFSA Form. **Deadline:** March 1. **Remarks:** The scholarship was established by the family and friends of Amy Elizabeth Spain who, at age 30, died in a car accident in 1995.

10175 ■ The Springfield Family Scholarships
(Undergraduate/Scholarship)

Purpose: To support the education of students at the University of Memphis. **Focus:** Law. **Qualif.:** Applicant must be an entering student at the University of Memphis who is a graduate of Rhodes College. **Criteria:** Selection is based on academic merit.

Funds Avail.: No specific amount. **Duration:** Annual. **Number Awarded:** 1. **To Apply:** Applicant must complete the

Awards are arranged alphabetically below their administering organizations

online scholarship application form along with the personal statement; resume; scholarship statement; and recommendation letters. Applicant must also complete the FAFSA Form.

10176 ■ Tennessee Bar Foundation IOLTA Law School Scholarships *(Undergraduate/Scholarship)*

Purpose: To support the education of law students at the University of Memphis. **Focus:** Law. **Qualif.:** Applicants must be Tennessee residents who are third year students in good academic standing. **Criteria:** Selection will be based on demonstrated concern for public interest law, financial need and diversity representation.

Funds Avail.: No specific amount. **Duration:** Annual. **To Apply:** Applicants must complete the online scholarship application form along with a personal statement; resume; scholarship statement; and recommendation letters. Applicants must also complete the FAFSA Form.

10177 ■ Wyatt, Tarrant & Combs, LLP, Dr. Benjamin L. Hooks Scholarship *(Undergraduate/Scholarship)*

Purpose: To support the education of law students at the University of Memphis. **Focus:** Law. **Qualif.:** Applicants must: be admitted as full-time students at the University of Memphis Cecil C. Humphreys School of Law; have a minimum GPA of 3.0 and a minimum LSAT score of 153; and, be Tennessee or Kentucky residents. **Criteria:** Selection will be based on academic merit and financial need. Preference will be given to Tennessee or Kentucky residents.

Funds Avail.: No specific amount. **Duration:** Triennial. **To Apply:** Applicants must complete the online scholarship application form along with a personal statement; resume; scholarship statement; and recommendation letters. Applicant must also complete the FAFSA Form. **Deadline:** March 1. **Remarks:** The scholarship is established in memory of Dr. Benjamin L. Hooks, and is made possible by the law firm of Wyatt, Tarrant & Combs, LLP.

10178 ■ University of Michigan - Biological Station (UMBS)
2541 Chemistry Bldg.
930 N University Ave.
Ann Arbor, MI 48109-1055
Ph: (734)763-4461
Fax: (734)647-1952
E-mail: umbs@umich.edu
URL: www.lsa.umich.edu/umbs

10179 ■ Howard A. Crum Student Scholarships *(Undergraduate/Scholarship)*

Purpose: To support individuals who wants to enhance their knowledge in the field of biology and related courses. **Focus:** Biology. **Qualif.:** Applicants must be students studying at UMBS. **Criteria:** Selection will be based on the committees' criteria.

Funds Avail.: No specific amount. **To Apply:** Applicants may contact the Center for application process and other information. **Deadline:** March 15.

10180 ■ Fred and Avery Test Scholarships *(Undergraduate/Scholarship)*

Purpose: To support individuals who wants to enhance their knowledge in the field of biology and related courses. **Focus:** Biology. **Qualif.:** Applicants must be students at UMBS with financial need. **Criteria:** Selection will be based on the committees' criteria.

Funds Avail.: No specific amount. **To Apply:** Applicants may contact the Center for application process and other information. **Deadline:** March 15.

10181 ■ Marian P. and David M. Gates Scholarship for Non-Residents *(Undergraduate/Scholarship)*

Purpose: To support individuals who wants to enhance their knowledge in the field of biology and related courses. **Focus:** Biology. **Qualif.:** Applicants must be out-of state students interested to study at UMBS. **Criteria:** Selection will be based on the committees' criteria.

Funds Avail.: No specific amount. **To Apply:** Applicants may contact the Center for application process and other information. **Deadline:** March 15.

10182 ■ Frank Caleb & Margaret Thompson Gates Student Scholarships *(Undergraduate/Scholarship)*

Purpose: To support individuals who wants to enhance their knowledge in the field of biology and related courses. **Focus:** Biology. **Qualif.:** Applicants must be students at UMBS. **Criteria:** Selection will be based on the committees' criteria.

Funds Avail.: No specific amount. **To Apply:** Applicants may contact the Center for application process and other information. **Deadline:** March 15.

10183 ■ Joel T. Heinen Undergraduate Support Scholarships *(Undergraduate/Scholarship)*

Purpose: To support individuals who wants to enhance their knowledge in the field of biology and related courses. **Focus:** Biology. **Qualif.:** Applicants must be undergraduate students taking classes at UMBS. **Criteria:** Selection will be based on the committees' criteria.

Funds Avail.: No specific amount. **To Apply:** Applicants may contact the Center for application process and other information. **Deadline:** March 15.

10184 ■ Douglas Lake Improvement Association Scholarships *(Undergraduate/Scholarship)*

Purpose: To support individuals who wants to enhance their knowledge in the field of biology and related courses. **Focus:** Biology. **Qualif.:** Applicants must be students who are residents of Northern Michigan planning to attend the spring or summer session. **Criteria:** Selection will be based on the committees' criteria.

Funds Avail.: No specific amount. **To Apply:** Applicants may contact the Center for application process and other information. **Deadline:** March 15.

10185 ■ Lowe Family First Summer Student Scholarships *(Undergraduate/Scholarship)*

Purpose: To support individuals who wants to enhance their knowledge in the field of biology and related courses. **Focus:** Biology. **Qualif.:** Applicants must be students spending their summer at UMBS. **Criteria:** Selection will be based on the committees' criteria.

Funds Avail.: No specific amount. **To Apply:** Applicants may contact the Center for application process and other information. **Deadline:** March 15.

10186 ■ J.B. and Marilyn McKenzie Graduate Student Fellowships *(Graduate/Fellowship)*

Purpose: To support outstanding students engaged in their research. **Focus:** Environmental science; Natural sciences.

Awards are arranged alphabetically below their administering organizations

Qualif.: Applicants must be graduate students. **Criteria:** Selection will be based on the committees' criteria.

Funds Avail.: No specific amount. **To Apply:** Applicants may contact the Center for application process and other information.

10187 ■ George E. Nichols Undergradute Scholarships *(Undergraduate/Scholarship)*

Purpose: To support individuals who wants to enhance their knowledge in the field of biology and related courses. **Focus:** Biology. **Qualif.:** Applicants must be out-of-state or international undergraduate students in LSA who are studying at the Biological Station. **Criteria:** Selection will be based on the committees' criteria.

Funds Avail.: No specific amount. **To Apply:** Applicants may contact the Center for application process and other information. **Deadline:** March 15.

10188 ■ James L. Plafkin Memorial Scholarships *(Undergraduate/Scholarship)*

Purpose: To support individuals who wants to enhance their knowledge in the field of biology and related courses. **Focus:** Biology. **Qualif.:** Applicants must be students studying aquatic ecology. **Criteria:** Selection will be based on the committees' criteria.

Funds Avail.: No specific amount. **Duration:** Annual. **To Apply:** Applicants may contact the Center for application process and other information. **Deadline:** March 15.

10189 ■ Schrank Family Scholarships *(Undergraduate/Scholarship)*

Purpose: To support individuals who wants to enhance their knowledge in the field of biology and related courses. **Focus:** Biology. **Qualif.:** Applicants must be students interested to study biology or other related courses. **Criteria:** Selection will be based on the committees' criteria.

Funds Avail.: No specific amount. **Duration:** Annual. **To Apply:** Applicants may contact the Center for application process and other information. **Deadline:** March 15.

10190 ■ UMBS Istock Family Scholarships *(Undergraduate/Scholarship)*

Purpose: To support individuals who wants to enhance their knowledge in the field of biology and related courses. **Focus:** Biology. **Qualif.:** Applicants must be students with financial need. **Criteria:** Selection will be based on the committees' criteria.

Funds Avail.: No specific amount. **To Apply:** Applicants may contact the Center for application process and other information. **Deadline:** March 15.

10191 ■ UMBS Returning Student Award *(Undergraduate/Scholarship)*

Purpose: To support individuals who wants to enhance their knowledge in the field of biology and related courses. **Focus:** Biology. **Qualif.:** Applicants must be returning students who are in their second or subsequent summer at the Biological Station. **Criteria:** Selection will be based on the committees' criteria.

Funds Avail.: No specific amount. **To Apply:** Applicants may contact the Center for application process and other information. **Deadline:** March 15.

10192 ■ Dr. Edward G. Voss Memorial Scholarships *(Undergraduate/Scholarship)*

Purpose: To support individuals who wants to enhance their knowledge in the field of biology and related courses. **Focus:** Biology. **Qualif.:** Applicants must be undergraduate students planning to attend at UMBS. **Criteria:** Preference will be given to students interested in botany or entomology.

Funds Avail.: No specific amount. **To Apply:** Applicants may contact the Center for application process and other information. **Deadline:** March 15.

10193 ■ Gary and Gussie Williams Scholarships *(Undergraduate/Scholarship)*

Purpose: To support individuals who wants to enhance their knowledge in the field of biology and related courses. **Focus:** Biology. **Qualif.:** Applicants must be students who are teaching science or pursuing a degree in science education. **Criteria:** Selection will be based on the committees' criteria.

Funds Avail.: No specific amount. **To Apply:** Applicants may contact the Center for application process and other information. **Deadline:** March 15.

10194 ■ University of Michigan - Center for the Education of Women

330 E Liberty St.
Ann Arbor, MI 48104-2274
Ph: (734)764-6005
Fax: (734)998-6203
E-mail: contactcew@umich.edu
URL: www.cew.umich.edu
Facebook: www.facebook.com/UM-Center-for-the-Education-of-Women-112501145249/?ref=mf
Twitter: twitter.com/CEWatUM

10195 ■ Center for the Education of Women Scholarships *(Graduate, Undergraduate/Scholarship)*

Purpose: To provide educational support to students who are completing their degree. **Focus:** General studies/Field of study not specified. **Qualif.:** Applicants must be undergraduates, graduates and full-time or part-time students attending the University of Michigan (Ann Arbor, Flint, Dearborn Campuses); must have experienced a lapse in education of at least 48 consecutive months and 48 non-consecutive; and must have not yet received a scholarship. **Criteria:** Recipients are selected based on strength of motivation; impact on the chosen field; academic record and potential; creativity; and contributions.

Funds Avail.: $1,000 to $10,000. **Duration:** Annual. **Number Awarded:** 40. **To Apply:** Applicants must submit a filled-out application form; transcript of records from all previous educational institutions attended; three letters of recommendation from either professors or supervisors; and completed financial statement. Provide the needed materials with five completed copies (original and four copies).

10196 ■ Center for the Education of Women Student Research Grants *(Graduate, Undergraduate/Grant)*

Purpose: To promote every woman's career, leadership, education, growth and development, healing and well-being. **Focus:** Women's studies. **Qualif.:** Applicants must be graduates and upper division undergraduate students attending University of Michigan-Ann Arbor who are doing dissertation, thesis, or research. **Criteria:** Recipients are selected based on submitted proposals.

Funds Avail.: Up to $1,000. **To Apply:** Applicants must

Awards are arranged alphabetically below their administering organizations

submit a filled-out application form with student ID number; two-page proposal accompanied by project budget; a letter of support from an advisor; a curriculum vitae; and proof of IRB approval for the project (if relevant). **Contact:** Submit application packets to: Susan Kaufmann at the above address; Email: kaufmann@umich.edu; Call at 734-764-7640.

10197 ■ University of Michigan - Dearborn - Armenian Research Center (ARC)
4901 Evergreen Rd.
Dearborn, MI 48128-1491
Ph: (313)593-5000
URL: www.umdearborn.edu/673901

10198 ■ George and Isabelle Elanjian Scholarships (Undergraduate/Scholarship)

Purpose: To provide financial assistance to those students who are in need. **Focus:** General studies/Field of study not specified. **Qualif.:** Applicants must be incoming freshmen students or enrolled for at least one year at the University of Michigan-Dearborn. **Criteria:** Selection will be based on the committee's criteria.

Funds Avail.: $700 for tuition to one incoming first year student; $2,000 for one continuing upper-class student. **Number Awarded:** 2. **To Apply:** Applicants must be incoming students and should apply to the UM-D Admissions Office and upperclassmen should apply to the UM-D Financial Aid Office. Applicants may also contact the Research Center for the application process and other required materials. **Deadline:** February 1.

10199 ■ University of Minnesota - Charles Babbage Institute Center for the History of Information Technology
211 Andersen Library
222 21st Ave., S
Minneapolis, MN 55455
Ph: (612)624-5050
Fax: (612)625-8054
URL: www.cbi.umn.edu

10200 ■ Arthur L. Norberg Travel Fund (Advanced Professional/Grant)

Purpose: To help scholars with travel expenses to use archival collections at the Charles Babbage Institute. **Focus:** Information science and technology. **Qualif.:** Applicants must be scholars intending to use CBI collections for research projects. They must be residents outside the Twin Cities metropolitan region. **Criteria:** Recipients will be selected based on eligibility.

Funds Avail.: $1,000 each. **Duration:** Annual. **Number Awarded:** 5. **To Apply:** Applicants must submit a two-page CV as well as a 500-word project description that describes the overall research project, identifies the importance of specific CBI collections and discusses the projected outcome (journal article, book chapter, museum exhibit, etc.). Materials must be submitted by email at cbi@umn.edu or mailed at: Charles Babbage Institute: Norberg Travel Fund, at the above address. **Deadline:** January 15.

10201 ■ The Adelle and Erwin Tomash Fellowship in the History of Information Technology (Doctorate, Graduate/Fellowship)

Purpose: To assist graduate students for doctoral dissertation research in the history of computing. **Focus:** Information science and technology. **Qualif.:** Applicants must be CBI students who have completed all requirements for the doctoral degree except the research and writing of the dissertation. **Criteria:** Preference will be given to applicants indicating a need to use CBI materials, planning research in residence at CBI, and willing to make a brief presentation of their research findings to CBI staff.

Funds Avail.: $14,000. **Duration:** Annual. **To Apply:** Applicants should send to CBI a curriculum vitae and a five-page (single-spaced) statement and justification of the research project including a discussion of methods, research materials, evidence of faculty support for the project, and bibliography (bibliography does not count toward page count). Applicants should also arrange for three letters of reference and certified copies of graduate school transcripts to be sent directly to CBI. **Deadline:** January 15. **Contact:** R. Arvid Nelsen, CBI Archivist, at nels0307@umn.edu.

10202 ■ University of Minnesota Office for Equity and Diversity - Women's Center
432 Morrill Hall
100 Church St., SE
Minneapolis, MN 55455
Ph: (612)624-0594
Fax: (612)626-0397
E-mail: oed@umn.edu
URL: diversity.umn.edu

10203 ■ Carol E. Macpherson Memorial Scholarship (Graduate, Undergraduate/Scholarship)

Purpose: To provide support for qualified individuals intending to pursue an educational career. **Focus:** General studies/Field of study not specified. **Qualif.:** Applicants must be women-identified; must have five-year or longer gap in college/university education; must have admission or pending admission to an undergraduate or graduate/professional degree or credit certificate program at any University of Minnesota campus. **Criteria:** Selection will be based on applicant's strength of personal statement, reference letters indicating educational goals and academic promise, status as a student parent, academic achievement and education status.

Funds Avail.: $1,000 - $6,000. **Duration:** Annual. **To Apply:** Applicants must submit the complete scholarship application, including the following: their personal statements; reference letters indicating educational goals and academic promise; academic transcripts of all related college/postsecondary enrollment; completed FAFSA for the academic year they are applying for (to be filed at least three weeks before the scholarship deadline). **Deadline:** June 3. **Contact:** Women's Center, 612-625-9837; Email: women@umn.edu.

10204 ■ University of Nebraska-Lincoln - Institute of Agriculture and Natural Resources - Agricultural Research Division (ARD)
207 Agricultural Hall
Lincoln, NE 68583
Ph: (402)472-2045
URL: ard.unl.edu

10205 ■ Shear-Miles Agricultural Fellowship (Graduate, Doctorate/Fellowship)

Purpose: To provide funds to individuals conducting basic research in agriculture. **Focus:** Agricultural sciences. **Qua-**

Awards are arranged alphabetically below their administering organizations

lif.: Nominees must be graduate research assistantships students, may be either beginning graduate students or students in progress, but all nominees must have identified a thesis topic that would clearly be considered "basic research in agriculture". Only students with high scholastic merit and research potential should be nominated. **Criteria:** Preference will be given to Ph.D. graduate research assistants, although exceptional M.S. students may also be considered.

Funds Avail.: $2,000. **To Apply:** Nominees may contact the Center for application process and other information. **Deadline:** June 17.

10206 ■ Shear-Miles Agricultural Scholarship *(Graduate, Doctorate/Scholarship)*

Purpose: To provide funds to individuals conducting basic research in agriculture. **Focus:** Agricultural sciences. **Qualif.:** Nominees must be graduate research assistantships students, may be either beginning graduate students or students in progress, but all nominees must have identified a thesis topic that would clearly be considered "basic research in agriculture". Only students with high scholastic merit and research potential should be nominated. **Criteria:** Preference will be given to Ph.D. graduate research assistants, although exceptional M.S. students may also be considered.

Funds Avail.: $2,000. **To Apply:** Nominees may contact the Center for application process and other information. **Deadline:** June 17.

10207 ■ University of New Hampshire (UNH)
Durham, NH 03824
Ph: (603)862-1234
Fax: (603)862-0077
E-mail: admission@unh.edu
URL: www.unh.edu
Facebook: www.facebook.com/universityofnewhampshire
Twitter: www.twitter.com/uofnh

10208 ■ College of Engineering and Physical Sciences Industry Scholarships *(Undergraduate/Scholarship)*

Purpose: To provide financial assistance to students who want to continue their education at UNH. **Focus:** Engineering; Physical sciences. **Qualif.:** Applicants must be first year students admitted to the University's College of Engineering and Physical Sciences. **Criteria:** Students who wish to be considered for the scholarship must present credentials that reflect outstanding academic achievement and promise. These include: rigorous program of study including a minimum of four years of mathematics and four years of science, with preference given to pre-engineering programs, advanced placement, and international baccalaureate courses; grades that indicate excellence; class rank in the top 10 percent (for schools that provide class rank) or equivalent; SAT Reasoning Test score of typically 1970+, or higher; or a composite ACT score of 29+, or higher.

Funds Avail.: No specific amount. **Duration:** Annual. **Number Awarded:** 2. **To Apply:** Applicants must have an application for admission to a major within the College of Engineering and Physical Sciences at the University of New Hampshire; must have official high school transcripts, including the first marking period of senior year; must have the official test scores for either the SAT Reasoning Test or ACT with writing test; must submit an additional scholarship essay through the online form; must submit a Free Application for Federal Student Aid (FAFSA) form. **Deadline:** November 15. **Contact:** Dr. Charles Zercher at 603-862-2697 or via email: chuck.zercher@unh.edu.

10209 ■ UNH Alumni Association Legacy Scholarships *(Undergraduate/Scholarship)*

Purpose: To provide financial assistance to students who want to continue their education at UNH. **Focus:** General studies/Field of study not specified. **Qualif.:** Applicants must be students who are directly descended from any relatives (i.e. parents, grandparents or great-grandparents, etc.) who are alumni/alumnae of the University of New Hampshire. **Criteria:** Selection will be based on merit; applicants shall be chosen based on the following criteria: leadership skills; academic record; broad extracurricular interests.

Funds Avail.: No specific amount. **Duration:** Annual. **To Apply:** Application details shall be determined by the University and program officers.

10210 ■ UNH Parents Association Endowment Scholarship Fund *(Undergraduate/Scholarship)*

Purpose: To provide financial assistance to students who want to continue their education at UNH. **Focus:** General studies/Field of study not specified. **Qualif.:** Applicants must: demonstrate academic achievement; be of good character; have a minimum cumulative GPA of 2.8; be involved in community service projects or in the university community; and, be making financial contributions to their education through employment. **Criteria:** Selection of recipients will be based on financial need.

Funds Avail.: $3,000 each. **Duration:** Annual. **Number Awarded:** Varies. **To Apply:** Applicants must submit the following: FAFSA for initial qualification; completed application form provided by UNH Program; employment verification letter/community service verification letter; background information statement; and, faculty recommendation **Deadline:** March 4. **Remarks:** Established in 1999. **Contact:** University of New Hampshire Parents Association, University of New Hampshire, at the above address.

10211 ■ University of North Carolina School of Media and Journalism
Carol Hall CB 3365
Chapel Hill, NC 27599-3365
Ph: (919)962-1204
Fax: (919)962-0620
E-mail: mjschool@unc.edu
URL: mj.unc.edu
Facebook: www.facebook.com/uncmjschool
LinkedIn: www.linkedin.com/edu/school?id=176010&trk
=tyah&trkInfo=clickedVertical%3Aschool%2CclickedEnti
tyId%3A176010%2Cidx%3A1-1-1%2CtarId%3A1443
580785264%2Ctas%3Aunc%20school%20of%20media
Twitter: twitter.com/uncmjschool

10212 ■ Floyd S. Alford Jr. Scholarships *(Undergraduate/Scholarship)*

Purpose: To educate journalists; to recognize students who demonstrate outstanding journalistic talent and a strong commitment to improve the community through honest and accurate work. **Focus:** Journalism. **Qualif.:** Applicants must be students who have pre-declared or are enrolled in the School of Media and Journalism. **Criteria:** Recipients will be selected based on their academic

Awards are arranged alphabetically below their administering organizations

interests, geographic location, financial need and programs of study.
Funds Avail.: No specific amount. **Duration:** Annual. **To Apply:** Applicants must submit a completed general application form, available at the website. **Deadline:** February 22. **Contact:** mjschoolscholarships@unc.edu.

10213 ■ Phillip Alston Scholarships *(Undergraduate/Scholarship)*

Purpose: To provide financial assistance to students interested in sports communication program. **Focus:** Communications; Journalism. **Qualif.:** Applicants must be students who have pre-declared or are enrolled in the School of Media and Journalism. **Criteria:** Recipients will be selected based on their academic interests, geographic location, financial need and programs of study.
Funds Avail.: No specific amount. **Duration:** Annual. **To Apply:** Applicants must submit a completed general application form, available at the website. **Deadline:** February 22. **Contact:** mjschoolscholarships@unc.edu.

10214 ■ AT&T Business Internship Awards *(Undergraduate/Internship)*

Purpose: To provide financial assistance to undergraduate or graduate students interested in business journalism. **Focus:** Journalism. **Qualif.:** Applicants must have arranged a business journalism internship and must be in the BellSouth service area. **Criteria:** Recipients will be selected based on their academic interests, geographic location, financial need and programs of study.
Funds Avail.: No specific. **Duration:** Annual. **To Apply:** Applicants must submit a completed general application form, available at the website. **Deadline:** February 22.

10215 ■ Jim Batten Community Newspaper Internships *(Undergraduate/Internship)*

Purpose: To provide financial assistance to students to fund their living expenses during their summer internship at a community newspaper. **Focus:** Communications; Journalism. **Qualif.:** Applicants must students who have pre-declared or are enrolled in the School of Media and Journalism. **Criteria:** Recipients will be selected based on the academic interests, geographic location, financial need and programs of study.
Funds Avail.: No specific amount. **Duration:** Annual. **To Apply:** Applicants must submit a completed general application form, available at the website. **Deadline:** February 22. **Contact:** Robin Jackson, Director of Alumni Affairs and Donor Relations at mjschoolscholarships@unc.edu.

10216 ■ Margaret Blanchard Dissertation Support Fund *(Graduate/Grant)*

Purpose: To provide educational assistance to students who are pursuing journalism career. **Focus:** Communications. **Qualif.:** Applicants must students who have pre-declared or are enrolled in the School of Media and Journalism. **Criteria:** Recipients will be selected based on their academic interests, geographic location, financial need and programs of study.
Funds Avail.: No specific amount. **Duration:** Annual. **To Apply:** Applicants must submit a completed special application form, available at the website. **Deadline:** February 22. **Contact:** mjschoolscholarships@unc.edu.

10217 ■ Tom Bost Scholarships *(Undergraduate/Scholarship)*

Purpose: To provide educational assistance to students who are studying journalism. **Focus:** Communications; Journalism. **Qualif.:** Applicants must be students who have pre-declared or are enrolled in the School of Media and Journalism. **Criteria:** Recipients will be selected based on their academic interests, geographic location, financial need and programs of study.
Funds Avail.: No specific amount. **Duration:** Annual. **To Apply:** Applicants must submit a completed general application form, available at the website. **Deadline:** February 22. **Contact:** mjschoolscholarships@unc.edu.

10218 ■ Rick Brewer Scholarships *(Undergraduate/Scholarship)*

Purpose: To provide educational assistance to students who have expressed an interest in pursuing a career in the field of sports journalism, broadcasting or public relations on the collegiate, amateur or professional levels. **Focus:** Broadcasting; Journalism; Public relations. **Qualif.:** Applicants must be undergraduate students with a keen interest in pursuing a career in sports journalism, broadcasting, or public relations. **Criteria:** Recipients will be selected based on their academic interests, geographic location, financial need and programs of study.
Funds Avail.: No specific amount. **Duration:** Annual. **To Apply:** Applicants must submit a completed general application form, available at the website. **Deadline:** February 22. **Contact:** mjschoolscholarships@unc.edu.

10219 ■ Elton Casey Scholarships *(Undergraduate/Scholarship)*

Purpose: To provide educational assistance to current MJ-school students. **Focus:** Communications. **Qualif.:** Applicants must be students who are pursuing a career in sports journalism with a preference given to students from Orange or Durham counties. **Criteria:** Recipients will be selected based on their academic interests, geographic location, financial need and programs of study.
Funds Avail.: No specific amount. **Duration:** Annual. **To Apply:** Applicants must submit a completed general application form, available at the website. **Deadline:** February 22. **Contact:** mjschoolscholarships@unc.edu.

10220 ■ Ardis Cohoon Scholarships *(Undergraduate/Scholarship)*

Purpose: To provide educational assistance for journalists who wish to improve their communication skills. **Focus:** Communications; Journalism. **Qualif.:** Applicants must be students who have pre-declared or are enrolled in the School of Media and Journalism. **Criteria:** Recipients will be selected based on their academic interests, geographic location, financial need and programs of study.
Funds Avail.: No specific amount. **Duration:** Annual. **To Apply:** Applicants must submit a completed general application form, available at the website. **Deadline:** February 22. **Contact:** mjschoolscholarships@unc.edu.

10221 ■ Louis M. Connor Jr. Scholarships *(Undergraduate/Scholarship)*

Purpose: To provide educational assistance to students in the public relations specialization. **Focus:** Public relations. **Qualif.:** Applicants must students who have pre-declared or are enrolled in the School of Media and Journalism. **Criteria:** Recipients will be selected based on their academic interests, geographic location, financial need and programs of study.
Funds Avail.: No specific amount. **To Apply:** Applicants must submit a completed general application form, avail-

Awards are arranged alphabetically below their administering organizations

able at the website. **Deadline:** February 22. **Contact:** mjschoolscholarships@unc.edu.

10222 ■ Kathryn M. Cronin Scholarships
(Undergraduate/Scholarship)

Purpose: To support outstanding students who shows through coursework and other activities an intent to pursue a career in medical journalism or health communication. **Focus:** Communications; Journalism. **Qualif.:** Applicants must students who have pre-declared or are enrolled in the School of Media and Journalism. **Criteria:** Recipients will be selected based on their academic interests, geographic location, financial need and programs of study.
Funds Avail.: No specific amount. **Duration:** Annual. **To Apply:** Applicants must submit a completed special application form, available at the website. **Deadline:** February 22. **Contact:** mjschoolscholarships@unc.edu.

10223 ■ Don and Barbara Curtis Excellence Fund for Extracurricular Student Activities
(Undergraduate/Grant)

Purpose: To provide financial assistance to undergraduate majors in the School of Media and Journalism to participate in meaningful out-of-classroom activities that will help them in their careers. **Focus:** Communications. **Qualif.:** Applicants must be students who are currently enrolled at the University of North Carolina and/or as members of a student organization. **Criteria:** Recipients are selected based on the academic performance, financial need, and potential for journalism-mass communication careers.
Funds Avail.: Maximum of $1,000. **To Apply:** Applicants must visit the website to complete the online application process. **Contact:** Dr. C.A. Tuggle, Senior Associate Dean at catuggle@unc.edu.

10224 ■ James Davis Scholarships *(Undergraduate/ Scholarship)*

Purpose: To provide educational assistance to current MJ-school students. **Focus:** Communications; Journalism. **Qualif.:** Applicants must students who have pre-declared or are enrolled in the School of Media and Journalism. **Criteria:** Recipients will be selected based on their academic interests, geographic location, financial need and programs of study. Preference will be given to North Carolina natives who have demonstrated a commitment to the study of state history.
Funds Avail.: No specific amount. **Duration:** Annual. **To Apply:** Applicants must submit a completed general application form, available at the website. **Deadline:** February 22. **Contact:** mjschoolscholarships@unc.edu.

10225 ■ Robert Winchester Dodson Scholarships
(Undergraduate/Scholarship)

Purpose: To provide educational assistance to students who are studying journalism. **Focus:** Communications; Journalism. **Qualif.:** Applicants must students who have pre-declared or are enrolled in the School of Media and Journalism. **Criteria:** Recipients will be selected based on their academic interests, geographic location, financial need and programs of study.
Funds Avail.: No specific amount. **Duration:** Annual. **To Apply:** Applicants must submit a completed general application form, available at the website. **Deadline:** February 22. **Contact:** mjschoolscholarships@unc.edu.

10226 ■ Reese Felts Scholarships *(Undergraduate/ Scholarship)*

Purpose: To support students who are pursuing broadcast and electronic journalism specialization. **Focus:** Communications; Journalism. **Qualif.:** Applicants must students who have pre-declared or are enrolled in the School of Media and Journalism. **Criteria:** Recipients will be selected based on their academic interests, geographic location, financial need and programs of study.
Funds Avail.: No specific amount. **Duration:** Annual. **To Apply:** Applicants must submit a completed general application form, available at the website. **Deadline:** February 22. **Contact:** mjschoolscholarships@unc.edu.

10227 ■ Ameel J. Fisher Scholarships
(Undergraduate/Scholarship)

Purpose: To provide educational assistance to current MJ-school students. **Focus:** Communications; Journalism. **Qualif.:** Applicants must students who have pre-declared or are enrolled in the School of Media and Journalism. **Criteria:** Recipients will be selected based on their academic interests, geographic location, financial need and programs of study.
Funds Avail.: No specific amount. **Duration:** Annual. **To Apply:** Applicants must submit a completed general application form, available at the website. **Deadline:** February 22.

10228 ■ Victoria M. Gardner Scholarships
(Undergraduate/Scholarship)

Purpose: To provide educational assistance to students who have an interest in health and family issues in the field of medical journalism. **Focus:** Education, Medical. **Qualif.:** Applicants must students who have pre-declared or are enrolled in the School of Media and Journalism. **Criteria:** Recipients will be selected based on their academic interests, geographic location, financial need and programs of study.
Funds Avail.: No specific amount. **Duration:** Annual. **To Apply:** Applicants must submit a completed general application form, available at the website. **Deadline:** February 22. **Contact:** mjschoolscholarships@unc.edu.

10229 ■ Kays Gary Scholarships *(Undergraduate/ Scholarship)*

Purpose: To provide educational assistance to students who are studying journalism. **Focus:** Communications; Journalism. **Qualif.:** Applicants must be students who have pre-declared or are enrolled in the School of Media and Journalism. **Criteria:** Recipients will be selected based on their academic interests, geographic location, financial need and programs of study.
Funds Avail.: No specific amount. **Duration:** Annual. **To Apply:** Applicants must submit a completed general application form, available at the website. **Deadline:** February 22. **Contact:** mjschoolscholarships@unc.edu.

10230 ■ Stephen Gates Scholarships
(Undergraduate/Scholarship)

Purpose: To support students who are studying electronic communication specialization with an interest in sports journalism. **Focus:** Broadcasting; Communications. **Qualif.:** Applicants must students who have pre-declared or are enrolled in the School of Media and Journalism. **Criteria:** Recipients will be selected based on their academic interests, geographic location, financial need and programs of study.
Funds Avail.: No specific amount. **Duration:** Annual. **To Apply:** Applicants must submit a completed general application form, available at the website. **Deadline:** February

22. **Contact:** mjschoolscholarships@unc.edu.

10231 ■ **Joy Gibson Scholarships** *(Undergraduate/ Scholarship)*

Purpose: To provide educational assistance to students who are studying journalism. **Focus:** Communications; Journalism. **Qualif.:** Applicants must be students who have pre-declared or are enrolled in the School of Media and Journalism. **Criteria:** Recipients will be selected based on their academic interests, geographic location, financial need and programs of study.

Funds Avail.: No specific amount. **Duration:** Annual. **To Apply:** Applicants must submit a completed general application form, available at the website. **Deadline:** February 22. **Contact:** mjschoolscholarships@unc.edu.

10232 ■ **Charles Hauser Scholarships** *(Undergraduate/Scholarship)*

Purpose: To provide educational assistance to students who are studying journalism. **Focus:** Communications; Journalism. **Qualif.:** Applicants must students who have pre-declared or are enrolled in the School of Media and Journalism. **Criteria:** Recipients will be selected based on their academic interests, geographic location, financial need and programs of study.

Funds Avail.: No specific amount. **Duration:** Annual. **To Apply:** Applicants must submit a completed general application form, available at the website. **Deadline:** February 22. **Contact:** mjschoolscholarships@unc.edu.

10233 ■ **Paul Green Houston Scholarships** *(Undergraduate/Scholarship)*

Purpose: To provide educational assistance to students who are studying journalism. **Focus:** Communications; Journalism. **Qualif.:** Applicants must students who have pre-declared or are enrolled in the School of Media and Journalism. **Criteria:** Recipients will be selected based on their academic interests, geographic location, financial need and programs of study.

Funds Avail.: No specific amount. **Duration:** Annual. **To Apply:** Applicants must submit a completed general application form, available at the website. **Deadline:** February 22. **Contact:** mjschoolscholarships@unc.edu.

10234 ■ **James F. Hurley III Bicentennial Merit Scholarships** *(Undergraduate/Scholarship)*

Purpose: To provide students the educational assistance they need. **Focus:** Communications; Journalism. **Qualif.:** Applicants must be rising juniors or seniors in the school who are in the reporting specialization. **Criteria:** Recipients will be selected based on the academic interests, geographic location, financial need and programs of study.

Funds Avail.: No specific amount. **Duration:** Annual. **To Apply:** Applicants must submit a completed general application form, available at the website. **Deadline:** February 22. **Contact:** mjschoolscholarships@unc.edu.

10235 ■ **Edward Jackson International Scholarships** *(Undergraduate/Scholarship)*

Purpose: To support students who wish to travel to a European country to learn about politics, culture and mass media. **Focus:** Communications; Journalism. **Qualif.:** Applicants must be news editorial undergraduate students, preferably from North Carolina. **Criteria:** Recipients will be selected based on their academic interests, geographic location, financial need and programs of study.

Funds Avail.: No specific amount. **Duration:** Annual. **To Apply:** Applicants must submit a completed special application form, available at the website. **Deadline:** February 22. **Contact:** Michael Penny, Assistant Director, Professional and International Programs; Phone: 919-843-2573; Email: mpenny@email.unc.edu.

10236 ■ **Glenn Keever Scholarships** *(Undergraduate/ Scholarship)*

Purpose: To educate journalists; to help defray expenses associated with travel to foreign countries for courses. **Focus:** Communications; Journalism. **Qualif.:** Applicants must be undergraduate students, preferably in North Carolina. **Criteria:** Recipient are selected based on academic performance and financial need.

Funds Avail.: No specific amount. **Duration:** Annual. **To Apply:** Applicants must complete the application form and submit through e-mail. **Deadline:** February 22. **Contact:** mjschoolscholarships@unc.edu.

10237 ■ **Mackey-Byars Scholarships for Communication Excellence** *(Undergraduate/Scholarship)*

Purpose: To provide educational assistance to students who are studying journalism. **Focus:** Communications. **Qualif.:** Applicants must be minority or disadvantaged students majoring in mass communications. **Criteria:** Recipients will be selected based on their academic interests, geographic location, financial need and programs of study.

Funds Avail.: No specific amount. **Duration:** Annual. **To Apply:** Applicants must submit a completed general application form, available at the website. **Deadline:** February 22. **Contact:** mjschoolscholarships@unc.edu.

10238 ■ **Raleigh Mann Scholarships** *(Undergraduate/ Scholarship)*

Purpose: To provide educational assistance to students who are studying journalism. **Focus:** Communications; Journalism. **Qualif.:** Applicants must be students who have pre-declared or are enrolled in the School of Media and Journalism. **Criteria:** Recipients will be selected based on their academic interests, geographic location, financial need and programs of study.

Funds Avail.: No specific amount. **Duration:** Annual. **To Apply:** Applicants must submit a completed general application form, available at the website. **Deadline:** February 22. **Contact:** mjschoolscholarships@unc.edu.

10239 ■ **Donald Mauer Scholarships** *(Undergraduate/ Scholarship)*

Purpose: To provide educational assistance to students who are interested in advertising career. **Focus:** Advertising. **Qualif.:** Applicants must students who have pre-declared or are enrolled in the School of Media and Journalism. **Criteria:** Recipients will be selected based on their academic interests, geographic location, financial need and programs of study.

Funds Avail.: No specific amount. **Duration:** Annual. **To Apply:** Applicants must submit a completed general application form, available at the website. **Deadline:** February 22. **Contact:** mjschoolscholarships@unc.edu.

10240 ■ **Maxwell Graduate Scholarships in Medical Journalism** *(Graduate/Scholarship)*

Purpose: To provide educational assistance to current MJ-school students. **Focus:** Journalism. **Qualif.:** Applicants must be master's students in the medical journalism

Awards are arranged alphabetically below their administering organizations

UNIVERSITY OF NORTH CAROLINA SCHOOL OF MEDIA AND JOURNALISM

program. **Criteria:** Recipients will be selected based on their academic interests, geographic location, financial need and programs of study.

Funds Avail.: No specific amount. **Duration:** Annual. **To Apply:** Applicants must submit a completed special application form, available at the website. **Deadline:** February 22. **Contact:** mjschoolscholarships@unc.edu.

10241 ■ Molly McKay Scholarships (Undergraduate/Scholarship)

Purpose: To provide education assistance to students who are pursuing journalism career. **Focus:** Religion. **Qualif.:** Applicants must students who have pre-declared or are enrolled in the School of Media and Journalism. **Criteria:** Recipients will be selected based on their academic interests, geographic location, financial need and programs of study.

Funds Avail.: No specific amount. **To Apply:** Applicants must submit a completed general application form, available at the website. **Deadline:** February 22. **Contact:** mjschoolscholarships@unc.edu.

10242 ■ C.A. "Pete" McKnight Scholarships (Undergraduate/Scholarship)

Purpose: To provide educational assistance to current MJ-school students. **Focus:** Journalism. **Qualif.:** Applicants must students who have pre-declared or are enrolled in the School of Media and Journalism. **Criteria:** Recipients will be selected based on their academic interests, geographic location, financial need and programs of study.

Funds Avail.: No specific amount. **Duration:** Annual. **To Apply:** Applicants must submit a completed general application form, available at the website. **Deadline:** February 22. **Contact:** mjschoolscholarships@unc.edu.

10243 ■ Edward Heywood Megson Scholarships (Undergraduate/Scholarship)

Purpose: To provide educational assistance to students who are studying journalism. **Focus:** Communications; Journalism. **Qualif.:** Applicants must be graduates of University of North Carolina- Chapel Hill. **Criteria:** Recipients will be selected based on their academic interests, geographic location, financial need and programs of study.

Funds Avail.: No specific amount. **Duration:** Annual. **To Apply:** Applicants must submit a completed general application form, available at the website. **Deadline:** February 22. **Contact:** mjschoolscholarships@unc.edu.

10244 ■ Quincy Sharpe Mills Memorial Scholarships (Undergraduate/Scholarship)

Purpose: To provide educational assistance to current MJ-school students. **Focus:** Communications; Journalism. **Qualif.:** Applicants must students who have pre-declared or are enrolled in the School of Media and Journalism. **Criteria:** Recipients will be selected based on the academic interests, geographic location, financial need and programs of study.

Funds Avail.: No specific amount. **Duration:** Annual. **To Apply:** Applicants must submit a completed general application form, available at the website. **Deadline:** February 22. **Contact:** mjschoolscholarships@unc.edu.

10245 ■ Robert Pittman Scholarships-Internships (Undergraduate/Scholarship, Internship)

Purpose: To provide educational assistance to current MJ-school students. **Focus:** Communications; Journalism.

Qualif.: Applicants must be outstanding students in the school who are in the reporting specialization; must have a strong interest in a newspaper career and excellence in academic and journalistic accomplishments. **Criteria:** Recipients will be selected based on the academic interests, geographic location, financial need and programs of study.

Funds Avail.: No specific amount. **Duration:** Annual. **To Apply:** Applicants must submit a completed general application form, available at the website. **Deadline:** Varies. **Contact:** Robin Jackson, Director of Alumni Affairs and Donor Relations at mjschoolscholarships@unc.edu.

10246 ■ Erwin Potts Scholarships (Undergraduate/Scholarship)

Purpose: To provide educational assistance to current MJ-school students. **Focus:** Communications; Journalism. **Qualif.:** Applicants must students who have pre-declared or are enrolled in the School of Media and Journalism. **Criteria:** Recipients will be selected based on their academic interests, geographic location, financial need and programs of study. Preference will be given to students studying newspaper journalism.

Funds Avail.: No specific amount. **Duration:** Annual. **To Apply:** Applicants must submit a completed general application form, available at the website. **Deadline:** February 22. **Contact:** mjschoolscholarships@unc.edu.

10247 ■ Peter DeWitt Pruden and Phyliss Harrill Pruden Scholarships (Undergraduate/Scholarship)

Purpose: To provide educational assistance to current MJ-school students. **Focus:** Communications; Journalism. **Qualif.:** Applicants must be students who have pre-declared or are enrolled in the School of Media and Journalism in North Carolina, Tennessee or Virginia. **Criteria:** Recipients will be selected based on their academic interests, geographic location, financial need and programs of study.

Funds Avail.: No specific amount. **Duration:** Annual. **To Apply:** Applicants must submit a completed general application form, available at the website. **Deadline:** February 22. **Contact:** mjschoolscholarships@unc.edu.

10248 ■ Bob Quincy Scholarships (Undergraduate/Scholarship)

Purpose: To provide educational assistance to current MJ-school students. **Focus:** Communications; Journalism. **Qualif.:** Applicants must students who have pre-declared or are enrolled in the School of Media and Journalism. **Criteria:** Recipients will be selected based on their academic interests, geographic location, financial need and programs of study.

Funds Avail.: No specific amount. **Duration:** Annual. **To Apply:** Applicants must submit a completed general application form, available at the website. **Deadline:** February 22. **Contact:** mjschoolscholarships@unc.edu.

10249 ■ Marjorie Usher Ragan Scholarships (Undergraduate/Scholarship)

Purpose: To provide educational assistance to current MJ-school students. **Focus:** Communications; Journalism. **Qualif.:** Applicants must students who have pre-declared or are enrolled in the School of Media and Journalism. **Criteria:** Recipients will be selected based on their academic interests, geographic location, financial need and programs of study.

Funds Avail.: No specific amount. **Duration:** Annual. **To**

Awards are arranged alphabetically below their administering organizations

Sponsors and Their Scholarships

Apply: Applicants must submit a completed general application form, available at the website. **Deadline:** February 22. **Contact:** mjschoolscholarships@unc.edu.

10250 ■ Eugene L. Roberts Jr. Prize (Undergraduate/ Prize)

Purpose: To educate journalists; to help defray expenses associated with travel to foreign countries for courses. **Focus:** Journalism. **Qualif.:** Applicants must be undergraduate students interested in print journalism who propose the best idea for a Gene Roberts-type story; applicants must be returning to School for at least one semester to research and write a story in JOMC 296. The course is "Independent Study" supervised by a faculty member for three credits. **Criteria:** Recipients will be selected based on their academic interests, geographic location, financial need and programs of study.

Funds Avail.: No specific amount. **To Apply:** Applicants must complete the application form, available at the website, and submit it through e-mail. **Deadline:** March 1. **Contact:** Return completed application and supporting documents to Charlie Tuggle at catuggle@unc.edu.

10251 ■ A.C. Snow and Katherine Snow Smith Scholarship (Undergraduate/Scholarship)

Purpose: To provide educational assistance to students who are studying journalism. **Focus:** Journalism. **Qualif.:** Applicants must be news editorial students with an interest in grammar. **Criteria:** Recipients will be selected based on their academic interests, geographic location, financial need and programs of study.

Funds Avail.: No specific amount. **Duration:** Annual. **To Apply:** Applicants must submit a completed general application form, available at the website. **Deadline:** February 22. **Contact:** mjschoolscholarships@unc.edu.

10252 ■ Hal Tanner Sr. Scholarships (Undergraduate/ Scholarship)

Purpose: To provide educational assistance to students who are studying journalism. **Focus:** Advertising; Communications. **Qualif.:** Applicants must be rising senior students majoring in advertising. **Criteria:** Recipients will be selected based on their academic interests, geographic location, financial need and programs of study.

Funds Avail.: No specific amount. **Duration:** Annual. **To Apply:** Applicants must submit a completed general application form, available at the website. **Deadline:** February 22. **Contact:** mjschoolscholarships@unc.edu.

10253 ■ Jim and Pat Thacker Sports Communication Internships (Undergraduate/Grant)

Purpose: To assist students to intern for a professional sports organization during the summer. **Focus:** Communications. **Qualif.:** Applicants must students who have pre-declared or are enrolled in the School of Media and Journalism. **Criteria:** Recipients will be selected based on their academic interests, geographic location, financial need and programs of study.

Funds Avail.: No specific amount. **To Apply:** Applicants must submit a completed general application form, available at the website. **Deadline:** February 22.

10254 ■ Tucker Family Scholarships (Undergraduate/ Scholarship)

Purpose: To provide financial assistance for students who are interested in print or broadcast journalism. **Focus:** Communications; Journalism. **Qualif.:** Applicants must students who have pre-declared or are enrolled in the School of Media and Journalism. **Criteria:** Recipients will be selected based on the academic interests, geographic location, financial need and programs of study.

Funds Avail.: No specific amount. **Duration:** Annual. **To Apply:** Applicants must submit a completed general application form, available at the website. **Deadline:** February 22. **Contact:** mjschoolscholarships@unc.edu.

10255 ■ David Julian Wichard Scholarships (Undergraduate/Scholarship)

Purpose: To provide educational assistance to current MJ-school students. **Focus:** Communications; Journalism. **Qualif.:** Applicants must be currently enrolled or planning to enroll in university; must be residents of North Carolina. **Criteria:** Recipients will be selected based on their academic interests, geographic location, financial need and programs of study.

Funds Avail.: No specific amount. **Duration:** Annual. **To Apply:** Applicants must submit a completed general application form, available at the website. **Deadline:** February 22. **Contact:** mjschoolscholarships@unc.edu.

10256 ■ Tom Wicker Scholarships (Graduate/ Scholarship)

Purpose: To provide financial assistance to news-editorial graduate students. **Focus:** Communications; Journalism. **Qualif.:** Applicants must be students who have pre-declared or are enrolled in the School of Media and Journalism. **Criteria:** Recipients will be selected based on their academic interests, geographic location, financial need and programs of study.

Funds Avail.: No specific amount. **Duration:** Annual. **To Apply:** Applicants must submit a completed special application form, available at the website. **Deadline:** February 22. **Contact:** mjschoolscholarships@unc.edu.

10257 ■ WTVD Endowment Scholarships (Undergraduate/Scholarship)

Purpose: To provide educational assistance to students who have demonstrated excellence in their studies in journalism and mass communication. **Focus:** Communications; Journalism. **Qualif.:** Applicants must be students who have pre-declared or are enrolled in the School of Media and Journalism and be residents of North Carolina. **Criteria:** Recipients will be selected based on their academic interests, geographic location, financial need and programs of study.

Funds Avail.: No specific amount. **Duration:** Annual. **To Apply:** Applicants must submit a completed general application form, available at the website. **Deadline:** February 22. **Contact:** mjschoolscholarships@unc.edu.

10258 ■ University of Oregon (UO)
1585 E 13th Ave.
Eugene, OR 97403
Ph: (541)346-1000
Fax: (541)346-5815
Free: 800-280-6218
E-mail: quarterly@uoregon.edu
URL: uoregon.edu
Facebook: www.facebook.com/universityoforegon
LinkedIn: www.linkedin.com/edu/
school?id=19207&trk=tyah&trkInfo=idx%3A2-1-4%2Ctarl

Awards are arranged alphabetically below their administering organizations

Twitter: twitter.com/univ_of_oregon

10259 ■ Robert W. and Bernice Ingalls Staton Scholarships *(Undergraduate/Scholarship)*

Purpose: To provide financial support to students who desire to further their education without financial burden at the University of Oregon. **Focus:** Education; Humanities; Music; Visual arts. **Qualif.:** Applicants must be Oregon residents and have an extraordinary financial need. **Criteria:** Recipients will be selected based on financial need. Preference will be given to students who declare a major in the Humanities, Department of Fine Arts, the College of Education, or the School of Music. Other factors taken into consideration include the students' major and professional objective; academic performance; and family educational history with priority given to first generation students. **Funds Avail.:** Amount varies. **Duration:** Annual. **To Apply:** Applicants must submit the Admission application and Free Application for Federal Student Aid (FAFSA) available online to the Office of Admission. **Deadline:** January 15 (Staton application); February 15 (FAFSA). **Remarks:** Established in 2001.

10260 ■ University of Oregon Dean's Scholarships *(Undergraduate/Scholarship)*

Purpose: To encourage qualified individuals to pursue their studies at University of Oregon. **Focus:** General studies/Field of study not specified. **Qualif.:** Applicants must be entering freshmen who have a minimum cumulative high school GPA of 3.0 and meet all current UO freshman admission requirements. They must have not attended another college after graduation from high school. **Criteria:** Recipients will be selected based on high school GPA and coursework. **Funds Avail.:** No specific amount. **Duration:** Annual. **To Apply:** Applicants may visit the University of Oregon website for further information. **Remarks:** Established in 1999.

10261 ■ University of Oregon Diversity Excellence Scholarships *(Undergraduate/Scholarship)*

Purpose: To encourage the undergraduate and graduate students to enhance their educational experience by sharing diverse cultural experiences at the University of Oregon. **Focus:** General studies/Field of study not specified. **Qualif.:** Applicants must be undergraduate and graduate students who enhance the educational experience of all students by sharing diverse cultural experiences. They must be U.S citizens or permanent residents currently enrolled as University of Oregon students in good academic standing, and meet the DBS minimum GPA requirements. Lastly, they must have a minimum cumulative GPA of 3.0 for freshmen, and 2.50 for other applicants. **Criteria:** UO Diversity - Building Scholarship Committee gives priority to students who demonstrate the following: (1) Strong academic background as documented by official high school and/or college transcript; (2) Financial need as defined by federal guidelines; (3) Family educational history; (4) Residency status; (5) Commitment to diversity through documented history of community service, leadership, or other activities; and (6) Ethnic background. **Funds Avail.:** $6,500 (undergraduate); $9,000 (graduate). **Duration:** Annual. **To Apply:** Application forms are available online. Applicants must submit a personal statement, letter of recommendation and official transcripts. Application form and other supporting materials must be submitted to the Office of Student Financial Aid & Scholarships. **Deadline:** January 15 (DES application); January 27 (other documents); February 1 (FAFSA).

10262 ■ University of Oregon General University Scholarships *(Undergraduate/Scholarship)*

Purpose: To support qualified individuals who wish to pursue their education at the University of Oregon. **Focus:** General studies/Field of study not specified. **Qualif.:** Applicants must be incoming University freshmen or non-freshmen students. Transferees, graduate studies and law students are also eligible to apply. **Criteria:** Selection is highly competitive. Applicants will be evaluated based on academic performance, SAT or ACT scores (Freshmen), extracurricular involvement, faculty recommendation (continuing, transfer, graduate and law students), as well as writing ability and creativity as demonstrated in the career aspirations and scholarship essay. **Funds Avail.:** $1,500 to $3,000. **Duration:** Annual. **Number Awarded:** Varies. **To Apply:** Application processes are of various forms since the recipients shall come from distinct levels of study. Visit the program website for further information regarding the application. **Deadline:** January 15 for incoming freshmen; February 15 for non-freshmen; February 25 for transferees, graduate and law students.

10263 ■ University of Oregon Presidential Scholarships *(Undergraduate/Scholarship)*

Purpose: To provide financial support to the state's brightest students entering University of Oregon. **Focus:** General studies/Field of study not specified. **Qualif.:** Applicants must: be Oregon residents who are incoming college or university freshmen; have a minimum GPA of 3.85; have at least 1240 combined math and critical reading SAT score or 28 ACT composite score; and, have significant history of leadership and volunteer service activities. **Criteria:** Selection process is highly competitive. Criteria for selection are the following: academic preparation through transcripts evaluation; test scores; activities/talents; leadership; volunteer services and work experiences. **Funds Avail.:** $9,000 per year. **Duration:** Annual; Up to 4 years. **Number Awarded:** 50. **To Apply:** Applicants must complete the Scholarship Application forms available online; and must submit official high school transcripts and SAT or ACT scores to the Office of Admissions. **Deadline:** January 15.

10264 ■ University of Oxford Department of Politics and International Relations - Reuters Institute for the Study of Journalism
13 Norham Gardens
Oxford OX2 6PS, United Kingdom
Ph: 44 1865 611080
Fax: 44 1865 611094
E-mail: reuters.institute@politics.ox.ac.uk
URL: reutersinstitute.politics.ox.ac.uk
Twitter: twitter.com/risj_oxford

10265 ■ Reuters Institute Visiting Fellowships *(Professional development/Fellowship)*

Purpose: To promote the educational and research interests of the Reuters Institute through relationships with people employed by other institutions. **Focus:** Journalism. **Qualif.:** Applicants must be distinguished practitioners from journalism and the new media or leading academics in fields closely related to the Institute's research projects.

Awards are arranged alphabetically below their administering organizations

Criteria: Selection will be based on the committee's criteria.
Funds Avail.: No specific amount. **To Apply:** Interested applicants may contact the RISJ Director to obtain application forms.

10266 ■ University of Pennsylvania - School of Nursing - Center for Health Outcomes and Policy Research (CHOPR)
Fagin Hall, Rm. 387
418 Curie Blvd.
Philadelphia, PA 19104-4217
Ph: (215)898-5673
URL: www.nursing.upenn.edu/chopr/Pages/default.aspx

10267 ■ CHOPR Postdoctoral Fellowships
(Postdoctorate/Fellowship)

Purpose: To further develop the individuals' research career in the area of health outcomes. **Focus:** Medical research; Nursing; Nursing administration. **Qualif.:** Applicants must be US citizens or permanent residents who have received a doctoral degree from an accredited university in nursing or a field relevant to nursing outcomes research, such as sociology, demography, economics and public health. **Criteria:** Candidates will be competitively evaluated based on the following criteria: match with the overall goals and objectives of the training grant and affiliated Center; match with the T32 and Center-affiliated faculty advisor; scholarly potential for nursing science inquiry that has a high impact; commitment to a research career in a research intensive environment; scholarly productivity during and/or after the research doctoral training.

Duration: Annual. **To Apply:** Interested candidates should send a letter of interest and a curriculum vitae describing their fellowship and career goals. **Deadline:** January 31.

10268 ■ University of Pittsburgh Department of Biological Sciences - Pymatuning Laboratory of Ecology
c/o Chris Davis, Assistant Director
13142 Hartstown Rd.
Linesville, PA 16424
Ph: (814)273-0416
E-mail: pymlab@pitt.edu
URL: www.biology.pitt.edu/facilities/pymatuning
Facebook: www.facebook.com/pages/Pymatuning-Lab-of-Ecology/376904956544?ref=hl

10269 ■ Arthur and Barbara Pape Endowments
(Graduate/Grant)

Purpose: To support early stages of ecological and evolutionary research conducted at PLE. **Focus:** Biological and clinical sciences; Ecology. **Qualif.:** Applicants must be graduate students in good standing; must be recent PhD, initiating new research at PLE. **Criteria:** Selection will be based on the submitted proposals.

Funds Avail.: Maximum of $3,500. **Duration:** Annual. **To Apply:** Applicants must submit a proposal and must use the following format: Cover page, containing project title and researcher contact information; Project summary, page containing a project summary of not more than 100 words; Project description, not exceeding 4, single-spaced pages; Literature cited; budget; Applicants' resume or CV; a letter of recommendation from the major advisor for non-University of Pittsburgh graduate student applicants. All margins should be set at one inch, all text should use a minimum 12-point font. All figures, figure captions and tables must use a minimum 10-point font. Applications should be submitted as an attachment in MS Word format on or before the deadline. **Deadline:** February 8.

10270 ■ University of Saskatchewan - Native Law Centre of Canada
Law Bldg., Rm. 160
15 Campus Dr.
Saskatoon, SK, Canada S7N 5A6
Ph: (306)966-6189
Fax: (306)966-6207
E-mail: native.law@usask.ca
URL: www.usask.ca/nativelaw

10271 ■ Harvey Bell Memorial Prize *(Graduate/Award)*

Purpose: To financially assist students in order to receive their LL.B. degree in Canada. **Focus:** Law. **Qualif.:** Applicants must be students of Native Canadian ancestry receiving their LL.B. degree in Canada. **Criteria:** Applications will be evaluated based on the following criteria: 1) contributions from which students might be expected in establishing the right of Native people in Canada; and 2) academic records in Law studies.

Funds Avail.: Up to $1,000. **Duration:** Annual. **Number Awarded:** Varies. **To Apply:** Applicants must enclose a resume of their career and education; must submit a transcript of records and letter of application concerning their academic achievement. **Deadline:** July 31.

10272 ■ Poundmaker Memorial Scholarships
(Undergraduate/Scholarship)

Purpose: To support a status of an Indian student born in Saskatchewan pursue their education. **Focus:** Education; Teaching. **Qualif.:** Applicants must be Indian students born in Saskatchewan; must have completed two years of a direct entry teacher education program or currently in their third or fourth year at the University of Saskatchewan, University of Regina, or the First Nation University of Canada. **Criteria:** Evaluation will be based on academic achievement, leadership ability and aspirations to Indian community.

Funds Avail.: 750 Canadian Dollars. **Duration:** Annual. **To Apply:** Applicants must submit a completed application form. **Deadline:** July 31.

10273 ■ University of Tennessee at Knoxville College of Arts & Sciences - Center for the Study of War and Society
217 Hoskins Library
Knoxville, TN 37996-4008
Ph: (865)974-0128
E-mail: csws@utk.edu
URL: csws.utk.edu

10274 ■ The Edgar C. Wilson Fellowship *(Graduate/Fellowship)*

Purpose: To promote the study of American military history. **Focus:** History, Military. **Qualif.:** Applicants must be

Awards are arranged alphabetically below their administering organizations

graduate students in history studying U.S. military; must be in good standing and making sufficient progress toward the completion of the degree. **Criteria:** Preference is given to those who focus on some aspect of the Second World War.

Funds Avail.: $1,000. **Duration:** Annual. **Number Awarded:** 1. **To Apply:** Applicants must submit a dissertation focusing of American military history; a letter of application no longer than two pages that outlines the dissertation topic and the progress toward degree; two letters of recommendation outlining the progress to the degree. At least one letter must be from a faculty member in the History Department of the University of Tennessee. **Deadline:** March 15.

10275 ■ University of Texas at Austin - Office of the Vice President for Research
Peter Flawn Academic Center Bldg., Ste. 426
Austin, TX 78713
Ph: (512)471-2877
Fax: (512)471-2827
E-mail: vp-research-sr@mail.utexas.edu
URL: www.utexas.edu/research/about

10276 ■ University of Texas at Austin Special Research Grants *(Professional development/Grant)*

Purpose: To cover unanticipated costs or special needs of individuals whose conducting research. **Focus:** Operations research. **Qualif.:** Applicants must be individual tenured and tenure-track faculty members who are planning to conduct modest research for specific project. **Criteria:** Selection will be based on the committees' criteria.

Funds Avail.: Up to $750. **To Apply:** Applicants must submit complete, signed application, via email to the office of the Vice President for Research and required one-page curriculum vitae.

10277 ■ University of Toronto (U of T)
563 Spadina Crescent
Toronto, ON, Canada M5S 2J7
Ph: (416)978-2011
E-mail: admissions.help@utoronto.ca
URL: www.utoronto.ca

10278 ■ Dr. Anderson Abbott Awards *(Undergraduate/Scholarship)*

Purpose: To support students in pursuing their educational career. **Focus:** Health sciences; Medicine. **Qualif.:** Applicant must be a black student of University of Toronto. **Criteria:** The selection committee may give preference to a student in the medical program or in a related health science program.

Funds Avail.: $4,000. **Duration:** Annual. **Number Awarded:** 1. **To Apply:** Applicant must submit a completed Abbot application form along with the required materials and information. **Deadline:** March 31.

10279 ■ Stephanie Ali Memorial Scholarships *(Undergraduate/Scholarship)*

Purpose: To provide educational support to students who are in need. **Focus:** Computer and information sciences; Engineering. **Qualif.:** Applicants must be University of Toronto students; must be committed to community works and/or participating in charitable activities. **Criteria:** Preference will be given to students who are past or present members of the University of Toronto Gospel Choir.

Funds Avail.: Approximately $600. **Duration:** Annual. **To Apply:** Applicants must submit a completed application form along with the required materials and information. **Deadline:** March 30. **Contact:** Enrolment Services: 172 Saint George St., Toronto, ON M5R 0A3.

10280 ■ Leon C. Bynoe Memorial Scholarships *(Undergraduate/Scholarship)*

Purpose: To provide educational support to students who are in need. **Focus:** General studies/Field of study not specified. **Qualif.:** Applicants must be enrolled in an undergraduate degree program; must demonstrate outstanding service to the Afro-Canadian community. **Criteria:** Selection will be based on financial need and outstanding academic achievement. Preference will be given to students from the Afro-Canadian community and MTHA residents.

Funds Avail.: Approximately $1300. **Duration:** Annual. **To Apply:** Applicants must submit a completed application form along with the required materials and information. **Deadline:** November 30. **Contact:** Enrolment Services: 172 Saint George St., Toronto, ON M5R A03.

10281 ■ Canadian Federation of University Women Etobicoke Bursary *(Undergraduate/Scholarship)*

Purpose: To provide educational support to students who are in need. **Focus:** General studies/Field of study not specified. **Qualif.:** Applicants must be female undergraduate students of University of Toronto who is just beginning her first year of studies; must be residents of Etobicoke. **Criteria:** Selection is based on general proficiency or outstanding achievements.

Funds Avail.: $1,500 each. **Duration:** Annual. **Number Awarded:** 2. **To Apply:** Applicants must submit a completed application form along with the required materials and information. **Deadline:** October 31. **Contact:** Enrolment Services: 172 Saint George St., Toronto, ON M5R 0A3.

10282 ■ City of Toronto Graduate Scholarships for Women in Mathematics *(Master's, Doctorate/Scholarship)*

Purpose: To provide financial support to students who are pursuing their educational career. **Focus:** Mathematics and mathematical sciences. **Qualif.:** Applicants must be female students of University of Toronto enrolled in a master's or doctoral program in mathematics. **Criteria:** Selection will be based on the applicants' financial need, academic merit and demonstrated interest in issues related to women in mathematics.

Funds Avail.: No specific amount. **Duration:** Annual. **To Apply:** Applicants must submit a completed application form along with the required materials and information. **Deadline:** November 1. **Contact:** Enrolment Services: 172 Saint George St., Toronto, ON M5R 0A3.

10283 ■ City of Toronto Queen Elizabeth II Sesquicentennial Scholarships in Community Health Nursing for Graduates *(Graduate/Scholarship)*

Purpose: To support students with their educational pursuit. **Focus:** Nursing. **Qualif.:** Applicants must be graduate students enrolled in the Graduate Department of Nursing Science; must have completed courses in community health and demonstrate a commitment to the aspect of

Awards are arranged alphabetically below their administering organizations

nursing. **Criteria:** Selection will be based on the applicants' general proficiency or outstanding achievements.
Funds Avail.: $1,200. **Duration:** Annual. **Number Awarded:** 1. **To Apply:** Applicants must submit a completed application form along with the required materials and information. **Deadline:** October 1. **Contact:** Enrolment Services: 172 Saint George St., Toronto, ON M5R 0A3.

10284 ■ City of Toronto Queen Elizabeth II Sesquicentennial Scholarships in Community Health Nursing for Undergraduates *(Undergraduate/Scholarship)*

Purpose: To provide financial support to students who are in need. **Focus:** Nursing. **Qualif.:** Applicants must be undergraduate students completing the first year of the second-entry two year BScN program. **Criteria:** Preference may be given to students who are proficient in a language besides English and whose interest is to work with multicultural families.
Funds Avail.: $5,000. **Duration:** Annual. **Number Awarded:** 1. **To Apply:** Applicants must submit a completed application form along with the required materials and information. **Deadline:** June 30. **Contact:** Enrolment Services: 172 Saint George St., Toronto, ON M5R 0A3.

10285 ■ City of Toronto Scholarships for Aboriginal Students *(Graduate, Undergraduate/Scholarship)*

Purpose: To provide financial support to students who are in need. **Focus:** Health services administration. **Qualif.:** Applicants must be undergraduate or graduate aboriginal students studying in any of the health professional programs. **Criteria:** Selection will be based on the applicants' financial need, academic merit and demonstrated community leadership skills.
Funds Avail.: $4,500. **Duration:** Annual. **To Apply:** Applicants must submit a completed application form along with the required materials and information. **Deadline:** October 31. **Contact:** Enrolment Services: 172 Saint George St., Toronto, ON M5R 0A3.

10286 ■ City of Toronto Women's Studies Scholarships *(Graduate, Undergraduate/Scholarship)*

Purpose: To support students with their educational pursuits. **Focus:** Women's studies. **Qualif.:** Applicants must be undergraduate or graduate students in Women's Studies: must be Canadian citizen or permanent residents and resident of Ontario. **Criteria:** Selection is based on financial need and academic merit.
Funds Avail.: Undergraduate - $5,000; Graduate scholarship valued at the balance of the annual income. **Duration:** Annual. **Number Awarded:** 2. **To Apply:** Applicants must submit a completed application form along with the required materials and information. **Deadline:** November 1. **Contact:** Enrolment Services: 172 Saint George St., Toronto, ON M5R 0A3.

10287 ■ Mary Jane Hendrie Memorial Scholarships *(Graduate, Undergraduate/Scholarship)*

Purpose: To provide financial support to students who are in need. **Focus:** Japanese studies. **Qualif.:** Applicants must be senior undergraduate or graduate students of University of Ontario who are interested in relations between Japan and Canada with studies in business, law, economics, international relations, or political science. **Criteria:** Selection is based on general proficiency or outstanding achievements.
Funds Avail.: $3,500. **Duration:** Annual. **To Apply:** Applicants must submit a completed application form along with the required materials and information. **Deadline:** November 30. **Contact:** Enrolment Services: 172 Saint George St., Toronto, ON M5R 0A3.

10288 ■ Irving J. Hoffman Memorial Scholarships *(Undergraduate/Scholarship)*

Purpose: To provide financial support to students who are in need. **Focus:** General studies/Field of study not specified. **Qualif.:** Applicants must be student enrolled on either a full-time or part-time basis, demonstrate superior academic achievement; have completed at least five university level courses, or the equivalent. **Criteria:** Selection will be based on applicants' academic achievement and financial need.
Funds Avail.: $500. **Duration:** Annual. **To Apply:** Applicants must submit a completed application form along with the required materials and information. **Deadline:** November 30. **Contact:** Enrolment Services: 172 Saint George St., Toronto, ON M5R 0A3.

10289 ■ Hosinec Family Scholarships *(Graduate, Undergraduate/Scholarship)*

Purpose: To support students with their educational pursuits. **Focus:** General studies/Field of study not specified. **Qualif.:** Applicants must be undergraduate or graduate students of the University of Toronto. **Criteria:** Selection will be based on financial need and academic merit.
Funds Avail.: $3,000. **Duration:** Annual. **Number Awarded:** 25. **To Apply:** Applicants must submit a completed application form and required materials and information. **Deadline:** November 30. **Contact:** Enrolment Services: 172 Saint George St., Toronto, ON M5R 0A3.

10290 ■ In-course Scholarships - Chinese Dance Workshop Scholarships *(Undergraduate/Scholarship)*

Purpose: To provide educational support to students who are in need. **Focus:** Dance. **Qualif.:** Applicants must be University of Toronto students. **Criteria:** Selection is based on academic excellence and demonstrated dance experience.
Funds Avail.: Approximately $2,400. **Duration:** Annual. **To Apply:** Applicants must submit a letter of application verifying at least three years of attendance at a recognized dance institute along with a transcript of marks. **Deadline:** October 31. **Contact:** Enrolment Services: 172 Saint George St., Toronto, ON M5R 0A3.

10291 ■ Khaki University and Y.M.C.A. Memorial Scholarships *(Undergraduate/Scholarship)*

Purpose: To provide financial support to students who are in need. **Focus:** General studies/Field of study not specified. **Qualif.:** Applicants must be enrolled in the second or higher year of an undergraduate course proceeding to a degree; and have at least first class honours standing. **Criteria:** Preference will be given to students who are descendent from one who has served in the armed forces.
Funds Avail.: Varies. **Duration:** Annual. **To Apply:** Applicants must submit completed application form along with the required materials and information. **Deadline:** November 30. **Contact:** Enrolment Services: 172 Saint George St., Toronto, ON M5R 0A3.

10292 ■ Joseph McCulley Educational Scholarships *(Graduate, Undergraduate/Scholarship)*

Purpose: To provide financial support to students who are in need. **Focus:** Social work. **Qualif.:** Applicants must be

Awards are arranged alphabetically below their administering organizations

University of Toronto graduate or undergraduate students, whose programs of study and career interests lie in the area of public life or social work, emphasizing on penology. **Criteria:** Selection will be based on applicants' financial need.

Funds Avail.: No specific amount. **Duration:** Annual. **To Apply:** Applicants must submit a completed application form together with the required materials and information. **Deadline:** November 30.

10293 ■ Al Mercury Scholarships *(Undergraduate/Scholarship)*

Purpose: To provide educational support to students who are in need. **Focus:** General studies/Field of study not specified. **Qualif.:** Applicants must be University of Toronto students with demonstrated community involvement, academic excellence, integrity and an appreciation and interest in music. **Criteria:** Selection will be based on general proficiency or outstanding achievements of the applicants.

Funds Avail.: No specific amount. **Duration:** Annual. **To Apply:** Applicants must submit a completed application form along with the required materials and information. **Deadline:** November 30. **Contact:** Enrolment Services: 172 Saint George St., Toronto, ON M5R 0A3.

10294 ■ John H. Moss Scholarships *(Undergraduate/Scholarship)*

Purpose: To provide educational support to students who are in need. **Focus:** Arts; Science. **Qualif.:** Applicants must be University of Toronto students having a minimum GPA of 3.3 (B+); must demonstrate outstanding academic and extra-curricular leadership; must be in the graduating year in Arts and Science at the University of Toronto (St. George, Mississauga and Scarborough campuses) and intended to pursue a second degree or studies at the graduate level. **Criteria:** Selection will be based on general proficiency or outstanding achievements of the applicants.

Funds Avail.: $16,650. **Duration:** Annual. **To Apply:** Applicants must submit a completed application form together with the required materials and information. **Deadline:** December 4. **Contact:** Enrolment Services: 172 Saint George St., Toronto, ON M5R 0A3.

10295 ■ Taylor Statten Memorial Fellowships *(Graduate/Scholarship)*

Purpose: To provide educational support to students who are in need. **Focus:** Education, Physical; Psychology; Social work. **Qualif.:** Applicants must be post-baccalaureate study in professional field or career related to youth services (such as physical and health education, psychology, teaching, the ministry and social work). **Criteria:** Consideration will be given to academically qualified students with career goals and past interests and experience indicating a serious commitment to working with young people.

Funds Avail.: Approximately $2,000. **Duration:** Annual. **To Apply:** Applicants must submit a completed application form together with the required documents and information. **Deadline:** March 30.

10296 ■ Evald Torokvei Foundation Scholarships *(Graduate/Scholarship)*

Purpose: To provide educational support to students who are in need. **Focus:** Engineering, Chemical. **Qualif.:** Applicants must be graduate students engaged in research in chemicals and plastics. **Criteria:** Selection will be based on applicants' academic standing, community and university involvement and financial need.

Funds Avail.: $1,000 each. **Duration:** Annual. **Number Awarded:** 2. **To Apply:** Applicants must submit a letter of application that includes the applicant's name, address, phone number, student number, area of research, name of Research Director, details of the applicants' involvement in the University community; a statement of financial need (if applicable), transcript of marks, and letters of reference. **Deadline:** April 30. **Contact:** Enrolment Services: 172 Saint George St., Toronto, ON M5R 0A3.

10297 ■ University of Toronto Accenture Scholarships *(Undergraduate/Scholarship)*

Purpose: To support students with their educational pursuits. **Focus:** Computer and information sciences; Engineering. **Qualif.:** Applicants must be students of University of Ontario enrolled in an Engineering, Computer Science or Bachelor of Commerce Degree; must be third year students entering the final year of study; must have maintained a strong academic background - minimum GPA of 3.0; and must be actively involved in two or more extracurricular activities. **Criteria:** Selection will be based on general proficiency or outstanding achievements of the applicants.

Funds Avail.: $1,500. **Duration:** Annual. **To Apply:** Applicants must submit a completed Accenture Scholarship application form along with the required materials and information. **Deadline:** October 1. **Contact:** Enrolment Services: 172 Saint George St., Toronto, ON M5R 0A3.

10298 ■ University of Toronto Nortel Institute Undergraduate Scholarships *(Undergraduate/Scholarship)*

Purpose: To provide educational support to students who are in need. **Focus:** Art industries and trade; Engineering. **Qualif.:** Applicants must be University of Toronto students; must be Canadian citizens or landed immigrants and residents of Ontario; must be in second or third year in the Faculty of Applied Science and Engineering, Faculty of Arts and Science, University of Toronto Mississauga and University of Toronto Scarborough. **Criteria:** Selection is based on financial need, academic merit and on the essay.

Funds Avail.: $5,000. **Duration:** Annual. **To Apply:** Applicants must submit a completed application form along with two references and an essay on a given topic (maximum of 500 words). **Deadline:** November 1. **Contact:** Enrolment Services: 172 Saint George St., Toronto, ON M5R 0A3.

10299 ■ University of Toronto SAC Undergraduate Grants *(Undergraduate/Grant)*

Purpose: To provide educational support to students who are in need. **Focus:** General studies/Field of study not specified. **Qualif.:** Applicants must be full-time undergraduate students of University of Toronto; must have maintaining minimum academic standing of "C". **Criteria:** Selection will be based on applicants' financial need, and extracurricular involvement in the University Community.

Funds Avail.: $1,300. **Duration:** Annual. **Number Awarded:** Varies. **To Apply:** Applicants must submit a completed application form together with the required materials and information. **Deadline:** November 30. **Contact:** Enrolment Services: 172 Saint George St., Toronto, ON M5R 0A3.

Awards are arranged alphabetically below their administering organizations

10300 ■ University of Virginia

PO Box 400160
Charlottesville, VA 22904-4132
Ph: (924)924-7923
URL: www.virginia.edu
Facebook: www.facebook.com/UVASCPS
Twitter: twitter.com/UVASCPS

10301 ■ Bayly-Tiffany Scholarships (Undergraduate/Scholarship)

Purpose: To support students at the University of Virginia in their educational pursuits. **Focus:** General studies/Field of study not specified. **Qualif.:** Applicants must be students of the University of Virginia and residents of Accomack or Northampton counties in Virginia. **Criteria:** Selection will be based on the committee's criteria.

Funds Avail.: No specific amount. **Duration:** Annual. **To Apply:** Students do not need to complete a separate application form but will be considered automatically when admitted.

10302 ■ V. Thomas Forehand, Jr. Scholarships (Undergraduate/Scholarship)

Purpose: To support students at the University of Virginia in their educational pursuits. **Focus:** General studies/Field of study not specified. **Qualif.:** Applicants must be UVA undergraduate students from the city of Chesapeake who attended Oscar F. Smith High School, Norfolk Academy, or Nansemond-Suffolk Academy. **Criteria:** Selection is based on need.

Funds Avail.: No specific amount. **Duration:** Annual. **To Apply:** Students do not need to complete a separate application form but will be considered automatically when admitted.

10303 ■ Kaprielian Memorial Scholarships (Undergraduate/Scholarship)

Purpose: To support Armenian-descent students at the University of Virginia in their educational pursuits. **Focus:** General studies/Field of study not specified. **Qualif.:** Applicants must be UVA students who are U.S. citizens or registered permanent residents of Armenian descent and who demonstrate financial need. **Criteria:** Selection will be based on the aforesaid qualifications.

Funds Avail.: No specific amount. **Duration:** Annual. **To Apply:** Students do not need to complete a separate application form but will be considered automatically when admitted.

10304 ■ John Allen Love Scholarships (Graduate, Undergraduate/Scholarship)

Purpose: To support students at the University of Virginia in their educational pursuits. **Focus:** Government; International affairs and relations. **Qualif.:** Applicants must be University of Virginia undergraduate or graduate students residing in Missouri. **Criteria:** Preference will be given to applicants residing in St. Louis or St. Louis County, and also to those enrolled in courses in the Department of Government and Foreign Affairs.

Funds Avail.: No specific amount. **Duration:** Annual. **To Apply:** Students do not need to complete a separate application form but will be considered automatically when admitted.

10305 ■ Margaret E. Phillips Scholarships (Undergraduate/Scholarship)

Purpose: To support deserving students who shall be preparing for and who propose to become ministers of the Protestant Episcopal Church in America. **Focus:** Religion. **Qualif.:** Applicants must be University of Virginia students preparing for and proposing to become ministers of the Protestant Episcopal Church in America. **Criteria:** Selection will be based on need.

Funds Avail.: No specific amount. **Duration:** Annual. **To Apply:** Students do not need to complete a separate application form but will be considered automatically when admitted.

10306 ■ Charles Fred Wonson Scholarships (Undergraduate/Scholarship)

Purpose: To support students at the University of Virginia in their educational pursuits. **Focus:** General studies/Field of study not specified. **Qualif.:** Applicants must be students who are graduates of Robert E. Lee High School in Staunton, Virginia. **Criteria:** Selection will be based on need.

Funds Avail.: No specific amount. **Duration:** Annual. **To Apply:** Students do not need to complete a separate application form but will be considered automatically when admitted.

10307 ■ University of Virginia - Institute for Advanced Studies in Culture (IASC)

Watson Manor
3 University Cir.
Charlottesville, VA 22903
Ph: (434)924-7705
Fax: (434)243-5590
E-mail: iasc@virginia.edu
URL: www.iasc-culture.org
Facebook: www.facebook.com/iasculture
Twitter: twitter.com/iasculture

10308 ■ IASC Associate Fellowships (Doctorate/Fellowship)

Purpose: To support students doing course work in the first years of their doctoral work. **Focus:** Culture. **Qualif.:** Applicants must be students doing course work in the first years of their doctoral work. **Criteria:** Selection will be based on the committee's criteria.

Funds Avail.: No specific amount. **To Apply:** Interested applicants must visit the website for the application process.

10309 ■ IASC Doctoral Fellowships - Dissertation (Doctorate/Fellowship)

Purpose: To support students through the research and writing stages of their dissertations. **Focus:** Culture. **Qualif.:** Eligible applicants are students through the research and writing stages of their dissertations. **Criteria:** Selection will be based on the demonstrated academic promise and how closely their scholarly interests fit with the Institute research priorities.

Funds Avail.: No specific amount. **Duration:** Annual. **To Apply:** Interested applicants must contact the Institute for the application process.

10310 ■ IASC Doctoral Fellowships - Pre-Dissertation (Doctorate/Fellowship)

Purpose: To support students through the research and writing stages of their dissertations. **Focus:** Culture. **Qualif.:** Applicants must be in their comprehensive examination and proposal-writing year. **Criteria:** Selection will be based on the demonstrated academic promise and how closely their scholarly interest fit with the Institute's research priorities. **Funds Avail.:** No specific amount. **Duration:** Annual. **To Apply:** Interested applicants must contact the Institute for the application process.

10311 ■ IASC Postdoctoral Fellowships
(Postdoctorate/Fellowship)

Purpose: To support work on first books by aspiring postdoctoral students. **Focus:** Culture. **Qualif.:** Applicants must be recent PhDs whose research directly contributes to the research priorities of the Institute. Applicants must successfully defend dissertations prior to the start of the academic year in which they have been awarded a fellowship. **Criteria:** Selection will be on a competitive basis.

Funds Avail.: No specific amount. **Duration:** Annual. **To Apply:** Interested applicants must contact the Institute for the application process.

10312 ■ IASC Visiting Fellowships *(Professional development/Fellowship)*

Purpose: To support established scholars in their advanced studies in culture. **Focus:** Culture. **Qualif.:** Applicants must be scholars looking for semester and year-long sabbaticals and whose work directly contributes to the intellectual priorities of the Institute's research programs. **Criteria:** Selection will be on a competitive basis.

Funds Avail.: No specific amount. **Duration:** Annual. **To Apply:** Interested applicants must contact the Institute for the application process.

10313 ■ U.V.A. Faculty Fellowships *(Professional development/Fellowship)*

Purpose: To support the next generation of scholars. **Focus:** Culture. **Qualif.:** Applicants must be members of the UVa Faculty. **Criteria:** Selection will be based on the interest and fit with the Institute's intellectual mission.

Funds Avail.: No specific amount. **Duration:** Annual. **To Apply:** Interested applicants must contact the Institute for the application process.

10314 ■ University of Wisconsin--Madison
1308 W Dayton St.
Madison, WI 53715-1149
Ph: (608)263-2400
E-mail: askbucky@uwmad.wisc.edu
URL: www.wisc.edu

10315 ■ Ahlswede, Norman & Marie Endowed Engineering Scholarship *(Undergraduate/Scholarship)*

Purpose: To support UW-Madison engineering students in their education. **Focus:** Engineering. **Qualif.:** Applicants must be UW-Madison undergraduate students enrolled in any engineering major. They must be in good academic standing, be enrolled full-time in the College of Engineering and have completed at least two semesters (excluding Summer Session) on the UW-Madison campus at the time of the award. **Criteria:** Selection will be based on the aforesaid qualifications and compliance with the application process.

Funds Avail.: No specific amount. **Duration:** Annual. **To Apply:** Applicants must apply by the scholarship deadline. Completed applications will be read and evaluated using criteria designated by the donor and the values of the College. In addition, scholarships with a required financial need component use information provided on the completed FAFSA form. **Remarks:** The scholarship is part of the UW-Madison College of Engineering scholarships. There are other various scholarships offered.

10316 ■ Bascom Hill Society Scholarships
(Undergraduate/Scholarship)

Purpose: To support a student with financial need who combines academic excellence with demonstrated leadership ability and outstanding service to the university or their community. **Focus:** General studies/Field of study not specified. **Qualif.:** Applicants must: enroll full-time as undergraduates during the current academic year (students who plan to study abroad are eligible to apply); plan to graduate between May the following year; and qualify for need-based financial aid (grants or subsidized loans). **Criteria:** Selection will be based on the following: outstanding record of campus or community service; demonstrated leadership capacity; and, academic ability and achievement.

Funds Avail.: No specific amount. **Duration:** Annual. **To Apply:** Applicants must apply online. **Deadline:** June 6. **Contact:** UAA Office, at awards@provost.wisc.edu.

10317 ■ Mary Ann Brichta Scholarships
(Undergraduate/Scholarship)

Purpose: To support underrepresented UW-Madison students in their education. **Focus:** Education, Secondary. **Qualif.:** Applicants must be undergraduate students in the final year of an elementary teacher certification program based on financial need of students of underrepresented groups showing academic promise. **Criteria:** Selection will be based on the aforesaid qualifications.

Funds Avail.: No specific amount. **Duration:** Annual. **To Apply:** Interested applicants may contact the Office of the Dean to obtain an application form. **Remarks:** The scholarship was established to help students in the Department of Curriculum & Instruction. Ms. Brichta was a 1938 graduate from the School of Education and became a librarian at Milwaukee County General Hospital. **Contact:** Education Scholarships in Education Academic Services; Phone: 262-1651; E-mail: scholarships-soe@education.wisc.edu.

10318 ■ Patricia Buchanan Memorial Scholarships
(Undergraduate/Scholarship)

Purpose: To support UW-Madison students in their education. **Focus:** Education, Secondary. **Qualif.:** Applicants must be undergraduate students in underrepresented groups from Madison Metropolitan School District high schools who are preparing to become teachers. **Criteria:** Selection will be based on academic record, need, evidence of community service, and the recommendation of the students' academic department.

Funds Avail.: No specific amount. **Duration:** Annual. **To Apply:** Interested applicants may contact the Office of the Dean to obtain an application form. **Remarks:** The scholarship was established by the family and friends of the award's namesake. Established in 1991. **Contact:** Education Scholarships in Education Academic Services; Phone: 262-1651; E-mail: scholarships-soe@education.wisc.edu.

10319 ■ Barry M. Goldwater Scholarships
(Undergraduate/Scholarship)

Purpose: To support and recognize promising undergraduates who plan to pursue a PhD or MD/PhD followed by a

Awards are arranged alphabetically below their administering organizations

research career in engineering, mathematics or the natural sciences. **Focus:** Engineering; Mathematics and mathematical sciences; Science. **Qualif.:** Applicants must be full-time sophomores or juniors during academic year of application (defined as two years or one year of undergraduate study remaining after application year) who are also planning to pursue a PhD and research career in mathematics, natural sciences or engineering research (MD alone does not qualify, but MD/PhD does). They must also have an outstanding undergraduate academic record (GPA greater than 3.8), engaged in undergraduate research, and be U.S. citizens, nationals or permanent residents. **Criteria:** Selection will be based on academic achievement, progress toward research goals, research essay, and letters of recommendation.

Funds Avail.: $7,500. **Duration:** Annual. **Number Awarded:** 300. **To Apply:** Applicants must submit the following materials electronically or in hard copy: official Goldwater Online Application form; three letters of recommendation from professors who have supervised undergraduate research and/or undergraduate coursework in the sciences, engineering or mathematics; transcripts; and research essay (typed, two pages (one side only), font size no smaller than 11 point (please include your name at the top of each page). **Deadline:** November 16. **Remarks:** The scholarship was established by Congress to honor the career of former Senator Barry Goldwater. Established in 1986. **Contact:** Office of Undergraduate Academic Awards, at awards@provost.wisc.edu.

10320 ■ Kemper K. Knapp Scholarships
(Undergraduate/Scholarship)

Purpose: To support UW-Madison students in their education. **Focus:** General studies/Field of study not specified. **Qualif.:** Applicants must be National Merit finalists who are Wisconsin residents and designate UW-Madison as their first-choice institution. Other finalists who notify the Office of Student Financial Services are eligible as funds permit. **Criteria:** Selection will be based on academic excellence.

Funds Avail.: No specific amount. **Duration:** Annual. **To Apply:** No application for the award. Students will be automatically considered when admitted. **Contact:** Student Financial Aid Scholarship Office at: 608-262-9996; Email: scholarships@em.wisc.edu.

10321 ■ George Koeppel Scholarships/All School
(Undergraduate/Scholarship)

Purpose: To support UW-Madison students in their education. **Focus:** Education, Secondary. **Qualif.:** Applicants must be full-time undergraduates in the School of Education who intend to become elementary school teachers. **Criteria:** Scholarships are awarded based on the students' academic record, need, and the department's recommendation. Preference will be given to prospective elementary teachers from Milwaukee County. Financial need will be considered.

Funds Avail.: No specific amount. **Duration:** Annual. **To Apply:** Interested applicant may contact the Office of the Dean to obtain an application form. **Remarks:** The scholarship was established by the late Charlotte E. Zinns in honor of her father, a grade school principal in Milwaukee. **Contact:** Education Scholarships in Education Academic Services; Phone: 262-1651; E-mail: scholarships-soe@education.wisc.edu.

10322 ■ Abby Marlatt Scholarship *(Undergraduate/Scholarship)*

Purpose: To support UW-Madison students in their education. **Focus:** Ecology. **Qualif.:** Applicant must be current School of Human Ecology majors at the UW-Madison. **Criteria:** Preference will be given to applicants with good academic standing, who have participated in extracurricular and/or leadership activities, and/or who have performed community service.

Funds Avail.: $2,000. **Duration:** Annual. **To Apply:** Applicants must submit the School of Human Ecology Continuing Undergraduate Student Scholarship online application along with one letter of recommendation and two short essays. **Deadline:** December 4. **Remarks:** The scholarship is provided in honor of Abby Marlatt. **Contact:** Human Ecology Scholarship and Awards Coordinator at scholarships@mail.sohe.wisc.edu.

10323 ■ McBurney General Scholarships
(Undergraduate/Scholarship)

Purpose: To support UW-Madison disabled students in their education. **Focus:** General studies/Field of study not specified. **Qualif.:** Applicants must be UW-Madison undergraduate, graduate and professional students whose disabilities have been verified through the McBurney Disability Resource Center. **Criteria:** Recipients will be selected based on the application materials submitted.

Funds Avail.: No specific amount. **Duration:** Annual. **To Apply:** Applicants must submit a completed McBurney Scholarship Application along with two letters of recommendation and a current transcript. **Contact:** McBurney scholarships at mcbscholarships@studentlife.wisc.edu.

10324 ■ John P. and Tashia F. Morgridge Scholarships *(Undergraduate/Scholarship)*

Purpose: To support UW-Madison underrepresented students in their education. **Focus:** Education, Elementary. **Qualif.:** Applicants must be underrepresented undergraduate or graduate students preparing to become teachers, preferably at the elementary level who have proven success in academic achievement and who have demonstrated financial need. **Criteria:** Selection will be based on academic achievement and financial need, with preference given to graduates of Wisconsin high schools. Recipients are selected by the All School Minority/Underserved Population Scholarship Committee.

Funds Avail.: No specific amount. **Duration:** Annual. **Number Awarded:** 6. **To Apply:** Scholarship applications are available from the Office of the Dean. **Contact:** Student Financial Aid Scholarship Office at 608-262-9996; Email: scholarships@em.wisc.edu.

10325 ■ Pi Lambda Theta Scholarships
(Undergraduate/Scholarship)

Purpose: To support UW-Madison students in their education. **Focus:** Education. **Qualif.:** Applicants must be UW-Madison junior students having the highest GPA in the School of Education, and have completed at least one full semester (12 credits). **Criteria:** Selection will be based on students with highest GPA in junior year enrolled in a teacher preparation program. One award is given to majority student with highest GPA and one award to a student of an underrepresented group.

Funds Avail.: No specific amount. **Duration:** Annual. **Number Awarded:** 2. **To Apply:** Scholarship applications are available from the Office of the Dean. **Contact:** Student Financial Aid Scholarship Office at 608-262-9996; Email: scholarships@em.wisc.edu.

10326 ■ Powers-Knapp Scholarships
(Undergraduate/Scholarship)

Purpose: To support UW-Madison students in their education. **Focus:** General studies/Field of study not specified.

Awards are arranged alphabetically below their administering organizations

Qualif.: Applicants must be U.S. citizens who plan to enroll as new freshmen in the fall following graduation from high school, and be members of one of the following groups: African American; American Indian; Hispanic/Latino; Southeast Asian (Cambodian, Hmong, Laotian, or Vietnamese); Socioeconomically disadvantaged. They should demonstrate outstanding academic performance (3.0/4.0 GPA or higher in academic units). **Criteria:** Recipients will be selected based on academic achievements.

Funds Avail.: $400 each semester. **Duration:** Annual. **To Apply:** Application is via online. **Deadline:** February 15.

10327 ■ University of Wisconsin-Madison/CALS Minority Scholarships (Undergraduate/Scholarship)

Purpose: To support UW-Madison students in their education. **Focus:** Agricultural sciences; Life sciences. **Qualif.:** Applicants must be UW-Madison students of color enrolled in the College of Agricultural and Life Sciences (CALS). **Criteria:** Selection is based on academic excellence.

Funds Avail.: $500-$2,000. **Duration:** Annual. **Number Awarded:** Varies. **To Apply:** Students must submit a completed CALS Scholarship Application along with the letter of recommendation. **Deadline:** February 3. **Contact:** CALS scholarships; Phone: 608-262-3003; E-mail: scholarships@cals.wisc.edu.

10328 ■ University of Wisconsin-Madison Chancellor's Scholarships (Undergraduate/Scholarship)

Purpose: To support UW-Madison students in their education. **Focus:** General studies/Field of study not specified. **Qualif.:** Applicants must be U.S. citizens who plan to enroll as new freshmen in the fall following graduation from high school, and be members of one of the following groups: African American; American Indian; Hispanic/Latino; Southeast Asian (Cambodian, Hmong, Laotian, or Vietnamese); Socioeconomically disadvantaged. They should demonstrate outstanding academic performance (3.0/4.0 GPA or higher in academic units). **Criteria:** Recipients will be selected based on academic achievements.

Funds Avail.: $400 each semester. **Duration:** Annual. **To Apply:** Application is via online. **Deadline:** February 15.

10329 ■ University of Wisconsin-Madison National Merit Scholarships (Undergraduate/Scholarship)

Purpose: To support UW-Madison students in their education. **Focus:** General studies/Field of study not specified. **Qualif.:** Applicants must be National Merit finalists who designate UW-Madison as their first-choice institution. **Criteria:** Recipients will be selected based on a review of all applications.

Funds Avail.: No specific amount. **Duration:** Annual. **Number Awarded:** 5. **To Apply:** There is no application for the scholarship. **Contact:** Office of Student Financial Services, Scholarship Section; Phone: 608-262-9996; Email: finaid@finaid.wisc.edu.

10330 ■ University of Wisconsin-Madison Single Parent Scholarships (Undergraduate/Scholarship)

Purpose: To support single parent students in their education. **Focus:** General studies/Field of study not specified. **Qualif.:** Applicant must be: the sole head of their household and the single parent of at least one dependent child supported by and living in that household; a new or continuing student pursuing their first undergraduate degree; able to demonstrate financial need; and, a U.S. citizen, permanent resident, asylee, or other eligible non-citizen. **Criteria:** Selection will be on competitive basis. Preference may be given to undergraduates who have completed at least 30 degree credits with a cumulative GPA of 3.0 or better.

Funds Avail.: $1,000 to $2,000. **Duration:** Annual. **To Apply:** Applicants must visit the program site for tips on putting together a competitive application. **Deadline:** March 1. **Remarks:** Established in 1993. **Contact:** UW-Madison's Adult Career and Special Student Services; Phone: 608-263-6960; E-mail: advising@dcs.wisc.edu.

10331 ■ UW-Madison Engineering Diversity Scholarships (Undergraduate/Scholarship)

Purpose: To encourage broadened participation in Engineering. **Focus:** Engineering. **Qualif.:** Applicants must be academically-talented incoming engineering undergraduate students who are underrepresented in engineering, including women of all ethnicities, African-American, Latina/o, Southeast Asian, Native American/Hawaiian Native/Alaskan Native, and Pacific Islander, low income and/or educationally disadvantaged students. **Criteria:** Selection will be based on academic merit, quality of application, match to the Diversity Affairs Office mission of broadening participation in engineering, and financial need.

Funds Avail.: $500 to $3,000. **Duration:** Annual. **Number Awarded:** Varies. **To Apply:** Application is via online. A FASFA is also required and should be submitted to the Office of Student Financial Aid as soon as possible to allow for verification prior to award disbursement. **Deadline:** February 1 (priority deadline); April 1 (application and recommendations).

10332 ■ UW-Madison GLBT Alumni Council Scholarships (Undergraduate, Graduate/Scholarship)

Purpose: To support UW-Madison LGBTQ students in their education. **Focus:** General studies/Field of study not specified. **Qualif.:** Applicants must be committed to the gay, lesbian, bisexual, and transgender community; and must maintain an outstanding academic achievement. **Criteria:** Priority will be given to students with financial need.

Funds Avail.: No specific amount. **Duration:** Annual. **To Apply:** Applicants must contact the Wisconsin Alumni Association for information about the program. **Contact:** GLBT Alumni Council; Phone 608-265-3344; Gabe Javier at gabe.javier@wisc.edu.

10333 ■ UW-Madison Reserve Officers Training Corps Scholarships (Undergraduate/Scholarship)

Purpose: To support UW-Madison ROTC students in their education. **Focus:** Military science and education. **Qualif.:** Applicants must be U.S. citizens enrolled in ROTC programs (Army, Navy, Air Force). **Criteria:** Selection is based on merit.

Funds Avail.: No specific amount. **Duration:** Annual. **To Apply:** Applicants may contact Air Force Aerospace Studies, Air Force ROTC; Military Science, Army ROTC; Naval Sciences, Navy ROTC for more information about the program.

10334 ■ UW-Madison School of Education Minority Scholarships (Undergraduate/Scholarship)

Purpose: To support UW-Madison minority students in their education. **Focus:** Education. **Qualif.:** Applicants must be undergraduate students from underrepresented groups pursuing degrees in the School of Education. **Criteria:** Selection will be based on academic achievement and financial need. Recipients are chosen by the School's

Awards are arranged alphabetically below their administering organizations

Minority/Underserved Scholarship Committee.

Funds Avail.: No specific amount. **Duration:** Annual. **To Apply:** Scholarship applications are available from the Office of the Dean. **Contact:** Student Financial Aid Scholarship Office at 608-262-9996; Email: scholarships@em.wisc.edu.

10335 ■ William F. Vilas Scholarships
(Undergraduate/Scholarship)

Purpose: To support UW-Madison students in their education. **Focus:** General studies/Field of study not specified. **Qualif.:** Applicants must be students who demonstrate strong academic performance based on class rank and GPA. **Criteria:** Selection is based on academic excellence.

Funds Avail.: No specific amount. **Duration:** Annual. **To Apply:** Students will be automatically considered when admitted. **Contact:** Office of Student Financial Aid, at 608-262-3060.

10336 ■ Wisconsin Lawton Minority Retention Grants *(Undergraduate/Grant)*

Purpose: To support UW-Madison students in their education. **Focus:** General studies/Field of study not specified. **Qualif.:** Applicants must: be sophomores, juniors, and seniors who are of African-American, Latino/a, American Indian, Vietnamese, Cambodian, Laotian, or Hmong heritage; have a minimum cumulative 2.0 grade point average; be enrolled full-time, pass 24 credits each academic year; have a program affiliation; and be United States citizens and residents of Wisconsin (current Minnesota recipients are grandfathered in through the current year). **Criteria:** Recipients will be selected based on financial need.

Funds Avail.: $1,000 to $3,000. **Duration:** Annual; Up to 4 years. **To Apply:** Applicants must file an application at FAFSA in order to be considered. In addition, applicants must contact the Minority and Disadvantaged Coordinator in the UW-Madison school or college where they are enrolled.

10337 ■ Upakar Indian-American Scholarship Foundation
101 Friars Rd.
Bethesda, MD 20817
E-mail: info@upakar.org
URL: www.upakarfoundation.org

10338 ■ Geeta Rastogi Memorial Scholarships
(Undergraduate/Scholarship)

Purpose: To support the educational and career aspirations of the Indian-American community. **Focus:** Dance; Music. **Qualif.:** Applicants must be students entering a Fine Arts (Music, Dance, Drama, etc.) undergraduate program in the United States; must have either been born or have at least one parent in the Republic of India; must either be U.S. citizens or U.S. Green Card holders; must have latest Family Adjusted Gross Income (AGI) on the IRS form 1040, 1040EZ or 1040A of less than $75,000; and must be graduating high school seniors living in the United States with a cumulative unweighted GPA of 3.6 or higher on a 4.0 scale. **Criteria:** Applicants will be evaluated based on academic achievement.

Funds Avail.: $8,000. **Duration:** Annual; up to 4 years. **To Apply:** Applicants must submit a completed application form and an essay. **Deadline:** April 30.

10339 ■ Upper Left, Inc.
540 N Willow Dr.
Long Lake, MN 55356
Ph: (612)328-7198
E-mail: jim@interagency.com
URL: www.enhancedinsurance.com

10340 ■ Enhanced Insurance Scholarships Program
(Undergraduate/Scholarship)

Purpose: To promote insurance industry as positive force. **Focus:** General studies/Field of study not specified. **Qualif.:** Applicants must be high school seniors or current undergraduate students who will be enrolled full-time in a two- or four-year public or private college or university located in the United States and/or in the District of Columbia for an academic school year. **Criteria:** Selection will be based on the following criteria: grammar, spelling, punctuation, content, creativity, clarity, and thoughtfulness.

Funds Avail.: $2,500. **Duration:** Annual. **Number Awarded:** Varies. **To Apply:** Applicants may visit the application website for the set of rules regarding the application process. **Deadline:** October 31.

10341 ■ Upsilon Pi Epsilon Association
158 Wetlands Edge Rd.
American Canyon, CA 94503
Ph: (530)518-8488
Fax: (707)647-3560
E-mail: upe@acm.org
URL: upe.acm.org

10342 ■ UPE Scholarship Awards *(Graduate, Undergraduate/Scholarship)*

Purpose: To provide educational support to students who are in need. **Focus:** Computer and information sciences. **Qualif.:** Applicants must be graduate or undergraduate students. **Criteria:** Application form and other documents will be evaluated by the Executive Council of UPE.

Funds Avail.: $1,000 to $2,500. **Duration:** Annual. **To Apply:** Interested applicants may visit the website (http://upe.acm.org/documents/Scholarship_Form.pdf) to obtain an application form and other application process. **Deadline:** June 15. **Contact:** upe@acm.org.

10343 ■ Urban Affairs Association (UAA)
University of Wisconsin-Milwaukee
Urban Studies Program
3210 N Maryland Ave.
Bolton 702
Milwaukee, WI 53211
Ph: (414)229-3025
E-mail: conf@uaamail.org
URL: urbanaffairsassociation.org
Facebook: www.facebook.com/urbanaffairsassociation
Twitter: twitter.com/UAAnews

10344 ■ Alma H. Young Emerging Scholar Awards
(Doctorate/Award, Monetary)

Purpose: To honor and support emerging scholars whose work exemplifies outstanding scholarship in urban affairs. **Focus:** General studies/Field of study not specified. **Qualif.:** Applicants must be pursuing doctoral research in urban affairs, regardless of academic discipline. They must have:

Awards are arranged alphabetically below their administering organizations

finished the required course work; passed the comprehensive examinations; and, an approved dissertation proposal. **Criteria:** Recipients will be selected based on scholarship and commitment to urban issues.

Funds Avail.: $1,000. **Duration:** Annual. **To Apply:** Applicants must submit the nomination letter from current UAA members; provide (two-to-three page, double-spaced) personal statement describing urban interests, engagement and career plans; a curriculum vitae; a prospectus for the dissertation of (1,500 to 2,000 words) that indicate the research questions, argument or hypotheses, literature and data resources, methodology and nature of expected findings. **Deadline:** December 1. **Remarks:** Established in 1997. **Contact:** Sent applications to awards@uaamail.org.

10345 ■ Urology Care Foundation
1000 Corporate Blvd.
Linthicum, MD 21090
Ph: (410)689-3700
Fax: (410)689-3998
Free: 800-828-7866
E-mail: info@urologycarefoundation.org
URL: www.urologyhealth.org
Facebook: www.facebook.com/UrologyCareFoundation
Twitter: twitter.com/UrologyCareFdn

10346 ■ AUA Foundation Urology Research Bridge Awards *(Postgraduate/Award)*

Purpose: To provide funds to individuals for interim support for a research grant that was competitive but did not get funded. **Focus:** Urology. **Qualif.:** Applicant must be a member of AUA; not a previous recipient of the award; must have competed for a peer-reviewed external funding for the project during the current federal fiscal year. **Criteria:** Applicants are selected based on the jury's review of the application materials.

Funds Avail.: No specific amount. **Duration:** Annual. **To Apply:** Applicants must register online at the AUA Foundation website in order to apply. Applicants must submit the following materials: a completed application form; a registration summary form; an application agreement form; a NIH-style biosketch; a statement of current other support; letter from the applicants; budget justification worksheet; and letter from the applicants' department chair. The form must be signed by the applicants, department chair and sponsoring institution representative. Scan all materials into one complete .pdf file.

10347 ■ Urology Care Foundation/Astellas Rising Star in Urology Research Awards *(Postdoctorate, Other/Award)*

Purpose: To encourage a young urology faculty to go into, or continue a research career. **Focus:** Urology. **Qualif.:** Applicants must be Board certified or eligible urologists and must have successfully competed for a career development award within the current federal fiscal year. **Criteria:** Applicants will be selected based on scholarship panel's review of the application materials.

Funds Avail.: No specific amount. **Duration:** Annual. **To Apply:** Applicants must complete the online application form. They must also prepare a registration summary form; curriculum vitae; application agreement form with all necessary signatures; letter of support from each mentor; letter from urology department chair; current NIH-style biosketch of each mentor; copy of career development grant award letter; copy of career development grant; and copy of career development grant review summary sheets and scores. All materials must be uploaded and scanned into a single .pdf file.

10348 ■ US-Ireland Alliance
2800 Clarendon Blvd., Ste. 502W
Arlington, VA 22201
URL: www.us-irelandalliance.org

10349 ■ George J. Mitchell Scholarships *(Postgraduate/Scholarship)*

Purpose: To introduce and connect generations of future American leaders to the island of Ireland, while recognizing and fostering intellectual achievement, leadership, and a commitment to public service and community. **Focus:** General studies/Field of study not specified. **Qualif.:** Applicants must be U.S. citizens between 18-30 years old and hold a bachelor's degree from an accredited college or university. **Criteria:** Applicants will be judged based on academic excellence and intellectual distinction, outstanding record of leadership, sustained commitment to service and community.

Funds Avail.: No specific amount. **Duration:** Annual. **Number Awarded:** Up to 12. **To Apply:** Application is via online. All information and supporting documents including recommendations and institutional endorsements must be submitted through the online application process. **Deadline:** September 30. **Contact:** Serena Wilson, Dir., George Mitchell Scholarship Program; Email: director@mitchellscholars.org.

10350 ■ USA Water Ski Foundation
1251 Holy Cow Rd.
Polk City, FL 33868-8200
Ph: (863)324-2472
Fax: (863)324-3996
E-mail: usa-wsf@waterskihalloffame.com
URL: www.waterskihalloffame.com
Facebook: www.facebook.com/USAWSF
LinkedIn: www.linkedin.com/company/usa-water-ski-foundation
Twitter: www.twitter.com/USAWSF

10351 ■ American Water Ski Educational Foundation Scholarships *(Undergraduate/Scholarship)*

Purpose: To preserve the traditions of one of America's most popular family recreational activities; to encourage and to educate the safe enjoyment of the challenges of water skiing. **Focus:** General studies/Field of study not specified. **Qualif.:** Applicant must be enrolled with a minimum of two-year course in secondary education; he/she must be a U.S. citizen and a current member of USA Water Ski Foundation. **Criteria:** Applicants will be evaluated based upon the academic qualifications, leadership, extracurricular involvement, recommendations and financial need.

Funds Avail.: No specific amount. **Duration:** Three years. **To Apply:** Applicant must fill out the application form; he/she must submit two letters of reference; a 500-word essay on topic, "AWSEF has a beautiful new facility"; an official transcript of grades; or high school transcript (if college freshman). **Deadline:** March 1. **Remarks:** Incomplete applications will not be accepted.

10352 ■ USAttorneys.com
1001 W Cypress Creek Rd., Ste. 405
Fort Lauderdale, FL 33309

Awards are arranged alphabetically below their administering organizations

Fax: (954)734-7131
Free: 866-335-8999
URL: divorce.usattorneys.com

10353 ■ USAttorneys.com Immigration Scholarships Essay Contest *(Undergraduate/Scholarship)*

Purpose: To assist students with the costs of college tuition and books. **Focus:** General studies/Field of study not specified. **Qualif.:** Applicants must be U.S. citizens who are accepted or currently attending an accredited American university or college. **Criteria:** Selection will be based on the committee's criteria.

Funds Avail.: $2,500. **Duration:** Up to 3 years. **Number Awarded:** 1. **To Apply:** Applicants must prepare a 800 to 1,000 word legal essay on any of the following topics: Immigration Reform; How to Apply for a Work Visa; The Importance of Having an Immigration Lawyer; How to Apply for Asylum. Applicants must submit their essay as an attachment, in PDF or Word format, including their full name, school they will be or are attending, and contact information. **Deadline:** July 1; February 1. **Contact:** immigration@usattorneys.com.

10354 ■ USAttorneys.com National Scholarships Essay Contest *(Undergraduate/Scholarship)*

Purpose: To assist students with the costs of tuition and books. **Focus:** General studies/Field of study not specified. **Qualif.:** Applicants must be U.S. citizens, planning to attend an accredited American university or college. **Criteria:** Selection will be based on the committee's criteria.

Funds Avail.: $2,500. Checks will be made payable to the college. **Number Awarded:** 1. **To Apply:** Applicants must prepare a 800 to 1,000 word legal essay on any of the following topics: Divorce Law; Child Custody; Divorce Mediation. Applicants must submit their essay as an attachment in PDF or Word format, including their full name, school they will attending and contact information. **Deadline:** June 1. **Contact:** scholarships@usattorneys.com; pcharles@damg.com.

10355 ■ USC Latino Alumni Association
Epstein Family Alumni Ctr.
3607 Trousdale Pky., TCC 324
Los Angeles, CA 90089-3104
Ph: (213)740-4735
Fax: (213)740-7250
E-mail: latinoalumni@usc.edu
URL: latinoalumni.usc.edu
Facebook: www.facebook.com/USCLAA

10356 ■ Mexican American Alumni Association Scholarships *(Graduate, Undergraduate/Scholarship)*

Purpose: To support financially those students who are pursuing undergraduate and graduate degrees at University of Southern California. **Focus:** General studies/Field of study not specified. **Qualif.:** Applicant have a demonstrated commitment to the Latino community; have demonstrated leadership; overall academic and professional promise; current full-time student at USC (potential incoming freshman and incoming transfer student should apply even if not yet admitted into the university); and must have completed 24 or more units with a GPA of 2.7 or better for continuing USC undergraduate student and incoming transfer student, graduate student must have completed 16 units or more with a GPA of 3.0 or better. **Criteria:** Selection is based on: completed application; financial aid need; availability of other financial aid resources; grade point average (2.7 for undergraduate students, 3.0 for graduate students); current student loan obligations; community/university involvement; and the legibility, completeness, accuracy and quality of information provided in the application.

Funds Avail.: $500-$5,000 per academic year for undergraduate students and $1,000-$5,000 per academic year for graduate students. **Duration:** Annual. **To Apply:** Applicants must submit a completed USC MAAA Scholarship application form together with a typed essay of no more than two pages, double spaced; a resume; original letter(s) of recommendation; and unofficial transcripts. Applications must be sent complete. **Deadline:** December 1 and February 2. **Contact:** USC Latino Alumni Association Scholarship Committee, at the above address.

10357 ■ USS Coral Sea CVA-43 Association
52 Woodland Pl.
Fort Thomas, KY 41075-1605
URL: www.usscoralsea.org

10358 ■ USS Coral Sea Remembrance Scholarships *(Undergraduate/Scholarship)*

Purpose: To help the beneficiaries of an individual working at USS Coral Sea CVA-43 Association. **Focus:** General studies/Field of study not specified. **Qualif.:** Applicants must: be children, grandchildren, step-children or step-grandchildren of: 1) a member in good standing; 2) a deceased member; 3) a non-member who was killed in the line of duty; 4) an individual who was captured as a prisoner of war; or 5) and individual who was injured while in duty; must be high school seniors with at least a "B" or 3.0 GPA; and must have plans to attend a two or four-year college, university, technical or vocational school. **Criteria:** Essays will be judged based on originality of thought, adherence to topic, completeness, quality, spelling and punctuation. Applicants with the highest GPA will be announced as the winner.

Funds Avail.: $500 and $2,000. **Duration:** Annual. **To Apply:** Applicants must submit an original essay; two dated and signed letters of recommendation; and an official transcript of records. Essay must be typed and double-spaced. Reference sources must be listed and footnoted. **Deadline:** April 1. **Contact:** Jon Lickey, 2321 N. Delaware St., Peoria, IL 616003-2645; Phone: 309-688-3939; Email: jjlickey47@yahoo.com.

10359 ■ Utility Workers Union of America (UWUA)
1300 L St. NW No. 1200
Washington, DC 20005
Ph: (202)899-2851
Fax: (202)974-8201
E-mail: webmaster@uwua.net
URL: uwua.net

10360 ■ Utility Workers Union of America Scholarship Program *(Undergraduate/Scholarship)*

Purpose: To provide a system of services for corporations, foundations and other organizations that wish to sponsor college undergraduate scholarships for outstanding students who interest them. **Focus:** General studies/Field of study not specified. **Qualif.:** Applicants must be high school students who are sons and daughters of active members of UWUA; must be U.S. citizens and have a permanent residence in the United States. **Criteria:** Recipients will be selected based on academic record throughout high school, significant activities and contributions to the school community, test scores, recommendations and the student's essay about personal characteristics, activities, plan and goals.

Funds Avail.: $500 - $2,000. **Duration:** Annual. **To Apply:** Applicants must fill out the application form; must take the PSAT/NMSQT; must obtain a copy of the Official Student Guide to the PSAT/NMSQT from the high school counselor and make arrangements with the school to take the PSAT/NMSQT. **Deadline:** March 1. **Remarks:** Established in 1961.

10361 ■ ValuePenguin
600 3rd Ave., Floor 8
New York, NY 10016
Ph: (646)248-5684
URL: www.valuepenguin.com

10362 ■ ValuePenguin Scholarships *(Undergraduate/Scholarship)*

Purpose: To provide financial assistance for students to afford basic necessities. **Focus:** General studies/Field of study not specified. **Qualif.:** Applicants must be enrolled in an accredited U.S. undergraduate program. **Criteria:** Selection will be based on the following criteria; creativity, novelty and thoughtfulness of the essay responses.

Funds Avail.: $2,000. **Duration:** Annual. **Number Awarded:** 1-3. **To Apply:** Applicants must submit a 500 to 750 word response (for a total word count of 1,000 to 1,500) to each of the following two questions: 1) Students encounter financial pitfalls of all types while attending colleges and universities. Explain a situation in which you spent too much (or not enough) money on a student expense and explain a creative solution you would share with future students. This could be something you did on your own or as part of a group. 2) How did you choose your college and/or major? Submit all responses along with the following information: name, school you are attending, expected graduation date, major and career goal, email address, phone number, and an applicants' picture. **Deadline:** November 10.

10363 ■ Vector Marketing Corp.
5301 Limestone Rd., Ste. 105
Wilmington, DE 19808
Ph: (302)372-8020
E-mail: campus@cutco.com
URL: www.vectorscholarships.com

10364 ■ All-American Vector Marketing Scholarship Program *(Undergraduate/Scholarship)*

Purpose: To support the education of students who are also top sales performers. **Focus:** Marketing and distribution. **Qualif.:** Applicants must be full-time students at an accredited college or university; active in the business at the conclusion of the Scholarship Race. **Criteria:** Selection will be based on sales performance. Scholastic achievement and financial need are not taken into consideration.

Funds Avail.: Amount varies. **Duration:** Annual. **To Apply:** Applicants must provide current official transcript as well as a copy of current semester registration. Applicants may contact Vector Marketing Corporation for other requirements.

10365 ■ Vector Marketing Canadian Scholarship Awards *(Undergraduate/Scholarship)*

Purpose: To provide financial assistance to student sales representatives and the institutions of higher education they attend. **Focus:** Marketing and distribution. **Qualif.:** Applicants must be full-time university or college students working with Vector; and must be currently active on Vector Marketing All-American program tracking system. **Criteria:** Scholarship recipients are selected based on the committee's review of the application materials.

Funds Avail.: Amount varies. **Duration:** Annual. **To Apply:** Applicants must provide current official transcript as well as a copy of current semester registration. Applicants may contact Vector Marketing Corporation for other requirements.

10366 ■ Vectorworks Inc.
7150 Riverwood Dr.
Columbia, MD 21046-1295
Ph: (410)290-5114
Fax: (410)290-8050
Free: 888-646-4223
E-mail: academicteam@vectorworks.net
URL: www.vectorworks.net
Facebook: www.facebook.com/nemetschekag
LinkedIn: www.linkedin.com/company/nemetschek

10367 ■ Vectorworks Design Scholarships *(Undergraduate, Graduate/Scholarship, Prize)*

Purpose: To support the next generation of creative potential by providing resources and scholarships to those with great designs. **Focus:** Architecture; Construction; Design; Engineering; Environmental design; Graphic art and design; Industrial design; Interior design; Landscape architecture and design; Urban affairs/design/planning. **Qualif.:** Applicants must be enrolled or accepted for enrollment in undergraduate or graduate studies for six or more credits at an accredited university or college; must be pursuing any design-oriented degree. **Criteria:** Selection will be based on the submitted designs of the applicants. Criteria include: design (20%); technology (20%); concept and originality (20%); presentation (20%); and writing (20%).

Funds Avail.: $10,000 for grand winner; $3,000 for finalists. **Duration:** Annual. **Number Awarded:** 1 grand winner; 10-17 finalists. **To Apply:** Applicants must submit their best design and answer three short questions online. **Deadline:** August 31. **Remarks:** Submissions can be created in any software, and can even be a project previously completed for school. Individual and group work is allowed. Additionally, winners' schools will receive free Vectorworks design software, as well as free in-person or virtual training for faculty and students.

10368 ■ VelvetJobs
1400 N Martel Ave., Ste. 108
Los Angeles, CA 90046
Free: 877-370-7552
E-mail: support@velvetjobs.com
URL: www.velvetjobs.com

Awards are arranged alphabetically below their administering organizations

10369 ■ Resume Template Design Scholarships
(Undergraduate, Graduate/Scholarship)

Purpose: To support students to achieved their educational goals. **Focus:** General studies/Field of study not specified. **Qualif.:** Applicants must be U.S. or international college or university undergraduate and graduate students. **Criteria:** Selection will be based on the committee's criteria.

Funds Avail.: $1,000. **Duration:** Annual. **Number Awarded:** 1. **To Apply:** Applicants must create a VelvetJobs Account at www.velvetjobs.com and fill out their profile with their education and work background, and must submit their essay and resume template online, including the following information: full name, phone number, College or University where the applicants are enrolled or plan to attend, and current school year. **Deadline:** December 31. **Contact:** scholarship@velvetjobs.com.

10370 ■ Vermont Paralegal Organization (VPO)
PO Box 5755
Burlington, VT 05402-5755
E-mail: vermont@paralegals.org
URL: www.vtparalegal.org
Facebook: www.facebook.com/Vermont-Paralegal-Organization-163232993708517

10371 ■ Vermont Paralegal Organization Scholarships *(Undergraduate/Scholarship)*

Purpose: To promote excellence in the paralegal profession, and support those who are want to take the said course. **Focus:** Paralegal studies. **Qualif.:** Applicants must be attending, at least part-time, accredited paralegal/legal studies program. **Criteria:** Selection will be based on the quality of submitted essays, individual's academic achievement and financial need.

Funds Avail.: $500. **Duration:** Annual. **To Apply:** Applicants must submit a completed application, including their essays. **Deadline:** March 6.

10372 ■ Vesalius Trust (VT)
491 Carlisle Dr., Ste. A
Herndon, VA 20170
Ph: (703)437-9555
Fax: (703)437-0727
E-mail: vesaliustrust@aol.com
URL: www.vesaliustrust.org
Facebook: www.facebook.com/Vesalius-Trust-240623966016954

10373 ■ Inez Demonet Scholarship *(Graduate/Scholarship)*

Purpose: To support students with promising contributions to the profession of medical illustration. **Focus:** Illustrators and illustrations. **Qualif.:** Applicant must be a second year graduate student enrolled in a medical illustration accredited by the Accreditation Review Committee for the Medical Illustrators (ARC-MI) and Commission on Accreditation of the Allied Health Education Program (CAAHEP). **Criteria:** Applicants are evaluated based on past performances and potential for significant contributions to the field.

Funds Avail.: $2,000. **Duration:** One academic year. **To Apply:** Application form is available at the website. Applicants must prepare a resume (one page); transcripts; references; portfolio of five portfolio pieces; and an essay. **Deadline:** February 1 and February 8. **Contact:** Original application form and three photocopies of supporting documents must be sent to: Tami Tolpa, VT Student Grants and Scholarships, Tolpa Studios Inc., 6523 California Ave. SW, No. 110, Seattle, WA 98136; Phone: 206-420-1754; E-mail: tami@tolpa.com.

10374 ■ Vesalius Trust Student Research Scholarships *(Graduate, Undergraduate/Scholarship)*

Purpose: To support students enrolled in medical illustration programs. **Focus:** Illustrators and illustrations. **Qualif.:** Applicants must be enrolled in a medical illustration program and must have completed one year of the curriculum. **Criteria:** Applicants are judged based on background, education and project concept, design and production plan.

Funds Avail.: No specific amount. **To Apply:** Applicants must submit an application form; a resume; graduate project description; budget and timeline; transcripts; preceptor form and faculty advisor form. **Deadline:** November 9. **Contact:** Tami Tolpa, VT Student Grants and Scholarships, 206-420-1754 or tami@tolpa.com.

10375 ■ Veterans Health Administration - Office of Research and Development - Health Services Research and Development Service - Center for Organization, Leadership, and Management Research (COLMR)
VA Boston Health Care System (152M)
150 S Huntington Ave.
Boston, MA 02130
Ph: (857)364-4433
URL: www.colmr.research.va.gov

10376 ■ CHOIR MD Post-Residency Fellowship in Health Services Research *(Postdoctorate/Fellowship)*

Purpose: To provide post-residency training and research opportunities for physicians and other health professionals. **Focus:** Health care services. **Qualif.:** Applicants must be US citizens and must have completed an ACGME-approved residency. **Criteria:** Selection will be based on the committee's criteria.

Funds Avail.: No specific amount. **To Apply:** Applicants must submit a letter of interest with a CV and a 1-2 page statement of prior research training and experience, reasons for seeking fellowships, specific health services research interests, goals for the fellowship and overall career objectives. Applicants must also indicates whether they are applying to the Boston or Bedford site. **Deadline:** January 15. **Contact:** Interested PhD applicants should contact Karen Quigley, PhD at Karen.quigley@va.gov or Jim Burgess, PhD at james.burgess@va.gov; Interested MD applicants should contact Adam Rose at adam.rose@va.gov or Steven Simon, MD at steven.simon2@va.gov.

10377 ■ Veterinary Orthopedic Society (VOS)
PO Box 665
Parker, CO 80134
Ph: (720)335-6051
E-mail: secretary@vosdvm.org
URL: www.vosdvm.org
Twitter: twitter.com/vosdvm

Awards are arranged alphabetically below their administering organizations

10378 ■ Wade O. Brinker Resident Research Award
(Undergraduate/Award)

Purpose: To foster research related to musculoskeletal problems confronting veterinarians today. **Focus:** Muscular dystrophy. **Qualif.:** Applicants must be individuals planning or conducting research in the field of orthopedics. **Criteria:** The VOS research committee will review grant applications. The proposals will be evaluated for the following criteria: scientific and technical quality of the idea; scientific and technological quality of the method; relevance to VOS goals and priorities; feasibility of accomplishing objectives within the proposed time line and; relevance of objectives to current literature.

Funds Avail.: Up to $12,000. **To Apply:** Applicants must send one original and one blind version of the proposal as two separate files in MS Word format. **Deadline:** October 1. **Contact:** Matt Stewart, VOS Research Chairman, matt1@illinois.edu.

10379 ■ Vietnam Education Foundation (VEF)
2111 Wilson Blvd., Ste. 700
Arlington, VA 22201
Ph: (703)351-5053
Fax: (703)351-1423
E-mail: information@vef.gov
URL: home.vef.gov

10380 ■ VEF Fellowship Program *(Doctorate, Master's/Fellowship)*

Purpose: To financially assist Vietnamese to pursue their graduate education in the United States. **Focus:** Engineering; Mathematics and mathematical sciences; Medicine; Science; Technology. **Qualif.:** Applicants must be Vietnamese nationals to begin graduate studies in the United States; must be interested in pursuing a PhD or Master's degree in the major disciplines of Sciences, Mathematics, Medicine, Engineering and Technology; must have GPA of 7.0-10.0; must demonstrate sufficient proficiency in the English language. **Criteria:** Winners will be chosen based on individual merit, including academic performance and preparation, intellectual capabilities, English proficiency, potential contribution to scientific education and research in Vietnam.

Funds Avail.: No specific amount. **Duration:** Annual. **Number Awarded:** Approximately 34. **To Apply:** Applicants must submit a completed application form; must submit their undergraduate/graduate certificate and transcripts, evidence of English language proficiency, GRE score, one-page academic statement and one-page personal statement, three letters of recommendation/reference, U.S. universities. **Deadline:** December 10. **Contact:** All questions related to the VEF Fellowship Program should be sent to: vef2016@vef.gov.

10381 ■ VEF Visiting Scholars Program *(Doctorate/Fellowship)*

Purpose: To support professional development training for doctorate students. **Focus:** Engineering; Mathematics and mathematical sciences; Medicine; Science; Technology. **Qualif.:** Applicants must be Vietnamese nationals who already hold a doctoral degree in a field supported by VEF; must demonstrate a high level of English proficiency. **Criteria:** Recipients will be chosen based on the following categories: a) evidence of superior academic achievement; b) quality and value of visiting scholar professional development plan; c) demonstrated commitment to the educational and scientific development of Vietnam; d) demonstrated commitment of support from the U.S. host institution; e) demonstrated commitment of support from the Vietnamese institution(s).

Funds Avail.: Amount varies. **Duration:** Annual; Five months to one year. **Number Awarded:** 3. **To Apply:** Applicants must submit a completed application form. **Deadline:** April 10. **Contact:** All questions regarding the VEF Visiting Scholar Program, please contact VEF via e-mail at vs@vef.gov.

10382 ■ Vietnamese American Bar Association of Northern California (VABANC)
772 N 1st St.
San Jose, CA 95112
Ph: (408)975-9321
E-mail: info@vabanc.org
Facebook: www.facebook.com/VABANC

10383 ■ VABANC Scholarships *(Graduate, Undergraduate/Scholarship)*

Purpose: To provide assistance to students with their public interest or social justice goals. **Focus:** Law. **Qualif.:** Applicants must be all currently enrolled law students who have demonstrated a commitment to serving the needs of the Vietnamese-American and Vietnamese communities. **Criteria:** Priority will be given to those who have demonstrated a commitment to serving the Vietnamese-American and/or Vietnamese communities in Northern California and to those who will be using the scholarship award to further their public interest or social justice work, either by pursuing post-graduate work or for a summer position.

Funds Avail.: $1,000 each. **Duration:** Annual. **Number Awarded:** 2. **To Apply:** Applicants must submit a completed application form along with a resume; three academic and/or professional references; and a personal statement of no more than 800 words describing the following: pressing concerns faced by the Vietnamese-American and/or Vietnamese community, and how they will contribute to or engage in addressing such concerns; and/or their contributions to or activism within the Vietnamese-American and/or Vietnamese community; and/or, their experiences in overcoming socioeconomic and/or other barriers. **Deadline:** August 10. **Contact:** Email at: scholarships@vabanc.org.

10384 ■ Vietnamese American Scholarship Foundation
PO Box 429
Stafford, TX 77497
E-mail: scholarships@vietscholarships.org
URL: www.vietscholarships.org

10385 ■ Danny T. Le Memorial Scholarships *(Undergraduate/Scholarship)*

Purpose: To provide financial assistance to students of Vietnamese descent from the Greater Houston area for pursuing further education. **Focus:** General studies/Field of study not specified. **Qualif.:** Applicants must be of Vietnamese descent; must be graduated or graduating from a high school in the Greater Houston Area and pursuing degree at an accredited four-year college or university. **Criteria:** Applicants are evaluated based on academic excellence; compassion and desire to help others; strong will and

Awards are arranged alphabetically below their administering organizations

determination to achieve their goals.

Funds Avail.: $2,000. **Duration:** Annual. **Number Awarded:** 1. **To Apply:** Applicants must download and complete the application form and submit it with their resume, an essay and a letter of recommendation. **Deadline:** May 31. **Contact:** All questions can be directed to scholarships@vietscholarships.org.

10386 ■ Le Hoang Nguyen College Scholarships (LHN) *(Undergraduate/Scholarship)*

Purpose: To provide financial assistance to outstanding graduating high school seniors attending college in the upcoming fall semester. **Focus:** General studies/Field of study not specified. **Qualif.:** Applicants must be Vietnamese descendants and residents of the state of Texas; must be graduating high school seniors with a GPA of 3.0 or higher; must be ranked in the top 10% of graduating high school class; must attend the first semester at an accredited college or university immediately following notification of the scholarship award. **Criteria:** Applicants are evaluated based on academic achievement and financial need.

Funds Avail.: $500. **Duration:** Annual. **Number Awarded:** 1. **To Apply:** Applicants must complete the online application form with uploaded resume, essay and recommendation; and must submit a transcript of records. **Deadline:** May 31. **Contact:** All questions can be directed to scholarships@vietscholarships.org.

10387 ■ The Thuy Nguyen Scholarships *(High School/Scholarship)*

Purpose: To provide financial assistance to high school senior students for furthering their education. **Focus:** General studies/Field of study not specified. **Qualif.:** Applicants must be graduating high school seniors from Houston or the surrounding area; must have a cumulative GPA of 3.5 or higher; must be descendants of at least one Vietnamese parent; and must have a family annual income of less than $50,000. **Criteria:** Applicants are evaluated based on financial need.

Funds Avail.: $2,000. **To Apply:** Applicants must complete the online application with resume, essay with a cover letter; must submit a transcript of records, recommendation and a copy of their parent's W-2 forms and a photo. **Contact:** All questions can be directed to scholarships@vietscholarships.org.

10388 ■ Vera Tran Memorial Scholarships *(Undergraduate/Scholarship)*

Purpose: To provide financial assistance to graduating high school seniors of Vietnamese descent wishing to pursue further education. **Focus:** General studies/Field of study not specified. **Qualif.:** Applicants must be of Vietnamese descent, graduating high school seniors from Houston or the surrounding area who are planning to pursue an education at an accredited four-year college or university. **Criteria:** Applicants are evaluated based on demonstrated dedication to academic excellence; passion for learning; compassion and desire to help others; pursuit of their dreams; and proven leadership.

Funds Avail.: $2,000. **Duration:** Annual. **Number Awarded:** 1. **To Apply:** Applicants must complete the online application and submit it with their resume; must also send one transcript and recommendation. **Deadline:** May 31. **Contact:** All questions can be directed to scholarships@vietscholarships.org.

10389 ■ Violin Society of America (VSA)
341 N Maitland Ave., Ste. 130
Maitland, FL 32751
Ph: (407)647-8839
Fax: (407)629-2502
E-mail: info@vsaweb.org
URL: www.vsaweb.org

10390 ■ Violin Society of America Scholarships *(Undergraduate/Scholarship)*

Purpose: To provide financial assistance for needy and deserving students of the art of violin and bow-making and restoration. **Focus:** Music. **Qualif.:** Applicant must be a U.S. citizen; a student who has satisfactorily completed at least one full year of study in the program and has shown serious effort, talent and future promise and has financial need. **Criteria:** Applicant will be evaluated by the administrator of the program and will be recommended to the VSA.

Funds Avail.: No specific amount. **Duration:** Annual. **To Apply:** Applicant must fill up completely the provided scholarship application form. Such should be returned (by paper copy) to the school administrator who will forward the form to the VSA. **Contact:** info@vsaweb.org.

10391 ■ Virgin Islands Bar Association
2155 King Cross St., Ste. 2
Christiansted, VI 00822
Ph: (340)778-7497
Fax: (340)773-5060
E-mail: vibasearch@vibar.org
URL: www.vibar.org
Facebook: www.facebook.com/Virgin-Islands-Bar-Association-201213679964576

10392 ■ Almeric Christian Memorial Scholarships *(Graduate/Scholarship)*

Purpose: To provide financial assistance to Virgin Island residents who desire to attend law school. **Focus:** Law. **Qualif.:** Applicants must be college graduate who has been accepted to or is attending a law school accredited by the American Bar Association; must be permanent resident of the United States Virgin Islands and plan to engage in the practice of law in the United States Virgin Islands within three years of graduation from law school. Applicants who are already attending the law school must have a 2.75 GPA and those who have not yet started a law study must have at least 3.25 GPA. **Criteria:** Selection is based on the application.

Funds Avail.: $15,000. **Duration:** Annual. **To Apply:** Applicants must submit a completed application form along with a letter of acceptance to a law school or most recent transcript if already enrolled in a law school; three letters of recommendation, one from a former college or law school professor and the rest from individuals that are not related to the applicant by blood or marriage; an essay on career objectives and how the schooling plan will prepare the applicant to attain these goals (typewritten); official copy of undergraduate college transcript (if entering the first year of law school) or a copy of latest official transcript (if presently attending law school); and a copy of Student Financial Aid form (FAF), or the equivalent thereof. **Deadline:** June 30.

10393 ■ Virginia Dental Hygienist's Association Foundation
c/o Marge Green, Treas.
1919 Old York Hampton Hwy.
Yorktown, VA 23692-4143

Awards are arranged alphabetically below their administering organizations

URL: vdhafoundation.org

10394 ■ Alice Hinchcliffe Williams, RDH, MS Graduate Scholarships *(Graduate/Scholarship)*

Purpose: To provide support and serve as the primary provider of lifelong learning for dental hygienists throughout Virginia. **Focus:** Dental hygiene. **Qualif.:** Applicants must be ADHA members who are Virginia residents enrolled in a graduate degree program in dental hygiene or any fields of study directly related to the professional roles of dental hygienist. They must demonstrate a minimum GPA of at least 3.0 on a 4.0 scale. **Criteria:** Applicants will be evaluated based on merit, fulfillment of the required criteria and approval of the written narrative.

Funds Avail.: $1,500. **Duration:** Annual. **To Apply:** Applicants must complete the application form and must submit a narrative. **Deadline:** February 1. **Remarks:** The scholarship is administered by ADHA Institute for Oral Health.

10395 ■ Virginia Historical Society (VHS)
428 North Blvd.
Richmond, VA 23220
Ph: (804)358-4901
URL: www.vahistorical.org
Facebook: www.facebook.com/Virginia-Historical-Society-29594152350

10396 ■ Betty Sams Christian Fellowships *(Doctorate/Fellowship)*

Purpose: To help scholars with their research and travel expenses. **Focus:** History, American. **Qualif.:** Applicants must be doctoral candidates. **Criteria:** Selection is based on applicants' scholarly qualifications, the merits of the proposals and the appropriateness of the topics as demonstrated by citation to specific sources in the collections.

Funds Avail.: $150/week for mileage to commuting researchers who live outside the area; $500/week for those who live farther away. **Duration:** three weeks. **To Apply:** Applicants must submit an original and three copies of a cover letter; a resume; two letters of recommendation (may be sent separately); and a description of the research project (no longer than two double-spaced pages). **Deadline:** January 30. **Contact:** Frances S. Pollard at fpollard@vahistorical.org; Phone: 804-342-9672; Fax: 804-355-2399.

10397 ■ Virginia Lakes and Watershed Association (VLWA)
c/o Shelly Frie
5700 Cleveland St., Ste. 101
Virginia Beach, VA 23462
Ph: (757)671-6222
URL: www.vlwa.org

10398 ■ Leo Bourassa Scholarships *(Undergraduate, Graduate/Scholarship)*

Purpose: To support and acknowledge students for academic and personal accomplishments in the field of water resources. **Focus:** Water resources. **Qualif.:** Applicants must be full-time undergraduate and full- or part-time graduate students enrolled in a curriculum related to water resources; must be students in good standing at any Virginia accredited college or university; must be residents of Virginia at the time of application and at the time of award. Undergraduate students must have successfully completed at least two semesters. **Criteria:** Recipients will be evaluated based on academic performance, educational plans and contribution to the field of water resources, and related extra-curricular activities.

Funds Avail.: Range from $1,000 to $3,000. **Duration:** Annual. **Number Awarded:** Up to 4. **To Apply:** Applicants must complete the application form; must attach a copy of current college transcripts, list of clubs and organizations related to water resources as proof of being a member, description of experience(s) to water resources and watershed management, no more than one-page explaining why you deserves to get the scholarship. **Deadline:** April 1. **Contact:** Shelly Frie at scholarship@vlwa.org, or call 757-671-6222.

10399 ■ Virginia Museum of Fine Arts (VMFA)
200 N Blvd.
Richmond, VA 23220-4007
Ph: (804)340-1400
E-mail: visitorservices@vmfa.museum
URL: vmfa.museum
Twitter: twitter.com/vmfa

10400 ■ Virginia Museum of Fine Arts Visual Arts Fellowships *(Graduate, Other, Undergraduate/Fellowship)*

Purpose: To support professional artists and art students who demonstrate exceptional creative ability in their chosen field. **Focus:** Art history; Visual arts. **Qualif.:** Applicants must be undergraduate or graduate students enrolled full-time in a degree-seeking program at an accredited university, college, or school of the arts. Professional applicants must not be enrolled in a degree-seeking program. College-bound high school seniors are also eligible to apply. All applicants must be legal residents of Virginia. **Criteria:** Awards will be given to those applicants of the highest artistic merit.

Funds Avail.: $4,000 (undergraduates); $6,000 (graduates); $8,000 (professionals). **Duration:** Annual. **To Apply:** Applicants must complete the required fields on the application form. Crafts, Drawing, Painting, Photography and Sculpture applicants must submit a work sample consists of eight digital images, at least six must represent individual works and two images for details. Professional applicants must submit all works that have been completed in the past three years. Students must submit at least four sample works. Submit images on a PC-formatted CD-R, labeled with the applicant's name. Format digital images as JPEGs, no larger than 2 MB and 1000 pixels on the longest side. Mixed Media applicants must submit six images representing individual works plus two images for details. Film/Video applicants must submit a 15-minute (maximum) DVD sample of three works. These should be on a PC-formatted DVD, labeled with applicant's name and must include a menu on a DVD with links to each work and running times. Format submissions as files that are compatible with both QuickTime and RealPlayer. Art History applicants must submit two hard copies of the three research papers or published articles. Applicants are also required to submit a current resume, one-page artistic statement for professionals and transcript of records for students. SASE envelope and confirmation postcard are optional. **Deadline:** November 4. **Remarks:** Established in 1940.

Awards are arranged alphabetically below their administering organizations

10401 ■ Virginia Society of Certified Public Accountants (VSCPA)
4309 Cox Rd.
Glen Allen, VA 23060
Fax: (804)270-5344
Free: 800-733-8272
E-mail: vscpa@vscpa.com
URL: www.vscpa.com/Content/vscpa.aspx
Facebook: www.facebook.com/VSCPA
LinkedIn: www.linkedin.com/company/virginia-society-of-cpas

10402 ■ H. Burton Bates Jr. Scholarships (Graduate, Undergraduate/Scholarship)

Purpose: To provide financial support to students pursuing a degree in accounting. **Focus:** Accounting. **Qualif.:** Applicants must be U.S. citizens; must be juniors or seniors accounting major currently enrolled full time at an accredited Virginia college/university, or have earned an undergraduate degree from an accredited Virginia college/university and enrolled at least part-time (as defined by the institution) during the term of application and throughout the term of scholarship in coursework required to qualify to take the Uniform CPA Examination; must be in good academic standing during the term of application and remain in good academic standing throughout the term of the scholarship. **Criteria:** Selection is based on the application materials submitted.

Funds Avail.: $2,000. **Duration:** Annual. **To Apply:** Applicants must submit a completed application together with a faculty letter of recommendation (may be mailed separately); an essay (500-word maximum); a current resume; and official transcript reflecting GPA (may be mailed separately).

10403 ■ Thomas M. Berry Jr. Scholarships (Graduate, Undergraduate/Scholarship)

Purpose: To provide financial support to students pursuing a degree in accounting. **Focus:** Accounting. **Qualif.:** Applicants must be U.S. citizens; must be currently enrolled in an accredited Virginia college/university undergraduate or graduate program with the intent to pursue a degree in accounting; must have completed at least three hours of accounting and be currently registered for at least three more accounting credit hours (supporting documentation required). **Criteria:** Selection is based on demonstrated academic excellence, financial need and exemplary leadership skills.

Funds Avail.: $2,500 each. **Duration:** Annual. **Number Awarded:** 2. **To Apply:** Applicants must submit a completed application form along with the following: a faculty letter of recommendation (may be mailed separately); leadership essay (500-word maximum); a current resume; and official transcript reflecting GPA (may be mailed separately).

10404 ■ Cocke, Szpanka and Taylor Scholarships (Undergraduate/Scholarship)

Purpose: To financially support undergraduate accounting students. **Focus:** Accounting. **Qualif.:** Applicants must be U.S. citizens; must be juniors or seniors accounting major at the University of Virginia or George Mason University with the intent to take the CPA Exam; from the Washington, D.C. metro area; must demonstrate a minimum overall and accounting GPA of 3.0. **Criteria:** Selection is based on academic excellence, financial need and plans to pursue a career in public accounting.

Funds Avail.: $2,500. **To Apply:** Applicants must submit a completed application together with a faculty letter of recommendation (may be mailed separately); an essay (500-word maximum); a current resume; and official transcript reflecting GPA (may be mailed separately).

10405 ■ Dixon Hughes Goodman Scholarships (Undergraduate, Graduate/Scholarship)

Purpose: To financially support undergraduate accounting students. **Focus:** Accounting. **Qualif.:** Applicants must be U.S. citizens; must be juniors or seniors accounting major currently enrolled at an accredited Virginia college/university with the intent to take the CPA exam; must demonstrate a minimum overall and accounting GPA of 3.3. **Criteria:** Selection is based on academic excellence, financial need and plans to pursue a career in public accounting.

Funds Avail.: $2,000 each. **Duration:** Annual. **Number Awarded:** 2. **To Apply:** Applicants must submit a completed application together with a faculty letter of recommendation (may be mailed separately); an essay (500-word maximum); a current resume; and official transcript reflecting GPA (may be mailed separately).

10406 ■ Virginia Tech Doctoral Scholarship (Doctorate/Scholarship)

Purpose: To provide financial support to students pursuing a doctoral degree in accounting. **Focus:** Accounting. **Qualif.:** Applicants must be U.S. citizens; must be accepted or currently enrolled in the doctoral accounting program at Virginia Tech; must demonstrate a minimum overall and accounting GPA of 3.0 or higher; must be full-time doctoral students at Virginia Tech. **Criteria:** Selection is based on the application materials submitted.

Funds Avail.: Up to $2,500. **Duration:** Annual. **To Apply:** Applicants must contact Tracey Zink to be considered for the scholarship. **Contact:** Molly Wash; Email: mwash@vscpa.com.

10407 ■ VSCPA Educational Foundation Graduate Scholarships (Graduate/Scholarship)

Purpose: To financially support graduate accounting students. **Focus:** Accounting. **Qualif.:** Applicants must be U.S. citizens; must be accepted or currently enrolled in a graduate accounting program at an accredited Virginia college/university; and must demonstrate a minimum overall and accounting undergraduate GPA of 3.0 or higher. **Criteria:** Selection is based on demonstrated academic excellence and financial need.

Funds Avail.: Up to $1,000. **Duration:** Annual. **To Apply:** Applicants must submit a completed application together with the following: a faculty letter of recommendation (may be mailed separately); an essay (500-word maximum); a current resume; and official transcript reflecting GPA (may be mailed separately).

10408 ■ VSCPA Educational Foundation Minority Scholarships (Graduate, Undergraduate/Scholarship)

Purpose: To financially support minority accounting students. **Focus:** Accounting. **Qualif.:** Applicants must be U.S. citizens; must be members of one of the race/ethnic groups (American Indian or Alaskan Native, Asian, Black or African American, Hispanic or Latino, Native Hawaiian or other Pacific Islander); must be currently enrolled in an accredited Virginia college/university undergraduate or graduate program with the intent to pursue a bachelor's degree in accounting; must have completed at least three hours of accounting and be currently registered for at least three more accounting credit hours (supporting documentation required); must demonstrate a minimum overall and accounting GPA of 3.0. **Criteria:** Selection is based on demonstrated academic excellence and financial need.

Funds Avail.: Up to $1,000. **Duration:** Annual. **To Apply:** Applicants must submit a completed application including the following: ethnicity section together with a faculty letter of recommendation (may be mailed separately); an essay (500-word maximum); current resume; and an official transcript reflecting GPA (may be mailed separately). **Contact:** Submit finalized materials to: VSCPA Educational Foundation, Inc. PO Box 4620 Glen Allen, VA 23058-4620.

10409 ■ VSCPA Educational Foundation Undergraduate Scholarships *(Undergraduate/Scholarship)*

Purpose: To financially support undergraduate accounting students. **Focus:** Accounting. **Qualif.:** Applicant must be a U.S. citizen; currently enrolled in an accredited Virginia college/university undergraduate program with the intent to pursue a bachelor's degree in accounting; must have completed at least three hours of accounting and be currently registered for at least three more accounting credit hours (supporting documentation required); and must demonstrate a minimum overall and accounting GPA of 3.0. **Criteria:** Selection is based on demonstrated academic excellence and financial need.

Funds Avail.: Up to $1,000. **Duration:** Annual. **To Apply:** Applicant must submit a completed application together with a faculty letter of recommendation (may be mailed separately); an essay (500-word maximum); current resume; and official transcript reflecting GPA (may be mailed separately).

10410 ■ VSCPA PhD Accounting Scholarships *(Doctorate, Graduate/Scholarship)*

Purpose: To financially support graduate students pursuing a PhD in accounting. **Focus:** Accounting. **Qualif.:** Applicants must be U.S. citizens; must be accepted or currently enrolled in a doctoral accounting program at an accredited Virginia college/university; must demonstrate a minimum overall and accounting GPA of 3.0 or higher; and must be full-time doctoral students. **Criteria:** Selection is based on demonstrated academic excellence and financial need.

Funds Avail.: Up to $5,000. **Duration:** Annual. **To Apply:** Applicants must submit a completed application along with a faculty letter of recommendation (may be mailed separately); an essay (500-word maximum); a current resume; and official undergraduate and graduate (if applicable) transcripts to date (may be mailed separately).

10411 ■ Yount, Hyde & Barbour Scholarships *(Undergraduate/Scholarship)*

Purpose: To provide financial support to students pursuing a degree in accounting. **Focus:** Accounting. **Qualif.:** Applicants must be U.S. citizens; must be juniors or seniors accounting major currently enrolled at an accredited Virginia college/university with the intent of taking the CPA exam; and must demonstrate a minimum overall and accounting GPA of 3.0. **Criteria:** Selection is based on academic excellence and financial need, and intent to pursue a career in public accounting.

Funds Avail.: $2,500. **Duration:** Annual. **To Apply:** Applicants must submit a completed application form together with the following: a faculty letter of recommendation (may be mailed separately); an essay (500-word maximum); a current resume; and official transcript reflecting GPA (may be mailed separately).

10412 ■ Vista Health Solutions
31 Park Ave.
Suffern, NY 10901
Ph: (845)753-2320
Fax: (845)510-1940
Free: 888-215-4045
E-mail: info@nyhealthinsurer.com
URL: www.nyhealthinsurer.com

10413 ■ Vista Health Solutions' Scholarships *(Undergraduate/Scholarship)*

Purpose: To financially support students who will be attending a public or private university. **Focus:** General studies/Field of study not specified. **Qualif.:** Applicants must be students in college or entering college; must be working towards an undergraduate degree. **Criteria:** Selection will be based on the committee's criteria.

Funds Avail.: $500. **To Apply:** Applicants must submit a 1,000 to 1,500 words essay on how they will control and take charge of their health during college; they should include their name, current school attended, current grade level, and GPA at the top of their essay. **Deadline:** August 1.

10414 ■ John D. Voelker Foundation
PO Box 15222
Lansing, MI 48901-5222
Ph: (616)897-1304
URL: www.voelkerfdn.org

10415 ■ John D. Voelker Foundation Native American Scholarships *(Undergraduate/Scholarship)*

Purpose: To assist Native American students to pursue the dream of a legal education. **Focus:** Law; Paralegal studies. **Qualif.:** Applicants must have a sincere interest in studying law and using a legal education to benefit Native American people; must be enrolled member of a federal recognized Michigan or Wisconsin tribe; must have the academic potential to succeed in school, as evidenced by past academic success or admission to an accredited law school; must have a greatest financial need; must be willing to provide an annual report to the Foundation on the progress of their studies for each academic year in which a grant is received. **Criteria:** Selection will be based on the committee's criteria.

Funds Avail.: $4,000. **Duration:** Annual. **To Apply:** Applicants must submit a simple letter addressing each of the eligibility criteria applicable to the applicants. Letters of reference from teachers or employers, transcripts and documentation confirming tribal membership are encouraged.

10416 ■ Voluntary Protection Programs Participants' Association (VPPPA)
7600E Leesburg Pke., Ste. 100
Falls Church, VA 22043-2004
Ph: (703)761-1146

Awards are arranged alphabetically below their administering organizations

Fax: (703)761-1148
URL: www.vpppa.org
Facebook: www.facebook.com/VPPPA
LinkedIn: www.linkedin.com/company/vpppa-inc-
Twitter: twitter.com/VPPPA

10417 ■ VPPPA Stephen Brown Scholarships
(Graduate, Undergraduate/Scholarship)

Purpose: To advance the field of occupational safety and health, as well as to support the members and their families in acquiring education relevant to the said field. **Focus:** Environmental conservation; Occupational safety and health. **Qualif.:** Applicants must be students pursuing a degree (undergraduate or graduate) in either trades or the environmental, safety and health areas; must be enrolled in or enrolling in a vocational, college or university; must have at least a 2.5 GPA on a scale of 4.0. **Criteria:** Recipients are chosen on the basis of demonstrated occupational safety, health and/or environmental outreach efforts in their schools, communities and/or workplace, leadership skills, extracurricular activities, involvement in professional organizations, communication skills and other awards and honors earned at educational institutions or at their place of employment.

Funds Avail.: No specific amount. **Duration:** Annual. **To Apply:** Applicants must submit a completed application form available at the website; a typewritten biography of at least 300 words describing interests and accomplishments; copy of current transcript; reference letters from the VPPPA site employee and from high school teacher, university's department head, professor or supervisor at current job. Forward all requirements to: VPPPA, Inc., Attn: Awards Committee. **Deadline:** June 3. **Remarks:** Established in 2005. **Contact:** Scholarship Committee at Awards@vpppa.org.

10418 ■ VPPPA William Sullivan Scholarships
(Graduate, Undergraduate/Scholarship)

Purpose: To recognize and support employee at a VPPPA full member site who has made significant contributions to the VPP program at his or her site. **Focus:** Environmental conservation; Occupational safety and health. **Qualif.:** Applicants must be employees enrolled in or enrolling in a vocational school, college or university; must be pursuing a degree (undergraduate or graduate) in the environmental, safety and health areas (either part-time or full-time); must have at least a 2.5 GPA on a scale of 4.0. **Criteria:** Recipients are chosen on the basis of demonstrated occupational safety, health and/or environmental outreach efforts in their schools, communities and/or workplace, leadership skills, extracurricular activities, involvement in professional organizations, communication skills and other awards and honors earned at educational institutions or at their place of employment.

Funds Avail.: No specific amount. **Duration:** Annual. **To Apply:** Applicants must submit completed application form available at the website; a typewritten biography of at least 300 words describing interests and accomplishments or current resume; copy of current transcript; reference letters from the VPPPA site employee and from a high school teacher, university's department head, professor or supervisor at current job. Forward all requirements to: VPPPA, Inc., Attn: Awards Committee. **Deadline:** June 3. **Remarks:** Established in 2007. **Contact:** Scholarship Committee at Awards@vpppa.org.

10419 ■ VPPPA June Brothers Scholarships *(Graduate, Undergraduate/Scholarship)*

Purpose: To advance the field of occupational safety and health, as well as to support the members and their families in acquiring education relevant to the said field. **Focus:** Environmental conservation; Occupational safety and health. **Qualif.:** Applicants must be students pursuing a degree (undergraduate or graduate) in the environmental, safety and health areas (either part-time or full-time); must have at least a 2.5 GPA on a scale of 4.0. **Criteria:** Recipients are chosen on the basis of demonstrated occupational safety, health and/or environmental outreach efforts in their schools, communities and/or workplace, leadership skills, extracurricular activities, involvement in professional organizations, communication skills and other awards and honors earned at educational institutions or at their place of employment.

Funds Avail.: No specific amount. **Duration:** Annual. **To Apply:** Applicants must submit completed application form available in the website; a typewritten biography of at least 300 words describing interests and accomplishments or current resume; copy of current transcript; reference letters from the VPPPA site employee and from a high school teacher, university's department head, professor or supervisor at current job. Forward all requirements to: VPPPA, Inc., Attn: Awards Committee. **Deadline:** June 3. **Remarks:** Established in 2005. **Contact:** Scholarship Committee at Awards@vpppa.org.

10420 ■ W. Garfield Weston Foundation
22 St. Clair Ave. E Ste. 2001
Toronto, ON, Canada M4T 2S3
URL: www.westonfoundation.org

10421 ■ W. Garfield Weston Awards for Northern Research *(Graduate, Postdoctorate/Fellowship)*

Purpose: To support significant research and studies about scientific issues facing the North. **Focus:** Canadian studies. **Qualif.:** Applicants must be Canadian students at the graduate and postdoctoral levels. **Criteria:** Selection will be on competitive basis.

Funds Avail.: No specific amount. **To Apply:** Applicants may visit the website or contact the Foundation for the application process and other required materials. **Remarks:** The awards are also administered by the Association of Canadian Universities for Northern Science and the Wildlife Conservation Society Canada.

10422 ■ Weston Brain Institute International Fellowships in Neuroscience Program *(Graduate/Fellowship)*

Purpose: To provide funding to students who wish to advance their research on neurodegenerative disease of aging abroad in world-renowned labs and research universities. **Focus:** Neuroscience. **Qualif.:** Applicants must be registered full-time senior Ph.D. graduate students at University of Toronto; must be Canadian citizens or permanent residents in Canada. **Criteria:** Selection will be based on applicants' distinguished record of academic achievement, as well as the ability to demonstrate their promise as top-tier researchers and future leaders of their respective field.

Funds Avail.: 60,000 Canadian Dollars per year. **Number Awarded:** 3. **To Apply:** Applicants must visit the website for the online application process. **Deadline:** June 15.

Awards are arranged alphabetically below their administering organizations

Remarks: The fellowships are administered through the Weston Brain Institute. **Contact:** Rachel Reeve at rachel.reeve@weston.ca.

10423 ■ Weston Brain Institute Rapid Response Program *(Postdoctorate, Advanced Professional, Professional development/Grant)*

Purpose: To catalyze and jumpstart the development of safe and effective treatments for neurodegenerative diseases of aging. **Focus:** Neuroscience. **Qualif.:** Applicants must be researchers or postdoctoral fellows from institutions that are Canada Revenue Agency qualified donees in Canada. **Criteria:** Selection will be based on the letters of intent, research proposals and other criteria of the committee.

Funds Avail.: Up to 150,000 Canadian Dollars. **Duration:** 12-18 months. **To Apply:** Applicants must submit a letter of intent, and they will receive feedback from the scientific review committee. Applicants with high potential projects will be invited to submit a Proposal; instructions will be forwarded along with the invitation in August of the current year. **Deadline:** June 16 (letter of intent); September 15 (proposal). **Remarks:** The grants are administered through the Weston Brain Institute.

10424 ■ Wal-Mart Foundation, Inc.
702 SW 8th St.
Bentonville, AR 72716-0555
Free: 800-530-9925
URL: giving.walmart.com/foundation

10425 ■ Walmart Associate Scholarships
(Undergraduate/Scholarship)

Purpose: To provide educational grants to deserving students who want to pursue their studies. **Focus:** General studies/Field of study not specified. **Qualif.:** Applicants must: be citizens or permanent legal residents of the United States; be employed part-time or full-time with any division of Walmart for at least six consecutive months prior to the appropriate application due date; have graduated high school/ home school or obtained a GED; be applying or graduating high school who intends to enroll in a college or university upon graduation; and have financial need and be able to demonstrate the need with required documents. **Criteria:** Awards are given based on merit and need.

Funds Avail.: No specific amount. **To Apply:** Applicants must submit a completed scholarship application available online. **Deadline:** March 1.

10426 ■ Warner Norcross and Judd L.L.P. (WNJ)
900 5th 3rd Ctr.
111 Lyon St. NW
Grand Rapids, MI 49503-2487
Ph: (616)752-2000
Fax: (616)752-2500
Free: 866-533-3018
E-mail: contactwnj@wnj.com
URL: www.wnj.com

10427 ■ Warner Norcross & Judd Minority Scholarships *(Undergraduate/Scholarship)*

Purpose: To provide encouragement and financial assistance to students of racial and ethnic minority heritage pursuing a career in law. **Focus:** Law; Paralegal studies.

Qualif.: Candidates for the law school scholarship must be accepted to or attending a Michigan law school or be Michigan residents attending an accredited law school in the United States. Candidates for the paralegal and secretarial scholarships must be Michigan residents majoring in paralegal or legal secretarial studies in an accredited program. **Criteria:** Applicants will be selected based on academic standing and financial need.

Funds Avail.: $5,000 to law school students; $2,000 to paralegals/legal assistant students;$1,000 to legal secretarial students. **Duration:** Annual. **To Apply:** Applicants must submit: completed application forms; a statement of goals and aspirations related to their studies in the legal profession, and must indicate the reason why they choose the legal profession/field as their area of study; and two letters of reference. **Deadline:** April 1. **Contact:** Ruth Bishop, Grand Rapids Community Foundation, at rbishop@grfoundation.org, or to Rodney Martin, Warner Norcross & Judd LLP, at rmartin@wnj.com.

10428 ■ Washburn University School of Law
1700 SW College Ave.
Topeka, KS 66621
Ph: (785)670-1060
E-mail: admissions@washburnlaw.edu
URL: washburnlaw.edu

10429 ■ Judge Delmas C. Hill Scholarships
(Undergraduate/Scholarship)

Purpose: To assist Washburn University students in their education. **Focus:** Law. **Qualif.:** Applicants to Washburn University School of Law for each fall semester whose credentials qualify for the top 10% of the class are invited to apply for the scholarship. Moreover, eligibility requirements to maintain the award after the first year are: maintain a 3.0 grade-point average; no sanctions under the School of Law Honor Code; and, enrolled full-time at the School of Law. **Criteria:** Selection will be based on the aforesaid qualifications and other criteria.

Funds Avail.: Total of $45,000 ($15,000 per year). **Duration:** Annual; Up to 3 years. **Number Awarded:** 1. **To Apply:** Applicants must submit a statement showing: the reason for interest in the law as a profession; public and community service activities; leadership activities; and potential for leadership.

10430 ■ Koch Scholars Program *(Undergraduate/Scholarship)*

Purpose: To assist Washburn University students in their education. **Focus:** Law. **Qualif.:** Applicants to Washburn University School of Law for each fall semester whose credentials qualify for the top 10% of the class are invited to apply for the award. Moreover, eligibility requirements to maintain the award after the first year are: maintain a 3.0 grade-point average; no sanctions under the School of Law Honor Code, and, enrolled full-time at the School of Law. **Criteria:** The School of Law's Financial Aid Committee reviews the applications and selects no more that five finalists. The selection of the Koch Scholar is made by the Financial Aid Committee after interviewing the finalists. The selection is made prior to the admission seat deposit deadline.

Funds Avail.: Total of $45,000 ($15,000 per year). **Duration:** Annual; Up to 3 years. **To Apply:** Applicants must submit a statement showing: the reason for interest in the

Awards are arranged alphabetically below their administering organizations

law as a profession; public and community service activities; and, leadership activities and potential for leadership. **Remarks:** Established in 1994.

10431 ■ **Shamberg Scholarships** *(Undergraduate/ Scholarship)*

Purpose: To assist Washburn University students in their education. **Focus:** Law. **Qualif.:** Applicants must be entering students at Washburn Law. **Criteria:** Selection will be based on academic achievements and leadership potential.

Funds Avail.: Total of $45,000 ($15,000 per year). **Duration:** Annual; Up to 3 years. **Number Awarded:** 3. **To Apply:** Admitted students who qualify will be automatically considered.

10432 ■ **Washburn University School of Law Business and Transactional Law Center Scholarships** *(Undergraduate/Scholarship)*

Purpose: To assist Washburn University law students in their education. **Focus:** Law. **Qualif.:** Applicants must be admitted to Washburn Law and have an interest in business law or transactional law. **Criteria:** Recipients will be selected based on the aforesaid qualifications and other criteria.

Funds Avail.: Maximum of $28,000. **Duration:** Annual; Up to 3 years. **To Apply:** To be considered for the scholarship, applicants must indicate their interest on the Washburn Law application. They will be automatically considered for the award upon admission and will be notified within two weeks of admission by letter if selected for the award. **Contact:** Washburn University School of Law Business and Transactional Law Center, 1700 SW College Ave., Topeka, Kansas 66621; phone: 785-670-1676; e-mail: transactional@washburnlaw.edu.

10433 ■ **Washburn University School of Law Child and Family Advocacy Fellowships** *(Undergraduate/ Fellowship)*

Purpose: To assist Washburn University students in their education. **Focus:** Law. **Qualif.:** Applicants must be entering Washburn law students who are also intending to pursue careers in child and family advocacy. **Criteria:** Selection will be based on the aforesaid qualifications and other criteria.

Funds Avail.: Maximum of $27,000, plus stipend of $3,000 for summer externship. **Duration:** Annual; Up to 3 years. **To Apply:** To be considered for the scholarship, applicants must indicate their interest on the Washburn Law application. They will be automatically considered for the award upon admission and will be notified within two weeks of admission by letter if selected for the award. **Contact:** Washburn University School of Law Children and Family Law Center, 1700 SW College Ave., Topeka, Kansas 66621; phone: 785-670-1676; e-mail: children@washburnlaw.edu.

10434 ■ **J.L. Weigand, Jr. Legal Education Trust Scholarships** *(Undergraduate/Scholarship)*

Purpose: To promote excellence in legal education and encourage the most scholastically qualified students who are long-term Kansas residents to remain in or return to Kansas to practice law. **Focus:** Law. **Qualif.:** Applicants must: be admitted full-time to Washburn Law; be in the top ten percent of the class; and, have been a legal residents of Kansas for at least ten years prior to their admission to law school. **Criteria:** Selection will be based on merit.

Funds Avail.: No specific amount. **Duration:** Annual. **To Apply:** Applicants must apply through the Weigand website. **Deadline:** March 1. **Contact:** Yolanda Ingram, Admissions Office, at the above address.

10435 ■ **Washington Association of School Business Officials (WASBO)**
284 Lee St. SW, Ste. 132
Tumwater, WA 98501
Ph: (360)528-2025
Fax: (360)528-2028
Free: 800-524-4706
E-mail: admin@wasbo.org
URL: www.wasbo.org
Facebook: www.facebook.com/WASBO.Organization
LinkedIn: www.linkedin.com/company/washington
-association-of-school-business-officials

10436 ■ **DA Davidson Presidential Scholarships** *(Undergraduate/Scholarship)*

Purpose: To support WASBO members, to enable them to continue their higher education in school business courses offered by colleges or universities. **Focus:** Business. **Qualif.:** Applicants must be WASBO members. **Criteria:** Selection will be based on the committee's criteria.

Funds Avail.: $500. **Duration:** Annual. **Number Awarded:** 2. **To Apply:** Interested applicant may contact the Washington Association of School Business Officials for the application process and other information. **Deadline:** September 15. **Contact:** Call Ruth at (360) 528-2025 or e-mail her at ruth@wasbo.org.

10437 ■ **Washington City/County Management Association (WCMA)**
2601 4th Ave., Ste. 800
Seattle, WA 98121
Ph: (206)625-1300
URL: www.wccma.org

10438 ■ **Washington City/County Management Association Scholarships** *(Graduate/Scholarship)*

Purpose: To provide financial assistance to students who have chosen to pursue a graduate degree in public administration and who have a desire to work in city or county management. **Focus:** Public administration. **Qualif.:** Applicants must be residing in Washington; must have bachelor's degree; must enrolled in or accepted for admission to a graduate school in Washington, Oregon, Idaho, or on-line graduate programs are acceptable with Washington State residency requirement; and must demonstrate serious commitment to pursue a career in local government. **Criteria:** Preference will be given to graduate students pursuing a degree in public administration, public affairs, or public policy.

Funds Avail.: $5,000. **Duration:** Annual; one academic year. **To Apply:** Applicants must submit a completed application form along with one official copy of undergraduate transcripts; one official copy of graduate transcripts (if applicable); two letters of reference, one from a previous or current undergraduate or graduate academic instructor and the other from a previous or current work supervisor; and a letter of application (no more than two pages). An initial unofficial copy of transcripts is sufficient to meet the deadline but must be followed by an official copy of them. **Deadline:** May 6.

10439 ■ The Washington Group (TWG)
Washington, DC
Facebook: www.facebook.com/TheWashingtonGroup

10440 ■ Alberta Ukrainian Centennial Commemorative Scholarships *(Graduate/Scholarship)*

Purpose: To encourage active participation in the Ukrainian community. **Focus:** General studies/Field of study not specified. **Qualif.:** Applicants must be graduate students intending to study in Alberta or Canadian graduate students from Alberta intending to study in Ukraine. **Criteria:** Recipients are chosen by a selection committee appointed by the Presidents of the universities in Alberta. Applicants are judged on previous academic accomplishments, program of study, appraiser's evaluations, answers to the essay question, and general impressions from the application form.

Funds Avail.: No specific amount. **Duration:** Annual. **Number Awarded:** 2. **To Apply:** Interested applicants may contact The Washington Group for the application process and other requirements. **Deadline:** February 1. **Contact:** Alberta Heritage Scholarship Fund at 9940 106th Street, Edmonton, Alberta, T5K 2V1, Canada; 1403-427-5538; 1403-422-4516. Website: alis.alberta.ca/scholarships.

10441 ■ Canada-Ukraine Parliamentary Program Internship Scholarships (CUPP) *(Undergraduate/Scholarship, Internship)*

Purpose: To encourage active participation in the Ukrainian community. **Focus:** General studies/Field of study not specified. **Qualif.:** Applicants must be Ukrainian citizens seeking scholarships for a three-month internship for Ukrainian undergraduates with a Member of Parliament of the House of Commons in Ottawa, Canada. **Criteria:** Recipients are selected based on academic records. Proficiency in English or French as well as in Ukrainian is a requirement.

Funds Avail.: No specific amount. **Duration:** Annual; every three months. **To Apply:** Interested applicants may contact The Washington Group for the application process and other requirements. **Remarks:** The internship is run by the Chair of Ukrainian Studies Foundation. **Contact:** Ukrainian Studies Foundation, 620 Spadina Avenue, Toronto, Ontario, Canada M5S 2H4; Fax: 416-234-9114; Email: cup@infoukes.com.

10442 ■ Chopivsky Fellowships *(Graduate/Fellowship)*

Purpose: To encourage active participation in the Ukrainian community. **Focus:** Economics; Environmental science; Forestry. **Qualif.:** Applicants must be Ukrainian citizens and must be first admitted to the appropriate faculties at Yale; must be in a graduate degree program leading to a master's degree at the Yale School of Management at the Yale School of Forestry and Environmental Studies, and in the Departments of International Relations, International Economics and Developmental Studies. **Criteria:** Recipients are selected based on academic records.

Funds Avail.: No specific amount. **To Apply:** Interested applicants may contact The Washington Group for the application process and other requirements. **Deadline:** January 1. **Contact:** Chopivsky Fellowships, Yale-Ukraine Initiative Committee, Russian and East European Studies, PO Box 208206, New Haven, CT 06520-8606; Phone: 203-432-3423; Fax: 203-432-5963; Email: rees@yale.edu.

10443 ■ Eugene and Elinor Kotur Scholarship Trust Fund *(Undergraduate, Graduate/Scholarship)*

Purpose: To encourage active participation in the Ukrainian community. **Focus:** General studies/Field of study not specified. **Qualif.:** Applicants must be students enrolled in the sophomore or higher year or graduate school of about thirty leading colleges and universities in the USA listed on the application form; must be member of the Ukrainian Fraternal Association for two years. **Criteria:** Selection will be based on demonstrated financial need.

Funds Avail.: $1,000. **Duration:** Annual. **To Apply:** Interested applicants may contact either The Washington Group or the Ukrainian Fraternal Association Scholarship Program for the application process and other information. **Contact:** Ukrainian Fraternal Association Scholarship Program at PO Box 350, Scranton, PA 18501-0350; Phone: 717-342-0937.

10444 ■ The Ivan Shandor Memorial Ukrainian American Bar Association Scholarships *(Graduate, Master's/Scholarship)*

Purpose: To encourage active participation in the Ukrainian community. **Focus:** Law. **Qualif.:** Applicants must be enrolled in the Masters of Law degree program at Georgetown University Law center; must be residents or resided in Ukraine; must be fluent in Ukrainian language; and must demonstrate a desire to promote democracy and uphold the rule of law in Ukraine. **Criteria:** Recipients are selected based on academic records.

Funds Avail.: No specific amount. **Duration:** Annual. **To Apply:** Applicants may contact The Washington Group to obtain an application and other information. **Remarks:** Established by Lidia Shandor in memory of her husband, Ivan Shandor, Georgetown University Law alumnus 1973. **Contact:** Scholarships for International Students, Georgetown University Law Center, Office of development, 600 New Jersey Avenue, N.W., Washington, DC 20001; 202-662-9000.

10445 ■ Marusia Yaworska Entrance Scholarships *(Graduate/Scholarship)*

Purpose: To encourage active participation in the Ukrainian community. **Focus:** Music. **Qualif.:** Applicants must be graduate level students from Ukraine or Canada who are willing to study anywhere in the world, and enrolled in the field of music. **Criteria:** Recipients are selected based on academic records.

Funds Avail.: 5,000 Canadian Dollars each. **Duration:** Annual. **Number Awarded:** 2. **To Apply:** Interested applicants may contact The Washington Group for the application process and other requirements. **Deadline:** March 31. **Contact:** Department of Music, Faculty of Arts, University of Ottawa, 50 University Private, Ottawa, Ontario, K1N 6N5, Canada.

10446 ■ Washington Hospital Healthcare System (WHHS)
2000 Mowry Ave.
Fremont, CA 94538-1716
Ph: (510)797-1111
E-mail: feedback@whhs.com
URL: www.whhs.com
Twitter: www.twitter.com/Geritrex

Awards are arranged alphabetically below their administering organizations

10447 ■ Service League Volunteer Scholarships
(Undergraduate/Scholarship)

Purpose: To support Washington Hospital District students who are pursuing studies in a health-related field. **Focus:** Health care services. **Qualif.:** Applicants must be graduating high school seniors or college students who are pursuing studies in a health-related field; must have 2.50 GPA or higher; must be U.S. citizens and residents of Washington Hospital District; must have been accepted by an accredited school, college or university offering a bachelor or higher degree program in a health-related field; must be full-time students and must have completed 100 hours of volunteer service or employment in a health-related field. **Criteria:** Recipients are selected based on academic performance. **Funds Avail.:** $1,000 (per year for four years). **Duration:** Annual. **Number Awarded:** 2. **To Apply:** Applicants must submit: completed application form; current letters of recommendation from a Director of Volunteer Services, employer, counselor, advisor or teacher; high school or college transcript and proof of citizenship. **Deadline:** April 1. **Contact:** Washington Hospital Service League Scholarship Committee; Phone: 510-791-3465.

10448 ■ WHHS Medical Staff Scholarships
(Undergraduate/Scholarship)

Purpose: To support students residing in the District who are pursuing careers in the health sciences field. **Focus:** Health sciences. **Qualif.:** Applicants must be students residing within the Washington Township Health Care District who are pursuing careers in the health sciences field; must be students enrolled in the nursing program at San Jose State University or Ohlone College. **Criteria:** Recipients are selected based on academic performance and demonstrated interest in a health-related field. **Funds Avail.:** Amount varies. **Duration:** Annual. **Number Awarded:** 7. **To Apply:** Applicants must submit a completed application form. **Deadline:** April 1. **Contact:** Medical Staff office at 510-791-3446.

10449 ■ Washington Indian Gaming Association (WIGA)
1110 Capitol Way S, Ste. 404
Olympia, WA 98501
Ph: (360)352-3248
Fax: (360)352-4819
URL: www.washingtonindiangaming.org

10450 ■ WIGA Scholarships *(Postgraduate, Other, Undergraduate/Scholarship)*

Purpose: To promote tribal economic development and self-sufficiency. **Focus:** General studies/Field of study not specified. **Qualif.:** Applicants must be Native American/Alaska Native students who are enrolled members of a Washington tribe or Washington state residents; or Native American students from Washington attending college in another state, as well as Native American students from outside of Washington who attend college in Washington. They must be pursuing a degree at a community/technical college, four-year college, post-graduate or professional school. **Criteria:** Selection shall be based on the aforementioned qualifications and compliance with the application details. **Funds Avail.:** Amount varies. **Duration:** Annual. **Number Awarded:** Varies. **To Apply:** Applicants may visit the website to verify the application process and other pieces of information. **Deadline:** March 31. **Contact:** Rebecca Kaldor, Deputy Director, at 360-352-3248 or email at rebeccakaldor@reachone.com.

10451 ■ Washington Society of Certified Public Accountants (WSCPA)
902 140th Ave. NE
Bellevue, WA 98005-3480
Ph: (425)644-4800
Fax: (425)562-8853
Free: 800-272-8273
E-mail: memberservices@wscpa.org
URL: www.wscpa.org/home?Site=WSCPA
Facebook: www.facebook.com/WashingtonCPAs

10452 ■ Washington CPA Foundation Scholarships
(Undergraduate/Scholarship)

Purpose: To support accounting students. **Focus:** Accounting. **Qualif.:** Applicants must: have junior status or higher in fall of the current year; have GPA minimum of 3.0 (on a 4.0 scale) in accounting courses and overall; be accepted into an accounting program at a 4-year college or university accredited in Washington state; be involved in on-campus, off-campus or community activities; and, attend school in Washington state. **Criteria:** Selection shall be based on the aforementioned qualifications and compliance with the application details. **Funds Avail.:** $3,000 each. **Duration:** Annual. **Number Awarded:** Varies. **To Apply:** Applicants may visit the website to verify the application process and other pieces of information. **Deadline:** February 15. **Contact:** Kimberly Scott at kscott@wscpa.org.

10453 ■ George Waterman Memorial Scholarships
(Undergraduate/Scholarship)

Purpose: To support accounting students. **Focus:** Accounting. **Qualif.:** Applicants must: have junior status or higher in fall of the current year; have GPA minimum of 3.0 (on a 4.0 scale) in accounting courses and overall; be accepted into an accounting program at a 4-year college or university accredited in Washington state; be involved in on-campus, off-campus or community activities; and, attend school in Washington state. **Criteria:** Selection shall be based on the aforementioned qualifications and compliance with the application details. **Funds Avail.:** $3,000. **Duration:** Annual. **Number Awarded:** Varies. **To Apply:** Applicants may visit the website to verify the application process and other pieces of information. **Contact:** Kimberly Scott at kscott@wscpa.org.

10454 ■ Washington Space Grant Consortium (WSGC)
Box 351310
141 Johnson Hall
Seattle, WA 98195-1310
Ph: (206)543-1943
Fax: (206)543-0179
Free: 800-659-1943
E-mail: nasa@uw.edu
URL: www.waspacegrant.org
Facebook: www.facebook.com/Washington-NASA-Space-Grant-Consortium-116910748327473

Awards are arranged alphabetically below their administering organizations

Twitter: twitter.com/WaSpaceGrant

10455 ■ WSGC Community College Transfer Scholarships *(Undergraduate/Scholarship)*

Purpose: To provide opportunities to deserving college students in Washington who are planning to continue their studies in science, technology and engineering. **Focus:** Engineering; Mathematics and mathematical sciences; Science; Technology. **Qualif.:** Applicants must be residents of Washington state and U.S. citizens; must have a minimum GPA of 3.3; must have applied to transfer into Washington University; must be pursuing an undergraduate degree in science, technology, engineering or mathematics. **Criteria:** Selection will be based on the committees' criteria.

Funds Avail.: $2,000 to $5,000. **Duration:** Annual. **To Apply:** Applicants may contact the University of Washington for the application process and other information.

10456 ■ WSGC Scholarships for Incoming Freshmen *(Undergraduate/Scholarship)*

Purpose: To provide opportunities to deserving students in Washington who are planning to study science, technology and engineering. **Focus:** Science. **Qualif.:** Applicants must be Washington state residents and U.S. citizens; must have a minimum GPA of 3.5. **Criteria:** Selection will be based on the committees' criteria.

Funds Avail.: No specific amount. **Duration:** Annual. **To Apply:** Applicants may contact the University of Washington for the application process and other information. **Deadline:** January 15.

10457 ■ Washington State Association for Justice (WSAJ)
1809 7th Ave., No. 1500
Seattle, WA 98101
Ph: (206)464-1011
E-mail: wsaj@washingtonjustice.org
URL: www.washingtonjustice.org
Facebook: www.facebook.com/washingtonjustice
Twitter: twitter.com/wajustice

10458 ■ Women of WSAJ Bar Preparation Scholarships *(Undergraduate/Scholarship)*

Purpose: To provide law school graduates a scholarship to defray the cost of bar review courses. **Focus:** Law. **Qualif.:** Applicants must be female individuals who will take the Washington State bar exam. **Criteria:** Recipients will be selected based on financial need, demonstrated interest and intent to practice in the plaintiff's bar.

Funds Avail.: No specific amount. **Duration:** Annual. **To Apply:** Applicants must submit a resume and an essay (not to exceed two pages, typed and double-spaced). Additional documents that will support the application are acceptable. **Deadline:** January 25. **Contact:** Washington State Association for Justice, at the above address.

10459 ■ WSAJ American Justice Essay Scholarships *(Undergraduate/Scholarship)*

Purpose: To help students pursue a post-secondary education. **Focus:** General studies/Field of study not specified. **Qualif.:** Applicants must be high school seniors who are currently attending high school in Washington and also residents of the state of Washington. **Criteria:** Recipients will be chosen based on excellence in writing and eloquence in addressing the essay topic.

Funds Avail.: No specific amount. **Duration:** Annual. **To Apply:** Applicants must submit an essay. It should be four-to-five pages, typewritten and double-spaced, original and should pertain to any subject within the scope of the topic. Applicants must also provide a cover sheet with the name and contact information.

10460 ■ WSAJ Diversity Bar Preparation Scholarships *(Undergraduate/Scholarship)*

Purpose: To provide scholarship monies for diverse individuals who are under-represented in the legal profession. **Focus:** Law. **Qualif.:** Applicants must be individuals who are under-represented in the legal profession based on disability, gender identity and expression, race, ethnicity, religion and sexual orientation. **Criteria:** Applicants will be chosen based on qualifications and submitted materials.

Funds Avail.: No specific amount. **Duration:** Annual. **To Apply:** Applicants must submit a resume and a brief essay (not to exceed two pages, typed and double-spaced). Additional documents that will support the application are accepted. **Deadline:** January 25.

10461 ■ WSAJ Presidents' Scholarships *(Undergraduate/Scholarship)*

Purpose: To support and encourage the efforts of high school students who have overcome obstacles to pursue their education. **Focus:** General studies/Field of study not specified. **Qualif.:** Applicants must be high school senior students who are residents of the state of Washington. **Criteria:** Winners will be selected based on the following criteria: 1) demonstrated academic achievements and planned advancement toward a degree in an institution of higher learning; 2) documented need for financial assistance; 3) history of achievement despite disability; 4) record of commitment in helping needy people or protecting the rights of injured persons; 5) plan or commitment to apply the education in helping people; and 6) residency.

Funds Avail.: No specific amount. **Duration:** Annual. **To Apply:** Applicants must submit all high school and community college academic transcripts; name, address and telephone numbers of two references, at least one of which must be outside the school environment; a brief written financial statement; and any other documentation that will support the application. Applicants are also required to send a letter to the scholarship committee describing the qualifications and explaining the reasons why they deserve the scholarship. **Deadline:** March 13. **Contact:** Washington State Association for Justice, at the above address.

10462 ■ Washington State Business Education Association
c/o Susan Dunaway, Chairperson
23814 61st Ave.
Graham, WA 98338-9447
URL: www.wsbea.org

10463 ■ Dr. F. Ross Byrd Scholarships *(Graduate, Vocational/Occupational, Postgraduate/Scholarship)*

Purpose: To provide financial support to those students who are in need. **Focus:** Business. **Qualif.:** Applicants must be graduate students with a minimum of one quarter or one semester of graduate classes to complete. Applicants must be pursuing an advanced degree in business education or a related education field (Vocational Adminis-

Awards are arranged alphabetically below their administering organizations

tration, Business & Marketing, Curriculum, etc.). **Criteria:** Preference will be given to those who meet the criteria.

Funds Avail.: No specific amount. **Duration:** Annual. **To Apply:** Applicants must submit a completed application form and 3 letters of recommendation, one of which must be from a member of the student's graduate advisory committee, another one from a local vocational director/vocational administrator/administrator, and one from a member of WSBEA. **Deadline:** May 1. **Contact:** WSBEA Awards/Scholarship Chair at dunawayrs@comcast.net.

10464 ■ Doris Y. and John J. Gerber Scholarships
(Undergraduate/Scholarship)

Purpose: To provide financial assistance to those students who are in need. **Focus:** Business. **Qualif.:** Applicants must be junior or senior students majoring in Business Education. Applicants must be nominated by their advisor who is a current dues-paying member of WSBEA. **Criteria:** Preference will be given to those who meet the criteria.

Funds Avail.: No specific amount. **Duration:** Annual. **To Apply:** Applicants must inquire online for the application process. **Deadline:** December 1. **Contact:** WSBEA Awards/Scholarship Chair at dunawayrs@comcast.net.

10465 ■ Washington State Lake Protection Association (WALPA)
PO Box 4245
Seattle, WA 98194
E-mail: info@walpa.org
URL: www.walpa.org
Facebook: www.facebook.com/walpa.org/?ref=search

10466 ■ WALPA Lake Student Scholarships
(Undergraduate, Graduate/Scholarship)

Purpose: To promote the study of limnology, hydrology, ecology, and management or restoration of lakes and watersheds in Washington or Idaho. **Focus:** Environmental science. **Qualif.:** Applicants must be enrolled as part or full time undergraduate or graduate students in an accredited college or university in Washington or Idaho and be completing course work or research related to biology, hydrology, ecology and management or restoration of lakes and watersheds in Washington and Idaho. **Criteria:** Selection will be based on the quality of research topic, its significance to the fields of Environmental Science, particularly limnology and hydrology, and relevance to the applicant's interests and career goals.

Funds Avail.: $1,000 each. **Duration:** Annual. **Number Awarded:** 2. **To Apply:** Applicants must provide a statement of interests, including: research interests and explain why their research is of importance to the field of limnology and/or watershed management, career goals, and intended use of scholarship funds (one-page limit); a one-page resume; and recent transcripts of all college/university course work. A recommendation from someone in the applicant's field of study is encouraged, but not required. **Deadline:** April 29.

10467 ■ Washington State Nurses Association (WSNA)
575 Andover Pk. W, Ste. 101
Seattle, WA 98188
Ph: (206)575-7979
Fax: (206)575-1908
Free: 800-231-8482
E-mail: wsna@wsna.org
URL: www.wsna.org
Facebook: www.facebook.com/myWSNA
Twitter: twitter.com/mywsna

10468 ■ Washington State Nurses Association Foundation Scholarships (WSNF) *(Graduate, Undergraduate/Scholarship)*

Purpose: To support the education of students preparing for a career as registered nurses in Washington State. **Focus:** Nursing. **Qualif.:** Applicants must be either residents of Washington State or enrolled in an approved RN program in Washington State. Undergraduate student applicants must be enrolled in an approved program leading to an associate or baccalaureate nursing degree, and must have completed at least 12 nursing credits (Credits from LPN programs do not apply towards the 12 completed credits). Graduate student applicants must be admitted to an approved graduate nursing program to be eligible to apply. **Criteria:** Selection is based on academic performance, nursing leadership, school and community involvement, professional activities and commitment to WSNA.

Funds Avail.: $1,000 each. **Duration:** Annual. **Number Awarded:** Varies. **To Apply:** Applicants must download the application form provided at the scholarship website. Other documents to be submitted are also enumerated thereof. **Deadline:** February 12.

10469 ■ Washington Student Achievement Council
917 Lakeridge Way SW
Olympia, WA 98502
Ph: (360)753-7800
E-mail: info@wsac.wa.gov
URL: www.wsac.wa.gov
Facebook: www.facebook.com/WSACouncil
Twitter: twitter.com/WSACouncil

10470 ■ American Indian Endowed Scholarships
(Graduate, Undergraduate/Scholarship)

Purpose: To provide financial support to students who are academically competitive. **Focus:** General studies/Field of study not specified. **Qualif.:** Applicants must be Washington state resident; must enrolled full-time as an undergraduate or graduate students in an eligible program. **Criteria:** Selection is based on academic merit and commitment to serve the American Indian community.

Funds Avail.: $608,267. **Duration:** Annual. **To Apply:** Applicants must submit an American Indian Endowed Scholarship application form together with the required materials and information.

10471 ■ Washington College Bound Scholarships
(Undergraduate/Scholarship)

Purpose: To provide financial assistance to low-income students who want to achieve the dream of a college education. **Focus:** General studies/Field of study not specified. **Qualif.:** Applicants must be seventh- and eighth-grade students whose family income meets the guidelines or who are in foster care. **Criteria:** Selection will be based on student's family income status.

Funds Avail.: No specific amount. **Duration:** Annual. **To Apply:** Applicants must submit the complete application.

Deadline: June 30. **Remarks:** Established in 2007.

10472 ■ Washington Higher Education Coordinating Board - State Need Grants (SNG) *(Undergraduate/Grant)*

Purpose: To help state's lowest-income undergraduate students pursue degrees, hone skills, or retrain for new careers. **Focus:** General studies/Field of study not specified. **Qualif.:** Applicant must have a family income of equal to or less than 70 percent of the state median; must be a Washington State resident; must be enrolled as an undergraduate student in an eligible program. **Criteria:** Selection is based on the applicant's family income.

Funds Avail.: Varies. **To Apply:** Interested applicant must file a FAFSA (Free Application for Federal Student Aid) to be considered.

10473 ■ Washington University School of Law (WashULaw)
Anheuser-Busch Hall
1 Brookings Dr.
Saint Louis, MO 63130-4899
Ph: (314)935-6400
URL: law.wustl.edu
Facebook: www.facebook.com/WashULaw
LinkedIn: www.linkedin.com/edu/school?id=18731&trk=edu-cp-title
Twitter: twitter.com/washulaw

10474 ■ Buder Scholarships for American Indian Law Students *(Juris Doctorate/Scholarship)*

Purpose: To provide financial assistance to American Indian law students. **Focus:** Law. **Qualif.:** Applicants must be American Indian Law students enrolled at the Washington University School of Law. **Criteria:** Selection will be based on the applicants' demonstrated potential for success in law school as evidenced by undergraduate academic performance, performance on the Law School Admission Test, and other relevant factors.

Funds Avail.: No specific amount. **Duration:** Annual; Up to 3 years. **To Apply:** Applicants must submit an application letter and other requirements to the office. **Contact:** Carrie Burns, Assistant Director of Financial Aid & Student Services; Phone: 314-935-4605; E-mail: cjburns@wustl.edu.

10475 ■ Walter Moran Farmer Scholarships *(Juris Doctorate/Scholarship)*

Purpose: To offer financial support to students of color with intellectual, leadership and community service achievements. **Focus:** Law; Public service. **Qualif.:** Applicants must Washington University Law students, of color. **Criteria:** Selection will be based on: intellectual, leadership and community service achievement; demonstrated commitment of bringing diverse people together; and demonstrated achievement in the face of personal challenges.

Funds Avail.: No specific amount. **Duration:** Annual. **To Apply:** Applicants must submit the application letter and other requirements.

10476 ■ Washington University Law School Chancellor's Graduate Fellowships *(Advanced Professional/Fellowship)*

Purpose: To provide academic and generous financial support to outstanding and diverse students interested in careers as college or university professors. **Focus:** Arts; Business; Engineering; Law; Social work. **Qualif.:** Applicants must be graduate students who are interested in becoming college or university professors. **Criteria:** Recipients will be selected based on potential contributions to the diversity of graduate education at Washington University.

Funds Avail.: No specific amount. **Duration:** Annual. **To Apply:** Applicants may download an application form from the website. **Deadline:** January 25. **Remarks:** Established in 1991. **Contact:** Carrie Burns, Assistant Director of Financial Aid & Student Services; Phone: 314-935-4605; E-mail: cjburns@wustl.edu.

10477 ■ Washington University Law School Olin Fellowships for Women *(Advanced Professional/Fellowship)*

Purpose: To provide financial assistance to women who wish to have careers in higher education. **Focus:** Architecture; Art; Business; Engineering; Law; Medicine; Social work. **Qualif.:** Applicants must be women. **Criteria:** Recipients will be selected based on the committee's review of all applications.

Funds Avail.: No specific amount. **Duration:** Annual. **To Apply:** Applicants must submit a completed application form; a one-page information form; a curriculum vitae; an essay; three letters of recommendation; a transcript; and test scores. **Deadline:** January 25. **Contact:** Carrie Burns, Assistant Director of Financial Aid & Student Services; Phone: 314-935-4605; E-mail: cjburns@wustl.edu.

10478 ■ Webster Society Scholarships *(Juris Doctorate/Scholarship)*

Purpose: To offer financial support to students with outstanding credentials and a demonstrated commitment to public service. **Focus:** Law; Public service. **Qualif.:** Applicants must be entering first-year J.D. students with exemplary academic credentials and an established commitment to public service. **Criteria:** Selection will be based on academic merit.

Funds Avail.: No specific amount. **Duration:** Annual. **To Apply:** Interested applicants should write a short statement summarizing their involvement in public service activities. **Deadline:** February 1. **Contact:** Carrie Burns, Assistant Director of Financial Aid & Student Services; Phone: 314-935-4605; E-mail: cjburns@wustl.edu.

10479 ■ Water Environment Federation (WEF)
601 Wythe St.
Alexandria, VA 22314-1994
Fax: (703)684-2492
Free: 800-666-0206
E-mail: inquiry@wef.org
URL: www.wef.org
Facebook: www.facebook.com/WaterEnvironmentFederation
Twitter: twitter.com/WEForg

10480 ■ WEF Canham Graduate Studies Scholarships *(Graduate/Scholarship)*

Purpose: To provide financial assistance to those post-baccalaureate students who are in the water environment field. **Focus:** Water resources. **Qualif.:** Applicants must be members of the Water Environment Federation; must be pursuing post-baccalaureate degrees in the water environment field; must have practical experience. Recipients are

Awards are arranged alphabetically below their administering organizations

expected to make a commitment to work in the water environment field for two years following the completion of the degree. **Criteria:** Selection will be based on evaluation of submitted documents and specific criteria.

Funds Avail.: $25,000. **To Apply:** Applicants must submit a completed application form providing a summary of academic and practical experience in the environmental field; official college/university transcripts; letter of acceptance to a graduate program in the water environment field; recommendations from three persons; detailed statement of degree objectives as related to career goals and intent to work in the water environment field (750-1000 words). **Deadline:** March 1.

10481 ■ Water and Sewer Distributors of America (WASDA)

100 N 20th St., Ste. 400
Philadelphia, PA 19103-1462
Ph: (215)320-3882
Fax: (215)564-2175
URL: www.wasda.com
Facebook: www.facebook.com/JoinWASDA/
LinkedIn: www.linkedin.com/company/water-&-sewer
  -distributors-of-america
Twitter: twitter.com/joinwasda

10482 ■ Matt Stager Memorial Scholarship Fund
(Undergraduate/Scholarship)

Purpose: To provide financial support to students who are pursuing their educational career. **Focus:** General studies/Field of study not specified. **Qualif.:** Applicants must be children of employees of distributor companies whose membership is in good standing with WASDA; must maintain a GPA of 3.0 or higher. **Criteria:** Selection will be based on objective standards such as academic performance, performance on tests designed to measure ability and aptitude for higher education, and the candidate's rank in school.

Funds Avail.: $1,000. **Duration:** Annual. **To Apply:** Applicants must prepare a one-page detailed narrative description of the academic plans for the future and the career goals; must attach two letters of recommendation from teachers who are not related or members of the Matt Stager Scholarship Section Committee who have knowledge in academic achievements and who are able to comment on the academic motivation and character; must have a WASDA member contact verify parent's employment; have the Counselor fill out the counselor's report; submit the required scores and forward all requirements to the WASDA Headquarters. **Deadline:** March 31.

10483 ■ Waterbury Bar Association

PO Box 1767
Waterbury, CT 06721
URL: www.waterburybar.org

10484 ■ Edward Traurig Scholarships
(Undergraduate/Scholarship)

Purpose: To provide financial support to deceased members' children who wish to continue their educations. **Focus:** Law; Paralegal studies. **Qualif.:** Applicants must be residents of the Waterbury Judicial District (Middlebury, Naugatuck, Prospect, Southbury, Watertown, Wolcott, Woodbury or Waterbury) but can be entering their second or final year of study as full or part-time students at an accredited institution. **Criteria:** Selection will be based on applicants' academic record, demonstrated interest in community affairs and professional and personal integrity.

Funds Avail.: $1,000. **Duration:** Annual. **To Apply:** Application forms are available in the Placement Office or may be obtained by contacting Attorney Petrokaitis, or via the Waterbury Bar Association's website. A certified transcript from applicants' Registrar, as well as recommendation from their faculty or advisor should accompany each application. **Deadline:** May 22. **Contact:** Attorney Gina M. Petrokaitis, 678 Chase Parkway, Waterbury, CT 06708; Phone: 203 756-6955.

10485 ■ Waterbury Bar Association Scholarships
(Undergraduate/Scholarship)

Purpose: To provide financial support to deceased members' children who wish to continue their educations. **Focus:** Law; Paralegal studies. **Qualif.:** Applicants must be residents of the Waterbury Judicial District (Middlebury, Naugatuck, Prospect, Southbury, Watertown, Wolcott, Woodbury or Waterbury) and be in or entering their final year of study at an accredited law school. **Criteria:** Selection will be based on applicants' academic record, demonstrated interest in community affairs and professional and personal integrity.

Funds Avail.: $1,500. **To Apply:** Application forms are available in the Placement Office or may be obtained by contacting Attorney Petrokaitis, or via the Waterbury Bar Association's website. A certified transcript from applicants' Registrar, as well as recommendation from their faculty or advisor should accompany each application. **Deadline:** May 22. **Contact:** Attorney Gina M. Petrokaitis, 678 Chase Parkway, Waterbury, CT 06708; Phone: 203 756-6955.

10486 ■ WBA Bar President's Scholarships
(Undergraduate/Scholarship)

Purpose: To provide financial support to deceased members' children who wish to continue their educations. **Focus:** Law; Paralegal studies. **Qualif.:** Applicants must be residents of the Waterbury Judicial District (Middlebury, Naugatuck, Prospect, Southbury, Watertown, Wolcott, Woodbury or Waterbury) and be in or entering their final year of study at an accredited law school. **Criteria:** Selection will be based on applicants' academic record, demonstrated interest in community affairs and professional and personal integrity.

Funds Avail.: $1,000. **Duration:** Annual. **To Apply:** Application forms are available in the Placement Office or may be obtained by contacting Attorney Petrokaitis, or via the Waterbury Bar Association's website. A certified transcript from applicants' Registrar, as well as recommendation from their faculty or advisor should accompany each application. **Deadline:** May 22. **Contact:** Attorney Gina M. Petrokaitis, 678 Chase Parkway, Waterbury, CT 06708; Phone: 203 756-6955.

10487 ■ WBA Paralegal/Legal Assistant Scholarships *(Undergraduate/Scholarship)*

Purpose: To provide financial support to deceased members' children who wish to continue their educations. **Focus:** Paralegal studies. **Qualif.:** Applicants must be residents of the Waterbury Judicial District (Middlebury, Naugatuck, Prospect, Southbury, Watertown, Wolcott, Woodbury or Waterbury) and must be enrolled in an accredited paralegal or legal assistant program. Applicants must have completed, or will complete within the current school year, at

Awards are arranged alphabetically below their administering organizations

least 30 credit hours toward the completion of the program and intend to seek employment within the Judicial District of Waterbury. **Criteria:** Selection will be based on applicants' academic record, demonstrated interest in community affairs and professional and personal integrity.

Funds Avail.: $500. **Duration:** Annual. **To Apply:** Application forms are available in the Placement Office or may be obtained by contacting Attorney Petrokaitis, or via the Waterbury Bar Association's website. A certified transcript from applicants' Registrar, as well as recommendation from their faculty or advisor should accompany each application. **Deadline:** May 22. **Contact:** Attorney Gina M. Petrokaitis, 678 Chase Parkway, Waterbury, CT 06708; Phone: 203 756-6955.

10488 ■ Watson-Brown Foundation
310 Tom Watson Way
Thomson, GA 30824-0037
Ph: (706)595-8886
Fax: (706)595-3948
E-mail: info@watson-brown.org
URL: www.watson-brown.org

10489 ■ Watson-Brown Scholarships
(Undergraduate/Scholarship)

Purpose: To provide assistance to those who are pursuing their educational goals. **Focus:** General studies/Field of study not specified. **Qualif.:** Applicants must be students from Georgia or South Carolina who are high school seniors or current undergraduate students in their respective colleges or universities. **Criteria:** Scholarship recipients are selected based on merit and need.

Funds Avail.: Amount varies. **Duration:** Annual. **To Apply:** Applicants must complete the online scholarship application and submit supporting documents (essay, financial need statement, letters of recommendation, high school/college transcript, IRS Form 1040 or 1040 EZ) which must be mailed separately. **Deadline:** February 15.

10490 ■ Jeannette K. Watson Fellowships (JKW)
11 Park Pl., Ste. 1503
New York, NY 10007
Ph: (212)655-0201
URL: watson.foundation/fellowships/jk

10491 ■ Jeannette K. Watson Fellowships
(Undergraduate/Fellowship, Internship)

Purpose: To provide internships, mentoring, and enriched educational opportunities to promising New York City undergraduates with the goal of increasing their life choices and developing their capacity to make a difference in their own and other people's lives. **Focus:** Liberal arts. **Qualif.:** Applicants must be second semester freshmen or sophomores at one of the twelve invited colleges, namely: Baruch College; Brooklyn College; College of Staten Island; Hunter College; John Jay College; Lehman College; Long Island University, Brooklyn Campus; Marymount Manhattan College; Pace University, Manhattan Campus; Queens College; St. John's University; and The City College of New York. Applicants must also have at least four semesters of full-time academic work remaining after the term; be registered in a liberal arts track; demonstrate competence in college level work; not more than 21 years old on March; be American citizens or "green card" holders. **Criteria:** Selection shall be based on the aforementioned applicants' qualifications and compliance with the application details.

Funds Avail.: $5,000-$6,000. **Duration:** Annual; up to three years. **Number Awarded:** Varies. **To Apply:** Applicants must submit two short essays, two long essays along with two letters of recommendation (sent directly to the Campus Representatives), resume, and transcript. **Remarks:** Established in 1999. **Contact:** Jeannette K. Watson Fellowships, at the above address.

10492 ■ Thomas J. Watson Foundation (TJW)
11 Park Pl., Ste. 1503
New York, NY 10007
E-mail: tjw@tjwf.org
URL: watson.foundation

10493 ■ Thomas J. Watson Fellowships
(Undergraduate/Fellowship)

Purpose: To support individuals in their purposeful, independent studies outside the United States. **Focus:** General studies/Field of study not specified. **Qualif.:** Applicants must be graduating seniors nominated by one of the 40 partner colleges. **Criteria:** Qualities sought in the selection of fellows include: leadership; imagination; independence; emotional maturity; courage; integrity; resourcefulness; and responsibility.

Funds Avail.: $30,000. **Duration:** Annual. **To Apply:** Applicants nominated by a participating college must submit the following: personal statement; project statement; 2 to 3 recommendation letters; and transcripts.

10494 ■ Wattpad
36 Wellington St. E Ste. 200
Toronto, ON, Canada M5E 1C7
Ph: (640)963-7730
E-mail: amber.wattpad@gmail.com
URL: www.wattpad.com
Facebook: www.facebook.com/wattpad
Twitter: www.twitter.com/wattpad

10495 ■ Tell Us Your Story Scholarships
(Undergraduate/Scholarship)

Purpose: To give students an opportunity to use the power of stories to further their education. **Focus:** General studies/Field of study not specified. **Qualif.:** Applicants must be U.S. or Canadian citizens enrolled in a four-year accredited college or university in the United States and have a cumulative GPA of 2.5 or higher. **Criteria:** Selection will be based on the applicants' submitted essays. Such essays reveal unique voice, depth of reflection, good grammar/structure/vocabulary.

Funds Avail.: Total of $7,500 ($1,500 for each winner). **Number Awarded:** 5. **To Apply:** Applicants must submit their respective essays (of 1,000-2,000 words). **Deadline:** August 15. **Contact:** Email at scholarship@wattpad.com.

10496 ■ Wayne County Foundation, Inc.
33 S 7th St.
Richmond, IN 47374
Ph: (765)962-1638
Fax: (765)939-0508
URL: www.waynecountyfoundation.org
Facebook: www.facebook.com/

Awards are arranged alphabetically below their administering organizations

WayneCountyFoundation?fref=ts
LinkedIn: www.linkedin.com/company/wayne-county-foundation?trk=fc_badge

10497 ■ Jonathan Alan Scholarship Fund
(Undergraduate/Scholarship)

Purpose: To provide support student who plans to enter a medical field and demonstrates financial need. **Focus:** Education, Medical. **Qualif.:** Applicants must be Richmond high school graduates who have plans to enter a medical field and must demonstrate financial need. **Criteria:** Recipients are selected based on academic standing and financial need.

Funds Avail.: No specific amount. **To Apply:** For further information about the application form and materials, applicants are advised to contact the Wayne County Foundation at the above address or visit the website.

10498 ■ Erika A. and George E. Brattain Sr. Scholarship Fund *(Undergraduate, High School/Scholarship)*

Purpose: To financially support students in pursuing their education in music. **Focus:** Music. **Qualif.:** Applicants must be Lincoln High School graduating seniors who are pursuing an education in music. **Criteria:** Applicants are selected based on the criteria.

Funds Avail.: No specific amount. **Duration:** Annual. **To Apply:** For further information about the application form and materials, applicants are advised to contact the Wayne County Foundation at the above address or visit the website. **Remarks:** Established in 2005. **Contact:** Wayne County Foundation, Inc., at the above address.

10499 ■ Ralph Burkhardt Scholarship Fund
(Undergraduate, High School/Scholarship)

Purpose: To support students in pursuing their career in the music industry. **Focus:** Music. **Qualif.:** Applicants must be graduating Richmond High School seniors who have been outstanding orchestra students and intend to study music in college. **Criteria:** Selection will be based on the committee's criteria.

Funds Avail.: $300. **Duration:** Annual. **To Apply:** For further information about the application form and materials, applicants are advised to contact the Wayne County Foundation at the above address or visit the website. **Remarks:** Established in 1997. **Contact:** Wayne County Foundation, Inc., at the above address.

10500 ■ Lucille Campbell Scholarship Fund
(Undergraduate, High School/Scholarship)

Purpose: To support graduating high school seniors of Wayne County obtain a higher education. **Focus:** General studies/Field of study not specified. **Qualif.:** Applicants must be Wayne County high school graduating seniors. **Criteria:** Applicants are selected based on proof of eligibility and relative financial need.

Funds Avail.: No specific amount. **Duration:** Annual. **To Apply:** For further information about the application form and materials, applicants are advised to contact the Wayne County Foundation at the above address or visit the website. **Remarks:** Established in 2004. **Contact:** Wayne County Foundation, Inc., at the above address.

10501 ■ Betty J. Cecere Memorial Scholarship Endowment Fund *(Undergraduate, High School/Scholarship)*

Purpose: To provide opportunities for deserving young female students to achieve higher education. **Focus:** General studies/Field of study not specified. **Qualif.:** Applicants must be Richmond High School graduating female seniors. **Criteria:** Selection will be based on the committee's criteria.

Funds Avail.: No specific amount. **Duration:** Annual. **To Apply:** For further information about the application form and materials, applicants are advised to contact the Wayne County Foundation at the above address or visit the website. **Remarks:** Established in 2006. **Contact:** Wayne County Foundation, Inc., at the above address.

10502 ■ Centerville-Abington Dollars for Scholars
(Undergraduate/Scholarship)

Purpose: To provide financial assistance to those students who are in need. **Focus:** General studies/Field of study not specified. **Qualif.:** Applicants must be enrolled in an accredited post-secondary institution pursuing a two or four year degree or attending a vocational or technical college. **Criteria:** Preference will be given to those who meet the criteria.

Funds Avail.: $9,100. **To Apply:** For further information about the application form and materials, applicants are advised to contact the Wayne County Foundation at the above address or visit the website.

10503 ■ Jason Chaney Memorial Scholarship Fund
(Undergraduate/Scholarship)

Purpose: To provide scholarship assistance to male student who wants to pursue his education. **Focus:** General studies/Field of study not specified. **Qualif.:** Applicants must be Hagerstown High School graduating male seniors. **Criteria:** Scholarship recipient will be selected based on scholastic ability.

Funds Avail.: No specific amount. **Duration:** Annual. **To Apply:** For further information about the application form and materials, applicants are advised to contact the Wayne County Foundation at the above address or visit the website. **Contact:** Wayne County Foundation, Inc., at the above address.

10504 ■ Melba Dawn Chiarenza Scholarship Fund
(Undergraduate/Scholarship)

Purpose: To provide financial support for Lincoln High School graduates. **Focus:** Business; Criticism (Art, Drama, Literary); Nursing. **Qualif.:** Applicants must be Lincoln High School graduates who plan to obtain a degree in business, nursing, or drama. **Criteria:** Applicants will be evaluated based on criteria designed by the Scholarship Selection Committee.

Funds Avail.: $3,500. **To Apply:** For further information about the application form and materials, applicants are advised to contact the Wayne County Foundation at the above address or visit the website.

10505 ■ Niqui McCown Honor and Memorial Scholarship Fund *(Undergraduate/Scholarship)*

Purpose: To provide scholarships to graduating seniors who intend to pursue careers relating to the law or criminal justice. **Focus:** Criminal justice; Law. **Qualif.:** Applicants must be graduating seniors of Richmond High School who intend to pursue careers relating to the law or criminal justice. **Criteria:** Selection of applicants will be based on the moral character and academic achievements.

Funds Avail.: No specific amount. **To Apply:** For further information about the application form and materials, applicants are advised to contact the Wayne County Foundation at the above address or visit the website.

Awards are arranged alphabetically below their administering organizations

10506 ■ Nixon Family Scholarship Fund
(Undergraduate, High School/Scholarship)

Purpose: To assist students pursuing a degree in engineering, technology or related fields. **Focus:** Construction; Engineering; Technology; Welding. **Qualif.:** Applicants must be graduating seniors of Centerville High School; must have completed a two-year course of vocational study at the Whitewater Technical Career in Computer Assisted Design, Precision Machining, Welding, Electricity, Construction, or Project Lead the Way Programs. **Criteria:** Applicants are judged based on financial need.

Funds Avail.: $500 each. **Duration:** Annual. **Number Awarded:** 4. **To Apply:** For further information about the application form and materials, applicants are advised to contact the Wayne County Foundation at the above address or visit the website. **Remarks:** Established in 2010. **Contact:** Wayne County Foundation, Inc., at the above address.

10507 ■ Reid Hospital Graduate Student Scholarships *(Graduate/Scholarship)*

Purpose: To provide scholarship opportunities and assistance for students engaged in practical nursing, pharmacy, physical therapy, occupational therapy, speech and language pathology. **Focus:** Health care services. **Qualif.:** Applicants must be pursuing a graduate degree at an accredited university or college; must be enrolled full-time and must be fifth year or greater graduate students; must be residents of one of the following Indiana counties: Wayne, Fayette, Henry, Randolph, or Union or residents of one of the following Ohio counties: Darke or Preble. **Criteria:** Preference will be given to those who meet the criteria.

Funds Avail.: $10,000 each. **Number Awarded:** 4. **To Apply:** Applicants must complete the application form available online; must provide an official transcript of grades and letter of recommendation from a professor, guidance counselor, or dean of program that they have known for at least one year; must submit a two-page maximum statement including: their future plans, why they should be selected for the scholarship, and what inspired them to the health care profession.

10508 ■ Wayne County Foundation Anonymous Scholarship Fund *(Graduate/Scholarship)*

Purpose: To provide college scholarships to graduates of Lincoln, Hagerstown, Northeastern or Centerville High Schools. **Focus:** Music. **Qualif.:** Applicants must be graduates of Lincoln, Hagerstown, Northeastern, Seton, or Centerville high schools who are pursuing a degree in music. **Criteria:** Selection is based on submitted application and supporting documents.

Funds Avail.: $1,000. **To Apply:** For further information about the application form and materials, applicants are advised to contact the Wayne County Foundation at the above address or visit the website.

10509 ■ Rob and Bessie Welder Wildlife Foundation
PO Box 1400
Sinton, TX 78387-1400
Ph: (361)364-2643
Fax: (361)364-2650
E-mail: conservationeducator@welderwildlife.org
URL: www.welderwildlife.org

10510 ■ Welder Wildlife Foundation Fellowships
(Graduate, Master's, Doctorate/Fellowship)

Purpose: To promote the education of exceptionally qualified students and provide research information to manage wildlife populations. **Focus:** Animal science and behavior; Biology; Botany; Conservation of natural resources; Ecology; Genetics; Ornithology; Veterinary science and medicine; Wildlife conservation, management, and science. **Qualif.:** Applicants must: be graduate students, at the M.S. and Ph.D. levels, from the continental United States; and, have a GPA of 3.0/4.0 and a combined verbal and analytical GRE score of 300 or above. **Criteria:** Selection shall be based on the aforesaid qualifications and the respective research proposals of the applicants.

Funds Avail.: No specific amount. **Duration:** Annual. **To Apply:** Applicants must provide and submit their respective research proposals in the following areas of study: animal behavior, biology, botany, conservation education, ecology, genetics, mammalogy, ornithology, parasitology, range science, veterinary pathology, and wildlife and fisheries sciences. The complete proposal should include the following: objectives, background and relevance, study site, methods, analytical procedures, itemized budget, and timetable. Application materials include biographical data, degree sought, three letters of recommendation, complete academic record, and GRE score (verbal and quantitative). **Deadline:** October 1. **Remarks:** Established in 1956. **Contact:** Terry Blankenship; Email: tblankenship@welderwildlife.org.

10511 ■ Wells Fargo & Co.
420 Montgomery St.
San Francisco, CA 94104
Free: 866-878-5865
E-mail: corpcsf@wellsfargo.com
URL: www.wellsfargo.com

10512 ■ Wells Fargo Veterans Scholarships Program *(Undergraduate/Scholarship)*

Purpose: To provide educational support to students to complete their post-secondary program. **Focus:** General studies/Field of study not specified. **Qualif.:** Applicants must be honorably-discharged veterans or spouses of disabled veterans who are high school or GED graduates and who have served in the U.S. military; must have a minimum GPA of 2.5 on a 4.0 scale or its equivalent and plan to enroll in full-time undergraduate or graduate study at an accredited two- or four-year college, university or vocational-technical school for the next academic year. **Criteria:** Selection will be based on the committee's criteria.

Funds Avail.: Up to $10,000. **Number Awarded:** 15. **To Apply:** Applicants must visit the website, https://www.scholarsapply.org/wellsfargoveterans, for the application process and other information. **Deadline:** February 29. **Contact:** Scholarship America, One Scholarship Way, Saint Peter, MN 56082; Toll Free: 800-537-4180; Email: wellsfargoveterans@scholarshipamerica.org.

10513 ■ Wenner-Gren Foundation
470 Park Ave. S, 8th Fl.
New York, NY 10016
Ph: (212)683-5000
Fax: (212)532-1492
E-mail: inquiries@wennergren.org
URL: www.wennergren.org

Awards are arranged alphabetically below their administering organizations

Facebook: www.facebook.com/wennergrenfoundation

10514 ■ Conference and Workshop Grants *(Professional development/Grant)*

Purpose: To foster the creation of an international community of research scholars in anthropology and advance significant and innovative anthropological research. **Focus:** Anthropology. **Qualif.:** Applicants must be professional anthropologists who will be the primary organizers of the proposed conference or workshop. Co-applicants can be specified on the application and must have a doctorate and hold an established academic position. **Criteria:** Selection will be based on the submitted applications.

Funds Avail.: Up to $20,000. **Duration:** Annual. **To Apply:** Applicants must complete and submit all materials using the Foundation's online application submission procedure as well as sending printed copies of these materials to the Foundation by regular mail. **Deadline:** June 1 and December 1. **Contact:** Wenner-Gren Foundation; Phone: 212-683-5000; Fax: 212-532-1492; E-mail: inquiries@wennergren.org.

10515 ■ Engaged Anthropology Grants *(Doctorate, Postdoctorate/Grant)*

Purpose: To enable grantees to return to their research locale to share their research results. **Focus:** Anthropology. **Qualif.:** Applicants must have been funded previously through dissertation fieldwork or a post-doctorate research grant, and the proposed engagement activities must be a direct outgrowth of this funded research; must have completed their dissertation fieldwork or post-doctorate research grant and fulfilled the final reporting requirements before this grant; must apply within five years of the original approval date of their dissertation fieldwork or postdoctorate research grant. **Criteria:** Applications are evaluated according to the project's capacity for producing engaged participation, cultivating mutually beneficial collaborations and forging equitable relationships among all parties involved.

Funds Avail.: $5,000. **Duration:** Annual. **To Apply:** Applications must be submitted on the most recent official application form online, along with all other required materials. If it is not possible to submit the application online because of inadequate access in your country of origin, applicants must notify the Foundation at least one week before the deadline to arrange to submit an application by conventional mail. A complete application must have the following categories of information: general information about yourself, your prior Wenner-Gren grant and your proposed project; an abstract of the proposed project; project description questions. All responses should be carefully prepared. Applicants are advised to read the questions and instructions as they develop their answers; a detailed budget; curriculum vitae. **Deadline:** February 1 and August 1.

10516 ■ Fejos Postdoctoral Fellowships in Ethnographic Film *(Postdoctorate/Fellowship)*

Purpose: To support the completion of ethnographic films based on anthropological research. **Focus:** Anthropology; Ethnography. **Qualif.:** Applicants must have a Ph.D. or equivalent in anthropology or a related discipline at the time of application; and must have received a Ph.D. or equivalent within ten years of the application deadline. **Criteria:** The main criterion of evaluation is the quality of the research underlying the film project and its potential contribution to anthropological knowledge, theory, and debate. Furthermore, applications for the Fellowship will also be judged on the following criteria: the degree to which the proposed film reflects and communicates the results of the research upon which it is based; the innovative aspects of the film project; integration of film/video with other media forms and/or written publication; and the quality of the film sample submitted by the applicants. Applicants whose applications that were unsuccessful in a prior funding cycle may be resubmitted only twice.

Funds Avail.: $40,000. **Duration:** Annual. **Number Awarded:** 2. **To Apply:** Applicants may contact the Foundation for the online application process and submission procedure. **Deadline:** May 1. **Remarks:** The fellowship is named after Paul Fejos, who was an early ethnographic film maker (1935-1941) and the first director of the Wenner-Gren Foundation (1941-1963). **Contact:** Email at applications@wennergren.org.

10517 ■ Hunt Postdoctoral Fellowships *(Postdoctorate/Fellowship)*

Purpose: To support basic research in anthropology. **Focus:** Anthropology. **Qualif.:** Applicants must have received a PhD or equivalent within ten years of the application deadline. Qualified scholars are eligible without regard to nationality or institutional or departmental affiliation. **Criteria:** The main criteria of evaluation are the quality of the research and its potential contribution to anthropological knowledge, theory and debate.

Funds Avail.: $40,000. **Duration:** Annual. **Number Awarded:** Maximum of 8. **To Apply:** The Foundation operates an online application submission procedure. All application forms and other required application materials must be submitted online. If it is not possible to submit an application online because of inadequate internet access in applicant's country of origin, applicant must notify the Foundation at least one week before the deadline to arrange a submission of application by conventional mail. In addition to online submission, five printed copies of the application form and other required materials must be sent to the Foundation. **Deadline:** May 1.

10518 ■ Wadsworth African Fellowships *(Doctorate/Fellowship)*

Purpose: To support African students undertaking study leading to a PhD at a South African university that can provide them with international-level training in anthropology. **Focus:** Anthropology. **Qualif.:** Applicants must be African scholars who may not otherwise be able to pursue a doctoral degree in anthropology. Normally, applicants must be under 35 years of age at the time they begin their fellowship. They must be citizens and residents of an African country at the time of application and also be members of an underrepresented group in academic anthropology/archaeology. Applicants must be prepared to demonstrate their reasons for choosing their host institution. Priority will be given to the applications from University of Witwatersrand and the University of Cape Town. At the time they submit their application, candidates must have an application for doctoral admission pending at a South African institution that will provide training. The applicants must have a host sponsor who is a member of the institution at which the applicants received their prior degree(s). **Criteria:** Priority is given to applicants with well-articulated training and research goals. It is also important to demonstrate a good fit between the host institution, host sponsor and the applicants' research goals.

Funds Avail.: $17,500. **Duration:** Annual. **To Apply:** The

Foundation operates an online application submission procedure. All application forms and other required application materials must be submitted online in a format compatible with Microsoft Word 2003, 2007 or 2010 or as an Adobe PDF. Acceptable document formats include .doc, .docx, .txt, .xls and .pdf extensions. Two printed copies of the applicants' materials must also be mailed to the Foundation. Application and all supporting materials such as CVs, transcripts, etc. must be in English. Complete applications must have the following categories of information: general information about the applicants, the home institution and sponsor and the host institution sponsor; the answers to three questions about the applicants' background and their proposed plan of study, their research interests and their professional goals or plans. Applicants are advised to read the questions and instructions carefully as they develop their answers; a detailed budget; copies of official transcripts from their home institution; language competency; curriculum vitae for the applicants and host sponsor. The applicants should request reference letters from both the home sponsor and the host sponsor, to be sent directly to the Foundation. **Deadline:** December 15. **Contact:** International Programs administrator at internationalprograms@wennergren.org.

10519 ■ Wadsworth International Fellowships
(Graduate/Fellowship)

Purpose: To offer support for students who are in the early stages of their doctoral programs. **Focus:** Anthropology. **Qualif.:** Applicants must be from countries where anthropology is underrepresented and where there are limited resources to send students overseas for training; must be under 35 years of age at the time they begin their fellowship; must have a Host Sponsor who holds an academic position at the Host Institution and in the department where the applicant will be registered. **Criteria:** Priority is given to applicants who have not already earned a prior degree from an institution outside of their home country and have not already begun their graduate training outside of their home country.

Funds Avail.: $17,500. **Duration:** Annual. **To Apply:** The Foundation operates an online application submission procedure. All application forms and other required application materials must be submitted online. If it is not possible to submit an application online because of inadequate internet access in applicant's country of origin, applicant must notify the Foundation at least one week before the deadline to arrange a submission of application by conventional mail. In addition to online submission, two printed copies of the application materials must also be mailed to the Foundation. **Deadline:** March 1.

10520 ■ Wenner-Gren Foundation Dissertation Fieldwork Grants *(Doctorate/Grant)*

Purpose: To support students who are enrolled in a doctoral program in anthropology. **Focus:** Anthropology. **Qualif.:** Applicants must be students enrolled in a doctoral program (or equivalent, if applying from outside the United States) at the time of application. Qualified doctoral students are eligible without regard to nationality or institutional or departmental affiliation. **Criteria:** The main criteria of evaluation are the quality of the research and its potential contribution to anthropological knowledge, theory and debate.

Funds Avail.: $20,000. **To Apply:** The Foundation operates an online application submission procedure. All application forms and other required application materials must be submitted online. If it is not possible to submit an application online because of inadequate internet access in applicant's country of origin, applicant must notify the Foundation at least one week before the deadline to arrange a submission of application by conventional mail. **Deadline:** May 1 and November 1. **Contact:** Wenner-Gren Foundation, at the above address.

10521 ■ Wenner-Gren Foundation Post-PhD Research Grants *(Doctorate/Grant)*

Purpose: To support individual who are holding a Ph.D. or equivalent degree to support their research projects. **Focus:** Anthropology. **Qualif.:** Applicants must be individuals holding a PhD or equivalent degree. Qualified scholars are eligible without regard to nationality or institutional or departmental affiliation. **Criteria:** The main criteria of evaluation are the quality of the research and its potential contribution to anthropological knowledge, theory, and debate.

Funds Avail.: $20,000. **To Apply:** The Foundation operates an online application submission procedure. All application forms and other required application materials must be submitted online. If it is not possible to submit an application online because of inadequate internet access in applicant's country of origin, applicant must notify the Foundation at least one week before the deadline to arrange a submission of application by conventional mail. In addition to online submission, five printed copies of the application form and other required materials must be sent to the Foundation. **Deadline:** May 1 and November 1.

10522 ■ West Virginia Coal Association (WVCA)
PO Box 3923
Charleston, WV 25339
Ph: (304)342-4153
URL: www.wvcoal.com

10523 ■ Friends of Coal Scholarships
(Undergraduate/Scholarship)

Purpose: To support students with financial needs. **Focus:** General studies/Field of study not specified. **Qualif.:** Applicants must be high school honor graduates; must have high GPA's in high school; must be living in West Virginia. **Criteria:** Recipients are selected based on academic performance and financial need.

Funds Avail.: $2,500. **Number Awarded:** 3. **To Apply:** Applicants must submit a filled-out application form.

10524 ■ West Virginia PTA (WV PTA)
PO Box 3557
Parkersburg, WV 26103-3557
Ph: (304)420-9576
Fax: (304)420-9577
E-mail: info@westvirginiapta.org
URL: www.wvpta.net

10525 ■ West Virginia PTA Scholarships
(Undergraduate/Scholarship)

Purpose: To support the education of WV students. **Focus:** General studies/Field of study not specified. **Qualif.:** Applicants must be high school seniors in a WV school, and have at least 2.0 grade point average. **Criteria:** Selection is based on the overall presence of the essay and application; volunteer service; honors received; extracurricular activities; GPA, ACT and SAT scores.

Awards are arranged alphabetically below their administering organizations

Funds Avail.: $500. **Duration:** Annual. **Number Awarded:** Varies. **To Apply:** Applicants must submit five sets (one original, four copies) of high school transcripts; (one-page) three letters of recommendation; ACT and SAT scores; and (one-page, double-spaced) essay reflecting long-term goals. Applications must have notarized signatures of parents, guardians and students.

10526 ■ West Virginia Space Grant Consortium (WVSGC)

Engineering Science Bldg., Rm. G-68
West Virginia University
Morgantown, WV 26506
Ph: (304)293-4099
Fax: (304)293-4970
E-mail: info@nasa.wvu.edu
URL: www.wvspacegrant.org
Facebook: www.facebook.com/WVSGC

10527 ■ NASA WVSGC Undergraduate Research Fellowship (Undergraduate/Fellowship)

Purpose: To provide support for undergraduate students to become involved in a research project under the supervision of their academic supervisor. **Focus:** Space and planetary sciences. **Qualif.:** Applicants must be undergraduate students in the Science, Technology, Engineering and Mathematics (STEM) fields enrolled in a WVSGC affiliate institution. Female and minority students are strongly encouraged to apply. **Criteria:** The consortium will award these grants based on the following criteria: soundness and technical merit of the proposed research; student's academic and extracurricular achievements; budget and plans for dissemination and publicizing of the results.

Funds Avail.: $4,500. **To Apply:** Applicants must complete the on-line application process and must upload the following materials: three-page summary, using the applicants' own words of the research plan including statement of the problem, methodology, expected results, proposed timeline and references (document must be in PDF format); resume and; official and unofficial copy of the applicants' transcript. Applicants are also required to submit a statement of no more than 600 words addressing the following items: applicants' research experience and career interests; applicants' plans for sharing research findings through participation in a professional conference and /or publication; lists of planned expenditures and justification for the expenditures and; acknowledgement prior WVSGC funding and brief description of previous projects funded.

10528 ■ Western Equipment Dealers Association (WEDA)

638 W 39th St.
Kansas City, MO 64111-2910
Ph: (816)561-5323
Fax: (816)561-1249
Free: 800-762-5616
E-mail: oholcombe@westerneda.com
URL: westerneda.com

10529 ■ WEDA Scholarship Program (Professional development/Scholarship)

Purpose: To assist in the training, re-training, or advancement of employees or potential employees of western Canadian farm, industrial and outdoor power equipment dealers. **Focus:** General studies/Field of study not specified. **Qualif.:** Applicants must be employees or potential employees of western Canadian farm, outdoor power and industrial equipment dealers, subject to the following conditions: such applicants must be approved by the dealer principal for training, re-training or professional advancement; enrolled and accepted in a higher education curriculum, which is approved by the dealer principal as training applicable to the dealership's needs; and, enrolled full-time in the approved course of study. Lastly, dealer principals must be willing to provide matching scholarship funds in the amount fixed by the WEDA and must be current members of Western Equipment Dealers Association. **Criteria:** Applicants will be selected based on submitted materials.

Funds Avail.: Up to $1,000. **Duration:** Annual. **To Apply:** Applicants may contact WEDA for further information. **Deadline:** April 1.

10530 ■ Western Golf Association (WGA)

1 Briar Rd.
Golf, IL 60029-0301
Ph: (847)724-4600
Fax: (847)724-7133
URL: www.wgaesf.org

10531 ■ Chick Evans Caddie Scholarships (Undergraduate/Scholarship)

Purpose: To help caddies to pursue education. **Focus:** General studies/Field of study not specified. **Qualif.:** Applicant must be caddies nominated by their club and have caddied, successfully and regularly, for a minimum of two years and also expected to caddie or work at their sponsoring club during the summer prior to the application; have completed junior year of high school with above B average in college preparatory courses and are required to take the ACT; have clearly established their need for financial assistance; and have an outstanding character. **Criteria:** Scholarship Committee will select finalist and will conduct an interview.

Funds Avail.: No specific amount. **Duration:** Annual. **To Apply:** Caddies must be nominated by their respective clubs. **Deadline:** September 30.

10532 ■ Western Michigan Society of Health-System Pharmacists (WMSHP)

c/o Brad Miller, Secretary
8835 Summerset Woods Ct. SE
Alto, MI 49302
Ph: (616)486-4019
E-mail: webmaster@wmshp.net
URL: www.wmshp.net

10533 ■ Western Michigan Society of Health-System Pharmacists Scholarships (Undergraduate/Scholarship)

Purpose: To support the financial needs of a local pharmacy student. **Focus:** Pharmacy. **Qualif.:** Applicants must be in good standing with the college of pharmacy at Ferris State University, University of Michigan, or Wayne State University; must be natives or current residents of the Western Michigan area. **Criteria:** Recipients are selected based on demonstrated interest in health-system pharmacy and involvement in or leadership positions with professional organizations.

Awards are arranged alphabetically below their administering organizations

Funds Avail.: $1,000. **Number Awarded:** 1. **To Apply:** Applicants must complete the application form. **Deadline:** April 3. **Contact:** Rebecca Maynard, PharmD, WMSHP President-Elect, Borgess Medical Center, Pharmacy Department, 1521 Gull Road, Kalamazoo, MI 49048.

10534 ■ Western Social Science Association (WSSA)
2307 Chof Trl.
Flagstaff, AZ 86005
URL: www.wssaweb.com

10535 ■ WSSA Student Paper Competition
(Undergraduate, Graduate/Award)

Purpose: To encourage undergraduate and graduate students to present their research papers. **Focus:** General studies/Field of study not specified. **Qualif.:** Both undergraduate and graduate students are eligible for the award. **Criteria:** Submitted papers will be judged based on 1) advancement of knowledge; 2) appropriateness for a broad social science audience; 3) quality and implementation of the research design; 4) definition and significance of topic; 5) analysis of findings and discussion of their implications; and 6) clarity and cogency of writing.

Funds Avail.: $800. **To Apply:** Paper should not exceed 25 pages and must be double-spaced in 12 pt. Arial font. Applicants must provide an abstract (not to exceed 200 words) with the title of the paper but not the author(s)/affiliation(s).

10536 ■ Western Society of Criminology (WSC)
c/o California State University
Department of Criminal Justice
1250 Bellflower Blvd.
Long Beach, CA 90840
E-mail: secretary-treasurer@westerncriminology.org
URL: westerncriminology.org

10537 ■ Libby Deschenes Prize for Applied Research *(Undergraduate/Prize)*

Purpose: To support criminology or criminal justice students. **Focus:** Criminal justice; Criminology. **Qualif.:** Applicants must be students interested in criminal justice or criminology field of study. **Criteria:** Award will be given to students who have demonstrated commitment in improving policy, practice, or programs in criminal justice through research or the application of research.

Funds Avail.: $500. **Duration:** Annual. **To Apply:** Applicants must contact WSC office for further information and other required documents. **Deadline:** December 15.

10538 ■ June Morrison Scholarship Fund
(Undergraduate/Scholarship)

Purpose: To financially assist undergraduate students and help defray the cost of attending the annual meeting. **Focus:** Criminal justice; Criminology. **Qualif.:** Applicants must be criminal justice students or individuals who are interested in criminology field. **Criteria:** Recipients will be selected based on submitted materials.

Funds Avail.: $200-$300. **Duration:** Annual. **Number Awarded:** 1-2. **To Apply:** Applicants must submit a paper and must contact WSC office for further information and other required documents. **Deadline:** October 9.

10539 ■ Miki Vohryzek-Bolden Student Paper Competition *(Undergraduate/Prize)*

Purpose: To support undergraduate students who are involved in criminal justice or criminology field. **Focus:** Criminal justice; Criminology. **Qualif.:** Applicants must be criminal justice students or individuals who are interested in criminology field. **Criteria:** Recipients will be selected based on submitted materials.

Funds Avail.: $125-$250 (First place); $100 (Second place). **Duration:** Annual. **To Apply:** Applicants must submit an original manuscript and must contact WSC office for further information and other required documents. **Deadline:** October 9.

10540 ■ Western Society of Weed Science (WSWS)
Bldg. 4, Ste. 5
205 W Boutz Rd.
Las Cruces, NM 88005
Ph: (575)649-7157
E-mail: wsws@marathonag.com
URL: www.wsweedscience.org

10541 ■ Western Society of Weed Science Outstanding Student Scholarship Program *(Graduate, Undergraduate/Scholarship)*

Purpose: To encourage new weed science research and future weed science careers. **Focus:** Agricultural sciences; General studies/Field of study not specified. **Qualif.:** Applicants must be undergraduate or graduate students enrolled in a degree program (B.S., M.S., or PhD) at an accredited college or university in the western region. Applicants must be current WSWS members at the time of application. **Criteria:** Applicants will be evaluated based on contribution of research to the discipline of weed science and to the WSWS objectives, academic record and scholarly achievements, potential contributions to the future of weed science, and participation in extracurricular pursuits contributing to the advancement on any of the following: weed science, natural resource management, and/or education and mentoring.

Funds Avail.: A total of $3,000. **Duration:** Annual. **Number Awarded:** 3. **To Apply:** Applicants must submit a completed and signed Application Form; one-page cover letter describing how applicant became interested in weed science, how applicant's research will contribute to the field of weed science and the WSWS objectives, and what future contributions applicant hopes to make to the field of weed science including career goals; 1 or 2-page resume highlighting recent relevant experience through school, work and/or internships; abstract submitted for paper or poster presentation at WSWS annual meeting; two letters of support, at least one of which must be from a college/university faculty member (preferably major advisor) familiar with the applicant's abilities, interests, and career goals; academic transcripts (unofficial copy is acceptable). **Deadline:** October1. **Contact:** WSWS Student Section, Liaison Chair Marcelo Moretti; Email: mlmoretti@ucdavis.edu.

10542 ■ Western Washington University Alumni Association
516 High St., MS 9199
Bellingham, WA 98225
Ph: (360)650-3353

Awards are arranged alphabetically below their administering organizations

Fax: (360)650-6555
Free: 800-676-6885
E-mail: alumni@wwu.edu
URL: alumni.wwu.edu/s/1710/start.aspx?gid=2&pgid=61
Facebook: www.facebook.com/WWUAlumni

10543 ■ Why Get Your Blue On? Video Scholarships *(Graduate, Undergraduate/Award, Scholarship)*

Purpose: To support current, full-time students enrolled at Western Washington University. **Focus:** General studies/Field of study not specified. **Qualif.:** Contestant must be a current, full-time student at Western Washington University, and must have a valid user account with YouTube. **Criteria:** Scholarship Committee will take into consideration the following factors when evaluating the video submission: Creativity: Originality, uniqueness, and ingenuity demonstrated in the video; Relevance: How well the video related to wearing the blue and WWU.

Funds Avail.: $250-$1,000. **Number Awarded:** 3. **To Apply:** Contestants must create a 5 minute (or less) video response to the question, "Why Get Your Blue On?". Submit a completed Official Entry Form, after successfully uploaded the video on YouTube. **Deadline:** December 10.

10544 ■ Wexner Foundation
8000 Walton Pky., Ste. 110
New Albany, OH 43054-7074
Ph: (614)939-6060
URL: www.wexnerfoundation.org
Facebook: www.facebook.com/WexnerFoundation
Twitter: twitter.com/Wexnertweets

10545 ■ Wexner Graduate Fellowships/Davidson Scholars *(Graduate/Fellowship)*

Purpose: To encourage promising candidates to successfully meet the challenges of professional Jewish leadership in the North American Jewish community. **Focus:** Jewish studies; Religion. **Qualif.:** Applicants must be entering (and not already matriculated in) a degree granting graduate program, based in North America, that will allow them to pursue a career as a professional Jewish leader in North America and commit to doing so; and must be between the ages of 21 and 40 upon entering the graduate program. Applicants who are not citizens of a North American country must have documentation that allows them to study and to work in that country. **Criteria:** Selection is based on applicant's strong personal commitment to the Jewish community; demonstrated excellence in academic achievement; and possess the potential to provide outstanding professional leadership that will shape the future of Jewish communal life in North America.

Funds Avail.: Up to $30,000 each year. **Duration:** Annual; Up to 2 years. **To Apply:** Applicants must complete the application online. In addition, applicants must submit academic transcripts (undergraduate and, if applicable, graduate); scores from the General Test of the Graduate Record Examination (Institution No. 3134); three letters of recommendation; and confirmation letter or acceptance letter. **Remarks:** Established in 1988.

10546 ■ Weyburn Credit Union
PO Box 1117
Weyburn, SK, Canada S4H 2L3
Ph: (306)842-6641

Free: 800-567-8111
E-mail: info@weyburn.cu.sk.ca
URL: www.weyburncu.ca

10547 ■ C.H.(Chuck) Hodgson Scholarships *(Undergraduate/Scholarship)*

Purpose: To provide financial assistance to students who want to pursue their college education. **Focus:** General studies/Field of study not specified. **Qualif.:** Applicants must be recently graduated grade 12 students under age 21 who have been out of High School for at least one year; must be member of Weyburn Credit Union; must be enrolled full time (3 or more classes) at the Southeast Regional College. **Criteria:** Scholarships will be awarded on the basis of academic excellence, good citizenship and effort.

Funds Avail.: 750 Canadian Dollars. **Duration:** Annual. **To Apply:** Applicants must submit the following: application form; resume; a brief description of any clubs, groups, organizations, etc. in which they are involved, what the group achieved and, most important, what part they played, time which they invested in working with the group and what they contributed to the group's success. On an individual level, applicants should include: any individual achievements over the past years and how they achieved them; how and why they chose their particular area of post-secondary study; applicants' future goals and ambitions. Applicants must also include letters of reference. These letters should come from people who can give a good evaluation and recommendation of the applicants' character (i.e. school counselors, principals, homeroom teachers, youth leaders, part-time employer; or any other individual). The application may include as many letters of reference as applicants wish.

10548 ■ Q. O. (Quint) Patrick Scholarships *(Undergraduate/Scholarship)*

Purpose: To provide financial assistance to graduated high school students who want to pursue their college education. **Focus:** General studies/Field of study not specified. **Qualif.:** Applicants must be mature students, defined as someone age 21 or older; must be members of Weyburn Credit Union; must be enrolled full time (3 or more classes) at the Southeast Regional College. **Criteria:** Scholarship will be awarded on the basis of academic excellence, good citizenship and effort.

Funds Avail.: 750 Canadian Dollars. **Duration:** Annual. **To Apply:** Applicants must submit the following: application form; resume; a brief description of any clubs, groups, organizations, etc. in which they are involved, what the group achieved and, most important, what part they played, time which they invested in working with the group and what they contributed to the group's success. On an individual level, applicants should include: any individual achievements over the past years and how they achieved them; how and why they chose their particular area of post-secondary study; applicants' future goals and ambitions. Applicants must also include letters of reference. These letters should come from people who can give a good evaluation and recommendation of the applicants' character (i.e. school counselors, principals, homeroom teachers, youth leaders, part-time employer; or any other individual). The application may include as many letters of reference as applicants wish. **Deadline:** November 15.

10549 ■ RS Williamson and Eliford Mott Memorial Scholarships *(Undergraduate/Scholarship)*

Purpose: To provide financial assistance to graduating high school students. **Focus:** General studies/Field of study

Awards are arranged alphabetically below their administering organizations

not specified. **Qualif.:** Applicants must be graduating students from a high school within the Weyburn Credit Union defined trade area; applicants or the parents of the applicants must be members of Weyburn Credit Union. **Criteria:** Scholarships will be awarded on the basis of academic excellence, good citizenship and effort.

Funds Avail.: 1,000 Canadian Dollars each. **Duration:** Annual; One year. **Number Awarded:** 3. **To Apply:** Applicants must submit the following: application form; resume; a brief description of any clubs, groups, organizations, etc. in which they are involved, what the group achieved and, most important, what part they played, time which they invested in working with the group and what they contributed to the group's success. On an individual level, applicants should include: any individual achievements over the past years and how they achieved them; how and why they chose their particular area of post-secondary study; applicants' future goals and ambitions. Applicants must also include letters of reference. These letters should come from people who can give a good evaluation and recommendation of the applicants' character (i.e. school counselors, principals, homeroom teachers, youth leaders, part-time employer; or any other individual). The application may include as many letters of reference as applicants wish. **Deadline:** March 15.

10550 ■ Helen Hay Whitney Foundation
20 Squadron Blvd., Ste. 630
New City, NY 10956
Ph: (845)639-6799
Fax: (845)639-6798
E-mail: hhwf@earthlink.net
URL: www.hhwf.org

10551 ■ Helen Hay Whitney Foundation Fellowships (Postdoctorate/Fellowship)

Purpose: To support early postdoctoral research training in all basic biomedical sciences. **Focus:** Biomedical research. **Qualif.:** Applicants must hold, or are in the final stages of obtaining a PhD, MD, or equivalent degree and are seeking beginning postdoctoral training in basic biomedical research. They must have no more than one year of postdoctoral research experience at the time of the deadline; or should have received a PhD (or D.Phil. or equivalent) degree no more than two years before the deadline, or an M.D. degree no more than three years before the deadline. **Criteria:** Selection shall be based on the aforementioned applicants' qualifications and compliance with the application details.

Funds Avail.: Amount varies. **Duration:** Annual; up to three years. **Number Awarded:** Varies. **To Apply:** Applicants are required to fill out and submit applications online. **Deadline:** July 1.

10552 ■ Elie Wiesel Foundation for Humanity
555 Madison Ave., 20th Fl.
New York, NY 10022
Ph: (212)490-7788
URL: www.eliewieselfoundation.org

10553 ■ Elie Wiesel Prize in Ethics (Undergraduate/Prize, Award)

Purpose: To challenge students to examine and analyze urgent ethical issues confronting them in today's complex world. **Focus:** General studies/Field of study not specified. **Qualif.:** Applicants must be full-time undergraduate juniors and seniors at accredited four-year colleges and universities in the United States. **Criteria:** Selection will be based on the committee's criteria.

Funds Avail.: 1st Prize-$5,000; 2nd Prize-$2,500; 3rd Prize-$1,500; Two Honorable Mentions-$500 each. **Duration:** Annual. **To Apply:** Applicants must submit the essays following the suggested essay topics. Essay format must be in 3,000 to 4,000 words, may be written in the formal or informal voice, but an individual voice should be evident. Essay should be developed from the applicant's point of view and may take the form of an analysis that is biographical, historical, literary, philosophical, sociological or theological. Essay must be the original, unpublished work of one student, have a title, and typed in 12-point font in English, double-spaced with 1" margins and numbered pages. Applicants must submit the following: three copies of essay (one copy paper-clipped and two stapled); completed Entry Form (signed by both the student and faculty sponsor); and a letter on school stationery from the Registrar's Office, verifying the applicant's eligibility. **Remarks:** Established in 1989.

10554 ■ Wild Felid Research and Management Association (WFA)
PO Box 3335
Montrose, CO 81402-3335
Ph: (970)252-1928
URL: www.wildfelid.com

10555 ■ Wild Felid Legacy Scholarships (Graduate/Scholarship)

Purpose: To provide financial support to a graduate-level university student conducting research on wild felids. **Focus:** Wildlife conservation, management, and science. **Qualif.:** Applicants must be student members of the Wild Felid Research and Management Association; must have completed a Bachelor of Science or Arts Degree and be enrolled in a graduate program in wildlife biology; wildlife management or any related natural resource field. **Criteria:** Applicants will be evaluated based on demonstrated need for financial aid; participation in a research project that aims to improve our understanding of wild felid biology, management and/or conservation; undergraduate and graduate GPA.

Funds Avail.: $1,000. **Duration:** Annual. **To Apply:** Applicants must submit a completed application form; current resume; Bachelor's Degree transcript; graduate studies transcript or copy of acceptance letter into a graduate program in wildlife biology, wildlife management or related natural resource fields; two reference letters from professor and supervisor; short essay (500-750 words) describing interests in wild felid research, career goals and usage of award to further professional development, demonstration of financial need. **Deadline:** March 30.

10556 ■ The Wilderness Society (TWS)
1615 M St. NW
Washington, DC 20036
Ph: (202)833-2300
Free: 800-THE-WILD
URL: wilderness.org

10557 ■ Gloria Barron Wilderness Society Scholarship (Graduate/Scholarship)

Purpose: To encourage individuals who have the potential to make a significant positive difference in the long term

Awards are arranged alphabetically below their administering organizations

protection of wilderness in North America. **Focus:** Conservation of natural resources. **Qualif.:** Applicants must be enrolled in an accredited graduate institution in North America; must have strong academic qualifications; and have academic and/or career goals focused on making a significant positive difference in the long-term protection of wilderness in the United States. **Criteria:** Selection is based on submitted application materials.

Funds Avail.: $10,000. **Duration:** Annual. **To Apply:** Applicants must submit a two-page double-spaced cover letter; 3-5 page double-spaced proposal; current resume or curriculum vitae; two letters of recommendation describing the applicant's ability to meet the objectives of the scholarship and proposed work; and undergraduate and graduate transcripts (official or unofficial). **Contact:** Email at barron_scholarship@tws.org.

10558 ■ Wilkinson & Company L.L.P.
PO Box 757
Belleville, ON, Canada K8N 5B5
Ph: (613)966-5105
Fax: (613)962-7072
Free: 888-728-3890
URL: www.wilkinson.net
LinkedIn: www.linkedin.com/company/wilkinson-&
 -company-llp

10559 ■ Wilkinson and Company LLP Scholarships *(Undergraduate/Scholarship)*

Purpose: To provide financial support to students with the highest marks in a business-related course so they may pursue further education. **Focus:** Business. **Qualif.:** Applicants must be students from secondary schools in the Quinte and Kingston area. **Criteria:** Selection shall be based on scholastic records of applicants.

Funds Avail.: 300 Canadian Dollars. **Duration:** Annual. **To Apply:** Applicants must submit a completed application form. **Contact:** hrdept@wilkinson.net.

10560 ■ Willamette University
900 State St.
Salem, OR 97301-3922
Ph: (503)370-6300
Fax: (503)370-6153
E-mail: ask@willamette.edu
URL: www.willamette.edu

10561 ■ Mary Stuart Rogers Scholarships *(Undergraduate/Scholarship)*

Purpose: To provide financial support to individuals who wish to pursue their studies. **Focus:** General studies/Field of study not specified. **Qualif.:** Applicants must be enrolled as full-time students and have 3.0 GPA to be considered. **Criteria:** Applicants will be selected based on academic credentials; strength in service; leadership and financial need.

Funds Avail.: $4,000. **Duration:** Annual. **To Apply:** For more information about the scholarship, applicants must contact the Office of Financial Aid. **Deadline:** March 13. **Contact:** Office of Financial Aid; Phone: 503-370-6273; E-mail: finaid@willamette.edu.

10562 ■ The Williams Chorale
c/o Liisa Niemi, President
25 Torrey St.
Attleboro, MA 02703
URL: www.thewilliamschorale.org

10563 ■ Williams Chorale Bacardi Fallon Performing Arts Scholarships *(Undergraduate/Award, Scholarship)*

Purpose: To help area high school juniors or seniors in their pursuit of a musical education. **Focus:** Education, Music. **Qualif.:** Applicant must be a high school junior or senior pursuing musical education. **Criteria:** Selection is based on the application recording.

Funds Avail.: 1st prize: $5,000; 2nd prize: $2,000; 3rd prize: $1,000; Director's Choice: $500; All other finalists: $250. **Duration:** Annual. **To Apply:** Application recording must include at least 5 minutes of total playing time and must include at least two movements of contrasting style. All recording submissions must be on compact discs. **Deadline:** March 16. **Remarks:** Established in 2001. **Contact:** Wayne Taylor; Email: wjtaylor@comcast.net or Liisa Niemi; Email: liisaniemi@verizon.net.

10564 ■ John G. Williams Foundation
PO Box 1229
Camp Hill, PA 17001-1229
Ph: (717)795-9880
Fax: (717)795-1002
URL: www.jgwfoundation.org

10565 ■ John G. Williams Scholarship Fund *(Undergraduate/Scholarship)*

Purpose: To provide financial assistance to deserving students for their pursuit of college and/or post-graduate educational opportunities. **Focus:** General studies/Field of study not specified. **Qualif.:** Applicants must be residents of Pennsylvania; must be high school graduates and enrolled full-time; must have a minimum GPA of 3.0 or its equivalent; must have been accepted by an institution of higher learning before making application for assistance. Application may be made at any time during a student's undergraduate or graduate career. **Criteria:** Recipients are selected based on demonstrated financial need, personal initiative and civic responsibility.

Funds Avail.: No specific amount. **To Apply:** Applicants must complete the standard financial need and financial aid form; must submit a transcript of grades for the most recent academic year; must provide evidence of acceptance and attendance by a college or graduate school and two character recommendations. **Deadline:** June 15. **Remarks:** Established in 1985.

10566 ■ Woodrow Wilson International Center for Scholars
1 Woodrow Wilson Plz.
1300 Pennsylvania Ave. NW
Washington, DC 20004-3027
Ph: (202)691-4000
Fax: (202)691-4001
E-mail: wwics@wilsoncenter.org
URL: www.wilsoncenter.org
Facebook: www.facebook.com/woodrowwilsoncenter
LinkedIn: www.linkedin.com/company/woodrow-wilson
 -international-center-for-scholars
Twitter: twitter.com/thewilsoncenter

10567 ■ Woodrow Wilson International Center for Scholars Fellowships *(Doctorate/Fellowship)*

Purpose: To support individuals conduct an independent research on national and/or international issues addressing

Awards are arranged alphabetically below their administering organizations

key public policy challenges. **Focus:** General studies/Field of study not specified. **Qualif.:** Applicants must be citizens or permanent residents from any country. Foreign nationals must be able to hold a valid passport and obtain a J1 Visa; men and women with outstanding capabilities and experience from a wide variety of backgrounds, including government, the corporate world, professions and academia; academic candidates holding a PhD; academic candidates demonstrating scholarly achievement by publications beyond their doctoral dissertations; practitioners or policymakers with an equivalent level of professional achievement; be English proficiency as the Center is designed to encourage the exchange of ideas among its fellows. **Criteria:** Fellowships will be awarded on a competitive basis. Selection will be based on the following criteria: significance of the proposed research, including the importance and originality of the project; quality of the proposal in definition, organization, clarity and scope; capabilities and achievements of the applicants and the likelihood that they will accomplish the proposed project; the relevance of the project to contemporary policy issues; potential as a fellow, including what is the applicant's potential for participating in the life and priorities of the Center and its outreach in fulfilling its mission.

Funds Avail.: No specific amount. **Duration:** Annual; Nine months. **To Apply:** Applicants may submit their applications online. If submitted by mail, a complete application must include the following: a two-page, single-sided Fellowship application form; not to exceed three page list of applicant's publications that include exact titles, names of the publishers, dates of publication and status of forthcoming publications; not to exceed five single-spaced typed pages, using 12-point, typed project proposal; maximum of three pages of bibliography for the project that includes primary sources and relevant secondary sources; and a one-page Financial Information Form. All application materials must be submitted in English. Two reference letters must be submitted directly to the Center by the referees or mailed with the application. **Deadline:** October 1. **Contact:** Woodrow Wilson International Center for Scholars, at the above address.

10568 ■ Winston-Salem Foundation
751 W 4th St., Ste. 200
Winston Salem, NC 27101-2702
Ph: (336)725-2382
Fax: (336)727-0581
E-mail: info@wsfoundation.org
URL: www.wsfoundation.org
Facebook: www.facebook.com/winstonsalemfoundation
Twitter: twitter.com/wsfoundation

10569 ■ William H. Andrews/HAWS Scholarships
(Undergraduate/Scholarship)

Purpose: To encourage and enable residents of public housing and Section Eight housing to pursue their education in an accredited post-secondary school. **Focus:** General studies/Field of study not specified. **Qualif.:** Applicants must be graduating high school seniors or adults; must be residents living in a property owned or managed by HAWS; must have cumulative GPA of 2.0 at the time of initial application; and must demonstrate evidence of community involvement or school activities including any awards or leadership roles. **Criteria:** Recipients will be selected based on the committee's review of applications.

Funds Avail.: $600-$1,200. **Duration:** Annual. **To Apply:** Applicants must download and complete the online application form; must submit a signed certification signature page; graduating high school seniors must provide a grade transcript through first semester of 12th grade. **Deadline:** April 1. **Contact:** Winston-Salem Foundation's Student Aid Department at 336-714-3445 or students@wsfoundation.org.

10570 ■ Chester Arzell and Helen Miller Montgomery Scholarships (Undergraduate/Scholarship)

Purpose: To provide educational support to deserving students from Stokes County public high schools. **Focus:** General studies/Field of study not specified. **Qualif.:** Applicants must be students at a Stokes County high schools; must have a minimum and cumulative GPA of 2.0; must participate in community service and extracurricular activities; must demonstrate good character and financial need. **Criteria:** Selection will be based on the committee's criteria.

Funds Avail.: $1,000. **To Apply:** Scholarship applications are available online or in the guidance offices of the three Stokes county high schools. **Deadline:** April 1. **Remarks:** Established in 2007. **Contact:** Winston-Salem Foundation's Student Aid Department at 336-714-3445 or students@wsfoundation.org.

10571 ■ F.A. and Charlotte Blount Scholarships
(Undergraduate/Scholarship)

Purpose: To support Forsyth County high school seniors who will pursue a four-year baccalaureate degree at an accredited college or university. **Focus:** General studies/Field of study not specified. **Qualif.:** Applicants must be African American or Hispanic; must demonstrate a minimum and cumulative GPA of 3.0; must demonstrate financial need, however, the scholarship is not restricted to lowest family incomes. **Criteria:** Preference will be given to minority students.

Funds Avail.: $3,000. **To Apply:** Applicants must submit a completed application form; grade transcript through first semester of the 12th grade; and one recommendation. **Deadline:** April 1. **Remarks:** Established in 1997. **Contact:** Winston-Salem Foundation's Student Aid Department at 336-714-3445 or students@wsfoundation.org.

10572 ■ Sam L. Booke, Sr. Scholarships
(Undergraduate/Scholarship)

Purpose: To provide financial support to students who are pursuing career in the mathematics field. **Focus:** Mathematics and mathematical sciences. **Qualif.:** Applicants must be graduating seniors from public high schools in the Winston-Salem/Forsyth County School; must demonstrate interest in Mathematics. **Criteria:** Recipients will be selected based on the following: evidence of excellence in Mathematics through both course selection and grades; intent to pursue a career in Mathematics; potential to achieve career goal; evidence of scholarship including appropriate selection of high school curriculum and academic standing; evidence that students have shown interest and concern for being members of the society.

Funds Avail.: $1,500. **Duration:** Annual. **To Apply:** Applicants must complete online application form. Applicants must also submit one teacher recommendation from math teacher; and official high school grade transcript (through at least first semester of the 12th grade and including SAT scores and class rank). **Deadline:** April 1. **Remarks:** Established in 1989. **Contact:** Winston-Salem Foundation's Student Aid Department; Phone: 336-714-3445; Email: Students@wsfoundation.org.

Awards are arranged alphabetically below their administering organizations

10573 ■ Tien Bui Memorial Scholarships
(Undergraduate/Scholarship)

Purpose: To assist graduating high school seniors who have attended the Winston-Salem/Forsyth County Schools' Career Center. **Focus:** General studies/Field of study not specified. **Qualif.:** Applicants must: demonstrate a minimum cumulative GPA of 3.5; must have strong SAT scores and challenging academic course selection as graduating high school seniors; must demonstrate financial need (award not restricted to lowest family income); have attended the Winston-Salem/Forsyth County Schools' Career Center during their high school and successfully completed either advanced placement in Math or Science. **Criteria:** Recipients will be selected based on the committee's review of application materials.

Funds Avail.: $1,000. **To Apply:** Scholarship applications are available online. Applicants must complete the Tien Bui Memorial Scholarship application; must submit grade transcript through 1st semester of 12th grade; submit letter of acceptance from NCSU that specifies enrollment in the College of Engineering; and must submit a signed certification signature page. **Deadline:** April 1. **Contact:** Winston-Salem Foundation's Student Aid Department; Phone: 336-714-3445; Email: Students@wsfoundation.org.

10574 ■ Wes Burton Memorial Scholarships
(Undergraduate/Scholarship)

Purpose: To provide students undergraduate tuition, fees room and board at an accredited college or university. **Focus:** Business administration; Computer and information sciences; Engineering; Mathematics and mathematical sciences. **Qualif.:** Applicants must have a minimum GPA of 3.5; must demonstrate community and school service; must have an intent to pursue a career in Mathematics, Computer Science, Business Administration, or Engineering; demonstrate financial need (award is not restricted to lowest family incomes). **Criteria:** Award will be given based on the committee's criteria.

Funds Avail.: No specific amount. **Duration:** Annual. **To Apply:** Students must complete the application in its entirety and include supplemental items and information requested in the various sections of the application. The supplemental items include: an interview with the Foundation; a grade transcript; a resume or list of student activities; one letter of recommendation from a math teacher, business teacher, or computer science teacher. **Deadline:** April 1. **Contact:** Winston-Salem Foundation's Student Aid Department; Phone: 336-714-3445; Email: Students@wsfoundation.org.

10575 ■ Elmer and Rosa Lee Collins Scholarships
(Undergraduate/Scholarship)

Purpose: To provide a college scholarship to a worthy graduating high school senior from a Forsyth County high school. **Focus:** General studies/Field of study not specified. **Qualif.:** Applicants must: be graduating high school seniors, be attending a Forsyth County high school and residents in The Winston-Salem's Foundation service area; demonstrate character and purpose as evidenced in school, community, church, and work activities; achieved a minimum cumulative GPA of 3.5 with strong course selection; demonstrate financial need (however, the scholarship is not restricted to lower family incomes); be US citizens. **Criteria:** Selection will be based on the committee's criteria.

Funds Avail.: $3,000. **Duration:** Annual. **To Apply:** Eligible high school seniors may complete an application online. Applicants are responsible for submitting the completed application and all supplemental items to the Foundation. Supplemental items include: grade transcript through the 1st semester of the 12th grade; one recommendation from a teacher, guidance counselor, coach, principal, employer, clergy, or other community leader who has supervised, counseled or coached applicant in some capacity. **Deadline:** April 1. **Remarks:** Established in 2006. **Contact:** Winston-Salem Foundation's Student Aid Department; Phone: 336-714-3445; Email: StudentAid@wsfoundation.org.

10576 ■ Lloyd E. and Rachel S. Collins Scholarships
(Undergraduate/Scholarship)

Purpose: To award scholarships to worthy graduating high school seniors from North, South, and West Stokes High Schools who will attend an accredited two or four-year college or university. **Focus:** General studies/Field of study not specified. **Qualif.:** Applicants must be graduating high school seniors attending North Stokes High School, South Stokes High School, or West Stokes High School; must have a minimum cumulative GPA of 3.0 and a transcript reflecting a challenging course selection; must demonstrate good character, school service, and community service; must demonstrate financial need, but not restricted to lower incomes (student's financial need and merit will be equally weighted). **Criteria:** Selection will be based on the committee's criteria.

Funds Avail.: $2,000. **Duration:** Annual. **To Apply:** Applicants must submit complete application form, high school grade transcript, one recommendation letter and signed copy of parents' federal tax return from previous year. **Deadline:** April 1. **Remarks:** Established in 1991. **Contact:** Winston-Salem Foundation's Student Aid Department; Phone: 336-714-3445; Email: StudentAid@wsfoundation.org.

10577 ■ D.C. Cornelius Memorial Scholarships
(Undergraduate/Scholarship)

Purpose: To provide students the educational support they need in pursuing a two-year associate degree, or a certificate or diploma. **Focus:** General studies/Field of study not specified. **Qualif.:** Applicants be U.S. citizens; must be graduating high school seniors from Forbush High School; must have a minimum GPA of 2.8; must demonstrate character, leadership, compassion for all people and dedication to service of community and school; must demonstrate financial need. **Criteria:** Award will be given based on the committee's criteria.

Funds Avail.: $1,000. **Duration:** Up to two years. **To Apply:** Scholarship applications will be available in the guidance office at Forbush High School and also online. Students must complete the application in its entirety; include grade transcripts with the application at time of submittal; and include two recommendations with the application. **Deadline:** April 1. **Remarks:** Established in 2005. **Contact:** Winston-Salem Foundation's Student Aid Department at 336-714-3445 or students@wsfoundation.org; donna.myers@me.com.

10578 ■ Serena D. Dalton Scholarships
(Undergraduate/Scholarship)

Purpose: To provide students the financial assistance they need. **Focus:** General studies/Field of study not specified. **Qualif.:** Applicants must have adjusted gross income within the table guidelines (table is based on up to 300% above the federal poverty level); must be residents of Forsyth County; must have achieved a current cumulative GPA of

Awards are arranged alphabetically below their administering organizations

at least 2.0; must be enrolled a minimum of six credit hours/semester during the academic year in a program leading to a first time two or four year degree, certificate, or diploma from an accredited institution which participates in the federal student aid program; must be US citizens. **Criteria:** Selection will be based on the committee's criteria.

Funds Avail.: No specific amount. **To Apply:** The following items are required to complete the application process: Submittal of completed application and signed signature page; Signed copy of parents'/guardians'/family's previous year's 1040, 1040A, or 1040EZ income tax return (for dependent students); Signed copy of applicant's previous year's tax return; Official high school grade transcript through at least 1st semester of the 12th grade or year-end college grade transcript, whichever is the most recent (request from the school's Registrar and forward to the Foundation); Copy of the Student Aid Report if they have applied for federal aid; Copy of the financial aid award letter. Please submit the application on-line and follow with additional items as soon as you receive them. **Deadline:** August 15. **Contact:** Winston-Salem Foundation's Student Aid Department at 336-714-3445 or students@wsfoundation.org.

10579 ■ Wade and Marcelene Duncan Scholarships
(Undergraduate/Scholarship)

Purpose: To provide scholarships to worthy high school seniors graduating from either North Stokes or South Stokes High schools. **Focus:** General studies/Field of study not specified. **Qualif.:** Applicants must be graduating seniors from either North Stokes or South Stokes high schools; must have a minimum cumulative GPA of 2.0; must demonstrate financial need, leadership, participation in community service, or in athletics. **Criteria:** Applications will be reviewed by the Wade and Marcelene Duncan Scholarship Fund Committee at each high school. Upon determination of the scholarship recipient each year, the selection committee will notify The Winston-Salem Foundation of that individual's name, address, college of choice, social security number, and telephone number.

Funds Avail.: $500. **To Apply:** Applications and all required materials must be delivered to high school guidance office. Students should contact the guidance office at North Stokes High School or South Stokes High School to request applications. Applications are also available online. **Deadline:** April 1. **Contact:** Winston-Salem Foundation's Student Aid Department at 336-714-3445 or students@wsfoundation.org.

10580 ■ Virginia Elizabeth and Alma Vane Taylor Nursing Scholarship *(Undergraduate/Scholarship)*

Purpose: To provide support to residents seeking associate or baccalaureate nursing degrees. **Focus:** Nursing. **Qualif.:** Applicants must: be accepted into an accredited North Carolina school of nursing program, as verified by an acceptance letter; demonstrate financial need; have a high school/college cumulative GPA of at least 2.5. Preference will be given to those seeking first time associate or baccalaureate degrees; those with master's degrees in any area will be ineligible to apply. **Criteria:** Selection will be based on the committee's criteria.

Funds Avail.: No specific amount. **To Apply:** The Winston-Salem Foundation's General Financial Aid Application will be used to apply for this scholarship. The General Financial Aid Application is available online or you may request an application to the Foundation's Student Aid Committee. **Deadline:** August 15. **Remarks:** Established in 1966. **Contact:** Winston-Salem Foundation's Student Aid Department; Phone: 336-714-3445; Email: Students@wsfoundation.org.

10581 ■ Forsyth County Nursing Scholarships
(Undergraduate/Scholarship)

Purpose: To support students seeking first-time RN degrees at accredited two and four-year colleges. **Focus:** Nursing. **Qualif.:** Applicants must be US citizens; must be residents of Forsyth County, NC; must have achieved a current cumulative GPA of at least 2.0; must demonstrate financial need, but not restricted to lowest incomes. **Criteria:** Preference will be given to those seeking first-time associate or baccalaureate nursing degrees.

Funds Avail.: No specific amount. **Duration:** Annual. **To Apply:** The following items are required to complete the application process: Submittal of completed application and signed signature page; Signed copy of parents'/guardians'/family's previous year's 1040, 1040A, or 1040EZ income tax return (for dependent students); Signed copy of applicant's previous year's tax return; Official high school grade transcript through at least 1st semester of the 12th grade or college grade transcript, whichever is the most recent (request from the school's Registrar and forward to the Foundation); Copy of the Student Aid Report if applicant has applied for federal aid; Copy of the financial aid award letter. Please submit the application on-line and follow with additional items as soon as you receive them. **Deadline:** August 15. **Contact:** Winston-Salem Foundation's Student Aid Department at 336-714-3445 or students@wsfoundation.org.

10582 ■ Gaddy Student Scholarships
(Undergraduate/Scholarship)

Purpose: To give priority consideration to those students who will attend Davidson College or Wake Forest University. **Focus:** General studies/Field of study not specified. **Qualif.:** Applicants must be students who: are graduating high school seniors from R.J. Reynolds High School; demonstrate academic promise; are US citizens; have participated as athletes or in support positions in high school athletics (broad consideration); have financial need (broad consideration given - not restricted to lower family incomes). **Criteria:** Selection will be based on the committee's criteria.

Funds Avail.: $1,000. **Duration:** Annual. **To Apply:** Students must provide the following: A completed application; grade transcript through 1st semester, 12th grade; one recommendation as described in the application guidelines. Schedule an interview, if so advised. **Deadline:** April 1. **Remarks:** Established in 1997. **Contact:** Winston-Salem Foundation's Student Aid Department at 336-714-3445 or students@wsfoundation.org.

10583 ■ Garden Club Council of Winston-Salem and Forsyth County Council Scholarships
(Undergraduate/Scholarship)

Purpose: To provide financial support for educational opportunities to legal residents of North Carolina. **Focus:** Horticulture; Landscape architecture and design. **Qualif.:** Applicants must be residents of Forsyth County, NC or one of the other counties in the Winston-Salem Foundation's service area; must maintain at least part-time enrollment; must have a minimum cumulative GPA of 2.0; must demonstrate financial need, but not restricted to lower incomes (student's financial need and merit will be equally weighted); must be in pursuit of undergraduate associate or baccalaureate degree (first-time degrees preferred); must be enrolled in a horticulture or landscaping curriculum.

Awards are arranged alphabetically below their administering organizations

Criteria: Applicants will be evaluated based on qualifications, academic standing and demonstrated financial need.

Funds Avail.: No specific amount. **To Apply:** Interested applicants must visit the website for the online application process and must submit the following required materials: high school grade transcript through the first semester of 12th grade or most recent college grade transcript; signed copy of parents' federal income tax return from previous year; signed copy of student's federal income tax return from previous year. **Deadline:** August 15. **Remarks:** Established in 2004. **Contact:** Winston-Salem Foundation's Student Aid Department at 336-714-3445 or students@wsfoundation.org.

10584 ■ Claude B. Hart Memorial Scholarships
(Undergraduate/Scholarship)

Purpose: To provide educational support to worthy graduating high school seniors from Elkin High School who are US citizens. **Focus:** Engineering; Mathematics and mathematical sciences. **Qualif.:** Applicant must demonstrate significant promise in academics, leadership, community service and school service and intend to major in mathematics (accounting, computer science, business administration) and/or engineering (mechanical, civil, chemical, etc.) in college. Demonstration of financial need is preferred, but award is not restricted to lowest family incomes. Renewal of the award after the first year will require that the student be a full-time undergraduate student at an accredited four-year institution, maintain a minimum cumulative grade point average of 2.5, and continue to major in mathematics or engineering. **Criteria:** Selection will be based on the committee's criteria.

Funds Avail.: $1,000. **To Apply:** Scholarship applications will be provided in the guidance office at Elkin High School; student must complete the application, requested transcripts, and financial information before being considered by the Elkin High School Scholarship Committee; the Scholarship Committee will submit up to 5 candidates to The Winston-Salem Foundation for review by the Elkin Advisory Committee or its appointed sub-committee. **Deadline:** April 1. **Remarks:** Established in 1994. **Contact:** Winston-Salem Foundation's Student Aid Department at 336-714-3445 or students@wsfoundation.org.

10585 ■ Oliver Joel and Ellen Pell Denny Healthcare Scholarship Fund *(Undergraduate/Scholarship)*

Purpose: To support students who are seeking a first-time associate or baccalaureate degree, certificate or diploma in a health field. **Focus:** Health care services. **Qualif.:** Applicants must be seeking a two or four year degree or be enrolled in a program leading to a certificate or diploma; must be attending an accredited North Carolina school pursuing healthcare education such as, but not limited, registered nursing, licensed practical nursing, nuclear medicine, radiography, and respiratory therapy; must provide an acceptance letter for all programs; must have a high school/college cumulative GPA of at least 2.5 for all healthcare programs, including nursing; must be North Carolina residents and US citizens. **Criteria:** Selection will be based on the committee's criteria. Preference will be given to those living in Forsyth, Davidson, Davie, and Stokes, Surry, and Yadkin counties.

Funds Avail.: $3,000. **Duration:** Annual. **To Apply:** The Winston-Salem Foundation's General Financial Aid Application will be used to apply for this scholarship; the General Financial Aid Applications are available in high school guidance office and on the website. **Deadline:** August 15. **Contact:** Winston-Salem Foundation's Student Aid Department at 336-714-3445 or students@wsfoundation.org.

10586 ■ Stella B. Johnson Scholarships
(Undergraduate/Scholarship)

Purpose: To provide educational aid to traditional and non-traditional age applicants from charitable funds established by generous supporters of the community. **Focus:** General studies/Field of study not specified. **Qualif.:** Applicants must: have a family adjusted gross income within the table guidelines (table is based on up to 330% above the federal poverty level); be residents of Forsyth County, NC; have achieved a current cumulative grade point average of at least 2.0; must be enrolled a minimum of six credit hours/semester during the academic year in a program leading to a first time two or four year degree, certificate, or diploma from an accredited institution which participates in the federal student aid program; must be US citizens. **Criteria:** Selection will be based on the committee's criteria.

Funds Avail.: No specific amount. **To Apply:** The following items are required to complete the application process: submittal of completed application and signed signature page; signed copy of parents'/guardians'/family's previous year's 1040, 1040A, or 1040EZ income tax return (for dependent students); signed copy of applicants' previous year's tax return; official high school grade transcript through at least 1st semester of the 12th grade or year-end college grade transcript, whichever is the most recent (request from the school's Registrar and forward to the Foundation); copy of the Student Aid Report if applicant has applied for federal aid; copy of the financial aid award letter; interview if so advised; submit the application on-line **Deadline:** August 15. **Contact:** Winston-Salem Foundation's Student Aid Department at 336-714-3445 or students@wsfoundation.org.

10587 ■ Douglas Gray Kimel Scholarships
(Undergraduate/Scholarship)

Purpose: To award freshman who will pursue a degree in music from one of the following institutions: North Carolina School of the Arts, Salem College, Wake Forest University, or Winston-Salem State University. **Focus:** Music. **Qualif.:** This scholarship seeks to identify those students who: will pursue a degree in music; demonstrate a minimum, cumulative GPA of 3.5; have financial need (scholarship is not restricted to lowest family incomes); are residents of Forsyth County; are Moravian, preferably; are studying to enter a church-related vocation, preferably. **Criteria:** Selection will be based on the committee's criteria.

Funds Avail.: $500. **To Apply:** Scholarship applications will be available online. Students must: complete the scholarship application; provide grade transcript through the 1st semester of 12th grade; submit one recommendation as outlined on the application; attend an interview if so advised. **Deadline:** April 1. **Remarks:** Established in 2007. **Contact:** Winston-Salem Foundation's Student Aid Department at 336-714-3445 or students@wsfoundation.org.

10588 ■ Johnny Lineberry Memorial Scholarships
(Undergraduate, Vocational/Occupational/Scholarship)

Purpose: To provide educational support to a worthy Forbush High School senior who will go directly to an accredited vocational/technical school, community college, or college/university in pursuit of a certificate, diploma or baccalaureate degree. **Focus:** Electronics. **Qualif.:** Applicants must be graduating high school seniors from Forsbush High School in East Bend, N.C.; must demonstrate a minimum

Awards are arranged alphabetically below their administering organizations

and cumulative GPA of at least 2.5; must demonstrate strong character and community involvement; must intend to study the field of electronics, preferably. **Criteria:** Selection will be based on the committee's criteria.

Funds Avail.: $500. **To Apply:** Applications for the scholarship are available in the guidance office at Forbush High School and from The Winston-Salem Foundation's web site. Completed applications should be submitted to the guidance office. **Deadline:** April 1. **Remarks:** Established in 1990. **Contact:** Winston-Salem Foundation's Student Aid Department at 336-714-3445 or students@wsfoundation.org.

10589 ■ L.D. and Elsie Long Memorial Scholarships
(Graduate/Scholarship)

Purpose: To provide financial support for Forsyth County residents who demonstrate financial need to attend Wake Forest University. **Focus:** General studies/Field of study not specified. **Qualif.:** Applicant must have a family adjusted gross income within the table guidelines (table is based on up to 330% above the federal poverty level); be a resident of Forsyth County; have achieved a current cumulative GPA of at least 2.0; must be enrolled a minimum of six credits hours/semester during the academic year in a program leading to a graduate degree from Wake Forest University. **Criteria:** Preference will be given to students enrolled or planning to enroll in graduate programs on the Reynolda Campus.

Funds Avail.: No specific amount. **To Apply:** The following items are required to complete the application process: submittal of completed application and signed signature page; signed copy of applicant's previous year's tax return; official high school grade transcript through at least 1st semester of the 12th grade or year-end college grade transcript, whichever is the most recent (request from the school's Registrar and forward to the Foundation); copy of the Student Aid Report (SAR) if applicant has applied for federal aid; copy of the financial award letter; interview if so advised. **Remarks:** Established in 1980.

10590 ■ Orthopaedic Specialists Nursing Scholarships *(Undergraduate/Scholarship)*

Purpose: To provide financial support for students who have been accepted into the nursing program at Forsyth Technical Community College or Winston-Salem State University. **Focus:** Nursing. **Qualif.:** Applicants must be enrolled on a full-time basis in the pursuit of a first associate degree or a bachelors degree in nursing; must provide a copy of letter of admission to the nursing program at FTCC or WSSU (students ineligible until accepted into nursing program); must have at least 3.0 cumulative GPA for graduating high school seniors and at least 2.6 cumulative GPA for college students. **Criteria:** Selection will be based on the committee's criteria.

Funds Avail.: $1,000. **Duration:** Annual. **To Apply:** Scholarship application may be obtained online. In addition to the application, the following items are required for first-time applicants: signed copy of parent/guardian federal income tax return (for dependent students); signed copy of applicants' federal income tax return; current official transcript of academic records (obtain from school Registrar); copy of Student Aid Report if student applied for federal aid; copy of financial aid notice from college if student applied for federal aid; and a letter of acceptance into a nursing program. **Deadline:** August 15. **Remarks:** Established in 2002. **Contact:** Winston-Salem Foundation's Student Aid Department at 336-714-3445 or students@wsfoundation.org.

10591 ■ Alice Conger Patterson Scholarships
(Undergraduate/Scholarship)

Purpose: To help deserving adult women achieve their educational goals. **Focus:** General studies/Field of study not specified. **Qualif.:** Applicants must be female students who: demonstrate financial need; are 23 years of age or older; have earned a high school diploma or equivalent certificate (GED, home school completion, adult high school diploma); are applying to or are currently enrolled in a four-year college or university in the Piedmont Triad of North Carolina in pursuit of an undergraduate degree; have a minimum cumulative GPA of 2.6. **Criteria:** Selection will be based on the committee's criteria. Preference will be given to students at Salem College who demonstrate a strong purpose in pursuing a liberal arts degree.

Funds Avail.: $1,000. **To Apply:** Scholarship applications will be available online. Students must submit: completed application and signed signature page; copy of federal tax return for previous year; copy of the financial aid award letter for upcoming year; grade transcripts with class ranking in high school and transcripts for all college or university work to date; one recommendation. **Deadline:** June 15. **Contact:** Winston-Salem Foundation's Student Aid Department at 336-714-3445 or students@wsfoundation.org.

10592 ■ William H. and Lena M. Petree Scholarships *(Undergraduate/Scholarship)*

Purpose: To provide educational support for Forsyth County residents who wish to enter in college. **Focus:** General studies/Field of study not specified. **Qualif.:** Applicants must be graduating high-school seniors who: demonstrate academic promise during high-school; have a minimum and cumulative GPA of 3.5 through 1st semester, 12th grade; demonstrate a willingness for self-help during high school; demonstrate leadership, school service, and community service during high school; demonstrate financial need for upcoming college expenses (award not restricted to lowest family incomes); are US citizens and residents of Forsyth County. **Criteria:** Selection will be based on the committee's criteria.

Funds Avail.: $5,000. **Duration:** Annual. **To Apply:** Application may be downloaded from the Foundation's web site. In addition to completing the application, students must: submit one recommendation; submit a grade transcript through first semester, 12th grade; be present for an interview; and a signed copy of student's and parent's federal tax return from previous year. **Deadline:** April 1. **Remarks:** Established in 1996. **Contact:** Winston-Salem Foundation's Student Aid Department at 336-714-3445 or students@wsfoundation.org.

10593 ■ Pfafftown Jaycees/Lynn Canada Memorial Scholarships *(Undergraduate/Scholarship)*

Purpose: To provide support to Forsyth County residents who are seeking nursing degrees at Forsyth Technical Community College. **Focus:** General studies/Field of study not specified. **Qualif.:** Applicants must be enrolled on a full-time basis in the pursuit of a first associate or a first baccalaureate degree; provide copy of admission letter into the nursing program at FTCC (ineligible until accepted into the nursing program) maintain high school or college cumulative GPA of 2.5. **Criteria:** Selection will be based on the committee's criteria.

Funds Avail.: $1,000. **To Apply:** Eligible applicants may obtain a scholarship application from the Winston-Salem Foundation's website. In addition to the completed/signed application, applicants are responsible for providing the fol-

Awards are arranged alphabetically below their administering organizations

lowing required supplemental items: signed copy of parent/guardian's federal income tax return; signed copy of student's federal income tax return, if applicable; applicant's official high school (as of 1st semester, 12th grade) or official college grade transcript (as of academic year-end); copy of Student Aid Report and financial aid notice if student applied for federal aid; and must provide a letter of acceptance into a nursing program. **Deadline:** August 15. **Remarks:** Established in 2005. **Contact:** Winston-Salem Foundation's Student Aid Department; Phone: 336-714-3445; Email: Students@wsfoundation.org.

10594 ■ L. Gordon, Jr. and June D. Pfefferkorn Scholarships *(Undergraduate/Scholarship)*

Purpose: To provide financial support to students who are attending a Forsyth County high school and reside in the Foundation's service area of Davidson, Davie, Forsyth, Stokes, Surry, Yadkin, and Wilkes counties. **Focus:** General studies/Field of study not specified. **Qualif.:** Applicants must: attend an accredited four-year college or university in North Carolina; be residents of Forsyth County; have achieved a current cumulative GPA of at least 3.5; demonstrate significant promise in leadership, community service, and school service; be US citizens; demonstrate financial need, (award not restricted to lowest family incomes); be graduating high school seniors. **Criteria:** Selection will be based on the committee's criteria.

Funds Avail.: $5,000. **To Apply:** The following items are required to complete the application process: submittal of completed application; signed copy of parents' federal tax return from previous year; high school grade transcript through the first semester of the 12th grade; one recommendation as described in the online Student Aid Application. **Deadline:** April 1. **Remarks:** Established in 2004. **Contact:** Winston-Salem Foundation's Student Aid Department; Phone: 336-714-3445; Email: Students@wsfoundation.org.

10595 ■ Dean Prim Scholarships *(Undergraduate/Scholarship)*

Purpose: To provide educational support and travel opportunities to juniors and seniors who attend high schools in Davie, Forsyth and Yadkin counties. **Focus:** General studies/Field of study not specified. **Qualif.:** Applicants must: be at least 16 years of age; be high school juniors or high school seniors; demonstrate excellence in schoolwork as evidenced by course selection and grades (minimum GPA of 3.0); participate in extracurricular school activities, community and/or church activities, and school or community athletics; demonstrate good character and show interest in and concern for being an active member of society; be committed to traveling and studying in China and have the full support of parent(s) to participate. The scholarship is available to students regardless of race, sex, national, origin, or religion. **Criteria:** Selection will be based on the committee's criteria.

Funds Avail.: $1,500. **Duration:** Annual. **To Apply:** The Prim scholarship application is on The Winston-Salem Foundation's web site. It is the student's responsibility to make sure that, along with submittal for the electronic application completed in its entirety, all supplemental materials are in the office of The Winston-Salem Foundation by the deadline. Supplemental materials include: a grade transcript, through 10th grade for juniors and 11th grade for seniors; two recommendations as described in the application; a recent photograph (include student's name on back of photo). **Deadline:** August 15. **Remarks:** Established in 1975. **Contact:** Winston-Salem Foundation's Student Aid Department; Phone: 336-714-3445; Email: Students@wsfoundation.org.

10596 ■ John S. and Jacqueline P. Rider Scholarships *(Undergraduate/Scholarship)*

Purpose: To provide financial support to a student who attend a Forsyth County high school. **Focus:** General studies/Field of study not specified. **Qualif.:** Applicants must: demonstrate financial need (not restricted to lower family incomes); be residents of Forsyth County; have achieved a current cumulative grade point average of at least 3.5; be enrolled full-time in a program leading to a two or four year degree, certificate, or diploma from an accredited institution which participates in the federal student aid program; be graduating high school seniors. **Criteria:** Selection will be based on merit and financial need though need is not restricted to lower incomes.

Funds Avail.: $500. **To Apply:** The following items are required to complete the application process: submittal of completed application and high school grade transcript through the first semester of 12th grade; one recommendation letter; signed copy of parents' federal tax return from previous year. **Deadline:** April 1. **Contact:** Winston-Salem Foundation's Student Aid Department; Phone: 336-714-3445; Email: Students@wsfoundation.org.

10597 ■ Ray and Pearl Sams Scholarships *(Undergraduate/Scholarship)*

Purpose: To provide financial assistance to students enrolled in a post-secondary institution. **Focus:** General studies/Field of study not specified. **Qualif.:** Applicants must be graduating high-school seniors who: have achieved excellence in school work as evidence by course selection and grades (minimum cumulative GPA of 3.5 on a 4.0 scale, or equivalent) through 1st semester of the 12th grade; have participated in school service clubs and/or other school activities; have participated in non-school community service activities; demonstrates good moral character; demonstrates evidence of financial need, although award is not restricted to lower incomes; are United States citizens. **Criteria:** Selection will be based on the committee's criteria.

Funds Avail.: $2,500. **Duration:** Annual. **To Apply:** Applicants must complete and submit the application online. The application and the following items must be received in the foundation's office by the deadline: official grade transcript through the 1st semester of the 12 grade; one recommendation from a teacher, guidance counselor, coach, principal, employer, clergy, or other community leader who has supervised, counseled or coached applicant in some capacity; an interview with the Foundation's Director of Student Aid, if so advised **Deadline:** April 1. **Remarks:** Established in 1999. **Contact:** Winston-Salem Foundation's Student Aid Department; Phone: 336-714-3445; Email: Students@wsfoundation.org.

10598 ■ Bruce Shelton Scholarships *(Undergraduate/Scholarship)*

Purpose: To support a graduating high school student from a Forsyth County school who displays the traits of athletic excellence, academic achievement, leadership, and social responsibility. **Focus:** General studies/Field of study not specified. **Qualif.:** Applicants must be students who exhibit the following qualities in equal measure: athletic excellence the student must have excelled in at least one varsity sport; social responsibility - the student must have participated in at least one extra-curricular or community activity; academic success - the student must have a minimum high school cumulative grade point average of at least 3.0, as of the 1st semester of the 12th grade and be ranked in the top 25% of the senior class; leadership - the student must possess qualities that exhibit a willingness to "go the extra mile". Recipients receiving renewal awards must maintain a minimum cumulative GPA of 2.5 and full time enrollment of at least 12 hours each semester at accredited four-year institutions. Official grade transcripts must be submitted each summer by July 1 for verification of acceptable academic pace and GPA. Recipients should request grade transcripts from the Registrar for themselves and forward to the Foundation. **Criteria:** Selection will be based on the committee's criteria.

Funds Avail.: $1,000. **Duration:** Annual. **To Apply:** Students should complete the application in its entirety and submit it by the deadline. In addition, the following supplemental items must be submitted: a grade transcript through the first semester of the 12th grade; one recommendation as described in the application. **Deadline:** April 1. **Remarks:** Established in 1991. **Contact:** Winston-Salem Foundation's Student Aid Department; Phone: 336-714-3445; Email: Students@wsfoundation.org.

10599 ■ Thomas E. Shown, M.D. Memorial Scholarships *(Undergraduate/Scholarship)*

Purpose: To support worthy students from the counties of Forsyth, Wikes, Surry, Yahkin, and Davie who plan to attend an accredited two or four year college or university, preferably in North Carolina. **Focus:** General studies/Field of study not specified. **Qualif.:** Applicants must: demonstrate financial need (award not restricted to lower incomes); have a cumulative, minimum high school GPA of 3.0 or college GPA of 2.5; must be employed a minimum of 20 hours, monthly (including college work study); be US citizens. **Criteria:** Selection will be based on the committee's criteria.

Funds Avail.: $1,000. **Duration:** Annual. **To Apply:** The General Financial Aid Application should be completed for this scholarship and is available online. Applicants are responsible for submitting the completed application and all supplemental items. Supplemental items include: Parent/guardian's tax return (for dependent students); applicant's tax return; official high school grade transcript through at least the first semester of the 12th grade or year-end college grade transcript; a copy of your Student Aid Report and financial aid notice if student applied for federal aid; an interview at The Winston-Salem Foundation. **Deadline:** April 1. **Contact:** Winston-Salem Foundation's Student Aid Department; Phone: 336-714-3445; Email: Students@wsfoundation.org.

10600 ■ Stultz Scholarships *(Undergraduate/Scholarship)*

Purpose: To support students with their financial need. **Focus:** General studies/Field of study not specified. **Qualif.:** Applicant must: have a family adjusted gross income within the table guidelines (table is based on up to 300% above the federal poverty level); be a resident of Forsyth County; have achieved a current cumulative grade point of at least 2.0; be enrolled a minimum of six credit hours/semester during the academic year, in a program leading to a first time two or four year degree, certificate, or diploma from an accredited institution which participates in the federal student aid program; be a US citizen. **Criteria:** Selection will be based on the committee's criteria.

Funds Avail.: No specific amount. **To Apply:** The following items are required to complete the application process: submittal of completed application and signed signature page; signed copy of parent's/guardians'/family's previous year's 1040, 1040A, or 1040EZ income tax return; signed copy of applicant's previous year's tax return; official high school grade transcript through at least 1st semester of the 12th grade or year-end college grade transcript, whichever is the most recent, (request from the school's Registrar and forward to the Foundation); copy of the Student Aid Report (SAR) and financial aid award letter if applicant has applied for federal aid; interview if so advised. **Deadline:** August 15. **Contact:** Winston-Salem Foundation's Student Aid Department; Phone: 336-714-3445; Email: Students@wsfoundation.org.

10601 ■ Jeff Turner-Forsyth Audubon Society Scholarships *(Undergraduate/Scholarship)*

Purpose: To support worthy graduating high school seniors from a Forsyth County High School and admitted to a four year accredited college or university. **Focus:** General studies/Field of study not specified. **Qualif.:** Applicants can be U.S. citizens or eligible non-citizen; must demonstrate character, leadership, and solid academic skills (minimum GPA of 3.0). Demonstration of financial needs will be considered but is not required. **Criteria:** Recipients will be evaluated on submitted materials and result of the interview.

Funds Avail.: $500. **To Apply:** Scholarship Applications will be available online. Student must: complete the Winston-Salem Foundation application in its entirety, including an attached listing of student activities as well as personal statement; provide grade transcript through 1st semester of 12th grade with the application, at time of submittal; include at least one letter of reference (3 maximum) which addresses the applicant's character as well as environmental interest/experiences. **Deadline:** April 1. **Remarks:** Established in 2005. **Contact:** Winston-Salem Foundation's Student Aid Department; Phone: 336-714-3445; Email: Students@wsfoundation.org.

10602 ■ Nell and Spencer Waggoner Scholarships *(Undergraduate/Scholarship)*

Purpose: To award merit-based scholarships to worthy graduating high school seniors in Forsyth County who intend to pursue baccalaureate degrees at accredited universities and colleges. **Focus:** General studies/Field of study not specified. **Qualif.:** Applicants must be students who: demonstrate evidence of excellence through course selection and academic achievement with a minimum cumulative GPA of 3.5 (D's are undesirable in any coursework in grades 9-12); outstanding community and school leadership; demonstrate community service and/or school service and concern for being a contributing member of society (work experience recognized for those who have less community involvement due to work obligations). **Criteria:** Selection will be based on the committee's criteria.

Funds Avail.: $3,000. **Duration:** Annual. **To Apply:** In addition to a completed application, the following items are required: a high school grade transcript through at least the first semester of the 12th grade; an interview if so advised; one recommendation; and signed certification signature page. **Deadline:** April 1. **Remarks:** Established in 2005. **Contact:** Winston-Salem Foundation's Student Aid Department; Phone: 336-714-3445; Email: Students@wsfoundation.org.

10603 ■ Art and Dannie Weber Scholarships *(Undergraduate/Scholarship)*

Purpose: To provide a consecutive four-year renewable award to a graduating high school senior form a Forsyth

Awards are arranged alphabetically below their administering organizations

County high school who will pursue post-secondary education. **Focus:** Education. **Qualif.:** Applicants must be graduating high school seniors; must have demonstrated character and purpose as evidenced in school, community, church, and work activities; must have financial need (however, the scholarship is not restricted to lower family incomes); demonstrate academic success by having achieved minimum high school cumulative grade point average (GPA) between 2.5-3.5. **Criteria:** Selection will be based on the committee's criteria.

Funds Avail.: $750. **Duration:** Annual. **To Apply:** Students who are interested in applying for this scholarship should complete the application in its entirety and submit it by the deadline. In addition, the following supplemental items must be submitted: a grade transcript through the first semester of the 12th grade; family federal tax return for last year; one recommendation from a teacher, guidance counselor, coach, principal, employer, clergy, or other community leader who has supervised or coached applicant in some capacity. **Deadline:** April 1. **Remarks:** Established in 2007. **Contact:** Winston-Salem Foundation's Student Aid Department; Phone: 336-714-3445; Email: Students@wsfoundation.org.

10604 ■ Edward Kent Welch Memorial Scholarships
(Undergraduate/Scholarship)

Purpose: To provide college scholarships to graduating high school seniors at Mt. Tabor High School who will attend the University of North Carolina at Chapel Hill. **Focus:** General studies/Field of study not specified. **Qualif.:** Applicants must: have academic promise; evidence of strong moral character; have a genuine concern for others; have school and/or community leadership. The scholarship is available to students regardless of race, sex, national origin, religion, or handicap. **Criteria:** Selection will be based on the committee's criteria.

Funds Avail.: $500. **To Apply:** The Mt. Tabor Guidance Office will select the recipient of this award from its pool of students admitted by and planning to attend UNC-Chapel Hill. **Deadline:** April 1. **Contact:** Winston-Salem Foundation's Student Aid Department; Phone: 336-714-3445; Email: Students@wsfoundation.org.

10605 ■ Edwin H. and Louise N. Williamson Endowed Scholarships *(Undergraduate/Scholarship)*

Purpose: To provide scholarships to a graduating high school senior who will pursue a bachelor's degree at the University of North Carolina-Greensboro. **Focus:** General studies/Field of study not specified. **Qualif.:** Applicants must be graduating high school seniors; demonstrate a minimum cumulative GPA of 3.0; demonstrate financial need (students' merit will be considered to a greater degree); attending the University of North Carolina at Greensboro. **Criteria:** Selection will be based on the committee's criteria.

Funds Avail.: $1,500. **Duration:** Annual. **To Apply:** Scholarship applications are available online. Students must: complete application in its entirety; provide grade transcript through the 1st semester of 12th grade; provide one recommendation, as described in the application; attend an interview, if so advised. **Deadline:** April 1. **Remarks:** Established in 2007. **Contact:** Winston-Salem Foundation's Student Aid Department; Phone: 336-714-3445; Email: Students@wsfoundation.org.

10606 ■ Winston-Salem Foundation Scholarships
(Undergraduate/Scholarship)

Purpose: To provide scholarships to Forsyth County graduating seniors who will pursue post-secondary education at accredited institutions. **Focus:** Education. **Qualif.:** Applicants must attend a Forsyth County high school and reside in The Winston-Salem's Foundation service area; must be graduating high school seniors; must have a minimum unweighted cumulative GPA between 3.0 and 3.5; must demonstrate outstanding leadership, school service and community involvement; must exemplify the Foundation's core values of generosity, integrity, inclusion and excellence. **Criteria:** Selection will be based on the committee's criteria.

Funds Avail.: $4,000. **To Apply:** Scholarship application will be available online. Students must: complete the scholarship application in its entirety; provide grade transcript through the 1st semester of the 12th grade; must submit a signed certification signature page; and last year's family federal tax return. **Deadline:** April 1. **Contact:** WSF Student Aid Department by calling 336-714-3445 or e-mail at studentaid@wsfoundation.org.

10607 ■ Blanche Raper Zimmerman Scholarships
(Other/Scholarship)

Purpose: To provide assistance for teachers to increase their understanding of and appreciation for various world cultures, with preference for teachers of social studies and history. **Focus:** History. **Qualif.:** Applicant must be history or social studies teachers of any grade, kindergarten through twelfth; must have a minimum of three years full-time teaching experience in Forsyth County. **Criteria:** Recipient are selected based on committee's review of application materials.

Funds Avail.: No specific amount. **To Apply:** Applicant should write a letter of application (no more than two pages single-spaced, typewritten) to Kay Dillon, describing the proposed participation in a conference, workshop or foreign travel, as specified in the purpose and requirements; should prepare an itemized statement of all costs associated with a conference, workshop, or travel, including costs of registration, transportation, housing, and meals; and should provide letter of recommendation from his or her principal which includes a verification of the number of years of teaching experience. **Remarks:** Established in 1986.

10608 ■ Winterthur Museum, Garden and Library
5105 Kennett Pke.
Winterthur, DE 19735
Ph: (302)888-4600
Free: 800-448-3883
E-mail: tourinfo@winterthur.org
URL: www.winterthur.org
Facebook: www.facebook.com/winterthurmuse/?ref=nf

10609 ■ Winterthur Research Fellowships
(Graduate/Fellowship)

Purpose: To support student's research in many areas of social and cultural history, including material culture, architecture, decorative arts, design, consumer culture, garden and landscape studies, Shaker studies, travel and tourism, the Atlantic World, and objects in literature. **Focus:** Humanities. **Qualif.:** Applicants must be academic, independent or museum scholars and graduate students conducting a research in the areas of social and cultural history. **Criteria:** Recipients are selected based on the significance of the research.

Funds Avail.: $1,750 per month. **Duration:** Annual; From one to three months. **Number Awarded:** Varies. **To Apply:**

Awards are arranged alphabetically below their administering organizations

Applicants must submit the application cover sheet; an application essay of no more than 1500 words which opens a concise overview of the project; a copy of the curriculum vitae; maximum of two pages bibliography; and two letters of reference addressing the previous scholarly record and current project. Applicants must mail six copies of the completed application package. **Deadline:** January 15. **Remarks:** Fellowships are divided into certain awards where the successful applicants be designated as: Faith Andrews Fellowships for the study of Shaker life and material culture; Robert Lee Gill Fellowships for research on American decorative arts, painting, architecture, or historic preservation; and the Cheryl A. Robertson Fellowships for the study of American domestic life and material culture.

10610 ■ Wire Reinforcement Institute (WRI)
942 Main St.
Hartford, CT 06103
Ph: (860)240-9545
URL: www.wirereinforcementinstitute.org

10611 ■ WRI Education Foundation Scholarships - Graduate (Graduate/Scholarship)
Purpose: To support students pursuing graduate level degrees in structural and/or civil engineering. **Focus:** Engineering, Civil. **Qualif.:** Applicants must be enrolled/registered graduate level students presently pursuing a graduate level degree in structural and/or civil engineering, and enrolled full-time in an accredited four year university program in the United States or Canada. **Criteria:** Selection is based on submitted application.

Funds Avail.: $2,000-$4,000. **Duration:** Annual. **To Apply:** Applicants must submit a completed application form along with an up-to-date transcript of university grades; two letters of recommendation from engineering department faculty members; a letter of recommendation from applicant's past or current employer (if presently working in the areas of construction, engineering or architectural design); a signed and notarized statement confirming the enrollment/registration in an accredited four year United States or Canadian university in pursuit of a graduate degree in structural and/or civil engineering. **Deadline:** April 15.

10612 ■ WRI Education Foundation Scholarships - High School Seniors (Undergraduate/Scholarship)
Purpose: To support students pursuing undergraduate degrees in structural and/or civil engineering. **Focus:** Engineering, Civil. **Qualif.:** Applicants must be high school seniors intending to pursue a four year undergraduate degree in structural and/or civil engineering that have been accepted to and will be registered/enrolled in a four year accredited university/college program in the United States or Canada. **Criteria:** Selection is based on the application materials submitted for review.

Funds Avail.: $2,000-$4,000. **Duration:** Annual. **To Apply:** Applicants must submit a completed application form along with the most recent transcript of high school grades (including ACT/SAT scores and high school class ranking); two letters of recommendation from faculty of math and science departments; and a proof of acceptance to a four year accredited university/college located in the United States or Canada accompanied; a signed statement of intent to enroll in the university/college and to major in structural and/or civil engineering (statement of intent must be signed by the applicant before a Notary Public). **Deadline:** April 15.

10613 ■ WRI Education Foundation Scholarships - Undergraduate (Undergraduate/Scholarship)
Purpose: To support undergraduate students pursuing structural and/or civil engineering. **Focus:** Engineering, Civil. **Qualif.:** Applicants must be currently enrolled/registered undergraduate level student presently pursuing a four year undergraduate level degree in structural and/or civil engineering; or either be enrolled full-time in a four year accredited university/college program in the United States or Canada. **Criteria:** Selection is based on submitted application.

Funds Avail.: $2,000-$4,000. **Duration:** Annual. **To Apply:** Applicants must submit a completed application form along with an up-to-date transcript of university/college grades; two letters of recommendation from engineering department faculty members; a letter of recommendation from applicant's past or current employer (if presently working in the areas of construction, engineering or architectural design); a signed and notarized statement confirming the registration or enrollment and intent to pursue an undergraduate degree in structural and/or civil engineering from a four year university/college in the United States or Canada. **Deadline:** April 15.

10614 ■ Wisconsin Association for Food Protection (WAFP)
PO Box 620705
Middleton, WI 53562
E-mail: wafp-lamb@charter.net
URL: www.wifoodprotection.org

10615 ■ E.H. Marth Food and Environmental Scholarships (Undergraduate/Scholarship)
Purpose: To promote and sustain interest in fields of study that may lead to a career in dairy, food, or environmental sanitation. **Focus:** Food science and technology. **Qualif.:** Applicants must be accepted or enrolled in an accredited post high school undergraduate degree or diploma program (university, college, or technical college) in Wisconsin or an out-of-state school with a reciprocal enrollment agreement with Wisconsin. They must be full-time students enrolled in a dairy science, food science, environmental sanitation or closely related major who are residents of Wisconsin. **Criteria:** Recipients will be selected based on academic performance, professional potential, activities and financial need.

Funds Avail.: $3,000. **Duration:** Annual. **Number Awarded:** 1. **To Apply:** Applicants must submit a complete application form; a copy of official transcript; recommendation of advisor or instructor which should address scholastic ability, professional potential, applicable work experience, extra-curricular activities, financial need and other relevant information. **Deadline:** July 1.

10616 ■ Wisconsin Athletic Trainers' Association (WATA)
c/o Lucus Solum, Treasurer
Bellin Health Sports Medicine
1630 Commanche Ave.
Green Bay, WI 54313
E-mail: watainc.president@gmail.com
URL: www.watainc.org

10617 ■ Founding Fathers Leadership Scholarships (Undergraduate/Scholarship)
Purpose: To support athletic training students who have distinguished themselves academically and performed with

distinction as a member of the Athletic Training Program. **Focus:** Athletics. **Qualif.:** Applicants must be members of the NATA and WATA; currently enrolled in the first year of an athletic training curriculum program at a college or university in Wisconsin; distinguished academically with an overall minimum accumulative GPA of 3.0 on a 4.0 scale or its equivalent; demonstrated qualities of leadership as members of the Athletic Training Student program. **Criteria:** Selection will be based on application.

Funds Avail.: $1,000. **To Apply:** Applicants must be nominated by a Licensed/Certified Athletic Trainer. Submit the following with the application: (signed by the nominating Licensed/Certified Athletic Trainer) Embossed undergraduate transcript at completion of the semester preceding the filing of the application; Letter of recommendation completed by the nominating Licensed/Certified Athletic Trainer (Section II); a second letter of recommendation completed by a nominating physician or coach. **Deadline:** March 1. **Contact:** Anna Linstedt, LAT, Awards & Scholarship Committee Chair; or Email: anna.linstedt@thedacare.org.

10618 ■ Mueller Undergraduate Scholarships
(Undergraduate/Scholarship)

Purpose: To provide support for future athletic training professionals. **Focus:** Athletics. **Qualif.:** Applicants must be members of NATA and WATA; distinguished academically with an overall minimum accumulative GPA of 3.0 on a 4.0 scale or its equivalent; performed with distinction as members of the Athletic Training Student program in the declared major. **Criteria:** Consideration will be given to students who will demonstrate qualities of leadership.

Funds Avail.: $1,000 each. **Duration:** Annual. **Number Awarded:** 2. **To Apply:** Applicants must be nominated by a Licensed/Certified Athletic Trainer. Nominee must submit a completed and signed application form together with the essay and embossed transcript. Evaluation form must be completed and signed by the Licensed/Certified Athletic Trainer supervisor. **Deadline:** March 1. **Contact:** Anna Linstedt, LAT, Awards & Scholarship Committee Chair, at the above address; or Email: anna.linstedt@thedacare.org.

10619 ■ Jeff Oliphant Memorial Post-Graduate Scholarships *(Postgraduate/Scholarship)*

Purpose: To support athletic training students who have distinguished themselves academically and performed with distinction as a member of the Athletic Training Program. **Focus:** Athletics. **Qualif.:** Applicants must be current members of WATA; must demonstrate enrollment in postgraduate program at an accredited institution of higher learning; distinguished academically with an overall minimum accumulative GPA of 3.0 on a 4.0 scale or its equivalent; have performed with distinction as participants with their athletic training program, academic major and institution; and have the intention to pursue certification by NATA, and confirm intent to pursue the athletic training profession as their primary means of livelihood. **Criteria:** Consideration will be given to students who will demonstrate qualities of leadership.

Funds Avail.: $1,000. **To Apply:** Applicants must complete all required sections in the application form. Section I General Information (to be completed and signed by the applicant); Section II Nomination Form (to be completed and signed by a BOC certified athletic trainer, who can attest to the applicant's skills, abilities and scholarly activities as they relate to the application); Section III Institutional Endorsement (to be completed and signed by the dean of the college or the department head responsible for the applicant's academic program); Section IV Applicant's Essay (to be written and signed by the applicant). **Deadline:** March 1. **Remarks:** Established in 2006. **Contact:** Anna Linstedt, LAT, Awards & Scholarship Committee Chair; or Email: anna.linstedt@thedacare.org.

10620 ■ Wisconsin Broadcasters Association (WBA)
44 E Mifflin St., Ste. 900
Madison, WI 53703
Ph: (608)255-2600
Fax: (608)256-3986
Free: 800-236-1922
E-mail: contact@wi-broadcasters.org
URL: www.wi-broadcasters.org
Facebook: www.facebook.com/Wisconsin.Broadcasters.Association
Twitter: www.twitter.com/MVetterkind

10621 ■ Wisconsin Broadcasters Association Foundation Student Scholarships *(Undergraduate/Scholarship)*

Purpose: To assist students enrolled in broadcasting-related educational programs. **Focus:** Broadcasting. **Qualif.:** Applicants must have completed at least one-half of their degree or graduation requirements in a broadcast or broadcast-related course of study; must be attending a Higher Educational Institution in Wisconsin that has been designated as eligible by the WBA Foundation Board; must have a Wisconsin connection in that they must have either graduated from a Wisconsin high school or attend a Wisconsin college or university; must be planning a career in radio or television broadcasting. **Criteria:** Recipients will be selected based on academic performance and quality of the essay.

Funds Avail.: $1,000-$2,000. **Number Awarded:** 4. **To Apply:** Applicants must submit a completed application form; a current official transcript of college/university grades; two brief letters of recommendation supporting the application; an original, typed, double-spaced essay (3 pages maximum) written by the applicants forecasting what the broadcasting industry will be like in five years and how the applicants believes they will contribute to radio or television during that time. **Deadline:** October 14. **Contact:** Linda Baun at the above address.

10622 ■ Wisconsin Health Information Management Association (WHIMA)
3817 Mormon Coulee Rd., Ste. B
La Crosse, WI 54601-7328
Ph: (608)787-0168
Fax: (608)787-0169
E-mail: whima@whima.org
URL: www.whima.org
Facebook: www.facebook.com/WHIMA-Wisconsin-Health-Information-Management-Association-1389469134607129
Twitter: twitter.com/WHIMAHIM

10623 ■ WHIMA Established Professional Scholarship *(Graduate/Scholarship)*

Purpose: To support and recognize Wisconsin students pursuing graduate education as health information professionals and members needing financial assistance for professional development. **Focus:** General studies/Field of study not specified. **Qualif.:** Applicants must be active members of WHIMA and AHIMA. **Criteria:** Selection will be based on the committee's criteria.

Funds Avail.: $100 to $1,500. **Duration:** Annual. **To Apply:** Applicants must provide evidence of attendance at a continuing education program and personal payment for program or successful completion of credentialing examination; must complete the application procedure; provide professional or personal references. **Deadline:** October 15; February 15.

10624 ■ Wisconsin Indian Education Association (WIEA)
PO Box 910
Keshena, WI 54135
Ph: (715)799-5110
URL: www.wiea.org

10625 ■ WIEA Scholarships *(Doctorate, Graduate, Undergraduate/Scholarship)*

Purpose: To provide financial assistance to American Indian students attending institutes of higher education. **Focus:** General studies/Field of study not specified. **Qualif.:** Applicants must be: Wisconsin residents who are Wisconsin Indians; maintaining at least a 2.5 semester GPA; carrying sufficient credits to maintain full0time status. **Criteria:** Selection shall be based on merit.

Funds Avail.: $1,000 each. **Duration:** Annual. **Number Awarded:** 4 (graduating high school senior, undergraduate college student, technical college student and Graduate or PhD student). **To Apply:** Applicants must provide a proof of tribal enrollment. They must also include the following: application form; transcripts; and two recommendation letters. **Deadline:** May 1. **Remarks:** Established in 1997.

10626 ■ Wisconsin Laboratory Association (WLA)
PO Box 177
Sun Prairie, WI 53590
Ph: (920)406-8300
URL: www.wisconsinlabassociation.org

10627 ■ Wisconsin Laboratory Association Graduate Student Scholarships *(Graduate/Scholarship)*

Purpose: To financially support students to pursue a career in a non-medical laboratory related field. **Focus:** Technology. **Qualif.:** Applicants must be graduate students at an accredited college or university having completed at least one semester of classes; must be enrolled in a curriculum that will enable them to pursue a career in a non-medical laboratory related field and have 3.0 or higher GPA. **Criteria:** Selection is based on submitted application.

Funds Avail.: $1,000. **Number Awarded:** 2. **To Apply:** Applicants must submit completed WLA application form, current transcript from the school, and two letters of recommendation from the student's instructors. **Deadline:** May 1. **Contact:** Gina Steiner, Address: PO Box 808, Fort Atkinson, WI 53538; Email: ginas@jonesdairyfarm.com.

10628 ■ Wisconsin Laboratory Association Technical Student Scholarships *(Undergraduate, Graduate/Scholarship)*

Purpose: To financially support students who plan to pursue a career in a non-medical laboratory related field. **Focus:** Technology. **Qualif.:** Applicants must be technical students enrolled in a curriculum that enables them to pursue a career in a non-medical laboratory related field and have at least a 3.0 or higher GPA. **Criteria:** Selection is based on application materials.

Funds Avail.: $1,000. **Number Awarded:** 2. **To Apply:** Applicants must submit a completed application form along with the supporting documents. **Deadline:** May 1. **Contact:** Gina Steiner, Address: PO Box 808, Fort Atkinson, WI 53538; Email: ginas@jonesdairyfarm.com.

10629 ■ Wisconsin Laboratory Association Undergraduate University Student Scholarships *(Undergraduate/Scholarship)*

Purpose: To financially support students who plan to pursue a career in a non-medical laboratory related field. **Focus:** Technology. **Qualif.:** Applicants must be undergraduate students at an accredited college or university having completed at least one semester of classes; must be enrolled in a curriculum that will enable them to pursue a career in a non-medical laboratory related field and have a 3.0 or higher GPA. **Criteria:** Selection is based on application.

Funds Avail.: $1,000. **Number Awarded:** 2. **To Apply:** Applicants must submit completed WLA application form, current transcript from the school, and two letters of recommendation from the student's instructors. **Deadline:** May 1. **Contact:** Gina Steiner, Address: PO Box 808, Fort Atkinson, WI 53538; Email: ginas@jonesdairyfarm.com.

10630 ■ Wolf Trap Foundation for the Performing Arts (WTFPA)
1645 Trap Rd.
Vienna, VA 22182
Ph: (703)255-1900
Free: 877-WOLFTRAP
E-mail: wolftrap@wolftrap.org
URL: www.wolftrap.org
Facebook: www.facebook.com/WolfTrapOfficialPage
Twitter: www.twitter.com/wolf_trap

10631 ■ Wolf Trap Grants for High School Performing Arts Teachers *(Other/Grant)*

Purpose: To reward and assist the teachers who make it all possible - particularly those creating innovative new programs. **Focus:** Performing arts. **Qualif.:** Applicants must be performing arts public high school teachers in Washington, DC; Montgomery County, MD; Prince George's County, MD; and Fairfax County, VA. **Criteria:** Selection is based on the submitted proposals.

Funds Avail.: $3,500. **Duration:** Annual. **To Apply:** Grant proposals are by invitation only. For more information, refer to the contact provided. **Remarks:** The program is made possible through a grant from the Catherine Filene Shouse Education Fund. **Contact:** Emily Smalling, Coordinator, Public Relations; Phone: 703-255-4096; Email: emilys@wolftrap.org; and Michelle Pendoley, Director, Public Relations; Phone: 703-255-1917; Email: michellep@wolftrap.org.

10632 ■ The Wolf Trap Internship Program *(Graduate, Other, Undergraduate/Internship)*

Purpose: To provide training program for the performing arts. **Focus:** Performing arts. **Qualif.:** Applicants must be undergraduate students (completed one year of study or equivalent), graduate students, or recent graduates (up to two years out of school); career-changers enrolled in a degree program; and international students (J-1 or F-1 Visa required). **Criteria:** Committee will review submitted materials.

Funds Avail.: No specific amount. **Duration:** Annual; 12 weeks internship program. **To Apply:** Applicants must submit a cover letter with a brief personal statement and an outline of career goals; a resume; two academic or professional recommendations; two contrasting writing samples, (maximum of 3 pages each). **Deadline:** February 1; March 1 (Summer internships); November 1 (Spring internships); July 1 (Fall internships). **Contact:** Phone: 703-937-6304, 800-404-8461; Email: internships@wolftrap.org.

10633 ■ Thomas Wolfe Society (TWS)
PO Box 1146
Bloomington, IN 47402-1146
URL: www.thomaswolfe.org
Facebook: www.facebook.com/pages/The-Thomas-Wolfe-Society/139828276033808

10634 ■ William B. Wisdom Grant in Aid of Research *(Professional development/Grant)*

Purpose: To provide funds for travel and living expenses for scholars and students working out of the William B. Wisdom Collection in the Houghton Library, Harvard University. **Focus:** Literature. **Qualif.:** Candidates at work on PhD dissertations are especially encouraged. **Criteria:** Selection will be based on the committee's criteria. Consideration will also be given to applicants who wish to use the Thomas Wolfe Collection in the University of North Carolina at Chapel Hill.

Funds Avail.: $1,000. **Duration:** Annual. **To Apply:** Applicants must provide letters of application, to be submitted in triplicate, and should include the following: a description of the proposed research project; an estimate of expenses; curriculum vitae; list of publications. Approved applicants are expected to submit a final report on the research at the following Thomas Wolfe Society meeting and two copies of any publication resulting from the research. **Deadline:** April 1. **Remarks:** Established in 1991. **Contact:** Dr. Joseph M. Flora, Chair of the Grants Committee, at jflora@email.unc.edu.

10635 ■ Women in Defense, a National Security Organization (WID)
2111 Wilson Blvd., Ste. 400
Arlington, VA 22201-3061
Ph: (703)522-1820
Fax: (703)522-1885
E-mail: wid@ndia.org
URL: www.womenindefense.net/Pages/default.aspx
Facebook: www.facebook.com/Women-In-Defense-857203097657993/
LinkedIn: www.linkedin.com/company/women-in-defense?trk=tyah&trkInfo=clickedVertical%3Acompany%2Cidx%3A1-3-3%2CtarId%3A1428669942035%2Ctas%3Awomen+in+defe
Twitter: twitter.com/WIDNational

10636 ■ Women In Defense HORIZONS Scholarships *(Graduate, Undergraduate/Scholarship)*

Purpose: To provide financial assistance to further educational objectives of women either employed or planning careers in defense or national security areas. **Focus:** Business; Computer and information sciences; Economics; Engineering; Government; History, Military; International affairs and relations; Law; Mathematics and mathematical sciences; National security; Physics; Political science. **Qualif.:** Applicant must be currently enrolled at an accredited university/college, either full-time or part-time; must have junior, senior or graduate status; demonstrate interest in pursuing a career related to national security or defense; demonstrate financial need; have a minimum GPA of 3.25. Applicant must be a female citizen of the United States. **Criteria:** Awards are given based on academic achievement, participation in defense and national security activities, field of study, work experience, statements of objectives, recommendations, and financial need.

Funds Avail.: No specific amount. **To Apply:** Applicants must submit a completed scholarship application form with the essays, recommendations, and transcripts. **Deadline:** July 15. **Remarks:** Established in 1988.

10637 ■ Women Divers Hall of Fame (WDHOF)
43 Mackey Ave.
Port Washington, NY 11050
E-mail: info@wdhof.org
URL: www.wdhof.org

10638 ■ Cecelia Connelly Memorial Scholarships in Underwater Archaeology *(Graduate, Undergraduate/Scholarship)*

Purpose: To provide financial and educational support to individuals of all ages, particularly those who are preparing for professional careers which involve scuba diving. **Focus:** Aquaculture; Archeology. **Qualif.:** Applicants must be either undergraduate or graduate students enrolled in an accredited course of study in the field of Underwater Archaeology. They must have an overall GPA of 2.5 or better (for undergraduate) or 3.0 or better (for graduate); and must be in good standing. First year graduate students may submit verification of a minimum overall GPA of 2.5 from the final year as undergraduate students. **Criteria:** Selection shall be based on the aforementioned qualifications and compliance with the application details.

Funds Avail.: $2,000 (Graduate); $750 (Undergraduate). **Duration:** Annual. **Number Awarded:** 2. **To Apply:** Applicants may visit the website to verify the application process and other pieces of information. **Contact:** Women Divers Hall of Fame, at the above address.

10639 ■ Elizabeth Greenhalgh Memorial Scholarships in Journalism, Graphic Arts, or Photography *(Undergraduate/Scholarship)*

Purpose: To provide financial and educational support to individuals of all ages, particularly those who are preparing for professional careers in scuba diving. **Focus:** Graphic art and design; Journalism; Photography. **Qualif.:** Applicants must be women divers who are furthering their education beyond high school in the field of journalism, graphic arts, or photography to better serve the ocean environment or ocean community. **Criteria:** Selection shall be based on the aforementioned qualifications and compliance with the application details.

Funds Avail.: $1,500. **Duration:** Annual. **To Apply:** Applicants may visit the website to verify the application process and other pieces of information. **Contact:** Women Divers Hall of Fame, at the above address.

Awards are arranged alphabetically below their administering organizations

10640 ■ WDHOF Undergraduate Scholarships in Marine Conservation *(Undergraduate/Scholarship)*
Purpose: To provide financial and educational support to individuals of all ages, particularly those who are preparing for professional careers in scuba diving. **Focus:** Conservation of natural resources. **Qualif.:** Applicants must be undergraduate women enrolled in an accredited academic or research program in the field of marine conservation. **Criteria:** Selection shall be based on the aforementioned qualifications and compliance with the application details.
Funds Avail.: $1,000. **Duration:** Annual. **To Apply:** Applicants may visit the website to verify the application process and other pieces of information.

10641 ■ Women in Federal Law Enforcement, Inc. (WIFLE)
2200 Wilson Blvd., Ste. 102
PMB 204
Arlington, VA 22201-3324
Ph: (301)805-2180
Fax: (301)560-8836
E-mail: wifle@comcast.net
URL: www.wifle.org
Facebook: www.facebook.com/wifleinc

10642 ■ WIFLE Regular Scholarship Program *(Graduate, Postdoctorate, Undergraduate/Scholarship)*
Purpose: To support women who are interested in pursuing a career in law enforcement. **Focus:** Law enforcement. **Qualif.:** Applicants must: be citizens of the United States; be physically attend and full-time students at an accredited four-year college or university, or be currently enrolled in a full-time in a fully accredited community college with the intention of transferring to a four-year degree; have completed at least one full academic year of college work at an accredited college or university or community college; have a minimum 3.0 overall grade point (GPA) average; and, be major in Criminal Justice or related discipline such as social sciences, public administration, computer science, finance, linguistic arts, chemistry, physics, etc., leading to a four-year degree (Students in graduate and postgraduate programs are also eligible; students pursuing Associate degrees are not eligible, unless as stated above, fully articulate in the application their intention to transfer to a four-year program). **Criteria:** Recipients will be selected based on academic potential, achievement and commitment to serving communities in the field of law enforcement.
Funds Avail.: No specific amount. **Duration:** Annual. **To Apply:** Applicants must complete the application with a 500-word essay describing the applicant's involvement in a community project and the results or impact of that involvement to the community. If the applicant is currently serving or has served an internship with a law enforcement agency, preferably a federal law enforcement agency, the applicant must provide details including the name of the agency, the dates served and the value of the experience and the accomplishment through the internship in a 500-word essay. Applicants must have at least one community leader or member of a community or police official sponsor their applications with a written statement of support.

10643 ■ Women Lawyers' Association of Greater St. Louis (WLA)
PO Box 775512
Saint Louis, MO 63177
E-mail: wla@wlastl.org
URL: wlastl.org

10644 ■ Linda J. Murphy Scholarships *(Undergraduate/Scholarship)*
Purpose: To support students who are pursuing legal education. **Focus:** Law. **Qualif.:** Applicants must be part-time or full-time female law students; must be currently enrolled in a Missouri law school and must be committed to continue law school enrollment in the fall semester following the award. **Criteria:** Selection of recipients is based on demonstrated commitment to causes that are consistent with the Mission of the WLA. Academic achievement and financial need are taken into account to a lesser extent.
Funds Avail.: $1,000 - $6,000 depending on the amount of funds available. **Duration:** Annual. **To Apply:** Applicants must submit a completed application form along with the personal statement and official or unofficial law school transcripts. Applications and all accompanying materials must be submitted via e-mail. **Deadline:** April 1. **Remarks:** Established in 1996. **Contact:** The Women Lawyers' Association of Greater St. Louis, at the above address.

10645 ■ Women Lawyers Association of Los Angeles (WLALA)
634 S Spring St., Ste. 617
Los Angeles, CA 90014-3906
Ph: (213)892-8982
Fax: (213)892-8948
E-mail: info@wlala.org
URL: www.wlala.org

10646 ■ WLALA Fran Kandel Public Interest Grants *(Postgraduate/Grant)*
Purpose: To support law students for projects that make governmental and social institutions and agencies more accessible and responsive to members of society whose interests are not otherwise adequately recognized or asserted. **Focus:** Law; Public service. **Qualif.:** Applicants must be law students who have the interest to know and gain experience about public interest. **Criteria:** Selection will be based on the committee's criteria. Strong preference will be given to those who have the support of a sponsoring organization.
Funds Avail.: Maximum of $5,000. **Number Awarded:** Up to 2. **To Apply:** Applicants should submit the completed application form which consists of: personal information; project information; and references (academic, personal, and work). Additional requirements include: essays of no more than 500 words, single-spaced, on separate sheets of paper (each discussing the specific proposal and the applicants' background); budget; resume; and letter of recommendation. **Deadline:** March 17. **Contact:** Questions can be directed to Ruth Pinkel; Phone: 213-894-6077; Email: ruth.pinkel@usdoj.gov.

10647 ■ WLALA Scholarships *(Postgraduate/Scholarship)*
Purpose: To assist law students whose prior and current activities and future plans demonstrate a commitment to issues affecting women and/or children. **Focus:** Law; Women's studies; Youth. **Qualif.:** Applicants must be currently enrolled in a law school that is accredited by the Committee of Bar Examiners of the State of California which is located in Los Angeles County, and plan to be so

Awards are arranged alphabetically below their administering organizations

enrolled in the upcoming academic year. Upon graduation from law school, they must have the plan to practice law in Southern California, and be in the top fifty percent of their class. **Criteria:** Selection of recipients will be based on the applicants' demonstrated commitment to issues affecting women and/or children.

Funds Avail.: $1,000. **To Apply:** Applicants must submit a personal statement addressing their commitment to issues affecting women and/or children (they must sure to address how their commitment will continue after law school graduation). The personal statement should also explain why they need the scholarship and how it will benefit them. Technical formats are typed, double-spaced, and no longer than 2 pages. Additional documents include: resume; certified law school transcript, including grades for fall semester last year; and minimum one letter of recommendation (no more than three). **Deadline:** April 30. **Contact:** Questions can be directed to Carmela T. Pagay; Levene, Neale, Bender, Yoo & Brill L.L.P., 10250 Constellation Blvd., Ste. 1700, Los Angeles, California 90067; Phone: 310-229-3362; Email: ctp@lnbyb.com.

10648 ■ Women Marines Association (WMA)
PO Box 377
Oaks, PA 19456-0377
Free: 888-525-1943
E-mail: wma@womenmarines.org
URL: www.womenmarines.org

10649 ■ The Agnes Sopcak Memorial Scholarship
(Undergraduate/Scholarship)

Purpose: To support students financially in pursuing their educational career. **Focus:** Maritime studies. **Qualif.:** Applicants must have served, or be serving in the United States Marine Corps or Reserve; must be direct descendants by blood; must be siblings or a descendant of siblings by blood. High school students must have a maintaining GPA of 3.0 on a scale of 4.0; College students must have a minimum GPA of 3.0. **Criteria:** A selection board of five members will review qualified applications.

Funds Avail.: $1,500 - $3,000. **Duration:** Annual. **To Apply:** Applicants must submit complete application form (typewritten form), readable copy of Sponsor's National Membership Card, 2x2 passport photos, and two letters from school personnel, and proof of relationship to a U.S. Marine. Male applicants must submit proof of draft registration. Applicants must submit SAT or ACT Scores; official transcript with grading key. **Deadline:** February 28. **Contact:** Dottie Stover-Kendrick, P.O. Box 134, Stilwell, KS 66085; Email: scholarship@womenmarines.org.

10650 ■ LaRue A. Ditmore Music Scholarships
(Undergraduate/Scholarship)

Purpose: To financially support those students who are in need. **Focus:** Maritime studies. **Qualif.:** Applicants must have served, or be serving in the United States Marine Corps or Reserve; must be direct descendants by blood; must be siblings or a descendant of siblings by blood. High school students must have maintaining GPA of 3.0 on a scale of 4.0; College students must have a minimum GPA of 3.0. **Criteria:** A selection board of five members will review qualified applications.

Funds Avail.: $1,500 - $3,000. **Duration:** Annual. **To Apply:** Applicants must submit complete application form (typewritten form), readable copy of Sponsor's National Membership Card, 2x2 passport photos, and two letters from school personnel, and proof of relationship to a U.S. Marine. Male applicants must submit proof of draft registration. Applicants must submit SAT or ACT Scores; official transcript with grading key. **Deadline:** February 28. **Contact:** Dottie Stover-Kendrick, P.O. Box 134, Stilwell, KS 66085; Email: scholarship@womenmarines.org.

10651 ■ Lily H. Gridley Memorial Scholarships
(Undergraduate/Scholarship)

Purpose: To financially support those students who are in need. **Focus:** Maritime studies. **Qualif.:** Applicants must have served, or be serving in the United States Marine Corps or Reserve; must be direct descendants by blood; must be siblings or a descendant of siblings by blood. High school students must have maintaining GPA of 3.0 on a scale of 4.0; College students must have a minimum GPA of 3.0. **Criteria:** A selection board of five members will review qualified applications.

Funds Avail.: $1,500. **Duration:** Annual. **To Apply:** Applicants must submit complete application form (typewritten form), readable copy of Sponsor's National Membership Card, 2x2 passport photos, and two letters from school personnel, and proof of relationship to a U.S. Marine. Male applicants must submit proof of draft registration. Applicants must submit SAT or ACT Scores; official transcript with grading key. **Deadline:** February 28. **Contact:** Dottie Stover-Kendrick, P.O. Box 134, Stilwell, KS 66085; Email: scholarship@womenmarines.org.

10652 ■ Ethyl and Armin Wiebke Memorial Scholarships
(Undergraduate/Scholarship)

Purpose: To financially support those students who are in need. **Focus:** Maritime studies. **Qualif.:** Applicants must have served, or be serving in the United States Marine Corps or Reserve; must be direct descendants by blood; must be siblings or a descendant of siblings by blood. High school students must have a maintaining GPA of 3.0 on a scale of 4.0; College students must have a minimum GPA of 3.0. **Criteria:** A selection board of five members will review qualified applications.

Funds Avail.: $1,500. **Duration:** Annual. **Number Awarded:** 1. **To Apply:** Applicants must submit complete application form (typewritten form), readable copy of Sponsor's National Membership Card, 2x2 passport photos, and two letters from school personnel, and proof of relationship to a U.S. Marine. Male applicants must submit proof of draft registration. Applicants must submit SAT or ACT Scores; official transcript with grading key. **Deadline:** February 28. **Contact:** Dottie Stover-Kendrick, P.O. Box 134, Stilwell KS 66085; Email: scholarship@womenmarines.org.

10653 ■ Women's Army Corps Veterans' Association (WACVA)
PO Box 663
Weaver, AL 36277
Ph: (256)820-6824
E-mail: info@armywomen.org
URL: www.armywomen.org

10654 ■ Women's Army Corps Veterans Association Scholarships *(Undergraduate/Scholarship)*

Purpose: To provide educational assistance to relatives of Army Service Women. **Focus:** General studies/Field of study not specified. **Qualif.:** Applicants must be relatives of

Awards are arranged alphabetically below their administering organizations

Army Service Women who are U.S. citizens; must be high school graduating seniors or planning to enroll as full-time students at an accredited college or university; and have 3.5 GPA on a 4.0 scale. **Criteria:** Selection is based on academic achievement; leadership as expressed through co-curricular activities and community involvement; biographical sketch; and recommendations.

Funds Avail.: $1,500. **Duration:** One year. **To Apply:** Applicants must submit the completed application form available from the website, an official 7-semester high school transcript, three letters of recommendation (one of which must be written by a teacher, counselor or principal); biographical sketch; and documentation of sponsor's military service. **Deadline:** May 1.

10655 ■ Women's Business Enterprise National Council (WBENC)
1120 Connecticut Ave. NW, Ste. 1000
Washington, DC 20036
Ph: (202)872-5515
Fax: (202)872-5505
E-mail: support@wbenc.org
URL: www.wbenc.org
Facebook: www.facebook.com/WBENC
LinkedIn: www.linkedin.com/company/wbenc
Twitter: twitter.com/WBENCLive

10656 ■ Dorothy B. Brothers Executive Scholarship Program (Undergraduate/Scholarship)
Purpose: To provide financial assistance and opportunities for women to attend an executive level course. **Focus:** General studies/Field of study not specified. **Qualif.:** Applicants must be currently certified as a woman business enterprise by WBENC; must have at least three-to-five years experience running a business; must employ at least three full-time employees; must maintain a minimum annual sales volume of $500,000 (the range is $500,000-$50,000); must not have previously attended a comparable executive management program (TUK-WBENC Executive Program). **Criteria:** Recipients are selected based on the quality of the essay.

Funds Avail.: Up to $11,000. **Duration:** Annual. **To Apply:** Applicants must fill out the application form and submit an essay stating the applicant's career goals related to business. **Deadline:** July 3.

10657 ■ Women's Health Research Foundation of Canada (WHRFC)
PO Box 61019
Winnipeg, MB, Canada R3M 3X8
E-mail: whrfc_inc@yahoo.ca
URL: whrfcinc.com
LinkedIn: www.linkedin.com/company/canadian-foundation-for-women's-health

10658 ■ Women's Health Research Foundation of Canada Scholarship Program (Graduate/Scholarship)
Purpose: To support graduate students who demonstrate academic excellence in the area of women's health. **Focus:** Women's studies. **Qualif.:** Applicants must be registered in a graduate program at the University of Manitoba; must have research concentration in some area of women's health. **Criteria:** Selection of applicants will be based on their research studies and application requirements.

Funds Avail.: 3,000 Canadian Dollars. **To Apply:** Applicants must complete the application form available online; must submit an official transcript or student history; must have an official transcript from all other universities attended; must have two letters of reference. **Deadline:** April 15. **Contact:** Mrs. Rosemary Visevic, Awards Assistant, Faculty of Graduate Studies at the above address.

10659 ■ Women's International Network of Utility Professionals (WiNUP)
PO Box 64
Grove City, OH 43123-0064
E-mail: winup@att.net
URL: www.winup.org
Facebook: www.facebook.com/WINUP-465604863532023
LinkedIn: www.linkedin.com/groups/7489510/profile
Twitter: twitter.com/winupint

10660 ■ Julia Kiene Fellowships in Electrical Energy (Graduate/Fellowship)
Purpose: To support students engaging in graduate work toward an advanced degree in any phase of electrical energy. **Focus:** Engineering, Electrical. **Qualif.:** Applicant must be a graduate student in an advanced degree in electrical energy. **Criteria:** Selection is based on the application.

Funds Avail.: $2000. **To Apply:** Applicants must submit a completed application form along with the required materials. **Deadline:** March 31. **Remarks:** Established in memory of Julia Kiene, past president of the organization.

10661 ■ Lyle Mamer Fellowships (Graduate/Fellowship, Award)
Purpose: To support students engaging in graduate work toward an advanced degree in any phase of electrical energy. **Focus:** Engineering, Electrical. **Qualif.:** Applicant must be a graduate student earning an advanced degree in electrical energy. **Criteria:** Selection is based on the application.

Funds Avail.: $1000. **To Apply:** Applicants must submit a completed application form along with the required materials. **Deadline:** March 31. **Remarks:** Established in memory of Lyle Mamer who served as an Associate Professor at the University of Tennessee College of Home Economics for 35 years.

10662 ■ Women's Jewelry Association (WJA)
82 Washington St., Ste. 203A
Poughkeepsie, NY 12601
Ph: (212)687-2722
Fax: (646)355-0219
E-mail: info@womensjewelryassociation.com
URL: www.womensjewelryassociation.com
Facebook: www.facebook.com/WomensJewelryAssociation

10663 ■ Women's Jewelry Association Member Grants (Professional development/Grant)
Purpose: To provide educational assistance to students in the international jewelry, watch and related industries. **Focus:** Design; Fashion design. **Qualif.:** Applicants must be WJA members. **Criteria:** Applicants are selected through a random drawing of the WJA Member Grant Committee.

Awards are arranged alphabetically below their administering organizations

Funds Avail.: $500. **Duration:** Annual. **To Apply:** Applicants must provide in a printed text limited to one 8 1/2 x 11 page: a short statement about applicant's personal information, work, the course and how the grant will benefit the applicant (mandatory); applicant's signature to accept all terms and conditions of the WJA Grants (mandatory); a brief description of the applicant's contributions to the jewelry and/or related industries (optional). Applicants must submit a completed application form and all supporting documents to WJA Member Grant Committee. **Deadline:** January 31. **Contact:** Fran Pennella, WJA National Grant Chairperson; Email: fran@benaliconsulting.com.

10664 ■ Women's Missionary Council of the Christian Methodist Episcopal Church
c/o Mrs. Princess A. Pegues, President
2309 Bonnie Ave.
Bastrop, LA 71220-4171
Ph: (318)281-3044
URL: www.womensmissionarycouncilcme.org
Facebook: www.facebook.com/Womens-Missionary
 -Council-of-the-Christian-Methodist-Episcopal-Church
 -125840330805430

10665 ■ The Helena B. Cobb Annual Scholarships *(Undergraduate, Vocational/Occupational/Scholarship)*

Purpose: To support students with their studies by emphasizing the importance of educational training beyond the high school level. **Focus:** General studies/Field of study not specified. **Qualif.:** Applicant must be a member of the Christian Methodist Episcopal Church; a high school graduate; and enrolled in a college, university, or vocational-technical school. **Criteria:** Selection is based on the application.

Funds Avail.: $100. **Duration:** Annual. **To Apply:** Applicant must submit a completed application form. **Deadline:** December 31.

10666 ■ The Helena B. Cobb Four-Year Higher Education Grants *(Undergraduate, Vocational/Occupational/Scholarship)*

Purpose: To support students with their studies by emphasizing the importance of educational training beyond the high school level. **Focus:** General studies/Field of study not specified. **Qualif.:** Applicant must be a member of the Christian Methodist Episcopal Church; a high school graduate; and enrolled in a college, university, or vocational-technical school. **Criteria:** Applicant are chosen through a four-year progressive competitive system from the local to Episcopal levels.

Funds Avail.: $1,000 - $4,000. **Duration:** Quadrennial. **To Apply:** Applicant must submit a completed application form. **Deadline:** December 31.

10667 ■ Women's National Book Association (WNBA)
PO Box 237
New York, NY 10150
Ph: (212)208-4629
Fax: (212)208-4629
E-mail: info@wnba-books.org
URL: www.wnba-books.org
Facebook: www.facebook.com/
 WomensNationalBookAssociation
Twitter: twitter.com/WNBA_National?ref_src=twsrc%5Etfw

10668 ■ WNBA Eastman Grants *(Other/Grant)*

Purpose: To provide funds for librarians who are interested in learning about the publishing process. **Focus:** Publishing. **Qualif.:** Applicant must be an MLS or its equivalent and must have at least two years of post-master's work experience in a library. **Criteria:** Recipients are selected based on the likelihood of career benefit to the person taking the course.

Funds Avail.: $500. **Duration:** Annual. **Number Awarded:** 1. **To Apply:** Applicants must provide a current resume; a personal statement of not more than 300 words concerning an ongoing interest in the publishing process and how a better understanding of this process would enhance the applicant's library career; a list of publishing courses to which the applicant would apply; and a signed acknowledgement of intent to submit to ALA and WNBA a simple report and verification of attendance at the chosen publishing course. **Deadline:** November 1. **Remarks:** Established in 1997.

10669 ■ Women's Overseas Service League (WOSL)
PO Box 124
Cedar Knolls, NJ 07927-0124
E-mail: carolhabgood@sbcglobal.net
URL: www.wosl.org

10670 ■ Women's Overseas and Service League Scholarships for Women *(Undergraduate/Scholarship)*

Purpose: To financially assist women who have served overseas in or with the Armed Forces. **Focus:** General studies/Field of study not specified. **Qualif.:** Applicants must be women who are committed to the advancement in military or other public service careers; must have demonstrated such commitment through life experiences; have successfully completed a minimum of 12 semester (18 quarter) hours of study in any institution of higher Education with a minimum of 2.5 grade point average; must be admitted for study in an institution of higher learning program leading to an academic degree (Associate Degree or higher). The program must be professional or technical in nature; must agree to enroll for a minimum of six semester (nine quarter) hours of study each academic period; and she must agree to maintain academic standards. **Criteria:** Scholarship Committee of the Women's Overseas Service League Board of Directors will evaluate the student's application based on academic records.

Funds Avail.: $500 - $1,000. **Duration:** Annual. **To Apply:** Applicants must fill out the application form; must include all needed documents such as resume, transcripts, essays and references. **Deadline:** March 1.

10671 ■ Women's Research and Education Institute (WREI)
714 G St. SE, Ste. 200
Washington, DC 20003
Ph: (202)506-9804
URL: www.wrei.org

10672 ■ Congressional Fellows on Women and Public Policy *(Doctorate, Graduate, Master's/Fellowship)*

Purpose: To encourage more effective participation by women in the formulation of policy options. **Focus:** General studies/Field of study not specified. **Qualif.:** Applicant must be currently enrolled in a master's or doctoral program at an accredited institution in the United States or have completed such a program within the past 18 months; have completed at least nine hours of graduate coursework; and have a demonstrated interest in research or political activity related to women's social and political status. **Criteria:** Fellows are selected on the basis of academic competence as well as their demonstrated interest in the public policy process.

Funds Avail.: $1,450 per month plus an additional sum of $500 for health insurance. **Duration:** Eight months. **To Apply:** Applicants must submit a completed application via regular mail or by email. Applicants must also present transcripts of previous academic work (college and graduate level) and three letters of reference sent directly to WREI. **Deadline:** June 14. **Remarks:** Established in 1980.

10673 ■ Women's Transportation Seminar (WTS)
1701 K St. NW, Ste. 800
Washington, DC 20006
Ph: (202)955-5085
Fax: (202)955-5088
E-mail: membership@wtsinternational.org
URL: www.wtsinternational.org
Facebook: www.facebook.com/womenstransportationseminar
Twitter: twitter.com/wts_org

10674 ■ Sharon D. Banks Undergraduate Memorial Scholarships (Undergraduate/Scholarship)

Purpose: To introduce cultural and organizational changes aimed at motivating the public transit work force. **Focus:** Finance; Logistics; Transportation. **Qualif.:** Applicants must be women pursuing undergraduate studies in transportation engineering, planning, finance or logistics, or related fields. Applicants must have at least a GPA of 3.0 or higher. **Criteria:** Recipients are selected based on specific transportation goals, academic record, transportation-related activities, or job skills.

Funds Avail.: $5,000. **To Apply:** Applicants must fill out and submit the scholarship application form to WTS Central Virginia Chapter. **Deadline:** November 4. **Contact:** WTS Central Virginia Chapter; Attn: Patsy Napier, c/o McCormick Taylor, North Shore Commons A, 4951 Lake Brook Drive, Suite 275, Richmond, Virginia 23060; Email: pgnapier@mccormicktaylor.com.

10675 ■ Helene M. Overly Memorial Scholarships (Undergraduate/Scholarship)

Purpose: To introduce cultural and organizational changes aimed at motivating the public transit work force. **Focus:** Finance; Logistics; Transportation. **Qualif.:** Applicants must be women pursuing undergraduate studies in transportation engineering, planning, finance or logistics, or related fields. Applicants must have at least a GPA of 3.0 or higher. **Criteria:** Recipients are selected based on specific transportation goals, academic record, transportation-related activities, or job skills.

Funds Avail.: $10,000 at the national level. **To Apply:** Applicants must fill out the scholarship application form **Remarks:** Established in 1981. **Contact:** Gabriella Yanez-Uribe, Parsons Brinckerhoff; Address: 3340 Peachtree Road, Suite 2400, Tower Place, Atlanta, GA 30326; Email: yanezuribe@pbworld.com.

10676 ■ Woodrow Wilson National Fellowship Foundation (WWNFF)
5 Vaughn Dr., Ste. 300
Princeton, NJ 08540-6313
Ph: (609)452-7007
Fax: (609)452-0066
URL: www.woodrow.org
Facebook: www.facebook.com/woodrowwilsonfoundation
LinkedIn: www.linkedin.com/company/woodrow-wilson-national-fellowship-foundation
Twitter: www.twitter.com/WWFoundation

10677 ■ Leonore Annenberg Teaching Fellowships (Graduate/Fellowship)

Purpose: To support future leaders who are developing their career in several critical fields. **Focus:** Education, Secondary. **Qualif.:** Applicants must be recent college graduates and career-changers who agree to work in urban and rural secondary schools serving high proportions of disadvantaged students. **Criteria:** Selection will be based on the committee's criteria.

Funds Avail.: $30,000. **To Apply:** Applicants may visit the website for further details and application information. **Deadline:** October 13; November 14 and January 31.

10678 ■ Doris Duke Conservation Fellows Program (Master's/Fellowship)

Purpose: To support future conservation leaders. **Focus:** Conservation of natural resources; General studies/Field of study not specified. **Qualif.:** Applicants must be students enrolled in master's program at eight universities - Yale, Duke, Cornell, Florida A&M University, Northern Arizona University and the universities of Michigan, Wisconsin, and California at Santa Barbara. **Criteria:** Selection will be based on the committee's criteria.

Funds Avail.: $5,000. **To Apply:** Applicant must submit a completed application form available on the website. **Deadline:** December 17. **Contact:** Woodrow Wilson National Fellowship Foundation, at the above address.

10679 ■ MMUF Dissertation Grants (Graduate/Grant)

Purpose: To support students who are in their critical juncture of completing their graduate degrees. **Focus:** General studies/Field of study not specified. **Qualif.:** Applicants must be Mellon Mays Undergraduate Fellows and candidates for the PhD degree in the fields recognized under the terms of the Mellon Mays Undergraduate Fellowship Program. Candidates must have completed all pre-dissertation requirements preceding the application deadline. Specifically, each applicant must have passed all comprehensive examination, completed all coursework for the degree, received approval of the dissertation topic, and completed most or all of the fieldwork and/or research necessary to begin writing. **Criteria:** Selection will be based on the committee's criteria.

Funds Avail.: Up to $20,000. **Duration:** 12-month period. **To Apply:** Applications must include the following: a three-page prospectus; a draft dissertation chapter; a three-page personal statement; an official graduate transcript; two letters of recommendation - one from the dissertation director and one from another academic knowledgeable about the Fellow's academic performance and/or familiar with the Fellow's dissertation project and its contribution to the field of scholarship; official budget form; a declaration of previous fellowship awards. **Deadline:** December 13.

Awards are arranged alphabetically below their administering organizations

10680 ■ MMUF Travel and Research Grants
(Graduate/Grant)

Purpose: To provide eligible graduate students with the financial means to complete their research prior to the start of dissertation writing. **Focus:** General studies/Field of study not specified. **Qualif.:** Applicants must be Mellon Mays Undergraduate Fellows and candidates for the PhD degree in the fields recognized under the terms of the Mellon Mays Undergraduate Fellowship Program. All candidates must have passed all comprehensive examinations, completed all course work for the degree, and selected a dissertation topic that has been approved by the dissertation advisor. **Criteria:** Selection will be based on the committee's criteria.

Funds Avail.: Up to $5,000. **Duration:** One summer or one semester. **To Apply:** Applications must include the following: official application form; a resume; a personal statement as outlined in the application; an official budget form (funding may be applied to travel to research sites, cost of meals and lodging at research sites, photocopying or microfilming of documents, purchase of access to research databases, fees for use of research facilities, and other research-related expenses); an official graduate transcript; and a brief letter of recommendation (two-page maximum) from the dissertation advisor endorsing the request for funding. **Deadline:** March 14.

10681 ■ Thomas R. Pickering Graduate Foreign Affairs Fellowships *(Graduate, Undergraduate/Fellowship)*

Purpose: To provide funding to participants as they are prepared academically and professionally to enter the United States Department of State Foreign Service. **Focus:** Business; Economics; Foreign languages; International affairs and relations; Political science; Public administration; Sociology. **Qualif.:** Applicants must be US citizens at the time of application; must have a minimum undergraduate GPA of 3.2 or higher on a 4.0 scale; must be seeking admission to graduate school for the following year; demonstrate financial need. Winners are expected to enroll in a two-year, full-time master's degree program in public policy, international affairs, or public administration, or in an academic field such as business, economic, political science, sociology, or foreign languages (US graduate institutions only).). **Criteria:** Selection will be based on the committee's criteria.

Funds Avail.: Up to $37,500. **Duration:** Annual. **To Apply:** Completed application includes both an online application form, which requires secure registration at the Woodrow Wilson Foundation Web site, and a series of hard-copy supporting documents, as follows: Certification of US citizenship (copy of US passport, birth certificate, or US citizen naturalization papers); copy of GRE scores; two letters of recommendation; official academic transcripts from every undergraduate school attended; two page resume. In addition, all applicants who received financial aid must also provide a copy of their most recent financial aid letter that list grants or loans. Applicants must also provide a copy of the Student Aid Report (SAR), which indicates the Estimated Family Contribution number. **Contact:** Contact the Pickering team at pickering@woodrow.org.

10682 ■ Woodrow Wilson-Rockefeller Brothers Fund Fellowships for Aspiring Teachers of Color
(Undergraduate/Fellowship)

Purpose: To support future leaders who are developing their career stages in several critical fields. **Focus:** Education, Secondary. **Qualif.:** Applicant must: be a person of color (African American/Black, Asian, Hispanic, Latino(a), Native American) in his/her senior year of undergraduate preparation; be nominated by an eligible nominating institution; demonstrate a commitment to the program and its goals; have US citizenship or permanent residency; expect to attain a bachelor's degree by June 30, 2011; have substantial background in the arts and sciences and high academic performance with a cumulative undergraduate GPA of 3.0 or better on a 4.0 scale (negotiable for applicants from institutions that do not employ a 4.0 GPA scale); not currently in a teacher preparation program which leads to initial teacher certification. **Criteria:** Selection will be based on the committee's criteria.

Funds Avail.: $30,000. **To Apply:** Applicants must visit the website for application and registration. Information required on the application includes: educational background; preference(s) of master's program(s); two 500-word essays; contact information for the two recommenders you've asked to write letters for you; personal information; additional information. In addition to online application, applicants must submit a resume, two recommendations, and official transcripts. **Contact:** Woodrow Wilson National Fellowship Foundation, at the above address.

10683 ■ Carter G. Woodson Institute for African-American and African Studies
University of Virginia
108 Minor Hall
108 Minor Hall
Charlottesville, VA 22904-4162
Ph: (434)924-3109
Fax: (434)924-8820
E-mail: woodson@virginia.edu
URL: artsandsciences.virginia.edu/woodson

10684 ■ Carter G. Woodson Institute Post-doctoral Residential Research and Teaching Fellowships
(Postdoctorate/Fellowship)

Purpose: To facilitate the writing of dissertations or manuscripts and provide successful applicants the opportunity to discuss and exchange works-in-progress both with each other and the larger intellectual community of the University. **Focus:** Humanities; Social sciences. **Qualif.:** Applicants for the post-doctoral fellowship must have been awarded their Ph.D. by the time of application or furnish proof from the relevant registrar that all documentation required for the Ph.D. has been submitted. **Criteria:** Selection will be based on the following criteria: significance of the proposed work; qualifications of the applicant; familiarity with existing relevant research literature; research design of the project; promise of completion within the award period. Preference will be given to applicants whose field research is already substantially completed.

Funds Avail.: $45,000 plus benefits. **Duration:** Up to 2 years. **To Apply:** Applicants must submit a Candidate Profile on-line through Jobs@UVA and must attach the following: a maximum of 250-word letter of application stating interest in the program; a curriculum vitae which must include the personal information, date(s) and location(s) of degree(s) earned, honors and awards, lectures and conference presentations, publications and the names of three referees. Applicants must also submit the following: a project abstract, including title, not to exceed 50 words as well as a project description, including title, not to exceed seven double-spaced pages (1,750 words). It must indicate the nature of the research to be completed during the period of the fellowship award, as well as the significance of this work. The project description must include a detailed research plan giving concrete objectives to be achieved during the award period. Project descriptions must be attached through Jobs@ under Writing Sample 1; a working bibliography not to exceed four double-spaced pages. The bibliography must list those scholarly works that the applicant considers most important to the intellectual development of the project. The working bibliography must be attached through Jobs@ under Writing Sample 2; an original, signed three confidential letters of reference sent directly to the Woodson Institute by persons qualified to evaluate the proposals for which support is being sought. **Deadline:** December 1. **Contact:** Deborah E. McDowell, at dem8z@virginia.edu.

10685 ■ Carter G. Woodson Institute Pre-doctoral Residential Research Fellowships (Doctorate/Fellowship)

Purpose: To facilitate the writing of dissertations or manuscripts and provide successful applicants the opportunity to discuss and exchange works-in-progress both with each other and the larger intellectual community of the University. **Focus:** Humanities; Social sciences. **Qualif.:** Open to all qualified candidates without restriction as to citizenship or current residence whose work focused on Africa and/or African Diaspora. **Criteria:** Selection will be based on the following criteria: significance of the proposed work; qualifications of the applicants; familiarity with existing relevant research literature; research design of the project; promise of completion within the award period. Preference will be given to applicants whose field research is already substantially completed.

Funds Avail.: $20,000 plus health insurance. **Duration:** Up to 2 years. **To Apply:** Applicants must submit a Candidate Profile on-line through Jobs@UVA and must attach the following: a maximum of 250-word letter of application stating interest in the program; a curriculum vitae which must include the personal information, date(s) and location(s) of degree(s) earned, honors and awards, lectures and conference presentations, publications and the names of three referees. Applicants must also submit the following: a project abstract, including title, not to exceed 50 words as well as a project description, including title, not to exceed seven double-spaced pages (1,750 words). It must indicate the nature of the research to be completed during the period of the fellowship award, as well as the significance of this work. The project description must include a detailed research plan giving concrete objectives to be achieved during the award period. Project descriptions must be attached through Jobs@ under Writing Sample 1; a working bibliography not to exceed four double-spaced pages. The bibliography must list those scholarly works that the applicant considers most important to the intellectual development of the project. The working bibliography must be attached through Jobs@ under Writing Sample 2; an original, signed three confidential letters of reference sent directly to the Woodson Institute by persons qualified to evaluate the proposals for which support is being sought. **Deadline:** December 1. **Contact:** Deborah E. McDowell, at dem8z@virginia.edu.

10686 ■ Worcester County Conservation District (WCCD)
52 Boyden Rd., Ste. 107
Holden, MA 01520
Ph: (508)829-4477
URL: worcesterconservation.org

10687 ■ Worcester County Conservation District Annual Scholarships Program (Undergraduate/Scholarship)

Purpose: To promote the conservation of the natural resources throughout all of Massachusetts. **Focus:** Agricultural sciences; Conservation of natural resources; Environmental conservation. **Qualif.:** Applicants must be Worcester County, MA residents; must be high school seniors who will be entering college and majoring in Natural Resource Conservation, Agriculture or Environmental Science. **Criteria:** Selection will be based on the submitted application and essay.

Funds Avail.: $500. **Duration:** Annual. **Number Awarded:** 1. **To Apply:** Applicants need to provide the following: an essay consisting of at least 300 words explaining why they are interested in pursuing the chosen degree program and hot it will apply to their career plans; a signed and sealed transcript from the applicants current high school; on e letter of recommendation from a teacher, guidance counselor, athletic coach or employer. **Deadline:** June 1. **Contact:** lisa.trotto@ma.usda.gov.

10688 ■ Worcester District Medical Society (WDMS)
Mechanics Hall
321 Main St.
Worcester, MA 01608-1532
Ph: (508)753-1579
Fax: (508)754-6246
E-mail: info@wdms.org
URL: www.wdms.org

10689 ■ Worcester District Medical Society Scholarship Fund (Undergraduate/Scholarship)

Purpose: To provide educational assistance to medical students. **Focus:** Medicine. **Qualif.:** Applicants must be second, third or fourth year students enrolled (with tuition obligation) in an accredited medical or osteopathic school; and must be legal residents of Central Massachusetts at the time of applying to medical school. **Criteria:** Recipients are selected based on academic achievement; community service; and financial need.

Funds Avail.: No specific amount. **Duration:** Annual. **To Apply:** Applicants must submit a completed application form; current transcript; two letters of recommendation; and an essay stating the reasons for selecting a career in medicine and why they deserve the award. **Deadline:** August 8. **Contact:** Scholarship Fund of WDMS at wordmsa@massmed.org.

10690 ■ Working for Farmers' Success (WFS)
233 W Ciro St.
Truman, MN 56088
Ph: (507)776-2831
Fax: (507)776-2871
Free: 800-657-3282
URL: www.cfscoop.com
Facebook: www.facebook.com/WFS.COOP

10691 ■ Working for Farmers' Success Scholarships (Undergraduate/Scholarship)

Purpose: To encourage young people to pursue an agricultural career. **Focus:** Agriculture, Economic aspects.

Awards are arranged alphabetically below their administering organizations

Qualif.: Applicants must be senior students who are graduating from the WFS trade territory. **Criteria:** Recipients will be selected based on academic performance, qualities of leadership, integrity and good community citizenship. Financial need is also given consideration.

Funds Avail.: $500 each. **Number Awarded:** Up to 20. **To Apply:** Applicants must submit a completed application form.

10692 ■ World Association for Cooperative Education (WACE)

Wannalancit Business Ctr., Ste. 125
600 Suffolk St.
Lowell, MA 01854
Ph: (978)934-1867
Fax: (978)934-4084
URL: www.waceinc.org

10693 ■ WACE National Co-op Scholarship Program
(Undergraduate/Scholarship)

Purpose: To assist students pursuing higher education at the WACE Partner Institutions. **Focus:** Engineering; Mathematics and mathematical sciences; Science. **Qualif.:** Applicants must have a cumulative high school GPA of 3.5 or better on a 4.0 scale, and have applied and be accepted for the academic year at one of the WACE Partner Institutions. **Criteria:** Selection shall be based on the aforementioned qualifications and compliance with the application details.

Funds Avail.: No specific amount. **Duration:** Annual. **Number Awarded:** Varies. **To Apply:** Applicants must submit a complete National Co-op Scholarship program Application including a typed, one-page essay (250-300 words). **Deadline:** February 15. **Remarks:** Established in 2003. **Contact:** Questions should be directed to Marty Ford at marty_ford@uml.edu.

10694 ■ World Bank Group (WBG)

1818 H St. NW
Washington, DC 20433
Ph: (202)473-1000
Fax: (202)477-6391
Free: 800-831-0463
E-mail: pic@worldbank.org
URL: www.worldbank.org

10695 ■ Japan Indonesia Presidential Scholarship Program *(Doctorate/Scholarship)*

Purpose: To provide scholars an opportunity to strengthen their skills and knowledge and to improve the quality of higher education and research in the country. **Focus:** General studies/Field of study not specified. **Qualif.:** Applicants must be in a Ph.D. level of study. **Criteria:** Selection will be based on the committee's criteria.

Funds Avail.: No specific amount. **To Apply:** Applicants may contact the Society for the online application process and other required materials.

10696 ■ Joint Japan/World Bank Graduate Scholarship Program for Developing Country National (JJ/WBGSP) *(Graduate/Scholarship)*

Purpose: To enable mid-career professionals from developing countries to access the latest techniques and knowledge through graduate studies at universities worldwide. **Focus:** General studies/Field of study not specified. **Qualif.:** Applicants must be a national of a World Bank member country eligible to borrow; must not be a dual citizen of any developed country; must not be an Executive Director, Executive Director's alternate staff, or consultant of the World Bank Group (the World Bank, International Finance Corporation, International Development Association, Multilateral Investment Guarantee Agency, and International Center for Settlement of Investments Disputes) or have any relatives or in-laws who are employed by the World Bank Group in any capacity; must hold a bachelor's degree (or equivalent university degree); and must have at least 3 years of development-related experience since earning a bachelor's degree. **Criteria:** Selection will be based on the committee's criteria.

Funds Avail.: No specific amount. **To Apply:** Applicants must submit a completed application form (either in English or in the language of his/her mater degree program) and recommendation letters from two people who have direct knowledge of the applicants' professional experience.

10697 ■ Joint Japan/World Bank Graduate Scholarship Program for Japanese National (JJ/WBGSP) *(Graduate, Master's, Doctorate/Scholarship)*

Purpose: To enable mid-career professionals from developing countries to access the latest techniques and knowledge through graduate studies at universities worldwide. **Focus:** General studies/Field of study not specified. **Qualif.:** Applicants must be Japanese national; must hold a bachelor's degree (or its equivalent university degree) earned at least three years prior to the application deadline; must be in good health with respect to the capacity to be a productive graduate student; must have, by the application deadline, at least 3 years but no more than 25 years of full time paid employment acquired after receiving the first bachelor's degree; must not be employed by the Government of Japan or its related agencies, including local governments and the Central Bank at the time of application; must not be an Executive Director, Executive Director's alternate staff, or consultant of the World Bank Group (the World Bank, International Finance Corporation, International Development Association, Multilateral Investment Guarantee Agency, and International Center for Settlement of Investments Disputes) or have any relatives or in-laws who are employed by the World Bank Group in any capacity; and have not received any scholarship funds from the Government of Japan to help finance a graduate degree. **Criteria:** Two qualified assessors independently review each eligible application and score the application on a scale of 1 to 10, taking into account three main factors and the degree of cohesion among them: quality of academic experience and recommendations; quality of professional experience and recommendations; and quality of commitment to development.

Funds Avail.: No specific amount. **Duration:** Two years. **To Apply:** Applicants must submit the following documents: cover form for the required documentation; current curriculum vitae not exceeding two pages, written in English; copy of the official letter of acceptance to at least one graduate program; copy of identification page of the applicant's passport or other legal document (birth or marriage certificate) that indicates nationality and date of birth with the name identical to the one submitted on the application form; proof of employment for each record of employment noted in the application form; certified copy of a certificate of the applicant's most advanced university degree earned and corresponding transcript of grades; and two academic recommendations and two professional recommendations, one for academic recommenders and one for professional recommenders. Once the application form is submitted online, the applicant will receive within 2 business days an email from JJ/WBGSP Secretariat that informs the applicant of his application identification number. The application number is needed to complete the package of required documentation. Documents mailed to the JJWBG Scholarship Program cannot be returned. Therefore, copies of all supporting documentation and not the originals should be sent.

10698 ■ Robert S. McNamara Fellowships Program (RSMFP) (Doctorate/Fellowship)

Purpose: To provide financial assistance to PhD students from developing countries for them to conduct innovative, development-related, PhD research under the supervision of a research advisor at a host institution abroad. **Focus:** General studies/Field of study not specified. **Qualif.:** Applicants must be a national of a World Bank member developing country; must not be a dual citizen of a developed country that is not a World Bank member; must be currently enrolled in a Ph.D. program in a World Bank member country; must have completed all course work and exam requirements for Ph.D. at the time of application; must have a master's degree or equivalent; must be 35 years old or younger; must not be an Executive Director, Executive Director's alternate staff, or consultant of the World Bank Group (the World Bank, International Finance Corporation, International Development Association, Multilateral Investment Guarantee Agency, and International Center for Settlement of Investments Disputes) or have any relatives or in-laws who are employed by the World Bank Group in any capacity, including consulting; must not previously been the recipient of the World Bank Robert S. McNamara Fellowship; and must be accepted as a visiting scholar for a period of six to ten months by a university or research center in a World Bank member country other than the applicants' home country. **Criteria:** Selection will be based on the committee's criteria.

Funds Avail.: Up to $25,000. **Duration:** Annual. **To Apply:** Applicants must submit all the required documents together with application form and reference letters: official document from host institution stating that he/she is currently enrolled as a Ph.D. student and already completed all course work and exam requirements for the applicant's doctoral program; proof of employment if the applicant is currently employed; official diploma of the applicant's highest degree earned; and a proposed budget for the fellowship using his/her own World Bank Fellowship budget template. All documents must submit in English or the language in which the applicant is completing his/her application, he/she should translate it into English. Both the document in the original language and the translated document must be uploaded into the application form. Finalists must submit an additional document, a copy of his/her passport or other legal document (birth or marriage certificate), with the name identical to the one submitted on the application form. **Remarks:** Established in 1982. **Contact:** rsm_fellowships@worldbank.org.

10699 ■ World Council of Credit Unions (WOCCU)
5710 Mineral Point Rd.
Madison, WI 53705-4454
Ph: (608)395-2000
Fax: (608)395-2001
E-mail: mail@woccu.org
URL: www.woccu.org
Facebook: www.facebook.com/woccu
LinkedIn: www.linkedin.com/company/world-council-of-credit-unions
Twitter: twitter.com/woccu

10700 ■ WYCUP Scholarships (Other/Scholarship)

Purpose: To engage and promote the next generation of credit union professionals and volunteers in the international credit union movement. **Focus:** General studies/Field of study not specified. **Qualif.:** Applicant must be 35 years of age or younger; must be actively involved either as an employee or volunteer with a credit union or credit organization affiliated with the international credit union movement; must demonstrate personal commitment and the ability to significantly influence credit unions in his/her country; must exhibit the potential to advance the international credit union system; must not have been a previous WYCUP Scholarship recipient. **Criteria:** Individual selected for the scholarship are those the committee believes have the greatest potential to contribute to the international credit union system.

Funds Avail.: Scholarship covers all costs associated with the event, including conference registration fee, travel costs, hotel accommodation and metals. **Duration:** Annual. **Number Awarded:** 5. **To Apply:** Applicant must have two Nomination Forms (attached) completed by the nominee and the sponsor; must provide the proof of age (photocopy of passport, driver's license, birth certificate or other official document); must prepare a brief 500-word essay describing the contribution made to the development of the candidate's credit union or credit union organization. **Deadline:** June 16. **Contact:** Liliana Tangwall, Credit Union Analyst, at 608-395-2043, or ltangwall@woccu.org.

10701 ■ World Forest Institute (WFI)
World Forestry Ctr.
4033 SW Canyon Rd.
Portland, OR 97221
Ph: (503)228-1367
E-mail: swu@worldforestry.org
URL: wfi.worldforestry.org
Facebook: www.facebook.com/worldforestrycenter
Twitter: twitter.com/World_Forestry

10702 ■ WFI International Fellowships (Undergraduate/Fellowship)

Purpose: To provide assistance to students interested in the forestry field. **Focus:** Forestry. **Qualif.:** Applicants must obtain a bachelor's degree or equivalent in the field of forestry, natural resources, or other related degree; must have written and oral proficiency in English; 21 years of age; must have an initial research proposal on a topic relevant to forestry; should be self-motivated, be able to work independently towards a clear research goal or output, be able to work with colleagues from diverse backgrounds; and should obtain funding from the fellowship. **Criteria:** Selection will be based on submitted documents and specific criteria.

Funds Avail.: $10,000 for six month fellowship and $20,000 for twelve month fellowship. **To Apply:** Applicants should submit a completed application form; project proposal; and curriculum vitae. The project should take advantage of being located in the Pacific Northwest which

Awards are arranged alphabetically below their administering organizations

involves collaboration with forest industry, local organizations, researchers, or communities. **Contact:** Sara Wu at the above address or send completed application to swu@worldforestry.org.

10703 ■ World Leisure Organization (WLO)
Faculty of Social & Human Sciences
Institute of Leisure Studies
University of Deusto
Avenida de las Universidades, 24
SP 48007 Bilbao, Spain
Ph: 34 94 4139086
URL: www.worldleisure.org

10704 ■ Thomas and Ruth River International Scholarships *(Undergraduate, Graduate/Scholarship)*

Purpose: To provide opportunities for seniors or graduate students who are studying recreation or tourism studies related fields. **Focus:** Parks and recreation; Travel and tourism. **Qualif.:** Applicants must be undergraduate or final year graduate students majoring in recreation, leisure studies, leisure services and resources, or tourism studies; must have a GPA of 3.5 on a 4.0 scale for undergraduates and 3.8 on a 4.0 scale if graduate students; must be recommended by two faculty members; must have demonstrated interest in recreation, leisure and/or tourism internationally; must have had either volunteer or paid work experience in the recreation, leisure services or tourism fields. **Criteria:** Applicants will be selected based on submitted application and supporting documents.

Funds Avail.: No specific amount. **Duration:** Biennial. **To Apply:** Applicants must complete the application form; must submit the Faculty Validation of Student Applicant form and a copy of the abstract submitted to the World Congress Program Committee. If the college or university does not have a major in required fields, applicants must obtain a letter from their major professor indicating the area of study. If the college or university does not require coursework, applicants must obtain a letter indicating the required learning/research activities and performance evaluation. **Deadline:** May 1. **Remarks:** Established in 1970. **Contact:** Stephen Anderson, Program Manger, Thomas and Ruth Rivers International Scholarship Award Committee, Florida International University, 11200 SW 8th Street PC 237C Miami, Florida, USA 33199; Telephone: 305-348-3848; Fax: 305-3483-685; E-mail: stepande@fiu.edu.

10705 ■ George Torkildsen Literary Awards *(Professional development/Award, Trophy)*

Purpose: To recognize individuals who made a significant contribution to the recreation, parks and leisure service literature by advancing innovative ideas, thoughts and/or philosophical perspectives. **Focus:** Parks and recreation. **Qualif.:** Applicants must be individuals who have made contributions in recreation, parks and leisure service literatures. **Criteria:** Applicants will be evaluated based on literary contributions to advance leisure concerns worldwide; impact of the contributions to influence the general public and/or profession; clarity, solutions and insights brought to emerging trends, issues and concepts.

Funds Avail.: No specific amount. **Duration:** Biennial. **To Apply:** Applicants must be include their full name, title, organizational affiliation and full contact details; must submit a written statement of no more than 1000 words that addresses the nominees scholarly efforts and other professional contributions, referencing the impact that the nominees contributions have made to the literature; and must submit a curriculum vitae. **Deadline:** February 29.

10706 ■ World Wildlife Fund (WWF)
1250 24th St. NW
Washington, DC 20037
Ph: (202)293-4800
Free: 800-960-0993
E-mail: membership@wwfus.org
URL: www.worldwildlife.org
Facebook: www.facebook.com/worldwildlifefund
Twitter: twitter.com/world_wildlife

10707 ■ Kathryn Fuller Science for Nature Post-Doctoral Fellowships *(Graduate, Postdoctorate/Fellowship)*

Purpose: To support early-career scientists working on issues of exceptional importance and relevance to conservation. **Focus:** Conservation of natural resources. **Qualif.:** Applicant must have earned the doctoral degree between June 1, 2006 and June 1, 2011; proposing a research plan that addresses the following topics: 1) ecosystem services; 2) measuring and monitoring carbon stocks in forests; 3) climate change impacts on/and adaptation of freshwater resources. Staff, directors and immediate family members are not eligible for the fellowship. **Criteria:** Selection is based on applicants' ability, accomplishments and potential to become a leader in the field; scientific merit, feasibility and significance of the research proposal; and relevance of the research to conservation practice in general, WWF's mission and programs. Preference will be given to those applicants whose research proposes their country of origin.

Funds Avail.: No specific amount. **Duration:** Annual; two years. **To Apply:** Applicants are required to apply online. In addition, applicants must submit two letters of recommendation, proof of PhD, curriculum vitae and an indirect cost waiver.

10708 ■ Worldstudio Foundation
200 Varick St., Ste. 507
New York, NY 10014
Ph: (212)366-1317
Fax: (212)807-0024
E-mail: info@worldstudio.org
URL: worldstudioinc.com/social-initiatives/case-studies/aiga-scholarships

10709 ■ Worldstudio AIGA Scholarships *(Graduate, Undergraduate/Scholarship)*

Purpose: To help the next generation of artists, architects and designers realize their dreams while being pro-actively involved in their communities. **Focus:** Advertising; Architecture; Art; Art, Caricatures and cartoons; Crafts; Environmental design; Fashion design; Filmmaking; Graphic art and design; Illustrators and illustrations; Industrial design; Interior design; Landscape architecture and design; Photography; Urban affairs/design/planning. **Qualif.:** Applicants must be U.S. citizens or in possession of a Green Card; pursuing an undergraduate or graduate degree in the fine or commercial arts, design or architecture and planning to enter a career in the creative professions; planning or matriculated at an accredited college/university in the United States; maintaining a full-time status; have at least 2.0 GPA; and must demonstrate financial need. Minority

students are encouraged to apply. **Criteria:** Selection is based on the quality of submitted work, financial need, minority status, academic record, recommendations and strength of written statement.
Funds Avail.: No specific amount. **Duration:** Annual. **To Apply:** Applicants must submit up to ten examples of their work and must follow the format indicated at the website. Applicants must mail the disks with film, motion graphics or interactive; transcript(s); and letters of recommendation. **Remarks:** Established in 1995.

10710 ■ Worldwide Assurance for Employees of Public Agencies (WAEPA)
433 Park Ave.
Falls Church, VA 22046
Ph: (703)790-8011
Free: 800-368-3484
E-mail: info@waepa.org
URL: www.waepa.org
Facebook: www.facebook.com/pages/Falls-Church-VA/ WAEPA/111622072195060
Twitter: www.twitter.com/WAEPA_News

10711 ■ WAEPA Scholarship Program
(Undergraduate/Scholarship)
Purpose: To assist policy holders' children who plan to continue education in college or vocational school programs. **Focus:** General studies/Field of study not specified. **Qualif.:** Applicants must be: children (under the age of 23) of WAEPA members insured under WAEPA's group term life insurance program; high school seniors or graduates who plan to enroll or students who are already enrolled in full-time undergraduate study at an accredited two-year or four-year college, university, or vocational-technical school for the entire upcoming academic year; and, maintaining a minimum grade point average of 3.0 on a 4.0 scale (or its equivalent). **Criteria:** Recipients will be selected based on academic record, demonstrated leadership and participation in school, community and volunteer activities, honors, work experience, statement of goals and aspirations, unusual personal or family circumstances and an outside appraisal.
Funds Avail.: No specific amount. **Duration:** Annual. **Number Awarded:** Up to 70. **To Apply:** Applicants must complete the application and mail it along with a current and complete transcript of grades to Scholarship America. **Deadline:** February 1. **Contact:** WAEPA Scholarship Program; Scholarship America; One Scholarship Way, PO Box 297, Saint Peter, MN 56082; Telephone: 507-931-1682.

10712 ■ Worthy Inc.
551 5th Ave., 22nd Flr.
New York, NY 10176
Free: 888-222-0208
E-mail: info@worthy.com
URL: www.worthy.com

10713 ■ Worthy Gemological Scholarships
(Undergraduate/Scholarship)
Purpose: To enhance the students' knowledge and expertise regarding jewelry and its industry. **Focus:** Gemology. **Qualif.:** Applicants must be students with creative, informative and innovative mind about jewelry and jewelry industry. **Criteria:** Selection will be based on the committee's criteria.

Funds Avail.: $1,500. **Duration:** Annual. **To Apply:** Applicants must complete and submit the application and provide a research paper in PDF format with the name template: LastName_FirstName_Date.pdf. **Deadline:** May 28. **Contact:** scholarships@worthy.com.

10714 ■ Wound, Ostomy and Continence Nurses Society (WOCN)
1120 Route 73, Ste. 200
Mount Laurel, NJ 08054
Fax: (856)439-0525
Free: 888-224-9626
E-mail: wocn_info@wocn.org
URL: www.wocn.org

10715 ■ WOCN Accredited Nursing Education Scholarships *(Graduate, Undergraduate/Scholarship)*
Purpose: To support individuals seeking education in wound, ostomy and continence nursing specialties. **Focus:** Nursing. **Qualif.:** Applicants must be students pursuing an education in wound, ostomy and continence nursing care; must be accepted in a WOCN-accredited WOC Educational Program; must be currently enrolled in a WOCN-accredited WOCNEP or Specialty Course. **Criteria:** Selection will be based on the committee's criteria.
Funds Avail.: No specific amount. **Duration:** Annual. **To Apply:** Applicants must have a certificate of completion from a WOCN-accredited WOCNEP or Specialty Course, within three months of graduation. Also, they must complete the application and submit three satisfactory letters of recommendation from professional associates who have known them for at least one year (one from current employer is preferred). **Contact:** WOCN National Office; Phone: 888-224-9626; Email: wocn_info@wocn.org.

10716 ■ WOCN Advanced Education Scholarships *(Graduate/Scholarship)*
Purpose: To support individual seeking education in wound, ostomy and continence nursing specialties. **Focus:** Nursing. **Qualif.:** Applicants should be individuals seeking a master's or doctoral degree or nurse practitioner certificate. They must be active members of WOCN with current or previous employment as a wound, ostomy and/or continence nurse for three years during the past five years, as well as current enrollment, acceptance, or completion/graduation (within 3 months of completion/graduation) from an NLN accredited nursing program/course or other accredited college and/or university program/course for non-nursing degrees. **Criteria:** Selection will be based on the committee's criteria.
Funds Avail.: No specific amount. **Duration:** Annual. **To Apply:** Applicants must have a Certification by the Wound, Ostomy and Continence Nursing Certification Board (WOC-NCB) in one or more areas of WOCN nursing. Also, they must complete the application and submit the following: three letters of recommendation; proof of current RN license; proof of WOCN Membership; proof of current or previous employment as a wound, ostomy, and/or continence nurse for three years within the past five years; and, proof of current enrollment, acceptance, or completion/graduation from an NLN accredited nursing program or other accredited program for non-nursing degree. **Deadline:** May 1; November 1. **Contact:** WOCN National Office; Phone: 888-224-9626; Email: wocn_info@wocn.org.

10717 ■ Xavier University
3800 Victory Pkwy.
Cincinnati, OH 45207

Awards are arranged alphabetically below their administering organizations

Sponsors and Their Scholarships — XAVIER UNIVERSITY

Ph: (513)745-3000
Free: 800-344-4698
URL: www.xavier.edu

10718 ■ Edgecliff Alumni Awards *(Undergraduate/Scholarship)*

Purpose: To provide financial support to students who are in need. **Focus:** General studies/Field of study not specified. **Qualif.:** Applicants must be incoming freshmen and the children, grandchildren, nieces or nephews of Edgecliff College alumni. **Criteria:** Selection is based on academic merit and financial need.

Funds Avail.: No specific amount. **Duration:** Annual. **To Apply:** Applicants admitted at the Xavier University are automatically considered. **Deadline:** February 1.

10719 ■ Edgecliff McAuley Art Scholarships *(Undergraduate/Scholarship)*

Purpose: To provide financial support to students who are in need. **Focus:** Arts. **Qualif.:** Applicants must be incoming first year students with good academic achievement and outstanding artistic talent, and must declare a major in the Arts. **Criteria:** Selection is based on the submitted portfolio.

Funds Avail.: No specific amount. **Duration:** Annual. **To Apply:** Students admitted at the Xavier University are automatically considered. Applicants must submit a portfolio (minimum of eight or maximum of twelve examples of applicant's best work). Portfolios must be clearly labeled with the applicant's name, home phone number, school, and must include an inventory list and a one page personal resume. All pieces must be matted (white mats are mandatory) unless in slide/digital format. All work must be original. **Deadline:** February 1. **Contact:** Department of Art/McAuley Art Scholarship, A.B. Cohen Center/Rm. 190a, 1658 Herald Ave., Cincinnati, OH 4520.

10720 ■ Edgecliff McAuley Music Scholarships *(Undergraduate/Scholarship)*

Purpose: To support outstanding musicians who intend to major in music or music education. **Focus:** Music. **Qualif.:** Applicants must be admitted to Xavier University; must be intended to major in music, music education or sacred music; must display musicianship and proficiency in their primary voice or instrument. **Criteria:** Scholarships are awarded on a competitive basis.

Funds Avail.: Varies. **Duration:** Annual. **To Apply:** Students admitted at the Xavier University are automatically considered and must pass the audition.

10721 ■ James E. Hoff, S.J. Scholars *(Undergraduate/Scholarship)*

Purpose: To provide financial support to students who are in need. **Focus:** General studies/Field of study not specified. **Qualif.:** Applicants must be the children, grandchildren, nieces or nephews of Edgecliff College alumni; must demonstrate exceptional leadership, vision, courage, service and compassion in academic and personal life. **Criteria:** Selection is based on academic merit and financial need.

Funds Avail.: Varies. **Duration:** Annual. **To Apply:** Applicants admitted at the Xavier University are automatically considered. **Deadline:** February 1.

10722 ■ Indiana Alumni Scholarships *(Undergraduate/Scholarship)*

Purpose: To provide financial support to students who are in need. **Focus:** General studies/Field of study not specified. **Qualif.:** Applicants must be incoming freshmen from Indiana. **Criteria:** Selection is based on need.

Funds Avail.: $2,000. **Duration:** Annual. **Number Awarded:** 3. **To Apply:** Applicants must apply for financial aid by completing the FAFSA. **Deadline:** February 1; February 15 for the FAFSA application.

10723 ■ Ohio War Orphan Scholarships *(Undergraduate/Scholarship)*

Purpose: To provide financial support to students who are in need. **Focus:** General studies/Field of study not specified. **Qualif.:** Applicants must be students with a parent who served at least 90 days of active duty during wartime and is disabled or deceased as a result of service; must be Ohio residents; must achieve a 2.0 GPA or higher. **Criteria:** Selection will be based on the committee's criteria.

Funds Avail.: No specific amount. **Duration:** Annual. **To Apply:** Applications available from high school guidance counselors or veterans offices. **Deadline:** July 1.

10724 ■ Miguel Pro Scholarships *(Undergraduate/Scholarship)*

Purpose: To provide support to students in promoting diversity in the society and demonstrating leadership in the classroom, on campus, and in the greater community. **Focus:** General studies/Field of study not specified. **Qualif.:** Applicants must be students ranking in the top 25 percent of their high school class with at least 3.0 GPA and a minimum SAT of 1070 (23 ACT). **Criteria:** Selection will be based on merit.

Funds Avail.: No specific amount. **Duration:** Annual. **To Apply:** Applicants admitted at the Xavier University are automatically considered. **Deadline:** February 1.

10725 ■ St. Francis Xavier Scholarships *(Undergraduate/Scholarship)*

Purpose: To provide financial support to students who are in need. **Focus:** General studies/Field of study not specified. **Qualif.:** Applicants must be incoming first-year students with exceptional academic achievement and outstanding leadership involvement in the community or school; must have at least 3.75GPA and a minimum SAT of 1360. **Criteria:** Selection is based on merit.

Funds Avail.: No specific amount. **Duration:** Annual; up to 4 years. **Number Awarded:** Up to 10. **To Apply:** Applicants admitted at the Xavier University are automatically considered. **Deadline:** February 1.

10726 ■ Francis X. Weninger Scholarships *(Undergraduate/Scholarship)*

Purpose: To provide support to students who are committed to the promotion of diversity in the society and who demonstrated leadership in the classroom, on campus and in the greater community. **Focus:** General studies/Field of study not specified. **Qualif.:** Applicants must be students ranking in the top 25 percent of their high school class with at least 3.0 GPA and a minimum SAT of 1070 (23 ACT). **Criteria:** Selection will be based on merit.

Funds Avail.: No specific amount. **Duration:** Annual. **To Apply:** Applicants admitted at the Xavier University are automatically considered. **Deadline:** February 1.

10727 ■ Xavier Community-Engaged Fellowships *(Undergraduate/Fellowship)*

Purpose: To support students who have demonstrated extraordinary leadership or initiative in the area of com-

Awards are arranged alphabetically below their administering organizations

munity engagement or service through their school, community or church. **Focus:** General studies/Field of study not specified. **Qualif.:** Applicants must be incoming first-year students who have demonstrated high academic achievement, outstanding service to community, school, or church, and leadership in encouraging others to serve. **Criteria:** Preference will be given to students demonstrating exemplary involvement in volunteer service; have shown potential for leading other students in service; have attained a minimum score of 29 on the ACT composite or 1280 on the SAT; and in the top ten percent of the high school senior class. **Funds Avail.:** $22,000. **Duration:** Annual. **Number Awarded:** 8. **To Apply:** Applicants admitted at the Xavier University are automatically considered. **Deadline:** February 1. **Remarks:** Established in 1989.

10728 ■ Xavier University Chancellor Scholarships (Undergraduate/Scholarship)

Purpose: To financially support students with their education. **Focus:** General studies/Field of study not specified. **Qualif.:** Applicants must be an incoming first-year student with excellent academic achievement. **Criteria:** Selection is based on merit. **Funds Avail.:** $17,000. **Duration:** Annual. **To Apply:** Applicants admitted at the Xavier University are automatically considered. **Deadline:** February 1.

10729 ■ Xavier University Departmental Scholarships (Undergraduate/Scholarship)

Purpose: To financially support students with their education. **Focus:** Chemistry; Classical studies; History; Mathematics and mathematical sciences; Modern languages; Physics. **Qualif.:** Applicants must top the score in either of the six departmental exams (chemistry, classics (Latin), history, mathematics, modern languages (French, German or Spanish) and physics). Students must major in the area for which the scholarship is awarded. **Criteria:** Scholarship is given to the highest scorer on the exams. **Funds Avail.:** $3,000. **Duration:** Annual. **Number Awarded:** 4. **To Apply:** Participants will take an exam in the appropriate subject area and have an opportunity to speak with faculty and learn more about the department. **Deadline:** February 1.

10730 ■ Xavier University Honors Bachelor of Arts Scholarships (Undergraduate/Scholarship)

Purpose: To financially support students with their education. **Focus:** Arts. **Qualif.:** Applicants must be students enrolled in the honor bachelor of arts program. **Criteria:** Selection will be bases on merit. **Funds Avail.:** No specific amount. **Duration:** Annual. **To Apply:** Applicants admitted at the Xavier University are automatically considered. **Remarks:** Established in 1948.

10731 ■ Xavier University Legacy Scholarships (Undergraduate/Scholarship)

Purpose: To provide financial support to students who are in need. **Focus:** General studies/Field of study not specified. **Qualif.:** Applicants must be full-time undergraduate students who are children or grandchildren of Xavier alumni. **Criteria:** Selection is based on academic merit, leadership and service activities. **Funds Avail.:** $3,000 renewable. **Number Awarded:** 2. **To Apply:** Applicants must submit a completed Legacy Scholarship Application along with the required supporting materials. **Deadline:** February 1.

10732 ■ Xavier University Presidential Scholarships (Undergraduate/Scholarship)

Purpose: To financially support students pursuing higher education. **Focus:** General studies/Field of study not specified. **Qualif.:** Applicants must be incoming first-year students with excellent academic achievement (rank at least in the top 25 percent of high school class, have appropriately high grades, and have a minimum SAT of 1130, 25 ACT). **Criteria:** Selection will be based on merit. **Funds Avail.:** No specific amount. **To Apply:** Students admitted at the Xavier University are automatically considered. **Deadline:** February 1.

10733 ■ Xavier University ROTC Scholarships - Air Force ROTC (Undergraduate/Scholarship)

Purpose: To provide financial support to students who are in need. **Focus:** Aerospace sciences. **Qualif.:** Applicants must be high school students pursuing an Air Force ROTC or college freshmen and sophomores pursuing an in-college Air Force ROTC. **Criteria:** Selection is based on merit. **Funds Avail.:** No specific amount. **To Apply:** Applicants must submit online application.

10734 ■ Xavier University ROTC Scholarships - Army ROTC (Undergraduate/Scholarship)

Purpose: To provide financial support to students who are in need. **Focus:** Military science and education. **Qualif.:** Applicants must students pursuing military science at Xavier University. Nursing students can also compete for an Army ROTC nursing scholarship and upon graduation become an Army Nurse. **Criteria:** Selection will be based on merit and grades. **Funds Avail.:** Full-tuition, $1,200 yearly book allowance and a monthly stipend starting at $300/month during the academic school year. **Duration:** Annual. **To Apply:** High School students may apply online for an Army ROTC Scholarship at www.goarmy.com/rotc. **Contact:** Detachment 665 Unit Admission Officer: 513-556-2237.

10735 ■ Xavier University Williams Scholarships (Undergraduate/Scholarship)

Purpose: To financially support students with their education. **Focus:** Business. **Qualif.:** Applicants must be first year students enrolled in the Williams College of Business. **Criteria:** Selection will be based on merit. **Funds Avail.:** $3000. **Duration:** Annual. **Number Awarded:** 4. **To Apply:** Applicants must complete the online application. **Deadline:** February 1.

10736 ■ Xerox Corp.
45 Glover Ave.
Norwalk, CT 06856-4505
Ph: (203)968-3000
Fax: (203)968-3218
Free: 800-275-9376
E-mail: info@xerox.com
URL: www.xerox.com

10737 ■ Xerox Technical Minority Scholarships (Graduate, Undergraduate/Scholarship)

Purpose: To provide financial support and experiences for minorities enrolled in a technical degree program. **Focus:**

Awards are arranged alphabetically below their administering organizations

Chemistry; Computer and information sciences; Engineering, Chemical; Engineering, Computer; Engineering, Electrical; Engineering, Mechanical; Engineering, Optical; Materials research/science; Optics; Physics; Printing trades and industries. **Qualif.:** Applicants must: be academic high-achievers (3.0 or better GPA); be U.S. citizens or visa-holding Permanent Resident of African American, Asian, Pacific Island, Native American, Native Alaskan, or Hispanic descent; enrolled as a full-time undergraduate or graduate student in any technical fields (Chemistry, Information Management, Computing & Software Systems, Material Science, Printing Management Science, Laser Optics, Physics, Material Science, Engineering: Chemical, Computer, Electrical, Imaging, Manufacturing, Mechanical, Optical, or Software). **Criteria:** Selection is based on the application materials submitted for review.

Funds Avail.: $1,000-$10,000. **Duration:** Annual. **To Apply:** Applicants must complete the scholarship application form, attach a resume and have the Financial Aid Office complete the bottom portion of the application. **Deadline:** September 30. **Contact:** Nancy Dempsey at nancy.dempsey@xerox.com, or xtmsp@rballiance.com.

10738 ■ York Art Association (YAA)
PO Box 74
York, ME 03909
Ph: (207)363-4049
URL: www.yorkartassociation.com

10739 ■ Letitia Moore Charitable Trust Scholarship
(Undergraduate/Scholarship)

Purpose: To support students majoring in art or art history. **Focus:** Art; Art history. **Qualif.:** Applicants must be enrolled in an accredited college or university; must be majoring in art or art history; must have completed their first year of study with a GPA of at least 3.0 or greater. **Criteria:** Recipients will be selected based on submitted materials.

Funds Avail.: $5,000. **Duration:** Annual. **To Apply:** Applicants must submit a letter of application and provide proof of their eligibility. The letter should describe the applicant's educational and career goals and should identify the names and telephone numbers of two or three references familiar with their ability and aspirations. **Deadline:** September 1. **Remarks:** Established in 2009.

10740 ■ York University - Schulich School of Business
111 Ian Macdonald Blvd.
Toronto, ON, Canada M3J 1P3
Ph: (416)736-2100
Fax: (416)736-5763
Free: 800-667-9380
E-mail: admissions@schulich.yorku.ca
URL: www.schulich.yorku.ca/client/schulich/
 schulich_lp4w_lnd_webstation.nsf/index.html?Readform
Facebook: www.facebook.com/SchulichSchool
LinkedIn: www.linkedin.com/company/schulichbusiness
Twitter: twitter.com/SchulichSchool

10741 ■ Lawrence Bloomberg Entrance Awards
(Postgraduate/Award)

Purpose: To financially support those students who are pursuing MBA degree. **Focus:** General studies/Field of study not specified. **Qualif.:** Applicants must have presented first class standing in previous academic work (A average); have an active participation in either extra-curricular activities or community involvement; and have demonstrated financial need. **Criteria:** Applicants are selected based on academic excellence and financial need.

Funds Avail.: 10,000 Canadian Dollars. **Duration:** Annual. **To Apply:** Applicants are advised to visit the organization for the application procedure.

10742 ■ Louis J. Brody Q.C. Entrance Scholarships
(Graduate/Scholarship)

Purpose: To support students by providing educational needs. **Focus:** General studies/Field of study not specified. **Qualif.:** Applicants must be incoming MBA students who have demonstrated academic excellence in previous studies. **Criteria:** Applicants are evaluated based on academic excellence and financial need.

Funds Avail.: 2,500 Canadian Dollars. **Duration:** Annual. **Number Awarded:** Up to 4. **To Apply:** Applicants are advised to visit the organization for the application procedure. **Remarks:** Established in 1996.

10743 ■ Peter F. Bronfman Entrance Awards
(Postgraduate/Award)

Purpose: To provide educational support to students who demonstrated academic excellence in the previous studies. **Focus:** General studies/Field of study not specified. **Qualif.:** Applicants must be full-time students in the Schulich program; must be active in their community; must have demonstrated leadership either in extracurricular activities or community involvement. **Criteria:** Applicants are selected based on academic excellence and financial need.

Funds Avail.: 5,000 Canadian Dollars. **Duration:** Annual. **Number Awarded:** 3. **To Apply:** Applicants are advised to visit the organization for the application procedure.

10744 ■ Peter F. Bronfman Scholarships of Merit
(Postgraduate/Scholarship)

Purpose: To provide educational support to students who demonstrated the highest academic standing. **Focus:** General studies/Field of study not specified. **Qualif.:** Applicants must be full-time students enrolled in the Schulich MBA program; must be active in their community; must have demonstrated leadership either in the workplace or through extracurricular activities; must have at least two years working experience; must be Canadian citizens or permanent residents of Ontario; and have demonstrated financial need. **Criteria:** Applicants are selected based on academic excellence and financial need.

Funds Avail.: 10,000 Canadian Dollars. **Duration:** Annual. **To Apply:** Applicants are advised to visit the organization for the application procedure.

10745 ■ Marshall A. Cohen Entrance Awards
(Postgraduate/Award)

Purpose: To provide educational support to students who are pursuing MBA, MBA/JD and Nonprofit degree. **Focus:** General studies/Field of study not specified. **Qualif.:** Applicants must be full-time MBA students who have an active participation in their community; must have demonstrated academic excellence in previous studies; and must have at least two years working experience. **Criteria:** Applicants are selected based on community involvement and extracurricular activities which have contributed to the well-being of others, academic excellence, and financial need.

Funds Avail.: 10,000 Canadian Dollars. **Duration:** Annual.

Awards are arranged alphabetically below their administering organizations

Number Awarded: 3. **To Apply:** Applicants are advised to visit the organization for the application procedure.

10746 ■ Bernie Kom Memorial Awards
(Postgraduate/Award)

Purpose: To help students attain financial independence. **Focus:** General studies/Field of study not specified. **Qualif.:** Applicants must be MBA students who are currently enrolled in the second year of study and have demonstrated academic excellence in previous studies. **Criteria:** Applicants are evaluated based on academic excellence and financial need.
Funds Avail.: 5,000 Canadian Dollars. **Duration:** Annual. **To Apply:** Applicants are advised to visit the organization for the application procedure.

10747 ■ Robert Krembil Scholarships of Merit
(Doctorate/Scholarship)

Purpose: To provide students the educational support they need. **Focus:** General studies/Field of study not specified. **Qualif.:** Applicants must be full-time MBA students who have demonstrated academic excellence; must have working experience of no less than four years; must have excellent communication skills and leadership ability. **Criteria:** Applicants are evaluated based on academic excellence and financial need.
Funds Avail.: 34,500 Canadian Dollars (plus 5,000 Canadian Dollars living subsidy). **Duration:** Annual. **To Apply:** Applicants are advised to visit the organization for the application procedure.

10748 ■ Allen T. Lambert Scholarships
(Postgraduate/Scholarship)

Purpose: To provide educational support to students who are pursuing full-time MBA degree. **Focus:** General studies/Field of study not specified. **Qualif.:** Applicants must be MBA students who are currently enrolled in the second year of study and have demonstrated academic excellence in previous studies. **Criteria:** Applicants are evaluated based on academic excellence and financial need.
Funds Avail.: 5,000 Canadian Dollars. **Duration:** Annual. **To Apply:** Applicants are advised to visit the organization for the application procedure.

10749 ■ Kenneth Laundy Entrance Scholarships
(Graduate/Scholarship)

Purpose: To provide educational support to those students who are entering MBA/JD degree. **Focus:** General studies/Field of study not specified. **Qualif.:** Applicants must be incoming MBA/JD students who have achieved academic excellence and merit. **Criteria:** Applicants are selected based on academic excellence and financial need.
Funds Avail.: 2,500 Canadian Dollars. **Duration:** Annual. **To Apply:** Applicants are advised to visit the organization for the application procedure.

10750 ■ Carol Anne Letheren Entrance Awards
(Postgraduate/Award, Scholarship)

Purpose: To support an incoming MBA student who has demonstrated the highest academic standing. **Focus:** General studies/Field of study not specified. **Qualif.:** Applicants must be full-time incoming MBA students who have an academic excellence in the previous studies; must be active in their community and must demonstrate leadership either in the workplace or through extracurricular activities; must have at least two years working experience. **Criteria:** Applicants are selected based on academic excellence and financial need.
Funds Avail.: 5,000 Canadian Dollars. **Duration:** Annual. **To Apply:** Applicants are advised to visit the organization for the application procedure.

10751 ■ Ian Lithgow Memorial Awards
(Master's/Award)

Purpose: To support an incoming MBA student who has demonstrated the highest academic standing. **Focus:** General studies/Field of study not specified. **Qualif.:** Applicants must be full-time MBA students who have demonstrated academic excellence in the previous studies. **Criteria:** Applicants are selected based on academic excellence and financial need.
Funds Avail.: 5,000 Canadian Dollars. **Duration:** Annual. **To Apply:** Applicants are advised to visit the organization for the application procedure.

10752 ■ Irwin Allen Nadal Entrance Awards
(Master's/Award)

Purpose: To support an incoming MBA student who has demonstrated the highest academic standing. **Focus:** General studies/Field of study not specified. **Qualif.:** Applicants must be incoming MBA or IMBA students; must have a minimum cumulative grade of 6.0 (B+). **Criteria:** Applicants are evaluated based on academic achievements and financial need.
Funds Avail.: 2,500 Canadian Dollars. **Duration:** Annual. **To Apply:** Applicants are advised to visit the organization for the application procedure.

10753 ■ Miles Spencer Nadal Entrance Awards
(Master's/Award)

Purpose: To support an incoming MBA student who has demonstrated the highest academic standing. **Focus:** General studies/Field of study not specified. **Qualif.:** Applicants must be incoming MBA or IMBA students who have demonstrated academic excellence; must have a minimum cumulative grade of 6.0 (B+). **Criteria:** Applicants are evaluated based on academic achievements and financial need.
Funds Avail.: 2,500 Canadian Dollars. **Duration:** Annual. **To Apply:** Applicants are advised to visit the organization for the application procedure.

10754 ■ Tanna H. Schulich MBA Entrance Scholarships
(Graduate/Scholarship)

Purpose: To provide educational support to students who are pursuing their MBA degree. **Focus:** General studies/Field of study not specified. **Qualif.:** Applicants must be full-time MBA students who have an active in their community; and have demonstrated leadership either in the workplace or through extracurricular activities; must have at least two years working experience. **Criteria:** Applicants are selected based on academic excellence and financial need.
Funds Avail.: 24,200 Canadian Dollars. **Duration:** Annual. **Number Awarded:** 5. **To Apply:** Applicants are advised to visit the organization for the application procedure.

10755 ■ Harry Steele Entrance Awards
(Postgraduate/Award)

Purpose: To provide students the educational support they need. **Focus:** General studies/Field of study not specified.

Awards are arranged alphabetically below their administering organizations

Qualif.: Applicants must have presented an excellent academic standing (A average) from previous studies; and have shown involvement either in extra-curricular activities or community service. **Criteria:** Applicants are selected based on academic excellence and financial need.

Funds Avail.: 10,000 Canadian Dollars. **Duration:** Annual. **To Apply:** Applicants are advised to visit the organization for the application procedure.

10756 ■ York Graduate Scholarships *(Graduate/Scholarship)*

Purpose: To provide educational support to students who are pursuing master's and doctoral levels. **Focus:** General studies/Field of study not specified. **Qualif.:** Applicants must be students at the master's or doctoral level; must have an unequivocal "A" standing in their previous two years of study. **Criteria:** Applicants are evaluated based on demonstrated academic excellence and financial need.

Funds Avail.: 2,000 Canadian Dollars. **Duration:** Annual. **To Apply:** Applicants are advised to visit the organization for the application procedure.

10757 ■ Yottabyte
1750 S Telegraph Rd., Ste. 200
Bloomfield Township, MI 48302
Ph: (248)464-6100
Free: 888-630-2983
E-mail: info@yottabyte.com
URL: www.yottabyte.com
LinkedIn: www.linkedin.com/company/yottabyte-llc
Twitter: www.twitter.com/YottabyteLLC

10758 ■ Innovations in Software Scholarships *(Undergraduate, Graduate/Scholarship)*

Purpose: To develop future talent in the IT and Computer Science related fields. **Focus:** Information science and technology. **Qualif.:** Applicants must be undergraduate or graduate students studying software programming, engineering or technology at an accredited university in the United States; and have a minimum 3.0 GPA. **Criteria:** Selection will be based on the committee's criteria.

Funds Avail.: $1,000 (grand prize); $500 (runner-up). **Number Awarded:** 2. **To Apply:** Applicants must complete the online application and submit a copy of their undergraduate transcript, as well as an essay of 1,500 words or fewer (along with diagrams if needed) answering the following: "What are the next, most impactful innovations in software?" **Deadline:** November 15.

10759 ■ Young Christian Leaders Scholarship Porgram
9 Broadman Pkwy.
Jersey City, NJ 07305
Ph: (201)432-7300
E-mail: info@yclscholarship.org
URL: www.yclscholarship.org

10760 ■ Young Christian Leaders Scholarships *(Undergraduate/Scholarship)*

Purpose: To support the next generation of dedicated Christian professionals who will use their talents to impact their families, communities and the world. **Focus:** General studies/Field of study not specified. **Qualif.:** Applicants must be 18 to 24 years old; must be high school to undergraduate seniors; must be residents of NY, NJ, PA or CT; and must be active members of a church and able to get a pastoral reference. **Criteria:** Selection will be based on the following: online votes and judges vote based on character, achievement and need.

Funds Avail.: $1,000. **Duration:** Monthly. **Number Awarded:** 2. **To Apply:** Applicants may download an application form from the website and mail it along with all the requirements. **Deadline:** 15th of every month. **Contact:** Maciel Almonte at the above address.

10761 ■ Young Musicians Foundation (YMF)
244 San Pedro St., 5th Fl., Ste. 506
Los Angeles, CA 90012
Ph: (213)617-7707
Fax: (218)617-7706
E-mail: info@ymf.org
URL: www.ymf.org

10762 ■ YMF Scholarships *(Undergraduate/Scholarship)*

Purpose: To provide financial assistance to young musicians for their private music instruction. **Focus:** Music. **Qualif.:** Applicant must demonstrate exceptional talent and financial need; be a resident of Southern California. Instrumentalist or pianist may apply through the completion of their senior year of high school. Vocalists must be between the ages of 8-26. Applicant who is not a U.S. citizen and is under age 18, applicant's parents must live in the state of California. **Criteria:** Recipients will be selected at the four days countrywide auditions. Selection is based on outstanding talent and financial need.

Funds Avail.: No specific amount. **Duration:** Annual. **To Apply:** Applicant must submit a completed application.

10763 ■ Young People For (YP4)
1101 15th St., NW, Ste. 600
Washington, DC 20005
Ph: (202)467-4999
URL: www.youngpeoplefor.org

10764 ■ Young People For Fellowships *(Professional development/Fellowship)*

Purpose: To provide leadership development for young people committed to creating positive social change in their communities. **Focus:** General studies/Field of study not specified. **Qualif.:** Candidates must be young leaders and activists with the leadership development, networks, skills and support they need to create positive change on their campuses and in their communities. **Criteria:** Preference will be given to those who meet the criteria.

Funds Avail.: No specific amount. **Duration:** Annual. **To Apply:** YP4 hopes the professors, administrators, community leaders and campus activists will nominated innovative and promising young progressive leaders for the program. Nominators play a crucial role in connecting young leaders and activists with the support and guidance that the YP4 Fellowship can provide. Anyone is encouraged to submit a nomination, and self-nominations are appropriate and encouraged. Nomination form can be completed online. **Contact:** Michael Glymph, at mglymph@pfaw.org.

10765 ■ Young Women's Alliance (YWA)
PO Box 684612
Austin, TX 78701

Awards are arranged alphabetically below their administering organizations

E-mail: administrator@youngwomensalliance.org
URL: www.youngwomensalliance.org

10766 ■ YWA Foundation Scholarships *(Graduate, Undergraduate/Scholarship)*

Purpose: To financially support female students with their educational pursuit. **Focus:** General studies/Field of study not specified. **Qualif.:** Applicants must be female U.S. residents under the age of 40, and be juniors or seniors in college or pursuing a graduate degree at a university or accredited institution of higher learning within Central Texas. **Criteria:** Selection is based on demonstrated financial need, commitment to community service, academic achievement and leadership potential.

Funds Avail.: No specific amount. **Duration:** Annual. **To Apply:** Applicants must submit a completed application form along with an official copy of college transcript; a personal statement; copy of Federal Tax Return (or parents') for the previous year; proof of current income (copy of recent paycheck or stub); and two letters of recommendation (from persons outside the family). **Deadline:** March 31.

10767 ■ Youth Maritime Training Association (YMTA)
PO Box 70425
Seattle, WA 98127-0425
Ph: (206)300-5559
URL: www.ymta.net
Facebook: www.facebook.com/youthmaritimetrainingassociation

10768 ■ Norm Manly Maritime Educational Scholarships *(Undergraduate/Scholarship)*

Purpose: To support students pursuing maritime training and education. **Focus:** Maritime studies. **Qualif.:** Applicants must: currently be enrolled as seniors in a high school or affiliated high school program (including GED program) in the State of Washington; plan to pursue post-secondary training or educational program leading to a maritime or marine-related career; and, have a grade point average of at least 2.5. **Criteria:** Selection will be based on the aforesaid qualifications and compliance with the application process.

Funds Avail.: $500 to $1,000. **Duration:** Annual. **To Apply:** Interested applicants are requested to submit a letter of support from one teacher. An optional letter of support from a member of the maritime community is encouraged but not required. An additional letter of recommendation from a second teacher is also encouraged to submit. **Deadline:** February 22. **Contact:** Alicia Barnes by e-mail: ymta@pugetmaritime.org, or phone: 206-812-5464.

10769 ■ Youth for Understanding (YFU)
641 S St. NW, Ste. 200
Washington, DC 20001
Ph: (202)774-5200
E-mail: admission@yfu.org
URL: www.yfu-usa.org

10770 ■ The YFU Americas Scholarships *(Undergraduate/Scholarship)*

Purpose: To provide students an opportunity to study abroad to gain intercultural understanding, learn mutual respect and develop a sense of social responsibility. **Focus:** General studies/Field of study not specified. **Qualif.:** Applicants must be US high school students with freshman, sophomore, junior or senior class standing; must have a 2.0 GPA or higher on a 4.0 scale; must meet age requirements. **Criteria:** Scholarships are awarded based on a comprehensive evaluation process. A selection committee reviews all application materials and you will be contacted for an interview.

Funds Avail.: No specific amount. **Duration:** Annual. **To Apply:** Applicants must confer to the program website for the application details. **Deadline:** December 1.

10771 ■ Yukon Conservation Society (YCS)
302 Hawkins St.
Whitehorse, YT, Canada Y1A 1X6
Ph: (867)668-5678
Fax: (867)668-6637
E-mail: ycs@ycs.yk.ca
URL: www.yukonconservation.org

10772 ■ Ted Parnell Scholarship *(Undergraduate/Scholarship)*

Purpose: To financially support students who are pursuing any aspect of environmental studies. **Focus:** Wildlife conservation, management, and science. **Qualif.:** Applicants must be Yukon Territory residents and should be entering or currently enrolled in a post-secondary school program (excluding graduate work). **Criteria:** Selection will be based on the committee's criteria.

Funds Avail.: $500. **Duration:** Annual. **To Apply:** Applicants must submit their most recent transcripts, resume and cover letter to Yukon Conservation Society. **Deadline:** June 30.

10773 ■ The Yukon Foundation
PO Box 31622
Whitehorse, YT, Canada Y1A 6L2
Ph: (867)393-2454
E-mail: yukonfoundation@klondiker.com
URL: www.yukonfoundation.com

10774 ■ Marjorie Almstrom Scholarships *(Undergraduate, Master's/Scholarship)*

Purpose: To provide funds for students to help them pay their college or university tuition. **Focus:** General studies/Field of study not specified. **Qualif.:** Applicants must be 4th or 5th year post-secondary students, or Masters or equivalent. **Criteria:** Selection will be based on the committee's criteria.

Funds Avail.: No specific amount. **Duration:** Annual. **To Apply:** Applicants must submit the application form (available online), copy of their transcripts, university acceptance letters, and/or reference letters. **Deadline:** May 31.

10775 ■ Jaedyn Amann Memorial Scholarships *(Undergraduate, Master's/Scholarship)*

Purpose: To provide funds for students to help them pay their college or university tuition. **Focus:** General studies/Field of study not specified. **Qualif.:** Applicants must be 4th or 5th year post-secondary students, or Masters or equivalent. **Criteria:** Selection will be based on the committee's criteria.

Awards are arranged alphabetically below their administering organizations

Funds Avail.: No specific amount. **Duration:** Annual. **To Apply:** Applicants must submit the application form (available online), copy of their transcripts, university acceptance letters, and/or reference letters. **Deadline:** May 31.

10776 ■ Robert Armstrong Memorial Scholarships
(Undergraduate, Graduate/Scholarship)

Purpose: To provide funds for students to help them pay their college or university tuition. **Focus:** General studies/Field of study not specified. **Qualif.:** Applicants must be 4th or 5th year post-secondary students, or Masters or equivalent. **Criteria:** Selection will be based on the committee's criteria.

Funds Avail.: No specific amount. **Duration:** Annual. **To Apply:** Applicants must submit the application form (available online), copy of their transcripts, university acceptance letters, and/or reference letters. **Deadline:** May 31.

10777 ■ Victoria Baldwin Memorial Scholarships
(Undergraduate, Master's/Award)

Purpose: To provide funds for students to help them pay their college or university tuition. **Focus:** General studies/Field of study not specified. **Qualif.:** Applicants must be 4th or 5th year post-secondary students, or Masters or equivalent. **Criteria:** Selection will be based on the committee's criteria.

Funds Avail.: No specific amount. **Duration:** Annual. **To Apply:** Applicants must submit the application form (available online), copy of their transcripts, university acceptance letters, and/or reference letters. **Deadline:** May 31.

10778 ■ Henry Besner Memorial Scholarships
(Undergraduate, Master's/Scholarship)

Purpose: To provide funds for students to help them pay their college or university tuition. **Focus:** General studies/Field of study not specified. **Qualif.:** Applicants must be 4th or 5th year post-secondary students, or Masters or equivalent. **Criteria:** Selection will be based on the committee's criteria.

Funds Avail.: No specific amount. **Duration:** Annual. **To Apply:** Applicants must submit the application form (available online), copy of their transcripts, university acceptance letters, and/or reference letters. **Deadline:** May 31.

10779 ■ Herbie Bouwman Memorial Scholarships
(Undergraduate, Master's/Scholarship)

Purpose: To provide funds for students to help them pay their college or university tuition. **Focus:** General studies/Field of study not specified. **Qualif.:** Applicants must be 4th or 5th year post-secondary students, or Masters or equivalent. **Criteria:** Selection will be based on the committee's criteria.

Funds Avail.: No specific amount. **Duration:** Annual. **To Apply:** Applicants must submit the application form (available online), copy of their transcripts, university acceptance letters, and/or reference letters. **Deadline:** May 31.

10780 ■ Geoffrey Bradshaw Memorial Scholarships
(Graduate/Scholarship)

Purpose: To provide funds for students to help them pay their college or university tuition. **Focus:** Geology. **Qualif.:** Candidates must be Canadian citizens enrolled in a Canadian university in the first or second year of a graduate Geology program and must be working on a thesis with a Yukon field component. **Criteria:** Preference will be given to applicants who have not previously received the scholarship.

Funds Avail.: No specific amount. **Duration:** Annual. **To Apply:** Applicants must submit a completed scholarship application form (available online), copy of their transcripts, university acceptance letters, and/or reference letters. **Deadline:** May 31.

10781 ■ Brian Campion Scholarship Scholarships
(Advanced Professional/Scholarship)

Purpose: To assist Yukon students to further their studies in Law. **Focus:** Law. **Qualif.:** Applicants must be Yukon law students. **Criteria:** Selection will be based on the committee's criteria.

Funds Avail.: No specific amount. **Duration:** Annual. **To Apply:** Applicants must submit a completed scholarship application form (available online), copy of their transcripts, university acceptance letters, and/or reference letters. **Deadline:** May 31.

10782 ■ Chechahko Consumers Co-Op Ltd. Scholarships *(Undergraduate, Master's/Scholarship)*

Purpose: To provide funds for students to help them pay their college or university tuition. **Focus:** General studies/Field of study not specified. **Qualif.:** Applicants must be 4th or 5th year post-secondary students, or Masters or equivalent. **Criteria:** Selection will be based on the committee's criteria.

Funds Avail.: No specific amount. **Duration:** Annual. **To Apply:** Applicants must submit the application form (available online), copy of their transcripts, university acceptance letters, and/or reference letters. **Deadline:** May 31.

10783 ■ Helen & Orval Couch Memorial Scholarships *(Undergraduate, Master's/Scholarship)*

Purpose: To provide funds for students to help them pay their college or university tuition. **Focus:** General studies/Field of study not specified. **Qualif.:** Applicants must be 4th or 5th year post-secondary students, or Masters or equivalent. **Criteria:** Selection will be based on the committee's criteria.

Funds Avail.: No specific amount. **Duration:** Annual. **To Apply:** Applicants must submit the application form (available online), copy of their transcripts, university acceptance letters, and/or reference letters. **Deadline:** May 31.

10784 ■ Jim Davie Memorial Scholarships
(Undergraduate, Master's/Scholarship)

Purpose: To provide funds for students to help them pay their college or university tuition. **Focus:** General studies/Field of study not specified. **Qualif.:** Applicants must be 4th or 5th year post-secondary students, or Masters or equivalent. **Criteria:** Selection will be based on the committee's criteria.

Funds Avail.: No specific amount. **Duration:** Annual. **To Apply:** Applicants must submit the application form (available online), copy of their transcripts, university acceptance letters, and/or reference letters. **Deadline:** May 31.

10785 ■ Dr. Allan Duncan Memorial Scholarships
(Undergraduate, Master's/Scholarship)

Purpose: To provide funds for students to help them pay their college or university tuition. **Focus:** General studies/Field of study not specified. **Qualif.:** Applicants must be 4th or 5th year post-secondary students, or Masters or

Awards are arranged alphabetically below their administering organizations

equivalent. **Criteria:** Selection will be based on the committee's criteria.

Funds Avail.: No specific amount. **Duration:** Annual. **To Apply:** Applicants must submit the application form (available online), copy of their transcripts, university acceptance letters, and/or reference letters. **Deadline:** May 31.

10786 ■ Nicky & Ted Harrison Memorial Scholarships *(Undergraduate, Master's/Scholarship)*

Purpose: To provide funds for students to help them pay their college or university tuition. **Focus:** General studies/Field of study not specified. **Qualif.:** Applicants must be 4th or 5th year post-secondary students, or Masters or equivalent. **Criteria:** Selection will be based on the committee's criteria.

Funds Avail.: No specific amount. **Duration:** Annual. **To Apply:** Applicants must submit the application form (available online), copy of their transcripts, university acceptance letters, and/or reference letters. **Deadline:** May 31.

10787 ■ Donald Hoy Memorial Scholarships *(Undergraduate, Master's/Scholarship)*

Purpose: To provide funds for students to help them pay their college or university tuition. **Focus:** General studies/Field of study not specified. **Qualif.:** Applicants must be 4th or 5th year post-secondary students, or Masters or equivalent. **Criteria:** Selection will be based on the committee's criteria.

Funds Avail.: No specific amount. **Duration:** Annual. **To Apply:** Applicants must submit the application form (available online), copy of their transcripts, university acceptance letters, and/or reference letters. **Deadline:** May 31.

10788 ■ John Hoyt Memorial Scholarships *(Undergraduate, Master's/Scholarship)*

Purpose: To provide funds for students to help them pay their college or university tuition. **Focus:** General studies/Field of study not specified. **Qualif.:** Applicants must be 4th or 5th year post-secondary students, or Masters or equivalent. **Criteria:** Selection will be based on the committee's criteria.

Funds Avail.: No specific amount. **Duration:** Annual. **To Apply:** Applicants must submit the application form (available online), copy of their transcripts, university acceptance letters, and/or reference letters. **Deadline:** May 31.

10789 ■ Helen Janko Memorial Scholarships *(Undergraduate, Master's/Scholarship)*

Purpose: To provide funds for students to help them pay their college or university tuition. **Focus:** General studies/Field of study not specified. **Qualif.:** Applicants must be 4th or 5th year post-secondary students, or Masters or equivalent. **Criteria:** Selection will be based on the committee's criteria.

Funds Avail.: No specific amount. **Duration:** Annual. **To Apply:** Applicants must submit the application form (available online), copy of their transcripts, university acceptance letters, and/or reference letters. **Deadline:** May 31.

10790 ■ Harry Johannes Scholarships *(Undergraduate, Graduate/Scholarship)*

Purpose: To provide funds for students to help them pay their college or university tuition. **Focus:** Geology. **Qualif.:** Applicants must be undergraduate or graduate students enrolled in engineering sciences, with emphasis on geology. **Criteria:** Selection will be based on the committee's criteria.

Funds Avail.: No specific amount. **Duration:** Annual. **To Apply:** Applicants must submit a completed scholarship application form (available online), copy of their transcripts, university acceptance letters, and/or reference letters. **Deadline:** May 31.

10791 ■ Douglas Johnson Memorial Scholarships *(Undergraduate, Master's/Scholarship)*

Purpose: To provide funds for students to help them pay their college or university tuition. **Focus:** General studies/Field of study not specified. **Qualif.:** Applicants must be 4th or 5th year post-secondary students, or Masters or equivalent. **Criteria:** Selection will be based on the committee's criteria.

Funds Avail.: No specific amount. **Duration:** Annual. **To Apply:** Applicants must submit the application form (available online), copy of their transcripts, university acceptance letters, and/or reference letters. **Deadline:** May 31.

10792 ■ Flo Kitz Memorial Scholarships *(Undergraduate, Master's/Scholarship)*

Purpose: To provide funds for students to help them pay their college or university tuition. **Focus:** General studies/Field of study not specified. **Qualif.:** Applicants must be 4th or 5th year post-secondary students, or Masters or equivalent. **Criteria:** Selection will be based on the committee's criteria.

Funds Avail.: No specific amount. **Duration:** Annual. **To Apply:** Applicants must submit the application form (available online), copy of their transcripts, university acceptance letters, and/or reference letters. **Deadline:** May 31.

10793 ■ Queenie Leader Memorial Scholarships *(Undergraduate, Master's/Scholarship)*

Purpose: To provide funds for students to help them pay their college or university tuition. **Focus:** General studies/Field of study not specified. **Qualif.:** Applicants must be 4th or 5th year post-secondary students, or Masters or equivalent. **Criteria:** Selection will be based on the committee's criteria.

Funds Avail.: No specific amount. **Duration:** Annual. **To Apply:** Applicants must submit the application form (available online), copy of their transcripts, university acceptance letters, and/or reference letters. **Deadline:** May 31.

10794 ■ Grant Livingston Memorial Scholarships *(Undergraduate, Master's/Scholarship)*

Purpose: To provide funds for students to help them pay their college or university tuition. **Focus:** General studies/Field of study not specified. **Qualif.:** Applicants must be 4th or 5th year post-secondary students, or Masters or equivalent. **Criteria:** Selection will be based on the committee's criteria.

Funds Avail.: No specific amount. **Duration:** Annual. **To Apply:** Applicants must submit the application form (available online), copy of their transcripts, university acceptance letters, and/or reference letters. **Deadline:** May 31.

10795 ■ Dr. Sally Macdonald Scholarships *(Undergraduate, Master's/Scholarship)*

Purpose: To provide funds for students to help them pay their college or university tuition. **Focus:** General studies/Field of study not specified. **Qualif.:** Applicants must be 4th

Awards are arranged alphabetically below their administering organizations

or 5th year post-secondary students, or Masters or equivalent. **Criteria:** Selection will be based on the committee's criteria.

Funds Avail.: No specific amount. **Duration:** Annual. **To Apply:** Applicants must submit the application form (available online), copy of their transcripts, university acceptance letters, and/or reference letters. **Deadline:** May 31.

10796 ■ Norman Matechuk Memorial Scholarships
(Undergraduate, Master's/Scholarship)

Purpose: To provide funds for students to help them pay their college or university tuition. **Focus:** General studies/Field of study not specified. **Qualif.:** Applicants must be 4th or 5th year post-secondary students, or Masters or equivalent. **Criteria:** Selection will be based on the committee's criteria.

Funds Avail.: No specific amount. **Duration:** Annual. **To Apply:** Applicants must submit the application form (available online), copy of their transcripts, university acceptance letters, and/or reference letters. **Deadline:** May 31.

10797 ■ Nedien Hoganson Memorial Scholarships
(Undergraduate, Master's/Scholarship)

Purpose: To provide funds for students to help them pay their college or university tuition. **Focus:** General studies/Field of study not specified. **Qualif.:** Applicants must be 4th or 5th year post-secondary students, or Masters or equivalent. **Criteria:** Selection will be based on the committee's criteria.

Funds Avail.: No specific amount. **Duration:** Annual. **To Apply:** Applicants must submit the application form (available online), copy of their transcripts, university acceptance letters, and/or reference letters. **Deadline:** May 31.

10798 ■ Erik Nielsen Memorial Scholarships
(Undergraduate, Master's/Scholarship)

Purpose: To provide funds for students to help them pay their college or university tuition. **Focus:** General studies/Field of study not specified. **Qualif.:** Applicants must be 4th or 5th year post-secondary students, or Masters or equivalent. **Criteria:** Selection will be based on the committee's criteria.

Funds Avail.: No specific amount. **Duration:** Annual. **To Apply:** Applicants must submit the application form (available online), copy of their transcripts, university acceptance letters, and/or reference letters. **Deadline:** May 31.

10799 ■ Diamond & James Quong Memorial Scholarships
(Undergraduate, Master's/Scholarship)

Purpose: To provide funds for students to help them pay their college or university tuition. **Focus:** General studies/Field of study not specified. **Qualif.:** Applicants must be 4th or 5th year post-secondary students, or Masters or equivalent. **Criteria:** Selection will be based on the committee's criteria.

Funds Avail.: No specific amount. **Duration:** Annual. **To Apply:** Applicants must submit the application form (available online), copy of their transcripts, university acceptance letters, and/or reference letters. **Deadline:** May 31.

10800 ■ Red Rogers Memorial Scholarships
(Undergraduate, Master's/Scholarship)

Purpose: To provide funds for students to help them pay their college or university tuition. **Focus:** General studies/Field of study not specified. **Qualif.:** Applicants must be 4th or 5th year post-secondary students, or Masters or equivalent. **Criteria:** Selection will be based on the committee's criteria.

Funds Avail.: No specific amount. **Duration:** Annual. **To Apply:** Applicants must submit the application form (available online), copy of their transcripts, university acceptance letters, and/or reference letters. **Deadline:** May 31.

10801 ■ Senyk Memorial Scholarships *(Undergraduate, Master's/Scholarship)*

Purpose: To provide funds for students to help them pay their college or university tuition. **Focus:** General studies/Field of study not specified. **Qualif.:** Applicants must be 4th or 5th year post-secondary students, or Masters or equivalent. **Criteria:** Selection will be based on the committee's criteria.

Funds Avail.: No specific amount. **Duration:** Annual. **To Apply:** Applicants must submit the application form (available online), copy of their transcripts, university acceptance letters, and/or reference letters. **Deadline:** May 31.

10802 ■ Evelyn Steele Memorial Scholarships
(Undergraduate, Master's/Scholarship)

Purpose: To provide funds for students to help them pay their college or university tuition. **Focus:** General studies/Field of study not specified. **Qualif.:** Applicants must be 4th or 5th year post-secondary students, or Masters or equivalent. **Criteria:** Selection will be based on the committee's criteria.

Funds Avail.: No specific amount. **Duration:** Annual. **To Apply:** Applicants must submit the application form (available online), copy of their transcripts, university acceptance letters, and/or reference letters. **Deadline:** May 31.

10803 ■ Betty & Charles Taylor Scholarships
(Advanced Professional/Scholarship)

Purpose: To provide funds for students to help them pay their college or university tuition. **Focus:** Medicine. **Qualif.:** Applicants must be students studying medicine. **Criteria:** Selection will be based on the committee's criteria.

Funds Avail.: No specific amount. **Duration:** Annual. **To Apply:** Applicants must submit a completed scholarship application form (available online), copy of their transcripts, university acceptance letters, and/or reference letters. **Deadline:** May 31.

10804 ■ Whitehorse Shotokan Karate Club Scholarships *(Undergraduate, Master's/Scholarship)*

Purpose: To provide funds for students to help them pay their college or university tuition. **Focus:** General studies/Field of study not specified. **Qualif.:** Applicants must be 4th or 5th year post-secondary students, or Masters or equivalent. **Criteria:** Selection will be based on the committee's criteria.

Funds Avail.: No specific amount. **Duration:** Annual. **To Apply:** Applicants must submit the application form (available online), copy of their transcripts, university acceptance letters, and/or reference letters. **Deadline:** May 31.

10805 ■ Jeff Young Memorial Scholarships
(Undergraduate, Master's/Scholarship)

Purpose: To provide funds for students to help them pay their college or university tuition. **Focus:** General studies/Field of study not specified. **Qualif.:** Applicants must be 4th or 5th year post-secondary students, or Masters or equivalent. **Criteria:** Selection will be based on the committee's criteria.

Funds Avail.: No specific amount. **Duration:** Annual. **To Apply:** Applicants must submit the application form (available online), copy of their transcripts, university acceptance letters, and/or reference letters. **Deadline:** May 31.

10806 ■ The Yukon Foundation Medical Laboratory Scholarships *(Undergraduate, Master's/Award)*

Purpose: To provide funds for students to help them pay their college or university tuition. **Focus:** General studies/Field of study not specified. **Qualif.:** Applicants must be 4th or 5th year post-secondary students, or Masters or equivalent. **Criteria:** Selection will be based on the committee's criteria.

Funds Avail.: No specific amount. **Duration:** Annual. **To Apply:** Applicants must submit the application form (available online), copy of their transcripts, university acceptance letters, and/or reference letters. **Deadline:** May 31.

10807 ■ Yukon Law Foundation
Box 31789
Whitehorse, YT, Canada Y1A 6L3
Ph: (867)667-7500
Fax: (867)393-3904
E-mail: info@yukonlawfoundation.com
URL: www.yukonlawfoundation.com

10808 ■ Yukon Law Foundation Scholarships *(Undergraduate/Scholarship)*

Purpose: To provide financial assistance to qualified students who want to pursue their studies. **Focus:** Law. **Qualif.:** Applicants must be students attending law or law related studies. **Criteria:** Selection shall be based on academic achievement, residency, community involvement, and financial need.

Funds Avail.: No specific amount. **Duration:** Annual. **To Apply:** Applicants must complete the application form available online; submit a transcript of record and two letters of recommendation. Application form and other supporting documents must be sent to contact provided. **Deadline:** August 31. **Contact:** Yukon Law Foundation, at the above address.

10809 ■ The Zebra
301 Chicon St.
Austin, TX 78702
URL: quoted.thezebra.com

10810 ■ The Zebra Safe Driver Scholarships *(Undergraduate, Graduate/Scholarship)*

Purpose: To promote awareness in road safety. **Focus:** General studies/Field of study not specified. **Qualif.:** Applicants must be currently enrolled in high school or up to graduate level. **Criteria:** Selection will be based on the committee's criteria.

Funds Avail.: $500. **Number Awarded:** Varies. **To Apply:** Applicants must submit an essay along with his/her personal information: name, address, phone number and copy of the current transcript. **Deadline:** August 31. **Contact:** scholarship@thezebra.com.

10811 ■ Zelle Hofmann, Voelbel and Mason, LLP
950 Winter St., Ste. 1300
Waltham, MA 02451
Ph: (781)466-0700
Fax: (781)466-0701
Free: 800-229-5294
URL: www.zelle.com

10812 ■ Zelle Hofmann Diversity in Law Scholarships *(Undergraduate/Scholarship)*

Purpose: To support students who are pursuing education in law. **Focus:** Law. **Qualif.:** Applicants must be law students who are either members of a diverse group that is historically underrepresented in the private practice of law, or demonstrate a long-standing commitment to diversity that will be furthered by award of the scholarship; must be first-year law students enrolled full-time at an ABA-accredited law school or be part-time or joint-degree students in their second year of law school at an ABA-accredited law school. **Criteria:** Selection will be based on the following: academic performance, writing kills, demonstrated leadership skill, interest in litigation, financial need and a desire to practice in one of the cities where Zelle Hofmann maintains an office.

Funds Avail.: No specific amount. **To Apply:** Application forms can be obtained at the website. Applicants must complete and submit the application including the following attachments: resume, cover letter, undergraduate transcript(s), law school transcripts, graduate school transcripts, legal writing sample, two references and personal essay of no more that 1,000 words explaining the interest in the scholarship program, how diversity has influenced their life, and how it impacts the legal profession. **Deadline:** April 1. **Contact:** Diversity Coordinator, Patricia St. Peter at pstpeter@zelle.com.

10813 ■ Zeta Phi Beta Sorority, Inc.
1734 New Hampshire Ave. NW
Washington, DC 20009
Ph: (202)387-3103
Fax: (202)232-4593
E-mail: info@zetaphibetasororityhq.org
URL: www.zphib1920.org
Facebook: www.facebook.com/ZPHIBHQ
LinkedIn: www.linkedin.com/company/zeta-phi-beta
-sorority-inc----official
Twitter: twitter.com/ZPHIBHQ

10814 ■ Mildred Cater Bradham Social Work Fellowships *(Graduate, Professional development/Fellowship)*

Purpose: To support students in pursuit of higher education. **Focus:** Social work. **Qualif.:** Applicant must be a Zeta Phi Beta Sorority, Inc. member; pursuing a full-time graduate or professional degree in social work in an accredited college or university program. **Criteria:** Selection is based on the application and supporting documents.

Funds Avail.: $500-$1,000. **Duration:** Annual. **To Apply:** Applicant must submit completed application forms along with the required materials.

10815 ■ Lullelia W. Harrison Scholarships in Counseling *(Graduate, Undergraduate/Scholarship)*

Purpose: To support students who are pursuing higher education. **Focus:** Counseling/Guidance. **Qualif.:** Applicant must be a full-time graduate or undergraduate level student enrolled in a degree program in counseling. **Criteria:** Selection is based on the application and supporting documents.

Awards are arranged alphabetically below their administering organizations

Funds Avail.: $500-$1,000. **Duration:** Annual. **To Apply:** Applicant must submit completed application forms along with the required materials.

10816 ■ Isabel M. Herson Scholarships in Education *(Graduate, Undergraduate/Scholarship)*

Purpose: To support students who are pursuing higher education. **Focus:** Education, Elementary; Education--Curricula. **Qualif.:** Applicant must be a graduate or undergraduate level student enrolled full-time in a degree program in either elementary or secondary education. **Criteria:** Selection is based on the application and supporting documents.

Funds Avail.: $500-$1,000. **Duration:** Annual. **To Apply:** Applicant must submit completed application forms along with the required materials.

10817 ■ Zora Neale Hurston Scholarships *(Graduate/Scholarship)*

Purpose: To support students who are pursuing higher education. **Focus:** Anthropology. **Qualif.:** Applicant must be a graduate student enrolled full-time and pursuing a degree in anthropology or any related field of study. **Criteria:** Selection is based on the application and supporting documents.

Funds Avail.: $500-$1,000. **Duration:** Annual. **To Apply:** Applicant must submit completed application forms along with the required materials.

10818 ■ S. Evelyn Lewis Memorial Scholarships in Medical Health Sciences *(Graduate, Undergraduate/Scholarship)*

Purpose: To provide educational support to students who are in need. **Focus:** Health sciences; Medicine. **Qualif.:** Applicant must be a female full-time graduate or undergraduate enrolled in a program leading to a degree in medicine or health sciences. **Criteria:** Selection is based on the application and supporting documents.

Funds Avail.: $500-$1,000. **Duration:** Annual. **To Apply:** Applicant must submit completed application forms along with the required materials.

10819 ■ Nancy B. Woolridge McGee Graduate Fellowships *(Graduate/Fellowship)*

Purpose: To support students in pursuit of higher education. **Focus:** General studies/Field of study not specified. **Qualif.:** Applicant must be a Zeta Phi Beta Sorority, Inc. member; pursuing a full-time graduate or professional degree in an accredited college or university program. **Criteria:** Selection is based on the application and supporting documents.

Funds Avail.: $500-$1,000. **Duration:** Annual. **To Apply:** Applicant must submit completed application forms along with the required materials.

10820 ■ Deborah Partridge Wolfe International Fellowships *(Graduate, Undergraduate/Fellowship)*

Purpose: To provide educational support to students who are in need. **Focus:** General studies/Field of study not specified. **Qualif.:** Applicant must be a full-time graduate or undergraduate U.S. student studying abroad; or full-time graduate or undergraduate foreign student studying in the U.S. **Criteria:** Selection is based on the application and supporting documents.

Funds Avail.: $500-$1,000. **Duration:** Annual. **To Apply:** Applicants must submit a completed application form and documented proof of academic study and plan of program to the Scholarship Chairperson with signature of school administrator or Program Director.

10821 ■ Zeta Phi Beta Sorority General Graduate Scholarships *(Graduate/Scholarship)*

Purpose: To provide educational support to students who are in need. **Focus:** General studies/Field of study not specified. **Qualif.:** Applicant must be a female full-time graduate on a professional degree, masters, doctoral or enrolled in post-doctoral study. **Criteria:** Selection is based on the application.

Funds Avail.: Not to exceed $2,500. **Duration:** Annual. **To Apply:** Applicants must submit a completed application form along with the required materials.

10822 ■ Zeta Phi Beta Sorority General Undergraduate Scholarships *(Undergraduate/Scholarship)*

Purpose: To provide educational support to students who are in need. **Focus:** General studies/Field of study not specified. **Qualif.:** Applicant must be a full-time undergraduate freshman, sophomore, junior, senior or graduating high school planning to enter college. **Criteria:** Selection is based on the application and supporting documents.

Funds Avail.: No specific amount. **Duration:** Annual. **To Apply:** Applicant must submit a completed application form along with the required materials. Applicant must submit a proof of enrollment or university acceptance.

10823 ■ Zonta Club of Hilo
PO Box 1915
Hilo, HI 96721-1915
E-mail: info@zontahilo.org
URL: www.zontahilo.org

10824 ■ Amelia Earhart Fellowship Program *(Doctorate, Postgraduate/Fellowship)*

Purpose: To provide financial support for qualified females intending to pursue their graduate Ph.D./doctoral degrees in aerospace-related science and aerospace-related engineering. **Focus:** Aerospace sciences; Engineering, Aerospace/Aeronautical/Astronautical. **Qualif.:** Applicants must be women of any nationality pursuing a Ph.D./doctoral degree who demonstrate a superior academic record in the field of aerospace-related sciences or aerospace-related engineering are eligible; registered in a full-time Ph.D./doctoral program when funds are received in September and will not graduate before April. **Criteria:** Selection of applicants will be based on the application requirements. The Zonta International Amelia Earhart Fellowship Committee reviews the applications and recommends recipients to the Zonta International Board.

Funds Avail.: $10,000. **Duration:** Annual. **Number Awarded:** 35. **To Apply:** Applicants must fill up completely the provided application form and such shall be submitted together with other requirements prescribed by the bestowing organization. **Deadline:** November 15. **Remarks:** Established in 1938.

10825 ■ Zonta International Foundation (ZIF)
1211 W 22nd St., Ste. 900
Oak Brook, IL 60523
Ph: (630)928-1400
Fax: (630)928-1559

Awards are arranged alphabetically below their administering organizations

E-mail: contributions@zonta.org
URL: foundation.zonta.org

10826 ■ Jane M. Klausman Women in Business Scholarships *(Graduate, Undergraduate/Scholarship)*
Purpose: To support women pursue their undergraduate and Master's degree in business management. **Focus:** Business. **Qualif.:** Applicants must be women pursuing a business or business-related degree who demonstrate outstanding potential in the chosen field; must be enrolled in the second year of an undergraduate program through the final year of a Master's program at the time of the application; must have achieved an outstanding academic record; and living or studying in a Zonta region/district. Online students are also eligible. **Criteria:** Recipients will be selected based on submitted applications.

Funds Avail.: $7,000. **Duration:** Annual. **To Apply:** Applicants must complete an application form; must submit one recommendation from a faculty member and from an employer, volunteer supervisor, or academic advisor; must submit a 500-word essay that describes academic and professional goals; verification of enrollment; and transcript of grades. All non-English documents must be translated in English. **Deadline:** July 1. **Contact:** Zonta International Foundation, at the above address.

Awards are arranged alphabetically below their administering organizations

Field of Study Index

This index classifies awards by one or more of some 400 specific subject categories. Citations are arranged alphabetically under all appropriate subject categories. Each citation is followed by the study level and award type, which appear in parentheses. The number following the parenthetical information indicates the book entry number for a particular award, not a page number.

Abortion (See Family planning)

Academic medicine (See Medicine)

Accounting

EFWA Moss Adams Foundation Scholarships *(Undergraduate/Scholarship)* [3800]
African American Network - Carolinas Scholarship Fund *(Undergraduate/Scholarship)* [4174]
AFWA Masters Degree Scholarships *(Undergraduate, Master's/Scholarship)* [49]
AFWA Undergraduate Scholarships *(Undergraduate/Scholarship)* [50]
ALPFA Scholarship Programs *(Graduate, Undergraduate/Scholarship)* [2013]
American Society of Military Comptrollers National Scholarship Program *(Undergraduate/Scholarship)* [1375]
APS/ASU Scholarships *(Undergraduate/Scholarship)* [8139]
APS/Maricopa County Community Colleges Scholarships *(Undergraduate/Scholarship)* [8140]
ASCPA High School Scholarships *(Undergraduate/Scholarship, Monetary)* [1641]
Association of Government Accountants Undergraduate/Graduate Scholarships for Community Service Accomplishments *(Graduate, Undergraduate/Scholarship)* [1971]
Association of Government Accountants Undergraduate/Graduate Scholarships for Full-time study *(Graduate, Undergraduate/Scholarship)* [1972]
Association of Government Accountants Undergraduate/Graduate Scholarships for Part-time study *(Graduate, Undergraduate/Scholarship)* [1973]
Attorney-CPA Foundation Scholarships *(Postgraduate/Scholarship)* [391]
Frank H. Ault Scholarships *(Undergraduate/Scholarship)* [8687]
AWSCPA National Scholarships *(Graduate/Scholarship)* [1530]
H. Burton Bates Jr. Scholarships *(Graduate, Undergraduate/Scholarship)* [10402]
Thomas M. Berry Jr. Scholarships *(Graduate, Undergraduate/Scholarship)* [10403]
Bill and Nell Biggs Scholarships *(Undergraduate/Scholarship)* [10088]
T. Frank Booth Memorial Scholarship Fund *(Undergraduate/Scholarship)* [4180]
Scott Brownlee Memorial Scholarships *(Undergraduate, Graduate/Scholarship)* [6582]
Stuart Cameron and Margaret McLeod Memorial Scholarships (SCMS) *(Graduate, Undergraduate/Scholarship)* [5205]
John L. Carey Scholarship Awards *(Graduate/Scholarship)* [901]
Cocke, Szpanka and Taylor Scholarships *(Undergraduate/Scholarship)* [10404]
Community Bank - Lee Guggisberg Foundation Memorial Scholarships *(Undergraduate/Scholarship)* [8464]
Mable B. Crawford Memorial Scholarships *(Undergraduate/Scholarship)* [10015]
CSCPA College Scholarships *(Graduate, Undergraduate/Scholarship)* [3147]
CSCPA High School Scholarships *(Undergraduate/Scholarship)* [3148]
CSCPA Sophomore Scholarships *(Undergraduate/Scholarship)* [3149]
Dixon Hughes Goodman LLP Annual Scholarship *(Undergraduate/Scholarship)* [3645]
The Steve Duckett Local Conservation Scholarships *(Undergraduate, Postgraduate/Scholarship)* [8232]
The Educational Foundation of KyCPA Scholarships *(Undergraduate/Scholarship)* [5821]
Ernst and Young Scholarships *(Undergraduate/Scholarship)* [1780]
FICPA Educational Foundation 1040K Race Scholarships *(Undergraduate/Scholarship)* [4098]
Clay Ford Florida Board of Accountancy Minority Scholarships *(Undergraduate/Scholarship)* [4083]
Future CPA Scholarships *(Undergraduate/Scholarship)* [1642]
Sam Gallant Memorial Scholarships *(Graduate, Undergraduate/Scholarship)* [1643]
Anthony Gerharz Scholarships *(Undergraduate, Graduate/Scholarship)* [6583]
GWSCPA Scholarships *(Undergraduate/Scholarship)* [4664]
Lenore and George Hedla Accounting Scholarship *(Undergraduate/Scholarship)* [10063]
HSF/Marathon Oil College Scholarship Program *(Undergraduate/Scholarship)* [4905]
Dixon Hughes Goodman Scholarships *(Undergraduate, Graduate/Scholarship)* [10405]
IAAI Scholarship Foundation Accounting Scholarships *(Undergraduate/Scholarship)* [5091]
Idaho Society of CPA's Scholarships *(Undergraduate/Scholarship)* [5043]
IMA Memorial Education Fund Scholarships (MEF) *(Graduate, Undergraduate/Scholarship)* [5206]
Institute of Management Accountants FAR Doctoral Student Grants Program *(Doctorate/Grant)* [5207]
Journyx Scholarships *(Undergraduate, Graduate/Scholarship)* [5628]
The Michael Kiely Strong Roots Scholarships *(Undergraduate/Scholarship)* [8233]
Robert A. Kleckner Scholarships *(Undergraduate, Graduate/Scholarship)* [9439]
KPMG Foundation Minority Accounting Doctoral Scholarships *(Doctorate/Scholarship)* [5885]
Michael B. Kruse Scholarships *(Graduate, Undergraduate/Scholarship)* [3234]
Eldon E. and JoAnn C. Kuhns Family Scholarships *(Undergraduate, Graduate/Scholarship)* [6584]
Paul J. Laninga Memorial Scholarship Fund *(Undergraduate/Scholarship)* [4529]
The Floyd Lietz Memorial Scholarship *(Undergraduate/Scholarship)* [8323]
MACPA Scholarships *(Undergraduate, Graduate/Scholarship)* [6298]
Michele L. McDonald Scholarships *(Undergraduate/Scholarship)* [3801]
The Tatiana Mendez Future Resources Scholarships *(Undergraduate/Scholarship)* [8234]
Harry Mestel Memorial Accounting Scholarship Fund *(Undergraduate/Scholarship)* [9525]
Michigan Accountancy Foundation Final Year Accounting Scholarship *(Graduate/Scholarship)* [6457]
MillerCoors National Scholarships *(Undergraduate/Scholarship)* [69]
Minnesota Association of Public Accountant Scholarships *(Undergraduate/Scholarship)* [6543]
David J. Moynihan Scholarships *(Undergraduate/Scholarship)* [7373]
MSCPA Scholarship - Montana Tech *(Undergraduate, Graduate/Scholarship)* [6585]
MSCPA Scholarship - MSU Bozeman *(Undergraduate, Graduate/Scholarship)* [6586]
MSCPA Scholarship - University of Montana *(Undergraduate, Graduate/Scholarship)* [6587]
MSCPA Undergraduate Scholarships *(Undergraduate/Scholarship)* [6562]
Mutual of Omaha Finance Careers Scholarships *(Undergraduate, Graduate/Scholarship)* [105]
NABA National Scholarship Program *(Graduate, Undergraduate/Scholarship)* [6716]
NAFA Corporate Aviation Business Scholarship *(Undergraduate, Graduate/Scholarship)* [6692]
National Society of Accountants Scholarship Program *(Undergraduate/Scholarship)* [7134]
NCACPA Outstanding Minority Accounting Student Scholarships *(Undergraduate/Scholarship)* [7451]
Hubert A. Nelson Scholarships *(Undergraduate/Scholarship)* [3718]
NESCPA Fifth-Year Scholarships *(Graduate/Scholarship)* [7251]
NESCPA General Scholarships *(Graduate, Undergraduate/Scholarship)* [7252]
NJSCPA College Scholarships *(Graduate, Undergraduate/Scholarship)* [7331]
NJSCPA High School Scholarships *(Undergraduate/Scholarship)* [7332]
North Carolina CPA Foundation Scholarships *(Undergraduate/Scholarship)* [7452]
OAIA Scholarships *(Undergraduate, Graduate/Scholarship)* [7690]
The Seth Okin Good Deeds Scholarships *(Undergraduate/Scholarship)* [8235]
Rhonda J.B. O'Leary Memorial Scholarship *(Undergraduate, Graduate/Scholarship)* [3802]
OSCPA Educational Foundation College Scholarships *(Undergraduate/Scholarship)* [7711]
OSCPA Educational Foundation High School Scholarships *(Undergraduate/Scholarship)* [7712]
Chet and Jannett Perry Rotary Club of Fort Myers Scholarship Fund *(Undergraduate/Scholarship)* [9444]
Ritchie-Jennings Memorial Scholarships *(Undergraduate, Graduate/Scholarship)* [1923]
Ross/Nickey Scholarships *(Graduate/Scholarship)* [6563]
John M. and Mary A. Shanley Memorial Scholarships *(Undergraduate, Graduate/Scholarship)* [9448]
Snodgrass Scholarships *(Undergraduate/Scholarship)* [10039]

Society of Louisiana Certified Public Accountants Scholarships (Undergraduate, Graduate/Scholarship) [9165]
The Thomas Soldan Healthy Communities Scholarships (Undergraduate, Graduate/Scholarship) [8237]
The Stanley H. Stearman Awards (Undergraduate/Scholarship) [7135]
Surety and Fidelity Industry Intern and Scholarship Program for Minority Students (Undergraduate/Scholarship) [9614]
Talbert Family Memorial Scholarships (Undergraduate/Scholarship) [3111]
The Ed Tayter Outstanding Citizen Scholarships (Undergraduate/Scholarship) [8238]
UAA Accounting Club Scholarship (Undergraduate/Scholarship) [10075]
University Senior and Master's Program Scholarships (Graduate/Scholarship) [1644]
Virginia Tech Doctoral Scholarship (Doctorate/Scholarship) [10406]
VSCPA Educational Foundation Graduate Scholarships (Graduate/Scholarship) [10407]
VSCPA Educational Foundation Minority Scholarships (Graduate, Undergraduate/Scholarship) [10408]
VSCPA Educational Foundation Undergraduate Scholarships (Undergraduate/Scholarship) [10409]
VSCPA PhD Accounting Scholarships (Doctorate, Graduate/Scholarship) [10410]
Washington CPA Foundation Scholarships (Undergraduate/Scholarship) [10452]
George Waterman Memorial Scholarships (Undergraduate/Scholarship) [10453]
Wells Fargo American Indian Scholarships - Graduate (Graduate/Scholarship) [883]
Wells Fargo Career Scholarship (Undergraduate/Scholarship) [10085]
Melissa J. Wolf Scholarship (Undergraduate/Scholarship) [10086]
Yount, Hyde & Barbour Scholarships (Undergraduate/Scholarship) [10411]
Harry and Angel Zerigian Scholarships (Undergraduate/Scholarship) [1708]

Acquired immune deficiency syndrome

OHTN Postdoctoral Fellowships (Doctorate/Fellowship) [7637]

Actuarial science

Actuarial Diversity Scholarship (Undergraduate/Scholarship) [60]
Caribbean Actuarial Scholarship (Undergraduate/Scholarship) [61]
CAS Trust Scholarship (Undergraduate/Scholarship) [2809]
Curtis E. Huntington Memorial Scholarship (Undergraduate/Scholarship) [62]
International Association of Black Actuaries Scholarships (Undergraduate/Scholarship) [5248]
Elizabeth M. Mauro Reimbursement Awards (Advanced Professional/Award) [63]
Mutual of Omaha Finance Careers Scholarships (Undergraduate, Graduate/Scholarship) [105]
Actuary of Tomorrow - Stuart A. Robertson Memorial Scholarship (Undergraduate/Scholarship) [64]
Saskatchewan Government Insurance Actuarial Science Scholarships (Undergraduate/Scholarship) [8769]
Harold W. Schloss Memorial Scholarship Fund (Undergraduate/Scholarship) [2810]
DW Simpson Actuarial Science Scholarship Program (Undergraduate/Scholarship) [8963]

Adult education

APSA/Health and Aging Policy Fellowships (Graduate, Advanced Professional, Professional development/Fellowship) [1112]
NASCOE Scholarships (Undergraduate/Scholarship) [6744]
Larry B. Wickham Memorial Scholarship for Graduate Studies (Graduate/Scholarship) [6608]

Advertising (See also Public relations)

ANA Multicultural Excellence Scholarship Fund (MAIP) (Graduate, Undergraduate/Internship) [456]
Bill Bernbach Diversity Scholarships (Undergraduate/Scholarship) [457]
Harold K. Douthit Regional Scholarships (Undergraduate/Scholarship) [7576]
The Steve Duckett Local Conservation Scholarships (Undergraduate, Postgraduate/Scholarship) [8232]
The Michael Kiely Strong Roots Scholarships (Undergraduate/Scholarship) [8233]
The Lagrant Foundation - Graduate Students Scholarships (Graduate/Scholarship) [5900]
The Lagrant Foundation - Undergraduate Students Scholarships (Undergraduate/Scholarship) [5901]
Donald Mauer Scholarships (Undergraduate/Scholarship) [10239]
The Tatiana Mendez Future Resources Scholarships (Undergraduate/Scholarship) [8234]
New York Women in Communications, Inc. Foundation Scholarships (Graduate, Undergraduate/Scholarship) [7406]
Ohio Newspaper Association Minority Scholarships (Undergraduate/Scholarship) [7577]
The Seth Okin Good Deeds Scholarships (Undergraduate/Scholarship) [8235]
ONWA Annual Scholarships (Undergraduate/Scholarship) [7579]
Operation JumpStart Scholarships (Graduate/Scholarship) [458]
The Thomas Soldan Healthy Communities Scholarships (Undergraduate, Graduate/Scholarship) [8237]
Jim Springer Memorial Scholarships (Undergraduate/Scholarship) [3110]
Jay A. Strassberg Memorial Scholarships (Undergraduate/Scholarship) [2517]
Hal Tanner Sr. Scholarships (Undergraduate/Scholarship) [10252]
The Ed Tayter Outstanding Citizen Scholarships (Undergraduate/Scholarship) [8238]
Worldstudio AIGA Scholarships (Graduate, Undergraduate/Scholarship) [10709]

Aeronautics (See also Aviation)

AIAA Foundation Scholarship Program (Graduate, Undergraduate/Scholarship) [891]
Civil Air Patrol Flight Scholarships (Undergraduate/Scholarship) [3039]
Glendale Latino Association Scholarships (Undergraduate/Scholarship) [4449]
AMA/Charles H. Grant Scholarships (Undergraduate/Scholarship) [39]
NDSGC American Indian Scholarships (Undergraduate/Scholarship) [7494]
NDSGC Graduate Fellowships (Graduate, Master's, Doctorate/Scholarship, Fellowship) [7495]
NDSGC Summer Faculty Fellowships (Professional development/Scholarship, Fellowship) [7496]
NDSGC Undergraduate Fellowships (Undergraduate, Fellowship) [7497]
NDSGC Undergraduate Scholarships (Undergraduate/Scholarship) [7498]
PSGC/NASA Space Grant Fellowships at the PSGC Affiliate Institutions (Graduate/Fellowship) [7945]
Telford Scholarships (Undergraduate/Scholarship) [40]
U.S. Air Force ROTC Express Scholarships (Undergraduate/Scholarship) [9872]
Pearl I. Young Scholarships (Undergraduate/Scholarship) [7499]

Aerospace sciences

Air Force Association/Grantham Scholarships (Undergraduate/Scholarship) [121]
Amelia Earhart Fellowship Program (Doctorate, Postgraduate/Fellowship) [10824]
Charles A. Lindbergh Fellowships (Graduate/Fellowship) [9021]
Daedalian Foundation Matching Scholarships Program (Undergraduate/Scholarship) [3499]
Kenneth J. De Witt NASA/OSGC Scholarship at The University of Toledo (Undergraduate/Scholarship) [7592]
Descendant Scholarships (Undergraduate/Scholarship) [3500]
DOE Computational Science Graduate Fellowships (DOE CSGF) (Doctorate, Graduate/Fellowship) [5887]
John and Alice Egan Multi-Year Mentioning Scholarships (Undergraduate/Scholarship) [3501]
Guggenheim Fellowships (Doctorate/Fellowship) [9022]
Thomas R. McGetchin Memorial Scholarship Awards (Undergraduate/Scholarship) [9997]
MSGC Undergraduate-Under-Represented Minority Fellowship Program (Undergraduate/Fellowship) [6485]
Navy, Army or Air Force ROTC Scholarship Program (Undergraduate/Scholarship) [3502]
NCSGC Undergraduate Research Scholarships (Undergraduate/Scholarship) [7484]
NCSGC Undergraduate Scholarships (Undergraduate/Scholarship) [7485]
Edward A. O'Connor Founder's Scholarships (Undergraduate/Scholarship) [83]
OSGC Community College Scholarships (Undergraduate/Scholarship) [7596]
OSGC Education Scholarships (Undergraduate/Scholarship) [7597]
Pitsenbarger Awards (Undergraduate/Grant, Award) [125]
John R. Sevier Memorial Scholarship Award (Undergraduate/Scholarship) [9998]
Frederick A. Tarantino Memorial Scholarship Award (Undergraduate/Scholarship) [9999]
U.S. Air Force ROTC Express Scholarships (Undergraduate/Scholarship) [9872]
A. Verville Fellowships (Professional development/Fellowship) [9023]
James B. Willett Educational Memorial Scholarship Award (Undergraduate/Scholarship) [10000]
Michael Wilson Scholarships (Undergraduate/Scholarship) [126]
Xavier University ROTC Scholarships - Air Force ROTC (Undergraduate/Scholarship) [10733]

Aesthetics

KCC-JEE Graduate Fellowships (Graduate/Fellowship) [5855]

African studies (See also Area and ethnic studies)

ACLS African Humanities Fellowships (Postdoctorate/Fellowship) [734]
TIAA-CREF Ruth Simms Hamilton Research Fellowships (Graduate/Fellowship) [9737]

African-American studies (See also Area and ethnic studies)

MHS African American Studies Fellowships (Professional development/Fellowship) [6331]
Muddy Waters Scholarships (Undergraduate/Scholarship) [2316]
Lydia Donaldson Tutt-Jones Memorial Research Grant (Graduate, Other, Master's/Grant) [93]

Aggression and violence (See also Sociology)

Belfer-Aptman Dissertation Research Awards (Doctorate/Grant) [6409]

Aging (See Gerontology)

Agribusiness (See also Agricultural sciences)

Louisiana Agricultural Consultants Association

Scholarships *(Graduate, Undergraduate/Scholarship)* [6112]
Douglas McRorie Memorial Scholarships *(Doctorate, Master's/Scholarship)* [114]
National Poultry and Food Distributors Association Scholarships *(Undergraduate/Scholarship)* [7102]
North Dakota Farmers Union Scholarships *(Undergraduate/Scholarship)* [7491]
NPC Scholarships *(Graduate/Scholarship)* [7100]
Progressive Dairy Producer Awards *(All/Grant)* [6905]

Agricultural economics (See Agriculture, Economic aspects)

Agricultural sciences

Myron "Ted" Asplin Foundation Scholarships *(Undergraduate/Scholarship)* [5097]
The Bentley Cropping Systems Fellowship *(Graduate/Fellowship)* [2886]
Eugene Boyko Memorial Scholarships *(Undergraduate/Scholarship)* [228]
CME Beef Industry Scholarships *(Undergraduate/Scholarship)* [6841]
Charles Dobbins FTA Scholarships *(Undergraduate, Vocational/Occupational/Scholarship)* [4316]
Edon Farmers Cooperative Scholarships *(Undergraduate/Scholarship)* [3794]
Florida Fertilizer and Agrichemical Association Scholarships *(Undergraduate/Scholarship)* [4096]
Carleton A. Friday Scholarship *(Undergraduate/Scholarship)* [6527]
GCSAA Student Essay Contest *(Graduate, Undergraduate/Prize)* [4484]
Jim Graham Scholarships *(Undergraduate/Scholarship)* [7482]
Ronald P. Guerrette Future Farmers of America Scholarship Fund *(Undergraduate/Scholarship)* [6196]
Don Jaques Memorial Fellowships *(Graduate/Fellowship)* [8777]
McCloy Fellowships in Agriculture *(Professional development/Fellowship)* [727]
Monsanto Commitment To Agriculture Scholarships *(Undergraduate/Scholarship)* [6574]
NAAE Upper Division Scholarships *(Undergraduate/Scholarship)* [6712]
National Poultry and Food Distributors Association Scholarships *(Undergraduate/Scholarship)* [7102]
Nebraska Farm Bureau Greater Horizon Scholarships *(Undergraduate/Scholarship)* [7240]
NGC College Scholarships *(Graduate, Undergraduate/Scholarship)* [6965]
North Dakota Farmers Union Scholarships *(Undergraduate/Scholarship)* [7491]
Progressive Dairy Producer Awards *(All/Grant)* [6905]
Saskatchewan Pulse Growers Undergraduate Scholarships *(Undergraduate/Scholarship)* [8778]
Herbert M. Saylor Memorial Scholarship *(Graduate/Scholarship)* [9341]
Shear-Miles Agricultural Fellowship *(Graduate, Doctorate/Fellowship)* [10205]
Shear-Miles Agricultural Scholarship *(Graduate, Doctorate/Scholarship)* [10206]
Everett Oscar Shimp Memorial Scholarships *(Undergraduate/Scholarship)* [7862]
Dr. Alfred E. Slinkard Scholarships *(Graduate/Scholarship)* [8779]
Stanley W. Strew Educational Fund Scholarships *(Undergraduate/Scholarship)* [2438]
University of Wisconsin-Madison/CALS Minority Scholarships *(Undergraduate/Scholarship)* [10327]
USDA-NIFA-AFRI Merit Awards *(Postdoctorate/Award)* [9308]
Kenneth G. Weckel Scholarships *(Undergraduate/Scholarship)* [6528]
Western Society of Weed Science Outstanding Student Scholarship Program *(Graduate, Undergraduate/Scholarship)* [10541]
Women's Leadership in Agriculture Scholarship Program *(Undergraduate/Scholarship)* [7574]
Worcester County Conservation District Annual Scholarships Program *(Undergraduate/Scholarship)* [10687]

Agriculture, Economic aspects

Kyutaro and Yasuo Abiko Memorial Scholarships *(Undergraduate/Scholarship)* [5547]
Agriculture Future of America Community Scholarships *(Undergraduate/Scholarship)* [116]
Agriculture Future of America Scholarships *(Undergraduate/Scholarship)* [117]
Alberta Holstein Association Scholarships *(Undergraduate/Scholarship)* [246]
Don Aron Scholarships *(Undergraduate/Scholarship)* [6875]
Clackamas County Farm Bureau Scholarships *(Undergraduate/Scholarship)* [7705]
Keith Gilmore Foundation - Diploma Scholarships *(Other/Scholarship)* [4423]
Keith Gilmore Foundation - Postgraduate Scholarships *(Postgraduate/Scholarship)* [4424]
Keith Gilmore Foundation - Undergraduate Scholarships *(Undergraduate/Scholarship)* [4425]
HAESF Professional Internship Program *(Doctorate/Internship)* [5009]
M.G. "Doc" Headley Scholarships *(Undergraduate/Scholarship)* [9570]
Independent Professional Seed Association Student Recognition Awards *(Undergraduate/Scholarship)* [5098]
Gregory D. Johnson Memorial Scholarships *(Doctorate, Graduate, Master's/Scholarship)* [7036]
Sam and Florice Kuwahara Memorial Scholarship *(Undergraduate/Scholarship)* [5553]
The Maschhoffs Pork Production Scholarships *(Undergraduate/Scholarship)* [7037]
National Junior Swine Association Outstanding Member Scholarships *(Graduate/Scholarship)* [7038]
National Poultry and Food Distributors Association Scholarships *(Undergraduate/Scholarship)* [7102]
Nebraska Farm Bureau Greater Horizon Scholarships *(Undergraduate/Scholarship)* [7240]
New York State Association of Agricultural Fairs Scholarships *(Undergraduate/Scholarship)* [7361]
NJSA Visionary Leader Scholarships *(Graduate/Scholarship)* [7039]
NMPF National Dairy Leadership Scholarships *(Graduate, Master's, Doctorate/Scholarship)* [7073]
North Dakota Farmers Union Scholarships *(Undergraduate/Scholarship)* [7491]
Nuffield Canada Farming Scholarships *(Undergraduate/Scholarship)* [7558]
Oregon Farm Bureau Memorial Scholarships *(Undergraduate/Scholarship)* [7706]
Claude Robinson Scholarships *(Undergraduate/Scholarship)* [7040]
Ellis W. Rowe Scholarships *(Undergraduate/Scholarship)* [4703]
John M. and Mary A. Shanley Memorial Scholarships *(Undergraduate, Graduate/Scholarship)* [9448]
Dr. Robert and Anna Shaw Scholarships *(Undergraduate/Scholarship)* [291]
Pat Shimp Memorial Scholarships *(Undergraduate/Scholarship)* [7863]
Jason Shipley Memorial Scholarships *(Undergraduate/Scholarship)* [7041]
Working for Farmers' Success Scholarships *(Undergraduate/Scholarship)* [10691]
Yamhill County Farm Bureau Scholarships *(Undergraduate/Scholarship)* [7707]

Agronomy (See Agricultural sciences)

AIDS (See also Acquired immune deficiency syndrome)

HIV Prevention Research Advocacy Fellowships *(Professional development/Fellowship)* [2140]
Mathilde Krim Fellowships in Basic Biomedical Research *(Doctorate/Fellowship)* [1536]
NYCT Paid Graduate Student Philanthropy Fellowships - Health and People with Special Needs *(Graduate/Fellowship)* [7352]

Air pollution

A&WMA Scholarships *(Graduate/Scholarship)* [139]
Dave Benferado Scholarships *(Graduate/Scholarship)* [140]
Milton Feldstein Memorial Scholarships *(Graduate/Scholarship)* [141]
GWS Scholarships *(Undergraduate, Graduate/Scholarship)* [145]
Walter A. Rosenblith New Investigator Award *(Postdoctorate/Award)* [4806]
Jacqueline Shields Memorial Scholarships *(Graduate/Scholarship)* [142]
SSAWMA Scholarships *(Graduate/Scholarship)* [9415]
Richard Stessel Memorial Scholarships *(Graduate/Scholarship)* [143]

Allied health (See Health sciences)

Alzheimer's disease

Firefly Foundation/ASRP Spark Award *(Postdoctorate, Advanced Professional/Grant)* [371, 4032]
NBHRF/ASRP Doctoral Training Awards *(Doctorate/Grant)* [372, 7267]
New Investigator Research Grant *(Postdoctorate/Grant)* [374]
Part the Cloud Translational Research Funds *(Postgraduate/Grant)* [375]
Sigma Kappa Foundation Alzheimer's/Gerontology Scholarships *(Graduate/Scholarship)* [8936]
Thome Foundation Awards Program in Alzheimer's Disease Drug Discovery Research *(Professional development/Grant)* [4825]
U.S.-U.K. Young Investigator Exchange Fellowship *(Postdoctorate/Fellowship)* [376]
The Zenith Fellows Award Program (Zenith) *(Postdoctorate/Fellowship)* [377]

American history (See History, American)

American Indian studies (See Native American studies)

American studies (See United States studies)

Amyotrophic lateral sclerosis

ALS Canada Bridge Grants *(Professional development/Grant)* [365]
ALS Canada Doctoral Research Awards *(Doctorate, Professional development/Fellowship)* [366]
ALS Canada and Tim E. Noel Postdoctoral Fellowships *(Postdoctorate, Professional development/Fellowship)* [367]
Brain Canada-ALS Canada Career Transition Awards *(Postdoctorate, Advanced Professional, Professional development/Grant)* [2351]
Brain Canada-ALS Canada Discovery Grants *(Advanced Professional, Professional development/Grant)* [2352]
Brain Canada-ALS Canada Hudson Translational Team Grants *(Advanced Professional, Professional development/Grant)* [2353]

Ancient Greece (See Classical studies)

Ancient history (See History, Ancient)

Anesthesiology

Baxter Corporation Canadian Research Awards in Anesthesia *(Other/Award, Monetary)* [2538]
Canadian Anesthesiologists' Society Research Awards *(Other/Award)* [2539]
CAS/Vitaid-LMA Residents' Research Grant Competition *(Other/Award)* [2541]
FAER Mentored Research Training Grants *(Professional development/Grant)* [4163]
FAER Research in Education Grants *(Advanced Professional/Grant)* [4164]
FAER Research Fellowship Grants *(Postdoctorate, Postgraduate, Graduate/Grant)* [4165]
Dale O. Heimberger CRNA Memorial Scholarship Fund *(Graduate/Scholarship)* [9509]
IARS Mentored Research Awards (IMRA) *(Professional development/Grant)* [5242]
Carl Koller Memorial Research Grants *(Professional development/Grant)* [1404]
Lansdale Public Policy Fellowship *(Advanced Professional, Professional development/Fellowship)* [1245]
David S. Sheridan Canadian Research Awards *(Other/Award)* [2542]
SOAP/Kybele International Outreach Grant *(Advanced Professional, Professional development/Grant)* [9231]

Animal rights

ABA Scholarships *(Undergraduate/Scholarship)* [626]
Richard E. Andrews Memorial Scholarships *(Undergraduate/Scholarship)* [627]
PETA Foundation Law Internships *(Graduate/Internship)* [7958]
Shaw-Worth Memorial Scholarship *(Undergraduate/Scholarship)* [5002]

Animal science and behavior (See also Zoology)

ABA Scholarships *(Undergraduate/Scholarship)* [626]
Richard E. Andrews Memorial Scholarships *(Undergraduate/Scholarship)* [627]
Angus Foundation Graduate Student Degree Scholarship Program *(Graduate/Scholarship)* [1558]
Angus/Talon Youth Educational Learning Program Endowment Fund *(Graduate, Undergraduate/Scholarship)* [1559]
ASI Sheep Heritage Foundation Memorial Scholarship *(Graduate/Scholarship)* [1241]
Marian Breland Bailey Award *(Graduate, Undergraduate/Award)* [1860]
W.D. Farr Scholarships *(Graduate/Scholarship)* [6842]
Minority Visiting Students Awards *(Undergraduate, Graduate/Award, Internship)* [9011]
A. Stanley Rand Fellowships Program *(Undergraduate, Doctorate, Postdoctorate/Fellowship)* [9037]
Stark County Dairy Promoters Scholarships *(Undergraduate/Scholarship)* [9536]
STRI Short-Term Fellowships *(Undergraduate, Graduate, Postdoctorate/Fellowship)* [9038]
Earl S. Tupper 3-year Postdoctoral Fellowships in Tropical Biology *(Postdoctorate/Fellowship)* [9039]
Welder Wildlife Foundation Fellowships *(Graduate, Master's, Doctorate/Fellowship)* [10510]

Anthropology

ARCE Funded Fellowships *(Doctorate, Postdoctorate/Fellowship)* [1195]
ARCE Research Associates Fellowships *(Doctorate, Postdoctorate, Professional development/Fellowship)* [1196]
Franklin Mosher Baldwin Memorial Fellowships *(Master's, Doctorate/Fellowship)* [5991]
Condon Prize for Best Student Essay in Psychological Anthropology *(Graduate, Undergraduate/Prize, Recognition)* [9281]
Conference and Workshop Grants *(Professional development/Grant)* [10514]
Engaged Anthropology Grants *(Doctorate, Postdoctorate/Grant)* [10515]
Fejos Postdoctoral Fellowships in Ethnographic Film *(Postdoctorate/Fellowship)* [10516]
Hunt Postdoctoral Fellowships *(Postdoctorate/Fellowship)* [10517]
Carrie Hunter-Tate Award *(Undergraduate, Graduate/Grant)* [6794]
Zora Neale Hurston Scholarships *(Graduate/Scholarship)* [10817]
Leakey Foundation Research Grants *(Doctorate, Advanced Professional/Grant)* [5992]
Lemelson Student Fellowships *(Graduate/Award)* [9282]
Larry Matfay Cultural Heritage Scholarships *(Undergraduate, Graduate/Scholarship)* [5868]
William P. McHugh Memorial Fund Award *(Doctorate, Graduate/Fellowship)* [1197]
Minority Visiting Students Awards *(Undergraduate, Graduate/Award, Internship)* [9011]
The National Endowment for the Humanities Fellowships *(Graduate/Fellowship)* [1198]
Pi Gamma Mu Scholarships *(Graduate/Scholarship)* [8133]
Kenneth W. Russell Memorial Fellowships *(Undergraduate, Graduate/Fellowship)* [661]
Society for Linguistic Anthropology Student Essay Prize *(Graduate, Undergraduate/Prize)* [9163]
STRI Short-Term Fellowships *(Undergraduate, Graduate, Postdoctorate/Fellowship)* [9038]
Earl S. Tupper 3-year Postdoctoral Fellowships in Tropical Biology *(Postdoctorate/Fellowship)* [9039]
The United States Department of State, Bureau of Educational & Cultural Affairs Fellowships *(Graduate/Fellowship)* [1199]
Wadsworth African Fellowships *(Doctorate/Fellowship)* [10518]
Wadsworth International Fellowships *(Graduate/Fellowship)* [10519]
Wenner-Gren Foundation Dissertation Fieldwork Grants *(Doctorate/Grant)* [10520]
Wenner-Gren Foundation Post-PhD Research Grants *(Doctorate/Grant)* [10521]

Applied art (See Art industries and trade)

Applied mathematics (See Mathematics and mathematical sciences)

Aquaculture

ACOR-CAORC Pre-Doctorate Fellowships *(Graduate, Doctorate/Fellowship)* [654]
Anchor QEA Environmental Scholarships *(Graduate/Scholarship)* [1551]
Lloyd Bridges Scholarships *(Graduate, Other/Scholarship)* [2835]
Cecelia Connelly Memorial Scholarships in Underwater Archaeology *(Graduate, Undergraduate/Scholarship)* [10638]
Nova Scotia Salmon Association Scholarships *(Undergraduate/Scholarship)* [7556]

Archeology

AIA Graduate Student Travel Awards *(Graduate/Grant)* [1603]
American Philological Association Minority Student Summer Fellowships *(Undergraduate/Fellowship)* [9106]
ARCE Funded Fellowships *(Doctorate, Postdoctorate/Fellowship)* [1195]
ARCE Research Associates Fellowships *(Doctorate, Postdoctorate, Professional development/Fellowship)* [1196]
Archaeological Institute of America Fellowships for Study in the U.S. *(Postdoctorate/Fellowship)* [1604]
Archaeology of Portugal Fellowships *(Professional development/Fellowship)* [1605]
ARIT National Endowment for the Humanities Advanced Fellowships for Research in Turkey *(Postdoctorate/Fellowship)* [1202]
Pierre and Patricia Bikai Fellowships *(Graduate/Fellowship)* [655]
Cave Conservancy Foundation Graduate and Undergraduate Fellowships *(Doctorate, Graduate, Undergraduate/Fellowship)* [2823]
Anna C. and Oliver C. Colburn Fellowships *(Doctorate/Fellowship)* [1606]
Cecelia Connelly Memorial Scholarships in Underwater Archaeology *(Graduate, Undergraduate/Scholarship)* [10638]
Conservation Department Program Fellowships *(Graduate/Fellowship)* [9028]
DAI Fellowships for Study in Berlin *(Doctorate/Fellowship)* [1607]
Bert and Sally de Vries Fellowships *(Undergraduate, Graduate/Fellowship)* [656]
Fieldwork Fellowships *(Undergraduate/Award, Fellowship)* [3927]
Jennifer C. Groot Memorial Fellowships *(Undergraduate, Graduate/Fellowship)* [657]
Harrell Family Fellowships *(Graduate/Fellowship)* [658]
Olivia James Traveling Fellowships *(Professional development/Fellowship)* [1608]
Samuel H. Kress Grants for Research and Publication in Classical Art and Architecture *(Professional development/Grant)* [1609]
Burton MacDonald and Rosemarie Sampson Fellowships *(Undergraduate, Graduate/Fellowship)* [659]
William P. McHugh Memorial Fund Award *(Doctorate, Graduate/Fellowship)* [1197]
Dorothy Mountain Memorial Scholarships *(Graduate/Scholarship)* [6135]
The National Endowment for the Humanities Fellowships *(Graduate/Fellowship)* [1198]
Harriet and Leon Pomerance Fellowships *(Professional development/Fellowship)* [1610]
Kenneth W. Russell Memorial Fellowships *(Undergraduate, Graduate/Fellowship)* [661]
SAA Native American Scholarships *(Undergraduate, Graduate, Professional development/Scholarship)* [9079]
James A. Sauer Memorial Fellowships *(Graduate/Fellowship)* [662]
Smithsonian Postgraduate Fellowships in Conservation of Museum Collection Program *(Postgraduate/Fellowship)* [9019]
The United States Department of State, Bureau of Educational & Cultural Affairs Fellowships *(Graduate/Fellowship)* [1199]
Jane C. Waldbaum Archaeological Field School Scholarships *(Undergraduate/Scholarship)* [1611]
Harry Walts Memorial Graduate Scholarships *(Graduate/Scholarship)* [6136]
Helen M. Woodruff Fellowships *(Professional development/Fellowship)* [1612]

Architectural engineering (See Engineering, Architectural)

Architecture (See also Landscape architecture and design)

AAUW Selected Professions Fellowships *(Graduate, Master's, Doctorate/Fellowship)* [22]
ACI Foundation Scholarships *(Graduate/Scholarship)* [703]
ACI W.R. Grace Scholarships *(Graduate/Scholarship)* [705]
AIA Northeast Illinois Student Scholarships *(Undergraduate, Graduate/Scholarship)* [895]

American Association of University Women Selected Professions Fellowships *(Other/Fellowship)* [603]
ARCE Funded Fellowships *(Doctorate, Postdoctorate/Fellowship)* [1195]
ARCE Research Associates Fellowships *(Doctorate, Postdoctorate, Professional development/Fellowship)* [1196]
Architects Association of PEI Scholarships *(Undergraduate/Scholarship)* [3309]
ASF/Annika Teig/Skidmore, Owings and Merrill Fellowships *(Postgraduate/Fellowship)* [1234]
Association for Women in Architecture Scholarships *(Undergraduate/Scholarship)* [2089]
Carpenters' Company Scholarships *(Undergraduate/Scholarship)* [2801]
Cintas Foundation Fellowships in Architecture *(Professional development/Fellowship)* [3031]
Tom Cory Memorial Scholarships *(Undergraduate/Scholarship)* [1614]
D&A Florida Scholarships *(Undergraduate/Scholarship)* [9425]
Charles Dubose Scholarships *(Undergraduate/Scholarship)* [4750]
Eastern Shore Building Industry Association Scholarships *(Undergraduate/Scholarship)* [3174]
Generation III Scholarships *(Undergraduate/Scholarship)* [3783]
Huber Engineered Woods Product Evaluation Scholarships *(Graduate/Scholarship)* [3977]
IALD Education Trust Scholarship Program *(Graduate, Undergraduate/Scholarship)* [5271]
JMA Architecture Studios Scholarships *(Undergraduate/Scholarship)* [8351]
Kluge Fellowships *(Doctorate, Graduate/Fellowship)* [5846]
Samuel H. Kress Foundation Dissertation Fellowships *(Doctorate/Fellowship)* [9084]
Samuel H. Kress Grants for Research and Publication in Classical Art and Architecture *(Professional development/Grant)* [1609]
Arnold "Les" Larsen, FAIA, Memorial Scholarships *(Graduate/Scholarship)* [896]
PCH Architects/Steven J. Lehnhof Memorial Architectural Scholarships *(Undergraduate/Scholarship)* [8491]
Dolores Zohrab Liebmann Fund - Graduate School Fellowships *(Graduate/Fellowship)* [6075]
Katharine & Bryant Mather Scholarship *(Graduate/Scholarship)* [708]
William P. McHugh Memorial Fund Award *(Doctorate, Graduate/Fellowship)* [1197]
Kumar Mehta Scholarship *(Graduate/Scholarship)* [709]
The National Endowment for the Humanities Fellowships *(Graduate/Fellowship)* [1198]
Stuart L. Noderer Memorial Scholarships *(Undergraduate/Scholarship)* [8719]
Pardee Community Building Scholarships *(Undergraduate/Scholarship)* [8359]
Resilience Action Fund Scholarships *(Graduate/Scholarship)* [3981]
SAH Study Tour Fellowships *(Graduate/Fellowship)* [9085]
Leo and Trinidad Sanchez Scholarships *(Undergraduate/Scholarship)* [8956]
Galvanize the Future: Edgar K. Schutz Scholarships *(Undergraduate, Graduate/Scholarship)* [838]
John M. and Mary A. Shanley Memorial Scholarships *(Undergraduate, Graduate/Scholarship)* [9448]
SOM Foundation Architecture, Design and Urban Design Prize *(Graduate, Undergraduate/Prize)* [8980]
SOM Foundation Travel Fellowships in Architecture, Design and Urban Design *(Graduate, Undergraduate/Fellowship)* [8982]
Study Scholarships for Artists or Musicians *(Graduate/Scholarship)* [3610]
UC MEXUS-CONACYT Doctoral Fellowships *(Doctorate/Fellowship)* [10117]
The United States Department of State, Bureau of Educational & Cultural Affairs Fellowships *(Graduate/Fellowship)* [1199]
Vectorworks Design Scholarships *(Undergraduate, Graduate/Scholarship, Prize)* [10367]
Dimitri J. Ververelli Memorial Scholarship for Architecture and/or Engineering *(Undergraduate/Scholarship)* [4851]
Washington University Law School Olin Fellowships for Women *(Advanced Professional/Fellowship)* [10477]
Bertold E. Weinberg Scholarship *(Graduate/Scholarship)* [711]
Polaire Weissman Funds *(Graduate/Fellowship)* [6439]
Beverly Willis Architecture Foundation Travel Fellowship *(Doctorate/Fellowship)* [9086]
Worldstudio AIGA Scholarships *(Graduate, Undergraduate/Scholarship)* [10709]

Architecture, Naval

Robert N. Herbert Undergraduate Scholarships *(Undergraduate/Scholarship)* [9216]
Malayalee Engineers Association Scholarships *(Undergraduate/Scholarship)* [6225]
NDSEG Fellowships *(Graduate/Fellowship)* [6911]
NRL-ASEE Postdoctoral Fellowships *(Postdoctorate/Fellowship)* [9966]
Mandell and Lester Rosenblatt Undergraduate Scholarships *(Undergraduate/Scholarship)* [9217]

Archival science (See Library and archival sciences)

Area and ethnic studies

David L. Boren Fellowships *(Graduate/Fellowship)* [5199]
David L. Boren Scholarships *(Undergraduate, College/Scholarship)* [5200]
Theodore E.D. Braun Research Travel Fellowships *(Other/Fellowship)* [1287]
Ruth B. Fein Prize *(Graduate/Prize)* [949]
Alan R. and Barbara D. Finberg Fellowships *(Graduate/Fellowship)* [4998]
Ford Foundation Dissertation Fellowships *(Graduate, Doctorate/Fellowship)* [6675]
Ford Foundation Diversity Fellowships *(Graduate, Doctorate, Postdoctorate, Postgraduate/Fellowship)* [6676]
Ford Foundation Postdoctoral Fellowships *(Postdoctorate/Fellowship)* [6677]
Ford Foundation Predoctoral Fellowships *(Graduate, Doctorate/Fellowship)* [6678]
HIAA Graduate Student Travel Grants *(Graduate/Grant)* [4908]
Houtan Scholarships *(Graduate/Scholarship)* [4972]
Pokross/Curhan Family Fund Prize *(Graduate, Undergraduate/Prize)* [950]
Short-term Senior Fellowships in Iranian Studies *(Professional development/Fellowship)* [914]

Armenian studies (See also Area and ethnic studies)

Karekin DerAvedision Memorial Endowment Fund *(Undergraduate/Scholarship)* [1692]
Garikian Scholarship Fund *(Undergraduate/Scholarship)* [1694]
Knights of Vartan, Fresno Lodge No. 9 Scholarships *(Undergraduate/Scholarship)* [1701]
Dolores Zohrab Liebmann Fund - Publication Grants *(Graduate/Grant)* [6077]

Art (See also Performing arts; Visual arts)

ADAC Foundation Scholarships *(Undergraduate/Scholarship)* [1767]
American Watercolor Society Scholarship Program for Art Teachers *(Other/Scholarship)* [1500]
ARCE Funded Fellowships *(Doctorate, Postdoctorate/Fellowship)* [1195]
ARCE Research Associates Fellowships *(Doctorate, Postdoctorate, Professional development/Fellowship)* [1196]
ARIT National Endowment for the Humanities Advanced Fellowships for Research in Turkey *(Postdoctorate/Fellowship)* [1202]
Artist-in-Residence Workspace Grant *(Professional development/Grant)* [2843]
Joan Auld Scholarships *(Undergraduate/Scholarship)* [3310]
Cynthia and Alan Baran Fine Arts and Music Scholarships *(Undergraduate/Scholarship)* [3211]
Jenny Panitch Beckow Memorial Scholarships Israel *(Graduate/Scholarship)* [5570]
BEF Scholarships of the Arts *(Graduate, Undergraduate/Scholarship)* [2337]
Beta Sigma Phi Visual Arts Scholarship *(Undergraduate/Scholarship)* [8869]
BRAF Grants *(Graduate/Grant)* [2301]
Edwin Anthony and Adelaide Boudreaux Cadogan Scholarships *(Graduate/Fellowship)* [8747]
Emi Chance for Aspiring Artists Scholarship *(Undergraduate/Scholarship)* [10054]
Chautauqua Scholarships Program *(Undergraduate/Scholarship)* [5367]
Paul Collins Scholarships *(Undergraduate/Scholarship)* [4583]
Convergence Assistantship Grants *(Undergraduate/Grant)* [4708]
Dewey Lee Curtis Scholarships *(Advanced Professional/Scholarship)* [3541]
Chester Dale Fellowships *(Doctorate/Fellowship)* [6429]
Mychajlo Dmytrenko Fine Arts Foundation Scholarships *(Undergraduate/Scholarship)* [9980]
Pauly D'Orlando Memorial Art Scholarships *(Graduate, Undergraduate/Scholarship)* [9834]
Douglass Foundation Fellowship in American Art *(Doctorate/Fellowship)* [9001]
The "Drawn to Art" Fellowships *(Doctorate/Fellowship)* [436]
Adrienne Zoe Fedok Art and Music Scholarships *(Undergraduate/Scholarship)* [4240]
Fine Arts Association Minority Scholarships *(Undergraduate/Scholarship)* [4026]
Fine Arts Association United Way Scholarships *(Undergraduate/Scholarship)* [4027]
Patricia and Phillip Frost Fellowships *(Doctorate, Postdoctorate/Fellowship)* [9002]
GAAC Project Grants *(Undergraduate, Professional development/Grant)* [4445]
Mearl K. Gable II Memorial Grants *(Other/Grant)* [4709]
The Gallery Collection's Create-A-Greeting Card Scholarships *(Undergraduate/Scholarship)* [4318]
Mathilda and Carolyn Gallmeyer Scholarships *(Undergraduate/Scholarship)* [4594]
Getty Scholar Grants *(Professional development/Grant)* [4412]
Mona Gray Creative Arts Scholarships *(Graduate, Undergraduate/Scholarship)* [5593]
George Gurney Fellowships *(Doctorate, Postdoctorate/Fellowship)* [9003]
HAESF Professional Internship Program *(Doctorate/Internship)* [5009]
Handweavers Guild of America and Dendel Scholarships *(Graduate, Undergraduate/Scholarship)* [4710]
Muriel Hannah Scholarships in Art *(Undergraduate, Graduate/Scholarship)* [10062]
Regina Higdon Scholarships *(Undergraduate/Scholarship)* [3229]
Lucy Hilty Research Grants *(Graduate/Grant)* [1173]
Indiana State University Creative and Performing Arts Awards *(Undergraduate/Scholarship)* [5127]
Donald Wills Jacobs Scholarships *(Undergraduate/Scholarship)* [10023]
Gregori Jakovina Endowment Scholarships *(Undergraduate/Scholarship)* [3920]
George E. Judd Scholarships *(Undergraduate/Scholarship)* [9436]
Martha Julian Memorial Scholarship *(Undergraduate/Scholarship)* [212]
Samuel H. Kress Grants for Research and Publication in Classical Art and Architecture *(Professional development/Grant)* [1609]
Jay and Deborah Last Fellowships *(Doctorate/Fellowship)* [440]
William P. McHugh Memorial Fund Award *(Doctorate, Graduate/Fellowship)* [1197]
Mill Creek Business Association Scholarships *(Undergraduate/Scholarship)* [6537]

J. Clawson Mills Scholarships *(Doctorate/Scholarship)* [6435]
Letitia Moore Charitable Trust Scholarship *(Undergraduate/Scholarship)* [10739]
Jack K. and Gertrude Murphy Fellowships *(Graduate/Fellowship)* [8748]
The National Endowment for the Humanities Fellowships *(Graduate/Fellowship)* [1198]
Northwest-Shoals Community College Fine Arts Scholarships - Art *(Undergraduate/Scholarship)* [7543]
Marvin R. and Pearl E. Patterson Family Scholarships Fund *(Undergraduate/Scholarship)* [4535]
Pennies for Art Scholarships *(Undergraduate/Scholarship)* [4355]
Silvio and Eugenia Petrini Grants *(Other/Grant)* [4711]
Phi Theta Kappa Scholarships *(Undergraduate/Scholarship)* [5124]
James Renwick Fellowship in American Craft *(Doctorate, Postdoctorate/Fellowship)* [9004]
David G. Robinson Arts Scholarships *(Undergraduate/Scholarship)* [9446]
Sara Roby Fellowship in Twentieth-Century American Realism *(Doctorate, Postdoctorate/Fellowship)* [9005]
Dr. Robert and Anna Shaw Scholarships *(Undergraduate/Scholarship)* [291]
Smithsonian Postgraduate Fellowships in Conservation of Museum Collection Program *(Postgraduate/Fellowship)* [9019]
John F. and Anna Lee Stacey Scholarships *(All/Scholarship)* [6901]
Marion Barr Stanfield Art Scholarships *(Graduate, Undergraduate/Scholarship)* [9840]
Cecilia Steinfeldt Fellowships for Research in the Arts and Material Culture *(Professional development/Fellowship)* [9717]
Study Scholarships for Artists or Musicians *(Graduate/Scholarship)* [3610]
Joshua C. Taylor Fellowships *(Doctorate, Postdoctorate/Fellowship)* [9006]
The Terra Foundation Fellowships in American Art *(Undergraduate, Doctorate, Postdoctorate/Fellowship)* [9007]
Terra Foundation Research Travel Grants *(Doctorate, Undergraduate/Grant)* [9683]
William H. Truettner Fellowships *(Undergraduate, Doctorate, Postdoctorate/Fellowship)* [9008]
UAA Kimura Scholarship Fund for Photography *(Undergraduate/Scholarship)* [10082]
The United States Department of State, Bureau of Educational & Cultural Affairs Fellowships *(Graduate/Fellowship)* [1199]
Philip F. Vineberg Travelling Fellowships in the Humanities *(Undergraduate/Scholarship)* [6368]
Washington University Law School Olin Fellowships for Women *(Advanced Professional/Fellowship)* [10477]
Jane and Morgan Whitney Fellowships *(Graduate/Fellowship)* [6440]
Worldstudio AIGA Scholarships *(Graduate, Undergraduate/Scholarship)* [10709]
Wyeth Foundation Predoctoral Fellowship *(Postdoctorate/Fellowship)* [9009]
Gwen Yarnell Theatre Scholarships *(Undergraduate/Scholarship)* [4028]
James and Joy Zana Memorial Scholarships *(Undergraduate/Scholarship)* [4569]

Art, Caricatures and cartoons

Worldstudio AIGA Scholarships *(Graduate, Undergraduate/Scholarship)* [10709]

Art, Performing (See Performing arts)

Art, Roman

Shohet Scholars Program *(Professional development/Grant)* [5290]

Art, Visual (See Visual arts)

Art conservation

Individual Professional Development Scholarship *(Professional development/Scholarship)* [4161]
Kress Conservation Fellowships *(Postgraduate/Fellowship)* [5889]
NGA Conservation Fellowships *(Graduate/Award)* [6963]

Art history

Hench Post-Dissertation Fellowship *(Postdoctorate/Fellowship)* [438]
Louis I. Jaffe Memorial Scholarships-ODU *(Graduate/Scholarship)* [4701]
Annette Kade Fellowships *(Graduate/Fellowship)* [6431]
Henry Luce Foundation/ACLS Dissertation Fellowships in American Art *(Graduate, Doctorate/Fellowship)* [742]
Metropolitan Museum of Art Bothmer Fellowship *(Doctorate/Fellowship)* [6432]
Letitia Moore Charitable Trust Scholarship *(Undergraduate/Scholarship)* [10739]
Margaret B. Ševčenko Prize in Islamic Art and Culture *(Doctorate/Prize)* [4909]
Eric E. Smoker Memorial Scholarships *(Undergraduate/Scholarship)* [7521]
Hanns Swarzenski and Brigitte Horney Swarzenski Fellowship *(Graduate/Fellowship)* [6438]
United States Capitol Historical Society Fellowships *(Graduate/Fellowship)* [9886]
Virginia Museum of Fine Arts Visual Arts Fellowships *(Graduate, Other, Undergraduate/Fellowship)* [10400]

Art industries and trade

Paul Collins Scholarships *(Undergraduate/Scholarship)* [4583]
Dr. Robert and Anna Shaw Scholarships *(Undergraduate/Scholarship)* [291]
University of Toronto Nortel Institute Undergraduate Scholarships *(Undergraduate/Scholarship)* [10298]
Kurt Wayne Scholarships *(Graduate/Scholarship)* [4346]

Art therapy

American Art Therapy Association Anniversary Scholarships *(Graduate/Scholarship)* [448]
Myra Levick Scholarships *(Graduate/Scholarship)* [449]
William Philpott Scholarships *(Undergraduate/Scholarship)* [2269]
Rawley Silver Awards for Excellence *(Graduate/Scholarship)* [450]
Rawley Silver Research Award *(Postgraduate, Postdoctorate/Award)* [451]

Arthritis (See also Rheumatology)

Arthritis Foundation Doctoral Dissertation Awards for Arthritis Health Professionals *(Doctorate/Fellowship)* [1769]
Arthritis Foundation Innovative Research Grants *(Doctorate/Grant)* [1770]
Arthritis Foundation Investigator Awards *(Doctorate/Award)* [1771]
Arthritis Foundation Postdoctoral Fellowships *(Doctorate/Fellowship)* [1772]

Arts

Aaron Copland Bogliasco Fellowships in Music *(Professional development/Fellowship)* [2325]
AFA Art Acquisition by Application Grants *(Professional development/Grant)* [237]
AFA Cultural Relations Project Grants *(Professional development/Grant)* [238]
AFA Dance Project Grants *(Professional development/Grant)* [239]
AFA Film and Video Arts Project Grants *(Professional development/Grant)* [240]
AFA Literary Arts Project Grants *(Professional development/Grant)* [241]
Albinas Elskus Scholarship *(All/Scholarship)* [9488]
American-Scandinavian Foundation Grants to Study in Scandinavia *(Graduate/Grant)* [1232]
Arts Graduate Scholarships *(Graduate/Scholarship)* [267]
William E. Barto Scholarships *(Undergraduate/Scholarship)* [3704]
Leo Biaggi de Blasys Bogliasco Fellowships *(Professional development/Fellowship)* [2326]
Hagop Bogigian Scholarship Fund *(Undergraduate/Scholarship)* [1689]
Bogliasco Fellowships *(Professional development/Fellowship)* [2327]
Regina Brown Undergraduate Student Fellowships *(Undergraduate/Fellowship)* [6879]
John Burroughs Bogliasco Fellowships *(Professional development/Fellowship)* [2328]
Bush Artist Fellowships *(Professional development/Fellowship)* [2419]
Antonio Cirino Memorial Art Education Fellowships *(Graduate/Fellowship)* [8603]
Diabetes Scholars Foundation College Scholarships *(Undergraduate/Scholarship)* [3616]
Douglass Foundation Fellowships in American Art *(Graduate/Fellowship)* [6430]
EAA Tuition Scholarships *(Undergraduate/Scholarship)* [3873]
EAA Workshop Scholarships *(Undergraduate/Scholarship)* [3874]
Edgecliff McAuley Art Scholarships *(Undergraduate/Scholarship)* [10719]
Bruce T. and Jackie Mahi Erickson Grant *(Graduate, Undergraduate/Grant)* [7907]
Helen R. Finley-Loescher and Stephen Loescher Scholarships *(Undergraduate/Scholarship)* [3283]
Florida Education Fund McKnight Doctoral Fellowships *(Graduate/Fellowship)* [4085]
Don Fox Memorial Scholarship *(Undergraduate/Scholarship)* [211]
William E. "Bill" Gallagher Scholarships *(Undergraduate/Scholarship)* [7829]
Graybar Canada Award of Excellence Scholarships *(Undergraduate/Scholarship)* [3832]
Andrew Gronholdt Arts Scholarship Awards *(Undergraduate, Vocational/Occupational, Graduate, Master's/Scholarship)* [310]
John Simon Guggenheim Memorial Fellowships - U.S. and Canadian Competition *(Advanced Professional/Fellowship)* [4684]
Guntley-Lorimer Science and Arts Scholarships *(Undergraduate/Scholarship)* [2284]
Ed Haas Memorial Scholarships *(Undergraduate/Scholarship)* [9568]
Jacob K. Javits Fellowships Program *(Master's, Doctorate/Fellowship)* [9894]
Jerome Robbins Bogliasco Fellowships in Dance *(Professional development/Fellowship)* [2329]
Jewish Federation Academic Scholarships *(Graduate, Undergraduate/Scholarship)* [5598]
Ladies Literary Club Scholarships *(Undergraduate/Scholarship)* [4605]
Ted Lewis Memorial Scholarship *(Undergraduate/Scholarship)* [213]
Dorothy L. Maddy Workshop/Seminar Scholarship *(All/Scholarship)* [9489]
Minority Visiting Students Awards *(Undergraduate, Graduate/Award, Internship)* [9011]
John H. Moss Scholarships *(Undergraduate/Scholarship)* [10294]
NCECA Graduate Student Fellowships *(Graduate/Fellowship)* [6880]
NHFA Scholarships *(Graduate/Scholarship)* [6998]
NYCT Paid Graduate Student Philanthropy Fellowships - Arts and Historic Preservation *(Graduate/Fellowship)* [7349]
Pembroke Center Faculty Seed Grants *(Professional development/Grant)* [2390]
Prescott Fine Arts Association Scholarship Program *(Undergraduate/Scholarship)* [8221]
Rome Prize *(Doctorate, Graduate/Prize, Award)* [424]

Leo S. Rowe Pan American Fund *(Graduate, Undergraduate/Loan)* [7730]
Scholarship Foundation of Santa Barbara Art Scholarship Program *(Undergraduate/Scholarship)* [8798]
Roger Sessions Memorial Bogliasco Fellowships in Music *(Professional development/Fellowship)* [2331]
Eric E. Smoker Memorial Scholarships *(Undergraduate/Scholarship)* [7521]
Terra Foundation Fellowships at the Smithsonian American Art Museum *(Postdoctorate/Fellowship)* [9680]
Terra Foundation Postdoctoral Teaching Fellowships at the Courtauld Institute of Art, London *(Postdoctorate/Fellowship)* [9681]
Terra Foundation Postdoctoral Teaching Fellowships at the Institut National d'Histoire de l'Art, Paris *(Postdoctorate/Fellowship)* [9682]
Terra Summer Residency Fellowships *(Master's, Doctorate/Fellowship)* [9684]
UC MEXUS Scholars in Residence Program - Graduate *(Graduate/Scholarship)* [10120]
The UCSD Black Alumni Scholarship for Arts and Humanities *(Undergraduate/Scholarship)* [8736]
Washington University Law School Chancellor's Graduate Fellowships *(Advanced Professional/Fellowship)* [10476]
Polaire Weissman Funds *(Graduate/Fellowship)* [6439]
Xavier University Honors Bachelor of Arts Scholarships *(Undergraduate/Scholarship)* [10730]

Asian studies (See Area and ethnic studies)

Astronautics

AIAA Foundation Scholarship Program *(Graduate, Undergraduate/Scholarship)* [891]

Astronomy and astronomical sciences (See also Space and planetary sciences)

Annie J. Cannon Award in Astronomy *(Doctorate/Award, Recognition)* [613]
Chambliss Astronomy Achievement Student Awards *(Undergraduate, Graduate/Award)* [614]
Chrétien International Research Grants *(Doctorate/Grant)* [615]
DOE Computational Science Graduate Fellowships (DOE CSGF) *(Doctorate, Graduate/Fellowship)* [5887]
Rodger Doxsey Travel Prizes *(Graduate, Postdoctorate/Prize)* [616]
Jeffress Trust Awards Program in Interdisciplinary Research *(Professional development/Award)* [4816]
NPSC Fellowships *(Graduate/Fellowship)* [7098]

Athletics

Canadian Seniors' Golf Association Scholarships *(Undergraduate/Scholarship)* [4477]
Diabetes Scholars Foundation College Scholarships *(Undergraduate/Scholarship)* [3616]
Earl and Countess of Wessex - World Championships in Athletics Scholarships *(Undergraduate/Scholarship)* [272]
Founding Fathers Leadership Scholarships *(Undergraduate/Scholarship)* [10617]
The Gene and John Athletic Scholarships *(Undergraduate/Scholarship)* [9589]
Harry Jerome Legacy Scholarships *(Undergraduate, Graduate/Scholarship)* [2287]
Terry Mellor Continuing Education Grant *(Undergraduate/Grant)* [9480]
Mueller Undergraduate Scholarships *(Undergraduate/Scholarship)* [10618]
Mike Niemeyer Memorial Football Scholarships *(Undergraduate/Scholarship)* [8506]
Northwest-Shoals Community College Athletic Scholarships *(Undergraduate/Scholarship)* [7541]
Jeff Oliphant Memorial Post-Graduate Scholarships *(Postgraduate/Scholarship)* [10619]
Redlands High School Boy's Varsity Volleyball Scholarships *(Undergraduate/Scholarship)* [8512]
James H. Roberts Athletic Scholarships *(Undergraduate/Scholarship)* [7855]
The Viking Voices - Mike Ruben Honorarium and John Rice Memorial Scholarship *(Undergraduate/Scholarship)* [7860]

Atmospheric science (See also Meteorology)

GWS Scholarships *(Undergraduate, Graduate/Scholarship)* [145]
NOAA EPP Undergraduate Scholarships (USP) *(Undergraduate/Scholarship)* [9891]
NOAA Graduate Sciences Scholarships *(Graduate/Scholarship)* [9892]
U.S. Air Force ROTC Express Scholarships *(Undergraduate/Scholarship)* [9872]
CASFM-Ben Urbonas Scholarships *(Graduate/Scholarship)* [3132]

Audiology (See Speech and language pathology/audiology)

Australian studies (See Area and ethnic studies)

Automotive technology

AIA and the Global Automotive Aftermarket Symposium Scholarships *(Undergraduate/Scholarship)* [2131]
ISA Aerospace Industries Division - William H. Atkinson Scholarships *(Graduate, Undergraduate/Scholarship)* [5396]
Auto Body Technician Certificate Scholarships *(Undergraduate/Scholarship)* [8765]
Automotive Technician Scholarship Program *(Undergraduate/Scholarship)* [6344]
Automotive Women's Alliance Foundation Scholarships *(Undergraduate/Scholarship)* [2138]
Tom Babcox Memorial Scholarships *(Professional development/Scholarship)* [2124]
Rob Copeland Memorial Scholarships *(Undergraduate/Scholarship)* [6022]
Florida Automotive Industry Scholarships *(Undergraduate/Scholarship)* [2125]
Friends of Mary Automotive Scholarships *(Undergraduate/Scholarship)* [8872]
Bob and Dawn Hardy Automotive Scholarships *(Undergraduate/Scholarship)* [5506]
Norman E. and Mary-Belle Huston Scholarships *(Graduate, Undergraduate/Scholarship)* [5397]
ISA Educational Foundation Scholarships *(Undergraduate/Scholarship)* [5398]
ISA Executive Board Scholarships *(Graduate, Undergraduate/Scholarship)* [5399]
ISA Section and District Scholarships - Houston *(Graduate, Undergraduate/Scholarship)* [5400]
ISA Section and District Scholarships - Lehigh Valley *(Graduate, Undergraduate/Scholarship)* [5401]
ISA Section and District Scholarships - Richmond Hopewell *(Graduate, Undergraduate/Scholarship)* [5402]
ISA Section and District Scholarships - Southwestern Wyoming *(Graduate, Undergraduate/Scholarship)* [5403]
ISA Section and District Scholarships - Texas, Louisiana and Mississippi *(Graduate, Undergraduate/Scholarship)* [5404]
ISA Section and District Scholarships - Wilmington *(Graduate, Undergraduate/Scholarship)* [5405]
ISA Technical Division Scholarships - Analysis Division *(Graduate, Undergraduate/Scholarship)* [5406]
ISA Technical Division Scholarships - Chemical and Petroleum Industries Division *(Graduate, Undergraduate/Scholarship)* [5407]
ISA Technical Division Scholarships - Food and Pharmaceutical Industries Division *(Graduate, Undergraduate/Scholarship)* [5408]
ISA Technical Division Scholarships - Power Industry Division *(Graduate, Undergraduate/Scholarship)* [5409]
ISA Technical Division Scholarships - Process Measurement and Control Division *(Graduate, Undergraduate/Scholarship)* [5410]
ISA Technical Division Scholarships - Pulp and Paper Industry Division *(Graduate, Undergraduate/Scholarship)* [5411]
ISA Technical Division Scholarships - Test Measurement Division *(Graduate, Undergraduate/Scholarship)* [5412]
ISA Technical Division Scholarships - Water and Wastewater Industries Division *(Graduate, Undergraduate/Scholarship)* [5413]
Bob and Mary Ives Scholarships *(Graduate, Undergraduate/Scholarship)* [5414]
Ken and Romaine Kauffman Scholarship Fund *(Undergraduate/Scholarship)* [4245]
Loan Forgiveness Scholarships *(Graduate, Undergraduate/Loan, Scholarship)* [9463]
Leon I. Lock and Barbara R. Lock Scholarship Fund *(Undergraduate/Scholarship)* [4246]
Hans McCorriston Motive Power Machinist Grant Programs *(Undergraduate/Scholarship)* [2132]
The Medallion Fund Scholarships *(Undergraduate/Scholarship)* [7302]
Arthur Paulin Automotive Aftermarket Scholarship Awards *(Postgraduate, Undergraduate/Scholarship)* [2133]
Carl C. and Abbie Rebman Trust Scholarships *(Undergraduate/Scholarship)* [4566]
Kenneth Rogers Memorial Scholarships *(Undergraduate/Scholarship)* [6051]
SEMA Memorial Scholarships *(Graduate, Undergraduate/Scholarship)* [9464]
APSAIL's Ralph Silverman Memorial Scholarships *(Undergraduate/Scholarship)* [2126]
Sloan Northwood University Heavy-Duty Scholarships *(Undergraduate/Scholarship)* [2127]
Specialty Equipment Market Association Scholarships *(Graduate, Undergraduate, Vocational/Occupational/Scholarship)* [9465]

Aviation (See also Aeronautics)

ACI-NA Scholarships *(Graduate, Undergraduate/Scholarship)* [180]
ADMA International Scholarship *(Undergraduate/Scholarship)* [2144]
AE Flight Training Scholarships *(Other/Scholarship)* [7436]
AE Jet Type Rating Scholarships *(Other/Scholarship)* [7437]
AE Technical Training Scholarships *(Other/Scholarship)* [7438]
Air Traffic Control Association Full-time Employee Student Scholarships *(Other/Scholarship)* [135]
Air Traffic Control Association Non-employee Student Scholarships *(Undergraduate/Scholarship)* [136]
Aircraft Owners and Pilots Association Scholarships *(Undergraduate/Scholarship)* [154]
AMACESP Student Scholarships *(Undergraduate/Scholarship)* [178]
David Arver Memorial Scholarships *(Undergraduate/Scholarship)* [155]
Dutch and Ginger Arver Scholarships *(Undergraduate/Scholarship)* [156]
Association of Flight Attendants Scholarship Fund *(Undergraduate/Scholarship)* [1963]
Donald A. Baldwin Sr. Business Aviation Management Scholarships *(Professional development/Scholarship)* [6829]
Charles A. Lindbergh Fellowships *(Graduate/Fellowship)* [9021]
Civil Air Patrol Flight Scholarships *(Undergraduate/Scholarship)* [3039]
Al Conklin and Bill de Decker Business Aviation Management Scholarships *(Undergraduate/Scholarship)* [6830]
John P. Culhane Professional Pilot Scholarships *(Undergraduate/Scholarship)* [215]
Johnny Davis Memorial Scholarships *(Undergraduate/Scholarship)* [157]

Arlene Davis Scholarships *(Undergraduate/Scholarship)* [3581]
Distinguished Flying Cross Society Scholarships *(Undergraduate/Scholarship)* [3641]
F. Atlee Dodge Maintenance Scholarships *(Undergraduate/Scholarship)* [216]
Duncan Aviation Scholarships *(Undergraduate/Scholarship)* [158]
Amelia Earhart Memorial Academic Scholarships *(Undergraduate/Scholarship)* [7439]
William M. Fanning Maintenance Scholarships *(Undergraduate/Scholarship)* [6831]
Field Aviation Co., Inc. Scholarships *(Undergraduate/Scholarship)* [159]
Flight Attendants/Flight Technician Scholarships *(Other/Scholarship)* [6832]
Joseph Frasca Excellence in Aviation Scholarships *(Undergraduate/Scholarship)* [10104]
Garmin Scholarships *(Undergraduate/Scholarship)* [160]
Lowell Gaylor Memorial Scholarships *(Undergraduate/Scholarship)* [161]
Lawrence Ginocchio Aviation Scholarships *(Undergraduate/Scholarship)* [6833]
Bud Glover Memorial Scholarships *(Undergraduate/Scholarship)* [162]
Guggenheim Fellowships *(Doctorate/Fellowship)* [9022]
Leon Harris/Les Nichols Memorial Scholarships to Spartan College of Aeronautics & Technology *(Undergraduate/Scholarship)* [163]
Don C. Hawkins Memorial Scholarships *(Undergraduate/Scholarship)* [164]
Helicopter Foundation International Commercial Helicopter Rating Scholarships *(Other/Scholarship)* [4838]
Helicopter Foundation International Maintenance Technician Certificate Scholarships *(Other/Scholarship)* [4839]
Honeywell Avionics Scholarships *(Undergraduate/Scholarship)* [165]
Edward L. Horne, Jr. Scholarships *(Advanced Professional/Scholarship)* [7732]
International Operators Scholarship *(Professional development/Scholarship)* [6834]
The ISASI Rudolf Kapustin Memorial Scholarships *(Undergraduate/Scholarship)* [5394]
Eugene S. Kropf Scholarship *(Undergraduate/Scholarship)* [10105]
L-3 Communications Avionics Systems Scholarships *(Undergraduate/Scholarship)* [166]
Leadership Conference Scholarship *(Other/Scholarship)* [6835]
MAF Canada Scholarship Fund *(Undergraduate/Scholarship)* [6560]
Maintenance Technical Reward and Career Scholarships *(Undergraduate/Scholarship)* [6836]
NBCFAE Mamie W. Mallory National Scholarship Program *(Undergraduate/Scholarship)* [6813]
Mid-Continent Instrument Scholarships *(Undergraduate/Scholarship)* [167]
Joshua Esch Mitchell Aviation Scholarships *(Undergraduate/Scholarship)* [4611]
Monte R. Mitchell Global Scholarships *(Undergraduate/Scholarship)* [168]
NAFA Corporate Aviation Business Scholarship *(Undergraduate, Graduate/Scholarship)* [6692]
Michelle North Scholarships for Safety *(Other/Scholarship)* [4840]
Organization of Black Aerospace Professionals General Scholarships *(All/Scholarship)* [7733]
Chuck Peacock Memorial Scholarships *(Undergraduate/Scholarship)* [169]
Bob Reeve Aviation Management Scholarships *(Undergraduate/Scholarship)* [217]
Rockwell Collins Scholarships *(Undergraduate/Scholarship)* [170]
Marty Rosness Student Scholarships *(Undergraduate/Scholarship)* [1623]
Bill Sanderson Aviation Maintenance Technician Scholarships *(Postgraduate/Scholarship)* [4841]
Schedulers and Dispatchers Monetary Scholarships *(Other/Scholarship)* [6837]
Thomas J. Slocum Memorial Scholarships to Redstone College *(Undergraduate/Scholarship)* [171]
Sporty's/Cincinnati Avionics Scholarships *(Undergraduate, Vocational/Occupational/Scholarship)* [172]
Tailhook Educational Foundation Scholarship Program *(Undergraduate/Scholarship)* [9632]
Kei Takemoto Memorial Scholarships *(Undergraduate/Scholarship)* [173]
Lee Tarbox Memorial Scholarships *(Undergraduate/Scholarship)* [174]
Tom Taylor Memorial Scholarships to Spartan College of Aeronautics and Technology *(Undergraduate/Scholarship)* [175]
Texas State Technical College Scholarships *(Undergraduate/Scholarship)* [176]
UAA Janice K. Barden Aviation Scholarships *(Undergraduate/Scholarship)* [6838]
U.S. Aircraft Insurance Group Professional Development Program (USAIG PDP) Scholarships *(Undergraduate/Scholarship)* [6839]
A. Verville Fellowships *(Professional development/Fellowship)* [9023]
Paul A. Whelan Aviation Scholarships *(Undergraduate, Graduate/Scholarship)* [10106]
Dr. Harold S. Wood Awards for Excellence *(Undergraduate/Award)* [4349]
The Frank Der Yuen Aviation Scholarship *(Undergraduate/Scholarship)* [7789]

Banking (See also Accounting; Finance)

Bank of Canada Fellowship Award *(Doctorate, Other/Fellowship, Grant)* [2187]
Norm Bromberger Research Bursaries *(Undergraduate, Graduate/Scholarship)* [3469]
Conference of State Bank Supervisors Graduate School Scholarships *(Graduate/Award)* [3343]
Amy and Tim Dauphinee Scholarships *(Graduate/Scholarship)* [2575]
Lloyd Houlden Memorial Research Fellowships *(Advanced Professional, Professional development/Fellowship)* [2559]
HSF/Wells Fargo Scholarship Program *(Undergraduate/Scholarship)* [4906]
Alexander Fraser Laidlaw Fellowships *(Graduate/Fellowship, Scholarship)* [2576]
Lemaire Co-operative Studies Awards *(Undergraduate, Graduate/Scholarship)* [2577]
Mutual of Omaha Finance Careers Scholarships *(Undergraduate, Graduate/Scholarship)* [105]
Wells Fargo American Indian Scholarships - Graduate *(Graduate/Scholarship)* [883]

Behavioral sciences

Owen F. Aldis Scholarship Fund *(Doctorate/Scholarship)* [5420]
CASBS Fellowships *(Doctorate, Other/Fellowship)* [2841]
EAPSI Fellowships *(Doctorate, Graduate/Fellowship)* [7124]
Epilepsy Foundation Behavioral Sciences Post-Doctoral Fellowships *(Postdoctorate/Fellowship)* [3902]
Epilepsy Foundation Behavioral Sciences Student Fellowships *(Graduate, Undergraduate/Fellowship)* [3903]
Epilepsy Foundation Research Grants *(Doctorate/Grant)* [3907]
Eleanor Guetzloe Undergraduate Scholarship *(Undergraduate/Scholarship)* [3433]
Ruth L. Kirschstein NRSA Individual Pre-Doctoral Fellowships *(Doctorate/Fellowship)* [9926]
Christine Mirzayan Science and Technology Policy Graduate Fellowships *(Graduate/Fellowship)* [6679]
National Institute of Health Undergraduate Scholarship Program (NIH UGSP) *(Undergraduate/Scholarship)* [9930]
NDSEG Fellowships *(Graduate/Fellowship)* [6911]
Wayne F. Placek Grants *(Graduate, Doctorate/Grant)* [1150]
Russell Sage Foundation Visiting Scholars *(Postdoctorate/Fellowship)* [8668]
SOPHE/ATSDR Student Fellowships in Environmental Health or Emergency Preparedness *(Doctorate, Graduate, Master's/Fellowship)* [9292]
SOPHE/CDC Student Fellowships in Child, Adolescent and School Health *(Doctorate, Graduate, Master's/Fellowship)* [9293]
SOPHE/CDC Student Fellowships in Injury Prevention *(Graduate/Fellowship)* [9294]
Louis Stokes Urban Health Policy Fellows Program *(Other/Fellowship)* [3350]
Student Research Awards from the Behavioral Gerontology SIG *(Undergraduate, Graduate/Award, Monetary)* [1861]
Targeted Research Initiative for Health Outcomes *(Doctorate/Grant)* [3909]

Bible studies (See also Religion; Theology)

Catholic Biblical Association of America Scholarships *(Undergraduate/Scholarship)* [2812]
CSF Graduate Fellowships *(Graduate/Fellowship)* [2936]
FTE Dissertation Fellowships *(Graduate, Doctorate/Fellowship)* [4153]
FTE Doctoral Fellowships *(Doctorate, Graduate/Fellowship)* [4154]
FTE North American Doctoral Fellowships *(Doctorate, Graduate/Fellowship)* [4155]

Bilingual and cross-cultural education (See Education, Bilingual and cross-cultural)

Biochemistry (See also Chemistry)

Career Awards at the Scientific Interface (CASI) *(Doctorate, Postdoctorate, Advanced Professional, Professional development/Grant)* [2416]
Epilepsy Foundation Pre-doctoral Research Training Fellowships *(Graduate/Fellowship)* [3906]
Kris Knudson Memorial Scholarship *(Graduate, Undergraduate/Scholarship)* [10065]
Larson Aquatic Research Support Scholarships (LARS) *(Graduate/Scholarship)* [1490]
MillerCoors Engineering and Sciences Scholarships *(Undergraduate/Scholarship)* [68]

Bioengineering (See Engineering, Biomedical)

Bioethics (See Ethics and bioethics)

Biological and clinical sciences (See also Biology)

Raymond B. Bauer Research Award *(Professional development/Grant)* [6479]
C. Lalor Burdick Scholarships *(Graduate, Master's, Doctorate/Scholarship)* [6245]
Max M. Burger Endowed Scholarships in Embryology *(Graduate, Master's, Doctorate/Scholarship)* [6246]
Burroughs Wellcome Travel Fellowships *(Undergraduate, Graduate/Fellowship, Grant)* [9305]
Clinical Research Fellowship for Medical Students *(Graduate/Fellowship)* [3699]
Daland Fellowships in Clinical Investigation *(Doctorate, Postgraduate/Fellowship)* [1079]
Dr. Biljan Memorial Awards *(Advanced Professional/Award)* [2636]
EAPSI Fellowships *(Doctorate, Graduate/Fellowship)* [7124]
Endowment Fund for Education Grants *(Undergraduate/Grant)* [2264]
Endowment Fund for Education, Loans/Grants for Educational Materials *(Undergraduate/Grant)* [2266]
Endowment Fund for Education, Loans/Grants for Equipment *(Undergraduate/Grant)* [2267]
Endowment Fund for Education, Loans *(Undergraduate/Loan)* [2265]

Everglades Foundation Fellowship *(Graduate, Doctorate, Master's/Fellowship)* [3931]
Everglades Foundation Internship *(Postgraduate, Postdoctorate/Internship)* [3932]
Everglades Foundation Scholarships *(Graduate, Master's, Doctorate/Scholarship)* [3933]
FASEB MARC Travel Awards *(Undergraduate, Graduate, Postdoctorate/Award)* [9306]
Jeffress Trust Awards Program in Interdisciplinary Research *(Professional development/Award)* [4816]
Charles A. King Trust Postdoctoral Research Fellowships *(Postdoctorate/Fellowship)* [4817]
Lewis and Clark Fund for Exploration and Field Research *(Graduate, Postdoctorate/Grant)* [1082]
March of Dimes General Research Grants *(Professional development/Grant)* [6233]
MDI Biological Laboratory High school Student Summer Research Fellowships *(Undergraduate/Fellowship)* [6606]
MGH Department of Psychiatry Global Psychiatric Clinical Research Training Program *(Advanced Professional/Fellowship)* [6323]
Christine Mirzayan Science and Technology Policy Graduate Fellowships *(Graduate/Fellowship)* [6679]
National GEM Consortium - PhD Science Fellowships *(Doctorate, Graduate/Fellowship)* [6969]
Basil O'Connor Starter Scholar Research Awards *(Professional development/Grant)* [6235]
OHTN Postdoctoral Fellowships *(Doctorate/Fellowship)* [7637]
Arthur and Barbara Pape Endowments *(Graduate/Grant)* [10269]
Lola Ellis Robertson Scholarships *(Graduate, Master's, Doctorate/Scholarship)* [6258]
SFP Mid-Career/Mentor Awards for Family Planning *(Other/Grant)* [9120]
Louis Stokes Urban Health Policy Fellows Program *(Other/Fellowship)* [3350]
UC MEXUS-CONACYT Doctoral Fellowships *(Doctorate/Fellowship)* [10117]
Susan C. Weiss Clinical Advancement Scholarships *(Other/Scholarship)* [9229]

Biology (See also Biological and clinical sciences)
AAA Postdoctoral Fellowship Program *(Postdoctorate/Fellowship)* [460]
AIST Ohio Valley Chapter Scholarships *(Undergraduate/Scholarship)* [1994]
Catherine H. Beattie Fellowships *(Graduate/Fellowship)* [2867]
B.O.G. Pest Control Scholarship Funds *(Undergraduate, Graduate/Scholarship)* [2323]
William L. Brown Fellowships *(Graduate/Fellowship)* [7735]
John and Elisabeth Buck Endowed Scholarships *(Graduate, Postdoctorate/Scholarship)* [6244]
Burroughs Wellcome Fund Collaborative Research Travel Grants (CRTG) *(Doctorate, Postdoctorate, Professional development/Grant)* [2413]
Career Awards at the Scientific Interface (CASI) *(Doctorate, Postdoctorate, Advanced Professional, Professional development/Grant)* [2416]
Julian E. Carnes Scholarship Fund *(Undergraduate/Scholarship)* [4183]
Cave Conservancy Foundation Graduate and Undergraduate Fellowships *(Doctorate, Graduate, Undergraduate/Fellowship)* [2823]
David and Deborah Clark Fellowships *(Graduate/Fellowship)* [7736]
CNS-UCSB Graduate Fellowships for Science and Engineering *(Doctorate/Fellowship)* [10127]
Howard A. Crum Student Scholarships *(Undergraduate/Scholarship)* [10179]
Rexford Daubenmire Fellowships *(Graduate/Fellowship)* [7737]
Charles Dobbins FTA Scholarships *(Undergraduate, Vocational/Occupational/Scholarship)* [4316]
DOE Computational Science Graduate Fellowships (DOE CSGF) *(Doctorate, Graduate/Fellowship)* [5887]
Dole Food Fellowships *(Graduate/Fellowship)* [7738]

Dow Chemical Company Fellowships *(Graduate/Fellowship)* [7085]
E.I. DuPont Graduate Fellowship *(Graduate/Fellowship)* [7086]
Emily P. Foster Fellowships *(Graduate/Fellowship)* [7739]
Fred and Avery Test Scholarships *(Undergraduate/Scholarship)* [10180]
Marian P. and David M. Gates Scholarship for Non-Residents *(Undergraduate/Scholarship)* [10181]
Frank Caleb & Margaret Thompson Gates Student Scholarships *(Undergraduate/Scholarship)* [10182]
Harry Hampton Fund Scholarship *(Undergraduate/Scholarship)* [4733]
Joel T. Heinen Undergraduate Support Scholarships *(Undergraduate/Scholarship)* [10183]
Helm Family Scholarships *(Undergraduate/Scholarship)* [8706]
Indspire Health Careers Bursary and Scholarships *(Graduate, Undergraduate/Scholarship)* [5132]
Investigators in the Pathogenesis of Infectious Disease Awards *(Doctorate, Postdoctorate, Professional development/Grant)* [2417]
AACT John Kitt Memorial Scholarship *(Undergraduate/Scholarship)* [477]
Jeffery P. LaFage Graduate Student Research Award *(Master's, Doctorate/Grant)* [3882]
Douglas Lake Improvement Association Scholarships *(Undergraduate/Scholarship)* [10184]
Lakselaget Foundation Scholarships *(Graduate, Undergraduate/Scholarship)* [5903]
Life Sciences Research Foundation Postdoctoral Fellowship Program *(Postdoctorate/Fellowship)* [6081]
Frank R. Lillie Fellowships and Scholarships *(Undergraduate, Graduate/Scholarship)* [6251]
Lowe Family First Summer Student Scholarships *(Undergraduate/Scholarship)* [10185]
Dolphus E. Milligan Graduate Fellowships *(Graduate/Fellowship)* [7087]
National Association of Biology Teachers BioClub Student Awards *(Undergraduate/Scholarship)* [6714]
NDSEG Fellowships *(Graduate/Fellowship)* [6911]
NGC College Scholarships *(Graduate, Undergraduate/Scholarship)* [6965]
George E. Nichols Undergradute Scholarships *(Undergraduate/Scholarship)* [10187]
NOBCChE Procter and Gamble Fellowships *(Graduate/Fellowship)* [7088]
NYU Langone Medical Center Science Student Scholarships *(Undergraduate, Graduate/Scholarship)* [109]
James L. Plafkin Memorial Scholarships *(Undergraduate/Scholarship)* [10188]
A. Stanley Rand Fellowships Program *(Undergraduate, Doctorate, Postdoctorate/Fellowship)* [9037]
Florence C. Rose and S. Meryl Rose Scholarships *(Graduate, Master's, Doctorate/Scholarship)* [6259]
Rowe Family Fellowships *(Graduate/Fellowship)* [7742]
Herbert M. Saylor Memorial Scholarship *(Graduate/Scholarship)* [9341]
Schrank Family Scholarships *(Undergraduate/Scholarship)* [10189]
Clifford G. Shull Fellowships *(Postdoctorate/Fellowship)* [9909]
SICB Fellowships of Graduate Student Travel (FGST) *(Graduate/Fellowship)* [9157]
SICB Grants-in-Aid of Research Program (GIAR) *(Graduate/Grant)* [9158]
Lillian and Murray Slatkin Fellowships *(Graduate/Fellowship)* [7743]
David H. Smith Conservation Research Fellowships *(Postdoctorate/Fellowship)* [9109]
Eastman Kodak Dr. Theophilus Sorrell Fellowships *(Graduate/Fellowship)* [7090]
STRI Short-Term Fellowships *(Undergraduate, Graduate, Postdoctorate/Fellowship)* [9038]
F. Christian and Betty Thompson Fellowships *(Graduate/Fellowship)* [7745]
J.P. and Madeline Trinkaus Endowed Scholarships in Embryology *(Graduate, Master's, Doctorate/Scholarship)* [6263]

Earl S. Tupper 3-year Postdoctoral Fellowships in Tropical Biology *(Postdoctorate/Fellowship)* [9039]
UMBS Istock Family Scholarships *(Undergraduate/Scholarship)* [10190]
UMBS Returning Student Award *(Undergraduate/Scholarship)* [10191]
Veterinary and Pre-Veterinary Academic Scholarships *(Undergraduate/Scholarship)* [3647]
Dr. Edward G. Voss Memorial Scholarships *(Undergraduate/Scholarship)* [10192]
Alvin M. Weinberg Fellowships *(Doctorate/Fellowship)* [9910]
Welder Wildlife Foundation Fellowships *(Graduate, Master's, Doctorate/Fellowship)* [10510]
E. E. Williams Research Grants *(Master's, Doctorate/Grant)* [4873]
Gary and Gussie Williams Scholarships *(Undergraduate/Scholarship)* [10193]

Biology, Marine
Atlantic Salmon Federation Olin Fellowships *(Graduate/Fellowship)* [2120]
Charles H. Bussmann Graduate Scholarship *(Graduate, Undergraduate/Scholarship)* [6271]
Dr. Nancy Foster Scholarship Program *(Postgraduate, Graduate/Scholarship)* [7077]
Dr. Nancy Foster Scholarships *(Graduate/Scholarship)* [4159]
Thomas B. Grave and Elizabeth F. Grave Scholarships *(Undergraduate, Graduate/Scholarship)* [6247]
Caswell Grave Scholarships *(Undergraduate, Graduate/Scholarship)* [6248]
International Women's Fishing Association Scholarship Trust *(Graduate/Scholarship)* [5456]
ISRS Graduate Fellowships *(Doctorate, Graduate/Fellowship)* [5429]
Arthur Klorfein Scholarship and Fellowship Fund *(Undergraduate, Graduate/Scholarship)* [6250]
Link Foundation/Smithsonian Graduate Fellowships in Marine Science *(Graduate/Fellowship)* [9033]
Boyd N. Lyon Scholarships *(Doctorate, Graduate, Master's/Scholarship)* [6162]
Marine Biological Laboratory Pioneers Fund *(Undergraduate, Graduate/Scholarship)* [6252]
Marine Technology Society ROV Scholarships (MTS ROV) *(Undergraduate, Graduate/Scholarship)* [6272]
MASNA Student Scholarships *(Undergraduate, Graduate/Scholarship)* [6241]
S.O. Mast Founder's Scholarships *(Undergraduate, Graduate/Scholarship)* [6253]
Frank Morrell Endowed Memorial Scholarships *(Graduate, Master's, Doctorate/Scholarship)* [6254]
The MTS Student Scholarship for Graduate Students *(Graduate/Scholarship)* [6273]
The MTS Student Scholarship for Graduating High School Seniors *(Undergraduate/Scholarship)* [6274]
The MTS Student Scholarship for Two-Year, Technical, Engineering and Community College Students *(Undergraduate/Scholarship)* [6275]
Oceanic Research Group Scholarships *(Graduate, Undergraduate/Scholarship)* [7570]
Our World Underwater Scholarship Society North American Rolex Scholarships *(Undergraduate, Professional development/Scholarship)* [7764]
The Paros-Digiquartz Scholarships *(Graduate, Undergraduate/Scholarship)* [6276]
Pfizer Scholarship Funds *(Undergraduate, Graduate/Scholarship)* [6256]
Herbert W. Rand Fellowships and Scholarships *(Undergraduate, Graduate/Scholarship)* [6257]
Ellis W. Rowe Scholarships *(Undergraduate/Scholarship)* [4703]
Ruth Sager Scholarships *(Undergraduate, Graduate/Scholarship)* [6260]
Ronald L. Schmied Scholarships *(Other, Undergraduate/Scholarship)* [4686]
Milton L. Shifman Endowed Scholarships *(Undergraduate, Graduate/Scholarship)* [6261]
Horace W. Stunkard Scholarships *(Undergraduate, Graduate/Scholarship)* [6262]

William Randolph Hearst Educational Endowments *(Undergraduate, Graduate/Scholarship)* [6265]

Biology, Molecular
NYU Langone Medical Center Science Student Scholarships *(Undergraduate, Graduate/Scholarship)* [109]
Sloan Research Fellowships *(Doctorate/Fellowship)* [8988]

Biomedical engineering (See Engineering, Biomedical)

Biomedical research (See also Medical research)
Henry Friesen Awards and Lectures *(Doctorate/Award)* [9074]
Gilliam Fellowships for Advanced Study *(Doctorate/Fellowship)* [4974]
HHMI International Student Research Fellowships *(Doctorate/Fellowship)* [4975]
HHMI Medical Research Fellowships *(Undergraduate/Fellowship)* [4976]
KFOC Biomedical Fellowships *(Postdoctorate/Fellowship)* [5827]
Donald A.B. Lindberg Research Fellowships *(Doctorate, Graduate/Fellowship)* [6388]
Abby and Howard Milstein Innovation Award in Reproductive Medicine *(Advanced Professional, Professional development/Award, Grant)* [5618]
Abby and Howard Milstein Reproductive Medicine Research Award *(Advanced Professional, Professional development/Award, Grant)* [5619]
National Institute of Health Undergraduate Scholarship Program (NIH UGSP) *(Undergraduate/Scholarship)* [9930]
National Space Biomedical Research Institute Postdoctoral Fellowships *(Postdoctorate/Fellowship)* [7177]
Pew Latin American Fellows Program in the Biomedical Sciences *(Other/Fellowship)* [8021]
SRF Post-doctoral Fellowships *(Postdoctorate/Fellowship)* [8819]
Helen Hay Whitney Foundation Fellowships *(Postdoctorate/Fellowship)* [10551]
Young Investigators Achievement Award *(Advanced Professional, Professional development/Award, Grant)* [5620]

Biomedical sciences
BMES Graduate and Undergraduate Student Awards *(Graduate, Undergraduate/Award)* [2271]
Career Awards for Medical Scientists (CAMS) *(Postdoctorate, Advanced Professional, Professional development/Grant)* [2414]
Ruth L. Kirschstein NRSA Individual Pre-Doctoral Fellowships *(Doctorate/Fellowship)* [9926]
Saul T. Wilson, Jr. Scholarships *(Graduate, Undergraduate/Scholarship)* [9888]

Biophysics (See also Physics)
Career Awards at the Scientific Interface (CASI) *(Doctorate, Postdoctorate, Advanced Professional, Professional development/Grant)* [2416]
Grass Fellowships at the Marine Biological Laboratory *(Doctorate, Postdoctorate/Fellowship)* [4643]
Lou Hochberg Awards - University/College Essay Awards *(Undergraduate/Award)* [7747]
Lou Hochberg Awards - University Thesis/Dissertation Awards *(Undergraduate, Graduate/Scholarship)* [7748]
Lou Hochberg Awards - University Thesis/Dissertation Research Improvement and Implementation Grants *(Graduate/Award, Grant)* [7749]
Graduate Fellowship Program - Peter Verhofstadt Fellowships *(Graduate/Fellowship)* [8836]

Blood banking
Canadian Blood Services Graduate Fellowship *(Graduate/Fellowship)* [2583]
Canadian Blood Services Postdoctoral Fellowship *(Postdoctorate/Fellowship)* [2584]

Botany
Arkansas Green Industry Association Student Scholarships *(Undergraduate/Scholarship)* [1652]
CSSA Research Grants *(Undergraduate, Graduate, Advanced Professional/Grant)* [2428]
Garden Club of America Awards in Tropical Botany (GCA) *(Doctorate/Award)* [4324]
Louisiana Agricultural Consultants Association Scholarships *(Graduate, Undergraduate/Scholarship)* [6112]
NGC College Scholarships *(Graduate, Undergraduate/Scholarship)* [6965]
Dennis Raveling Scholarships *(Undergraduate/Scholarship)* [2488]
Richard E. Schultes Research Awards *(Graduate/Grant, Award)* [9113]
Welder Wildlife Foundation Fellowships *(Graduate, Master's, Doctorate/Fellowship)* [10510]

British studies (See also Scottish studies)
Carl H. Pforzheimer, Jr. Research Grants *(Graduate, Other/Grant)* [5800]

Broadcasting (See also Media arts)
APSA Congressional Fellowships for Journalists *(Advanced Professional, Professional development/Fellowship)* [1109]
Atkinson Fellowships in Public Policy *(Professional development/Fellowship)* [2111]
John Bayliss Broadcast Foundation Internship Programs *(Undergraduate/Internship)* [2203]
John Bayliss Broadcast Foundation Radio Scholarships *(Undergraduate/Scholarship)* [2204]
Rick Brewer Scholarships *(Undergraduate/Scholarship)* [10218]
Broadcast Education and Development Program *(Other/Scholarship)* [3134]
Mary L. Brown Scholarships *(Undergraduate/Scholarship)* [5467]
APTRA-Clete Roberts/Kathryn Dettman Memorial Journalism Scholarship *(Undergraduate/Scholarship)* [1818]
Joe Durso, Jr. Memorial Scholarship *(Undergraduate/Scholarship)* [6576]
Harold E. Ennes Scholarships *(Graduate, Other/Award, Scholarship)* [9092]
E. Lanier Finch Scholarships *(Undergraduate/Scholarship)* [4375]
Stephen Gates Scholarships *(Undergraduate/Scholarship)* [10230]
Great Falls Broadcasters Association Scholarships *(Undergraduate/Scholarship)* [6577]
Howard L. Green Scholarships *(Undergraduate/Scholarship)* [7317]
Robert D. Greenberg Scholarships *(Graduate, Other/Scholarship)* [9093]
HACU/NASCAR Scholarships *(Graduate, Undergraduate/Scholarship)* [4888]
Indiana Broadcasters Association College Scholarship Program *(Undergraduate/Scholarship)* [5108]
ISBA General Scholarships *(Undergraduate/Scholarship)* [5052]
Kansas Association of Broadcasters Scholarships *(Undergraduate/Scholarship)* [5652]
Anna-Maria and Stephen M. Kellen Fellowships *(Professional development/Fellowship)* [726]
Montana Broadcasters Association Broadcast Engineering Scholarships *(Undergraduate/Scholarship)* [6578]
New York Women in Communications, Inc. Foundation Scholarships *(Graduate, Undergraduate/Scholarship)* [7406]
Ohio Association of Broadcaster's Kids Scholarships *(Undergraduate/Scholarship)* [7572]
Oregon Association of Broadcasters Scholarships *(Undergraduate/Scholarship)* [7688]
Walter S. Patterson Scholarships *(Graduate/Scholarship)* [2370]
SBE/Ennes Youth Scholarships *(Undergraduate/Scholarship)* [9094]
Linda Simmons Memorial Scholarships *(Undergraduate/Scholarship)* [219]
Helen J. Sioussat/Fay Wells Scholarships *(Graduate/Scholarship)* [2371]
Alexander M. Tanger Scholarships *(Graduate/Scholarship)* [2372]
Two Year/Community Broadcast Education Association Scholarship Awards *(Graduate/Scholarship)* [2373]
Abe Voron Scholarships *(Graduate/Scholarship)* [2374]
Vincent T. Wasilewski Scholarships *(Graduate/Scholarship)* [2375]
Glenn Wilson Broadcast Journalism Scholarships *(Undergraduate/Scholarship)* [7873]
Wisconsin Broadcasters Association Foundation Student Scholarships *(Undergraduate/Scholarship)* [10621]

Business
Evelyn Abrams Memorial Scholarships *(Undergraduate/Scholarship)* [8327]
Accenture American Indian Scholarship Program *(Graduate, Undergraduate/Scholarship)* [880]
AfterCollege Business Student Scholarships *(Undergraduate, Graduate, Doctorate/Scholarship)* [97]
Alaska Aerospace Development Corporation Scholarships *(Undergraduate/Scholarship)* [10004]
ALPFA Scholarship Programs *(Graduate, Undergraduate/Scholarship)* [2013]
American Business Women's Association Sarasota Sunrise Chapter Scholarships *(Undergraduate, Vocational/Occupational/Scholarship)* [3317]
American Indian Fellowship in Business Scholarships *(Graduate, Master's, Undergraduate/Scholarship)* [6844]
ARA Scholarship Awards *(Undergraduate/Scholarship)* [2136]
Arkansas Green Industry Association Professional Grants *(Professional development, Undergraduate/Grant)* [1651]
ARS of Eastern USA Lazarian Graduate Scholarship *(Master's, Doctorate/Scholarship)* [1680]
ASBPE Young Leaders Scholarships *(Professional development/Scholarship)* [1250]
ASEE/NSF Small Business Postdoctoral Research Diversity Fellowships *(Postdoctorate/Fellowship)* [1303]
Auto-Pets "Out-of-the-Box Thinking" Scholarships *(All/Award, Scholarship)* [2129]
Bank of America Junior Achievement Scholarship Fund *(Undergraduate/Scholarship)* [4177]
Bank of Canada Governor's Awards *(Doctorate, Other/Award, Grant)* [2188]
Banner Bank Business Scholarships *(Undergraduate/Scholarship)* [6057]
Quincy Brown Memorial Scholarships *(Undergraduate/Scholarship)* [8461]
Buick Achievers Scholarship Program *(Undergraduate/Scholarship)* [4359]
Dr. F. Ross Byrd Scholarships *(Graduate, Vocational/Occupational, Postgraduate/Scholarship)* [10463]
C200 Scholar Awards *(Graduate/Scholarship)* [3156]
Canadian Association for Studies in Co-operation Scholarships Lemaire Co-operative Studies Awards (CASC) *(Graduate, Undergraduate/Scholarship)* [2611]
C.C.H.R.M.A. Scholarships *(Undergraduate/Scholarship)* [3092]
CERT College Scholarships *(Graduate, Undergraduate/Scholarship)* [3435]
Melba Dawn Chiarenza Scholarship Fund *(Undergraduate/Scholarship)* [10504]
Citi/TELACU Scholars Mentoring Program *(Undergraduate/Scholarship)* [9659]
Clark High School Academy of Finance Scholarships *(Undergraduate/Scholarship)* [8338]
Community Bank - Lee Guggisberg Foundation Memorial Scholarships *(Undergraduate/Scholarship)* [8464]
Connecticut Mortgage Bankers Social Affairs Com-

BUSINESS

mittee Scholarships *(Undergraduate/Scholarship)* [4745]
Mable B. Crawford Memorial Scholarships *(Undergraduate/Scholarship)* [10015]
Critical Language Scholarships for Intensive Summer Institutes *(Graduate, Undergraduate/Scholarship)* [1204]
DA Davidson Presidential Scholarships *(Undergraduate/Scholarship)* [10436]
D&A Florida Scholarships *(Undergraduate/Scholarship)* [9425]
Canadian Association for Studies in Co-operation Scholarships - Amy and Tim Dauphinee Scholarships (CASC) *(Graduate/Scholarship)* [2612]
Kenneth D. and Katherine D. Davis Scholarships *(Undergraduate/Scholarship)* [7823]
Don Debolt Franchising Scholarship Program *(Undergraduate/Scholarship)* [5335]
Delta Faucet Scholarships *(Undergraduate/Scholarship)* [8160]
Denton Scholarships *(Graduate/Scholarship)* [8897]
Diabetes Scholars Foundation College Scholarships *(Undergraduate/Scholarship)* [3616]
The Angie Dipietro Women in Business Scholarships *(Undergraduate/Scholarship)* [8231]
Discover MBA Loans *(Graduate/Loan)* [3638]
The Steve Duckett Local Conservation Scholarships *(Undergraduate, Postgraduate/Scholarship)* [8232]
Josephine P. White Eagle Scholarships *(Undergraduate, Graduate/Scholarship)* [4911]
Economic Club of Grand Rapids Scholarships *(Undergraduate/Scholarship)* [4590]
EDC International Business Scholarships *(Undergraduate/Scholarship)* [2603]
Wayne G. Failor Scholarships *(Undergraduate/Scholarship)* [7947]
Harry Feldman Memorial Scholarships *(Undergraduate/Scholarship)* [5576]
Brendan Flores Alumni Leadership Circle Scholarship - Clark High School *(Undergraduate/Scholarship)* [8344]
Florida Education Fund McKnight Doctoral Fellowships *(Graduate/Fellowship)* [4085]
Floto-Peel Family Scholarship Fund *(Undergraduate, Vocational/Occupational/Scholarship)* [4517]
Michael D. Ford Memorial Scholarship *(Graduate, Undergraduate/Scholarship)* [10057]
Forté Fellowships *(Master's/Fellowship)* [4151]
Jan and Glenn Fredericks Scholarship *(Graduate, Undergraduate/Scholarship)* [10058]
G.E. Lighting Canada Community Leadership Awards *(Undergraduate/Award)* [3830]
Generation III Scholarships *(Undergraduate/Scholarship)* [3783]
Doris Y. and John J. Gerber Scholarships *(Undergraduate/Scholarship)* [10464]
Senator James Gladstone Memorial Scholarships *(Graduate, Undergraduate/Scholarship)* [249]
William R. Goldfarb Memorial Scholarships *(Undergraduate/Scholarship)* [1739]
Goldman Sachs/Matsuo Takabuki Commemorative Scholarships *(Graduate/Scholarship)* [7908]
Graybar Canada Award of Excellence Scholarships *(Undergraduate/Scholarship)* [3832]
HACU/JCPenny Leadership Excellence Scholarships *(Graduate, Undergraduate, Graduate/Scholarship)* [4886]
HACU/NASCAR Scholarships *(Graduate, Undergraduate/Scholarship)* [4888]
HAESF Professional Internship Program *(Doctorate/Internship)* [5009]
HAESF Senior Leaders and Scholars Fellowships *(Other/Fellowship)* [5010]
Gene Halker Memorial Scholarships *(Graduate, Undergraduate/Scholarship)* [4145]
Anna E. Hall Memorial Scholarships *(Undergraduate, Graduate/Scholarship)* [8055]
Harvey Fellows Program *(Graduate/Fellowship)* [6632]
Raymond T. Hoge Scholarship Fund *(Undergraduate/Scholarship)* [9510]
IAAP Wings Chapter Scholarships *(Undergraduate/Scholarship)* [5244]
IBEA Graduate Scholarships *(Graduate/Scholarship)* [5056]

IBEA Undergraduate Scholarships *(Undergraduate/Scholarship)* [5057]
Indspire Post-Secondary Education Scholarships *(Graduate, Undergraduate/Scholarship)* [5133]
International Dairy-Deli-Bakery Association Undergraduate/Graduate Scholarships *(Graduate, Undergraduate/Scholarship)* [5314]
International Management Council Scholarships (IMC) *(Undergraduate/Scholarship)* [3288]
Dwight P. Jacobus Scholarships *(Undergraduate/Scholarship)* [2058]
Margaret G. Johnson and Marge J. Stout Scholarships *(Undergraduate/Scholarship)* [6034]
The Johnson & Wales Scholarships *(Undergraduate/Scholarship)* [5631]
Kerrwil's J.W. Kerr Continuing Education Scholarship Awards *(Undergraduate/Scholarship)* [3837]
The Michael Kiely Strong Roots Scholarships *(Undergraduate/Scholarship)* [8233]
Jane M. Klausman Women in Business Scholarships *(Graduate, Undergraduate/Scholarship)* [10826]
Vivian M. Kommer Scholarships *(Undergraduate/Scholarship)* [4603]
Canadian Association for Studies in Co-operation Scholarships - Alexander Fraser Laidlaw Fellowships *(Graduate/Fellowship)* [2613]
Lance Surety College Scholarships *(Undergraduate, Graduate/Scholarship)* [5911]
Paul J. Laninga Memorial Scholarship Fund *(Undergraduate/Scholarship)* [4529]
Las Vegas Chinatown Scholarships *(Undergraduate/Scholarship)* [8352]
Rick and Beverly Lattin Education Scholarship Fund *(Undergraduate/Scholarship)* [4530]
League of Latin American Citizens General Electric Scholarships *(Undergraduate/Scholarship)* [5987]
Doreen Legg Memorial Scholarships *(Undergraduate/Scholarship)* [8490]
David C. Lizárraga Graduate Fellowships *(Graduate/Fellowship)* [9660]
Luso-American Education Foundation C-1 General Scholarships *(Undergraduate/Scholarship)* [6145]
Kaia Lynn Markwalter Endowed Scholarships *(Undergraduate/Scholarship)* [6044]
Mas Family Scholarships *(Graduate, Undergraduate/Scholarship)* [6304]
The Tatiana Mendez Future Resources Scholarships *(Undergraduate/Scholarship)* [8234]
Ruth Messmer Memorial Scholarships *(Undergraduate/Scholarship)* [9441]
Mill Creek Business Association Scholarships *(Undergraduate/Scholarship)* [6537]
MillerCoors National Scholarships *(Undergraduate/Scholarship)* [69]
Christine Mirzayan Science and Technology Policy Graduate Fellowships *(Graduate/Fellowship)* [6679]
Robert E. and Judy More Scholarship Fund *(Undergraduate/Scholarship)* [4053]
Morgan Stanley Tribal Scholars Program *(Undergraduate/Scholarship)* [870]
MPI-WI Founders Grant Program *(Professional development/Grant)* [6405]
NABA National Scholarship Program *(Graduate, Undergraduate/Scholarship)* [6716]
NAFA Corporate Aviation Business Scholarship *(Undergraduate, Graduate/Scholarship)* [6692]
NAIFA West Michigan Scholarships *(Undergraduate/Scholarship)* [4614]
NASE Future Entrepreneur *(Undergraduate/Scholarship)* [6784]
National Technical Honor Society Scholarships *(Professional development/Scholarship)* [2424]
NBMBAA Graduate Scholarships Program *(Graduate/Scholarship)* [6821]
Paul and Ruth Neidhold Business Scholarships *(Undergraduate/Scholarship)* [3294]
Hubert A. Nelson Scholarships *(Undergraduate/Scholarship)* [3718]
Dr. Ezra Nesbeth Scholarships *(Undergraduate/Scholarship)* [5526]
New York Financial Writers' Associations Scholarships *(Graduate, Undergraduate/Scholarship)* [7354]
North American Van Lines Military Scholarship Competition *(Undergraduate/Scholarship)* [7449]

Novak Awards *(Doctorate/Monetary)* [58]
Peggy Kommer Novosad Scholarships *(Graduate, Postgraduate/Scholarship)* [4615]
NSHMBA Scholarships *(Graduate/Scholarship)* [7164]
NYFWA Scholarships *(Undergraduate, Graduate/Scholarship)* [7355]
The Seth Okin Good Deeds Scholarships *(Undergraduate/Scholarship)* [8235]
Open Society Presidential Fellowships *(Advanced Professional/Fellowship)* [7663]
Pardee Community Building Scholarships *(Undergraduate/Scholarship)* [8359]
Patriot Education Scholarships *(Undergraduate/Scholarship)* [6209]
Pepperdine University School of Law JD/MBA Endowed Scholarships *(Undergraduate/Scholarship)* [7999]
Thomas R. Pickering Graduate Foreign Affairs Fellowships *(Graduate, Undergraduate/Fellowship)* [10681]
Pignalberi Public Policy Scholarship *(Graduate/Scholarship)* [10068]
Julia T. Pingree Student Scholarship *(Undergraduate/Scholarship)* [7300]
PlasticPlace Young Entrepreneurs Scholarships *(Undergraduate/Scholarship)* [8148]
Plumbing-Heating-Cooling Contractors Association Educational Foundation Massachusetts Auxiliary Scholarships *(Undergraduate/Scholarship)* [8161]
Plumbing-Heating-Cooling Contractors Association Educational Foundation Need-Based Scholarships *(Undergraduate/Scholarship)* [8162]
Plumbing-Heating-Cooling Contractors Association Educational Foundation Scholarships *(Undergraduate/Scholarship)* [8163]
Progressive Dairy Producer Awards *(All/Grant)* [6905]
Resilience Action Fund Scholarships *(Graduate/Scholarship)* [3981]
RFDF MBA Preparation Fellowships *(Graduate, Undergraduate/Fellowship)* [8619]
RFDF Pre-MBA Fellowships *(Graduate/Fellowship)* [8620]
Dorothy Worden Ronken Scholarships *(Graduate/Scholarship)* [3594]
Scotiabank Scholarships *(Undergraduate/Scholarship)* [2291]
David and Sharon Seaver Family Scholarship Fund *(Undergraduate/Scholarship)* [4544]
SGI Business Insurance Diploma Scholarships *(Undergraduate/Scholarship)* [8772]
Pat Shimp Memorial Scholarships *(Undergraduate/Scholarship)* [7863]
A.O. Smith Scholarships *(Undergraduate/Scholarship)* [8164]
Helen D. Snow Memorial Scholarships *(Undergraduate/Scholarship)* [8056]
Frank H. Sobey Awards for Excellence in Business Studies *(Undergraduate/Award)* [9048]
The Thomas Soldan Healthy Communities Scholarships *(Undergraduate, Graduate/Scholarship)* [8237]
Gabe Stepetin Business Scholarship Awards *(Undergraduate, Vocational/Occupational, Graduate, Master's/Scholarship)* [312]
Edward P. Suchecki Family Scholarship Fund *(Undergraduate/Scholarship)* [4549]
Surety and Fidelity Industry Intern and Scholarship Program for Minority Students *(Undergraduate/Scholarship)* [9614]
TaskEasy Scholarships for Future Entrepreneurs *(Undergraduate/Scholarship)* [9646]
The Ed Tayter Outstanding Citizen Scholarships *(Undergraduate/Scholarship)* [8238]
TechChecks Business Leadership Scholarships *(Undergraduate/Scholarship)* [9650]
TFAS Congressional Scholarship Awards *(Undergraduate/Award, Scholarship)* [4309]
Toyota/TELACU Scholarships *(Undergraduate/Scholarship)* [9661]
Jacki Tuckfield Memorial Graduate Business Scholarship Fund *(Doctorate, Graduate, Master's/Scholarship)* [6453]
UAA College of Business and Public Policy Scholar-

ships *(Graduate, Undergraduate/Scholarship)* [10078]
Undergraduate/Graduate Scholarships *(Undergraduate, Graduate/Scholarship)* [5315]
Martin Walmsley Fellowships for Technological Entrepreneurship *(Graduate/Fellowship)* [7627]
Washington University Law School Chancellor's Graduate Fellowships *(Advanced Professional/Fellowship)* [10476]
Washington University Law School Olin Fellowships for Women *(Advanced Professional/Fellowship)* [10477]
Wells Fargo Career Scholarship *(Undergraduate/Scholarship)* [10085]
Jerry Wheeler Scholarships *(Undergraduate/Scholarship)* [9377]
Bradford White Corporation Scholarships *(Undergraduate/Scholarship)* [8165]
Wilkinson and Company LLP Scholarships *(Undergraduate/Scholarship)* [10559]
Women In Defense HORIZONS Scholarships *(Graduate, Undergraduate/Scholarship)* [10636]
Xavier University Williams Scholarships *(Undergraduate/Scholarship)* [10735]

Business administration

AACE International Competitive Scholarships *(Undergraduate/Scholarship)* [14]
AAUW Selected Professions Fellowships *(Graduate, Master's, Doctorate/Fellowship)* [22]
African American Network - Carolinas Scholarship Fund *(Undergraduate/Scholarship)* [4174]
American Association of University Women Selected Professions Fellowships *(Other/Fellowship)* [603]
American Society of Military Comptrollers National Scholarship Program *(Undergraduate/Scholarship)* [1375]
ASAC-CJAS PhD Research Grant Awards *(Doctorate/Grant)* [73]
Lawrence Bayer Business Administration Scholarships *(Undergraduate/Scholarship)* [10008]
Mark A. Beltz Scholarship *(Graduate, Undergraduate/Scholarship)* [10052]
Bill and Nell Biggs Scholarships *(Undergraduate/Scholarship)* [10088]
Wes Burton Memorial Scholarships *(Undergraduate/Scholarship)* [10574]
Rick Crane Group Real Estate Scholarship Fund *(Undergraduate/Scholarship)* [6023]
CTRF Scholarships for Graduate Study in Transportation *(Graduate/Scholarship)* [2764]
GFOA Minorities in Government Finance Scholarship *(Graduate, Undergraduate/Scholarship)* [4502]
Geordie Hilton Academic Scholarships *(Undergraduate/Scholarship)* [4480]
Conrad N. Hilton Scholarships *(Undergraduate/Scholarship)* [4414]
IPMA-HR Graduate Study Fellowships *(Graduate, Master's/Fellowship)* [5376]
ISU Networks Scholarships College of Business *(Undergraduate/Scholarship)* [5122]
Ron LaFreniere Business Administration Scholarship *(Undergraduate/Scholarship)* [8877]
Lazarian Graduate Scholarships *(Graduate/Scholarship)* [1678]
Mary Elizabeth Lockwood Beneventi MBA Scholarship *(Graduate/Scholarship)* [7153]
Native Hawaiian Chamber of Commerce Scholarships *(Graduate, Undergraduate/Scholarship)* [7916]
Osram Sylvania Scholastic Achievement Awards *(Undergraduate/Scholarship)* [3838]
Philips Lighting Continuing Education Awards *(Undergraduate/Scholarship)* [3839]
Dan M. Reichard, Jr. Scholarships *(Undergraduate, Graduate/Scholarship)* [1168]
Ritchie-Jennings Memorial Scholarships *(Undergraduate, Graduate/Scholarship)* [1923]
Royal Bank Scholarships *(Undergraduate, Master's/Scholarship)* [2290]
Schneider Electric Student Merit Awards *(Undergraduate/Scholarship)* [3841]
Snodgrass Scholarships *(Undergraduate/Scholarship)* [10039]

WESCO Student Achievement Awards *(Undergraduate/Scholarship)* [3848]
Urashi Zen Scholarships *(Undergraduate/Scholarship)* [8272]

Business Communications

McAllister Fellowships *(Professional development/Fellowship)* [1867]

Byzantine studies (See also Area and ethnic studies)

Dumbarton Oaks Fellowships *(Doctorate, Graduate/Fellowship)* [3728]
Dumbarton Oaks Junior Fellowships *(Graduate/Fellowship)* [3729]
Dumbarton Oaks Research Library and Collection Bliss Symposium Awards *(Undergraduate, Graduate/Award)* [3730]
Dumbarton Oaks Research Library and Collection Graduate Research Workshops *(Undergraduate, Graduate/Fellowship)* [3731]
Dumbarton Oaks Research Library and Collection One-Month Research Stipends *(Doctorate/Monetary)* [3732]
Dumbarton Oaks Research Library and Collection Post-Baccalaureate Media Fellowships *(Graduate/Fellowship)* [3733]
Dumbarton Oaks Research Library and Collection Project Grants *(Doctorate/Grant)* [3734]
Dumbarton Oaks Research Library and Collection Short-Term Predoctoral Residencies Grants *(Doctorate/Grant)* [3735]
Dumbarton Oaks Research Library and Collection Summer Fellowships *(Graduate/Fellowship)* [3736]
Dumbarton Oaks Research Library and Collection Summer Internships for Harvard Students *(Undergraduate, Graduate/Internship)* [3737]
Dumbarton Oaks Research Library and Collection Post-Doctoral Teaching Fellowships *(Postdoctorate/Fellowship)* [3738]
William R. Tyler Fellowships *(Graduate/Fellowship)* [3740]

Canadian studies (See also Area and ethnic studies)

ALIS Fellowships for Full-time Studies in French *(Undergraduate/Fellowship)* [263]
Canadian Studies Postdoctoral Fellowships *(Postdoctorate/Fellowship)* [3398]
Jane Glassco Northern Fellowships *(Professional development/Fellowship)* [4500]
International Council for Canadian Studies Graduate Student Scholarships *(Graduate/Scholarship)* [3399]
Shastri Scholar Travel Subsidy Grants (SSTSG) *(Graduate, Professional development/Grant)* [8857]
W. Garfield Weston Awards for Northern Research *(Graduate, Postdoctorate/Fellowship)* [10421]

Cancer (See Oncology)

Cardiology (See Medicine, Cardiology)

Career planning

Allman Medical Scholarship *(Undergraduate/Scholarship)* [6555]
Miss America Community Service Scholarship *(Undergraduate/Scholarship)* [6557]
Miss America Quality of Life Awards *(Undergraduate/Scholarship)* [6558]

Caricature (See Art, Caricatures and cartoons)

Cartography/Surveying

Connecticut Association of Land Surveyors Memorial Scholarships *(Undergraduate/Scholarship)* [3358]
Arthur and Janet Holzheimer Fellowship in the History of Cartography *(Postdoctorate, Doctorate/Fellowship)* [7411]
MALSCE Memorial Scholarships *(Undergraduate/Scholarship)* [6306]
Marek Nawrot Memorial Scholarships *(Undergraduate/Scholarship)* [8586]
Norman Nicholson Scholarships *(Undergraduate/Scholarship)* [2607]
NSPS Scholarships *(Undergraduate/Scholarship)* [7175]
Pennsylvania Land Surveyors Foundation Scholarships *(Undergraduate/Scholarship)* [7941]

Cartooning (See Art, Caricatures and cartoons)

Cave studies

Cave Conservancy Foundation Graduate and Undergraduate Fellowships *(Doctorate, Graduate, Undergraduate/Fellowship)* [2823]
CCF Academic Fellowships in Karst Studies - Graduate *(Master's, Doctorate/Fellowship)* [2820]
CCF Academic Fellowships in Karst Studies - Undegraduate *(Undergraduate/Fellowship)* [2821]
NSS Sara Corrie Memorial Grants *(Professional development/Grant)* [7181]
NSS Conservation Grants *(Advanced Professional/Grant)* [7182]
NSS Education Grants *(Undergraduate/Grant)* [7183]
Ralph W. Stone Graduate Fellowships *(Graduate/Fellowship, Grant)* [7184]

Central European studies (See European studies)

Chemical engineering (See Engineering, Chemical)

Chemistry (See also Biochemistry; Electrochemistry)

ACS Rubber Division Undergraduate Scholarships *(Undergraduate/Scholarship)* [666]
AESF Foundation Scholarships *(Undergraduate, Graduate/Scholarship)* [6796]
AIST Ohio Valley Chapter Scholarships *(Undergraduate/Scholarship)* [1994]
B.O.G. Pest Control Scholarship Funds *(Undergraduate, Graduate/Scholarship)* [2323]
Burroughs Wellcome Fund Collaborative Research Travel Grants (CRTG) *(Doctorate, Postdoctorate, Professional development/Grant)* [2413]
Career Awards at the Scientific Interface (CASI) *(Doctorate, Postdoctorate, Advanced Professional, Professional development/Grant)* [2416]
Julian E. Carnes Scholarship Fund *(Undergraduate/Scholarship)* [4183]
Chemical Heritage Foundation Travel Grants (CHF) *(All/Grant)* [2891]
CNS-UCSB Graduate Fellowships for Science and Engineering *(Postdoctorate/Fellowship)* [10127]
D&A Florida Scholarships *(Undergraduate/Scholarship)* [9425]
DEPS Graduate Scholarship Program *(Graduate/Scholarship)* [3624]
William Donald Dixon Research Grants *(Graduate, Undergraduate, Advanced Professional/Grant)* [2665]
DOE Computational Science Graduate Fellowships (DOE CSGF) *(Doctorate, Graduate/Fellowship)* [5887]

Robert E. Dougherty Scholarships (*Undergraduate, Postgraduate/Scholarship*) [3339]
Dow Chemical Company Fellowships (*Graduate/Fellowship*) [7085]
E.I. DuPont Graduate Fellowship (*Graduate/Fellowship*) [7086]
William Robert Findley Graduate Chemistry Scholarship (*Graduate/Scholarship*) [7151]
Ardell French Memorial Scholarship (*Undergraduate/Scholarship*) [10059]
Getty Postdoctoral Fellowships in Conservation Science (*Postdoctorate/Fellowship*) [4410]
Helm Family Scholarships (*Undergraduate/Scholarship*) [8706]
Indspire Health Careers Bursary and Scholarships (*Graduate, Undergraduate/Scholarship*) [5132]
Jeffress Trust Awards Program in Interdisciplinary Research (*Professional development/Award*) [4816]
AACT John Kitt Memorial Scholarship (*Undergraduate/Scholarship*) [477]
Larson Aquatic Research Support Scholarships (LARS) (*Graduate/Scholarship*) [1490]
Imelda "Mel" and Ralph LeMar Scholarship (*Undergraduate/Scholarship*) [3330]
Dolphus E. Milligan Graduate Fellowships (*Graduate/Fellowship*) [7087]
National GEM Consortium - PhD Science Fellowships (*Doctorate, Graduate/Fellowship*) [6969]
NDSEG Fellowships (*Graduate/Fellowship*) [6911]
NOBCChE Procter and Gamble Fellowships (*Graduate/Fellowship*) [7088]
NPSC Fellowships (*Graduate/Fellowship*) [7098]
Lendon N. Pridgen, GlaxoSmithKline - NOBCChE Fellowships (*Graduate/Fellowship*) [7089]
Clifford G. Shull Fellowships (*Postdoctorate/Fellowship*) [9909]
Sloan Research Fellowships (*Doctorate/Fellowship*) [8988]
Eastman Kodak Dr. Theophilus Sorrell Fellowships (*Graduate/Fellowship*) [7090]
Graduate Fellowship Program - Peter Verhofstadt Fellowships (*Graduate/Fellowship*) [8836]
Xavier University Departmental Scholarships (*Undergraduate/Scholarship*) [10729]
Xerox Technical Minority Scholarships (*Graduate, Undergraduate/Scholarship*) [10737]

Child care
Alberta Child Care Association Professional Development Grants (*Professional development/Grant*) [232]
HACU/Denny's Hungry for Education Scholarships (*Undergraduate, Graduate/Scholarship*) [4883]
Pilot Project Award (*Professional development/Award, Grant*) [9239]

Child development
AACPDM Student Scholarships (*Professional development/Scholarship*) [399]
Depression and ADHD Fellowships (*Postdoctorate/Fellowship*) [5840]
Huenefeld/Denton Scholarships (*Undergraduate/Scholarship*) [3588]
Mister Rogers Memorial Scholarship (*Graduate, Master's, Doctorate/Scholarship*) [47]

Chinese studies (See also Area and ethnic studies)
Comparative Perspectives on Chinese Culture and Society Grants (*Doctorate/Grant*) [739]
Louise Wallace Hackney Fellowships for the Study of Chinese Art (*Doctorate, Postdoctorate/Fellowship*) [1058]

Chiropractic medicine (See Medicine, Chiropractic)

Choreography (See also Dance)
Jerome Robbins Bogliasco Fellowships in Dance (*Professional development/Fellowship*) [2329]

Christian education
Lewis B. Barber Memorial Scholarships (*Undergraduate/Scholarship*) [9419]
Beatitudes Fellowships (*Professional development/Fellowship*) [2208]
Chester H. Bruce Memorial Scholarships (*Undergraduate/Scholarship*) [7816]
Pamfil and Maria Bujea Family Orthodox Christian Seminarian Scholarships (*Undergraduate/Scholarship*) [1225]
Doris W. Frey Memorial Scholarships (*Undergraduate, Graduate/Scholarship*) [9430]
Louisville Institute Dissertation Fellowships (*Doctorate/Fellowship*) [6128]
Louisville Institute First Book Grants for Minority Scholars (*Doctorate/Grant*) [6129]
Louisville Institute Project Grant for Researchers (*Doctorate/Grant*) [6130]
Louisville Institute Sabbatical Grants for Researchers (*Doctorate/Grant*) [6131]

Church occupations (See Religion)

Cinema
William A. Fraker Student Heritage Awards (*Graduate, Undergraduate/Award*) [1256]
Gerald Pratley Award (*Doctorate, Graduate/Award*) [1884]

Civil engineering (See Engineering, Civil)

Civil rights
Kalmen Kaplansky Scholarships in Economic and Social Rights (*Graduate/Scholarship*) [3657]
MALDEF Dream Act Student Activist Scholarships (*Undergraduate, Graduate/Scholarship*) [6446]
NARAL Pro-Choice America Development Internships (*Undergraduate, Graduate, Professional development/Internship*) [6659]
NARAL Pro-Choice America Policy Internships (*Professional development/Internship*) [6660]
Minoru Yasui Memorial Scholarships (*Graduate, Master's, Doctorate/Scholarship*) [5560]

Classical music (See Music, Classical)

Classical studies (See also Area and ethnic studies)
American Philological Association Minority Student Summer Fellowships (*Undergraduate/Fellowship*) [9106]
Desmond Conacher Scholarships (*Graduate/Scholarship*) [9071]
Glenn Knudsvig Memorial Scholarships (*Graduate, Undergraduate/Scholarship*) [679]
Arthur Patch McKinlay Scholarships (*Graduate, Undergraduate/Scholarship*) [680]
Ed Phinney Commemorative Scholarships (*Graduate, Undergraduate/Scholarship*) [681]
Clair Shirey Scholarships (*Undergraduate/Scholarship*) [10037]
Xavier University Departmental Scholarships (*Undergraduate/Scholarship*) [10729]

Clinical laboratory sciences
AACPDM Transformative Practice Grants (*Professional development/Grant*) [400]
Alpha Mu Tau Undergraduate Scholarships (*Undergraduate/Scholarship*) [1258]
Lawrence Livermore National Laboratory Fellowships (*Doctorate/Fellowship*) [9905]
Dorothy Morrison Undergraduate Scholarships (*Undergraduate/Scholarship*) [1260]
Siemens-ASCP Scholarship (*Undergraduate/Scholarship*) [1263]

Clinical sciences (See Biological and clinical sciences)

Commercial design (See Design)

Communications
AAFSW College Merit Scholarship (*College, Undergraduate/Scholarship*) [1820]
AFCEA Scholarship for Working Professionals (*Undergraduate, Graduate/Scholarship*) [86]
Afghanistan and Iraq War Veterans Scholarship (*Undergraduate/Scholarship*) [88]
Phillip Alston Scholarships (*Undergraduate/Scholarship*) [10213]
American Speech Language Hearing Foundation Clinical Research Grants (*Doctorate/Grant*) [1450]
American Speech Language Hearing Foundation Endowed Scholarships (*Graduate, Master's, Doctorate/Scholarship*) [1451]
American Speech Language Hearing Foundation General Scholarships (*Graduate, Master's, Doctorate/Scholarship*) [1452]
American Speech Language Hearing Foundation Scholarships for International Students (*Graduate, Master's, Doctorate/Scholarship*) [1453]
American Speech Language Hearing Foundation Scholarships for Minority Students (*Graduate, Master's, Doctorate/Scholarship*) [1454]
APC High School Scholarship Awards (*Undergraduate/Scholarship*) [78]
APSA Congressional Fellowship for Communications Scholars and Journalists (*Advanced Professional, Professional development/Fellowship*) [1108]
ARRLF Mississippi Scholarships (*Undergraduate/Scholarship*) [1725]
ASHFoundation New Century Scholars Doctoral Scholarships (*Doctorate/Scholarship*) [1455]
ASHFoundation New Century Scholars Research Grants (*Doctorate/Grant*) [1456]
ASHFoundation Speech Science Research Grants (*Doctorate/Grant*) [1459]
ASHFoundation Student Research Grants in Audiology (*Doctorate/Grant*) [1460]
ASHFoundation Student Research Grants in Early Childhood Language Development (*Doctorate, Master's/Grant*) [1461]
Francis Warren Baker Memorial Scholarships (*Undergraduate/Scholarship*) [8910]
Jim Batten Community Newspaper Internships (*Undergraduate/Internship*) [10215]
Beaverbrook Media at McGill Student Paper Prize (*Graduate/Prize*) [2615]
Margaret Blanchard Dissertation Support Fund (*Graduate/Grant*) [10216]
Tom Bost Scholarships (*Undergraduate/Scholarship*) [10217]
Lt. General Douglas D. Buchholz Memorial Scholarship (*Undergraduate/Scholarship*) [89]
CEJIL Communications Internships (*Undergraduate, Graduate/Internship*) [2860]
George H. Clinton Scholarship Fund (*Undergraduate/Scholarship*) [7818]
Ardis Cohoon Scholarships (*Undergraduate/Scholarship*) [10220]
Irving W. Cook WA0CGS Scholarships (*Undergraduate/Scholarship*) [1735]
Charles Clarke Cordle Memorial Scholarships (*Undergraduate/Scholarship*) [1736]
Kathryn M. Cronin Scholarships (*Undergraduate/Scholarship*) [10222]
Don and Barbara Curtis Excellence Fund for Extracurricular Student Activities (*Undergraduate/Grant*) [10223]
James Davis Scholarships (*Undergraduate/Scholarship*) [10224]
Disabled War Veterans Scholarships (*Undergraduate/Scholarship*) [90]
Robert Winchester Dodson Scholarships (*Under-

COMMUNICATIONS TECHNOLOGIES

graduate/Scholarship) [10225]
Harold K. Douthit Regional Scholarships (Undergraduate/Scholarship) [7576]
ECA Applied Urban Communication Research Grants (Professional development/Grant) [3768]
ECA Centennial Scholarships (Master's, Doctorate/Scholarship) [3769]
Palmer Farley Memorial Scholarships (Graduate/Scholarship) [4696]
The Judy Felt Memorial Volunteerism Scholarship (College, Undergraduate/Scholarship) [1821]
Reese Felts Scholarships (Undergraduate/Scholarship) [10226]
Charles N. Fisher Memorial Scholarships (Undergraduate/Scholarship) [1738]
Ameel J. Fisher Scholarships (Undergraduate/Scholarship) [10227]
Florida Outdoor Writers Association Scholarships (Undergraduate/Scholarship) [4104]
Paul B. and Aline Flynn Scholarships (Undergraduate/Scholarship) [9429]
Kays Gary Scholarships (Undergraduate/Scholarship) [10229]
Stephen Gates Scholarships (Undergraduate/Scholarship) [10230]
Joy Gibson Scholarships (Undergraduate/Scholarship) [10231]
Keith Gilmore Foundation - Diploma Scholarships (Other/Scholarship) [4423]
Keith Gilmore Foundation - Postgraduate Scholarships (Postgraduate/Scholarship) [4424]
Keith Gilmore Foundation - Undergraduate Scholarships (Undergraduate/Scholarship) [4425]
GLAAD Communications/PR Internships - New York (Undergraduate, Graduate/Internship) [4434]
GLAAD Spanish-Language and Latino Media Internships - Los Angeles (Undergraduate, Graduate/Internship) [4436]
GLAAD Youth Issues Internships - New York (Undergraduate, Graduate/Internship) [4437]
Paul and Helen L. Grauer Scholarships (Undergraduate/Scholarship) [1740]
Howard L. Green Scholarships (Undergraduate/Scholarship) [7317]
HAESF Professional Internship Program (Doctorate/Internship) [5009]
Charles Hauser Scholarships (Undergraduate/Scholarship) [10232]
Paul Green Houston Scholarships (Undergraduate/Scholarship) [10233]
James F. Hurley III Bicentennial Merit Scholarships (Undergraduate/Scholarship) [10234]
International Foodservice Editorial Council Scholarships (Graduate, Undergraduate/Scholarship) [5331]
Iowa Journalism Institute Scholarships (Undergraduate/Scholarship) [5473]
Harriet Irsay Scholarships (Graduate, Undergraduate/Scholarship) [927]
Edward Jackson International Scholarships (Undergraduate/Scholarship) [10235]
Glenn Keever Scholarships (Undergraduate/Scholarship) [10236]
Dr. James L. Lawson Memorial Scholarships (Undergraduate/Scholarship) [1745]
Mackey-Byars Scholarships for Communication Excellence (Undergraduate/Scholarship) [10237]
Raleigh Mann Scholarships (Undergraduate/Scholarship) [10238]
Mas Family Scholarships (Graduate, Undergraduate/Scholarship) [6304]
Fred R. McDaniel Memorial Scholarships (Undergraduate/Scholarship) [1746]
Edward Heywood Megson Scholarships (Undergraduate/Scholarship) [10243]
MillerCoors National Scholarships (Undergraduate/Scholarship) [69]
Quincy Sharpe Mills Memorial Scholarships (Undergraduate/Scholarship) [10244]
New York Women in Communications, Inc. Foundation Scholarships (Graduate, Undergraduate/Scholarship) [7406]
NHFA Scholarships (Graduate/Scholarship) [6998]
Ohio Newspaper Association Minority Scholarships (Undergraduate/Scholarship) [7577]
ONWA Annual Scholarships (Undergraduate/Scholarship) [7579]
Chuck Pezzano Scholarships (Undergraduate/Scholarship) [5286]
Stephen D. Pisinski Memorial Scholarships (Undergraduate/Scholarship) [8376]
Robert Pittman Scholarships-Internships (Undergraduate/Scholarship, Internship) [10245]
Erwin Potts Scholarships (Undergraduate/Scholarship) [10246]
Print and Graphics Scholarship Foundation Awards (PGSF-GATF) (Graduate, Undergraduate/Scholarship, Fellowship) [8282]
PRSA Diversity Multicultural Scholarships (Undergraduate/Scholarship) [8378]
Peter DeWitt Pruden and Phyliss Harrill Pruden Scholarships (Undergraduate/Scholarship) [10247]
Bob Quincy Scholarships (Undergraduate/Scholarship) [10248]
Marjorie Usher Ragan Scholarships (Undergraduate/Scholarship) [10249]
Gertrude J. Robinson Book Prize (Professional development/Prize) [2616]
William C. Rogers Scholarships (Undergraduate/Scholarship) [4389]
Richard J. Roth Journalism Fellowships (Graduate/Fellowship) [7369]
Bert Saperstein Communication Scholarships (Undergraduate/Scholarship) [8758]
Soros Justice Media Fellowships - Track II (Professional development/Fellowship) [7667]
Soros Justice Media Fellowships - Track I (Professional development/Fellowship) [7666]
Sports Internships - Los Angeles (Undergraduate, Graduate/Internship) [4440]
Kirk Sutlive Scholarships (Undergraduate/Scholarship) [4390]
Hal Tanner Sr. Scholarships (Undergraduate/Scholarship) [10252]
TCAdvance Scholarships (Undergraduate/Scholarship) [9814]
Jim and Pat Thacker Sports Communication Internships (Undergraduate/Grant) [10253]
Trans Issues Internships - New York (Undergraduate, Graduate/Internship) [4441]
Tucker Family Scholarships (Undergraduate/Scholarship) [10254]
Turf and Ornamental Communicators Association Scholarship Program (Undergraduate/Scholarship) [9809]
USGLC Internships - Communications (Undergraduate, Doctorate/Internship) [9949]
David Julian Wichard Scholarships (Undergraduate/Scholarship) [10255]
The L. Phil and Alice J. Wicker Scholarship (Undergraduate/Scholarship) [1763]
Tom Wicker Scholarships (Graduate/Scholarship) [10256]
Glenn Wilson Broadcast Journalism Scholarships (Undergraduate/Scholarship) [7873]
WTVD Endowment Scholarships (Undergraduate/Scholarship) [10257]

Communications technologies

Document Management and Graphic Communications Industry Scholarships (Undergraduate/Scholarship) [3852]
OAS Scholarships for Professional Development - Disaster Communications Management (Professional development/Scholarship) [7723]
OAS Scholarships for Professional Development - Satellite Communications (Professional development/Scholarship) [7725]

Community leadership (See Leadership, Institutional and community)

Computer and information sciences

AAUW Selected Professions Fellowships (Graduate, Master's, Doctorate/Fellowship) [22]
Aerospace Corporation Science and Engineering Student Scholarships (Undergraduate, Graduate/Scholarship) [95]
AFCEA Cyber Studies and Intelligence Scholarships (Undergraduate, Graduate/Scholarship) [85]
African American Network - Carolinas Scholarship Fund (Undergraduate/Scholarship) [4174]
Air Products and Chemicals, Inc. Scholarships (Undergraduate/Scholarship) [1975]
AISES Intel Scholarships (Graduate, Undergraduate/Scholarship) [887]
AIST Ohio Valley Chapter Scholarships (Undergraduate/Scholarship) [1994]
Stephanie Ali Memorial Scholarships (Undergraduate/Scholarship) [10279]
American Association of University Women Selected Professions Fellowships (Other/Fellowship) [603]
Arlyn Scales Awards for Science and Technology (Undergraduate/Scholarship) [3035]
ARRL Foundation PHD Scholarships (Undergraduate/Scholarship) [1724]
Dr. Anita Borg Memorial Scholarships - USA (Graduate, Undergraduate/Scholarship) [4493]
William (Billbo) Boston/Harold Knopp Scholarship (Undergraduate/Scholarship) [7815]
Kathi Bowles Scholarships for Women in Technology (Undergraduate, Graduate/Scholarship) [2091]
AFCEA San Diego Buck Bragunier Leadership Scholarship (Undergraduate/Scholarship) [1667]
Richard A. Brown Student Scholarships (Undergraduate/Scholarship) [9691]
Burroughs Wellcome Fund Collaborative Research Travel Grants (CRTG) (Doctorate, Postdoctorate, Professional development/Grant) [2413]
Wes Burton Memorial Scholarships (Undergraduate/Scholarship) [10574]
Career Awards at the Scientific Interface (CASI) (Doctorate, Postdoctorate, Advanced Professional, Professional development/Grant) [2416]
Julian E. Carnes Scholarship Fund (Undergraduate/Scholarship) [4183]
CDC Public Health Informatics Fellowships (Professional development, Master's, Graduate/Fellowship) [9919]
CERT College Scholarships (Graduate, Undergraduate/Scholarship) [3435]
Chambersburg/Fannett-Metal School District Scholarship Fund (Undergraduate/Scholarship) [4234]
China Google PhD Fellowships (Doctorate/Fellowship) [4494]
D&A Florida Scholarships (Undergraduate/Scholarship) [9425]
Document Management and Graphic Communications Industry Scholarships (Undergraduate/Scholarship) [3852]
DOE Computational Science Graduate Fellowships (DOE CSGF) (Doctorate, Graduate/Fellowship) [5887]
EAPSI Fellowships (Doctorate, Graduate/Fellowship) [7124]
ESA Foundation Scholarship Program (Undergraduate/Scholarship) [3878]
Facebook Fellowships Program (Doctorate/Fellowship) [3950]
Frank Fong Scholarships (Undergraduate/Scholarship) [9076]
William R. Goldfarb Memorial Scholarships (Undergraduate/Scholarship) [1739]
Google-American Indian Science and Engineering Society Scholarships (Graduate, Undergraduate/Scholarship) [4495]
Google European Doctoral Fellowships (Doctorate/Fellowship) [4496]
Google Hispanic College Fund Scholarships (Graduate, Undergraduate/Scholarship) [4497]
Google US/Canada PhD Fellowships (Graduate, Doctorate/Fellowship) [4498]
Jimmy Guild Memorial Scholarships (Undergraduate/Scholarship) [6030]
Helm Family Scholarships (Undergraduate/Scholarship) [8706]
IBEA Undergraduate Scholarships (Undergraduate/Scholarship) [5057]
Influenster Code Like a Girl Scholarships (Undergraduate, Graduate/Scholarship) [5140]

Internet Society Fellowships to the IETF *(Doctorate, Master's/Fellowship)* [5460]
(ISC)2 Foundation Information Security Scholarships *(Graduate, Undergraduate/Scholarship)* [5348]
Jeffress Trust Awards Program in Interdisciplinary Research *(Professional development/Award)* [4816]
Robert E. Knight Professional Scholarships *(Graduate/Scholarship)* [9692]
Malayalee Engineers Association Scholarships *(Undergraduate/Fellowship)* [6225]
John Mazurek Memorial-Morgex Insurance Scholarship *(Other/Scholarship)* [296]
Microsoft Research Graduate Women's Scholarships *(Graduate/Scholarship)* [6506]
Microsoft Research PhD Fellowships *(Doctorate/Fellowship)* [6507]
MillerCoors Engineering and Sciences Scholarships *(Undergraduate/Scholarship)* [68]
National GEM Consortium - PhD Science Fellowships *(Doctorate, Graduate/Fellowship)* [6969]
NDSEG Fellowships *(Graduate/Fellowship)* [6911]
Dr. Ezra Nesbeth Scholarships *(Undergraduate/Scholarship)* [5526]
Edsel Newman Scholarships *(Undergraduate/Scholarship)* [6065]
Northrop Grumman Engineering Scholarships *(Undergraduate/Scholarship)* [7527]
NPSC Fellowships *(Graduate/Fellowship)* [7098]
NSA Mathematics and Computer Science Student Scholarships *(Undergraduate, Graduate, Doctorate/Scholarship)* [108]
NVIDIA Graduate Fellowships *(Graduate/Fellowship)* [7566]
Ray, NORP and Katie, WOKTE Pautz Scholarships *(Undergraduate/Scholarship)* [1750]
John Riddick Student Grants *(Graduate/Grant)* [7446]
Faye Lynn Roberts Educational Scholarships *(Undergraduate, Graduate/Scholarship)* [9445]
Paul and Ellen Ruckes Scholarships *(Graduate, Undergraduate/Scholarship)* [823]
John M. and Mary A. Shanley Memorial Scholarships *(Undergraduate, Graduate/Scholarship)* [9448]
Everett Oscar Shimp Memorial Scholarships *(Undergraduate/Scholarship)* [7862]
Ralph W. Shrader Diversity Scholarship *(Graduate/Scholarship)* [91]
Sloan Research Fellowships *(Doctorate/Fellowship)* [8988]
Snodgrass Scholarships *(Undergraduate/Scholarship)* [10039]
Henry D. and Ruth G. Swartz Family Scholarship Fund *(Undergraduate/Scholarship)* [4550]
SWE Scholarships *(Undergraduate, Graduate/Scholarship)* [9329]
Syncrude/Athabasca University Aboriginal Scholarships *(Undergraduate/Scholarship)* [9627]
Tech Mastery Scholarships *(Undergraduate/Scholarship)* [8551]
Texas Computer Education Association Professional Educator Grants *(Other/Grant)* [9693]
University of Toronto Accenture Scholarships *(Undergraduate/Scholarship)* [10297]
UPE Scholarship Awards *(Graduate, Undergraduate/Scholarship)* [10342]
Edwin F. Wiegand Science and Technology Scholarships *(Undergraduate/Scholarship)* [8370]
Women In Defense HORIZONS Scholarships *(Graduate, Undergraduate/Scholarship)* [10636]
Frank and Betty Woodhams Memorial Scholarships *(Undergraduate/Scholarship)* [6422]
Xerox Technical Minority Scholarships *(Graduate, Undergraduate/Scholarship)* [10737]
Ralph Yetka Memorial Scholarships *(Undergraduate/Scholarship)* [10045]
Urashi Zen Scholarships *(Undergraduate/Scholarship)* [8272]

Conservation of natural resources

American Society of Mining and Reclamation Memorial Scholarships *(Undergraduate/Scholarship, Recognition)* [1377]
Gloria Barron Wilderness Society Scholarship *(Graduate/Scholarship)* [10557]
CCF Academic Fellowships in Karst Studies - Undegraduate *(Undergraduate/Fellowship)* [2821]
Doris Duke Conservation Fellows Program *(Master's/Fellowship)* [10678]
Kathryn Fuller Science for Nature Post-Doctoral Fellowships *(Graduate, Postdoctorate/Fellowship)* [10707]
Getty Conservation Guest Scholar Grants *(Professional development/Grant)* [4406]
Getty Postdoctoral Fellowships in Conservation Science *(Postdoctorate/Fellowship)* [4410]
National Geographic Young Explorers Grants *(Advanced Professional/Grant)* [6974]
NCEA Postdoctoral Research Program *(Postdoctorate, Advanced Professional, Professional development/Fellowship)* [9943]
Paul W. Rodgers Scholarship *(Undergraduate, Master's, Doctorate/Scholarship)* [5261]
Kenneth W. Russell Memorial Fellowships *(Undergraduate, Graduate/Fellowship)* [661]
WDHOF Undergraduate Scholarships in Marine Conservation *(Undergraduate/Scholarship)* [10640]
Welder Wildlife Foundation Fellowships *(Graduate, Master's, Doctorate/Fellowship)* [10510]
Worcester County Conservation District Annual Scholarships Program *(Undergraduate/Scholarship)* [10687]

Construction

AACE International Competitive Scholarships *(Undergraduate/Scholarship)* [14]
ACI BASF Construction Chemicals Student Fellowships *(Graduate, Undergraduate/Fellowship)* [701]
ACI President's Fellowships *(Doctorate, Master's/Fellowship)* [704]
Herb Adrian Memorial Scholarship Fund *(Undergraduate/Scholarship)* [4173]
AGC Foundation Outstanding Educator Awards *(Other/Award)* [1812]
American Society of Safety Engineers Construction Safety Scholarships *(Undergraduate/Scholarship)* [1407]
APS/ASU Scholarships *(Undergraduate/Scholarship)* [8139]
ASA Graduate Scholarships *(Graduate/Scholarship)* [1243]
Associated General Contractors of Connecticut Scholarships *(Undergraduate/Scholarship)* [3365]
ACI Elmer Baker Student Fellowships *(Undergraduate, Graduate/Fellowship)* [707]
ACI Baker Student Fellowships *(Undergraduate, Graduate/Fellowship)* [706]
Bechtel Group Foundation Scholarships for Safety & Health *(Undergraduate/Scholarship)* [1409]
O.J. Beck, Jr. Memorial Scholarships *(Undergraduate/Scholarship)* [3087]
Carpenters' Company Scholarships *(Undergraduate/Scholarship)* [2801]
Darooge Family Scholarships *(Undergraduate/Scholarship)* [4586]
Eastern Shore Building Industry Association Scholarships *(Undergraduate/Scholarship)* [3174]
Lee S. Evans/National Housing Endowment Scholarships *(Undergraduate, Graduate/Scholarship)* [7003]
Huber Engineered Woods Product Evaluation Scholarships *(Graduate/Scholarship)* [3977]
International Code Council Scholarships *(Graduate/Scholarship)* [3978]
Melvin Kruger Endowed Scholarships *(Graduate, Undergraduate/Scholarship)* [8644]
National Association of Women in Construction Construction Trades Scholarships *(Undergraduate/Scholarship)* [6800]
National Association of Women in Construction Founders Undergraduate Scholarships *(Undergraduate/Scholarship)* [6801]
Nixon Family Scholarship Fund *(Undergraduate, High School/Scholarship)* [10506]
ACI Charles Pankow Foundation ACI Student Fellowships *(Graduate, Undergraduate/Fellowship)* [710]
Pardee Community Building Scholarships *(Undergraduate/Scholarship)* [8359]
Pipe Line Contractors Association of Canada Student Bursary *(Undergraduate, Postgraduate/Scholarship)* [8142]
Portland Cement Association Scholarships *(Graduate/Scholarship)* [3980]
Resilience Action Fund Scholarships *(Graduate/Scholarship)* [3981]
Herman J. Smith Scholarships *(Undergraduate, Graduate/Scholarship)* [7004]
United States Society on Dams Scholarships *(Graduate, Undergraduate/Scholarship)* [9971]
Vectorworks Design Scholarships *(Undergraduate, Graduate/Scholarship, Prize)* [10367]
Ted G. Wilson Memorial Scholarships *(Undergraduate/Scholarship)* [8288]

Consulting

PON Graduate Student Grants *(Graduate/Grant)* [4789]
PON Next Generation Grants *(Doctorate, Postdoctorate/Grant)* [4790]
PON Summer Fellowships *(Graduate/Fellowship)* [4791]

Consumer affairs

Geraldine Clewell Fellowships - Doctoral Student *(Graduate/Fellowship)* [8086]
Geraldine Clewell Fellowships - Masteral *(Graduate/Fellowship)* [8087]
Geraldine Clewell Scholarships - Undergraduate *(Undergraduate/Scholarship)* [8088]
Closs/Parnitzke/Clarke Scholarships *(Undergraduate/Scholarship)* [8089]
Jean Dearth Dickerscheid Fellowships *(Graduate/Fellowship)* [8090]
Margaret Drew Alpha Fellowships *(Graduate/Fellowship)* [8091]
Lydia Fohn-Hansen/Lola Hill Memorial Scholarships *(Undergraduate, Graduate/Scholarship)* [10018]
Genevieve Forthun Scholarships *(Undergraduate/Scholarship)* [8092]
Mary Weiking Franken Scholarships *(Undergraduate/Scholarship)* [8093]
Tommie J. Hamner Scholarships *(Undergraduate/Scholarship)* [8094]
Jackman Scholarships *(Undergraduate/Scholarship)* [8095]
Martha Combs Jenkins Scholarships *(Undergraduate/Scholarship)* [8096]
Treva C. Kintner Scholarships *(Undergraduate/Scholarship)* [8097]
Phi Upsilon Omicron Candle Fellowships *(Graduate/Fellowship)* [8098]
Phi Upsilon Omicron Challenge Scholarships *(Undergraduate/Scholarship)* [8099]
Phi Upsilon Omicron Diamond Anniversary Fellowships *(Graduate/Fellowship)* [8100]
Phi Upsilon Omicron Founders Fellowships *(Graduate/Fellowship)* [8101]
Phi Upsilon Omicron Golden Anniversary Scholarships *(Undergraduate/Scholarship)* [8102]
Phi Upsilon Omicron Past Presidents Scholarships *(Undergraduate/Scholarship)* [8103]
Phi Upsilon Omicron Presidents Research Fellowships *(Graduate/Fellowship)* [8104]
Nell Bryant Robinson Scholarships *(Undergraduate/Scholarship)* [8105]
Lucile Rust Scholarships *(Undergraduate/Scholarship)* [8106]
Margaret Jerome Sampson Scholarships *(Undergraduate/Scholarship)* [8107]
Lillian P. Schoephoerster Scholarships *(Undergraduate/Scholarship)* [8108]

Cooley's anemia
Vern Parish *(Graduate, Undergraduate/Scholarship)* [964]

Cosmetology
Melissa Eleanor Ernest Scholarships *(Undergraduate/Scholarship)* [5503]
Sue Fleming Memorial Scholarships *(Undergraduate/Scholarship)* [2440]
Joe Francis Haircare Scholarships *(Undergraduate/Scholarship)* [4289]
Helen F. "Jerri" Rand Memorial Scholarships *(Undergraduate, Vocational/Occupational/Scholarship)* [3323]
Sally Beauty Scholarships for High School Graduates *(Undergraduate/Scholarship)* [8286]
Salon Supply Store Cosmetology Scholarships *(Undergraduate/Scholarship)* [8678]
H. Wayne Van Agtmael Cosmetology Scholarship Fund *(Undergraduate/Scholarship)* [4551]

Counseling/Guidance
Jane Engelberg Memorial Fellowship *(Professional development/Fellowship)* [7156]
Lullelia W. Harrison Scholarships in Counseling *(Graduate, Undergraduate/Scholarship)* [10815]
Dottie Martin Teacher Scholarships *(Graduate, Undergraduate/Scholarship)* [7464]
NAJA Scholarships *(Graduate/Scholarship)* [6760]
OSCA Graduate Student Scholarship Program *(Graduate/Scholarship)* [7590]
Ross Trust Future School Counselors Essay Competition *(Master's, Doctorate/Award, Prize)* [750]
TCA Outstanding Graduate Student Awards *(Graduate/Award)* [9695]
Colin Wasacase Scholarship *(Undergraduate/Scholarship)* [7659]

Crafts
Joan Auld Scholarships *(Undergraduate/Scholarship)* [3310]
Craft Research Fund Grants *(Other/Grant)* [2845]
EAIA Research Grants *(Other/Grant)* [3748]
Bruce T. and Jackie Mahi Erickson Grant *(Graduate, Undergraduate/Grant)* [7907]
Piscataqua Region Artist Advancement Grants *(Professional development/Grant)* [7305]
Worldstudio AIGA Scholarships *(Graduate, Undergraduate/Scholarship)* [10709]

Creative arts (See Arts)

Creative writing
Jack Kent Cooke Graduate Arts Awards *(Graduate/Award)* [5493]
Dr. Julianne Malveaux Scholarships *(Undergraduate/Scholarship)* [6762]
Milton Postgraduate Fellowships *(Postgraduate/Fellowship)* [5080]
Eleanor M. Wolfson Memorial Scholarship Fund *(Undergraduate/Scholarship)* [4063]

Criminal justice
ACJA-LAE Student Paper Competitions *(Undergraduate, Graduate/Scholarship)* [752]
Affirmative Action Student Scholarship Mini-Grant Travel Awards *(Undergraduate, Master's, Doctorate/Grant)* [30]
American Criminal Justice Association - Lambda Alpha Epsilon Student Scholarships - Graduate Level *(Graduate, Master's, Doctorate/Scholarship)* [753]
American Criminal Justice Association - Lambda Alpha Epsilon Student Scholarships - Upper and Lower Division Levels *(Undergraduate/Scholarship)* [754]
Richard E. Arnason Court Scholarships *(Undergraduate/Scholarship)* [3409]
ASC Graduate Fellowships for Ethnic Minorities *(Doctorate/Fellowship)* [1280]
Officer Brian A. Aselton Memorial Scholarships *(Undergraduate/Scholarship)* [4737]
Robert C. Carson Memorial Bursary *(Undergraduate/Scholarship)* [270]
Gene Carte Student Paper Competition Awards *(Undergraduate, Graduate/Prize)* [1281]
Jorge Espejel Contreras IALEIA Scholarship Award *(Undergraduate/Scholarship)* [5266]
Correctional Education Association Scholarships *(Graduate, Undergraduate/Scholarship)* [3427]
Colonel Richard M. Dawson Highway Patrol Scholarship Fund *(Undergraduate/Scholarship)* [3222]
Libby Deschenes Prize for Applied Research *(Undergraduate/Prize)* [10537]
Thomas J. Drinan Memorial Fellowships *(Undergraduate/Fellowship)* [8434]
Carli Edwards Memorial Scholarships *(Undergraduate/Scholarship)* [8871]
Brian Jimenez Memorial Scholarships *(Undergraduate/Scholarship)* [8483]
Niqui McCown Honor and Memorial Scholarship Fund *(Undergraduate/Scholarship)* [10505]
Richard McGrath Memorial Fund Awards *(Undergraduate/Award)* [755]
Paul R. McLaughlin Fellowship *(Undergraduate/Fellowship)* [8436]
Minnesota Association County Probation Officers Scholarships *(Undergraduate/Scholarship)* [6541]
June Morrison Scholarship Fund *(Undergraduate/Scholarship)* [10538]
National Sheriffs' Association Scholarship Program *(Graduate, Undergraduate/Scholarship)* [7130]
NIJ Visiting Fellowships *(Other/Fellowship)* [7012]
Ottawa Police 150th Anniversary Scholarships *(Undergraduate/Scholarship)* [2347]
Michael Oykhman Criminal Law and Evidence Scholarships *(Juris Doctorate, Advanced Professional/Scholarship)* [6455]
Pi Gamma Mu Scholarships *(Graduate/Scholarship)* [8133]
Ritchie-Jennings Memorial Scholarships *(Undergraduate, Graduate/Scholarship)* [1923]
Soros Justice Advocacy Fellowships - Track II *(Professional development/Fellowship)* [7665]
Soros Justice Advocacy Fellowships - Track I *(Professional development/Fellowship)* [7664]
Soros Justice Media Fellowships - Track II *(Professional development/Fellowship)* [7667]
Soros Justice Media Fellowships - Track I *(Professional development/Fellowship)* [7666]
Tiftickjian Law Firm, P.C. Juvenile Justice Law School Scholarships *(Postgraduate/Scholarship)* [9741]
Emmett H. Turner Scholarships *(Undergraduate/Scholarship)* [3255]
Miki Vohryzek-Bolden Student Paper Competition *(Undergraduate/Prize)* [10539]
W.E.B. Du Bois Fellowships *(Doctorate/Fellowship)* [7013]

Criminology
ASC Graduate Fellowships for Ethnic Minorities *(Doctorate/Fellowship)* [1280]
Canadian Identification Society Essay/Scholarship Awards *(Advanced Professional, Professional development/Prize)* [2664]
Robert C. Carson Memorial Bursary *(Undergraduate/Scholarship)* [270]
Gene Carte Student Paper Competition Awards *(Undergraduate, Graduate/Prize)* [1281]
Libby Deschenes Prize for Applied Research *(Undergraduate/Prize)* [10537]
Edward Foster Awards *(Advanced Professional/Award)* [2666]
FSF Student Travel Grant *(Undergraduate, Graduate/Grant)* [4135]
June Morrison Scholarship Fund *(Undergraduate/Scholarship)* [10538]
Miki Vohryzek-Bolden Student Paper Competition *(Undergraduate/Prize)* [10539]

Criticism (Art, Drama, Literary)
Melba Dawn Chiarenza Scholarship Fund *(Undergraduate/Scholarship)* [10504]
Northwest-Shoals Community College Fine Arts Scholarships - Drama *(Undergraduate/Scholarship)* [7544]
Wendy Y. Wolfson Memorial Scholarship Fund *(Undergraduate/Scholarship)* [4064]

Cross-cultural studies
Edith and Arnold N. Bodtker Grants *(Undergraduate, Graduate/Grant, Internship)* [3522]
IAESTE United States Internships *(Undergraduate/Internship)* [3489]
University of Hawaii at Manoa Japan Travel Bureau Scholarships *(Graduate, Undergraduate/Scholarship)* [10142]

Culinary arts
Alliance of Black Culinarians Scholarships *(Undergraduate/Scholarship)* [8330]
Balestreri/Cutino Scholarships *(Undergraduate/Scholarship)* [757]
Canadian Hospitality Foundation College Entrance Scholarships *(Undergraduate/Scholarship)* [2658]
CANFIT Nutrition, Physical Education and Culinary Arts Scholarships *(Graduate, Undergraduate/Scholarship)* [3167]
Letitia B. Carter Scholarships *(Undergraduate, Advanced Professional/Scholarship)* [8563]
Chaîne des Rôtisseurs Scholarships *(Undergraduate/Scholarship)* [758]
Vickie Clark-Flaherty Scholarships *(Undergraduate/Scholarship)* [7471]
Geri Coccodrilli Culinary Scholarship Fund *(Undergraduate/Scholarship)* [4511]
Culinary (1-Year Program) Scholarships *(Undergraduate/Scholarship)* [2660]
Linda Cullen Memorial Scholarships *(Undergraduate/Scholarship)* [759]
For the Love of Chocolate Foundation Scholarships *(Undergraduate, Graduate, Professional development/Scholarship)* [4133]
The French Culinary Institute Classic Pastry Arts Scholarships *(Other, Undergraduate/Scholarship)* [3487]
Marcia S. Harris Legacy Fund Scholarships *(Undergraduate, Advanced Professional/Scholarship)* [8564]
International Dairy-Deli-Bakery Association Undergraduate/Graduate Scholarships *(Graduate, Undergraduate/Scholarship)* [5314]
International Foodservice Editorial Council Scholarships *(Graduate, Undergraduate/Scholarship)* [5331]
Stanley "Doc" Jensen Scholarships *(Undergraduate/Scholarship)* [760]
The Johnson & Wales Scholarships *(Undergraduate/Scholarship)* [5631]
K & W Cafeterias Scholarships *(Undergraduate/Scholarship)* [7472]
Andrew Macrina Scholarships *(Undergraduate/Scholarship)* [761]
Ray and Gertrude Marshall Scholarships *(Undergraduate/Scholarship)* [762]
Karl Mehlmann Scholarships *(Undergraduate/Scholarship)* [3138]
NC Hospitality Education Foundation Scholarships - Four Year College or University *(Undergraduate/Scholarship)* [7473]
NC Hospitality Education Foundation Scholarships - Graduate *(Graduate/Scholarship)* [7474]
NC Hospitality Education Foundation Scholarships - High School *(Undergraduate/Scholarship)* [7475]
NC Hospitality Education Foundation Scholarships - Two Year Community or Junior College *(Undergraduate/Scholarship)* [7476]
NCRLA Golden Corral Scholarships *(Undergraduate/Scholarship)* [7477]
Oklahoma Restaurant Association Scholarships *(Graduate, Undergraduate/Scholarship)* [7604]
RAMEF/NRAEF Co-Branded Scholarships *(Undergraduate/Scholarship)* [8565]
Hermann G. Rusch Scholarships *(Other/Scholarship, Grant)* [763]
Elizabeth Shafer Memorial Scholarships *(Undergraduate/Scholarship)* [8362]

South Carolina Undergraduate Scholarships (Undergraduate/Scholarship) [9367]
Spice Box Grants (Advanced Professional/Grant) [764]
The AIWF/Patricia Tillinghast Memorial Scholarships (Graduate, Undergraduate/Scholarship) [939]
Charlie Trotters's Culinary Education Foundation Scholarships (Other, Undergraduate/Scholarship) [765]
UAF Community and Technical College Culinary Arts Scholarships (Undergraduate/Scholarship) [9823]

Culture

AAS Fellowships for Creative and Performing Artists and Writers (Professional development/Fellowship, Award) [430]
AFA Aboriginal Traditional Arts Individual Project Grants (Professional development/Grant) [236]
AFA Cultural Relations Project Grants (Professional development/Grant) [238]
Jenny Panitch Beckow Memorial Scholarships Israel (Graduate/Scholarship) [5570]
Stephen Botein Fellowships (Doctorate/Fellowship) [433]
Shirley Cheshire Memorial Scholarship Awards (Undergraduate/Scholarship) [6853]
Conservation Department Program Fellowships (Graduate/Fellowship) [9028]
Jenny d'Héricourt Fellowships (Doctorate/Fellowship) [435]
The "Drawn to Art" Fellowships (Doctorate/Fellowship) [436]
Fieldwork Fellowships (Undergraduate/Award, Fellowship) [3927]
Gabriel Dumont College Graduate Student Bursary (Postgraduate, Master's, Doctorate/Scholarship) [3742]
Guelph Caribbean Canadian Association Graduate Scholarships (Undergraduate/Scholarship) [4678]
IAF Fellowships (Doctorate/Fellowship) [5232]
IASC Associate Fellowships (Doctorate/Fellowship) [10308]
IASC Doctoral Fellowships - Dissertation (Doctorate/Fellowship) [10309]
IASC Doctoral Fellowships - Pre-Dissertation (Doctorate/Fellowship) [10310]
IASC Postdoctoral Fellowships (Postdoctorate/Fellowship) [10311]
IASC Visiting Fellowships (Professional development/Fellowship) [10312]
Lapides Fellowships in Pre-1865 Juvenile Literature and Ephemera (Graduate, Postdoctorate/Fellowship) [439]
Jay and Deborah Last Fellowships (Doctorate/Fellowship) [440]
The Legacy Fellowships (Doctorate/Fellowship) [441]
Audrey Lumsden-Kouvel Fellowships (Postdoctorate/Fellowship) [7415]
Minority Visiting Students Awards (Undergraduate, Graduate/Award, Internship) [9011]
NMNH American Indian Program Fellowships (Graduate/Fellowship) [9034]
Barbara L. Packer Fellowships (Doctorate, Postdoctorate/Fellowship) [442]
Kate B. and Hall J. Peterson Fellowships (Doctorate/Fellowship) [443]
Justin G. Schiller Fellowships (Doctorate, Postdoctorate/Fellowship) [445]
Margaret B. Ševčenko Prize in Islamic Art and Culture (Doctorate/Prize) [4909]
The Joyce Tracy Fellowships (Doctorate/Fellowship) [446]
U.V.A. Faculty Fellowships (Professional development/Fellowship) [10313]

Cystic fibrosis

CCFF Clinical Fellowships (Doctorate, Graduate/Fellowship) [4013]
CCFF Fellowships (Doctorate, Graduate/Fellowship) [4014]
CCFF Scholarships (Doctorate, Graduate/Scholarship) [4015]

Rimington Trophy Scholarships (Undergraduate, Graduate/Scholarship) [2340]
Rosemary Quigley Memorial Scholarships (Undergraduate, Graduate/Scholarship) [2341]

Dairy science

Dairy Farmers of America Scholarships (Undergraduate/Scholarship) [3506]
NMPF National Dairy Leadership Scholarships (Graduate, Master's, Doctorate/Scholarship) [7073]
Progressive Dairy Producer Awards (All/Grant) [6905]
South Dakota Division Scholarships (Undergraduate/Scholarship) [6525]
Stark County Dairy Promoters Scholarships (Undergraduate/Scholarship) [9536]

Dance (See also Choreography; Performing arts)

AFA Dance Project Grants (Professional development/Grant) [239]
Deloris Carter Hampton Scholarships (Undergraduate/Scholarship) [8247]
James Echols Scholarship Award (Undergraduate/Scholarship) [2434]
FCA Grants to Artists (Advanced Professional/Grant) [4227]
Flamenco Student Scholarships (Undergraduate, Professional development/Scholarship) [4070]
Graduate Student Travel Grants (Graduate, Other/Grant) [9111]
In-course Scholarships - Chinese Dance Workshop Scholarships (Undergraduate/Scholarship) [10290]
Indiana State University Creative and Performing Arts Awards (Undergraduate/Scholarship) [5127]
John F. Kennedy Scholarship Award (Undergraduate/Scholarship) [2435]
Caroline H. Newhouse Scholarship Fund (Professional development/Scholarship, Grant) [2793]
Geeta Rastogi Memorial Scholarships (Undergraduate/Scholarship) [10338]
Study Scholarships for Artists or Musicians (Graduate/Scholarship) [3610]
Winifred Van Hagen/Rosalind Cassidy Scholarship Award (Undergraduate/Scholarship) [2436]

Data processing (See Computer and information sciences)

Dental hygiene

ADHA IOH Sigma Phi Alpha Graduate Scholarships (Graduate/Scholarship) [775]
American Dental Hygienists' Association Institute for Oral Health Research Grants (Master's/Fellowship) [776]
Bailey/Hollister Scholarships (Graduate, Professional development/Scholarship) [7935]
Brown Dental Scholarships (Undergraduate/Scholarship) [5521]
CDA Foundation Allied Dental Student Scholarships (Undergraduate/Scholarship) [2828]
CDA Foundation Dental Student Scholarships (All/Scholarship) [2829]
Colgate-Palmolive/HDA Foundation Scholarships (Master's, Postgraduate/Scholarship) [4892]
Ken LaFountaine First Nations Scholarships (Undergraduate/Scholarship) [8876]
Latinos for Dental Careers Scholarships (Undergraduate/Scholarship) [2830]
Wilma Motley Memorial California Merit Scholarships (Undergraduate/Scholarship) [777]
National Dental Hygienists' Association Scholarships (Undergraduate/Scholarship) [6916]
Procter & Gamble Professional Oral Health/HDA Foundation Scholarships (Undergraduate/Scholarship) [4893]
Dr. Sidney Rafal Memorial Scholarships (Undergraduate/Scholarship) [4770]
IADR David B. Scott Fellowship (Professional development/Fellowship, Award) [5254]
Bettie Underwood Dental Assisting Scholarships (Undergraduate/Scholarship) [2831]
Dr. Juan D. Villarreal/HDA Foundation Scholarships (Undergraduate/Scholarship) [4894]
Alice Hinchcliffe Williams, RDH, MS Graduate Scholarships (Graduate/Scholarship) [10394]
Irene Woodall Graduate Scholarships (Master's/Scholarship) [778]

Dental laboratory technology

Brown Dental Scholarships (Undergraduate/Scholarship) [5521]
CDA Foundation Allied Dental Student Scholarships (Undergraduate/Scholarship) [2828]
CDA Foundation Dental Student Scholarships (All/Scholarship) [2829]
Chinese American Medical Society Summer Research Fellowships Program (Undergraduate/Fellowship) [2917]
Paul W. Clopper Scholarship Grant for Junior Dental Students (Undergraduate/Scholarship) [5068]
Latinos for Dental Careers Scholarships (Undergraduate/Scholarship) [2830]
Esther Lim Memorial Scholarships (Undergraduate/Scholarship) [2918]
Ruth Liu Memorial Scholarships (Undergraduate/Scholarship) [2919]
Procter & Gamble Professional Oral Health/HDA Foundation Scholarships (Undergraduate/Scholarship) [4893]
Bettie Underwood Dental Assisting Scholarships (Undergraduate/Scholarship) [2831]

Dentistry

1Dental Dentistry Scholarships (Undergraduate/Scholarship) [6]
AACD Dentist Fellowships (Professional development/Fellowship) [405]
AACD Laboratory Fellowships (Professional development/Fellowship) [406]
American Academy of Periodontology Educator Scholarships (Postdoctorate/Scholarship) [420]
American Dental Association Allied Dental Student Scholarships (Undergraduate/Scholarship) [769]
American Dental Association Dental Assisting Scholarship Program (Undergraduate/Scholarship) [770]
American Dental Association Dental Hygiene Scholarship Program (Undergraduate/Scholarship) [771]
American Dental Association Dental Laboratory Technology Scholarship Program (Undergraduate/Scholarship) [772]
American Dental Association Minority Dental Student Scholarships (Undergraduate/Scholarship) [773]
AMSUS Dentist Awards (Professional development/Recognition) [1538]
Army Health Professions Scholarships Program (Professional development/Scholarship) [9878]
AvaCare Medical Scholarships (Undergraduate/Scholarship) [2142]
Brown Dental Scholarships (Undergraduate/Scholarship) [5521]
CDA Foundation Allied Dental Student Scholarships (Undergraduate/Scholarship) [2828]
CDA Foundation Dental Student Scholarships (All/Scholarship) [2829]
IADR John Clarkson Fellowship (Postdoctorate/Fellowship) [5250]
American Academy of Periodontology Dr. D. Walter Cohen Teaching Fellowships (Postdoctorate/Fellowship) [421]
Colgate-Palmolive/HDA Foundation Scholarships (Master's, Postgraduate/Scholarship) [4892]
DAAD Study Scholarship Awards (Graduate/Scholarship) [3604]
Discover Health Professions Loans (Graduate/Loan) [3638]
Discover Residency Loans (Graduate/Loan) [3639]
Dr. Mac Scholarships (Undergraduate/Scholarship) [3225]

Endodontic Educator Fellowship Award *(Graduate/Fellowship)* [492]
Endodontic Research Grants *(Graduate/Grant)* [493]
IADR John Gray Fellowship *(Other/Fellowship)* [5251]
Nicholas S. Hetos, DDS, Memorial Graduate Scholarships *(Graduate, Doctorate/Scholarship)* [4848]
Howard B. Higgins South Carolina Dental Scholarships *(Undergraduate/Scholarship)* [4197]
Indspire Health Careers Bursary and Scholarships *(Graduate, Undergraduate/Scholarship)* [5132]
Kansas Dental Education Opportunities Program *(Graduate/Scholarship)* [5654]
Kendrick Foundation, Inc. Scholarships *(Undergraduate/Scholarship)* [5813]
Jason Lang Scholarships *(Undergraduate/Scholarship)* [276]
Latinos for Dental Careers Scholarships *(Undergraduate/Scholarship)* [2830]
NAAMA Scholarships *(Undergraduate/Scholarship)* [6701]
IADR Toshio Nakao Fellowship *(Other/Fellowship)* [5252]
Nicholas J. Piergrossi Scholarships *(Undergraduate/Scholarship)* [4768]
Procter & Gamble Professional Oral Health/HDA Foundation Scholarships *(Undergraduate/Scholarship)* [4893]
Dr. Sidney Rafal Memorial Scholarships *(Undergraduate/Scholarship)* [4770]
IADR Norton Ross Fellowship *(Postgraduate/Fellowship)* [5253]
Jeptha Wade Schureman Scholarship Program *(Undergraduate/Scholarship)* [3333]
Dr. Eugene M. Seidner Student Scholarship Program *(Undergraduate, Graduate/Scholarship)* [35]
John M. and Mary A. Shanley Memorial Scholarships *(Undergraduate, Graduate/Scholarship)* [9448]
SmileMarketing Dental Scholarships *(Doctorate/Scholarship)* [8990]
Dr. Kiyoshi Sonoda Memorial Scholarships *(Graduate, Master's, Doctorate/Scholarship)* [5559]
Bud and Linda Tarrson Fellowships *(Professional development/Fellowship)* [422]
Bettie Underwood Dental Assisting Scholarships *(Undergraduate/Scholarship)* [2831]
Dr. Juan D. Villarreal/HDA Foundation Scholarships *(Undergraduate/Scholarship)* [4894]

Dermatology

American Acne and Rosacea Society Mentorship Grant *(Professional development/Grant)* [426]
ASPIRE Rheumatology and Dermatology Research Awards *(Postdoctorate/Award)* [8023]
International Society Annual Meeting Travel Grant *(Professional development/Grant)* [408]

Design

ACI Cagley ACI Student Fellowships *(Graduate, Master's, Undergraduate/Fellowship)* [702]
ACI President's Fellowships *(Doctorate, Master's/Fellowship)* [704]
Joan Auld Scholarships *(Undergraduate/Scholarship)* [3310]
BedwettingStore.com Design a Mascot Scholarships *(Undergraduate, Graduate/Scholarship)* [5635]
Buick Achievers Scholarship Program *(Undergraduate/Scholarship)* [4359]
ITAA Graduate Student Best Paper Award *(Graduate/Monetary)* [5442]
Dorothy L. Maddy Workshop/Seminar Scholarship *(All/Scholarship)* [9489]
MJSA Education Foundation Scholarship Fund *(Undergraduate/Scholarship)* [6231]
SOM Foundation Architecture, Design and Urban Design Prize *(Graduate, Undergraduate/Prize)* [8980]
SOM Foundation Travel Fellowships in Architecture, Design and Urban Design *(Graduate, Undergraduate/Fellowship)* [8982]
Vectorworks Design Scholarships *(Undergraduate, Graduate/Scholarship, Prize)* [10367]

Polaire Weissman Funds *(Graduate/Fellowship)* [6439]
Women's Jewelry Association Member Grants *(Professional development/Grant)* [10663]

Diabetes

Diabetes Scholars Foundation College Scholarships *(Undergraduate/Scholarship)* [3616]
Early-Career Patient-Oriented Diabetes Research Awards *(Professional development/Award)* [5640]
Eli Lilly Graduate Scholarship *(Graduate, Postgraduate/Scholarship)* [1886]
Innovative Grants-Pilot and Research Tool Grants *(Postdoctorate/Grant)* [5641]
JDRF Advanced Postdoctoral Fellowships *(Postdoctorate/Fellowship)* [5642]
JDRF Career Development Awards *(Professional development, Postdoctorate/Grant)* [5643]
JDRF Postdoctoral Fellowships *(Postdoctorate/Fellowship)* [5644]
The Youth Scholarship Program *(Undergraduate/Scholarship)* [2871]

Dietetics (See Nutrition)

Disabilities

AACPDM Student Scholarships *(Professional development/Scholarship)* [399]
AAHD Scholarships *(Graduate, Undergraduate/Scholarship)* [502]
AAIDD Fellowship *(Advanced Professional, Professional development/Fellowship)* [511]
American Speech Language Hearing Foundation Clinical Research Grants *(Doctorate/Grant)* [1450]
American Speech Language Hearing Foundation Endowed Scholarships *(Graduate, Master's, Doctorate/Scholarship)* [1451]
American Speech Language Hearing Foundation General Scholarships *(Graduate, Master's, Doctorate/Scholarship)* [1452]
Ethel Louise Armstrong Foundation Scholarships *(Graduate/Scholarship)* [8750]
ASHFoundation New Century Scholars Doctoral Scholarships *(Doctorate/Scholarship)* [1455]
ASHFoundation New Century Scholars Research Grants *(Doctorate/Grant)* [1456]
ASHFoundation Student Research Grants in Audiology *(Doctorate/Grant)* [1460]
BMO Capital Markets Lime Connect Equity through Education Scholarships *(Undergraduate, Graduate/Scholarship)* [6087]
BMO Financial Group Lime Connect Canada Scholarship Program for Students with Disbliities *(Undergraduate, Graduate/Scholarship)* [6088]
BSF Science and Medicine Research Grants *(Professional development/Grant)* [2199]
California Council of the Blind Scholarships *(Undergraduate, Graduate/Scholarship)* [8751]
ChairScholars Florida Scholarship Program *(Undergraduate/Scholarship)* [2888]
Google Lime Scholarships for Students with Disabilities *(Undergraduate, Graduate, Doctorate/Scholarship)* [6089]
JustWalkers.com Mobility Scholarships *(Undergraduate, Graduate/Scholarship)* [5638]
P. Johnson and C. Kolb Memorial Scholarships *(Undergraduate, Graduate, Master's, Doctorate/Scholarship)* [8752]
Katie MacDonald Memorial Scholarships *(Graduate, Undergraduate/Scholarship)* [9865]
NBCUniversal Tony Coelho Media Scholarships *(Undergraduate, Graduate/Scholarship)* [555]
Deborah Munroe Noonan Memorial Research Awards *(Professional development/Grant)* [4822]
NYCT Paid Graduate Student Philanthropy Fellowships - Health and People with Special Needs *(Graduate/Fellowship)* [7352]
Parkinson Canada Clinical Movement Disorder Fellowships *(Advanced Professional, Professional development/Fellowship)* [7877]
Siobhan Isabella Reid Memorial Scholarships *(Graduate, Undergraduate/Scholarship)* [5994]
Dale M. Schoettler Scholarships *(Undergraduate,

Graduate/Scholarship)* [8753]
Mary Switzer Research Fellowships - Distinguished Fellowships *(Doctorate/Fellowship)* [9896]
Mary Switzer Research Fellowships - Merit Fellowships *(Professional development/Fellowship)* [9897]
Whitaker-Minard Memorial Scholarships *(Undergraduate/Scholarship)* [7871]
Timothy Wiese Memorial Scholarships *(Undergraduate, Graduate/Scholarship)* [8754]

Discrimination, Sex

ASA Minority Fellowship Program (ASA MFP) *(Graduate, Doctorate, Professional development/Fellowship)* [1445]

Drafting

Dry Defender Protect Your Bed Scholarships *(Undergraduate, Graduate/Scholarship)* [5636]

Drawing (See also Art; Visual arts)

Yvonne L. Bombardier Visual Arts Scholarships *(Master's, Doctorate/Scholarship)* [1665]

Early childhood education (See Education, Early childhood)

Earth sciences

American Association of Stratigraphic Palynologists Student Scholarships *(Graduate/Scholarship)* [16]
W.L. Calvert Memorial Scholarships *(Graduate/Scholarship)* [4966]
EERI/FEMA Graduate Fellowship in Earthquake Hazard Reduction *(Graduate/Fellowship)* [3750]
El Dorado County Mineral and Gem Society Scholarships *(Undergraduate/Scholarship)* [3816]
Everglades Foundation Fellowship *(Graduate, Doctorate, Master's/Fellowship)* [3931]
Everglades Foundation Internship *(Postgraduate, Postdoctorate/Internship)* [3932]
Everglades Foundation Scholarships *(Graduate, Master's, Doctorate/Scholarship)* [3933]
Minority Visiting Students Awards *(Undergraduate, Graduate/Award, Internship)* [9011]
National GEM Consortium - PhD Science Fellowships *(Doctorate, Graduate/Fellowship)* [6969]
NWF Campus Ecology Fellowships *(Graduate, Undergraduate/Fellowship)* [7216]
Paleontological Society Student Research Grants *(Graduate, Undergraduate/Grant)* [17]
UC MEXUS-CONACYT Doctoral Fellowships *(Doctorate/Fellowship)* [10117]

East European studies (See Central European studies)

Ecology (See also Environmental science)

CTEC Internships *(Undergraduate/Internship)* [1567]
B. Harper Bull Conservation Fellowships *(Graduate/Fellowship)* [9749]
Maude Keisling/Cumberland County Extension Homemakers Scholarships *(Undergraduate/Scholarship)* [3231]
Abby Marlatt Scholarship *(Undergraduate/Scholarship)* [10322]
Andrew W. Mellon Foundation Fellowships *(Graduate/Fellowship)* [7740]
NERL Postdoctoral Research Program *(Postdoctorate, Advanced Professional, Professional development/Fellowship)* [9935]
NERRS Graduate Research Fellowships (GRF) *(Graduate/Fellowship)* [6945]
NGC College Scholarships *(Graduate, Undergraduate/Scholarship)* [6965]

Field of Study Index   EDUCATION

Arthur and Barbara Pape Endowments *(Graduate/Grant)* [10269]
A. Stanley Rand Fellowships Program *(Undergraduate, Doctorate, Postdoctorate/Fellowship)* [9037]
Dennis Raveling Scholarships *(Undergraduate/Scholarship)* [2488]
STRI Short-Term Fellowships *(Undergraduate, Graduate, Postdoctorate/Fellowship)* [9038]
Earl S. Tupper 3-year Postdoctoral Fellowships in Tropical Biology *(Postdoctorate/Fellowship)* [9039]
Welder Wildlife Foundation Fellowships *(Graduate, Master's, Doctorate/Fellowship)* [10510]
Mary and Elliot Wood Foundation Graduate Scholarship Fund *(Graduate/Scholarship)* [4222]

Economic history (See History, Economic)

Economics

American Enterprise Institute National Research Initiative Fellowships (NRI) *(Graduate/Fellowship)* [786]
American Institute for Economic Research Student Summer Fellowships *(Doctorate, Graduate, Undergraduate/Fellowship)* [911]
American Society of Military Comptrollers National Scholarship Program *(Undergraduate/Scholarship)* [1375]
ANSER Graduate Student Awards for Research on Nonprofits and the Social Economy *(Graduate/Award)* [2030]
APS/ASU Scholarships *(Undergraduate/Scholarship)* [8139]
APS/Maricopa County Community Colleges Scholarships *(Undergraduate/Scholarship)* [8140]
ARCE Funded Fellowships *(Doctorate, Postdoctorate/Fellowship)* [1195]
ARCE Research Associates Fellowships *(Doctorate, Postdoctorate, Professional development/Fellowship)* [1196]
ARS of Eastern USA Lazarian Graduate Scholarship *(Master's, Doctorate/Scholarship)* [1680]
ASEE/NSF Small Business Postdoctoral Research Diversity Fellowships *(Postdoctorate/Fellowship)* [1303]
Association of Government Accountants Undergraduate/Graduate Scholarships for Community Service Accomplishments *(Graduate, Undergraduate/Scholarship)* [1971]
Association of Government Accountants Undergraduate/Graduate Scholarships for Full-time study *(Graduate, Undergraduate/Scholarship)* [1972]
Association of Government Accountants Undergraduate/Graduate Scholarships for Part-time study *(Graduate, Undergraduate/Scholarship)* [1973]
Bank of Canada Fellowship Award *(Doctorate, Other/Fellowship, Grant)* [2187]
Bank of Canada Governor's Awards *(Doctorate, Other/Award, Grant)* [2188]
Mark A. Beltz Scholarship *(Graduate, Undergraduate/Scholarship)* [10052]
Calihan Academic Fellowships *(Graduate, Professional development/Fellowship, Grant)* [56]
Calihan Travel Grants *(Graduate/Grant)* [57]
Chopivsky Fellowships *(Graduate/Fellowship)* [10442]
Clark High School Academy of Finance Scholarships *(Undergraduate/Scholarship)* [8338]
Mable B. Crawford Memorial Scholarships *(Undergraduate/Scholarship)* [10015]
CTRF Scholarships for Graduate Study in Transportation *(Graduate/Scholarship)* [2764]
Denton Scholarships *(Graduate/Scholarship)* [8897]
The Angie Dipietro Women in Business Scholarships *(Undergraduate/Scholarship)* [8231]
Jack Ervin EDI Scholarships *(Other/Scholarship)* [7460]
Everglades Foundation Fellowship *(Graduate, Doctorate, Master's/Fellowship)* [3931]
Everglades Foundation Internship *(Postgraduate, Postdoctorate/Internship)* [3932]

Everglades Foundation Scholarships *(Graduate, Master's, Doctorate/Scholarship)* [3933]
Brendan Flores Alumni Leadership Circle Scholarship - Clark High School *(Undergraduate/Scholarship)* [8344]
GFOA Minorities in Government Finance Scholarship *(Graduate, Undergraduate/Scholarship)* [4502]
Senator James Gladstone Memorial Scholarships *(Graduate, Undergraduate/Scholarship)* [249]
Enid Hall Griswold Memorial Scholarships *(Undergraduate/Scholarship)* [7152]
Gene Halker Memorial Scholarships *(Graduate, Undergraduate/Scholarship)* [4145]
Anna E. Hall Memorial Scholarships *(Undergraduate, Graduate/Scholarship)* [8055]
Harkness Fellowships in Health Care Policy and Practice *(Doctorate, Graduate/Fellowship)* [3160]
Harvey Fellows Program *(Graduate/Fellowship)* [6632]
Conrad N. Hilton Scholarships *(Undergraduate/Scholarship)* [4414]
Governor James E. Holshouser Professional Development Scholarships *(Other/Scholarship)* [7461]
Lloyd Houlden Memorial Research Fellowships *(Advanced Professional, Professional development/Fellowship)* [2559]
Kalmen Kaplansky Scholarships in Economic and Social Rights *(Graduate/Scholarship)* [3657]
Lazarian Graduate Scholarships *(Graduate/Scholarship)* [1678]
Dr. Julianne Malveaux Scholarships *(Undergraduate/Scholarship)* [6762]
Mas Family Scholarships *(Graduate, Undergraduate/Scholarship)* [6304]
William P. McHugh Memorial Fund Award *(Doctorate, Graduate/Fellowship)* [1197]
Douglas McRorie Memorial Scholarships *(Doctorate, Master's/Scholarship)* [114]
MillerCoors National Scholarships *(Undergraduate/Scholarship)* [69]
MPAC-DC Graduate Policy Fellowships *(Graduate/Fellowship)* [6630]
NAFA Corporate Aviation Business Scholarship *(Undergraduate, Graduate/Scholarship)* [6692]
The National Endowment for the Humanities Fellowships *(Graduate/Fellowship)* [1198]
National Iranian American Council Fellowships *(Graduate, Undergraduate/Fellowship)* [7022]
NGC College Scholarships *(Graduate, Undergraduate/Scholarship)* [6965]
NMPF National Dairy Leadership Scholarships *(Graduate, Master's, Doctorate/Scholarship)* [7073]
Novak Awards *(Doctorate/Monetary)* [58]
Diane Olsen Memorial Scholarship *(Undergraduate/Scholarship)* [10067]
Open Society Baltimore Community Fellowships *(Advanced Professional/Fellowship)* [7661]
Pi Gamma Mu Scholarships *(Graduate/Scholarship)* [8133]
Thomas R. Pickering Graduate Foreign Affairs Fellowships *(Graduate, Undergraduate/Fellowship)* [10681]
PlasticPlace Young Entrepreneurs Scholarships *(Undergraduate/Scholarship)* [8148]
Doug Purvis Prize *(Other/Prize)* [2546]
Betty Rendel Scholarships *(Undergraduate/Scholarship)* [6955]
Resilience Action Fund Scholarships *(Graduate/Scholarship)* [3981]
Royal Bank Scholarships *(Undergraduate, Master's/Scholarship)* [2290]
Sloan Research Fellowships *(Doctorate/Fellowship)* [8988]
Helen D. Snow Memorial Scholarships *(Undergraduate/Scholarship)* [8056]
Dan Stewart Scholarships *(Other/Scholarship)* [7462]
Steven M. Teutsch Prevention Effectiveness Fellowships *(Doctorate/Fellowship)* [9921]
The United States Department of State, Bureau of Educational & Cultural Affairs Fellowships *(Graduate/Fellowship)* [1199]
Wells Fargo Career Scholarship *(Undergraduate/Scholarship)* [10085]

Women In Defense HORIZONS Scholarships *(Graduate, Undergraduate/Scholarship)* [10636]
Mary and Elliot Wood Foundation Graduate Scholarship Fund *(Graduate/Scholarship)* [4222]

Editors and editing

ASBPE Young Leaders Scholarships *(Professional development/Scholarship)* [1250]
Aubespin Scholarships *(Undergraduate/Scholarship)* [718]
Kaiser Media Fellowships in Health Reporting *(Advanced Professional, Professional development/Fellowship)* [5648]
Eugene C. Pulliam Fellowships for Editorial Writing *(Other/Fellowship)* [8902]
Claudette Upton Scholarships *(Undergraduate/Scholarship)* [3787]

Education

Evelyn Abrams Memorial Scholarships *(Undergraduate/Scholarship)* [8327]
Gladys Ross Carlson Adelphe Scholarship Fund *(Undergraduate, Graduate/Award)* [5688]
AECT Foundation Mentor Endowment Scholarships *(Doctorate, Graduate/Scholarship)* [1942]
AERA-AIR Fellows Program *(Postdoctorate/Fellowship)* [782]
AERA Minority Fellowship Program in Education Research *(Doctorate/Fellowship)* [784]
AFCEA Science, Technology, Engineering and Math Teachers Scholarships *(Graduate/Scholarship, Grant)* [87]
AIEA Presidential Fellows Program *(Graduate/Fellowship)* [1985]
Alberta Teachers Association Doctoral Fellowships in Education *(Doctorate/Fellowship)* [294]
Alberta Teachers Association Educational Research Award *(Other/Award)* [295]
William Tasse Alexander Scholarship Fund *(Undergraduate/Scholarship)* [4175]
Margaret M. Alkek Scholarships *(Undergraduate/Scholarship)* [3548]
American Quarter Horse Foundation Scholarships *(Undergraduate/Scholarship)* [1171]
AMS Teacher Education Scholarships *(Undergraduate/Scholarship)* [1007]
Charles Lee Anderson Memorial Scholarships *(Undergraduate/Scholarship)* [3275]
APS/Maricopa County Community Colleges Scholarships *(Undergraduate/Scholarship)* [8140]
Mike Ardaw Scholarships *(Undergraduate/Scholarship)* [10007]
ASA Minority Fellowship Program (ASA MFP) *(Graduate, Doctorate, Professional development/Fellowship)* [1445]
ASM Science Teaching Fellowships - Student *(Undergraduate/Fellowship)* [1371]
Associated Women for Pepperdine Scholarships *(Undergraduate/Scholarship)* [7962]
George C. Balch Scholarships *(Graduate, Undergraduate/Scholarship)* [9958]
Barbara Jordan Memorial Scholarships *(Undergraduate, Graduate/Scholarship)* [2078]
Jean Clark Berry Scholarships *(Graduate, Undergraduate/Scholarship)* [5693]
Beta Lambda Project 2000 Scholarship *(Undergraduate/Scholarship)* [5694]
Beta Mu Project 2000 Scholarships *(Undergraduate/Scholarship)* [5695]
Beta Pi Project 2000 Scholarship in Memory of Kristy LeMond *(Undergraduate/Scholarship)* [5696]
Beta Province Project 2000 Scholarships *(Undergraduate/Scholarship)* [5697]
Beta Tau Scholarship Fund *(Undergraduate/Scholarship)* [5698]
Beta Theta Memorial Scholarships *(Graduate, Undergraduate/Scholarship)* [5699]
Beta Xi Project 2000 Scholarships *(Undergraduate/Scholarship)* [5700]
Beta Zeta Project 2000 Scholarships *(Undergraduate/Scholarship)* [5701]
Thomas M. Blake Memorial Scholarships *(Undergraduate/Scholarship)* [3360]

EDUCATION

Boston Intercollegiate Alumnae Association Adelphe Scholarship (Undergraduate/Scholarship) [5702]
TACS/A. Bragas and Associates Student Scholarships (Undergraduate/Scholarship) [9686]
Susan Brager Occupational Education Scholarships (Undergraduate/Scholarship) [8333]
Houston Alumnae Association, Doris Krikham Brokaw Memorial Adelphe Scholarship (Undergraduate, Graduate/Scholarship) [5703]
Cecil E. Burney Scholarships (Undergraduate/Scholarship) [3091]
Canadian Society for the Study of Education New Scholar Fellowships (CSSE) (Professional development/Fellowship) [9068]
CAPE Scholarships (Undergraduate, Postdoctorate/Scholarship) [2768]
Deloris Carter Hampton Scholarships (Undergraduate/Scholarship) [8247]
Cengage Travel Award for Teachers of Reading at a Community College (Professional development/Monetary) [3123]
CHCI Graduate Fellowships (Graduate/Fellowship) [3352]
Lula Faye Clegg Memorial Scholarship Fund (Undergraduate/Scholarship) [4188]
Coleopterists Society - Youth Incentive Award (Undergraduate/Award) [3117]
Maridell Braham Condon Scholarships (Undergraduate/Scholarship) [8915]
Rosemary Cook Education Scholarships (Undergraduate/Scholarship) [4584]
Jack Kent Cooke Foundation College Scholarships (Undergraduate/Scholarship) [3411]
Judy Crocker Memorial Scholarship Fund (Undergraduate/Scholarship) [4191]
CSSE ARTS Graduate Research Awards (Graduate/Award) [9069]
CSSHE Masters Thesis/Project Awards (Master's/Award) [2756]
CSSHE Research Awards (Professional development/Award) [2757]
Dallas Alumnae Association Adelphe Scholarships (Undergraduate/Scholarship) [5704]
Dallas Alumnae Association Gamma Phi Chapter Scholarships (Undergraduate/Scholarship) [5705]
June Danby and Pat Pearse Education Scholarships (Undergraduate/Scholarship) [5500]
Ruth and Victor David Scholarships (Undergraduate, Graduate/Scholarship) [5575]
Lucile Caswell Davids Memorial Adelphe Scholarships (Undergraduate, Graduate/Scholarship) [5706]
Delta Kappa Project 2000 Scholarships (Undergraduate/Scholarship) [5707]
Delta Nu Project 2000 Scholarships (Undergraduate/Scholarship) [5708]
Delta Project 2000 Scholarships (Undergraduate/Scholarship) [5709]
Delta Tau Project 2000 Scholarships (Undergraduate/Scholarship) [5710]
Delta Upsilon Project 2000 Nowell Memorial Scholarships (Undergraduate/Scholarship) [5711]
Rudolph Dillman Memorial Scholarships (Graduate, Undergraduate/Scholarship) [820]
Disability Care Center Special Education Scholarships (Undergraduate/Scholarship) [3630]
Helen Cashatt Drais Memorial Adelphe Scholarships (Undergraduate/Scholarship) [5712]
Josephine P. White Eagle Scholarships (Undergraduate, Graduate/Scholarship) [4911]
EAPSI Fellowships (Doctorate, Graduate/Fellowship) [7124]
Epsilon Delta Project 2000 Scholarships (Undergraduate/Scholarship) [5713]
Epsilon Mu Scholarships (Graduate, Undergraduate/Scholarship) [5714]
Erickson Education Scholarships (Undergraduate/Scholarship) [4513]
Bertha M. Fase Memorial Scholarship Fund (Undergraduate/Scholarship) [4515]
James R. Favor Risk Management Scholarship Fund (Undergraduate/Scholarship) [5715]
Diane Ross Fennekohl Endowment Fund for Education (Undergraduate/Scholarship) [5716]
Marjorie Gosselin Fitzgerald, Upsilon, Permanently Restricted Scholarship Fund (Undergraduate/Scholarship) [5717]
Stephen J. Fortgang/University of Northern Iowa Chapter Scholarship (Undergraduate/Scholarship) [5670]
Mary Metzger Fouse Memorial Scholarship Fund (Undergraduate/Scholarship) [5718]
FREA Scholarship (Undergraduate/Scholarship) [4111]
Mary Alice Fry Memorial Scholarships (Undergraduate, Graduate/Scholarship) [5719]
William E. "Bill" Gallagher Scholarships (Undergraduate/Scholarship) [7829]
Gamma Chi Project 2000 Scholarships (Undergraduate/Scholarship) [5720]
Gamma Mu Project 2000 Scholarships (Undergraduate/Scholarship) [5721]
Gamma Pi Project 2000 Scholarships (Undergraduate/Scholarship) [5722]
Gamma Theta Project 2000 Scholarships (Undergraduate/Scholarship) [5723]
Gamma Zeta Project 2000 Scholarships (Undergraduate/Scholarship) [5724]
Garikian Scholarship Fund (Undergraduate/Scholarship) [1694]
The Gates Millennium Scholars (Undergraduate/Scholarship) [4903]
Kappa Kappa Gamma Foundation - Mary Maxwell Gates Scholarships (Undergraduate, Graduate/Scholarship) [5725]
Elizabeth Tucker Gessley Scholarship (Undergraduate/Scholarship) [5727]
Laverne L. Gibson Memorial Scholarships (Undergraduate/Scholarship) [7830]
FAMU Presidential Scholarship - George W. Gore Assistantship Scholarship (Undergraduate/Scholarship) [4077]
Sarah "Sally" Ives Gore Gamma Kappa Sapphire Scholarships (Graduate, Undergraduate/Scholarship) [5728]
Anna Munger Greenwood Memorial Adelphe Scholarship (Undergraduate/Scholarship) [5729]
Mary Ewing Guthrey/Mary Keller Moyer Memorial Scholarship (Undergraduate, Graduate/Scholarship) [5730]
Suzanne Lovell Hadsell Memorial Scholarship (Undergraduate, Graduate/Scholarship) [5731]
Caitlin Hammaren Memorial Scholarship (Undergraduate/Scholarship) [5732]
Martha and Oliver Hansen Memorial Scholarships (Undergraduate/Scholarship) [5505]
Dolores Ruth Heady Hardy Memorial Scholarship (Undergraduate/Scholarship) [5733]
Eileen Harrison Education Scholarships (Graduate, Undergraduate/Scholarship) [4146]
Delta Gamma Foundation Florence Margaret Harvey Memorial Scholarships (Graduate, Undergraduate/Scholarship) [822]
Dick and Pat Hazel Minority Scholarships (Undergraduate/Scholarship) [3180]
HECUA Scholarship for Social Justice (Undergraduate/Scholarship) [4879]
Jessica M. Herron, Epsilon Nu, Memorial Scholarship (Undergraduate/Scholarship) [5734]
Raymond T. Hoge Scholarship Fund (Undergraduate/Scholarship) [9510]
Houston Alumnae Association, Eunice "Scotty" Scott Siverson Memorial Adelphe Scholarship (Undergraduate, Graduate/Scholarship) [5735]
Huenefeld/Denton Scholarships (Undergraduate/Scholarship) [3588]
Betty Jo Creighton Hunkele Adelphe Scholarship (Undergraduate/Scholarship) [5736]
IARSLCE Graduate Student Scholarships (Graduate/Scholarship) [5273]
IASP Visiting Professor Grants (Professional development/Grant) [5275]
IBEA Undergraduate Scholarships (Undergraduate/Scholarship) [5057]
Indspire Post-Secondary Education Scholarships (Graduate, Undergraduate/Scholarship) [5133]
Inspire our Future Scholarships (All/Scholarship) [9648]
IPPR Events Internships (Undergraduate/Internship) [5209]
Iris Scholarship (Undergraduate/Scholarship) [5737]
Harriet Irsay Scholarships (Graduate, Undergraduate/Scholarship) [927]
Dwight P. Jacobus Scholarships (Undergraduate/Scholarship) [2058]
Jewish Federation Academic Scholarships (Graduate, Undergraduate/Scholarship) [5598]
Wilma Winberg Johnson Adelphe Scholarship for Chapter Consultants (Undergraduate/Scholarship) [5738]
Edward G. Kaelber Scholarships (Undergraduate/Scholarship) [6201]
Kappa Kappa Gamma Foundation Project 2000 Scholarships (Undergraduate/Scholarship) [5739]
Kappa Project 2000 Scholarships (Undergraduate/Scholarship) [5742]
KDP Huntington Bank Scholarship (Undergraduate/Scholarship) [5673]
KDP International Scholarship Program - President Scholarship (Undergraduate, Graduate, Doctorate/Scholarship) [5674]
Maude Keisling/Cumberland County Extension Homemakers Scholarships (Undergraduate/Scholarship) [3231]
Emily Day Koppell Memorial Adelphe Scholarship (Undergraduate, Graduate/Scholarship) [5743]
Kovaluk Scholarship Fund (Undergraduate/Scholarship) [9984]
Liela Klinger Kurztman Memorial Scholarships (Undergraduate/Scholarship) [5583]
Elaine Johnson Lampert Journalism Memorial Adelphe Scholarship (Graduate/Award) [5745]
Katherine Roberts LaPorte Memorial Adelphe Scholarship (Undergraduate/Scholarship) [5746]
Lee Womack Scholarship Fund (Undergraduate/Scholarship) [6570]
Miriam "Doc" Locke Memorial Adelphe Scholarships (Graduate/Scholarship) [5747]
Louise Loomis Memorial Adelphe Scholarships (Undergraduate/Scholarship) [5748]
James Madison Foundation - Junior Fellowships (Advanced Professional/Fellowship) [6174]
James Madison Foundation - Senior Fellowships (Graduate/Fellowship) [6175]
Shirley Stone Marinkovich Memorial Scholarships (Undergraduate/Scholarship) [5749]
Marisol Scholarship (Undergraduate/Scholarship) [5750]
Marsh Writing/Research Scholarship Awards (Undergraduate, Graduate/Scholarship, Award) [5677]
Edna L. Martin Scholarships (Undergraduate/Scholarship) [3237]
Dottie Martin Teacher Scholarships (Graduate, Undergraduate/Scholarship) [7464]
Margaret Edwards Mason Adelphe Scholarship (Undergraduate, Graduate/Scholarship) [5751]
Mary Bowles McInnis Adelphe Scholarship (Undergraduate/Scholarship) [5752]
McJulien Minority Graduate Scholarships (Graduate/Scholarship) [1944]
John Alexander McLean Scholarships (Undergraduate/Scholarship) [9731]
Minority Teacher Loans (Undergraduate, Graduate/Loan) [9554]
ARTC Glenn Moon Scholarships (Undergraduate/Scholarship) [4765]
NAAE Upper Division Scholarships (Undergraduate/Scholarship) [6712]
NAED/Spencer Dissertation Fellowship Program (Graduate, Doctorate/Fellowship) [6681]
Carol Nelson Scholarship (Undergraduate/Scholarship) [5753]
NHS Regional Scholarships (Undergraduate/Scholarship) [7001]
North Dakota Division Scholarships (Undergraduate/Scholarship) [6523]
North Mecklenburg Teachers' Memorial Scholarships (Undergraduate/Scholarship) [4208]
Nicholas H. Noyes, Jr. Scholarship (Undergraduate/Scholarship) [5680]
NYCT Paid Graduate Student Philanthropy Fellowships - Children, Youth, Families, Education, Human Justice and Workforce (Graduate/Fellowship) [7350]
WillEtta Long Oates, Gamma Nu, Memorial Scholar-

ship *(Undergraduate, Graduate/Scholarship)* [5754]
O'Brien Foundation Fellowships *(Postgraduate, Master's, Doctorate/Fellowship)* [7568]
Overflow/PLUS Tax Credit Scholarships *(Undergraduate/Scholarship)* [1628]
Elvina Jane Owen Awards *(Graduate, Undergraduate/Scholarship)* [9855]
PDF Student Travel Award *(Graduate, Undergraduate/Scholarship)* [7887]
Martha Mitchell Pearson Memorial Scholarship *(Undergraduate, Graduate/Scholarship)* [5755]
Pi Lambda Theta Scholarships *(Undergraduate/Scholarship)* [10325]
Pi Project 2000 Tali James Memorial Scholarships *(Undergraduate/Scholarship)* [5756]
A. H. Pollard Travelling PhD Scholarships *(Postdoctorate/Scholarship)* [5163]
Poundmaker Memorial Scholarships *(Undergraduate/Scholarship)* [10272]
Phillis Brinton Pryor Panhellenic Scholarship *(Undergraduate/Scholarship)* [5757]
Rosa Quezada Memorial Education Scholarships *(Undergraduate/Scholarship)* [3361]
R&E Foundation Education Scholarships *(Graduate, Other/Scholarship)* [8416]
Marie Mathew Rask-Gamma Omicron Educational Endowment *(Undergraduate/Scholarship)* [5758]
Lois McDonald Rinehart Adelphe Scholarship *(Undergraduate, Graduate/Scholarship)* [5759]
Sandra Journey Rolf Scholarship Fund *(Undergraduate, Graduate/Scholarship)* [5760]
Charles and Ruth Ronin Memorial Scholarships *(Undergraduate/Scholarship)* [8524]
Dorothy Worden Ronken Scholarships *(Graduate/Scholarship)* [3594]
Susanna Stover Root Memorial Scholarship *(Undergraduate/Scholarship)* [5761]
A.J. and Lynda Hare Scribante Scholarship Fund *(Undergraduate/Scholarship)* [5762]
Josephine Kerbey Shaw Memorial Undergraduate Scholarship *(Undergraduate/Scholarship)* [5763]
Donna Gail Shaw Scholarship for Chapter Service *(Undergraduate, Graduate, Doctorate/Scholarship)* [5684]
Susan Goldsmith Shelley Scholarship *(Undergraduate/Scholarship)* [5764]
Marion A. and Ruth Sherwood Family Fund Education Scholarships *(Undergraduate/Scholarship)* [4546]
Everett Oscar Shimp Memorial Scholarships *(Undergraduate/Scholarship)* [7862]
Lynn Brower Shonk Memorial Scholarship *(Undergraduate/Scholarship)* [5765]
Skooblie Scholarships *(Undergraduate/Scholarship)* [8984]
Lillian Smith Scholarship for Teaching Students *(Graduate, Undergraduate/Scholarship)* [10072]
John Soto Scholarships *(Undergraduate/Scholarship)* [3362]
Robert W. and Bernice Ingalls Staton Scholarships *(Undergraduate/Scholarship)* [10259]
Sheri Stears Education Scholarship *(Undergraduate/Scholarship)* [10073]
Peter T. Steinwedell Scholarships *(Undergraduate/Scholarship)* [4772]
Step Up Scholarships *(Undergraduate, Graduate/Scholarship)* [8731]
Dell Chenoweth Stifel Scholarship *(Graduate/Scholarship)* [5767]
Sturgulewski Family Scholarship *(Graduate, Undergraduate/Scholarship)* [10074]
John A. and Jean Quinn Sullivan Scholarship Funds *(Undergraduate/Scholarship)* [3725]
Hatton W. Sumners Endowed Undergraduate School Scholarships *(Undergraduate/Scholarship)* [9609]
Hatton W. Sumners Non-Endowed Undergraduate and Graduate Scholarships *(Undergraduate, Graduate/Scholarship)* [9610]
TACS/Texas Tech University ISD Scholarships *(Undergraduate/Scholarship)* [9687]
Tarkanian Teacher Education Academy at Clark High School Scholarships *(Undergraduate/Scholarship)* [8367]
Teacher of the Visually Impaired Loans *(Undergraduate, Graduate/Loan)* [9556]
Nadene M. Thomas Graduate Research Scholarships *(Graduate/Scholarship)* [297]
Tortuga Backpacks Study Abroad Scholarships *(Undergraduate/Scholarship)* [9756]
Charles A. Townsend Scholarships *(Undergraduate/Scholarship)* [7868]
UW-Madison School of Education Minority Scholarships *(Undergraduate/Scholarship)* [10334]
Marta Vallin Memorial Scholarships *(Undergraduate/Scholarship)* [3363]
Philip F. Vineberg Travelling Fellowships in the Humanities *(Undergraduate/Scholarship)* [6368]
Jane and Gregg Waddill Memorial Adelphe Scholarship *(Undergraduate/Scholarship)* [5768]
Helen Zick Walker Adelphe Scholarship *(Undergraduate/Scholarship)* [5769]
Lynn McNabb Walton Adelphe Scholarhship *(Undergraduate/Scholarship)* [5770]
Wayne-Meador-Elliott Scholarships *(Undergraduate/Scholarship)* [7869]
Richard M. Weaver Fellowships *(Graduate/Fellowship)* [5235]
Faye and Rendell Webb Scholarships *(Undergraduate/Scholarship)* [3112]
Art and Dannie Weber Scholarships *(Undergraduate/Scholarship)* [10603]
Jean Hess Wells Memorial Adelphe Graduate Scholarship *(Graduate/Scholarship)* [5771]
Jean Hess Wells Memorial Adelphe Scholarship *(Undergraduate/Scholarship)* [5772]
Mary Elizabeth Westpheling - Long Beach Alumnae Association Memorial Scholarhips *(Undergraduate/Scholarship)* [5773]
Louise Wachter Wickham Scholarships *(Undergraduate/Scholarship)* [4553]
Fred Wiesner Educational Excellence Scholarships *(Undergraduate, Graduate/Scholarship)* [2079]
Dr. Dana Williams Scholarships *(Undergraduate/Scholarship)* [3113]
Winston-Salem Foundation Scholarships *(Undergraduate/Scholarship)* [10606]
Paul R. Wolf Memorial Scholarships *(Graduate/Scholarship)* [1809]
Nona Hobbs Wolfe Memorial Scholarship *(Undergraduate/Scholarship)* [5774]
Mary and Elliot Wood Foundation Graduate Scholarship Fund *(Graduate/Scholarship)* [4222]
Geoffrey H. Wood Scholarships *(Undergraduate/Scholarship)* [2740]
Minoru Yasui Memorial Scholarships *(Graduate, Master's, Doctorate/Scholarship)* [5560]
Zeta Sigma Project 2000 Scholarships *(Undergraduate/Scholarship)* [5775]
Amelia Zollner IPPR/UCL Internship Award *(Undergraduate/Internship)* [5210]

Education, Bilingual and cross-cultural

AECT Legacy Scholarship *(Master's, Graduate, Professional development/Scholarship)* [1943]
New Mexico Association for Bilingual Education Scholarships *(Undergraduate/Scholarship)* [7339]
Robert Roy Awards *(Advanced Professional/Award, Recognition)* [1897]
SANS Inc./Mead Leadership Fellows Program *(Professional development/Fellowship)* [7509]
H.H. Stern Grant Awards *(Advanced Professional, Professional development/Award, Grant)* [1898]

Education, Early childhood

Early Childhood Educators Scholarship Program *(Undergraduate/Scholarship)* [6342]
Patty Hamilton Early Childhood Development Scholarships *(Undergraduate/Scholarship)* [10021]
Carol Hoy Scholarship Fund *(Undergraduate/Scholarship)* [4243]
JCC Association Graduate Education Scholarships *(Graduate/Scholarship)* [5562]
Molly Ann Mishler Memorial Scholarships *(Undergraduate/Scholarship)* [10030]
Morgan Stanley Pediatrics Fellowships *(Doctorate, Postdoctorate, Postgraduate, Graduate/Fellowship)* [618]
NKA Dr. Violet B. Robinson Memorial Graduate Scholarship *(Advanced Professional/Scholarship)* [7043]
Mister Rogers Memorial Scholarship *(Graduate, Master's, Doctorate/Scholarship)* [47]
Katharine Whiteside Taylor Bursary *(Professional development/Scholarship)* [7807]

Education, Elementary

AECT Legacy Scholarship *(Master's, Graduate, Professional development/Scholarship)* [1943]
Albert Einstein Distinguished Educator Fellowships (AEF) *(Graduate, Other/Fellowship)* [9794]
APS/ASU Scholarships *(Undergraduate/Scholarship)* [8139]
Gina L. Barnhart Memorial Scholarship Fund *(Undergraduate/Scholarship)* [4040]
Marion Jones Donaldson Scholarship Fund *(Undergraduate/Scholarship)* [4043]
Harold D. Drummond Scholarships *(Undergraduate, Graduate/Scholarship)* [5668]
Lindsay M. Entz Memorial Scholarships *(Undergraduate/Scholarship)* [4044]
Norma Gotwalt Scholarship Fund *(Undergraduate/Scholarship)* [4241]
Isabel M. Herson Scholarships in Education *(Graduate, Undergraduate/Scholarship)* [10816]
Carol Hoy Scholarship Fund *(Undergraduate/Scholarship)* [4243]
Dr. Eva Kleinpeter Scholarship *(Undergraduate/Scholarship)* [5676]
Carie and George Lyter Scholarship Fund *(Undergraduate/Scholarship)* [4247]
Linda and Vincent McGrath Scholarship *(Undergraduate/Scholarship)* [5679]
John P. and Tashia F. Morgridge Scholarships *(Undergraduate/Scholarship)* [10324]
Ruth Cook Pfautz Memorial Scholarship Fund *(Undergraduate/Scholarship)* [4251]
R.M. Princ Scholarships *(Undergraduate/Scholarship)* [8361]
Jack Rosen Scholarship *(Undergraduate/Scholarship)* [5683]
Mary Kean White Memorial Scholarship Fund *(Undergraduate/Scholarship)* [9544]
Ralph Yetka Memorial Scholarships *(Undergraduate/Scholarship)* [10045]

Education, English as a second language

Douglas-Coldwell Foundation Scholarships in Social Affairs *(Graduate/Scholarship)* [3656]
Sarah Jane Houston Scholarships *(Undergraduate/Scholarship)* [3587]
Arlene Kuhner Memorial Scholarship *(Undergraduate/Scholarship)* [10066]
William R. Pfalzgraf Scholarships *(Undergraduate/Scholarship)* [7852]

Education, Industrial

American Rental Association Foundation Scholarships *(Graduate, Undergraduate, Vocational/Occupational/Scholarship)* [1191]
Gary L. Buffington Memorial Scholarships *(Undergraduate/Scholarship)* [5138]
FPA Summer Internships Program *(Undergraduate/Internship)* [4072]
Daniel Lasky Scholarship Fund *(Undergraduate/Scholarship)* [7081]
Ron Marshall Scholarships *(Undergraduate/Scholarship)* [1192]
Material Handling Education Foundation Scholarships *(Doctorate, Graduate, Undergraduate/Scholarship)* [6346]
Dorothy Wellnitz Canadian Scholarships *(Undergraduate, Vocational/Occupational/Scholarship)* [1193]

Education, Medical

AAMA Houston Chapter Health Training Scholarships *(Other/Scholarship)* [1601]

Jonathan Alan Scholarship Fund *(Undergraduate/Scholarship)* [10497]
Dulemba Aleksander and Stefania Scholarship *(Undergraduate/Scholarship)* [8571]
Canadian Pain Society Post-Doctoral Fellowship Awards *(Postdoctorate/Fellowship)* [2724]
CPS Clinical Pain Management Fellowship Awards *(Postgraduate/Fellowship)* [2725]
CPS Excellence in Interprofessional Pain Education Awards *(Other/Award)* [2726]
CPS Interprofessional Nursing Project Awards *(Other/Award)* [2727]
CPS Knowledge Translation Research Awards *(Other/Grant)* [2728]
CPS Nursing Excellence in Pain Management Awards *(Other/Award)* [2729]
CPS Nursing Research and Education Awards *(Other/Grant)* [2730]
CPS Outstanding Pain Mentorship Awards *(Other/Award)* [2731]
CPS Trainee Research Awards *(Doctorate/Grant, Award)* [2732]
Clifford W. and Doris E. Davis Educational Scholarship Fund *(Undergraduate, Vocational/Occupational/Scholarship)* [3319]
Victoria M. Gardner Scholarships *(Undergraduate/Scholarship)* [10228]
Victor and Ruth N. Goodman Memorial Scholarships *(Graduate/Scholarship)* [4697]
Zelma Gray Medical School Scholarships *(Graduate, Doctorate/Fellowship)* [4168]
Alice Newell Joslyn Medical Fund *(Undergraduate/Scholarship)* [2211]
John and Lois Lamont Graduate Scholarship *(Graduate/Scholarship)* [2627]
Lapeer County Medical Scholarship Fund *(Undergraduate/Scholarship)* [5932]
Albert and Eloise Midyette Memorial Scholarship Fund *(Undergraduate/Scholarship)* [4204]
John J. Mingenback Memorial Scholarships *(Graduate, Undergraduate/Scholarship)* [4468]
Herbert W. Nickens Medical Student Scholarships *(Advanced Professional/Scholarship)* [1840]
Gilberto and Lennetta Pesquera Medical School Scholarships *(Graduate, Doctorate/Scholarship, Grant)* [4453]
Florence L. Smith Medical Scholarships *(Graduate/Scholarship)* [4705]
U.S. Medical Supplies' Medical Professionals of Tomorrow Scholarships *(Undergraduate, Graduate/Scholarship)* [9964]
S. William and Martha R. Goff Educational Scholarships *(Undergraduate/Scholarship)* [7872]

Education, Music

AOSA Research Grants *(Undergraduate/Grant)* [1053]
Bach Organ Scholarship *(Undergraduate/Scholarship)* [8602]
TCDA Carroll Barnes Student Scholarships *(Undergraduate/Scholarship)* [668]
Brent R. Churchill Memorial Scholarships *(Undergraduate/Scholarship)* [6191]
TCDA Jim and Glenda Casey Professional Scholarships *(Other/Scholarship)* [669]
Constant Memorial Scholarship *(Undergraduate/Scholarship)* [8604]
Dalcroze Society of America Memorial Scholarships *(Graduate/Scholarship)* [3510]
William R. Gard Memorial Scholarships *(Undergraduate/Scholarship)* [6654]
TCDA Bill Gorham Student Scholarships *(Undergraduate/Scholarship)* [670]
Robert C. and Judith L. Knapp Scholarships *(Graduate, Undergraduate/Scholarship)* [4147]
Muddy Waters Scholarships *(Undergraduate/Scholarship)* [2316]
Nickels for Notes Music Scholarship *(Undergraduate/Scholarship)* [4354]
Jerry Robbins Scholarship *(Undergraduate/Scholarship)* [5682]
TCDA Abbott IPCO Professional Scholarships *(Other/Scholarship)* [671]
TCDA Gandy Ink Professional Scholarships *(Professional development/Scholarship)* [672]
TCDA General Fund Scholarships *(Undergraduate/Scholarship)* [673]
TCDA Past Presidents Student Scholarships *(Undergraduate/Scholarship)* [674]
TCDA Cloys Webb Student Scholarships *(Undergraduate/Scholarship)* [675]
Williams Chorale Bacardi Fallon Performing Arts Scholarships *(Undergraduate/Award, Scholarship)* [10563]

Education, Physical

Ruth Abernathy Presidential Scholarships *(Graduate, Undergraduate/Scholarship)* [9128]
American Sokol Merit Awards *(Undergraduate/Scholarship, Recognition)* [1448]
Dr. Andy Anderson Young Professional Awards *(Professional development/Award)* [8117]
CANFIT Nutrition, Physical Education and Culinary Arts Scholarships *(Graduate, Undergraduate/Scholarship)* [3167]
James Echols Scholarship Award *(Undergraduate/Scholarship)* [2434]
William E. "Bill" Gallagher Scholarships *(Undergraduate/Scholarship)* [7829]
Veronica Gantt Memorial Scholarships *(Undergraduate/Scholarship)* [8346]
Gretchen Hauff Memorial Scholarships *(Undergraduate/Scholarship)* [8349]
Indiana State University Creative and Performing Arts Awards *(Undergraduate/Scholarship)* [5127]
JCC Association Graduate Education Scholarships *(Graduate/Scholarship)* [5562]
John F. Kennedy Scholarship Award *(Undergraduate/Scholarship)* [2435]
R. Tait Mckenzie Awards *(Professional development/Award)* [8118]
North American Society Fellowships *(Professional development/Fellowship)* [8119]
PHE Canada National Award for Teaching Excellence in Physical Education *(Professional development/Recognition)* [8120]
PHE Canada Student Awards *(Undergraduate/Award)* [8121]
James H. Roberts Athletic Scholarships *(Undergraduate/Scholarship)* [7855]
Bonnie Sorenson Scudder Scholarships *(Undergraduate/Scholarship)* [3301]
Taylor Statten Memorial Fellowships *(Graduate/Scholarship)* [10295]
Winifred Van Hagen/Rosalind Cassidy Scholarship Award *(Undergraduate/Scholarship)* [2436]

Education, Religious

Mary E. Bivins Foundation Religious Scholarship Program *(Graduate, Undergraduate/Scholarship)* [2275]
Emmanuel Bible College Scholarships *(Undergraduate/Scholarship)* [1693]
International Scholarship Programs for Community Service *(Undergraduate/Scholarship)* [6413]
Margaret Lynch Religious Study Fellowships *(Graduate/Scholarship)* [7634]
MACC Scholarships *(Other/Scholarship)* [6444]
William P. McHugh Memorial Fund Award *(Doctorate, Graduate/Fellowship)* [1197]
The National Endowment for the Humanities Fellowships *(Graduate/Fellowship)* [1198]
Cecilia Rowan Religious Study Fellowships *(Graduate/Fellowship)* [7635]
The United States Department of State, Bureau of Educational & Cultural Affairs Fellowships *(Graduate/Fellowship)* [1199]
Philip F. Vineberg Travelling Fellowships in the Humanities *(Undergraduate/Fellowship)* [6368]

Education, Secondary

Albert Einstein Distinguished Educator Fellowships (AEF) *(Graduate, Other/Fellowship)* [9794]
Leonore Annenberg Teaching Fellowships *(Graduate/Fellowship)* [10677]
APS/ASU Scholarships *(Undergraduate/Scholarship)* [8139]
Mary Ann Brichta Scholarships *(Undergraduate/Scholarship)* [10317]
Patricia Buchanan Memorial Scholarships *(Undergraduate/Scholarship)* [10318]
Marion Jones Donaldson Scholarship Fund *(Undergraduate/Scholarship)* [4043]
George Koeppel Scholarships/All School *(Undergraduate/Scholarship)* [10321]
La Voz Latina Scholarships *(Undergraduate/Scholarship)* [3290]
Noyce Scholarships for Secondary Math and Science Education *(Undergraduate/Scholarship)* [5123]
R.M. Princ Scholarships *(Undergraduate/Scholarship)* [8361]
Carl Rose Memorial Scholarships *(Undergraduate/Scholarship)* [7858]
Woodrow Wilson-Rockefeller Brothers Fund Fellowships for Aspiring Teachers of Color *(Undergraduate/Fellowship)* [10682]
Ralph Yetka Memorial Scholarships *(Undergraduate/Scholarship)* [10045]

Education, Special

AECT Legacy Scholarship *(Master's, Graduate, Professional development/Scholarship)* [1943]
APS/ASU Scholarships *(Undergraduate/Scholarship)* [8139]
Antonia Dellas Memorial Scholarships *(Undergraduate/Scholarship)* [5501]
Disability Care Center Special Education Scholarships *(Undergraduate/Scholarship)* [3630]
J. Everett and Louise Light Scholarships *(Undergraduate, Graduate/Scholarship)* [5669]
Laverne L. Gibson Memorial Scholarships *(Undergraduate/Scholarship)* [7830]
Illinois Special Education Teacher Tuition Waiver Scholarships (SETTW) *(Undergraduate/Scholarship)* [5073]
KDP MBNA Scholarships *(Undergraduate, Graduate/Scholarship)* [5675]
Lewis-Clark State College - Military Order of the Purple Heart Scholarships *(Undergraduate/Scholarship)* [6041]
Mollie Lukken Memorial Scholarships *(Graduate, Other/Scholarship)* [5633]
William B. Martin East Carolina University Scholarships *(Undergraduate/Scholarship)* [5678]
NAJA Scholarships *(Graduate/Scholarship)* [6760]
Siobhan Isabella Reid Memorial Scholarships *(Graduate, Undergraduate/Scholarship)* [5994]
UCT Scholarships *(Graduate, Other, Undergraduate/Scholarship)* [7686]
Workshops, Inc. and Stark MRDD Fostering Diversity Through Special Needs Scholarship Fund *(Undergraduate/Scholarship)* [9545]

Education, Vocational-technical

ALOA Scholarship Foundation *(Undergraduate/Scholarship)* [1816]
APS/Maricopa County Community Colleges Scholarships *(Undergraduate/Scholarship)* [8140]
ARA Scholarship Awards *(Undergraduate/Scholarship)* [2136]
Laura M. Fleming Scholarships *(Undergraduate, Vocational/Occupational/Scholarship)* [4194]
Harrisville Lions Club Scholarships *(Undergraduate/Scholarship)* [7836]
Wilbert L. and Zora F. Holmes Scholarship Endowment Fund *(Undergraduate/Scholarship)* [4198]
IOIA Organic Community Initiative Scholarships *(Other/Scholarship)* [5369]
Virginia C. Jack and Ralph L. Jack Scholarships *(Undergraduate/Scholarship)* [9513]
Margaret G. Johnson and Marge J. Stout Scholarships *(Undergraduate/Scholarship)* [6034]
Lake Dollars for Scholars Endowment Fund *(Undergraduate/Scholarship)* [9518]
The Leaders of Tomorrow Scholarships *(Undergraduate, Vocational/Occupational/Scholarship)* [3765]
Lt. Colonel Robert G. Moreland Vocational/Technical Fund *(Undergraduate/Scholarship)* [9527]
National Dairy Herd Information Association Scholarship Program *(Undergraduate/Scholarship)* [6903]

National Slovak Society Senior Scholarships (Undergraduate, Vocational/Occupational/Scholarship) [7132]
Northwest-Shoals Community College Applied Technology Scholarships (Undergraduate/Scholarship) [7540]
William Reaser Scholarships (Undergraduate/Scholarship) [7854]
Faye Lynn Roberts Educational Scholarships (Undergraduate, Graduate/Scholarship) [9445]
IOIA Andrew Rutherford Scholarships (Other/Scholarship) [5370]
Bill Sawyer Memorial Scholarships (Undergraduate/Scholarship) [6052]
Shinn Family Scholarships (Undergraduate/Scholarship) [6054]
Mary K. Smith Rector Scholarships (Undergraduate/Scholarship) [7866]
Beatrice Drinnan Spence Scholarships (Undergraduate, Vocational/Occupational/Scholarship) [3766]
Texas Mutual Scholarship Program (Undergraduate, Vocational/Occupational/Scholarship) [9709]
Turner Family Scholarships (Undergraduate, Vocational/Occupational/Scholarship) [4217]
Harriet Glen Wilmore Scholarship (Undergraduate, Vocational/Occupational/Scholarship) [4221]

Educational administration

AASA Educational Administration Scholarship Awards (Postgraduate/Scholarship) [572]
Cindy Andrews Educational Scholarships (Undergraduate/Scholarship) [8447]
William J. Brennan Graduate Assistant Fellowships (Graduate/Fellowship) [7678]
CSSHE Masters Thesis/Project Awards (Master's/Award) [2756]
CSSHE Research Awards (Professional development/Award) [2757]
Jacque Placette Chapman Master's Fellowships (Graduate, Master's/Fellowship) [7679]
Order of Omega Doctoral Fellowships (Doctorate, Graduate/Fellowship) [7680]

Education--Curricula

Louise Berman Fellows Award (Graduate, Master's, Doctorate/Fellowship, Award) [5667]
Ed Haas Memorial Scholarships (Undergraduate/Scholarship) [9568]
Isabel M. Herson Scholarships in Education (Graduate, Undergraduate/Scholarship) [10816]
Louisa Anne Oriente Scholarships (Graduate/Scholarship) [5681]
Audrey L. Wright Scholarships (Undergraduate/Scholarship) [4637]

Electrical engineering (See Engineering, Electrical)

Electrochemistry (See also Chemistry)

Oronzio de Nora Industrial Electrochemistry Fellowships (Postdoctorate/Fellowship) [3850]

Electronics

ARRL Foundation PHD Scholarships (Undergraduate/Scholarship) [1724]
ARRLF Mississippi Scholarships (Undergraduate/Scholarship) [1725]
Convectair Sustainable Development Scholarship Awards (Undergraduate/Scholarship) [3824]
Irving W. Cook WA0CGS Scholarships (Undergraduate/Scholarship) [1735]
Charles Clarke Cordle Memorial Scholarships (Undergraduate/Scholarship) [1736]
SRC NRI Hans J. Coufal Fellowships (Graduate/Fellowship) [8838]
Bob Dyer/OEL Apprenticeship Scholarships (Undergraduate/Scholarship) [3825]
Eaton Awards of Academic Achievement (Undergraduate/Scholarship) [3826]
EFC Atlantic Region Scholarships (Undergraduate/Scholarship) [3827]
EFC University and College Scholarships (Undergraduate/Scholarship) [3828]
Charles N. Fisher Memorial Scholarships (Undergraduate/Scholarship) [1738]
Paul and Helen L. Grauer Scholarships (Undergraduate/Scholarship) [1740]
Graybar Canada Award of Excellence Scholarships (Undergraduate/Scholarship) [3832]
Hammond Power Solutions Inc. Outstanding Electrical Scholar Awards (Undergraduate/Award) [3833]
Hubbell Canada LP "Electrical Industry Leadership" Scholarship Awards (Undergraduate/Scholarship) [3835]
Ideal Supply Scholarship Awards (Undergraduate/Scholarship) [3836]
Kerrwil's J.W. Kerr Continuing Education Scholarship Awards (Undergraduate/Scholarship) [3837]
Dr. James L. Lawson Memorial Scholarships (Undergraduate/Scholarship) [1745]
Johnny Lineberry Memorial Scholarships (Undergraduate, Vocational/Occupational/Scholarship) [10588]
Fred R. McDaniel Memorial Scholarships (Undergraduate/Scholarship) [1746]
Ray, NORP and Katie, WOKTE Pautz Scholarships (Undergraduate/Scholarship) [1750]
RAB Design Lighting Award of Excellence (Undergraduate/Scholarship) [3840]
IRARC Memorial Joseph P. Rubino WA4MMD Scholarships (Undergraduate/Scholarship) [1754]
Sonepar Canada Scholarship Awards (Undergraduate/Scholarship) [3843]
Standard Recognition of Excellence Awards (Undergraduate/Scholarship) [3844]
Stelpro Scholarships 360: Energizing Potential (Undergraduate/Scholarship) [3845]
WESCO Student Achievement Awards (Undergraduate/Scholarship) [3848]
The L. Phil and Alice J. Wicker Scholarship (Undergraduate/Scholarship) [1763]

Emergency and disaster services

Gail L. Hartshorn Memorial Fund (Undergraduate/Scholarship) [7838]
Johns Hopkins Department of Emergency Medicine Administration Fellowships (Advanced Professional, Professional development/Fellowship) [5607]
IAEM Scholarship Program (Undergraduate/Scholarship) [5256]
Johns Hopkins Medicine Disaster Fellowships (Professional development/Fellowship) [5608]
Johns Hopkins Medicine Emergency Medical Services Fellowship (Professional development/Fellowship) [5609]
Johns Hopkins Medicine International Emergency and Public Health Fellowships (Graduate/Fellowship) [5610]
Johns Hopkins Medicine Medical Education Fellowships (Professional development/Fellowship) [5611]
Johns Hopkins Medicine Research Fellowships (Professional development/Fellowship) [5613]
Johns Hopkins Medicine Ultrasound Fellowships (Professional development/Fellowship) [5614]
William C. Leary Memorial Emergency Services Scholarships (Undergraduate/Scholarship) [9822]
Harry J. Morris, Jr. Emergency Services Scholarships (Undergraduate/Scholarship) [4613]
Mary Fran Myers Scholarships (Professional development, Undergraduate/Scholarship) [10129]
John I. and Madeleine R. Taeni Scholarships (Undergraduate/Scholarship) [9452]

Endocrinology

Dr. Biljan Memorial Awards (Advanced Professional/Award, Grant) [2636]
Endocrine Society Summer Research Fellowships (Graduate, Undergraduate/Fellowship) [3864]
Lilly Endocrine Scholars Fellowship Awards (Doctorate, Other/Fellowship) [3865]

Energy-related areas

AIPN Student Scholarships (All/Scholarship) [1987]
Alberta Innovates Graduate Student Scholarships (Graduate/Scholarship) [256]
American Association of Blacks in Energy Scholarships (Undergraduate/Scholarship) [464]
American Planning Association ENRE Student Fellowship Program (Graduate/Fellowship) [1103]
Association of Desk and Derrick Clubs Education Trust Scholarships (Undergraduate/Scholarship) [1931]
Association of Energy Engineers Foundation Scholarship Program (Graduate, Undergraduate/Scholarship) [1946]
Calgary USAEE/IAEE North American Conference Registration Fee Scholarships (Undergraduate/Scholarship) [9883]
DEED Student Research Grant/Internships (Undergraduate, Graduate/Grant, Scholarship, Internship) [1160]
e8 Sustainable Energy Development Post-Doctoral Scholarship Programme (ESED) (Postdoctorate/Scholarship) [4460]
EMLF Law Student Scholarships (Undergraduate/Scholarship) [3869]
Joseph L. Fisher Doctoral Dissertation Fellowships (Graduate/Fellowship) [8561]
Purdue University Ray W. Herrick Laboratories Research Fellowship (Graduate/Fellowship) [8388]
Dennis J. O'Brien USAEE/IAEE Best Student Paper Award (Undergraduate/Award) [9884]
Rocky Mountain Coal Mining Institute Technical Scholarships (Undergraduate/Scholarship) [8633]
Schatz Energy Fellowships for Graduate Studies (Graduate/Fellowship) [5004]
Alvin M. Weinberg Fellowships (Doctorate/Fellowship) [9910]

Engineering

AAAS Mass Media Science and Engineering Fellowship (Undergraduate, Graduate, Postdoctorate/Fellowship, Award) [453]
AAAS Science and Technology Policy Fellowships (Professional development/Fellowship) [454]
AAUW Selected Professions Fellowships (Graduate, Master's, Doctorate/Fellowship) [22]
Accenture American Indian Scholarship Program (Graduate, Undergraduate/Scholarship) [880]
ACI Foundation Scholarships (Graduate/Scholarship) [703]
ACI W.R. Grace Scholarships (Graduate/Scholarship) [705]
Henry Adams Scholarships (Undergraduate/Scholarship) [1326]
AES Educational Foundation Grants (Graduate/Grant, Award) [2122]
AFCEA Cyber Studies and Intelligence Scholarships (Undergraduate, Graduate/Scholarship) [85]
AFCEA Scholarship for Working Professionals (Undergraduate, Graduate/Scholarship) [86]
AFCEA Science, Technology, Engineering and Math Teachers Scholarships (Graduate/Scholarship, Grant) [87]
Afghanistan and Iraq War Veterans Scholarship (Undergraduate/Scholarship) [88]
African American Network - Carolinas Scholarship Fund (Undergraduate/Scholarship) [4174]
AfterCollege Engineering Student Scholarships (Undergraduate, Graduate, Doctorate, Master's/Scholarship) [98]
AfterCollege STEM Inclusion Scholarships (Undergraduate, Graduate/Scholarship) [102]
AHETEMS General Scholarships (Undergraduate, Graduate/Scholarship) [8888]
AHETEMS Professional Scholarships (Graduate/Scholarship) [8889]
Ahlswede, Norman & Marie Endowed Engineering Scholarship (Undergraduate/Scholarship) [10315]
AIST Baltimore Member Chapter Scholarships (Undergraduate/Scholarship) [1989]
AIST Midwest Member Chapter - Engineering Scholarships (Undergraduate/Scholarship) [1990]

ENGINEERING

AIST Midwest Member Chapter - Western States Scholarships *(Undergraduate/Scholarship)* [1992]
AIST Northwest Member Chapter Scholarships *(Undergraduate/Scholarship)* [1993]
Alaska Aerospace Development Corporation Scholarships *(Undergraduate/Scholarship)* [10004]
Alberta Innovates - Technology Futures Graduate Student Scholarships in Nanotechnology *(Doctorate, Graduate/Scholarship)* [258]
Alberta Innovates - Technology Futures Graduate Student Scholarships in Omics *(Doctorate, Graduate/Scholarship)* [259]
Stephanie Ali Memorial Scholarships *(Undergraduate/Scholarship)* [10279]
American Association of University Women Selected Professions Fellowships *(Other/Fellowship)* [603]
American Council of Engineering Companies of Illinois Scholarships *(Undergraduate/Scholarship)* [722]
American Railway Engineering and Maintenance-of-Way Association Scholarships *(Undergraduate/Scholarship)* [1175]
American Society of Heating, Refrigerating, and Air-Conditioning Memorial Scholarships *(Undergraduate/Scholarship)* [1327]
A.T. Anderson Memorial Scholarships *(Graduate, Undergraduate/Scholarship)* [889]
Mike Ardaw Scholarships *(Undergraduate/Scholarship)* [10007]
AREMA Committee 12 - Rail Transit Scholarships *(Undergraduate/Scholarship)* [1176]
AREMA Committee 18 - Light Density and Short Line Railways Scholarships *(Undergraduate/Scholarship)* [1177]
AREMA Committee 24 - Education and Training Scholarships *(Undergraduate/Scholarship)* [1178]
AREMA Committee 27 - Maintenance-of-Way Work Equipment Scholarships *(Undergraduate/Scholarship)* [1179]
AREMA Committee 33 - Electric Energy Utilization Scholarships *(Undergraduate/Scholarship)* [1180]
AREMA Michigan Tech Alumni Scholarships *(Graduate, Undergraduate/Scholarship)* [1181]
AREMA Presidential Spouse Scholarships *(Undergraduate/Scholarship)* [1182]
Arlyn Scales Awards for Science and Technology *(Undergraduate/Scholarship)* [3035]
ASGP Graduate Research Fellowships *(Graduate/Fellowship)* [223]
ASHARE Undergraduate Engineering Scholarships *(Undergraduate/Scholarship)* [1328]
ASNT Fellowship Award *(Graduate/Fellowship, Award)* [1384]
Astronaut Scholarship Foundation Scholarships *(Undergraduate/Scholarship)* [2105]
Auto-Pets "Out-of-the-Box Thinking" Scholarships *(All/Award, Scholarship)* [2129]
AWMA Louisiana Section Scholarships *(Undergraduate, Graduate/Scholarship)* [147]
B&W Y-12 Scholarship Fund *(Undergraduate/Scholarship)* [3752]
Bechtel Engineering and Science Scholarships *(Undergraduate/Scholarship)* [6278]
Charles E. Behlke Engineering Memorial Scholarships *(Undergraduate/Scholarship)* [10009]
Bill and Nell Biggs Scholarships *(Undergraduate/Scholarship)* [10088]
Boeing Company Scholarships *(Undergraduate/Scholarship)* [8870]
AFCEA San Diego Buck Bragunier Leadership Scholarship *(Undergraduate/Scholarship)* [1667]
Henry Broughton, K2AE Memorial Scholarships *(Undergraduate/Scholarship)* [1728]
Lt. General Douglas D. Buchholz Memorial Scholarship *(Undergraduate/Scholarship)* [89]
Buick Achievers Scholarship Program *(Undergraduate/Scholarship)* [4359]
Graduate Fellowship Program - Robert M. Burger Fellowships *(Doctorate, Graduate/Fellowship)* [8832]
Dorothy and Dick Burgess Scholarships *(Undergraduate/Scholarship)* [5499]
Burroughs Wellcome Fund Collaborative Research Travel Grants (CRTG) *(Doctorate, Postdoctorate, Professional development/Grant)* [2413]

Wes Burton Memorial Scholarships *(Undergraduate/Scholarship)* [10574]
Cesar A. Calas/FES Miami Chapter Scholarships *(Undergraduate/Scholarship)* [4087]
Dave Caldwell Scholarships *(Graduate/Scholarship)* [1485]
Canadian Council of Technicians and Technologists Scholarships for Technology Students *(Undergraduate/Scholarship)* [3392]
Career Awards at the Scientific Interface (CASI) *(Doctorate, Postdoctorate, Advanced Professional, Professional development/Grant)* [2416]
Julian E. Carnes Scholarship Fund *(Undergraduate/Scholarship)* [4183]
Willis H. Carrier Scholarships *(Undergraduate/Scholarship, Award)* [1329]
CEMF Undergraduate Engineering Scholarships *(Undergraduate/Scholarship)* [2622]
Center for Engineering in Medicine Predoctoral Fellows Program *(Postdoctorate/Fellowship)* [6316]
CERT College Scholarships *(Graduate, Undergraduate/Scholarship)* [3435]
CH2M Hill/AEESP Outstanding Doctoral Dissertation Award *(Graduate, Doctorate/Award)* [1951]
Channabasappa Memorial Scholarships *(Graduate, Doctorate/Scholarship)* [5319]
CHCI Graduate Fellowships *(Graduate/Fellowship)* [3352]
The Churchill Scholarships *(Postgraduate/Scholarship)* [2940]
Frank M. Coda Scholarships *(Undergraduate/Scholarship)* [1330]
College of Engineering and Physical Sciences Industry Scholarships *(Undergraduate/Scholarship)* [10208]
Roy Cooper Memorial Scholarships *(Undergraduate/Scholarship)* [5998]
Richard P. Covert, Ph.D./FHIMSS Scholarships for Management Systems *(Graduate, Postgraduate, Undergraduate/Scholarship)* [4830]
Critical Language Scholarships for Intensive Summer Institutes *(Graduate, Undergraduate/Scholarship)* [1204]
CSX Scholarships *(Undergraduate/Scholarship)* [1183]
John J. Cunningham Memorial Scholarships *(Undergraduate/Scholarship)* [1184]
Jason Dahnert Memorial Scholarships *(Undergraduate/Scholarship)* [4143]
D&A Florida Scholarships *(Undergraduate/Scholarship)* [9425]
Frank L. Dautriel Memorial Scholarships for Graduates *(Graduate/Scholarship)* [6116]
Frank L. Dautriel Memorial Scholarships for Undergraduates *(Undergraduate/Scholarship)* [6117]
Decommissioning, Decontamination and Reutilization Scholarships *(Graduate, Master's/Scholarship)* [1035]
Disabled War Veterans Scholarships *(Undergraduate/Scholarship)* [90]
Document Management and Graphic Communications Industry Scholarships *(Undergraduate/Scholarship)* [3852]
Robert E. Dougherty Scholarships *(Undergraduate, Postgraduate/Scholarship)* [3339]
EAPSI Fellowships *(Doctorate, Graduate/Fellowship)* [7124]
Eastern Shore Building Industry Association Scholarships *(Undergraduate/Scholarship)* [3174]
W. Wesley Eckenfelder Gradute Research Award *(Graduate, Master's, Doctorate/Award)* [1952]
John R. Eidson Jr., Scholarships *(Undergraduate/Scholarship)* [3096]
Harold E. Ennes Scholarships *(Graduate, Other/Award, Scholarship)* [9092]
Larry L. Etherton Scholarships *(Graduate, Undergraduate/Scholarship)* [1185]
Everglades Foundation Fellowship *(Graduate, Doctorate, Master's/Fellowship)* [3931]
Everglades Foundation Internship *(Postgraduate, Postdoctorate/Internship)* [3932]
Everglades Foundation Scholarships *(Graduate, Master's, Doctorate/Scholarship)* [3933]
Facebook Fellowships Program *(Doctorate/Fellowship)* [3950]
AIST Benjamin F. Fairless Scholarships *(Undergraduate/Scholarship)* [1996]
Fecon Scholarships *(Undergraduate/Scholarship)* [4088]
Fermilab Science Undergraduate Laboratory Internship *(Undergraduate/Internship)* [9900]
Fermilab Summer Internships in Science and Technology *(Undergraduate/Internship)* [9901]
Lt. Colonel Romeo and Josephine Bass Ferretti Scholarships *(Undergraduate/Scholarship)* [124]
FICE Scholarships *(Undergraduate/Scholarship)* [4089]
Herb and Anne Fincher Memorial Scholarships *(Undergraduate/Scholarship)* [3176]
FLASH Social Science Scholarships *(Graduate/Scholarship)* [3976]
Reuben H. Fleet Memorial Scholarships *(Undergraduate/Scholarship)* [8704]
Grant H. Flint International Scholarships - Category II *(Undergraduate/Scholarship)* [9338]
Florida Education Fund McKnight Doctoral Fellowships *(Graduate/Fellowship)* [4085]
Florida Engineering Society University Scholarships *(Undergraduate/Scholarship)* [4090]
Frank Fong Scholarships *(Undergraduate/Scholarship)* [9076]
Ford Motor Company Scholarship *(Undergraduate/Scholarship)* [10113]
Michael W. and Jean D. Franke Family Foundation Scholarships *(Graduate, Undergraduate/Scholarship)* [1186]
Future Leaders of Manufacturing Scholarships *(Graduate, Undergraduate/Scholarship)* [9181]
Michael and Gina Garcia Rail Engineering Scholarships *(Undergraduate, Graduate/Scholarship)* [1187]
The Gates Millennium Scholars *(Undergraduate/Scholarship)* [4903]
Gauthier Family Scholarship Fund *(Undergraduate/Scholarship)* [4519]
Generation III Scholarships *(Undergraduate/Scholarship)* [3783]
Georgia Engineering Foundation Scholarships *(Graduate/Scholarship)* [4380]
AIST Midwest Member Chapter - Jack Gill Scholarships *(Undergraduate/Scholarship)* [1997]
Benjamin A. Gilman International Scholarship *(Undergraduate/Scholarship)* [10060]
Glendale Latino Association Scholarships *(Undergraduate/Scholarship)* [4449]
Alfred B. Glossbrenner Scholarships *(Undergraduate/Scholarship)* [1999]
Dr. Robert H. Goddard Memorial Scholarships *(Graduate, Undergraduate/Scholarship)* [7179]
William R. Goldfarb Memorial Scholarships *(Undergraduate/Scholarship)* [1739]
Barry M. Goldwater Scholarships *(Undergraduate/Scholarship)* [10319]
Graduate Fellowship Program - Research Fellowships (GFP) *(Doctorate, Graduate/Fellowship)* [8833]
GREAT MINDS Collegiate Scholarship Program *(Undergraduate/Scholarship)* [338]
Robert D. Greenberg Scholarships *(Graduate, Other/Scholarship)* [9093]
HACU/NASCAR Scholarships *(Graduate, Undergraduate/Scholarship)* [4888]
Jerome Hake Engineering Scholarships *(Undergraduate/Scholarship)* [4144]
Hamilton Industrial Environmental Association Bursaries-Mohawk College *(Undergraduate/Scholarship)* [4691]
Duane Hanson Scholarships *(Undergraduate/Scholarship)* [1331]
Claude B. Hart Memorial Scholarships *(Undergraduate/Scholarship)* [10584]
Rona Hatt Master's Scholarships in Chemical Engineering *(Master's/Scholarship)* [2623]
Helm Family Scholarships *(Undergraduate/Scholarship)* [8706]
Purdue University Ray W. Herrick Laboratories Research Fellowship *(Graduate/Fellowship)* [8388]
Herschede Engineering Scholarships *(Graduate/Scholarship)* [8898]
Hertz Foundation Graduate Fellowship Award *(Graduate/Fellowship)* [4875]
Hertz Foundation Graduate Fellowships *(Graduate,

Master's, Doctorate/Fellowship) [6748]
Hertz Foundation Thesis Prize *(Graduate/Prize)* [4876]
Huber Engineered Woods Product Evaluation Scholarships *(Graduate/Scholarship)* [3977]
IDA Fellowship Awards *(Other/Fellowship)* [5320]
Indspire Post-Secondary Education Scholarships *(Graduate, Undergraduate/Scholarship)* [5133]
Industrial R&D Fellowships *(Postdoctorate/Fellowship)* [3403]
Influenster Code Like a Girl Scholarships *(Undergraduate, Graduate/Scholarship)* [5140]
International Code Council Scholarships *(Graduate/Scholarship)* [3978]
ISPE Foundation Scholarships *(Undergraduate/Scholarship)* [5066]
ITEEA Greer/FTE Grants *(Other/Grant)* [5437]
Jeffress Trust Awards Program in Interdisciplinary Research *(Professional development/Award)* [4816]
Nancy Lorraine Jensen Memorial Scholarships *(Undergraduate/Scholarship)* [9345]
Joseph C. Johnson Memorial Grants *(Undergraduate/Grant, Scholarship)* [1252]
Graduate Fellowship Program - Mahboob Khan/Advanced Micro Devices Fellowships *(Doctorate, Graduate/Fellowship)* [8834]
Robert C. and Judith L. Knapp Scholarships *(Graduate, Undergraduate/Scholarship)* [4147]
AIST Willy Korf Memorial Fund *(Undergraduate/Scholarship)* [2000]
Lamar University College of Engineering Scholarships *(Undergraduate/Scholarship)* [6928]
Laser Technology, Engineering and Applications Scholarships *(Graduate, Undergraduate/Scholarship)* [9469]
Dolores Zohrab Liebmann Fund - Graduate School Fellowships *(Graduate/Fellowship)* [6075]
AIST Ronald E. Lincoln Memorial Scholarships *(Undergraduate/Scholarship)* [2001]
David C. Lizárraga Graduate Fellowships *(Graduate/Fellowship)* [9660]
David F. Ludovici Scholarships *(Undergraduate/Scholarship)* [4091]
Robert Mack Scholarships *(Graduate, Undergraduate/Scholarship)* [6166]
CEMF Claudette MacKay-Lassonde Graduate Scholarships *(Doctorate, Postdoctorate/Scholarship)* [2624]
MAES Founders Scholarships *(Graduate, Undergraduate/Scholarship)* [6178]
MAES General Scholarships *(Graduate, Undergraduate/Scholarship)* [6179]
MAES Graduate Scholarships *(Graduate/Scholarship)* [6180]
MAES Padrino/Madrina Scholarships *(Graduate, Undergraduate/Scholarship)* [6181]
MAES Pipeline Scholarships *(Graduate, Undergraduate/Scholarship)* [6182]
MAES Presidential Scholarships *(Graduate, Undergraduate/Scholarship)* [6183]
Malayalee Engineers Association Scholarships *(Undergraduate/Fellowship)* [6225]
Maley/FTE Scholarships *(Graduate/Scholarship)* [5439]
Mas Family Scholarships *(Graduate, Undergraduate/Scholarship)* [6304]
Katharine & Bryant Mather Scholarship *(Graduate/Scholarship)* [708]
MCEA Financial Assistance Award *(Undergraduate/Scholarship)* [6267]
Thomas R. McGetchin Memorial Scholarship Awards *(Undergraduate/Scholarship)* [9997]
AIST Midwest Member Chapter - Betty McKern Scholarships *(Undergraduate/Scholarship)* [2002]
Kumar Mehta Scholarship *(Graduate/Scholarship)* [709]
Bernard Michel Scholarships *(Undergraduate/Scholarship)* [2526]
Michigan Society of Professional Engineers Scholarships *(Undergraduate/Scholarship)* [6483]
John G. and Betty J. Mick Scholarship Fund *(Undergraduate/Scholarship)* [9526]
Raymond W. Miller, PE and Alice E. Miller Scholarships *(Undergraduate/Scholarship)* [4092]

Raymond W. Miller, PE Scholarships *(Undergraduate/Scholarship)* [4093]
Christine Mirzayan Science and Technology Policy Graduate Fellowships *(Graduate/Fellowship)* [6679]
Ralph Modjeski Scholarships *(Graduate, Undergraduate/Scholarship)* [8198]
Montana Broadcasters Association Broadcast Engineering Scholarships *(Undergraduate/Scholarship)* [6578]
Robert E. and Judy More Scholarship Fund *(Undergraduate/Scholarship)* [4053]
National Board Technical Scholarships *(Undergraduate/Scholarship)* [6827]
National GEM Consortium - MS Engineering Fellowships *(Graduate/Fellowship)* [6967]
National GEM Consortium - PhD Engineering Fellowships *(Doctorate, Graduate/Fellowship)* [6968]
National Science Foundation Graduate Research Fellowship Program (NSF-GRFP) *(Graduate/Fellowship)* [7125]
National Security Technologies Engineering and Science Scholarships *(Undergraduate/Scholarship, Internship)* [8356]
AIST Midwest Member Chapter - Don Nelson Scholarships *(Undergraduate/Scholarship)* [2003]
Edsel Newman Scholarships *(Undergraduate/Scholarship)* [6065]
Alwin B. Newton Scholarships *(Undergraduate/Scholarship)* [1332]
Donald E. Nichols Scholarships *(Undergraduate/Scholarship)* [1333]
AIST Midwest Member Chapter - Mel Nickel Scholarships *(Undergraduate/Scholarship)* [2004]
Nixon Family Scholarship Fund *(Undergraduate, High School/Scholarship)* [10506]
Stuart L. Noderer Memorial Scholarships *(Undergraduate/Scholarship)* [8719]
Norfolk Southern Foundation Scholarships *(Undergraduate/Scholarship)* [1188]
Northrop Grumman Engineering Scholarships *(Undergraduate/Scholarship)* [7527]
Nuts, Bolts and Thingamajigs Scholarships *(Undergraduate, Vocational/Occupational/Scholarship)* [7562]
Ocean Industries Student Research Awards *(Undergraduate, Graduate, Postdoctorate/Award)* [8557]
Ohio Space Grant Consortium Graduate Fellowships *(Graduate, Doctorate, Master's/Fellowship)* [7594]
Ohio Space Grant Consortium Special Minority Fellowships *(Doctorate, Graduate, Master's/Fellowship)* [7595]
Patricia and Armen Oumedian Scholarships *(Undergraduate/Scholarship)* [4616]
Packard Fellowships for Science and Engineering *(Professional development/Fellowship)* [7793]
Joseph M. Parish Memorial Grants *(Undergraduate/Scholarship, Grant)* [1253]
Pennsylvania Engineering Foundation Undergradaute Scholarships *(Undergraduate/Scholarship)* [7943]
Physics of Accelerators and Related Technology for International Students *(Undergraduate/Internship)* [9902]
William Pigott Memorial Scholarships *(Undergraduate/Scholarship)* [3296]
Polymer Modifiers and Additives Division Scholarships *(Undergraduate/Scholarship)* [9267]
Eric Primavera Memorial Scholarships *(Undergraduate/Scholarship)* [4094]
Josef Princ Memorial Scholarships *(Undergraduate/Scholarship)* [8360]
AIST Judith A. Quinn Detroit Member Chapter Scholarship *(Undergraduate/Scholarship)* [2005]
REMSA Scholarships *(Undergraduate/Scholarship)* [1189]
Paul V. Roberts/AEESP Outstanding Doctoral Dissertation Award *(Graduate, Doctorate/Prize, Monetary)* [1953]
Rocky Mountain Coal Mining Institute Engineering/Geology Scholarships *(Undergraduate/Scholarship)* [8632]
Barnes W. Rose, Jr. and Eva Rose Nichol Scholarship Fund *(Undergraduate/Scholarship)* [304]
Paul and Ellen Ruckes Scholarships *(Graduate, Un-

dergraduate/Scholarship)* [823]
Liane B. Russell Fellowships *(Postdoctorate/Fellowship)* [9908]
AIST David H. Samson Canadian Scholarships *(Undergraduate/Scholarship)* [2006]
Saskatchewan Pulse Growers Undergraduate Scholarships *(Undergraduate/Scholarship)* [8778]
Kurt H. and Donna M. Schuler Cash Grants *(Undergraduate/Scholarship, Grant)* [1254]
AIST William E. Schwabe Memorial Scholarships *(Undergraduate/Scholarship)* [2007]
Science, Mathematics And Research for Transformation Scholarship for Service Program (SMART) *(Undergraduate, Graduate/Scholarship)* [1305]
John R. Sevier Memorial Scholarship Award *(Undergraduate/Scholarship)* [9998]
SGI Research Grants *(Graduate/Grant)* [8773]
John M. and Mary A. Shanley Memorial Scholarships *(Undergraduate, Graduate/Scholarship)* [9448]
Dr. Robert and Anna Shaw Scholarships *(Undergraduate/Scholarship)* [291]
Shell Incentive Scholarship Fund *(Undergraduate/Scholarship)* [8861]
Shell Oil Company Technical Scholarships *(Undergraduate/Scholarship)* [8862]
Shell Process Technology Scholarships *(Undergraduate/Scholarship)* [8863]
Marion A. and Ruth K. Sherwood Family Fund Engineering Scholarships *(Undergraduate/Scholarship)* [4547]
SHPE Dissertation Scholarship *(Doctorate/Scholarship)* [9130]
SHPE Professional Scholarship *(Master's, Doctorate/Scholarship)* [9131]
Clifford G. Shull Fellowships *(Postdoctorate/Fellowship)* [9909]
Alfred P. Sloan Foundation Graduate Scholarships - Sloan Indigenous Graduate Partnership *(Master's, Doctorate/Scholarship)* [6683]
Alfred P. Sloan Foundation Graduate Scholarships - Sloan Minority Ph.D. Program *(Doctorate/Scholarship)* [6684]
William Brewster Snow Award *(Graduate/Award, Monetary)* [1954]
Society of Manufacturing Engineers Ford PAS Scholarships (SME) *(Undergraduate/Scholarship)* [9197]
Sons of Norway Foundation Scholarships to Oslo International Summer School *(Undergraduate/Scholarship)* [9346]
SPE Thermoplastic Materials and Foams Division Scholarships *(Undergraduate/Scholarship)* [9274]
SPEATBC Scholarships *(Undergraduate, High School/Scholarship)* [9296]
SRC Master's Scholarships Program (MSP) *(Graduate, Master's/Scholarship)* [8835]
SREB-State Doctoral Scholars Program - Doctoral Awards *(Doctorate, Graduate/Scholarship)* [9411]
Robert P. Stearns/SCS Engineers Scholarships *(Graduate/Scholarship)* [9339]
Sturgulewski Family Scholarship *(Graduate, Undergraduate/Scholarship)* [10074]
AIST Southeast Member Chapter Gene Suave Scholarships *(Undergraduate/Scholarship)* [2008]
SWE Scholarships *(Undergraduate, Graduate/Scholarship)* [9329]
Frederick A. Tarantino Memorial Scholarship Award *(Undergraduate/Scholarship)* [9999]
Texas Society of Professional Engineers Scholarships *(Undergraduate/Scholarship)* [9711]
Anil and Neema Thakrar Family Fund No. 1 *(Undergraduate/Scholarship)* [4257]
Thompson Scholarships for Women in Safety *(Graduate/Scholarship)* [1430]
Toronto Rehabilitation Institute Graduate Student Scholarships - Ontario Student Opportunities Trust Fund (OSOTF) *(Graduate/Scholarship)* [9754]
Toyota/TELACU Scholarships *(Undergraduate/Scholarship)* [9661]
Reuben Trane Scholarships *(Undergraduate/Scholarship)* [1334]
UAA Quanterra Scholarship *(Graduate/Scholarship)* [10083]
UC MEXUS-CONACYT Doctoral Fellowships *(Doctorate/Fellowship)* [10117]

ENGINEERING, AEROSPACE/AERONAUTICAL/ASTRONAUTICAL

The UCSD Black Alumni Scholarships for Engineering, Mathematics and Science (Undergraduate/Scholarship) [8737]
UNCF/Merck Graduate Science Research Dissertation Fellowships (Graduate/Fellowship) [6426, 9862]
UNCF/Merck Postdoctoral Science Research Fellowships (Postdoctorate/Fellowship) [6427, 9863]
United Engineering Foundation Grants (All/Grant) [9845]
U.S. Air Force ROTC Express Scholarships (Undergraduate/Scholarship) [9872]
University of Toronto Accenture Scholarships (Undergraduate/Scholarship) [10297]
University of Toronto Nortel Institute Undergraduate Scholarships (Undergraduate/Scholarship) [10298]
USGA/Chevron STEM Scholarship Program (Undergraduate/Scholarship) [9954]
UW-Madison Engineering Diversity Scholarships (Undergraduate/Scholarship) [10331]
Vale Master's in Engineering Scholarships (Master's/Scholarship) [2625]
Vectorworks Design Scholarships (Undergraduate, Graduate/Scholarship, Prize) [10367]
VEF Fellowship Program (Doctorate, Master's/Fellowship) [10380]
VEF Visiting Scholars Program (Doctorate/Fellowship) [10381]
Dimitri J. Ververelli Memorial Scholarship for Architecture and/or Engineering (Undergraduate/Scholarship) [4851]
Virginia Tech Student Travel Award (Undergraduate, Graduate/Award) [1955]
WACE National Co-op Scholarship Program (Undergraduate/Scholarship) [10693]
Gary Wagner, K3OMI Scholarships (Undergraduate/Scholarship) [1762]
Washington University Law School Chancellor's Graduate Fellowships (Advanced Professional/Fellowship) [10476]
Washington University Law School Olin Fellowships for Women (Advanced Professional/Fellowship) [10477]
Allen and Loureena Weber Scholarships (Undergraduate/Scholarship) [9200]
Bertold E. Weinberg Scholarship (Graduate/Scholarship) [711]
William E. Weisel Scholarships (Undergraduate/Scholarship) [9201]
James B. Willett Educational Memorial Scholarship Award (Undergraduate/Scholarship) [10000]
Ted G. Wilson Memorial Scholarships (Undergraduate/Scholarship) [8288]
Women In Defense HORIZONS Scholarships (Graduate, Undergraduate/Scholarship) [10636]
WSGC Community College Transfer Scholarships (Undergraduate/Scholarship) [10455]
Yasme Foundation Scholarships (Undergraduate/Scholarship) [1765]
Ralph Yetka Memorial Scholarships (Undergraduate/Scholarship) [10045]

Engineering, Aerospace/Aeronautical/Astronautical

Aerospace Corporation Science and Engineering Student Scholarships (Undergraduate, Graduate/Scholarship) [95]
Amelia Earhart Fellowship Program (Doctorate, Postgraduate/Fellowship) [10824]
DEPS Graduate Scholarship Program (Graduate/Scholarship) [3624]
NDSEG Fellowships (Graduate/Fellowship) [6911]
Science Foundation Arizona Graduate Research Fellowships (GRF) (Graduate/Fellowship) [8814]

Engineering, Agricultural

AACE International Competitive Scholarships (Undergraduate/Scholarship) [14]
NPC Scholarships (Graduate/Scholarship) [7100]

Engineering, Architectural

AACE International Competitive Scholarships (Undergraduate/Scholarship) [14]
AISC/Great Lakes Fabricators and Erectors Association Fellowships (Graduate/Fellowship) [933]
AISC/Ohio Structural Steel Association Scholarships (Graduate/Scholarship) [934]
AISC/Rocky Mountain Steel Construction Association Scholarships (Graduate/Scholarship) [935]
AISC/Southern Association of Steel Fabricators Scholarships (Graduate/Scholarship) [936]
Michael Baker Corp. Scholarship for Diversity in Engineering (Undergraduate/Scholarship) [1976]
Carpenters' Company Scholarships (Undergraduate/Scholarship) [2801]
Edilia and François Auguste de Montêquin Fellowships (Doctorate/Fellowship) [9083]
AISC Education Foundation - Fred R. Havens Fund (Undergraduate, Graduate/Scholarship) [937]
Drzymala Janusz and Roma Scholarship (Undergraduate/Scholarship) [8577]
PCH Architects/Steven J. Lehnhof Memorial Architectural Scholarships (Undergraduate/Scholarship) [8491]
J.W. "Bill" Neese Scholarships (Undergraduate/Scholarship) [5300]
Snodgrass Scholarships (Undergraduate/Scholarship) [10039]
SOM Foundation Structural Engineering Travel Fellowships (Doctorate, Graduate, Master's, Undergraduate/Fellowship) [8981]
William J. Tangye Scholarships (Undergraduate/Scholarship) [5302]

Engineering, Biomedical

BMES Graduate and Undergraduate Student Awards (Graduate, Undergraduate/Award) [2271]
Detroit Section/Robert G. Dailey Scholarship (Undergraduate/Scholarship) [9260]
DOE Computational Science Graduate Fellowships (DOE CSGF) (Doctorate, Graduate/Fellowship) [5887]

Engineering, Chemical

SEE Education Foundation Scholarships (Undergraduate, Graduate, Doctorate/Scholarship) [5418]
AACE International Competitive Scholarships (Undergraduate/Scholarship) [14]
ACI BASF Construction Chemicals Student Fellowships (Graduate, Undergraduate/Fellowship) [701]
ACS Rubber Division Undergraduate Scholarships (Undergraduate/Scholarship) [666]
AESF Foundation Scholarships (Undergraduate, Graduate/Scholarship) [6796]
AIChE Minority Scholarship Awards for College Students (Undergraduate/Scholarship) [903]
AIChE Minority Scholarship Awards for Incoming College Freshmen (Undergraduate/Scholarship) [904]
Air Products and Chemicals, Inc. Scholarships (Undergraduate/Scholarship) [1975]
AISES Intel Scholarships (Graduate, Undergraduate/Scholarship) [887]
APS/ASU Scholarships (Undergraduate/Scholarship) [8139]
APS/Maricopa County Community Colleges Scholarships (Undergraduate/Scholarship) [8140]
B.O.G. Pest Control Scholarship Funds (Undergraduate, Graduate/Scholarship) [2323]
Canadian Technical Asphalt Association Scholarships (Undergraduate/Scholarship) [2762]
Robert E. Cramer Product Design and Development Scholarship (Undergraduate/Scholarship) [9259]
DEPS Graduate Scholarship Program (Graduate/Scholarship) [3624]
Dow Chemical Company Fellowships (Graduate/Fellowship) [7085]
E.I. DuPont Graduate Fellowship (Graduate/Fellowship) [7086]
Extrusion Division/Lew Erwin Memorial Scholarship (Graduate, Postgraduate/Scholarship) [9261]
Fleming/Blaszcak Scholarships (Undergraduate, Graduate/Scholarship) [9262]
Composites Division/Harold Giles Scholarship (Undergraduate, Graduate/Scholarship) [9263]
HSF/Marathon Oil College Scholarship Program (Undergraduate/Scholarship) [4905]
Thermoset Division/James I. Mackenzie and James H. Cunningham Scholarships (Undergraduate, Graduate/Scholarship) [9264]
John J. McKetta Undergraduate Scholarships (Undergraduate/Scholarship) [905]
Dolphus E. Milligan Graduate Fellowships (Graduate/Fellowship) [7087]
NDSEG Fellowships (Graduate/Fellowship) [6911]
Ted and Ruth Neward Scholarships (Undergraduate, Graduate/Scholarship) [9265]
NOBCChE Procter and Gamble Fellowships (Graduate/Fellowship) [7088]
NPSC Fellowships (Graduate/Fellowship) [7098]
Donald F. and Mildred Topp Othmer National Scholarship Awards (Undergraduate/Scholarship) [906]
Ralph W. Shrader Diversity Scholarship (Graduate/Scholarship) [91]
Carrie Fox Solin Blow Molding Division Memorial Scholarships (Undergraduate/Scholarship) [9268]
Eastman Kodak Dr. Theophilus Sorrell Fellowships (Graduate/Fellowship) [7090]
SPE Foundation General Scholarships (Undergraduate, Graduate/Scholarship) [9269]
SPE Gulf Coast Hurricane Scholarships (Undergraduate/Scholarship) [9270]
SPE Injection Molding Division Scholarships (Undergraduate, Graduate/Scholarship) [9271]
SPE Thermoforming Division Memorial Scholarships (Undergraduate, Graduate/Scholarship) [9272]
SPE Thermoplastic Elastomers Special Interest Group Scholarship (Undergraduate, Graduate/Scholarship) [9273]
SPE Vinyl Plastics Division Educational Grants (Undergraduate/Grant) [9275]
Evald Torokvei Foundation Scholarships (Graduate/Scholarship) [10296]
Xerox Technical Minority Scholarships (Graduate, Undergraduate/Scholarship) [10737]

Engineering, Civil

AACE International Competitive Scholarships (Undergraduate/Scholarship) [14]
AGC New York State Chapter Scholarship Program (Undergraduate/Scholarship) [1814]
AHETEMS/ExxonMobil Scholarships (Undergraduate/Scholarship) [8887]
AISC/Ohio Structural Steel Association Scholarships (Graduate/Scholarship) [934]
AISC/Rocky Mountain Steel Construction Association Scholarships (Graduate/Scholarship) [935]
AISC/Southern Association of Steel Fabricators Scholarships (Graduate/Scholarship) [936]
Arsham Amirikian Engineering Scholarships (Undergraduate/Scholarship) [1508]
APS/ASU Scholarships (Undergraduate/Scholarship) [8139]
APS/Maricopa County Community Colleges Scholarships (Undergraduate/Scholarship) [8140]
Associated General Contractors of Connecticut Scholarships (Undergraduate/Scholarship) [3365]
Association of State Dam Safety Officials Undergraduate Scholarships (Undergraduate/Scholarship) [2074]
Michael Baker Corp. Scholarship for Diversity in Engineering (Undergraduate/Scholarship) [1976]
ACI Baker Student Fellowships (Undergraduate, Graduate/Fellowship) [706]
Canadian Technical Asphalt Association Scholarships (Undergraduate/Scholarship) [2762]
Warren E. "Whitey" Cole American Society of Highway Engineers Scholarships (Undergraduate/Scholarship) [4042]
AISC Education Foundation - Fred R. Havens Fund (Undergraduate, Graduate/Scholarship) [937]
HSF/Marathon Oil College Scholarship Program (Undergraduate/Scholarship) [4905]
International Association of Foundation Drilling Scholarships for Civil Engineering Students (Graduate/Scholarship) [75]
International Association of Foundation Drilling

Scholarships for Part-time Civil Engineering Graduate School Students *(Graduate/Scholarship)* [76]
MALSCE Memorial Scholarships *(Undergraduate/Scholarship)* [6306]
NDSEG Fellowships *(Graduate/Fellowship)* [6911]
Pardee Community Building Scholarships *(Undergraduate/Scholarship)* [8359]
Plastics Pioneers Association Scholarships *(Undergraduate/Scholarship)* [9266]
Galvanize the Future: Edgar K. Schutz Scholarships *(Undergraduate, Graduate/Scholarship)* [838]
SOM Foundation Structural Engineering Travel Fellowships *(Doctorate, Graduate, Master's, Undergraduate/Fellowship)* [8981]
WRI Education Foundation Scholarships - Graduate *(Graduate/Scholarship)* [10611]
WRI Education Foundation Scholarships - High School Seniors *(Undergraduate/Scholarship)* [10612]
WRI Education Foundation Scholarships - Undergraduate *(Undergraduate/Scholarship)* [10613]

Engineering, Computer

AISES Intel Scholarships *(Graduate, Undergraduate/Scholarship)* [887]
Zachary Barriger Memorial Scholarships *(Undergraduate/Scholarship)* [3086]
Dr. Anita Borg Memorial Scholarships - USA *(Graduate, Undergraduate/Scholarship)* [4493]
Chambersburg/Fannett-Metal School District Scholarship Fund *(Undergraduate/Scholarship)* [4234]
Google-American Indian Science and Engineering Society Scholarships *(Graduate, Undergraduate/Scholarship)* [4495]
Google Hispanic College Fund Scholarships *(Graduate, Undergraduate/Scholarship)* [4497]
NSA Mathematics and Computer Science Student Scholarships *(Undergraduate, Graduate, Doctorate/Scholarship)* [108]
NVIDIA Graduate Fellowships *(Graduate/Fellowship)* [7566]
Xerox Technical Minority Scholarships *(Graduate, Undergraduate/Scholarship)* [10737]

Engineering, Electrical

AACE International Competitive Scholarships *(Undergraduate/Scholarship)* [14]
Aerospace Corporation Science and Engineering Student Scholarships *(Undergraduate, Graduate/Scholarship)* [95]
Affiliated Distributors Electrical Industry Scholarship Awards *(Undergraduate/Scholarship)* [3822]
AHETEMS/ExxonMobil Scholarships *(Undergraduate/Scholarship)* [8887]
AISES Intel Scholarships *(Graduate, Undergraduate/Scholarship)* [887]
AIST Ohio Valley Chapter Scholarships *(Undergraduate/Scholarship)* [1994]
APS/ASU Scholarships *(Undergraduate/Scholarship)* [8139]
APS/Maricopa County Community Colleges Scholarships *(Undergraduate/Scholarship)* [8140]
Zachary Barriger Memorial Scholarships *(Undergraduate/Scholarship)* [3086]
Burndy Canada Inc. Academic Achievement Awards *(Undergraduate/Scholarship)* [3823]
Convectair Sustainable Development Scholarship Awards *(Undergraduate/Scholarship)* [3824]
DEPS Graduate Scholarship Program *(Graduate/Scholarship)* [3624]
DOE Computational Science Graduate Fellowships (DOE CSGF) *(Doctorate, Graduate/Fellowship)* [5887]
Bob Dyer/OEL Apprenticeship Scholarships *(Undergraduate/Scholarship)* [3825]
Eaton Awards of Academic Achievement *(Undergraduate/Scholarship)* [3826]
EFC Atlantic Region Scholarships *(Undergraduate/Scholarship)* [3827]
EFC University and College Scholarships *(Undergraduate/Scholarship)* [3828]
Franklin Empire Scholarship Awards *(Undergraduate/Scholarship)* [3829]
G.E. Lighting Canada Community Leadership Awards *(Undergraduate/Award)* [3830]
Gerrie Electric Memorial Scholarship Awards *(Undergraduate/Scholarship)* [3831]
Graybar Canada Award of Excellence Scholarships *(Undergraduate/Scholarship)* [3832]
Perry F. Hadlock Memorial Scholarships *(Undergraduate/Scholarship)* [1742]
Hammond Power Solutions Inc. Outstanding Electrical Scholar Awards *(Undergraduate/Award)* [3833]
E.B. Horsman & Son Scholarships *(Undergraduate/Scholarship)* [3834]
HSF/Marathon Oil College Scholarship Program *(Undergraduate/Scholarship)* [4905]
Hubbell Canada LP "Electrical Industry Leadership" Scholarship Awards *(Undergraduate/Scholarship)* [3835]
Ideal Supply Scholarship Awards *(Undergraduate/Scholarship)* [3836]
Kerrwil's J.W. Kerr Continuing Education Scholarship Awards *(Undergraduate/Scholarship)* [3837]
Julia Kiene Fellowships in Electrical Energy *(Graduate/Fellowship)* [10660]
Louis T. Klauder Scholarships *(Undergraduate, Graduate/Scholarship)* [1166]
League of Latin American Citizens General Electric Scholarships *(Undergraduate/Scholarship)* [5987]
Imelda "Mel" and Ralph LeMar Scholarship *(Undergraduate/Scholarship)* [3330]
Lyle Mamer Fellowships *(Graduate/Fellowship, Award)* [10661]
Edmond A. Metzger Scholarships *(Undergraduate/Scholarship)* [1747]
Microsoft Research Graduate Women's Scholarships *(Graduate/Scholarship)* [6506]
Microsoft Research PhD Fellowships *(Doctorate/Fellowship)* [6507]
MillerCoors Engineering and Sciences Scholarships *(Undergraduate/Scholarship)* [68]
NDSEG Fellowships *(Graduate/Fellowship)* [6911]
NPSC Fellowships *(Graduate/Fellowship)* [7098]
NSA Electrical Engineering Student Scholarships *(Undergraduate, Graduate, Doctorate/Scholarship)* [107]
NVIDIA Graduate Fellowships *(Graduate/Fellowship)* [7566]
Osram Sylvania Scholastic Achievement Awards *(Undergraduate/Scholarship)* [3838]
Philips Lighting Continuing Education Awards *(Undergraduate/Scholarship)* [3839]
RAB Design Lighting Award of Excellence *(Undergraduate/Scholarship)* [3840]
Schneider Electric Student Merit Awards *(Undergraduate/Scholarship)* [3841]
Ralph W. Shrader Diversity Scholarship *(Graduate/Scholarship)* [91]
Siemens Canada Academic Awards *(Undergraduate/Scholarship)* [3842]
Sonepar Canada Scholarship Awards *(Undergraduate/Scholarship)* [3843]
Standard Recognition of Excellence Awards *(Undergraduate/Scholarship)* [3844]
Stelpro Scholarships 360: Energizing Potential *(Undergraduate/Scholarship)* [3845]
Thomas & Betts Scholarship Awards *(Undergraduate/Scholarship)* [3847]
WESCO Student Achievement Awards *(Undergraduate/Scholarship)* [3848]
Xerox Technical Minority Scholarships *(Graduate, Undergraduate/Scholarship)* [10737]

Engineering, Geological

Cave Conservancy Foundation Graduate and Undergraduate Fellowships *(Doctorate, Graduate, Undergraduate/Fellowship)* [2823]
Marliave Scholarship Fund *(Undergraduate/Scholarship, Grant)* [1948]
Rocky Mountain Coal Mining Institute Engineering/Geology Scholarships *(Undergraduate/Scholarship)* [8632]
Martin L. Stout Scholarships *(Undergraduate, Graduate/Scholarship)* [1949]

Engineering, Hydraulic

Channabasappa Memorial Scholarships *(Graduate, Doctorate/Scholarship)* [5319]
IDA Fellowship Awards *(Other/Fellowship)* [5320]

Engineering, Industrial

AACE International Competitive Scholarships *(Undergraduate/Scholarship)* [14]
Chapter 17 - St. Louis Scholarships *(Undergraduate/Scholarship)* [9170]
Chapter 31 - Peoria Endowed Scholarships *(Undergraduate/Scholarship)* [9173]
Chapter 52 - Wichita Scholarships *(Graduate, Undergraduate/Scholarship)* [9175]
Chapter 56 - Fort Wayne Scholarships *(Graduate, Undergraduate/Scholarship)* [9176]
Chapter 67 - Phoenix Scholarships *(Undergraduate/Scholarship)* [9178]
Chapter 198 - Downriver Detroit Scholarships *(Graduate, Undergraduate/Scholarship)* [9171]
Chapter 311 - Tri City Scholarships *(Undergraduate/Scholarship)* [9174]
Robert E. Cramer Product Design and Development Scholarship *(Undergraduate/Scholarship)* [9259]
Detroit Section/Robert G. Dailey Scholarship *(Undergraduate/Scholarship)* [9260]
Extrusion Division/Lew Erwin Memorial Scholarship *(Graduate, Postgraduate/Scholarship)* [9261]
John S.W. Fargher, Jr. Scholarships *(Graduate/Scholarship)* [5185]
Fleming/Blaszcak Scholarships *(Undergraduate, Graduate/Scholarship)* [9262]
Future Leaders of Manufacturing Scholarships *(Graduate, Undergraduate/Scholarship)* [9181]
Dwight D. Gardner Scholarships *(Undergraduate/Scholarship)* [5186]
Gilbreth Memorial Fellowships *(Graduate/Scholarship, Fellowship)* [5187]
Composites Division/Harold Giles Scholarship *(Undergraduate, Graduate/Scholarship)* [9263]
IIE Council of Fellows Undergraduate Scholarships *(Undergraduate/Scholarship)* [5188]
IISE Presidents Scholarships *(Undergraduate/Scholarship)* [5189]
John L. Imhoff Scholarships *(Graduate, Undergraduate/Scholarship)* [5190]
Thermoset Division/James I. Mackenzie and James H. Cunningham Scholarships *(Undergraduate, Graduate/Scholarship)* [9264]
Harold and Inge Marcus Scholarships *(Undergraduate/Scholarship)* [5191]
Marvin Mundel Memorial Scholarships *(Undergraduate/Scholarship)* [5192]
Clarence & Josephine Myers Undergraduate Scholarships *(Graduate, Undergraduate/Scholarship)* [9190]
Ted and Ruth Neward Scholarships *(Undergraduate, Graduate/Scholarship)* [9265]
North Central, Region 9 Scholarships *(Undergraduate/Scholarship)* [9191]
Plastics Pioneers Association Scholarships *(Undergraduate/Scholarship)* [9266]
A.O. Putnam Memorial Scholarships *(Undergraduate/Scholarship)* [5193]
Carrie Fox Solin Blow Molding Division Memorial Scholarships *(Undergraduate/Scholarship)* [9268]
SPE Foundation General Scholarships *(Undergraduate, Graduate/Scholarship)* [9269]
SPE Gulf Coast Hurricane Scholarships *(Undergraduate/Scholarship)* [9270]
SPE Injection Molding Division Scholarships *(Undergraduate, Graduate/Scholarship)* [9271]
SPE Thermoforming Division Memorial Scholarships *(Undergraduate, Graduate/Scholarship)* [9272]
SPE Thermoplastic Elastomers Special Interest Group Scholarship *(Undergraduate, Graduate/Scholarship)* [9273]
SPE Vinyl Plastics Division Educational Grants *(Undergraduate/Grant)* [9275]
Steven M. Teutsch Prevention Effectiveness Fellowships *(Doctorate/Fellowship)* [9921]
Thomas & Betts Scholarship Awards *(Undergraduate/Scholarship)* [3847]
United Parcel Service Scholarships for Female Students *(Undergraduate/Scholarship)* [5195]

United Parcel Service Scholarships for Minority Students (Undergraduate/Scholarship) [5196]
Chapter 4 - Lawrence A. Wacker Memorial Scholarships (Undergraduate/Scholarship) [9198]
Allen and Loureena Weber Scholarships (Undergraduate/Scholarship) [9200]
Lisa Zaken Awards For Excellence (Graduate, Undergraduate/Award, Monetary) [5197]

Engineering, Marine

Charles H. Bussmann Graduate Scholarship (Graduate, Undergraduate/Scholarship) [6271]
Robert N. Herbert Undergraduate Scholarships (Undergraduate/Scholarship) [9216]
Marine Technology Society ROV Scholarships (MTS ROV) (Undergraduate, Graduate/Scholarship) [6272]
The MTS Student Scholarship for Two-Year, Technical, Engineering and Community College Students (Undergraduate/Scholarship) [6275]
Mandell and Lester Rosenblatt Undergraduate Scholarships (Undergraduate/Scholarship) [9217]
SUT Houston Graduate Scholarships (Graduate/Scholarship) [9317]
SUT Houston Undergraduate Scholarships (Undergraduate/Scholarship) [9318]
John V. Wehausen Graduate Scholarships for Advanced Study in Ship Hydrodynamics and Wave Theory (Graduate/Scholarship) [9218]

Engineering, Materials

AISES Intel Scholarships (Graduate, Undergraduate/Scholarship) [887]
Robert E. Cramer Product Design and Development Scholarship (Undergraduate/Scholarship) [9259]
Detroit Section/Robert G. Dailey Scholarship (Undergraduate/Scholarship) [9260]
Extrusion Division/Lew Erwin Memorial Scholarship (Graduate, Postgraduate/Scholarship) [9261]
Fleming/Blaszcak Scholarships (Undergraduate, Graduate/Scholarship) [9262]
Composites Division/Harold Giles Scholarship (Undergraduate, Graduate/Scholarship) [9263]
Electronics Division Lewis C. Hoffman Scholarships (Undergraduate/Scholarship) [664]
Thermoset Division/James I. Mackenzie and James H. Cunningham Scholarships (Undergraduate, Graduate/Scholarship) [9264]
NDSEG Fellowships (Graduate/Fellowship) [6911]
Ted and Ruth Neward Scholarships (Undergraduate, Graduate/Scholarship) [9265]
Plastics Pioneers Association Scholarships (Undergraduate/Scholarship) [9266]
Galvanize the Future: Edgar K. Schutz Scholarships (Undergraduate, Graduate/Scholarship) [838]
Carrie Fox Solin Blow Molding Division Memorial Scholarships (Undergraduate/Scholarship) [9268]
SPE Gulf Coast Hurricane Scholarships (Undergraduate/Scholarship) [9270]
SPE Injection Molding Division Scholarships (Undergraduate, Graduate/Scholarship) [9271]
SPE Thermoforming Division Memorial Scholarships (Undergraduate, Graduate/Scholarship) [9272]
SPE Thermoplastic Elastomers Special Interest Group Scholarship (Undergraduate, Graduate/Scholarship) [9273]
SPE Vinyl Plastics Division Educational Grants (Undergraduate/Grant) [9275]
ACI Richard N. White Student Fellowships (Master's/Fellowship) [712]

Engineering, Mechanical

AACE International Competitive Scholarships (Undergraduate/Scholarship) [14]
ACS Rubber Division Undergraduate Scholarships (Undergraduate/Scholarship) [666]
Aerospace Corporation Science and Engineering Student Scholarships (Undergraduate, Graduate/Scholarship) [95]
AESF Foundation Scholarships (Undergraduate, Graduate/Scholarship) [6796]
AHETEMS/ExxonMobil Scholarships (Undergraduate/Scholarship) [8887]
Air Products and Chemicals, Inc. Scholarships (Undergraduate/Scholarship) [1975]
AIST Ohio Valley Chapter Scholarships (Undergraduate/Scholarship) [1994]
APS/ASU Scholarships (Undergraduate/Scholarship) [8139]
APS/Maricopa County Community Colleges Scholarships (Undergraduate/Scholarship) [8140]
Association of Desk and Derrick Clubs Education Trust Scholarships (Undergraduate/Scholarship) [1931]
Auxiliary Undergraduate Scholarships (Undergraduate/Scholarship) [1796]
Chapter 198 - Downriver Detroit Scholarships (Graduate, Undergraduate/Scholarship) [9171]
Lucy and Charles W.E. Clarke Scholarships (Undergraduate/Scholarship) [1797]
Convectair Sustainable Development Scholarship Awards (Undergraduate/Scholarship) [3824]
DOE Computational Science Graduate Fellowships (DOE CSGF) (Doctorate, Graduate/Fellowship) [5887]
HSF/Marathon Oil College Scholarship Program (Undergraduate/Scholarship) [4905]
Louis T. Klauder Scholarships (Undergraduate, Graduate/Scholarship) [1166]
Paul C. K. Lam Memorial Scholarship at The University of Akron (Undergraduate/Scholarship) [7593]
Imelda "Mel" and Ralph LeMar Scholarship (Undergraduate/Scholarship) [3330]
MillerCoors Engineering and Sciences Scholarships (Undergraduate/Scholarship) [68]
Clarence & Josephine Myers Undergraduate Scholarships (Graduate, Undergraduate/Scholarship) [9190]
North Central, Region 9 Scholarships (Undergraduate/Scholarship) [9191]
NPSC Fellowships (Graduate/Fellowship) [7098]
Osram Sylvania Scholastic Achievement Awards (Undergraduate/Scholarship) [3838]
Elisabeth M. and Winchell M. Parsons Scholarships (Graduate/Scholarship) [1798]
Philips Lighting Continuing Education Awards (Undergraduate/Scholarship) [3839]
RAB Design Lighting Award of Excellence (Undergraduate/Scholarship) [3840]
Rice-Cullimore Scholarships (Graduate/Scholarship) [1799]
Marjorie Roy Rothermel Scholarships (Master's/Scholarship) [1800]
Siemens Canada Academic Awards (Undergraduate/Scholarship) [3842]
Thomas & Betts Scholarship Awards (Undergraduate/Scholarship) [3847]
Chapter 4 - Lawrence A. Wacker Memorial Scholarships (Undergraduate/Scholarship) [9198]
Allen and Loureena Weber Scholarships (Undergraduate/Scholarship) [9200]
Albert E. Wischmeyer Memorial Scholarships (Undergraduate/Scholarship) [9202]
Xerox Technical Minority Scholarships (Graduate, Undergraduate/Scholarship) [10737]

Engineering, Metallurgical

AESF Foundation Scholarships (Undergraduate, Graduate/Scholarship) [6796]
AIST Ohio Valley Chapter Scholarships (Undergraduate/Scholarship) [1994]

Engineering, Mining and Mineral

American Society of Mining and Reclamation Memorial Scholarships (Undergraduate/Scholarship, Recognition) [1377]
SME Coal and Energy Division Scholarships (Undergraduate/Scholarship) [9212]
SME Environmental Division Scholarships (Undergraduate, Graduate/Scholarship) [9213]

Engineering, Naval

American Society of Naval Engineers Scholarships (ASNE) (Graduate, Undergraduate/Scholarship) [1379]

Engineering, Nuclear

SEE Education Foundation Scholarships (Undergraduate, Graduate, Doctorate/Scholarship) [5418]
American Nuclear Society Incoming Freshman Scholarships (Undergraduate/Scholarship) [1032]
American Nuclear Society Nevada Section Scholarships (Undergraduate/Scholarship) [8331]
American Nuclear Society Undergraduates Scholarships (Undergraduate/Scholarship) [1033]
Association of Desk and Derrick Clubs Education Trust Scholarships (Undergraduate/Scholarship) [1931]
DOE Computational Science Graduate Fellowships (DOE CSGF) (Doctorate, Graduate/Fellowship) [5887]
Alvin M. Weinberg Fellowships (Doctorate/Fellowship) [9910]

Engineering, Ocean

Canadian Hydrographic Association Student Awards (Undergraduate/Award, Monetary, Medal) [2662]
Robert N. Herbert Undergraduate Scholarships (Undergraduate/Scholarship) [9216]
NDSEG Fellowships (Graduate/Fellowship) [6911]
Mandell and Lester Rosenblatt Undergraduate Scholarships (Undergraduate/Scholarship) [9217]

Engineering, Optical

BACUS Scholarships (Graduate, Undergraduate/Scholarship) [9467]
Raymond Davis Scholarships (Undergraduate, Graduate/Scholarship) [9150]
DEPS Graduate Scholarship Program (Graduate/Scholarship) [3624]
Robert S. Hilbert Memorial Student Travel Grants (Graduate, Undergraduate/Grant) [7673]
Michael Kidger Memorial Scholarships in Optical Design (Undergraduate/Scholarship) [9468]
D.J. Lovell Scholarships (Graduate, Undergraduate/Scholarship) [9470]
Optical Design and Engineering Scholarships (Graduate, Undergraduate/Scholarship) [9471]
SPIE Student Author Travel Grants (Graduate, Undergraduate/Grant) [9472]
Xerox Technical Minority Scholarships (Graduate, Undergraduate/Scholarship) [10737]

Engineering, Petroleum

AHETEMS/ExxonMobil Scholarships (Undergraduate/Scholarship) [8887]
Association of Desk and Derrick Clubs Education Trust Scholarships (Undergraduate/Scholarship) [1931]
CADE Bursary (Undergraduate/Scholarship) [2550]
CADE Scholarships (Undergraduate/Scholarship) [2551]
HSF/Marathon Oil College Scholarship Program (Undergraduate/Scholarship) [4905]
Petroleum Engineering Scholarships (Undergraduate/Scholarship) [9250]
Wayne-Meador-Elliott Scholarships (Undergraduate/Scholarship) [7869]

English language and literature (See also Linguistics; Literature)

The Steve Duckett Local Conservation Scholarships (Undergraduate, Postgraduate/Scholarship) [8232]
Wilhelmina Gordon Foundation Scholarships (Undergraduate/Scholarship) [6854]
Indiana State University Creative and Performing Arts Awards (Undergraduate/Scholarship) [5127]
The Michael Kiely Strong Roots Scholarships (Undergraduate/Scholarship) [8233]
The Langfitt-Ambrose Trust Scholarship (Undergraduate/Scholarship) [7846]
The Tatiana Mendez Future Resources Scholarships (Undergraduate/Scholarship) [8234]

Field of Study Index   ENVIRONMENTAL SCIENCE

NCTE Research Foundation Grants *(Other/Grant)* [6885]
The Seth Okin Good Deeds Scholarships *(Undergraduate/Scholarship)* [8235]
William R. Pfalzgraf Scholarships *(Undergraduate/Scholarship)* [7852]
Susan P. Schroeder Memorial Scholarships *(Undergraduate/Scholarship)* [6053]
The Thomas Soldan Healthy Communities Scholarships *(Undergraduate, Graduate/Scholarship)* [8237]
Swensrud Teacher Fellowships at MHS (Massachusetts Historical Society) *(Professional development/Fellowship)* [6338]
The Ed Tayter Outstanding Citizen Scholarships *(Undergraduate/Scholarship)* [8238]
Edwyna Wheadon Postgraduate Training Scholarship Fund *(Postgraduate/Scholarship)* [6886]

Enology

American Wine Society Educational Foundation Scholarships *(Graduate/Scholarship)* [1528]
Nancy Johnston Memorial Scholarships *(Graduate, Undergraduate/Scholarship)* [9675]

Entomology

American Association of Professional Apiculturists Research Scholarships *(Graduate, Undergraduate/Scholarship)* [568]
Ed Becker Conference Travel Awards *(Undergraduate, Graduate/Award)* [3886]
Biological Survey of Canada Scholarships *(Postgraduate/Scholarship)* [3887]
John H. Borden Scholarships *(Postgraduate/Scholarship)* [3888]
Brooks Scholarships *(Graduate/Scholarship)* [3894]
Lloyd M. Dosdall Memorial Scholarships *(Postgraduate/Scholarship)* [3889]
Entomological Society of Canada Postgraduate Awards *(Postgraduate/Award)* [3890]
Entomological Society of Saskatchewan Student Presentation Awards *(Undergraduate/Award)* [3895]
Entomological Society of Saskatchewan Travel Awards *(Professional development/Award)* [3896]
Lillian and Alex Feir Graduate Student Travel Awards *(Master's, Doctorate/Award)* [3880]
Graduate Research-Travel Scholarships *(Graduate/Scholarship)* [3891]
Nancy Johnston Memorial Scholarships *(Graduate, Undergraduate/Scholarship)* [9675]
Shripat Kamble Urban Entomology Graduate Student Awards for Innovative Research *(Doctorate/Recognition, Grant)* [3881]
Keith Kevan Award *(Postgraduate/Award)* [3892]
Jeffery P. LaFage Graduate Student Research Award *(Master's, Doctorate/Grant)* [3882]
Louisiana Agricultural Consultants Association Scholarships *(Graduate, Undergraduate/Scholarship)* [6112]
North Carolina Commercial Flower Growers Association Floriculture Scholarships *(Graduate, Undergraduate/Scholarship)* [7456]
Henry and Sylvia Richardson Research Grant *(Postdoctorate/Grant)* [3883]
Rove Pest Control Scholarships *(Undergraduate/Scholarship)* [8650]
Kenneth and Barbara Starks Plant Resistance to Insects Graduate Student Research Awards *(Graduate/Grant)* [3884]

Environmental conservation

VPPPA Stephen Brown Scholarships *(Graduate, Undergraduate/Scholarship)* [10417]
CCF Academic Fellowships in Karst Studies - Graduate *(Master's, Doctorate/Fellowship)* [2820]
CTEC Internships *(Undergraduate/Internship)* [1567]
Antenore C. "Butch" Davanzo Scholarships *(Graduate, Undergraduate/Scholarship)* [6502]
Ellen Eberhardt Memorial Scholarships *(Undergraduate/Scholarship)* [9565]
Joseph L. Fisher Doctoral Dissertation Fellowships *(Graduate/Fellowship)* [8561]

Grand Canyon Historical Society Scholarships *(Graduate/Scholarship)* [4508]
John P. Hennessey Scholarships *(Graduate, Undergraduate/Scholarship)* [6503]
National Geographic Conservation Trust Grants *(Doctorate, Advanced Professional/Grant)* [6971]
National Geographic Expedition Council Grants *(Advanced Professional/Grant)* [6972]
National Geographic Society/Waitt Grants *(Advanced Professional/Grant)* [6973]
National Geographic Young Explorers Grants *(Advanced Professional/Grant)* [6974]
NGC College Scholarships *(Graduate, Undergraduate/Scholarship)* [6965]
NYCT Paid Graduate Student Philanthropy Fellowships - Community Development and the Environment *(Graduate/Fellowship)* [7351]
VPPPA William Sullivan Scholarships *(Graduate, Undergraduate/Scholarship)* [10418]
Switzer Environmental Fellowships *(Graduate/Fellowship)* [9623]
VPPPA June Brothers Scholarships *(Graduate, Undergraduate/Scholarship)* [10419]
Jack H. Wagner Scholarships *(Graduate, Undergraduate/Scholarship)* [6504]
Frederick K. Weyerhaeuser Forest History Fellowships *(Graduate/Fellowship)* [4138]
Worcester County Conservation District Annual Scholarships Program *(Undergraduate/Scholarship)* [10687]

Environmental design

Vectorworks Design Scholarships *(Undergraduate, Graduate/Scholarship, Prize)* [10367]
Worldstudio AIGA Scholarships *(Graduate, Undergraduate/Scholarship)* [10709]

Environmental law

A&WMA Scholarships *(Graduate/Scholarship)* [139]
EMLF Law Student Scholarships *(Undergraduate/Scholarship)* [3869]
McCloy Fellowships in Environmental Policy *(Professional development/Fellowship)* [728]
Property and Environment Research Center Graduate Fellowships *(Graduate/Fellowship)* [8297]
SSAWMA Scholarships *(Graduate/Scholarship)* [9415]
Switzer Environmental Fellowships *(Graduate/Fellowship)* [9623]

Environmental science (See also Ecology)

American Society of Mining and Reclamation Memorial Scholarships *(Undergraduate/Scholarship, Recognition)* [1377]
Anchor QEA Environmental Scholarships *(Graduate/Scholarship)* [1551]
Max Bell Senior Fellow Grants *(Advanced Professional/Grant)* [2219]
B.O.G. Pest Control Scholarship Funds *(Undergraduate, Graduate/Scholarship)* [2323]
Carol Bond Community College Scholarships *(Undergraduate/Scholarship)* [7479]
Carol Bond University Scholarships *(Undergraduate/Scholarship)* [7480]
Stephen Bronfman Scholarship Funds in Environmental Studies *(Graduate/Scholarship)* [5572]
Rachel Carson Prize *(Other/Prize)* [1310]
CH2M Hill/AEESP Outstanding Doctoral Dissertation Award *(Graduate, Doctorate/Award)* [1951]
Chopivsky Fellowships *(Graduate/Fellowship)* [10442]
Community-based Natural Resource Management Assistantships *(Undergraduate, Advanced Professional/Internship)* [3169]
Convectair Sustainable Development Scholarship Awards *(Undergraduate/Scholarship)* [3824]
CTFS Research Grants Program *(Graduate, Postdoctorate, Professional development/Grant)* [9036]
Frank L. Dautriel Memorial Scholarships for Graduates *(Graduate/Scholarship)* [6116]
Frank L. Dautriel Memorial Scholarships for Under-

graduates *(Undergraduate/Scholarship)* [6117]
DOE Computational Science Graduate Fellowships (DOE CSGF) *(Doctorate, Graduate/Fellowship)* [5887]
The Steve Duckett Local Conservation Scholarships *(Undergraduate, Postgraduate/Scholarship)* [8232]
W. Wesley Eckenfelder Gradute Research Award *(Graduate, Master's, Doctorate/Award)* [1952]
EMLF Law Student Scholarships *(Undergraduate/Scholarship)* [3869]
EPA Science to Achieve Results Fellowships (STAR) *(Graduate/Fellowship)* [7403]
FAMU Presidential Scholarship - Florida Community College Scholarships *(Undergraduate/Scholarship)* [4076]
Grant H. Flint International Scholarships - Category II *(Undergraduate/Scholarship)* [9338]
GFLC AWMA Scholarships *(Undergraduate, Graduate/Scholarship)* [4361]
Greater Research Opportunities (GRO) Undergraduate Fellowships *(Undergraduate/Fellowship)* [9933]
GWS Scholarships *(Undergraduate, Graduate/Scholarship)* [145]
HACU/Empacadora Fruticola Santa Ines S.A. de C.V. Scholarships *(Undergraduate, Graduate/Scholarship)* [4884]
HACU/Gilberto Salazar Escoboza Scholarships *(Undergraduate, Graduate/Scholarship)* [4885]
HACU/Videxport S.A. de C.V. Scholarships *(Undergraduate, Graduate/Scholarship)* [4889]
Harry Hampton Fund Scholarship *(Undergraduate/Scholarship)* [4733]
Samuel P. Hays Research Fellowships *(Other/Fellowship)* [1312]
Marjorie M. Hendricks Environmental Education Scholarship Fund *(Undergraduate/Scholarship)* [4523]
Jeffress Trust Awards Program in Interdisciplinary Research *(Professional development/Award)* [4816]
N.G. Kaul Memorial Scholarships *(Doctorate, Graduate/Scholarship)* [7403]
The Michael Kiely Strong Roots Scholarships *(Undergraduate/Scholarship)* [8233]
Legacy Inc. College Undergraduate and Graduate Scholarships *(Graduate, Undergraduate/Scholarship)* [6002]
George Perkins Marsh Prize *(Other/Prize)* [1313]
Randall Matthis for Environmental Studies Scholarships *(Graduate, Undergraduate/Scholarship)* [1649]
J.B. and Marilyn McKenzie Graduate Student Fellowships *(Graduate/Fellowship)* [10186]
Ben Meadows Natural Resource Scholarships - Academic Achievement Scholarships *(Undergraduate/Scholarship)* [2221]
Ben Meadows Natural Resource Scholarships - Leadership Scholarships *(Undergraduate/Scholarship)* [2222]
The Tatiana Mendez Future Resources Scholarships *(Undergraduate/Scholarship)* [8234]
MHS/Cushing Academy Fellowships on Environmental History *(Professional development/Fellowship)* [6332]
NCNJ-AWMA Undergraduate Scholarship *(Undergraduate/Scholarship)* [152]
NEHA/AAS Scholarship *(Graduate, Undergraduate/Scholarship)* [6943]
New York Water Environment Association Scholarships *(Undergraduate/Scholarship)* [7404]
Eric Niemitalo Scholarships in Earth and Environmental Science *(Undergraduate/Scholarship)* [8879]
NMPF National Dairy Leadership Scholarships *(Graduate, Master's, Doctorate/Scholarship)* [7073]
The Seth Okin Good Deeds Scholarships *(Undergraduate/Scholarship)* [8235]
A. Stanley Rand Fellowships Program *(Undergraduate, Doctorate, Postdoctorate/Fellowship)* [9037]
Hal Rothman Dissertation Fellowships *(Doctorate, Graduate/Fellowship)* [1316]
SAEMS Environmental Scholarships *(Undergraduate, Graduate/Scholarship)* [9396]

Scholarships, Fellowships and Loans, 34th Ed.   1497

Miller G. Sherwood Family Scholarship Fund (Undergraduate/Scholarship) [4548]
William Brewster Snow Award (Graduate/Award, Monetary) [1954]
The Thomas Soldan Healthy Communities Scholarships (Undergraduate, Graduate/Scholarship) [8237]
Robert P. Stearns/SCS Engineers Scholarships (Graduate/Scholarship) [9339]
Switzer Environmental Fellowships (Graduate/Fellowship) [9623]
The Ed Tayter Outstanding Citizen Scholarships (Undergraduate/Scholarship) [8238]
UC MEXUS-CONACYT Doctoral Fellowships (Doctorate/Fellowship) [10117]
Virginia Tech Student Travel Award (Undergraduate, Graduate/Award) [1955]
WALPA Lake Student Scholarships (Undergraduate, Graduate/Scholarship) [10466]
Mary and Elliot Wood Foundation Graduate Scholarship Fund (Graduate/Scholarship) [4222]

Environmental technology

AESF Foundation Scholarships (Undergraduate, Graduate/Scholarship) [6796]
Alberta Innovates Graduate Student Scholarships (Graduate/Scholarship) [256]
Jim Bourque Scholarship (Undergraduate/Scholarship) [1617]
Frank L. Dautriel Memorial Scholarships for Graduates (Graduate/Scholarship) [6116]
Frank L. Dautriel Memorial Scholarships for Undergraduates (Undergraduate/Scholarship) [6117]
Hamilton Industrial Environmental Association Bursaries-Mohawk College (Undergraduate/Scholarship) [4691]
Hampton Roads Sanitation District Environmental Scholarships (Graduate/Scholarship) [4699]
NCNJ-AWMA Undergraduate Scholarship (Undergraduate/Scholarship) [152]
Switzer Environmental Fellowships (Graduate/Fellowship) [9623]
Thompson Scholarships for Women in Safety (Graduate/Scholarship) [1430]
Morris K. Udall Scholarships (Undergraduate/Scholarship) [9825]

Epidemiology (See also Infectious diseases)

Alex's Lemonade Stand Foundation Epidemiology Grants (Doctorate, Master's, Professional development/Grant) [318]
Raymond B. Bauer Research Award (Professional development/Grant) [6479]
OHTN Postdoctoral Fellowships (Doctorate/Fellowship) [7637]

Epilepsy

Epilepsy Foundation Behavioral Sciences Post-Doctoral Fellowships (Postdoctorate/Fellowship) [3902]
Epilepsy Foundation Behavioral Sciences Student Fellowships (Graduate, Undergraduate/Fellowship) [3903]
Epilepsy Foundation Health Sciences Student Fellowships (Doctorate, Graduate/Fellowship) [3904]
Epilepsy Foundation Post-doctoral Research and Training Fellowships (Postdoctorate/Fellowship) [3905]
Epilepsy Foundation Pre-doctoral Research Training Fellowships (Graduate/Fellowship) [3906]
Epilepsy Foundation Research Grants (Doctorate/Grant) [3907]
Epilepsy Foundation Research and Training Fellowships for Clinicians (Doctorate, Other/Grant) [3908]
Savoy Foundation Postdoctoral and Clinical Research Fellowships (Postdoctorate/Fellowship) [4123]
Targeted Research Initiative for Health Outcomes (Doctorate/Grant) [3909]

Equine studies

Alabama Horse Council Scholarships (Undergraduate/Scholarship) [203]

Ethics and bioethics

ARRS/Leonard Berlin Scholarships in Medical Professionalism (Other/Scholarship) [1222]

Ethnography

Conservation Department Program Fellowships (Graduate/Fellowship) [9028]
Fejos Postdoctoral Fellowships in Ethnographic Film (Postdoctorate/Fellowship) [10516]

European studies (See also Central European studies; East European studies)

CES Conference Travel Grants (Graduate, Professional development/Grant) [3437]
CES First Article Prize (Professional development/Prize) [3438]
CES Pre-Dissertation Research Fellowships (Graduate/Fellowship) [3439]
Dissertation Fellowships in East European Studies (Doctorate/Fellowship) [740]
Early Career Postdoctoral Fellowships in East European Studies (Postdoctorate/Fellowship) [741]
Educational and Cultural Affairs Alumni Small Grants Program (ECA) (Other/Grant) [5380]
Dr. Guido Goldman Fellowships (Doctorate, Postdoctorate/Fellowship) [724]
Individual Advanced Research Opportunities Program For Master's Students (Graduate, Master's/Fellowship) [5381]
IREX Individual Advanced Research Opportunities Program For Pre-doctoral Students (Doctorate/Fellowship) [5382]
IREX Individual Advanced Research Opportunities Program For Professionals (Other/Fellowship) [5383]
IREX Individual Advanced Research Opportunities Program for Postdoctoral Scholars (Postdoctorate/Fellowship) [5384]
Kress Fellowships in Art History at Foreign Institutions (Graduate/Fellowship) [5890]
Mellon-CES Dissertation Completion Fellowships (Graduate/Fellowship) [3440]
NEH Fellowships for Senior Scholars (Doctorate/Fellowship) [2853]
Prins Foundation Fellowship for Senior Scholars (Doctorate/Fellowship) [2854]
Prins Foundation Post-Doctoral and Early Career Fellowship for Emigrating Scholars (Professional development, Postdoctorate/Fellowship) [2855]

Family planning

Geraldine Clewell Fellowships - Doctoral Student (Graduate/Fellowship) [8086]
Geraldine Clewell Fellowships - Masteral (Graduate/Fellowship) [8087]
Geraldine Clewell Scholarships - Undergraduate (Undergraduate/Scholarship) [8088]
Closs/Parnitzke/Clarke Scholarships (Undergraduate/Scholarship) [8089]
Jean Dearth Dickerscheid Fellowships (Graduate/Fellowship) [8090]
Margaret Drew Alpha Fellowships (Graduate/Fellowship) [8091]
Lydia Fohn-Hansen/Lola Hill Memorial Scholarships (Undergraduate, Graduate/Scholarship) [10018]
Genevieve Forthun Scholarships (Undergraduate/Scholarship) [8092]
Mary Weiking Franken Scholarships (Undergraduate/Scholarship) [8093]
Tommie J. Hamner Scholarships (Undergraduate/Scholarship) [8094]
Jackman Scholarships (Undergraduate/Scholarship) [8095]
Martha Combs Jenkins Scholarships (Undergraduate/Scholarship) [8096]
Treva C. Kintner Scholarships (Undergraduate/Scholarship) [8097]
NYCT Paid Graduate Student Philanthropy Fellowships - Children, Youth, Families, Education, Human Justice and Workforce (Graduate/Fellowship) [7350]
Phi Upsilon Omicron Candle Fellowships (Graduate/Fellowship) [8098]
Phi Upsilon Omicron Challenge Scholarships (Undergraduate/Scholarship) [8099]
Phi Upsilon Omicron Diamond Anniversary Fellowships (Graduate/Fellowship) [8100]
Phi Upsilon Omicron Founders Fellowships (Graduate/Fellowship) [8101]
Phi Upsilon Omicron Golden Anniversary Scholarships (Undergraduate/Scholarship) [8102]
Phi Upsilon Omicron Past Presidents Scholarships (Undergraduate/Scholarship) [8103]
Phi Upsilon Omicron Presidents Research Fellowships (Graduate/Fellowship) [8104]
Nell Bryant Robinson Scholarships (Undergraduate/Scholarship) [8105]
Lucile Rust Scholarships (Undergraduate/Scholarship) [8106]
Margaret Jerome Sampson Scholarships (Undergraduate/Scholarship) [8107]
Lillian P. Schoephoerster Scholarships (Undergraduate/Scholarship) [8108]
SFP Junior Investigator's Career Development Awards (Other/Grant) [9119]
SFP Mid-Career/Mentor Awards for Family Planning (Other/Grant) [9120]
SFP Student Research Grants (Graduate/Grant) [9121]

Family/Marital therapy (See also Rehabilitation, Physical/Psychological)

AAMFT Minority Fellowships (Doctorate, Graduate/Fellowship) [538]

Fashion design

Paul Arnold Memorial Scholarships (Undergraduate/Scholarship) [8241]
California Association of Family and Consumer Sciences - San Diego Chapter Scholarships (CAFCS) (Undergraduate, Graduate/Scholarship) [8695]
S. Penny Chappell Scholarships (Undergraduate/Scholarship) [8085]
Hadar Chemtob Memorial Scholarships (Undergraduate/Scholarship) [5574]
Edith Head Scholarships (Undergraduate/Scholarship) [3584]
Sutherland/Purdy Scholarships (Undergraduate/Scholarship) [8109]
Women's Jewelry Association Member Grants (Professional development/Grant) [10663]
Worldstudio AIGA Scholarships (Graduate, Undergraduate/Scholarship) [10709]

Fashion modeling

Miss America Community Service Scholarship (Undergraduate/Scholarship) [6557]
Miss America Quality of Life Awards (Undergraduate/Scholarship) [6558]

Filmmaking (See also Media arts)

AAS Fellowships for Creative and Performing Artists and Writers (Professional development/Fellowship, Award) [430]
AFA Film and Video Arts Project Grants (Professional development/Grant) [240]
Anne Friedberg Innovative Scholarship Awards (Other/Scholarship) [9104]
Canadian Picture Pioneers Scholarships (Undergraduate/Scholarship) [2734]
Documentary Film Grants (Professional development/Grant) [369]

Field of Study Index

FOOD SCIENCE AND TECHNOLOGY

Carole Fielding Student Grant *(Undergraduate, Graduate/Grant)* [10131]
Harvey Fellows Program *(Graduate/Fellowship)* [6632]
Steve Kaplan TV and Film Studies Scholarships *(Other/Scholarship)* [1273]
MANAA Media Scholarships *(Graduate, Undergraduate/Scholarship)* [6382]
Scott Pearlman Field Awards for Science and Exploration *(Other/Award)* [3946]
Mister Rogers Memorial Scholarship *(Graduate, Master's, Doctorate/Scholarship)* [47]
Betty Rose Scholarships *(Undergraduate/Scholarship)* [1276]
Worldstudio AIGA Scholarships *(Graduate, Undergraduate/Scholarship)* [10709]

Finance (See also Accounting; Banking)

Herb Adrian Memorial Scholarship Fund *(Undergraduate/Scholarship)* [4173]
African American Network - Carolinas Scholarship Fund *(Undergraduate/Scholarship)* [4174]
AFWA Masters Degree Scholarships *(Undergraduate, Master's/Scholarship)* [49]
AFWA Undergraduate Scholarships *(Undergraduate/Scholarship)* [50]
ALPFA Scholarship Programs *(Graduate, Undergraduate/Scholarship)* [2013]
American Society of Military Comptrollers National Scholarship Program *(Undergraduate/Scholarship)* [1375]
APS/ASU Scholarships *(Undergraduate/Scholarship)* [8139]
APS/Maricopa County Community Colleges Scholarships *(Undergraduate/Scholarship)* [8140]
Bank of Canada Fellowship Award *(Doctorate, Other/Fellowship, Grant)* [2187]
Bank of Canada Governor's Awards *(Doctorate, Other/Award, Grant)* [2188]
Sharon D. Banks Undergraduate Memorial Scholarships *(Undergraduate/Scholarship)* [10674]
Stuart Cameron and Margaret McLeod Memorial Scholarships (SCMS) *(Graduate, Undergraduate/Scholarship)* [5205]
The Canadian Derivatives Exchange Scholars Program *(Graduate, Postgraduate/Scholarship)* [2345]
Clark High School Academy of Finance Scholarships *(Undergraduate/Scholarship)* [8338]
Amy and Tim Dauphinee Scholarships *(Graduate/Scholarship)* [2575]
Ernst and Young Scholarships *(Undergraduate/Scholarship)* [1780]
FINCAD Women in Finance Scholarships *(Graduate/Scholarship)* [4024]
Brendan Flores Alumni Leadership Circle Scholarship - Clark High School *(Undergraduate/Scholarship)* [8344]
GFOA Minorities in Government Finance Scholarship *(Graduate, Undergraduate/Scholarship)* [4502]
Senator James Gladstone Memorial Scholarships *(Graduate, Undergraduate/Scholarship)* [249]
Daniel B. Goldberg Scholarship *(Graduate/Scholarship)* [4503]
Frank L. Greathouse Government Accounting Scholarship *(Graduate, Undergraduate/Scholarship)* [4504]
Harvey Fellows Program *(Graduate/Fellowship)* [6632]
HSF/Wells Fargo Scholarship Program *(Undergraduate/Scholarship)* [4906]
IMA Memorial Education Fund Scholarships (MEF) *(Graduate, Undergraduate/Scholarship)* [5206]
ISU Networks Scholarships College of Business *(Undergraduate/Scholarship)* [5122]
Robert A. Kleckner Scholarships *(Undergraduate, Graduate/Scholarship)* [9439]
Alexander Fraser Laidlaw Fellowships *(Graduate/Fellowship, Scholarship)* [2576]
Lemaire Co-operative Studies Awards *(Undergraduate, Graduate/Scholarship)* [2577]
Douglas McRorie Memorial Scholarships *(Doctorate, Master's/Scholarship)* [114]

Robert E. and Judy More Scholarship Fund *(Undergraduate/Scholarship)* [4053]
Mutual of Omaha Finance Careers Scholarships *(Undergraduate, Graduate/Scholarship)* [105]
NABA National Scholarship Program *(Graduate, Undergraduate/Scholarship)* [6716]
NAFA Corporate Aviation Business Scholarship *(Undergraduate, Graduate/Scholarship)* [6692]
NAIFA West Michigan Scholarships *(Undergraduate/Scholarship)* [4614]
New York Financial Writers' Associations Scholarships *(Graduate, Undergraduate/Scholarship)* [7354]
NYFWA Scholarships *(Undergraduate, Graduate/Scholarship)* [7355]
Helene M. Overly Memorial Scholarships *(Undergraduate/Scholarship)* [10675]
Ritchie-Jennings Memorial Scholarships *(Undergraduate, Graduate/Scholarship)* [1923]
Royal Bank Scholarships *(Undergraduate, Master's/Scholarship)* [2290]
South Carolina Association for Financial Professionals Certified Treasury Professional Scholarships *(Other/Scholarship)* [9358]
South Carolina Association for Financial Professionals College Education Scholarships *(Undergraduate/Scholarship)* [9359]
Surety and Fidelity Industry Intern and Scholarship Program for Minority Students *(Undergraduate/Scholarship)* [9614]
Robert Toigo Foundation Fellowships *(Master's/Fellowship)* [9747]
Wells Fargo American Indian Scholarships - Graduate *(Graduate/Scholarship)* [883]
Wells Fargo Career Scholarship *(Undergraduate/Scholarship)* [10085]

Fine arts (See Art)

Finnish studies (See Area and ethnic studies)

Fires and fire prevention

CFSA Randal Brown & Associates Awards *(Undergraduate/Award)* [1911]
CFSA Aon Fire Protection Engineering Award *(Undergraduate/Scholarship)* [1912]
CFSA City of Markham, Buildings Standards Department Award *(Undergraduate/Scholarship)* [1913]
CFSA Fire Safety Awards *(Postgraduate/Award, Monetary)* [1914]
CFSA Leber Rubes Inc. Awards *(Postgraduate/Award, Monetary)* [1915]
CFSA LRI Engineering Award *(Undergraduate/Scholarship)* [1916]
CFSA Nadine International Inc. Awards *(Undergraduate/Award)* [1917]
CFSA Siemens Canada Award *(Undergraduate/Scholarship)* [1918]
CFSA Underwriters' Laboratories of Canada Awards *(Undergraduate/Award)* [1919]
International Association of Wildland Fire Graduate-Level Scholarships *(Doctorate, Graduate/Scholarship)* [5278]
Junior Firefighter Scholarships *(Undergraduate/Scholarship)* [7211]
Friends and Family of Christopher J. Kohlmeier Scholarships *(Undergraduate/Scholarship)* [8489]
Joseph C. Menezes Scholarship *(Undergraduate/Scholarship)* [6189]
Harry J. Morris, Jr. Emergency Services Scholarships *(Undergraduate/Scholarship)* [4613]
Snodgrass Scholarships *(Undergraduate/Scholarship)* [10039]
Thompson Scholarships for Women in Safety *(Graduate/Scholarship)* [1430]
John Charles Wilson and Robert Doran Sr. Scholarships *(Undergraduate/Scholarship)* [5246]

Fisheries sciences/management

Anchor QEA Environmental Scholarships *(Graduate/Scholarship)* [1551]
Norman S. Baldwin Fishery Science Scholarship *(Doctorate, Graduate/Scholarship)* [5260]
Ted Bjornn University of Idaho Graduate Student Scholarships *(Graduate/Scholarship)* [5033]
Ted Bjornn University of Idaho Undergraduate Student Scholarships *(Undergraduate/Scholarship)* [5034]
Jack B. Fisher Scholarship Fund *(Undergraduate/Scholarship)* [9501]
Harry Hampton Fund Scholarship *(Undergraduate/Scholarship)* [4733]
B. Harper Bull Conservation Fellowships *(Graduate/Fellowship)* [9749]
ICAFS Idaho Graduate Student Scholarships *(Graduate/Scholarship)* [5035]
ICAFS Idaho High School Student Scholarships *(Undergraduate/Scholarship)* [5036]
ICAFS Idaho Undergraduate Student Scholarships *(Undergraduate/Scholarship)* [5037]
Susan B. Martin Memorial Scholarships *(Graduate/Scholarship)* [5038]
Ben Meadows Natural Resource Scholarships - Academic Achievement Scholarships *(Undergraduate/Scholarship)* [2221]
Ben Meadows Natural Resource Scholarships - Leadership Scholarships *(Undergraduate/Scholarship)* [2222]
Ronald L. Schmied Scholarships *(Other, Undergraduate/Scholarship)* [4686]
Vern Parish *(Graduate, Undergraduate/Scholarship)* [964]

Floriculture

NGC College Scholarships *(Graduate, Undergraduate/Scholarship)* [6965]
Joseph Shinoda Memorial Scholarships *(Undergraduate/Scholarship)* [8867]

Folklore

Muddy Waters Scholarships *(Undergraduate/Scholarship)* [2316]

Food science and technology

American Association of Cereal Chemists Graduate Fellowships *(Graduate/Fellowship)* [12]
Margaret J. Andrew Memorial Scholarships *(Undergraduate, Graduate/Scholarship)* [8909]
ASBC Foundation Graduate Scholarships *(Graduate/Scholarship)* [1247]
ASBC Foundation Undergraduate Scholarships *(Undergraduate/Scholarship)* [1248]
Clifford L. Bedford Scholarship Award *(Undergraduate/Scholarship)* [5177]
The Bentley Cropping Systems Fellowship *(Graduate/Fellowship)* [2886]
California Association of Family and Consumer Sciences - San Diego Chapter Scholarships (CAFCS) *(Undergraduate, Graduate/Scholarship)* [8695]
Career Development Scholarships *(Postdoctorate, Postgraduate/Scholarship)* [4129]
Letitia B. Carter Scholarships *(Undergraduate, Advanced Professional/Scholarship)* [8563]
Carleton A. Friday Scholarship *(Undergraduate/Scholarship)* [6527]
Great Lakes Section Diversity Scholarship *(Graduate, Undergraduate/Scholarship)* [5178]
Marcia S. Harris Legacy Fund Scholarships *(Undergraduate, Advanced Professional/Scholarship)* [8564]
Institute of Food Technologists Graduate Scholarships *(Graduate/Scholarship)* [5171]
Institute of Food Technologists Junior/Senior Scholarships *(Undergraduate/Scholarship)* [5172]
Institute of Food Technologists Sophomore Scholarships *(Undergraduate/Scholarship)* [5173]
International Association for Food Protection - Student Travel Scholarship Program *(Undergraduate,*

Scholarships, Fellowships and Loans, 34th Ed.

Graduate/Scholarship) [5258]
International Foodservice Editorial Council Scholarships *(Graduate, Undergraduate/Scholarship)* [5331]
AACT John Kitt Memorial Scholarship *(Undergraduate/Scholarship)* [477]
LionsDeal Scholarships *(Undergraduate/Scholarship)* [6095]
Maine Nutrition Council Scholarships *(Undergraduate/Scholarship)* [6219]
E.H. Marth Food and Environmental Scholarships *(Undergraduate/Scholarship)* [10615]
National Poultry and Food Distributors Association Scholarships *(Undergraduate/Scholarship)* [7102]
NMPF National Dairy Leadership Scholarships *(Graduate, Master's, Doctorate/Scholarship)* [7073]
PMCA/Penn State Fellowship in Confectionery Research *(Graduate/Fellowship)* [8293]
RAMEF/NRAEF Co-Branded Scholarships *(Undergraduate/Scholarship)* [8565]
School Nutrition Association of Kansas Education Scholarship *(Undergraduate/Scholarship)* [8810]
Stark County Dairy Promoters Scholarships *(Undergraduate/Scholarship)* [9536]
Undergraduate/Graduate Scholarships *(Undergraduate, Graduate/Scholarship)* [5315]
John D. Utterback Scholarship Program *(Undergraduate/Scholarship)* [322]
Kenneth G. Weckel Scholarships *(Undergraduate/Scholarship)* [6528]

Food service careers

California Association of Family and Consumer Sciences - San Diego Chapter Scholarships (CAFCS) *(Undergraduate, Graduate/Scholarship)* [8695]
Career Development Scholarships *(Postdoctorate, Postgraduate/Scholarship)* [4129]
Letitia B. Carter Scholarships *(Undergraduate, Advanced Professional/Scholarship)* [8563]
Nancy Curry Scholarships *(Vocational/Occupational/Scholarship)* [8804]
David Meador Foundation - Hospitality-Food Service Scholarships *(Undergraduate/Scholarship)* [7294]
GED Jump Start Scholarships *(Professional development/Scholarship)* [8805]
Marcia S. Harris Legacy Fund Scholarships *(Undergraduate, Advanced Professional/Scholarship)* [8564]
IFSEA Worthy Goal Scholarships *(Two Year College, Undergraduate, Vocational/Occupational/Scholarship)* [5329]
International Dairy-Deli-Bakery Association Undergraduate/Graduate Scholarships *(Graduate, Undergraduate/Scholarship)* [5314]
International Foodservice Editorial Council Scholarships *(Graduate, Undergraduate/Scholarship)* [5331]
Les Dames D'Escoffier New York Scholarships *(Undergraduate/Scholarship)* [6009]
Oklahoma Restaurant Association Scholarships *(Graduate, Undergraduate/Scholarship)* [7604]
RAMEF/NRAEF Co-Branded Scholarships *(Undergraduate/Scholarship)* [8565]
Al Schuman/Ecolab Undergraduate Entrepreneurial Scholarships *(Undergraduate/Scholarship)* [7120]
Schwan's Food Service Scholarships *(Vocational/Occupational/Scholarship)* [8806]
Jeff Siegel Scholarships *(Undergraduate/Scholarship)* [7359]
SNF Professional Growth Scholarships *(Graduate, Undergraduate/Scholarship)* [8807]
Winston Build Your Future Scholarship *(Graduate, Undergraduate, Vocational/Occupational/Scholarship)* [8808]

Foreign languages

AISLS Grants for Language Instruction *(Doctorate/Grant)* [931]
ARIT Summer Fellowships for Intensive Advanced Turkish Language Study *(Graduate, Undergraduate/Fellowship)* [1203]
Pete and Ellen Bensley Memorial Scholarship Fund *(Undergraduate/Scholarship)* [4178]
Blakemore Freeman Fellowships *(Undergraduate, Advanced Professional/Fellowship)* [2307]
Blakemore Refresher Grants *(Professional development/Grant)* [2308]
Palo Verde High School - Barbara Edwards Memorial Scholarships *(Undergraduate/Scholarship)* [8342]
German Society Scholarships *(Undergraduate/Scholarship)* [4404]
Michael J. Hogan Language Fellowships *(Graduate/Fellowship)* [9138]
ISCALC International Scholarship Fund *(Undergraduate/Scholarship)* [4049]
Italian Language Scholarships *(Undergraduate/Scholarship)* [7682]
Kor Memorial Scholarships *(Undergraduate, Graduate/Scholarship)* [5842]
Language Teacher Bursary Program Awards *(Other/Award)* [277]
Languages In Teacher Education Scholarships *(Undergraduate/Scholarship)* [278]
MACC Scholarships *(Other/Scholarship)* [6444]
National Security Education Program - David L. Boren Fellowships *(Graduate/Fellowship)* [10137]
Thomas R. Pickering Graduate Foreign Affairs Fellowships *(Graduate, Undergraduate/Fellowship)* [10681]
SANS Inc./Mead Leadership Fellows Program *(Professional development/Fellowship)* [7509]
Richard J. Schmeelk Fellowships *(Graduate/Fellowship)* [8790]
UF Center for Latin American Studies FLAS Summer Fellowships *(Master's, Graduate, Undergraduate/Award, Fellowship)* [10133]
UH Manoa Starr Foundation Graduate Fellowships in Asian Studies *(Graduate/Grant)* [10138]
Audrey L. Wright Scholarships *(Undergraduate/Scholarship)* [4637]

Forestry

Chopivsky Fellowships *(Graduate/Fellowship)* [10442]
Cecil Earl Clapp, Sr. Memorial Scholarship *(Undergraduate/Scholarship)* [7531]
Robert E. Dougherty Scholarships *(Undergraduate, Postgraduate/Scholarship)* [3339]
James L. and Genevieve H. Goodwin Scholarships *(Undergraduate/Scholarship)* [4753]
Harry Hampton Fund Scholarship *(Undergraduate/Scholarship)* [4733]
B. Harper Bull Conservation Fellowships *(Graduate/Fellowship)* [9749]
Ben Meadows Natural Resource Scholarships - Academic Achievement Scholarships *(Undergraduate/Scholarship)* [2221]
Ben Meadows Natural Resource Scholarships - Leadership Scholarships *(Undergraduate/Scholarship)* [2222]
NGC College Scholarships *(Graduate, Undergraduate/Scholarship)* [6965]
NTHA Forest Resources Scholarships for College Students *(Undergraduate/Scholarship)* [7525]
Dr. Harry V. Pfautz Memorial Scholarship Fund *(Undergraduate/Scholarship)* [4250]
Frederick K. Weyerhaeuser Forest History Fellowships *(Graduate/Fellowship)* [4138]
WFI International Fellowships *(Undergraduate/Fellowship)* [10702]

French studies (See also Area and ethnic studies)

ALIS Fellowships for Full-time Studies in French *(Undergraduate/Fellowship)* [263]
Alliance Francaise of Hartford Harpin/Rohinsky Scholarships *(Undergraduate/Scholarship)* [4736]
Walter J. Jensen Fellowships *(Other/Fellowship)* [8052]
Mary Isabel Sibley Fellowships *(Doctorate/Fellowship)* [8053]

Funeral services (See also Mortuary science)

ABFSE National Scholarship Program *(Undergraduate/Scholarship)* [629]
NFDA Professional Women's Conference Scholarships *(Undergraduate/Scholarship)* [4314]

Gaming industry

Wells Fargo American Indian Scholarships - Graduate *(Graduate/Scholarship)* [883]

Gastroenterology

Crohn's and Colitis Canada Grants in Aid of Research *(Advanced Professional, Professional development/Grant)* [3473]
Crohn's and Colitis Canada Innovations in IBD Research Grants *(Advanced Professional, Professional development/Grant)* [3474]
International GI Training Grant Award *(Professional development/Grant)* [685]

Gemology

ColorMasters Scholarships *(Undergraduate/Scholarship)* [4333]
GIA Scholarship- Distance Education eLearning *(Graduate/Scholarship)* [4334]
GIA Scholarships - On Campus *(Graduate/Scholarship)* [4335]
William Goldberg Diamond Corp. Scholarships *(Undergraduate/Scholarship)* [4336]
Goldia.com Jewelry Scholarships *(Undergraduate, Graduate/Scholarship)* [4474]
Morris Hanauer Scholarships *(Undergraduate/Scholarship)* [4337]
George W. Juno Memorial Scholarships *(Undergraduate/Scholarship)* [4339]
Richard T. Liddicoat Scholarships *(Graduate/Scholarship)* [4340]
Mikimoto Scholarships *(Graduate/Scholarship)* [4342]
Daniel Swarovski and Company Scholarships *(Graduate/Scholarship)* [4345]
Kurt Wayne Scholarships *(Graduate/Scholarship)* [4346]
Worthy Gemological Scholarships *(Undergraduate/Scholarship)* [10713]

Genealogy

ASG Scholar Awards *(Professional development/Scholarship)* [1321]

General studies/Field of study not specified

4th Infantry Division Association Memorial Scholarships *(All/Scholarship)* [6670]
The "21" Endowed Scholarships *(Undergraduate/Scholarship)* [6015]
AAAA Scholarship Program *(Undergraduate, Graduate/Scholarship)* [1710]
AAIB Scholarships *(Undergraduate/Scholarship)* [509]
AAJUW Scholarships *(Graduate, Undergraduate/Scholarship)* [513]
AAS-American Society for Eighteenth Century Studies Fellowships *(Postdoctorate/Fellowship)* [429]
AAS CIAC Small Grants *(Graduate/Grant)* [1857]
AAS Korean Studies Scholarship Program *(Graduate/Scholarship)* [1858]
The AASSC Gurli Aagaard Woods Undergraduate Publication Awards *(Undergraduate/Award)* [1825]
The AASSC Marna Feldt Graduate Publication Awards *(Graduate/Award)* [1826]
AASSC Norwegian Travel Grants *(Professional development/Grant)* [1827]
AAUW American Fellowships *(Doctorate, Postdoctorate/Fellowship)* [19]
AAUW Career Development Grants *(Graduate, Advanced Professional, Professional development/Grant)* [20]

GENERAL STUDIES/FIELD OF STUDY NOT SPECIFIED

AAUW International Fellowships *(Master's, Doctorate, Postdoctorate/Fellowship)* [21]
Anthony Abbene Scholarships *(Undergraduate/Scholarship)* [5025]
Clifford V. Abbott Memorial Scholarships *(Undergraduate/Scholarship)* [9561]
Jordan Abdo Memorial Scholarship *(Undergraduate/Scholarship)* [9417]
Alejandro "Alex" Abecia Reaching High Scholarships *(Undergraduate/Scholarship)* [3084]
Abercrombie and Fitch Global Diversity and Leadership Scholar Awards *(Undergraduate/Scholarship)* [7158]
Aboriginal Canadians Scholarship *(Undergraduate/Scholarship)* [7204]
Emily and Roland Abraham Educational Funds *(Undergraduate/Scholarship)* [3316]
Frederick B. Abramson Memorial Foundation Scholarships *(Undergraduate/Scholarship)* [28]
ACHE/American Legion Auxiliary Scholarships *(Undergraduate/Scholarship)* [184]
ACHE Junior and Community College Athletic Scholarships *(Undergraduate/Scholarship)* [185]
ACHE Police Officers and Firefighters Survivors' Educational Assistance Programs *(Undergraduate/Scholarship)* [187]
ACHE Senior Adult Scholarships *(Undergraduate/Scholarship)* [188]
ACHE Two-Year College Academic Scholarships *(Undergraduate/Scholarship)* [189]
Wayne D. Ackerman Family Scholarship Fund *(Undergraduate/Scholarship)* [9491]
ACMS Intensive Mongolian Language Fellowship Program *(Undergraduate/Fellowship)* [648]
ACMS U.S.-Mongolia Field Research Fellowship Program *(Graduate, Undergraduate/Fellowship)* [650]
ACPA Foundation Annual Fund *(Professional development/Grant)* [695]
ACSO Scholarships *(Undergraduate/Scholarship)* [1633]
ACSUS Distinguished Dissertation Awards *(Doctorate/Award)* [1875]
ACUI Research and Education Grant *(Undergraduate, Graduate, Professional development/Grant)* [1925]
Nancy Ashley Adams/Ashley Adams Koetje Scholarships *(Undergraduate/Scholarship)* [3547]
Ruth D. Adams Fund *(Undergraduate/Scholarship)* [4037]
Mamie Adams Memorial Awards *(Undergraduate/Scholarship)* [6016]
The Clarke B. Adams Memorial Foundation Lapeer County Community Foundation Fund *(Undergraduate/Scholarship)* [5928]
Lt. Holly Adams Memorial Scholarships *(Undergraduate/Scholarship)* [3209]
Ruth Adams Memorial Scholarships *(Undergraduate/Scholarship)* [8442]
Henry S. and Carolyn Adams Scholarship Fund *(Undergraduate/Scholarship)* [4172]
Frederick G. Adams Scholarships *(Undergraduate/Scholarship)* [4735]
Adelante Fund Hope Scholarships, CPS Energy Dependents *(Undergraduate/Scholarship)* [66]
Adelante Fund Hope Scholarships, San Antonio, TX Students *(Undergraduate/Scholarship)* [67]
Carl Joseph Adelhardt Memorial Scholarships *(Undergraduate/Scholarship)* [4329]
Adelson Family Scholarships *(Undergraduate/Scholarship)* [8328]
Adult Students in Scholastic Transition Scholarships (ASIST) *(Professional development/Scholarship)* [3935]
Advance Prevention Lawsuit Legal Scholarships *(Undergraduate/Scholarship)* [5982]
"Advice to Your High School Self" Scholarships *(Undergraduate/Scholarship)* [2534]
AEBC Toronto Chapter Scholarships *(Undergraduate/Scholarship)* [333]
AEF Educational Scholarship *(Undergraduate/Scholarship)* [234]
AFSA Chapter 155 Division 1 Scholarships - Category 1 *(Undergraduate/Scholarship)* [130]
AFSA Chapter 155 Division 1 Scholarships - Category 2 *(Undergraduate/Scholarship)* [131]
AFSA Chapter 155 Division 1 Scholarships - Category 3 *(Undergraduate/Scholarship)* [132]
AFT-Oregon Union Plus Credit Card Scholarship *(Undergraduate/Scholarship)* [792]
AfterCollege Succurro Scholarships *(Undergraduate, Graduate, Doctorate/Scholarship)* [103]
AGBU Heritage Scholar Grant *(Undergraduate/Scholarship, Grant)* [1673]
Patty Ahearn Victoria Elementary Scholarships *(Undergraduate/Scholarship)* [8443]
Ahepa Buckeye Scholarship Awards *(Undergraduate/Scholarship)* [119]
AHEPA Family District No. 1 Scholarships *(Graduate, Undergraduate/Scholarship)* [849]
AIBS Junior Fellowships *(Doctorate/Fellowship)* [898]
AIBS Senior Fellowships *(Doctorate/Fellowship)* [899]
AIGC Fellowships - Graduate *(Graduate/Fellowship)* [881]
AIMS Long-term Research Grants *(Doctorate, Graduate/Grant)* [916]
AIMS Short-term Research Grants *(Doctorate/Grant)* [917]
AIR Dissertation Grants *(Doctorate/Grant)* [1980]
Air Force Sergeants Association Scholarship Program *(Undergraduate/Scholarship)* [128]
AIR Research Grants *(Professional development/Grant)* [1981]
AISES Summer Internships *(Undergraduate, Graduate/Internship)* [888]
AIST Midwest Member Chapter - Non-Engineering Scholarships *(Undergraduate/Scholarship)* [1991]
AIST San Francisco Member Chapter Scholarships *(Undergraduate/Scholarship)* [1995]
AJL Conference Stipends *(Graduate/Grant)* [2010]
Ak-Sar-Ben Scholarships *(Undergraduate/Scholarship)* [4935]
Crown Prince Akihito Scholarship Foundation *(Graduate/Scholarship)* [5535]
Alabama Gi Dependents' Educational Benefit Program *(Undergraduate/Scholarship)* [190]
Alabama National Guard Educational Assistance Program *(Undergraduate/Scholarship)* [191]
Alabama Power Scholarships *(Undergraduate/Scholarship)* [7529]
Alabama Scholarships for Dependents of Blind Parents *(Undergraduate/Scholarship)* [192]
Alabama Student Assistance Programs *(Undergraduate/Scholarship)* [193]
Alabama Student Grant Programs *(Undergraduate, Vocational/Occupational/Grant)* [194]
Alamo IFT Scholarship *(Undergraduate/Scholarship)* [5175]
Alaska Native Medical Center Auxiliary Scholarships *(Undergraduate/Scholarship)* [10005]
Bette Lou Albert, New Mexico, Memorial Scholarship Fund *(Undergraduate, Graduate, Doctorate/Scholarship)* [5689]
Alberta Blue Cross Scholarships for Aboriginal Students *(Undergraduate/Scholarship)* [230]
Alberta Centennial Scholarships - Alberta *(Undergraduate/Scholarship)* [262]
Alberta Ukrainian Centennial Commemorative Scholarships *(Graduate/Scholarship)* [10440]
ALCOA Foundation Corporate Scholarships *(Undergraduate, Graduate/Scholarship)* [4645]
ALD Graduate Fellowships *(Graduate/Fellowship)* [6696]
Alex Scholarship Funds *(Undergraduate/Scholarship)* [6280]
Anne L. Alexander and Blaise Robert Alexander Memorial Scholarships *(Undergraduate/Scholarship)* [4038]
Hon. Lincoln Alexander Scholarships *(Undergraduate, Graduate/Scholarship)* [2277]
Horatio Alger Delaware Scholarships *(Undergraduate/Scholarship)* [4936]
Horatio Alger District of Columbia, Maryland and Virginia Scholarships *(Undergraduate/Scholarship)* [4937]
Horatio Alger Florida Scholarships *(Undergraduate/Scholarship)* [4938]
Horatio Alger Georgia Scholarships *(Undergraduate/Scholarship)* [4939]
Horatio Alger Illinois Scholarships *(Undergraduate/Scholarship)* [4940]
Horatio Alger Indiana Scholarships *(Undergraduate/Scholarship)* [4941]
Horatio Alger Kentucky Scholarships *(Undergraduate/Scholarship)* [4942]
Horatio Alger Lola and Duane Hagadone Idaho Scholarships *(Undergraduate/Scholarship)* [4943]
Horatio Alger Louisiana Scholarships *(Undergraduate/Scholarship)* [4944]
Horatio Alger Minnesota Scholarships *(Undergraduate/Scholarship)* [4945]
Horatio Alger Missouri Scholarships *(Undergraduate/Scholarship)* [4946]
Horatio Alger Montana Scholarships *(Undergraduate/Scholarship)* [4947]
Horatio Alger National Scholarships *(Undergraduate/Scholarship)* [4948]
Horatio Alger North Dakota Scholarships *(Undergraduate/Scholarship)* [4949]
Horatio Alger Pennsylvania Scholarships *(Undergraduate/Scholarship)* [4950]
Horatio Alger South Dakota Scholarships *(Undergraduate/Scholarship)* [4951]
Horatio Alger Texas - Fort Worth Scholarships *(Undergraduate/Scholarship)* [4952]
Horatio Alger Texas Scholarships *(Undergraduate/Scholarship)* [4953]
Horatio Alger Utah Scholarships *(Undergraduate/Scholarship)* [4954]
Horatio Alger Washington Scholarships *(Undergraduate/Scholarship)* [4955]
Horatio Alger Wyoming Scholarships *(Undergraduate/Scholarship)* [4956]
ALIS Graduate Student Scholarships *(Graduate/Scholarship)* [264]
ALIS International Education Awards - Ukraine *(Undergraduate/Scholarship)* [265]
Robinson G. Allen Athletic Memorial Scholarships *(Undergraduate/Scholarship)* [8444]
Frances C. Allen Fellowships *(Graduate/Fellowship)* [7408]
William A. Allen Memorial Metal Shop/Auto Body Scholarships *(Undergraduate/Scholarship)* [8445]
Dorothea E. Allen Scholarship *(Undergraduate/Scholarship)* [4427]
Marjorie Almstrom Scholarships *(Undergraduate, Master's/Scholarship)* [10774]
Alpha Chi Omega Love and Loyalty Grants *(Professional development/Grant)* [346]
Alpha Chi Sigma Scholarship Awards *(Graduate, Undergraduate/Scholarship)* [348]
Alpha Delta Gamma Educational Foundation Scholarships *(Undergraduate, Graduate/Scholarship)* [350]
Alpha Kappa Alpha - Educational Advancement Foundation Financial Need-Based Scholarships *(Graduate, Undergraduate/Scholarship)* [352]
Alpha Kappa Alpha - Educational Advancement Foundation Merit Scholarships *(Graduate, Undergraduate/Scholarship)* [353]
Alpha Tau Omega Graduate Scholarships *(Graduate/Scholarship)* [359]
Alpha Tau Omega Undergraduate Scholarships *(Undergraduate/Scholarship)* [360]
Justin Scot Alston Memorial Scholarships *(Undergraduate/Scholarship)* [5026]
Altrusa International of Grand Rapids Scholarships *(Undergraduate/Scholarship)* [4573]
Jaedyn Amann Memorial Scholarships *(Undergraduate, Master's/Scholarship)* [10775]
Lou Amen Legacy Scholarships *(Undergraduate/Scholarship)* [2446]
American Association of University Women American Fellowships *(Doctorate, Postdoctorate/Fellowship)* [599]
American Association of University Women Career Development Grants *(Postgraduate/Grant)* [600]
American Association of University Women International Fellowships *(Graduate, Postgraduate/Fellowship)* [601]
American Association for Women in Community Colleges Regional Scholarships *(Undergraduate/Scholarship)* [605]
American Association for Women in Community Col-

GENERAL STUDIES/FIELD OF STUDY NOT SPECIFIED

leges Scholarship LEADERS Institute *(Other/Scholarship)* [606]
American Council of the Blind Scholarships *(Graduate, Undergraduate/Scholarship)* [720]
American Darts Organization Memorial Scholarship *(Undergraduate/Scholarship)* [767]
American Division Veterans Association Scholarships *(Undergraduate/Scholarship)* [383]
American Foreign Service Association Scholarship Fund *(Undergraduate/Scholarship)* [816]
American GI Forum of San Jose Scholarships *(Undergraduate/Scholarship)* [8756]
American Indian Endowed Scholarships *(Graduate, Undergraduate/Scholarship)* [10470]
American Legion Boys/Girls State Scholarships *(Undergraduate/Scholarship)* [6017]
American Legion Department of Vermont Scholarships *(Undergraduate, High School/Scholarship)* [959]
American Legion Eagle Scout of the Year Scholarships *(Undergraduate/Scholarship)* [6918]
The American Legion Legacy Scholarships *(Undergraduate/Scholarship)* [954]
American Lung Association Scholar Program *(Professional development/Grant)* [979]
American-Scandinavian Foundation Fellowships and Grants to Study in America *(Graduate, Professional development/Fellowship, Grant)* [1230]
American-Scandinavian Foundation Fellowships to Study in Scandinavia *(Graduate/Fellowship)* [1231]
American-Scandinavian Foundation Translation Prize *(Other/Prize)* [1233]
American Water Ski Educational Foundation Scholarships *(Undergraduate/Scholarship)* [10351]
AmeriGlide Achiever Scholarships *(Undergraduate/Scholarship)* [1534]
AMLN Scholarships for Arab American Students *(Graduate, Undergraduate/Scholarship)* [1003]
Bernard Amtmann Fellowships *(Postgraduate, Other/Fellowship)* [2258]
AMVETS National Scholarships - Entering College Freshmen *(Undergraduate/Scholarship)* [1545]
AMVETS National Scholarships - For Veterans *(Undergraduate/Scholarship)* [1546]
AMVETS National Scholarships - JROTC *(Undergraduate/Scholarship)* [1547]
Anaheim Police Survivors and Scholarship Fund *(Undergraduate/Scholarship)* [1549]
Anchor Scholarship Foundation Scholarships *(Undergraduate/Scholarship)* [9616]
Andersen Nontraditional Scholarships for Women's Education and Retraining (ANSWER) *(Undergraduate/Scholarship)* [4176]
Judge Isaac Anderson, Jr. Scholarships *(Undergraduate/Scholarship)* [9418]
Kathy D. and Stephen J. Anderson Scholarships *(Undergraduate/Scholarship)* [3210]
Redlands Rotary Club - Donald C. Anderson Scholarships *(Undergraduate/Scholarship)* [8446]
Warren M. Anderson Scholarships *(Undergraduate/Scholarship)* [5115]
William H. Andrews/HAWS Scholarships *(Undergraduate/Scholarship)* [10569]
Androscoggin County Chamber of Commerce Adult Scholarships *(Professional development/Scholarship)* [1555]
Angus Foundation General Undergraduate Student Scholarships *(Undergraduate/Scholarship)* [1557]
Angus Foundation Scholarships *(Undergraduate/Scholarship)* [7032]
Annuity.org Scholarships *(Undergraduate, Graduate/Scholarship)* [1565]
APHF Academic Scholarships *(Undergraduate/Scholarship)* [1069]
APIASF Scholarships *(Undergraduate/Scholarship)* [1792]
APT US&C Scholarships *(Advanced Professional/Scholarship)* [2050]
Aquatics Booster Club Scholarships *(Undergraduate/Scholarship)* [8448]
ARAFCS Doctoral Scholarships *(Doctorate/Scholarship)* [1646]
ARAFCS Masters Scholarships *(Graduate/Scholarship)* [1647]
Frank G. Araujo Memorial Scholarships *(Undergraduate/Scholarship)* [8449]
Arctic Physical Therapy Scholarship *(Undergraduate/Scholarship)* [1619]
A.R.F.O.R.A. Undergraduate Scholarships for Women *(Undergraduate/Scholarship)* [1224]
ARIT Summer Fellowships for Intensive Advanced Turkish Language Study *(Graduate, Undergraduate/Fellowship)* [1203]
Rick Arkans Eagle Scout Scholarships *(Undergraduate/Scholarship)* [6919]
Arkansas Single Parent Scholarships *(Undergraduate, Graduate/Scholarship)* [1661]
Arkansas State University Mountain Home Scholarships *(Undergraduate/Scholarship)* [1663]
Connie "Chelo" Armendariz Memorial Scholarships *(Undergraduate/Scholarship)* [8450]
Armenian American Citizen's League Scholarships *(Undergraduate/Scholarship)* [1682]
Armenian General Athletic Union Scholarships *(Undergraduate/Scholarship)* [1685]
Armenian Professional Society Graduate Student Scholarships *(Graduate/Scholarship)* [1675]
Armenian Relief Society Scholarships *(Graduate, Undergraduate/Scholarship)* [1686]
Robert Armstrong Memorial Scholarships *(Undergraduate, Graduate/Scholarship)* [10776]
Norma Arnold Clerical Scholarships *(Undergraduate/Scholarship)* [6221]
Aaron Edward Arnoldsen Memorial Scholarships *(Undergraduate/Scholarship)* [1719]
Judge Sidney M. Aronovitz Memorial Scholarships *(Undergraduate/Scholarship)* [6451]
Kush Arora Federal Criminal Justice Reform Scholarships *(Undergraduate, Graduate/Scholarship)* [8227]
Luis Arreola Memorial Scholarships *(Undergraduate/Scholarship)* [8686]
ARS Undergraduate Scholarships *(Undergraduate/Scholarship)* [1677]
Chester Arzell and Helen Miller Montgomery Scholarships *(Undergraduate/Scholarship)* [10570]
ASBA College Scholarship Grant Program *(Postgraduate/Scholarship)* [1239]
ASECS Graduate Student Research Paper Awards *(Graduate/Award)* [1283]
ASECS Innovative Course Design Competition *(Undergraduate/Award)* [1284]
ASEH Minority Travel Grants *(Graduate, Other/Grant)* [1309]
Asia Pacific Foundation of Canada Junior Research Fellowships *(Undergraduate, Master's/Fellowship)* [4113]
Asia Pacific Foundation of Canada Post-Graduate Research Fellowships *(Master's, Doctorate/Fellowship)* [4115]
Asian Development Bank - Japan Scholarships *(Graduate/Scholarship)* [3759]
Asian and Pacific Islander Queers Sisters Scholarships *(Undergraduate/Scholarship)* [8242]
ASIS Foundation Chapter Matching Scholarships *(Undergraduate/Scholarship)* [1794]
Michael M. Assarian Scholarships *(Undergraduate/Scholarship)* [1687]
Darrell and Palchie Asselin Scholarships *(Undergraduate/Scholarship)* [3703]
Association for the Advancement of Baltic Studies Dissertation Grants for Graduate Students *(Doctorate/Grant)* [1823]
Association for Compensatory Educators of Texas Paraprofessionals Scholarships *(Other/Scholarship)* [1928]
Association for Compensatory Educators of Texas Scholarships *(Undergraduate/Scholarship)* [1929]
Association of Donor Recruitment Professionals Hughes Scholarships *(Other/Scholarship)* [1937]
Association of Donor Recruitment Professionals Presidential Scholarships *(Other/Scholarship)* [1938]
Association of the United States Navy Scholarships *(Undergraduate/Scholarship)* [2083]
Atlantic Provinces Library Association Memorial Awards *(Undergraduate/Scholarship)* [2117]
Atlas Shrugged Essay Contest *(Graduate, Undergraduate, High School/Prize)* [2163]
A. B. and Hazel Augenstein Scholarship Funds *(Undergraduate/Scholarship)* [6281]
Herzog August Bibliothek Wolfenbüttel Fellowships *(Postdoctorate/Fellowship)* [7409]
Austin Alumnae Association Beta Xi Scholarship *(Undergraduate/Scholarship)* [5690]
Auto Accident Law Firm Survivor Scholarships *(Graduate/Scholarship)* [1592]
AWMA Niagara Frontier Section College Scholarships *(Graduate, Undergraduate/Scholarship)* [149]
AXA Achievement Scholarships *(Undergraduate/Scholarship)* [2161]
Susan Ayers Memorial Scholarships *(Undergraduate/Scholarship)* [8332]
Ayn Rand Institute Anthem Essay Contest *(High School, Undergraduate/Prize)* [2164]
Ayn Rand Institute Fountainhead Essay Contest *(High School, Undergraduate/Prize)* [2165]
John M. Azarian Memorial Armenian Youth Scholarship Fund *(Undergraduate/Scholarship)* [1688]
B-Brave McMahon/Stratton Scholarship Fund *(Undergraduate/Scholarship)* [4039]
Paula Backscheider Archival Fellowships *(Other/Fellowship)* [1286]
BAFTX Early Starters Awards *(Undergraduate/Scholarship)* [2365]
BAFTX Graduate Awards *(Undergraduate/Scholarship)* [2366]
BAFTX Junior Achievers Awards *(Undergraduate/Scholarship)* [2367]
BAFTX Undergraduate Awards *(Undergraduate/Scholarship)* [2368]
Baha'i Faith Scholarships for Racial Harmony *(Undergraduate/Scholarship)* [8451]
Morton Bahr Scholarships *(Undergraduate/Scholarship)* [3165]
The Bailey Family Foundation College Scholarship Program *(Undergraduate/Scholarship)* [2167]
The Bailey Family Foundation High School Scholarships Program *(Undergraduate/Scholarship)* [2168]
Lincoln C. Bailey Memorial Scholarship Fund *(Undergraduate/Scholarship)* [5390]
Esther Tuttle Bailey Memorial Scholarships *(Undergraduate/Scholarship)* [5691]
Bambi Bailey Scholarships *(Undergraduate/Scholarship)* [3197]
Barbara Bailey Scholarships *(Undergraduate/Scholarship)* [8244]
Sandra Sebrell Bailey Scholarships *(Undergraduate/Scholarship)* [3579]
Mark B. Bain Graduate Fellowship *(Doctorate, Master's, Graduate/Fellowship)* [4980]
Marian Wood Baird Scholarships *(Undergraduate/Scholarship)* [9973]
Richard L. Baker Memorial Scholarships *(Undergraduate/Scholarship)* [9563]
Robby Baker Memorial Scholarships *(Undergraduate/Scholarship)* [299]
Victoria Baldwin Memorial Scholarships *(Undergraduate, Master's/Award)* [10777]
Ballard Family Foundation Scholarships *(Undergraduate/Scholarship)* [8688]
G. Thomas Balsbaugh Memorial Scholarship Fund *(Undergraduate/Scholarship)* [4231]
Brenda S. Bank Educational Workshop Scholarships *(Undergraduate/Scholarship)* [9123]
Banting Postdoctoral Fellowships *(Postdoctorate/Fellowship)* [3402]
Michael Bany Memorial Scholarships *(Undergraduate/Scholarship)* [2944]
Barakat Trust and Barakat Foundation Scholarships *(Graduate, Postdoctorate/Scholarship)* [1598]
Joe Barbarow Memorial Scholarships *(Undergraduate/Scholarship)* [7813]
Edgar Barge Memorial Scholarships *(Undergraduate/Scholarship)* [4559]
Robbie Barron Memorial Scholarships *(Undergraduate/Scholarship)* [4232]
Walter and Marilyn Bartlett Scholarships *(Undergraduate/Scholarship)* [2945]
Elsa Barton Educational Scholarship Fund *(Undergraduate, Vocational/Occupational/Scholarship)* [1127]
Guthikonda BasavapunnaRao and Umadevi Scholarships *(Graduate/Scholarship)* [9667]

Field of Study Index

GENERAL STUDIES/FIELD OF STUDY NOT SPECIFIED

Bascom Hill Society Scholarships *(Undergraduate/Scholarship)* [10316]
Charles A. Bassett Endowed Memorial Scholarship Fund *(Undergraduate/Scholarship)* [4510]
Lewis and Gurry Batten/Sand Plains Educational Trust Scholarships *(Undergraduate/Scholarship)* [7814]
Marian Sims Baughn Scholarships *(Undergraduate/Scholarship)* [5692]
Hazel Reed Baumeister Scholarship Program *(Undergraduate/Scholarship)* [8947]
Timothy Baylink Good Fellowship Awards *(Undergraduate/Fellowship)* [8452]
Bayly-Tiffany Scholarships *(Undergraduate/Scholarship)* [10301]
BCCC Foundation General Scholarship Fund *(Undergraduate/Scholarship)* [2178]
BCCC Workforce Creation Scholarships *(Undergraduate/Scholarship)* [2179]
BCPF Bursaries *(Undergraduate/Scholarship)* [9476]
BCSF Scholarships *(Undergraduate/Scholarship)* [2294]
BDC Visiting Fellowships *(Advanced Professional, Professional development/Fellowship)* [2382]
Jane Beattie Memorial Scholarships *(Graduate, Professional development/Scholarship)* [9160]
Suzanne Beauregard Scholarships *(Undergraduate/Scholarship)* [4476]
Beaver Medical Clinic-Glen Adams Scholarship Awards *(Undergraduate/Scholarship)* [8453]
Beaver Medical Clinic-H.E.A.R.T. Scholarship Awards *(Undergraduate/Scholarship)* [8454]
Beaver Medical Clinic-Premed Scholarship Awards *(Undergraduate/Scholarship)* [8455]
Don C. Beaver Memorial Scholarships *(Undergraduate/Scholarship)* [2447]
BECA Foundation General Scholarships Fund *(Undergraduate/Scholarship)* [2210]
Becas Univision Scholarship Program *(Undergraduate, Graduate/Scholarship)* [4902]
Dennis J. Beck Memorial Scholarships *(Undergraduate/Scholarship)* [5498]
Garvin L. Beck Scholarships *(Undergraduate/Scholarship)* [8456]
Raymond and Donald Beeler Memorial Scholarships *(Undergraduate/Scholarship)* [8457]
Notah Begay III Scholarship Program *(Undergraduate/Scholarship)* [300]
Alfred D. Bell, Jr. Travel Grants *(Graduate/Grant)* [4137]
John Bell and Lawrence Thornton Scholarship Fund *(Undergraduate/Scholarship)* [4738]
Ray and Mary Bell Memorial Scholarships *(Undergraduate/Scholarship)* [8690]
Betty Bell Scholarship Fund *(Undergraduate/Scholarship)* [4922]
A.G. Bell School Age Financial Aid Program *(Undergraduate/Scholarship)* [315]
Bellevue PFLAG Scholarships *(Undergraduate/Scholarship)* [8245]
H. Y. Benedict Fellowships *(Graduate/Fellowship)* [340]
Reverend E.F. Bennett Scholarships *(Undergraduate/Scholarship)* [3088]
Bergman Scholarships *(Undergraduate/Scholarship)* [7487]
Bergmann Family Scholarship Funds *(Undergraduate/Scholarship)* [6282]
The Joseph Berkman, and Michael and Sarah Chipkin Holocaust/Genocide Studies Award *(Graduate/Scholarship)* [9581]
Richard L. Bernardi Memorial Scholarships *(Undergraduate/Scholarship)* [3276]
Donald H. Bernstein/John B. Talbert, Jr. Scholarships *(Undergraduate/Scholarship)* [4179]
James R. and Geraldine F. Bertelsen Scholarships *(Undergraduate/Scholarship)* [8691]
Henry Besner Memorial Scholarships *(Undergraduate, Master's/Scholarship)* [10778]
Best Price Nutrition and Health Scholarships *(Undergraduate/Scholarship)* [2237]
Beta Omega Scholarships *(Undergraduate/Scholarship)* [8911]
Beta Pi Sigma Sorority Scholarships (BPSSS) *(Undergraduate/Scholarship)* [2244]

Beta Sigma Scholarships *(Undergraduate/Scholarship)* [8912]
Bethune-Cookman University Excelsior Scholarship Level 1 *(Undergraduate/Scholarship)* [2250]
Bethune-Cookman University Presidential Scholarships *(Undergraduate/Scholarship)* [2251]
BIE-Loan for Service for Graduates *(Graduate/Loan)* [882]
James L. Biggane Fellowships in Finance *(Graduate/Fellowship)* [7367]
James Bilder Scholarships *(Undergraduate/Scholarship)* [9420]
Helen & Bob Bintz Scholarship Funds *(Undergraduate/Scholarship)* [6283]
BioRx/Hemophilia of North Carolina Educational Scholarships *(Undergraduate/Scholarship)* [6985]
Birmingham-Southern College Eagle Scout Scholarships *(Undergraduate/Scholarship)* [6920]
Birmingham Student Scholarships *(Undergraduate/Scholarship)* [2273]
The Bishop James C. Baker Award *(Doctorate/Scholarship)* [9850]
Lebbeus F. Bissell Scholarships *(Undergraduate/Scholarship)* [4739]
Dr. Richard E. Bjork Memorial Graduate Study Award *(Graduate/Scholarship)* [9582]
Law Offices of David A. Black Annual Hearing Impaired Scholarships *(All/Scholarship)* [5957]
Black Men Building Resources Scholarships *(Undergraduate/Scholarship)* [4576]
William T. Blackwell Scholarship Fund *(Undergraduate/Scholarship)* [7019]
Alex Blaski Memorial Scholarships *(Undergraduate/Scholarship)* [8572]
Lawrence Bloomberg Entrance Awards *(Postgraduate/Award)* [10741]
F.A. and Charlotte Blount Scholarships *(Undergraduate/Scholarship)* [10571]
Sandra Bobbitt Continuing Education Scholarship *(Undergraduate/Scholarship)* [2032]
Gerald J. and Helen Bogen Fund *(Undergraduate/Scholarship)* [4660]
Therese and David Bohbot Scholarships *(Undergraduate/Scholarship)* [5571]
Bolick Foreign Student Scholarships *(Undergraduate/Scholarship)* [10010]
Brian Bolton Graduate/Mature Student Essay Awards *(Undergraduate, Graduate/Award)* [4301]
Friends of Megan Bolton Memorial Fund *(Undergraduate/Scholarship)* [4233]
Dorothy M. Bolyard Memorial Scholarships *(Undergraduate/Scholarship)* [8692]
BOMA/NY Scholarships *(Undergraduate/Scholarship)* [2404]
Steve Bonk Scholarships *(Postgraduate/Scholarship)* [2766]
Lorne and Ruby Bonnell Scholarships *(Undergraduate/Scholarship)* [3311]
Barbara Bonnema Memorial Scholarships *(Undergraduate/Scholarship)* [8459]
Boomer Benefits Scholarships *(Undergraduate/Scholarship)* [2335]
Admiral Mike Boorda Loans Program *(Undergraduate/Loan)* [7234]
Maria and Czeslaw Borek Scholarships *(Undergraduate/Scholarship)* [8573]
David L. Boren Undergraduate Scholarships *(Graduate, Undergraduate/Scholarship)* [1968]
Geraldine Geistert Boss Scholarships *(Undergraduate/Scholarship)* [4577]
Boston City Federation "Return to School" Scholarships *(Undergraduate, Graduate/Scholarship)* [4351]
Dr. George T. Bottomley Scholarships *(Undergraduate/Scholarship)* [6350]
Herbie Bouwman Memorial Scholarships *(Undergraduate, Master's/Scholarship)* [10779]
William R. Bowen Scholarships *(Undergraduate/Scholarship)* [3171]
Billy Bowling Memorial Scholarship *(Undergraduate/Scholarship)* [7530]
Boy Scouts of America Troop 3 Scholarships - Art Till/Nathan E. Smith Memorial Scholarships *(Undergraduate, Vocational/Occupational/Scholarship)* [8460]
Dr. Betty J. Boyd-Beu and Edwin G. Beu, Jr. Scholarships *(Undergraduate/Scholarship)* [10011]
W. Scott Boyd Group Grants *(Advanced Professional/Grant)* [5282]
Dody Boyd Scholarships *(Undergraduate/Scholarship)* [3214]
BPW Foundation Career Advancement Scholarships *(Undergraduate/Scholarship)* [2422]
Charles Bradley Memorial Scholarships *(Undergraduate/Scholarship)* [4723]
Doreen Brady Memorial Scholarships *(Postgraduate/Scholarship)* [7630]
W. Philip Braender and Nancy Coleman Braender Scholarships *(Undergraduate/Scholarship)* [4741]
Byard Braley Scholarship *(Undergraduate/Scholarship)* [5462]
The Helen and Edward Brancati Teacher Development Scholarships *(Other/Scholarship)* [2783]
Kenneth H. Breeden Scholarships *(Undergraduate/Scholarship)* [5924]
Marion Luna Brem/Pat McNeil Health and Education Scholarships *(Undergraduate/Scholarship)* [3089]
Breslauer Family Scholarships *(Undergraduate/Scholarship)* [8693]
Hilda E. Bretzlaff Foundation Scholarships *(Undergraduate/Scholarship, Grant)* [2363]
Tommy Bright Scholarship Fund *(Undergraduate/Scholarship)* [4923]
Margaret Brine Graduate Scholarships *(Graduate/Scholarship)* [2634]
Louise A. Broderick San Diego County Scholarships *(Undergraduate/Scholarship)* [8694]
Louis J. Brody Q.C. Entrance Scholarships *(Graduate/Scholarship)* [10742]
Ross P. Broesamle Educational Scholarship Fund *(Undergraduate/Scholarship)* [5929]
John G. Brokaw Scholarships *(Undergraduate/Scholarship)* [7227]
Peter F. Bronfman Entrance Awards *(Postgraduate/Award)* [10743]
Peter F. Bronfman Scholarships of Merit *(Postgraduate/Scholarship)* [10744]
Seth R. and Corrine H. Brooks Memorial Scholarships *(Undergraduate/Scholarship)* [2246]
Carl E. Brooks Scholarships *(Undergraduate/Scholarship)* [9421]
Dorothy B. Brothers Executive Scholarship Program *(Undergraduate/Scholarship)* [10656]
Diana Brown Endowed Scholarships *(Undergraduate/Scholarship)* [6018]
John Carter Brown Library Long-Term Fellowships *(Graduate, Doctorate/Fellowship)* [2384]
John Carter Brown Library Short-Term Fellowships *(Doctorate, Postdoctorate/Fellowship)* [2385]
Catherine Amelia Thew Brown Memorial Scholarship Funds *(Undergraduate/Scholarship)* [6284]
Milton and Edith Brown Memorial Scholarships *(Undergraduate/Scholarship)* [2946]
Jesse Brown Memorial Youth Scholarship Program *(Advanced Professional/Scholarship)* [3632]
JoAhn Brown-Nash Memorial Scholarships *(Undergraduate/Scholarship)* [3215]
Ron Brown Scholars Program *(Undergraduate/Scholarship)* [2387]
D.C. and Virginia Brown Scholarships *(Undergraduate/Scholarship)* [3090]
Harry and Lucille Brown Scholarships *(Undergraduate/Scholarship)* [4578]
Jack H. Brown Scholarships *(Undergraduate/Scholarship)* [2448]
Robert W. Brunsman Memorial Scholarship *(Professional development/Scholarship)* [5360]
Bernard B. and Mary L. Brusin Scholarships *(Undergraduate/Scholarship)* [3705]
William and Clara Bryan Scholarships *(Undergraduate/Scholarship)* [3216]
Bryant Essay Scholarships *(Undergraduate, Graduate/Scholarship)* [2396]
Bryant Visual Content Scholarships *(Undergraduate, Graduate/Scholarship)* [2397]
BSA Educational Scholarships *(Undergraduate/Scholarship)* [2426]
Peter Buck Fellowships Program - Graduate *(Graduate/Fellowship)* [9030]
Peter Buck Fellowships Program - Postdoctoral *(Postdoctorate/Fellowship)* [9031]
Walter and Louise Buell Graduate Scholarships

Scholarships, Fellowships and Loans, 34th Ed.

1503

GENERAL STUDIES/FIELD OF STUDY NOT SPECIFIED

(Graduate/Scholarship) [4142]
Susan Thompson Buffett Foundation Scholarships *(Undergraduate/Scholarship)* [2402]
Tien Bui Memorial Scholarships *(Undergraduate/Scholarship)* [10573]
Armen H. Bululian Scholarships *(Undergraduate/Scholarship)* [1690]
Bunnell Scholarships *(Undergraduate/Scholarship)* [10012]
William T. Burbage Family Memorial Scholarships *(Undergraduate/Scholarship)* [3172]
George M. Burditt Scholarships *(Undergraduate/Scholarship)* [1965]
Freda Burge Scholarships *(Undergraduate/Scholarship)* [7817]
Burger King Employee Scholars Program *(Undergraduate/Scholarship)* [2410]
Burger King Scholars Program *(Undergraduate/Scholarship)* [2411]
Loyal D. Burkett Memorial Scholarships *(Undergraduate/Scholarship)* [10013]
Business, Education and Technology Scholarships *(Graduate, Undergraduate/Scholarship)* [334]
Lindsay Buster Memorial Scholarships *(Undergraduate/Scholarship)* [3277]
Leon C. Bynoe Memorial Scholarships *(Undergraduate/Scholarship)* [10280]
Robert C. Byrd Honors Scholarships *(Undergraduate/Scholarship)* [5071]
George J. Bysiewicz Scholarship Fund *(Undergraduate/Scholarship)* [3198]
CAAO Scholarship *(Professional development/Scholarship)* [3356]
CAG Health and Health Care Study Group Awards *(Graduate/Award)* [1881]
Cal State San Macros Alumna Scholarships *(Undergraduate/Scholarship)* [2486]
Tese Caldarelli Memorial Scholarships *(Graduate, Undergraduate/Scholarship)* [6723]
Caledonia Alumni Association Scholarship Funds *(Undergraduate/Scholarship)* [6285]
Calhoun County Auburn University Scholarships *(Undergraduate/Scholarship)* [3260]
Calhoun Valedictorian, Salutatorian/Top 5 Scholarships *(Undergraduate/Scholarship)* [2432]
California Groundwater Association Scholarships *(Undergraduate/Scholarship)* [2462]
California Scottish Rite Foundation Scholarships *(Undergraduate/Scholarship)* [2477]
Calista Education and Culture Scholarships *(Graduate, Undergraduate, Vocational/Occupational/Scholarship)* [2490]
Harry D. Callahan Educational Trust *(Undergraduate/Scholarship)* [9495]
Captain Jodi Callahan Memorial Scholarships *(Graduate, Master's/Scholarship)* [122]
Calvin Alumni Association British Columbia Scholarships *(Undergraduate/Scholarship)* [2492]
Calvin Alumni Association California- Bay Area Scholarships *(Undergraduate/Scholarship)* [2493]
Calvin Alumni Association Florida-Gulf Coast Scholarships *(Undergraduate/Scholarship)* [2494]
Calvin Alumni Association-Illinois Scholarships *(Undergraduate/Scholarship)* [2495]
Calvin Alumni Association-Michigan Lakeshore Scholarships *(Undergraduate/Scholarship)* [2496]
Calvin Alumni Association-Michigan, Lansing Scholarships *(Undergraduate/Scholarship)* [2497]
Calvin Alumni Association-New Jersey Scholarships *(Undergraduate/Scholarship)* [2498]
Calvin Alumni Association-South Florida Scholarships *(Undergraduate/Scholarship)* [2499]
Calvin Alumni Association-Southeast Michigan Scholarships *(Undergraduate/Scholarship)* [2500]
Calvin Alumni Association-Southeastern Wisconsin Scholarships *(Undergraduate/Scholarship)* [2501]
Calvin Alumni Association Southern California Chapter Scholarships *(Undergraduate/Scholarship)* [2502]
Calvin Alumni Association-Southwest Michigan, Kalamazoo Scholarships *(Undergraduate/Scholarship)* [2503]
Calvin Alumni Association-Washington, D.C. Scholarships *(Undergraduate/Scholarship)* [2504]
Calvin Alumni Association-Washington, Lynden Scholarships *(Undergraduate/Scholarship)* [2505]

Camden County College Foundation Scholarships *(Undergraduate/Scholarship)* [2522]
Wesley C. Cameron Scholarships *(Undergraduate/Scholarship)* [7228]
Camp Network Counselor Appreciation Scholarships *(Undergraduate/Scholarship)* [2528]
Lucille Campbell Scholarship Fund *(Undergraduate, High School/Scholarship)* [10500]
Robert G. Campbell Scholarships *(Undergraduate/Scholarship)* [8462]
Theodore R. Campbell Scholarships *(Undergraduate/Scholarship)* [268]
Campus Discovery Scholarships *(Undergraduate/Scholarship)* [2532]
Canada-Ukraine Parliamentary Program Internship Scholarships (CUPP) *(Undergraduate/Scholarship, Internship)* [10441]
Canadian Evaluation Society Educational Fund Scholarships *(Graduate/Scholarship)* [4125]
Canadian Federation of Independent Grocers National Scholarships *(Undergraduate/Scholarship)* [4003]
Canadian Federation of University Women Etobicoke Bursary *(Undergraduate/Scholarship)* [10281]
Canadian Hard of Hearing Association Scholarship Programs *(Undergraduate/Scholarship)* [2651]
Canadian Iranian Foundation Scholarships *(Undergraduate/Scholarship)* [2677]
Canadian Parking Association Scholarships *(Undergraduate/Scholarship)* [1921]
Canadian Polar Commission Scholarships *(Doctorate, Graduate/Scholarship)* [1933]
Canadian Sanitation Supply Association Scholarships *(Undergraduate/Scholarship)* [2738]
Canadian Seniors' Golf Association Scholarships *(Undergraduate/Scholarship)* [4477]
Canadian Society for the Study of Education Mentorship Awards *(Other/Award)* [9067]
Cancer for College Scholarships *(Graduate, Undergraduate/Scholarship)* [2770]
Cancer Survivors' Fund Scholarships *(Undergraduate/Scholarship)* [2779]
Agustin C. Cano Memorial Scholarships *(Undergraduate/Scholarship)* [8334]
Commander Ronald J. Cantin Scholarships *(Undergraduate/Scholarship)* [3075]
CAODC Occupational Health and Safety Scholarships *(Professional development/Scholarship)* [2570]
CAODC Scholarship Program *(Undergraduate/Scholarship)* [2571]
John Caoile Memorial Scholarships *(Undergraduate/Scholarship)* [8335]
Cape Fear Community College Merit Scholarships *(Undergraduate/Scholarship)* [2786]
Kasie Ford Capling Memorial Scholarship Endowment Fund *(Undergraduate/Scholarship)* [4182]
Lester J. Cappon Fellowships in Documentary Editing *(Postdoctorate/Fellowship)* [7410]
Daniel Cardillo Charitable Fund *(Professional development/Scholarship)* [6192]
CareerFitter Scholarships *(Undergraduate, Graduate/Scholarship)* [2795]
Beth Carew Memorial Scholarships *(Undergraduate/Scholarship)* [6986]
William F. Carl Scholarships *(Undergraduate/Scholarship)* [7470]
AABA Read Carlock Memorial Scholarship Fund *(Other/Scholarship)* [1625]
Glen and Babs Carlson Endowed Scholarships *(Undergraduate/Scholarship)* [6019]
Carmangay Home and School Association Scholarships *(Undergraduate/Scholarship)* [269]
Walta Wilkinson Carmichael Scholarships *(Undergraduate/Scholarship)* [8913]
Carnegie Observatories Graduate Research Fellowships *(Graduate, Doctorate/Fellowship)* [2799]
Herb Carnegie Scholarships *(Undergraduate/Scholarship)* [2279]
Carolinas-Virginias Retail Hardware Scholarships *(Undergraduate/Scholarship)* [4184]
Walter and Elsie Carr Endowed Scholarships *(Undergraduate/Scholarship)* [6020]
Eugene Carroll Scholarships *(Undergraduate/Scholarship)* [2947]

Karen D. Carsel Memorial Scholarships *(Graduate/Scholarship)* [819]
Orin Carver Scholarships *(Undergraduate/Scholarship)* [3312]
Cascara Vacation Rentals Hospitality Matters Scholarships *(Undergraduate, Graduate/Scholarship)* [2805]
Local 827 Peter J. Casey Scholarships *(Undergraduate/Scholarship)* [5288]
George H. and Anna Casper Fund *(Undergraduate/Scholarship)* [9496]
Orrie and Dorothy Cassada Scholarships *(Undergraduate/Scholarship)* [4579]
Rose Cassin Memorial Scholarships *(Postgraduate/Scholarship)* [7631]
The Kerri Castellini Women's Leadership Scholarships *(Undergraduate/Scholarship)* [8229]
Catholic Aid Association's Post-High School Tuition Scholarships *(Undergraduate/Scholarship)* [2818]
Catholic Relief Services Summer Internships *(Undergraduate, Graduate, Professional development/Internship)* [2816]
Christine Kerr Cawthorne Scholarships *(Undergraduate/Scholarship)* [8914]
CBC Spouses Education Scholarship Fund *(Graduate, Undergraduate/Scholarship)* [3345]
CBCF Congressional Fellows Program *(Other/Fellowship)* [3348]
CC Times Scholarships *(Undergraduate/Scholarship)* [2921]
CCSD School Counselors' Scholarships *(Undergraduate/Scholarship)* [8336]
CCU Alumni Endowed Scholarships *(Undergraduate/Scholarship)* [3136]
Betty J. Cecere Memorial Scholarship Endowment Fund *(Undergraduate, High School/Scholarship)* [10501]
Cedarcrest Farms Scholarships *(Graduate, Undergraduate/Scholarship)* [944]
Celler Legal P.A. Employment Skills Scholarship Program *(Undergraduate/Scholarship)* [2837]
Cengage Learning Scholarships Program *(Undergraduate/Scholarship)* [2839]
Center for the Education of Women Scholarships *(Graduate, Undergraduate/Scholarship)* [10195]
Centerville-Abington Dollars for Scholars *(Undergraduate/Scholarship)* [10502]
Certified Municipal Clerk Scholarships (CMC) *(Other/Scholarship)* [5350]
Cerutti Group Scholarships *(Undergraduate/Scholarship)* [4646]
CFNIL Community Foundation Scholarships *(Undergraduate/Scholarship)* [3278]
CFNIL Senior Memorial Scholarships *(Undergraduate/Scholarship)* [3279]
CFT/ACPSOP Scholarships *(Undergraduate/Scholarship)* [2948]
CGPF Endowments Conference Scholarships *(Undergraduate/Scholarship)* [2648]
ChairScholars National Scholarship Program *(Undergraduate/Scholarship)* [2889]
Logan S. Chambers Individual Scholarships *(Other/Scholarship)* [5283]
Mary Anne Chambers Scholarships *(Undergraduate/Scholarship)* [5522]
Jason Chaney Memorial Scholarship Fund *(Undergraduate/Scholarship)* [10503]
Harry H. and Floy B. Chapin Scholarships *(Undergraduate/Scholarship)* [3280]
Nancy J. Chapman Scholarships *(Other/Scholarship)* [1939]
Charlotte Housing Authority Scholarship Fund (CHASF) *(Undergraduate, Vocational/Occupational/Scholarship)* [4185]
Charlotte-Mecklenburg Schools Scholarship Incentive Program *(Undergraduate/Scholarship)* [4186]
Cesar E. Chavez Scholarships *(Undergraduate/Scholarship)* [8463]
CHCI Scholarships *(Undergraduate, Graduate/Scholarship)* [3354]
CHEA Undergraduate Scholarship Program for Students with Disabilities *(Undergraduate/Scholarship)* [2464]
CHEA Vocational Grants *(Undergraduate/Grant)* [2465]
Cheatham County Community Foundation Scholar-

GENERAL STUDIES/FIELD OF STUDY NOT SPECIFIED

ships *(Undergraduate/Scholarship)* [3218]
Chechahko Consumers Co-Op Ltd. Scholarships *(Undergraduate, Master's/Scholarship)* [10782]
Cheerful Giver Scholarships *(Undergraduate/Scholarship)* [8696]
Bernard Chernos Essay Competition *(Undergraduate/Prize)* [1893]
Cherokee Nation Graduate Scholarships *(Graduate/Scholarship)* [2893]
Cherokee Nation Pell Scholarships *(Undergraduate/Scholarship)* [2894]
Cherokee Nation Scholarships *(Undergraduate/Scholarship)* [2895]
Sgt. Cherven Scholarship *(Undergraduate/Scholarship)* [6312]
Chevalier Award Scholarship *(Undergraduate/Scholarship)* [2618]
Cheyenne High School Desert Shields Scholarship *(Undergraduate/Scholarship)* [8337]
Chicana Latina Scholarship Fund *(Graduate, Undergraduate/Scholarship)* [2901]
Kevin Child Scholarships *(Undergraduate/Scholarship)* [6987]
John and Ruth Childe Scholarships *(Undergraduate/Scholarship)* [9422]
Children of Evangeline Section Scholarships *(Graduate, Undergraduate/Scholarship)* [9249]
Children of Unitarian Universalist Ministers College Scholarships *(Undergraduate/Scholarship)* [9833]
Children's Scholarship Fund of Charlotte *(Undergraduate/Scholarship)* [4187]
Chinese Professionals Association of Canada BMO Diversity Scholarships *(Undergraduate/Scholarship)* [2922]
Chinese Professionals Association of Canada Education Foundation Awards *(High School/Award)* [2923]
Chinese Professionals Association of Canada Journalism Scholarships *(Undergraduate/Scholarship)* [2924]
Chinese Professionals Association of Canada Professional Achievement Awards *(Other/Award)* [2925]
Choose Your Future Scholarships *(Undergraduate/Scholarship)* [3219]
Commander Daniel J. Christovich Scholarship Fund *(Undergraduate/Scholarship)* [3076]
Chrysler Technical Scholarship Fund *(Undergraduate/Scholarship)* [3545]
CHS - Bursary Program Scholarships *(Undergraduate/Scholarship)* [2653]
CHS - Mature Student Bursary Program Scholarships *(Undergraduate/Scholarship)* [2654]
CHS Scholarships *(Undergraduate/Scholarship)* [2655]
CIA Undergraduate Scholarships *(Undergraduate/Scholarship)* [1969]
CIFAR Global Scholars Program *(Advanced Professional, Professional development/Scholarship)* [2670]
Cincinnati High School Scholarships *(Undergraduate/Scholarship)* [2949]
CIP Fellow's Travel Scholarships *(Undergraduate/Scholarship)* [2672]
Citi Foundation Scholarship Program *(Undergraduate/Scholarship)* [866]
City of Sanibel Employee Dependent Scholarships *(Undergraduate/Scholarship)* [9423]
Civitan Shropshire Scholarships *(Undergraduate, Vocational/Occupational/Scholarship)* [3041]
Claes Nobel Academic Scholarships for Members *(High School/Scholarship)* [7159]
Thomas Arkle Clark Scholar-Leader of the Year Endowed Scholarships *(Graduate, Undergraduate/Scholarship)* [8061]
Classic Wines of California Scholarships *(Undergraduate/Scholarship)* [2449]
Clay Maitland CGF Scholarship *(Undergraduate/Scholarship)* [3077]
James L. Clifford Prize *(Other/Prize, Monetary)* [1289]
Bryan Cline Memorial Soccer Scholarship Program *(Undergraduate/Scholarship)* [301]
The Club at Morningside Scholarships *(Undergraduate, Graduate/Scholarship)* [8697]
The Clubs of America Scholarships Award for Career Success *(Undergraduate/Scholarship)* [3065]
CMSF Scholarships *(Undergraduate, Graduate/Scholarship)* [2932]
CNIB Master's Scholarships *(Master's/Scholarship)* [2688]
CNST Scholarships *(Doctorate, Graduate/Scholarship)* [1934]
Coast Guard Foundation Enlisted Education Grants *(Advanced Professional/Grant)* [3078]
The Helena B. Cobb Annual Scholarships *(Undergraduate, Vocational/Occupational/Scholarship)* [10665]
The Helena B. Cobb Four-Year Higher Education Grants *(Undergraduate, Vocational/Occupational/Scholarship)* [10666]
Coca-Cola First Generation Scholarships *(Undergraduate/Scholarship)* [867]
Coca-Cola Scholars Program Scholarships *(Undergraduate/Scholarship)* [3115]
The April Cockerham DREAM Act Scholarships *(Undergraduate, Graduate/Scholarship)* [8230]
CODY Foundation Fund *(Undergraduate/Scholarship)* [4235]
Coeur d'Alene Alumni Scholarships *(Undergraduate/Scholarship)* [6021]
Steven L. Coffey Memorial Scholarships *(Undergraduate/Scholarship)* [3755]
Thomas D. Coffield Scholarships *(Undergraduate/Scholarship)* [4582]
Donald O. Coffman Scholarships *(Undergraduate/Scholarship)* [8248]
COHEAO Scholarships *(Undergraduate/Scholarship)* [3071]
Marshall A. Cohen Entrance Awards *(Postgraduate/Award)* [10745]
Cole Family Scholarships *(Undergraduate/Scholarship)* [8249]
Cole Foundation Undergraduate Scholarship Program *(Undergraduate/Scholarship)* [4189]
The College Club of Hartford Scholarships *(Undergraduate/Scholarship)* [4743]
College Success Foundation Chateau Ste. Michelle Scholarship Fund *(Undergraduate/Scholarship)* [3125]
College Success Foundation Leadership 1000 Scholarships *(Undergraduate/Scholarship)* [3126]
College Success Foundation Realize the Dream Scholarships *(Undergraduate/Scholarship)* [3127]
College Success Foundation Washington State Governors' Scholarship for Foster Youth *(Undergraduate/Scholarship)* [3128]
Irene Culver Collins and Louis Franklin Collins Scholarships *(Undergraduate/Scholarship)* [3173]
Captain Winifred Quick Collins Scholarships *(Undergraduate/Scholarship)* [7229]
Elmer and Rosa Lee Collins Scholarships *(Undergraduate/Scholarship)* [10575]
Lloyd E. and Rachel S. Collins Scholarships *(Undergraduate/Scholarship)* [10576]
Colombian Education Fund Scholarships *(Undergraduate/Scholarship)* [3130]
Columbus Citizens Foundation College Scholarships *(Undergraduate/Scholarship)* [3151]
Columbus Citizens Foundation High School Scholarships *(Undergraduate/Scholarship)* [3152]
Commonwealth "Good Citizen" Scholarships *(Undergraduate/Scholarship)* [1977]
Communal Studies Association Research Fellowships *(Graduate/Fellowship)* [3163]
Community Foundation of the Fox River Valley Scholarships *(Undergraduate/Scholarship)* [3192]
The Community Foundation Student Education Loan Funds for Gay and Lesbians *(Undergraduate/Loan)* [3221]
Community Foundation of Western Massachusetts Community Scholarship Program *(Undergraduate/Scholarship)* [3335]
Alan Compton and Bob Stanley Professional Scholarships *(Professional development/Scholarship)* [2192]
Congressional Fellows on Women and Public Policy *(Doctorate, Graduate, Master's/Fellowship)* [10672]
T.L. Conlan Scholarships *(Undergraduate/Scholarship)* [2950]
Connecticut Association of Latinos in Higher Education Scholarships *(Undergraduate/Scholarship)* [4744]
Dwight O. Conner and Ellen Conner Lepp/Danhart Scholarships *(Undergraduate/Scholarship)* [7819]
Karen Connick Memorial Scholarships *(Undergraduate/Scholarship)* [4560]
Connor/Spafford Scholarships *(Undergraduate/Scholarship)* [4478]
Constantinople Armenian Relief Society Scholarships (CARS) *(Undergraduate/Scholarship)* [1691]
Jack Kent Cooke Dissertation Fellowship Award *(Doctorate/Fellowship)* [5492]
Jack Kent Cooke Foundation Graduate Scholarships *(Graduate/Scholarship)* [3412]
Jack Kent Cooke Foundation Undergraduate Transfer Scholarships *(Undergraduate/Scholarship)* [3413]
Jack Kent Cooke Foundation Young Scholars *(Undergraduate/Scholarship)* [3414]
Madison and Edith Cooper Scholarships *(Undergraduate/Scholarship)* [8698]
COPA Scholarship Fund *(Undergraduate/Scholarship)* [2722]
Cope Middle School PTSA Scholarships *(Undergraduate/Scholarship)* [8466]
Copper and Brass Servicenter Association Inc. Scholarship Program *(Undergraduate/Scholarship)* [3421]
Beta Nu/Caryl Cordis D'hondt Scholarships *(Undergraduate/Scholarship)* [8916]
Theta/Caryl Cordis D'hondt Scholarships *(Undergraduate/Scholarship)* [8917]
Cornaro Scholarships for Graduate Studies *(Graduate/Scholarship)* [5686]
D.C. Cornelius Memorial Scholarships *(Undergraduate/Scholarship)* [10577]
The Corp - More Uncommon Grounds Scholarships *(Undergraduate/Scholarship)* [9604]
The Corp - Students of Georgetown Inc. Coke Scholarships *(Undergraduate/Scholarship)* [9605]
The Corp - Students of Georgetown Inc. Textbook Scholarships *(Undergraduate/Scholarship)* [9606]
Helen & Orval Couch Memorial Scholarships *(Undergraduate, Master's/Scholarship)* [10783]
Courage to Grow Scholarships *(Undergraduate/Scholarship)* [3461]
Pfizer Soozie Courter Hemophilia Scholarship Program *(Undergraduate/Scholarship)* [6988]
COUSE-Gram Scholarships *(Undergraduate/Scholarship)* [9424]
The Joe E. Covington Awards for Research on Bar Admissions Testing *(Doctorate, Graduate/Award)* [6873]
Steve Cowan Memorial Scholarships *(Undergraduate/Scholarship)* [3471]
Reuben R. Cowles Youth Awards *(Undergraduate/Award)* [945]
Justin Forrest Cox "Beat the Odds" Memorial Scholarships *(Undergraduate/Scholarship)* [3093]
Crafton Elementary School PTA Scholarships *(Undergraduate/Scholarship)* [8467]
Crafton Hills College Foundation Scholarships *(Undergraduate/Scholarship)* [8468]
Margaret T. Craig Community Service Scholarships *(Undergraduate/Scholarship)* [3281]
J. Craig and Page T. Smith Scholarships *(Undergraduate/Scholarship)* [8999]
Crain Educational Grant Program *(Undergraduate/Scholarship)* [8948]
Crawford Scholarships *(Undergraduate/Scholarship)* [8699]
Creative Glass Center of America Fellowships *(Advanced Professional/Fellowship)* [3467]
CRMA Scholarships *(Graduate, Undergraduate/Scholarship)* [2899]
Redlands Rotary Club - Ernest L. Cronemeyer Memorial Scholarships *(Undergraduate/Scholarship)* [8469]
CrossLites Scholarships *(Undergraduate, Graduate/Scholarship)* [3481]
R.G. and Ruth Crossno Memorial Scholarships *(Undergraduate/Scholarship)* [3756]
Crowder Scholarships *(Undergraduate/Scholarship)* [4192]
Lydia Cruz and Sandra Maria Ramos Scholarships

GENERAL STUDIES/FIELD OF STUDY NOT SPECIFIED

(Undergraduate/Scholarship) [3577]
CSA Fraternal Life Scholarships (Undergraduate/Scholarship) [3483]
CSF Ach Family Scholarships (Undergraduate/Scholarship) [2951]
CSF Barr Foundation Scholarships (Undergraduate/Scholarship) [2952]
CSF Barrett Family Scholarships (Undergraduate/Scholarship) [2953]
CSF Borden Inc. Scholarships (Undergraduate/Scholarship) [2954]
CSF Castellini Foundation Scholarships (Undergraduate/Scholarship) [2955]
CSF Cincinnati Bell Scholarships (Undergraduate/Scholarship) [2956]
CSF Cincinnati Financial Corporation Scholarships (Undergraduate/Scholarship) [2957]
CSF Crosset Family Scholarships (Undergraduate/Scholarship) [2958]
CSF Dater Foundation Scholarships (Undergraduate/Scholarship) [2959]
CSF Duke Energy Scholarships (Undergraduate/Scholarship) [2960]
CSF Farmer Family Foundation Scholarships (Undergraduate/Scholarship) [2961]
CSF Fifth Third Bank Combined Scholarships (Undergraduate/Scholarship) [2962]
CSF Fletemeyer Family Scholarships (Undergraduate/Scholarship) [2963]
CSF Gardner Foundation Scholarships (Undergraduate/Scholarship) [2964]
CSF Goldman, Sachs and Company Scholarships (Undergraduate/Scholarship) [2965]
CSF H.C. Schott Foundation Scholarships (Undergraduate/Scholarship) [2966]
CSF Heidelberg Distributing Co. Scholarships (Undergraduate/Scholarship) [2967]
CSF Heinz Pet Products Scholarships (Undergraduate/Scholarship) [2968]
CSF Juilfs Foundation Scholarships (Undergraduate/Scholarship) [2969]
CSF Kroger Cincinnati/Dayton Scholarships (Undergraduate/Scholarship) [2970]
CSF McCall Educational Scholarships (Undergraduate/Scholarship) [2971]
CSF Midland Company Scholarships (Undergraduate/Scholarship) [2972]
CSF Nethercott Family Scholarships (Undergraduate/Scholarship) [2973]
CSF Ohio National Foundation Scholarships (Undergraduate/Scholarship) [2974]
CSF Pepper Family Scholarships (Undergraduate/Scholarship) [2975]
CSF Pichler Family Scholarships (Undergraduate/Scholarship) [2976]
CSF PNC Bank Scholarships (Undergraduate/Scholarship) [2977]
CSF Procter and Gamble Scholarships (Undergraduate/Scholarship) [2978]
CSF Scripps Headliners Scholarships (Undergraduate/Scholarship) [2979]
CSF Semple Foundation Scholarships (Undergraduate/Scholarship) [2980]
CSF Union Central 135th Anniversary Scholarships (Undergraduate/Scholarship) [2981]
CSF U.S. Bank N.A. Scholarships (Undergraduate/Scholarship) [2982]
CSF Western-Southern Foundation Scholarships (Undergraduate/Scholarship) [2983]
CSF Woodward Trustees Scholarships (Undergraduate/Scholarship) [2984]
CSF Wynne Family Memorial Scholarships (Undergraduate/Scholarship) [2985]
CSLA Leaders of Distinction Award (Professional development/Recognition) [2759]
CSLA Leadership Scholarships (Undergraduate/Scholarship) [2760]
CSOHNS Fellowships (Graduate/Fellowship) [2752]
Murtha Cullina LLP Scholarships Fund (Undergraduate/Scholarship) [3199]
Brian Cummins Memorial Scholarships (Undergraduate/Scholarship) [4746]
John S. and Marjoria R. Cunningham Camp Scholarships (Professional development/Scholarship) [6193]
Laura Moore Cunningham Foundation General Scholarships (Undergraduate/Scholarship) [6024]
Tsutako Curo Scholarships (Undergraduate/Scholarship) [8339]
Curry Awards for Girls and Young Women (Undergraduate/Scholarship) [8949]
Cindy Curry Memorial Scholarships (Undergraduate/Scholarship) [7822]
Michael D. Curtin Renaissance Student Memorial Scholarships (Undergraduate/Scholarship) [3757]
Curtis/Breeden Scholarships (Doctorate/Scholarship) [2986]
Cystic Fibrosis Scholarship Foundation (Undergraduate/Scholarship) [3494]
DAAD Undergraduate Scholarship Program (Undergraduate/Scholarship) [3605]
Daily Lineups Scholarship Awards (Undergraduate, Master's/Award, Scholarship) [3504]
Dalai Lama Trust Graduate Scholarships (Graduate/Scholarship) [3508]
George Dale Scholarship Fund (Undergraduate/Scholarship) [1776]
Serena D. Dalton Scholarships (Undergraduate/Scholarship) [10578]
Marvin E. Daly Memorial Scholarship (Undergraduate/Scholarship) [7532]
Damon Runyon Physician-Scientist Training Awards (Postdoctorate, Professional development/Award) [3515]
D&R Sobey Scholarships (Undergraduate/Scholarship) [9047]
Arthur H. Daniels Scholarships (Undergraduate/Scholarship) [8470]
Mary Mouzon Darby Undergraduate Scholarships (Undergraduate/Scholarship) [4985]
David Library Fellowships (Doctorate, Postdoctorate/Fellowship) [3527]
Jim Davie Memorial Scholarships (Undergraduate, Master's/Scholarship) [10784]
Davis Family Scholarships (Undergraduate/Scholarship) [8700]
The William H. Davis, Jr. Scholarship Fund (Undergraduate/Scholarship) [3204]
Davis Memorial Foundation Scholarships (Graduate, Undergraduate/Scholarship) [3533]
Dwight F. Davis Memorial Scholarships (Undergraduate/Scholarship) [9974]
Estelle Davis Memorial Scholarships (Undergraduate/Scholarship) [2987]
Davis-Putter Scholarships Fund (Undergraduate, Graduate/Scholarship) [8659]
Larry Dean Davis Scholarship Program (Undergraduate/Scholarship) [7924]
Lawrence E. and Jean L. Davis Scholarships (Undergraduate/Scholarship) [7824]
Brian M. Day Scholarships (Undergraduate/Scholarship) [8252]
DBI Scholarships Fund (Undergraduate/Scholarship) [3223]
B.J. Dean Scholarships (Undergraduate/Scholarship) [3224]
Derek Lee Dean Soccer Scholarships (Undergraduate/Scholarship) [3094]
Debt.com Scholarships (All/Scholarship) [3539]
Julia B. DeCapua Fund (Undergraduate/Scholarship) [4661]
Walter M. Decker Point Scholarships (Graduate, Undergraduate/Scholarship) [8173]
Laurence Decore Awards for Student Leadership (Undergraduate/Scholarship) [8271]
Anthony R. Dees Educational Workshop Scholarships (Undergraduate/Scholarship) [9124]
DefensiveDriving.com Scholarships (Undergraduate/Scholarship) [3543]
Edward Delaney Scholarships (Professional development/Scholarship) [1982]
Jan DiMartino Delany Memorial Scholarships (Undergraduate/Scholarship) [4236]
Vine Deloria Jr. Memorial Scholarships (Graduate, Professional development/Scholarship) [868]
Delta Chi Alumnae Memorial Scholarships (Undergraduate/Scholarship) [8918]
Delta Epsilon Sigma Graduate Fellowships (Graduate/Fellowship) [3566]
Delta Epsilon Sigma Undergraduate Scholarships (Undergraduate/Scholarship) [3567]
Delta Iota Alumni Scholarships (Undergraduate/Scholarship) [8967]
Delta Kappa Gamma Society International World Fellowships (Professional development/Fellowship) [3571]
Delta Phi Epsilon Educational Foundation Scholarships (Undergraduate, Graduate/Scholarship) [3575]
Delta Zeta Undergraduate Scholarships (Undergraduate/Scholarship) [3582]
C. Rodney Demarest Memorial Scholarships (Undergraduate/Scholarship) [4747]
Law Offices of Michael A. DeMayo Scholarships (Undergraduate/Scholarship) [5963]
Enkhbaatar Demchig Field Research Fellowship Program (Undergraduate/Fellowship) [651]
Ruth DeMoss Scholarships (Undergraduate/Scholarship) [8701]
Michael Denton Scholarship (Undergraduate/Scholarship) [7533]
Denver Scholarship Foundation Scholarships (Undergraduate/Scholarship) [3600]
Dick Depaolis Memorial Scholarships (Undergraduate/Scholarship) [3325]
Herman H. Derksen Scholarships (Undergraduate/Scholarship) [8702]
Pat Dermargosian Memorial Scholarships (Undergraduate/Scholarship) [8471]
Achille and Irene Despres, William and Andre Scholarships (Undergraduate/Scholarship) [4587]
Detroit Economic Club Scholarship (Undergraduate/Scholarship) [3326]
Helen L. Dewar Scholarships (Undergraduate/Scholarship) [9729]
Albert and Jane Dewey Scholarships (Undergraduate/Scholarship) [4748]
Donald J. DeYoung Scholarships (Undergraduate/Scholarship) [4588]
Diabetes Hope Foundation Scholarships (Undergraduate/Scholarship) [3614]
Julio C. Diaz Academic Scholarship (Undergraduate/Scholarship) [9498]
Bill Dickey Scholarship Association Scholarships (Undergraduate/Scholarship) [3620]
Robert Martz DiGiacomo Memorial Scholarship Fund (Undergraduate/Scholarship) [9499]
The E.R. and Lilian B. Dimmette Scholarship Fund (Undergraduate/Scholarship) [4193]
Disability Care Center Disabled Student Scholarships (Undergraduate/Scholarship) [3629]
Discover Graduate Loans (Graduate, Master's, Doctorate/Loan) [3635]
Distinguished Young Women Scholarships (Undergraduate/Scholarship) [3643]
Dr. Allan A. Dixon Memorial Scholarships (Postgraduate/Scholarship) [2742]
Julian Dobranowski Memorial Scholarships (Undergraduate/Scholarship) [8574]
Doctoral Dissertation Grants (Doctorate/Grant) [5386]
Doddridge County Promise Scholarships (Undergraduate/Scholarship) [7825]
Jim Dodson Law Scholarships (Undergraduate/Scholarship) [5600]
Emmett J. Doerr Memorial Distinguished Scout Scholarships (Undergraduate/Scholarship) [6921]
Dofflemyer Scholarships (Undergraduate/Scholarship) [6922]
Dollar-A-Day Academic Scholarships (Graduate, Undergraduate/Scholarship) [3649]
Dolphin Scholarships (Undergraduate/Scholarship) [3651]
Doniphan Community Foundation Scholarships (Undergraduate/Scholarship) [4561]
Mike and Gail Donley Spouse Scholarships (Undergraduate, Graduate, Postgraduate/Scholarship) [123]
Harry A. Donn Scholarships (Undergraduate/Scholarship) [4749]
Mickey Donnelly Memorial Scholarships (Undergraduate/Scholarship) [8340]
Jim Doogan Memorial Scholarships (Undergraduate/Scholarship) [10096]
Father Connie Dougherty Scholarships (Undergraduate, Vocational/Occupational/Scholarship) [3320]

GENERAL STUDIES/FIELD OF STUDY NOT SPECIFIED

Tommy Douglas Memorial Scholarship *(Undergraduate/Scholarship)* [7205]
Downeast Energy Scholarships *(Undergraduate/Scholarship)* [3659]
Jay and Rheba Downes Memorial Scholarships *(Undergraduate/Scholarship)* [3095]
Wilma Sackett Dressel Scholarships *(Undergraduate/Scholarship)* [8919]
Charles Drew Scholarships *(Other/Scholarship)* [1940]
Drinkwater Family Scholarships *(Undergraduate/Scholarship)* [8703]
Mary Ellen Driscoll Scholarships *(Undergraduate/Scholarship)* [4479]
Sergeant Major Douglas R. Drum Memorial Scholarship Fund *(Undergraduate/Scholarship)* [1005]
DSACF Modern Woodmen of America Scholarships *(Undergraduate/Scholarship)* [3706]
Henry Belin du Pont Dissertation Fellowships *(Doctorate, Graduate/Fellowship)* [4688]
Julia M. Duckwall Scholarships *(Professional development/Scholarship)* [1983]
Deborah Gandee Dudding Memorial Scholarships *(Undergraduate/Scholarship)* [7826]
Edward Leon Duhamel Scholarship Fund *(Undergraduate/Scholarship)* [8605]
Doris Duke Conservation Fellows Program *(Master's/Fellowship)* [10678]
H.J. "Duke" Ellington Memorial Scholarship Award *(Undergraduate/Scholarship)* [7513]
Duluth Central High School Alumni Scholarships *(Undergraduate/Scholarship)* [3708]
Dunbar Heritage Scholarships *(Undergraduate/Scholarship)* [9427]
Dr. Allan Duncan Memorial Scholarships *(Undergraduate, Master's/Scholarship)* [10785]
Wade and Marcelene Duncan Scholarships *(Undergraduate/Scholarship)* [10579]
Travis Dunning Memorial Scholarships *(Undergraduate/Scholarship)* [8341]
Durning Sisters Scholarships *(Graduate/Scholarship)* [3549]
Joshua Dyke Family Scholarships *(Undergraduate/Scholarship)* [9730]
Howard G. and Gladys A. Eakes Memorial Scholarships *(Undergraduate/Scholarship)* [4562]
East-West Center Graduate Degree Fellowships *(Master's, Doctorate, Graduate/Fellowship)* [3760]
Eastern Orthodox Scouting Scholarships *(Undergraduate/Scholarship)* [6923]
École Polytechnique Commemorative Awards *(Master's, Doctorate, Graduate/Award, Fellowship)* [2630]
Economic Club Business Study Abroad Scholarships *(Undergraduate/Scholarship)* [4589]
Edgecliff Alumni Awards *(Undergraduate/Scholarship)* [10718]
Melanie and Todd Edmonson Memorial Scholarships *(Undergraduate/Scholarship)* [3261]
Edmonton Epilepsy Continuing Education Scholarships *(Undergraduate/Scholarship)* [3792]
Education Factor Scholarships *(Graduate, Undergraduate/Scholarship)* [6378]
"Education is Power" Scholarships *(Undergraduate/Scholarship)* [6989]
EDvestinU(r) National Monthly Scholarships *(Undergraduate/Scholarship)* [7309]
The Edwards Annual College Scholarships *(Undergraduate/Scholarship)* [3810]
Esther Edwards Graduate Scholarships *(Doctorate, Professional development/Scholarship)* [9851]
Jimmy Edwards Scholarships *(Undergraduate/Scholarship)* [3226]
Hillel Einhorn New Investigator Award *(Doctorate/Award)* [9161]
Eisbrouch & Marsh Scholarship Awards *(Undergraduate, Graduate/Scholarship)* [3814]
El Pomar Fellowships *(Graduate/Fellowship)* [3818]
George and Isabelle Elanjian Scholarships *(Undergraduate/Scholarship)* [10198]
W. Eldridge and Emily Lowe Scholarships *(Undergraduate/Scholarship)* [8968]
A.C. Elias, Jr. Irish-American Research Travel Fellowships *(Other/Fellowship)* [1290]
Elie Wiesel Prize in Ethics *(Undergraduate/Prize, Award)* [10553]
Dr. Robert Elliott Memorial Scholarships *(Undergraduate/Scholarship)* [6351]
Clay Elliott Scholarship Foundation Scholarships *(Undergraduate/Scholarship)* [3856]
Optimist Club of Redlands - Virginia Elliott Scholarships *(Undergraduate/Scholarship)* [8472]
Pauline Elliott Scholarships *(Undergraduate/Scholarship)* [6352]
Thomas J. Emery Memorial Scholarships *(Undergraduate/Scholarship)* [2988]
Thomas O. Enders Graduate Fellowships *(Graduate/Fellowship)* [1876]
ENF Most Valuable Student Scholarships *(Undergraduate/Scholarship)* [3854]
Enhanced Insurance Scholarships Program *(Undergraduate/Scholarship)* [10340]
Ensurify Safe Driving Scholarships *(Undergraduate/Scholarship)* [3876]
Epsilon Epsilon Scholarships *(Undergraduate/Scholarship)* [8920]
Epsilon Tau Pi's Soaring Eagle Scholarships *(Undergraduate/Scholarship)* [6924]
Epsilon Tau Scholarships *(Undergraduate/Scholarship)* [8921]
Alan R. Epstein "Reach for the Stars" Scholarships *(Undergraduate/Scholarship)* [6452]
Robert C. Erb Sr. Scholarships *(Undergraduate/Scholarship)* [6353]
ERCA Community Contribution Scholarships *(Undergraduate/Scholarship)* [3804]
Harriet Erich Graduate Fellowships *(Graduate/Fellowship, Scholarship)* [3550]
Ernest Hemingway Research Grants *(Other/Grant)* [4855]
The Eleonor A. Ernest Scholarships *(Undergraduate/Scholarship)* [5502]
Robert P. Ernest Scholarships *(Undergraduate/Scholarship)* [5504]
Boomer Esiason Foundation General Academic Scholarships *(Undergraduate, Graduate/Scholarship)* [2338]
European College of Liberal Arts Scholarships *(Undergraduate/Scholarship)* [9981]
Eustace-Kwan Family Foundation Scholarships *(Undergraduate/Scholarship)* [8950]
Chick Evans Caddie Scholarships *(Undergraduate/Scholarship)* [10531]
Lyle and Rlene Everingham Family Scholarships *(Undergraduate/Scholarship)* [2989]
Lyle Everingham Scholarships *(Undergraduate/Scholarship)* [2990]
Excel Staffing Companies Scholarships for Excellence in Continuing Education *(Undergraduate/Scholarship)* [302]
Executive Women International Scholarship Program (EWISP) *(Undergraduate/Scholarship)* [3936]
Exercise For Life Athletic Scholarships Program *(Undergraduate/Scholarship)* [2339]
Experts Exchange Scholarships Contest *(Undergraduate, Graduate/Scholarship)* [3944]
Express Medical Supply Scholarships *(Undergraduate/Scholarship)* [3948]
FACT "Second Chance" Scholarship Program *(Undergraduate/Scholarship)* [3999]
Faculty Research Visit Grants *(Doctorate/Grant, Award)* [3606]
Fairbanks Chapter Legacy Scholarships *(Undergraduate/Scholarship)* [10097]
The Fallen Heroes Scholarships *(Undergraduate/Scholarship)* [3079]
James Mackenzie Fallows Scholarships Honoring Gertrude Baccus *(Undergraduate/Scholarship)* [8473]
Families of Freedom Scholarship Fund - America Scholarships *(Undergraduate, Vocational/Occupational/Scholarship)* [3956]
The Fantasy Sports Daily Scholarship Program - General Scholarship for Advanced Education *(Undergraduate, Graduate, Master's/Scholarship)* [3966]
Farmington UNICO Scholarships *(Undergraduate/Scholarship)* [4751]
David Edward Farson Scholarships *(Undergraduate/Scholarship)* [7827]
Anne M. Fassett Scholarships *(Undergraduate, Graduate/Scholarship)* [9428]
FCBA Foundation College Scholarship Program *(Undergraduate/Scholarship)* [3972]
Federalsburg Rotary Club Scholarships *(Undergraduate/Scholarship)* [3175]
FEEA-NTEU Scholarships *(Graduate, Postgraduate, Undergraduate/Scholarship)* [3989]
Nolan W. Feeser Scholarship Fund *(Undergraduate/Scholarship)* [4045]
FEF Scholarships *(Undergraduate/Scholarship)* [3952]
Virginia Valk Fehsenfeld Scholarships *(Undergraduate/Scholarship)* [4591]
Symee Ruth Feinberg Memorial Scholarships *(Undergraduate/Scholarship)* [4752]
Feldman Law Firm Disabled Veterans Scholarships *(All/Scholarship)* [4009]
Feldman & Royle, Attorneys at Law Autism Scholarships *(All/Scholarship)* [4011]
Fellowships in the PMAC-AGPC *(Professional development/Fellowship)* [8295]
Field Museum Graduate Student Fellowships *(Graduate/Fellowship)* [4017]
Beth K. Fields Scholarships *(Undergraduate/Scholarship)* [10144]
Sakura Finetek Student Scholarships *(Undergraduate/Scholarship)* [7167]
Gordy Fink Memorial Scholarships *(Undergraduate/Scholarship)* [8343]
Martin Fischer Awards *(Undergraduate/Award)* [2649]
The Fisher-Clark Memorial Endowed Scholarships *(Undergraduate/Scholarship)* [6026]
Arthur and Juna Fisher Memorial Track Scholarships *(Undergraduate/Scholarship)* [8475]
Sergeant Paul Fisher Scholarships *(Undergraduate/Scholarship)* [6907]
Gloria Flaherty Scholarships *(Graduate/Scholarship)* [4466]
Albert Flegenheimer Memorial Scholarships *(Undergraduate/Scholarship)* [6494]
FLEOA Foundation Scholarship Program *(Undergraduate/Scholarship)* [3991]
Grant H. Flint International Scholarships - Category I *(Undergraduate/Scholarship)* [9337]
Barney Flynn Memorial Scholarships *(Undergraduate/Scholarship)* [3097]
John Flynn Memorial Scholarships *(Undergraduate/Scholarship)* [3284]
FMA-FEEA Scholarship Program *(Undergraduate/Scholarship)* [3993]
Alice J. Foit Scholarships *(Undergraduate/Scholarship)* [9502]
Foot Locker Scholar Athletes *(Undergraduate/Scholarship)* [4131]
Anne Ford Scholarships *(Undergraduate/Scholarship)* [6850]
V. Thomas Forehand, Jr. Scholarships *(Undergraduate/Scholarship)* [10302]
Foresters Scholarships *(Undergraduate/Scholarship)* [5095]
The FormsBirds Scholarships *(Undergraduate/Scholarship)* [4140]
Forsyth County United Way Scholarships *(Undergraduate/Scholarship)* [5925]
Andrew Foster Scholarships *(Undergraduate/Scholarship)* [6815]
Fostering Hope Scholarships Fund *(Undergraduate/Scholarship)* [7828]
Foundation for the Advancement of Aboriginal Youth Bursary Program *(Undergraduate/Scholarship)* [3389]
Foundation for the Advancement of Aboriginal Youth Scholarships *(Undergraduate/Scholarship)* [3390]
Foundation for the Carolinas Rotary Scholarship Fund *(Undergraduate/Scholarship)* [4195]
Foundation of the Federal Bar Association Public Service Scholarship Award *(Undergraduate/Scholarship)* [4260]
Terry Fox Memorial Scholarship *(Undergraduate/Scholarship)* [7206]
Captain Ernest Fox Perpetual Scholarships *(Undergraduate/Scholarship)* [3080]
Frame My Future Scholarships Contest *(Undergraduate, Graduate/Scholarship)* [2938]

GENERAL STUDIES/FIELD OF STUDY NOT SPECIFIED

Joe Francomano Scholarships *(Undergraduate/Scholarship)* [5630]
Johnny & Sarah Frank Scholarships *(Undergraduate/Scholarship)* [10019]
John Hope Franklin Dissertation Fellowships *(Doctorate/Fellowship)* [1080]
James Franklin and Dorothy J. Warnell Scholarship Fund *(Undergraduate, Vocational/Occupational/Scholarship)* [3321]
Franklin Elementary School PTA Scholarships *(Undergraduate/Scholarship)* [8476]
Franklin Research Grants *(Doctorate/Grant)* [1081]
Benjamin Franklin Trust Fund *(Undergraduate, Vocational/Occupational/Scholarship)* [4046]
John L. and Victory E. Frantz Scholarship *(Undergraduate/Scholarship)* [4518]
Fraser Family Scholarships *(Undergraduate/Scholarship)* [8345]
FRAXA Postdoctoral Fellowships *(Postdoctorate, Master's/Fellowship)* [4295]
Freedom Alliance Scholarships *(Undergraduate/Scholarship)* [4299]
Dale E. Fridell Memorial Scholarships *(Undergraduate, Vocational/Occupational/Scholarship)* [9593]
William A. Friedlander Scholarships *(Undergraduate/Scholarship)* [2991]
A.E. Robert Friedman Scholarships *(Undergraduate/Scholarship)* [7795]
Phil Friel Scholarships *(Undergraduate/Scholarship)* [6354]
Joel R. Friend Scholarships *(Undergraduate/Scholarship)* [2227]
Kennedy T. Friend Scholarships *(Graduate, Undergraduate/Scholarship)* [325]
Friends of Coal Scholarships *(Undergraduate/Scholarship)* [10523]
Dean A. Froehlich Endowed Scholarships *(Undergraduate/Scholarship)* [6027]
Melbourne and Alice E. Frontjes Scholarships *(Undergraduate/Scholarship)* [4592]
"Frugal Student" Scholarships *(Undergraduate/Scholarship)* [7950]
Marian Johnson Frutiger Scholarships *(Undergraduate/Scholarship)* [8922]
Gerard Swartz Fudge Memorial Scholarships *(Undergraduate/Scholarship)* [5027]
Keiko Fukuda Scholarships *(Undergraduate/Scholarship)* [9960]
Daniel G. and Helen I. Fultz Scholarship Fund *(Undergraduate/Scholarship)* [4047]
Gaddy Student Scholarships *(Undergraduate/Scholarship)* [10582]
Gaebe Eagle Scout Awards *(Undergraduate/Scholarship)* [6925]
Harry Gairey Scholarships *(Undergraduate/Scholarship)* [2282]
Farley Moody Galbraith Scholarship Fund *(Undergraduate/Scholarship)* [3262]
Louise Bales Gallagher Scholarships *(Undergraduate/Scholarship)* [3551]
Whitney Laine Gallahar Memorial Scholarship Fund *(Undergraduate/Scholarship)* [3263]
Carolyn Gallmeyer Scholarships *(Undergraduate/Scholarship)* [4593]
Gallo Blue Chip Scholarships *(Undergraduate/Scholarship)* [4724]
Priscilla Gamble Scholarships *(Undergraduate/Scholarship)* [2992]
Gamma Iota Scholarships - Gamma Tau *(Undergraduate/Scholarship)* [8923]
Gamma Iota Scholarships - Kappa Eta *(Undergraduate/Scholarship)* [8924]
Gamma Iota Scholarships - Zeta Kappa *(Undergraduate/Scholarship)* [8925]
Gamma Iota Scholarships - Zeta Nu *(Undergraduate/Scholarship)* [8926]
Gamma Sigma Alpha Graduate Scholarships *(Graduate/Scholarship)* [4322]
Peter M. Gargano Scholarship Fund *(Undergraduate/Scholarship)* [3709]
Gail Garner R.I.S.E. Memorial Scholarships *(Undergraduate/Scholarship)* [8477]
Edwin W. Gaston Scholarships *(Undergraduate/Scholarship)* [341]
Gates Cambridge Scholarships *(Graduate, Master's,
Doctorate, Postgraduate, Postdoctorate/Scholarship)* [6746]
David A. and Pamela A. Gault Charitable Fund *(Undergraduate/Scholarship)* [9504]
A.R.F.O.R.A. Martha Gavrila Scholarships for Women *(Postgraduate/Scholarship)* [1226]
GAWP Graduate Scholarships *(Graduate/Scholarship)* [4377]
GCABC Youth Scholarship Awards *(Undergraduate/Scholarship)* [4419]
G.E. Aviation Scholarships *(Undergraduate/Scholarship)* [2993]
Gehring Memorial Foundation Scholarships *(Graduate, Undergraduate/Scholarship)* [5100]
Milacron Geier Scholarships *(Undergraduate/Scholarship)* [2994]
Victoria S. and Bradley L. Geist Scholarships *(Undergraduate/Scholarship)* [4795]
Irma Gelhausen Scholarship Fund *(Undergraduate/Scholarship)* [5930]
General Falcon Scholarships *(Undergraduate/Scholarship)* [8201]
General Mills Foundation Scholarships *(Undergraduate/Scholarship)* [869]
General Scholarships for Higher Learning *(Undergraduate, Graduate, Master's/Scholarship)* [4960]
George W. and Ethel B. Hoefler Fund *(Undergraduate/Scholarship)* [3322]
Georgetown Working League Scholarships *(Undergraduate/Scholarship)* [4368]
Gerber Foundation Merit Scholarships *(Undergraduate/Scholarship)* [4392]
Daniel Gerber, Sr. Medallion Scholarships *(Undergraduate/Scholarship)* [4393]
German Historical Institute Fellowships at the Horner Library *(Doctorate/Fellowship)* [4396]
Bunny Kline Gerner and Robin Gerner Doty Memorial Adelphe Scholarships *(Undergraduate/Scholarship)* [5726]
Getty GRI-NEH Postdoctoral Fellowships *(Postdoctorate/Fellowship)* [4408]
Getty Postdoctoral Fellowships *(Postdoctorate/Fellowship)* [4409]
Getty Predoctoral Fellowships *(Doctorate/Fellowship)* [4411]
Getty Research Exchange Fellowship Program for Cultural Heritage Preservation *(Doctorate/Fellowship)* [1205]
GFWC Women's Club of South County Scholarships *(Undergraduate/Scholarship)* [8606]
Tom Gifford Scholarships *(Undergraduate/Scholarship)* [4520]
Shane Gilbert Memorial Scholarships *(Undergraduate/Scholarship)* [7831]
William Harrison Gill Education Fund *(Undergraduate/Scholarship)* [2228]
Benjamin A. Gilman International Scholarship *(Undergraduate/Scholarship)* [10060]
Leo Gilmartin Scholarships *(Undergraduate/Scholarship)* [8167]
Susan Kay Munson Gilmore Memorial Scholarships *(Undergraduate, Vocational/Occupational/Scholarship)* [3285]
Alex Gissler Memorial Scholarships *(Undergraduate/Scholarship)* [6355]
GLATA Living Memorial Doctorate Scholarships *(Doctorate, Graduate/Fellowship)* [4653]
GLATA Living Memorial Graduate Scholarships *(Graduate/Fellowship, Scholarship)* [4654]
Herman and Bess Glazer Scholarship Fund *(Undergraduate/Scholarship)* [4662]
Glazing Industry Scholarships *(Undergraduate/Scholarship)* [8347]
Gleaner Life Insurance Society Scholarships *(Undergraduate/Scholarship)* [4447]
Franciszek Glogowski Memorial Scholarships *(Undergraduate/Scholarship)* [8576]
Irene Carlson Gnaedinger Memorial Scholarships *(Undergraduate/Scholarship)* [6028]
Glenn Godfrey Memorial Scholarships *(Undergraduate, Graduate/Scholarship)* [5864]
Godparents for Tanzania Scholarship *(Undergraduate/Scholarship)* [4464]
Shirley J. Gold Scholarship *(Undergraduate/Scholarship)* [793]
Golden Eagle Coins Scholarships *(Undergraduate/Scholarship)* [4470]
Golden Key Graduate Scholar Awards *(Graduate, Master's, Doctorate/Scholarship)* [6747]
Golden Key Study Abroad Scholarships *(Undergraduate/Scholarship)* [4472]
Rhode Island Commission on Women/Freda H. Goldman Education Awards *(Undergraduate/Award, Scholarship)* [8607]
Alois and Marie Goldmann Scholarship Fund *(Undergraduate/Scholarship)* [5041]
Joshua Gomes Memorial Scholarship Fund *(Undergraduate, Graduate/Scholarship)* [6990]
Millie Gonzalez Memorial Scholarships *(Undergraduate/Scholarship)* [4859]
Richard Goolsby Scholarship Fund *(Graduate, Undergraduate/Scholarship)* [4196]
Lucille May Gopie Scholarships *(Undergraduate, Graduate/Scholarship)* [2283]
Barnett D. Gordon Scholarships *(Graduate, Undergraduate/Scholarship)* [5101]
Pauline LaFon Gore Scholarships *(Undergraduate/Scholarship)* [3227]
Richard C. Gorecki Scholarships *(Undergraduate/Scholarship)* [8202]
Nettie and Jesse Gorov Scholarships *(Undergraduate/Scholarship)* [3286]
American Association of University Women Sue Gottcent Memorial Scholarship Fund *(Undergraduate, Graduate/Scholarship)* [9431]
Charles F. Gould Endowment Scholarships *(Undergraduate/Scholarship)* [10020]
Rachel Graham Memorial Scholarships *(Undergraduate/Scholarship)* [8478]
Grand Rapids Scholarship Association *(Undergraduate/Scholarship)* [4595]
Grand Rapids University Prep Founder's Scholarships *(Undergraduate/Scholarship)* [4596]
Grande Prairie 4-H District Scholarships *(Undergraduate/Scholarship)* [8]
Granger Business Association College Scholarships *(Undergraduate/Scholarship)* [4641]
Russ Grant Memorial Scholarship for Tennis *(Undergraduate/Scholarship)* [7832]
Lucille Cheever Graubart/Lambda Scholarships *(Undergraduate/Scholarship)* [8927]
Grays Harbor Community Foundation Scholarships *(Undergraduate, Graduate/Scholarship)* [4651]
Greater Cincinnati Scholarships Association *(Undergraduate/Scholarship)* [2995]
Greater Seattle Business Association Scholarships (GSBA Scholarships) *(Undergraduate/Scholarship)* [4658]
Bishop Charles P. Greco Graduate Fellowships *(Graduate, Master's/Fellowship)* [5853]
Greek Orthodox Archdiocese of America Paleologos Graduate Scholarships *(Graduate/Scholarship)* [4666]
Green Hill Yacht and Country Club Scholarships *(Undergraduate/Scholarship)* [3177]
Green Knight Economic Development Corporation Scholarships *(Undergraduate/Scholarship)* [4668]
Crystal Green Memorial Scholarship *(Undergraduate/Scholarship)* [2314]
James H. and Shirley L. Green Scholarship Fund *(Undergraduate/Scholarship)* [9506]
Curt Greene Memorial Scholarships *(Undergraduate/Scholarship)* [4725]
Greenwich Scholarship Association Scholarships (GSA) *(Undergraduate/Scholarship)* [4672]
Francis Harris Gresham Scholarships *(Undergraduate/Scholarship)* [9433]
Griffin Foundation Scholarships *(Undergraduate/Scholarship)* [4674]
Homajean Grisham Memorial Scholarship *(Undergraduate/Scholarship)* [7534]
Reginald K. Groome Memorial Scholarships *(Undergraduate/Scholarship)* [8823]
Kathern F. Gruber Scholarship Program *(Undergraduate/Scholarship)* [2312]
Jack M. and Mary Lou Gruber Scholarships *(Undergraduate/Scholarship)* [6029]
Gruwell Scholarships *(Undergraduate/Scholarship)* [3178]
Guelph Caribbean Canadian Association Under-

graduate Scholarships *(Undergraduate/Scholarship)* [4679]
Melissa Ann Guerra Scholarships *(Undergraduate/Scholarship)* [3098]
Bobette Bibo Gugliotta Memorial Scholarships for Creative Writing *(Undergraduate/Scholarship)* [8951]
GuildScholar Awards *(Undergraduate/Scholarship)* [5596]
Hai Guin Scholarships Association *(Undergraduate/Scholarship)* [1695]
Guin-Stanford Scholarships *(Advanced Professional/Scholarship)* [3264]
Calouste Gulbenkian Foundation Scholarships *(Undergraduate/Scholarship)* [1696]
Larry Gulley Scholarships *(Undergraduate/Scholarship)* [9125]
Patricia S. Gustafson '56 Memorial Scholarships *(Undergraduate/Scholarship)* [3710]
Sara Gwisdalla Memorial Scholarships *(Undergraduate/Scholarship)* [7833]
Wesley R. Habley NACADA Summer Institute Scholarships *(Other/Scholarship)* [6672]
Hackett Family Scholarships *(Undergraduate/Scholarship)* [4597]
HACU/KIA Motors America, Inc. Scholarships *(Undergraduate, Graduate/Scholarship)* [4887]
HAESF Graduate Scholarships *(Graduate/Scholarship)* [5008]
Leslie Jane Hahn Memorial Scholarships *(Undergraduate/Scholarship)* [8705]
Hall of Achievement Scholarships *(Undergraduate/Scholarship)* [2450]
Joyce C. Hall College Scholarships *(Undergraduate/Scholarship)* [7960]
Chappie Hall Scholarship Program *(Undergraduate/Scholarship)* [2]
Guy D. and Mary Edith Halladay Graduate Scholarships *(Undergraduate/Scholarship)* [4598]
Harold B. Halter Memorial Scholarship *(Undergraduate/Scholarship)* [3970]
Alice Hamilton Prize *(Other/Prize)* [1311]
Al Hamilton Scholarships *(Undergraduate/Scholarship)* [2285]
Stan Hamilton Scholarships *(Undergraduate/Scholarship)* [8766]
George and Mary Josephine Hamman Foundation Scholarships *(Undergraduate/Scholarship)* [4693]
Jay Hammond Memorial Scholarships *(Undergraduate/Scholarship)* [10098]
HANA Scholarships *(Undergraduate, Graduate, Doctorate/Scholarship)* [9852]
Hancock Family Snow Hill High School Scholarships *(Undergraduate/Scholarship)* [3179]
Pauline Hand Memorial Scholarships *(Undergraduate/Scholarship)* [9569]
Byron Hanke Fellowships *(Doctorate, Graduate, Undergraduate/Fellowship)* [4225]
Clayburn and Garnet R. Hanna Scholarships *(Undergraduate/Scholarship)* [7834]
Zenon C.R. Hansen Leadership Scholarships *(Undergraduate/Scholarship)* [6926]
Clement T. Hanson Scholarships *(Undergraduate/Scholarship)* [6569]
Haraldson Foundation Scholarships *(Undergraduate, Graduate/Scholarship)* [4713]
Isaac and Mary Harbottle Scholarships *(Graduate, Undergraduate/Scholarship)* [7909]
Matt Harmon Memorial Scholarships *(Undergraduate/Scholarship)* [9434]
North Las Vegas Firefighters William J. Harnedy Memorial Scholarships *(Undergraduate/Scholarship)* [8348]
Harness Tracks of America Scholarship Fund *(Undergraduate/Scholarship)* [4727]
Father J. Harold Conway Memorial Scholarships *(Postgraduate/Fellowship)* [7632]
Walter and Lucille Harper Scholarships *(Undergraduate/Scholarship)* [5806]
Frank and Charlene Harris Scholarships *(Undergraduate/Scholarship)* [3228]
Nicky & Ted Harrison Memorial Scholarships *(Undergraduate, Master's/Scholarship)* [10786]
Peg Hart Harrison Memorial Scholarships *(Undergraduate/Scholarship)* [3552]
Morton and Beatrice Harrison Scholarship Fund *(Undergraduate/Scholarship)* [4048]
Carroll Hart Scholarship *(Graduate/Scholarship)* [9126]
Hartford Grammar School Scholarships *(Undergraduate/Scholarship)* [4756]
Hartford Whalers Booster Club Scholarships *(Undergraduate/Scholarship)* [4778]
Harry Hartleben Scholarships *(Undergraduate/Scholarship)* [7837]
William T. Hartzell Memorial Scholarships *(Undergraduate/Scholarship)* [8480]
Gregory Linn Haught Citizenship Awards *(Undergraduate/Award, Scholarship)* [7839]
Dorcas Edmonson Haught Scholarships *(Undergraduate/Scholarship)* [7840]
R. Garn Haycock Memorial Scholarships *(Undergraduate/Scholarship)* [8481]
HCF Community Scholarships Fund *(Undergraduate, Graduate/Scholarship)* [4796]
Dr. James H. Heckman Memorial Scholarship Fund *(Undergraduate/Scholarship)* [9508]
Professor Ulla Hedner Scholarships *(Undergraduate/Scholarship)* [6991]
Richard Heekin Scholarships *(Undergraduate/Scholarship)* [2996]
Howell Heflin Memorial Scholarship *(Undergraduate/Scholarship)* [7535]
Lavonne Heghinian Scholarships *(Undergraduate/Scholarship)* [3585]
Barbara and Nicole Heacox Foreign Travel and Study Scholarship Fund *(Undergraduate/Scholarship)* [4522]
Helen Steiner Rice Scholarships *(Undergraduate/Scholarship)* [2997]
Hellenic Times Scholarships *(Undergraduate, Graduate/Scholarship)* [4843]
Hemlow Prize in Burney Studies *(Graduate/Prize)* [1292]
Jeanne H. Hemmingway Scholarships *(Undergraduate/Scholarship)* [3711]
John Henderson Endowment Scholarships *(Undergraduate/Scholarship)* [10022]
The Henderson Memorial Endowed Scholarships *(Undergraduate/Scholarship)* [6031]
Dr. E. Bruce Hendrick Scholarships *(All/Scholarship)* [9474]
Gene Henson Scholarships *(Undergraduate/Scholarship)* [2113]
Herbert Hoover Uncommon Student Awards *(Undergraduate/Scholarship)* [4931]
Michael Herman Scholarships *(Undergraduate, Vocational/Occupational/Scholarship)* [4524]
Manuel Hernandez, Jr. Foundation Scholarships *(Undergraduate/Scholarship)* [3099]
Ella Beren Hersch Scholarships *(Undergraduate/Scholarship)* [7841]
Wayne E. Hesch Memorial Scholarship *(Undergraduate, Graduate/Scholarship)* [1543]
Peter Hess Scholarships *(Undergraduate/Scholarship)* [4338]
Dwight Hibbard Scholarships *(Undergraduate/Scholarship)* [2998]
Jim Hierlihy Memorial Scholarship *(Undergraduate/Scholarship)* [3911]
High School Academic Scholarship *(Undergraduate/Scholarship)* [8873]
Gus and Henrietta Hill Scholarships *(Undergraduate/Scholarship)* [3712]
D. Glenn Hilts Scholarships *(Graduate, Undergraduate/Scholarship)* [2069]
Jim and Nancy Hinkle Travel Grants *(Graduate/Grant)* [4856]
Hispanic Association of Colleges and Universities Scholarships *(Undergraduate/Scholarship)* [4890]
Hispanic Metropolitan Chamber Scholarships *(Graduate, Undergraduate/Scholarship)* [4900]
Hispanic Scholarship Fund General College Scholarship Program (HSF) *(Undergraduate/Scholarship)* [4904]
Hispanic Serving Institution Scholarships (HSIS) *(Undergraduate/Scholarship)* [9870]
Historically Black College or University Scholarships (HBCUS) *(Undergraduate/Scholarship)* [9871]
Lucy Hsu Ho Scholarships *(Undergraduate/Scholarship)* [2229]
C.H.(Chuck) Hodgson Scholarships *(Undergraduate/Scholarship)* [10547]
James E. Hoff, S.J. Scholars *(Undergraduate/Scholarship)* [10721]
Florette B. Hoffheimer Scholarships *(Undergraduate/Scholarship)* [2999]
Hoffman Family Scholarship Fund *(Undergraduate/Scholarship)* [4526]
Henry Hoffman Memorial Scholarship Fund *(Undergraduate/Scholarship)* [6740]
Irving J. Hoffman Memorial Scholarships *(Undergraduate/Scholarship)* [10288]
The Thelma S. Hoge Memorial Scholarship Fund *(Undergraduate/Scholarship)* [3205]
Michael J. Hoggard Memorial Scholarships *(Undergraduate/Scholarship)* [8350]
Cleve Holloway Memorial Scholarship Fund *(Undergraduate/Scholarship)* [3265]
Robert Holmes Scholarship *(Undergraduate/Scholarship)* [3327]
Hope Through Learning Awards *(Undergraduate/Scholarship)* [4927]
Hope for the Warriors Spouse/Caregiver Scholarships *(Undergraduate, Graduate/Scholarship)* [4933]
Frank and Gladys Hopkins Endowed Scholarships *(Undergraduate/Scholarship)* [6033]
Minnie Hopkins Memorial Scholarship Fund of Lathrop/Compton School *(Undergraduate/Scholarship)* [9511]
Harry Hopmeyer Memorial Scholarships *(Undergraduate/Scholarship)* [5578]
Horatio Alger Ak-Sar-Ben Scholarships *(Undergraduate/Scholarship)* [4957]
Horatio Alger Idaho University Scholarships *(Undergraduate/Scholarship)* [4958]
Sam J. Hord Memorial Scholarships *(Undergraduate/Scholarship)* [9381]
Sandra Jo Hornick Scholarships *(Undergraduate/Scholarship)* [5671]
Detroit Tigers Willie Horton Scholarship *(Undergraduate/Scholarship)* [3328]
Hosinec Family Scholarships *(Graduate, Undergraduate/Scholarship)* [10289]
Max and Julia Houghton Duluth Central Scholarships *(Undergraduate/Scholarship)* [3713]
Kaspar Hovannisian Memorial Scholarships *(Graduate/Scholarship)* [1697]
Hirair and Anna Hovnanian Foundation Presidential Scholarships *(Undergraduate/Scholarship)* [1698]
Hirair and Anna Hovnanian Foundation Scholarships *(Undergraduate/Scholarship)* [1699]
C.D. Howard Scholarships *(Undergraduate/Scholarship)* [5298]
Roger and Joyce Howe Scholarships *(Undergraduate/Scholarship)* [3000]
Donald Hoy Memorial Scholarships *(Undergraduate, Master's/Scholarship)* [10787]
John Hoyt Memorial Scholarships *(Undergraduate, Master's/Scholarship)* [10788]
Albert W. and Mildred Hubbard Scholarships *(Undergraduate/Scholarship)* [8708]
Amber Huber Memorial Scholarships *(Undergraduate/Scholarship)* [3287]
A. Joseph Huerta "Puedo" Scholarships *(Undergraduate/Scholarship)* [3100]
Dale Hughes, Jr. Memorial Scholarships *(Undergraduate/Scholarship)* [9571]
Roger K. Hughes Legacy Scholarships *(Undergraduate/Scholarship)* [2451]
Hughes Memorial Foundation Scholarships *(Graduate/Scholarship)* [4983]
Paul A. Hughes Memorial Scholarships *(Undergraduate/Scholarship)* [2452]
Humane Studies Fellowships *(Graduate/Fellowship, Scholarship)* [5183]
Anna C. Hume Scholarship *(Undergraduate/Scholarship)* [4428]
Kevin Hummer Point Scholarships *(Graduate, Undergraduate/Scholarship)* [8178]
Donald and Florence Hunting Scholarships *(Undergraduate/Scholarship)* [4600]
Walter Doc Hurley Scholarship *(Undergraduate/Scholarship)* [4757]
Mike Hylton and Ron Niederman Memorial Scholarships *(Undergraduate/Scholarship)* [4861]

GENERAL STUDIES/FIELD OF STUDY NOT SPECIFIED

I Have a Dream Scholarships *(Undergraduate/Scholarship)* [5525]
IAHCSMM-Purdue University Scholarship Awards *(Other/Scholarship)* [5263]
Iberdrola USA Scholarships *(Undergraduate/Scholarship)* [6198]
ICDA Graduate Scholarships *(Graduate/Scholarship)* [5464]
ICDA Research Grants *(Graduate/Grant)* [5465]
Ice Skating Institute of America Education Foundation Scholarships *(Undergraduate/Scholarship)* [5031]
Idaho Opportunity Scholarships *(Undergraduate/Scholarship)* [9547]
IDTA Freestyle Scholarships *(Undergraduate/Scholarship)* [5317]
Ella R. Ifill Fund *(Undergraduate/Scholarship)* [6199]
Illinois Association of Chamber of Commerce Executives Scholarships *(Professional development/Scholarship)* [5054]
Illinois Division Scholarships *(Undergraduate/Scholarship)* [6519]
Illinois Student Assistance Commission Merit Recognition Scholarships (MRS) *(Undergraduate/Scholarship)* [5075]
Illuminator Educational Foundation Scholarships *(Undergraduate/Scholarship)* [2453]
Imagine America College Scholarships for High School Students *(Undergraduate/Scholarship)* [5083]
Imagine America Military Awards Program *(Undergraduate/Scholarship, Grant)* [5084]
Imagine America Scholarships for Adult Students *(Undergraduate/Scholarship)* [5085]
Independent Lubricant Manufacturers Association Scholarships *(Undergraduate/Scholarship)* [5093]
Independent University Alumni Association Scholarships *(Graduate, Undergraduate/Scholarship)* [5102]
Indiana Alumni Scholarships *(Undergraduate/Scholarship)* [10722]
Indiana FFA Association State Fair Scholarship *(Undergraduate/Scholarship)* [5110]
Indiana State University Academic Excellence Scholarships *(Undergraduate/Scholarship)* [5116]
Indiana State University Academic Promise Scholarships *(Undergraduate/Scholarship)* [5126]
Indiana State University Incentive Scholarships *(Undergraduate/Scholarship)* [5117]
Indiana State University President's Scholarships *(Undergraduate/Scholarship)* [5118]
Indiana State University Transfer Student Scholarships *(Undergraduate/Scholarship)* [5120]
Indonesian Directorate General of Higher Education Scholarships *(Graduate/Scholarship)* [3761]
Informatics Post Doctoral Fellowships *(Doctorate/Fellowship)* [8027]
Informatics Pre Doctoral Fellowships *(Doctorate/Fellowship)* [8028]
Informatics Sabbatical Fellowships *(Doctorate, Postdoctorate/Fellowship)* [8029]
Information Age Publishing Graduate Student Book Scholarships *(Doctorate, Graduate/Scholarship)* [5142]
Jennifer Ingrum Scholarships *(Undergraduate/Scholarship)* [3230]
INIA Scholarship Program *(Undergraduate/Scholarship)* [5363]
Injury Scholarships *(Undergraduate/Scholarship)* [4731]
Inland Northwest Business Alliance Scholarships (INBA) *(Undergraduate/Scholarship)* [8254]
Institute for the International Education of Students Faculty Fellowships *(Other/Fellowship)* [7412]
Instructional Design & Learning Technologies Scholarships *(Undergraduate, Graduate/Scholarship)* [3820]
International Code Council Foundation General Scholarship Fund *(Undergraduate/Scholarship)* [5299]
International Door Association Scholarship Foundation Program *(Undergraduate, Vocational/Occupational/Scholarship)* [5322]
International Executive Housekeepers Association Education Foundation Scholarship Awards *(Undergraduate/Scholarship)* [5324]
International Executive Housekeepers Association Spartan Scholarship Awards *(Undergraduate/Scholarship)* [5325]
International Grenfell Association Bursary *(Undergraduate/Scholarship)* [5341]
International Grenfell Association Post-Secondary Bursaries *(Undergraduate/Scholarship)* [5342]
International Grenfell Association Secondary/High School Bursaries *(Undergraduate/Scholarship)* [5343]
International Order of the King's Daughters and Sons North American Indian Scholarship Program *(Undergraduate/Scholarship)* [876]
International Radio and Television Society Foundation Summer Fellowships Program *(Undergraduate, Graduate/Fellowship)* [5378]
International Sanitary Supply Association Foundation Scholarships *(Undergraduate/Scholarship)* [5392]
Interracial Scholarship Fund of Greater Hartford *(Undergraduate/Scholarship)* [4758]
IODE Canada Labrador Bursary *(Undergraduate/Scholarship)* [6855]
Iowa Division Scholarships *(Undergraduate/Scholarship)* [6520]
Greg Irons Award Fund *(Undergraduate/Scholarship)* [3714]
Hazel D. Isbell Fellowships *(Graduate/Fellowship, Scholarship)* [3553]
ISDS Graduate Student Scholarships *(Doctorate, Graduate/Scholarship)* [5416]
ISF Excellence in Community Service Scholarships *(Undergraduate/Scholarship)* [5478]
ISF Undergraduate Scholarships *(Undergraduate/Scholarship)* [5479]
Islamic Scholarship Fund Scholarships (ISF) *(Postgraduate, Undergraduate/Scholarship)* [5484]
Island Institute Scholarship Fund *(Undergraduate/Scholarship)* [6200]
Broughton Isom Memorial Scholarship *(Undergraduate/Scholarship)* [7536]
ISU Child of Alumni Book Voucher Awards *(Undergraduate/Scholarship)* [5128]
Italian Language Scholarships *(Undergraduate/Scholarship)* [7682]
Jack Family Scholarships *(Undergraduate/Scholarship)* [4601]
Jack and Jill of America National Scholarships Program *(Undergraduate/Scholarship)* [5490]
Jackie Robinson Scholarships *(Undergraduate/Scholarship)* [5495]
The Jackson Club Scholarships *(Undergraduate/Scholarship)* [3715]
Jackson High School Alumni Scholarship Fund *(Undergraduate/Scholarship)* [9514]
Holly Jackson-Wuller Memorial Scholarships *(Undergraduate/Scholarship)* [7842]
Freddy L. Jacobs Scholarships *(Undergraduate/Scholarship)* [5284]
Eric L. Jacobson Memorial Scholarships *(Undergraduate/Scholarship)* [8482]
Louis I. Jaffe Memorial Scholarships-NSU Alumni *(Graduate/Scholarship)* [4700]
Cory Jam Memorial Award Fund *(Undergraduate/Scholarship)* [3716]
Jamaican Canadian Association Alberta Scholarship Program *(Undergraduate/Scholarship)* [5533]
Jamail/Long Challenge Grant Scholarships *(Undergraduate/Scholarship)* [4896]
Helen Janko Memorial Scholarships *(Undergraduate, Master's/Scholarship)* [10789]
Japan Indonesia Presidential Scholarship Program *(Doctorate/Scholarship)* [10695]
Dr. Ali Jarrahi Merit Scholarships *(Undergraduate/Scholarship)* [5480]
Carl and Lucille Jarrett Scholarship Fund *(Undergraduate/Scholarship)* [4050]
Hon. Michaelle Jean Scholarships *(Undergraduate/Scholarship)* [2286]
Jefferson Graduate Fellowships *(Doctorate, Graduate/Fellowship)* [5564]
Erin L. Jenkins Memorial Scholarship Fund *(Undergraduate/Scholarship)* [4244]
Elise Reed Jenkins Memorial Scholarships - Gamma Lambda *(Undergraduate/Scholarship)* [8928]
Elise Reed Jenkins Memorial Scholarships - Gamma Psi *(Undergraduate/Scholarship)* [8929]
Ruth E. Jenkins Scholarships *(Undergraduate/Scholarship)* [8709]
Kenneth Jernigan Scholarships *(Undergraduate/Scholarship)* [6947]
Reverend H. John and Asako Yamashita Memorial Scholarships *(Graduate/Scholarship)* [5551]
Johnny Bench Scholarships *(Undergraduate/Scholarship)* [3001]
Douglas Johnson Memorial Scholarships *(Undergraduate, Master's/Scholarship)* [10791]
James V. Johnson Scholarship Fund *(Undergraduate/Scholarship)* [4199]
Camilla C. Johnson Scholarships *(Undergraduate/Scholarship)* [4602]
Chip Johnson Scholarships *(Undergraduate/Scholarship)* [9435]
Ella Wilson Johnson Scholarships *(Undergraduate/Scholarship)* [3002]
Stella B. Johnson Scholarships *(Undergraduate/Scholarship)* [10586]
OOIDA Mary Johnston Scholarships *(Undergraduate/Scholarship)* [7785]
Joint Japan/World Bank Graduate Scholarship Program for Developing Country National (JJ/WB-GSP) *(Graduate/Scholarship)* [10696]
Joint Japan/World Bank Graduate Scholarship Program for Japanese National (JJ/WBGSP) *(Graduate, Master's, Doctorate/Scholarship)* [10697]
Redlands Council PTA - Dorothy Jolley Memorial Scholarships *(Undergraduate/Scholarship)* [8484]
George E. Jonas Scholarships *(Graduate, Undergraduate/Scholarship)* [5616]
Napoleon A. Jones, III Memorial Scholarships *(Undergraduate/Scholarship)* [8710]
Annabel Lambeth Jones Scholarships *(Undergraduate/Scholarship)* [4200]
David J. Joseph Company Scholarships *(Undergraduate/Scholarship)* [3003]
Kazimiera Juchniewicz Memorial Scholarships *(Undergraduate/Scholarship)* [8578]
Junior Achievement of East Central Ohio, Inc. Scholarship Fund *(Undergraduate/Scholarship)* [9515]
James W. Junior and Jane T. Brown Scholarships *(Undergraduate, Vocational/Occupational/Scholarship)* [4527]
JW Surety Bonds Scholarships *(Undergraduate, Graduate/Scholarship)* [5646]
Stefan and Weronika Kacperski Memorial Scholarships *(Undergraduate/Scholarship)* [8579]
Daniel Kahikina and Millie Akaka Scholarships *(Graduate, Undergraduate/Scholarship)* [7910]
David A. Kaiser Memorial Scholarship Fund *(Undergraduate/Scholarship)* [9516]
Gladys Kamakakūokalani 'Ainoa Brandt Scholarships *(Graduate, Undergraduate/Scholarship)* [7911]
Kamehameha Schools Class of 1968 "Ka Poli O Kaiona" Scholarships *(Graduate, Undergraduate/Scholarship)* [7912]
Kamehameha Schools Class of 1972 Scholarships *(Graduate, Undergraduate/Scholarship)* [7913]
Joan Kamps Memorial Bursaries *(Undergraduate, Graduate, Postgraduate, Professional development/Scholarship)* [7633]
Martin S. Kane Memorial Community Service Award Scholarships *(Undergraduate/Scholarship)* [3181]
Kansas City Division Scholarships *(Undergraduate/Scholarship)* [6521]
Kansas Distinguished Scholarship Program *(Graduate/Scholarship)* [5655]
Walter Kapala Scholarships *(Undergraduate/Scholarship)* [4759]
Joseph Kaplan Fund *(Graduate, Undergraduate/Scholarship)* [5103]
Don Kaplan Legacy Scholarships *(Undergraduate/Scholarship)* [2454]
Kappa Kappa Gamma Foundation of Canada Graduate Scholarships *(Graduate, Doctorate/Scholarship)* [5777]
Kappa Kappa Gamma Graduate Scholarships *(Graduate/Scholarship)* [5740]

GENERAL STUDIES/FIELD OF STUDY NOT SPECIFIED

Kappa Kappa Gamma Undergraduate Scholarships *(Undergraduate/Scholarship)* [5741]
Kappa Sigma Scholarship/Leadership Awards *(Undergraduate/Scholarship)* [5792]
Kappa Zeta Scholarships *(Undergraduate/Scholarship)* [8930]
Kaprielian Memorial Scholarships *(Undergraduate/Scholarship)* [10303]
Josephine de Karman Fellowships *(Graduate, Undergraduate/Fellowship)* [5796]
Philip R. Karr, III Scholarship Fund *(Graduate/Scholarship)* [4378]
K.A.S.A Memorial Scholarships *(Undergraduate/Scholarship)* [7843]
KASF Chair Scholarships *(Graduate, Undergraduate/Scholarship)* [5873]
KASF Designated Scholarships *(Graduate, Undergraduate/Scholarship)* [5874]
KASF General Scholarships *(Undergraduate, Graduate, Professional development/Scholarship)* [5875]
Joseph Katz Memorial Scholarships *(Undergraduate/Scholarship)* [5580]
Ka'u Chamber of Commerce College Scholarships *(Undergraduate/Scholarship)* [5798]
William and Beatrice Kavanaugh Scholarships *(Undergraduate/Scholarship)* [5507]
Kawano Family Scholarships *(Undergraduate/Scholarship)* [8711]
KCC Foundation Gold Key Scholarships *(Undergraduate/Scholarship)* [5807]
KCC Foundation Scholarships *(Undergraduate/Scholarship)* [5808]
KCC Trustee Scholarships *(Undergraduate/Scholarship)* [5809]
Doc Keen Memorial Scholarships *(Undergraduate/Scholarship)* [9437]
Keepers Preservation Education Fund *(Undergraduate/Award)* [6202]
Micki and Norm Keesal Scholarships *(Undergraduate/Scholarship)* [5581]
KEF Academic Scholarships *(Undergraduate, Graduate/Scholarship)* [5865]
KEF College/University Basic Scholarships *(Undergraduate/Scholarship)* [5866]
KEF Vocational Education Scholarship *(Undergraduate/Scholarship)* [5867]
Annette and Ernest Keith Scholarships *(Undergraduate/Scholarship)* [8485]
Kelly Law Team Annual Down Syndrome Scholarships *(All/Scholarship)* [5811]
Dr. Charles Kelly Memorial Scholarships *(Undergraduate/Scholarship)* [7844]
Southwest Ohio Environmental Horticulture Association (SOEHA) Lloyd W. Kennedy Scholarship *(Undergraduate/Scholarship)* [7584]
Raymond A. Kent-Navy V-12/ROTC Scholarships *(Undergraduate/Scholarship)* [10145]
Kentucky Alumni Club Scholarships - Frankfort/Capital Region Alumni Club *(Undergraduate/Scholarship)* [10146]
Kentucky Alumni Club Scholarships - Lexington/Central Kentucky Alumni Club *(Undergraduate/Scholarship)* [10147]
Kentucky Alumni Club Scholarships - Somerset/Lake Cumberland Area Alumni Club *(Undergraduate/Scholarship)* [10148]
Kentucky Educational Excellence Scholarships *(Undergraduate/Scholarship)* [2261]
Edgar Kerstan Memorial Scholarships *(Undergraduate/Scholarship)* [6420]
Judge Oliver Kessel Memorial Scholarships - Ripley Rotary *(Undergraduate/Scholarship)* [7845]
Ashley E. Ketcher Memorial Scholarships *(Undergraduate/Scholarship)* [3289]
Khaki University and Y.M.C.A. Memorial Scholarships *(Undergraduate/Scholarship)* [10291]
Mary and Millard Kiker Scholarships *(Undergraduate/Scholarship)* [4201]
Kilbuck Family Native American Scholarships *(Undergraduate/Scholarship)* [2230]
Helen and George Kilik Scholarships *(Undergraduate/Scholarship)* [274]
Killam Fellowships *(Undergraduate/Fellowship)* [4229]

Killingworth Foundation Scholarships *(Undergraduate/Scholarship)* [5830]
Kimberly Elementary School PTA Scholarships *(Undergraduate/Scholarship)* [8486]
Arthur M. and Berdena King Eagle Scout Scholarships *(Undergraduate/Scholarship)* [6927]
King Ice Scholarships *(Undergraduate, Graduate/Scholarship)* [5834]
Mackenzie King Open Scholarships *(Graduate/Scholarship)* [6366]
Kingsbury Elementary School PTA Scholarships *(Undergraduate/Scholarship)* [8487]
Isabel Mayer Kirkpatrick Scholarships *(Undergraduate/Scholarship)* [9438]
Dr. Elemér and Éva Kiss Scholarship Fund *(Undergraduate/Scholarship)* [5006]
Tamo Kitaura Scholarships *(Other/Scholarship)* [9961]
Flo Kitz Memorial Scholarships *(Undergraduate, Master's/Scholarship)* [10792]
Kiwanis Club of Escondido Scholarships *(Undergraduate/Scholarship)* [8712]
Kiwanis Club of Redlands Foundation Academic Excellence Scholarships *(Undergraduate/Scholarship)* [8488]
Gerda and Kurt Klein Scholarships *(Undergraduate/Scholarship)* [4962]
Stefan and Janina Klimt Scholarships *(Undergraduate/Scholarship)* [8580]
Raymond and Augusta Klink Scholarships *(Undergraduate/Scholarship)* [3004]
J. Merrill Knapp Research Fellowship *(Undergraduate/Fellowship)* [843]
Kemper K. Knapp Scholarships *(Undergraduate/Scholarship)* [10320]
Iver and Cora Knapstad Scholarships *(Undergraduate/Scholarship)* [10024]
Jane Shaw Knox Graduate Scholarships *(Graduate/Scholarship)* [4148]
Knox-Hume Scholarships *(Undergraduate/Scholarship)* [3232]
Ina Knutsen Scholarships *(Undergraduate/Scholarship)* [8875]
Seth Koehler Central High School Scholarship Fund *(Undergraduate, Vocational/Occupational/Scholarship)* [4528]
Herb Kohl Educational Foundation Excellence Scholarships *(Undergraduate/Scholarship)* [5857]
Herb Kohl Educational Foundation Initiative Scholarships *(Undergraduate/Scholarship)* [5858]
Bob and Linda Kohlhepp Scholarships *(Undergraduate/Scholarship)* [3005]
George Kokociński Memorial Scholarships *(Undergraduate/Scholarship)* [8581]
Gwin J. and Ruth Kolb Research Travel Fellowships *(Doctorate, Other/Fellowship)* [1294]
Anna and John Kolesay Memorial Scholarships *(Undergraduate/Scholarship)* [275]
Bernie Kom Memorial Awards *(Postgraduate/Award)* [10746]
Susan G. Komen for the Cure College Scholarship Awards *(Two Year College/Award, Scholarship)* [5861]
KON/GEICO LeaderShape Undergraduate Scholarship *(Undergraduate/Scholarship)* [5789]
Herman P. Kopplemann Scholarships *(Undergraduate/Scholarship)* [4761]
Robert W. Korn Scholarships *(Undergraduate/Scholarship)* [10025]
Henriette and Marcel Korner Scholarships *(Undergraduate/Scholarship)* [5582]
Eugene and Elinor Kotur Scholarship Trust Fund *(Undergraduate, Graduate/Scholarship)* [10443]
Marjorie Kovler Research Fellowships *(Professional development/Fellowship)* [5602]
Eve Kraft Education and College Scholarships *(Undergraduate/Scholarship)* [9975]
Norman Kramer Scholarship Awards *(Undergraduate/Scholarship)* [6499]
Schmidt Kramer Scholarships for Academic Excellence *(Undergraduate/Scholarship)* [8792]
Krawczyk-Krane Family Scholarships *(Undergraduate/Scholarship)* [8582]
Sharon Kreikemeier Memorial Scholarships *(Undergraduate/Scholarship)* [7242]

Robert Krembil Scholarships of Merit *(Doctorate/Scholarship)* [10747]
Kristin Bjurstrom Krueger Student Scholarship Program *(Undergraduate/Scholarship)* [6404]
Melvin Kruger Endowed Scholarship Program *(Undergraduate, Vocational/Occupational/Scholarship)* [7122]
Judith Keller Marx Krumholz Scholarships *(Undergraduate/Scholarship)* [8713]
KTA Chapter Adviser Research Grant Award *(Professional development/Grant)* [5794]
Heloise Werthan Kuhn Scholarships *(Undergraduate/Scholarship)* [3235]
Kumin Scholars Program *(Undergraduate/Scholarship)* [8953]
Jan Kuropas Memorial Scholarships *(Undergraduate/Scholarship)* [8583]
Chris Kurzweil Scholarship *(Undergraduate/Scholarship)* [3329]
Henry and Chiyo Kuwahara Memorial Scholarships *(Undergraduate, Graduate/Scholarship)* [5554]
LA Tutors Innovation in Education Scholarships *(All/Scholarship)* [5896]
Roger and Jacquelyn Vander Laan Family Scholarships *(Undergraduate/Scholarship)* [4604]
Gretchen Laatsch Scholarships *(Graduate/Scholarship)* [1926]
LAFS - Cal State University San Marcos General Scholarships *(Undergraduate/Scholarship)* [2212]
Lavina Laible Scholarships *(Undergraduate/Scholarship)* [4606]
Casey Laine Armed Forces Scholarships *(Undergraduate/Scholarship)* [3101]
Lalor Foundation Post-Doctoral Fellowships *(Postdoctorate/Fellowship)* [5905]
Allen T. Lambert Scholarships *(Postgraduate/Scholarship)* [10748]
Frank S. Land Scholarships *(Undergraduate/Scholarship)* [3598]
The Lanford Family Highway Worker Memorial Scholarship Program *(Undergraduate/Scholarship)* [1219]
Stephen Lankester Scholarships *(Undergraduate/Scholarship)* [4607]
The Otis and Florence Lapham Memorial Scholarships *(Undergraduate/Scholarship)* [5508]
Peter and Jody Larkin Legacy Scholarships *(Undergraduate/Scholarship)* [2455]
Austin E. Lathrop Scholarships *(Undergraduate/Scholarship)* [10026]
Kenneth Laundy Entrance Scholarships *(Graduate/Scholarship)* [10749]
Willie D. Lawson, Jr. Memorial Scholarships *(Doctorate, Graduate, Other/Scholarship)* [6819]
Sue Kay Lay Memorial Scholarships *(Undergraduate/Scholarship)* [3102]
LCSC Presidential Out-of-State Tuition Scholarships *(Undergraduate/Scholarship)* [6035]
Danny T. Le Memorial Scholarships *(Undergraduate/Scholarship)* [10385]
Franklin M. Leach Scholarships *(Undergraduate/Scholarship)* [10027]
Queenie Leader Memorial Scholarships *(Undergraduate, Master's/Scholarship)* [10793]
LEAGUE Foundation Scholarships *(Undergraduate/Scholarship)* [8660]
Jack W. Leatherman Family Scholarship Fund *(Undergraduate, Vocational/Occupational/Scholarship)* [4531]
Patrick Ledden Honorary Scholarships *(Undergraduate/Scholarship)* [8714]
Jay C. and B. Nadine Leggett Charitable Scholarship Fund *(Undergraduate/Scholarship)* [9519]
Herbert Lehman Education Scholarships *(Undergraduate/Scholarship)* [6646]
Lehman Family Scholarships *(Undergraduate/Scholarship)* [8715]
Lemelson Center Fellowships *(Doctorate, Postdoctorate, Professional development/Fellowship)* [9025]
Lemelson Center Travel to Collections Awards *(Graduate, Professional development/Award)* [9026]
The Lemon Grove Education Foundation Scholarships *(Undergraduate/Scholarship)* [8716]

GENERAL STUDIES/FIELD OF STUDY NOT SPECIFIED

Stan Lencki Scholarships *(Undergraduate/Scholarship)* [6356]
Franklin A. Lenfesty Memorial Scholarship *(Undergraduate/Scholarship)* [7537]
V.A. Leonard Scholarships *(Graduate, Undergraduate/Scholarship)* [356]
Leopold Education Project Scholarships *(Undergraduate/Scholarship)* [3291]
Sherman L. and Mabel C. Lepard Scholarships *(Undergraduate/Scholarship)* [4608]
Irwin S. Lerner Student Scholarships *(Undergraduate/Scholarship)* [7168]
Carol Anne Letheren Entrance Awards *(Postgraduate/Award, Scholarship)* [10750]
Jack A. and Louise S. Levine Memorial Scholarships *(Undergraduate/Scholarship)* [8492]
Lewis-Clark Coin Club Endowed Scholarships *(Undergraduate/Scholarship)* [6037]
Lewis-Clark State College Foundation Scholars Scholarships *(Undergraduate/Scholarship)* [6038]
Lewis-Clark State College In-State Non-Traditional Student Scholarships *(Undergraduate/Scholarship)* [6040]
Lewis-Clark State College Provost Scholarships *(Undergraduate/Scholarship)* [6042]
Lewis-Clark State College Transfer Scholarships *(Undergraduate/Scholarship)* [6058]
George T. Lewis, Jr. Academic Scholarship Fund *(Undergraduate/Scholarship)* [4203]
Jonathan D. Lewis Point Scholarships *(Graduate, Undergraduate/Scholarship)* [8184]
Lewis-Reynolds-Smith Founders Fellowship *(Graduate/Fellowship)* [4857]
Marvin Lewis Scholarships *(Undergraduate/Scholarship)* [6060]
Lewiston Service League Memorial Scholarships *(Undergraduate/Scholarship)* [6043]
Lexington Alumni Scholarships *(Undergraduate/Scholarship)* [6062]
Lexington Community Foundation Annual Scholarships *(Undergraduate/Scholarship)* [6063]
Lexington Community Foundation/CCC Scholarships *(Undergraduate/Scholarship)* [6064]
Irene Brand Lieberman Memorial Scholarships *(Graduate, Postgraduate/Scholarship)* [5585]
Dolores Zohrab Liebmann Fund - Independent Research/Study Grants *(Graduate/Grant)* [6076]
LIFE Lessons Scholarship Program *(Undergraduate/Scholarship)* [6079]
Lighthouse International Scholarships - College-bound Awards *(High School, Undergraduate/Scholarship)* [6083]
Lighthouse International Scholarships - Graduate Awards *(Graduate/Scholarship)* [6084]
Lighthouse International Scholarships - Undergraduate Awards *(Undergraduate/Scholarship)* [6085]
Lindenwood University Scouting Scholarships *(Undergraduate/Scholarship)* [6929]
Carl H. Lindner Family Scholarships *(Undergraduate/Scholarship)* [3006]
Obrzut Ling Scholarships *(Undergraduate/Scholarship)* [8255]
Linsley Scholarship Fund *(Undergraduate/Scholarship)* [2913]
Lawrence Lipking Fellowships at the Newberry Library *(Graduate/Fellowship)* [7414]
Hushy Lipton Memorial Scholarship Funds *(Undergraduate, Graduate, Postgraduate/Scholarship)* [2641]
Ian Lithgow Memorial Awards *(Master's/Award)* [10751]
LiveCareer Scholarships *(Undergraduate/Scholarship)* [6099]
Grant Livingston Memorial Scholarships *(Undergraduate, Master's/Scholarship)* [10794]
LLN Student Scholarships *(Undergraduate/Scholarship)* [5939]
E.C. Lloyd and J.C.U. Johnson Scholarship Fund *(Undergraduate/Scholarship)* [3266]
Virgil K. Lobring Scholarship *(Undergraduate/Scholarship)* [3331]
Local 564 Scholarship Award *(High School/Scholarship)* [5454]
Local Internet Service Scholarships *(Undergraduate/Scholarship)* [6103]

Audrey Loftus Memorial Scholarships *(Undergraduate/Scholarship)* [10099]
Stephen Logan Memorial Scholarships *(Undergraduate/Scholarship)* [4330]
London Goodenough Association of Canada Scholarships *(Graduate/Scholarship)* [6105]
Lone Star GIA Associate and Alumni Scholarships *(Undergraduate/Scholarship)* [4341]
Lawrence A. Long Memorial Law Scholarships *(Undergraduate/Scholarship)* [362]
L.D. and Elsie Long Memorial Scholarships *(Graduate/Scholarship)* [10589]
Megan Nicole Longwell Scholarships *(Undergraduate/Scholarship)* [7847]
Sir James Lougheed Awards of Distinction *(Doctorate, Graduate/Award)* [279]
Love of Bonita Empowerment Scholarships *(Undergraduate/Scholarship)* [9440]
First Lieutenant Scott McClean Love Memorial Scholarship - Children of Soldiers *(Undergraduate, Vocational/Occupational/Scholarship)* [1714]
First Lieutenant Scott McClean Love Memorial Scholarship - Spouses of Soldiers *(Undergraduate, Vocational/Occupational/Scholarship)* [1715]
Diane G. Lowe and John Gomez, IV Scholarships *(Undergraduate/Scholarship)* [3236]
Lowry Awards for Women of Excellence *(Undergraduate, Graduate, Advanced Professional/Award, Scholarship)* [3789]
Elsa Ludeke Graduate Scholarships *(Graduate/Scholarship)* [3590]
Lugonia Alumni/Harrison Lightfoot Scholarships *(Undergraduate/Scholarship)* [8493]
Luso-American Fraternal Federation B-2 Scholarships *(Postgraduate/Scholarship)* [6149]
Luso-American Fraternal Federation B-3 Scholarships *(Professional development/Scholarship)* [6150]
Luso-American Fraternal Federation B-4 Scholarships *(Professional development/Scholarship)* [6151]
Charles Luttman Scholarship *(Undergraduate/Scholarship)* [2536]
John Mabry Forestry Scholarships *(Undergraduate/Scholarship)* [8423]
MAC Emeritus Scholarships for First-Time Meeting Attendees *(Professional development/Scholarship)* [6516]
Bill MacAloney Legacy Scholarships *(Undergraduate/Scholarship)* [2456]
MacArthur Fellows Program *(Professional development/Fellowship)* [6164]
Dr. Sally Macdonald Scholarships *(Undergraduate, Master's/Scholarship)* [10795]
Nate Mack/Cindi Turner Scholarships *(Undergraduate/Scholarship)* [8353]
Carol E. Macpherson Memorial Scholarship *(Graduate, Undergraduate/Scholarship)* [10203]
Lawrence Madeiros Scholarships *(Undergraduate/Scholarship)* [6992]
James Madison Graduate Fellowships *(Graduate/Fellowship)* [6176]
Madson Graduate Scholarships *(Graduate/Scholarship)* [8899]
Keith Maffioli Scholarships *(Undergraduate/Scholarship)* [3292]
The Brandon Magalassi Memorial Scholarship Foundation Scholarships *(Undergraduate/Scholarship)* [6185]
John T. and Frances J. Maghielse Scholarships *(Undergraduate/Scholarship)* [4609]
Sonia S. Maguire Outstanding Scholastic Achievement Awards *(Graduate, Undergraduate/Scholarship)* [9618]
Dan and Rachel Mahi Educational Scholarships *(Graduate, Undergraduate/Scholarship)* [7914]
Rick Mahoney Scholarships *(Undergraduate/Scholarship)* [6357]
Mary Main Memorial Scholarships *(Undergraduate/Scholarship)* [4762]
Maine Community College Scholarships *(Undergraduate/Scholarship)* [6222]
Maine Community Foundation - Rice Scholarships *(Undergraduate/Scholarship)* [6203]
Maine Vietnam Veterans Scholarships *(Advanced Professional/Scholarship)* [6204]

The Make It Move Scholarships *(Undergraduate/Scholarship)* [1594]
Make Us Proud Scholarships *(Undergraduate/Scholarship)* [4793]
Joseph J. Malone Fellowships in Arab and Islamic Studies *(Professional development/Fellowship)* [6895]
Optimist Club Of Redlands - Ralph Maloof Scholarships *(Undergraduate/Scholarship)* [8494]
Manchester Scholarship Foundation - Adult Learners Scholarships *(Undergraduate/Scholarship)* [4763]
Mangasar M. Mangasarian Scholarship Fund *(Graduate/Scholarship)* [1702]
Manhattan Street Capital Annual National Scholarships *(Undergraduate, Graduate, Doctorate/Scholarship)* [6227]
Mansfield Soccer Association Scholarships *(Undergraduate/Scholarship)* [6229]
Stephen T. Marchello Scholarships *(Undergraduate/Scholarship)* [6237]
Aurella Varallo Mariani Scholarship Program *(Undergraduate/Scholarship)* [6665]
Marine Corps League National Scholarships *(Undergraduate/Scholarship)* [6269]
Mariposa Elementary School PTA Scholarships *(Undergraduate/Scholarship)* [8495]
Markley Family Scholarship Fund *(Undergraduate/Scholarship)* [9522]
Markley Scholarships *(Undergraduate/Scholarship)* [6724]
Marshall Memorial Fellowships *(Other/Fellowship)* [4399]
Sarah Shinn Marshall Scholarships *(Undergraduate/Scholarship)* [3554]
Marshall Undergraduate Scholars Program *(Undergraduate/Award)* [6296]
Bryce-Lietzke Martin Scholarships *(Undergraduate/Scholarship)* [7848]
Martin Sisters Scholarships *(Undergraduate/Scholarship)* [3555]
John S. Martinez and Family Scholarship Fund *(Undergraduate/Scholarship)* [3200]
Eric Martinez Memorial Scholarships *(Graduate, Undergraduate/Scholarship)* [9866]
Corporal Joseph Martinez U.S. Army/Durango High School AFJROTC *(Undergraduate/Scholarship)* [8354]
Anthony A. Martino Memorial Scholarships *(Undergraduate/Scholarship)* [4462]
Beverley Mascoll Scholarships *(Undergraduate/Scholarship)* [2288]
Master Municipal Clerks Academy Scholarships *(Other/Scholarship)* [5351]
Matanuska-Susitna College Regent's Scholarships *(Undergraduate/Scholarship)* [10089]
Norman Matechuk Memorial Scholarships *(Undergraduate, Master's/Scholarship)* [10796]
Rene Matos Memorial Scholarships *(Undergraduate, Vocational/Occupational/Scholarship)* [6996]
The Renardo A. Matteucci Scholarship Fund *(Undergraduate/Scholarship)* [3206]
Antonio Mattos Memorial Scholarships *(Undergraduate/Scholarship)* [6152]
Mature Student Scholarship *(Undergraduate/Scholarship)* [3912]
Edmund F. Maxwell Scholarships *(Undergraduate/Scholarship)* [6348]
Juliann and Joe Maxwell Scholarships *(Undergraduate/Scholarship)* [3238]
Juliann King Maxwell Scholarships for Riverview High School *(Undergraduate, Vocational/Occupational/Scholarship)* [3239]
May-Cassioppi Scholarships *(Undergraduate/Scholarship)* [3293]
John E. Mayfield ABLE Scholarships *(Undergraduate/Scholarship)* [3240]
John E. Mayfield Scholarship Fund for Cheatham County Central High School *(Undergraduate/Scholarship)* [3241]
John E. Mayfield Scholarship Fund for Harpeth High School *(Undergraduate/Scholarship)* [3242]
John E. Mayfield Scholarship Fund for Pleasant View Christian High School *(Undergraduate/Scholarship)* [3243]
John E. Mayfield Scholarship Fund for Sycamore

High School *(Undergraduate/Scholarship)* [3244]
Bill Maynes Fellowships *(Professional development/Fellowship)* [3929]
Joseph W. Mayo ALS Scholarships *(Undergraduate/Scholarship)* [6205]
Tadeusz Maziarz Scholarships *(Undergraduate/Scholarship)* [8584]
Charles "Chuck" McAdams Memorial Scholarships *(Graduate, Undergraduate/Scholarship)* [9644]
McBurney General Scholarships *(Undergraduate/Scholarship)* [10323]
Bill McCarthy Scout Scholarship Fund *(Undergraduate/Scholarship)* [9523]
Dave McCloud Aviation Memorial Scholarships *(Undergraduate/Scholarship)* [10028]
McDaniel College Eagle Scout Scholarships *(Undergraduate/Scholarship)* [6930]
McFarffels Scholarships *(Undergraduate/Scholarship)* [8256]
Nancy B. Woolridge McGee Graduate Fellowships *(Graduate/Fellowship)* [10819]
Lucille E. McGee Scholarships *(Undergraduate/Scholarship)* [5509]
McKinley Elementary School PTA Scholarships *(Undergraduate/Scholarship)* [8496]
John L. and Eleanore I. Mckinley Scholarships *(Undergraduate/Scholarship)* [3591]
Louise McKinney Post-secondary Scholarships *(Undergraduate/Scholarship)* [280]
McKinney Sisters Undergraduate Scholarships *(Undergraduate/Scholarship)* [3556]
Elizabeth McKissick Memorial Scholarships *(Undergraduate/Scholarship)* [6045]
McNeely Stephenson of New Albany Community Involvement Scholarships *(Undergraduate/Scholarship)* [6372]
Joan Reagin McNeill Scholarships - Alpha Theta *(Undergraduate/Scholarship)* [8931]
Joan Reagin McNeill Scholarships - Theta Phi *(Undergraduate/Scholarship)* [8932]
MCRTA Book Scholarships *(Undergraduate/Scholarship)* [6449]
David Meador Foundation - Club Management Student Scholarships *(Undergraduate/Scholarship)* [7295]
The Medalist Club Post Graduate Scholarships *(Postgraduate/Scholarship)* [6376]
Medford Rogue Rotary Scholarship *(Undergraduate/Scholarship)* [6380]
Medicus Student Exchange Scholarships *(Graduate, Undergraduate/Scholarship)* [9619]
Medina County Retired Teachers Association Scholarship *(Undergraduate/Scholarship)* [6400]
MEFA Graduate Loans *(Graduate/Loan)* [6314]
Dr. Ernest and Minnie Mehl Scholarships *(Undergraduate/Scholarship)* [281]
Fred & Lena Meijer Scholarships *(Undergraduate/Scholarship)* [4610]
Carl J. Mejel Scholarship *(Undergraduate/Scholarship)* [794]
Ilse Hanfmann, George Hanfmann and Machteld Mellink Fellowships *(Doctorate/Fellowship)* [1206]
Richard Mellon Scholarships *(Undergraduate/Scholarship)* [10029]
E.V. and Nancy Melosi Travel Grants *(Graduate, Other/Grant)* [1314]
Menominee Tribal Scholarships *(Undergraduate, Graduate/Scholarship)* [6418]
Mensa Canada General Scholarships *(Undergraduate/Scholarship)* [6421]
Mensa Education and Research Foundation U.S. Scholarships *(Undergraduate/Scholarship)* [6424]
Benchwarmers of Redlands-Jess Mercado Football Scholarships *(Undergraduate/Scholarship)* [8497]
Al Mercury Scholarships *(Undergraduate/Scholarship)* [10293]
Erickson Merkel Foundation Scholarships *(Undergraduate/Scholarship)* [3925]
MESA Student Travel Fund *(Undergraduate/Grant)* [6511]
Mesothelioma Memorial Scholarships *(Undergraduate, Vocational/Occupational/Scholarship)* [9594]
Mesquite Club Evening Chapter Inc. Scholarships *(Undergraduate/Scholarship)* [8355]
Mexican American Alumni Association Scholarships *(Graduate, Undergraduate/Scholarship)* [10356]

MICA Scholarships *(Undergraduate/Scholarship)* [6532]
Michigan Education Association Scholarships *(Undergraduate/Scholarship)* [6470]
Michigan Sugar Queen Scholarships *(Undergraduate/Scholarship)* [6496]
Bronislaw Michno Memorial Scholarships *(Undergraduate/Scholarship)* [8585]
Beth Middleton Memorial Scholarships *(Undergraduate/Scholarship)* [3961]
Midlothian Rotary Club "Service Above Self" Scholarship *(Undergraduate/Scholarship)* [6513]
Midwest Modern Language Association Fellowships *(Doctorate, Postdoctorate/Fellowship)* [7416]
Mihaly Russin Scholarship Awards *(Graduate/Scholarship)* [8656]
Milan Getting Scholarships *(Undergraduate/Scholarship)* [9335]
Eunice Miles Scholarships *(Undergraduate/Scholarship)* [4343]
Military Service Scholarships *(Graduate, Undergraduate/Scholarship)* [8900]
Brian and Colleen Miller Math and Science Scholarships *(Undergraduate/Scholarship)* [3103]
Robbie Miller Memorial Scholarships *(Undergraduate/Scholarship)* [6046]
Carolina Panthers Players Sam Mills Memorial Scholarship Fund *(Undergraduate/Scholarship)* [4205]
Carolina Panthers Players Sam Mills Memorial Scholarships *(Graduate/Scholarship)* [4206]
Minerva Scholarships *(Undergraduate/Scholarship)* [2289]
Minneapolis Jewish Federation Camp Scholarships *(Undergraduate/Scholarship)* [6539]
Minnesota Division Scholarships *(Undergraduate/Scholarship)* [6522]
Minnesota GLBT Educational Fund *(Undergraduate/Scholarship)* [8661]
Minnesota Power Community Involvement Scholarships *(Undergraduate/Scholarship)* [3717]
Minnesota State Archery Association Scholarships Program *(Undergraduate/Scholarship)* [6551]
Missigman Scholarship Fund *(Undergraduate/Scholarship)* [4052]
George J. Mitchell Postgraduate Scholarships *(Postgraduate/Scholarship)* [6749]
Dorothy Mitchell Scholarships *(Undergraduate/Scholarship)* [8498]
George J. Mitchell Scholarships *(Postgraduate/Scholarship)* [10349]
Robert L. and Hilda Treasure Mitchell Scholarships *(Undergraduate/Scholarship)* [4612]
Sam Mizrahi Memorial Scholarships *(Undergraduate/Scholarship)* [4248]
MKC/Preuss Scholarship Fund *(Undergraduate/Scholarship)* [8718]
MMUF Dissertation Grants *(Graduate/Grant)* [10679]
MMUF Travel and Research Grants *(Graduate/Grant)* [10680]
MOAA American Patriot Scholarships *(Undergraduate/Scholarship)* [6534]
Molecular Evolution Fellowships *(Doctorate/Fellowship)* [9012]
Momeni Foundation Scholastic Achievement Scholarships *(Undergraduate/Scholarship)* [7021]
Mongan Commonwealth Fund Fellowship in Minority Health Policy *(Other/Fellowship)* [3161]
Murray Montague Memorial Scholarships *(Undergraduate/Scholarship)* [4571]
Hugh and Elizabeth Montgomery Scholarships *(Undergraduate/Scholarship)* [6208]
Moore Middle School PTA Scholarships *(Undergraduate/Scholarship)* [8499]
Annabelle Moore Scholarship *(Undergraduate/Scholarship)* [2408]
Farmers Union Industries Foundation Stanley Moore Scholarships *(Undergraduate/Scholarship)* [7488]
NFU Foundation Stanley Moore Scholarships *(Undergraduate/Scholarship)* [7489]
Dr. Blanca Moore-Velez Woman of Substance Scholarships *(Undergraduate/Scholarship)* [6763]
Kyle R. Moreland Memorial Scholarships *(Undergraduate/Scholarship)* [4533]
Robert L. Morlan Redlands Area Interfaith Council

Scholarships *(Undergraduate/Scholarship)* [8500]
Leo F. Moro Baseball Memorial Scholarships *(Undergraduate/Scholarship)* [4249]
James B. Morris Scholarships *(Undergraduate/Scholarship)* [6598]
Mortar Board National Foundation Fellowships *(Postdoctorate/Fellowship)* [6600]
Dwight Mosley Scholarships *(Undergraduate/Scholarship)* [9976]
John R. Mott Scholarships *(Undergraduate/Scholarship)* [6604]
MPI CRV Scholarships *(Other/Scholarship)* [6402]
MSEA/SEIU Part-time Student Members Scholarships *(Undergraduate/Scholarship)* [6223]
Dudley Mullins/Cabot Corporation Scholarships *(Undergraduate/Scholarship)* [7849]
Muncy Rotary Club Scholarship Fund *(Undergraduate/Scholarship)* [4054]
Muncy Scholars Award Fund *(Undergraduate/Scholarship)* [4055]
Harry Munoz Memorial Scholarships *(Undergraduate/Scholarship)* [8501]
Rick Munoz Memorial Scholarships *(Undergraduate/Scholarship)* [8502]
Anthony Munoz Scholarships *(Undergraduate/Scholarship)* [6618]
Kiwanis Club of Redlands Foundation - Martin and Dorothy Munz Scholarships *(Undergraduate/Scholarship)* [8503]
Daniel Murphy Scholarships *(High School/Scholarship)* [6620]
Muscle Shoals Kiwanis/Wal-Mart Scholarship *(Undergraduate/Scholarship)* [7538]
MyApartmentMap Housing Scholarships *(Undergraduate/Scholarship)* [6634]
MyMozaic.com Annual Scholarships *(Undergraduate/Scholarship)* [6639]
NACA Foundation Graduate Scholarships *(Graduate, Master's, Postdoctorate/Scholarship)* [6725]
NACA Mid Atlantic Graduate Student Scholarships *(Graduate, Master's, Doctorate/Scholarship)* [6726]
NACA Mid Atlantic Higher Education Research Scholarships *(Master's/Scholarship)* [6727]
NACA Mid Atlantic Undergraduate Scholarships for Student Leaders *(Undergraduate/Scholarship)* [6728]
NACA Northern Plains Regional Student Leadership Scholarships *(Undergraduate/Scholarship)* [6730]
NACA South Student Leadership Scholarships *(Undergraduate/Scholarship)* [6731]
NACADA Scholarships *(Graduate/Scholarship)* [6673]
Irwin Allen Nadal Entrance Awards *(Master's/Award)* [10752]
Miles Spencer Nadal Entrance Awards *(Master's/Award)* [10753]
NAFA Scholarship Programs *(Undergraduate/Scholarship)* [6690]
Jack Nagasaka Memorial Scholarships *(Undergraduate/Scholarship)* [8504]
NANBPWC National Scholarships *(Undergraduate/Scholarship)* [6764]
Robyn Nance Memorial Scholarships *(Undergraduate/Scholarship)* [8505]
Chereddi NarayanaRao and Radhamanohari Scholarships *(Graduate/Scholarship)* [9668]
NARFE-FEEA Scholarship Awards Program *(Undergraduate/Scholarship)* [6686]
Kermit B. Nash Academic Scholarships *(Undergraduate/Scholarship)* [8891]
Elizabeth Nash Foundation Scholarships *(Undergraduate, Graduate/Scholarship)* [6663]
Archie Hartwell Nash Memorial Scholarships *(Graduate, Undergraduate/Scholarship)* [3245]
National AAHAM Scholarships *(Undergraduate/Scholarship)* [504]
National Association for Armenian Studies and Research Scholarships *(Graduate, Postgraduate/Scholarship)* [1703]
National Association of Campus Activities Scholarships for Student Leaders *(Undergraduate/Scholarship)* [6732]
National Association for the Self-Employed Scholar-

ships *(Professional development/Scholarship)* [6785]
National Beta Club Scholarships *(Undergraduate/Scholarship)* [6809]
National Black Deaf Advocate Scholarships *(Graduate, Undergraduate/Scholarship)* [6816]
National Center for Health Statistics Postdoctoral Research Awards *(Postdoctorate/Fellowship)* [9920]
National Collegiate Athletic Association Postgraduate Scholarships *(Postgraduate/Scholarship)* [6863]
National Costumers Association Scholarships *(Undergraduate/Scholarship)* [6877]
National Court Reporters Association Student Intern Scholarship *(Undergraduate/Scholarship)* [6897]
National Guard Association of Rhode Island Scholarship *(Undergraduate/Scholarship)* [6978]
National High School Oratorical Contest Scholarship *(Undergraduate/Scholarship)* [956]
National Huguenot Society College and Postgraduate Student Scholarships *(Undergraduate, Postgraduate/Scholarship)* [7006]
National Merit Harris Corporation Scholarship Program *(Undergraduate/Scholarship)* [4729]
National Merit Scholarship Program *(Undergraduate/Scholarship)* [7063]
National MS Society New Jersey Metro Chapter Scholarship Program *(Undergraduate/Scholarship)* [7075]
National Organization of Italian-American Women Scholarships *(Undergraduate, Graduate/Scholarship)* [7083]
National Pathfinder Scholarships *(Graduate, Master's, Undergraduate/Scholarship)* [6954]
National Preservation Institute Scholarships *(Professional development/Scholarship)* [7104]
National Technical Honor Society Scholarships *(Undergraduate/Scholarship)* [3962]
Native American Community Scholars Awards *(Graduate/Fellowship)* [9013]
Native American Education Grants *(Graduate, Undergraduate/Grant)* [877]
Native American Visiting Student Awards *(Graduate/Fellowship)* [9014]
Naval Helicopter Association Scholarships *(Undergraduate, Graduate/Scholarship)* [7223]
The Nazareth Scholarships *(Undergraduate/Scholarship)* [7238]
NCBWL Scholarships *(Undergraduate/Scholarship)* [6666]
NCCF Survivor Scholarships *(Undergraduate/Scholarship)* [6865]
NCRF New Professional Reporter Grant *(Other/Grant)* [6898]
Nedien Hoganson Memorial Scholarships *(Undergraduate, Master's/Scholarship)* [10797]
Bill Nelson Scholarship Endowment (BNSE) *(Undergraduate, Graduate/Scholarship)* [7768]
Judge William J. Nelson Scholarships *(Undergraduate/Scholarship)* [9442]
Law Offices of Judd S. Nemiro Dyslexia Scholarships *(All/Scholarship)* [5961]
NEMLA Summer Fellowships *(Graduate, Other/Fellowship)* [7511]
NEMRA Educational Scholarship Foundation *(Undergraduate, Vocational/Occupational/Scholarship)* [6941]
Andrew Nerland Scholarships *(Undergraduate/Scholarship)* [10031]
Amelia and Emanuel Nessell Scholarships *(Undergraduate/Scholarship)* [3719]
Netfloor USA Access Flooring College Scholarships *(Undergraduate/Scholarship)* [7261]
Reverend John S. Nettles Scholarships *(Undergraduate/Scholarship)* [3268]
Alan H. Neville Memorial Scholarships *(Undergraduate/Scholarship)* [335]
New Hampshire Snowmobile Association Book Scholarships *(Undergraduate/Scholarship)* [7313]
New Mexico Manufactured Housing Association Scholarship Program *(Undergraduate/Scholarship)* [303]
New Orleans Ghost Tours Scholarships *(Undergraduate/Scholarship)* [7341]
New York State Senate - Legislative Fellowships *(Graduate, Postgraduate/Fellowship)* [7368]
The New York Times College Scholarships *(Undergraduate/Scholarship, Internship)* [7396]
Newberry Consortium on American Indian Studies Graduate Student Fellowships *(Doctorate/Fellowship)* [7418]
Newberry Library ACM/GLCA Faculty Fellowships *(Other/Fellowship)* [7419]
Newberry Library/Ecole Nationale des Chartes Exchange Fellowships *(Graduate/Fellowship)* [7420]
Newberry Library Short-Term Resident Fellowships for Individual Research *(Postdoctorate, Doctorate/Fellowship)* [7422]
Newcomer Supply Student Scholarships *(Undergraduate/Scholarship)* [7169]
Newman Civic Fellows Awards *(Undergraduate/Award)* [2530]
Newman University Scouting Scholarships *(Undergraduate/Scholarship)* [6931]
Jerry Newson Scholarships *(Undergraduate/Scholarship)* [3246]
NFPA Youth Scholarships *(Undergraduate, Vocational/Occupational/Scholarship)* [6961]
NGAT Educational Scholarships *(Graduate, Undergraduate/Scholarship)* [6980]
Le Hoang Nguyen College Scholarships (LHN) *(Undergraduate/Scholarship)* [10386]
The Thuy Nguyen Scholarships *(High School/Scholarship)* [10387]
NHAEOP Member Scholarships *(Undergraduate/Scholarship)* [7299]
NHEERL Postdoctoral Research Program *(Postdoctorate, Advanced Professional, Professional development/Fellowship)* [9937]
NHPGA Apprentice Scholarships *(Undergraduate/Scholarship)* [6358]
NHS National Scholarships *(Undergraduate/Scholarship)* [7000]
NIAC Iranian-American Scholarship Fund *(Undergraduate, Graduate/Scholarship)* [7023]
NIAF Scholarships - General Category I *(Undergraduate, Graduate, Postgraduate/Scholarship)* [7027]
NIBA Presidential Scholarships *(Undergraduate/Scholarship)* [7010]
Erik Nielsen Memorial Scholarships *(Undergraduate, Master's/Scholarship)* [10798]
Mike Niemeyer Memorial Football Scholarships *(Undergraduate/Scholarship)* [8506]
Nikko Cosmetic Surgery Center Annual Breast Cancer Survivor Scholarships *(All/Scholarship)* [7434]
Evelyn S. Nish Scholarships *(Undergraduate/Scholarship)* [8933]
Anderson Niskanen Scholarships *(Undergraduate/Scholarship)* [3720]
Nissan North America, Inc. Scholarships *(Undergraduate/Scholarship)* [871]
Corwin Nixon Scholarships *(Undergraduate/Scholarship)* [3007]
NLBRA National Royalty Scholarships *(Undergraduate/Scholarship)* [7054]
NLBRA Rainwater Scholarships *(Undergraduate/Scholarship)* [7055]
NLBRA World All Around Scholarships *(Undergraduate/Scholarship)* [7056]
NLBRA World Event Scholarships *(Undergraduate/Scholarship)* [7057]
NLBRA/Wrangler Academic Scholarships *(Undergraduate/Scholarship)* [7058]
NLBRA Youth Board Officer Scholarships *(Undergraduate/Scholarship)* [7059]
NMCRS Gold Star Scholarship Program *(Undergraduate/Scholarship)* [7235]
NMSC College and University Sponsorship of Merit Scholarship Awards *(Undergraduate/Scholarship)* [7064]
NMSC Corporate-Sponsored Achievement Scholarship Awards *(Undergraduate/Scholarship)* [7065]
NMSC National Achievement Scholarship Program *(Undergraduate/Scholarship)* [7066]
NMSC Special Scholarships *(Undergraduate/Scholarship)* [7067]
Charles S. Noble Scholarships for Study at Harvard *(Undergraduate/Scholarship)* [282]
Edna A. Noblin Dawsonville Lions Club Scholarships *(Undergraduate/Scholarship)* [5926]
Alfred H. Nolle Scholarships *(Undergraduate/Scholarship)* [342]
Non Commissioned Officers Association Scholarships *(Undergraduate/Scholarship)* [7441]
Nor' Easters Scholarships - Four-year Program *(Undergraduate/Scholarship)* [4915]
Nor' Easters Scholarships - Two-year Program *(Undergraduate/Scholarship)* [4916]
Norall Scholarship Trust *(Undergraduate/Scholarship)* [6066]
Nordic Ski Association of Anchorage Scholarships *(Undergraduate/Scholarship)* [221]
North Carolina Heroes Financial Hardship Grant *(All/Grant)* [7466]
North Dakota Farmers Union Co-op House Scholarships *(Undergraduate/Scholarship)* [7490]
North Texas GIA Alumni Association Scholarships *(Undergraduate/Scholarship)* [4344]
North Texas Relocation Professionals Scholarships *(Undergraduate/Scholarship)* [7505]
Northern Alberta Development Council Bursary Awards *(Undergraduate/Award)* [283]
Northern Alberta Development Council Bursary Partnership Program *(Undergraduate/Award)* [284]
Northern Arizona Native-American Foundation Scholarships *(Undergraduate, Vocational/Occupational/Scholarship)* [7516]
Northern Resident Scholarships *(Doctorate, Graduate/Scholarship)* [1935]
Eugene Northrup Scholarships *(Undergraduate/Scholarship)* [6047]
Northwest Community Center Scholarships *(Undergraduate/Scholarship)* [3295]
Northwest-Shoals Community College Academic Scholarships *(Undergraduate/Scholarship)* [7539]
Northwest-Shoals Community College Bank Independent Scholarships *(Undergraduate/Scholarship)* [7542]
Northwest-Shoals Community College High School Academic Scholarships *(Undergraduate/Scholarship)* [7546]
Northwest-Shoals Community College Independent Computer Scholarships *(Undergraduate/Scholarship)* [7547]
Northwest-Shoals Community College Student Activities Scholarships *(Undergraduate/Scholarship)* [7548]
Notre Dame Club of Canton Scholarships *(Undergraduate/Scholarship)* [9528]
NSHSS Academic Paper Awards *(High School/Scholarship)* [7160]
NSHSS National Scholar Awards *(High School/Scholarship)* [7161]
NSSA/NSCA Collegiate Scholarships *(Undergraduate/Scholarship)* [7186]
The Nuts.com Healthy Eating Scholarships *(Undergraduate, Graduate/Scholarship)* [7564]
NWAG Georgia, USA Scholarships *(Undergraduate/Scholarship)* [7431]
NWAG Nigeria Scholarships *(Undergraduate/Scholarship)* [7432]
NWSA Graduate Scholarships *(Graduate/Scholarship)* [7219]
AEBC Rick Oakes Scholarships for the Arts *(Undergraduate/Scholarship)* [336]
OAS Academic Scholarship for Undergraduate Studies *(Undergraduate/Scholarship)* [7721]
OAS Academic Scholarships - Graduate *(Graduate/Scholarship)* [7722]
Obuchi Student Scholarships *(Graduate/Scholarship)* [3762]
Odd Fellows Lodge No. 8 Endowed Scholarships *(Undergraduate/Scholarship)* [6048]
Captain Jennifer Shafer Odom Memorial Scholarships - Children of Soldiers *(Undergraduate, Vocational/Occupational/Scholarship)* [1716]
Captain Jennifer Shafer Odom Memorial Scholarships - Spouses of Soldiers *(Undergraduate/Scholarship)* [1717]
Don and Jan O'Dowd/SAA Statewide Scholarships *(Undergraduate/Scholarship)* [10033]
Ohio War Orphan Scholarships *(Undergraduate/Scholarship)* [10723]
O'Jays Scholarship Fund *(Undergraduate/Scholarship)* [9529]
Roy C. and Dorothy Jean Olson Memorial Scholar-

ships *(Undergraduate/Scholarship)* [5361]
Olympia Tumwater Foundation Traditional Scholarships *(Undergraduate/Scholarship)* [7608]
Olympia Tumwater Foundation Transitional (non-traditional) Scholarships *(Undergraduate/Scholarship)* [7609]
Charlie O'Meilia Scholarships *(Undergraduate/Scholarship)* [5301]
Omicron Delta Kappa Foundation Scholarships *(Graduate/Scholarship)* [7611]
ONECA Four Directions Scholarship *(Undergraduate/Scholarship)* [7658]
ONLA President's Scholarship *(Undergraduate/Scholarship)* [7586]
OOBS Student Leadership Scholarships *(Undergraduate/Scholarship)* [7766]
Open Society Fellowships *(Other/Fellowship)* [7662]
Order Sons of Italy Foundation General Scholarships *(Graduate, Undergraduate/Scholarship)* [7683]
Organization of American States AOS-Placed Scholarships *(Graduate, Undergraduate/Scholarship)* [7727]
Organization of American States Graduate Scholarships *(Doctorate, Graduate/Scholarship)* [7728]
Organization of American States Self-Placed Scholarships *(Doctorate, Graduate/Scholarship)* [7729]
Organization of Chinese Americans Scholarships *(Undergraduate/Scholarship)* [1784]
Original Tax Credit Scholarship *(Undergraduate/Scholarship)* [1627]
Alvin G. Ott Fish and Wildlife Scholarships *(Undergraduate/Scholarship)* [10034]
Ted H. Ousley Scholarship Fund *(Undergraduate/Scholarship)* [4209]
Outlaw Student's Minority Scholarships *(Undergraduate/Scholarship)* [9596]
Victoria Ovis Memorial Scholarships *(Undergraduate/Scholarship)* [7045]
Charles and Melva T. Owen Memorial Scholarships *(Undergraduate/Scholarship)* [6948]
Ozarks Division Scholarships *(Undergraduate/Scholarship)* [6524]
The Pac-10 Postgraduate Scholarships *(Graduate/Scholarship)* [7787]
Dr. Nicholas Padis Memorial Graduate Scholarships *(Graduate/Scholarship)* [4849]
Casilda Pagan Educational/Vocational Scholarships *(Graduate, Undergraduate, Postgraduate/Scholarship)* [4964]
Ben Palacio Scholarships *(Undergraduate/Scholarship)* [9962]
Robert R. Palmer Research Travel Fellowships *(Other/Fellowship)* [1296]
Palo Verde High School Faculty Follies Scholarships *(Undergraduate/Scholarship)* [8357]
The PanHellenic Scholarships *(Undergraduate/Scholarship)* [7797]
Panther Cafe Scholarships *(Undergraduate/Scholarship)* [8358]
Paper Stock Industries Chapter ISRI RRF Scholarship *(Undergraduate/Scholarship)* [7801]
Cissy McDaniel Parker Scholarships *(Undergraduate/Scholarship)* [3557]
E.U. and Gene Parker Scholarships *(Undergraduate/Scholarship)* [6949]
Parking Industry Institute Scholarship Program *(Undergraduate/Scholarship)* [7094]
Carl Parsell Scholarship Fund *(Undergraduate/Scholarship)* [6459]
Pasteur Foundation Postdoctoral Fellowships *(Postdoctorate/Fellowship)* [7899]
PATCH Early Childhood Education Scholarships *(Other/Scholarship)* [7903]
James H. Patrenos Memorial Scholarships *(Undergraduate/Scholarship)* [8969]
Gail Patrick Charitable Trust Scholarships *(Undergraduate/Scholarship)* [3593]
Q. O. (Quint) Patrick Scholarships *(Undergraduate/Scholarship)* [10548]
Alice Conger Patterson Scholarships *(Undergraduate/Scholarship)* [10591]
Joanne Holbrook Patton Military Spouse Scholarships *(Graduate, Undergraduate/Scholarship)* [7069]

Paul and Inger Friend 4-H Scholarships *(Undergraduate/Scholarship)* [9574]
PEA Bursaries *(Undergraduate/Scholarship)* [8290]
PEA Scholarships *(Undergraduate/Scholarship)* [8291]
Pearman Family Scholarships *(Undergraduate/Scholarship)* [8720]
Mario Pedrozzi Scholarships *(Undergraduate, Graduate/Scholarship)* [7931]
Pellegrini Scholarships *(Undergraduate, Graduate/Scholarship)* [9620]
Pembroke Center Faculty Fellowships *(Professional development/Fellowship)* [2389]
Pembroke Center Graduate Fellowships *(Graduate/Fellowship)* [2391]
Pembroke Center for Teaching and Research on Women Postdoctoral Fellowships *(Postdoctorate/Fellowship)* [2392]
Dorothy E. Hofmann Pembroke Scholarships *(Undergraduate/Scholarship)* [4767]
Robert B. and Dorothy Pence Scholarships *(Undergraduate/Scholarship)* [9443]
Pennsboro Alumni Scholarship Fund *(Undergraduate/Scholarship)* [7850]
P.E.O. Chapter DS Scholarships *(Undergraduate, Vocational/Occupational/Scholarship)* [4536]
PEO Educational Loan Funds *(Undergraduate, Master's, Doctorate/Loan)* [7954]
PEO International Peace Scholarships *(Graduate, Master's, Doctorate/Scholarship)* [7955]
PEO Scholars Awards *(Doctorate/Award, Scholarship)* [7956]
Pepsi Wood County Technical/Caperton Center Scholarship Fund *(Undergraduate/Scholarship)* [7851]
Joaquim Pereira Memorial Scholarships *(Undergraduate/Scholarship)* [6153]
Nalini Perera Little Lotus Bud Master's Scholarships *(Master's/Scholarship)* [2689]
Eleanor Perry Memorial Endowed Scholarships *(Undergraduate/Scholarship)* [6050]
Perry Township School Memorial Scholarship Fund *(Undergraduate/Scholarship)* [9530]
Persons Case Scholarships *(Undergraduate, Graduate/Scholarship)* [285]
Jerome Peters Family Scholarships *(Undergraduate/Scholarship)* [6210]
Captain James H. Peterson Memorial Scholarships *(Undergraduate/Scholarship)* [4715]
Charles E. Peterson Senior Fellowships *(Other/Fellowship)* [2107]
William H. and Lena M. Petree Scholarships *(Undergraduate/Scholarship)* [10592]
Pfafftown Jaycees/Lynn Canada Memorial Scholarships *(Undergraduate/Scholarship)* [10593]
L. Gordon, Jr. and June D. Pfefferkorn Scholarships *(Undergraduate/Scholarship)* [10594]
PFLAG Columbia-Howard County Scholarship *(Undergraduate/Scholarship)* [8025]
Marshall Phelps Athletic Memorial Scholarships *(Undergraduate/Scholarship)* [8507]
Phi Delta Gamma Academic Achievement Awards *(Undergraduate/Scholarship)* [8059]
Phi Eta Sigma Distinguished Member Scholarships - Graduate or Professional *(Graduate, Other/Scholarship)* [8062]
Phi Eta Sigma Distinguished Member Scholarships - Undergraduate *(Undergraduate/Scholarship)* [8063]
Phi Eta Sigma Undergraduate Scholarship Awards *(Undergraduate/Scholarship)* [8064]
Phi Kappa Phi Fellowships *(Graduate, Undergraduate/Fellowship)* [8066]
Phi Kappa Sigma Foundation Scholarship *(Undergraduate/Scholarship)* [8068]
Phi Kappa Sigma Need-Based Scholarships *(Undergraduate/Scholarship)* [8069]
Phi Kappa Sigma Participation-Based Scholarships *(Undergraduate/Scholarship)* [8070]
Walter T. Philippy Scholarships *(Undergraduate/Scholarship)* [6359]
CSF Charles and Claire Phillips Scholarships *(Undergraduate/Scholarship)* [3008]
Lowell Phillips Scholarships *(Undergraduate/Scholarship)* [3313]
PhRMA Foundation Informatics Research Starter Grants *(Doctorate/Grant)* [8038]
Eleonora Pidperyhora Scholarship *(Undergraduate/Scholarship)* [8587]
Herschel Pifer Memorial Scholarships *(Undergraduate/Scholarship)* [7853]
Christopher Mark Pitkin Memorial Scholarships *(Undergraduate/Scholarship)* [6994]
Day Pitney LLP Scholarships *(Undergraduate/Scholarship)* [4769]
Al Plamann Legacy Scholarships *(Undergraduate/Scholarship)* [2457]
TFC Edward A. Plank, Jr. Memorial Scholarships *(Undergraduate/Scholarship)* [3182]
Katherine Barton Platt Excavation Fellowships *(Other, Undergraduate/Fellowship)* [1237]
Pleasantview Public Schools Fund *(Undergraduate/Scholarship)* [4564]
PLSCA Scholarships *(Undergraduate/Scholarship)* [6101]
PLUS Foundation Financial Aid Scholarships *(Undergraduate/Scholarship)* [8168]
Henry DeWitt Plyler Scholarship Fund *(Undergraduate/Scholarship)* [4210]
Point Foundation Scholarships *(Undergraduate/Scholarship)* [8662]
Tibor T. Polgar Fellowships *(Graduate, Undergraduate/Fellowship)* [4981]
Pollard-Bailey Scholarships *(Undergraduate/Scholarship)* [8722]
David J. Pollini Scholarships *(Undergraduate/Scholarship)* [6360]
Buster Pool Memorial Scholarships *(Undergraduate/Scholarship)* [3248]
Pope Scholarship Awards *(Undergraduate/Scholarship)* [6361]
Karin Riley Porter Good Works Scholarships *(Undergraduate, Graduate/Scholarship)* [8236]
AFT Robert Porter Scholarship Program *(Undergraduate/Scholarship)* [795]
Portland Area Business Association Scholarships *(Undergraduate/Scholarship)* [3921]
Portuguese-American Scholarship Foundation *(Undergraduate/Scholarship)* [8209]
Poteet Strawberry Festival Association Scholarships *(Graduate, Undergraduate/Scholarship)* [8213]
Gerald Powell Scholarships *(Undergraduate/Scholarship)* [3269]
Susan Kelly Power and Helen Hornbeck Tanner Fellowships *(Doctorate, Postdoctorate/Fellowship)* [7423]
J.R. (Joe) Power National Scholarships *(Postgraduate/Scholarship)* [8383]
Powers-Knapp Scholarships *(Undergraduate/Scholarship)* [10326]
Prairie Baseball Academy Scholarships *(Undergraduate/Scholarship)* [286]
Jim and Dee Price Scholarships *(Undergraduate/Scholarship)* [4565]
Pride Foundation Regional Scholarships *(Undergraduate/Scholarship)* [8259]
Pride Foundation Scholarships *(Undergraduate/Scholarship)* [8663]
Pride of the Rose Scholarship Fund *(Undergraduate/Scholarship)* [3922]
Dean Prim Scholarships *(Undergraduate/Scholarship)* [10595]
Prince Henry Society Scholarships *(Undergraduate/Scholarship)* [8278]
Miguel Pro Scholarships *(Undergraduate/Scholarship)* [10724]
Professional Women of Redlands, PoWeR to Continue Learning Scholarships *(Undergraduate/Scholarship)* [8508]
Progress Lane Scholarships *(Undergraduate/Scholarship)* [3183]
Provincial and Regional 4-H Scholarships *(Undergraduate/Scholarship)* [9]
Joseph E. Pryor Graduate Fellowships *(Graduate/Fellowship, Scholarship)* [343]
Cheryl White Pryor Memorial Scholarships *(Undergraduate/Scholarship)* [3558]
PSAC-AGR National Scholarships *(Postgraduate/Scholarship)* [8384]
PSAC - Coughlin National Scholarships *(Postgraduate/Scholarship)* [8385]

PSAC Regional Scholarships *(Postgraduate/Scholarship)* [8386]
PSHF Good Idea Grants *(Other/Grant)* [8381]
Pt. Lay Memorial Scholarships *(Undergraduate/Scholarship)* [10035]
Public Service Fellows Internship Program - Center for Government Leadership *(Undergraduate, Graduate/Internship)* [7890]
Public Service Fellows Internship Program - Communications *(Undergraduate, Graduate, Professional development/Internship)* [7891]
Public Service Fellows Internship Program - Development *(Undergraduate, Graduate, Professional development/Internship)* [7892]
Public Service Fellows Internship Program - Education and Outreach *(Undergraduate, Graduate, Professional development/Internship)* [7893]
Public Service Fellows Internship Program - Government Affairs *(Undergraduate, Graduate, Professional development/Internship)* [7894]
Public Service Fellows Internship Program - Government Transformation and Agency Partnerships *(Undergraduate, Graduate, Professional development/Internship)* [7895]
Public Service Fellows Internship Program - Human Resources *(Undergraduate, Graduate, Professional development/Internship)* [7896]
Public Service Fellows Internship Program - Research *(Undergraduate, Graduate, Professional development/Internship)* [7897]
Duane V. Puerde Memorial Scholarships *(Undergraduate/Scholarship)* [3184]
Morris M. Pulver Scholarship Funds *(Undergraduate, Graduate, Postgraduate/Scholarship)* [2642]
Harry B. Pulver Scholarships *(Undergraduate/Scholarship)* [4454]
Elizabeth Pusey Scholarships *(Undergraduate/Scholarship)* [3185]
Qualcomm San Diego Science, Technology, Engineering and Mathematics Scholarships *(Undergraduate/Scholarship)* [8723]
Queen Elizabeth II Graduate Scholarship Program *(Doctorate, Graduate/Scholarship)* [287]
Queer Foundation Effective Writing and Scholarships *(Undergraduate/Prize, Scholarship)* [8394]
Michael J. Quill Scholarships *(Undergraduate/Scholarship)* [9766]
Diamond & James Quong Memorial Scholarships *(Undergraduate, Master's/Scholarship)* [10799]
Dr. J. Glenn Radcliffe Memorial Scholarships *(Undergraduate/Scholarship)* [9575]
The Raffin-Gathercole Scholarships *(Undergraduate/Scholarship)* [4331]
Railroad and Mine Workers Memorial Scholarships *(Graduate/Scholarship)* [5556]
J.J. Rains Memorial Scholarships *(Undergraduate/Scholarship)* [3104]
The NASSCO Jeffrey D. Ralston Memorial Scholarship *(Undergraduate/Scholarship)* [6668]
Guthikonda Ramabrahmam and Balamani *(Graduate/Scholarship)* [9669]
Marvin Rammelsberg Scholarships *(Undergraduate/Scholarship)* [3009]
Rancho Bernardo/Smith Scholarships *(Undergraduate/Scholarship)* [8724]
James Randi Educational Foundation Scholarships *(Graduate, Undergraduate/Scholarship)* [8427]
Jeannette Rankin Scholarships *(Undergraduate, Vocational/Occupational/Scholarship)* [8431]
General John Paul Ratay Educational Grants *(Undergraduate/Grant)* [6535]
Dr. Mark Rathke Family Scholarships *(Undergraduate/Scholarship)* [3721]
Mary C. Rawlins Scholarships *(Undergraduate/Scholarship)* [4771]
W.B. Ray HS Class of '56 Averill Johnson Scholarships *(Undergraduate/Scholarship)* [3105]
Raytheon Scholarship Program *(Undergraduate/Scholarship)* [8440]
Reach for Your Goal Scholarships *(Undergraduate/Scholarship)* [4617]
Robert H. Reakirt Scholarships *(Undergraduate/Scholarship)* [3010]
Redlands Baseball/Softball for Youth Scholarship *(Undergraduate/Scholarship)* [8509]
Redlands Community Scholarship Foundation Awards *(Undergraduate/Scholarship)* [8510]
Redlands High School Academic Decathlon Scholarships *(Undergraduate/Scholarship)* [8511]
Redlands High School Boy's Varsity Volleyball Scholarships *(Undergraduate/Scholarship)* [8512]
Redlands High School Girls' Volleyball Boosters Scholarship Awards *(Undergraduate/Scholarship)* [8513]
Redlands High School Mock Trial Scholarships *(Undergraduate/Scholarship)* [8514]
Redlands High School-PTSA Scholarships *(Undergraduate/Scholarship)* [8515]
Redlands High School Softball Booster Scholarship Awards *(Undergraduate/Scholarship)* [8516]
Redlands High School Spiritleaders Scholarships *(Undergraduate/Scholarship)* [8517]
Redlands Morning Kiwanis Club Foundation Scholarships *(Undergraduate/Scholarship)* [8520]
Redlands Rotary Club Foundation Discretionary Scholarships *(Undergraduate/Scholarship)* [8521]
Regions Riding Forward Scholarships Essay Contest *(Undergraduate/Scholarship)* [8536]
Registered Apprenticeship Program/CTS Scholarships (RAP) *(Undergraduate/Scholarship)* [288]
J.H. Stewart Reid Memorial Fellowship Trust *(Doctorate/Fellowship, Award)* [8547]
Jacob L. Reinecke Memorial Scholarship Fund *(Undergraduate/Scholarship)* [4538]
Daniel L. Reiss Memorial Scholarship Fund *(Undergraduate/Scholarship)* [4539]
Reservation Counter College Scholarships *(Undergraduate, Graduate, Advanced Professional/Scholarship)* [8559]
Resume Template Design Scholarships *(Undergraduate, Graduate/Scholarship)* [10369]
Retired League Postmasters Scholarship Program *(Undergraduate/Scholarship)* [8569]
W. Reymont Scholarships *(Undergraduate/Scholarship)* [8589]
Reynoldsburg-Pickerington Rotary Club High School Scholarship *(Undergraduate/Scholarship)* [8595]
Lori Rhett Memorial Scholarships *(Graduate, Undergraduate/Scholarship)* [6733]
Rhode Island Association of Former Legislators Scholarships *(Undergraduate/Scholarship)* [8608]
Barbara Hagan Richards Scholarships *(Undergraduate/Scholarship)* [3249]
James Edward "Bill" Richards Scholarships *(Undergraduate/Scholarship)* [3250]
Ellen Swallow Richards Travel Grants *(Graduate, Other/Grant)* [1315]
Phillip Guy Richardson Memorial Scholarships *(Undergraduate/Scholarship)* [5510]
John S. and Jacqueline P. Rider Scholarships *(Undergraduate/Scholarship)* [10596]
Jasper Ridge Restoration Fellowships Jasper Ridge Biological Preserve *(Graduate, Postdoctorate/Fellowship)* [3777]
William J. Rielly/MCURC Scholarships *(Undergraduate/Scholarship)* [3011]
Riggs Cove Foundation Scholarships *(Undergraduate/Scholarship)* [4369]
Benjamin Riggs Scholarships *(Undergraduate/Scholarship)* [4370]
Lana K. Rinehart Scholarships *(Undergraduate/Scholarship)* [3186]
Harold and Eleanor Ringelberg Scholarships *(Undergraduate/Scholarship)* [4540]
Josephine Ringold Scholarships *(Undergraduate/Scholarship)* [4618]
RISLA Student Loans *(Undergraduate, Graduate, Loan)* [8615]
Riverside Sheriffs Association Member Scholarship Program *(Graduate, Undergraduate/Scholarship)* [8622]
Anthony Rizzo Scholarship Award *(Professional development/Scholarship)* [7514]
RMNP Research Fellowship *(Graduate/Fellowship)* [8635]
Lawrence and Louise Robbins Scholarships *(Undergraduate/Scholarship)* [6211]
Robert S. McNamara Fellowships Program (RSMFP) *(Doctorate/Fellowship)* [10698]
Marion Roberts Memorial Scholarships *(Undergraduate/Scholarship)* [2134]
Smiley Elementary School PTA - Beverly Roberts Memorial Scholarships *(Undergraduate/Scholarship)* [8523]
Mary Roberts Scholarships *(Undergraduate/Scholarship)* [3012]
Thomas Warren Roberts Scholarships *(Undergraduate/Scholarship)* [7856]
A.D. Al and Maxine Robertson Memorial Scholarship *(Undergraduate/Scholarship)* [10036]
Ben Robinette Scholarship Endowment Fund *(Undergraduate/Scholarship)* [4211]
Robinhood Marine Center Scholarships *(Undergraduate/Scholarship)* [4371]
James Robinson Memorial Scholarship - Ripley Rotary *(Undergraduate/Scholarship)* [7857]
August M. Rocco Scholarship Fund *(Undergraduate/Scholarship)* [9531]
James and Marilyn Rockefeller Scholarships *(Undergraduate/Scholarship)* [6212]
Rockford Area Habitat for Humanity College Scholarships *(Undergraduate/Scholarship)* [3298]
R.O.E.A. Dumitru Golea Goldy-Gemu Scholarships *(Undergraduate/Scholarship)* [1227]
Roy Seymour Rogers and Geraldine Ruth Rogers Scholarships *(Undergraduate/Scholarship)* [9732]
Kimberly Marie Rogers Memorial Scholarship Fund *(Undergraduate, Vocational/Occupational/Scholarship)* [4057]
Red Rogers Memorial Scholarships *(Undergraduate, Master's/Scholarship)* [10800]
Pat and Cliff Rogers Nursing Scholarships *(Undergraduate/Scholarship)* [10090]
Mary Stuart Rogers Scholarships *(Undergraduate/Scholarship)* [10561]
Ronald McDonald House Charities African American Future Achievers Scholarships *(Undergraduate/Scholarship)* [8639]
Ronald McDonald House Charities/HACER Scholarships *(Undergraduate/Scholarship)* [8640]
Ronald McDonald House Charities Scholarships in Asia *(Undergraduate/Scholarship)* [8642]
Ronald McDonald House Charities Scholarships *(Undergraduate/Scholarship)* [8641]
Roothbert Fund Scholarships *(Undergraduate/Scholarship)* [8646]
Dr. Wayne F. Rose Scholarship Fund *(Undergraduate/Scholarship)* [4058]
Ollie Rosenberg Educational Trust *(Undergraduate/Scholarship)* [4253]
Rosenberg-Ibarra Scholarships *(Undergraduate/Scholarship)* [8263]
Jean and Tom Rosenthal Scholarship Program *(Undergraduate/Scholarship)* [3332]
The Bea and Harry Ross Scholarship Endowment *(Graduate/Scholarship)* [9586]
Rotary Club of Annapolis Scholarships *(Undergraduate/Scholarship)* [1561]
The Rotary Club of Cape Coral Goldcoast Scholarship Fund *(Undergraduate/Scholarship)* [2784]
Rotary Club of Corpus Christi Scholarships *(Undergraduate/Scholarship)* [3106]
The Rotary Club of Rancho Bernardo Sunrise Community Service Scholarships *(Undergraduate/Scholarship)* [8725]
Rotary Foundation Global Grant Scholarships *(Graduate/Scholarship)* [8648]
Rothberg International School Graduate Merit Scholarships *(Graduate, Master's/Scholarship)* [2643]
Lawrence E. and Mabel Jackson Rudberg Scholarships *(Undergraduate/Scholarship)* [3722]
Ruppert Educational Grant Program *(Undergraduate/Grant)* [8955]
Russell Athletics Scholarship *(Undergraduate/Scholarship)* [2109]
Dave & Laurie Russell Family Scholarships for Habitat for Humanity of Kent County Families *(Undergraduate/Scholarship)* [4619]
Norman K. Russell Scholarships *(Graduate, Doctorate/Scholarship)* [7092]
Alexander Rutherford Scholarships for High School Achievement *(Undergraduate/Scholarship)* [290]
Rutherford Scholars *(Undergraduate/Scholarship)* [289]
Ralph and Clara Rutledge Memorial Scholarships *(Graduate/Scholarship)* [4149]
Charles and Eleanor Rycenga Education Scholar-

GENERAL STUDIES/FIELD OF STUDY NOT SPECIFIED

ship Fund *(Undergraduate/Scholarship)* [4541]
Deborah Jean Rydberg Memorial Scholarships *(Undergraduate/Scholarship)* [3299]
Ryerson Scholarships *(Undergraduate/Scholarship)* [5527]
SAC Scholarships for Higher Education *(Undergraduate/Scholarship)* [9558]
Sacks For CF Scholarships *(Professional development/Scholarship)* [2342]
Safelink Internet Scholarships *(Undergraduate/Scholarship)* [8666]
Saint Andrews Scholarships *(Undergraduate/Scholarship)* [8670]
St. Francis Xavier Scholarships *(Undergraduate/Scholarship)* [10725]
St. James Armenian Church Memorial Scholarships *(Undergraduate/Scholarship)* [1704]
Saint Paul University Excellence Scholarships *(Undergraduate/Scholarship, Medal)* [8675]
Saint Paul University Financial Aid Bursaries *(Undergraduate, Graduate/Scholarship)* [8676]
Saints Cyril and Methodius Scholarships *(Undergraduate/Scholarship)* [8657]
Joseph and Amelia Saks Scholarship Fund *(Undergraduate/Scholarship)* [3270]
Henry Salvatori Scholarships *(Undergraduate/Scholarship)* [7684]
The Walter Samek III Memorial Scholarship Fund *(Undergraduate/Scholarship)* [3207]
SAMFund Grants *(Advanced Professional/Grant)* [8682]
Ray and Pearl Sams Scholarships *(Undergraduate/Scholarship)* [10597]
Samsung American Legion Scholarships *(Undergraduate/Scholarship)* [957]
San Angelo Area Foundation Scholarships *(All/Scholarship)* [8684]
The San Diego Foundation Community Scholarships II *(Undergraduate/Scholarship)* [8727]
The San Diego Foundation Community Scholarships I *(Undergraduate/Scholarship)* [8726]
San Pasqual Academy Scholarships *(Undergraduate/Scholarship)* [8728]
Sand Hill Scholars Program *(Undergraduate/Scholarship)* [8957]
The Amato Sanita Brighter Future Scholarships *(Undergraduate, Graduate, Advanced Professional/Scholarship)* [379]
Frank Sarli Memorial Scholarship *(Undergraduate/Scholarship)* [6899]
SARP Education Assistance Grants *(Professional development/Grant)* [8762]
SARP Professional Development Grants *(Professional development/Grant)* [8763]
Saskatchewan Government Insurance Anniversary Scholarships *(Undergraduate/Scholarship)* [8770]
Saskatchewan Government Insurance Corporate Scholarships *(Undergraduate/Scholarship)* [8771]
Saskatchewan School Boards Association Graduate Student Awards *(Graduate/Monetary)* [8782]
Saskatchewan Trucking Association Scholarships *(Undergraduate/Scholarship)* [8784]
Roger C. Sathre Memorial Scholarship Fund *(Undergraduate/Scholarship)* [5045]
Malini E. Sathyadev Memorial Scholarships *(Undergraduate/Scholarship)* [8729]
Dave Sauer Memorial College Scholarships *(Undergraduate/Scholarship)* [150]
Kevin Saunders Wheelchair Success Scholarships *(Undergraduate/Scholarship)* [3107]
Dr. William A. and Marceleine J. Sautter Hanover-Horton High School Youth of Promise Scholarships *(Undergraduate/Scholarship)* [5511]
Save Mart Legacy Scholarships *(Undergraduate/Scholarship)* [2458]
John A. Savoy Scholarship Fund *(Undergraduate/Scholarship)* [4059]
S.C. Johnson, A Family Company Scholarships *(Undergraduate/Scholarship)* [3013]
Leslie and Mary Ella Scales Memorial Scholarships *(Undergraduate/Scholarship)* [3271]
Mary Turnbull Schacht Memorial Scholarships *(Undergraduate/Scholarship)* [8934]
David W. Schacht Native American Student Scholarships *(Undergraduate/Scholarship)* [2231]
Millicent M. Schaffner Endowed Memorial Scholarships *(Undergraduate/Scholarship)* [4542]
Leopold Schepp Foundation Scholarships *(Undergraduate, Graduate/Scholarship)* [8788]
Robert C. and Margaret A. Schikora Scholarships *(Undergraduate/Scholarship)* [9447]
Henry L.P. Schmelzer College Transitions Scholarships *(Undergraduate/Scholarship)* [6213]
CSF Charlotte R. Schmidlapp Scholarships *(Undergraduate/Scholarship)* [3014]
Richard J. Schnell Memorial Scholarships *(Postdoctorate/Scholarship)* [3300]
Scholarship Award of the Bell Aliant Pioneer Volunteers *(Undergraduate/Scholarship)* [2690]
The Scholarship Foundation of St. Louis Scholarships *(Graduate, Undergraduate/Scholarship)* [8796]
Scholarship Foundation of Santa Barbara General Undergraduate, Vocational and Graduate/Medical Scholarships and Loans Program *(Undergraduate, Graduate/Scholarship)* [8799]
The Scholarship Foundation of Wakefield Scholarships *(All/Scholarship)* [8802]
Scholarship for Junior PHS Commissioned Officers *(Undergraduate/Scholarship)* [8115]
Scholarships for Veterans with Post-Traumatic Stress Disorder *(All/Scholarship)* [8624]
Schoolsfirst Federal Credit Union Scholarships *(Undergraduate/Scholarship)* [8526]
Tanna H. Schulich MBA Entrance Scholarships *(Graduate/Scholarship)* [10754]
Alice Southworth Schulman, Class of 1954, Simmons Scholarships for Unitarian Universalist Women *(Undergraduate/Scholarship)* [9838]
David and Jinny Schultz Family Scholarship *(Undergraduate/Scholarship)* [4543]
Nelson Schwab Jr. Scholarships *(Undergraduate/Scholarship)* [3015]
Judge Benjamin Schwartz Scholarships *(Undergraduate/Scholarship)* [3016]
Evalee C. Schwarz Educational Loans *(Undergraduate, Graduate/Loan)* [8812]
SCLEOA Scholarships *(Undergraduate/Scholarship)* [9361]
CSF E.W. Scripps Foundation Scholarship Fund *(Undergraduate/Scholarship)* [3017]
Seabee Memorial Scholarship Association Scholarships *(Undergraduate/Scholarship)* [9043]
Seaman Family Scholarships *(Undergraduate/Scholarship)* [3108]
Margery J. Seeger Scholarships *(Undergraduate/Scholarship)* [4620]
Aaron Seesan Memorial Scholarship Fund *(Undergraduate/Scholarship)* [9532]
Seldovia Native Association Achievement Scholarships *(Undergraduate, Graduate/Scholarship)* [8829]
Seldovia Native Association General Scholarships *(Undergraduate, Graduate/Scholarship)* [8830]
D. Mitchell Self Memorial Scholarship *(Undergraduate/Scholarship)* [7549]
SeniorAdvice Caregiver Scholarships *(Undergraduate/Scholarship)* [8840]
SeniorAdvice Volunteer Scholarships *(Undergraduate/Scholarship)* [8841]
Sentinels of Freedom Scholarships *(Advanced Professional/Scholarship)* [8843]
William "Buddy" Sentner Scholarship Awards *(Undergraduate/Scholarship)* [566]
Senyk Memorial Scholarships *(Undergraduate, Master's/Scholarship)* [10801]
SEO Optimizers Scholarships *(All/Scholarship)* [8845]
Sequoyah Graduate Scholarships *(Master's/Scholarship)* [1834]
Servus Credit Union 4-H Scholarships *(Undergraduate/Scholarship)* [10]
Frank B. Sessa Scholarship *(Professional development/Scholarship)* [2241]
Hubert K. and JoAnn Seymour Scholarships *(Undergraduate/Scholarship)* [7492]
SFP Undergraduate Scholarships *(Undergraduate/Scholarship)* [8794]
Al Shackleford and Dan Martin Professional Scholarships *(Professional development/Scholarship)* [2193]
Charles Shafae Scholarships *(Undergraduate/Scholarship)* [7799]
Josephine Hooker Shain Scholarships *(Undergraduate/Scholarship)* [4372]
Judge Terry Shamsie Scholarships *(Undergraduate/Scholarship)* [3109]
Albert F. Shanker Scholarship *(Undergraduate/Scholarship)* [796]
William H. Shannon Fellowships *(Graduate, Undergraduate/Fellowship)* [5445]
Law Office of David P. Shapiro Annual Leukemia Scholarships *(All/Scholarship)* [5949]
Ken and Sandy Sharkey Family Scholarship Fund *(Undergraduate/Scholarship)* [4545]
W.L. Shattuck Scholarships *(Undergraduate/Scholarship)* [5046]
Regina B. Shearn Scholarships *(Graduate, Undergraduate/Scholarship)* [357]
Jim Sheerin Scholarships *(Undergraduate/Scholarship)* [6362]
Nettie and Edward Shelah Scholarships *(Undergraduate/Scholarship)* [9576]
Bruce Shelton Scholarships *(Undergraduate/Scholarship)* [10598]
Robert P. Sheppard Leadership Awards *(High School/Scholarship)* [7162]
Morgan and Jeanie Sherwood Travel Grants *(Graduate, Other/Grant)* [1317]
Chiyoko and Thomas Shimazaki Scholarships *(Graduate/Scholarship)* [5558]
S. David Shor Scholarships *(Undergraduate/Scholarship)* [3018]
Shoreline Community College Full-Time Continuing Students Scholarships *(Undergraduate/Scholarship)* [8881]
Shoreline Community College Part-Time Students Scholarships *(Undergraduate/Scholarship)* [8882]
Shoreline - Lake Forest Park High School Scholarship *(Undergraduate/Scholarship)* [8883]
Thomas E. Shown, M.D. Memorial Scholarships *(Undergraduate/Scholarship)* [10599]
Law Office of Matthew Shrum Annual Scholarships for Single Mothers *(Undergraduate/Scholarship)* [5953]
Phil Shykes Memorial Scholarships *(Undergraduate/Scholarship)* [3723]
Don and Madalyn Sickafoose Educational Trust *(Undergraduate/Scholarship)* [9533]
Sigma Diagnostics Student Scholarships *(Undergraduate/Scholarship)* [7171]
Sigma Kappa Foundation Alumnae Continuing Education Scholarships *(Undergraduate/Scholarship)* [8935]
Sigma Kappa Foundation Founders' Scholarships *(Undergraduate/Scholarship)* [8937]
Sigma Kappa Foundation Michigan Scholarships *(Undergraduate/Scholarship)* [8939]
Meyer D. and Dorothy C. Silverman Scholarship *(Undergraduate/Scholarship)* [3251]
Harvey L. Simmons Memorial Scholarships *(Undergraduate/Scholarship)* [8730]
Simon Youth Foundation Community Scholarships *(Undergraduate/Scholarship)* [8959]
Simonton Windows Scholarships *(Undergraduate/Scholarship)* [7864]
Lowe Simpson Scholarships *(Undergraduate/Scholarship)* [3019]
Aaron B. Singleton Memorial Scholarship *(Undergraduate/Scholarship)* [7550]
Gadde Sitaramamma and Tirupataiah Scholarships *(Graduate/Scholarship)* [9670]
Bill Six Memorial Scholarship Fund *(Undergraduate/Scholarship)* [7865]
Sixt Rent a Car Scholarships *(Undergraduate/Scholarship)* [8973]
Ruth Skeeles Memorial Scholarship Fund *(Undergraduate/Scholarship)* [9534]
Frank Foster Skillman Scholarships *(Undergraduate/Scholarship)* [3020]
Francelene Skinner Memorial Scholarships *(Undergraduate/Scholarship)* [6067]
SLEAMC Scholarships *(Graduate, Undergraduate/Scholarship)* [8865]
Robert W. Sledge Fellowships *(Graduate/Fellowship)* [344]

GENERAL STUDIES/FIELD OF STUDY NOT SPECIFIED

Sleeping Angels Co. Scholarships *(All/Scholarship)* [8986]

J. Ward Sleichter and Frances F. Sleichter Memorial Scholarship Fund *(Undergraduate/Scholarship)* [4254]

Eva Smith Bursary *(Undergraduate/Scholarship)* [5528]

Ryan and Jamie Smith Essay Contest *(Graduate, Postgraduate/Scholarship)* [8992]

Ronald T. Smith Family Scholarships *(Undergraduate, Graduate/Scholarship)* [4621]

Gladys Ann Smith Greater Los Angeles Women's Council Scholarships *(Undergraduate/Scholarship)* [7230]

Brian Smith Memorial Scholarships *(Undergraduate/Scholarship)* [2348]

Tacy Anna Smith Memorial Scholarships *(Undergraduate/Scholarship)* [4213]

Ralph and Josephine Smith Scholarship Fund *(Undergraduate/Scholarship)* [4060]

Esther M. Smith Scholarships *(Undergraduate/Scholarship)* [3188]

Helen J. and Harold Gilman Smith Scholarships *(Graduate, Undergraduate/Scholarship)* [2232]

Joseph Sumner Smith Scholarships *(Undergraduate/Scholarship)* [9839]

Smith's Personal Best Scholarships *(Undergraduate/Scholarship)* [8363]

Gladys Snauble Scholarships *(Undergraduate/Scholarship)* [4622]

SNMMI-TS Bachelor's Degree Completion Scholarships *(Undergraduate/Scholarship)* [9225]

Boleslaw & Irena Sobczak Scholarships *(Undergraduate/Scholarship)* [8591]

Arnold Sobel Scholarships *(Undergraduate/Scholarship)* [3081]

Sobeys & Empire Work Experience & Scholarship Program - Future Leaders Awards *(Other/Scholarship)* [9049]

Society of Allied Weight Engineers Scholarships *(Undergraduate/Scholarship)* [9077]

Society of Marine Port Engineers Scholarship Loans *(Undergraduate/Scholarship loan)* [9204]

Dale and Betty George Sola Scholarships *(Undergraduate/Scholarship)* [3724]

Sons of Union Veterans of the Civil War Scholarships *(Undergraduate/Scholarship)* [9348]

Christine Soper Scholarships *(Undergraduate/Scholarship)* [4623]

Soroptimist International of Chambersburg Scholarship Fund *(Undergraduate/Scholarship)* [4255]

Soroptimist International of Redlands Scholarships *(Undergraduate/Scholarship)* [8528]

Paul & Daisy Soros Fellowships *(Graduate/Fellowship)* [9350]

SORP Student Conference Scholarship *(Graduate, Undergraduate/Scholarship)* [9237]

Lily and Catello Sorrentino Memorial Scholarships *(Undergraduate/Scholarship)* [8609]

Sourdough Reunion Memorial Endowment Scholarships *(Undergraduate/Scholarship)* [10040]

South Central Modern Language Association Fellowships *(Doctorate, Postdoctorate/Fellowship)* [7424]

South Central Power Scholarships *(Undergraduate/Scholarship)* [9373]

South Coast Area High School Senior Honors Scholarship Program *(Undergraduate/Scholarship)* [8800]

South Jersey Golf Association Scholarships *(Undergraduate/Scholarship)* [9379]

South Kentucky RECC High School Senior Scholarships *(Undergraduate/Scholarship)* [9382]

Southeast Asian Ministers of Education Organization-Vietnam Scholarship Program *(Graduate/Scholarship)* [3763]

Southern Maine Women's Golf Association Scholarships *(Professional development/Scholarship)* [9403]

Southern Nevada Sports Hall of Fame Scholarships *(Undergraduate/Scholarship)* [8364]

Southern Scholarship Foundation Scholarships *(Undergraduate/Scholarship)* [9413]

Southwest Florida Community Foundation College Assistance Scholarships *(Undergraduate/Scholarship)* [9449]

Southwest Florida Deputy Sheriffs Association Fund Scholarships *(Undergraduate/Scholarship)* [9450]

Southwest Movers Association Scholarships *(Undergraduate/Scholarship)* [9454]

Sovereign Nations Scholarships *(Undergraduate/Scholarship)* [872]

Master Sergeant William Sowers Memorial Scholarships *(Undergraduate/Scholarship)* [133]

Kathy Spadoni Memorial Scholarships *(Undergraduate/Scholarship)* [8264]

Nathan Sparks Memorial Scholarships *(Undergraduate/Scholarship)* [3272]

Spartan Staff Scholarships *(Undergraduate/Scholarship)* [8365]

Faith Speckhard Scholarships *(Undergraduate/Scholarship)* [5513]

Phillip A. Spiegel IASP Congress Trainee Scholarship *(College, Graduate, Undergraduate/Scholarship)* [5276]

Lawrence Alan Spiegel Remembrance Scholarships *(Undergraduate/Scholarship)* [4920]

Jean and Manny Spinner Scholarships *(Undergraduate/Scholarship)* [5587]

The Spirit Square Center for Arts and Education Scholarship Fund *(Undergraduate/Scholarship)* [4214]

Spokeo Connections Scholarships *(Undergraduate/Scholarship)* [9478]

Spouse Tuition Aid Loan Program (STAP) *(Undergraduate, Graduate/Loan)* [7236]

SREB-State Doctoral Scholars Program - Dissertation Awards *(Doctorate/Scholarship, Award)* [9410]

SSOC Scholarships *(Undergraduate/Scholarship)* [8786]

Ernest and Charlene Stachowiak Memorial Scholarships *(Undergraduate/Scholarship)* [3302]

Stafford Loan for Graduate Students - Unsubsidized Stafford Loans *(Graduate/Loan)* [9486]

Matt Stager Memorial Scholarship Fund *(Undergraduate/Scholarship)* [10482]

Lasek Stanisław and Aniela Scholarship *(Undergraduate/Scholarship)* [8592]

A.R.O.Y. Stanitz Scholarships *(Undergraduate/Scholarship)* [1228]

Minnie Patton Stayman Scholarships *(Undergraduate/Scholarship)* [7948]

Harry Steele Entrance Awards *(Postgraduate/Award)* [10755]

Evelyn Steele Memorial Scholarships *(Undergraduate, Master's/Scholarship)* [10802]

Elin J. Stene/Xi Scholarships *(Undergraduate/Scholarship)* [8940]

Elizabeth Coulter Stephenson Scholarships *(Undergraduate/Scholarship, Grant)* [3595]

Joseph S. Stern, Jr. Scholarships *(Undergraduate/Scholarship)* [3021]

Richie Stevenson Scholarships *(Undergraduate, Vocational/Occupational/Scholarship)* [3253]

Mary Stewart and William T. Covington, Jr. Scholarship Fund *(Undergraduate/Scholarship)* [4215]

Dr. Gunnar B. Stickler Scholarships *(Undergraduate, Vocational/Occupational/Scholarship)* [9578]

The Richard Stockton College of New Jersey Foundation Alumni Association Graduate Awards *(Graduate/Scholarship)* [9587]

Stop Hunger Scholarships *(Undergraduate/Scholarship)* [573]

Stop-Painting.com Scholarships *(Undergraduate/Scholarship)* [5147]

Bonnie Strangio Education Scholarships *(Graduate, Undergraduate/Scholarship)* [2343]

Marlene Streit Golf Scholarships *(Undergraduate/Scholarship)* [4481]

George and Pearl Strickland Scholarships *(Graduate, Undergraduate/Scholarship)* [3195]

Mark and Karla Stuart Family Scholarship *(Undergraduate/Scholarship)* [8732]

Stultz Scholarships *(Undergraduate/Scholarship)* [10600]

Subic Bay-Cubi Point Scholarships *(Undergraduate/Scholarship)* [7231]

Vallabhaneni Sukundamma and Lakshmaiah Scholarships *(Graduate/Scholarship)* [9671]

Phil Sullivan Scholarships *(Undergraduate/Scholarship)* [8265]

William A. Sullivan Scholarships *(Undergraduate/Scholarship)* [7232]

Summerside-Natick International Friendship Hockey Scholarships *(Undergraduate/Scholarship)* [3314]

Bruce and Marjorie Sundlun Scholarships *(Undergraduate/Scholarship)* [8610]

SuperKutz Scholarships *(Undergraduate/Scholarship)* [5892]

Sussman-Miller Educational Assistance Award Program *(Undergraduate/Scholarship)* [305]

Lorraine E. Swain Scholarships *(Undergraduate/Scholarship)* [8941]

Jeffrey Tyler Sweitzer Wrestling Memorial Scholarship Fund *(Undergraduate/Scholarship)* [9537]

Timothy S. Sweterlitsch Memorial Scholarship Fund *(Undergraduate/Scholarship)* [9538]

Hazaros Tabakoglu Scholarship Fund *(Undergraduate/Scholarship)* [1705]

Taiwanese American Community Scholarships *(Undergraduate/Scholarship)* [9634]

Tall Awareness Scholarships *(Undergraduate/Scholarship)* [8366]

Tall Clubs International Student Scholarships *(Undergraduate/Scholarship)* [9638]

TANA Foundation Graduate Scholarships *(Graduate/Scholarship)* [9672]

Martha W. Tanner Memorial Scholarships *(Undergraduate/Scholarship)* [3022]

Jack Tate/ThinkCOLLEGE Scholarship Fund *(Undergraduate/Scholarship)* [4216]

Ryan "Munchie" Taylor Memorial Scholarships *(Undergraduate/Scholarship)* [6154]

TCA-ACBH Scholarships *(Undergraduate/Scholarship)* [9812]

TCA Scholarship *(Undergraduate/Scholarship)* [9800]

TCA-UMD Scholarships *(Undergraduate/Scholarship)* [9813]

TCATA College Scholarship Program *(Undergraduate/Scholarship)* [9721]

Teammates Mentoring Scholarship Program *(Undergraduate/Scholarship)* [4567]

Technical Women's Organization Education Scholarships (TWO) *(Undergraduate/Scholarship)* [9652]

Dwight Teed Scholarships *(Undergraduate/Scholarship)* [9612]

Telecommunications Association of Michigan Scholarship Fund *(Undergraduate/Scholarship)* [9663]

Tell Us Your Story Scholarships *(Undergraduate/Scholarship)* [10495]

Telluride Association Summer Program Scholarships *(Undergraduate/Scholarship)* [9665]

Tennessee Trucking Foundation Scholarships *(Undergraduate/Scholarship)* [3254]

Texas Elks State Association Eagle Scout Scholarships *(Undergraduate/Scholarship)* [9697]

Texas Elks State Association Girl Scout Gold Award Scholarships *(Undergraduate/Scholarship)* [9698]

Texas Elks State Association Scholarships *(Undergraduate/Scholarship)* [9699]

Texas Scholarships of Academic Excellence *(Undergraduate, Graduate/Scholarship)* [9559]

Texas Telephone Association Foundation Scholarships *(Undergraduate/Scholarship)* [9719]

ThanksUSA Scholarships *(Undergraduate, Vocational/Occupational/Scholarship)* [9723]

The Cover Guy Annual Scholarships *(Undergraduate, Graduate/Scholarship)* [3463]

Elizabeth R. Thomas Alumni Nursing Scholarship *(Undergraduate/Scholarship)* [8885]

Barbara Thomas Bursary *(Undergraduate/Scholarship)* [5529]

Barber Owen Thomas Scholarships *(Undergraduate/Scholarship)* [8942]

C.R. Thomas Scholarships *(Undergraduate/Scholarship)* [7867]

Dorothy B. and Charles E. Thomas Scholarships *(Undergraduate/Scholarship)* [4625]

Matilda B. Thompson Scholarship *(Undergraduate/Scholarship)* [4929]

Thornberg/Havens Scholarships *(Undergraduate/Scholarship)* [3596]

Dorothy J. Thurston Graduate Scholarships *(Undergraduate/Scholarship)* [4626]

Raymond A. Tice Scholarships I *(Undergraduate/Scholarship)* [8733]

Raymond A. Tice Scholarships II *(Undergraduate/Scholarship)* [8734]
Tidewater Builders Association Scholarships *(Undergraduate/Scholarship)* [9739]
Tillman Scholars Program *(Undergraduate, Graduate/Scholarship)* [7901]
Louise Tillotson Teaching Fellowships *(Professional development/Fellowship)* [7306]
Louise Tillotson Teaching Professional Development Scholarships *(Professional development/Scholarship)* [7307]
TMCF Scholarships *(Undergraduate/Scholarship)* [9735]
Mario J. Tocco Hydrocephalus Foundation Scholarships *(Undergraduate/Scholarship)* [5028]
Richard Cecil Todd and Clauda Pennock Todd Tripod Scholarships *(Graduate, Undergraduate/Scholarship)* [8082]
CSF Christopher Todd Grant Memorial Scholarships *(Undergraduate/Scholarship)* [3023]
Aram Torossian Memorial Scholarships *(Undergraduate/Scholarship)* [1706]
Ferdinand Torres Scholarships *(Graduate, Undergraduate/Scholarship)* [824]
Touchstone Special Achievement Scholarships *(Undergraduate/Scholarship)* [7588]
Town and County Club Scholarships *(Undergraduate/Scholarship)* [4773]
Toyota Earth Day Scholarships *(Undergraduate/Scholarship)* [9764]
TRALA Industry Scholarship Awards *(Undergraduate/Scholarship)* [9798]
Vera Tran Memorial Scholarships *(Undergraduate/Scholarship)* [10388]
Transatlantic Fellows Program *(Other/Fellowship)* [4400]
Traub-Dicker Rainbow Scholarships *(Undergraduate/Scholarship)* [9590]
Trelut Family Legacy Scholarships *(Undergraduate/Scholarship)* [2459]
Marie Tremaine Fellowships *(Postgraduate, Other/Fellowship)* [2259]
Tri Delta Alpha Eta Scholarships *(Undergraduate/Scholarship)* [3559]
Tri Delta Alpha Rho Leadership Scholarships *(Undergraduate/Scholarship)* [3560]
Tri Delta Atlanta Alumnae Achievement Scholarships *(Undergraduate/Scholarship)* [3561]
Tri Delta Beta Gamma Memorial Scholarships *(Undergraduate/Scholarship)* [3562]
Tri Delta Houston Alumnae Chapter Graduate Fellowships *(Graduate/Fellowship, Scholarship)* [3563]
Tri Delta Northern Virginia Alumnae Chapter Scholarships *(Undergraduate/Scholarship)* [3564]
Tim Triner Letter Carriers Scholarship Fund *(Undergraduate/Scholarship)* [9539]
Tristin Memorial Scholarships *(Undergraduate, Vocational/Occupational/Scholarship)* [5996]
Mildred E. Troske Music Scholarships *(Undergraduate/Scholarship)* [4627]
Jo Anne J. Trow Scholarships *(Undergraduate/Scholarship)* [6697]
Truckload Carriers Association Scholarships *(Undergraduate/Scholarship)* [9801]
Trudeau Fellowships - Regular *(Advanced Professional, Professional development/Fellowship)* [8135]
Trudeau Fellowships - Visiting *(Advanced Professional, Professional development/Fellowship)* [8136]
TrustedPros Scholarships *(Undergraduate/Scholarship)* [9805]
Norman J. Tschantz/Walter C. Deuble Scholarships *(Undergraduate/Scholarship)* [9540]
Tschudy Family Scholarships *(Undergraduate/Scholarship)* [5050]
Richard R. Tufenkian Memorial Scholarships *(Undergraduate/Scholarship)* [1671]
Hans Turley Prize in Queer Eighteenth-Century Studies *(Graduate, Other/Prize)* [1297]
Jeff Turner-Forsyth Audubon Society Scholarships *(Undergraduate/Scholarship)* [10601]
Mark and Vera Turner Memorial Scholarships *(Undergraduate/Scholarship)* [6068]

Ira G. Turpin Scholars Fund *(Undergraduate/Scholarship)* [9541]
Tuscumbia Kiwanis Scholarship *(Undergraduate/Scholarship)* [7551]
U-M Alumnae Club (University of Michigan) Scholarships *(Undergraduate/Scholarship)* [4628]
UAA Alumni Association Scholarship *(Undergraduate/Scholarship)* [10077]
UAF Alumni Association Scholarships *(Undergraduate/Scholarship)* [10100]
UC MEXUS-CICESE Short-term Research & Training Program *(Graduate/Award, Grant)* [10115]
UC MEXUS-CONACYT Collaborative Grants *(Professional development/Grant)* [10116]
UC MEXUS-CONACYT Postdoctoral Research Fellowships *(Postdoctorate/Fellowship)* [10118]
UC MEXUS Scholars in Residence Program - Recent University Graduates *(Postgraduate/Scholarship)* [10121]
UC MEXUS Scholars in Residence Program - Visiting Faculty *(Professional development/Scholarship)* [10122]
UFCW Local Union Scholarships *(Undergraduate/Scholarship)* [9847]
UH Manoa Starr Foundation Graduate Fellowships in Asian Studies *(Graduate/Grant)* [10138]
Umialik Scholarships *(Undergraduate/Scholarship)* [10041]
UNC-CGI C.V. Starr Scholarships *(Undergraduate, Graduate/Scholarship)* [2847]
UNH Alumni Association Legacy Scholarships *(Undergraduate/Scholarship)* [10209]
UNH Parents Association Endowment Scholarship Fund *(Undergraduate/Scholarship)* [10210]
Union of Marash Armenian Scholarships *(Undergraduate, Graduate/Scholarship)* [1707]
Union Plus Scholarship Program *(Undergraduate/Scholarship)* [5451]
United Methodist General Scholarships *(Undergraduate, Graduate/Scholarship)* [9856]
United South and Eastern Tribes Scholarship Fund *(Undergraduate/Scholarship)* [9868]
U.S. Air Force ROTC High School Scholarships *(Undergraduate/Scholarship)* [9873]
U.S. Air Force ROTC In-College Scholarships *(Undergraduate/Scholarship)* [9874]
U.S. Bank Scholarships *(Undergraduate/Scholarship)* [8738]
U.S. Bates Scholarship Program *(Undergraduate/Scholarship)* [5452]
U.S. BIA Indian Higher Education Grants *(Undergraduate/Grant)* [878]
UnitedAg Scholarship Program *(Undergraduate/Scholarship)* [9988]
University of Alaska Scholars Program *(Undergraduate/Scholarship)* [10042]
University of Hawaii at Manoa East-West Center Graduate Fellowships *(Graduate, Postdoctorate/Fellowship)* [10139]
University of Hawaii at Manoa Graduate Student Organization Travel Funds *(Graduate/Grant)* [10141]
University of Louisville Eagle Scout Scholarships *(Undergraduate/Scholarship)* [6932]
University of Oregon Dean's Scholarships *(Undergraduate/Scholarship)* [10260]
University of Oregon Diversity Excellence Scholarships *(Undergraduate/Scholarship)* [10261]
University of Oregon General University Scholarships *(Undergraduate/Scholarship)* [10262]
University of Oregon Presidential Scholarships *(Undergraduate/Scholarship)* [10263]
University of Puget Sound LGBT Leadership Scholarships Fund *(Undergraduate/Scholarship)* [8664]
University of Southern Mississippi Eagle Scout/Gold Award Scholarship *(Undergraduate/Scholarship)* [6933]
University of Toronto SAC Undergraduate Grants *(Undergraduate/Grant)* [10299]
University of Wisconsin-Madison Chancellor's Scholarships *(Undergraduate/Scholarship)* [10328]
University of Wisconsin-Madison National Merit Scholarships *(Undergraduate/Scholarship)* [10329]
University of Wisconsin-Madison Single Parent Scholarships *(Undergraduate/Scholarship)* [10330]
Urban and Regional Policy (Comparative Domestic Policy) Fellowships *(Other/Fellowship)* [4401]
The Urban Scholarship Fund *(Undergraduate/Scholarship)* [9689]
USA Freestyle Martial Arts Scholarships *(Undergraduate/Scholarship)* [8739]
USA Funds Access to Education Scholarships *(Graduate, Undergraduate/Scholarship)* [9986]
USA/USA-Ukramerazha Scholarships *(Undergraduate/Scholarship)* [9982]
USAttorneys.com Immigration Scholarships Essay Contest *(Undergraduate/Scholarship)* [10353]
USAttorneys.com National Scholarships Essay Contest *(Undergraduate/Scholarship)* [10354]
USAWOASF/Grantham University On-Line Scholarships *(Graduate, Undergraduate/Scholarship)* [9880]
USAWOASF Regular Scholarships *(Undergraduate/Scholarship)* [9881]
USHJA General Scholarships *(Undergraduate/Scholarship)* [9956]
USPAACC Ampcus Hallmark Scholarships *(Undergraduate/Scholarship)* [9968]
USPAACC Denny's Hungry for Education Scholarship *(Undergraduate/Scholarship)* [9969]
USS Coral Sea Remembrance Scholarships *(Undergraduate/Scholarship)* [10358]
USTA Serves College Education Scholarships *(Undergraduate/Scholarship)* [9977]
USTA Serves College Textbook Scholarship *(Undergraduate/Scholarship)* [9978]
Utility Workers Union of America Scholarship Program *(Undergraduate/Scholarship)* [10360]
UW-Madison GLBT Alumni Council Scholarships *(Undergraduate, Graduate/Scholarship)* [10332]
Vale Manitoba Operations Scholarships *(Undergraduate/Scholarship, Internship)* [9995]
ValuePenguin Scholarships *(Undergraduate/Scholarship)* [10362]
The Vander Putten Family Scholarships *(Advanced Professional/Scholarship)* [3082]
Keith C. Vanderhyde Scholarships *(Undergraduate/Scholarship)* [4629]
Jacob R. and Mary M. VanLoo and Lenore K. VanLoo Scholarships *(Undergraduate/Scholarship)* [4630]
Kodali Veeraiah and Sarojini Scholarships *(Graduate/Scholarship)* [9673]
Helen Veress-Mitchell Scholarship Fund *(Undergraduate/Scholarship)* [2788]
Chester M. Vernon Memorial Eagle Scout Scholarships *(Undergraduate/Scholarship)* [6934]
Veterans of Foreign Wars Scout of the Year *(Undergraduate/Scholarship)* [6935]
William F. Vilas Scholarships *(Undergraduate/Scholarship)* [10335]
Visible Minorities Scholarship *(Undergraduate/Scholarship)* [7207]
Vista Health Solutions' Scholarships *(Undergraduate/Scholarship)* [10413]
Irma E. Voigt Memorial Scholarships *(Undergraduate/Scholarship)* [8943]
Chad Vollmer Scholarships *(Undergraduate/Scholarship)* [4631]
Dee Wacksman Scholarships *(Undergraduate/Scholarship)* [3024]
Robert & Barbara Wade Scholarships *(Undergraduate/Scholarship)* [6069]
WAEPA Scholarship Program *(Undergraduate/Scholarship)* [10711]
Covington-Cincinnati/Northern Kentucky Alumni Club - Dane Wagge Scholarships *(Undergraduate/Scholarship)* [10149]
Nell and Spencer Waggoner Scholarships *(Undergraduate/Scholarship)* [10602]
Laramie Walden Memorial Fund *(Undergraduate/Scholarship)* [4219]
Margaret E. Waldron Scholarship Fund *(Undergraduate/Scholarship)* [4061]
Walmart Associate Scholarships *(Undergraduate/Scholarship)* [10425]
Flis Walter and Anna Memorial Scholarship *(Undergraduate/Scholarship)* [8593]
Robert E. Walter Memorial Scholarship *(Under-*

graduate/Scholarship) [6168]
War Memorial Doctoral Scholarships *(Postgraduate/Scholarship)* [6856]
Judith Warner Memorial Scholarships *(Undergraduate/Scholarship)* [8369]
Washington College Bound Scholarships *(Undergraduate/Scholarship)* [10471]
Washington Higher Education Coordinating Board - State Need Grants (SNG) *(Undergraduate/Grant)* [10472]
Stand Watie Scholarships *(Undergraduate/Scholarship)* [9343]
Watson-Brown Scholarships *(Undergraduate/Scholarship)* [10489]
Thomas J. Watson Fellowships *(Undergraduate/Fellowship)* [10493]
Glenn Watson Scholarships *(Undergraduate/Scholarship)* [9394]
Wayne County Bank Scholarships *(Undergraduate/Scholarship)* [7552]
Lester and Eleanor Webster Foundation Scholarships *(Undergraduate/Scholarship)* [9542]
WEDA Scholarship Program *(Professional development/Scholarship)* [10529]
Frank L. Weil Memorial Eagle Scout Scholarships *(Undergraduate/Scholarship)* [6936]
Arthur and Lila Weinberg Fellowship for Independent Scholars and Researchers *(Other/Fellowship)* [7425]
The Bee Winkler Weinstein Scholarship Fund *(Undergraduate, Vocational/Occupational/Scholarship)* [9591]
Weissbuch Family Scholarships *(Undergraduate/Scholarship)* [8740]
Edward Kent Welch Memorial Scholarships *(Undergraduate/Scholarship)* [10604]
Wells Fargo Scholarships *(Undergraduate/Scholarship)* [8268]
Wells Fargo Veterans Scholarships Program *(Undergraduate/Scholarship)* [10512]
Donald M. Wells Scholarships *(Undergraduate/Scholarship)* [4632]
Peter R. Weitz Prize *(Other/Prize)* [4402]
Francis X. Weninger Scholarships *(Undergraduate/Scholarship)* [10726]
John R. and Joan F. Werren Scholarships Fund *(Undergraduate/Scholarship)* [9543]
West Virginia PTA Scholarships *(Undergraduate/Scholarship)* [10525]
Redlands Evening Lions Club - Barbara Westen Memorial Scholarships *(Undergraduate/Scholarship)* [8529]
Western Society of Weed Science Outstanding Student Scholarship Program *(Graduate, Undergraduate/Scholarship)* [10541]
Robert B. Westover Scholarships *(Undergraduate/Scholarship)* [4347]
Whidbey Island Giving Circle Scholarships *(Undergraduate/Scholarship)* [8269]
WHIMA Established Professional Scholarship *(Graduate/Scholarship)* [10623]
Law Office of David D. White Annual Traumatic Brain Injury Scholarships *(All/Scholarship)* [5947]
Wayne F. White and Bob Evans Legacy Scholarships *(Undergraduate, High School/Scholarship)* [4170]
White Collar Defense Diversity Scholarships *(Undergraduate, Advanced Professional/Scholarship)* [8239]
White House Fellows *(Other/Fellowship)* [8223]
Whitehorse Shotokan Karate Club Scholarships *(Undergraduate, Master's/Scholarship)* [10804]
Robert B. and Sophia Whiteside Scholarships *(Undergraduate/Scholarship)* [3726]
Ann Cook Whitman Scholarships for Perry High School *(Undergraduate/Scholarship)* [4416]
Ann Cook Whitman Washington, DC Scholarships *(Undergraduate/Scholarship)* [4417]
Why Get Your Blue On? Video Scholarships *(Graduate, Undergraduate/Award, Scholarship)* [10543]
Wi-Hi Class of '55 Scholarship *(Undergraduate/Scholarship)* [3189]
Alice Hersey Wick Scholarships *(Undergraduate/Scholarship)* [8944]
WIEA Scholarships *(Doctorate, Graduate, Undergraduate/Scholarship)* [10625]

Barbara Wiedner and Dorothy Vandercook Memorial Peace Scholarships *(Undergraduate/Scholarship)* [4639]
Elmo Wierenga Alumni Scholarships *(Undergraduate/Scholarship)* [4633]
WIGA Scholarships *(Postgraduate, Other, Undergraduate/Scholarship)* [10450]
Fred C. Wikoff, Jr. Scholarships *(Undergraduate, Vocational/Occupational/Scholarship)* [4220]
Teddy Wilburn Scholarships *(Undergraduate/Scholarship)* [3256]
Andrea Will Memorial Scholarships *(Undergraduate/Scholarship)* [8945]
M. William and Frances J. Tilghman Scholarships *(Undergraduate/Scholarship)* [3190]
Rodney Williams Legacy Scholarships *(Undergraduate/Scholarship)* [10150]
John G. Williams Scholarship Fund *(Undergraduate/Scholarship)* [10565]
CSM Virgil R. Williams Scholarships *(Undergraduate/Scholarship)* [3871]
Randy Williams Scholarships *(Undergraduate/Scholarship)* [8742]
RS Williamson and Eliford Mott Memorial Scholarships *(Undergraduate/Scholarship)* [10549]
Edwin H. and Louise N. Williamson Endowed Scholarships *(Undergraduate/Scholarship)* [10605]
Mary Katherine "Kathy" Williamson Scholarship Fund *(Undergraduate/Scholarship)* [3273]
Dr. Alice E. Wilson Awards *(Graduate, Doctorate/Award, Fellowship)* [2632]
Bob Wilson Legacy Scholarships *(Undergraduate/Scholarship)* [2460]
Walter C. Winchester Scholarships *(Undergraduate/Scholarship)* [4634]
John D. Wirth Travel Grants for International Scholars *(Graduate, Other/Grant)* [1318]
Wisconsin Lawton Minority Retention Grants *(Undergraduate/Grant)* [10336]
HCRTA/Glen O. and Wyllabeth Wise Scholarships *(Undergraduate/Scholarship)* [3025]
Woksape Oyate: "Wisdom of the People" Distinguished Scholars Awards *(Undergraduate/Scholarship)* [873]
Michael J. Wolf Scholarships *(Undergraduate/Scholarship)* [4635]
Deborah Partridge Wolfe International Fellowships *(Graduate, Undergraduate/Fellowship)* [10820]
Woman In Rural Electrification Scholarships *(Undergraduate/Scholarship)* [9383]
The Woman's Club of Nashville Scholarship Endowment Fund *(Undergraduate/Scholarship)* [3257]
Women in Coaching National Coaching Institute Scholarships *(Undergraduate/Scholarship)* [3069]
Women on Par Scholarships *(Undergraduate/Scholarship)* [3938]
Women's Army Corps Veterans Association Scholarships *(Undergraduate/Scholarship)* [10654]
Women's Club of Grand Haven Scholarships *(Undergraduate/Scholarship)* [4554]
Women's Overseas and Service League Scholarships for Women *(Undergraduate/Scholarship)* [10670]
Carolyn Wones Recruitment Scholarship Grants *(Undergraduate/Scholarship)* [3305]
Charles Fred Wonson Scholarships *(Undergraduate/Scholarship)* [10306]
Mary and Elliot Wood Foundation Undergraduate Scholarship Fund *(Undergraduate/Scholarship)* [4223]
Rolla F. Wood Graduate Scholarships *(Graduate/Scholarship)* [8083]
Hugh and Helen Wood Nepales Scholarships *(Undergraduate/Scholarship)* [2233]
Woodex Bearing Company Scholarships *(Undergraduate/Scholarship)* [4373]
Woodrow Wilson International Center for Scholars Fellowships *(Doctorate/Fellowship)* [10567]
Betsy B. Woodward Scholarships *(Undergraduate/Scholarship)* [1966]
Woodyard Family Scholarships *(Undergraduate/Scholarship)* [4568]
L and T Woolfolk Memorial Scholarships *(Undergraduate/Scholarship)* [3026]
Donald Worster Travel Grants *(Graduate, Other/Grant)* [1319]

Wozumi Family Scholarships *(Undergraduate/Scholarship)* [8270]
WSAJ American Justice Essay Scholarships *(Undergraduate/Scholarship)* [10459]
WSAJ Presidents' Scholarships *(Undergraduate/Scholarship)* [10461]
WSSA Student Paper Competition *(Undergraduate, Graduate/Award)* [10535]
WYCUP Scholarships *(Other/Scholarship)* [10700]
Margaret Wyeth Scholarships *(Undergraduate/Scholarship)* [3306]
Xavier Community-Engaged Fellowships *(Undergraduate/Fellowship)* [10727]
Xavier University Chancellor Scholarships *(Undergraduate/Scholarship)* [10728]
Xavier University Legacy Scholarships *(Undergraduate/Scholarship)* [10731]
Xavier University Presidential Scholarships *(Undergraduate/Scholarship)* [10732]
Pang Xiaoyan Scholarships *(Undergraduate/Scholarship)* [2926]
William J. Yankee Memorial Scholarships *(Undergraduate/Scholarship)* [1125]
The YFU Americas Scholarships *(Undergraduate/Scholarship)* [10770]
York Graduate Scholarships *(Graduate/Scholarship)* [10756]
York Regional Police Scholarships *(Undergraduate/Scholarship)* [5530]
Jack and Edna May Yost Scholarships *(Undergraduate/Scholarship)* [4258]
You Go Girl! Scholarships *(Undergraduate/Scholarship)* [8271]
Young Christian Leaders Scholarships *(Undergraduate/Scholarship)* [10760]
Alma H. Young Emerging Scholar Awards *(Doctorate/Award, Monetary)* [10344]
Jeff Young Memorial Scholarships *(Undergraduate, Master's/Scholarship)* [10805]
Young People For Fellowships *(Professional development/Fellowship)* [10764]
Donnell B. Young Scholarships *(Undergraduate/Scholarship)* [308]
Elmer Cooke Young - Taylor Young Scholarships *(Undergraduate/Scholarship)* [4774]
Your Skin Is In College Ambassador Scholarships *(Undergraduate/Scholarship)* [6407]
Youth Affairs Committee Rising Star Scholarships *(Undergraduate/Scholarship)* [5531]
Youth Empowerment Summit Scholarships *(Undergraduate/Scholarship)* [6817]
Youth Leadership Scholarships *(Undergraduate/Scholarship)* [2469]
Youth Partners Accessing Capital (PAC) *(Undergraduate/Scholarship)* [354]
The Yukon Foundation Medical Laboratory Scholarships *(Undergraduate, Master's/Award)* [10806]
YWA Foundation Scholarships *(Graduate, Undergraduate/Scholarship)* [10766]
Zagunis Student Leader Scholarships *(Graduate, Undergraduate/Scholarship)* [6734]
Louis B. Zapoleon Memorial Scholarships *(Undergraduate/Scholarship)* [3027]
The Zebra Safe Driver Scholarships *(Undergraduate, Graduate/Scholarship)* [10810]
Zenko Family Scholarship Fund *(Undergraduate/Scholarship)* [4555]
Zeta Chapter Memorial Scholarship Awards *(Undergraduate/Scholarship)* [3307]
Zeta Phi Beta Sorority General Graduate Scholarships *(Graduate/Scholarship)* [10821]
Zeta Phi Beta Sorority General Undergraduate Scholarships *(Undergraduate/Scholarship)* [10822]
Zimmermann Scholarships *(Graduate/Scholarship)* [9621]
Jacob Ziskind Memorial Fund for Upperclassmen *(Graduate, Undergraduate/Scholarship)* [5104]
Morris L. and Rebecca Ziskind Memorial Scholarships *(Undergraduate/Scholarship)* [5029]
Ruth and Sherman Zudekoff Scholarships *(Undergraduate/Scholarship)* [3202]

Genetics
BSF Science and Medicine Research Grants *(Professional development/Grant)* [2199]
Jane Engelberg Memorial Fellowship *(Professional development/Fellowship)* [7156]
Epilepsy Foundation Pre-doctoral Research Training Fellowships *(Graduate/Fellowship)* [3906]
NYU Langone Medical Center Science Student Scholarships *(Undergraduate, Graduate/Scholarship)* [109]
Welder Wildlife Foundation Fellowships *(Graduate, Master's, Doctorate/Fellowship)* [10510]

Geography (See also Cartography/Surveying)
AAG Dissertation Research Grants *(Doctorate/Grant)* [1829]
Robin P. Armstrong Memorial Prize for Excellence in Native Studies Awards *(Graduate/Award)* [1880]
Canadian Association of Geographers Historical Geography Study Group Awards *(Master's, Graduate, Undergraduate/Award)* [1882]
Cave Conservancy Foundation Graduate and Undergraduate Fellowships *(Doctorate, Graduate, Undergraduate/Fellowship)* [2823]
CTRF Scholarships for Graduate Study in Transportation *(Graduate/Scholarship)* [2764]
Everglades Foundation Fellowship *(Graduate, Doctorate, Master's/Fellowship)* [3931]
Everglades Foundation Internship *(Postgraduate, Postdoctorate/Internship)* [3932]
Everglades Foundation Scholarships *(Graduate, Master's, Doctorate/Scholarship)* [3933]
Excellence in Geographic Information Systems Scholarships *(Undergraduate/Scholarship)* [10017]
Darrel Hess Community College Geography Scholarships *(Undergraduate/Scholarship)* [1830]
Eric Niemitalo Scholarships in Earth and Environmental Science *(Undergraduate/Scholarship)* [8879]
Pi Gamma Mu Scholarships *(Graduate/Scholarship)* [8133]

Geology
American Association of Stratigraphic Palynologists Student Scholarships *(Graduate/Scholarship)* [16]
Association of Desk and Derrick Clubs Education Trust Scholarships *(Undergraduate/Scholarship)* [1931]
Geoffrey Bradshaw Memorial Scholarships *(Graduate/Scholarship)* [10780]
Cameco Corporation Scholarships in the Geological Sciences - Continuing Students *(Undergraduate/Scholarship)* [2524]
Cameco Corporation Scholarships in the Geological Sciences - Entering Students *(Undergraduate/Scholarship)* [2525]
Cave Conservancy Foundation Graduate and Undergraduate Fellowships *(Doctorate, Graduate, Undergraduate/Fellowship)* [2823]
Farouk El-Baz Student Research Grants *(Graduate, Undergraduate/Grant)* [4363]
Geological Society of America Graduate Student Research Grants *(Doctorate, Graduate/Grant)* [4364]
A. Allen Graffham Research Grants *(Advanced Professional, Professional development/Grant)* [1842]
HSF/Marathon Oil College Scholarship Program *(Undergraduate/Scholarship)* [4905]
Harry Johannes Scholarships *(Undergraduate, Graduate/Scholarship)* [10790]
Eric Niemitalo Scholarships in Earth and Environmental Science *(Undergraduate/Scholarship)* [8879]
NPSC Fellowships *(Graduate/Fellowship)* [7098]
Paleontological Society Student Research Grants *(Graduate, Undergraduate/Grant)* [17]
Dan Rigel Memorial Educational Grants *(Professional development, Advanced Professional/Grant)* [1843]
René M. Vandervelde Research Grants *(Undergraduate, Professional development/Grant)* [1845]
Wayne-Meador-Elliott Scholarships *(Undergraduate/Scholarship)* [7869]

Geophysics (See also Physics)
Association of Desk and Derrick Clubs Education Trust Scholarships *(Undergraduate/Scholarship)* [1931]
CfA Postdoctoral Fellowships *(Postdoctorate/Fellowship)* [4780]
Clay Postdoctoral Fellowships *(Postdoctorate/Fellowship)* [4781]
CSEG Scholarship Trust Fund *(Graduate, Undergraduate/Scholarship)* [2748]
HSF/Marathon Oil College Scholarship Program *(Undergraduate/Scholarship)* [4905]
SAO (Smithsonian Astrophysical Observatory) Predoctoral Fellowships *(Graduate/Fellowship)* [4782]

Geosciences
AWG Minority Scholarships *(Undergraduate/Scholarship)* [2093]
Chrysalis Scholarships *(Graduate/Scholarship)* [2094]
AWG Maria Luisa Crawford Field Camp Scholarships *(Undergraduate/Scholarship)* [2095]
EAPSI Fellowships *(Doctorate, Graduate/Fellowship)* [7124]
Global Volcanism Program for Visiting Scientist/Postdoctoral Fellowships *(Postdoctorate/Fellowship)* [9032]
HGS Foundation Undergraduate Scholarships *(Undergraduate/Scholarship)* [4967]
NDSEG Fellowships *(Graduate/Fellowship)* [6911]
Glen Ruby Memorial Scholarships *(Undergraduate/Scholarship)* [2754]
Shell Incentive Scholarship Fund *(Undergraduate/Scholarship)* [8861]
Shell Oil Company Technical Scholarships *(Undergraduate/Scholarship)* [8862]
Shell Process Technology Scholarships *(Undergraduate/Scholarship)* [8863]
Society of Exploration Geophysicists Foundation Scholarships *(Graduate, Undergraduate/Scholarship)* [9117]
Janet Cullen Tanaka Scholarships *(Undergraduate/Scholarship)* [2096]
United States Geospatial Intelligence Foundation Graduate Scholarships *(Graduate/Scholarship)* [9945]
United States Geospatial Intelligence Foundation High School Scholarships *(Undergraduate/Scholarship)* [9946]
United States Geospatial Intelligence Foundation Undergraduate Scholarships *(Undergraduate/Scholarship)* [9947]

Geriatric medicine (See Medicine, Geriatric)

German studies (See also Area and ethnic studies)
Leo Baeck Institute - DAAD Fellowships *(Doctorate/Fellowship)* [3602]
DAAD Learn German in Germany Grants *(Doctorate/Grant)* [3603]
German Historical Institute Doctoral and Postdoctoral Fellowships *(Doctorate, Postgraduate/Fellowship)* [4395]
German Society Scholarships *(Undergraduate/Scholarship)* [4404]
German Studies Research Grants *(Graduate/Grant, Award)* [3607]
Dr. Guido Goldman Fellowships *(Doctorate, Postdoctorate/Fellowship)* [724]
Hochschulsommerkurse *(Undergraduate/Grant, Award)* [3608]
Dr. Richard M. Hunt Fellowships *(Doctorate, Postdoctorate/Fellowship)* [725]
Intensive Language Course Grants *(Doctorate/Grant)* [3609]
NEH Fellowships for Senior Scholars *(Doctorate/Fellowship)* [2853]
Prins Foundation Fellowship for Senior Scholars *(Doctorate/Fellowship)* [2854]
Prins Foundation Post-Doctoral and Early Career Fellowship for Emigrating Scholars *(Professional development, Postdoctorate/Fellowship)* [2855]

Gerontology
Alberta Association of Gerontology Student Awards - Edmonton Chapter *(Graduate, Undergraduate/Award)* [226]
Alberta Association of Gerontology Student Awards *(Graduate/Award)* [225]
Ann C. Beckingham Scholarships *(Graduate, Other/Scholarship)* [2645]
CAG Margery Boyce Bursary Awards *(Undergraduate/Award, Scholarship)* [2553]
Brookdale Leadership in Aging Fellowships *(Other/Fellowship)* [2380]
CFN Interdisciplinary Fellowships Program *(Graduate, Postdoctorate, Advanced Professional/Fellowship)* [2638]
CGNA Memorial Scholarship *(Graduate, Other/Scholarship)* [2646]
Extendicare Scholarships in Gerontology *(Master's/Scholarship)* [2699]
Glenn/AFAR Scholarships for Research in the Biology of Aging *(Graduate, Doctorate/Scholarship)* [788]
HPGS/ALOH Graduate Scholarships *(Graduate/Scholarship)* [4801]
HPGS Undergraduate Scholarships *(Undergraduate/Scholarship)* [4802]
Annie Kirshenblatt Memorial Scholarships *(Graduate, Undergraduate/Scholarship)* [9751]
CAG Donald Menzies Bursary Awards *(Postgraduate/Scholarship, Award)* [2554]
Partners HealthCare Geriatric Psychiatry Fellowships *(Professional development/Fellowship)* [6324]
Shoshana Philipp (Kirshenblatt) R.N. Memorial Scholarships *(Graduate, Undergraduate/Scholarship)* [9752]
Schlegel-UW RIA Scholarships *(Doctorate/Scholarship)* [2555]
Sigma Kappa Foundation Alzheimer's/Gerontology Scholarships *(Graduate/Scholarship)* [8936]
Sigma Kappa Foundation Gerontology Scholarships *(Undergraduate/Scholarship)* [8938]
Virginia M. Smyth Scholarships *(Graduate/Scholarship)* [4382]
Student Research Awards from the Behavioral Gerontology SIG *(Undergraduate, Graduate/Award, Monetary)* [1861]

Government (See also Political science)
ARS of Eastern USA Lazarian Graduate Scholarship *(Master's, Doctorate/Scholarship)* [1680]
ASA/NSF/BLS Fellowships *(Graduate/Fellowship)* [1463]
George Oliver Benton Memorial Scholarships *(Undergraduate/Scholarship)* [3213]
Congressional Research Awards *(Graduate/Award)* [3626]
Fellowship on Women & Public Policy *(Graduate/Fellowship)* [10102]
Enid Hall Griswold Memorial Scholarships *(Undergraduate/Scholarship)* [7152]
Bryce Harlow Fellowship Program *(Graduate/Fellowship)* [4721]
Conrad N. Hilton Scholarships *(Undergraduate/Scholarship)* [4414]
IAF Fellowships *(Doctorate/Fellowship)* [5232]
Ray and Kathy LaHood Scholarships for the Study of American Government *(Undergraduate/Scholarship)* [3627]
John Allen Love Scholarships *(Graduate, Undergraduate/Scholarship)* [10304]
Gary Merrill Memorial Scholarships *(Undergraduate/Scholarship)* [6206]

GRAPHIC ART AND DESIGN

Minnesota Association of Township Scholarships *(Undergraduate, Vocational/Occupational/Scholarship)* [6545]
Police Explorer Scholarships Program *(Undergraduate/Scholarship)* [4106]
Betty Rendel Scholarships *(Undergraduate/Scholarship)* [6955]
USGLC Internships - Government Relations *(Undergraduate, Graduate/Internship)* [9950]
USGLC Internships - Policy *(Undergraduate, Graduate/Internship)* [9952]
Paul A. Volcker Endowment for Public Service Research and Education *(Doctorate/Grant)* [1116]
Women In Defense HORIZONS Scholarships *(Graduate, Undergraduate/Scholarship)* [10636]
Mary and Elliot Wood Foundation Graduate Scholarship Fund *(Graduate/Scholarship)* [4222]

Graphic art and design (See also Art)

APC High School Scholarship Awards *(Undergraduate/Scholarship)* [78]
Paul Arnold Memorial Scholarships *(Undergraduate/Scholarship)* [8241]
Cadmus Communications Corporation Graphics Scholarship Endowment Fund *(Undergraduate/Scholarship)* [4181]
ESA Foundation Scholarship Program *(Undergraduate/Scholarship)* [3878]
The Gallery Collection's Create-A-Greeting Card Scholarships *(Undergraduate/Scholarship)* [4318]
GEF Scholarship Program *(Undergraduate, Graduate/Scholarship)* [4647]
Elizabeth Greenhalgh Memorial Scholarships in Journalism, Graphic Arts, or Photography *(Undergraduate/Scholarship)* [10639]
International Foodservice Editorial Council Scholarships *(Graduate, Undergraduate/Scholarship)* [5331]
Maine Graphic Arts Association Scholarships *(Undergraduate/Scholarship)* [6215]
MHS Andrew Oliver Research Fellowships *(Professional development/Fellowship)* [6336]
PGSF Scholarships *(Undergraduate/Scholarship)* [8284]
Print and Graphics Scholarship Foundation Awards (PGSF-GATF) *(Graduate, Undergraduate/Scholarship, Fellowship)* [8282]
Harry V. Quadracci Memorial Scholarships *(Undergraduate, Graduate/Scholarship)* [4649]
Society of Graphic Designers of Canada Adobe Scholarships *(Undergraduate/Scholarship)* [9063]
Society of Graphic Designers of Canada Applied Arts Scholarships *(Undergraduate/Scholarship)* [9064]
Society of Graphic Designers of Canada Veer Scholarships *(Undergraduate/Scholarship)* [9065]
Tag and Label Manufacturers Institute Scholarships - Four-Year Colleges *(Undergraduate/Scholarship)* [9629]
Vectorworks Design Scholarships *(Undergraduate, Graduate/Scholarship, Prize)* [10367]
Worldstudio AIGA Scholarships *(Graduate, Undergraduate/Scholarship)* [10709]

Greek studies (See also Area and ethnic studies)

Christopher Demetris Memorial Scholarships *(Undergraduate/Scholarship)* [4845]
Dr. Michael Dorizas Memorial Scholarships *(Undergraduate/Scholarship)* [4846]
Hellenic University Club of Philadelphia Founders Scholarships *(Undergraduate/Scholarship)* [4847]
Mary Isabel Sibley Fellowships *(Doctorate/Fellowship)* [8053]

Handicapped

American Speech Language Hearing Foundation General Scholarships *(Graduate, Master's, Doctorate/Scholarship)* [1452]
ASHFoundation Student Research Grants in Audiology *(Doctorate/Grant)* [1460]

Health care services

ACMPE Scholarship Fund Program *(Graduate, Undergraduate/Scholarship)* [6384]
Adelson Scholarships *(Undergraduate/Scholarship)* [8329]
AHCJ Reporting Fellowships on Health Care Performance *(Other/Fellowship)* [3158]
American Cancer Society - Postdoctoral Fellowships *(Doctorate/Fellowship)* [644]
AMSUS Physician Awards *(Advanced Professional/Recognition)* [1540]
APS/Maricopa County Community Colleges Scholarships *(Undergraduate/Scholarship)* [8140]
APSA/Health and Aging Policy Fellowships *(Graduate, Advanced Professional, Professional development/Fellowship)* [1112]
Australian-American Health Policy Fellowships *(Doctorate, Graduate/Fellowship)* [3159]
Leslie Baranowski Scholarships for Professional Excellence *(Professional development/Scholarship)* [5144]
Ellis J. Bonner Scholarships *(Graduate/Scholarship)* [6754]
Maria Gonzales Borrero Scholarships *(Undergraduate/Scholarship)* [4740]
Corris Boyd Scholarships *(Master's/Scholarship)* [2085]
Dvora Brodie Scholarships *(Graduate, Postgraduate, Undergraduate/Scholarship)* [4829]
Rhea Sourifman Caplin Memorial Scholarships *(Undergraduate/Scholarship)* [4742]
Cardiac Health Foundation of Canada Scholarships *(Graduate/Scholarship)* [2790]
Leigh Carter Scholarships *(Undergraduate/Scholarship)* [3217]
Casey Family Services Alumni Scholarships *(Graduate, Undergraduate, Vocational/Occupational/Scholarship)* [4157]
CentraState Associated Auxiliaries Scholarships *(Undergraduate/Scholarship)* [2875]
CentraState Healthcare Foundation Health Professions Scholarships *(Undergraduate/Scholarship)* [2877]
CHCI Graduate Fellowships *(Graduate/Fellowship)* [3352]
CHOIR MD Post-Residency Fellowship in Health Services Research *(Postdoctorate/Fellowship)* [10376]
Albert W. Dent Graduate Student Scholarships *(Undergraduate/Scholarship)* [687]
Diabetes Scholars Foundation College Scholarships *(Undergraduate/Scholarship)* [3616]
Duluth Building and Construction Trades Council Scholarships *(Undergraduate/Scholarship)* [3707]
Eagles Fly for Leukemia Scholarships *(Undergraduate/Scholarship)* [2906]
Foundation for Seacoast Health Scholarships *(Undergraduate, Graduate/Scholarship)* [4283]
Gardner Foundation Infusion Nurses Society Education Scholarships *(Professional development/Scholarship)* [5145]
Florence S. Gaynor Scholarships *(Graduate/Scholarship)* [6755]
John Glaser Scholarships *(Undergraduate/Scholarship)* [3121]
Harkness Fellowships in Health Care Policy and Practice *(Doctorate, Graduate/Fellowship)* [3160]
Health Services Research Dissertation Awards *(Doctorate/Award)* [9914]
Healthcare Information Management Systems Scholarships *(Graduate, Postgraduate, Undergraduate/Scholarship)* [4831]
HFMA Connecticut Chapter Scholarships *(Undergraduate, Graduate/Scholarship)* [4827]
Lillie Hope-McGarvey Health Scholarship Awards *(Undergraduate, Vocational/Occupational, Graduate, Master's/Scholarship)* [311]
HRET Health Career Scholarships *(Postgraduate, Undergraduate/Scholarship)* [7319]
Michael A. Hunter Memorial Scholarships *(Undergraduate/Scholarship)* [2907]
Gaynold Jensen Education Stipends *(Postdoctorate, Other/Scholarship)* [3622]
Oliver Joel and Ellen Pell Denny Healthcare Scholarship Fund *(Undergraduate/Scholarship)* [10585]
Robert Wood Johnson Foundation Health Policy Fellows Program *(Advanced Professional, Professional development/Fellowship)* [8629]
Kaiser Permanente Northern California Delivery Science Fellowships Program *(Postgraduate/Fellowship)* [5650]
Dr. Terry Kavanagh Fellowships *(Graduate/Fellowship)* [2791]
Kendrick Foundation, Inc. Scholarships *(Undergraduate/Scholarship)* [5813]
David A. Kronick Travelling Fellowships *(Doctorate, Graduate/Fellowship)* [6387]
Donald A.B. Lindberg Research Fellowships *(Doctorate, Graduate/Fellowship)* [6388]
Ann & Robert H. Lurie Children's Memorial Hospital Postgraduate Administrative Fellowships *(Postgraduate/Fellowship)* [6143]
Robert Mack Scholarships *(Graduate, Undergraduate/Scholarship)* [6166]
Foster G. McGaw Graduate Student Scholarships *(Graduate/Scholarship)* [688]
Mentored Clinical Scientist Development Awards *(Doctorate/Award)* [9915]
NOHIMSS Student Scholarship Program *(Undergraduate, Master's, Doctorate/Scholarship)* [7523]
North Carolina Association of Health Care Recruiters Scholarships *(Undergraduate/Scholarship)* [7454]
Northern California Chapter of HIMSS Scholarships *(Graduate, Postgraduate, Undergraduate/Scholarship)* [4832]
NTHS/HOSA Scholarships *(Undergraduate/Scholarship)* [7197]
NYCT Paid Graduate Student Philanthropy Fellowships - Health and People with Special Needs *(Graduate/Fellowship)* [7352]
Outlaw Student's Medical Professions Scholarships *(Undergraduate/Scholarship)* [9595]
Portuguese American Police Association Scholarships *(Undergraduate/Scholarship)* [8211]
Reid Hospital Graduate Student Scholarships *(Graduate/Scholarship)* [10507]
Haynes Rice Scholarships *(Graduate/Scholarship)* [6756]
SALEF Health Career Scholarships *(Undergraduate, Graduate/Scholarship)* [8680]
Lewis L. Seaman Junior Enlisted Awards for Outstanding Operational Support *(Professional development/Recognition)* [1541]
Service League Volunteer Scholarships *(Undergraduate/Scholarship)* [10447]
Pat Shimp Memorial Scholarships *(Undergraduate/Scholarship)* [7863]
The Eileen J. Smith, R.N. Memorial Scholarships *(Undergraduate/Scholarship)* [5512]
Society for the Arts in Healthcare Student Scholarships *(Doctorate, Graduate, Undergraduate/Scholarship)* [9088]
Louis Stokes Health Scholars Program *(Undergraduate/Scholarship)* [3349]
Paul Tejada Memorial Scholarships *(Undergraduate/Scholarship)* [5514]
Vincent Trotter Health Care Scholarships *(Undergraduate/Scholarship)* [8735]
Villers Fellowships for Health Care Justice *(Graduate/Fellowship)* [3958]
Leon Williams Scholarships *(Undergraduate/Scholarship)* [8741]
David A. Winston Health Policy Scholarship *(Graduate/Scholarship)* [2087]
Violet Wondergem Health Science Scholarships *(Undergraduate/Scholarship)* [4636]

Health education

AAHD Scholarships *(Graduate, Undergraduate/Scholarship)* [502]
Ruth Abernathy Presidential Scholarships *(Graduate, Undergraduate/Scholarship)* [9128]
ACS/ASA Health Policy and Management Scholarships *(Professional development/Scholarship)* [1468]
Dr. Andy Anderson Young Professional Awards *(Professional development/Award)* [8117]
APSA/Health and Aging Policy Fellowships *(Graduate, Advanced Professional, Professional development/Fellowship)* [1112]

Jane B. Aron Doctoral Fellowships *(Doctorate/Fellowship)* [6787]
Association of American Indian Physicians Scholarships *(Graduate, Undergraduate/Scholarship)* [1838]
Astra Zeneca Medical Scholarships *(Advanced Professional/Scholarship)* [7275]
Max Bell Senior Fellow Grants *(Advanced Professional/Grant)* [2219]
BMO Harris Scholarships *(Advanced Professional/Scholarship)* [7277]
Cathy L. Brock Memorial Scholarships *(Graduate/Scholarship)* [5167]
CIBC Medical Education Scholarships *(Advanced Professional/Scholarship)* [7278]
Evelyn L. Cockrell Memorial Scholarship Award *(Undergraduate/Scholarship)* [9701]
Emergency Medicine Physician Scholarships for Health Information Management Program *(Undergraduate/Scholarship)* [9500]
NSPF Ray B. Essick Scholarship Awards *(Other/Scholarship)* [7192]
Dr. Isaac Keillor Farrer, Advanced Medical Education Scholarships *(Advanced Professional/Scholarship)* [7279]
Foundation for Seacoast Health Scholarships *(Undergraduate, Graduate/Scholarship)* [4283]
Friends of the Christofor Foundation Scholarships *(Advanced Professional/Scholarship)* [7280]
Horizon Health Network Scholarships *(Advanced Professional/Scholarship)* [7281]
Steven Huesing Scholarships *(Graduate, Undergraduate/Scholarship)* [3067]
Berton W. Huestis Memorial Scholarships *(Advanced Professional/Scholarship)* [7282]
JCC Association Graduate Education Scholarships *(Graduate/Scholarship)* [5562]
Kaiser Media Fellowships in Health Reporting *(Advanced Professional, Professional development/Fellowship)* [5648]
KHIMA Graduate Scholarships *(Graduate/Scholarship)* [5661]
David B. Larson Fellowships in Health and Spirituality *(Doctorate/Fellowship)* [5847]
Sue A. Malone Scholarships *(Doctorate, Graduate, Professional development/Scholarship)* [5662]
Randall Matthis for Environmental Studies Scholarships *(Graduate, Undergraduate/Scholarship)* [1649]
Robert R. McCain Memorial Scholarships *(Advanced Professional/Scholarship)* [7283]
R. Tait Mckenzie Awards *(Professional development/Award)* [8118]
G. William McQuade Memorial Scholarships *(Advanced Professional/Scholarship)* [7284]
Migrant Health Scholarships *(Other/Scholarship)* [6846]
Minnesota Health Information Management Association Scholarships *(Undergraduate/Scholarship)* [6547]
National Swimming Pool Foundation Scholarship Awards *(Other/Scholarship)* [7193]
NB College of Physicians and Surgeons Medical Education Scholarships *(Advanced Professional/Scholarship)* [7285]
North American Society Fellowships *(Professional development/Fellowship)* [8119]
PHE Canada Student Awards *(Undergraduate/Award)* [8121]
Terry Linda Potter Scholarship Fund *(Undergraduate/Scholarship)* [4537]
RBC Medical Education Scholarships *(Advanced Professional/Scholarship)* [7286]
Regional Development Corporation Scholarships *(Advanced Professional/Scholarship)* [7287]
Resident Research Grants *(Postgraduate, Professional development/Grant)* [8126]
Elliott C. Roberts Scholarships *(Graduate/Scholarship)* [5168]
SALEF Health Career Scholarships *(Undergraduate, Graduate/Scholarship)* [8680]
Karen Schuvie Scholarships *(Undergraduate/Scholarship, Loan)* [5663]
Scotiabank Medical Education Scholarships *(Advanced Professional/Scholarship)* [7288]
Dr. Paul and Gayle Sohi Medical Education Scholarships *(Advanced Professional/Scholarship)* [7289]
SOPHE/ATSDR Student Fellowships in Environmental Health or Emergency Preparedness *(Doctorate, Graduate, Master's/Fellowship)* [9292]
SOPHE/CDC Student Fellowships in Child, Adolescent and School Health *(Doctorate, Graduate, Master's/Fellowship)* [9293]
SOPHE/CDC Student Fellowships in Injury Prevention *(Graduate/Fellowship)* [9294]
Louis Stokes Health Scholars Program *(Undergraduate/Scholarship)* [3349]
TD Bank Medical Education Scholarships *(Advanced Professional/Scholarship)* [7290]
Dr. Henrik and Wanda Tonning Memorial Scholarships *(Advanced Professional/Scholarship)* [7291]
Transamerica Retirement Solutions Leaders in Health Care Scholarships *(Graduate/Scholarship)* [5169]
TxHIMA HIA-HIT Scholarship *(Undergraduate/Scholarship)* [9703]
TxHIMA Outstanding Student Scholarship *(Undergraduate/Scholarship)* [9704]
Dr. Frank and Audrey Wanamaker Medical Scholarships *(Advanced Professional/Scholarship)* [7292]

Health sciences

AASLD Advanced/Transplant Hepatology Fellowships *(Professional development/Fellowship)* [581]
AASLD Autoimmune Liver Diseases Pilot Research Awards *(Graduate, Doctorate, Postdoctorate, Professional development/Award, Grant)* [582]
AASLD Career Development Awards in Liver Transplantation *(Professional development/Grant)* [583]
AASLD Clinical and Translational Research Awards *(Professional development/Grant)* [584]
AASLD NP/PA Clinical Hepatology Fellowships *(Professional development/Fellowship)* [585]
AASLD Pinnacle Research Awards in Liver Disease *(Professional development/Grant)* [586]
AATS Cardiothoracic Surgery Resident Poster Competition *(Professional development/Award)* [593]
AATS Perioperative/Team-Based Care Poster Competition *(Professional development/Award)* [595]
AATS Resident Critical Care Scholarships *(Professional development/Scholarship)* [596]
AATS/STS Cardiothoracic Ethics Forum Scholarships *(Professional development/Scholarship)* [597]
Dr. Anderson Abbott Awards *(Undergraduate/Scholarship)* [10278]
Afdhal/McHutchison LIFER Awards *(Postdoctorate, Professional development/Grant)* [587]
AIHS Graduate Studentships *(Master's, Doctorate, Professional development/Fellowship)* [251]
AIHS Postgraduate Fellowships *(Postgraduate, Advanced Professional/Fellowship)* [253]
ALA Allergic Respiratory Diseases Research Award *(Doctorate/Grant)* [969]
Alberta Innovates Graduate Student Scholarships *(Graduate/Scholarship)* [256]
Allied Health Care Professional Scholarships *(Undergraduate/Scholarship)* [5070]
American Lung Association Biomedical Research Grants *(Doctorate/Grant)* [970]
American Lung Association Clinical Patient Care Research Grants *(Doctorate/Grant)* [971]
American Lung Association Dalsemer Research Grants *(Doctorate/Grant)* [972]
American Lung Association DeSousa Awards *(Doctorate/Grant)* [973]
American Lung Association Lung Cancer Discovery Awards *(Doctorate/Grant)* [974]
American Lung Association Senior Research Training Fellowships *(Doctorate/Fellowship)* [975]
American Lung Association Social-Behavioral Research Grants *(Doctorate/Grant)* [976]
American Society of Electroneurodiagnostic Technologists Student Education Grants (ASET) *(Undergraduate/Grant)* [1300]
ATS Abstract Scholarships *(Undergraduate, Graduate, Doctorate/Scholarship)* [1473]
Bill Bendiner and Doug Morgenson Scholarships *(Undergraduate/Scholarship)* [8246]
Board of Young Adult Advisors Scholarships *(Graduate/Scholarship)* [9827]
Richard J. Burk, Jr. Fellowships *(Graduate/Fellowship)* [4808]
Joseph R. Calder, Jr., MD Scholarship Fund *(Undergraduate/Scholarship)* [4041]
Canadian Cancer Society Travel Awards *(Doctorate, Master's, Postdoctorate/Award)* [2605]
CareFusion Fellowships for Neonatal and Pediatric Therapists *(Professional development/Fellowship)* [1209]
CentraState Band Aid Open Committee Scholarships *(Undergraduate/Scholarship)* [2876]
Gordon W. and Agnes P. Cobb Scholarships *(Undergraduate/Scholarship)* [3754]
Davis Foundation Postdoctoral Fellowships *(Doctorate, Master's/Fellowship)* [4814]
DCH Freehold Toyota Scholarships *(Undergraduate/Scholarship)* [2878]
Matthew Debono Memorial Scholarship Funds *(Undergraduate, Graduate/Scholarship)* [1588]
Josephine P. White Eagle Scholarships *(Undergraduate, Graduate/Scholarship)* [4911]
James Echols Scholarship Award *(Undergraduate/Scholarship)* [2434]
Jeri Eiserman, RRT Professional Education Research Fellowships *(Professional development/Fellowship)* [1210]
Epilepsy Foundation Health Sciences Student Fellowships *(Doctorate, Graduate/Fellowship)* [3904]
Fanconi Anemia Research Grants *(Postdoctorate/Grant)* [3964]
Sue Fleming Memorial Scholarships *(Undergraduate/Scholarship)* [2440]
Florida Education Fund McKnight Doctoral Fellowships *(Graduate/Fellowship)* [4085]
AIHS Cy Frank Fellowships: Impact Assessment *(Doctorate, Professional development/Fellowship)* [254]
Robert Gardner Memorial Fellowships *(Graduate/Fellowship)* [4809]
HLS/MLA Professional Development Grants *(Other/Grant)* [6386]
Houston/Nancy Holliman Scholarships *(Undergraduate/Scholarship)* [3586]
HRET Health Career Scholarships *(Postgraduate, Undergraduate/Scholarship)* [7319]
HRSA Scholarships for Disadvantaged Students *(Undergraduate/Scholarship)* [9923]
Indian Health Service Professionals Program *(Undergraduate/Scholarship)* [875]
International Trainee Scholarships (ITS) *(Doctorate/Scholarship)* [1474]
John F. Kennedy Scholarship Award *(Undergraduate/Scholarship)* [2435]
Robert Wood Johnson Foundation Health Policy Fellows Program *(Advanced Professional, Professional development/Fellowship)* [8629]
KFOC Allied Health Doctoral Fellowship *(Doctorate/Fellowship)* [5825]
KFOC Allied Health Scholarships *(Graduate/Scholarship)* [5826]
Charles A. King Trust Postdoctoral Research Fellowships *(Postdoctorate/Fellowship)* [4817]
Robert S. Landauer, Sr. Memorial Fellowships *(Graduate/Fellowship)* [4810]
S. Evelyn Lewis Memorial Scholarships in Medical Health Sciences *(Graduate, Undergraduate/Scholarship)* [10818]
Lung Health Dissertation Grants *(Graduate/Grant)* [977]
Sue A. Malone Scholarships *(Doctorate, Graduate, Professional development/Scholarship)* [5662]
Olivia M. Marquart Scholarships *(Graduate, Master's, Doctorate/Scholarship)* [9828]
Medical Library Association Scholarships for Minority Students *(Graduate/Scholarship)* [6389]
George Hi'ilani Mills Perpetual Fellowships *(Graduate/Fellowship)* [7915]
MLA/NLM Spectrum Scholarship Program *(Undergraduate/Scholarship)* [6391]
MLA Research, Development, and Demonstration Project Grants *(Graduate/Grant)* [6392]
Monaghan/Trudell Fellowships for Aerosol Technique Development *(Professional development/Fellowship)* [1212]

HEALTH SERVICES ADMINISTRATION

Burton J. Moyer Memorial Fellowships *(Graduate/Fellowship)* [4811]
National Biosafety and Biocontainment Training Program Fellowships *(Graduate, Postgraduate/Fellowship)* [6811]
NBHRF Bridge Grants *(Professional development/Grant)* [7268]
NBHRF Establishment Grants *(Professional development/Grant)* [7270]
NBHRF Health Research Strategic Initiative Grants *(Professional development/Grant)* [7271]
NEDA Eating Recovery Center Foundation Early Career Investigator Grants *(Professional development/Grant)* [6938]
NEDA Feeding Hope Fund for Clinical Research Grants *(Professional development/Grant)* [6939]
Dr. Ezra Nesbeth Scholarships *(Undergraduate/Scholarship)* [5526]
NLM Associate Fellowships *(Postgraduate/Fellowship)* [9928]
Helen Woodruff Nolop Scholarships in Audiology and Allied Fields *(Graduate/Scholarship)* [3592]
Pembroke Center Faculty Seed Grants *(Professional development/Grant)* [2390]
Philips Respironics Fellowships in Mechanical Ventilation *(Professional development/Award)* [1214]
Philips Respironics Fellowships in Non-Invasive Respiratory Care *(Professional development/Fellowship)* [1215]
PhRMA Foundation Health Outcomes Post Doctoral Fellowships *(Postdoctorate/Fellowship)* [8034]
PhRMA Foundation Health Outcomes Pre Doctoral Fellowships *(Doctorate/Fellowship)* [8035]
PhRMA Foundation Health Outcomes Research Starter Grants *(Doctorate/Grant)* [8036]
PhRMA Foundation Health Outcomes Sabbatical Fellowships *(Postdoctorate/Fellowship)* [8037]
Rehabmart.com Scholarships *(Undergraduate/Scholarship)* [8545]
Thomson Reuters/MLA Doctoral Fellowships *(Doctorate, Graduate/Fellowship)* [6393]
Robert Browning Scholarships *(Undergraduate/Scholarship)* [8262]
Charles W. Serby COPD Research Fellowships *(Professional development/Fellowship)* [1216]
Dr. Robert Norman Shaw Scholarships *(Undergraduate/Scholarship)* [292]
J. Newell Stannard Fellowships *(Graduate/Fellowship)* [4812]
Peggy P. Starks Scholarship *(Postgraduate/Scholarship)* [9702]
Louis Stokes Health Scholars Program *(Undergraduate/Scholarship)* [3349]
Louis Stokes Urban Health Policy Fellows Program *(Other/Fellowship)* [3350]
Jerome M. Sullivan Research Funds *(Professional development/Grant)* [1217]
Steven M. Teutsch Prevention Effectiveness Fellowships *(Doctorate/Fellowship)* [9921]
TMA Research Fellowships *(Postdoctorate/Grant, Fellowship)* [6641]
UMDF Clinical Research Fellowship Training Awards *(Professional development/Fellowship)* [9860]
Winifred Van Hagen/Rosalind Cassidy Scholarship Award *(Undergraduate/Scholarship)* [2436]
Vanier Canada Graduate Scholarships *(Graduate/Scholarship)* [3405]
WHHS Medical Staff Scholarships *(Undergraduate/Scholarship)* [10448]
Marilyn Yetso Memorial Scholarships *(Graduate/Scholarship)* [9829]

Health services administration

Ellis J. Bonner Scholarships *(Graduate/Scholarship)* [6754]
Cathy L. Brock Memorial Scholarships *(Graduate/Scholarship)* [5167]
City of Toronto Scholarships for Aboriginal Students *(Graduate, Undergraduate/Scholarship)* [10285]
Florence S. Gaynor Scholarships *(Graduate/Scholarship)* [6755]
Foster G. McGaw Scholarships *(Undergraduate, Graduate/Scholarship)* [2086]
Haynes Rice Scholarships *(Graduate/Scholarship)* [6756]
Elliott C. Roberts Scholarships *(Graduate/Scholarship)* [5168]
Louis Stokes Health Scholars Program *(Undergraduate/Scholarship)* [3349]
Steven M. Teutsch Prevention Effectiveness Fellowships *(Doctorate/Fellowship)* [9921]
Toronto Rehabilitation Institute Graduate Student Scholarships - Ontario Student Opportunities Trust Fund (OSOTF) *(Graduate/Scholarship)* [9754]
Transamerica Retirement Solutions Leaders in Health Care Scholarships *(Graduate/Scholarship)* [5169]
TxHIMA Outstanding Student Scholarship *(Undergraduate/Scholarship)* [9704]
UAB Health Policy Fellowship *(Graduate, Master's, Doctorate/Scholarship)* [10002]

Hearing and deafness

American Speech Language Hearing Foundation Clinical Research Grants *(Doctorate/Grant)* [1450]
American Speech Language Hearing Foundation Endowed Scholarships *(Graduate, Master's, Doctorate/Scholarship)* [1451]
American Speech Language Hearing Foundation General Scholarships *(Graduate, Master's, Doctorate/Scholarship)* [1452]
American Speech Language Hearing Foundation Scholarships for International Students *(Graduate, Master's, Doctorate/Scholarship)* [1453]
American Speech Language Hearing Foundation Scholarships for Minority Students *(Graduate, Master's, Doctorate/Scholarship)* [1454]
ANS Research Grants *(Professional development/Grant)* [1030]
ASHFoundation New Century Scholars Research Grants *(Doctorate/Grant)* [1456]
ASHFoundation Student Research Grants in Audiology *(Doctorate/Grant)* [1460]
ASHFoundation Student Research Grants in Early Childhood Language Development *(Doctorate, Master's/Grant)* [1461]
AG Bell College Scholarship Awards *(Undergraduate, Graduate/Scholarship)* [314]
A.G. Bell School Age Financial Aid Program *(Undergraduate/Scholarship)* [315]
Elizabeth Benson Scholarship Awards *(Undergraduate/Scholarship)* [8542]
Houston/Nancy Holliman Scholarships *(Undergraduate/Scholarship)* [3586]
NAJA Scholarships *(Graduate/Scholarship)* [6760]
George H. Nofer Scholarships for Law and Public Policy *(Graduate/Scholarship)* [316]
Daniel H. Pokorny Memorial Scholarship Awards *(Undergraduate/Scholarship)* [8543]
Sertoma Communicative Disorders Scholarship *(Undergraduate/Scholarship)* [8849]
Sertoma Hard of Hearing and Deaf Scholarships *(Undergraduate/Scholarship)* [8850]
THFC Medical Research Grants *(Professional development/Grant)* [4834]

Heating, air conditioning, and refrigeration

Dave Nelsen Scholarships *(Undergraduate/Scholarship)* [6766]
Snodgrass Scholarships *(Undergraduate/Scholarship)* [10039]

Hematology

Adolescent/Young Adult Lymphoma Cooperative Groups Correlative Studies Grants *(Advanced Professional/Grant)* [6156]
Aplastic Anemia and Myelodysplasia Association of Canada Scholarships *(Graduate/Scholarship)* [2694]
Chronic Lymphocytic Leukemia Collaborative Grants *(Advanced Professional/Grant)* [6157]
Diffuse Large B-Cell Lymphoma Explorations Grants *(Advanced Professional/Grant)* [6158]
Follicular Lymphoma Research Grants *(Advanced Professional/Grant)* [6159]
Mantle Cell Lymphoma Research Grants *(Advanced Professional/Grant)* [6160]

Hemophilia

Biogen Idec Hemophilia Scholarship Program *(Undergraduate, Graduate, Doctorate/Scholarship)* [2310]
Hemophilia Federation of America Educational Scholarships *(Undergraduate/Scholarship)* [4860]
Doreen McMullan McCarthy Memorial Academic Scholarship for Women with Bleeding Disorders *(Undergraduate/Scholarship)* [6993]
Gail Posluns Fellowships in Hematology *(Postdoctorate/Fellowship)* [6139]

Herpetology

The Herpetologists' League Graduate Research Award *(Graduate/Award)* [4871]
Jones-Lovich Grants in Southwestern Herpetology *(Master's, Doctorate/Grant)* [4872]
Peace Frogs Fellowships *(Graduate/Fellowship)* [7741]
E. E. Williams Research Grants *(Master's, Doctorate/Grant)* [4873]

Hispanic American studies

LAEF Scholarships *(Undergraduate/Scholarship)* [5937]
LULAC GM Scholarships *(Graduate, High School, Undergraduate, Vocational/Occupational/Award)* [5988]
LULAC National Scholarship Fund (LNSF) *(Graduate, Undergraduate/Scholarship)* [5989]

Histology

Robert A. Clark Memorial Educational Scholarships *(Professional development/Scholarship)* [7166]
Leonard Noble Educational Scholarships *(Professional development/Scholarship)* [7170]
Thermo Scientific Educational Scholarships *(Professional development/Scholarship)* [7172]
Ventana Medical Systems In Situ Hybridization Awards *(Other/Award)* [7173]

Historic preservation

Association for Preservation Technology International Student Scholarships *(Graduate, Undergraduate/Scholarship)* [2041]
DAR Centennial Scholarship *(Undergraduate/Scholarship)* [7150]
Death Valley '49ers Scholarships *(Undergraduate/Scholarship)* [3537]
Grand Canyon Historical Society Scholarships *(Graduate/Scholarship)* [4508]
Herb Stovel Scholarship Funds - Conference Bursaries *(Undergraduate, Graduate, Professional development/Scholarship)* [7199]
Herb Stovel Scholarship Funds - Project Bursaries *(Undergraduate, Graduate, Professional development/Scholarship)* [7200]
Mildred Colodny Diversity Scholarships for Graduate Study in Historic Preservation *(Graduate/Scholarship)* [7202]
NAPC FORUM Scholarships *(Undergraduate/Scholarship)* [6694]
NYCT Paid Graduate Student Philanthropy Fellowships - Arts and Historic Preservation *(Graduate/Fellowship)* [7349]
The Aaron and Rita Slom Scholarships *(Undergraduate/Scholarship)* [9762]

History

Dr. Feroz Ahmed Memorial Educational Post-Graduate Scholarships *(Doctorate, Postgraduate/Scholarship)* [8965]
American Historical Association Fellowships in Aerospace History *(Doctorate/Fellowship)* [851]
ARCE Funded Fellowships *(Doctorate, Postdoctorate/Fellowship)* [1195]
ARCE Research Associates Fellowships *(Doctorate,*

Postdoctorate, Professional development/Fellowship) [1196]
ARIT National Endowment for the Humanities Advanced Fellowships for Research in Turkey (Postdoctorate/Fellowship) [1202]
ARS of Eastern USA Lazarian Graduate Scholarship (Master's, Doctorate/Scholarship) [1680]
Albert J. Beveridge Grants for Research in the Western Hemisphere (Doctorate/Grant) [852]
Cecil E. Burney Scholarships (Undergraduate/Scholarship) [3091]
Rachel Carson Prize (Other/Prize) [1310]
CCWH/Berkshire Conference of Women Historians Graduate Student Fellowships (Doctorate/Fellowship) [3418]
CCWH Nupur Chaudhuri First Article Prizes (Professional development/Prize) [3419]
Jenny d'Héricourt Fellowships (Doctorate/Fellowship) [435]
Douglas-Coldwell Foundation Scholarships in Social Affairs (Graduate/Scholarship) [3656]
The Steve Duckett Local Conservation Scholarships (Undergraduate, Postgraduate/Scholarship) [8232]
UAA Governor William A. Egan Scholarship (Undergraduate/Scholarship) [10056]
Franciszek Gadzala Memorial Scholarships (Undergraduate/Scholarship) [8575]
William E. "Bill" Gallagher Scholarships (Undergraduate/Scholarship) [7829]
Margaret S. Gilbert Scholarship Fund (Undergraduate/Scholarship) [9505]
Louis Gottschalk Prize (Other/Prize) [1291]
Grand Canyon Historical Society Scholarships (Graduate/Scholarship) [4508]
Velma Shotwell Griffin Memorial Scholarship Fund (Undergraduate/Scholarship) [9507]
Enid Hall Griswold Memorial Scholarships (Undergraduate/Scholarship) [7152]
Samuel P. Hays Research Fellowships (Other/Fellowship) [1312]
Hench Post-Dissertation Fellowship (Postdoctorate/Fellowship) [438]
Conrad N. Hilton Scholarships (Undergraduate/Scholarship) [4414]
Brooke Hindle Postdoctoral Fellowships (Postdoctorate/Fellowship) [9142]
Mary M. Hughes Research Fellowships in Texas History (Professional development/Fellowship) [9714]
Huguenot Society of South Carolina Graduate Scholarships (Graduate/Scholarship) [4986]
Harriet Irsay Scholarships (Graduate, Undergraduate/Scholarship) [927]
J. Franklin Jameson Fellowships in American History (Professional development/Fellowship) [853]
John H. Jenkins Research Fellowships in Texas History (Professional development/Fellowship) [9715]
Mary Jon and J. P. Bryan Leadership in Education Awards (Advanced Professional/Award) [9716]
The Michael Kiely Strong Roots Scholarships (Undergraduate/Scholarship) [8233]
Melvin Kranzberg Dissertation Fellowships (Doctorate/Fellowship) [9143]
Michael Kraus Research Grants (Doctorate/Grant) [854]
Lapides Fellowships in Pre-1865 Juvenile Literature and Ephemera (Graduate, Postdoctorate/Fellowship) [439]
Lazarian Graduate Scholarships (Graduate/Scholarship) [1678]
Gilder Lehrman Short-Term Fellowships (Graduate, Postdoctorate/Fellowship) [6007]
Lerner-Scott Prize (Doctorate/Prize) [7717]
Littleton-Griswold Research Grants (Doctorate/Grant) [855]
George Perkins Marsh Prize (Other/Prize) [1313]
Larry Matfay Cultural Heritage Scholarships (Undergraduate, Graduate/Scholarship) [5868]
William P. McHugh Memorial Fund Award (Doctorate, Graduate/Fellowship) [1197]
The Tatiana Mendez Future Resources Scholarships (Undergraduate/Scholarship) [8234]
Thomas S. Morgan Memorial Scholarship (Graduate, Master's/Scholarship) [8044]

National Council on Public History Graduate Student Travel Awards (Doctorate, Graduate/Grant) [6882]
National Council on Public History Student Project Awards (Undergraduate/Grant) [6883]
The National Endowment for the Humanities Fellowships (Graduate/Fellowship) [1198]
NMNH American Indian Program Fellowships (Graduate/Fellowship) [9034]
North American Conference on British Studies Dissertation Year Fellowships (Doctorate, Postdoctorate/Fellowship) [7443]
North American Conference on British Studies-Huntington Library Fellowships (Doctorate, Postdoctorate/Fellowship) [7444]
OAH-IEHS Huggins-Quarles Dissertation Awards (Doctorate, Graduate/Fellowship) [7718]
The Seth Okin Good Deeds Scholarships (Undergraduate/Scholarship) [8235]
Barbara L. Packer Fellowships (Doctorate, Postdoctorate/Fellowship) [442]
William E. Parrish Scholarships (Graduate, Master's/Scholarship) [8045]
Louis Pelzer Memorial Awards (Graduate/Award) [7719]
Petroleum History Society Graduate Scholarships (Graduate/Scholarship) [8017]
Phi Alpha Theta Doctoral Scholarships (Doctorate/Scholarship) [8046]
Phi Alpha Theta Faculty Advisor Research Grant (Other/Grant) [8047]
Pi Gamma Mu Scholarships (Graduate/Scholarship) [8133]
John Pine Memorial Scholarships (Doctorate, Graduate/Scholarship) [8048]
D.F. Plett Graduate Fellowships (Doctorate/Scholarship) [8158]
A. Stanley Rand Fellowships Program (Undergraduate, Doctorate, Postdoctorate/Fellowship) [9037]
Charles and Ruth Ronin Memorial Scholarships (Undergraduate/Scholarship) [8524]
Hal Rothman Dissertation Fellowships (Doctorate, Graduate/Fellowship) [1316]
Justin G. Schiller Fellowships (Doctorate, Postdoctorate/Fellowship) [445]
Bernadotte E. Schmitt Grants (Doctorate/Grant) [856]
Everett Oscar Shimp Memorial Scholarships (Undergraduate/Scholarship) [7862]
The Thomas Soldan Healthy Communities Scholarships (Undergraduate, Graduate/Scholarship) [8237]
Hatton W. Sumners Endowed Undergraduate School Scholarships (Undergraduate/Scholarship) [9609]
Hatton W. Sumners Non-Endowed Undergraduate and Graduate Scholarships (Undergraduate, Graduate/Scholarship) [9610]
The Ed Tayter Outstanding Citizen Scholarships (Undergraduate/Scholarship) [8238]
Terra Foundation Fellowships at the Smithsonian American Art Museum (Postdoctorate/Fellowship) [9680]
Terra Foundation Postdoctoral Teaching Fellowships at the Courtauld Institute of Art, London (Postdoctorate/Fellowship) [9681]
Terra Foundation Postdoctoral Teaching Fellowships at the Institut National d'Histoire de l'Art, Paris (Postdoctorate/Fellowship) [9682]
Terra Summer Residency Fellowships (Master's, Doctorate/Fellowship) [9684]
Barbara and Howard Thompson Scholarships (Undergraduate/Scholarship) [5515]
Graydon A. Tunstall Undergraduate Student Scholarships (Undergraduate/Scholarship) [8049]
The United States Department of State, Bureau of Educational & Cultural Affairs Fellowships (Graduate/Fellowship) [1199]
Frederick K. Weyerhaeuser Forest History Fellowships (Graduate/Fellowship) [4138]
Xavier University Departmental Scholarships (Undergraduate/Scholarship) [10729]
A.F. Zimmerman Scholarships (Graduate, Master's/Scholarship) [8050]
Blanche Raper Zimmerman Scholarships (Other/Scholarship) [10607]

History, American

AAS Fellowships for Creative and Performing Artists and Writers (Professional development/Fellowship, Award) [430]
AAS-Northeast Modern Language Association Fellowships (Undergraduate/Fellowship) [432]
APSA Presidency Research Group Fellowships (Graduate, Postdoctorate/Fellowship) [1118]
Stephen Botein Fellowships (Doctorate/Fellowship) [433]
Betty Sams Christian Fellowships (Doctorate/Fellowship) [10396]
College Art Association Wyeth Publication Grants (Other/Grant) [3119]
Cromwell Fellowships (Graduate/Fellowship) [1354]
W.B.H. Dowse Fellowships (Professional development/Fellowship) [6326]
MHS Marc Friedlaender Fellowships (Professional development/Fellowship) [6328]
German Historical Institute Doctoral and Postdoctoral Fellowships (Doctorate, Postgraduate/Fellowship) [4395]
John Higham Travel Grants (Graduate/Grant) [5087, 7716]
ICJS Short-Term Fellowships (Doctorate, Postdoctorate, Advanced Professional/Fellowship) [8997]
The Legacy Fellowships (Doctorate/Fellowship) [441]
Lloyd Lewis Fellowships in American History (Postdoctorate/Fellowship) [7413]
Suzanne and Caleb Loring Research Fellowships (Professional development/Fellowship) [6329]
James Madison Foundation - Junior Fellowships (Advanced Professional/Fellowship) [6174]
James Madison Foundation - Senior Fellowships (Graduate/Fellowship) [6175]
MHS Andrew W. Mellon Fellowships (Professional development/Fellowship) [6330]
MHS Long-Term Research Fellowships (Professional development/Fellowship) [6333]
MHS/Massachusetts Society of the Cincinnati Fellowships (Professional development/Fellowship) [6334]
Kate B. and Hall J. Peterson Fellowships (Doctorate/Fellowship) [443]
Dr. Aura-Lee A. and James Hobbs Pittenger American History Scholarships (Undergraduate/Scholarship) [7154]
Platt Family Scholarship Prize Essay Contest (Graduate, Undergraduate/Scholarship, Monetary) [6091]
Arthur M. Schlesinger, Jr. Fellowships (Professional development/Fellowship) [5603]
Benjamin F. Stevens Fellowships (Professional development/Fellowship) [6337]
Swensrud Teacher Fellowships at MHS (Massachusetts Historical Society) (Professional development/Fellowship) [6338]
The Joyce Tracy Fellowships (Doctorate/Fellowship) [446]
United States Capitol Historical Society Fellowships (Graduate/Fellowship) [9886]
Woody Guthrie Fellowship (Professional development/Fellowship) [2321]

History, Ancient

ARIT Fellowships in the Humanities and Social Sciences in Turkey (Postdoctorate, Graduate/Fellowship) [1201]

History, Art (See Art history)

History, Economic

Arthur H. Cole Grants in Aid (Doctorate/Grant, Award) [3779]
EHA Exploratory Travel and Data Grants (Doctorate/Grant) [3780]
EHA Graduate Dissertation Fellowships (Doctorate/Fellowship) [3781]

History, Military

ABC-Clio Research Grants (Graduate/Grant) [9208]
CMH Dissertation Fellowships (Graduate/Fellowship) [9876]
Marshall-Baruch Fellowships (Doctorate/Fellowship) [6295]
The Edgar C. Wilson Fellowship (Graduate/Fellowship) [10274]
Women In Defense HORIZONS Scholarships (Graduate, Undergraduate/Scholarship) [10636]

History, United States (See History, American)

History of printing (See Printing--History)

History of science (See Science--History)

Home Economics

California Association of Family and Consumer Sciences - San Diego Chapter Scholarships (CAFCS) (Undergraduate, Graduate/Scholarship) [8695]
Canadian Home Economics Association Fellowships (Master's, Doctorate/Fellowship) [2629]
FACS Graduate Fellowships (Graduate/Fellowship) [6798]
Kappa Omicron Nu National Alumni Fellowships (Graduate/Fellowship) [5782]
Eileen C. Maddex Fellowships (Graduate/Fellowship) [5785]

Homosexuality

Center for Lesbian and Gay Studies Fellowships (Graduate/Fellowship) [2863]
Martin Duberman Fellowships (Other/Fellowship) [2864]
GAPA Scholarships (Undergraduate/Scholarship) [4327]
Joan Heller-Diane Bernard Fellowships (Graduate, Undergraduate/Fellowship) [2865]

Horticulture

American Conifer Society Scholarships (Undergraduate/Scholarship) [714]
American Society for Horticultural Science Student Travel Grants (Graduate, Undergraduate/Grant) [1336]
Arizona Nursery Association Scholarships (Undergraduate/Scholarship) [1637]
Arkansas Green Industry Association Professional Grants (Professional development, Undergraduate/Grant) [1651]
The Artist in Landscape Design Scholarship by Fullmer's Landscaping (Undergraduate/Scholarship) [7581]
ASHS Industry Division Student Travel Grants (Graduate, Undergraduate/Grant) [1337]
ASHS Scholars Awards (Undergraduate/Scholarship) [1338]
Ball Horticultural Company Scholarships (Undergraduate/Scholarship) [798]
Vic and Margaret Ball Student Intern Scholarships (Undergraduate/Internship) [799]
Catherine H. Beattie Fellowships (Graduate/Fellowship) [2867]
Harold Bettinger Scholarships (Undergraduate, Graduate/Scholarship) [800]
Leonard Bettinger Vocational Scholarships (Undergraduate, Vocational/Occupational/Scholarship) [801]
James Bridenbaugh Memorial Scholarships (Undergraduate/Scholarship) [802]
John Carew Memorial Scholarships (Graduate/Scholarship) [803]
Bryan A. Champion Memorial Scholarship (Undergraduate/Scholarship) [7582]

Christmas Tree Chapter Scholarship Awards (Undergraduate/Scholarship) [7692]
Clackamas Chapter Scholarship Awards (Undergraduate/Scholarship) [7693]
Howard A. Clark Horticulture Scholarships (Undergraduate/Scholarship) [3220]
James H. Davis Scholarships (Undergraduate/Scholarship) [4100]
Earl Dedman Memorial Scholarships (Undergraduate/Scholarship) [804]
Bill Egan Scholarship Program (Undergraduate/Scholarship) [7694]
Emerald Empire Chapter Scholarship Awards (Undergraduate/Scholarship) [7695]
Miklos Faust International Travel Awards (Doctorate/Grant) [1339]
FFA Scholarship (Undergraduate/Scholarship) [7583]
Fruits and Vegetable Industries Scholarships (Undergraduate/Scholarship) [6487]
Garden Club Council of Winston-Salem and Forsyth County Council Scholarships (Undergraduate/Scholarship) [10583]
Katherine M. Grosscup Scholarships (Undergraduate, Graduate/Scholarship) [4325]
Hill Country Master Gardeners Horticulture Scholarships (Undergraduate/Scholarship) [4881]
Idaho Nursery and Landscape Association Scholarships (Undergraduate/Scholarship) [5048]
Illinois Landscape Contractors Association Scholarships (Undergraduate/Scholarship) [5064]
Joseph H. Klupenger Scholarship Awards (Undergraduate/Scholarship) [7696]
ONLA Phil Kozel Memorial Scholarship (Undergraduate/Scholarship) [7585]
Louisiana Agricultural Consultants Association Scholarships (Graduate, Undergraduate/Scholarship) [6112]
Markham-Colegrave International Scholarships (Undergraduate/Scholarship) [805]
MELNA Scholarship (Undergraduate, Graduate/Scholarship) [6217]
Mt. Hood Chapter Scholarship Awards (Undergraduate/Scholarship) [7697]
Nashville Unit Scholarships (Undergraduate/Scholarship) [4863]
National Greenhouse Manufacturers Association Scholarships (Undergraduate/Scholarship) [806]
National Junior Horticultural Association Alumni Scholarships (Undergraduate/Scholarship) [7034]
NGC College Scholarships (Graduate, Undergraduate/Scholarship) [6965]
North Carolina Commercial Flower Growers Association Floriculture Scholarships (Graduate, Undergraduate/Scholarship) [7456]
North Carolina Nursery and Landscape Association Horticulture Scholarships (Undergraduate/Scholarship) [7468]
Mike and Flo Novovesky Scholarships (Undergraduate/Scholarship) [807]
Nurseries Foundation Scholarship Awards (Undergraduate/Scholarship) [7698]
Nurseries Memorial Scholarship Awards (Graduate/Scholarship) [7699]
Lawrence "Bud" Ohlman Memorial Scholarships (Undergraduate/Scholarship) [808]
Oregon Association of Nurseries Scholarship Program (Undergraduate/Scholarship) [7700]
Pennsylvania Heartland Unit Scholarships (Undergraduate/Scholarship) [4864]
Jim Perry Vocational Scholarships (Undergraduate, Vocational/Occupational/Scholarship) [809]
Rain Bird Intelligent Use of Water Scholarships (Undergraduate/Scholarship) [5917]
James K. Rathmell Jr. Memorial Scholarships (Undergraduate, Graduate/Scholarship) [810]
Bertha and Byron L. Reppert Scholarship Fund (Undergraduate/Scholarship) [4252]
Retail Chapter Scholarship Awards (Undergraduate/Scholarship) [7701]
Seed Companies Scholarships (Undergraduate, Graduate/Scholarship) [811]
Stanley Smith Horticultural Fellowships (Graduate, Undergraduate/Fellowship) [7744]
South Texas Unit Scholarships (Undergraduate/Scholarship) [4865]

Jordan B. Tatter Scholarships (Undergraduate/Scholarship) [6488]
John L. Tomasovic, Sr. Scholarships (Undergraduate/Scholarship) [812]
Edward Tuinier Memorial Scholarships (Undergraduate/Scholarship) [813]
Jacob and Rita Van Namen Marketing Scholarships (Undergraduate/Scholarship) [814]
West Michigan Nursery and Landscape Association Scholarship Fund (Undergraduate/Scholarship) [4552]
Western Reserve Herb Society Scholarships (Undergraduate/Scholarship) [4866]
Willamette Chapter Scholarship Awards (Undergraduate/Scholarship) [7702]
Ed Wood Memorial Scholarship Awards (Undergraduate/Scholarship) [7703]
Francis Sylvia Zverina Scholarships (Undergraduate/Scholarship) [4867]

Hotel, institutional, and restaurant management

AH&LEF American Express Scholarship (Undergraduate/Scholarship) [858]
American Express Professional Development Scholarships (Other/Scholarship) [859]
Applied Hospitality Degree Scholarships (Undergraduate/Scholarship) [2657]
Canadian Hospitality Foundation College Entrance Scholarships (Undergraduate/Scholarship) [2658]
Canadian Hospitality Foundation University Entrance Scholarships (Undergraduate/Scholarship) [2659]
Caribbean Hotel and Tourism Association Academic Scholarships (Graduate, Undergraduate/Scholarship) [2797]
Letitia B. Carter Scholarships (Undergraduate, Advanced Professional/Scholarship) [8563]
Vickie Clark-Flaherty Scholarships (Undergraduate/Scholarship) [7471]
FHSMAI Scholarship Program (Graduate/Scholarship) [4264]
Marcia S. Harris Legacy Fund Scholarships (Undergraduate, Advanced Professional/Scholarship) [8564]
R.W. "Bob" Holden Memorial Scholarships (Undergraduate/Scholarship) [4798]
The Hyatt Hotels Fund For Minority Lodging Management Students (Undergraduate/Scholarship) [860]
The Steve Hymans Extended Stay Scholarship Program (Undergraduate/Scholarship) [861]
International Foodservice Editorial Council Scholarships (Graduate, Undergraduate/Scholarship) [5331]
Clem Judd Jr. Memorial Scholarships (Undergraduate/Scholarship) [4799]
K & W Cafeterias Scholarships (Undergraduate/Scholarship) [7472]
Les Dames D'Escoffier New York Scholarships (Undergraduate/Scholarship) [6009]
Michigan Sugar Company Hotel Restaurant/Resort Management Scholarships (Undergraduate/Scholarship) [6495]
NC Hospitality Education Foundation Scholarships - Four Year College or University (Undergraduate/Scholarship) [7473]
NC Hospitality Education Foundation Scholarships - Graduate (Graduate/Scholarship) [7474]
NC Hospitality Education Foundation Scholarships - High School (Undergraduate/Scholarship) [7475]
NC Hospitality Education Foundation Scholarships - Two Year Community or Junior College (Undergraduate/Scholarship) [7476]
NCRLA Golden Corral Scholarships (Undergraduate/Scholarship) [7477]
Oklahoma Restaurant Association Scholarships (Graduate, Undergraduate/Scholarship) [7604]
Ontario Women's Institute Scholarships (Undergraduate/Scholarship) [3997]
The Arthur J. Packard Memorial Scholarship Competition (Undergraduate/Scholarship) [862]
Pepsi Scholarships (Undergraduate/Scholarship) [863]
Rama Scholarships for the American Dream

(Graduate, Undergraduate/Scholarship) [864]
RAMEF/NRAEF Co-Branded Scholarships (Undergraduate/Scholarship) [8565]

Housing

California Association of Family and Consumer Sciences - San Diego Chapter Scholarships (CAFCS) (Undergraduate, Graduate/Scholarship) [8695]
CHCI Graduate Fellowships (Graduate/Fellowship) [3352]
NACCED Annual John C. Murphy Scholarships (Graduate, Undergraduate/Scholarship) [6742]

Human relations

AAFSW College Merit Scholarship (College, Undergraduate/Scholarship) [1820]
Bill Bendiner and Doug Morgenson Scholarships (Undergraduate/Scholarship) [8246]
Derivative Duo Scholarships (Undergraduate/Scholarship) [8253]
The Judy Felt Memorial Volunteerism Scholarship (College, Undergraduate/Scholarship) [1821]
David C. Maloney Scholarships (Undergraduate/Scholarship) [7079]
April Relyea Scholarship (Graduate, Undergraduate/Scholarship) [10069]

Human rights

Alberta Award for the Study of Canadian Human Rights and Multiculturalism (Doctorate, Graduate/Award) [261]
Beverlee Bell Scholarships in Human Rights and Democracy (Graduate/Scholarship) [3655]
Robert L. Bernstein Fellowships in International Human Rights (Graduate/Fellowship) [4994]
Canadian Japanese-Mennonite Scholarships (Graduate/Scholarship) [6416]
CEJIL Communications Internships (Undergraduate, Graduate/Internship) [2860]
CEJIL Legal Internships (Graduate, Professional development/Internship) [2861]
CHRGJ Emerging Human Rights Scholarship Conference (Graduate/Scholarship) [7398]
CHRGJ International Human Rights Fellowships (Doctorate, Professional development/Fellowship, Internship) [7399]
CHRGJ Students Human Rights Scholars Program (Graduate, Advanced Professional, Professional development/Scholarship) [7400]
ASIL Arthur C. Helton Fellowship Program (Professional development/Fellowship) [1344]
Arthur Helton Fellowships (Graduate/Fellowship) [7401]
Henigson Human Rights Fellowships (Graduate, Master's, Juris Doctorate/Fellowship) [4786]
Kovaluk Scholarship Fund (Undergraduate/Scholarship) [9984]
NYCT Paid Graduate Student Philanthropy Fellowships - Children, Youth, Families, Education, Human Justice and Workforce (Graduate/Fellowship) [7350]
Satter Human Rights Fellowships (Graduate, Master's, Juris Doctorate/Fellowship) [4787]
Spirit of Anne Frank Outstanding Scholarship Award (Undergraduate/Scholarship) [1563]
Upper Midwest Human Rights Fellowship Program (Graduate/Scholarship, Fellowship) [4996]
George Watt Prize (Undergraduate, Graduate/Prize) [26]
Minoru Yasui Memorial Scholarships (Graduate, Master's, Doctorate/Scholarship) [5560]

Humanities

AAS National Endowment for the Humanities Long-Term Fellowships (Postdoctorate/Fellowship) [431]
ACLS African Humanities Fellowships (Postdoctorate/Fellowship) [734]
ACLS Collaborative Research Fellowships (Doctorate/Fellowship) [735]
ACLS Fellowships (Advanced Professional, Professional development/Fellowship) [736]

ACOR-CAORC Post-Graduate Fellowships (Doctorate, Postdoctorate/Award) [653]
Dr. Feroz Ahmed Memorial Educational Post-Graduate Scholarships (Doctorate, Postgraduate/Scholarship) [8965]
AISLS Dissertation Planning Grants (Graduate/Grant) [929]
AISLS Fellowships Program (Doctorate/Fellowship) [930]
American Philosophical Society Library Resident Research Fellowships (Doctorate/Fellowship) [1078]
American Research in the Humanities in China Fellowships (Doctorate/Fellowship) [737]
ARCE Funded Fellowships (Doctorate, Postdoctorate/Fellowship) [1195]
ARCE Research Associates Fellowships (Doctorate, Postdoctorate, Professional development/Fellowship) [1196]
ARIT Fellowships in the Humanities and Social Sciences in Turkey (Postdoctorate, Graduate/Fellowship) [1201]
ARIT National Endowment for the Humanities Advanced Fellowships for Research in Turkey (Postdoctorate/Fellowship) [1202]
Leo Biaggi de Blasys Bogliasco Fellowships (Professional development/Fellowship) [2326]
Bogliasco Fellowships (Professional development/Fellowship) [2327]
ACLS Frederick Burkhardt Residential Fellowships (Other/Fellowship) [434]
Frederick Burkhardt Residential Fellowships for Recently Tenured Scholars (Advanced Professional, Professional development/Fellowship) [738]
CES First Article Prize (Professional development/Prize) [3438]
Critical Language Scholarships for Intensive Summer Institutes (Graduate, Undergraduate/Scholarship) [1204]
Dissertation Fellowships in East European Studies (Doctorate/Fellowship) [740]
Dissertation Proposal Development Fellowships (Doctorate/Fellowship) [9053]
Early Career Postdoctoral Fellowships in East European Studies (Postdoctorate/Fellowship) [741]
Getty Scholar Grants (Professional development/Grant) [4412]
Harry Frank Guggenheim Dissertation Fellowships (Doctorate/Fellowship) [4681]
Harry Frank Guggenheim Foundation Research Grants (Professional development/Grant) [4682]
John Simon Guggenheim Memorial Fellowships - U.S. and Canadian Competition (Advanced Professional/Fellowship) [4684]
Ed Haas Memorial Scholarships (Undergraduate/Scholarship) [9568]
Lois Hole Humanities and Social Sciences Scholarships (Undergraduate/Scholarship) [273]
Institute of Turkish Studies Post-Doctoral Summer Travel-Research Grants (Postdoctorate/Grant) [5224]
Institute of Turkish Studies Summer Language Study Grants in Turkey (Graduate/Grant) [5226]
International Dissertation Research Fellowship (IDRF) (Graduate, Doctorate/Fellowship) [9054]
International Society for Humor Studies Graduate Student Awards (GSA) (Graduate/Award, Scholarship) [5422]
International Society for Humor Studies Scholarly Contribution Awards (SCA) (Other/Award) [5423]
Louis I. Jaffe Memorial Scholarships-ODU (Graduate/Scholarship) [4701]
Japan Society for the Promotion of Science Fellowship Program (Doctorate/Fellowship) [9055]
Jacob K. Javits Fellowships Program (Master's, Doctorate/Fellowship) [9894]
Robert E. Kelsey Annual Scholarship (Undergraduate/Scholarship) [7933]
Kluge Fellowships (Doctorate, Graduate/Fellowship) [5846]
Korean Studies Dissertation Workshop Funds (Graduate/Fellowship) [9056]
Dolores Zohrab Liebmann Fund - Graduate School Fellowships (Graduate/Fellowship) [6075]
David C. Maloney Scholarships (Undergraduate/Scholarship) [7079]

O. Ruth McQuown Scholarship - Graduate Award for Current Students (Graduate/Scholarship) [10135]
Mellon/ACLS Dissertation Completion Fellowships (Graduate, Doctorate/Fellowship) [743]
Mellon Fellowships for Dissertation Research in the Humanities (Doctorate, Graduate/Fellowship, Scholarship) [3450]
Mellon Fellowships for Dissertation Research in Original Sources (Doctorate/Fellowship) [3451]
Multi-Country Research Fellowships (Doctorate/Fellowship) [3431]
NAFA International Dissertation Research Fellowships (Graduate, Doctorate/Fellowship) [6750]
National Endowment for the Humanities Research Fellowships (Doctorate/Fellowship) [660]
National Humanities Center Fellowships (Doctorate, Postdoctorate/Fellowship) [7008]
NEH Fellowships for Senior Scholars (Doctorate/Fellowship) [2853]
Newberry Library National Endowment for the Humanities Fellowships (Postdoctorate/Fellowship) [7421]
Pembroke Center Faculty Seed Grants (Professional development/Grant) [2390]
Prins Foundation Fellowship for Senior Scholars (Doctorate/Fellowship) [2854]
Prins Foundation Post-Doctoral and Early Career Fellowship for Emigrating Scholars (Professional development, Postdoctorate/Fellowship) [2855]
Rome Prize (Doctorate, Graduate/Prize, Award) [424]
Rovelstad Scholarship in International Librarianship (Undergraduate, Graduate/Award, Scholarship) [3452]
Ellis W. Rowe Scholarships (Undergraduate/Scholarship) [4703]
Charles A. Ryskamp Research Fellowships (Postgraduate, Postdoctorate, Professional development/Fellowship) [744]
Musia and Leon Schwartz Scholarships (Undergraduate, Graduate/Scholarship) [5586]
SHAFR Dissertation Completion Fellowships (Doctorate/Fellowship) [9140]
Short-term Senior Fellowships in Iranian Studies (Professional development/Fellowship) [914]
SSHRC Doctoral Fellowship Program (Doctorate/Fellowship, Scholarship) [3396]
Robert W. and Bernice Ingalls Staton Scholarships (Undergraduate/Scholarship) [10259]
Trudeau Foundation Doctoral Scholarships (Doctorate/Scholarship) [8137]
UC MEXUS-CONACYT Doctoral Fellowships (Doctorate/Fellowship) [10117]
The UCSD Black Alumni Scholarship for Arts and Humanities (Undergraduate/Scholarship) [8736]
Vanier Canada Graduate Scholarships (Graduate/Scholarship) [3405]
Winterthur Research Fellowships (Graduate/Fellowship) [10609]
Mary and Elliot Wood Foundation Graduate Scholarship Fund (Graduate/Scholarship) [4222]
Carter G. Woodson Institute Post-doctoral Residential Research and Teaching Fellowships (Postdoctorate/Fellowship) [10684]
Carter G. Woodson Institute Pre-doctoral Residential Research Fellowships (Doctorate/Fellowship) [10685]
Woody Guthrie Fellowship (Professional development/Fellowship) [2321]

Huntington's disease

HDSA Research Grants (Graduate/Grant) [5019]
Hereditary Disease Foundation Basic Research Grants (Advanced Professional/Grant) [4869]
Huntington's Disease Society of America Research Fellowships (Postdoctorate/Fellowship) [5020]
Don King Student Fellowships (Undergraduate/Fellowship) [5021]

Hydrology

Arizona Hydrological Society Scholarships (Graduate, Undergraduate/Scholarship) [1635]
Canadian Hydrographic Association Student Awards

ILLUSTRATORS AND ILLUSTRATIONS

(Undergraduate/Award, Monetary, Medal) [2662]
B. Harper Bull Conservation Fellowships (Graduate/Fellowship) [9749]
Hydro Research Foundation Fellowships (Advanced Professional/Fellowship) [5023]
CASFM-Ben Urbonas Scholarships (Graduate/Scholarship) [3132]

Illustrators and illustrations

Inez Demonet Scholarship (Graduate/Scholarship) [10373]
UAA Kimura Scholarship Fund for Illustration (Undergraduate/Scholarship) [10081]
Vesalius Trust Student Research Scholarships (Graduate, Undergraduate/Scholarship) [10374]
Worldstudio AIGA Scholarships (Graduate, Undergraduate/Scholarship) [10709]

Immigration

John Higham Travel Grants (Graduate/Grant) [5087, 7716]
Abba P. Schwartz Research Fellowships (Professional development/Fellowship) [5604]

Immunology

AAI Careers in Immunology Fellowship Program (Graduate, Doctorate, Postdoctorate/Fellowship) [506]
AAI Public Policy Fellows Program (PPFP) (Doctorate, Postdoctorate/Fellowship) [507]
CRI Clinic and Laboratory Integration Program Grants (CLIP) (Professional development/Grant) [2772]
CRI Irvington Postdoctoral Fellowship Program (Postdoctorate/Fellowship) [2773]
CRI Irvington Postdoctoral Fellowships (Postdoctorate, Doctorate/Fellowship) [2774]
Kris Knudson Memorial Scholarship (Graduate, Undergraduate/Scholarship) [10065]
Student Training and Research in Tumor Immunology Grants (Graduate/Grant) [2775]
Dr. Steven S. Zalcman Memorial Scholarships (Graduate, Postgraduate/Scholarship) [5589]

Indian studies (Asia)

Shastri Scholar Travel Subsidy Grants (SSTSG) (Graduate, Professional development/Grant) [8857]
SHOT-NASA Fellowships (Doctorate, Postdoctorate/Fellowship) [9144]

Industrial and labor relations

Mary Babcock Fellowships for Labour Studies Application (Graduate/Fellowship) [7629]
Mackenzie King Travelling Scholarships (Graduate/Scholarship) [6367]
The Anthony C. Russo Scholarships (Graduate/Scholarship) [7115]
NPELRA Foundation - Anthony C. Russo Scholarships (Graduate/Scholarship) [7116]

Industrial design

FPA Summer Internships Program (Undergraduate/Internship) [4072]
IDSA Gianninoto Graduate Scholarships (Graduate, Undergraduate/Scholarship) [5136]
Tom D. Ralls Memorial Scholarship (Professional development/Scholarship) [4285]
Tag and Label Manufacturers Institute Scholarships - Two-Year Colleges (Undergraduate/Scholarship) [9630]
Vectorworks Design Scholarships (Undergraduate, Graduate/Scholarship, Prize) [10367]
Worldstudio AIGA Scholarships (Graduate, Undergraduate/Scholarship) [10709]

Industrial education (See Education, Industrial)

Industrial hygiene

Thompson Scholarships for Women in Safety (Graduate/Scholarship) [1430]

Industry and trade

Bruce Clement Post-Secondary Education Scholarships (Undergraduate/Scholarship) [7311]
EAIA Research Grants (Other/Grant) [3748]
Oil & Gas, Trades & Technology (OGTT) Bursary and Scholarship Awards (OGTT) (Undergraduate/Scholarship) [5134]
Syncrude/Athabasca University Aboriginal Scholarships (Undergraduate/Scholarship) [9627]

Infectious diseases (See also Epidemiology)

Dr. James A. Ferguson Emerging Infectious Diseases Fellowships (Graduate/Fellowship) [5815]
Investigators in the Pathogenesis of Infectious Disease Awards (Doctorate, Postdoctorate, Professional development/Grant) [2417]
ISID Small Grant (Postdoctorate, Professional development/Grant) [5425]

Information science and technology

Aerospace Corporation Science and Engineering Student Scholarships (Undergraduate, Graduate/Scholarship) [95]
AFCEA Cyber Studies and Intelligence Scholarships (Undergraduate, Graduate/Scholarship) [85]
AFFIRM University Scholarships (Undergraduate/Scholarship) [1961]
Afghanistan and Iraq War Veterans Scholarship (Undergraduate/Scholarship) [88]
Alberta Innovates Graduate Student Scholarships (Graduate/Scholarship) [256]
Alberta Innovates - Technology Futures Graduate Student Scholarships in ICT (Doctorate, Graduate, Master's/Scholarship) [257]
APALA Scholarship Award (Doctorate, Master's/Scholarship) [1788]
APS/ASU Scholarships (Undergraduate/Scholarship) [8139]
APS/Maricopa County Community Colleges Scholarships (Undergraduate/Scholarship) [8140]
Boeing Company Scholarships (Undergraduate/Scholarship) [8870]
Kathi Bowles Scholarships for Women in Technology (Undergraduate, Graduate/Scholarship) [2091]
Disabled War Veterans Scholarships (Undergraduate/Scholarship) [90]
Eli Lilly and Company/Black Data Processing Associates Scholarships (Undergraduate/Scholarship) [2206]
Eugene Garfield Doctoral Dissertation Fellowship (Doctorate/Fellowship) [2239]
Graybar Canada Award of Excellence Scholarships (Undergraduate/Scholarship) [3832]
Indspire Post-Secondary Education Scholarships (Graduate, Undergraduate/Scholarship) [5133]
Innovations in Software Scholarships (Undergraduate, Graduate/Scholarship) [10758]
Iowa Library Association Foundation Scholarships (Graduate/Scholarship) [5469]
(ISC)2 Foundation Information Security Scholarships (Graduate, Undergraduate/Scholarship) [5348]
Christian Larew Memorial Scholarships (Graduate/Scholarship) [6071]
Robert V. McKenna Scholarships (Undergraduate/Scholarship) [9654]
Arthur L. Norberg Travel Fund (Advanced Professional/Grant) [10200]
Paul Evan Peters Fellowship (Master's, Doctorate/Fellowship) [3073]
Thomson Reuters/MLA Doctoral Fellowships (Doctorate, Graduate/Fellowships) [6393]
Fritz Schwartz Serials Education Scholarships (Graduate, Other/Scholarship) [7447]
SWE Scholarships (Undergraduate, Graduate/Scholarship) [9329]
Symantec Research Labs Graduate Fellowships (Doctorate, Graduate/Fellowship) [9625]
Syncrude/Athabasca University Aboriginal Scholarships (Undergraduate/Scholarship) [9627]
Jack E. Tillson Scholarships (Graduate/Scholarship) [5470]
The Adelle and Erwin Tomash Fellowship in the History of Information Technology (Doctorate, Graduate/Fellowship) [10201]
Wells Fargo American Indian Scholarships - Graduate (Graduate/Scholarship) [883]
Edwin F. Wiegand Science and Technology Scholarships (Undergraduate/Scholarship) [8370]

Insurance and insurance-related fields

Intermediaries and Reinsurance Underwriters Association Summer Intern Scholarships Program (Undergraduate/Scholarship) [5237]
ISU Gongaware Scholarships (Undergraduate/Scholarship) [5121]
William H. McGannon Foundation Scholarships (Graduate, Undergraduate/Scholarship) [6364]
Mutual of Omaha Finance Careers Scholarships (Undergraduate, Graduate/Scholarship) [105]
Patriot Education Scholarships (Undergraduate/Scholarship) [6209]
Risk Management and Insurance Scholarships - University of Calgary (Undergraduate/Scholarship) [8768]
Risk Management and Insurance Scholarships (Undergraduate/Scholarship) [8767]
Surety and Fidelity Industry Intern and Scholarship Program for Minority Students (Undergraduate/Scholarship) [9614]

Intelligence service

Afghanistan and Iraq War Veterans Scholarship (Undergraduate/Scholarship) [88]
CFR National Intelligence Fellowships (Professional development/Fellowship) [3443]
Jorge Espejel Contreras IALEIA Scholarship Award (Undergraduate/Scholarship) [5266]
Disabled War Veterans Scholarships (Undergraduate/Scholarship) [90]
Henley-Putnam University Scholarships (Other/Scholarship) [5267]

Interdisciplinary studies

BSF General Scholarship Awards (Undergraduate, Vocational/Occupational/Scholarship) [2197]
Ford Foundation Dissertation Fellowships (Graduate, Doctorate/Fellowship) [6675]
Ford Foundation Diversity Fellowships (Graduate, Doctorate, Postdoctorate, Postgraduate/Fellowship) [6676]
Ford Foundation Postdoctoral Fellowships (Postdoctorate/Fellowship) [6677]
Ford Foundation Predoctoral Fellowships (Graduate, Doctorate/Fellowship) [6678]
Heather McCallum Scholarships (Doctorate, Other/Scholarship) [1903]
O. Ruth McQuown Scholarship - Graduate Award for Current Students (Graduate/Scholarship) [10135]

Interior design

Paul Arnold Memorial Scholarships (Undergraduate/Scholarship) [8241]
ASID Foundation Legacy Scholarships for Graduate Students (Graduate/Scholarship) [1341]
Irene Winifred Eno Grants (Professional development/Grant) [1342]
IFDA Student Member Scholarships (Undergraduate/Scholarship) [5338]
International Furnishings and Design Association

Part-time Student Scholarships (Undergraduate/Scholarship) [5339]
Eloise Pitts O'More Scholarships (Undergraduate/Scholarship) [3247]
Vectorworks Design Scholarships (Undergraduate, Graduate/Scholarship, Prize) [10367]
Worldstudio AIGA Scholarships (Graduate, Undergraduate/Scholarship) [10709]

Internal medicine (See Medicine, Internal)

International affairs and relations

Americans for Informed Democracy Global Scholar Program (Undergraduate/Scholarship) [1532]
ARS of Eastern USA Lazarian Graduate Scholarship (Master's, Doctorate/Scholarship) [1680]
Samuel Flagg Bemis Dissertation Research Grants (Doctorate, Graduate/Grant) [9133]
Stuart L. Bernath Dissertation Grants (Doctorate, Graduate/Grant) [9134]
Myrna F. Bernath Fellowships (Doctorate, Graduate/Fellowship) [9135]
David L. Boren Fellowships (Graduate/Fellowship) [5199]
David L. Boren Scholarships (Undergraduate, College/Scholarship) [5200]
CFR Military Fellowships (Professional development/Fellowship) [3442]
CFR National Intelligence Fellowships (Professional development/Fellowship) [3443]
CFR Stanton Nuclear Security Fellowships (Doctorate, Postdoctorate, Advanced Professional/Fellowship) [3444]
CFR Volunteer Internships (Undergraduate, Graduate/Internship) [3445]
DACOR Graduate Fellowships for Study of International Affairs (Graduate, Master's/Fellowship) [3496]
D&A Florida Scholarships (Undergraduate/Scholarship) [9425]
Denton Scholarships (Graduate/Scholarship) [8897]
Robert A. and Barbara Divine Graduate Student Travel Grants (Graduate/Grant) [9136]
Alan R. and Barbara D. Finberg Fellowships (Graduate/Fellowship) [4998]
Mayme and Herb Frank Scholarship Program (Graduate, Undergraduate/Scholarship) [1782]
Lawrence Gelfand - Armin Rappaport - Walter LaFeber Dissertation Fellowships (Doctorate, Graduate/Fellowship) [9137]
ASIL Arthur C. Helton Fellowship Program (Professional development/Fellowship) [1344]
Conrad N. Hilton Scholarships (Undergraduate/Scholarship) [4414]
W. Stull Holt Dissertation Fellowships (Doctorate, Graduate/Fellowship) [9139]
International Affairs Fellowships in Japan (IAF-J) (Professional development/Fellowship) [3447]
International Affairs Fellowships in Nuclear Security (IAF-NS) (Professional development/Fellowship) [3448]
Harriet Irsay Scholarships (Graduate, Undergraduate/Scholarship) [927]
ISCALC International Scholarship Fund (Undergraduate/Scholarship) [4049]
Mackenzie King Travelling Scholarships (Graduate/Scholarship) [6367]
Lazarian Graduate Scholarships (Graduate/Scholarship) [1678]
John Allen Love Scholarships (Graduate, Undergraduate/Scholarship) [10304]
Mas Family Scholarships (Graduate, Undergraduate/Scholarship) [6304]
MPAC-DC Graduate Policy Fellowships (Graduate/Fellowship) [6630]
National Iranian American Council Fellowships (Graduate, Undergraduate/Fellowship) [7022]
James B. Pearson Fellowships (Graduate/Scholarship) [5659]
Pi Gamma Mu Scholarships (Graduate/Scholarship) [8133]
Thomas R. Pickering Graduate Foreign Affairs Fellowships (Graduate, Undergraduate/Fellowship) [10681]
Rangel Graduate Fellowship (Graduate/Fellowship) [8429]
Harold W. Rosenthal Fellowships in International Relations (Professional development/Fellowship, Internship) [2043]
SHAFR Dissertation Completion Fellowships (Doctorate/Fellowship) [9140]
TCAdvance Scholarships (Undergraduate/Scholarship) [9814]
University of Hawaii at Manoa Japan Travel Bureau Scholarships (Graduate, Undergraduate/Scholarship) [10142]
USGLC Internships - Communications (Undergraduate, Doctorate/Internship) [9949]
USGLC Internships - Government Relations (Undergraduate, Graduate/Internship) [9950]
USGLC Internships - Outreach (Undergraduate, Graduate/Internship) [9951]
USGLC Internships - Policy (Undergraduate, Graduate/Internship) [9952]
Women In Defense HORIZONS Scholarships (Graduate, Undergraduate/Scholarship) [10636]

Italian studies (See also Area and ethnic studies)

Italian Language Scholarships (Undergraduate/Scholarship) [7682]
NIAF Scholarships - General Category II (Undergraduate, Graduate, Postgraduate/Scholarship) [7028]

Japanese studies (See also Area and ethnic studies)

Mary Jane Hendrie Memorial Scholarships (Graduate, Undergraduate/Scholarship) [10287]
Japan Foundation, New York Doctoral Fellowship Program (Doctorate/Fellowship) [5537]
Japan Foundation, New York Long-Term Research Fellowship Program (Professional development/Fellowship) [5538]
Japan Foundation, New York Short-Term Fellowship Program (Professional development/Fellowship) [5539]
KCC-JEE Graduate Fellowships (Graduate/Fellowship) [5855]
The Shincho Graduate Fellowships for Study in Japan (Graduate/Fellowship) [5802]

Jazz (See Music, Jazz)

Jewish studies (See also Area and ethnic studies)

Evelyn Joy Abramowicz Memorial Scholarships (Undergraduate/Scholarship) [5568]
Awards for Judaic Studies and/or Studies in Israel (Undergraduate, Postgraduate/Scholarship) [5591]
Jenny Panitch Beckow Memorial Scholarships Canada (Undergraduate, Graduate/Scholarship) [5569]
Berkowitz Fellowships (Professional development/Fellowship) [9743]
Bernice and Gordon Brown Scholarships (Undergraduate, Graduate/Scholarship) [5573]
CJH Graduate Research Fellowships (Doctorate/Fellowship) [2851]
CJH Visiting Scholars Program (Doctorate/Fellowship) [2852]
Mark & Dorothy Danzker Scholarships (Postgraduate/Scholarship) [5592]
Jack Gitlitz CA Memorial Scholarships for Study in Israel (Undergraduate/Scholarship) [5577]
HBI-BGI Scholar-in-Residence Program (Undergraduate/Scholarship) [2359]
International Doctoral Scholarships for Studies Specializing in Jewish Fields (Doctorate/Scholarship, Award) [6411]
International Fellowships in Jewish Studies and Jewish Culture (Professional development/Fellowship) [6412]
International Scholarship Programs for Community Service (Undergraduate/Scholarship) [6413]
Mitchell Karper Memorial Scholarships (Undergraduate/Scholarship) [5579]
Loewenstein-Wiener Fellowship Award (Professional development/Fellowship) [947]
MFJC International Fellowships in Jewish Studies (Other/Fellowship) [6414]
NEH Fellowships for Senior Scholars (Doctorate/Fellowship) [2853]
Prins Foundation Fellowship for Senior Scholars (Doctorate/Fellowship) [2854]
Prins Foundation Post-Doctoral and Early Career Fellowship for Emigrating Scholars (Professional development, Postdoctorate/Fellowship) [2855]
Joseph S. Steinberg Emerging Jewish Filmmaker Fellowships (Undergraduate, Graduate/Fellowship) [2856]
Bernard Michael Tarshis Memorial Scholarships for Jewish Studies (Undergraduate/Scholarship) [5588]
Tikvah Fellowships (Graduate, Professional development/Fellowship) [9745]
Joel A. Weinstein Memorial Scholarships (Postgraduate, Undergraduate/Scholarship) [5594]
Wexner Graduate Fellowships/Davidson Scholars (Graduate/Fellowship) [10545]

Journalism

Leroy F. Aarons Scholarships (Graduate, Undergraduate/Scholarship) [7049]
AAS Fellowships for Creative and Performing Artists and Writers (Professional development/Fellowship, Award) [430]
Abe Fellowships for Journalists (Professional development/Fellowship) [9052]
Kyutaro and Yasuo Abiko Memorial Scholarships (Undergraduate/Scholarship) [5547]
Alaska Press Club Scholarships (Undergraduate/Scholarship) [10006]
Floyd S. Alford Jr. Scholarships (Undergraduate/Scholarship) [10212]
Phillip Alston Scholarships (Undergraduate/Scholarship) [10213]
American Quarter Horse Foundation Scholarships (Undergraduate/Scholarship) [1171]
APSA Congressional Fellowship for Communications Scholars and Journalists (Advanced Professional, Professional development/Fellowship) [1108]
APSA Congressional Fellowships for Journalists (Advanced Professional, Professional development/Fellowship) [1109]
ARRL Foundation PHD Scholarships (Undergraduate/Scholarship) [1724]
Asia Pacific Foundation of Canada Media Fellowships (Professional development/Fellowship) [4114]
AT&T Business Internship Awards (Undergraduate/Internship) [10214]
Atkinson Fellowships in Public Policy (Professional development/Fellowship) [2111]
Elaine Atwood Scholarship (Undergraduate/Scholarship) [10049]
Francis Warren Baker Memorial Scholarships (Undergraduate/Scholarship) [8910]
Jim Batten Community Newspaper Internships (Undergraduate/Internship) [10215]
Bob Baxter Scholarships (Graduate, Undergraduate/Scholarship) [7106]
N.S. Beinstock Fellowships (Other/Fellowship) [8402]
Pete and Ellen Bensley Memorial Scholarship Fund (Undergraduate/Scholarship) [4178]
Lester G. Benz Memorial Scholarships for College Journalism Study (Other/Scholarship) [8396]
Reid Blackburn Scholarships (Undergraduate/Scholarship) [7107]
Tom Bost Scholarships (Undergraduate/Scholarship) [10217]
William (Billbo) Boston/Harold Knopp Scholarship (Undergraduate/Scholarship) [7815]
Rick Brewer Scholarships (Undergraduate/Scholarship) [10218]
Carlos M. Castaneda Journalism Scholarships

JOURNALISM

(Graduate/Scholarship) [2807]
CJF Canadian Journalism Fellowships *(Graduate, Other, Undergraduate/Fellowship)* [4117]
Michele Clark Fellowships *(Undergraduate/Fellowship)* [8403]
Greg Clerk Awards *(Advanced Professional, Professional development/Award)* [4118]
Ardis Cohoon Scholarships *(Undergraduate/Scholarship)* [10220]
Kathryn M. Cronin Scholarships *(Undergraduate/Scholarship)* [10222]
D&A Florida Scholarships *(Undergraduate/Scholarship)* [9425]
James Davis Scholarships *(Undergraduate/Scholarship)* [10224]
Robert Winchester Dodson Scholarships *(Undergraduate/Scholarship)* [10225]
Harold K. Douthit Regional Scholarships *(Undergraduate/Scholarship)* [7576]
Richard Drukker Memorial Scholarships *(Undergraduate/Scholarship)* [7326]
Bob East Scholarships *(Graduate, Undergraduate/Scholarship)* [7108]
Ed Bradley Scholarships *(Undergraduate/Scholarship)* [8404]
Edward R. Murrow Press Fellowships *(Professional development/Fellowship)* [3446]
Faith Initiatives Internships - New York *(Undergraduate, Graduate/Internship)* [4432]
Reese Felts Scholarships *(Undergraduate/Scholarship)* [10226]
Alan R. and Barbara D. Finberg Fellowships *(Graduate/Fellowship)* [4998]
Allison E. Fisher Scholarships *(Undergraduate, Graduate/Scholarship)* [4068]
Ameel J. Fisher Scholarships *(Undergraduate/Scholarship)* [10227]
Florida Outdoor Writers Association Scholarships *(Undergraduate/Scholarship)* [4104]
Paul B. and Aline Flynn Scholarships *(Undergraduate/Scholarship)* [9429]
Emanuel R. Freedman Scholarships *(Graduate, Undergraduate/Scholarship)* [7772]
Guy P. Gannett Scholarships *(Undergraduate/Scholarship)* [6195]
Joel Garcia Memorial Scholarship *(Undergraduate/Scholarship)* [2825]
Garikian Scholarship Fund *(Undergraduate/Scholarship)* [1694]
Kays Gary Scholarships *(Undergraduate/Scholarship)* [10229]
George Foreman Tribute to Lyndon B. Johnson Scholarships *(Undergraduate/Scholarship)* [8405]
Joy Gibson Scholarships *(Undergraduate/Scholarship)* [10231]
Keith Gilmore Foundation - Diploma Scholarships *(Other/Scholarship)* [4423]
Keith Gilmore Foundation - Postgraduate Scholarships *(Postgraduate/Scholarship)* [4424]
Keith Gilmore Foundation - Undergraduate Scholarships *(Undergraduate/Scholarship)* [4425]
GLAAD Spanish-Language and Latino Media Internships - Los Angeles *(Undergraduate, Graduate/Internship)* [4436]
GLAAD Youth Issues Internships - New York *(Undergraduate, Graduate/Internship)* [4437]
Howard L. Green Scholarships *(Undergraduate/Scholarship)* [7317]
Elizabeth Greenhalgh Memorial Scholarships in Journalism, Graphic Arts, or Photography *(Undergraduate/Scholarship)* [10639]
Harvey Fellows Program *(Graduate/Fellowship)* [6632]
Charles Hauser Scholarships *(Undergraduate/Scholarship)* [10232]
Paul Green Houston Scholarships *(Undergraduate/Scholarship)* [10233]
James F. Hurley III Bicentennial Merit Scholarships *(Undergraduate/Scholarship)* [10234]
INF Scholarships *(Undergraduate/Scholarship)* [5472]
Inter American Press Association Scholarships *(Undergraduate/Scholarship)* [9061]
International Foodservice Editorial Council Scholarships *(Graduate, Undergraduate/Scholarship)* [5331]

Iowa Journalism Institute Scholarships *(Undergraduate/Scholarship)* [5473]
Harriet Irsay Scholarships *(Graduate, Undergraduate/Scholarship)* [927]
Edward Jackson International Scholarships *(Undergraduate/Scholarship)* [10235]
JCCF Equal Voice Journalism Scholarship *(Professional development/Scholarship)* [10152]
JEA Future Teacher Scholarships *(Undergraduate, Master's/Scholarship)* [5625]
Sister Rita Jeanne Scholarships *(Undergraduate/Monetary, Scholarship)* [5626]
Kaiser Media Fellowships in Health Reporting *(Advanced Professional, Professional development/Fellowship)* [5648]
Glenn Keever Scholarships *(Undergraduate/Scholarship)* [10236]
Anna-Maria and Stephen M. Kellen Fellowships *(Professional development/Fellowship)* [726]
Alexander Kendrick Memorial Scholarships *(Graduate, Undergraduate/Scholarship)* [7773]
Bernard Kilgore Memorial Scholarships *(Undergraduate/Scholarship)* [7327]
Kit C. King Graduate Scholarships *(Graduate/Scholarship)* [7109]
Kiplinger Fellowship *(Professional development/Fellowship)* [7599]
John S. Knight Fellowships *(Other/Fellowship)* [5849]
Knight-Wallace Fellowship *(Professional development/Fellowship)* [5851]
William D. Krahling Excellence in Journalism Scholarships *(Undergraduate/Scholarship)* [361]
Irene Corbally Kuhn Scholarships *(Graduate, Undergraduate/Scholarship)* [7774]
Elaine Johnson Lampert Journalism Memorial Adelphe Scholarship *(Graduate/Award)* [5745]
Lazarian Graduate Scholarships *(Graduate/Scholarship)* [1678]
Flora Lewis Memorial Scholarships *(Graduate, Undergraduate/Scholarship)* [7775]
Lilly Scholarships in Religion for Journalists *(Other/Scholarship)* [8549]
Kay Longcope Scholarships *(Graduate, Undergraduate/Scholarship)* [7050]
Warren Mack Scholarship *(Undergraduate/Scholarship)* [5622]
Dr. Julianne Malveaux Scholarships *(Undergraduate/Scholarship)* [6762]
Raleigh Mann Scholarships *(Undergraduate/Scholarship)* [10238]
Art Margosian Scholarship *(Undergraduate/Scholarship)* [5623]
Mas Family Scholarships *(Graduate, Undergraduate/Scholarship)* [6304]
Maxwell Graduate Scholarships in Medical Journalism *(Graduate/Scholarship)* [10240]
Durwood McAlister Scholarships *(Undergraduate/Scholarship)* [4387]
McClatchy Minority Scholarship and Fellowship *(Undergraduate/Scholarship)* [9369]
McCloy Fellowships in Environmental Policy *(Professional development/Fellowship)* [728]
McCloy Fellowships in Journalism *(Professional development/Fellowship)* [729]
Anne O'Hare McCormick Scholarship Fund *(Graduate/Scholarship)* [7429]
C.A. "Pete" McKnight Scholarships *(Undergraduate/Scholarship)* [10242]
Edward Heywood Megson Scholarships *(Undergraduate/Scholarship)* [10243]
Michener-Deacon Fellowship for Journalism Education *(Professional development/Fellowship)* [4121]
Quincy Sharpe Mills Memorial Scholarships *(Undergraduate/Scholarship)* [10244]
Jacque I. Minnotte Health Reporting Fellowships *(Other/Fellowship)* [8406]
Morris Newspaper Corp. Scholarships *(Undergraduate/Scholarship)* [4388]
Muddy Waters Scholarships *(Undergraduate/Scholarship)* [2316]
National Iranian American Council Fellowships *(Graduate, Undergraduate/Fellowship)* [7022]
Edward J. Nell Memorial Scholarships in Journalism *(Undergraduate/Scholarship)* [8397]

Elizabeth Neuffer Fellowships *(Other/Fellowship)* [5458]
New York Financial Writers' Associations Scholarships *(Graduate, Undergraduate/Scholarship)* [7354]
New York Women in Communications, Inc. Foundation Scholarships *(Graduate, Undergraduate/Scholarship)* [7406]
NPPF Still and Multimedia Scholarships *(Undergraduate/Scholarship)* [7110]
NPPF TV News Scholarships *(Undergraduate/Scholarship)* [7111]
NYFWA Scholarships *(Undergraduate, Graduate/Scholarship)* [7355]
Ohio Newspaper Association Minority Scholarships *(Undergraduate/Scholarship)* [7577]
Ohio Newspaper Association University Journalism Scholarships *(Undergraduate/Scholarship)* [7578]
Frank del Olmo Memorial Scholarships *(Undergraduate/Scholarship)* [2826]
ONWA Annual Scholarships *(Undergraduate/Scholarship)* [7579]
Overseas Press Club Foundation Harper's Magazine Scholarships *(Graduate, Undergraduate/Scholarship)* [7776]
Overseas Press Club Foundation Reuters Scholarships *(Graduate, Undergraduate/Scholarship)* [7777]
Scott Pearlman Field Awards for Science and Exploration *(Other/Award)* [3946]
Pete Wilson Graduate Scholarships *(Graduate, Undergraduate/Scholarship)* [8407]
Pete Wilson Journalism Scholarships *(Graduate, Undergraduate/Scholarship)* [8408]
Steve Petix Journalism Scholarships *(Undergraduate/Scholarship)* [8721]
Stephen D. Pisinski Memorial Scholarships *(Undergraduate/Scholarship)* [8376]
Robert Pittman Scholarships-Internships *(Undergraduate/Scholarship, Internship)* [10245]
Carter Pitts Scholarships *(Undergraduate/Scholarship)* [5474]
Erwin Potts Scholarships *(Undergraduate/Scholarship)* [10246]
Lou and Carole Prato Sports Reporting Scholarships *(Undergraduate/Scholarship)* [8409]
Peter DeWitt Pruden and Phyliss Harrill Pruden Scholarships *(Undergraduate/Scholarship)* [10247]
Pulliam/Kilgore Freedom of Information Internships *(Undergraduate/Internship)* [9279]
Bob Quincy Scholarships *(Undergraduate/Scholarship)* [10248]
Marjorie Usher Ragan Scholarships *(Undergraduate/Scholarship)* [10249]
Reuters Institute Visiting Fellowships *(Professional development/Fellowship)* [10265]
Mike Reynolds Journalism Scholarships *(Undergraduate/Scholarship)* [8410]
Eugene L. Roberts Jr. Prize *(Undergraduate/Prize)* [10250]
William C. Rogers Scholarships *(Undergraduate/Scholarship)* [4389]
Richard J. Roth Journalism Fellowships *(Graduate/Fellowship)* [7369]
Roy Rowan Scholarships *(Graduate, Undergraduate/Scholarship)* [7778]
RTDNA Presidents Scholarships *(Undergraduate/Scholarship)* [8411]
SAJA Journalism Scholarships *(Undergraduate, Graduate/Scholarship)* [9356]
David R. Schweisberg Memorial Scholarships *(Graduate, Undergraduate/Scholarship)* [7779]
Carole Simpson Scholarships *(Undergraduate/Scholarship)* [8412]
Ward Sims Memorial Scholarships *(Undergraduate/Scholarship)* [10038]
Drue Smith/Society of Professional Journalists Scholarships *(Undergraduate/Scholarship)* [3252]
A.C. Snow and Katherine Snow Smith Scholarship *(Undergraduate/Scholarship)* [10251]
South Carolina Scholastic Press Association Scholarships *(Undergraduate/Scholarship)* [9370]
South Carolina Scholastic Press Association Yearbook Scholarships *(Undergraduate/Scholarship)* [9371]

Sports Internships - Los Angeles *(Undergraduate, Graduate/Internship)* [4440]
Standard and Poor's Award for Economic and Business Reporting - S&P Scholarships *(Graduate, Undergraduate/Scholarship)* [7780]
H.L. Stevenson Scholarships *(Graduate, Undergraduate/Scholarship)* [7781]
Jay A. Strassberg Memorial Scholarships *(Undergraduate/Scholarship)* [2517]
Sturgulewski Family Scholarship *(Graduate, Undergraduate/Scholarship)* [10074]
Hatton W. Sumners Endowed Undergraduate School Scholarships *(Undergraduate/Scholarship)* [9609]
Hatton W. Sumners Non-Endowed Undergraduate and Graduate Scholarships *(Undergraduate, Graduate/Scholarship)* [9610]
Kirk Sutlive Scholarships *(Undergraduate/Scholarship)* [4390]
Stan Swinton Scholarships *(Graduate, Undergraduate/Scholarship)* [7782]
Taylor/Blakeslee University Fellowships *(Other, Undergraduate/Fellowship)* [3429]
Trans Issues Internships - New York *(Undergraduate, Graduate/Internship)* [4441]
Tucker Family Scholarships *(Undergraduate/Scholarship)* [10254]
UAA GCI, Inc. Scholarship *(Undergraduate/Scholarship)* [10080]
UAA Kimura Scholarship Fund for Photography *(Undergraduate/Scholarship)* [10082]
UAF College of Liberal Arts - Anchorage Daily News Journalism Awards *(Undergraduate/Scholarship)* [10094]
David Julian Wichard Scholarships *(Undergraduate/Scholarship)* [10255]
Tom Wicker Scholarships *(Graduate/Scholarship)* [10256]
Glenn Wilson Broadcast Journalism Scholarships *(Undergraduate/Scholarship)* [7873]
Theo Wilson Scholarships *(Graduate, Undergraduate/Scholarship)* [7783]
WTVD Endowment Scholarships *(Undergraduate/Scholarship)* [10257]

Korean studies

Fall Fellowships in Korean Studies *(Other/Fellowship)* [5870]
Korean Language Study Awards *(Graduate/Scholarship)* [5871]

Labor relations (See Industrial and labor relations)

Laboratory technology (See Medical laboratory technology)

Land economics (See Land management)

Land management

Anchor QEA Environmental Scholarships *(Graduate/Scholarship)* [1551]
Appraisal Institute Education Trust Undergraduate Scholarships *(Undergraduate/Scholarship)* [1596]
HSF/Marathon Oil College Scholarship Program *(Undergraduate/Scholarship)* [4905]
Ivanhoe Foundation Fellowships *(Master's/Fellowship)* [5488]
NASLR Mined Land Reclamation Educational Grant *(Undergraduate/Scholarship, Grant)* [6792]
NGC College Scholarships *(Graduate, Undergraduate/Scholarship)* [6965]

Landscape architecture and design

AIA Alaska Scholarships *(Graduate, Undergraduate/Scholarship)* [893]
Anchor QEA Environmental Scholarships *(Graduate/Scholarship)* [1551]

ASLA Council of Fellow Scholarships *(Undergraduate/Scholarship)* [1346]
ASLA Council of Fellows Scholarships *(Undergraduate/Scholarship)* [5913]
CLCA Landscape Educational Advancement Foundation Educational Grant Program *(Undergraduate/Grant)* [2467]
Garden Club Council of Winston-Salem and Forsyth County Council Scholarships *(Undergraduate/Scholarship)* [10583]
Steven G. King Play Environments Scholarships *(Undergraduate/Scholarship)* [5914]
LAF Landscape Forms Design for People Scholarships *(Undergraduate/Scholarship)* [5915]
Mellon Fellowships in Urban Landscape Studies *(Graduate, Master's, Doctorate/Fellowship)* [3739]
MNLA Academic Scholarships *(Undergraduate/Scholarship)* [6474]
NGC College Scholarships *(Graduate, Undergraduate/Scholarship)* [6965]
Peridian International, Inc./Rae L. Price, FASLA Scholarship *(Undergraduate/Scholarship)* [1347]
Peridian International, Inc./Rae L. Price, FASLA Scholarships *(Undergraduate/Scholarship)* [5916]
Rain Bird Intelligent Use of Water Scholarships *(Undergraduate/Scholarship)* [5917]
Enid W. and Bernard B. Spigel Architectural Scholarships *(Graduate, Undergraduate/Scholarship)* [4706]
Vectorworks Design Scholarships *(Undergraduate, Graduate/Scholarship, Prize)* [10367]
Hawaii Chapter/David T. Woolsey Scholarships *(Undergraduate, Graduate, Professional development/Scholarship)* [5918]
Worldstudio AIGA Scholarships *(Graduate, Undergraduate/Scholarship)* [10709]

Languages (See Foreign languages)

Latin American studies (See also Area and ethnic studies)

FAIC Latin American and Caribbean Scholars Program *(Other/Scholarship)* [908]
Foundation of American Institute for Conservation Lecture Grants *(Other/Grant)* [909]
Catarino and Evangelina Hernández Research Fellowships in Latino History *(Advanced Professional/Fellowship)* [9713]
IAF Fellowships *(Doctorate/Fellowship)* [5232]
Leo S. Rowe Pan American Fund *(Graduate, Undergraduate/Loan)* [7730]
Arthur M. Schlesinger, Jr. Fellowships *(Professional development/Fellowship)* [5603]
Thesaurus Linguae Latinae Fellowships (TTL) *(Doctorate/Fellowship)* [9107]
UC MEXUS-CICESE Graduate Student Short-Term Research and Training Program *(Master's, Doctorate, Postdoctorate/Grant)* [10110]
UC MEXUS Dissertation Research Grants *(Graduate/Grant)* [10119]
UC MEXUS Grants for Dissertation Research *(Graduate/Grant)* [10111]
UC MEXUS Small Grants for UC Faculty *(Graduate/Grant)* [10123]
UC MEXUS Small Grants for UC Postdocs *(Postdoctorate/Grant)* [10124]
UC MEXUS Small Grants for UC Students *(Graduate, Postdoctorate/Grant)* [10125]
UF Center for Latin American Studies FLAS Summer Fellowships *(Master's, Graduate, Undergraduate/Award, Fellowship)* [10133]

Law

AAJ Trial Advocacy Scholarships *(Undergraduate/Scholarship)* [515]
AALL Leadership Academy Grants *(Professional development/Grant)* [519]
AALL Minority Leadership Development Award *(Graduate/Award)* [520]
AALL Research Funds *(Professional development/Grant)* [521]
AALL Technical Services SIS Active Member Grant

(Professional development/Grant) [523]
AALL Technical Services SIS Experienced Member General Grant *(Professional development/Grant)* [524]
AALL Technical Services SIS Leadership Academy Grant *(Professional development/Grant)* [525]
AALL Technical Services SIS Management Institute Grant *(Professional development/Grant)* [526]
AALL Technical Services SIS New Member General Grant *(Professional development/Grant)* [527]
AAUW Selected Professions Fellowships *(Graduate, Master's, Doctorate/Fellowship)* [22]
ABF Doctoral/Post-Doctoral Fellowships *(Doctorate, Graduate/Fellowship)* [622]
ABF Law and Social Science Dissertation Fellowship and Mentoring Program *(Graduate/Fellowship)* [623]
ABF Montgomery Summer Research Diversity Fellowships in Law and Social Science *(Undergraduate/Scholarship)* [624]
Accenture American Indian Scholarship Program *(Graduate, Undergraduate/Scholarship)* [880]
ACS Law Fellowships *(Graduate/Fellowship)* [716]
Adler Pollock & Sheehan Diversity Scholarships *(Undergraduate/Scholarship)* [71]
Affirmative Action Student Scholarship Mini-Grant Travel Awards *(Undergraduate, Master's, Doctorate/Grant)* [30]
Justice John F. Aiso Scholarships *(Undergraduate/Scholarship)* [5541]
Akron Bar Association Foundation Scholarships *(Undergraduate/Scholarship)* [182]
Neil Alexander Scholarships *(Undergraduate/Scholarship)* [6688]
ALL-SIS Conference of Newer Law Librarians Grants *(Professional development/Grant)* [528]
Alliance Defending Freedom - Blackstone Legal Fellowships *(Undergraduate/Fellowship)* [331]
Tillie B. Alperin Scholarship *(Undergraduate/Scholarship)* [10156]
American Association of University Women Selected Professions Fellowships *(Other/Fellowship)* [603]
American Counsel Association Scholarships *(Undergraduate/Scholarship)* [748]
American Criminal Justice Association - Lambda Alpha Epsilon Student Scholarships - Graduate Level *(Graduate, Master's, Doctorate/Scholarship)* [753]
American Enterprise Institute National Research Initiative Fellowships (NRI) *(Graduate/Fellowship)* [786]
American Judges Association Law Student Essay Competition *(Undergraduate/Prize)* [952]
American Psychology-Law Society Dissertation Awards *(Graduate/Award)* [1155]
American Psychology-Law Society Early Career Professional Grants-In-Aid *(Other/Grant)* [1156]
American Psychology-Law Society Student Grants-In-Aid *(Graduate/Grant)* [1157]
Grace Andow Memorial Scholarships *(Undergraduate, Graduate/Scholarship)* [5548]
Anheuser-Busch NAPABA Law Foundation Presidential Scholarships *(Undergraduate/Scholarship)* [6703]
APABA-SV Scholarships *(Advanced Professional/Scholarship)* [1786]
Appalachian School of Law Merit Scholarship Program *(Undergraduate/Scholarship)* [1590]
Arent Fox Diversity Scholarships *(Graduate, Juris Doctorate/Scholarship)* [1621]
Armenian Bar Association Graduate Scholarships in Law *(Graduate/Scholarship)* [1669]
ARS of Eastern USA Lazarian Graduate Scholarship *(Master's, Doctorate/Scholarship)* [1680]
Benjamin Asbell Memorial Scholarships *(Undergraduate/Scholarship)* [2507]
Asian/Pacific Bar Association of Sacramento Law Foundation Scholarship *(Graduate, Postgraduate/Scholarship)* [1790]
Associated Women for Pepperdine Scholarships *(Undergraduate/Scholarship)* [7962]
Attorney-CPA Foundation Scholarships *(Postgraduate/Scholarship)* [391]
H. Thomas Austern Memorial Writing Competition *(Doctorate/Award, Prize)* [4127]

William Stone Ayres Scholarship *(Undergraduate/Scholarship)* [3661]
Baker Donelson Diversity Scholarships *(Undergraduate/Scholarship)* [2170]
Baker and Hostetler Diversity Fellowships *(Undergraduate/Fellowship)* [2172]
Baker and McKenzie Diversity Fellowships *(Postgraduate, Professional development/Fellowship)* [2175]
Baker and McKenzie Graduate Legal Studies Scholarships *(Graduate, Professional development/Scholarship)* [2176]
Donald W. Banner Diversity Scholarships for Law Students *(Graduate/Scholarship)* [2190]
Mark T. Banner Scholarships for Law Students *(Postgraduate/Scholarship)* [6093]
Eivind H. Barth, Jr. Memorial Scholarships *(Undergraduate/Scholarship)* [2508]
Helen Bassett Commemorative Student Award *(Undergraduate, Graduate/Scholarship)* [7221]
Bay Area Minority Law Student Scholarships *(Graduate, Undergraduate/Scholarship)* [2195]
Beck-Pfann Memorial Scholarships *(Undergraduate/Scholarship)* [7964]
Harvey Bell Memorial Prize *(Graduate/Award)* [10271]
Arthur Lockwood Beneventi Law Scholarships *(Undergraduate/Scholarship)* [7149]
Viscount Bennett Fellowships *(Graduate/Fellowship)* [2581]
Berkowitz Fellowships *(Professional development/Fellowship)* [9743]
Hon. Peggy Bernheim Memorial Scholarships *(Undergraduate/Scholarship)* [2377]
Robert L. Bernstein Fellowships in International Human Rights *(Graduate/Fellowship)* [4994]
Beverly Estate Scholarship *(Undergraduate/Scholarship)* [3662]
Thomas F. Black, Jr. Memorial Scholarships *(Undergraduate/Scholarship)* [8600]
William Verbon Black Scholarships *(Undergraduate/Scholarship)* [205]
Lucie and Thornton Blackburn Scholarships *(Graduate, Juris Doctorate/Scholarship)* [2544]
David and Camille Boatwright Endowed Scholarships *(Undergraduate/Scholarship)* [7965]
Bohemian Lawyers Association of Chicago Scholarships *(Graduate/Scholarship)* [2333]
George and Mary Brammer Scholarship *(Undergraduate/Scholarship)* [3663]
Farella Braun + Martel LLP 1L Diversity Scholarship Program *(Undergraduate/Scholarship)* [3968]
Ann Marie Bredefeld Scholarships *(Undergraduate/Scholarship)* [7966]
Margaret Martin Brock Scholarships in Law *(Undergraduate/Scholarship)* [7967]
Kae and Kay Brockermeyer Endowed Scholarships *(Undergraduate/Scholarship)* [7968]
Shirley J. Brooke Endowed Scholarships *(Undergraduate/Scholarship)* [7969]
Peggy Browning Fund - Chicago School-Year Fellowships *(Graduate, Undergraduate/Fellowship)* [2394]
Buckfire & Buckfire, P.C. Law School Diversity Scholarships *(Graduate/Scholarship)* [2399]
Buder Scholarships for American Indian Law Students *(Juris Doctorate/Scholarship)* [10474]
Sam Bull Memorial Scholarships *(Undergraduate/Scholarship)* [248]
William S. Bullinger Scholarships *(Doctorate/Scholarship)* [3983]
Johnston Cabaniss Scholarships *(Graduate/Scholarship)* [206]
California Bar Foundation 1L Diversity Scholarships *(Graduate/Scholarship)* [2442]
California Bar Foundation 3L Diversity Scholarships *(Undergraduate/Scholarship)* [2443]
CALL/ACBD Education Reserve Fund Grants *(Professional development/Grant)* [2561]
CALL/ACBD Research Grants *(Graduate/Grant)* [2562]
Brian Campion Scholarship Scholarships *(Advanced Professional/Scholarship)* [10781]
Canadian Association of Law Teachers Award for Academic Excellence *(Other/Award)* [2566]
Canadian Association for the Practical Study of Law in Education Fellowships *(Graduate/Fellowship)* [2573]
Canadian Energy Law Foundation Graduate Scholarships in Law *(Advanced Professional/Scholarship)* [2620]
Canadian Institute for Advanced Legal Studies French Language Scholarships *(Graduate, Advanced Professional/Scholarship)* [5149]
Canadian IT Law Association Student Writing Contest *(Undergraduate/Prize)* [2020]
Dan Carman Attorney at Law Criminal Defense Scholarships *(Advanced Professional/Scholarship)* [3520]
Robert C. Carson Memorial Bursary *(Undergraduate/Scholarship)* [270]
Fraser Milner Casgrain LLP Scholarships *(Graduate, Juris Doctorate/Scholarship)* [2280]
Catzman Awards for Professionalism and Civility *(Advanced Professional, Professional development/Award)* [80]
CCLA Summer Legal Internships *(Graduate/Internship)* [1892]
CEJIL Legal Internships *(Graduate, Professional development/Internship)* [2861]
CF Abogados Legal Scholarships *(Graduate/Scholarship)* [2781]
CHCI Graduate Fellowships *(Graduate/Fellowship)* [3352]
CHRGJ Emerging Human Rights Scholarship Conference *(Graduate/Scholarship)* [7398]
CHRGJ International Human Rights Fellowships *(Doctorate, Professional development/Fellowship, Internship)* [7399]
CHRGJ Students Human Rights Scholars Program *(Graduate, Advanced Professional, Professional development/Scholarship)* [7400]
Almeric Christian Memorial Scholarships *(Graduate/Scholarship)* [10392]
CIHR Health Law, Ethics and Policy Fellowships *(Graduate/Fellowship)* [2942]
CISDL Global Research Fellowship - Associate Fellows *(Graduate/Fellowship)* [2880]
CISDL Global Research Fellowship - Legal Research Fellows *(Graduate/Fellowship)* [2881]
CISDL Global Research Fellowships - Senior Research Fellows *(Other/Fellowship)* [2882]
City Bar Diversity Fellowships Program *(Undergraduate/Fellowship)* [7343]
CJA Legal Internships *(Professional development/Internship)* [2858]
CLA-ACE Internship Program *(Graduate, Juris Doctorate/Internship)* [6013]
Athalie Clarke Endowed Scholarships *(Undergraduate/Scholarship)* [7970]
Brian Dane Cleary Memorial Scholarships *(Undergraduate/Scholarship)* [7971]
Justice Robert L. Clifford Fellowships *(Undergraduate/Fellowship)* [6593]
Claude T. Coffman Memorial Scholarships *(Undergraduate/Scholarship)* [10157]
John R. Colvin Legal Scholarships *(Graduate/Scholarship)* [3154]
Community Legal Services of Philadelphia Fellowships *(Postgraduate/Fellowship)* [3337]
Constangy, Brooks and Smith Diversity Scholars Awards *(Undergraduate/Award)* [3407]
Consumer Law Public Service Fellowships *(Undergraduate/Fellowship)* [8433]
Cooley Diversity Fellowship *(Graduate, Undergraduate/Fellowship)* [3416]
Valdemar A. Cordova Scholarships *(Undergraduate/Award)* [6110]
Hon. Joseph W. Cowgill Memorial Scholarships *(Undergraduate/Scholarship)* [2509]
Mable B. Crawford Memorial Scholarships *(Undergraduate/Scholarship)* [10015]
CTRF Scholarships for Graduate Study in Transportation *(Graduate/Scholarship)* [2764]
Cuban American Bar Association Scholarships *(All/Scholarship)* [3485]
John J. Curtin, Jr. Fellowships *(Undergraduate/Fellowship)* [620]
D&A Florida Scholarships *(Undergraduate/Scholarship)* [9425]
The Hugh and Hazel Darling Dean Scholarships *(Undergraduate/Scholarship)* [7972]
Darling Foundation Endowed School of Law Scholarships *(Undergraduate/Scholarship)* [7973]
DBA Student Scholarships *(Undergraduate/Scholarship)* [3653]
Martha Delman and Milton Arthur Krug Endowed Scholarships *(Undergraduate/Scholarship)* [7974]
Dezao Legal Awards *(Advanced Professional/Scholarship)* [5959]
Edward D. Di Loreto-Odell S. McConnell Scholarships *(Undergraduate/Scholarship)* [7975]
Carol DiMaiti Scholarship Awards *(Undergraduate/Scholarship)* [6308]
Raymond DiPaglia Endowment Scholarship *(Undergraduate/Scholarship)* [3664]
Discover Bar Exam Loans *(Graduate/Loan)* [3634]
Discover Law Loans *(Graduate/Loan)* [3637]
Diversity Fellowship Program (DFP) *(Undergraduate/Fellowship)* [6589]
Daniel B. Dixon Scholarships *(Undergraduate/Scholarship)* [324]
Grace O. Doane Scholarship *(Undergraduate/Scholarship)* [3665]
Hon. Ralph W.E. Donges Memorial Scholarships *(Undergraduate/Scholarship)* [2510]
Joseph M. Dorgan Scholarship *(Undergraduate/Scholarship)* [3666]
Drake University Law School Law Opportunity Scholarships - Disadvantage *(Undergraduate/Scholarship)* [3667]
Drake University Law School Law Opportunity Scholarships - Diversity *(Undergraduate/Scholarship)* [3668]
Drake University Law School Public Service Scholarships *(Undergraduate/Scholarship)* [3669]
C. Cleveland Drennon, Jr. Memorial Scholarships *(Undergraduate/Scholarship)* [10158]
Thomas J. Drinan Memorial Fellowships *(Undergraduate/Fellowship)* [8434]
DuBois Brothers Scholarships *(Undergraduate/Scholarship)* [2511]
Josephine P. White Eagle Scholarships *(Undergraduate, Graduate/Scholarship)* [4911]
Earl Warren Civil Rights Training Scholarships *(Graduate/Scholarship)* [6645]
Robert E. Early Memorial Scholarship *(Undergraduate/Scholarship)* [3670]
Mike Eidson Scholarships *(Graduate, Undergraduate/Scholarship)* [516]
Herman E. Elgar Memorial Scholarship *(Undergraduate/Scholarship)* [3671]
Equal Justice Works Fellowship Program *(Graduate, Undergraduate/Fellowship)* [3918]
Judge Samuel J. Ervin, III Fellowships *(Graduate/Fellowship)* [6004]
R. Wayne Estes Endowed Scholarships *(Undergraduate/Scholarship)* [7976]
Evans and Petree Law Firm Scholarship *(Undergraduate/Scholarship)* [10159]
Clifton W. Everett, Sr. Community Lawyer Fellowships *(Graduate/Fellowship)* [6005]
The Expert Institute Legal Blog Post Writing Contest *(Graduate/Award)* [3942]
Faegre Baker Daniels Diversity & Inclusion Fellowships *(Graduate/Fellowship)* [3954]
D.J. Fairgrave Education Trust *(Undergraduate/Scholarship)* [3672]
Judge McIntyre Faries Scholarships *(Undergraduate/Scholarship)* [7977]
Walter Moran Farmer Scholarships *(Juris Doctorate/Scholarship)* [10475]
FCBA Foundation Internship Stipends for Law Students *(Professional development/Internship)* [3973]
FCBA Foundation Law School Scholarships *(Postgraduate/Scholarship)* [3974]
FCIL Schaffer Grants for Foreign Law Librarians *(Professional development/Grant)* [529]
Federal Court Bench and Bar Scholarships *(Undergraduate/Scholarship)* [10160]
John E. Fenton, Jr. Public Service Awards *(Postgraduate/Fellowship)* [8435]
Filipino Bar Association of Northern California Scholarships (FBANC) *(Advanced Professional/Scholarship)* [4022]
Alan R. and Barbara D. Finberg Fellowships *(Graduate/Fellowship)* [4998]

LAW

Fred Finch Scholarships *(Undergraduate/Scholarship)* [9816]
Finnegan Diversity Scholarships *(Juris Doctorate/Scholarship)* [4030]
Fish & Richardson 1L Diversity Fellowships *(Undergraduate/Scholarship)* [4066]
Scott A. Flahive Memorial Scholarship Fund *(Undergraduate/Scholarship)* [4516]
Florence Young Memorial Scholarships *(Master's/Scholarship)* [1833]
Leland Stanford Forrest Scholarship *(Undergraduate/Scholarship)* [3673]
Howard Fox Memorial Law Scholarships *(Graduate/Scholarship)* [2235]
Franchise Law Diversity Scholarship Awards *(Undergraduate/Scholarship)* [5336]
John Hope Franklin Prize *(Other/Prize)* [5971]
Fraser Stryker Diversity Scholarships *(Undergraduate/Scholarship)* [4293]
Fredrikson and Byron Foundation Minority Scholarships *(Undergraduate/Scholarship)* [4297]
Fried, Frank, Harris, Shriver and Jacobson Fellowships *(Graduate/Fellowship)* [4303]
Froberg-Suess JD/MBA Scholarships *(Undergraduate/Scholarship)* [7978]
Gerald Garner Memorial Scholarships *(Undergraduate/Scholarship)* [7979]
NWT Law Foundation/Graeme Garson Scholarships *(Advanced Professional/Scholarship)* [7554]
Joseph H. Gellert/Dutchess County Bar Association Scholarships *(Undergraduate/Scholarship)* [3744]
John J. Gibbons Fellowships in Public Interest and Constitutional Law *(Professional development/Fellowship)* [4421]
Terry M. Giles Honor Scholar Program *(Undergraduate/Scholarship)* [7980]
Jane S. Glenn Memorial Endowed Scholarships *(Undergraduate/Scholarship)* [8626]
Goodman Acker Scholarships *(Graduate/Scholarship)* [4489]
Government Documents Special Interest Section - Veronica Maclay Student Grants *(Master's/Grant)* [530]
Wilford Hayes Gowen Scholarship Fund *(Undergraduate/Scholarship)* [10161]
William L. Graddy Law School Scholarships *(Graduate/Scholarship)* [9432]
Graduate Research Awards for Disarmament, Arms Control and Non-Proliferation *(Master's, Doctorate/Award)* [8961]
Graham and Dunn 1L Diversity Fellowships *(Graduate/Fellowship)* [4506]
Camille F. Gravel, Jr. Scholarships *(Professional development/Scholarship)* [6114]
Alexander G. Gray, Jr. Scholarships *(Graduate/Scholarship)* [6340]
Philip F. Greco Memorial Scholarships *(Undergraduate/Scholarship)* [6170]
Priscilla Green Scholarships *(Undergraduate/Scholarship)* [3465]
Leslie C. Green Veterans Scholarships *(Juris Doctorate, Advanced Professional/Scholarship)* [3458]
Michael Greenberg Student Writing Competition *(Graduate/Monetary, Scholarship)* [7052]
Guy P. Greenwald Jr. Endowed Scholarships *(Undergraduate/Scholarship)* [7981]
F.C. Grote Fund Scholarships *(Graduate, Undergraduate/Scholarship)* [326]
Guajardo & Marks Law School Scholarships *(Graduate/Scholarship)* [4676]
Warren and Rosalie Gummow Endowed Scholarships *(Undergraduate/Scholarship)* [7982]
Vincent S. Haneman-Joseph B. Perskie Memorial Foundation Scholarships *(Graduate, Undergraduate/Scholarship)* [2115]
Lex and Scott Hawkins Endowed Scholarship *(Undergraduate/Scholarship)* [3674]
Thomas T. Hayashi Memorial Scholarships *(Graduate/Scholarship)* [5550]
Edward and Cora Hayes Scholarship *(Undergraduate/Scholarship)* [3675]
Annamae Heaps Law Scholarship *(Undergraduate/Scholarship)* [3676]
Steven H. Heisler Law Scholarships *(Graduate/Scholarship)* [4836]

Joseph T. Helling Scholarship Fund *(Undergraduate/Scholarship)* [5106]
John M. Helmick Law Scholarship *(Undergraduate/Scholarship)* [3677]
ASIL Arthur C. Helton Fellowship Program *(Professional development/Fellowship)* [1344]
Arthur Helton Fellowships *(Graduate/Fellowship)* [7401]
Douglas B. Henderson Leadership Scholarships *(Doctorate/Scholarship)* [3984]
Henigson Human Rights Fellowships *(Graduate, Master's, Juris Doctorate/Fellowship)* [4786]
Herbert Herff Presidential Law Scholarships *(Undergraduate/Scholarship)* [10162]
Mark and Michelle Hiepler Endowed Scholarships *(Undergraduate/Scholarship)* [7983]
Hierholzer-Fojtik Scholarship Fund *(Undergraduate/Scholarship)* [4525]
Judge Delmas C. Hill Scholarships *(Undergraduate/Scholarship)* [10429]
HIPLA Judicial Fellowships *(Undergraduate/Fellowship)* [4969]
HIPLA Scholarships for University of Houston Law Center Students *(Graduate, Undergraduate/Scholarship)* [4970]
Robert and Elaine Hoffman Memorial Scholarships *(Undergraduate/Scholarship)* [10163]
Zelle Hofmann Diversity in Law Scholarships *(Undergraduate/Scholarship)* [10812]
Alan Holoch Memorial Grants *(Professional development/Grant)* [531]
Kathryn Hookanson Law Fellowship *(Undergraduate/Scholarship)* [10164]
John C. "Jack" Hough Memorial Law Scholarship *(Undergraduate/Scholarship)* [10165]
Lloyd Houlden Memorial Research Fellowships *(Advanced Professional, Professional development/Fellowship)* [2559]
John Peters Humphrey Student Fellowships *(Graduate/Fellowship)* [3459]
Cecil C. Humphreys Law Fellowships *(Undergraduate/Fellowship, Internship)* [10166]
IABA Scholarships *(Graduate/Scholarship)* [5476]
IALL Regular Bursaries *(Other/Scholarship)* [5269]
IBA Law Student Scholarship Foundation Scholarships *(Undergraduate/Scholarship)* [5130]
ICNL Research Fellowships *(Advanced Professional, Professional development/Fellowship)* [5292]
IILJ Scholarships *(Doctorate/Scholarship)* [5202]
IILJ Visiting Fellowships and Research *(Postdoctorate/Fellowship)* [5203]
ILSA Internships *(Graduate/Internship)* [5353]
Indspire Post-Secondary Education Scholarships *(Graduate, Undergraduate/Scholarship)* [5133]
International Law Research Program Fellowships *(Advanced Professional, Professional development/Fellowship)* [2884]
International Trademark Association-Ladas Memorial Awards *(Other, Undergraduate/Award)* [5447]
Iowa Association of Electric Cooperatives - Electric Cooperative Pioneer Trust Fund Scholarship *(Undergraduate/Scholarship)* [3678]
IPMA-HR Graduate Study Fellowships *(Graduate, Master's/Fellowship)* [5376]
James P. Irish Scholarship *(Undergraduate/Scholarship)* [3679]
Jan Jancin Competition Awards *(Undergraduate/Award)* [941]
Jewish Federation Academic Scholarships *(Graduate, Undergraduate/Scholarship)* [5598]
JLTLA Judge's Scholarships *(Undergraduate/Scholarship)* [9817]
JLTLA Minority Law Student Scholarships *(Undergraduate/Scholarship)* [9818]
MCCA Lloyd M. Johnson, Jr. Scholarships *(Graduate/Scholarship)* [6553]
Bernadine Johnson-Marshall and Martha Bell Williams Scholarships *(Undergraduate/Scholarship)* [1863]
Barbara Jordan Scholarships *(Undergraduate/Scholarship)* [9819]
JSR Foundation Endowed School of Law Scholarships *(Undergraduate/Scholarship)* [7984]
Woodrow Judkins Endowed Scholarships *(Undergraduate/Scholarship)* [7985]

Judge Edward Y. Kakita Memorial Scholarships *(Undergraduate/Scholarship)* [5542]
WLALA Fran Kandel Public Interest Grants *(Postgraduate/Grant)* [10646]
Kaplan Lawyers PC Legal Scholarships *(Graduate/Scholarship)* [5665]
Kaplan Scholarships *(Graduate/Scholarship)* [4898]
Kegler Brown Diversity Scholarship *(Graduate/Scholarship)* [5804]
Kerrigan Scholarships *(Undergraduate/Scholarship)* [7986]
James N. Kincanon Scholarships *(Undergraduate/Scholarship)* [8627]
Martin Luther King Law Scholarship *(Undergraduate/Scholarship)* [3680]
Forest A. King Scholarship *(Undergraduate/Scholarship)* [3681]
Kluge Fellowships *(Doctorate, Graduate/Fellowship)* [5846]
AALL/Wolters Kluwer Law & Business Grants *(Professional development/Grant)* [532]
Koch Scholars Program *(Undergraduate/Scholarship)* [10430]
Senator Carl O. Koella, Jr. Memorial Scholarships *(Undergraduate/Scholarship)* [3233]
Marcia J. Koslov Scholarship *(Professional development/Scholarship)* [533]
Krist-Reavley Minority Scholarships *(Undergraduate/Scholarship)* [7987]
George F. Kugler, Jr. Scholarships *(Undergraduate/Scholarship)* [2512]
Julia Kwan Endowed Scholarships *(Graduate/Scholarship)* [7988]
Ladah Law Firm, PLLC Injury Scholarships *(Undergraduate, Graduate/Scholarship)* [5898]
James D. Lang Memorial Scholarships *(Graduate/Scholarship)* [2563]
Frank H. Lang Merit Scholarships *(Undergraduate/Scholarship)* [5922]
Jason Lang Scholarships *(Undergraduate/Scholarship)* [276]
Latham Diversity Scholars *(Undergraduate/Scholarship)* [5935]
Law Fellows Program *(Undergraduate/Fellowship)* [6710]
Law Foundation of British Columbia Graduate Fellowships *(Graduate/Fellowship)* [5941]
Law Foundation of Newfoundland and Labrador Law School Scholarships *(Advanced Professional/Scholarship)* [5943]
Law Foundation of Ontario Community Leadership in Justice Fellowships *(Other/Fellowship)* [5945]
Law and Society Association Article Prize *(Other/Prize)* [5972]
Law and Society Association Dissertation Prize *(Other/Prize)* [5973]
Law and Society Association International Prize *(Other/Prize)* [5974]
Law and Society Association Undergraduate Student Paper Prize *(Undergraduate/Prize)* [5975]
Law Society of British Columbia Scholarships *(Graduate, Undergraduate/Scholarship)* [5978]
Verne Lawyer Scholarship *(Undergraduate/Scholarship)* [3682]
Lazarian Graduate Scholarships *(Graduate/Scholarship)* [1678]
Steven A. Leahy Law Office Marine Service/Law School Scholarships *(Postgraduate/Scholarship)* [5955]
LeClairRyan Diversity Scholarships *(Undergraduate/Scholarship)* [6000]
Albert J. and Mae Lee Memorial Scholarships *(Undergraduate/Scholarship)* [7989]
The Leesfield/AAJ Law Student Scholarships *(Undergraduate/Scholarship)* [517]
Judge William B. Leffler Scholarships *(Undergraduate/Scholarship)* [10167]
Craig Lensch Memorial Scholarships *(Undergraduate/Scholarship)* [2378]
Frederick D. Lewis Jr. Scholarships *(Undergraduate/Scholarship)* [3683]
Dolores Zohrab Liebmann Fund - Graduate School Fellowships *(Graduate/Fellowship)* [6075]
Lim, Ruger & Kim Scholarships *(Undergraduate/Scholarship)* [6704]
George N. Lindsay Civil Rights Legal Fellowships

(Graduate/Fellowship) [5985]
Davis Levin Livingston Public Interest Law Scholarships (Postgraduate/Scholarship) [3531]
Abram D. and Maxine H. Londa Scholarships (Undergraduate/Scholarship) [7334]
Louthian Law School Scholarships (Advanced Professional/Scholarship) [6133]
LSAC Research Grant Program (Professional development/Grant) [5967]
The C. Lyons Fellowship Program (Advanced Professional/Fellowship) [7047]
MABF Scholarships (Postgraduate/Scholarship) [6442]
Gordon and Delores Madson Scholarship (Undergraduate/Scholarship) [3684]
MALDEF Dream Act Student Activist Scholarships (Undergraduate, Graduate/Scholarship) [6446]
Mann Law Firm Scholarships (Advanced Professional/Scholarship) [3529]
Honorable Carol Los Mansmann Memorial Scholarships (Graduate, Undergraduate/Scholarship) [327]
The Margarian Scholarships (Undergraduate, Graduate/Scholarship) [6239]
Howard T. Markey Memorial Scholarship (Undergraduate/Scholarship) [3985]
Abraham Lincoln Marovitz Public Interest Law Scholarships (Undergraduate/Scholarship) [2897]
Right Honourable Paul Martin Sr. Scholarships (Graduate/Scholarship) [5150]
Massachusetts Bar Foundation Legal Intern Fellowship Program (LIFP) (Undergraduate/Fellowship) [6310]
Greg Matthews Memorial Scholarships (Undergraduate/Scholarship) [7990]
McCleary Law Fellows Program (Graduate, Undergraduate/Fellowship) [4992]
Niqui McCown Honor and Memorial Scholarship Fund (Undergraduate/Scholarship) [10505]
J. McDonald and Judy Williams School of Law Scholarships (Undergraduate/Scholarship) [7991]
H. H. McKnight Memorial Scholarships (Undergraduate/Scholarship) [10168]
Paul R. McLaughlin Fellowship (Undergraduate/Fellowship) [8436]
R. Roy McMurtry Fellowships in Legal History (Doctorate, Graduate/Fellowship) [7760]
Memphis Access and Diversity Scholarships (Undergraduate/Scholarship) [10169]
John Merrick Law Scholarships (Undergraduate/Scholarship) [7992]
Sanders J. Mestel Legal Scholarship Fund (Undergraduate/Scholarship) [9524]
Mexican American Legal Defense and Educational Fund Law School Scholarships (Undergraduate/Scholarship) [6447]
Michigan Auto Law Student Diversity Scholarships (Undergraduate/Scholarship) [6463]
Milbank Diversity Scholars Program (Undergraduate/Scholarship) [6530]
Christine Mirzayan Science and Technology Policy Graduate Fellowships (Graduate/Fellowship) [6679]
Jake S. More Scholarship (Undergraduate/Scholarship) [3685]
Thomas More Scholarships (Undergraduate/Scholarship) [4487]
Sonia Morgan Scholarships (Undergraduate/Scholarship) [7335]
Linda J. Murphy Scholarships (Undergraduate/Scholarship) [10644]
My Life As A Lawyer Scholarships (Graduate, Undergraduate/Scholarship) [3425]
Sam A. Myar Jr. Law Scholarship (Undergraduate/Scholarship) [10170]
NALS of Michigan Scholarships (Undergraduate/Scholarship) [6652]
NAPABA Law Foundation Scholarships (Undergraduate/Scholarship) [6705]
National Judges Association Scholarships (Other/Scholarship) [7030]
National Sheriffs' Association Scholarship Program (Graduate, Undergraduate/Scholarship) [7130]
NAWJ Equal Access to Justice Scholarships (Graduate/Scholarship) [6803]
NCLEJ Law School Graduate Fellows and Volunteers (Graduate/Fellowship) [6848]
Nebraska Paralegal Association Student Scholarships (Undergraduate/Scholarship) [7247]
Need-Based Scholarships (Doctorate/Scholarship) [3986]
Charles I. Nelson Endowed Scholarships (Undergraduate/Scholarship) [7993]
Tad Nelson Law Firm Scholarships (Undergraduate/Scholarship) [5965]
NIABA/NIAF Scholarships (Graduate/Scholarship) [7025]
Gunnar Nicholson Endowed Scholarships (Undergraduate/Scholarship) [7994]
Helen W. Nies Memorial Scholarship (Postgraduate/Scholarship) [3987]
NJSBF Labor Law Scholarships (Undergraduate/Scholarship) [7336]
Peggy Kommer Novosad Scholarships (Graduate, Postgraduate/Scholarship) [4615]
NYU School of Law Fellowships at HRW (Graduate/Fellowship) [4999]
Justice Sandra Day O'Connor Scholarship (Undergraduate/Scholarship) [6804]
Oklahoma City University Full-Time Merit Scholarships (Graduate/Scholarship) [7601]
Olin/Searle Fellows in Law (Other/Fellowship) [3995]
Omatsu FACL Scholarships (Juris Doctorate, Advanced Professional/Scholarship) [4001]
Faith E. O'Neal Scholarships (Undergraduate/Scholarship) [8392]
Open Society Presidential Fellowships (Advanced Professional/Fellowship) [7663]
Dwight D. Opperman Scholarships (Undergraduate/Scholarship) [3686]
Mary Reiko Osaka Memorial Scholarships (Undergraduate, Graduate/Scholarship) [5555]
M. Dick Osumi Civil Rights and Public Interest Scholarship (Graduate, Undergraduate/Scholarship) [5543]
Michael Oykhman Criminal Law and Evidence Scholarships (Juris Doctorate, Advanced Professional/Scholarship) [6455]
Patterson Belknap Webb & Tyler LLP Diversity Fellowships (Doctorate/Fellowship) [7905]
Pepperdine University Diversity Scholarships (Doctorate, Graduate/Scholarship) [7995]
Pepperdine University School of Law Armenian Student Scholarships (Undergraduate/Scholarship) [7996]
Pepperdine University School of Law Dean's Merit Scholarships (Doctorate, Graduate/Scholarship) [7997]
Pepperdine University School of Law Faculty Scholars Award (Doctorate, Graduate/Scholarship) [7998]
Pepperdine University School of Law JD/MBA Endowed Scholarships (Undergraduate/Scholarship) [7999]
Pepperdine University School of Law Special Law School Scholarships (Undergraduate/Scholarship) [8000]
Perkins Coie 1L Diversity Fellowships (Postgraduate/Fellowship) [8011]
Perkins Coie 1L Patent Litigation and Patent Fellowships (Postgraduate/Fellowship) [8012]
Perkins Coie 1L Political Law Fellowships (Postgraduate/Fellowship) [8013]
PETA Foundation Law Internships (Graduate/Internship) [7958]
William R. Pfalzgraf Scholarships (Undergraduate/Scholarship) [7852]
Philadelphia Public Interest Fellowships (Undergraduate/Fellowship) [8111]
Jamie Phillips Endowed Scholarships (Undergraduate/Scholarship) [8001]
Pi Gamma Mu Scholarships (Graduate/Scholarship) [8133]
Harold and Harriet Plum Memorial Scholarships (Undergraduate/Scholarship) [2513]
Donald and Susie Polden Dean's Scholarships (Undergraduate/Scholarship) [10171]
Justice Stewart G. Pollock Scholarships (Undergraduate/Fellowship) [6594]
PON Graduate Student Grants (Graduate/Grant) [4789]
PON Next Generation Grants (Doctorate, Postdoctorate/Grant) [4790]
PON Summer Fellowships (Graduate/Fellowship) [4791]
Louis C. Portella Memorial Scholarships (Graduate/Scholarship) [2514]
George V. Powell Diversity Scholarships (Graduate/Scholarship) [5920]
Practising Law Institute Law Student Scholarships (Advanced Professional, Professional development/Scholarship) [8215]
Pride Foundation Political Leadership Scholarships (Undergraduate/Scholarship) [8258]
Diana M. Priestly Memorial Scholarships (Undergraduate/Scholarship) [2564]
Prince Edward Island Law Student Scholarships (Undergraduate/Scholarship) [5980]
Alexander Pringle Criminal Law Scholarships (Advanced Professional/Scholarship) [8280]
Prudential 1L Summer Internships (Postgraduate/Internship) [6706]
Public Interest Environmental Law Fellowships (Graduate/Fellowship) [3898]
Public Interest Fellowships for Law Students of Color (Undergraduate/Fellowship) [4491]
John Purfield Endowed Scholarships (Undergraduate/Scholarship) [8002]
Frederick Rakestraw Law Scholarships (Graduate/Scholarship) [7520]
Rappaport Fellows Program in Law and Public Policy (Undergraduate/Fellowship) [8437]
Ratner and Sugarmon Scholarship (Undergraduate/Scholarship) [10172]
Janet Reynoldson Memorial Scholarships (Undergraduate/Scholarship) [3687]
William S. Richardson Commemorative Scholarships (Graduate/Scholarship) [7918]
Honorable Joseph H. Ridge Memorial Scholarships (Undergraduate/Scholarship) [328]
Rosenthal Bar Exam Scholarship Fund (Advanced Professional/Scholarship) [2444]
Hon. Rudolph J. Rossetti Memorial Scholarships (Undergraduate/Scholarship) [2515]
Joe Rudd Scholarships (Master's, Juris Doctorate/Scholarship) [8637]
Lim Ruger Foundation Scholarships (Undergraduate/Scholarship) [5544]
SABA NC - Organizational Fellowships (Undergraduate/Fellowship) [9352]
SABA NC - Pro Bono Fellowships (Undergraduate/Fellowship) [9353]
SABA NC - Public Interest Fellowships (Undergraduate/Fellowship) [9354]
Leonard H. Sandler Fellowships (Graduate/Fellowship) [5000]
Santa Clara La Raza Lawyers Scholarships (Graduate/Scholarship) [5894]
Saratoga County Bar Association Law Student Scholarships (Undergraduate/Scholarship) [8760]
Sho Sato Memorial Scholarships (Undergraduate, Graduate/Scholarship) [5557]
Satter Human Rights Fellowships (Graduate, Master's, Juris Doctorate/Fellowship) [4787]
SCCLA Fellowships (Graduate/Fellowship) [9398]
SCCLA Scholarships (Graduate/Scholarship) [9399]
Scholarships for an Education Towards Law (Graduate/Scholarship) [3812]
Scholarships for a Higher Education in Law (Graduate/Scholarship) [2361]
Jeptha Wade Schureman Scholarship Program (Undergraduate/Scholarship) [3333]
Marla Schwartz Education Grant (Graduate, Professional development/Grant) [534]
Marla Schwartz Grants (Professional development, Graduate/Grant) [535]
Walter and Rita Selvy Scholarship (Undergraduate/Scholarship) [3688]
Serbian Bar Association of America Scholarships (Graduate/Scholarship) [8847]
Seton Hall Law Merit Scholarships (Graduate/Scholarship) [8855]
Barbara A. Shacochis Scholarships (Undergraduate/Scholarship) [8003]
Saleem Shah Early Career Award (Doctorate/Recognition) [1158]

Field of Study Index

Shamberg Scholarships *(Undergraduate/Scholarship)* [10431]

The Ivan Shandor Memorial Ukrainian American Bar Association Scholarships *(Graduate, Master's/Scholarship)* [10444]

John M. and Mary A. Shanley Memorial Scholarships *(Undergraduate, Graduate/Scholarship)* [9448]

Benjamin G. Shatz Scholarships *(Undergraduate/Scholarship)* [8004]

Bill and Ann Sheperd Legal Scholarship Fund *(Undergraduate/Scholarship)* [3923]

Joseph Henry Shepherd Scholarship *(Undergraduate/Scholarship)* [10173]

Justice Janie L. Shores Scholarships *(Undergraduate/Scholarship)* [207]

Sidley Diversity and Inclusion Scholarships *(Undergraduate/Scholarship)* [8894]

Sidley Prelaw Scholars Initiative *(Undergraduate/Scholarship)* [8895]

Stuart Silverman Scholarships *(Undergraduate/Scholarship)* [8005]

Skadden Fellowships *(Graduate/Fellowship)* [8978]

Ann Kelsay Small Scholarship *(Undergraduate/Scholarship)* [5766]

James I. Smith, III Notre Dame Law School Scholarship Fund *(Graduate, Undergraduate/Scholarship)* [329]

C. Bainbridge Smith Scholarships *(Undergraduate/Scholarship)* [7344]

Louis B. Sohn Fellowships in Human Rights and Environment *(Graduate/Fellowship)* [2849]

Amy E. Spain Memorial Scholarships *(Undergraduate/Scholarship)* [10174]

Spangenberg Shibley & Liber Video PSA Scholarship Awards *(Undergraduate/Scholarship)* [9456]

The Springfield Family Scholarships *(Undergraduate/Scholarship)* [10175]

Otto M. Stanfield Law Scholarships *(Graduate/Scholarship)* [9841]

Stark County Bar Association Fund *(Undergraduate/Scholarship)* [9535]

Tom Steel Post-Graduate Fellowships *(Postgraduate, Other/Fellowship)* [8274]

Mike Stephenson Legal Scholarships *(Graduate/Scholarship)* [6370]

David Stockwood Memorial Prize *(Advanced Professional, Professional development/Prize)* [81]

Jay A. Strassberg Memorial Scholarships *(Undergraduate/Scholarship)* [2517]

Robby Strong Cancer Survivor Scholarships *(Graduate/Scholarship)* [6596]

Suffolk Public Interest Law Group Summer Fellowships (SPILG) *(Undergraduate/Fellowship)* [8438]

Hatton W. Sumners Endowed Law Schools Scholarships *(Undergraduate, Graduate/Scholarship)* [9608]

Hatton W. Sumners Endowed Undergraduate School Scholarships *(Undergraduate/Scholarship)* [9609]

Hatton W. Sumners Non-Endowed Undergraduate and Graduate Scholarships *(Undergraduate, Graduate/Scholarship)* [9610]

Hatton W. Sumners Scholarships *(Undergraduate/Scholarship)* [7602]

Robert M. Takasugi Public Interest Fellowships *(Postgraduate/Fellowship)* [9636]

Justice Stephen K. Tamura Scholarships *(Undergraduate/Scholarship)* [5545]

Charles "Buck" and Dora Taylor Scholarship *(Undergraduate/Scholarship)* [3689]

Tennessee Bar Foundation IOLTA Law School Scholarships *(Undergraduate/Scholarship)* [10176]

The Honorable Raymond Thompson Endowed Scholarships *(Undergraduate/Scholarship)* [8006]

Thomas P. Thornton Scholarships *(Undergraduate/Scholarship)* [5089]

Thurgood Marshall Fellowships Program *(Undergraduate/Fellowship)* [7345]

Tiftickjian Law Firm, P.C. Juvenile Justice Law School Scholarships *(Postgraduate/Scholarship)* [9741]

Daniel B. Toll Memorial Scholarships *(Undergraduate/Scholarship)* [2518]

William Tomar Memorial Scholarships *(Undergraduate/Scholarship)* [2519]

Marie Trahan/Susman Godfrey Scholarships *(Undergraduate/Scholarship)* [9820]

Edward Traurig Scholarships *(Undergraduate/Scholarship)* [10484]

Thomas and Glenna Trimble Endowed Scholarships *(Undergraduate/Scholarship)* [8007]

Trustees College Scholarships *(Undergraduate/Scholarship)* [6171]

Trustees Law School Scholarships *(Undergraduate/Scholarship)* [6172]

UC MEXUS-CONACYT Doctoral Fellowships *(Doctorate/Fellowship)* [10117]

VABANC Scholarships *(Graduate, Undergraduate/Scholarship)* [10383]

Wallace Vail Scholarships *(Undergraduate/Scholarship)* [7337]

Philip F. Vineberg Travelling Fellowships in the Humanities *(Undergraduate/Scholarship)* [6368]

Viscount Bennett Scholarships *(Postgraduate, Advanced Professional/Scholarship)* [5969]

Vision Zero Auto Accident Prevention Scholarships *(Postgraduate/Scholarship)* [5951]

John D. Voelker Foundation Native American Scholarships *(Undergraduate/Scholarship)* [10415]

Gary Walker Memorial Scholarships *(Other/Scholarship)* [4266]

Bruce A. Wallace Memorial Scholarships *(Undergraduate/Scholarship)* [2520]

Warner Norcross & Judd Minority Scholarships *(Undergraduate/Scholarship)* [10427]

Earl Warren Scholarships *(Graduate/Scholarship)* [6648]

Washburn University School of Law Business and Transactional Law Center Scholarships *(Undergraduate/Scholarship)* [10432]

Washburn University School of Law Child and Family Advocacy Fellowships *(Undergraduate/Fellowship)* [10433]

Washington University Law School Chancellor's Graduate Fellowships *(Advanced Professional/Fellowship)* [10476]

Washington University Law School Olin Fellowships for Women *(Advanced Professional/Fellowship)* [10477]

Waterbury Bar Association Scholarships *(Undergraduate/Scholarship)* [10485]

WBA Bar President's Scholarships *(Undergraduate/Scholarship)* [10486]

Webster Society Scholarships *(Juris Doctorate/Scholarship)* [10478]

J.L. Weigand, Jr. Legal Education Trust Scholarships *(Undergraduate/Scholarship)* [10434]

Haemer Wheatcraft Scholarship *(Undergraduate/Scholarship)* [3690]

Stan Wheeler Mentorship Awards *(Other/Award)* [5976]

The Brian J. White Endowed Law Scholarships *(Undergraduate/Scholarship)* [8008]

Howard A. White Endowed Scholarships *(Undergraduate/Scholarship)* [8009]

Richard S. White Fellowships *(Undergraduate/Fellowship)* [4853]

Paul D. White Scholarship *(Undergraduate/Scholarship)* [2173]

Sidney B. Williams, Jr. Scholarships *(Undergraduate/Scholarship)* [942]

WLALA Scholarships *(Postgraduate/Scholarship)* [10647]

Women In Defense HORIZONS Scholarships *(Graduate, Undergraduate/Scholarship)* [10636]

Women of WSAJ Bar Preparation Scholarships *(Undergraduate/Scholarship)* [10458]

Wood County Bar Association Memorial Scholarships *(Graduate/Scholarship)* [7874]

Marilynne Graboys Wool Scholarships *(Graduate/Scholarship)* [8611]

Davis Wright Tremaine 1L Diversity Scholarships *(Undergraduate/Scholarship)* [3535]

WSAJ Diversity Bar Preparation Scholarships *(Undergraduate/Scholarship)* [10460]

Wyatt, Tarrant & Combs, LLP, Dr. Benjamin L. Hooks Scholarship *(Undergraduate/Scholarship)* [10177]

Minoru Yasui Memorial Scholarships *(Graduate, Master's, Doctorate/Scholarship)* [5560]

Yukon Law Foundation Scholarships *(Undergraduate/Scholarship)* [10808]

Zarley, McKee, Thomte, Voorhees, Sease Law Scholarship *(Undergraduate/Scholarship)* [3691]

Law enforcement

Jack Ackroyd Scholarships *(Other/Scholarship)* [1878]

American Association of State Troopers Scholarship Foundation First Scholarships *(Undergraduate/Scholarship)* [577]

American Association of State Troopers Scholarship Foundation Second Scholarships *(Undergraduate/Scholarship)* [578]

American Federation of Police and Concerned Citizen Scholarships *(Undergraduate/Scholarship)* [790]

Benjamin Asbell Memorial Scholarships *(Undergraduate/Scholarship)* [2507]

Sheriff W. Bruce Umpleby Law Enforcement Scholarship Fund *(Undergraduate/Scholarship)* [9494]

Canadian Identification Society Essay/Scholarship Awards *(Advanced Professional, Professional development/Prize)* [2664]

Alphonso Deal Scholarship Awards *(Undergraduate/Scholarship)* [6825]

William Donald Dixon Research Grants *(Graduate, Undergraduate, Advanced Professional/Grant)* [2665]

Hardy, Wolf & Downing Scholarships *(Undergraduate, Graduate/Scholarship)* [4719]

Wayne Hildebrant Police Scholarship Fund *(Undergraduate/Scholarship)* [5931]

IAWP International Scholarship Award *(Other/Scholarship)* [5280]

V.J. Johnson Memorial Scholarships *(Undergraduate/Scholarship)* [579]

John W. Kelley Memorial Scholarships *(Undergraduate/Scholarship)* [9572]

Friends and Family of Christopher J. Kohlmeier Scholarships *(Undergraduate/Scholarship)* [8489]

Law Enforcement Memorial Scholarship Fund *(Undergraduate/Scholarship)* [4202]

NASSLEO Scholarships - Region I *(Undergraduate/Scholarship)* [6782]

Pan Pacific Law Enforcement Scholarships *(Undergraduate/Scholarship)* [8745]

Portuguese American Police Association Scholarships *(Undergraduate/Scholarship)* [8211]

Commander Newell S. Rand Jr. Scholarship Program *(Undergraduate/Scholarship)* [7809]

WIFLE Regular Scholarship Program *(Graduate, Postdoctorate, Undergraduate/Scholarship)* [10642]

Leadership, Institutional and community

Alliance Pipeline Scholarships *(Other/Scholarship)* [2181]

Americans for Informed Democracy Global Scholar Program *(Undergraduate/Scholarship)* [1532]

Bush Fellowship Program *(Other/Fellowship)* [2420]

Fraser Milner Casgrain Scholarships *(Other/Scholarship)* [2182]

CMC-KLI Leadership Research Fellowship *(Undergraduate/Fellowship)* [3045]

CMC-KLI Social Sector Internship Program *(Undergraduate/Internship)* [3046]

CMC-KLI Social Sector Research Fellowship *(Undergraduate/Fellowship)* [3047]

Diversity Executive Leadership Program Scholarships *(Other/Scholarship)* [1778]

Echoing Green Global Fellowships *(Professional development/Fellowship)* [3775]

ESA Foundation Life Grants *(Undergraduate/Grant)* [3914]

Founding Mothers' Student Scholarships - Graduate *(Graduate/Scholarship)* [2015]

Greenlining Institute Fellowships *(Graduate/Fellowship)* [4670]

Kathryn Huget Leadership Awards *(Master's, Doctorate/Award)* [2430]

Humber College Institute of Technology and Ad-

vanced Learning Scholarships *(Undergraduate/Scholarship)* [5524]
Investors Group Scholarships for Not-For-Profit Leaders *(Other/Scholarship)* [2183]
Kappa Omicron Nu Leadership Undergraduate Scholarships *(Undergraduate/Scholarship)* [5781]
KDP International Scholarship Program - President Scholarship *(Undergraduate, Graduate, Doctorate/Scholarship)* [5674]
Lafarge Community Leaders Scholarships *(Other/Scholarship)* [2184]
Lambda Project 2000 Scholarship *(Undergraduate/Scholarship)* [5744]
NCSEA Judge Ross Leadership Scholarships *(Professional development/Scholarship)* [6858]
NCSEA New Leader Scholarships *(Professional development/Scholarship)* [6859]
USGLC Internships - Outreach *(Undergraduate, Graduate/Internship)* [9951]
Youth or the Environment Scholarships *(Other/Scholarship)* [2185]

Leukemia

Hollis Brownstein Research Grants *(Professional development/Grant)* [6011]

Liberal arts

Cecil E. Burney Scholarships *(Undergraduate/Scholarship)* [3091]
Stephen J. Fortgang/University of Northern Iowa Chapter Scholarship *(Undergraduate/Scholarship)* [5670]
Elizabeth M. Gruber Scholarships *(Graduate/Scholarship)* [3583]
Doris Hendren Memorial Scholarships *(Undergraduate/Scholarship)* [8707]
Harriet Irsay Scholarships *(Graduate, Undergraduate/Scholarship)* [927]
Bernard Michel Scholarships *(Undergraduate/Scholarship)* [2526]
Jeannette K. Watson Fellowships *(Undergraduate/Fellowship, Internship)* [10491]
Denis Wong and Associates Scholarships *(Graduate, Undergraduate/Scholarship)* [7920]

Library and archival sciences

AALL Leadership Academy Grants *(Professional development/Grant)* [519]
AALL Minority Leadership Development Award *(Graduate/Award)* [520]
AALL Scholarships for Continuing Education Classes *(Postgraduate/Scholarship)* [522]
ACMS Library Fellowships *(Graduate, Other/Fellowship)* [649]
AECT Legacy Scholarship *(Master's, Graduate, Professional development/Scholarship)* [1943]
AJL Scholarship Fund *(Graduate/Scholarship)* [2011]
ALL-SIS Conference of Newer Law Librarians Grants *(Professional development/Grant)* [528]
APALA Scholarship Award *(Doctorate, Master's/Scholarship)* [1788]
ArLA Scholarships *(Graduate/Scholarship)* [1654]
Atlantic Provinces Library Association Memorial Awards *(Undergraduate/Scholarship)* [2117]
Beinecke Rare Book and Manuscript Library Visiting Postdoctoral Scholar Fellowships *(Postdoctorate/Fellowship)* [2214]
Bound to Stay Bound Books Scholarships *(Graduate/Scholarship)* [2017]
Rev. Andrew L. Bouwhuis Memorial Scholarship Program *(Graduate/Scholarship)* [2814]
MAC Louisa Bowen Memorial Scholarships for Graduate Students in Archival Administration *(Graduate/Scholarship)* [6515]
Carol June Bradley Awards *(Professional development/Grant)* [6625]
Rick Chace Foundation Scholarships *(Graduate/Scholarship)* [2024]
CLA/ACB Dafoe Scholarships *(Graduate/Scholarship)* [2679]
David H. Clift Scholarships *(Graduate/Scholarship)* [961]
DEMCO New Leaders Travel Grants *(Professional development/Grant)* [8372]
Henry Belin du Pont Research Grants *(Graduate/Fellowship)* [4689]
Dena Epstein Awards for Archival and Library Research in American Music *(Professional development/Grant)* [6626]
Sherman Fairchild Post Graduate Fellowships in Conservation *(Postgraduate/Fellowship)* [6591]
FCIL Schaffer Grants for Foreign Law Librarians *(Professional development/Grant)* [529]
Kevin Freeman Travel Grants *(Graduate, Other/Grant)* [6627]
Jewell Gardiner Scholarships *(Undergraduate/Scholarship)* [2473]
Eugene Garfield Doctoral Dissertation Fellowship *(Doctorate/Fellowship)* [2239]
The Gates Millennium Scholars *(Undergraduate/Scholarship)* [4903]
Walter Gerboth Awards *(Other/Award)* [6628]
Getty Foundation Library Research Grants *(Professional development/Grant)* [4407]
GLA Beard Scholarships *(Master's/Scholarship)* [4384]
GLA Hubbard Scholarships *(Master's/Scholarship)* [4385]
Government Documents Special Interest Section - Veronica Maclay Student Grants *(Master's/Grant)* [530]
Caroline M. Hewins Scholarships *(Graduate/Scholarship)* [4776]
D. Glenn Hilts Scholarships *(Graduate, Undergraduate/Scholarship)* [2069]
HLS/MLA Professional Development Grants *(Other/Grant)* [6386]
Alan Holoch Memorial Grants *(Professional development/Grant)* [531]
Christopher Hoy/ERT Scholarships *(Graduate/Scholarship)* [962]
Huenefeld/Denton Scholarships *(Undergraduate/Scholarship)* [3588]
Iowa Library Association Foundation Scholarships *(Graduate/Scholarship)* [5469]
E.J. Josey Scholarships *(Graduate/Scholarship, Award)* [2296]
Kodak Fellowships in Film Preservation *(Graduate/Fellowship)* [2025]
Marcia J. Koslov Scholarship *(Professional development/Scholarship)* [533]
Harold Lancour Scholarship for Foreign Study *(Professional development/Scholarship)* [2240]
Christian Larew Memorial Scholarships *(Graduate/Scholarship)* [6071]
LITA/LSSI Minority Scholarships *(Graduate/Scholarship)* [6072]
LITA/OCLC Minority Scholarships *(Graduate/Scholarship)* [6073]
Louisiana Library Association Scholarships *(Graduate/Scholarship)* [6119]
Lillian Grace Mahan Scholarship Fund *(Graduate/Scholarship)* [9520]
AILA Virginia Mathews Memorial Scholarships *(Graduate/Scholarship)* [885]
Medical Library Association Scholarships for Minority Students *(Graduate/Scholarship)* [6389]
Frederic G. Melcher Scholarships *(Graduate/Scholarship)* [2018]
Mary Moore Mitchell Scholarships *(Graduate/Scholarship)* [6120]
MLA Continuing Education Awards (CE) *(Graduate/Grant)* [6390]
MLA Research, Development, and Demonstration Project Grants *(Graduate/Grant)* [6392]
Archie Motley Memorial Scholarships for Minority Students *(Graduate/Scholarship)* [6517]
NELA Conference Scholarships *(All/Scholarship)* [7297]
Louise A. Nixon Scholarships *(Graduate/Scholarship)* [7245]
NJLA Scholarships *(Graduate, Postgraduate/Scholarship)* [7321]
NYLA-Dewey Scholarship *(Master's, Undergraduate/Scholarship)* [7357]
Katharine Pantzer Fellowships in the British Book Trades *(Other/Fellowship)* [2256]
Pennsylvania Library Association MLS Scholarships *(Graduate/Scholarship)* [7937]
Paul Evan Peters Fellowship *(Master's, Doctorate/Fellowship)* [3073]
Mary Pickford Scholarships *(Graduate/Scholarship)* [2026]
REFORMA Scholarship Program *(Doctorate, Graduate, Other/Scholarship)* [8534]
Thomson Reuters/MLA Doctoral Fellowships *(Doctorate, Graduate/Fellowship)* [6393]
Rovelstad Scholarship in International Librarianship *(Undergraduate, Graduate/Award, Scholarship)* [3452]
Esther Schlundt Memorial Scholarships *(Graduate/Scholarship)* [5112]
School Library Paraprofessional Scholarships - Southern Region *(Advanced Professional/Scholarship)* [2474]
Marla Schwartz Education Grant *(Graduate, Professional development/Grant)* [534]
Marla Schwartz Grants *(Professional development, Graduate/Grant)* [535]
Fritz Schwartz Serials Education Scholarships *(Graduate, Other/Scholarship)* [7447]
Carin Alma E. Somers Scholarship Trust *(Undergraduate/Scholarship)* [2118]
Sony Pictures Scholarships *(Graduate/Scholarship)* [2027]
George A. Strait Minority Scholarship *(Graduate/Scholarship)* [536]
Roger K. Summit Scholarships for North America *(Graduate/Scholarship)* [8302]
Teacher Librarian Scholarships *(Master's/Scholarship)* [2475]
Jack E. Tillson Scholarships *(Graduate/Scholarship)* [5470]
Universal Studios Preservation Scholarships *(Graduate/Scholarship)* [2028]
Philip F. Vineberg Travelling Fellowships in the Humanities *(Undergraduate/Scholarship)* [6368]
Sue Marsh Weller Memorial Scholarships *(Graduate/Scholarship)* [5113]
Blanche E. Woolls Scholarships *(Graduate/Scholarship)* [2242]
World Book Graduate Scholarships in Library and Information Science *(Graduate/Scholarship)* [2680]
Yale Graduate and Professional Students Research Fellowships *(Graduate, Professional development/Fellowship)* [2215]

Life sciences

C. Lalor Burdick Scholarships *(Graduate, Master's, Doctorate/Scholarship)* [6245]
Max M. Burger Endowed Scholarships in Embryology *(Graduate, Master's, Doctorate/Scholarship)* [6246]
Dow Chemical Company Fellowships *(Graduate/Fellowship)* [7085]
E.I. DuPont Graduate Fellowship *(Graduate/Fellowship)* [7086]
Foundation for the Preservation of Honey Bees Graduate Scholarships *(Graduate/Scholarship)* [4281]
Life Sciences Research Foundation Postdoctoral Fellowship Program *(Postdoctorate/Fellowship)* [6081]
Michigan Society of Fellows Three-Year Fellowships *(Postdoctorate/Fellowship)* [6481]
Dolphus E. Milligan Graduate Fellowships *(Graduate/Fellowship)* [7087]
NOBCChE Procter and Gamble Fellowships *(Graduate/Fellowship)* [7088]
NYU Langone Medical Center Science Student Scholarships *(Undergraduate, Graduate/Scholarship)* [109]
Lola Ellis Robertson Scholarships *(Graduate, Master's, Doctorate/Scholarship)* [6258]
Florence C. Rose and S. Meryl Rose Scholarships *(Graduate, Master's, Doctorate/Scholarship)* [6259]
Paul and Ellen Ruckes Scholarships *(Graduate, Undergraduate/Scholarship)* [823]
Everett Oscar Shimp Memorial Scholarships *(Undergraduate/Scholarship)* [7862]
Sino-American Pharmaceutical Professionals Asso-

ciation Scholarships *(Undergraduate/Scholarship)* [8971]
Eastman Kodak Dr. Theophilus Sorrell Fellowships *(Graduate/Fellowship)* [7090]
J.P. and Madeline Trinkaus Endowed Scholarships in Embryology *(Graduate, Master's, Doctorate/Scholarship)* [6263]
UNCF/Merck Graduate Science Research Dissertation Fellowships *(Graduate/Fellowship)* [6426, 9862]
UNCF/Merck Postdoctoral Science Research Fellowships *(Postdoctorate/Fellowship)* [6427, 9863]
UNESCO-L'Oreal for Women in Science International Fellowships *(Doctorate, Postdoctorate/Fellowship)* [6108]
University of Wisconsin-Madison/CALS Minority Scholarships *(Undergraduate/Scholarship)* [10327]
Selman A. Waksman Endowed Scholarships in Microbial Diversity *(Graduate, Master's, Doctorate/Scholarship)* [6264]

Lighting science

IALD Education Trust Scholarship Program *(Graduate, Undergraduate/Scholarship)* [5271]

Linguistics

AIIrS Persian Language Study in Tehran Fellowships *(Graduate, Master's, Doctorate/Fellowship)* [913]
American Councils for International Education Critical Language Scholarships *(Undergraduate, Graduate/Scholarship)* [746]
ARIT National Endowment for the Humanities Advanced Fellowships for Research in Turkey *(Postdoctorate/Fellowship)* [1202]
ETS Postdoctoral Fellowships *(Postdoctorate/Fellowship)* [3806]
Graduate Student Travel Grants *(Doctorate, Master's/Grant)* [462]
Harold Gulliksen Psychometric Research Fellowships *(Doctorate, Graduate/Fellowship)* [3807]
Sylvia Taylor Johnson Fellowships in Educational Measurement *(Doctorate/Fellowship)* [3808]
NIU-CSEAS Foreign Language and Area Studies (FLAS) Fellowships *(Undergraduate, Graduate/Fellowship)* [7518]
Robert Roy Awards *(Advanced Professional/Award, Recognition)* [1897]
Mary Isabel Sibley Fellowships *(Doctorate/Fellowship)* [8053]

Literature

AFA Literary Arts Project Grants *(Professional development/Grant)* [241]
ARCE Funded Fellowships *(Doctorate, Postdoctorate/Fellowship)* [1195]
ARCE Research Associates Fellowships *(Doctorate, Postdoctorate, Professional development/Fellowship)* [1196]
ARIT National Endowment for the Humanities Advanced Fellowships for Research in Turkey *(Postdoctorate/Fellowship)* [1202]
Jenny Panitch Beckow Memorial Scholarships Israel *(Graduate/Scholarship)* [5570]
John Burroughs Bogliasco Fellowships *(Professional development/Fellowship)* [2328]
CAA National Capital Region Writing Contests *(All/Award, Prize, Monetary)* [2579]
D&A Florida Scholarships *(Undergraduate/Scholarship)* [9425]
Jenny d'Héricourt Fellowships *(Doctorate/Fellowship)* [435]
R.L. Gillette Scholarships *(Undergraduate/Scholarship)* [821]
Louis Gottschalk Prize *(Other/Prize)* [1291]
Gene Halker Memorial Scholarships *(Graduate, Undergraduate/Scholarship)* [4145]
Hench Post-Dissertation Fellowship *(Postdoctorate/Fellowship)* [438]
Oscar Kenshur Book Prize *(Other/Prize)* [1293]
Lapides Fellowships in Pre-1865 Juvenile Literature and Ephemera *(Graduate, Postdoctorate/Fellowship)* [439]

William P. McHugh Memorial Fund Award *(Doctorate, Graduate/Fellowship)* [1197]
The National Endowment for the Humanities Fellowships *(Graduate/Fellowship)* [1198]
Oregon Literary Fellowships *(Advanced Professional/Fellowship)* [6097]
Barbara L. Packer Fellowships *(Doctorate, Postdoctorate/Fellowship)* [442]
Ameen Rihani Scholarship Program *(Undergraduate/Scholarship)* [1599]
Luci Shaw Fellowship *(Undergraduate/Fellowship)* [5081]
Leif and Inger Sjöberg Awards *(Advanced Professional, Professional development/Award, Grant, Prize)* [1235]
The United States Department of State, Bureau of Educational & Cultural Affairs Fellowships *(Graduate/Fellowship)* [1199]
Aubrey L. Williams Research Travel Fellowships *(Doctorate/Fellowship)* [1298]
William B. Wisdom Grant in Aid of Research *(Professional development/Grant)* [10634]

Literature, Children's

Hannah Beiter Graduate Student Research Grants *(Doctorate, Graduate/Grant)* [2909]
Don Freeman Work-in-Progress Grants *(Advanced Professional/Grant)* [9096]
Martha Weston Grant *(Advanced Professional/Grant)* [9097]
Multicultural Work-in-Progress Grant *(Advanced Professional/Grant)* [9098]
SCBWI Student Illustrator Scholarship *(Undergraduate, Graduate, Grant, Scholarship)* [9099]
SCBWI Student Writer Scholarship *(Graduate, Doctorate, Undergraduate/Grant, Scholarship)* [9100]
SCBWI Work-in-Progress Awards *(Advanced Professional/Grant, Award)* [9101]
Tribute Fund Community Grant *(Professional development/Grant)* [9102]

Local government

ICMA Local Government Management Fellowships *(Master's/Fellowship)* [5296]
TFAS Congressional Scholarship Awards *(Undergraduate/Award, Scholarship)* [4309]

Logistics

Sharon D. Banks Undergraduate Memorial Scholarships *(Undergraduate/Scholarship)* [10674]
Delta Nu Alpha Foundation Scholarships *(Undergraduate/Scholarship)* [3573]
HSF/Marathon Oil College Scholarship Program *(Undergraduate/Scholarship)* [4905]
NDTA Academic Scholarship Program A *(Undergraduate/Scholarship)* [6913]
NDTA Academic Scholarship Program B *(Undergraduate/Scholarship)* [6914]
North American Van Lines Military Scholarship Competition *(Undergraduate/Scholarship)* [7449]
Helene M. Overly Memorial Scholarships *(Undergraduate/Scholarship)* [10675]

Lou Gehrig's disease (See Amyotrophic lateral sclerosis)

Management

AACE International Competitive Scholarships *(Undergraduate/Scholarship)* [14]
Herb Adrian Memorial Scholarship Fund *(Undergraduate/Scholarship)* [4173]
APS/Maricopa County Community Colleges Scholarships *(Undergraduate/Scholarship)* [8140]
George M. Brooker, CPM Diversity Collegiate Scholarship *(Graduate, Undergraduate/Scholarship)* [5215]
California Association of Family and Consumer Sciences - San Diego Chapter Scholarships (CAFCS) *(Undergraduate, Graduate/Scholarship)* [8695]
Stuart Cameron and Margaret McLeod Memorial Scholarships (SCMS) *(Graduate, Undergraduate/Scholarship)* [5205]
CDC Presidential Management Fellows Program *(Graduate/Fellowship)* [9917]
The Club Foundation Faculty Research Grants *(Professional development/Grant)* [3060]
CMAA Student Conference Travel Grants *(Undergraduate/Grant)* [3061]
CTP Scholarship Program *(Other/Scholarship)* [7113]
Diversity Executive Leadership Program Scholarships *(Other/Scholarship)* [1778]
The Steve Duckett Local Conservation Scholarships *(Undergraduate, Postgraduate/Scholarship)* [8232]
Harold E. Eisenberg Foundation Scholarships *(Other/Scholarship)* [5304]
Donald M. Furbush Professional Development Grants *(Other/Grant)* [5216]
HACU/NASCAR Scholarships *(Graduate, Undergraduate/Scholarship)* [4888]
Robert Hancock Memorial Scholarship Awards *(Undergraduate/Scholarship)* [6498]
HRH Prince Alwaleed Bin Talal ISNA Fellowships *(Graduate/Fellowship)* [5486]
IFMA Foundation Scholarships *(Undergraduate, Graduate/Scholarship)* [5327]
IMA Memorial Education Fund Scholarships (MEF) *(Graduate, Undergraduate/Scholarship)* [5206]
Willmoore H. Kendall Scholarships *(Professional development/Scholarship)* [3062]
The Michael Kiely Strong Roots Scholarships *(Undergraduate/Scholarship)* [8233]
Jessica King Scholarships *(Other/Scholarship)* [3490]
David A. Kronick Travelling Fellowships *(Doctorate, Graduate/Fellowship)* [6387]
Val Mason Scholarships *(Postgraduate/Scholarship)* [2746]
The Tatiana Mendez Future Resources Scholarships *(Undergraduate/Scholarship)* [8234]
Mutual of Omaha Finance Careers Scholarships *(Undergraduate, Graduate/Scholarship)* [105]
NAGAP Graduate Student Enrollment Management Research Grants *(Graduate/Grant)* [6752]
North American Van Lines Military Scholarship Competition *(Undergraduate/Scholarship)* [7449]
The Seth Okin Good Deeds Scholarships *(Undergraduate/Scholarship)* [8235]
Ontario Women's Institute Scholarships *(Undergraduate/Scholarship)* [3997]
PARMA Scholarships *(Undergraduate/Scholarship)* [8325]
Kenyon T. Payne Outstanding Student Awards *(Undergraduate/Award)* [6500]
Joe Perdue Scholarships *(Undergraduate/Scholarship)* [3063]
John T. Riordan Professional Education Scholarships *(Other/Scholarship)* [5307]
Paul H. Rittle Sr. Professional Development Grants *(Other/Grant)* [5217]
Stanley M. Schoenfeld Memorial Scholarship *(Postgraduate/Scholarship)* [7363]
The Thomas Soldan Healthy Communities Scholarships *(Undergraduate, Graduate/Scholarship)* [8237]
Surety and Fidelity Industry Intern and Scholarship Program for Minority Students *(Undergraduate/Scholarship)* [9614]
Syncrude/Athabasca University Aboriginal Scholarships *(Undergraduate/Scholarship)* [9627]
Tag and Label Manufacturers Institute Scholarships - Four-Year Colleges *(Undergraduate/Scholarship)* [9629]
The Ed Tayter Outstanding Citizen Scholarships *(Undergraduate/Scholarship)* [8238]
Wells Fargo American Indian Scholarships - Graduate *(Graduate/Scholarship)* [883]
Wells Fargo Career Scholarship *(Undergraduate/Scholarship)* [10085]

Manufacturing

AACE International Competitive Scholarships *(Undergraduate/Scholarship)* [14]
Walt Bartram Memorial Education Award, Region 12

MARINE BIOLOGY

and Chapter 119 *(Undergraduate/Scholarship)* [9167]
Boeing Company Scholarships *(Undergraduate/Scholarship)* [8870]
Arthur and Gladys Cervenka Scholarships *(Undergraduate/Scholarship)* [9168]
Chapter 1 - Detroit Founding Chapter Undergraduate Scholarships *(Undergraduate/Scholarship)* [9169]
Chapter 6 Fairfield County Scholarships *(Undergraduate/Scholarship)* [9177]
Chapter 17 - St. Louis Scholarships *(Undergraduate/Scholarship)* [9170]
Chapter 23 - Quad Cities Iowa/Illinois Scholarships *(Undergraduate/Scholarship)* [9172]
Chapter 31 - Peoria Endowed Scholarships *(Undergraduate/Scholarship)* [9173]
Chapter 52 - Wichita Scholarships *(Graduate, Undergraduate/Scholarship)* [9175]
Chapter 56 - Fort Wayne Scholarships *(Graduate, Undergraduate/Scholarship)* [9176]
Chapter 67 - Phoenix Scholarships *(Undergraduate/Scholarship)* [9178]
Chapter 93 - Albuquerque Scholarships *(Undergraduate/Scholarship)* [9179]
Chapter 198 - Downriver Detroit Scholarships *(Graduate, Undergraduate/Scholarship)* [9171]
Chapter 311 - Tri City Scholarships *(Undergraduate/Scholarship)* [9174]
Dake Community Manufacturing Scholarships *(Undergraduate/Scholarship)* [4512]
Chapter 116 - Kalamazoo - Roscoe Douglas Scholarships *(Undergraduate/Scholarship)* [9180]
Future Leaders of Manufacturing Scholarships *(Graduate, Undergraduate/Scholarship)* [9181]
SME Education Foundation Connie & Robert T. Gunter Scholarships *(Undergraduate/Scholarship)* [9182]
Clinton J. Helton Manufacturing Scholarships *(Undergraduate/Scholarship)* [9183]
Lucile B. Kaufman Women's Scholarships *(Undergraduate/Scholarship)* [9184]
E. Wayne Kay Co-op Scholarships *(Undergraduate/Scholarship)* [9185]
E. Wayne Kay Community College Scholarships *(Undergraduate/Scholarship)* [9186]
E. Wayne Kay High School Scholarships *(Undergraduate/Scholarship)* [9187]
Giuliano Mazzetti Scholarships *(Undergraduate/Scholarship)* [9188]
Chapter 63 - Portland James E. Morrow Scholarships *(Graduate, Undergraduate/Scholarship)* [9189]
Clarence & Josephine Myers Undergraduate Scholarships *(Graduate, Undergraduate/Scholarship)* [9190]
North Central, Region 9 Scholarships *(Undergraduate/Scholarship)* [9191]
Nuts, Bolts and Thingamajigs Scholarships *(Undergraduate, Vocational/Occupational/Scholarship)* [7562]
Edward S. Roth Manufacturing Engineering Scholarships *(Graduate, Undergraduate/Scholarship)* [9192]
Prof. George Schneider, Jr. Manufacturing Technology Education Scholarships *(Undergraduate/Scholarship)* [9193]
SME Directors Scholarships *(Undergraduate/Scholarship)* [9194]
SME Education Foundation Family Scholarships *(Undergraduate/Scholarship)* [9195]
Chapter 63 - Portland Uncle Bud Smith Scholarships *(Undergraduate/Scholarship)* [9196]
Chapter 4 - Lawrence A. Wacker Memorial Scholarships *(Undergraduate/Scholarship)* [9198]
Myrtle & Earl Walker Scholarships *(Undergraduate/Scholarship)* [9199]
Allen and Loureena Weber Scholarships *(Undergraduate/Scholarship)* [9200]
Albert E. Wischmeyer Memorial Scholarships *(Undergraduate/Scholarship)* [9202]
Women of Today's Manufacturing Scholarships *(Undergraduate/Scholarship)* [3304]

Marine biology (See Biology, Marine)

Marine engineering (See Engineering, Marine)

Maritime studies

The Agnes Sopcak Memorial Scholarship *(Undergraduate/Scholarship)* [10649]
LaRue A. Ditmore Music Scholarships *(Undergraduate/Scholarship)* [10650]
Dr. Nancy Foster Scholarship Program *(Postgraduate, Graduate/Scholarship)* [7077]
Dr. Nancy Foster Scholarships *(Graduate/Scholarship)* [4159]
Lily H. Gridley Memorial Scholarships *(Undergraduate/Scholarship)* [10651]
Norm Manly Maritime Educational Scholarships *(Undergraduate/Scholarship)* [10768]
Ethyl and Armin Wiebke Memorial Scholarships *(Undergraduate/Scholarship)* [10652]

Marketing and distribution

All-American Vector Marketing Scholarship Program *(Undergraduate/Scholarship)* [10364]
Anchor Plastics Scholarships *(Graduate, Undergraduate/Scholarship)* [8072]
APS/Maricopa County Community Colleges Scholarships *(Undergraduate/Scholarship)* [8140]
Auto-Pets "Out-of-the-Box Thinking" Scholarships *(All/Award, Scholarship)* [2129]
Bank of Canada Fellowship Award *(Doctorate, Other/Fellowship, Grant)* [2187]
Mike Buoncristiano Memorial Scholarship Fund *(Undergraduate/Scholarship)* [6287]
Harold K. Douthit Regional Scholarships *(Undergraduate/Scholarship)* [7576]
The Steve Duckett Local Conservation Scholarships *(Undergraduate, Postgraduate/Scholarship)* [8232]
Mark Duda Scholarship Fund *(Graduate, Undergraduate/Scholarship)* [6288]
Harold E. Eisenberg Foundation Scholarships *(Other/Scholarship)* [5304]
Enterprise Rent-A-Car Scholarships *(Graduate, Undergraduate/Scholarship)* [8073]
Lee Epstein Scholarship Fund *(Graduate, Undergraduate/Scholarship)* [6289]
Federated Insurance Scholarships *(Graduate, Undergraduate/Scholarship)* [8074]
Dave Florence Scholarship Fund *(Undergraduate/Scholarship)* [6290]
Richard A. Hammill Scholarship Fund *(Undergraduate/Scholarship)* [981]
William H. Harris Memorial Scholarships *(Graduate, Undergraduate/Scholarship)* [8075]
HSF/Marathon Oil College Scholarship Program *(Undergraduate/Scholarship)* [4905]
IBEA Undergraduate Scholarships *(Undergraduate/Scholarship)* [5057]
Kerrwil's J.W. Kerr Continuing Education Scholarship Awards *(Undergraduate/Scholarship)* [3837]
Debbie Khalil Memorial Scholarships *(Graduate, Undergraduate/Scholarship)* [8076]
The Michael Kiely Strong Roots Scholarships *(Undergraduate/Scholarship)* [8233]
American Marketing Association-Connecticut Chapter, Anna C. Klune Memorial Scholarships *(Graduate/Scholarship)* [4760]
Don Kuhn Memorial Scholarship Fund *(Graduate/Scholarship)* [6291]
The Lagrant Foundation - Graduate Students Scholarships *(Graduate/Scholarship)* [5900]
The Lagrant Foundation - Undergraduate Students Scholarships *(Undergraduate/Scholarship)* [5901]
Robert J. Lavidge Nonprofit Marketing Research Scholarships *(Other/Scholarship)* [982]
Reba Malone Scholarships *(Undergraduate, Graduate/Scholarship)* [1167]
The Tatiana Mendez Future Resources Scholarships *(Undergraduate/Scholarship)* [8234]
MillerCoors National Scholarships *(Undergraduate/Scholarship)* [69]
Mutual of Omaha Sales and Marketing Student Scholarships *(Undergraduate, Graduate/Scholarship)* [106]
New York Women in Communications, Inc. Foundation Scholarships *(Graduate, Undergraduate/Scholarship)* [7406]
Northwestern Mutual Financial Network Scholarships *(Graduate, Undergraduate/Scholarship)* [8077]
Ohio Newspaper Association Minority Scholarships *(Undergraduate/Scholarship)* [7577]
The Seth Okin Good Deeds Scholarships *(Undergraduate/Scholarship)* [8235]
ONWA Annual Scholarships *(Undergraduate/Scholarship)* [7579]
Phi Sigma Epsilon Past National President Scholarships *(Graduate, Undergraduate/Scholarship)* [8078]
John T. Riordan Professional Education Scholarships *(Other/Scholarship)* [5307]
The Thomas Soldan Healthy Communities Scholarships *(Undergraduate, Graduate/Scholarship)* [8237]
Jim Springer Memorial Scholarships *(Undergraduate/Scholarship)* [3110]
Tag and Label Manufacturers Institute Scholarships - Four-Year Colleges *(Undergraduate/Scholarship)* [9629]
The Ed Tayter Outstanding Citizen Scholarships *(Undergraduate/Scholarship)* [8238]
Undergraduate/Graduate Scholarships *(Undergraduate, Graduate/Scholarship)* [5315]
Valuing Diversity PhD Scholarships *(Doctorate/Scholarship)* [983]
Vector Marketing Canadian Scholarship Awards *(Undergraduate/Scholarship)* [10365]
Vector Marketing Scholarships *(Graduate, Undergraduate/Scholarship)* [8079]
Whan Memorial Scholarships *(Graduate, Undergraduate/Scholarship)* [8080]
Glenn Wilson Broadcast Journalism Scholarships *(Undergraduate/Scholarship)* [7873]
Willa Yeck Memorial Scholarship Fund *(Undergraduate/Scholarship)* [6292]
Lorraine Zitone Memorial Scholarship Fund *(Undergraduate/Scholarship)* [6293]

Material and process engineering (See Engineering, Materials)

Materials handling

IFMA Foundation Scholarships *(Undergraduate, Graduate/Scholarship)* [5327]

Materials research/science

ACI Foundation Scholarships *(Graduate/Scholarship)* [703]
ACI W.R. Grace Scholarships *(Graduate/Scholarship)* [705]
AESF Foundation Scholarships *(Undergraduate, Graduate/Scholarship)* [6796]
ASNT Fellowship Award *(Graduate/Fellowship, Award)* [1384]
DEPS Graduate Scholarship Program *(Graduate/Scholarship)* [3624]
DOE Computational Science Graduate Fellowships (DOE CSGF) *(Doctorate, Graduate/Fellowship)* [5887]
Electronics Division Lewis C. Hoffman Scholarships *(Undergraduate/Scholarship)* [664]
Huber Engineered Woods Product Evaluation Scholarships *(Graduate/Scholarship)* [3977]
Jeffress Trust Awards Program in Interdisciplinary Research *(Professional development/Award)* [4816]
Katharine & Bryant Mather Scholarship *(Graduate/Scholarship)* [708]
Kumar Mehta Scholarship *(Graduate/Scholarship)* [709]
NPSC Fellowships *(Graduate/Fellowship)* [7098]
Robert B. Oliver ASNT Scholarships *(Undergraduate/Scholarship)* [1385]

Bertold E. Weinberg Scholarship *(Graduate/Scholarship)* [711]
Xerox Technical Minority Scholarships *(Graduate, Undergraduate/Scholarship)* [10737]

Mathematics and mathematical sciences

AAPM Summer Undergraduate Fellowships *(Undergraduate/Fellowship)* [559]
AAUW Selected Professions Fellowships *(Graduate, Master's, Doctorate/Fellowship)* [22]
Actuarial Diversity Scholarship *(Undergraduate/Scholarship)* [60]
Aerospace Corporation Science and Engineering Student Scholarships *(Undergraduate, Graduate/Scholarship)* [95]
AFCEA Scholarship for Working Professionals *(Undergraduate, Graduate/Scholarship)* [86]
AFCEA Science, Technology, Engineering and Math Teachers Scholarships *(Graduate/Scholarship, Grant)* [87]
Afghanistan and Iraq War Veterans Scholarship *(Undergraduate/Scholarship)* [88]
African American Network - Carolinas Scholarship Fund *(Undergraduate/Scholarship)* [4174]
AfterCollege STEM Inclusion Scholarships *(Undergraduate, Graduate/Scholarship)* [102]
AHETEMS General Scholarships *(Undergraduate, Graduate/Scholarship)* [8888]
AHETEMS Professional Scholarships *(Graduate/Scholarship)* [8889]
Alaska Aerospace Development Corporation Scholarships *(Undergraduate/Scholarship)* [10004]
AMS Centennial Fellowships *(Postdoctorate/Fellowship)* [985]
A.T. Anderson Memorial Scholarships *(Graduate, Undergraduate/Scholarship)* [889]
Arlyn Scales Awards for Science and Technology *(Undergraduate/Scholarship)* [3035]
ASGP Graduate Research Fellowships *(Graduate/Fellowship)* [223]
Astronaut Scholarship Foundation Scholarships *(Undergraduate/Scholarship)* [2105]
AWM Mathematics Travel Grants *(Doctorate/Grant)* [2098]
B&W Y-12 Scholarship Fund *(Undergraduate/Scholarship)* [3752]
Bill and Nell Biggs Scholarships *(Undergraduate/Scholarship)* [10088]
Sam L. Booke, Sr. Scholarships *(Undergraduate/Scholarship)* [10572]
AFCEA San Diego Buck Bragunier Leadership Scholarship *(Undergraduate/Scholarship)* [1667]
Lt. General Douglas D. Buchholz Memorial Scholarship *(Undergraduate/Scholarship)* [89]
Buick Achievers Scholarship Program *(Undergraduate/Scholarship)* [4359]
Burroughs Wellcome Fund Collaborative Research Travel Grants (CRTG) *(Doctorate, Postdoctorate, Professional development/Grant)* [2413]
Wes Burton Memorial Scholarships *(Undergraduate/Scholarship)* [10574]
Career Awards for Science and Mathematics Teachers *(Other/Award)* [2415]
Career Awards at the Scientific Interface (CASI) *(Doctorate, Postdoctorate, Advanced Professional, Professional development/Grant)* [2416]
Caribbean Actuarial Scholarship *(Undergraduate/Scholarship)* [61]
CERT College Scholarships *(Graduate, Undergraduate/Scholarship)* [3435]
CHCI Graduate Fellowships *(Graduate/Fellowship)* [3352]
The Churchill Scholarships *(Postgraduate/Scholarship)* [2940]
City of Toronto Graduate Scholarships for Women in Mathematics *(Master's, Doctorate/Scholarship)* [10282]
Mike Crapo Math and Science Scholarship Fund *(Undergraduate/Scholarship)* [5040]
CRM-ISM Postdoctoral Fellowships *(Postdoctorate/Fellowship)* [9993]
Disabled War Veterans Scholarships *(Undergraduate/Scholarship)* [90]
DOE Computational Science Graduate Fellowships (DOE CSGF) *(Doctorate, Graduate/Fellowship)* [5887]
EAPSI Fellowships *(Doctorate, Graduate/Fellowship)* [7124]
Kevin Ernst Memorial Scholarship Fund *(Undergraduate/Scholarship)* [4514]
Lt. Colonel Romeo and Josephine Bass Ferretti Scholarships *(Undergraduate/Scholarship)* [124]
Fields Institute - Fields Research Immersion Fellowships *(Postdoctorate/Fellowship)* [4019]
Herb and Anne Fincher Memorial Scholarships *(Undergraduate/Scholarship)* [3176]
Reuben H. Fleet Memorial Scholarships *(Undergraduate/Scholarship)* [8704]
Frank Fong Scholarships *(Undergraduate/Scholarship)* [9076]
Future Leader Initial NCTM Annual Meeting Attendance Awards *(Advanced Professional/Award, Monetary)* [6888]
The Gates Millennium Scholars *(Undergraduate/Scholarship)* [4903]
Margaret S. Gilbert Scholarship Fund *(Undergraduate/Scholarship)* [9505]
Glendale Latino Association Scholarships *(Undergraduate/Scholarship)* [4449]
Barry M. Goldwater Scholarships *(Undergraduate/Scholarship)* [10319]
GREAT MINDS Collegiate Scholarship Program *(Undergraduate/Scholarship)* [338]
Jimmy Guild Memorial Scholarships *(Undergraduate/Scholarship)* [6030]
H.G. Hardbarger Science and Mathematics Awards *(Undergraduate/Award)* [7835]
Claude B. Hart Memorial Scholarships *(Undergraduate/Scholarship)* [10584]
Alston S. Householder Fellowships *(Doctorate/Fellowship)* [9907]
Curtis E. Huntington Memorial Scholarship *(Undergraduate/Scholarship)* [62]
ISM Doctoral Fellowships *(Doctorate/Fellowship)* [5160]
ISM Scholarships for Graduate Studies *(Graduate/Scholarship)* [5161]
Jeffress Trust Awards Program in Interdisciplinary Research *(Professional development/Award)* [4816]
Professor Emeritus Dr. Bill Johnson Memorial Scholarships *(Undergraduate/Scholarship)* [8874]
Robert C. and Judith L. Knapp Scholarships *(Graduate, Undergraduate/Scholarship)* [4147]
Lakselaget Foundation Scholarships *(Graduate, Undergraduate/Scholarship)* [5903]
The Langfitt-Ambrose Trust Scholarship *(Undergraduate/Scholarship)* [7846]
Carie and George Lyter Scholarship Fund *(Undergraduate/Scholarship)* [4247]
MAES Founders Scholarships *(Graduate, Undergraduate/Scholarship)* [6178]
MAES General Scholarships *(Graduate, Undergraduate/Scholarship)* [6179]
MAES Graduate Scholarships *(Graduate/Scholarship)* [6180]
MAES Padrino/Madrina Scholarships *(Graduate, Undergraduate/Scholarship)* [6181]
MAES Pipeline Scholarships *(Graduate, Undergraduate/Scholarship)* [6182]
MAES Presidential Scholarships *(Graduate, Undergraduate/Scholarship)* [6183]
Mathematics Mentoring Travel Grants for Women *(Doctorate/Scholarship)* [2099]
Microsoft Research Graduate Women's Scholarships *(Graduate/Scholarship)* [6506]
Microsoft Research PhD Fellowships *(Doctorate/Fellowship)* [6507]
Mu Alpha Theta Summer Grants *(Undergraduate, Graduate/Grant)* [6610]
National GEM Consortium - PhD Science Fellowships *(Doctorate, Graduate/Fellowship)* [6969]
NCTM Emerging Teacher-Leaders in Elementary School Mathematics Grants for Grades K-5 Teachers *(Other/Grant)* [6889]
NCTM Prospective 7-12 Secondary Teacher Course Work Scholarships *(Professional development/Scholarship)* [6890]
NCTM School In-Service Training Grants for Grades 6-8 Teachers *(Undergraduate/Grant)* [6891]
NCTM School In-Service Training Grants for Grades 9-12 Teachers *(Undergraduate/Grant)* [6892]
NCTM School In-Service Training Grants for Grades K-5 Teachers *(Undergraduate/Grant)* [6893]
Northrop Grumman Engineering Scholarships *(Undergraduate/Scholarship)* [7527]
Noyce Scholarships for Secondary Math and Science Education *(Undergraduate/Scholarship)* [5123]
NSA Mathematics and Computer Science Student Scholarships *(Undergraduate, Graduate, Doctorate/Scholarship)* [108]
Ohio Space Grant Consortium Graduate Fellowships *(Graduate, Doctorate, Master's/Fellowship)* [7594]
Ohio Space Grant Consortium Special Minority Fellowships *(Doctorate, Graduate, Master's/Fellowship)* [7595]
Laura Ann Peck Memorial Endowed Scholarships *(Undergraduate/Scholarship)* [6049]
PIMS Postdoctoral Fellowships *(Doctorate/Fellowship)* [7791]
Postdoctoral Fellowships at the Fields Institute *(Postdoctorate/Fellowship)* [4020]
Josef Princ Memorial Scholarships *(Undergraduate/Scholarship)* [8360]
Actuary of Tomorrow - Stuart A. Robertson Memorial Scholarship *(Undergraduate/Scholarship)* [64]
Joseph Wood Rogers Memorial Scholarships *(Undergraduate/Scholarship)* [8880]
Carl Rose Memorial Scholarships *(Undergraduate/Scholarship)* [7858]
Jack Rosen Scholarship *(Undergraduate/Scholarship)* [5683]
Science, Mathematics And Research for Transformation Scholarship for Service Program (SMART) *(Undergraduate, Graduate/Scholarship)* [1305]
Everett Oscar Shimp Memorial Scholarships *(Undergraduate/Scholarship)* [7862]
SHPE Dissertation Scholarship *(Doctorate/Scholarship)* [9130]
SHPE Professional Scholarship *(Master's, Doctorate/Scholarship)* [9131]
Ralph W. Shrader Diversity Scholarship *(Graduate/Scholarship)* [91]
Alfred P. Sloan Foundation Graduate Scholarships - Sloan Indigenous Graduate Partnership *(Master's, Doctorate/Scholarship)* [6683]
Alfred P. Sloan Foundation Graduate Scholarships - Sloan Minority Ph.D. Program *(Doctorate/Scholarship)* [6684]
Sloan Research Fellowships *(Doctorate/Fellowship)* [8988]
SREB-State Doctoral Scholars Program - Doctoral Awards *(Doctorate, Graduate/Scholarship)* [9411]
Margaret Svec Scholarships *(Undergraduate/Scholarship)* [8884]
Anil and Neema Thakrar Family Fund No. 1 *(Undergraduate/Scholarship)* [4257]
The UCSD Black Alumni Scholarships for Engineering, Mathematics and Science *(Undergraduate/Scholarship)* [8737]
USGA/Chevron STEM Scholarship Program *(Undergraduate/Scholarship)* [9954]
VEF Fellowship Program *(Doctorate, Master's/Fellowship)* [10380]
VEF Visiting Scholars Program *(Doctorate/Fellowship)* [10381]
Graduate Fellowship Program - Peter Verhofstadt Fellowships *(Graduate/Fellowship)* [8836]
WACE National Co-op Scholarship Program *(Undergraduate/Scholarship)* [10693]
Women In Defense HORIZONS Scholarships *(Graduate, Undergraduate/Scholarship)* [10636]
Woodcock Family Education Scholarship Program *(Undergraduate/Scholarship)* [306]
Frank and Betty Woodhams Memorial Scholarships *(Undergraduate/Scholarship)* [6422]
WSGC Community College Transfer Scholarships *(Undergraduate/Scholarship)* [10455]
Xavier University Departmental Scholarships *(Undergraduate/Scholarship)* [10729]
Leo Zupin Memorial Scholarship Fund *(Undergraduate, Vocational/Occupational/Scholarship)* [4556]

Mechanical engineering (See Engineering, Mechanical)

Mechanics and repairs

ISOPE Offshore Mechanics Scholarships for Outstanding Students *(Graduate/Scholarship)* [5427]

Media arts

AAAS Mass Media Science and Engineering Fellowship *(Undergraduate, Graduate, Postdoctorate/Fellowship, Award)* [453]
Academy of Motion Picture Arts and Sciences Student Academy Awards *(Undergraduate/Award)* [42]
AFA Aboriginal Traditional Arts Individual Project Grants *(Professional development/Grant)* [236]
AFA Visual Arts and New Media Project Grants *(Professional development/Grant)* [244]
AIHS Media Fellowships - CBC Radio *(Undergraduate, Graduate/Fellowship)* [252]
Anne Friedberg Innovative Scholarship Awards *(Other/Scholarship)* [9104]
Association for Women in Sports Media Internship/Scholarship Program *(Undergraduate/Scholarship, Internship)* [2101]
Dalton Camp Awards *(Undergraduate/Award, Monetary)* [4305]
Canadian Picture Pioneers Scholarships *(Undergraduate/Scholarship)* [2734]
Greg Clerk Awards *(Advanced Professional, Professional development/Award)* [4118]
Design and Multimedia Internships - New York *(Undergraduate, Graduate/Internship)* [4430]
Entertainment Media Internships - Los Angeles *(Undergraduate, Graduate/Internship)* [4431]
Faith Initiatives Internships - New York *(Undergraduate, Graduate/Internship)* [4432]
Foundation Relations Internships - Los Angeles *(Undergraduate, Graduate/Internship)* [4433]
GLAAD News Internships - New York *(Undergraduate, Graduate/Internship)* [4435]
HAESF Professional Internship Program *(Doctorate/Internship)* [5009]
HBO Point Scholarships *(Graduate, Undergraduate/Scholarship)* [8177]
Harriet Irsay Scholarships *(Graduate, Undergraduate/Scholarship)* [927]
New York Women in Communications, Inc. Foundation Scholarships *(Graduate, Undergraduate/Scholarship)* [7406]
NHFA Scholarships *(Graduate/Scholarship)* [6998]
Mister Rogers Memorial Scholarship *(Graduate, Master's, Doctorate/Scholarship)* [47]
William C. Rogers Scholarships *(Undergraduate/Scholarship)* [4389]
Special Events Internships - Los Angeles *(Undergraduate, Graduate/Internship)* [4438]
Special Events Internships - New York *(Undergraduate, Graduate/Internship)* [4439]
Kirk Sutlive Scholarships *(Undergraduate/Scholarship)* [4390]
TFI Latin America Media Arts Fund *(Professional development/Grant)* [9796]
Sandy Ulm Scholarships *(Undergraduate/Scholarship)* [4081]

Medical assisting

AASLD NP/PA Clinical Hepatology Fellowships *(Professional development/Fellowship)* [585]
Buckfire & Buckfire, P.C. Medical Diversity Scholarships *(Advanced Professional/Scholarship)* [2400]
Discover Health Professions Loans *(Graduate/Loan)* [3636]
Discover Residency Loans *(Graduate/Loan)* [3639]
Northampton County Medical Society Alliance Scholarships *(Undergraduate/Scholarship)* [7507]
TMA Research Fellowships *(Postdoctorate/Grant, Fellowship)* [6641]
Susan Vincent Memorial Scholarship *(Undergraduate/Scholarship)* [6187]
Maxine Williams Scholarships *(Undergraduate/Scholarship)* [540]

Medical education (See Education, Medical)

Medical laboratory technology

CSMLS Student Scholarship Awards *(Postgraduate/Scholarship)* [2750]
Indspire Health Careers Bursary and Scholarships *(Graduate, Undergraduate/Scholarship)* [5132]
Johns Hopkins Medicine Ultrasound Fellowships *(Professional development/Fellowship)* [5614]
Siemens-ASCP Scholarship *(Undergraduate/Scholarship)* [1263]

Medical library science (See Library and archival sciences)

Medical research (See also Biomedical research)

AACR Scholar-in-Training Awards: Other Conferences and Meetings *(Graduate, Postdoctorate, Professional development/Grant)* [471]
ABTA Discovery Grant Program *(Professional development/Grant)* [631]
ABTA Medical Student Summer Fellowship Program *(Undergraduate/Grant, Fellowship)* [632]
AHNS/AAO-HNS Young Investigator Award *(Other/Grant)* [845]
AHNS Pilot Research Grants *(Other/Grant)* [846]
AIHS Graduate Studentships *(Master's, Doctorate, Professional development/Fellowship)* [251]
AIHS Postgraduate Fellowships *(Postgraduate, Advanced Professional/Fellowship)* [253]
ALF Postdoctoral Research Fellowship Award *(Postdoctorate, Professional development/Fellowship)* [966]
American Cancer Society - Research Scholar Grants *(Doctorate, Professional development/Grant)* [645]
American Diabetes Association and Boehringer Ingelheim Research Award: Chronic Kidney Disease and Renal Insufficiency in the Setting of Diabetes *(Doctorate, Professional development/Award)* [780]
American Liver Foundation Liver Scholar Awards *(Doctorate/Award)* [967]
Annual Research Doctoral and Postgraduate Fellowship Grant Program *(Doctorate, Postdoctorate, Postgraduate, Advanced Professional/Fellowship, Grant)* [2586]
Asia-Pacific Biomedical Research Foundation Merit Awards *(Postdoctorate/Award)* [9304]
Ballantyne Resident Research Grants *(Other/Grant)* [847]
Raymond B. Bauer Research Award *(Professional development/Grant)* [6479]
Bradley Stuart Beller Special Merit Award *(Doctorate, Postdoctorate/Award)* [3370]
CAHR Master's Level Scholarships *(Master's/Scholarship)* [2557]
Career Awards for Medical Scientists (CAMS) *(Postdoctorate, Advanced Professional, Professional development/Grant)* [2414]
CareFusion Fellowships for Neonatal and Pediatric Therapists *(Professional development/Fellowship)* [1209]
CAS/GE Healthcare Canada Inc. Research Awards *(Other/Award)* [2540]
CHOPR Postdoctoral Fellowships *(Postdoctorate/Fellowship)* [10267]
Crohn's and Colitis Canada Innovations in IBD Research Grants *(Advanced Professional, Professional development/Grant)* [3474]
CSCI Distinguished Scientist Lectures and Awards *(Advanced Professional/Award)* [9073]
Damon Runyon Cancer Research Foundation Fellowships *(Doctorate, Graduate, Postdoctorate/Fellowship)* [3514]
Damon Runyon-Rachleff Innovation Awards *(Postdoctorate/Fellowship)* [3516]
Damon Runyon-Sohn Pediatric Cancer Fellowship Awards *(Master's, Doctorate/Fellowship)* [3517]
Drug Development Research Professorship *(Professional development/Internship)* [3375]
Educational Fellowships for Practicing Physicians *(Advanced Professional, Professional development/Fellowship)* [8123]
PSI Graham Farquharson Knowledge Translation Fellowships *(Advanced Professional, Professional development/Fellowship)* [8124]
Parker B. Francis Respiratory Research Grants *(Advanced Professional, Professional development/Grant)* [1211]
AIHS Cy Frank Fellowships: Impact Assessment *(Doctorate, Professional development/Fellowship)* [254]
FXRFC Medical Research Postdoctoral Fellowships *(Postdoctorate/Fellowship)* [4287]
Carl W. Gottschalk Research Scholar Grants *(Professional development/Grant)* [1381]
Charles H. Hood Foundation Child Health Research Awards Program *(Doctorate/Grant)* [4815]
International GI Training Grant Award *(Professional development/Grant)* [685]
ITNS Research Grants *(Other/Grant)* [5449]
Klarman Family Foundation Grants Program in Eating Disorders Research *(Professional development/Grant)* [4818]
Susan G. Komen for the Cure Post-doctoral Fellowships - Clinical Research Grants *(Postdoctorate/Grant, Fellowship)* [5862]
Lalor Foundation Merit Awards *(Postdoctorate/Award)* [9307]
LAM Pilot Project Awards *(Master's, Postdoctorate/Grant)* [5907]
LCRF Grants *(Advanced Professional, Professional development/Grant)* [6141]
Robert E. Leet and Clara Guthrie Patterson Trust Awards Program in Clinical Research *(Professional development/Grant)* [4819]
Lymphatic Research Foundation Additional Support for NIH-funded F32 Postdoctoral Fellows Awards *(Postdoctorate/Award)* [4820]
Lymphatic Research Foundation Postdoctoral Fellowship Awards Program *(Postdoctorate/Fellowship)* [4821]
Mentored Research Scholar Grant in Applied and Clinical Research *(Doctorate, Professional development/Grant)* [646]
Metcalf Innovation Fellowships *(Advanced Professional, Professional development/Fellowship)* [4366]
Abby and Howard Milstein Innovation Award in Reproductive Medicine *(Advanced Professional, Professional development/Award, Grant)* [5618]
Abby and Howard Milstein Reproductive Medicine Research Award *(Advanced Professional, Professional development/Award, Grant)* [5619]
MMRF Research Fellow Awards *(Postdoctorate, Professional development/Grant)* [6612]
Monaghan/Trudell Fellowships for Aerosol Technique Development *(Professional development/Fellowship)* [1212]
Movember Clinical Trials *(Advanced Professional/Grant)* [8304]
Movember Discovery Grants *(Advanced Professional, Professional development/Grant)* [8305]
Movember Rising Star in Prostate Cancer Research Awards *(Advanced Professional, Professional development/Grant)* [8306]
Movember Team Grants *(Advanced Professional, Professional development/Grant)* [8307]
MSFHR Scholar Awards *(Advanced Professional, Professional development/Grant)* [8994]
MSFHR Trainee Awards *(Postdoctorate, Professional development/Grant)* [8995]
NBHRF/ASRP Doctoral Training Awards *(Doctorate/Grant)* [372, 7267]
NBHRF Doctoral Studentships *(Doctorate/Grant)* [7269]
NBHRF Master's Studentships *(Master's/Grant)* [7272]
NBHRF Postdoctoral Fellowships *(Postdoctorate/Fellowship)* [7273]
NCCT Postdoctoral Research Program *(Postdoctorate, Advanced Professional, Professional development/Fellowship)* [9941]
NINR Mentored Patient-Oriented Research Career Development Award *(Doctorate/Grant)* [7015]

NINR Midcareer Investigator Award in Patient-Oriented Research *(Doctorate/Grant)* [7016]
NINR Pathway to Independence Award *(Doctorate/Grant)* [7017]
Deborah Munroe Noonan Memorial Research Awards *(Professional development/Grant)* [4822]
Parkinson Canada Basic Research Fellowships *(Advanced Professional/Fellowship)* [7876]
Parkinson Canada New Investigator Award Grants *(Professional development/Grant)* [7880]
Parkinson Canada Pilot Project Grants *(Advanced Professional/Grant)* [7881]
Patient Advocate Scholarship Program *(Professional development/Scholarship)* [3385]
Philips Respironics Fellowships in Non-Invasive Respiratory Care *(Professional development/Fellowship)* [1215]
Prostate Cancer Canada Clinical Research Fellowships *(Advanced Professional/Fellowship)* [8308]
Prostate Cancer Canada Graduate Studentships *(Graduate, Doctorate/Grant)* [8309]
Prostate Cancer Canada Postdoctoral Research Fellowships *(Postdoctorate, Advanced Professional/Fellowship)* [8310]
PSI Healthcare Research by Community Physicians Grants *(Advanced Professional, Professional development/Grant)* [8125]
Resident Research Grants *(Postgraduate, Professional development/Grant)* [8126]
Robert Wood Johnson Clinical Scholarships *(Graduate, Professional development/Fellowship)* [8630]
Damon Runyon Clinical Investigator Awards *(Doctorate, Graduate, Postdoctorate/Fellowship, Award)* [3518]
Scholarships for the Next Generation of Scientists *(Postdoctorate/Scholarship)* [2777]
Smith Family Awards Program for Excellence in Biomedical Research *(Advanced Professional, Professional development/Grant)* [4823]
SSF Research Grants *(Other/Grant)* [8975]
SSF Student Fellowships *(Doctorate, Undergraduate/Fellowship)* [8976]
Lee Summer Student Fellowship *(Undergraduate, Master's/Fellowship)* [8553]
THFC Medical Research Grants *(Professional development/Grant)* [4834]
Toronto Rehab Scholarships in Rehabilitation-Related Research *(Graduate/Scholarship)* [9753]
Translational Research Professorship *(Professional development/Internship)* [3387]
USDA-NIFA-AFRI Merit Awards *(Postdoctorate/Award)* [9308]
Young Investigators Achievement Award *(Advanced Professional, Professional development/Award, Grant)* [5620]

Medical technology

ASCP Phlebotomy Scholarships *(Undergraduate/Scholarship)* [1262]
Chinese American Medical Society Summer Research Fellowships Program *(Undergraduate/Fellowship)* [2917]
Margaret Dowell-Gravatt, M.D. Scholarships *(Undergraduate/Scholarship)* [2226]
Illinois Student Assistance Commission Medical Student Scholarships *(Undergraduate/Scholarship)* [5074]
Esther Lim Memorial Scholarships *(Undergraduate/Scholarship)* [2918]
Ruth Liu Memorial Scholarships *(Undergraduate/Scholarship)* [2919]
Med Technology and Clinical Lab Science Scholarships *(Undergraduate/Scholarship)* [104]
SPSmedical CS Scholarships *(Other/Scholarship)* [5264]

Medicine (See also specific diseases)

AAMA Houston Chapter Health Training Scholarships *(Other/Scholarship)* [1601]
AASLD Advanced/Transplant Hepatology Fellowships *(Professional development/Fellowship)* [581]
AASLD Autoimmune Liver Diseases Pilot Research Awards *(Graduate, Doctorate, Postdoctorate, Professional development/Award, Grant)* [582]
AASLD Career Development Awards in Liver Transplantation *(Professional development/Grant)* [583]
AASLD Clinical and Translational Research Awards *(Professional development/Grant)* [584]
AASLD Pinnacle Research Awards in Liver Disease *(Professional development/Grant)* [586]
AATS Medical Students Summer Intern Scholarships *(Undergraduate/Scholarship, Internship)* [594]
AAUW Selected Professions Fellowships *(Graduate, Master's, Doctorate/Fellowship)* [22]
Dr. Anderson Abbott Awards *(Undergraduate/Scholarship)* [10278]
Accenture American Indian Scholarship Program *(Graduate, Undergraduate/Scholarship)* [880]
Afdhal/McHutchison LIFER Awards *(Postdoctorate, Professional development/Grant)* [587]
AFPPA Student Scholarships *(Undergraduate/Scholarship)* [1959]
Ahrens Charitable Trust Scholarship *(Undergraduate/Scholarship)* [4558]
AIHS Media Fellowships - CBC Radio *(Undergraduate, Graduate/Fellowship)* [252]
Allegheny County Medical Society Medical Student Scholarships (ACMS) *(Undergraduate/Scholarship)* [4274]
Alliance Medical Education Scholarship Fund (AMES) *(Undergraduate/Scholarship)* [4275]
AMA Foundation Minority Scholars Awards *(Graduate/Scholarship)* [989]
AMA Foundation Physicians of Tomorrow Scholarships *(Graduate/Scholarship)* [990]
American Association of University Women Selected Professions Fellowships *(Other/Fellowship)* [603]
AMSN Career Mobility Scholarship Awards *(Undergraduate, Doctorate/Scholarship)* [37]
AMTF Graduate Scholarships *(Graduate/Scholarship)* [1259]
A.T. Anderson Memorial Scholarships *(Graduate, Undergraduate/Scholarship)* [889]
Annual Research Doctoral and Postgraduate Fellowship Grant Program *(Doctorate, Postdoctorate, Postgraduate, Advanced Professional/Fellowship, Grant)* [2586]
APDA Medical Students Summer Fellowships *(Graduate, Professional development/Fellowship)* [1071]
Armenian American Medical Association Scholarships *(Undergraduate/Scholarship)* [1683]
Army Health Professions Scholarships Program *(Professional development/Scholarship)* [9878]
ARS of Eastern USA Lazarian Graduate Scholarship *(Master's, Doctorate/Scholarship)* [1680]
ASA Minority Fellowship Program (ASA MFP) *(Graduate, Doctorate, Professional development/Fellowship)* [1445]
ASLMS Research Grants *(Postdoctorate/Grant)* [1349]
ASLMS Student Research Grants *(Undergraduate, Graduate, Professional development/Grant)* [1350]
AvaCare Medical Scholarships *(Undergraduate/Scholarship)* [2142]
Dr. Noyes L. Avery, Jr. and Ann E. Avery Scholarships *(Undergraduate, Graduate/Scholarship)* [4575]
Jenny Panitch Beckow Memorial Scholarships Israel *(Graduate/Scholarship)* [5570]
Benign Essential Blepharospasm Research Foundation Research Grants *(Doctorate, Postdoctorate/Grant)* [2224]
Linn-Benton County Scholarships *(Undergraduate/Scholarship)* [7709]
Board of Young Adult Advisors Scholarships *(Graduate/Scholarship)* [9827]
Linda Brandt Research Awards *(Postgraduate/Award)* [2039]
Joseph R. Calder, Jr., MD Scholarship Fund *(Undergraduate/Scholarship)* [4041]
Career Awards at the Scientific Interface (CASI) *(Doctorate, Postdoctorate, Advanced Professional, Professional development/Grant)* [2416]
CCFA Career Development Awards *(Doctorate/Grant)* [3476]
CCFA Research Fellowship Awards *(Doctorate, Graduate/Fellowship)* [3477]
CCFA Student Research Fellowship Awards *(Graduate, Undergraduate/Grant)* [3478]
CDC Preventive Medicine Residency and Fellowships *(Other/Fellowship)* [9918]
Center for Engineering in Medicine Predoctoral Fellows Program *(Postdoctorate/Fellowship)* [6316]
Chronic Pain Medicine Research Grants *(Professional development/Grant)* [1403]
Crohn's and Colitis Foundation of America Senior Research Awards *(Doctorate, Graduate/Grant)* [3479]
Rebecca Lee Crumpler, M.D. Scholarships *(Advanced Professional/Scholarship)* [1865]
The Cure Starts Now Foundation Grants *(Graduate, Doctorate/Grant)* [3492]
DAAD Study Scholarship Awards *(Graduate/Scholarship)* [3604]
D&A Florida Scholarships *(Undergraduate/Scholarship)* [9425]
Steve Dearduff Scholarships *(Graduate, Undergraduate/Scholarship)* [3194]
Matthew Debono Memorial Scholarship Funds *(Undergraduate, Graduate/Scholarship)* [1588]
Margaret Dowell-Gravatt, M.D. Scholarships *(Undergraduate/Scholarship)* [2226]
Family and Children's Services of Lebanon County Fund *(Undergraduate/Scholarship)* [4239]
Dr. Joseph Fitzsimmons Scholarships *(Doctorate/Scholarship)* [9959]
A. Ward Ford Memorial Research Grants *(Postdoctorate, Professional development/Grant)* [1351]
Doris W. Frey Memorial Scholarships *(Undergraduate, Graduate/Scholarship)* [9430]
William and Francis Fry Honorary Fellowships for Contributions to Therapeutic Ultrasound *(Professional development/Fellowship)* [5431]
Dr. Horace Furumoto Innovations Professional Development - Young Investigator Awards *(Professional development/Award)* [1352]
Gantenbein Medical Fund Fellowship *(Graduate/Fellowship)* [3497]
William R. Goldfarb Memorial Scholarships *(Undergraduate/Scholarship)* [1739]
Scott A. Gunder, MD, DCMS Presidential Scholarships *(Undergraduate/Scholarship)* [4276]
HAESF Professional Internship Program *(Doctorate/Internship)* [5009]
Hall County Medical Society Scholarships *(Undergraduate/Scholarship)* [4563]
Lillie Hope-McGarvey Health Scholarship Awards *(Undergraduate, Vocational/Occupational, Graduate, Master's/Scholarship)* [311]
Johns Hopkins Department of Emergency Medicine Administration Fellowships *(Advanced Professional, Professional development/Fellowship)* [5607]
Dr. Gilbert Hopson Medical Student Bursaries *(Undergraduate/Grant)* [7639]
HRSA Scholarships for Disadvantaged Students *(Undergraduate/Scholarship)* [9923]
Dr. James L. Hutchinson and Evelyn Ribbs Hutchinson Medical School Scholarship Fund *(Undergraduate/Scholarship)* [8952]
Indiana State University Rural Health Scholarships *(Graduate/Scholarship)* [5119]
Indspire Health Careers Bursary and Scholarships *(Graduate, Undergraduate/Scholarship)* [5132]
International Scholars Program for Young Vascular Surgeons *(Graduate/Scholarship)* [9325]
ISTU Student Prize *(Undergraduate/Prize)* [5432]
Jewish Federation Academic Scholarships *(Graduate, Undergraduate/Scholarship)* [5598]
Johns Hopkins Medicine Emergency Medical Services Fellowship *(Professional development/Fellowship)* [5609]
Johns Hopkins Medicine Medical Education Fellowships *(Professional development/Fellowship)* [5611]
Johns Hopkins Medicine Observation Medicine Fellowships *(Professional development/Fellowship)* [5612]
Johns Hopkins Medicine Research Fellowships *(Professional development/Fellowship)* [5613]
Magoichi and Shizuko Kato Memorial Scholarships

(Graduate, Master's, Doctorate/Scholarship) [5552]
Kendrick Foundation, Inc. Scholarships *(Undergraduate/Scholarship)* [5813]
Jason Lang Scholarships *(Undergraduate/Scholarship)* [276]
Karen E. Latt Memorial Scholarships *(Graduate/Scholarship)* [5584]
Lazarian Graduate Scholarships *(Graduate/Scholarship)* [1678]
S. Evelyn Lewis Memorial Scholarships in Medical Health Sciences *(Graduate, Undergraduate/Scholarship)* [10818]
Dolores Zohrab Liebmann Fund - Graduate School Fellowships *(Graduate/Fellowship)* [6075]
Lycoming County Medical Society Scholarships (LCMS) *(Undergraduate/Scholarship)* [4277]
Dr. Arlene MacIntyre Medical Student Bursaries *(Undergraduate/Grant)* [7640]
Dr. Edward May Magruder Medical Scholarships *(Undergraduate/Scholarship)* [677]
Dr. Frank and Florence Marino Scholarships *(Undergraduate/Scholarship)* [4764]
Olivia M. Marquart Scholarships *(Graduate, Master's, Doctorate/Scholarship)* [9828]
Abby and Howard Milstein Innovation Award in Reproductive Medicine *(Advanced Professional, Professional development/Award, Grant)* [5618]
Abby and Howard Milstein Reproductive Medicine Research Award *(Advanced Professional, Professional development/Award, Grant)* [5619]
Mission Bay Hospital Auxiliary Scholarships *(Undergraduate/Scholarship)* [8717]
Montgomery County Medical Society Scholarships (MCMS) *(Undergraduate/Scholarship)* [4278]
National Ataxia Foundation Research Fellowships *(Other/Fellowship)* [6806]
National Ataxia Foundation Research Grants *(Other/Grant)* [6807]
National Biosafety and Biocontainment Training Program Fellowships *(Graduate, Postgraduate/Fellowship)* [6811]
National Medical Fellowships Need-Based Scholarships *(Undergraduate/Scholarship)* [7061]
OMSBF Burlington Medical Student Bursaries *(Undergraduate/Grant)* [7641]
OMSBF District Four - Physician Care Bursaries *(Undergraduate/Grant)* [7642]
OMSBF Durham Medical Society Medical Student Bursaries *(Undergraduate/Grant)* [7643]
OMSBF Sun Life Financial Medical Student Bursaries *(Undergraduate/Grant)* [7644]
Pappaioanou Veterinary Public Health and Applied Epidemiology Fellowships *(Undergraduate/Fellowship)* [2833]
Sylvia Parkinson Scholarships *(Undergraduate/Scholarship)* [4766]
Gilberto and Lennetta Pesquera Medical School Scholarships *(Graduate, Doctorate/Scholarship, Grant)* [4453]
PKD Foundation Fellowships *(Doctorate, Graduate/Fellowship)* [8144]
Paul S. Robinson Scholarships *(Undergraduate/Scholarship)* [9115]
RSDSA Research Grants *(Other/Grant)* [8532]
Michael A. Russo Memorial Scholarships *(Undergraduate/Scholarship)* [8525]
Meta M. Sawyer Bursary Fund *(Undergraduate/Grant)* [7645]
Jeptha Wade Schureman Scholarship Program *(Undergraduate/Scholarship)* [3333]
SCLMA Medical Student Scholarships *(Undergraduate, Graduate/Scholarship)* [9401]
John M. and Mary A. Shanley Memorial Scholarships *(Undergraduate, Graduate/Scholarship)* [9448]
Myrtle Siegfried, MD and Michael Vigilante, MD Scholarships *(Undergraduate/Scholarship)* [4279]
Nadine Barrie Smith Student Awards *(Undergraduate/Award)* [5433]
SOHN Allied Health to BSN Degree Scholarship *(Undergraduate/Scholarship)* [9233]
Dr. William E. and Norma Sprague Scholarships *(Undergraduate, Graduate/Scholarship)* [4624]
Betty & Charles Taylor Scholarships *(Advanced Professional/Scholarship)* [10803]

Marvin H. and Kathleen G. Teget Leadership Scholarships *(Undergraduate/Scholarship)* [9602]
Dr. Peter A. Theodos Memorial Graduate Scholarships *(Undergraduate, Graduate/Scholarship)* [4850]
Thompson Scholarships for Women in Safety *(Graduate/Scholarship)* [1430]
Sam Tughan Scholarships *(Undergraduate/Scholarship)* [2739]
Dr. Csaba Oliver Vargha Medical Student Bursaries *(Undergraduate/Grant)* [7646]
Vascular Surgery Trainee Advocacy Travel Scholarship *(Advanced Professional, Professional development/Scholarship, Grant)* [9326]
VEF Fellowship Program *(Doctorate, Master's/Fellowship)* [10380]
VEF Visiting Scholars Program *(Doctorate/Fellowship)* [10381]
The Sybil Jennings Vorheis Memorial Undergraduate Scholarships *(Undergraduate/Scholarship)* [4218]
Percy W. Wadman, M.D. Scholarship *(Postgraduate/Scholarship)* [4291]
Washington University Law School Olin Fellowships for Women *(Advanced Professional/Fellowship)* [10477]
Arthur N. Wilson, MD, Scholarships *(Undergraduate/Scholarship)* [991]
Women's Leadership Training Grant *(Advanced Professional, Professional development/Grant)* [9327]
Worcester District Medical Society Scholarship Fund *(Undergraduate/Scholarship)* [10689]
Marilyn Yetso Memorial Scholarships *(Graduate/Scholarship)* [9829]
Young Investigators Achievement Award *(Advanced Professional, Professional development/Award, Grant)* [5620]

Medicine, Cardiology

Canadian Association of Cardiac Rehabilitation Graduate Scholarship Awards *(Graduate/Scholarship)* [2548]
Wagner-Torizuka Fellowships *(Professional development/Fellowship)* [9228]

Medicine, Cardiovascular (See also Medicine, Cardiology)

International Scholars Program for Young Vascular Surgeons *(Graduate/Scholarship)* [9325]
Vascular Surgery Trainee Advocacy Travel Scholarship *(Advanced Professional, Professional development/Scholarship, Grant)* [9326]
Women's Leadership Training Grant *(Advanced Professional, Professional development/Grant)* [9327]

Medicine, Cerebrovascular

International Scholars Program for Young Vascular Surgeons *(Graduate/Scholarship)* [9325]
Vascular Surgery Trainee Advocacy Travel Scholarship *(Advanced Professional, Professional development/Scholarship, Grant)* [9326]
Women's Leadership Training Grant *(Advanced Professional, Professional development/Grant)* [9327]

Medicine, Chiropractic

Beatrice K. Blair Scholarships *(Undergraduate/Scholarship)* [2305]
F. Maynard Lipe Scholarship Award *(Master's, Postgraduate/Scholarship)* [683]

Medicine, Geriatric

APDA Postdoctoral Research Fellowships *(Other/Fellowship)* [1072]
NHCGNE Patricia G. Archbold Predoctoral Scholar Award *(Doctorate/Scholarship)* [6982]
Claire M. Fagin Fellow Award *(Doctorate/Fellowship)* [6983]

HPGS/ALOH Graduate Scholarships *(Graduate/Scholarship)* [4801]
HPGS Undergraduate Scholarships *(Undergraduate/Scholarship)* [4802]
T. Franklin Williams Research Scholars Award Program *(Other/Grant)* [4804]

Medicine, Gynecological and obstetrical

SMFM/AAOGF Scholarship Awards *(Graduate/Scholarship)* [9206]

Medicine, Internal

Epilepsy Foundation Research and Training Fellowships for Clinicians *(Doctorate, Other/Grant)* [3908]

Medicine, Nuclear

Mitzi and William Blahd, MD Pilot Research Grants *(Doctorate/Grant)* [9220]
Paul Cole Scholarships *(Undergraduate/Scholarship)* [9221]
SNMMI Robert E. Henkin, MD, Government Relations Fellowship *(Professional development/Fellowship)* [9222]
Professional Development and Education Fund (PDEF) Professional Development Scholarships *(Professional development/Scholarship)* [9223]
R&E Foundation Education Scholarships *(Graduate, Other/Scholarship)* [8416]
SNMMI-TS Advanced Practitioner Program Scholarship *(Professional development/Scholarship)* [9224]
SNNMI Predoctoral Molecular Imaging Scholar Program *(Doctorate/Scholarship)* [9226]
Marc Tetalman, MD, Memorial Award *(Professional development, Doctorate/Recognition)* [9227]

Medicine, Orthopedic

AOFAS Research Grants Program *(Graduate/Grant)* [1060]
F. Maynard Lipe Scholarship Award *(Master's, Postgraduate/Scholarship)* [683]
Orthopaedic Foot and Ankle Fellowships *(Graduate, Professional development/Fellowship)* [1061]
Orthopaedic Trauma Association Research Grants *(Other/Grant)* [7753]

Medicine, Osteopathic

AACOM Scholar in Residence Program *(Professional development/Scholarship)* [482]
William G. Anderson, DO, Minority Scholarships *(Undergraduate/Scholarship)* [1063]
Discover Health Professions Loans *(Graduate/Loan)* [3636]
Discover Residency Loans *(Graduate/Loan)* [3639]
Humanism in Medicine Scholarships *(Undergraduate/Scholarship)* [9600]
Illinois Student Assistance Commission Medical Student Scholarships *(Undergraduate/Scholarship)* [5074]
Kansas Osteopathic Medical Service Scholarships *(Graduate, Other/Scholarship)* [5658]
McCaughan Heritage Scholarships *(Undergraduate/Scholarship)* [1064]
Morgan Stanley Pediatrics Fellowships *(Doctorate, Postdoctorate, Postgraduate, Graduate/Fellowship)* [618]
NAAMA Scholarships *(Undergraduate/Scholarship)* [6701]
NJOEF Scholarships *(Undergraduate/Scholarship)* [7315]
Scleroderma Foundation Established Investigator Grants *(Doctorate/Grant)* [8816]
Scleroderma Foundation New Investigator Grants *(Doctorate/Grant)* [8817]
SOMA Student Research Fellowships *(Undergraduate/Fellowship)* [9601]
Marvin H. and Kathleen G. Teget Leadership Scholarships *(Undergraduate/Scholarship)* [9602]

Welch Scholars Grants *(Undergraduate/Grant)* [1065]

Medicine, Pediatric

American Pediatric Surgical Nurses Association Educational Grants *(Other/Grant)* [1076]
Antimicrobial Stewardship Fellowship Award *(Professional development/Award, Fellowship)* [7929]
Daland Fellowships in Clinical Investigation *(Doctorate, Postgraduate/Fellowship)* [1079]
John W. Duckett Jr., AFUD Pediatric Research Scholarships *(Undergraduate/Scholarship)* [9246]
National Association of Pediatric Nurse Practitioners McNeil Rural and Underserved Scholarships *(Graduate/Scholarship)* [6774]
Morgan Stanley Pediatrics Fellowships *(Doctorate, Postdoctorate, Postgraduate, Graduate/Fellowship)* [618]
Lizette Peterson Homer Injury Prevention Grant Awards *(Other, Undergraduate, Graduate/Grant)* [1571]
Marion and Donald Routh Student Research Grants *(Undergraduate/Grant)* [1572]
Norman Siegel Research Scholar Grants *(Doctorate/Grant)* [1382]
Society for Pediatric Urology Research Grant Program *(Undergraduate/Grant)* [9247]

Medicine, Sports

AMSSM-ACSM Clinical Research Grants *(Professional development/Grant)* [993]
Swede Swanson Memorial Scholarships *(Undergraduate/Scholarship)* [7243]

Medicine, Veterinary (See Veterinary science and medicine)

Medieval studies

ARIT Fellowships in the Humanities and Social Sciences in Turkey *(Postdoctorate, Graduate/Fellowship)* [1201]
Birgit Baldwin Fellowships *(Graduate/Fellowship)* [6395]
Medieval Academy Dissertation Grants *(Graduate/Grant)* [6396]
Schallek Awards *(Graduate/Award)* [6397]
Schallek Fellowships *(Graduate/Fellowship)* [6398]

Meniere's disease

AOS Research Training Fellowships *(Graduate/Fellowship)* [1067]

Mental health

AACPDM Student Scholarships *(Professional development/Scholarship)* [399]
ADAA Career Development Travel Awards *(Other/Award)* [1569]
AED Student Early Career Investigator Travel Fellowships *(Undergraduate, Graduate, Postdoctorate, Postgraduate/Fellowship)* [32]
AED Student Research Grants *(Undergraduate, Graduate, Postgraduate/Grant)* [33]
Azrieli Neurodevelopmental Research Program *(Advanced Professional/Grant)* [2350]
Bell Aliant Medical Education Scholarships *(Advanced Professional/Scholarship)* [7276]
Brain Canada-ALS Canada Discovery Grants *(Advanced Professional, Professional development/Grant)* [2352]
Brain Canada-ALS Canada Hudson Translational Team Grants *(Advanced Professional, Professional development/Grant)* [2353]
Brain Canada/CQDM "Focus on Brain" Partnership Program *(Advanced Professional/Grant)* [2354]
Brain Canada/NeuroDevNet Developmental Neurosciences Research Training Awards *(Postdoctorate, Advanced Professional, Professional development/Grant)* [2355]
Brain Canada/RBC Research Partnership in Mental Health Services for Children and Youth Funds *(Advanced Professional/Grant)* [2356]
Council on Social Work Education Minority Fellowship Program for Doctoral Students *(Postdoctorate/Fellowship)* [3454]
Derivative Duo Scholarships *(Undergraduate/Scholarship)* [8253]
Diabetes Scholars Foundation College Scholarships *(Undergraduate/Scholarship)* [3616]
Family and Children's Services of Lebanon County Fund *(Undergraduate/Scholarship)* [4239]
Grant Assistance Program for Autism Professionals - College Programs *(Undergraduate/Grant)* [7650]
Grant Assistance Program for Autism Professionals - Doctoral Programs *(Doctorate/Grant)* [7651]
Grant Assistance Program for Autism Professionals - Institutional Standards *(Undergraduate, Graduate/Grant)* [7652]
Grant Assistance Program for Autism Professionals - Masters Programs *(Master's/Grant)* [7653]
Grant Assistance Program for Autism Professionals - Professional Certification Programs *(Undergraduate, Professional development/Grant)* [7654]
Grant Assistance Program for Autism Professionals - Retroactive Assistance *(Advanced Professional, Professional development/Grant)* [7655]
Grant Assistance Program for Autism Professionals - Undergraduate Programs *(Undergraduate/Grant)* [7656]
Catharine Wilder Guiles Scholarships *(Graduate/Scholarship)* [6197]
HRSA Scholarships for Disadvantaged Students *(Undergraduate/Scholarship)* [9923]
Lutheran Student Scholastic and Service Scholarships - College and University Students *(Undergraduate/Scholarship)* [2248]
MGH Department of Psychiatry Behavioral Neurology and Neuropsychiatry Fellowships *(Advanced Professional, Professional development/Fellowship)* [6320]
NAJA Scholarships *(Graduate/Scholarship)* [6760]
OMHF Postdoctoral Fellowships *(Postdoctorate/Fellowship)* [7648]
Platform Support Grants *(Advanced Professional/Grant)* [2357]
Don Renschler Scholarships *(Graduate/Scholarship)* [8261]

Mental retardation

AAIDD Fellowship *(Advanced Professional, Professional development/Fellowship)* [511]
NYCT Paid Graduate Student Philanthropy Fellowships - Health and People with Special Needs *(Graduate/Fellowship)* [7352]

Metallurgy

AIST Baltimore Member Chapter Scholarships *(Undergraduate/Scholarship)* [1989]
AIST Benjamin F. Fairless Scholarships *(Undergraduate/Scholarship)* [1996]
Globe-Trotters Member Chapter Scholarships *(Undergraduate, Postgraduate/Scholarship)* [1998]
Alfred B. Glossbrenner Scholarships *(Undergraduate/Scholarship)* [1999]
H.H. Harris Foundation Scholarships *(Professional development, Undergraduate/Scholarship)* [836]
Gerald V. Henderson Memorial Scholarships *(Undergraduate, Graduate/Scholarship)* [9210]
AIST Willy Korf Memorial Fund *(Undergraduate/Scholarship)* [2000]
AIST Ronald E. Lincoln Memorial Scholarships *(Undergraduate/Scholarship)* [2001]
Mineral & Metallurgical Processing Division Scholarships and Richard Klimpel Memorial Scholarships *(Undergraduate, Graduate/Scholarship)* [9211]
AIST Judith A. Quinn Detroit Member Chapter Scholarship *(Undergraduate/Scholarship)* [2005]
IPMI Richard Rubin Memorial Scholarship Award *(Graduate/Award)* [5374]
AIST William E. Schwabe Memorial Scholarships *(Undergraduate/Scholarship)* [2007]
Sheet Metal And Air Conditioning Contractors' National Association College of Fellows Scholarships *(Undergraduate/Scholarship)* [8859]
SME Coal and Energy Division Scholarships *(Undergraduate/Scholarship)* [9212]
SME Environmental Division Scholarships *(Undergraduate, Graduate/Scholarship)* [9213]
Henry DeWitt Smith Graduate Scholarships *(Graduate/Scholarship)* [9214]

Meteorology (See also Atmospheric science)

AMS Freshman Undergraduate Scholarships *(Undergraduate/Scholarship)* [997]
AMS/Industry/Government Graduate Fellowships *(Graduate/Fellowship)* [999]
AMS/Industry Minority Scholarships *(Undergraduate/Scholarship)* [1000]
AMS Undergraduate Named Scholarships *(Undergraduate/Scholarship)* [1001]
CMOS-SCMO President's Prize *(Professional development/Prize)* [2682]
Roger Daley Postdoctoral Publication Awards *(Postdoctorate/Monetary)* [2683]
Tertia M.C. Hughes Memorial Graduate Student Prize *(Graduate/Award, Prize)* [2684]
John Jeffries Meteorology Scholarships *(Graduate/Scholarship)* [3979]
Naval Weather Service Association Scholarships *(Undergraduate/Scholarship)* [7225]
François J. Saucier Prize in Applied Oceanography *(Professional development/Award, Prize)* [2685]
Dr. Andrew Thomson Prize in Applied Meteorology *(Professional development/Award, Prize)* [2686]
CASFM-Ben Urbonas Scholarships *(Graduate/Scholarship)* [3132]

Microbiology (See also Biology)

AIST Ohio Valley Chapter Scholarships *(Undergraduate/Scholarship)* [1994]
American Society for Microbiology International Fellowships for Africa *(Postdoctorate/Fellowship)* [1365]
American Society for Microbiology International Fellowships for Asia *(Postdoctorate/Fellowship)* [1366]
American Society for Microbiology International Fellowships for Latin America and the Caribbean *(Postdoctorate/Fellowship)* [1367]
American Society for Microbiology Undergraduate Research Fellowships *(Undergraduate/Fellowship)* [1368]
ASM/CDC Program in Infectious Disease and Public Health Microbiology *(Postdoctorate/Fellowship)* [1369]
ASM Undergraduate Research Capstone Program *(Undergraduate/Fellowship)* [1372]
Margaret Dowell-Gravatt, M.D. Scholarships *(Undergraduate/Scholarship)* [2226]
International Association for Food Protection - Student Travel Scholarship Program *(Undergraduate, Graduate/Scholarship)* [5258]
Kris Knudson Memorial Scholarship *(Graduate, Undergraduate/Scholarship)* [10065]
National Biosafety and Biocontainment Training Program Fellowships *(Graduate, Postgraduate/Fellowship)* [6811]
Selman A. Waksman Endowed Scholarships in Microbial Diversity *(Graduate, Master's, Doctorate/Scholarship)* [6264]
ASM Robert D. Watkins Graduate Research Fellowships *(Postdoctorate/Fellowship)* [1373]

Middle Eastern studies (See Near Eastern studies)

Midwifery

ACNM Foundation, Inc. Fellowships for Graduate Education *(Doctorate, Postdoctorate/Fellowship, Grant)* [692]
ACNM Foundation Midwives of Color-Watson Midwifery Student Scholarship *(Undergraduate/Scholarship)* [693]

Military history (See History, Military)

Military science and education

NMIA Scholarship Program *(Undergraduate, Graduate/Scholarship)* [7071]
Colonel Nate Smith Memorial Scholarships *(Graduate, Undergraduate/Scholarship)* [6374]
UW-Madison Reserve Officers Training Corps Scholarships *(Undergraduate/Scholarship)* [10333]
Xavier University ROTC Scholarships - Army ROTC *(Undergraduate/Scholarship)* [10734]

Mineralogy

EMLF Law Student Scholarships *(Undergraduate/Scholarship)* [3869]
Ludo Frevel Crystallography Scholarships *(Graduate/Scholarship)* [5294]
Mineral & Metallurgical Processing Division Scholarships and Richard Klimpel Memorial Scholarships *(Undergraduate, Graduate/Scholarship)* [9211]
Mineralogical Association of Canada Scholarships *(Doctorate, Graduate/Scholarship)* [2022]
SME Coal and Energy Division Scholarships *(Undergraduate/Scholarship)* [9212]
SME Environmental Division Scholarships *(Undergraduate, Graduate/Scholarship)* [9213]

Mining (See also Engineering, Mining and Mineral)

American Society of Mining and Reclamation Memorial Scholarships *(Undergraduate/Scholarship, Recognition)* [1377]
Gerald V. Henderson Memorial Scholarships *(Undergraduate, Graduate/Scholarship)* [9210]
Joseph A. Holmes Safety Association Scholarships *(Undergraduate, Graduate/Scholarship)* [4918]
National Association of Abandoned Mine Land Programs Scholarships *(Undergraduate/Scholarship)* [6708]
SME Coal and Energy Division Scholarships *(Undergraduate/Scholarship)* [9212]
SME Environmental Division Scholarships *(Undergraduate, Graduate/Scholarship)* [9213]
Henry DeWitt Smith Graduate Scholarships *(Graduate/Scholarship)* [9214]

Ministry (See Religion)

Minorities

Actuarial Diversity Scholarship *(Undergraduate/Scholarship)* [60]
American Speech Language Hearing Foundation Endowed Scholarships *(Graduate, Master's, Doctorate/Scholarship)* [1451]
American Speech Language Hearing Foundation Scholarships for Minority Students *(Graduate, Master's, Doctorate/Scholarship)* [1454]
ASA Minority Fellowship Program (ASA MFP) *(Graduate, Doctorate, Professional development/Fellowship)* [1445]
Baker and McKenzie Diversity Fellowships *(Postgraduate, Professional development/Fellowship)* [2175]
Marcus Mosiah Garvey Scholarships *(Undergraduate/Scholarship)* [5523]
NACA Multicultural Professional Development Grant *(Undergraduate, Graduate, Professional development/Grant)* [6729]

Modern languages

ARIT Fellowships in the Humanities and Social Sciences in Turkey *(Postdoctorate, Graduate/Fellowship)* [1201]
MLA Financial Assistance *(Graduate, Advanced Professional/Grant)* [6567]
Xavier University Departmental Scholarships *(Undergraduate/Scholarship)* [10729]

Molecular biology (See Biology, Molecular)

Mortuary science (See also Funeral services)

ABFSE National Scholarship Program *(Undergraduate/Scholarship)* [629]
Joseph E. Hagan Memorial Scholarships *(Undergraduate/Scholarship)* [4312]
Brenda Renee Horn Memorial Scholarship *(Undergraduate/Scholarship)* [4313]
NFDA Professional Women's Conference Scholarships *(Undergraduate/Scholarship)* [4314]

Motherhood

Childbirth Educator Program Scholarships *(All/Scholarship)* [5909]

Multiple sclerosis

endMS Doctoral Studentship Awards *(Doctorate/Internship)* [6614]
endMS Master's Studentship Awards *(Master's/Internship)* [6615]
endMS Postdoctoral Fellowships *(Postdoctorate/Fellowship)* [6616]

Muscular dystrophy

Wade O. Brinker Resident Research Award *(Undergraduate/Award)* [10378]
Dystonia Medical Research Foundation Clinical Fellowships *(Postdoctorate/Fellowship)* [3746]
J. Robert Gladden Orthopaedic Society International Traveling Fellowship *(Undergraduate/Fellowship)* [4443]
Jain Foundation Merit-Based Scholarships *(All/Scholarship)* [5518]
Jain Foundation Social-Media Scholarships *(All/Scholarship)* [5519]
MDA Development Grants *(Doctorate/Grant)* [6622]
MDA Research Grants *(Advanced Professional/Grant)* [6623]
MDF Post-Doctoral Fellowships *(Postdoctorate/Fellowship)* [6643]
RSDSA Research Grants *(Other/Grant)* [8532]

Museum science

AAMC Foundation Engagement Program for International Curators Grants *(Advanced Professional, Professional development/Grant)* [1854]
Rick Chace Foundation Scholarships *(Graduate/Scholarship)* [2024]
Douglass Foundation Fellowship in American Art *(Doctorate/Fellowship)* [9001]
Patricia and Phillip Frost Fellowships *(Doctorate, Postdoctorate/Fellowship)* [9002]
George Gurney Fellowships *(Doctorate, Postdoctorate/Fellowship)* [9003]
Kodak Fellowships in Film Preservation *(Graduate/Fellowship)* [2025]
Kress/AAR Fellowships *(Professional development/Fellowship)* [1855]
Betsy B. and Garold A. Leach Scholarships for Museum Studies *(Undergraduate/Scholarship)* [3589]
Lee Kimche McGrath Worldwide Fellowships *(Other/Fellowship)* [2067]
Metropolitan Museum of Art Conservation and Scientific Research Fellowships *(Graduate/Fellowship)* [6433]
Metropolitan Museum of Art Research Scholarship in Photograph Conservation *(Graduate/Scholarship)* [6434]
Mary Pickford Scholarships *(Graduate/Scholarship)* [2026]
James Renwick Fellowship in American Craft *(Doctorate, Postdoctorate/Fellowship)* [9004]
Sara Roby Fellowship in Twentieth-Century American Realism *(Doctorate, Postdoctorate/Fellowship)* [9005]
Sony Pictures Scholarships *(Graduate/Scholarship)* [2027]
Joshua C. Taylor Fellowships *(Doctorate, Postdoctorate/Fellowship)* [9006]
The Terra Foundation Fellowships in American Art *(Undergraduate, Doctorate, Postdoctorate/Fellowship)* [9007]
William H. Truettner Fellowships *(Undergraduate, Doctorate, Postdoctorate/Fellowship)* [9008]
United States Capitol Historical Society Fellowships *(Graduate/Fellowship)* [9886]
Universal Studios Preservation Scholarships *(Graduate/Scholarship)* [2028]
Wyeth Foundation Predoctoral Fellowship *(Postdoctorate/Fellowship)* [9009]

Music

Aaron Copland Bogliasco Fellowships in Music *(Professional development/Fellowship)* [2325]
RPMDA/Ed Adams Memorial Scholarships *(Other/Scholarship)* [8567]
AFA Music Project Grants *(Professional development/Grant)* [242]
Margaret M. Alkek Scholarships *(Undergraduate/Scholarship)* [3548]
Allen - Marty Allen Scholarships *(Undergraduate/Scholarship)* [3085]
Martin K. Alsup Scholarships *(Undergraduate/Scholarship)* [7811]
American Guild of Organists, Canton Chapter Charitable Fund *(Undergraduate/Scholarship)* [9492]
The Anderson Group Summer Institute Scholarships *(Other/Scholarship)* [1553]
AOSA Research Grants *(Undergraduate/Grant)* [1053]
AOSA Research Partnership Grants *(Professional development/Grant)* [1054]
Louis Armstrong Scholarships *(Undergraduate/Scholarship)* [1268]
Bernt Balchen, Jr. and Olav Jorgen Hegge Hardingfele Scholarships *(Other/Scholarship)* [4717]
Cynthia and Alan Baran Fine Arts and Music Scholarships *(Undergraduate/Scholarship)* [3211]
Barta-Lehman Musical Scholarships *(Undergraduate/Scholarship)* [8689]
Willa Beach-Porter Music Scholarships *(Undergraduate/Scholarship)* [2873]
Jenny Panitch Beckow Memorial Scholarships Israel *(Graduate/Scholarship)* [5570]
Belmont University Commercial Music Showcase Scholarships *(Undergraduate/Scholarship)* [3212]
Charlotte V. Bergen Scholarships *(Undergraduate/Scholarship)* [1269]
Carol June Bradley Awards *(Professional development/Grant)* [6625]
Erika A. and George E. Brattain Sr. Scholarship Fund *(Undergraduate, High School/Scholarship)* [10498]
Ralph Burkhardt Scholarship Fund *(Undergraduate, High School/Scholarship)* [10499]
Cecil E. Burney Scholarships *(Undergraduate/Scholarship)* [3091]
Jeffrey Carollo Music Scholarships *(Undergraduate/Scholarship)* [7323]
Llewellyn L. Cayvan String Instrument Scholarships *(Undergraduate/Scholarship)* [4580]
Irene R. Christman Scholarship *(Undergraduate/Scholarship)* [7939]
Edward Rollin Clinton Memorial for Music *(Undergraduate/Scholarship)* [10055]
CMA Private Lesson Program: Instrumental Scholarships for Elementary and Middle School Students *(Undergraduate/Scholarship)* [3037]
Ruth M. Cogan Scholarship Fund *(Undergraduate/Scholarship)* [9497]
Dennis Coleman Choral Conducting Scholarships *(Undergraduate/Scholarship)* [8250]
Dennis Coleman Memorial Scholarships *(Undergraduate/Scholarship)* [8251]
Contemporary Club Scholarships *(Undergraduate/Scholarship)* [8465]
Bill Cormack Scholarships *(Undergraduate/Scholarship)* [9706]
Gerald M. Crane Music Award Scholarships *(Undergraduate/Scholarship)* [4585]

Fran Morgenstern Davis Scholarships *(Undergraduate/Scholarship)* [1270]
John Denver Music Scholarships *(Undergraduate/Scholarship)* [1271]
Louis Dreyfus Warner-Chappell City College Scholarships *(Undergraduate/Scholarship)* [1272]
ECMS Scholarships *(Undergraduate/Scholarship)* [3771]
Edgecliff McAuley Music Scholarships *(Undergraduate/Scholarship)* [10720]
Dena Epstein Awards for Archival and Library Research in American Music *(Professional development/Grant)* [6626]
FCA Grants to Artists *(Advanced Professional/Grant)* [4227]
Adrienne Zoe Fedok Art and Music Scholarships *(Undergraduate/Scholarship)* [4240]
Brandon Fradd Fellowship *(Professional development/Fellowship)* [3033]
Kevin Freeman Travel Grants *(Graduate, Other/Grant)* [6627]
William R. Gard Memorial Scholarships *(Undergraduate/Scholarship)* [6654]
Garikian Scholarship Fund *(Undergraduate/Scholarship)* [1694]
Walter Gerboth Awards *(Other/Award)* [6628]
R.L. Gillette Scholarships *(Undergraduate/Scholarship)* [821]
Glenn Miller Scholarships *(Undergraduate/Scholarship)* [4451]
Velma Shotwell Griffin Memorial Scholarship Fund *(Undergraduate/Scholarship)* [9507]
Guy D. and Mary Edith Halladay Music Scholarships *(Graduate, Undergraduate/Scholarship)* [4599]
Hench Post-Dissertation Fellowship *(Postdoctorate/Fellowship)* [438]
Miriam Hoffman Scholarships *(Undergraduate, Graduate/Scholarship)* [9853]
Indiana State University Creative and Performing Arts Awards *(Undergraduate/Scholarship)* [5127]
Ruth K. Jacobs Memorial Scholarships *(Graduate, Undergraduate/Scholarship)* [2930]
Alvin H. Johnson AMS 50 Dissertation Fellowships *(Doctorate/Fellowship)* [1020]
Steve Kaplan TV and Film Studies Scholarships *(Other/Scholarship)* [1273]
Gunild Keetman Scholarships *(Other, Undergraduate/Scholarship)* [7714]
Douglas Gray Kimel Scholarships *(Undergraduate/Scholarship)* [10587]
Emily Day Koppell Memorial Adelphe Scholarship *(Undergraduate, Graduate/Scholarship)* [5743]
Leiber and Stoller Music Scholarships *(Undergraduate/Scholarship)* [1274]
Paul Mansur Scholarships *(Undergraduate/Scholarship)* [5345]
American Turkish Society Arif Mardin Music Fellowships *(Other/Fellowship)* [9811]
Howard Mayer Brown Fellowship *(Graduate/Fellowship)* [1021]
MCBA Scholarship *(Undergraduate/Scholarship)* [6465]
Christopher Mesi Memorial Music Scholarships *(Undergraduate/Scholarship)* [2803]
Muddy Waters Scholarships *(Undergraduate/Scholarship)* [2316]
Albert and Alice Nacinovich Music Scholarships *(Undergraduate/Scholarship)* [4056]
Northwest-Shoals Community College Fine Arts Scholarships - Music *(Undergraduate/Scholarship)* [7545]
NPM Academic Scholarships *(Graduate, Undergraduate/Scholarship)* [6768]
NPM Program Scholarships *(Undergraduate/Scholarship)* [6769]
Rudy Perez Songwriting Scholarships *(Undergraduate/Scholarship)* [1275]
William R. Pfalzgraf Scholarships *(Undergraduate/Scholarship)* [7852]
Barbara Potter Scholarships *(Professional development/Scholarship)* [1055]
Presbyterian Association of Musicians Scholarships *(All/Scholarship)* [8217]
Geeta Rastogi Memorial Scholarships *(Undergraduate/Scholarship)* [10338]
Redlands High School Terrier Band Boosters Club Scholarships *(Undergraduate/Scholarship)* [8518]
Redlands High School Vocal Music Boosters Scholarship Awards *(Undergraduate/Scholarship)* [8519]
Mark A. Reid Memorial Scholarship Grants *(Undergraduate/Scholarship)* [3297]
Mister Rogers Memorial Scholarship *(Graduate, Master's, Doctorate/Scholarship)* [47]
Betty Rose Scholarships *(Undergraduate/Scholarship)* [1276]
S. Byrl Ross Memorial Scholarship Fund *(Undergraduate/Scholarship)* [7859]
Curtis M. Saulsbury Scholarship Fund *(Undergraduate/Scholarship)* [3201]
Brown Schoenheit Memorial Scholarship *(Undergraduate/Scholarship)* [10070]
Roger Sessions Memorial Bogliasco Fellowships in Music *(Professional development/Fellowship)* [2331]
Shields-Gillespie Scholarships *(Other/Scholarship)* [1056]
Robert W. and Bernice Ingalls Staton Scholarships *(Undergraduate/Scholarship)* [10259]
Joseph L. and Vivian E. Steele Music Scholarship Fund *(Undergraduate/Scholarship)* [4256]
Study Scholarships for Artists or Musicians *(Graduate/Scholarship)* [3610]
Texas Music Educators Association Past-Presidents Memorial Scholarships *(Undergraduate/Scholarship)* [9707]
Johnny Trombly Scholarships *(Undergraduate/Scholarship)* [6572]
Barry Tuckwell Scholarships *(All/Scholarship)* [5346]
Philip F. Vineberg Travelling Fellowships in the Humanities *(Undergraduate/Scholarship)* [6368]
Violin Society of America Scholarships *(Undergraduate/Scholarship)* [10390]
Wayne County Foundation Anonymous Scholarship Fund *(Graduate/Scholarship)* [10508]
Wayne-Meador-Elliott Scholarships *(Undergraduate/Scholarship)* [7869]
Portia White Scholarships *(Undergraduate/Scholarship)* [2292]
Gary S. Wilmer/RAMI Music Scholarships *(Undergraduate/Scholarship)* [3303]
Wendy Y. Wolfson Memorial Scholarship Fund *(Undergraduate/Scholarship)* [4064]
Women's Italian Club of Boston Scholarships *(Undergraduate/Scholarship)* [4357]
John W. Work III Memorial Foundation Scholarships *(Undergraduate/Scholarship)* [3258]
Marusia Yaworska Entrance Scholarships *(Graduate/Scholarship)* [10445]
YMF Scholarships *(Undergraduate/Scholarship)* [10762]

Music, Classical

Gladys C. Anderson Memorial Scholarships *(Graduate, Undergraduate/Scholarship)* [818]
Lou Drane Music Scholarships *(Undergraduate/Scholarship)* [4237]

Music, Jazz

Central Florida Jazz Society Scholarships *(Undergraduate/Award, Scholarship)* [2869]

Music, Opera (See Opera)

Music, Piano

Chopin Foundation of the United States Scholarships *(Undergraduate/Scholarship)* [2928]
Nickels for Notes Music Scholarship *(Undergraduate/Scholarship)* [4354]

Music, Vocal

Dorchester Woman's Club Music Scholarship - Voice *(Undergraduate/Scholarship)* [4352]
Nickels for Notes Music Scholarship *(Undergraduate/Scholarship)* [4354]
S. Byrl Ross Memorial Scholarship Fund *(Undergraduate/Scholarship)* [7859]

Music composition

Pete Carpenter Fellowship *(Professional development/Fellowship)* [2318]
John Lennon Scholarships *(Undergraduate/Scholarship)* [2319]
Peermusic Latin Scholarship *(Undergraduate/Scholarship)* [2320]

Music education (See Education, Music)

Music therapy

AMTA Past Presidents' Conference Scholar Awards *(Professional development/Award)* [1010]
AMTA Student Conference Scholar Awards *(Undergraduate, Graduate/Award)* [1011]
Edwina Eustis Dick Scholarship for Music Therapy Interns *(Graduate/Scholarship)* [1012]
Arthur Flagler Fultz Research Awards *(Professional development/Grant)* [1013]
Anne Emery Kyllo Professional Scholarships *(Professional development/Scholarship)* [1014]
Theodore Meyer Scholarships *(Undergraduate, Graduate/Scholarship)* [1015]
Nickels for Notes Music Scholarship *(Undergraduate/Scholarship)* [4354]
Brian and Cathy Smith Memorial Fund *(Graduate/Scholarship)* [1016]
Christine K. Stevens Development Scholarships *(Undergraduate, Graduate/Scholarship)* [1017]
Florence Tyson Grants to Study Music Pyschotherapy *(Professional development/Grant)* [1018]

Musicology

Martin K. Alsup Scholarships *(Undergraduate/Scholarship)* [7811]
Howard Mayer Brown Fellowship *(Graduate/Fellowship)* [1021]
Woody Guthrie Fellowship *(Professional development/Fellowship)* [2321]

Myasthenia Gravis

Myasthenia Gravis Foundation of America Nursing Research Fellowships *(Undergraduate/Fellowship)* [6636]
Myasthenia Gravis Foundation of America Student Research Fellowships *(Graduate, Undergraduate/Fellowship)* [6637]

National security

AFCEA Cyber Studies and Intelligence Scholarships *(Undergraduate, Graduate/Scholarship)* [85]
CFR Stanton Nuclear Security Fellowships *(Doctorate, Postdoctorate, Advanced Professional/Fellowship)* [3444]
(ISC)2 Foundation Information Security Scholarships *(Graduate, Undergraduate/Scholarship)* [5348]
Rieser Fellowships *(Undergraduate/Fellowship)* [2406]
Samuel S. Wilks Awards *(Advanced Professional/Award, Monetary)* [1466]
Women In Defense HORIZONS Scholarships *(Graduate, Undergraduate/Scholarship)* [10636]

Native American studies

Larry Matfay Cultural Heritage Scholarships *(Undergraduate, Graduate/Scholarship)* [5868]
Newberry Consortium on American Indian Studies Faculty Fellowships *(Other/Fellowship)* [7417]
Phillips Fund Grants for Native American Research *(Doctorate, Master's/Grant)* [1083]
Allogan Slagle Memorial Scholarships *(Undergraduate/Scholarship)* [1835]
Morris K. Udall Scholarships *(Undergraduate/Scholarship)* [9825]
Adolph Van Pelt Special Fund for Indians Scholar-

ships *(Undergraduate/Scholarship)* [1836]

Natural resources

American Planning Association ENRE Student Fellowship Program *(Graduate/Fellowship)* [1103]
A.T. Anderson Memorial Scholarships *(Graduate, Undergraduate/Scholarship)* [889]
EMLF Law Student Scholarships *(Undergraduate/Scholarship)* [3869]
Grand Haven Offshore Challenge Scholarship Fund *(Undergraduate/Scholarship)* [4521]
Great Lakes Commission Sea Grant Fellowships *(Graduate/Scholarship)* [4656]
Randall Matthis for Environmental Studies Scholarships *(Graduate, Undergraduate/Scholarship)* [1649]
Ben Meadows Natural Resource Scholarships - Academic Achievement Scholarships *(Undergraduate/Scholarship)* [2221]
Ben Meadows Natural Resource Scholarships - Leadership Scholarships *(Undergraduate/Scholarship)* [2222]
Property and Environment Research Center Graduate Fellowships *(Graduate/Fellowship)* [8297]
Property and Environment Research Center Lone Mountain Fellowships *(Other/Fellowship)* [8298]
Property and Environment Research Center Media Fellowships *(Other/Fellowship)* [8299]
Julian Simon Fellowships *(Other/Fellowship)* [8300]
Smithsonian Institution Graduate Student Fellowships *(Graduate/Fellowship)* [9015]
Smithsonian Institution Postdoctoral Fellowships *(Doctorate/Fellowship)* [9016]
Smithsonian Institution Predoctoral Fellowships *(Doctorate/Fellowship)* [9017]
Smithsonian Institution Senior Fellowships *(Doctorate/Fellowship)* [9018]
Guy A. Woodings Scholarships *(Undergraduate/Scholarship)* [10044]

Natural sciences

ACOR-CAORC Post-Graduate Fellowships *(Doctorate, Postdoctorate/Award)* [653]
Alexander Graham Bell Canada Graduate Scholarship Program *(Doctorate, Master's/Scholarship)* [3401]
Lorraine Allison Scholarship *(Graduate/Scholarship)* [1616]
Ora E. Anderson Scholarships *(Undergraduate, High School/Scholarship)* [4167]
AWMA Louisiana Section Scholarships *(Undergraduate, Graduate/Scholarship)* [147]
AFCEA San Diego Buck Bragunier Leadership Scholarship *(Undergraduate/Scholarship)* [1667]
CTFS-ForestGEO Research Grants Program *(Graduate, Postdoctorate, Advanced Professional/Grant)* [9041]
CTFS Research Grants Program *(Graduate, Postdoctorate, Professional development/Grant)* [9036]
Margaret S. Gilbert Scholarship Fund *(Undergraduate/Scholarship)* [9505]
John Simon Guggenheim Memorial Fellowships - U.S. and Canadian Competition *(Advanced Professional/Fellowship)* [4684]
Dolores Zohrab Liebmann Fund - Graduate School Fellowships *(Graduate/Fellowship)* [6075]
J.B. and Marilyn McKenzie Graduate Student Fellowships *(Graduate/Fellowship)* [10186]
Multi-Country Research Fellowships *(Doctorate/Fellowship)* [3431]
Natural Sciences and Engineering Research Council Postgraduate Scholarships *(Doctorate/Scholarship)* [3404]
Newkirk Center for Science and Society Graduate Student Fellowships *(Doctorate, Graduate/Fellowship)* [7427]
Laura Ann Peck Memorial Endowed Scholarships *(Undergraduate/Scholarship)* [6049]
Saskatchewan Pulse Growers Undergraduate Scholarships *(Undergraduate/Scholarship)* [8778]
Susan P. Schroeder Memorial Scholarships *(Undergraduate/Scholarship)* [6053]
Alfred P. Sloan Foundation Graduate Scholarships - Sloan Indigenous Graduate Partnership *(Master's, Doctorate/Scholarship)* [6683]
Alfred P. Sloan Foundation Graduate Scholarships - Sloan Minority Ph.D. Program *(Doctorate/Scholarship)* [6684]
Vanier Canada Graduate Scholarships *(Graduate/Scholarship)* [3405]

Naval architecture (See Architecture, Naval)

Naval art and science

Naval Research Enterprise Internship Program (NREIP) *(Undergraduate, Graduate, Professional development/Internship)* [1304]
NRL-ASEE Postdoctoral Fellowships *(Postdoctorate/Fellowship)* [9966]

Naval engineering (See Engineering, Naval)

Near Eastern studies

Garikian Scholarship Fund *(Undergraduate/Scholarship)* [1694]

Nephrology

American Nephrology Nurses' Association Evidence-Based Research Grants *(Other/Grant)* [1025]
American Nephrology Nurses' Association Research Grants *(Doctorate, Graduate/Grant)* [1026]
ANNA Nephrology Nurse Researcher Awards *(Doctorate, Graduate/Award)* [1027]
KFOC Allied Health Doctoral Fellowship *(Doctorate/Fellowship)* [5825]
KFOC Allied Health Scholarships *(Graduate/Scholarship)* [5826]
KFOC Biomedical Scholarships *(Doctorate/Scholarship)* [5828]
Barbara F. Prowant Nursing Research Grants *(Graduate/Grant)* [1028]

Neurology

AAN Clinical Research Training Fellowships *(Other/Fellowship)* [410]
AAN International Scholarship Award *(Professional development/Scholarship)* [411]
AAN Medical Student Summer Research Scholarships *(Graduate/Scholarship)* [412]
AANS Medical Student Summer Research Fellowships (MSSRF) *(Undergraduate/Fellowship)* [542]
Brain Canada-ALS Canada Career Transition Awards *(Postdoctorate, Advanced Professional, Professional development/Grant)* [2351]
Brain Canada-ALS Canada Discovery Grants *(Advanced Professional, Professional development/Grant)* [2352]
Brain Canada-ALS Canada Hudson Translational Team Grants *(Advanced Professional, Professional development/Grant)* [2353]
Dr. George C. Cotzias Memorial Fellowship *(Other/Fellowship)* [1074]
Daland Fellowships in Clinical Investigation *(Doctorate, Postgraduate/Fellowship)* [1079]
Epilepsy Foundation Research and Training Fellowships for Clinicians *(Doctorate, Other/Grant)* [3908]
Grass Fellowships at the Marine Biological Laboratory *(Doctorate, Postdoctorate/Fellowship)* [4643]
Massachusetts General Hospital Clinical Translational Fellowships at Pfizer *(Advanced Professional/Fellowship)* [6318]
MGH Department of Psychiatry Behavioral Neurology and Neuropsychiatry Fellowships *(Advanced Professional, Professional development/Fellowship)* [6320]
MGH Department of Psychiatry Global Psychiatric Clinical Research Training Program *(Advanced Professional/Fellowship)* [6323]

NJCBIR Individual Research Grants *(Other/Grant)* [9549]
NJCBIR Pilot Research Grants *(Other/Grant)* [9550]
NJCBIR Postdoctoral and Graduate Student Fellowships *(Graduate, Postdoctorate/Fellowship)* [9551]
NJCBIR Programmatic Multi-Investigator Project Grants *(Other/Grant)* [9552]
Postdoctoral Fellowships for Clinical Neurologists *(Postdoctorate/Fellowship)* [7888]
William P. Van Wagenen Fellowships *(Undergraduate/Fellowship)* [543]
Wagner-Torizuka Fellowships *(Professional development/Fellowship)* [9228]
Dr. Steven S. Zalcman Memorial Scholarships *(Graduate, Postgraduate/Scholarship)* [5589]

Neurophysiology

Grass Fellowships at the Marine Biological Laboratory *(Doctorate, Postdoctorate/Fellowship)* [4643]

Neuroscience

ASET Scholarships *(Other/Scholarship)* [1301]
Azrieli Neurodevelopmental Research Program *(Advanced Professional/Grant)* [2350]
Lynn Ann Baldwin Scholarships *(Master's/Scholarship)* [1888]
Brain Canada-ALS Canada Discovery Grants *(Advanced Professional, Professional development/Grant)* [2352]
Brain Canada-ALS Canada Hudson Translational Team Grants *(Advanced Professional, Professional development/Grant)* [2353]
Brain Canada/CQDM "Focus on Brain" Partnership Program *(Advanced Professional/Grant)* [2354]
Brain Canada/NeuroDevNet Developmental Neurosciences Research Training Awards *(Postdoctorate, Advanced Professional, Professional development/Grant)* [2355]
Certified Neuroscience Registered Nurse Recertification Grant Program *(Other/Grant)* [545]
CTF Young Investigator Awards (CTF-YIA) *(Graduate, Postdoctorate, Doctorate/Award)* [2911]
Epilepsy Foundation Post-doctoral Research and Training Fellowships *(Postdoctorate/Fellowship)* [3905]
Epilepsy Foundation Pre-doctoral Research Training Fellowships *(Graduate/Fellowship)* [3906]
Grass Fellowships at the Marine Biological Laboratory *(Doctorate, Postdoctorate/Fellowship)* [4643]
Integra Foundation NNF Research Grant Awards *(Other/Grant)* [546]
IRSF Mentored Training Fellowships *(Advanced Professional, Postdoctorate/Fellowship)* [5388]
Janelia Farm Graduate Program *(Graduate/Award)* [4978]
Herbert H. Jasper Fellowships in Neurosciences *(Postdoctorate/Fellowship)* [2568]
Klingenstein Fellowships in the Neurosciences *(Doctorate, Other/Fellowship)* [5838]
Massachusetts General Hospital Clinical Translational Fellowships at Pfizer *(Advanced Professional/Fellowship)* [6318]
Neuroscience Certification Bursary Awards *(Other/Award)* [1889]
NYU Langone Medical Center Science Student Scholarships *(Undergraduate, Graduate/Scholarship)* [109]
Platform Support Grants *(Advanced Professional/Grant)* [2357]
Sloan Research Fellowships *(Doctorate/Fellowship)* [8988]
STRI Short-Term Fellowships *(Undergraduate, Graduate, Postdoctorate/Fellowship)* [9038]
Earl S. Tupper 3-year Postdoctoral Fellowships in Tropical Biology *(Postdoctorate/Fellowship)* [9039]
Weston Brain Institute International Fellowships in Neuroscience Program *(Graduate/Fellowship)* [10422]
Weston Brain Institute Rapid Response Program *(Postdoctorate, Advanced Professional, Professional development/Grant)* [10423]

Jessie Young Bursary Awards *(Other/Award)* [1890]
Dr. Steven S. Zalcman Memorial Scholarships *(Graduate, Postgraduate/Scholarship)* [5589]

Nonprofit sector

ANSER Graduate Student Awards for Research on Nonprofits and the Social Economy *(Graduate/Award)* [2030]
ARNOVA Emerging Scholar Awards *(Graduate/Award)* [2056]
EJI Justice Fellowship *(Graduate, Postgraduate, Professional development/Fellowship)* [3916]

Nuclear medicine (See Medicine, Nuclear)

Nuclear science

American Nuclear Society Nevada Section Scholarships *(Undergraduate/Scholarship)* [8331]
American Nuclear Society Undergraduates Scholarships *(Undergraduate/Scholarship)* [1033]
Everitt P. Blizard Scholarships *(Graduate/Scholarship)* [1034]
Allan F. Henry/Paul A. Greebler Scholarships *(Graduate/Scholarship)* [1036]
Saul Levine Memorial Scholarships *(Graduate/Scholarship)* [1037]
Nuclear Criticality Safety Pioneers Scholarships *(Graduate/Scholarship)* [1038]
James F. Schumar Scholarships *(Graduate/Fellowship)* [1039]
Glenn T. Seaborg Congressional Science and Engineering Fellowships *(Professional development/Fellowship)* [1040]

Nursing

AAACN Conference Scholarships for Nursing Students *(Undergraduate/Scholarship)* [385]
AAACN Education Scholarships *(Undergraduate/Scholarship)* [386]
AAACN Research Grants *(Undergraduate/Grant)* [387]
AAACN Scholarships *(Undergraduate/Scholarship)* [388]
AACN Continuing Professional Development Scholarships *(Advanced Professional, Other/Scholarship)* [490]
AASLD NP/PA Clinical Hepatology Fellowships *(Professional development/Fellowship)* [585]
ACNL Research Scholarships *(Graduate/Scholarship)* [1869]
ACNM Foundation Midwives of Color-Watson Midwifery Student Scholarship *(Undergraduate/Scholarship)* [693]
ACS Doctoral Degree Scholarships in Cancer Nursing *(Doctorate, Graduate/Scholarship)* [642]
ACS Graduate Scholarships in Cancer Nursing Practice *(Graduate, Master's, Doctorate/Scholarship)* [643]
AfterCollege/AACN Nursing Scholarships *(Graduate, Undergraduate/Scholarship)* [479]
AfterCollege-AACN Scholarships *(Undergraduate, Master's, Doctorate/Scholarship)* [96]
Dr. Feroz Ahmed Memorial Educational Post-Graduate Scholarships *(Doctorate, Postgraduate/Scholarship)* [8965]
Alabama ARN Scholarship *(Professional development/Scholarship)* [2054]
American Pediatric Surgical Nurses Association Educational Grants *(Other/Grant)* [1076]
American Quarter Horse Foundation Scholarships *(Undergraduate/Scholarship)* [1171]
AMSN Career Mobility Scholarship Awards *(Undergraduate, Doctorate/Scholarship)* [37]
AMSUS Nursing Awards *(Advanced Professional/Recognition)* [1539]
ANCA Scholarships *(Undergraduate/Scholarship)* [1712]
Roy Anderson Memorial Scholarships *(Graduate, Undergraduate/Scholarship)* [3140]
ANF/ENRS Nursing Research Grants *(Professional development/Grant)* [1043]
ANF/STTI Nursing Research Grants *(Master's, Doctorate/Grant)* [1044]
AORN Academic Scholarships *(Undergraduate, Master's, Doctorate/Scholarship)* [2035]
AORN Administrator Skills Course *(Professional development/Recognition, Grant)* [2036]
AORN Foundation Scholarship Program *(Undergraduate, Doctorate, Master's/Scholarship)* [2037]
APS/ASU Scholarships *(Undergraduate/Scholarship)* [8139]
Arizona Nurses Foundation Scholarships *(Doctorate, Graduate, Undergraduate/Scholarship)* [1639]
AstraZeneca Scholarships *(Doctorate/Scholarship)* [2695]
AvaCare Medical Scholarships *(Undergraduate/Scholarship)* [2142]
Bachelor of Science in Nursing Academic Scholarships *(Graduate/Scholarship)* [6656]
Dr. Johnella Banks Memorial Scholarships *(Undergraduate/Scholarship)* [2298]
Leslie Baranowski Scholarships for Professional Excellence *(Professional development/Scholarship)* [5144]
Raymond B. Bauer Research Award *(Professional development/Grant)* [6479]
Ann C. Beckingham Scholarships *(Graduate, Other/Scholarship)* [2645]
Dr. Ann C. Beckingham Scholarships *(Doctorate/Scholarship)* [2696]
Reckitt Benckiser Student Scholarships *(Graduate/Scholarship)* [6771]
Linn-Benton County Scholarships *(Undergraduate/Scholarship)* [7709]
Dr. Noorali and Sabiya Bharwani Endowment *(Undergraduate/Scholarship)* [2253]
Hussein Jina Bharwani Memorial Endowment *(Undergraduate/Scholarship)* [2254]
Jan Bingle Scholarships *(Master's, Doctorate/Scholarship)* [3055]
Joan Blend Scholarship Fund *(Undergraduate/Scholarship)* [9493]
Board of Certification for Emergency Nursing (BCEN) Undergraduate Scholarships *(Undergraduate/Scholarship)* [3860]
Breakthrough to Nursing Scholarships *(Undergraduate/Scholarship)* [4268]
Ruby A. Brown Memorial Scholarships *(Undergraduate/Scholarship)* [3753]
Katie Brush Memorial Scholarships *(Master's, Doctorate/Scholarship)* [3056]
Joan Butler Award in Perinatal Intensive Care Nursing *(Advanced Professional/Award)* [6852]
byourself Scholarship Fund *(Undergraduate, Vocational/Occupational/Scholarship)* [3318]
Joseph R. Calder, Jr., MD Scholarship Fund *(Undergraduate/Scholarship)* [4041]
Canadian Nurses Foundation Northern Award *(Undergraduate/Scholarship)* [2697]
Canadian Nurses Foundation Scholarships *(Undergraduate, Master's, Doctorate/Scholarship)* [2698]
CANS/SNRS Dissertation Research Grants *(Doctorate/Grant)* [9405]
Rhea Sourifman Caplin Memorial Scholarships *(Undergraduate/Scholarship)* [4742]
Career Mobility Scholarships *(Graduate, Undergraduate, Vocational/Occupational/Scholarship)* [4269]
Certified Neuroscience Registered Nurse Recertification Grant Program *(Other/Grant)* [545]
CGNA Memorial Scholarship *(Graduate, Other/Scholarship)* [2646]
Melba Dawn Chiarenza Scholarship Fund *(Undergraduate/Scholarship)* [10504]
CHOPR Postdoctoral Fellowships *(Postdoctorate/Fellowship)* [10267]
Frances N. Christian Memorial Endowment Nursing Scholarship *(Graduate, Undergraduate/Scholarship)* [9583]
City of Toronto Queen Elizabeth II Sesquicentennial Scholarships in Community Health Nursing for Graduates *(Graduate/Scholarship)* [10283]
City of Toronto Queen Elizabeth II Sesquicentennial Scholarships in Community Health Nursing for Undergraduates *(Undergraduate/Scholarship)* [10284]
Colorado Nurses Foundation Nightingale Scholarships *(Graduate, Undergraduate/Scholarship)* [3141]
Conduct and Utilization of Research in Nursing (CURN) Awards *(Professional development/Award)* [6476]
Doctors Ira and Udaya Dash Nursing Scholarships *(Undergraduate, Graduate/Scholarship)* [9426]
Jane Delano Student Nurse Scholarships *(Undergraduate, Graduate/Scholarship)* [1023]
Diabetes Scholars Foundation College Scholarships *(Undergraduate/Scholarship)* [3616]
Gretchen Dimico Memorial Scholarships *(Undergraduate/Scholarship)* [6025]
Discover Health Professions Loans *(Graduate/Loan)* [3636]
Discover Residency Loans *(Graduate/Loan)* [3639]
Margaret Dowell-Gravatt, M.D. Scholarships *(Undergraduate/Scholarship)* [2226]
Education Advancement Scholarships *(Graduate, Master's, Doctorate/Scholarship)* [548]
Virginia Elizabeth and Alma Vane Taylor Nursing Scholarship *(Undergraduate/Scholarship)* [10580]
ENA Foundation Annual Conference Scholarships *(Advanced Professional, Professional development/Scholarship)* [3861]
ENA Foundation Seed Research Grants *(Master's, Advanced Professional/Grant)* [3862]
ENA Foundation State Challenge Undergraduate Scholarship *(Undergraduate/Scholarship)* [3858]
ExeptionalNurse.com Scholarships *(Undergraduate, Graduate/Scholarship)* [3940]
Family and Children's Services of Lebanon County Fund *(Undergraduate/Scholarship)* [4239]
Lola Fehr: Nightingale Scholarships *(Graduate, Undergraduate/Scholarship)* [3142]
Christine Filipovich Scholarships *(Master's, Doctorate/Scholarship)* [3057]
Sue Fleming Memorial Scholarships *(Undergraduate/Scholarship)* [2440]
Florida Education Fund McKnight Doctoral Fellowships *(Graduate/Fellowship)* [4085]
Florida Nurses Foundation Scholarships *(Undergraduate, Master's, Doctorate/Scholarship)* [4102]
Floto-Peel Family Scholarship Fund *(Undergraduate, Vocational/Occupational/Scholarship)* [4517]
Forsyth County Nursing Scholarships *(Undergraduate/Scholarship)* [10581]
The Foundation of the National Student Nurses' Association Scholarships *(Graduate, Undergraduate/Scholarship)* [7190]
Doris W. Frey Memorial Scholarships *(Undergraduate, Graduate/Scholarship)* [9430]
Don and Eileen Fulton Nursing Scholarships *(Undergraduate/Scholarship)* [9566]
Arkansas Nursing Foundation - Dorothea Fund Scholarships *(Other/Scholarship)* [1656]
Gardner Foundation Infusion Nurses Society Education Scholarships *(Professional development/Scholarship)* [5145]
Elaine Gelman Scholarship Awards *(Undergraduate/Scholarship)* [6772]
Dr. Helen Preston Glass Fellowships *(Doctorate/Fellowship)* [2700]
William R. Goldfarb Memorial Scholarships *(Undergraduate/Scholarship)* [1739]
Baxter Corporation - Jean Goodwill Scholarships *(Graduate/Scholarship)* [24]
Arkansas Nursing Foundation - Mary Gray Scholarships *(Other/Scholarship)* [1657]
William G. and Mayme J. Green Scholarships *(Undergraduate/Scholarship)* [4754]
Helen R. Greenamyer Memorial Scholarships *(Undergraduate/Scholarship)* [9567]
GSA Scholarships for International Nurses *(Undergraduate, Master's/Scholarship)* [4458]
Health Professional Nursing Student Loans *(Undergraduate, Graduate/Loan)* [6565]
Judy Hill Memorial Scholarships *(Undergraduate/Scholarship)* [2701]
Roberta L. Houpt Scholarship Fund *(Undergraduate/Scholarship)* [4242]
HRET Health Career Scholarships *(Postgraduate, Undergraduate/Scholarship)* [7319]
HRSA Scholarships for Disadvantaged Students *(Undergraduate/Scholarship)* [9923]

Idaho Nursing and Health Professions Scholarships *(Undergraduate/Scholarship)* [5042]
Illinois Student Assistance Commission Nurse Educator Scholarships (NESP) *(Undergraduate/Scholarship)* [5076]
Illinois Student Assistance Commission Nursing Education Scholarships *(Undergraduate/Scholarship)* [5077]
Indspire Health Careers Bursary and Scholarships *(Graduate, Undergraduate/Scholarship)* [5132]
Integra Foundation NNF Research Grant Awards *(Other/Grant)* [546]
Susan K. Ipacs Nursing Legacy Scholarships *(Undergraduate, High School/Scholarship)* [4169]
Virginia C. Jack and Ralph L. Jack Scholarships *(Undergraduate/Scholarship)* [9513]
Johnson and Johnson/AACN Minority Nurse Faculty Scholars *(Graduate/Scholarship)* [480]
Johnson & Johnson Scholarships *(Undergraduate/Scholarship)* [2702]
Kansas Nurse Educator Service Scholarships *(Graduate/Scholarship)* [5656]
Kendrick Foundation, Inc. Scholarships *(Undergraduate/Scholarship)* [5813]
Dr. Dorothy J. Kergin Fellowships *(Doctorate, Master's/Fellowship)* [2703]
Lake Dollars for Scholars Endowment Fund *(Undergraduate/Scholarship)* [9518]
Candia Baker Laughlin Certification Scholarships *(Undergraduate/Scholarship)* [389]
Mandel and Lauretta Abrahamer Scholarships *(Undergraduate/Scholarship)* [9573]
Lawsuit Legal American Nursing Support Scholarships *(Undergraduate/Scholarship)* [5983]
Tecla Lin & Nelia Laroza Memorial Scholarships *(Undergraduate/Scholarship)* [2704]
Gertie S. Lowe Nursing Scholarship Awards *(Undergraduate/Scholarship)* [3267]
Margaret Mallett Nursing Scholarship *(Undergraduate/Scholarship)* [8878]
March of Dimes Graduate Nursing Scholarships *(Graduate/Scholarship)* [6234]
Eleanor Jean Martin Award *(Master's/Scholarship)* [2705]
Master's Degree with a Major in Nursing Academic Scholarships *(Graduate/Scholarship)* [6657]
John Mazurek Memorial-Morgex Insurance Scholarship *(Other/Scholarship)* [296]
Senator Patricia K. McGee Nursing Faculty Scholarships *(Doctorate, Graduate/Scholarship)* [7365]
McLean Scholarships *(Undergraduate/Scholarship)* [1978]
National Association of Pediatric Nurse Practitioners McNeil Annual Scholarships *(Undergraduate/Scholarship)* [6773]
National Association of Pediatric Nurse Practitioners McNeil Rural and Underserved Scholarships *(Graduate/Scholarship)* [6774]
Michigan League for Nursing Scholarships *(Undergraduate/Scholarship)* [6472]
Michigan Nurses Foundation Scholarships *(Undergraduate, Graduate/Scholarship)* [6477]
Albert and Eloise Midyette Memorial Scholarship Fund *(Undergraduate/Scholarship)* [4204]
Mary Ann Mikulic Scholarships *(Other/Scholarship)* [2052]
Ruth Milan-Altrusa Scholarships *(Undergraduate/Scholarship)* [6207]
Military Nurses Association Scholarships *(Master's/Scholarship)* [2706]
Joseph and Catherine Missigman Memorial Nursing Scholarships *(Undergraduate/Scholarship)* [4051]
MODNA Nursing Education Scholarships *(Doctorate, Graduate/Fellowship)* [6509]
Dan Mordecai Educational Scholarships *(Graduate, Undergraduate/Scholarship)* [7265]
H.M. Muffly Memorial Scholarships *(Graduate, Undergraduate/Scholarship)* [3143]
Margaret Munro Award *(Undergraduate/Scholarship)* [2707]
Dr. Helen K. Mussallem Fellowships *(Master's/Scholarship)* [2708]
National American Arab Nurses Association Scholarships *(Undergraduate, Master's/Scholarship)* [6699]
National Black Nurses Association Scholarships *(Undergraduate/Scholarship)* [6823]
National Slovak Society Senior Scholarships *(Undergraduate, Vocational/Occupational/Scholarship)* [7132]
New Brunswick Nurses Association Scholarships *(Master's/Scholarship)* [2709]
Sharon Nield Memorial Scholarships *(Undergraduate/Scholarship)* [2710]
North Carolina League for Nursing Academic Scholarships *(Graduate/Scholarship)* [4207]
North Ottawa Hospital Auxiliary Scholarship Fund *(Undergraduate/Scholarship)* [4534]
Northampton County Medical Society Alliance Scholarships *(Undergraduate/Scholarship)* [7507]
NOVA Foundation Scholarships *(Doctorate, Graduate, Master's/Scholarship)* [7560]
NURSE Corps Scholarship Program *(Professional development/Scholarship)* [9924]
Nursing Student Loans *(Graduate/Loan)* [9555]
Orthopaedic Specialists Nursing Scholarships *(Undergraduate/Scholarship)* [10590]
Outlaw Student's Nursing School Scholarships *(Undergraduate/Scholarship)* [9597]
Senator Norman Paterson Fellowships *(Doctorate/Scholarship)* [2711]
Colorado Nurses Association: Virginia Paulson Memorial Scholarships *(Graduate, Undergraduate/Scholarship)* [3144]
Margaret Pemberton Scholarships *(Undergraduate/Scholarship)* [2299]
Shoshana Philipp (Kirshenblatt) R.N. Memorial Scholarships *(Graduate, Undergraduate/Scholarship)* [9752]
Donald E. Pizzini Memorial Nurse Scholarships *(Undergraduate, Professional development/Scholarship)* [6580]
PNAA Nursing Scholarship Award *(Master's, Doctorate/Scholarship)* [8113]
Carl C. and Abbie Rebman Trust Scholarships *(Undergraduate/Scholarship)* [4566]
Faye Lynn Roberts Educational Scholarships *(Undergraduate, Graduate/Scholarship)* [9445]
Ellis W. Rowe Scholarships *(Undergraduate/Scholarship)* [4703]
Lucille and Edward R. Roybal Foundation Public Health Scholarships *(Graduate, Undergraduate/Scholarship)* [8654]
St. Joseph's Hospital School of Nursing Alumnae Scholarship *(Undergraduate/Scholarship)* [7861]
Sanofi Pasteur Scholarships *(Master's/Scholarship)* [2712]
Jeptha Wade Schureman Scholarship Program *(Undergraduate/Scholarship)* [3333]
Senior Innovation Scholarships *(Undergraduate, Graduate/Scholarship)* [8146]
Pat Shimp Memorial Scholarships *(Undergraduate/Scholarship)* [7863]
Sigma Theta Tau International Scholarships *(Doctorate/Scholarship)* [2713]
Hazel Simms Nursing Scholarships *(Other/Scholarship)* [5933]
Ann Kelsay Small Scholarship *(Undergraduate/Scholarship)* [5766]
SNRS Dissertation Research Grants *(Doctorate/Grant)* [9406]
SNRS Research Grants *(Professional development/Grant)* [9407]
SNRS/STTI Research Grants *(Professional development/Grant)* [9408]
Society of Pediatric Nurses Educational Scholarships *(Graduate, Other/Scholarship)* [9241]
SOHN Allied Health to BSN Degree Scholarship *(Undergraduate/Scholarship)* [9233]
SOHN Graduate Degree Scholarship *(Undergraduate/Scholarship)* [9234]
SOHN RN to BSN Degree Scholarship *(Undergraduate/Scholarship)* [9235]
Specialty Nursing Scholarships *(Undergraduate/Scholarship)* [4270]
Spotlight on Nursing Graduate Nursing Student Scholarships *(Graduate/Scholarship)* [9484]
Marianne M. Stenvig Scholarships *(Master's, Doctorate/Scholarship)* [9375]
Anne Sturrock Nursing Scholarships *(Undergraduate, Graduate/Scholarship)* [9451]
Syncrude/Athabasca University Aboriginal Scholarships *(Undergraduate/Scholarship)* [9627]
John I. and Madeleine R. Taeni Scholarships *(Undergraduate/Scholarship)* [9452]
TD Meloche-Monnex Scholarships *(Doctorate/Scholarship)* [2714]
Paul Tejada Memorial Scholarships *(Undergraduate/Scholarship)* [5514]
UAA Alaska Kidney Foundation Scholarship *(Graduate, Undergraduate/Scholarship)* [10076]
UAA RRANN Program Scholarships *(Undergraduate/Scholarship)* [10084]
United Health Foundation National Association of Hispanic Nurses Scholarships *(Graduate, Undergraduate/Scholarship)* [6758]
John Vanderlee Award *(Undergraduate/Scholarship)* [2715]
The Sybil Jennings Vorheis Memorial Undergraduate Scholarships *(Undergraduate/Scholarship)* [4218]
Sue Walicki Nursing Scholarships *(Undergraduate/Scholarship)* [5516]
Patty Walter Memorial Scholarships *(Graduate, Undergraduate/Scholarship)* [3145]
Imogene Ward Nursing Scholarships *(Undergraduate/Scholarship)* [4079]
Washington State Nurses Association Foundation Scholarships (WSNF) *(Graduate, Undergraduate/Scholarship)* [10468]
West Virginia Nurses Association District No. 3 Scholarships *(Undergraduate/Scholarship)* [7870]
Lois Widley Student Scholarships *(Graduate, Undergraduate/Scholarship)* [5365]
Lippincott Williams and Wilkins Scholarships *(Master's, Doctorate/Scholarship)* [3058]
WOCN Accredited Nursing Education Scholarships *(Graduate, Undergraduate/Scholarship)* [10715]
WOCN Advanced Education Scholarships *(Graduate/Scholarship)* [10716]
Jean Wright-Elson Scholarships *(Doctorate, Graduate, Undergraduate/Scholarship)* [8743]
Joan C. Yoder Memorial Nursing Scholarships *(Undergraduate/Scholarship)* [10046]
Yukon Delta Fisheries Development Association Scholarships *(Undergraduate, Graduate/Scholarship)* [10047]

Nursing, Cardiovascular and cerebrovascular

Epilepsy Foundation Pre-doctoral Research Training Fellowships *(Graduate/Fellowship)* [3906]

Nursing, Neonatal

Academy of Neonatal Nursing Conference Scholarships *(Professional development/Scholarship)* [44]
ANF/ANN-FNRE Nursing Research Grants *(Professional development/Grant)* [1042]
Foundation for Neonatal Research and Education Scholarships *(Doctorate, Graduate, Postgraduate, Undergraduate/Scholarship)* [4272]
ANN Ingrid Josefin Ridky Academic Scholarships *(Undergraduate, Graduate/Scholarship)* [45]

Nursing, Oncological

CBCF - Ontario Nurse and Allied Health Professional Fellowships *(Advanced Professional, Professional development/Fellowship)* [2592]
Clinical Project Funding for Advanced Practice Oncology Nurses *(Advanced Professional, Professional development/Grant)* [7616]
Leadership Development Online Course Scholarships *(Professional development/Scholarship)* [7617]
Pearl Moore Career Development Awards *(Professional development/Grant)* [7618]
Oncology Nursing Society Foundation - Bachelor's Scholarships *(Undergraduate/Scholarship)* [7619]
Oncology Nursing Society Foundation - Doctoral Scholarships *(Doctorate/Scholarship)* [7620]
Oncology Nursing Society Foundation - Master's Scholarships *(Graduate, Master's/Scholarship)* [7621]
ONS Foundation Congress Scholarships *(Profes-

sional development/Scholarship) [7622]
ONS Foundation Dissertation Research Grants (Doctorate, Professional development/Grant) [7623]
ONS Foundation Research Grants (Advanced Professional/Grant) [7624]
Research Career Development Awards (Professional development/Fellowship, Grant) [7625]

Nursing, Pediatric

Eight and Forty Lung and Respiratory Disease Nursing Scholarships (Other/Scholarship) [955]
Pediatric Endocrinology Nursing Society Academic Education Scholarships (Undergraduate/Scholarship) [7926]
Pediatric Endocrinology Nursing Society Convention Reimbursement Awards (Undergraduate/Award) [7927]

Nursing, Psychiatric

Associates in Behavioral Health Scholarships (Graduate/Scholarship) [8243]
RPNAS Baccalaureate Level Program Scholarships (Undergraduate/Scholarship) [8538]
RPNAS Doctorate Level Program Scholarship (Doctorate/Scholarship) [8539]
RPNAS Master's Level Program Scholarship (Master's/Scholarship) [8540]

Nursing administration

CHOPR Postdoctoral Fellowships (Postdoctorate/Fellowship) [10267]

Nutrition

ASBC Foundation Graduate Scholarships (Graduate/Scholarship) [1247]
ASBC Foundation Undergraduate Scholarships (Undergraduate/Scholarship) [1248]
AvaCare Medical Scholarships (Undergraduate/Scholarship) [2142]
Birmingham District Alabama Dietetic Association Scholarships (Graduate, Undergraduate/Scholarship) [196]
California Association of Family and Consumer Sciences - San Diego Chapter Scholarships (CAFCS) (Undergraduate, Graduate/Scholarship) [8695]
CANFIT Nutrition, Physical Education and Culinary Arts Scholarships (Graduate, Undergraduate/Scholarship) [3167]
Margaret Drew Alpha Fellowships (Graduate/Fellowship) [8091]
International Foodservice Editorial Council Scholarships (Graduate, Undergraduate/Scholarship) [5331]
Les Dames D'Escoffier New York Scholarships (Undergraduate/Scholarship) [6009]
Maine Nutrition Council Scholarships (Undergraduate/Scholarship) [6219]
NMPF National Dairy Leadership Scholarships (Graduate, Master's, Doctorate/Scholarship) [7073]
North Alabama Dietetic Association Scholarships (Graduate, Undergraduate/Scholarship) [197]
North Dakota Division Scholarships (Undergraduate/Scholarship) [6523]
Northeast Alabama District Dietetic Association Scholarships (Graduate, Undergraduate/Scholarship) [198]
Nell Bryant Robinson Scholarships (Undergraduate/Scholarship) [8105]
Margaret Jerome Sampson Scholarships (Undergraduate/Scholarship) [8107]
Saskatchewan Pulse Growers Undergraduate Scholarships (Undergraduate/Scholarship) [8778]
William E. Smith Scholarships (Graduate/Scholarship) [199]
Southeast Alabama Dietetic Association Scholarships (Graduate, Undergraduate/Scholarship) [200]
Stark County Dairy Promoters Scholarships (Undergraduate/Scholarship) [9536]
Mary and Elliot Wood Foundation Graduate Scholarship Fund (Graduate/Scholarship) [4222]
Wood Fruitticher Grocery Company, Inc. Scholarships (Graduate, Undergraduate/Scholarship) [201]

Occupational safety and health

AAOHN Professional Development Scholarships - Academic Study (Graduate, Undergraduate/Scholarship) [550]
AAOHN Professional Development Scholarships - Continuing Education (Other/Scholarship) [551]
America Responds Memorial Scholarships (Undergraduate/Scholarship) [1406]
American Society of Safety Engineers Construction Safety Scholarships (Undergraduate/Scholarship) [1407]
ASSE Diversity Committee Scholarships (Graduate, Undergraduate/Scholarship) [1408]
Bechtel Group Foundation Scholarships for Safety & Health (Undergraduate/Scholarship) [1409]
VPPPA Stephen Brown Scholarships (Graduate, Undergraduate/Scholarship) [10417]
Warren K. Brown Scholarships (Undergraduate/Scholarship) [1410]
CNA Foundation Scholarships (Graduate, Undergraduate/Scholarship) [1411]
Scott Dominguez - Craters of the Moon Chapter Scholarships (Graduate, Undergraduate/Scholarship) [1412]
Gulf Coast Past President's Scholarships (Undergraduate/Scholarship) [1413]
George Gustafson HSE Memorial Scholarships (Graduate, Undergraduate/Scholarship) [1414]
David Iden Memorial Safety Scholarships (Undergraduate/Scholarship) [1415]
IRSST Doctoral Scholarship (Doctorate/Fellowship) [5152]
IRSST Doctoral Scholarships Abroad (Doctorate/Fellowship) [5153]
IRSST Doctoral Scholarships Supplement (Doctorate/Fellowship) [5154]
IRSST Masters Scholarships Supplement (Master's/Fellowship) [5156]
IRSST Masters Scholarships (Master's/Scholarship) [5155]
IRSST Postdoctoral Scholarships Abroad (Postdoctorate/Fellowship) [5158]
IRSST Postdoctoral Scholarships (Postdoctorate/Fellowship) [5157]
Greater Baton Rouge Chapter - Don Jones Excellence in Safety Scholarships (Undergraduate/Scholarship) [1416]
Southwest Chapter Roy Kinslow Scholarships (Undergraduate/Scholarship) [1417]
James P. Kohn Memorial Scholarships (Graduate/Scholarship) [1418]
Central Indiana ASSE Jim Kriner Memorial Scholarships (Graduate, Undergraduate/Scholarship) [1419]
Liberty Mutual Scholarships (Undergraduate/Scholarship) [1420]
Marsh Risk Consulting Scholarships (Undergraduate/Scholarship) [1421]
Dick Martin Scholarships (Postgraduate/Scholarship) [2609]
Rixio Medina and Associates Hispanics in Safety Scholarships (Graduate, Undergraduate/Scholarship) [1422]
North Florida Chapter Safety Education Scholarships (Graduate, Undergraduate/Scholarship) [1423]
Northeastern Illinois Chapter Scholarships (Graduate, Undergraduate/Scholarship) [1424]
PDC Scholarships (Undergraduate/Scholarship) [1425]
Harold F. Polston Scholarships (Graduate, Undergraduate/Scholarship) [1426]
William C. Ray, CIH, CSP Arizona Scholarships (Graduate, Undergraduate/Scholarship) [1427]
Region II Scholarships (Graduate, Undergraduate/Scholarship) [1428]
Julie Schmid Research Scholarship (Advanced Professional/Scholarship) [2033]
Louis Stokes Health Scholars Program (Undergraduate/Scholarship) [3349]
VPPPA William Sullivan Scholarships (Graduate, Undergraduate/Scholarship) [10418]
Harry Taback 9/11 Memorial Scholarships (Undergraduate/Scholarship) [1429]
Thompson Scholarships for Women in Safety (Graduate/Scholarship) [1430]
UPS Diversity Scholarships (Undergraduate/Scholarship) [1431]
VPPPA June Brothers Scholarships (Graduate, Undergraduate/Scholarship) [10419]

Occupational therapy

AfterCollege Occupational Therapy Scholarships (Master's, Doctorate/Scholarship) [99]
AMBUCS Scholarships for Therapists Program (Graduate, Undergraduate/Scholarship) [381]
Canadian Occupational Therapy Foundation Graduate Scholarships (Doctorate, Master's/Scholarship) [2717]
Canadian Occupational Therapy Foundation Invacare Master's Scholarships (Master's/Scholarship) [2718]
Thelma Cardwell Scholarships (Graduate/Scholarship) [2719]
COTA Scholarships for Occupational Therapy Assistants (Undergraduate/Scholarship) [7762]
Dave Couch Memorial Scholarships (Undergraduate/Scholarship) [7820]
Discover Health Professions Loans (Graduate/Loan) [3636]
Discover Residency Loans (Graduate/Loan) [3639]
Margaret Dowell-Gravatt, M.D. Scholarships (Undergraduate/Scholarship) [2226]
Goldwin Howland Scholarships (Graduate/Scholarship) [2720]
Kappa Delta Phi Scholarship Program (Postgraduate/Scholarship) [1046]
Mary Minglen Scholarship Program (Postgraduate/Scholarship) [1047]
NorthCoast Medical Scholarship Program (Postgraduate/Scholarship) [1048]
Frank Oppenheimer Scholarship Program (Postgraduate/Scholarship) [1049]
Edith Weingarten Scholarship Program (Postgraduate/Scholarship) [1050]
Willard & Spackman Scholarship Program (Postgraduate/Scholarship) [1051]

Ocean engineering (See Engineering, Ocean)

Oceanography

Canadian Hydrographic Association Student Awards (Undergraduate/Award, Monetary, Medal) [2662]
CMOS-SCMO President's Prize (Professional development/Prize) [2682]
Roger Daley Postdoctoral Publication Awards (Postdoctorate/Monetary) [2683]
DOE Computational Science Graduate Fellowships (DOE CSGF) (Doctorate, Graduate/Fellowship) [5887]
Dr. Nancy Foster Scholarship Program (Postgraduate, Graduate/Scholarship) [7077]
Dr. Nancy Foster Scholarships (Graduate/Scholarship) [4159]
Tertia M.C. Hughes Memorial Graduate Student Prize (Graduate/Award, Prize) [2684]
Boyd N. Lyon Scholarships (Doctorate, Graduate, Master's/Scholarship) [6162]
Naval Weather Service Association Scholarships (Undergraduate/Scholarship) [7225]
NDSEG Fellowships (Graduate/Fellowship) [6911]
NOAA EPP Undergraduate Scholarships (USP) (Undergraduate/Scholarship) [9891]
NOAA Graduate Sciences Scholarships (Graduate/Scholarship) [9892]
François J. Saucier Prize in Applied Oceanography (Professional development/Award, Prize) [2685]
Dr. Andrew Thomson Prize in Applied Meteorology (Professional development/Award, Prize) [2686]

Oncology

ABTA Translational Grant Program *(Postdoctorate/Grant)* [633]
Adolescent/Young Adult Lymphoma Cooperative Groups Correlative Studies Grants *(Advanced Professional/Grant)* [6156]
Alex's Lemonade Stand Foundation Epidemiology Grants *(Doctorate, Master's, Professional development/Grant)* [318]
Alex's Lemonade Stand Foundation Innovation Grants *(Other/Grant)* [319]
Alex's Lemonade Stand Foundation Young Investigator Grants *(Doctorate, Master's, Professional development/Grant)* [320]
American Association for Cancer Research Minority Scholar Awards *(Graduate/Award)* [472]
Annual Research Doctoral and Postgraduate Fellowship Grant Program *(Doctorate, Postdoctorate, Postgraduate, Advanced Professional/Fellowship, Grant)* [2586]
Aplastic Anemia and Myelodysplasia Association of Canada Scholarships *(Graduate/Scholarship)* [2694]
ASCO/CCF Young Investigator Awards *(Professional development, Advanced Professional/Grant)* [3369]
ASTRO Junior Faculty Career Research Training Awards *(Advanced Professional, Professional development/Grant)* [1392]
ASTRO Minority Summer Fellowship Awards *(Postgraduate, Professional development/Fellowship)* [1393]
ASTRO Residents/Fellows in Radiation Oncology Research Seed Grants *(Advanced Professional, Professional development/Grant)* [1394]
ASTRO/ROI Comparative Effectiveness Research Awards *(Professional development/Grant)* [1395]
Basic Research Fellowship Program *(Postdoctorate/Fellowship)* [634]
Bradley Stuart Beller Special Merit Award *(Doctorate, Postdoctorate/Award)* [3370]
BHCRI Bridge Funds *(Advanced Professional, Professional development/Grant)* [5012]
BHCRI Cancer Research Training Program Awards *(Graduate, Postdoctorate, Advanced Professional, Professional development/Grant)* [5013]
BHCRI Matching Funds *(Advanced Professional, Professional development/Grant)* [5014]
BHCRI Miscellaneous Funds *(Advanced Professional, Professional development/Grant)* [5015]
BHCRI Seed Funds *(Advanced Professional, Professional development/Grant)* [5016]
BHCRI Studentship Awards *(Undergraduate, Graduate, Advanced Professional/Grant)* [5017]
CARO-ELEKTA Research Fellowship Program *(Professional development/Fellowship)* [1900]
CBCF - BC/Yukon Region Breast Cancer Research Grants Competition *(Advanced Professional/Grant)* [2587]
CBCF - BC/Yukon Region Breast Cancer Survivor Dragon Boat Grants *(Professional development/Grant)* [2588]
CBCF - BC/Yukon Region Community Health Grants *(Professional development/Grant)* [2589]
CBCF - BC/Yukon Region Small Initiative Funds *(Professional development/Grant)* [2590]
CBCF - Ontario Nurse and Allied Health Professional Fellowships *(Advanced Professional, Professional development/Fellowship)* [2592]
CBCF - Ontario Physician Fellowships *(Doctorate, Professional development/Fellowship)* [2593]
CBCF - Ontario Research Fellowships *(Doctorate, Postdoctorate, Professional development/Fellowship)* [2594]
CBCF - Ontario Research Project Grants *(Advanced Professional, Professional development/Grant)* [2595]
CBCF - Prairies/NWT Grants in Basic Biomedical Research *(Advanced Professional, Professional development/Grant)* [2597]
CBCF - Prairies/NWT Grants in Clinical Research *(Advanced Professional, Professional development/Grant)* [2598]
CBCF - Prairies/NWT Grants in Health Services and Policy Research *(Advanced Professional, Professional development/Grant)* [2599]
CBCF - Prairies/NWT Postdoctoral Fellowships *(Postdoctorate, Professional development/Fellowship)* [2600]
CBCF - Prairies/NWT Research Grants in Psychosocial, Cultural and Environmental Determinants of Health *(Advanced Professional, Professional development/Grant)* [2601]
CCF Career Development Award *(Professional development/Grant)* [3371]
CCF Improving Cancer Care Grants *(Professional development, Doctorate/Grant)* [3372]
CCF Merit Award *(Professional development, Doctorate/Award)* [3373]
Childhood Cancer Survivor Scholarships *(Undergraduate/Scholarship)* [2903]
Jane Coffin Childs Memorial Fund - Medical Research Fellowships *(Postdoctorate/Fellowship)* [2915]
Chronic Lymphocytic Leukemia Collaborative Grants *(Advanced Professional/Grant)* [6157]
Comparative Effectiveness Research Professorship (CERP) *(Professional development, Doctorate/Grant)* [3374]
The Cure Starts Now Foundation Grants *(Graduate, Doctorate/Grant)* [3492]
Diffuse Large B-Cell Lymphoma Explorations Grants *(Advanced Professional/Grant)* [6158]
Follicular Lymphoma Research Grants *(Advanced Professional/Grant)* [6159]
Norm Hollend Fellowships in Oncology *(Postdoctorate/Fellowship)* [6138]
Institute Community Support Program ICR Publication Prizes *(Undergraduate, Graduate, Postgraduate, Postdoctorate/Prize)* [5230]
International Development and Education Award in Palliative Care *(Professional development/Award)* [3376]
International Development and Education Awards *(Professional development, Doctorate/Grant)* [3377]
International Innovation Grants *(Professional development/Grant)* [3378]
Kimmel Scholars Award *(Doctorate/Grant)* [5832]
LCRF Grants *(Advanced Professional, Professional development/Grant)* [6141]
Brigid Leventhal Special Merit Award *(Postdoctorate, Professional development/Award)* [3379]
Long-term International Fellowships *(Professional development/Fellowship)* [3380]
Mantle Cell Lymphoma Research Grants *(Advanced Professional/Grant)* [6160]
Medical Student Rotation for Underrepresented Populations *(Graduate/Grant)* [3381]
Minority-Serving Institution Faculty Scholar Awards *(Doctorate/Award)* [474]
Morgan Stanley Pediatrics Fellowships *(Doctorate, Postdoctorate, Postgraduate, Graduate/Fellowship)* [618]
Movember Clinical Trials *(Advanced Professional/Grant)* [8304]
Movember Discovery Grants *(Advanced Professional, Professional development/Grant)* [8305]
Movember Rising Star in Prostate Cancer Research Awards *(Advanced Professional, Professional development/Grant)* [8306]
Movember Team Grants *(Advanced Professional, Professional development/Grant)* [8307]
James B. Nachman ASCO Junior Faculty Award in Pediatric Oncology *(Doctorate, Professional development/Grant)* [3382]
Oncology Trainee Travel Awards *(Professional development/Grant)* [3383]
The Pain Special Merit Award *(Postdoctorate, Professional development/Award)* [3384]
Patient Advocate Scholarship Program *(Professional development/Scholarship)* [3385]
PCF Challenge Awards *(Professional development/Grant)* [8312]
PCF Young Investigator Awards *(Professional development/Grant)* [8313]
Prevent Cancer Foundation Fellowships *(Postdoctorate/Fellowship)* [8225]
Prostate Cancer Canada Clinical Research Fellowships *(Advanced Professional/Fellowship)* [8308]
Prostate Cancer Canada Graduate Studentships *(Graduate, Doctorate/Grant)* [8309]
Prostate Cancer Canada Postdoctoral Research Fellowships *(Postdoctorate, Advanced Professional/Fellowship)* [8310]
Resident Travel Award for Underrepresented Populations *(Professional development/Award)* [3386]
Barbara Rosenblum Cancer Dissertation Scholarships *(Doctorate/Fellowship, Scholarship)* [9333]
TEVA Canada Scholarship *(Undergraduate/Scholarship)* [2904]
Wagner-Torizuka Fellowships *(Professional development/Fellowship)* [9228]
Women in Cancer Research Scholar Awards *(Graduate, Postdoctorate/Award)* [475]

Opera

Bel Canto Vocal Scholarship Foundation Vocal Competition *(Graduate/Award, Scholarship)* [2217]
Opera Foundation Scholarships *(Other/Scholarship)* [7669]

Operations research

Steven M. Teutsch Prevention Effectiveness Fellowships *(Doctorate/Fellowship)* [9921]
University of Texas at Austin Special Research Grants *(Professional development/Grant)* [10276]

Ophthalmology

Army Health Professions Scholarships Program *(Professional development/Scholarship)* [9878]
LSU Eye Center Clinical Retina Fellowships *(Undergraduate/Fellowship)* [6126]

Optical engineering (See Engineering, Optical)

Optics

BACUS Scholarships *(Graduate, Undergraduate/Scholarship)* [9467]
Jean Bennett Memorial Student Travel Grants *(Graduate, Undergraduate/Grant)* [7671]
Corning Outstanding Student Paper Competition *(Graduate, Undergraduate/Award)* [7672]
Michael Kidger Memorial Scholarships in Optical Design *(Undergraduate/Scholarship)* [9468]
D.J. Lovell Scholarships *(Graduate, Undergraduate/Scholarship)* [9470]
Maiman Student Paper Competition *(Graduate, Undergraduate/Award)* [7674]
Optical Design and Engineering Scholarships *(Graduate, Undergraduate/Scholarship)* [9471]
Harvey M. Pollicove Memorial Scholarships *(Undergraduate/Scholarship)* [7675]
SPIE Student Author Travel Grants *(Graduate, Undergraduate/Grant)* [9472]
Emil Wolf Outstanding Student Paper Competition *(Graduate, Undergraduate/Award)* [7676]
Xerox Technical Minority Scholarships *(Graduate, Undergraduate/Scholarship)* [10737]

Optometry

ACVO Best Resident Manuscript Awards *(Undergraduate/Recognition)* [699]
AOF/Johnson & Johnson Vision Care - Innovation in Education Grants *(Advanced Professional, Professional development/Grant)* [414]
Army Health Professions Scholarships Program *(Professional development/Scholarship)* [9878]
Discover Health Professions Loans *(Graduate/Loan)* [3636]
Discover Residency Loans *(Graduate/Loan)* [3639]
William C. Ezell Fellowships *(Postdoctorate/Fellowship)* [415]
FFB-C Postdoctoral Fellowships *(Postdoctorate/Fellowship)* [4262]
Terrance N. Ingraham Pediatric Optometry Residency Support *(Graduate/Fellowship)* [416]
Kansas Optometry Service Scholarships *(Graduate, Undergraduate/Scholarship)* [5657]

Antoinette M. Molinari Memorial Scholarships *(Doctorate/Scholarship)* [417]
Lucille and Edward R. Roybal Foundation Public Health Scholarships *(Graduate, Undergraduate/Scholarship)* [8654]
Sheldon Wechsler and George Mertz Contact Lens Residency Awards *(Professional development, Advanced Professional/Award)* [418]

Ornithology

Welder Wildlife Foundation Fellowships *(Graduate, Master's, Doctorate/Fellowship)* [10510]

Orthotics prosthetics technology

OPERF/ABC Resident Travel Award *(Professional development/Grant)* [7755]
OPERF Educator and Student Awards *(Professional development/Grant)* [7756]
OPERF Fellowships *(Graduate, Master's, Doctorate/Fellowship)* [7757]
OPERF Small Grants *(Doctorate/Grant)* [7758]

Osteopathic medicine (See Medicine, Osteopathic)

Otolaryngology

ANS Research Grants *(Professional development/Grant)* [1030]

Otology

ANS Research Grants *(Professional development/Grant)* [1030]
AOS Research Training Fellowships *(Graduate/Fellowship)* [1067]

Otosclerosis

AOS Research Training Fellowships *(Graduate/Fellowship)* [1067]

Packaging

Petroleum Packaging Council Scholarships *(Undergraduate/Scholarship)* [8019]

Painting (See also Art)

Albinas Elskus Scholarship *(All/Scholarship)* [9488]
American Watercolor Society Scholarship Program for Art Teachers *(Other/Scholarship)* [1500]
Yvonne L. Bombardier Visual Arts Scholarships *(Master's, Doctorate/Scholarship)* [1665]
Theodore Rousseau Fellowships *(Graduate/Fellowship)* [6436]
Slifka Foundation Interdisciplinary Fellowships *(Doctorate, Master's/Fellowship)* [6437]

Pakistani studies

AIPS Long Term Fellowships *(Doctorate, Postdoctorate/Fellowship)* [919]
AIPS Post-Doctoral Fellowships *(Postdoctorate/Fellowship)* [920]
AIPS Pre-Doctoral Fellowships *(Doctorate, Graduate/Fellowship)* [921]
AIPS Short Term Fellowships *(Doctorate, Postdoctorate/Fellowship)* [922]

Paleontology

A. Allen Graffham Research Grants *(Advanced Professional, Professional development/Grant)* [1842]
Dan Rigel Memorial Educational Grants *(Professional development, Advanced Professional/Grant)* [1843]
Charles Sternberg Scholarship *(Graduate/Scholarship)* [1844]
STRI Short-Term Fellowships *(Undergraduate, Graduate, Postdoctorate/Fellowship)* [9038]

Earl S. Tupper 3-year Postdoctoral Fellowships in Tropical Biology *(Postdoctorate/Fellowship)* [9039]
René M. Vandervelde Research Grants *(Undergraduate, Professional development/Grant)* [1845]
James R. Welch Scholarship *(Graduate/Scholarship)* [1846]

Paralegal studies

AAFPE LEX Scholarships *(Undergraduate/Scholarship)* [553]
AALL Research Funds *(Professional development/Grant)* [521]
ACJA-LAE Student Paper Competitions *(Undergraduate, Graduate/Scholarship)* [752]
Alamo Area Paralegal Association Educational Scholarships *(Undergraduate, Professional development/Scholarship)* [209]
Therese A. Cannon Educational Scholarships *(Other/Scholarship)* [5372]
Gene Carte Student Paper Competition Awards *(Undergraduate, Graduate/Prize)* [1281]
CLA/CP Scholarship *(Other/Scholarship)* [8672]
Community Legal Services of Philadelphia Fellowships *(Postgraduate/Fellowship)* [3337]
DAPA Student Member Scholarships *(Undergraduate/Scholarship)* [3512]
Lise M. Duchesneau Scholarship *(Undergraduate/Scholarship)* [1895]
Gail Goodell Folsom Memorial Scholarships *(Undergraduate/Scholarship)* [6650]
Judge and Mrs. Robert D. Horowitz Legal Scholarship Fund *(Graduate/Scholarship)* [9512]
Kentucky Paralegal Association Student Scholarships *(Undergraduate/Scholarship)* [5819]
AALL/Wolters Kluwer Law & Business Grants *(Professional development/Grant)* [532]
Samuel Krugliak Legal Scholarship Fund *(Undergraduate/Scholarship)* [9517]
Richard McGrath Memorial Fund Awards *(Undergraduate/Award)* [755]
NALS of Michigan Scholarships *(Undergraduate/Scholarship)* [6652]
NFPA/PACE Scholarships *(Other/Scholarship)* [6951]
PCCE Scholarship *(Undergraduate/Scholarship)* [6952]
Rochelle Scholarship *(College/Scholarship)* [6124]
St. Louis Paralegal Association Student Scholarships *(Undergraduate/Scholarship)* [8673]
Ann S. Salsberg Scholarship Awards *(Undergraduate/Award, Scholarship)* [2516]
Edward Traurig Scholarships *(Undergraduate/Scholarship)* [10484]
Vermont Paralegal Organization Scholarships *(Undergraduate/Scholarship)* [10371]
John D. Voelker Foundation Native American Scholarships *(Undergraduate/Scholarship)* [10415]
Warner Norcross & Judd Minority Scholarships *(Undergraduate/Scholarship)* [10427]
Waterbury Bar Association Scholarships *(Undergraduate/Scholarship)* [10485]
WBA Bar President's Scholarships *(Undergraduate/Scholarship)* [10486]
WBA Paralegal/Legal Assistant Scholarships *(Undergraduate/Scholarship)* [10487]

Paramedics

EMS Scholarship Awards *(All/Award)* [8150]
Gail L. Hartshorn Memorial Fund *(Undergraduate/Scholarship)* [7838]
Harry J. Morris, Jr. Emergency Services Scholarships *(Undergraduate/Scholarship)* [4613]
John I. and Madeleine R. Taeni Scholarships *(Undergraduate/Scholarship)* [9452]

Parapsychology

Parapsychological Association Research Endowments *(All/Grant)* [7805]
Alex Tanous Scholarship Award *(Undergraduate/Scholarship)* [9642]

Parkinson's disease

APDA Postdoctoral Research Fellowships *(Other/Fellowship)* [1072]
APDA Research Grants *(Other/Grant)* [1073]
Clinician Scientist Development Awards *(Postgraduate/Fellowship)* [7883]
Parkinson Canada Basic Research Fellowships *(Advanced Professional/Fellowship)* [7876]
Parkinson Canada Clinical Movement Disorder Fellowships *(Advanced Professional, Professional development/Fellowship)* [7877]
Parkinson Canada Clinical Research Fellowships *(Professional development/Fellowship)* [7878]
Parkinson Canada Graduate Student Awards *(Graduate, Advanced Professional/Award)* [7879]
Parkinson Canada New Investigator Award Grants *(Professional development/Grant)* [7880]
Parkinson Canada Pilot Project Grants *(Advanced Professional/Grant)* [7881]
Parkinson's Disease Foundation International Research Grants Program *(Postdoctorate/Grant)* [7884]
PDF-APDA Summer Student Fellowships *(Undergraduate, Graduate/Fellowship)* [7885]
PDF-PSG Mentored Clinical Research Awards *(Professional development/Award)* [7886]

Parks and recreation

National Recreation and Park Association Diversity Scholarships *(Undergraduate/Scholarship)* [7118]
Thomas and Ruth River International Scholarships *(Undergraduate, Graduate/Scholarship)* [10704]
George Torkildsen Literary Awards *(Professional development/Award, Trophy)* [10705]

Pathology

Investigators in the Pathogenesis of Infectious Disease Awards *(Doctorate, Postdoctorate, Professional development/Grant)* [2417]
Siemens-ASCP Scholarship *(Undergraduate/Scholarship)* [1263]

Peace studies

Ford Foundation Dissertation Fellowships *(Graduate, Doctorate/Fellowship)* [6675]
Ford Foundation Diversity Fellowships *(Graduate, Doctorate, Postdoctorate, Postgraduate/Fellowship)* [6676]
Ford Foundation Postdoctoral Fellowships *(Postdoctorate/Fellowship)* [6677]
Ford Foundation Predoctoral Fellowships *(Graduate, Doctorate/Fellowship)* [6678]
Jennings Randolph Peace Scholarship Dissertation Program *(Doctorate/Scholarship)* [9990]
United States Institute of Peace Jennings Randolph Senior Fellowship Program *(Advanced Professional/Fellowship)* [9991]
Rieser Fellowships *(Undergraduate/Fellowship)* [2406]
Rotary Peace Fellowship Program *(Graduate, Master's/Fellowship)* [3701]
Herbert Scoville Jr. Peace Fellowships *(Graduate/Fellowship)* [8825]
Mary and Elliot Wood Foundation Graduate Scholarship Fund *(Graduate/Scholarship)* [4222]

Pediatric medicine (See Medicine, Pediatric)

Performing arts

AAS Fellowships for Creative and Performing Artists and Writers *(Professional development/Fellowship, Award)* [430]
ACHE Junior and Community College Performing Arts Scholarships *(Undergraduate/Scholarship)* [186]
AFA Theatre & Performance Art Project Grants *(Professional development/Grant)* [243]
Arts Council of Greater Grand Rapids Minority Scholarships *(Undergraduate/Scholarship)* [4574]

PERSONNEL ADMINISTRATION/HUMAN RESOURCES

ASTR Research Fellowships *(Other/Fellowship)* [1433]
CBC Spouses Heineken USA Performing Arts Scholarships *(Undergraduate/Scholarship)* [3346]
Jack Kent Cooke Graduate Arts Awards *(Graduate/Award)* [5493]
John L. Dales Standard Scholarship *(Undergraduate/Scholarship)* [8827]
FCA Grants to Artists *(Advanced Professional/Grant)* [4227]
Eugenia Vellner Fischer Award for the Performing Arts *(Undergraduate/Scholarship)* [6556]
Florida Education Fund McKnight Doctoral Fellowships *(Graduate/Fellowship)* [4085]
Ken Gray Endowment Scholarship *(Undergraduate/Scholarship)* [10061]
George E. Judd Scholarships *(Undergraduate/Scholarship)* [9436]
Muddy Waters Scholarships *(Undergraduate/Scholarship)* [2316]
PWC Internships *(Undergraduate, Graduate/Internship)* [8156]
Star-Ledger Scholarships for the Performing Arts *(Undergraduate/Scholarship)* [7324]
Theatre Guild Scholarship *(Undergraduate/Scholarship)* [9725]
UAA Friends of the Performing Arts Scholarship *(Undergraduate/Scholarship)* [10079]
Wolf Trap Grants for High School Performing Arts Teachers *(Other/Grant)* [10631]
The Wolf Trap Internship Program *(Graduate, Other, Undergraduate/Internship)* [10632]

Personnel administration/human resources

C.C.H.R.M.A. Scholarships *(Undergraduate/Scholarship)* [3092]
Susan R. Meisinger Fellowship for Graduate Study in HR *(Graduate, Master's, Advanced Professional/Fellowship)* [9146]
NPELRA Foundation - Anthony C. Russo Scholarships *(Graduate/Scholarship)* [7116]
SHRM Certification Scholarships - Individual *(Professional development/Scholarship)* [9147]
SHRM Foundation Academic Scholarships *(Graduate, Undergraduate/Scholarship)* [9148]

Pesticide science

Professional Women in Pest Management Scholarships *(Graduate, Other/Scholarship)* [7096]

Petroleum engineering (See Engineering, Petroleum)

Pharmaceutical sciences

AFPE Gateway Research Scholarships *(Doctorate/Scholarship)* [826]
AFPE Pre-Doctoral Fellowships in Pharmaceutical Sciences for Underrepresented Minorities *(Doctorate, Graduate/Fellowship)* [828]
AFPE Pre-Doctoral Fellowships in Pharmaceutical Sciences *(Doctorate/Fellowship)* [827]
Dr. Feroz Ahmed Memorial Educational Post-Graduate Scholarships *(Doctorate, Postgraduate/Scholarship)* [8965]
NACDS Foundation Merit-Based Scholarships *(All/Scholarship)* [6736]

Pharmacology

Epilepsy Foundation Pre-doctoral Research Training Fellowships *(Graduate/Fellowship)* [3906]
Pharmacology/Toxicology Pre Doctoral Fellowships *(Doctorate/Fellowship)* [8033]
PhRMA Foundation Pharmacology/Toxicology Research Starter Grants *(Doctorate/Grant)* [8040]
PhRMA Foundation Pharmacology/Toxicology Sabbatical Fellowships *(Postdoctorate/Fellowship)* [8041]
PhRMA Foundation Pharmacology/Toxicology Post Doctoral Fellowships *(Postdoctorate/Fellowship)* [8042]

Pharmacy

Mary Louise Andersen Scholarship *(Undergraduate/Scholarship)* [1574]
APhA Auxilliary Scholarship *(Undergraduate/Scholarship)* [1575]
George F. Archambault Scholarship *(Undergraduate/Scholarship)* [1576]
Armenian American Pharmacists' Association Scholarships *(Graduate/Scholarship)* [1684]
ASHP Student Research Awards *(Doctorate/Award)* [1323]
Boyle Family Scholarship *(Undergraduate/Scholarship)* [1577]
Joseph R. Calder, Jr., MD Scholarship Fund *(Undergraduate/Scholarship)* [4041]
Christian Pharmacists Fellowship International *(Advanced Professional/Fellowship)* [2934]
J.C. and Rheba Cobb Memorial Scholarships *(Undergraduate/Fellowship)* [6867]
DAAD Study Scholarship Awards *(Graduate/Scholarship)* [3604]
Discover Health Professions Loans *(Graduate/Loan)* [3636]
Discover Residency Loans *(Graduate/Loan)* [3639]
Marvin and Joanell Dyrstad Scholarship *(Undergraduate/Scholarship)* [1578]
Epilepsy Foundation Pre-doctoral Research Training Fellowships *(Graduate/Fellowship)* [3906]
Gloria Francke Scholarship *(Undergraduate/Scholarship)* [1579]
Thomas W. Gallagher Scholarships Fund *(Undergraduate/Scholarship)* [9503]
John A. Gans Scholarship *(Undergraduate/Scholarship)* [1580]
Robert D. Gibson Scholarship *(Undergraduate/Scholarship)* [1581]
Indspire Health Careers Bursary and Scholarships *(Graduate, Undergraduate/Scholarship)* [5132]
Sam Kalman Scholarship *(Undergraduate/Scholarship)* [1582]
Jason Lang Scholarships *(Undergraduate/Scholarship)* [276]
Juan and Esperanza Luna Scholarship *(Undergraduate/Scholarship)* [1583]
Maryland Poison Center Clinical Toxicology Fellowships *(Doctorate, Graduate/Fellowship)* [6300]
Merck Frosst Canada Ltd. Postgraduate Pharmacy Fellowships *(Graduate/Fellowship)* [1957]
NACDS Foundation Merit-Based Scholarships *(All/Scholarship)* [6736]
National Community Pharmacists Association Summer Internship Programs *(Undergraduate/Internship)* [6868]
NCPA Foundation Presidential Scholarships *(Undergraduate/Scholarship)* [6869]
Pharmaceutics Post Doctoral Fellowships *(Postdoctorate/Fellowship)* [8030]
Pharmaceutics Research Starter Grants *(Doctorate/Grant)* [8031]
Pharmaceutics Sabbatical Fellowships *(Postdoctorate/Fellowship)* [8032]
PhRMA Foundation Pharmaceutics Pre Doctoral Fellowships *(Doctorate/Fellowship)* [8039]
Neil Pruitt, Sr. Memorial Scholarships *(Undergraduate/Scholarship)* [6870]
Paul Pumpian Scholarship *(Undergraduate/Scholarship)* [1584]
Rho Chi, AFPE First Year Graduate Fellowships *(Doctorate, Graduate/Fellowship)* [8597]
Rho Chi Society Clinical Research Scholarships *(Postdoctorate/Scholarship)* [8598]
Colonel Jerry W. Ross Scholarship *(Undergraduate/Scholarship)* [1585]
Lucille and Edward R. Roybal Foundation Public Health Scholarships *(Graduate, Undergraduate/Scholarship)* [8654]
Willard B. Simmons Sr. Memorial Scholarships *(Undergraduate/Scholarship)* [6871]
Ann Kelsay Small Scholarship *(Undergraduate/Scholarship)* [5766]
Charles C. Thomas Scholarship *(Undergraduate/Scholarship)* [1586]
TSHP R&E Foundation Scholarship Program *(Undergraduate, Graduate/Scholarship)* [9807]
John W. Webb Lecture Awards *(Other/Recognition)* [1324]
Western Michigan Society of Health-System Pharmacists Scholarships *(Undergraduate/Scholarship)* [10533]

Philanthropy

Edward G. Kaelber Scholarships *(Undergraduate/Scholarship)* [6201]

Philology

Thesaurus Linguae Latinae Fellowships (TTL) *(Doctorate/Fellowship)* [9107]

Philosophy

Calihan Academic Fellowships *(Graduate, Professional development/Fellowship, Grant)* [56]
Calihan Travel Grants *(Graduate/Grant)* [57]
The Steve Duckett Local Conservation Scholarships *(Undergraduate, Postgraduate/Scholarship)* [8232]
Marcus Mosiah Garvey Scholarships *(Undergraduate/Scholarship)* [5523]
The Michael Kiely Strong Roots Scholarships *(Undergraduate/Scholarship)* [8233]
The Tatiana Mendez Future Resources Scholarships *(Undergraduate/Scholarship)* [8234]
Novak Awards *(Doctorate/Monetary)* [58]
The Seth Okin Good Deeds Scholarships *(Undergraduate/Scholarship)* [8235]
Ameen Rihani Scholarship Program *(Undergraduate/Scholarship)* [1599]
The Thomas Soldan Healthy Communities Scholarships *(Undergraduate, Graduate/Scholarship)* [8237]
The Ed Tayter Outstanding Citizen Scholarships *(Undergraduate/Scholarship)* [8238]

Photogrammetry

Robert E. Altenhofen Memorial Scholarships *(Graduate, Undergraduate/Scholarship)* [1802]
ERDAS Internship *(Graduate/Internship, Award)* [1804]
Francis H. Moffitt Memorial Scholarships *(Graduate, Undergraduate/Scholarship)* [1807]
The Kenneth J. Osborn Memorial Scholarships *(Undergraduate/Scholarship)* [1808]
Paul R. Wolf Memorial Scholarships *(Graduate/Scholarship)* [1809]
Z/I Imaging Scholarships *(Graduate/Scholarship)* [1810]

Photography

Bob Baxter Scholarships *(Graduate, Undergraduate/Scholarship)* [7106]
Reid Blackburn Scholarships *(Undergraduate/Scholarship)* [7107]
Yvonne L. Bombardier Visual Arts Scholarships *(Master's, Doctorate/Scholarship)* [1665]
Raymond Davis Scholarships *(Undergraduate, Graduate/Scholarship)* [9150]
Bob East Scholarships *(Graduate, Undergraduate/Scholarship)* [7108]
Bruce T. and Jackie Mahi Erickson Grant *(Graduate, Undergraduate/Grant)* [7907]
Allison E. Fisher Scholarships *(Undergraduate, Graduate/Scholarship)* [4068]
The Gallery Collection's Create-A-Greeting Card Scholarships *(Undergraduate/Scholarship)* [4318]
Glendale Latino Association Scholarships *(Undergraduate/Scholarship)* [4449]
Elizabeth Greenhalgh Memorial Scholarships in Journalism, Graphic Arts, or Photography *(Undergraduate/Scholarship)* [10639]
International Foodservice Editorial Council Scholarships *(Graduate, Undergraduate/Scholarship)* [5331]
Kit C. King Graduate Scholarships *(Graduate/Scholarship)* [7109]
Manzer-Keener-Wefler Scholarships *(Undergraduate/Scholarship)* [9521]
NPPF Still and Multimedia Scholarships *(Undergraduate/Scholarship)* [7110]

NPPF TV News Scholarships *(Undergraduate/Scholarship)* [7111]
Scott Pearlman Field Awards for Science and Exploration *(Other/Award)* [3946]
SPE Student Awards for Innovations in Imaging *(Undergraduate, Graduate/Scholarship)* [9252]
UAA Kimura Scholarship Fund for Photography *(Undergraduate/Scholarship)* [10082]
Worldstudio AIGA Scholarships *(Graduate, Undergraduate/Scholarship)* [10709]

Photography, Journalistic
Tom Hanson Photojournalism Awards *(All/Internship)* [4119]

Physical education (See Education, Physical)

Physical rehabilitation (See Rehabilitation, Physical/Psychological)

Physical sciences
AIST Ohio Valley Chapter Scholarships *(Undergraduate/Scholarship)* [1994]
American Council of Independent Laboratories Scholarships *(Undergraduate/Scholarship)* [732]
American Sokol Merit Awards *(Undergraduate/Scholarship, Recognition)* [1448]
AWMA Louisiana Section Scholarships *(Undergraduate, Graduate/Scholarship)* [147]
Casey Bennett Scholarships *(Undergraduate/Scholarship)* [4007]
College of Engineering and Physical Sciences Industry Scholarships *(Undergraduate/Scholarship)* [10208]
Roy Cooper Memorial Scholarships *(Undergraduate/Scholarship)* [5998]
Discover Residency Loans *(Graduate/Loan)* [3639]
Getty Postdoctoral Fellowships in Conservation Science *(Postdoctorate/Fellowship)* [4410]
IAF Fellowships *(Doctorate/Fellowship)* [5232]
Michigan Society of Fellows Three-Year Fellowships *(Postdoctorate/Fellowship)* [6481]
Christine Mirzayan Science and Technology Policy Graduate Fellowships *(Graduate/Fellowship)* [6679]
Paul and Ellen Ruckes Scholarships *(Graduate, Undergraduate/Scholarship)* [823]
Alfred P. Sloan Foundation Graduate Scholarships - Sloan Minority Ph.D. Program *(Doctorate/Scholarship)* [6684]
UC MEXUS-CONACYT Doctoral Fellowships *(Doctorate/Fellowship)* [10117]
UNCF/Merck Graduate Science Research Dissertation Fellowships *(Graduate/Fellowship)* [6426, 9862]
UNCF/Merck Postdoctoral Science Research Fellowships *(Postdoctorate/Fellowship)* [6427, 9863]
Graduate Fellowship Program - Peter Verhofstadt Fellowships *(Graduate/Fellowship)* [8836]

Physical therapy
The Achieve Physical Therapy and Fitness Scholarship *(Doctorate/Scholarship)* [9580]
AfterCollege Physical Therapist Student Scholarships *(Undergraduate, Master's, Doctorate/Scholarship)* [100]
AMBUCS Scholarships for Therapists Program *(Graduate, Undergraduate/Scholarship)* [381]
APTA Minority Scholarships - Faculty Development Scholarships *(Postdoctorate/Scholarship)* [1096]
APTA Minority Scholarships - Physical Therapist Assistant Students *(Undergraduate/Scholarship)* [1097]
APTA Minority Scholarships - Physical Therapist Students *(Undergraduate/Scholarship)* [1098]
Dave Couch Memorial Scholarships *(Undergraduate/Scholarship)* [7820]
Discover Health Professions Loans *(Graduate/Loan)* [3636]
Margaret Dowell-Gravatt, M.D. Scholarships *(Undergraduate/Scholarship)* [2226]
The Shanon Newberry Physical Therapy Scholarship Endowment *(Doctorate/Scholarship)* [9584]
The Physical Therapy Faculty Scholarship Endowment *(Graduate/Scholarship)* [9585]
Everett Oscar Shimp Memorial Scholarships *(Undergraduate/Scholarship)* [7862]
The Sybil Jennings Vorheis Memorial Undergraduate Scholarships *(Undergraduate/Scholarship)* [4218]
Monica M. Weaver Memorial Fund *(Undergraduate/Scholarship)* [4062]

Physics
AAPM Diversity Recruitment through Education and Mentoring Program (MUSE) *(Undergraduate/Fellowship)* [557]
AAPM Fellowships for Graduate Study in Medical Physics *(Graduate/Fellowship)* [558]
AAPM Summer Undergraduate Fellowships *(Undergraduate/Fellowship)* [559]
Andreas Acrivos Dissertation Award in Fluid Dynamics *(Graduate, Doctorate/Award)* [1085]
ACS Rubber Division Undergraduate Scholarships *(Undergraduate/Scholarship)* [666]
AFCEA Scholarship for Working Professionals *(Undergraduate, Graduate/Scholarship)* [86]
Afghanistan and Iraq War Veterans Scholarship *(Undergraduate/Scholarship)* [88]
Alaska Aerospace Development Corporation Scholarships *(Undergraduate/Scholarship)* [10004]
American Institute of Physics Congressional Science Fellowships *(Doctorate/Fellowship)* [924]
American Institute of Physics State Department Science Fellowships *(Doctorate/Fellowship)* [925]
Michael P. Anderson Scholarships in Space Science *(Undergraduate/Scholarship)* [7137]
APS Scholarships for Minority Undergraduate Physics Majors *(Undergraduate/Scholarship)* [7138]
Award for Outstanding Doctoral Dissertation in Laser Science *(Doctorate/Award)* [1086]
Award for Outstanding Doctoral Thesis Research in Biological Physics *(Doctorate/Award)* [1087]
Harvey Washington Banks Scholarships in Astronomy *(Undergraduate/Scholarship)* [7139]
M. Hildred Blewett Fellowships *(Postdoctorate/Fellowship)* [1088]
Charles S. Brown Scholarships in Physics *(Graduate, Undergraduate/Scholarship)* [7140]
Lt. General Douglas D. Buchholz Memorial Scholarship *(Undergraduate/Scholarship)* [89]
Burroughs Wellcome Fund Collaborative Research Travel Grants (CRTG) *(Doctorate, Postdoctorate, Professional development/Grant)* [2413]
Career Awards at the Scientific Interface (CASI) *(Doctorate, Postdoctorate, Advanced Professional, Professional development/Grant)* [2416]
Julian E. Carnes Scholarship Fund *(Undergraduate/Scholarship)* [4183]
CfA Postdoctoral Fellowships *(Postdoctorate/Fellowship)* [4780]
Clay Postdoctoral Fellowships *(Postdoctorate/Fellowship)* [4781]
CNS-UCSB Graduate Fellowships for Science and Engineering *(Postdoctorate/Fellowship)* [10127]
SRC NRI Hans J. Coufal Fellowships *(Graduate/Fellowship)* [8838]
D&A Florida Scholarships *(Undergraduate/Scholarship)* [9425]
DEPS Graduate Scholarship Program *(Graduate/Scholarship)* [3624]
Disabled War Veterans Scholarships *(Undergraduate/Scholarship)* [90]
Dissertation Award in Hadronic Physics *(Doctorate/Award)* [1089]
Peggy Dixon Two-Year Scholarships *(Undergraduate/Scholarship)* [9254]
DOE Computational Science Graduate Fellowships (DOE CSGF) *(Doctorate, Graduate/Fellowship)* [5887]
Robert A. Ellis Scholarships in Physics *(Undergraduate/Scholarship)* [7141]
Fermilab Internships for Physics Majors *(Undergraduate/Internship)* [9899]
Fermilab Science Undergraduate Laboratory Internship *(Undergraduate/Internship)* [9900]
Fermilab Summer Internships in Science and Technology *(Undergraduate/Internship)* [9901]
Frank Fong Scholarships *(Undergraduate/Scholarship)* [9076]
Glendale Latino Association Scholarships *(Undergraduate/Scholarship)* [4449]
Richard L. Greene Dissertation Award *(Doctorate/Award)* [1090]
Helm Family Scholarships *(Undergraduate/Scholarship)* [8706]
Elmer S. Imes Scholarships in Physics *(Undergraduate/Scholarship)* [7142]
Jeffress Trust Awards Program in Interdisciplinary Research *(Professional development/Award)* [4816]
Robert C. and Judith L. Knapp Scholarships *(Graduate, Undergraduate/Scholarship)* [4147]
Imelda "Mel" and Ralph LeMar Scholarship *(Undergraduate/Scholarship)* [3330]
Herbert Levy Memorial Scholarship *(Undergraduate/Scholarship)* [9255]
Barbara Lotze Scholarships for Future Teachers *(Undergraduate/Scholarship)* [562]
Walter Samuel McAfee Scholarships in Space Physics *(Undergraduate/Scholarship)* [7143]
Ronald E. McNair Scholarships in Space and Optical Physics *(Undergraduate/Scholarship)* [7144]
Nicholas Metropolis Award for Outstanding Doctoral Thesis Work in Computational Physics *(Doctorate/Award)* [1091]
Willie Hobbs Moore Scholarships *(Undergraduate/Scholarship)* [7145]
Harry L. Morrison Scholarships *(Undergraduate/Scholarship)* [7146]
National GEM Consortium - PhD Science Fellowships *(Doctorate, Graduate/Fellowship)* [6969]
NDSEG Fellowships *(Graduate/Fellowship)* [6911]
Northampton County Medical Society Alliance Scholarships *(Undergraduate/Scholarship)* [7507]
Northrop Grumman Engineering Scholarships *(Undergraduate/Scholarship)* [7527]
NPSC Fellowships *(Graduate/Fellowship)* [7098]
Outstanding Doctoral Thesis in Astrophysics *(Doctorate/Award)* [1092]
Physics of Accelerators and Related Technology for International Students *(Undergraduate/Internship)* [9902]
Marshall N. Rosenbluth Outstanding Doctoral Thesis Award *(Doctorate/Award)* [1093]
RSNA/AAPM Fellowships for Graduate Study in Medical Physics *(Graduate/Fellowship)* [560]
SAO (Smithsonian Astrophysical Observatory) Predoctoral Fellowships *(Graduate/Fellowship)* [4782]
Ralph W. Shrader Diversity Scholarship *(Graduate/Scholarship)* [91]
Clifford G. Shull Fellowships *(Postdoctorate/Fellowship)* [9909]
Sloan Research Fellowships *(Doctorate/Fellowship)* [8988]
SPS Future Teacher Scholarships *(Undergraduate/Scholarship)* [9256]
SPS Leadership Scholarships *(Undergraduate/Scholarship)* [9257]
Mitsuyoshi Tanaka Dissertation Award in Experimental Particle Physics *(Doctorate/Award)* [1094]
Lee Teng Undergraduate Fellowships in Accelerator Science and Engineering *(Undergraduate/Fellowship)* [9903]
Graduate Fellowship Program - Peter Verhofstadt Fellowships *(Graduate/Fellowship)* [8836]
Arthur BC Walker Scholarships *(Undergraduate/Scholarship)* [7147]
Alvin M. Weinberg Fellowships *(Doctorate/Fellowship)* [9910]
Women In Defense HORIZONS Scholarships *(Graduate, Undergraduate/Scholarship)* [10636]
Xavier University Departmental Scholarships *(Undergraduate/Scholarship)* [10729]
Xerox Technical Minority Scholarships *(Graduate, Undergraduate/Scholarship)* [10737]

Physiology

Bruce and Betty Alberts Endowed Scholarships in Physiology *(Undergraduate/Scholarship)* [6243]
Dominio of Canada Insurance Scholarships *(Graduate/Scholarship)* [8128]
Epilepsy Foundation Pre-doctoral Research Training Fellowships *(Graduate/Fellowship)* [3906]
Benjamin Kaminer Endowed Scholarships in Physiology *(Graduate, Master's, Doctorate/Scholarship)* [6249]
Mountain Memorial Funds *(Graduate, Master's, Doctorate/Award)* [6255]
Physiotherapy Foundation of Canada Research Grant *(Other/Grant)* [8129]
Porter Physiology Development Fellowship Awards *(Doctorate/Fellowship)* [1100]
B.E. Schnurr Memorial Fund Research Grants *(Other/Grant)* [8130]
STRI Short-Term Fellowships *(Undergraduate, Graduate, Postdoctorate/Fellowship)* [9038]
Caroline tum Suden/Frances Hellebrandt Professional Opportunity Awards *(Postdoctorate, Other/Award)* [1101]
Earl S. Tupper 3-year Postdoctoral Fellowships in Tropical Biology *(Postdoctorate/Fellowship)* [9039]
Ann Collins Whitmore Memorial Scholarship (ACWMS) *(Graduate/Scholarship)* [8131]

Piano music (See Music, Piano)

Planetary sciences (See Space and planetary sciences)

Plastic surgery

American Association of Plastic Surgeons Academic Scholars Program *(Professional development/Scholarship)* [564]

Podiatry

Discover Health Professions Loans *(Graduate/Loan)* [3636]
Discover Residency Loans *(Graduate/Loan)* [3639]
Zelda Walling Vicha Memorial Scholarships *(Undergraduate/Scholarship)* [1387]

Poetry

FCA Grants to Artists *(Advanced Professional/Grant)* [4227]

Polish studies (See also Area and ethnic studies)

Falcon Achievement Scholarships *(Undergraduate/Scholarship)* [8200]
Harriet Irsay Scholarships *(Graduate, Undergraduate/Scholarship)* [927]
Jagiellonian University Summer Program Scholarship *(Professional development/Scholarship)* [8204]
Kosciuszko Foundation Graduate Study and Research in Poland Scholarships *(Graduate/Scholarship)* [5877]
Kosciuszko Foundation Tuition Scholarships *(Graduate/Scholarship)* [5878]
Kosciuszko Foundation Year Abroad Scholarships *(Graduate, Undergraduate/Scholarship)* [5879]
Massachusetts Federation of Polish Women's Clubs Scholarships *(Undergraduate/Scholarship)* [5880]
Polish American Club of North Jersey Scholarships *(Graduate, Undergraduate/Scholarship)* [5881]
Polish National Alliance of Brooklyn, USA Scholarships *(Undergraduate/Scholarship)* [5882]
Remkus-Sochaki Academmic Achievement Scholarships *(Undergraduate/Scholarship)* [8205]
Dr. Marie E. Zakrzewski Medical Scholarships *(Doctorate/Scholarship)* [5883]

Political science

American Enterprise Institute National Research Initiative Fellowships (NRI) *(Graduate/Fellowship)* [786]
American Institute for Economic Research Student Summer Fellowships *(Doctorate, Graduate, Undergraduate/Fellowship)* [911]
APSA Congressional Fellowship for Communications Scholars and Journalists *(Advanced Professional, Professional development/Fellowship)* [1108]
APSA Congressional Fellowships for Journalists *(Advanced Professional, Professional development/Fellowship)* [1109]
APSA Congressional Fellowships for Political Scientists *(Advanced Professional, Professional development/Fellowship)* [1110]
APSA Congressional Fellowships *(Other/Fellowship)* [4398]
APSA Fund for Latino Scholarship *(Undergraduate, Graduate/Scholarship)* [1111]
APSA Minority Fellows Program *(Doctorate/Fellowship)* [1113]
APSA Presidency Research Group Fellowships *(Graduate, Postdoctorate/Fellowship)* [1118]
APSA Small Research Grant Program *(Doctorate/Grant)* [1114]
APSA U.S. Federal Executives Fellowships *(Advanced Professional, Professional development/Fellowship)* [1115]
ARCE Funded Fellowships *(Doctorate, Postdoctorate/Fellowship)* [1195]
ARCE Research Associates Fellowships *(Doctorate, Postdoctorate, Professional development/Fellowship)* [1196]
ARS of Eastern USA Lazarian Graduate Scholarship *(Master's, Doctorate/Scholarship)* [1680]
Marguerite Ross Barnett Research Grant *(Graduate, Postdoctorate/Grant)* [1119]
Mark A. Beltz Scholarship *(Graduate, Undergraduate/Scholarship)* [10052]
Pat Brakke Political Science Scholarship *(Undergraduate/Scholarship)* [10053]
Sam Bull Memorial Scholarships *(Undergraduate/Scholarship)* [248]
Cecil E. Burney Scholarships *(Undergraduate/Scholarship)* [3091]
CIGNA Healthcare Graduate Scholarships *(Graduate/Scholarship)* [6957]
CIGNA Healthcare Undergraduate Scholarships *(Undergraduate/Scholarship)* [6958]
D&A Florida Scholarships *(Undergraduate/Scholarship)* [9425]
Denton Scholarships *(Graduate/Scholarship)* [8897]
Diabetes Scholars Foundation College Scholarships *(Undergraduate/Scholarship)* [3616]
Douglas-Coldwell Foundation Scholarships in Social Affairs *(Graduate/Scholarship)* [3656]
The Steve Duckett Local Conservation Scholarships *(Undergraduate, Postgraduate/Scholarship)* [8232]
UAA Governor William A. Egan Scholarship *(Undergraduate/Scholarship)* [10056]
Garikian Scholarship Fund *(Undergraduate/Scholarship)* [1694]
GFOA Minorities in Government Finance Scholarship *(Graduate, Undergraduate/Scholarship)* [4502]
Enid Hall Griswold Memorial Scholarships *(Undergraduate/Scholarship)* [7152]
Guzkowski Family Scholarships *(Undergraduate/Scholarship)* [8479]
Harkness Fellowships in Health Care Policy and Practice *(Doctorate, Graduate/Fellowship)* [3160]
Hench Post-Dissertation Fellowship *(Postdoctorate/Fellowship)* [438]
Chun-tu Hsueh Fellowship for International Scholars *(Graduate, Postdoctorate/Grant)* [1120]
John Peters Humphrey Student Fellowships *(Graduate/Fellowship)* [3459]
Rita Mae Kelly Fund *(Graduate, Doctorate/Fellowship)* [1121]
The Michael Kiely Strong Roots Scholarships *(Undergraduate/Scholarship)* [8233]
Lazarian Graduate Scholarships *(Graduate/Scholarship)* [1678]
William P. McHugh Memorial Fund Award *(Doctorate, Graduate/Fellowship)* [1197]
The Tatiana Mendez Future Resources Scholarships *(Undergraduate/Scholarship)* [8234]
Warren E. Miller Fellowship in Electoral Politics *(Advanced Professional, Graduate, Postdoctorate/Fellowship)* [1122]
MPAC-DC Graduate Policy Fellowships *(Graduate/Fellowship)* [6630]
NARAL Pro-Choice America Political Internships *(Undergraduate, Graduate, Professional development/Internship)* [6661]
The National Endowment for the Humanities Fellowships *(Graduate/Fellowship)* [1198]
National Iranian American Council Fellowships *(Graduate, Undergraduate/Fellowship)* [7022]
The Seth Okin Good Deeds Scholarships *(Undergraduate/Scholarship)* [8235]
Perkins Coie 1L Political Law Fellowships *(Postgraduate/Fellowship)* [8013]
Pi Gamma Mu Scholarships *(Graduate/Scholarship)* [8133]
Thomas R. Pickering Graduate Foreign Affairs Fellowships *(Graduate, Undergraduate/Fellowship)* [10681]
Pride Foundation Political Leadership Scholarships *(Undergraduate/Scholarship)* [8258]
Betty Rendel Scholarships *(Undergraduate/Scholarship)* [6955]
Bertha and Byron L. Reppert Scholarship Fund *(Undergraduate/Scholarship)* [4252]
Ameen Rihani Scholarship Program *(Undergraduate/Scholarship)* [1599]
Fauneil J. Rinn Scholarships *(Undergraduate/Scholarship)* [8954]
Charles and Ruth Ronin Memorial Scholarships *(Undergraduate/Scholarship)* [8524]
NPELRA Foundation - Anthony C. Russo Scholarships *(Undergraduate/Scholarship)* [7116]
Donald Smiley Prize *(Advanced Professional/Prize, Award, Recognition)* [1908]
The Thomas Soldan Healthy Communities Scholarships *(Undergraduate, Graduate/Scholarship)* [8237]
Special Fund for the Study of Women and Politics *(Graduate, Postdoctorate/Grant)* [1123]
John Streiff Memorial Scholarships *(Undergraduate/Scholarship)* [6055]
Hatton W. Sumners Endowed Undergraduate School Scholarships *(Undergraduate/Scholarship)* [9609]
Hatton W. Sumners Non-Endowed Undergraduate and Graduate Scholarships *(Undergraduate, Graduate/Scholarship)* [9610]
The Ed Tayter Outstanding Citizen Scholarships *(Undergraduate/Scholarship)* [8238]
TCAdvance Scholarships *(Undergraduate/Scholarship)* [9814]
Barbara and Howard Thompson Scholarships *(Undergraduate/Scholarship)* [5515]
The United States Department of State, Bureau of Educational & Cultural Affairs Fellowships *(Graduate/Fellowship)* [1199]
Jill Vickers Prize *(Other/Award)* [1909]
Women In Defense HORIZONS Scholarships *(Graduate, Undergraduate/Scholarship)* [10636]
Urashi Zen Scholarships *(Undergraduate/Scholarship)* [8272]

Portuguese studies (See also Area and ethnic studies)

Luso-American Education Foundation G-1 Grants *(Other/Grant)* [6146]
Luso-American Education Foundation G-2 Grants *(Other/Grant)* [6147]
Luso-American Education Foundation G-3 Grants *(Postgraduate/Grant)* [6148]

Poultry science

Canadian Poultry Research Council Postgraduate Scholarships *(Postgraduate/Scholarship)* [2736]
National Poultry and Food Distributors Association Scholarships *(Undergraduate/Scholarship)* [7102]

Practical nursing (See Nursing)

Pre-Columbian studies
Alexander Graham Bell Canada Graduate Scholarship Program *(Doctorate, Master's/Scholarship)* [3401]
Dumbarton Oaks Fellowships *(Doctorate, Graduate/Fellowship)* [3728]
Dumbarton Oaks Junior Fellowships *(Graduate/Fellowship)* [3729]
Dumbarton Oaks Research Library and Collection Post-Doctoral Teaching Fellowships *(Postdoctorate/Fellowship)* [3738]
Natural Sciences and Engineering Research Council Postgraduate Scholarships *(Doctorate/Scholarship)* [3404]

Preservation
SPOOM Research Grants *(Graduate/Grant)* [9277]

Printing trades and industries
FIRST Operator Certification Awards *(Professional development/Internship)* [4074]
TCAdvance Scholarships *(Undergraduate/Scholarship)* [9814]
Xerox Technical Minority Scholarships *(Graduate, Undergraduate/Scholarship)* [10737]

Printing--History
Katharine Pantzer Fellowships in the British Book Trades *(Other/Fellowship)* [2256]

Printmaking
Gravure Publishing Council Scholarships *(Undergraduate, Graduate/Scholarship)* [4648]
Harry V. Quadracci Memorial Scholarships *(Undergraduate, Graduate/Scholarship)* [4649]

Psychiatry
Associates in Behavioral Health Scholarships *(Graduate/Scholarship)* [8243]
Daland Fellowships in Clinical Investigation *(Doctorate, Postgraduate/Fellowship)* [1079]
Depression and ADHD Fellowships *(Postdoctorate/Fellowship)* [5840]
Epilepsy Foundation Research and Training Fellowships for Clinicians *(Doctorate, Other/Grant)* [3908]
Massachusetts General Hospital Clinical Translational Fellowships at Pfizer *(Advanced Professional/Fellowship)* [6318]
MGH Department of Psychiatry Behavioral Neurology and Neuropsychiatry Fellowships *(Advanced Professional, Professional development/Fellowship)* [6320]
MGH Department of Psychiatry Eating Disorders Summer Research Fellowships *(Advanced Professional, Professional development/Fellowship)* [6321]
MGH Department of Psychiatry Forensic Psychiatry Fellowships *(Professional development/Fellowship)* [6322]
MGH Department of Psychiatry Global Psychiatric Clinical Research Training Program *(Advanced Professional/Fellowship)* [6323]
Partners HealthCare Geriatric Psychiatry Fellowships *(Professional development/Fellowship)* [6324]
SOBP Travel Fellowship Award-Early Career Investigator(International) *(Postdoctorate/Award)* [9090]

Psychology
AED Student Early Career Investigator Travel Fellowships *(Undergraduate, Graduate, Postdoctorate, Postgraduate/Fellowship)* [32]
AED Student Research Grants *(Undergraduate, Graduate, Postgraduate/Grant)* [33]
Gordon Allport Intergroup Relations Prize *(Professional development/Monetary, Award)* [9289]
American Psychoanalytic Association Fellowships *(Doctorate, Postdoctorate, Other/Fellowship)* [1129]
American Psychology-Law Society Dissertation Awards *(Graduate/Award)* [1155]
American Psychology-Law Society Early Career Professional Grants-In-Aid *(Other/Grant)* [1156]
American Psychology-Law Society Student Grants-In-Aid *(Graduate/Grant)* [1157]
Annette Urso Rickel Foundation Dissertation Award for Public Policy *(Graduate/Scholarship)* [1137]
APA Society Convention Research Awards *(Undergraduate, Graduate/Award)* [8317]
APAGS-CLGBTC Grant Program *(Graduate/Grant)* [1131]
APF/COGDOP Graduate Research Scholarships *(Doctorate, Graduate/Scholarship)* [1138]
APF High School Psychology Teacher Network Grants *(Advanced Professional, Professional development/Grant)* [1139]
APF Professional Development Awards for High School Psychology Teachers *(Advanced Professional, Professional development/Grant)* [1140]
APF Visionary Grants *(Graduate/Grant)* [1141]
APS Society Convention Research Awards *(Undergraduate, Graduate/Award)* [8318]
APS Student Research Award *(Undergraduate, Graduate/Award)* [2045]
Army Health Professions Scholarships Program *(Professional development/Scholarship)* [9878]
Tara Lynn Arnold Scholarships *(Undergraduate/Scholarship)* [9562]
ASA Minority Fellowship Program (ASA MFP) *(Graduate, Doctorate, Professional development/Fellowship)* [1445]
Associated Women for Pepperdine Scholarships *(Undergraduate/Scholarship)* [7962]
Associates in Behavioral Health Scholarships *(Graduate/Scholarship)* [8243]
Association for Psychological Science Student Grants (APS) *(Graduate, Undergraduate/Grant)* [2046]
Dr. Jon Baker Memorial Scholarship *(Graduate, Undergraduate/Scholarship)* [10050]
Raymond B. Bauer Research Award *(Professional development/Grant)* [6479]
Benton-Meier Neuropsychology Graduate Scholarships *(Graduate/Scholarship)* [1142]
William and Dorothy Bevan Scholarship *(Graduate, Master's, Doctorate/Scholarship)* [1143]
Bisexual Foundation Scholarships *(Graduate/Scholarship)* [9284]
Ellin Bloch and Pierre Ritchie Diversity Dissertation Grant *(Graduate/Grant)* [1132]
CPA Foundation Minority Scholarships *(Graduate/Scholarship)* [2471]
Meredith P. Crawford Fellowships in I/O Psychology *(Doctorate/Fellowship)* [4990]
The Steve Duckett Local Conservation Scholarships *(Undergraduate, Postgraduate/Scholarship)* [8232]
Early Childhood Educators Scholarship Program *(Undergraduate/Scholarship)* [6342]
Epilepsy Foundation Pre-doctoral Research Training Fellowships *(Graduate/Fellowship)* [3906]
ETS Postdoctoral Fellowships *(Postdoctorate/Fellowship)* [3806]
Nancy B. Forest and L. Michael Honaker Master's Grant for Research in Psychology *(Graduate/Grant)* [1133]
Violet and Cyril Franks Scholarship *(Graduate/Scholarship)* [1144]
Garikian Scholarship Fund *(Undergraduate/Scholarship)* [1694]
Grant Assistance Program for Autism Professionals - College Programs *(Undergraduate/Grant)* [7650]
Grant Assistance Program for Autism Professionals - Doctoral Programs *(Doctorate/Grant)* [7651]
Grant Assistance Program for Autism Professionals - Institutional Standards *(Undergraduate, Graduate/Grant)* [7652]
Grant Assistance Program for Autism Professionals - Masters Programs *(Master's/Grant)* [7653]
Grant Assistance Program for Autism Professionals - Professional Certification Programs *(Undergraduate, Professional development/Grant)* [7654]
Grant Assistance Program for Autism Professionals - Retroactive Assistance *(Advanced Professional, Professional development/Grant)* [7655]
Grant Assistance Program for Autism Professionals - Undergraduate Programs *(Undergraduate/Grant)* [7656]
Harold Gulliksen Psychometric Research Fellowships *(Doctorate, Graduate/Fellowship)* [3807]
Lee Hakel Graduate Student Scholarship *(Doctorate/Scholarship)* [9152]
William C. Howell Scholarship *(Graduate, Master's, Doctorate/Scholarship)* [1145]
Peter and Malina James and Dr. Louis P. James Legacy Scholarships *(Graduate, Master's, Doctorate/Scholarship)* [1146]
Sylvia Taylor Johnson Fellowships in Educational Measurement *(Doctorate/Fellowship)* [3808]
Leslie W. Joyce and Paul W. Thayer Graduate Fellowship in I-O Psychology *(Doctorate/Fellowship)* [9153]
The Michael Kiely Strong Roots Scholarships *(Undergraduate/Scholarship)* [8233]
Chris L. Kleinke Scholarship *(Graduate/Scholarship)* [10064]
Elizabeth Munsterberg Koppitz Child Psychology Graduate Fellowships *(Graduate, Doctorate/Fellowship)* [1147]
Lemelson Student Fellowships *(Graduate/Award)* [9282]
Harry and Miriam Levinson Scholarship *(Graduate, Master's, Doctorate/Scholarship)* [1148]
Malyon-Smith Scholarship Award *(Graduate/Scholarship)* [9285]
Massachusetts General Hospital/Harvard Medical School Internships *(Doctorate/Internship)* [6319]
Ruth G. and Joseph D. Matarazzo Scholarship *(Graduate, Master's, Doctorate/Scholarship)* [1149]
Clara Mayo Grants Program *(Graduate/Grant)* [9290]
The Tatiana Mendez Future Resources Scholarships *(Undergraduate/Scholarship)* [8234]
Scott Mesh Honorary Grant for Research in Psychology *(Graduate/Grant)* [1134]
NAJA Scholarships *(Graduate/Scholarship)* [6760]
NASP-ERT Minority Scholarships for Graduate Training in School Psychology *(Graduate/Scholarship)* [6780]
NJPA Foundation Scholarship for Research on Diversity Issues *(Graduate/Scholarship)* [7329]
The Seth Okin Good Deeds Scholarships *(Undergraduate/Scholarship)* [8235]
Pi Gamma Mu Scholarships *(Graduate/Scholarship)* [8133]
David Pilon Scholarships for Training in Professional Psychology *(Graduate/Scholarship)* [1135]
Wayne F. Placek Grants *(Graduate, Doctorate/Grant)* [1150]
Psychology Association of Saskatchewan Student Scholarships - Academic Achievement *(Master's, Doctorate/Scholarship)* [8320]
Psychology Association of Saskatchewan Student Scholarships - Research Based *(Master's, Doctorate/Scholarship)* [8321]
Clarence J. Rosecrans Scholarship *(Graduate, Master's, Doctorate/Scholarship)* [1151]
Esther Katz Rosen Fund Grants *(Graduate, Doctorate/Grant)* [1152]
Saleem Shah Early Career Award *(Doctorate/Recognition)* [1158]
The Thomas Soldan Healthy Communities Scholarships *(Undergraduate, Graduate/Scholarship)* [8237]
Charles and Carol Spielberger Scholarships *(Graduate, Master's, Doctorate/Scholarship)* [1153]
SPSSI Grants-In-Aid Program *(Graduate, Postdoctorate/Grant)* [9287]
Taylor Statten Memorial Fellowships *(Graduate/Scholarship)* [10295]
The Ed Tayter Outstanding Citizen Scholarships *(Undergraduate/Scholarship)* [8238]
Mary L. Tenopyr Graduate Student Scholarships *(Doctorate/Scholarship)* [9154]

Public administration

Marvin A. Andrews Scholarships/Internships (Graduate/Internship, Scholarship) [1630]
APSA Congressional Fellowship for Communications Scholars and Journalists (Advanced Professional, Professional development/Fellowship) [1108]
Association of Government Accountants Undergraduate/Graduate Scholarships for Community Service Accomplishments (Graduate, Undergraduate/Scholarship) [1971]
Association of Government Accountants Undergraduate/Graduate Scholarships for Full-time study (Graduate, Undergraduate/Scholarship) [1972]
Association of Government Accountants Undergraduate/Graduate Scholarships for Part-time study (Graduate, Undergraduate/Scholarship) [1973]
James M. Banovetz Illinois Local Government Fellowships (Graduate, Master's/Fellowship) [5059]
CHCI Graduate Fellowships (Graduate/Fellowship) [3352]
CHCI Public Policy Fellowships (Professional development/Fellowship) [3353]
CIGNA Healthcare Graduate Scholarships (Graduate/Scholarship) [6957]
CIGNA Healthcare Undergraduate Scholarships (Undergraduate/Scholarship) [6958]
Charles A. Esser Memorial Scholarships (Graduate/Scholarship) [1631]
Fellowship on Women & Public Policy (Graduate/Fellowship) [10102]
GFOA Minorities in Government Finance Scholarship (Graduate, Undergraduate/Scholarship) [4502]
GLAAD Communications/PR Internships - New York (Undergraduate, Graduate/Internship) [4434]
Jane R. Glaser Scholarships (Undergraduate/Scholarship) [1476]
Goya Scholarships (Graduate/Scholarship) [8852]
Guzkowski Family Scholarships (Undergraduate/Scholarship) [8479]
HAESF Professional Internship Program (Doctorate/Internship) [5009]
HAESF Senior Leaders and Scholars Fellowships (Other/Fellowship) [5010]
IPMA-HR Graduate Study Fellowships (Graduate, Master's/Fellowship) [5376]
Kathleen Kelly Undergraduate Scholarship Award (Undergraduate/Scholarship) [8374]
Michael Koizumi APWA Scholarships (Undergraduate/Scholarship, Internship) [7263]
Dr. Julianne Malveaux Scholarships (Undergraduate/Scholarship) [6762]
Christine Mirzayan Science and Technology Policy Graduate Fellowships (Graduate/Fellowship) [6679]
George H. Nofer Scholarships for Law and Public Policy (Graduate/Scholarship) [316]
Pi Gamma Mu Scholarships (Graduate/Scholarship) [8133]
Thomas R. Pickering Graduate Foreign Affairs Fellowships (Graduate, Undergraduate/Fellowship) [10681]
Stephen D. Pisinski Memorial Scholarships (Undergraduate/Scholarship) [8376]
Pride Foundation Political Leadership Scholarships (Undergraduate/Scholarship) [8258]
Fauneil J. Rinn Scholarships (Undergraduate/Scholarship) [8954]
NPELRA Foundation - Anthony C. Russo Scholarships (Graduate/Scholarship) [7116]
Thomas J. Stanton, Jr. Scholarships (Graduate/Scholarship) [8853]
Paul A. Volcker Endowment for Public Service Research and Education (Doctorate/Grant) [1116]
Washington City/County Management Association Scholarships (Graduate/Scholarship) [10438]
Gary Yoshimura Scholarships (Undergraduate/Scholarship) [8379]

Public affairs

Americans for Informed Democracy Global Scholar Program (Undergraduate/Scholarship) [1532]
Atkinson Fellowships in Public Policy (Professional development/Fellowship) [2111]
Elaine Atwood Scholarship (Undergraduate/Scholarship) [10049]
Cleveland Executive Fellowships (CEF) (Other/Fellowship) [3051]
Coro Fellows Program in Public Affairs (Postgraduate/Fellowship) [3423]
Jennifer Curtis Byler Scholarships (Undergraduate/Scholarship) [7188]
Bryce Harlow Fellowship Program (Graduate/Fellowship) [4721]
MPAC-DC Graduate Policy Fellowships (Graduate/Fellowship) [6630]
Open Society Presidential Fellowships (Advanced Professional/Fellowship) [7663]
Clifford Roberts Graduate Fellowships (Doctorate/Fellowship) [4415]
William C. Rogers Scholarships (Undergraduate/Scholarship) [4389]
Stanley M. Schoenfeld Memorial Scholarship (Postgraduate/Scholarship) [7363]
Theodore C. Sorensen Research Fellowships (Professional development/Fellowship) [5605]
Kirk Sutlive Scholarships (Undergraduate/Scholarship) [4390]
TCAdvance Scholarships (Undergraduate/Scholarship) [9814]
UAA GCI, Inc. Scholarship (Undergraduate/Scholarship) [10080]

Public health

AAHD Scholarships (Graduate, Undergraduate/Scholarship) [502]
AAI Public Policy Fellows Program (PPFP) (Doctorate, Postdoctorate/Fellowship) [507]
ALA Allergic Respiratory Diseases Research Award (Doctorate/Grant) [969]
American Lung Association Biomedical Research Grants (Doctorate/Grant) [970]
American Lung Association Clinical Patient Care Research Grants (Doctorate/Grant) [971]
American Lung Association Dalsemer Research Grants (Doctorate/Grant) [972]
American Lung Association DeSousa Awards (Doctorate/Grant) [973]
American Lung Association Lung Cancer Discovery Awards (Doctorate/Grant) [974]
American Lung Association Senior Research Training Fellowships (Doctorate/Fellowship) [975]
American Lung Association Social-Behavioral Research Grants (Doctorate/Grant) [976]
APHL Emerging Infectious Diseases Fellowships (Doctorate/Fellowship) [2048]
Arkansas Public Health Association Scholarships (Undergraduate/Scholarship) [1659]
Elizabeth and Sherman Asche Memorial Scholarships (Graduate, Undergraduate/Scholarship) [1832]
ASPPH/CDC Public Health Fellowship Program (Doctorate, Graduate/Fellowship) [2060]
ASPPH/EPA Environmental Health Fellowship Program (Doctorate, Postdoctorate/Fellowship) [2061]
ASPPH/NHTSA Public Health Fellowship Program (Postdoctorate/Fellowship) [2062]
ASPPH Public Health Policy Fellowship Program (Doctorate, Postdoctorate/Fellowship) [2063]
ASPPH Public Health Preparedness Fellowship Program (Postdoctorate/Fellowship) [2064]
AWMA Louisiana Section Scholarships (Undergraduate, Graduate/Scholarship) [147]
Max Bell Senior Fellow Grants (Advanced Professional/Grant) [2219]
CANFIT Nutrition, Physical Education and Culinary Arts Scholarships (Graduate, Undergraduate/Scholarship) [3167]
Malcolm U. Dantzler Scholarships (Other/Scholarship) [9363]
Frank L. Dautriel Memorial Scholarships for Graduates (Graduate/Scholarship) [6116]
Frank L. Dautriel Memorial Scholarships for Undergraduates (Undergraduate/Scholarship) [6117]
Fahs-Beck Fund for Research and Experimentation - Doctoral Dissertation Grants (Doctorate/Grant) [7347]
Fahs-Beck Fund for Research and Experimentation - Postdoctoral Grants (Postdoctorate/Grant) [7348]
Florida Public Health Association Public Health Graduate Scholarships (Graduate/Scholarship) [4108]
Florida Public Health Association Public Health Undergraduate Scholarships (Undergraduate/Scholarship) [4109]
The Gates Millennium Scholars (Undergraduate/Scholarship) [4903]
Great Lakes Commission Sea Grant Fellowships (Graduate/Scholarship) [4656]
GWS Scholarships (Undergraduate, Graduate/Scholarship) [145]
HAESF Professional Internship Program (Doctorate/Internship) [5009]
HRSA Scholarships for Disadvantaged Students (Undergraduate/Scholarship) [9923]
Institute for Health Metrics and Evaluation Post Bachelor Fellowships (Graduate/Fellowship) [5180]
Institute for Health Metrics and Evaluation Post Graduate Fellowships (Doctorate, Postdoctorate/Fellowship) [5181]
Jewish Federation Academic Scholarships (Graduate, Undergraduate/Scholarship) [5598]
Johns Hopkins Medicine International Emergency and Public Health Fellowships (Graduate/Fellowship) [5610]
LPHA Scholarships (Graduate, Undergraduate/Scholarship) [6122]
Lung Health Dissertation Grants (Graduate/Grant) [977]
National Biosafety and Biocontainment Training Program Fellowships (Graduate, Postgraduate/Fellowship) [6811]
Catherine E. Philbin Scholarships (Undergraduate, Graduate/Scholarship) [4356]
PhRMA Foundation Health Outcomes Post Doctoral Fellowships (Postdoctorate/Fellowship) [8034]
PhRMA Foundation Health Outcomes Pre Doctoral Fellowships (Doctorate/Fellowship) [8035]
PhRMA Foundation Health Outcomes Research Starter Grants (Doctorate/Grant) [8036]
PhRMA Foundation Health Outcomes Sabbatical Fellowships (Postdoctorate/Fellowship) [8037]
ASPPH/CDC Allan Rosenfield Global Health Fellowship Program (Postdoctorate, Postgraduate/Fellowship) [2065]
Lucille and Edward R. Roybal Foundation Public Health Scholarships (Graduate, Undergraduate/Scholarship) [8654]
South Carolina Public Health Association Scholarships (Undergraduate/Scholarship) [9364]
Louis Stokes Health Scholars Program (Undergraduate/Scholarship) [3349]
UAB Health Policy Fellowship (Graduate, Master's, Doctorate/Scholarship) [10002]

Public relations (See also Advertising)

Rick Brewer Scholarships (Undergraduate/Scholarship) [10218]
Louis M. Connor Jr. Scholarships (Undergraduate/Scholarship) [10221]
GLAAD Spanish-Language and Latino Media Internships - Los Angeles (Undergraduate, Graduate/Internship) [4436]
HACU/NASCAR Scholarships (Graduate, Undergraduate/Scholarship) [4888]
International Foodservice Editorial Council Scholarships (Graduate, Undergraduate/Scholarship) [5331]
IPR Pathfinder Award (Advanced Professional/Recognition, Grant) [5212]
Harriet Irsay Scholarships (Graduate, Undergraduate/Scholarship) [927]
Ketchum Excellence in Public Relations Research Award (Graduate/Fellowship, Internship) [5213]
Jessica King Scholarships (Other/Scholarship) [3490]
The Lagrant Foundation - Graduate Students Schol-

arships *(Graduate/Scholarship)* [5900]
The Lagrant Foundation - Undergraduate Students Scholarships *(Undergraduate/Scholarship)* [5901]
MillerCoors National Scholarships *(Undergraduate/Scholarship)* [69]
New York Women in Communications, Inc. Foundation Scholarships *(Graduate, Undergraduate/Scholarship)* [7406]
Stephen D. Pisinski Memorial Scholarships *(Undergraduate/Scholarship)* [8376]
Betsy Plank/PRSSA Scholarships *(Undergraduate/Scholarship)* [8377]
PRSA Diversity Multicultural Scholarships *(Undergraduate/Scholarship)* [8378]
William C. Rogers Scholarships *(Undergraduate/Scholarship)* [4389]
Richard J. Roth Journalism Fellowships *(Graduate/Fellowship)* [7369]
Jim Springer Memorial Scholarships *(Undergraduate/Scholarship)* [3110]
Jay A. Strassberg Memorial Scholarships *(Undergraduate/Scholarship)* [2517]
Kirk Sutlive Scholarships *(Undergraduate/Scholarship)* [4390]
TCAdvance Scholarships *(Undergraduate/Scholarship)* [9814]
Gary Yoshimura Scholarships *(Undergraduate/Scholarship)* [8379]

Public service

ARS of Eastern USA Lazarian Graduate Scholarship *(Master's, Doctorate/Scholarship)* [1680]
CAPAL Public Service Scholarships *(Graduate, Undergraduate/Scholarship)* [3341]
CHCI Graduate Fellowships *(Graduate/Fellowship)* [3352]
CHCI Public Policy Fellowships *(Professional development/Fellowship)* [3353]
Willis W. and Ethel M. Clark Foundation Fellowships *(Graduate/Fellowship)* [3049]
Alice Yuriko Endo Memorial Scholarships *(Undergraduate/Scholarship)* [5549]
James Mackenzie Fallows Scholarships Honoring William Cunningham *(Undergraduate/Scholarship)* [8474]
Walter Moran Farmer Scholarships *(Juris Doctorate/Scholarship)* [10475]
John E. Fenton, Jr. Public Service Awards *(Postgraduate/Fellowship)* [8435]
IGS John Gardner Fellowship *(Undergraduate/Fellowship)* [10108]
Caroline L. Gross Fellowships *(Professional development/Fellowship)* [7304]
Harry S. Truman Scholarships *(Postgraduate/Scholarship)* [9803]
WLALA Fran Kandel Public Interest Grants *(Postgraduate/Grant)* [10646]
Lazarian Graduate Scholarships *(Graduate/Scholarship)* [1678]
Lewis-Clark State College Governor's Cup Scholarships *(Undergraduate/Scholarship)* [6039]
CH2M - Willie T. Loud Scholarships *(Undergraduate, Graduate/Scholarship)* [6959]
Al Maurer Awards *(Undergraduate, Graduate, Advanced Professional/Award, Scholarship)* [3790]
NUF Fellowships *(Graduate, Postgraduate, Other/Fellowship)* [7209]
Pignalberi Public Policy Scholarship *(Graduate/Scholarship)* [10068]
Rotary Public Safety Scholarships *(Undergraduate/Scholarship)* [4212]
Sheila Tarr-Smith Memorial Scholarships *(Undergraduate/Scholarship)* [8368]
UAA College of Business and Public Policy Scholarships *(Graduate, Undergraduate/Scholarship)* [10078]
Undergraduate Session Assistants Program *(Undergraduate/Other)* [7370]
Webster Society Fellowships *(Juris Doctorate/Scholarship)* [10478]
Richard A. Wiebe Public Service Fellowships *(Graduate/Fellowship)* [7371]

Publishing

College Art Association Wyeth Publication Grants *(Other/Grant)* [3119]
Malcolm and Mildred Freidberg Fellowships *(Professional development/Fellowship)* [6327]
Durwood McAlister Scholarships *(Undergraduate/Scholarship)* [4387]
Morris Newspaper Corp. Scholarships *(Undergraduate/Scholarship)* [4388]
WNBA Eastman Grants *(Other/Grant)* [10668]

Quality assurance and control

Richard A. Freund International Scholarships *(Graduate/Scholarship)* [1389]
Ellis R. Ott Scholarships *(Graduate, Master's/Scholarship)* [1390]

Radio and television

American Radio Relay League Louisiana Memorial Scholarships *(Undergraduate/Scholarship)* [1721]
Earl I. Anderson Scholarships *(Undergraduate/Scholarship)* [1722]
ARRL Foundation General Fund Scholarships *(Undergraduate/Scholarship)* [1723]
ARRL Foundation PHD Scholarships *(Undergraduate/Scholarship)* [1724]
ARRLF Mississippi Scholarships *(Undergraduate/Scholarship)* [1725]
Richard W. Bendicksen Memorial Scholarships *(Undergraduate/Scholarship)* [1726]
William Bennett W7PHO Memorial Scholarships *(Undergraduate/Scholarship)* [1727]
Henry Broughton, K2AE Memorial Scholarships *(Undergraduate/Scholarship)* [1728]
Mary Lou Brown Scholarships *(Undergraduate/Scholarship)* [1729]
L.B. Cebik, W4RNL, and Jean Cebik, N4TZP, Memorial Scholarships *(Undergraduate/Scholarship)* [1730]
Central Arizona DX Association Scholarships *(Undergraduate/Scholarship)* [1731]
Challenge Met Scholarships *(Undergraduate/Scholarship)* [1732]
Chicago FM Club Scholarships *(Undergraduate/Scholarship)* [1733]
Greg Clerk Awards *(Advanced Professional, Professional development/Award)* [4118]
Tom and Judith Comstock Scholarships *(Undergraduate/Scholarship)* [1734]
Irving W. Cook WA0CGS Scholarships *(Undergraduate/Scholarship)* [1735]
Charles Clarke Cordle Memorial Scholarships *(Undergraduate/Scholarship)* [1736]
Dayton Amateur Radio Association Scholarships *(Undergraduate/Scholarship)* [1737]
Charles N. Fisher Memorial Scholarships *(Undergraduate/Scholarship)* [1738]
Allison E. Fisher Scholarships *(Undergraduate, Graduate/Scholarship)* [4068]
William R. Goldfarb Memorial Scholarships *(Undergraduate/Scholarship)* [1739]
Paul and Helen L. Grauer Scholarships *(Undergraduate/Scholarship)* [1740]
K2TEO Martin J. Green, Sr. Memorial Scholarships *(Undergraduate/Scholarship)* [1741]
Perry F. Hadlock Memorial Scholarships *(Undergraduate/Scholarship)* [1742]
Albert H. Hix, W8AH Memorial Scholarships *(Undergraduate/Scholarship)* [1743]
Seth Horen, K1LOM Memorial Scholarships *(Undergraduate/Scholarship)* [1744]
Ken Kashiwahara Scholarships *(Undergraduate/Scholarship)* [8399]
Dr. James L. Lawson Memorial Scholarships *(Undergraduate/Scholarship)* [1745]
MANAA Media Scholarships *(Graduate, Undergraduate/Scholarship)* [6382]
Fred R. McDaniel Memorial Scholarships *(Undergraduate/Scholarship)* [1746]
Edmond A. Metzger Scholarships *(Undergraduate/Scholarship)* [1747]
Muddy Waters Scholarships *(Undergraduate/Scholarship)* [2316]
New England FEMARA Scholarships *(Undergraduate/Scholarship)* [1748]
Northern California DX Foundation Scholarships *(Undergraduate/Scholarship)* [1749]
OAS Scholarships for Professional Development - Radio Spectrum Monitoring Techniques and Procedures *(Professional development/Scholarship)* [7724]
Ray, NORP and Katie, WOKTE Pautz Scholarships *(Undergraduate/Scholarship)* [1750]
Peoria Area Amateur Radio Club Scholarships *(Undergraduate/Scholarship)* [1751]
Thomas W. Porter, W8KYZ Scholarships Honoring Michael Daugherty, W8LSE *(Undergraduate/Scholarship)* [1752]
Quarter Century Wireless Association Scholarships *(Undergraduate/Scholarship)* [8390]
Donald Riebhoff Memorial Scholarships *(Undergraduate/Scholarship)* [1753]
Mister Rogers Memorial Scholarship *(Graduate, Master's, Doctorate/Scholarship)* [47]
RTDNF Scholarships *(Undergraduate, Graduate/Scholarship)* [8414]
IRARC Memorial Joseph P. Rubino WA4MMD Scholarships *(Undergraduate/Scholarship)* [1754]
The Bill, W2ONV, and Ann Salerno Memorial Scholarship *(Undergraduate/Scholarship)* [1755]
Eugene Gene Sallee, W4YFR Memorial Scholarships *(Undergraduate/Scholarship)* [1756]
Abe Schechter Graduate Scholarships *(Graduate/Scholarship)* [8400]
Scholarships of the Morris Radio Club of New Jersey *(Undergraduate/Scholarship)* [1757]
Six Meter Club of Chicago Scholarships *(Undergraduate/Scholarship)* [1758]
Zachary Taylor Stevens Memorial Scholarships *(Undergraduate/Scholarship)* [1759]
Carole J. Streeter, KB9JBR Scholarships *(Undergraduate/Scholarship)* [1760]
Norman E. Strohmeier, W2VRS Memorial Scholarships *(Undergraduate/Scholarship)* [1761]
Gary Wagner, K3OMI Scholarships *(Undergraduate/Scholarship)* [1762]
The L. Phil and Alice J. Wicker Scholarship *(Undergraduate/Scholarship)* [1763]
Yankee Clipper Contest Club, Inc. Youth Scholarships *(Undergraduate/Scholarship)* [1764]
Yasme Foundation Scholarships *(Undergraduate/Scholarship)* [1765]

Radiology

American Roentgen Ray Society Scholarships *(Other/Scholarship)* [1221]
Anna Ames Clinical Excellence Student Grants *(Undergraduate/Grant)* [2481]
Richard J. Burk, Jr. Fellowships *(Graduate/Fellowship)* [4808]
Robert Gardner Memorial Fellowships *(Graduate/Fellowship)* [4809]
Jerman-Cahoon Student Scholarship *(Undergraduate/Scholarship)* [1397]
Robert S. Landauer, Sr. Memorial Fellowships *(Graduate/Fellowship)* [4810]
Ruth McMillan Student Grants *(Undergraduate/Grant)* [2482]
Burton J. Moyer Memorial Fellowships *(Graduate/Fellowship)* [4811]
Royce Osborn Minority Scholarship *(Undergraduate/Scholarship)* [1398]
Professional Research Grants *(Professional development/Grant)* [1399]
R&E Foundation Education Scholarships *(Graduate, Other/Scholarship)* [8416]
Research Resident/Fellow Grants *(Professional development/Grant)* [8417]
RSNA/AUR/APDR/SCARD Radiology Education Research Development Grant *(Professional development/Grant)* [8418]
RSNA Education Scholar Grant *(Professional development/Grant)* [8419]
RSNA Research Scholar Grants *(Professional development/Grant)* [8420]
RSNA Research Seed Grants *(Professional development/Grant)* [8421]
Siemens Clinical Advancement Scholarship *(Under-

graduate, Master's/Scholarship) [1400]
Society for Pediatric Radiology Research Fellows (Graduate, Other/Fellowship) [9243]
Society for Pediatric Radiology Seed Grants (Graduate, Other/Grant) [9244]
J. Newell Stannard Fellowships (Graduate/Fellowship) [4812]
Superior District Legislative Mentoring Student Grants RT to DC (Undergraduate/Grant) [2484]
Superior District Legislative Mentoring Student Grants (Undergraduate/Grant) [2483]
Varian Radiation Therapy Advancement Scholarship (Undergraduate, Master's, Doctorate/Scholarship) [1401]

Reading

Cengage Travel Award for Teachers of Reading at a Community College (Professional development/Monetary) [3123]
Jeanne S. Chall Research Fellowship (Doctorate, Graduate/Fellowship) [5355]
Malcolm and Mildred Freidberg Fellowships (Professional development/Fellowship) [6327]
Elva Knight Research Grants (Professional development/Grant) [5356]
Helen M. Robinson Grants (Doctorate/Award, Monetary, Grant) [5357]
Steven A. Stahl Research Grants (Graduate/Grant) [5358]

Real estate

Appraisal Institute Education Trust Undergraduate Scholarships (Undergraduate/Scholarship) [1596]
George M. Brooker, CPM Diversity Collegiate Scholarship (Graduate, Undergraduate/Scholarship) [5215]
Connecticut Mortgage Bankers Social Affairs Committee Scholarships (Undergraduate/Scholarship) [4745]
Rick Crane Group Real Estate Scholarship Fund (Undergraduate/Scholarship) [6023]
Mary Lou Fiala Fellowships (Other/Fellowship) [5305]
Donald M. Furbush Professional Development Grants (Other/Grant) [5216]
Graduate Realtor Institute Scholarships (Graduate/Scholarship) [5817]
Charles Grossman Graduate Scholarships (Graduate/Scholarship) [5306]
HomeCity Real Estate Scholarships (Undergraduate/Scholarship) [4925]
Michigan Realtors Scholarship Trust (Graduate, Undergraduate/Scholarship) [6461]
Pension Real Estate Association Scholarships (Undergraduate, Graduate/Scholarship) [7952]
Paul H. Rittle Sr. Professional Development Grants (Other/Grant) [5217]
Schurgin Family Foundation Scholarships (Undergraduate/Scholarship) [5308]

Recreational therapy

The Dave Family "Humor Studies" Scholarships (Undergraduate, Graduate/Scholarship) [1848]
Ed Dunkelblau Scholarships (All/Scholarship, Award) [1849]
The Margie Klein "Paper Plate" Scholarships (Undergraduate/Scholarship) [1850]
Lenny Ravich "Shalom" Scholarships (Advanced Professional/Scholarship) [1851]
Patty Wooten Scholarships (Professional development/Scholarship, Award, Recognition) [1852]

Rehabilitation, Physical/Psychological

Alabama ARN Scholarship (Professional development/Scholarship) [2054]
Raymond B. Bauer Research Award (Professional development/Grant) [6479]
Rudolph Dillman Memorial Scholarships (Graduate, Undergraduate/Scholarship) [820]
Delta Gamma Foundation Florence Margaret Harvey Memorial Scholarships (Graduate, Undergraduate/Scholarship) [822]
Mary Switzer Research Fellowships - Distinguished Fellowships (Doctorate/Fellowship) [9896]
Mary Switzer Research Fellowships - Merit Fellowships (Professional development/Fellowship) [9897]

Religion

The Ambrose-Ramsey Trust (Undergraduate/Scholarship) [7812]
ARCE Funded Fellowships (Doctorate, Postdoctorate/Fellowship) [1195]
ARCE Research Associates Fellowships (Doctorate, Postdoctorate, Professional development/Fellowship) [1196]
Martha and Robert Atherton Ministerial Scholarships (Master's/Scholarship) [9831]
Lewis B. Barber Memorial Scholarships (Undergraduate/Scholarship) [9419]
TCDA Carroll Barnes Student Scholarships (Undergraduate/Scholarship) [668]
Rosalie Bentzinger Scholarships (Doctorate/Scholarship) [9849]
Olympia Brown and Max Kapp Awards (Master's/Scholarship) [9832]
Pamfil and Maria Bujea Family Orthodox Christian Seminarian Scholarships (Undergraduate/Scholarship) [1225]
Calihan Academic Fellowships (Graduate, Professional development/Fellowship, Grant) [56]
Calihan Travel Grants (Graduate/Grant) [57]
Chautauqua Scholarships Program (Undergraduate/Scholarship) [5367]
Richard D. and Sheppard R. Cooke Memorial Scholarships (Graduate/Scholarship) [4695]
CSBS Student Prize Competition (Graduate/Prize) [2744]
CSF Graduate Fellowships (Graduate/Fellowship) [2936]
CTRF Scholarships for Graduate Study in Transportation (Graduate/Scholarship) [2764]
David Eaton Scholarships (Master's/Scholarship) [9835]
Doris W. Frey Memorial Scholarships (Undergraduate, Graduate/Scholarship) [9430]
FTE Dissertation Fellowships (Graduate, Doctorate/Fellowship) [4153]
FTE Doctoral Fellowships (Doctorate, Graduate/Fellowship) [4154]
FTE North American Doctoral Fellowships (Doctorate, Graduate/Fellowship) [4155]
TCDA Bill Gorham Student Scholarships (Undergraduate/Scholarship) [670]
Joseph H. Fichter Research Grants (Other/Grant) [2071]
Journey Toward Ordained Ministry Scholarships (Undergraduate, Graduate/Scholarship) [9854]
KCC-JEE Graduate Fellowships (Graduate/Fellowship) [5855]
David B. Larson Fellowships in Health and Spirituality (Doctorate/Fellowship) [5847]
Molly McKay Scholarships (Undergraduate/Scholarship) [10241]
William F. Miles Scholarships (Undergraduate/Scholarship) [4702]
Novak Awards (Doctorate/Monetary) [58]
Peale Scholarship Grant (Professional development/Scholarship) [8058]
Margaret E. Phillips Scholarships (Undergraduate/Scholarship) [10305]
David Pohl Scholarships (Master's/Scholarship) [9836]
Roy H. Pollack Scholarships (Graduate, Master's/Scholarship) [9837]
Robert J. McNamara Student Paper Awards (Graduate/Award) [2072]
Samuel Robinson Awards (Undergraduate/Award) [8219]
John M. and Mary A. Shanley Memorial Scholarships (Undergraduate, Graduate/Scholarship) [9448]
Hy Smith Endowment Fund (Undergraduate/Scholarship) [4704]
Richard S. Smith Scholarships (Undergraduate/Scholarship) [9858]
Iwalani Carpenter Sowa Scholarships (Graduate/Scholarship) [7919]
IRFI Dr. Mubin I. Syed Scholarship and Mohtarama Afshan J. Syed Scholarship (Undergraduate/Scholarship) [5482]
The Tabat Scholarship Fund (Graduate/Scholarship) [4005]
TCDA Gandy Ink Professional Scholarships (Professional development/Scholarship) [672]
TCDA General Fund Scholarships (Undergraduate/Scholarship) [673]
TCDA Past Presidents Student Scholarships (Undergraduate/Scholarship) [674]
Rev. Chuck and Nancy Thomas Scholarships (Professional development/Scholarship) [9842]
Von Ogden Vogt Scholarships (Master's/Scholarship) [9843]
TCDA Cloys Webb Student Scholarships (Undergraduate/Scholarship) [675]
Wexner Graduate Fellowships/Davidson Scholars (Graduate/Fellowship) [10545]

Religious education (See Education, Religious)

Remote sensing

Robert N. Colwell Memorial Fellowships (Doctorate, Graduate/Fellowship) [1803]
ERDAS Internship (Graduate/Internship, Award) [1804]
William A. Fischer Memorial Scholarships (Graduate/Scholarship) [1805]
Ta Liang Memorial Awards (Graduate/Grant, Award) [1806]
Francis H. Moffitt Memorial Scholarships (Graduate, Undergraduate/Scholarship) [1807]
NERL Postdoctoral Research Program (Postdoctorate, Advanced Professional, Professional development/Fellowship) [9935]

Renaissance studies

DSA Dante Prizes (Undergraduate/Prize, Monetary) [3524]
Charles Hall Grandgent Awards (Graduate/Award, Monetary) [3525]

Resource management

American Society of Military Comptrollers National Scholarship Program (Undergraduate/Scholarship) [1375]
Everglades Foundation Fellowship (Graduate, Doctorate, Master's/Fellowship) [3931]
Everglades Foundation Internship (Postgraduate, Postdoctorate/Internship) [3932]
Everglades Foundation Scholarships (Graduate, Master's, Doctorate/Scholarship) [3933]
Susan R. Meisinger Fellowship for Graduate Study in HR (Graduate, Master's, Advanced Professional/Fellowship) [9146]

Respiratory therapy

Advance Degree and Clinical Research Training Grants in Alpha-1 Antitrypsin Deficiency (Master's/Grant) [1208]
Parker B. Francis Respiratory Research Grants (Advanced Professional, Professional development/Grant) [1211]
JustNebulizers.com Respiratory Care Scholarships (Undergraduate, Graduate/Scholarship) [5637]
NBRC/AMP H. Frederic Helmholz, Jr., MD Educational Research Funds (Master's, Doctorate/Grant) [1213]

Rheumatology (See also Arthritis)

ASPIRE Rheumatology and Dermatology Research Awards (Postdoctorate/Award) [8023]
Winterhoff Scholarships (Undergraduate, Graduate/Scholarship) [1774]

Field of Study Index

SCIENCE

Risk management

FLASH Social Science Scholarships *(Graduate/Scholarship)* [3976]
ISU Gongaware Scholarships *(Undergraduate/Scholarship)* [5121]
William H. McGannon Foundation Scholarships *(Graduate, Undergraduate/Scholarship)* [6364]
Mutual of Omaha Finance Careers Scholarships *(Undergraduate, Graduate/Scholarship)* [105]
NCEA Postdoctoral Research Program *(Postdoctorate, Advanced Professional, Professional development/Fellowship)* [9943]
NRMRL Postdoctoral Research Program *(Postdoctorate, Advanced Professional, Professional development/Fellowship)* [9939]
Risk Management and Insurance Scholarships - University of Calgary *(Undergraduate/Scholarship)* [8768]
Risk Management and Insurance Scholarships *(Undergraduate/Scholarship)* [8767]
Thompson Scholarships for Women in Safety *(Graduate/Scholarship)* [1430]

Roman art (See Art, Roman)

Romanian studies (See Area and ethnic studies)

Russian studies

NEH Fellowships for Senior Scholars *(Doctorate/Fellowship)* [2853]
Prins Foundation Fellowship for Senior Scholars *(Doctorate/Fellowship)* [2854]
Prins Foundation Post-Doctoral and Early Career Fellowship for Emigrating Scholars *(Professional development, Postdoctorate/Fellowship)* [2855]

Science

AAAS Science and Technology Policy Fellowships *(Professional development/Fellowship)* [454]
AFCEA Science, Technology, Engineering and Math Teachers Scholarships *(Graduate/Scholarship, Grant)* [87]
African American Network - Carolinas Scholarship Fund *(Undergraduate/Scholarship)* [4174]
AfterCollege Science Student Scholarships *(Undergraduate, Graduate, Doctorate/Scholarship)* [101]
AfterCollege STEM Inclusion Scholarships *(Undergraduate, Graduate/Scholarship)* [102]
AHETEMS General Scholarships *(Undergraduate, Graduate/Scholarship)* [8888]
AHETEMS Professional Scholarships *(Graduate/Scholarship)* [8889]
Alberta Innovates - Technology Futures Graduate Student Scholarships in Nanotechnology *(Doctorate, Graduate/Scholarship)* [258]
Alberta Innovates - Technology Futures Graduate Student Scholarships in Omics *(Doctorate, Graduate/Scholarship)* [259]
Janet and Horace Allen Scholarships *(Undergraduate/Scholarship)* [266]
American Association of Family and Consumer Sciences Undergraduate Scholarships *(Undergraduate/Scholarship)* [498]
American Philosophical Society Library Resident Research Fellowships *(Doctorate/Fellowship)* [1078]
American Society of Crime Laboratory Directors Scholarships *(Graduate, Undergraduate, Master's, Doctorate/Scholarship)* [1278]
AMSA Graduate Student Research Poster Competition Award *(Undergraduate, Doctorate, Master's/Award)* [987]
A.T. Anderson Memorial Scholarships *(Graduate, Undergraduate/Scholarship)* [889]
Hettie Margaret Anthony Fellowship *(Doctorate/Fellowship)* [5779]
Hettie M. Anthony Fellowships *(Doctorate/Fellowship)* [5787]
Mike Ardaw Scholarships *(Undergraduate/Scholarship)* [10007]
Arlyn Scales Awards for Science and Technology *(Undergraduate/Scholarship)* [3035]
Elizabeth and Sherman Asche Memorial Scholarships *(Graduate, Undergraduate/Scholarship)* [1832]
ASGP Graduate Research Fellowships *(Graduate/Fellowship)* [223]
Asia-Pacific Biomedical Research Foundation Merit Awards *(Postdoctorate/Award)* [9304]
ASM Congressional Science Fellowships *(Postdoctorate/Fellowship)* [1370]
ASMS Research Awards *(Other/Grant)* [1363]
Astronaut Scholarship Foundation Scholarships *(Undergraduate/Scholarship)* [2105]
B&W Y-12 Scholarship Fund *(Undergraduate/Scholarship)* [3752]
Thomas J. Bardos Science Education Awards for Undergraduate Students *(Undergraduate/Award)* [473]
Bechtel Engineering and Science Scholarships *(Undergraduate/Scholarship)* [6278]
Jenny Panitch Beckow Memorial Scholarships Israel *(Graduate/Scholarship)* [5570]
Bill and Nell Biggs Scholarships *(Undergraduate/Scholarship)* [10088]
Rev. Andrew L. Bouwhuis Memorial Scholarship Program *(Graduate/Scholarship)* [2814]
AFCEA San Diego Buck Bragunier Leadership Scholarship *(Undergraduate/Scholarship)* [1667]
Henry Broughton, K2AE Memorial Scholarships *(Undergraduate/Scholarship)* [1728]
Marjorie M. Brown Dissertation Fellowship *(Doctorate/Fellowship)* [5780]
Marjorie M. Brown Fellowship Program *(Postdoctorate/Fellowship)* [5788]
Buick Achievers Scholarship Program *(Undergraduate/Scholarship)* [4359]
Graduate Fellowship Program - Robert M. Burger Fellowships *(Doctorate, Graduate/Fellowship)* [8832]
Camille and Henry Dreyfus Foundation - Senior Scientist Mentor Program *(Professional development/Grant)* [3695]
Canadian Identification Society Essay/Scholarship Awards *(Advanced Professional, Professional development/Prize)* [2664]
Career Awards for Science and Mathematics Teachers *(Other/Award)* [2415]
CERT College Scholarships *(Graduate, Undergraduate/Scholarship)* [3435]
Channabasappa Memorial Scholarships *(Graduate, Doctorate/Scholarship)* [5319]
CHCI Graduate Fellowships *(Graduate/Fellowship)* [3352]
Charlie Chilson Scholarships *(Undergraduate/Scholarship)* [3580]
Cottrell Scholar Awards (CSA) *(Graduate, Advanced Professional, Professional development/Grant)* [8555]
Robert E. Cramer Product Design and Development Scholarship *(Undergraduate/Scholarship)* [9259]
Critical Language Scholarships for Intensive Summer Institutes *(Graduate, Undergraduate/Scholarship)* [1204]
Detroit Section/Robert G. Dailey Scholarship *(Undergraduate/Scholarship)* [9260]
Decommissioning, Decontamination and Reutilization Scholarships *(Graduate, Master's/Scholarship)* [1035]
Delta Gamma Undergraduate Merit-Based Scholarships *(Undergraduate/Scholarship)* [3569]
Development Fund for Black Students in Science and Technology Scholarships *(Undergraduate/Scholarship)* [3612]
William Donald Dixon Research Grants *(Graduate, Undergraduate, Advanced Professional/Grant)* [2665]
Extrusion Division/Lew Erwin Memorial Scholarship *(Graduate, Postgraduate/Scholarship)* [9261]
Lt. Colonel Romeo and Josephine Bass Ferretti Scholarships *(Undergraduate/Scholarship)* [124]
Reuben H. Fleet Memorial Scholarships *(Undergraduate/Scholarship)* [8704]
Fleming/Blaszcak Scholarships *(Undergraduate, Graduate/Scholarship)* [9262]
Florida Education Fund McKnight Doctoral Fellowships *(Graduate/Fellowship)* [4085]
Edward Foster Awards *(Advanced Professional/Award)* [2666]
The Ginny Frankenthaler Memorial Scholarships *(Undergraduate/Scholarship)* [9385]
The Gates Millennium Scholars *(Undergraduate/Scholarship)* [4903]
Eloise Gerry Fellowships *(Graduate, Postdoctorate/Fellowship)* [8904]
Composites Division/Harold Giles Scholarship *(Undergraduate, Graduate/Scholarship)* [9263]
Benjamin A. Gilman International Scholarship *(Undergraduate/Scholarship)* [10060]
Glendale Latino Association Scholarships *(Undergraduate/Scholarship)* [4449]
Dr. Robert H. Goddard Memorial Scholarships *(Graduate, Undergraduate/Scholarship)* [7179]
William R. Goldfarb Memorial Scholarships *(Undergraduate/Scholarship)* [1739]
Barry M. Goldwater Scholarships *(Undergraduate/Scholarship)* [10319]
Graduate Fellowship Program - Research Fellowships (GFP) *(Doctorate, Graduate/Fellowship)* [8833]
GREAT MINDS Collegiate Scholarship Program *(Undergraduate/Scholarship)* [338]
Guntley-Lorimer Science and Arts Scholarships *(Undergraduate/Scholarship)* [2284]
H.G. Hardbarger Science and Mathematics Awards *(Undergraduate/Award)* [7835]
Hertz Foundation Graduate Fellowship Award *(Graduate/Fellowship)* [4875]
Hertz Foundation Graduate Fellowships *(Graduate, Master's, Doctorate/Fellowship)* [6748]
Hertz Foundation Thesis Prize *(Graduate/Prize)* [4876]
Hinman-Jensen Endowed Scholarships *(Undergraduate/Scholarship)* [6032]
IDA Fellowship Awards *(Other/Fellowship)* [5320]
Indspire Post-Secondary Education Scholarships *(Graduate, Undergraduate/Scholarship)* [5133]
Drzymala Janusz and Roma Scholarship *(Undergraduate/Scholarship)* [8577]
Nancy Lorraine Jensen Memorial Scholarships *(Undergraduate/Scholarship)* [9345]
JSA/Jefferson Lab Graduate Fellowships *(Doctorate, Graduate/Fellowship)* [5566]
Graduate Fellowship Program - Mahboob Khan/Advanced Micro Devices Fellowships *(Doctorate, Graduate/Fellowship)* [8834]
KON National Alumni Chapter Grant *(Professional development/Grant)* [5783]
KON New Initiatives Grant *(Professional development/Grant)* [5784]
Lakselaget Foundation Scholarships *(Graduate, Undergraduate/Scholarship)* [5903]
Lalor Foundation Merit Awards *(Postdoctorate/Award)* [9307]
Carie and George Lyter Scholarship Fund *(Undergraduate/Scholarship)* [4247]
Thermoset Division/James I. Mackenzie and James H. Cunningham Scholarships *(Undergraduate, Graduate/Scholarship)* [9264]
Pat and John MacTavish Scholarship Fund *(Undergraduate/Scholarship)* [4532]
MAES Founders Scholarships *(Graduate, Undergraduate/Scholarship)* [6178]
MAES General Scholarships *(Graduate, Undergraduate/Scholarship)* [6179]
MAES Graduate Scholarships *(Graduate/Scholarship)* [6180]
MAES Padrino/Madrina Scholarships *(Graduate, Undergraduate/Scholarship)* [6181]
MAES Pipeline Scholarships *(Graduate, Undergraduate/Scholarship)* [6182]
MAES Presidential Scholarships *(Graduate, Undergraduate/Scholarship)* [6183]
Masonic-Range Science Scholarships *(Undergraduate/Scholarship)* [9298]
Thomas R. McGetchin Memorial Scholarship Awards *(Undergraduate/Scholarship)* [9997]
Nell I. Mondy Fellowships *(Graduate, Doctorate/Fellowship)* [8905]
Robert E. and Judy More Scholarship Fund *(Undergraduate/Scholarship)* [4053]
John H. Moss Scholarships *(Undergraduate/Scholarship)* [10294]

SCIENCE TECHNOLOGIES

National GEM Consortium - MS Engineering Fellowships *(Graduate/Fellowship)* [6967]
National Science Foundation Graduate Research Fellowship Program (NSF-GRFP) *(Graduate/Fellowship)* [7125]
National Security Technologies Engineering and Science Scholarships *(Undergraduate/Scholarship, Internship)* [8356]
Ted and Ruth Neward Scholarships *(Undergraduate, Graduate/Scholarship)* [9265]
Stuart L. Noderer Memorial Scholarships *(Undergraduate/Scholarship)* [8719]
Maureen E. Nolan-Cahill Memorial Scholarships *(Undergraduate/Scholarship)* [10032]
Vessa Notchev Fellowships *(Doctorate, Graduate/Fellowship)* [8906]
Noyce Scholarships for Secondary Math and Science Education *(Undergraduate/Scholarship)* [5123]
Ocean Industries Student Research Awards *(Undergraduate, Graduate, Postdoctorate/Award)* [8557]
Office of Science Graduate Fellowships *(Graduate/Fellowship)* [9912]
Ohio Space Grant Consortium Graduate Fellowships *(Graduate, Doctorate, Master's/Fellowship)* [7594]
Ohio Space Grant Consortium Special Minority Fellowships *(Doctorate, Graduate, Master's/Fellowship)* [7595]
Omicron Nu Research Fellowships *(Postdoctorate/Fellowship)* [5790]
L'Oreal USA Fellowships for Women in Science *(Postdoctorate/Fellowship)* [6107]
Packard Fellowships for Science and Engineering *(Professional development/Fellowship)* [7793]
Phi Theta Kappa Scholarships *(Undergraduate/Scholarship)* [5124]
Plastics Pioneers Association Scholarships *(Undergraduate/Scholarship)* [9266]
Polymer Modifiers and Additives Division Scholarships *(Undergraduate/Scholarship)* [9267]
Carl Rose Memorial Scholarships *(Undergraduate/Scholarship)* [7858]
Jack Rosen Scholarship *(Undergraduate/Scholarship)* [5683]
Leo S. Rowe Pan American Fund *(Graduate, Undergraduate/Loan)* [7730]
Liane B. Russell Fellowships *(Postdoctorate/Fellowship)* [9908]
Chester & Maria Sadowski Memorial Scholarships *(Undergraduate/Scholarship)* [8590]
Science, Mathematics And Research for Transformation Scholarship for Service Program (SMART) *(Undergraduate, Graduate/Scholarship)* [1305]
John R. Sevier Memorial Scholarship Award *(Undergraduate/Scholarship)* [9998]
Everett Oscar Shimp Memorial Scholarships *(Undergraduate/Scholarship)* [7862]
SHPE Dissertation Scholarship *(Doctorate/Scholarship)* [9130]
SHPE Professional Scholarship *(Master's, Doctorate/Scholarship)* [9131]
Clifford G. Shull Fellowships *(Postdoctorate/Fellowship)* [9909]
Sigma Delta Epsilon Fellowships *(Graduate, Postdoctorate/Fellowship)* [8907]
Carrie Fox Solin Blow Molding Division Memorial Scholarships *(Undergraduate/Scholarship)* [9268]
Sons of Norway Foundation Scholarships to Oslo International Summer School *(Undergraduate/Scholarship)* [9346]
SPE Foundation General Scholarships *(Undergraduate, Graduate/Scholarship)* [9269]
SPE Gulf Coast Hurricane Scholarships *(Undergraduate/Scholarship)* [9270]
SPE Injection Molding Division Scholarships *(Undergraduate, Graduate/Scholarship)* [9271]
SPE Thermoforming Division Memorial Scholarships *(Undergraduate, Graduate/Scholarship)* [9272]
SPE Thermoplastic Elastomers Special Interest Group Scholarship *(Undergraduate, Graduate/Scholarship)* [9273]
SPE Thermoplastic Materials and Foams Division Scholarships *(Undergraduate/Scholarship)* [9274]
SPE Vinyl Plastics Division Educational Grants *(Undergraduate/Grant)* [9275]
SRC Master's Scholarships Program (MSP) *(Graduate, Master's/Scholarship)* [8835]
SREB-State Doctoral Scholars Program - Doctoral Awards *(Doctorate, Graduate/Scholarship)* [9411]
Frederick A. Tarantino Memorial Scholarship Award *(Undergraduate/Scholarship)* [9999]
Anil and Neema Thakrar Family Fund No. 1 *(Undergraduate/Scholarship)* [4257]
UAA Quanterra Scholarship *(Graduate/Scholarship)* [10083]
The UCSD Black Alumni Scholarships for Engineering, Mathematics and Science *(Undergraduate/Scholarship)* [8737]
USGA/Chevron STEM Scholarship Program *(Undergraduate/Scholarship)* [9954]
VEF Fellowship Program *(Doctorate, Master's/Fellowship)* [10380]
VEF Visiting Scholars Program *(Doctorate/Fellowship)* [10381]
WACE National Co-op Scholarship Program *(Undergraduate/Scholarship)* [10693]
Alvin M. Weinberg Fellowships *(Doctorate/Fellowship)* [9910]
James B. Willett Educational Memorial Scholarship Award *(Undergraduate/Scholarship)* [10000]
William S. Wilson Memorial Scholarships *(Undergraduate/Scholarship)* [10043]
Ross A. Wilson Science Scholarships *(Undergraduate/Scholarship)* [9733]
Denis Wong and Associates Scholarships *(Graduate, Undergraduate/Scholarship)* [7920]
Woodcock Family Education Scholarship Program *(Undergraduate/Scholarship)* [306]
WSGC Community College Transfer Scholarships *(Undergraduate/Scholarship)* [10455]
WSGC Scholarships for Incoming Freshmen *(Undergraduate/Scholarship)* [10456]
Yasme Foundation Scholarships *(Undergraduate/Scholarship)* [1765]

Science technologies

AAAS Mass Media Science and Engineering Fellowship *(Undergraduate, Graduate, Postdoctorate/Fellowship, Award)* [453]
AAAS Science and Technology Policy Fellowships *(Professional development/Fellowship)* [454]
AVS Applied Surface Science Division Awards *(Graduate/Award)* [2146]
AVS Biomaterial Interfaces Division - Early Career Researchers Awards *(Graduate/Monetary)* [2147]
AVS Electronic Materials and Photonic Division Postdoctoral Award *(Postdoctorate/Award)* [2148]
AVS Manufacturing Science and Technology Group Awards *(Graduate/Award)* [2149]
AVS MEMS and NEMS Technical Group Best Paper Awards *(Undergraduate, Graduate/Monetary)* [2150]
AVS Nanometer-Scale Science and Technology Division Graduate Award *(Graduate/Monetary)* [2151]
AVS Spectroscopic Ellipsometry Focus Topic Graduate Student Awards *(Graduate/Award)* [2152]
AVS Thin Film Division James Harper Awards *(Graduate/Monetary)* [2153]
Mark A. Beltz Scholarship *(Graduate, Undergraduate/Scholarship)* [10052]
Canadian Council of Technicians and Technologists Scholarships for Technology Students *(Undergraduate/Scholarship)* [3392]
John Coburn and Harold Winters Student Award in Plasma Science and Technology *(Graduate/Award)* [2154]
Magnetic Interfaces and Nanostructures Division - The Leo M. Falicov Student Award *(Graduate/Grant)* [2155]
Graduate Fellowships in Alternatives in Scientific Research *(Doctorate, Graduate/Fellowship)* [5333]
Dorothy M. and Earl S. Hoffman Award *(Graduate/Award)* [2156]
Pembroke Center Faculty Seed Grants *(Professional development/Grant)* [2390]
Saskatchewan School Boards Association Education Scholarships *(Undergraduate/Scholarship)* [8781]
Morton M. Traum Surface Science Student Awards *(Graduate, Doctorate/Prize)* [2157]
Russell and Sigurd Varian Award *(Graduate/Recognition)* [2158]
Nellie Yeoh Whetten Award *(Graduate/Recognition)* [2159]

Science--History
AMS Graduate Fellowships in the History of Science *(Graduate/Fellowship)* [998]

Scottish studies (See also British studies)
Clan Ross Foundation Scholarships *(Undergraduate/Scholarship)* [3043]

Screenwriting
Cinestory Fellowship *(Professional development/Fellowship)* [3029]

Sculpture
Yvonne L. Bombardier Visual Arts Scholarships *(Master's, Doctorate/Scholarship)* [1665]
Alex J. Ettl Grants *(Other/Grant)* [7127]
Ken Gray Endowment Scholarship *(Undergraduate/Scholarship)* [10061]
National Sculpture Society Scholarships *(Undergraduate/Scholarship)* [7128]

Sexuality
George Benes, MD & Michael Mallee, EdD Point Scholarships *(Undergraduate, Graduate, Doctorate/Scholarship)* [8170]
Tyler Clementi Point Scholarship *(Undergraduate/Scholarship)* [8171]
Darden Restaurants Point Scholarships *(Undergraduate, Graduate, Doctorate/Scholarship)* [8172]
Erickson-Zoellers Point Scholarships *(Undergraduate, Graduate, Doctorate/Scholarship)* [8174]
Loren Frankel Memorial Scholarships *(Undergraduate, Graduate/Scholarship)* [995]
Friends of Project 10 Models of Excellence Scholarships *(Undergraduate/Scholarship)* [4307]
Allan Gilmour & Eric Jirgens Point Scholarships *(Undergraduate, Graduate, Doctorate/Scholarship)* [8175]
GJEC Dissertation Completion Fellowships *(Postdoctorate/Fellowship)* [6490]
Rosen Goertz Point Scholarship *(Undergraduate, Graduate, Doctorate/Scholarship)* [8176]
Janssen Therapeutics Point Scholarships *(Undergraduate, Graduate, Doctorate/Scholarship)* [8179]
Larry King/Jeffrey Fashion Cares Point Scholarship *(Undergraduate, Graduate, Doctorate/Scholarship)* [8180]
KPMG Point Scholarship *(Undergraduate, Graduate, Doctorate/Scholarship)* [8181]
Estée Lauder Point Scholarships *(Undergraduate, Graduate, Doctorate/Scholarship)* [8182]
William J. Levy Point Scholarship *(Undergraduate, Graduate, Doctorate/Scholarship)* [8183]
Minton-Spidell Point Scholarship *(Undergraduate, Graduate, Doctorate/Scholarship)* [8185]
Motorola Solutions Point Scholarship *(Undergraduate, Graduate, Doctorate/Scholarship)* [8186]
NBCUniversal Point Scholarship *(Undergraduate, Graduate, Doctorate/Scholarship)* [8187]
New York Point Honors Point Scholarship *(Undergraduate, Graduate, Doctorate/Scholarship)* [8188]
Northern Trust Point Scholarship *(Undergraduate, Graduate, Doctorate/Scholarship)* [8189]
RBPA Scholarships *(All/Scholarship)* [8425]
Rim-Freeman Point Scholarship *(Undergraduate/Scholarship)* [8190]
Rand Skolnick Point Scholarship *(Undergraduate, Graduate, Doctorate/Scholarship)* [8191]
Society for the Scientific Study of Sexuality Student Research Grants *(Undergraduate/Grant)* [9302]

Took Trust Point Scholarship *(Undergraduate, Graduate, Doctorate/Scholarship)* [8192]
Toyota Financial Services Point Scholarship *(Undergraduate, Graduate, Doctorate/Scholarship)* [8193]
Voices On Point Scholarship *(Undergraduate, Graduate, Doctorate/Scholarship)* [8194]
Vorobek Point Scholarship *(Undergraduate, Graduate, Doctorate/Scholarship)* [8195]
Wells Fargo Point Scholarship *(Undergraduate/Scholarship)* [8196]

Social sciences

Abe Fellowship Program *(Professional development/Fellowship)* [9051]
ABF Law and Social Science Dissertation Fellowship and Mentoring Program *(Graduate/Fellowship)* [623]
ABF Montgomery Summer Research Diversity Fellowships in Law and Social Science *(Undergraduate/Fellowship)* [624]
ACLS Collaborative Research Fellowships *(Doctorate/Fellowship)* [735]
ACLS Fellowships *(Advanced Professional, Professional development/Fellowship)* [736]
ACOR-CAORC Post-Graduate Fellowships *(Doctorate, Postdoctorate/Award)* [653]
Dr. Feroz Ahmed Memorial Educational Post-Graduate Scholarships *(Doctorate, Postgraduate/Scholarship)* [8965]
AISLS Dissertation Planning Grants *(Graduate/Grant)* [929]
AISLS Fellowships Program *(Doctorate/Fellowship)* [930]
Lorraine Allison Scholarship *(Graduate/Scholarship)* [1616]
Gordon Allport Intergroup Relations Prize *(Professional development/Monetary, Award)* [9289]
American Enterprise Institute National Research Initiative Fellowships (NRI) *(Graduate/Fellowship)* [786]
American Research in the Humanities in China Fellowships *(Doctorate/Fellowship)* [737]
ARIT Fellowships in the Humanities and Social Sciences in Turkey *(Postdoctorate, Graduate/Fellowship)* [1201]
ARIT National Endowment for the Humanities Advanced Fellowships for Research in Turkey *(Postdoctorate/Fellowship)* [1202]
UAA Michael Baring-Gould Memorial Scholarship *(Graduate, Undergraduate/Scholarship)* [10051]
Raymond B. Bauer Research Award *(Professional development/Grant)* [6479]
Price Benowitz Social Justice Scholarships *(Undergraduate/Scholarship)* [8228]
Jeanne Humphrey Block Dissertation Award *(Postdoctorate/Award)* [4784]
ACLS Frederick Burkhardt Residential Fellowships *(Other/Fellowship)* [434]
Frederick Burkhardt Residential Fellowships for Recently Tenured Scholars *(Advanced Professional, Professional development/Fellowship)* [738]
Cave Conservancy Foundation Graduate and Undergraduate Fellowships *(Doctorate, Graduate, Undergraduate/Fellowship)* [2823]
CES First Article Prize *(Professional development/Prize)* [3438]
Mariam K. Chamberlain Fellowships in Women and Public Policy *(Graduate/Fellowship)* [5228]
Critical Language Scholarships for Intensive Summer Institutes *(Graduate, Undergraduate/Scholarship)* [1204]
CTFS-ForestGEO Research Grants Program *(Graduate, Postdoctorate, Advanced Professional/Grant)* [9041]
Dissertation Fellowships in East European Studies *(Doctorate/Fellowship)* [740]
Dissertation Proposal Development Fellowships *(Doctorate/Fellowship)* [9053]
EAPSI Fellowships *(Doctorate, Graduate/Fellowship)* [7124]
Early Career Postdoctoral Fellowships in East European Studies *(Postdoctorate/Fellowship)* [741]
Epilepsy Foundation Behavioral Sciences Postdoctoral Fellowships *(Postdoctorate/Fellowship)* [3902]
FLASH Social Science Scholarships *(Graduate/Scholarship)* [3976]
AIHS Cy Frank Fellowships: Impact Assessment *(Doctorate, Professional development/Fellowship)* [254]
Getty Scholar Grants *(Professional development/Grant)* [4412]
Charles D. Gonthier Research Fellowships *(Graduate, Advanced Professional/Fellowship)* [2668]
Harry Frank Guggenheim Dissertation Fellowships *(Doctorate/Fellowship)* [4681]
Harry Frank Guggenheim Foundation Research Grants *(Professional development/Grant)* [4682]
John Simon Guggenheim Memorial Fellowships - U.S. and Canadian Competition *(Advanced Professional/Fellowship)* [4684]
HAESF Professional Internship Program *(Doctorate/Internship)* [5009]
TIAA-CREF Ruth Simms Hamilton Research Fellowships *(Graduate/Fellowship)* [9737]
Lois Hole Humanities and Social Sciences Scholarships *(Undergraduate/Scholarship)* [273]
IAF Fellowships *(Doctorate/Fellowship)* [5232]
Indspire Post-Secondary Education Scholarships *(Graduate, Undergraduate/Scholarship)* [5133]
Institute of Turkish Studies Post-Doctoral Summer Travel-Research Grants *(Postdoctorate/Grant)* [5224]
Institute of Turkish Studies Summer Language Study Grants in Turkey *(Graduate/Grant)* [5226]
International Dissertation Research Fellowship (IDRF) *(Graduate, Doctorate/Fellowship)* [9054]
Japan Society for the Promotion of Science Fellowship Program *(Doctorate/Fellowship)* [9055]
Jacob K. Javits Fellowships Program *(Master's, Doctorate/Fellowship)* [9894]
Robert E. Kelsey Annual Scholarship *(Undergraduate/Scholarship)* [7933]
Martin Luther King Jr. Scholarships *(Undergraduate/Scholarship)* [5836]
Kluge Fellowships *(Doctorate, Graduate/Fellowship)* [5846]
Korean Studies Dissertation Workshop Funds *(Graduate/Fellowship)* [9056]
Dolores Zohrab Liebmann Fund - Graduate School Fellowships *(Graduate/Fellowship)* [6075]
Clara Mayo Grants Program *(Graduate/Grant)* [9290]
O. Ruth McQuown Scholarship - Graduate Award for Current Students *(Graduate/Scholarship)* [10135]
Philip H. Melanson Memorial Scholarships *(Undergraduate, Graduate/Scholarship)* [10154]
Mellon/ACLS Dissertation Completion Fellowships *(Graduate, Doctorate/Fellowship)* [743]
Mellon Fellowships for Dissertation Research in the Humanities *(Doctorate, Graduate, Postdoctorate, Scholarship)* [3450]
Mellon Fellowships for Dissertation Research in Original Sources *(Doctorate/Fellowship)* [3451]
Michigan Society of Fellows Three-Year Fellowships *(Postdoctorate/Fellowship)* [6481]
Minority Visiting Students Awards *(Undergraduate, Graduate/Award, Internship)* [9011]
Christine Mirzayan Science and Technology Policy Graduate Fellowships *(Graduate/Fellowship)* [6679]
Multi-Country Research Fellowships *(Doctorate/Fellowship)* [3431]
NAFA International Dissertation Research Fellowships *(Graduate, Doctorate/Fellowship)* [6750]
NAPRHSW Scholarships *(Undergraduate, Graduate/Scholarship)* [6776]
National Endowment for the Humanities Research Fellowships *(Doctorate/Fellowship)* [660]
National Institute of Health Undergraduate Scholarship Program (NIH UGSP) *(Undergraduate/Scholarship)* [9930]
Newkirk Center for Science and Society Graduate Student Fellowships *(Doctorate, Graduate/Fellowship)* [7427]
Next Generation Social Sciences in Africa: Doctoral Dissertation Completion Fellowships *(Doctorate/Fellowship)* [9057]
Next Generation Social Sciences in Africa: Doctoral Dissertation Proposal Fellowships *(Doctorate/Fellowship)* [9058]
Next Generation Social Sciences in Africa: Doctoral Dissertation Research Fellowship *(Doctorate/Fellowship)* [9059]
Open Society Baltimore Community Fellowships *(Advanced Professional/Fellowship)* [7661]
Pembroke Center Faculty Seed Grants *(Professional development/Grant)* [2390]
Charles A. Ryskamp Research Fellowships *(Postgraduate, Postdoctorate, Professional development/Fellowship)* [744]
Russell Sage Foundation Visiting Scholars *(Postdoctorate/Fellowship)* [8668]
SFP Mid-Career/Mentor Awards for Family Planning *(Other/Grant)* [9120]
SGI Research Grants *(Graduate/Grant)* [8773]
SHAFR Dissertation Completion Fellowships *(Doctorate/Fellowship)* [9140]
Short-term Senior Fellowships in Iranian Studies *(Professional development/Fellowship)* [914]
Spirit of Anne Frank Outstanding Scholarship Award *(Undergraduate/Scholarship)* [1563]
SSHRC Doctoral Fellowship Program *(Doctorate/Fellowship, Scholarship)* [3396]
Louis Stokes Urban Health Policy Fellows Program *(Other/Fellowship)* [3350]
John Streiff Memorial Scholarships *(Undergraduate/Scholarship)* [6055]
Trudeau Foundation Doctoral Scholarships *(Doctorate/Scholarship)* [8137]
UC MEXUS-CONACYT Doctoral Fellowships *(Doctorate/Fellowship)* [10117]
Vanier Canada Graduate Scholarships *(Graduate/Scholarship)* [3405]
Carter G. Woodson Institute Post-doctoral Residential Research and Teaching Fellowships *(Postdoctorate/Fellowship)* [10684]
Carter G. Woodson Institute Pre-doctoral Residential Research Fellowships *(Doctorate/Fellowship)* [10685]
Woody Guthrie Fellowship *(Professional development/Fellowship)* [2321]

Social work

Emma and Meloid Algood Tuition Scholarships *(Graduate, Undergraduate/Scholarship)* [6718]
APSA/Health and Aging Policy Fellowships *(Graduate, Advanced Professional, Professional development/Fellowship)* [1112]
Associates in Behavioral Health Scholarships *(Graduate/Scholarship)* [8243]
Dr. Joyce Beckett Scholarships *(Graduate, Undergraduate/Scholarship)* [6719]
Eileen Blackey Doctoral Fellowships *(Doctorate/Fellowship)* [6788]
Mildred Cater Bradham Social Work Fellowships *(Graduate, Professional development/Fellowship)* [10814]
Selena Danette Brown Book Scholarships *(Graduate, Undergraduate/Scholarship)* [6720]
Robert K. Brown Scholarships *(Undergraduate, Master's/Scholarship)* [2278]
CIBC Scholarships *(Undergraduate, Graduate/Scholarship)* [2281]
Council on Social Work Education Minority Fellowship Program for Doctoral Students *(Postdoctorate/Fellowship)* [3454]
Council on Social Work Education Scholars Program *(Doctorate/Scholarship)* [3455]
Steve Dearduff Scholarships *(Graduate, Undergraduate/Scholarship)* [3194]
Douglas-Coldwell Foundation Scholarships in Social Affairs *(Graduate/Scholarship)* [3656]
The Steve Duckett Local Conservation Scholarships *(Undergraduate, Postgraduate/Scholarship)* [8232]
Echoing Green Black Male Achievement Fellowships *(Professional development/Fellowship)* [3773]
Echoing Green Climate Fellowships *(Professional development/Fellowship)* [3774]
EJI Justice Fellowship *(Graduate, Postgraduate, Professional development/Fellowship)* [3916]

SOCIOLOGY

Alice Yuriko Endo Memorial Scholarships *(Undergraduate/Scholarship)* [5549]
Family and Children's Services of Lebanon County Fund *(Undergraduate/Scholarship)* [4239]
Consuelo W. Gosnell Memorial Scholarships *(Graduate/Fellowship)* [6789]
Hampton Roads Association of Social Workers Scholarships *(Graduate/Scholarship)* [4698]
HFMH Bilingual Scholarships for Mental Health Workforce Diversity *(Graduate/Scholarship)* [4913]
Indspire Post-Secondary Education Scholarships *(Graduate, Undergraduate/Scholarship)* [5133]
International Scholarship Programs for Community Service *(Undergraduate/Scholarship)* [6413]
Jewish Federation Academic Scholarships *(Graduate, Undergraduate/Scholarship)* [5598]
Maude Keisling/Cumberland County Extension Homemakers Scholarships *(Undergraduate/Scholarship)* [3231]
The Michael Kiely Strong Roots Scholarships *(Undergraduate/Scholarship)* [8233]
Verne LaMarr Lyons Memorial Scholarships *(Graduate, Master's/Fellowship)* [6790]
Joseph McCulley Educational Scholarships *(Graduate, Undergraduate/Scholarship)* [10292]
The Tatiana Mendez Future Resources Scholarships *(Undergraduate/Scholarship)* [8234]
NYCT Paid Graduate Student Philanthropy Fellowships - Community Development and the Environment *(Graduate/Fellowship)* [7351]
The Seth Okin Good Deeds Scholarships *(Undergraduate/Scholarship)* [8235]
Pi Gamma Mu Scholarships *(Graduate/Scholarship)* [8133]
Portuguese American Police Association Scholarships *(Undergraduate/Scholarship)* [8211]
Pride Foundation Social Work Scholarships *(Undergraduate/Scholarship)* [8260]
Carl A. Scott Book Scholarships *(Undergraduate/Scholarship)* [3456]
The Thomas Soldan Healthy Communities Scholarships *(Undergraduate, Graduate/Scholarship)* [8237]
Taylor Statten Memorial Fellowships *(Graduate/Scholarship)* [10295]
The Ed Tayter Outstanding Citizen Scholarships *(Undergraduate/Scholarship)* [8238]
Philip F. Vineberg Travelling Fellowships in the Humanities *(Undergraduate/Scholarship)* [6368]
Washington University Law School Chancellor's Graduate Fellowships *(Advanced Professional/Fellowship)* [10476]
Washington University Law School Olin Fellowships for Women *(Advanced Professional/Fellowship)* [10477]
Wellstone Fellowships for Social Justice *(Graduate/Fellowship)* [3959]
Cenie Jomo Williams Tuition Scholarships *(Graduate, Undergraduate/Scholarship)* [6721]

Sociology (See also Aggression and violence)

Dr. Feroz Ahmed Memorial Educational Post-Graduate Scholarships *(Doctorate, Postgraduate/Scholarship)* [8965]
ASA Minority Fellowship Program (ASA MFP) *(Graduate, Doctorate, Professional development/Fellowship)* [1445]
ASA Student Forum Travel Awards *(Undergraduate, Graduate/Grant)* [1446]
UAA Michael Baring-Gould Memorial Scholarship *(Graduate, Undergraduate/Scholarship)* [10051]
Douglas-Coldwell Foundation Scholarships in Social Affairs *(Graduate/Scholarship)* [3656]
Early Childhood Educators Scholarship Program *(Undergraduate/Scholarship)* [6342]
Garikian Scholarship Fund *(Undergraduate/Scholarship)* [1694]
Marcus Mosiah Garvey Scholarships *(Undergraduate/Scholarship)* [5523]
Beth B. Hess Memorial Scholarships *(Doctorate, Graduate/Fellowship, Award)* [9331]
IARSLCE Graduate Student Scholarships *(Graduate/Scholarship)* [5273]
Cheryl Allyn Miller Award *(Doctorate, Graduate/Monetary)* [9332]
National Women's Studies Association Lesbian Caucus Award *(Master's, Doctorate/Award, Grant)* [7218]
Pi Gamma Mu Scholarships *(Graduate/Scholarship)* [8133]
Thomas R. Pickering Graduate Foreign Affairs Fellowships *(Graduate, Undergraduate/Fellowship)* [10681]
Eveline Schuster Memorial Award/Scholarship *(Graduate, Undergraduate/Scholarship)* [10071]
Minoru Yasui Memorial Scholarships *(Graduate, Master's, Doctorate/Scholarship)* [5560]

Soil science

Dr. Karl C. Ivarson Scholarships *(Master's, Doctorate/Scholarship)* [113]
STRI Short-Term Fellowships *(Undergraduate, Graduate, Postdoctorate/Fellowship)* [9038]
Earl S. Tupper 3-year Postdoctoral Fellowships in Tropical Biology *(Postdoctorate/Fellowship)* [9039]

South Asian studies

NIU-CSEAS Foreign Language and Area Studies (FLAS) Fellowships *(Undergraduate, Graduate/Fellowship)* [7518]

Space and planetary sciences (See also Astronomy and astronomical sciences)

ASGP Graduate Research Fellowships *(Graduate/Fellowship)* [223]
Connecticut Space Grant College Consortium Undergraduate Research Fellowships *(Undergraduate/Fellowship)* [3367]
Thomas R. McGetchin Memorial Scholarship Awards *(Undergraduate/Scholarship)* [9997]
NASA RISGC Graduate Fellowships *(Master's, Postdoctorate, Graduate/Scholarship)* [8613]
NASA WVSGC Undergraduate Research Fellowship *(Undergraduate/Fellowship)* [10527]
PSGC/NASA Space Grant Fellowships at the PSGC Affiliate Institutions *(Graduate/Fellowship)* [7945]
John R. Sevier Memorial Scholarship Award *(Undergraduate/Scholarship)* [9998]
Frederick A. Tarantino Memorial Scholarship Award *(Undergraduate/Scholarship)* [9999]
James B. Willett Educational Memorial Scholarship Award *(Undergraduate/Scholarship)* [10000]

Spanish studies (See Area and ethnic studies)

Special education (See Education, Special)

Specific diseases

SCDAA Post-Doctoral Research Fellowships *(Doctorate/Fellowship)* [8892]

Speech, Debate, and Forensics

William R. Pfalzgraf Scholarships *(Undergraduate/Scholarship)* [7852]

Speech and language pathology/Audiology

Acoustical Society of America Minority Fellowships *(Graduate/Fellowship)* [52]
AMBUCS Scholarships for Therapists Program *(Graduate, Undergraduate/Scholarship)* [381]
American Speech Language Hearing Foundation Clinical Research Grants *(Doctorate/Grant)* [1450]
American Speech Language Hearing Foundation Endowed Scholarships *(Graduate, Master's, Doctorate/Scholarship)* [1451]
American Speech Language Hearing Foundation General Scholarships *(Graduate, Master's, Doctorate/Scholarship)* [1452]
American Speech Language Hearing Foundation Scholarships for International Students *(Graduate, Master's, Doctorate/Scholarship)* [1453]
American Speech Language Hearing Foundation Scholarships for Minority Students *(Graduate, Master's, Doctorate/Scholarship)* [1454]
ASHFoundation New Century Scholars Doctoral Scholarships *(Doctorate/Scholarship)* [1455]
ASHFoundation New Century Scholars Research Grants *(Doctorate/Grant)* [1456]
ASHFoundation New Investigators Research Grants *(Doctorate/Grant)* [1457]
ASHFoundation Scholarships for NSSLHA Members *(Graduate/Scholarship)* [1458]
ASHFoundation Speech Science Research Grants *(Doctorate/Grant)* [1459]
ASHFoundation Student Research Grants in Audiology *(Doctorate/Grant)* [1460]
ASHFoundation Student Research Grants in Early Childhood Language Development *(Doctorate, Master's/Grant)* [1461]
Fred Berg Awards *(Undergraduate/Award)* [3796]
Educational Audiology Association Doctoral Scholarships *(Doctorate/Scholarship)* [3797]
ETS Postdoctoral Fellowships *(Postdoctorate/Fellowship)* [3806]
GFWCMA Communication Disorder/Speech Therapy Scholarships *(Graduate/Scholarship)* [4353]
Harold Gulliksen Psychometric Research Fellowships *(Doctorate, Graduate/Fellowship)* [3807]
Dwight A. Hamilton Scottish Rite Foundation of Colorado Graduate Scholarships *(Graduate/Scholarship)* [8821]
Houston/Nancy Holliman Scholarships *(Undergraduate/Scholarship)* [3586]
Frederick V. Hunt Postdoctoral Research Fellowships in Acoustics *(Postdoctorate/Fellowship)* [53]
Sylvia Taylor Johnson Fellowships in Educational Measurement *(Doctorate/Fellowship)* [3808]
Maryland Speech Language Hearing Association Graduate Scholarships *(Graduate/Scholarship)* [6302]
Noel D. Matkin Awards *(Undergraduate/Award)* [3798]
NAJA Scholarships *(Graduate/Scholarship)* [6760]
New Investigator Research Grant *(Doctorate/Grant)* [393]
Helen Woodruff Nolop Scholarships in Audiology and Allied Fields *(Graduate/Scholarship)* [3592]
OSHA Graduate Scholarships *(Graduate/Scholarship)* [7606]
Raymond H. Stetson Scholarships in Phonetics and Speech Science *(Graduate/Scholarship)* [54]
Student Investigator Research Grant - General Audiology/Hearing Science *(Graduate, Doctorate/Grant)* [394]
Student Investigator Research Grant - Hearing Aids, Clinical Protocols and Patient Outcomes *(Graduate, Doctorate/Grant)* [395]
Student Investigator Research Grant - Vestibular *(Graduate, Doctorate/Grant)* [396]
Student Summer Research Fellowship *(Undergraduate, Graduate/Fellowship)* [397]

Spinal cord injuries and research

180 Medical College Scholarship Program *(Undergraduate, Graduate/Scholarship)* [4]
Individual K-Grants *(All/Grant)* [5823]
Morton Cure Paralysis Fund Research Grants *(Professional development, Postdoctorate/Grant)* [6602]
Neilsen Psychosocial Research Grants - Pilot Psychosocial Research Grants *(Professional development/Grant)* [7254]
Neilsen Psychosocial Research Grants - Postdoctoral Psychosocial Fellowships *(Postdoctorate/Fellowship)* [7255]
Neilsen Psychosocial Research Grants - Proof of Concept Research Grants *(Professional development/Grant)* [7256]

Field of Study Index

PVA Research Foundation Fellowships *(Postdoctorate/Fellowship)* [7803]
Bryon Riesch Paralysis Foundation Research Grants *(Professional development/Grant)* [8617]
Travis Roy Foundation Individual Grants *(All/Grant)* [8652]
SCIRTS (Spinal Cord Injury Research on the Translational Spectrum) Pilot Research Grants *(Professional development/Grant)* [7257]
SCIRTS (Spinal Cord Injury Research on the Translational Spectrum) Postdoctoral Fellowships *(Postdoctorate/Fellowship)* [7258]
SCIRTS (Spinal Cord Injury Research on the Translational Spectrum) Senior Research Grants *(Professional development/Grant)* [7259]

Sports medicine (See Medicine, Sports)

Sports studies

Henry H. Anderson, Jr. Sail Training Scholarship *(Professional development/Scholarship)* [9640]
Bernice Barabash Sports Scholarships *(Undergraduate/Scholarship)* [5497]
Walter Byers Postgraduate Scholarships *(Graduate, Postgraduate/Scholarship)* [6861]
Ethnic Minority and Women's Enhancement Postgraduate Scholarships *(Graduate/Scholarship)* [6862]
Veronica Gantt Memorial Scholarships *(Undergraduate/Scholarship)* [8346]
Geordie Hilton Academic Scholarships *(Undergraduate/Scholarship)* [4480]
John McLendon Memorial Minority Postgraduate Scholarships *(Postdoctorate/Scholarship)* [6738]
MMJGA Scholarships *(Undergraduate/Scholarship)* [6549]
James H. Roberts Athletic Scholarships *(Undergraduate/Scholarship)* [7855]
Safer Athletic Field Environments Scholarships (SAFE) *(Graduate, Undergraduate/Scholarship)* [9481]
Saskatchewan Hockey Association Scholarships *(Undergraduate/Scholarship)* [8775]
Felix R. Sepulveda Memorial Scholarships - Northside Booster Club *(Undergraduate/Scholarship)* [8527]
Gary Vanden Berg Internship Grant *(Undergraduate/Grant)* [9482]

Sports writing

Association for Women in Sports Media Internship/Scholarship Program *(Undergraduate/Scholarship, Internship)* [2101]
Chuck Pezzano Scholarships *(Undergraduate/Scholarship)* [5286]

Statistics

AAUW Selected Professions Fellowships *(Graduate, Master's, Doctorate/Fellowship)* [22]
ASA/NSF/BLS Fellowships *(Graduate/Fellowship)* [1463]
Edward C. Bryant Scholarship for an Outstanding Graduate Student in Survey Statistics *(Graduate/Scholarship)* [1464]
Burroughs Wellcome Fund Collaborative Research Travel Grants (CRTG) *(Doctorate, Postdoctorate, Professional development/Grant)* [2413]
Career Awards at the Scientific Interface (CASI) *(Doctorate, Postdoctorate, Advanced Professional, Professional development/Grant)* [2416]
Mariam K. Chamberlain Fellowships in Women and Public Policy *(Graduate/Fellowship)* [5228]
Jorge Espejel Contreras IALEIA Scholarship Award *(Undergraduate/Scholarship)* [5266]
Gertrude M. Cox Scholarships *(Graduate, Master's, Doctorate/Scholarship)* [1465]
ETS Postdoctoral Fellowships *(Postdoctorate/Fellowship)* [3806]
Harold Gulliksen Psychometric Research Fellowships *(Doctorate, Graduate/Fellowship)* [3807]
Sylvia Taylor Johnson Fellowships in Educational Measurement *(Doctorate/Fellowship)* [3808]
Ellis R. Ott Scholarships *(Graduate, Master's/Scholarship)* [1390]
Samuel S. Wilks Awards *(Advanced Professional/Award, Monetary)* [1466]

Suicide

AFSP - Distinguished Investigator Grants *(Postgraduate/Grant)* [830]
AFSP Postdoctoral Research Fellowships *(Postgraduate/Fellowship)* [831]
AFSP Standard Research Grants *(Postgraduate/Grant)* [832]
AFSP Young Investigator Grants *(Postgraduate/Grant)* [833]
American Foundation for Suicide and Prevention Pilot Grants *(Postgraduate/Grant)* [834]

Surgery

AAST/ETHICON Research Grants in Local Wound Haemostatics and Hemorrhage Control Scholarships *(Graduate, Postgraduate/Scholarship)* [589]
AAST/KCI Research Grant *(Doctorate/Grant)* [590]
AAST Medical Student, Resident and In-Training Fellow Scholarships *(Advanced Professional/Scholarship)* [591]
AATS Cardiothoracic Surgery Resident Poster Competition *(Professional development/Award)* [593]
AATS Perioperative/Team-Based Care Poster Competition *(Professional development/Award)* [595]
AATS/STS Cardiothoracic Ethics Forum Scholarships *(Professional development/Scholarship)* [597]
American Association for Hand Surgery Annual Research Awards *(Other/Award)* [500]
American Pediatric Surgical Nurses Association Educational Grants *(Other/Grant)* [1076]
American Society of Colon and Rectal Surgeons International Fellowships *(Other/Fellowship)* [1265]
American Society of Colon and Rectal Surgeons Travel Scholarships *(Other/Scholarship)* [1266]
AMSN Career Mobility Scholarship Awards *(Undergraduate, Doctorate/Scholarship)* [37]
Daland Fellowships in Clinical Investigation *(Doctorate, Postgraduate/Fellowship)* [1079]
Foundation for Surgical Technology Scholarships *(Graduate/Scholarship)* [2076]
Health Policy Scholarship for General Surgeons *(Professional development/Scholarship)* [697]
SUS Foundation Junior Faculty Grants *(Other/Grant)* [9320]
Wyeth-SUS Clinical Scholar Awards *(Other/Award)* [9321]

Surveying (See Cartography/Surveying)

Swedish studies

Lilly Lorenzen Scholarships *(Undergraduate/Scholarship)* [1470]
Malmberg Scholarships *(Undergraduate/Scholarship)* [1471]

Systems engineering

ISA Aerospace Industries Division - William H. Atkinson Scholarships *(Graduate, Undergraduate/Scholarship)* [5396]
Norman E. and Mary-Belle Huston Scholarships *(Graduate, Undergraduate/Scholarship)* [5397]
ISA Educational Foundation Scholarships *(Undergraduate/Scholarship)* [5398]
ISA Executive Board Scholarships *(Graduate, Undergraduate/Scholarship)* [5399]
ISA Section and District Scholarships - Houston *(Graduate, Undergraduate/Scholarship)* [5400]
ISA Section and District Scholarships - Lehigh Valley *(Graduate, Undergraduate/Scholarship)* [5401]
ISA Section and District Scholarships - Richmond Hopewell *(Graduate, Undergraduate/Scholarship)* [5402]
ISA Section and District Scholarships - Southwestern Wyoming *(Graduate, Undergraduate/Scholarship)* [5403]
ISA Section and District Scholarships - Texas, Louisiana and Mississippi *(Graduate, Undergraduate/Scholarship)* [5404]
ISA Section and District Scholarships - Wilmington *(Graduate, Undergraduate/Scholarship)* [5405]
ISA Technical Division Scholarships - Analysis Division *(Graduate, Undergraduate/Scholarship)* [5406]
ISA Technical Division Scholarships - Chemical and Petroleum Industries Division *(Graduate, Undergraduate/Scholarship)* [5407]
ISA Technical Division Scholarships - Food and Pharmaceutical Industries Division *(Graduate, Undergraduate/Scholarship)* [5408]
ISA Technical Division Scholarships - Power Industry Division *(Graduate, Undergraduate/Scholarship)* [5409]
ISA Technical Division Scholarships - Process Measurement and Control Division *(Graduate, Undergraduate/Scholarship)* [5410]
ISA Technical Division Scholarships - Pulp and Paper Industry Division *(Graduate, Undergraduate/Scholarship)* [5411]
ISA Technical Division Scholarships - Test Measurement Division *(Graduate, Undergraduate/Scholarship)* [5412]
ISA Technical Division Scholarships - Water and Wastewater Industries Division *(Graduate, Undergraduate/Scholarship)* [5413]
Bob and Mary Ives Scholarships *(Graduate, Undergraduate/Scholarship)* [5414]
Johns Hopkins University/Applied Physics Laboratory Alexander Kossiakoff Scholarships *(Doctorate, Graduate, Master's/Scholarship)* [5310]
James E. Long Memorial Post Doctoral Fellowships *(Postdoctorate/Fellowship)* [5311]
Stevens Doctoral Awards *(Doctorate/Award)* [5312]

Taxonomy

Charlie Fleming Education Fund Scholarships *(Undergraduate/Scholarship)* [7195]

Teaching

AACTE Outstanding Book Awards *(Other/Recognition)* [484]
AACTE Outstanding Dissertation Awards *(Doctorate/Award)* [485]
AMS Teacher Education Scholarships *(Undergraduate/Scholarship)* [1007]
Cindy Andrews Educational Scholarships *(Undergraduate/Scholarship)* [8447]
APF High School Psychology Teacher Network Grants *(Advanced Professional, Professional development/Grant)* [1139]
Verna Curry Boyer Scholarships *(Undergraduate/Scholarship)* [9564]
Leon Bradley Scholarship Program *(Undergraduate/Scholarship)* [575]
Quincy Brown Memorial Scholarships *(Undergraduate/Scholarship)* [8461]
Jennifer Coulter Memorial Scholarships *(Undergraduate/Scholarship)* [7821]
June Danby and Pat Pearse Education Scholarships *(Undergraduate/Scholarship)* [5500]
Patricia Hughes Eastaugh Teaching Scholarship *(Undergraduate/Scholarship)* [10016]
ETS Postdoctoral Fellowships *(Postdoctorate/Fellowship)* [3806]
Future Leader Initial NCTM Annual Meeting Attendance Awards *(Advanced Professional/Award, Monetary)* [6888]
Harold Gulliksen Psychometric Research Fellowships *(Doctorate, Graduate/Fellowship)* [3807]
Ida L. Hartenberg Charitable Scholarships *(Undergraduate/Scholarship)* [4755]
Harvey Fellows Program *(Graduate/Fellowship)* [6632]
J. Jay Hostetler Scholarships *(Undergraduate/Scholarship)* [5672]

Illinois Future Teacher Corps Scholarships *(Undergraduate/Scholarship)* [5072]
David G. Imig Awards for Distinguished Achievement in Teacher Education *(Other/Recognition)* [486]
ITEEA Greer/FTE Grants *(Other/Grant)* [5437]
Sylvia Taylor Johnson Fellowships in Educational Measurement *(Doctorate/Fellowship)* [3808]
The Johnson & Wales Scholarships *(Undergraduate/Scholarship)* [5631]
Mary Jon and J. P. Bryan Leadership in Education Awards *(Advanced Professional/Award)* [9716]
KHEAA Teacher Scholarship *(Undergraduate/Scholarship)* [2262]
Herb Kohl Educational Foundation Teacher Fellowships *(Professional development/Fellowship)* [5859]
Canadian Zionist Federation - Dr. Leon Aryeh Kronitz Scholarships *(Undergraduate, Graduate/Scholarship)* [2640]
Doreen Legg Memorial Scholarships *(Undergraduate/Scholarship)* [8490]
Margaret B. Lindsey Award for Distinguished Research in Teacher Education *(Other/Award, Recognition)* [487]
James Madison Foundation - Junior Fellowships *(Advanced Professional/Fellowship)* [6174]
James Madison Foundation - Senior Fellowships *(Graduate/Fellowship)* [6175]
Maley/FTE Scholarships *(Graduate/Scholarship)* [5439]
Minority Teacher Loans *(Undergraduate, Graduate/Loan)* [9554]
Minority Teachers of Illinois Scholarships (MTI) *(Undergraduate/Scholarship)* [5078]
North Carolina Council of Epsilon Sigma Alpha Scholarships *(Graduate, Other, Undergraduate/Scholarship)* [7458]
Louisa Anne Oriente Scholarships *(Graduate/Scholarship)* [5681]
Outlaw Student's Teacher Scholarships *(Undergraduate/Scholarship)* [9598]
Edward C. Pomeroy Awards for Outstanding Contributions to Teacher Education *(Other/Recognition)* [488]
Poundmaker Memorial Scholarships *(Undergraduate/Scholarship)* [10272]
Redlands Teachers Association Scholarships *(Undergraduate/Scholarship)* [8522]
Don Sahli-Kathy Woodall Graduate Scholarships *(Graduate/Scholarship)* [9677]
Sons and Daughters Don Sahli-Kathy Woodall Scholarships *(Graduate, Undergraduate/Scholarship)* [9678]
John M. and Mary A. Shanley Memorial Scholarships *(Undergraduate, Graduate/Scholarship)* [9448]
Donna Gail Shaw Scholarship for Chapter Service *(Undergraduate, Graduate, Doctorate/Scholarship)* [5684]
Step Up Scholarships *(Undergraduate, Graduate/Scholarship)* [8731]
John I. and Madeleine R. Taeni Scholarships *(Undergraduate/Scholarship)* [9452]
Teacher Education Scholarships *(Advanced Professional/Scholarship)* [1008]
Teacher of the Visually Impaired Loans *(Undergraduate, Graduate/Loan)* [9556]
University of Hawaii at Manoa Graduate Assistantship Awards *(Graduate/Award)* [10140]
Edwyna Wheadon Postgraduate Training Scholarship Fund *(Postgraduate/Scholarship)* [6886]

Technical communications

Alaska Aerospace Development Corporation Scholarships *(Undergraduate/Scholarship)* [10004]
Marian Norby Scholarships *(Other/Scholarship)* [9310]
Melissa Pellegrin Memorial Scholarships *(Undergraduate, Graduate/Scholarship)* [7751]
SBE/Ennes Youth Scholarships *(Undergraduate/Scholarship)* [9094]
STC-Lone Star Chapter Traditional Education Scholarships *(Graduate, Undergraduate/Scholarship)* [9313]
STC-PSC Scholarships *(Undergraduate, Graduate/Scholarship)* [9315]
STC Scholarships *(Graduate, Undergraduate/Scholarship)* [9311]

Technical training (See Education, Vocational-technical)

Technology

Accenture American Indian Scholarship Program *(Graduate, Undergraduate/Scholarship)* [880]
AFCEA Science, Technology, Engineering and Math Teachers Scholarships *(Graduate/Scholarship, Grant)* [87]
AFFIRM University Scholarships *(Undergraduate/Scholarship)* [1961]
AfterCollege STEM Inclusion Scholarships *(Undergraduate, Graduate/Scholarship)* [102]
AGE-WELL Graduate Student and Postdoctoral Awards in Technology and Aging *(Master's, Doctorate, Postdoctorate/Award)* [111]
AHETEMS General Scholarships *(Undergraduate, Graduate/Scholarship)* [8888]
AHETEMS Professional Scholarships *(Graduate/Scholarship)* [8889]
A.T. Anderson Memorial Scholarships *(Graduate, Undergraduate/Scholarship)* [889]
ASGP Graduate Research Fellowships *(Graduate/Fellowship)* [223]
Bank of America Junior Achievement Scholarship Fund *(Undergraduate/Scholarship)* [4177]
Kathi Bowles Scholarships for Women in Technology *(Undergraduate, Graduate/Scholarship)* [2091]
Buick Achievers Scholarship Program *(Undergraduate/Scholarship)* [4359]
Graduate Fellowship Program - Robert M. Burger Fellowships *(Doctorate, Graduate/Fellowship)* [8832]
Arthur and Gladys Cervenka Scholarships *(Undergraduate/Scholarship)* [9168]
Chapter 6 Fairfield County Scholarships *(Undergraduate/Scholarship)* [9177]
CHCI Graduate Fellowships *(Graduate/Fellowship)* [3352]
CN Scholarships for Women *(Undergraduate/Scholarship)* [2692]
CNS-UCSB Graduate Fellowships for Science and Engineering *(Postdoctorate/Fellowship)* [10127]
Development Fund for Black Students in Science and Technology Scholarships *(Undergraduate/Scholarship)* [3612]
William P. Elrod Memorial Scholarships *(Undergraduate/Scholarship)* [9656]
Lt. Colonel Romeo and Josephine Bass Ferretti Scholarships *(Undergraduate/Scholarship)* [124]
Future STEM Teacher Scholarship *(Undergraduate/Scholarship)* [9657]
Graduate Fellowship Program - Research Fellowships (GFP) *(Doctorate, Graduate/Fellowship)* [8833]
GREAT MINDS Collegiate Scholarship Program *(Undergraduate/Scholarship)* [338]
HACU/NASCAR Scholarships *(Graduate, Undergraduate/Scholarship)* [4888]
Perry F. Hadlock Memorial Scholarships *(Undergraduate/Scholarship)* [1742]
Hamilton Industrial Environmental Association Bursaries-Mohawk College *(Undergraduate/Scholarship)* [4691]
Helm Family Scholarships *(Undergraduate/Scholarship)* [8706]
Hinman-Jensen Endowed Scholarships *(Undergraduate/Scholarship)* [6032]
ITEEA Greer/FTE Grants *(Other/Grant)* [5437]
Janelia Farm Graduate Program *(Graduate/Award)* [4978]
The Johnson & Wales Scholarships *(Undergraduate/Scholarship)* [5631]
Lucile B. Kaufman Women's Scholarships *(Undergraduate/Scholarship)* [9184]
Graduate Fellowship Program - Mahboob Khan/Advanced Micro Devices Fellowships *(Doctorate, Graduate/Fellowship)* [8834]
Laser Technology, Engineering and Applications Scholarships *(Graduate, Undergraduate/Scholarship)* [9469]
Litherland/FTEE Scholarships *(Undergraduate/Scholarship)* [5438]
MAES Founders Scholarships *(Graduate, Undergraduate/Scholarship)* [6178]
MAES General Scholarships *(Graduate, Undergraduate/Scholarship)* [6179]
MAES Graduate Scholarships *(Graduate/Scholarship)* [6180]
MAES Padrino/Madrina Scholarships *(Graduate, Undergraduate/Scholarship)* [6181]
MAES Pipeline Scholarships *(Graduate, Undergraduate/Scholarship)* [6182]
MAES Presidential Scholarships *(Graduate, Undergraduate/Scholarship)* [6183]
Malayalee Engineers Association Scholarships *(Undergraduate/Fellowship)* [6225]
Maley/FTE Scholarships *(Graduate/Scholarship)* [5439]
Maley/FTEE Teacher Scholarships *(Professional development/Scholarship)* [5440]
Giuliano Mazzetti Scholarships *(Undergraduate/Scholarship)* [9188]
Michigan Council of Women in Technology High School Scholarship Program *(Undergraduate/Scholarship)* [6467]
Michigan Council of Women in Technology Undergraduate Scholarship Program *(Undergraduate/Scholarship)* [6468]
National Science Foundation Graduate Research Fellowship Program (NSF-GRFP) *(Graduate/Fellowship)* [7125]
NDIA Picatinny Chapter Scholarships *(Undergraduate/Scholarship)* [6909]
Dr. Ezra Nesbeth Scholarships *(Undergraduate/Scholarship)* [5526]
Nixon Family Scholarship Fund *(Undergraduate, High School/Scholarship)* [10506]
Ocean Industries Student Research Awards *(Undergraduate, Graduate, Postdoctorate/Award)* [8557]
Ohio Space Grant Consortium Graduate Fellowships *(Graduate, Doctorate, Master's/Fellowship)* [7594]
Ohio Space Grant Consortium Special Minority Fellowships *(Doctorate, Graduate, Master's/Fellowship)* [7595]
Portable Sanitation Association International Scholarship Fund *(Undergraduate/Scholarship)* [8207]
Proven Data Recovery Technology Scholarships *(All/Scholarship)* [8315]
Jack Rosen Scholarship *(Undergraduate/Scholarship)* [5683]
Science, Mathematics And Research for Transformation Scholarship for Service Program (SMART) *(Undergraduate, Graduate/Scholarship)* [1305]
SHPE Dissertation Scholarship *(Doctorate/Scholarship)* [9130]
SHPE Professional Scholarship *(Master's, Doctorate/Scholarship)* [9131]
Society of Manufacturing Engineers Ford PAS Scholarships (SME) *(Undergraduate/Scholarship)* [9197]
SPEATBC Scholarships *(Undergraduate, High School/Scholarship)* [9296]
SRC Master's Scholarships Program (MSP) *(Graduate, Master's/Scholarship)* [8835]
SREB-State Doctoral Scholars Program - Doctoral Awards *(Doctorate, Graduate/Scholarship)* [9411]
Eben Tisdale Fellowships *(Undergraduate/Fellowship)* [4310]
USGA/Chevron STEM Scholarship Program *(Undergraduate/Scholarship)* [9954]
VEF Fellowship Program *(Doctorate, Master's/Fellowship)* [10380]
VEF Visiting Scholars Program *(Doctorate/Fellowship)* [10381]
Myrtle & Earl Walker Scholarships *(Undergraduate/Scholarship)* [9199]
William E. Weisel Scholarships *(Undergraduate/Scholarship)* [9201]
Samuel S. Wilks Awards *(Advanced Professional/Award, Monetary)* [1466]
Wisconsin Laboratory Association Graduate Student Scholarships *(Graduate/Scholarship)* [10627]

Wisconsin Laboratory Association Technical Student Scholarships *(Undergraduate, Graduate/Scholarship)* [10628]
Wisconsin Laboratory Association Undergraduate University Student Scholarships *(Undergraduate/Scholarship)* [10629]
WSGC Community College Transfer Scholarships *(Undergraduate/Scholarship)* [10455]

Telecommunications systems

APS/ASU Scholarships *(Undergraduate/Scholarship)* [8139]
Jim Bourque Scholarship *(Undergraduate/Scholarship)* [1617]
Dickey Rural Networks College Scholarship Program *(Undergraduate, Vocational/Occupational/Scholarship)* [3618]
Future Leader in Radiocommunications Scholarships *(Undergraduate/Scholarship)* [3394]
OAS Scholarships for Professional Development - Disaster Communications Management *(Professional development/Scholarship)* [7723]
OAS Scholarships for Professional Development - Radio Spectrum Monitoring Techniques and Procedures *(Professional development/Scholarship)* [7724]
OAS Scholarships for Professional Development - Satellite Communications *(Professional development/Scholarship)* [7725]
OAS Scholarships for Professional Development - The ABC of Telecommunications *(Professional development/Scholarship)* [7726]
Snodgrass Scholarships *(Undergraduate/Scholarship)* [10039]
The SSPI Mid-Atlantic Chapter Scholarships *(Graduate, Undergraduate/Scholarship)* [9300]
RABC William Taylor Scholarships *(Undergraduate/Scholarship)* [3846]

Television (See Radio and television)

Testing, educational/psychological

AERA-ETS Fellowship Program in Measurement and Education Research *(Doctorate/Fellowship)* [783]
ASNT Fellowship Award *(Graduate/Fellowship, Award)* [1384]
Robert B. Oliver ASNT Scholarships *(Undergraduate/Scholarship)* [1385]

Textile science

California Association of Family and Consumer Sciences - San Diego Chapter Scholarships (CAFCS) *(Undergraduate, Graduate/Scholarship)* [8695]
S. Penny Chappell Scholarships *(Undergraduate/Scholarship)* [8085]
ITAA Graduate Student Best Paper Award *(Graduate/Monetary)* [5442]
Charles H. Stone Scholarships *(Undergraduate/Scholarship)* [2081]
Sutherland/Purdy Scholarships *(Undergraduate/Scholarship)* [8109]

Theater arts

AFA Theatre & Performance Art Project Grants *(Professional development/Grant)* [243]
Margaret M. Alkek Scholarships *(Undergraduate/Scholarship)* [3548]
ASTR Research Fellowships *(Other/Fellowship)* [1433]
Leighton M. Ballew Directing Scholarships *(Undergraduate/Scholarship)* [9387]
David Beltran Memorial Scholarships *(Undergraduate/Scholarship)* [8458]
Helen Krich Chinoy Dissertation Research Fellowships *(Doctorate/Fellowship)* [1434]
William R. Durham/Theater Scholarships *(Undergraduate/Scholarship)* [3282]
S. Randolph Edmonds Young Scholars Competition *(Graduate, Undergraduate/Scholarship)* [2303]
Polly Holliday Scholarships *(Undergraduate/Scholarship)* [9388]
Indiana State University Creative and Performing Arts Awards *(Undergraduate/Scholarship)* [5127]
Jerome Fellowships *(Other/Fellowship)* [8152]
Robert G. Lawrence Prize *(Doctorate, Other, Graduate/Prize, Award)* [1902]
Many Voices Fellowships *(Other/Fellowship)* [8153]
McKnight Advancement Grants *(Other/Grant)* [8154]
McKnight Theater Artist Fellowships *(Other/Fellowship)* [8155]
Robert Porterfield Graduate Scholarships *(Graduate/Scholarship)* [9389]
PWC Internships *(Undergraduate, Graduate/Internship)* [8156]
Stephen Schwartz Musical Theatre Scholarships *(Undergraduate/Scholarship)* [4988]
Anne Shaw Fellowships *(Graduate/Fellowship)* [9727]
Marian A. Smith Scholarships *(Graduate/Scholarship)* [9390]
Southeastern Theatre Conference Secondary School Scholarships *(Undergraduate/Scholarship)* [9391]
Theatre Guild Scholarship *(Undergraduate/Scholarship)* [9725]
Patricia Van Kirk Scholarships *(Undergraduate/Scholarship)* [8267]
Wilder Dimension Scholarships for Advanced Study in Theatre Arts *(Graduate/Scholarship)* [3693]
Redlands Footlighters, Inc. - Merle and Peggy Williams Scholarships *(Undergraduate/Scholarship)* [8530]
William E. Wilson Scholarships *(Graduate/Scholarship)* [9392]
Gwen Yarnell Theatre Scholarships *(Undergraduate/Scholarship)* [4028]

Theology (See also Religion)

Ellen Blodgett Memorial Scholarships *(Undergraduate/Scholarship)* [7375]
William L. Bradley Memorial Scholarships *(Undergraduate/Scholarship)* [7376]
Paul W. Bradley Scholarships *(Undergraduate/Scholarship)* [7377]
Pamfil and Maria Bujea Family Orthodox Christian Seminarian Scholarships *(Undergraduate/Scholarship)* [1225]
Calihan Academic Fellowships *(Graduate, Professional development/Fellowship, Grant)* [56]
Calihan Travel Grants *(Graduate/Grant)* [57]
CSF Graduate Fellowships *(Graduate/Fellowship)* [2936]
Esther Cummings Memorial Scholarships *(Undergraduate/Scholarship)* [7378]
Margaret Eddy Scholarships *(Graduate/Scholarship)* [7379]
FTE Dissertation Fellowships *(Graduate, Doctorate/Fellowship)* [4153]
FTE Doctoral Fellowships *(Doctorate, Graduate/Fellowship)* [4154]
FTE North American Doctoral Fellowships *(Doctorate, Graduate/Fellowship)* [4155]
Ethel Mae Gaston Memorial Scholarships *(Undergraduate/Scholarship)* [7380]
Emily V. Gibbes Scholarships *(Undergraduate/Scholarship)* [7381]
William Randolph Hearst Endowed Scholarships *(Undergraduatz/Scholarship)* [7382]
Melvyn F. Hester Scholarships *(Master's, Professional development/Scholarship)* [7383]
Barbara J. and M. William Howard Jr. Scholarships *(Undergraduate/Scholarship)* [7384]
Sang Ok Hur Scholarships *(Undergraduate/Scholarship)* [7385]
Rev. and Mrs. A.K. Jizmejian Educational Fund *(Undergraduate/Scholarship)* [1700]
Hwain Chang Lee scholarships *(Undergraduate/Scholarship)* [7386]
William K. Lee Scholarships *(Undergraduate/Scholarship)* [7387]
Margaret Smith Maase Scholarships *(Undergraduate/Scholarship)* [7388]
Ann M. Mallouk Scholarships *(Master's/Scholarship)* [7389]
Rev. Richard S. McCarroll and Mrs. E. Allison McCarroll Scholarships *(Undergraduate, Graduate/Scholarship)* [7390]
Ella and Harold Midtbo Scholarships *(Undergraduate/Scholarship)* [7391]
William Howard Morton Scholarships *(Undergraduate, Graduate/Scholarship)* [7392]
Novak Awards *(Doctorate/Monetary)* [58]
Abraham A. Oyedeji Scholarships *(Undergraduate/Scholarship)* [7393]
J. Milton Richardson Theological Fellowships *(Graduate/Fellowship)* [363]
The Tabat Scholarship Fund *(Graduate/Scholarship)* [4005]
George D. Younger Scholarships *(Undergraduate/Scholarship)* [7394]

Tourette syndrome

Tourette Association of America Research Grant Awards *(Master's, Doctorate/Grant)* [9758]

Toxicology

AACT Junior Investigator Research Grants *(Professional development/Grant)* [402]
AACT Toxicology Trainee Research Grants *(Professional development/Grant)* [403]
GWS Scholarships *(Undergraduate, Graduate/Scholarship)* [145]
International Association for Food Protection - Student Travel Scholarship Program *(Undergraduate, Graduate/Scholarship)* [5258]
NCCT Postdoctoral Research Program *(Postdoctorate, Advanced Professional, Professional development/Fellowship)* [9941]
Pharmacology/Toxicology Pre Doctoral Fellowships *(Doctorate/Fellowship)* [8033]
PhRMA Foundation Pharmacology/Toxicology Research Starter Grants *(Doctorate/Grant)* [8040]
PhRMA Foundation Pharmacology/Toxicology Sabbatical Fellowships *(Postdoctorate/Fellowship)* [8041]
PhRMA Foundatiion Pharmacology/Toxicology Post Doctoral Fellowships *(Postdoctorate/Fellowship)* [8042]
Michael P. Spadafora Medical Toxicology Travel Awards *(Professional development/Grant)* [690]

Trades training (See Education, Vocational-technical)

Traffic management (See Transportation)

Translating

Beca #Traductor Scholarships *(All/Scholarship)* [9458]
Institute for Anarchist Studies Grants for Radical Writers and Translators *(Professional development/Grant)* [5165]
Leif and Inger Sjöberg Awards *(Advanced Professional, Professional development/Award, Grant, Prize)* [1235]

Transportation

ABA Diversity Scholarships *(Undergraduate/Scholarship)* [636]
ABA Members Scholarships for ABA Bus and Tour Operators Only *(Undergraduate/Scholarship)* [637]
ABA Members Scholarships for All ABA Member Companies *(Undergraduate, Graduate/Scholarship)* [638]
Air Traffic Control Association Full-time Employee Student Scholarships *(Other/Scholarship)* [135]
American Bus Association Academic Merit Scholar-

TRAVEL AND TOURISM

ships *(Undergraduate, Graduate/Scholarship)* [639]
Sharon D. Banks Undergraduate Memorial Scholarships *(Undergraduate/Scholarship)* [10674]
Richard J. Bouchard AECOM Scholarships *(Undergraduate, Graduate/Scholarship)* [1162]
Parsons Brinckerhoff-Jim Lammie Scholarships *(Undergraduate, Graduate/Scholarship)* [1163]
Continuing Education Awards *(Undergraduate/Scholarship, Award)* [6778]
CTP Scholarship Program *(Other/Scholarship)* [7113]
Delta Nu Alpha Foundation Scholarships *(Undergraduate/Scholarship)* [3573]
Florida Public Transportation Association Scholarships (FPTA) *(Undergraduate, Graduate/Scholarship)* [1164]
Jack R. Gilstrap Scholarships *(Undergraduate, Graduate/Scholarship)* [1165]
Gabe A. Hartl Scholarships *(Undergraduate/Scholarship)* [137]
HSF/Marathon Oil College Scholarship Program *(Undergraduate/Scholarship)* [4905]
Institute of Transportation Engineers - Texas District Fellowships *(Graduate/Fellowship)* [5219]
Institute of Transportation Engineers - Western District Fellowships *(Graduate/Fellowship)* [5220]
Louis T. Klauder Scholarships *(Undergraduate, Graduate/Scholarship)* [1166]
Reba Malone Scholarships *(Undergraduate, Graduate/Scholarship)* [1167]
NDTA Academic Scholarship Program A *(Undergraduate/Scholarship)* [6913]
NDTA Academic Scholarship Program B *(Undergraduate/Scholarship)* [6914]
Helene M. Overly Memorial Scholarships *(Undergraduate/Scholarship)* [10675]
Peter L. Picknelly Honorary Scholarships *(Undergraduate/Scholarship)* [640]
Dan M. Reichard, Jr. Scholarships *(Undergraduate, Graduate/Scholarship)* [1168]
Frank J. Richter Scholarships *(Graduate, Undergraduate/Scholarship)* [570]
SC and R Foundation Scholarships *(Undergraduate/Scholarship)* [9460]
SC&R Foundation Grant Program *(Undergraduate/Grant)* [9461]
E.J. Sierleja Memorial Fellowships *(Graduate/Fellowship)* [5194]
Dr. George M. Smerk Scholarships *(Undergraduate, Graduate/Scholarship)* [1169]
Snowmobile Association of Massachusetts Scholarships *(Undergraduate/Scholarship)* [9045]
TAC Foundation-3M Canada Company Scholarships *(Graduate, Undergraduate/Scholarship)* [9768]
TAC Foundation-407 ETR Scholarships *(Undergraduate, Graduate/Scholarship)* [9769]
TAC Foundation-Amec Foster Wheeler Scholarships *(Undergraduate, Graduate/Scholarship)* [9770]
TAC Foundation-ATS Traffic Group of Companies Scholarships *(Undergraduate, Graduate/Scholarship)* [9771]
TAC Foundation-Canadian Council of Independent Laboratories Graduate Student Scholarships *(Graduate/Scholarship)* [9772]
TAC Foundation-CCMTA Road Safety Scholarships *(Undergraduate, Graduate/Scholarship)* [9773]
TAC Foundation-Cement Association of Canada Scholarships *(Graduate, Undergraduate/Scholarship)* [9774]
TAC Foundation-Dillon Consulting Scholarships *(Undergraduate, Graduate/Scholarship)* [9775]
TAC Foundation-Dr. Ralph Haas Graduate Student Scholarships *(Graduate/Scholarship)* [9776]
TAC Foundation-EllisDon Community College/CEGEP Scholarships *(Undergraduate/Scholarship)* [9777]
TAC Foundation-exp Scholarships *(Undergraduate, Graduate/Scholarship)* [9778]
TAC Foundation-Golder Associates Ltd. Scholarships *(Undergraduate, Graduate/Scholarship)* [9779]
TAC Foundation-HDR Corporation Graduate Student Scholarships *(Graduate/Scholarship)* [9780]
TAC Foundation-IBI Group Scholarships *(Undergraduate, Graduate/Scholarship)* [9781]

TAC Foundation-ISL Engineering Scholarships *(Undergraduate, Graduate/Scholarship)* [9782]
TAC Foundation-LEA Consulting Ltd. Scholarships *(Undergraduate, Graduate/Scholarship)* [9783]
TAC Foundation-MMM Group Limited Scholarships *(Undergraduate, Graduate/Scholarship)* [9784]
TAC Foundation-Municipalities Scholarships *(Undergraduate, Graduate/Scholarship)* [9785]
TAC Foundation-Parsons Scholarships *(Undergraduate, Graduate/Scholarship)* [9786]
TAC Foundation-Peto MacCallum Undergraduate & College Scholarships *(Undergraduate/Scholarship)* [9787]
TAC Foundation-Provinces and Territories Scholarships *(Undergraduate, Graduate/Scholarship)* [9788]
TAC Foundation-SNC Lavalin Scholarships *(Undergraduate, Graduate/Scholarship)* [9789]
TAC Foundation-Stantec Consulting Scholarships *(Graduate/Scholarship)* [9790]
TAC Foundation-Tetra Tech EBA Inc. Scholarships *(Undergraduate, Graduate/Scholarship)* [9791]
Transoft Solutions, Inc. Ahead of the Curve Scholarships (AOTC) *(Graduate, Undergraduate/Scholarship)* [5221]
Transportation Association of Canada Foundation Scholarships *(Graduate, Undergraduate/Scholarship)* [9792]

Travel and tourism

ABA Diversity Scholarships *(Undergraduate/Scholarship)* [636]
ABA Members Scholarships for ABA Bus and Tour Operators Only *(Undergraduate/Scholarship)* [637]
ABA Members Scholarships for All ABA Member Companies *(Undergraduate, Graduate/Scholarship)* [638]
America Express Travel Scholarships *(Undergraduate/Scholarship)* [1436]
American Bus Association Academic Merit Scholarships *(Undergraduate, Graduate/Scholarship)* [639]
Applied Hospitality Degree Scholarships *(Undergraduate/Scholarship)* [2657]
ASTA Alaska Airlines Scholarships *(Undergraduate/Scholarship)* [1437]
ASTA Holland America Line Graduate Research Scholarships *(Graduate/Scholarship)* [1438]
ASTA Rigby, Healy, Simmons Scholarships *(Graduate/Scholarship)* [1439]
Avis Budget Group Scholarships *(Graduate/Scholarship)* [1440]
Canadian Hospitality Foundation College Entrance Scholarships *(Undergraduate/Scholarship)* [2658]
Canadian Hospitality Foundation University Entrance Scholarships *(Undergraduate/Scholarship)* [2659]
Sue and Ken Dyer Foundation Travel Scholarships *(Undergraduate/Scholarship)* [4238]
Graduate Student Travel Grants *(Doctorate, Master's/Grant)* [462]
David J. Hallissey Memorial Internships *(Graduate, Undergraduate/Internship)* [1441]
ISTTE Scholarships *(Graduate, Undergraduate/Scholarship)* [5435]
Mike Kabo Global Scholarships *(Other/Scholarship)* [4456]
NC Hospitality Education Foundation Scholarships - Four Year College or University *(Undergraduate/Scholarship)* [7473]
NC Hospitality Education Foundation Scholarships - High School *(Undergraduate/Scholarship)* [7475]
NC Hospitality Education Foundation Scholarships - Two Year Community or Junior College *(Undergraduate/Scholarship)* [7476]
Peter L. Picknelly Honorary Scholarships *(Undergraduate/Scholarship)* [640]
George Reinke Scholarships *(Other/Scholarship)* [1442]
Thomas and Ruth River International Scholarships *(Undergraduate, Graduate/Scholarship)* [10704]
South Carolina Tourism and Hospitality Educational Foundation Scholarships *(Undergraduate/Scholarship)* [9366]

Allegheny Branch of Mid-America Chapter - Nancy Stewart Professional Development Scholarships *(Professional development/Scholarship)* [1443]
TIAC / Parks Canada Sustainable Tourism Scholarships *(Undergraduate, Master's/Scholarship)* [9760]

Tuberculosis

Firland Foundation Graduate Pulmonary Nursing Fellowships *(Professional development/Fellowship)* [4034]
Cedric Northrop Fellowships *(Professional development/Fellowship)* [4035]

Turfgrass management

GCSAA Scholars Competition *(Undergraduate/Scholarship)* [4483]
GCSAA Student Essay Contest *(Graduate, Undergraduate/Prize)* [4484]
Drew Smith Memorial Scholarships *(Undergraduate/Scholarship)* [3187]
Dr. James Watson Fellowship Program *(Doctorate, Graduate/Fellowship)* [4485]

Turkish studies

Institute of Turkish Studies Dissertation Writing Grants *(Graduate/Grant)* [5223]
Institute of Turkish Studies Post-Doctoral Summer Travel-Research Grants *(Postdoctorate/Grant)* [5224]
Institute of Turkish Studies Sabbatical Research Grants *(Other/Grant)* [5225]
Institute of Turkish Studies Summer Language Study Grants in Turkey *(Graduate/Grant)* [5226]

Ukrainian studies

Leo J. Krysa Family Undergraduate Scholarships *(Undergraduate/Scholarship)* [2674]
Ukrainian Canadian Professional and Business Club Scholarships in Education *(Undergraduate/Scholarship)* [2675]

United States studies

AAS-American Historical Print Collectors Society Fellowships *(Doctorate/Fellowship)* [428]
The Christoph Daniel Ebeling Fellowships *(Postdoctorate, Postgraduate/Fellowship)* [437]
Hench Post-Dissertation Fellowship *(Postdoctorate/Fellowship)* [438]
Institute-NEH Postdoctoral Fellowships *(Doctorate, Other/Fellowship)* [7613]
Kislak Fellowships in American Studies *(Graduate, Postdoctorate/Fellowship)* [5844]
Kislak Short Term Fellowships Opportunities in American Studies *(Undergraduate, Graduate/Fellowship)* [5845]
Marshall-Baruch Fellowships *(Doctorate/Fellowship)* [6295]
Institute Andrew W. Mellon Postdoctoral Research Fellowships *(Doctorate/Fellowship)* [7614]
The Reese Fellowships *(Doctorate/Fellowship)* [444]
Salvatori Fellowships *(Graduate/Fellowship)* [5234]
United States Capitol Historical Society Fellowships *(Graduate/Fellowship)* [9886]

Urban affairs/design/planning

American Planning Association ENRE Student Fellowship Program *(Graduate/Fellowship)* [1103]
Robert A. Catlin/David W. Long Memorial Fellowships *(Graduate/Fellowship)* [1104]
CIGNA Healthcare Graduate Scholarships *(Graduate/Scholarship)* [6957]
CIGNA Healthcare Undergraduate Scholarships *(Undergraduate/Scholarship)* [6958]
HECUA Scholarship for Community Engagement *(Undergraduate/Scholarship)* [4878]
Holzheimer Memorial Student Scholarship for Economic Development Planning *(Graduate, Master's/Scholarship)* [1105]
Jewish Federation Academic Scholarships *(Gradu-*

ate, Undergraduate/Scholarship) [5598]
McCloy Fellowships in Urban Affairs (Professional development/Fellowship) [730]
Judith McManus Price Scholarships (Undergraduate, Graduate/Scholarship) [1106]
Resilience Action Fund Scholarships (Graduate/Scholarship) [3981]
UC MEXUS-CONACYT Doctoral Fellowships (Doctorate/Fellowship) [10117]
Vectorworks Design Scholarships (Undergraduate, Graduate/Scholarship, Prize) [10367]
Worldstudio AIGA Scholarships (Graduate, Undergraduate/Scholarship) [10709]

Urology

AUA Foundation Urology Research Bridge Awards (Postgraduate/Award) [10346]
Endourological Society Fellowships (Professional development/Fellowship) [3867]
KFOC Allied Health Scholarships (Graduate/Scholarship) [5826]
KFOC Biomedical Scholarships (Doctorate/Scholarship) [5828]
Urology Care Foundation/Astellas Rising Star in Urology Research Awards (Postdoctorate, Other/Award) [10347]

Vacuum science and technology

Society of Vacuum Coaters Foundation Scholarships (Vocational/Occupational, Two Year College, Undergraduate, Graduate/Scholarship) [9323]

Veterinary science and medicine

AABP Amstutz Scholarships (Undergraduate/Scholarship) [466]
AABP Bovine Veterinary Student Recognition Awards (Undergraduate/Scholarship) [467]
AABP Education Grants (Undergraduate/Grant) [468]
AABP Student Externship Program (Undergraduate/Scholarship) [469]
AAEP/ALSIC Scholarships (Undergraduate/Scholarship) [495]
AAEP Foundation Past Presidents' Research Fellowships (Graduate, Professional development/Scholarship) [496]
ACVO Best Resident Manuscript Awards (Undergraduate/Recognition) [699]
American Quarter Horse Foundation Scholarships (Undergraduate/Scholarship) [1171]
Animal Compassion Undergraduate Scholarships (Undergraduate/Scholarship) [8015]
Army Health Professions Scholarships Program (Professional development/Scholarship) [9878]
AVMA Fellowship Program (Professional development/Fellowship) [1478]
DAAD Study Scholarship Awards (Graduate/Scholarship) [3604]
Discover Health Professions Loans (Graduate/Loan) [3636]
Discover Residency Loans (Graduate/Loan) [3639]
Downeast Feline Scholarships (Graduate/Scholarship) [6194]
Keith Gilmore Foundation - Postgraduate Scholarships (Postgraduate/Scholarship) [4424]
Keith Gilmore Foundation - Undergraduate Scholarships (Undergraduate/Scholarship) [4425]
M.G. "Doc" Headley Scholarships (Undergraduate/Scholarship) [9570]
Investigators in the Pathogenesis of Infectious Disease Awards (Doctorate, Postdoctorate, Professional development/Grant) [2417]
Dr. Roger E. Meisner Veterinary Medicine Educational Scholarship Fund (Undergraduate/Scholarship) [7501]
North Dakota Veterinary Medical Association Scholarships (Undergraduate/Scholarship) [7502]
Laurie Page-Peck Scholarship Fund (Undergraduate/Scholarship) [2103]
Pappaioanou Veterinary Public Health and Applied Epidemiology Fellowships (Undergraduate/Fellowship) [2833]
Stark County Dairy Promoters Scholarships (Undergraduate/Scholarship) [9536]
Veterinary and Pre-Veterinary Academic Scholarships (Undergraduate/Scholarship) [3647]
Welder Wildlife Foundation Fellowships (Graduate, Master's, Doctorate/Fellowship) [10510]
Dr. William "Tim" Whalen Memorial Scholarships (Undergraduate/Scholarship) [7503]
Saul T. Wilson, Jr. Scholarships (Graduate, Undergraduate/Scholarship) [9888]

Video

AFA Film and Video Arts Project Grants (Professional development/Grant) [240]
Carole Fielding Student Grant (Undergraduate, Graduate/Grant) [10131]

Vietnamese studies

Gamewarden Scholarship program (High School, Undergraduate, Vocational/Occupational/Scholarship) [4320]
BM1 James Elliott Williams Memorial Scholarship Fund (Undergraduate/Scholarship) [7922]

Violence (See Aggression and violence)

Violin (See Music, Violin)

Visual arts

AFA Visual Arts and New Media Project Grants (Professional development/Grant) [244]
Arts Council of Greater Grand Rapids Minority Scholarships (Undergraduate/Scholarship) [4574]
William E. Barto Scholarships (Undergraduate/Scholarship) [3704]
Bill Bendiner and Doug Morgenson Scholarships (Undergraduate/Scholarship) [8246]
CBC Spouses Visual Arts Scholarships (Undergraduate/Scholarship) [3347]
Cintas Foundation Fellowships in Visual Arts (Professional development/Fellowship) [3032]
Sally Cole Visual Arts Scholarship Fund (Undergraduate/Scholarship) [4190]
College Art Association Wyeth Publication Grants (Other/Grant) [3119]
Constant Memorial Scholarship (Undergraduate/Scholarship) [8604]
Jack Kent Cooke Graduate Arts Awards (Graduate/Award) [5493]
FCA Grants to Artists (Advanced Professional/Grant) [4227]
Florida Education Fund McKnight Doctoral Fellowships (Graduate/Fellowship) [4085]
Manzer-Keener-Wefler Scholarships (Undergraduate/Scholarship) [9521]
Elizabeth Massey Award (Postgraduate/Award) [2631]
Jack D. Motteler Scholarships (Undergraduate/Scholarship) [8257]
Native Hawaiian Visual Arts Scholarships (Graduate, Undergraduate/Scholarship) [7917]
New Museum Bogliasco Fellowship in Visual Art (Professional development/Fellowship) [2330]
Dr. Adolph Piotrowski Memorial Art Scholarships (Undergraduate/Scholarship) [8588]
Piscataqua Region Artist Advancement Grants (Professional development/Grant) [7305]
Robert W. and Bernice Ingalls Staton Scholarships (Undergraduate/Scholarship) [10259]
Ric Ulrich and Chuck Pischke Scholarships (Undergraduate/Scholarship) [8266]
Patricia Van Kirk Scholarships (Undergraduate/Scholarship) [8267]
Virginia Museum of Fine Arts Visual Arts Fellowships (Graduate, Other, Undergraduate/Fellowship) [10400]

Visual impairment

Teacher of the Visually Impaired Loans (Undergraduate, Graduate/Loan) [9556]
Thome Foundation Awards Program in Age-Related Macular Degeneration Research (Professional development/Grant) [4824]

Viticulture

American Society for Enology and Viticulture Scholarships (Graduate, Undergraduate/Scholarship) [1307]
American Wine Society Educational Foundation Scholarships (Graduate/Scholarship) [1528]
Nancy Johnston Memorial Scholarships (Graduate, Undergraduate/Scholarship) [9675]

Vocational-technical education (See Education, Vocational-technical)

Waste management

A&WMA Scholarships (Graduate/Scholarship) [139]
Dave Benferado Scholarships (Graduate/Scholarship) [140]
Environmental Research and Education Foundation Scholarships (Master's, Doctorate, Postdoctorate/Scholarship) [3900]
Milton Feldstein Memorial Scholarships (Graduate/Scholarship) [141]
GWS Scholarships (Undergraduate, Graduate/Scholarship) [145]
Ivanhoe Foundation Fellowships (Master's/Fellowship) [5488]
Jacqueline Shields Memorial Scholarships (Graduate/Scholarship) [142]
SSAWMA Scholarships (Graduate/Scholarship) [9415]
Richard Stessel Memorial Scholarships (Graduate/Scholarship) [143]

Water resources

AGWT Baroid Scholarships (Undergraduate/Scholarship) [840]
ARCADIS Scholarships (Master's, Doctorate/Scholarship) [1482]
Association of California Water Agencies Scholarships (Undergraduate/Scholarship) [1871]
AWWA American Water Scholarships (Master's, Doctorate/Scholarship) [1483]
AWWA Illinois Section Safe Water Scholarship Awards (Undergraduate, Master's, Doctorate/Scholarship) [1496]
HDR/Henry "Bud" Benjes Scholarships (Master's/Scholarship) [1484]
Leo Bourassa Scholarships (Undergraduate, Graduate/Scholarship) [10398]
Dave Caldwell Scholarships (Graduate/Scholarship) [1485]
California Sea Grant State Fellowship (Graduate/Fellowship) [2479]
Thomas R. Camp Scholarships (Graduate/Scholarship) [1486]
Canadian Water Resources Association Scholarships (Undergraduate/Scholarship) [1905]
Carollo Engineers Scholarships (Master's/Scholarship) [1487]
Channabasappa Memorial Scholarships (Graduate, Doctorate/Scholarship) [5319]
Holly Cornell Scholarship (Master's/Scholarship) [1488]
Robert Esser Student Achievement Scholarships (Graduate, Undergraduate/Scholarship) [5061]
GWS Scholarships (Undergraduate, Graduate/Scholarship) [145]
Stephen K. Hall ACWA Water Law and Policy Scholarships (Graduate/Scholarship) [1872]
B. Harper Bull Conservation Fellowships (Graduate/Fellowship) [9749]
Hazen and Sawyer Scholarships (Master's/Scholarship) [1489]
Richard A. Herbert Memorial Scholarships (Under-

graduate/Scholarship) [1480]
Clair A. Hill Scholarships *(Undergraduate/Scholarship)* [1873]
IDA Fellowship Awards *(Other/Fellowship)* [5320]
Illinois Lake Management Association Undergraduate/Graduate Scholarships *(Graduate, Undergraduate/Scholarship)* [5062]
IMS AWWA Graduate Science and Engineering Scholarships *(Graduate/Scholarship)* [5239]
Ivanhoe Foundation Fellowships *(Master's/Fellowship)* [5488]
John A. Knauss Marine Policy Fellowship *(Graduate/Fellowship)* [9890]
DSRSD James B. Kohnen Scholarships *(Undergraduate, High School/Scholarship)* [3697]
Larson Aquatic Research Support Scholarships (LARS) *(Graduate/Scholarship)* [1490]
Colonel Theodore A. Leisen Memorial and Training Endowment Funds *(Graduate, Professional development/Grant, Scholarship)* [7249]
Roy W. Likins Scholarships *(Undergraduate, Graduate/Scholarship)* [1494]
Ronald B. Linsky Fellowships for Outstanding Water Research *(Graduate, Master's, Doctorate/Fellowship)* [7213]
MWH Scholarships *(Master's/Scholarship)* [1491]
Eva Nieminski Honorary Graduate Science and Engineering Scholarships *(Graduate/Scholarship)* [5240]
NWRI Fellowships *(Graduate, Master's, Doctorate/Fellowship)* [7214]
AGWT Thomas M. Stetson Scholarships *(Undergraduate/Scholarship)* [841]
Ken Thomson Scholarships *(Undergraduate/Scholarship)* [1906]
VA AWWA Graduate Student Scholarships *(Graduate/Scholarship)* [1498]
WEF Canham Graduate Studies Scholarships *(Graduate/Scholarship)* [10480]
Abel Wolman Fellowships *(Doctorate/Fellowship)* [1492]

Water supply industry

ARCADIS Scholarships *(Master's, Doctorate/Scholarship)* [1482]
Len Assante Scholarship Fund *(Undergraduate/Scholarship)* [6976]
AWWA American Water Scholarships *(Master's, Doctorate/Scholarship)* [1483]
AWWA Illinois Section Safe Water Scholarship Awards *(Undergraduate, Master's, Doctorate/Scholarship)* [1496]
HDR/Henry "Bud" Benjes Scholarships *(Master's/Scholarship)* [1484]
Dave Caldwell Scholarships *(Graduate/Scholarship)* [1485]
Thomas R. Camp Scholarships *(Graduate/Scholarship)* [1486]
Carollo Engineers Scholarships *(Master's/Scholarship)* [1487]
Holly Cornell Scholarship *(Master's/Scholarship)* [1488]
Hazen and Sawyer Scholarships *(Master's/Scholarship)* [1489]
IMS AWWA Graduate Science and Engineering Scholarships *(Graduate/Scholarship)* [5239]
Larson Aquatic Research Support Scholarships (LARS) *(Graduate/Scholarship)* [1490]
Colonel Theodore A. Leisen Memorial and Training Endowment Funds *(Graduate, Professional development/Grant, Scholarship)* [7249]
Roy W. Likins Scholarships *(Undergraduate, Graduate/Scholarship)* [1494]
Michigan Stormwater-Floodplain Association Scholarships *(Graduate, Undergraduate/Scholarship)* [6492]
MWH Scholarships *(Master's/Scholarship)* [1491]
Eva Nieminski Honorary Graduate Science and Engineering Scholarships *(Graduate/Scholarship)* [5240]
VA AWWA Graduate Student Scholarships *(Graduate/Scholarship)* [1498]
Abel Wolman Fellowships *(Doctorate/Fellowship)* [1492]

Welding

Howard E. and Wilma J. Adkins Memorial Scholarships *(Undergraduate/Scholarship)* [1502]
American Welding Society District Scholarships *(Undergraduate/Scholarship)* [1503]
American Welding Society Graduate Research Fellowships *(Graduate/Fellowship)* [1504]
American Welding Society International Scholarships *(Undergraduate, Graduate/Scholarship)* [1505]
American Welding Society National Scholarships *(Undergraduate/Scholarship)* [1506]
American Welding Society Past Presidents Scholarships *(Undergraduate, Graduate/Scholarship)* [1507]
Arsham Amirikian Engineering Scholarships *(Undergraduate/Scholarship)* [1508]
Airgas - Jerry Baker Scholarships *(Undergraduate/Scholarship)* [1509]
Jack R. Barckhoff Welding Management Scholarships *(Undergraduate/Scholarship)* [1510]
Edward J. Brady Memorial Scholarships *(Undergraduate/Scholarship)* [1511]
William A. and Ann M. Brothers Scholarships *(Undergraduate/Scholarship)* [1512]
Aim High Jerry Clay Scholarships *(Undergraduate/Scholarship)* [4581]
Donald F. Hastings Scholarships *(Undergraduate/Scholarship)* [1513]
Donald and Shirley Hastings Scholarships *(Undergraduate/Scholarship)* [1514]
William B. Howell Scholarships *(Undergraduate/Scholarship)* [1515]
Hypertherm International HyTech Leadership Scholarships *(Graduate/Scholarship)* [1516]
ITW Welding Companies Scholarships *(Undergraduate/Scholarship)* [1517]
Airgas - Terry Jarvis Memorial Scholarships *(Undergraduate/Scholarship)* [1518]
LCSC Welding Club Scholarships *(Undergraduate/Scholarship)* [6036]
John C. Lincoln Memorial Scholarships *(Undergraduate/Scholarship)* [1519]
Miller Electric International WorldSkills Competition Scholarships *(Undergraduate/Scholarship)* [1520]
Nixon Family Scholarship Fund *(Undergraduate, High School/Scholarship)* [10506]
Robert L. Peaslee-Detroit Brazing and Soldiering Division Scholarships *(Undergraduate/Scholarship)* [1521]
Ronald C. and Joyce Pierce - Mobile Section Named Scholarships *(Undergraduate/Scholarship)* [1522]
Praxair International Scholarships *(Undergraduate/Scholarship)* [1523]
Resistance Welder Manufacturers' Association Scholarships *(Undergraduate/Scholarship)* [1524]
James A. Turner, Jr. Memorial Scholarships *(Undergraduate/Scholarship)* [1525]
Amos and Marilyn Winsand - Detroit Section Named Scholarships *(Undergraduate/Scholarship)* [1526]

Wildlife conservation, management, and science

Bat Conservation International Student Research Scholarships *(Graduate, Undergraduate/Scholarship)* [2201]
Lyle Carlson Wildlife Management Scholarships *(Undergraduate/Scholarship)* [10014]
CROW Fellowships *(All/Fellowship)* [3053]
Charles Dobbins FTA Scholarships *(Undergraduate, Vocational/Occupational/Scholarship)* [4316]
Harry Hampton Fund Scholarship *(Undergraduate/Scholarship)* [4733]
B. Harper Bull Conservation Fellowships *(Graduate/Fellowship)* [9749]
Ben Meadows Natural Resource Scholarships - Academic Achievement Scholarships *(Undergraduate/Scholarship)* [2221]
Ben Meadows Natural Resource Scholarships - Leadership Scholarships *(Undergraduate/Scholarship)* [2222]
NGC College Scholarships *(Graduate, Undergraduate/Scholarship)* [6965]
Ted Parnell Scholarship *(Undergraduate/Scholarship)* [10772]
Dennis Raveling Scholarships *(Undergraduate/Scholarship)* [2488]
Dr. Orrin Rongstad Wildlife Scholarship *(Undergraduate/Scholarship)* [10091]
Russian/Central Asian Student Scholarships *(Undergraduate/Scholarship)* [10092]
Welder Wildlife Foundation Fellowships *(Graduate, Master's, Doctorate/Fellowship)* [10510]
Wild Felid Legacy Scholarships *(Graduate/Scholarship)* [10555]

Women's studies

American Association of University Women Master's and First Professional Awards *(Other/Award)* [602]
Tara Lynn Arnold Scholarships *(Undergraduate/Scholarship)* [9562]
ASECS Women's Caucus Editing and Translation Fellowships *(Doctorate/Fellowship)* [1285]
Center for the Education of Women Student Research Grants *(Graduate, Undergraduate/Grant)* [10196]
Mariam K. Chamberlain Fellowships in Women and Public Policy *(Graduate/Fellowship)* [5228]
Emilie Du Chatelet Awards *(Doctorate/Award)* [1288]
City of Toronto Women's Studies Scholarships *(Graduate, Undergraduate/Scholarship)* [10286]
Fellowship on Women & Public Policy *(Graduate/Fellowship)* [10102]
Joseph H. Fichter Research Grants *(Other/Grant)* [2071]
Catharine Macaulay Prize *(Graduate/Prize)* [1295]
O. Ruth McQuown Scholarship - Graduate Award for Current Students *(Graduate/Scholarship)* [10135]
Ruth R. and Alyson R. Miller Fellowships *(Professional development/Fellowship)* [6335]
National Women's Studies Association Lesbian Caucus Award *(Master's, Doctorate/Award, Grant)* [7218]
Special Fund for the Study of Women and Politics *(Graduate, Postdoctorate/Grant)* [1123]
WLALA Scholarships *(Postgraduate/Scholarship)* [10647]
Women's Health Research Foundation of Canada Scholarship Program *(Graduate/Scholarship)* [10658]

Writing

AAS Fellowships for Creative and Performing Artists and Writers *(Professional development/Fellowship, Award)* [430]
CAA National Capital Region Writing Contests *(All/Award, Prize, Monetary)* [2579]
The Edit My Paper Proofreading Scholarships *(Undergraduate/Scholarship)* [3785]
Velma Shotwell Griffin Memorial Scholarship Fund *(Undergraduate/Scholarship)* [9507]
Institute for Anarchist Studies Grants for Radical Writers and Translators *(Professional development/Grant)* [5165]
Bodie McDowell Scholarships *(Graduate, Undergraduate/Scholarship)* [7770]
Melissa Pellegrin Memorial Scholarships *(Undergraduate, Graduate/Scholarship)* [7751]
Jim Poore Memorial Scholarships *(Undergraduate/Scholarship)* [5044]

Youth

NYCT Paid Graduate Student Philanthropy Fellowships - Children, Youth, Families, Education, Human Justice and Workforce *(Graduate/Fellowship)* [7350]
Tiftickjian Law Firm, P.C. Juvenile Justice Law School Scholarships *(Postgraduate/Scholarship)* [9741]
WLALA Scholarships *(Postgraduate/Scholarship)* [10647]

Zoology

AAZK/AZA Advances in Animal Keeping Course Grants *(Professional development/Grant)* [608]
AAZK Conservation, Preservation and Restoration Grants *(Professional development/Grant)* [609]
AAZK Professional Development Grants *(Professional development/Grant)* [610]
AAZK Research Grants *(Professional development/Grant)* [611]
American Society of Mammalogists - Fellowships in Mammalogy *(Graduate/Fellowship)* [1356]
American Society of Mammalogists Grants-in-Aid of Research *(Graduate, Undergraduate/Grant)* [1357]
Graduate Student Honoraria - Elmer C. Birney Awards *(Master's, Doctorate/Award)* [1358]
Margaret Dowell-Gravatt, M.D. Scholarships *(Undergraduate/Scholarship)* [2226]
Harry Hampton Fund Scholarship *(Undergraduate/Scholarship)* [4733]
Graduate Student Honoraria - A. Brazier Howell Awards *(Master's, Doctorate/Award)* [1359]
Libbie H. Hyman Memorial Scholarships *(Graduate, Undergraduate/Scholarship)* [9156]
Graduate Student Honoraria - Anna M. Jackson Awards *(Master's, Doctorate/Award)* [1360]
Primate Conservation Grants *(Graduate, Professional development/Grant)* [8276]
Dennis Raveling Scholarships *(Undergraduate/Scholarship)* [2488]
Albert R. and Alma Shadle Fellowships *(Graduate/Fellowship)* [1361]

Legal Residence Index

This index lists awards that are restricted by the applicant's residence of legal record. Award citations are arranged alphabetically by country and subarranged by region, state or province. Each citation is followed by the study level and award type, which appear in parentheses. The numbers following the parenthetical information indicate book entry numbers for awards, not page numbers.

UNITED STATES

180 Medical College Scholarship Program *(Undergraduate, Graduate/Scholarship)* [4]
1Dental Dentistry Scholarships *(Undergraduate/Scholarship)* [6]
4th Infantry Division Association Memorial Scholarships *(All/Scholarship)* [6670]
AAA Postdoctoral Fellowship Program *(Postdoctorate/Fellowship)* [460]
AAAA Scholarship Program *(Undergraduate, Graduate/Scholarship)* [1710]
AAACN Conference Scholarships for Nursing Students *(Undergraduate/Scholarship)* [385]
AAACN Education Scholarships *(Undergraduate/Scholarship)* [386]
AAACN Research Grants *(Undergraduate/Grant)* [387]
AAACN Scholarships *(Undergraduate/Scholarship)* [388]
AAAS Mass Media Science and Engineering Fellowship *(Undergraduate, Graduate, Postdoctorate/Fellowship, Award)* [453]
AAAS Science and Technology Policy Fellowships *(Professional development/Fellowship)* [454]
AABP Amstutz Scholarships *(Undergraduate/Scholarship)* [466]
AABP Bovine Veterinary Student Recognition Awards *(Undergraduate/Scholarship)* [467]
AABP Education Grants *(Undergraduate/Grant)* [468]
AABP Student Externship Program *(Undergraduate/Scholarship)* [469]
AACD Dentist Fellowships *(Professional development/Fellowship)* [405]
AACD Laboratory Fellowships *(Professional development/Fellowship)* [406]
AACE International Competitive Scholarships *(Undergraduate/Scholarship)* [14]
AACN Continuing Professional Development Scholarships *(Advanced Professional, Other/Scholarship)* [490]
AACOM Scholar in Residence Program *(Professional development/Scholarship)* [482]
AACPDM Student Scholarships *(Professional development/Scholarship)* [399]
AACPDM Transformative Practice Grants *(Professional development/Grant)* [400]
AACR Scholar-in-Training Awards: Other Conferences and Meetings *(Graduate, Postdoctorate, Professional development/Grant)* [471]
AACT Junior Investigator Research Grants *(Professional development/Grant)* [402]
AACT Toxicology Trainee Research Grants *(Professional development/Grant)* [403]
AACTE Outstanding Book Awards *(Other/Recognition)* [484]
AACTE Outstanding Dissertation Awards *(Doctorate/Award)* [485]
AAEP/ALSIC Scholarships *(Undergraduate/Scholarship)* [495]
AAEP Foundation Past Presidents' Research Fellowships *(Graduate, Professional development/Scholarship)* [496]
AAFPE LEX Scholarships *(Undergraduate/Scholarship)* [553]
AAFSW College Merit Scholarship *(College, Undergraduate/Scholarship)* [1820]
AAG Dissertation Research Grants *(Doctorate/Grant)* [1829]
AAHD Scholarships *(Graduate, Undergraduate/Scholarship)* [502]
AAI Careers in Immunology Fellowship Program *(Graduate, Doctorate, Postdoctorate/Fellowship)* [506]
AAI Public Policy Fellows Program (PPFP) *(Doctorate, Postdoctorate/Fellowship)* [507]
AAIB Scholarships *(Undergraduate/Scholarship)* [509]
AAIDD Fellowship *(Advanced Professional, Professional development/Fellowship)* [511]
AAJ Trial Advocacy Scholarships *(Undergraduate/Scholarship)* [515]
AAJUW Scholarships *(Graduate, Undergraduate/Scholarship)* [513]
AALL Leadership Academy Grants *(Professional development/Grant)* [519]
AALL Minority Leadership Development Award *(Graduate/Award)* [520]
AALL Research Funds *(Professional development/Grant)* [521]
AALL Scholarships for Continuing Education Classes *(Postgraduate/Scholarship)* [522]
AALL Technical Services SIS Active Member Grant *(Professional development/Grant)* [523]
AALL Technical Services SIS Experienced Member General Grant *(Professional development/Grant)* [524]
AALL Technical Services SIS Leadership Academy Grant *(Professional development/Grant)* [525]
AALL Technical Services SIS Management Institute Grant *(Professional development/Grant)* [526]
AALL Technical Services SIS New Member General Grant *(Professional development/Grant)* [527]
AAMA Houston Chapter Health Training Scholarships *(Other/Scholarship)* [1601]
AAMC Foundation Engagement Program for International Curators Grants *(Advanced Professional, Professional development/Grant)* [1854]
AAMFT Minority Fellowships *(Doctorate, Graduate/Fellowship)* [538]
AAN Clinical Research Training Fellowships *(Other/Fellowship)* [410]
AAN Medical Student Summer Research Scholarships *(Graduate/Scholarship)* [412]
A&WMA Scholarships *(Graduate/Scholarship)* [139]
AANS Medical Student Summer Research Fellowships (MSSRF) *(Undergraduate/Fellowship)* [542]
AAOHN Professional Development Scholarships - Academic Study *(Graduate, Undergraduate/Scholarship)* [550]
AAOHN Professional Development Scholarships - Continuing Education *(Other/Scholarship)* [551]
AAPM Diversity Recruitment through Education and Mentoring Program (MUSE) *(Undergraduate/Fellowship)* [557]
AAPM Fellowships for Graduate Study in Medical Physics *(Graduate/Fellowship)* [558]
AAPM Summer Undergraduate Fellowships *(Undergraduate/Fellowship)* [559]
Aaron Copland Bogliasco Fellowships in Music *(Professional development/Fellowship)* [2325]
Leroy F. Aarons Scholarships *(Graduate, Undergraduate/Scholarship)* [7049]
AAS-American Historical Print Collectors Society Fellowships *(Doctorate/Fellowship)* [428]
AAS-American Society for Eighteenth Century Studies Fellowships *(Postdoctorate/Fellowship)* [429]
AAS CIAC Small Grants *(Graduate/Grant)* [1857]
AAS Fellowships for Creative and Performing Artists and Writers *(Professional development/Fellowship, Award)* [430]
AAS Korean Studies Scholarship Program *(Graduate/Scholarship)* [1858]
AAS National Endowment for the Humanities Long-Term Fellowships *(Postdoctorate/Fellowship)* [431]
AAS-Northeast Modern Language Association Fellowships *(Undergraduate/Fellowship)* [432]
AASA Educational Administration Scholarship Awards *(Postgraduate/Scholarship)* [572]
AASLD Advanced/Transplant Hepatology Fellowships *(Professional development/Fellowship)* [581]
AASLD Autoimmune Liver Diseases Pilot Research Awards *(Graduate, Doctorate, Postdoctorate, Professional development/Award, Grant)* [582]
AASLD Career Development Awards in Liver Transplantation *(Professional development/Grant)* [583]
AASLD Clinical and Translational Research Awards *(Professional development/Grant)* [584]
AASLD NP/PA Clinical Hepatology Fellowships *(Professional development/Fellowship)* [585]
AASLD Pinnacle Research Awards in Liver Disease *(Professional development/Grant)* [586]
AAST/ETHICON Research Grants in Local Wound Haemostatics and Hemorrhage Control Scholarships *(Graduate, Postgraduate/Grant)* [589]
AAST/KCI Research Grant *(Doctorate/Grant)* [590]
AAST Medical Student, Resident and In-Training Fellow Scholarships *(Advanced Professional/Scholarship)* [591]
AATS Medical Students Summer Intern Scholarships *(Undergraduate/Scholarship, Internship)* [594]
AATS Perioperative/Team-Based Care Poster Competition *(Professional development/Award)* [595]
AATS Resident Critical Care Scholarships *(Professional development/Scholarship)* [596]
AATS/STS Cardiothoracic Ethics Forum Scholarships *(Professional development/Scholarship)* [597]
AAUW American Fellowships *(Doctorate, Postdoctorate/Fellowship)* [19]
AAUW Career Development Grants *(Graduate, Advanced Professional, Professional development/Grant)* [20]
AAUW International Fellowships *(Master's, Doctorate, Postdoctorate/Fellowship)* [21]
AAUW Selected Professions Fellowships *(Graduate, Master's, Doctorate/Fellowship)* [22]
AAZK/AZA Advances in Animal Keeping Course Grants *(Professional development/Grant)* [608]
AAZK Conservation, Preservation and Restoration

Grants *(Professional development/Grant)* [609]
AAZK Professional Development Grants *(Professional development/Grant)* [610]
AAZK Research Grants *(Professional development/Grant)* [611]
ABA Diversity Scholarships *(Undergraduate/Scholarship)* [636]
ABA Members Scholarships for ABA Bus and Tour Operators Only *(Undergraduate/Scholarship)* [637]
ABA Members Scholarships for All ABA Member Companies *(Undergraduate, Graduate/Scholarship)* [638]
ABA Scholarships *(Undergraduate/Scholarship)* [626]
Anthony Abbene Scholarships *(Undergraduate/Scholarship)* [5025]
ABC-Clio Research Grants *(Graduate/Grant)* [9208]
Abe Fellowship Program *(Professional development/Fellowship)* [9051]
Abe Fellowships for Journalists *(Professional development/Fellowship)* [9052]
Alejandro "Alex" Abecia Reaching High Scholarships *(Undergraduate/Scholarship)* [3084]
Abercrombie and Fitch Global Diversity and Leadership Scholar Awards *(Undergraduate/Scholarship)* [7158]
Ruth Abernathy Presidential Scholarships *(Graduate, Undergraduate/Scholarship)* [9128]
ABF Doctoral/Post-Doctoral Fellowships *(Doctorate, Graduate/Fellowship)* [622]
ABF Law and Social Science Dissertation Fellowship and Mentoring Program *(Graduate/Fellowship)* [623]
ABF Montgomery Summer Research Diversity Fellowships in Law and Social Science *(Undergraduate/Fellowship)* [624]
ABFSE National Scholarship Program *(Undergraduate/Scholarship)* [629]
Kyutaro and Yasuo Abiko Memorial Scholarships *(Undergraduate/Scholarship)* [5547]
Evelyn Abrams Memorial Scholarships *(Undergraduate/Scholarship)* [8327]
ABTA Discovery Grant Program *(Professional development/Grant)* [631]
ABTA Medical Student Summer Fellowship Program *(Undergraduate/Grant, Fellowship)* [632]
ABTA Translational Grant Program *(Postdoctorate/Grant)* [633]
Academy of Motion Picture Arts and Sciences Student Academy Awards *(Undergraduate/Award)* [42]
Academy of Neonatal Nursing Conference Scholarships *(Professional development/Scholarship)* [44]
Accenture American Indian Scholarship Program *(Graduate, Undergraduate/Scholarship)* [880]
ACHE Junior and Community College Athletic Scholarships *(Undergraduate/Scholarship)* [185]
ACHE Junior and Community College Performing Arts Scholarships *(Undergraduate/Scholarship)* [186]
ACHE Two-Year College Academic Scholarships *(Undergraduate/Scholarship)* [189]
The Achieve Physical Therapy and Fitness Scholarship *(Doctorate/Scholarship)* [9580]
ACI BASF Construction Chemicals Student Fellowships *(Graduate, Undergraduate/Fellowship)* [701]
ACI Cagley ACI Student Fellowships *(Graduate, Master's, Undergraduate/Fellowship)* [702]
ACI Foundation Scholarships *(Graduate/Scholarship)* [703]
ACI-NA Scholarships *(Graduate, Undergraduate/Scholarship)* [180]
ACI President's Fellowships *(Doctorate, Master's/Fellowship)* [704]
ACI W.R. Grace Scholarships *(Graduate/Scholarship)* [705]
ACJA-LAE Student Paper Competitions *(Undergraduate, Graduate/Scholarship)* [752]
Wayne D. Ackerman Family Scholarship Fund *(Undergraduate/Scholarship)* [9491]
ACLS Collaborative Research Fellowships *(Doctorate/Fellowship)* [735]
ACLS Fellowships *(Advanced Professional, Professional development/Fellowship)* [736]
ACMPE Scholarship Fund Program *(Graduate, Undergraduate/Scholarship)* [6384]
ACMS Intensive Mongolian Language Fellowship Program *(Undergraduate/Fellowship)* [648]
ACMS Library Fellowships *(Graduate, Other/Fellowship)* [649]
ACMS U.S.-Mongolia Field Research Fellowship Program *(Graduate, Undergraduate/Fellowship)* [650]
ACNL Research Scholarships *(Graduate/Scholarship)* [1869]
ACNM Foundation, Inc. Fellowships for Graduate Education *(Doctorate, Postdoctorate/Fellowship, Grant)* [692]
ACNM Foundation Midwives of Color-Watson Midwifery Student Scholarship *(Undergraduate/Scholarship)* [693]
ACOR-CAORC Post-Graduate Fellowships *(Doctorate, Postdoctorate/Award)* [653]
ACOR-CAORC Pre-Doctorate Fellowships *(Graduate, Doctorate/Fellowship)* [654]
Acoustical Society of America Minority Fellowships *(Graduate/Fellowship)* [52]
ACPA Foundation Annual Fund *(Professional development/Grant)* [695]
Andreas Acrivos Dissertation Award in Fluid Dynamics *(Graduate, Doctorate/Award)* [1085]
ACS/ASA Health Policy and Management Scholarships *(Professional development/Scholarship)* [1468]
ACS Doctoral Degree Scholarships in Cancer Nursing *(Doctorate, Graduate/Scholarship)* [642]
ACS Graduate Scholarships in Cancer Nursing Practice *(Graduate, Master's, Doctorate/Scholarship)* [643]
ACS Law Fellowships *(Graduate/Fellowship)* [716]
ACS Rubber Division Undergraduate Scholarships *(Undergraduate/Scholarship)* [666]
ACSUS Distinguished Dissertation Awards *(Doctorate/Award)* [1875]
Actuarial Diversity Scholarship *(Undergraduate/Scholarship)* [60]
ACUI Research and Education Grant *(Undergraduate, Graduate, Professional development/Grant)* [1925]
ACVO Best Resident Manuscript Awards *(Undergraduate/Recognition)* [699]
ADAA Career Development Travel Awards *(Other/Award)* [1569]
Nancy Ashley Adams/Ashley Adams Koetje Scholarships *(Undergraduate/Scholarship)* [3547]
EFWA Moss Adams Foundation Scholarships *(Undergraduate/Scholarship)* [3800]
Ruth D. Adams Fund *(Undergraduate/Scholarship)* [4037]
Mamie Adams Memorial Awards *(Undergraduate/Scholarship)* [6016]
Lt. Holly Adams Memorial Scholarships *(Undergraduate/Scholarship)* [3209]
RPMDA/Ed Adams Memorial Scholarships *(Other/Scholarship)* [8567]
Ruth Adams Memorial Scholarships *(Undergraduate/Scholarship)* [8442]
Henry Adams Scholarships *(Undergraduate/Scholarship)* [1326]
Adelante Fund Hope Scholarships, CPS Energy Dependents *(Undergraduate/Scholarship)* [66]
Adelante Fund Hope Scholarships, San Antonio, TX Students *(Undergraduate/Scholarship)* [67]
Carl Joseph Adelhardt Memorial Scholarships *(Undergraduate/Scholarship)* [4329]
Gladys Ross Carlson Adelphe Scholarship Fund *(Undergraduate, Graduate/Award)* [5688]
Adelson Scholarships *(Undergraduate/Scholarship)* [8329]
ADHA IOH Sigma Phi Alpha Graduate Scholarships *(Graduate/Scholarship)* [775]
Howard E. and Wilma J. Adkins Memorial Scholarships *(Undergraduate/Scholarship)* [1502]
ADMA International Scholarship *(Undergraduate/Scholarship)* [2144]
Adolescent/Young Adult Lymphoma Cooperative Groups Correlative Studies Grants *(Advanced Professional/Grant)* [6156]
Herb Adrian Memorial Scholarship Fund *(Undergraduate/Scholarship)* [4173]
Adult Students in Scholastic Transition Scholarships (ASIST) *(Professional development/Scholarship)* [3935]
Advance Degree and Clinical Research Training Grants in Alpha-1 Antitrypsin Deficiency *(Master's/Grant)* [1208]
Advance Prevention Lawsuit Legal Scholarships *(Undergraduate/Scholarship)* [5982]
"Advice to Your High School Self" Scholarships *(Undergraduate/Scholarship)* [2534]
AE Flight Training Scholarships *(Other/Scholarship)* [7436]
AE Jet Type Rating Scholarships *(Other/Scholarship)* [7437]
AE Technical Training Scholarships *(Other/Scholarship)* [7438]
AECT Foundation Mentor Endowment Scholarships *(Doctorate, Graduate/Scholarship)* [1942]
AECT Legacy Scholarship *(Master's, Graduate, Professional development/Scholarship)* [1943]
AED Student Early Career Investigator Travel Fellowships *(Undergraduate, Graduate, Postdoctorate, Postgraduate/Fellowship)* [32]
AED Student Research Grants *(Undergraduate, Graduate, Postgraduate/Grant)* [33]
AERA-AIR Fellows Program *(Postdoctorate/Fellowship)* [782]
AERA-ETS Fellowship Program in Measurement and Education Research *(Doctorate/Fellowship)* [783]
AERA Minority Fellowship Program in Education Research *(Doctorate/Fellowship)* [784]
Aerospace Corporation Science and Engineering Student Scholarships *(Undergraduate, Graduate/Scholarship)* [95]
AES Educational Foundation Grants *(Graduate/Grant, Award)* [2122]
AESF Foundation Scholarships *(Undergraduate, Graduate/Scholarship)* [6796]
AFCEA Cyber Studies and Intelligence Scholarships *(Undergraduate, Graduate/Scholarship)* [85]
AFCEA Scholarship for Working Professionals *(Undergraduate, Graduate/Scholarship)* [86]
AFCEA Science, Technology, Engineering and Math Teachers Scholarships *(Graduate/Scholarship, Grant)* [87]
AFFIRM University Scholarships *(Undergraduate/Scholarship)* [1961]
Affirmative Action Student Scholarship Mini-Grant Travel Awards *(Undergraduate, Master's, Doctorate/Grant)* [30]
Afghanistan and Iraq War Veterans Scholarship *(Undergraduate/Scholarship)* [88]
AFPE Gateway Research Scholarships *(Doctorate/Scholarship)* [826]
AFPE Pre-Doctoral Fellowships in Pharmaceutical Sciences for Underrepresented Minorities *(Doctorate, Graduate/Fellowship)* [828]
AFPE Pre-Doctoral Fellowships in Pharmaceutical Sciences *(Doctorate/Fellowship)* [827]
AFPPA Student Scholarships *(Undergraduate/Scholarship)* [1959]
AFSA Chapter 155 Division 1 Scholarships - Category 1 *(Undergraduate/Scholarship)* [130]
AFSA Chapter 155 Division 1 Scholarships - Category 2 *(Undergraduate/Scholarship)* [131]
AFSA Chapter 155 Division 1 Scholarships - Category 3 *(Undergraduate/Scholarship)* [132]
AFSP - Distinguished Investigator Grants *(Postgraduate/Grant)* [830]
AFSP Postdoctoral Research Fellowships *(Postgraduate/Fellowship)* [831]
AFSP Standard Research Grants *(Postgraduate/Grant)* [832]
AFSP Young Investigator Grants *(Postgraduate/Grant)* [833]
AFT-Oregon Union Plus Credit Card Scholarship *(Undergraduate/Scholarship)* [792]
AfterCollege/AACN Nursing Scholarships *(Graduate, Undergraduate/Scholarship)* [479]
AfterCollege-AACN Scholarships *(Undergraduate, Master's, Doctorate/Scholarship)* [96]
AfterCollege Business Student Scholarships *(Undergraduate, Graduate, Doctorate/Scholarship)* [97]
AfterCollege Engineering Student Scholarships *(Un-*

dergraduate, Graduate, Doctorate, Master's/Scholarship) [98]
AfterCollege Occupational Therapy Scholarships (Master's, Doctorate/Scholarship) [99]
AfterCollege Physical Therapist Student Scholarships (Undergraduate, Master's, Doctorate/Scholarship) [100]
AfterCollege Science Student Scholarships (Undergraduate, Graduate, Doctorate/Scholarship) [101]
AfterCollege STEM Inclusion Scholarships (Undergraduate, Graduate/Scholarship) [102]
AfterCollege Succurro Scholarships (Undergraduate, Graduate, Doctorate/Scholarship) [103]
AFWA Masters Degree Scholarships (Undergraduate, Master's/Scholarship) [49]
AFWA Undergraduate Scholarships (Undergraduate/Scholarship) [50]
AGBU Heritage Scholar Grant (Undergraduate/Scholarship, Grant) [1673]
AGC Foundation Outstanding Educator Awards (Other/Award) [1812]
AGC New York State Chapter Scholarship Program (Undergraduate/Scholarship) [1814]
The Agnes Sopcak Memorial Scholarship (Undergraduate/Scholarship) [10649]
Agriculture Future of America Community Scholarships (Undergraduate/Scholarship) [116]
Agriculture Future of America Scholarships (Undergraduate/Scholarship) [117]
AGWT Baroid Scholarships (Undergraduate/Scholarship) [840]
AH&LEF American Express Scholarship (Undergraduate/Scholarship) [858]
AHCJ Reporting Fellowships on Health Care Performance (Other/Fellowship) [3158]
Patty Ahearn Victoria Elementary Scholarships (Undergraduate/Scholarship) [8443]
Ahepa Buckeye Scholarship Awards (Undergraduate/Scholarship) [119]
AHEPA Family District No. 1 Scholarships (Graduate, Undergraduate/Scholarship) [849]
AHETEMS/ExxonMobil Scholarships (Undergraduate/Scholarship) [8887]
AHETEMS General Scholarships (Undergraduate, Graduate/Scholarship) [8888]
AHETEMS Professional Scholarships (Graduate/Scholarship) [8889]
Ahlswede, Norman & Marie Endowed Engineering Scholarship (Undergraduate/Scholarship) [10315]
Dr. Feroz Ahmed Memorial Educational Post-Graduate Scholarships (Doctorate, Postgraduate/Scholarship) [8965]
AHNS/AAO-HNS Young Investigator Award (Other/Grant) [845]
AHNS Pilot Research Grants (Other/Grant) [846]
Ahrens Charitable Trust Scholarship (Undergraduate/Scholarship) [4558]
AIA and the Global Automotive Aftermarket Symposium Scholarships (Undergraduate/Scholarship) [2131]
AIA Graduate Student Travel Awards (Graduate/Grant) [1603]
AIAA Foundation Scholarship Program (Graduate, Undergraduate/Scholarship) [891]
AIBS Junior Fellowships (Doctorate/Fellowship) [898]
AIBS Senior Fellowships (Doctorate/Fellowship) [899]
AIChE Minority Scholarship Awards for College Students (Undergraduate/Scholarship) [903]
AIChE Minority Scholarship Awards for Incoming College Freshmen (Undergraduate/Scholarship) [904]
AIEA Presidential Fellows Program (Undergraduate/Fellowship) [1985]
AIGC Fellowships - Graduate (Graduate/Fellowship) [881]
AIIrS Persian Language Study in Tehran Fellowships (Graduate, Master's, Doctorate/Fellowship) [913]
AIMS Long-term Research Grants (Doctorate, Graduate/Grant) [916]
AIMS Short-term Research Grants (Doctorate/Grant) [917]
AIPN Student Scholarships (All/Scholarship) [1987]

AIPS Long Term Fellowships (Doctorate, Postdoctorate/Fellowship) [919]
AIPS Post-Doctoral Fellowships (Postdoctorate/Fellowship) [920]
AIPS Pre-Doctoral Fellowships (Doctorate, Graduate/Fellowship) [921]
AIPS Short Term Fellowships (Doctorate, Postdoctorate/Fellowship) [922]
AIR Dissertation Grants (Doctorate/Grant) [1980]
Air Force Association/Grantham Scholarships (Undergraduate/Scholarship) [121]
Air Force Sergeants Association Scholarship Program (Undergraduate/Scholarship) [128]
Air Products and Chemicals, Inc. Scholarships (Undergraduate/Scholarship) [1975]
AIR Research Grants (Professional development/Grant) [1981]
Air Traffic Control Association Full-time Employee Student Scholarships (Other/Scholarship) [135]
Air Traffic Control Association Non-employee Student Scholarships (Undergraduate/Scholarship) [136]
Aircraft Owners and Pilots Association Scholarships (Undergraduate/Scholarship) [154]
AISC/Great Lakes Fabricators and Erectors Association Fellowships (Graduate/Fellowship) [933]
AISC/Rocky Mountain Steel Construction Association Scholarships (Graduate/Scholarship) [935]
AISC/Southern Association of Steel Fabricators Scholarships (Graduate/Scholarship) [936]
AISES Intel Scholarships (Graduate, Undergraduate/Scholarship) [887]
AISES Summer Internships (Undergraduate, Graduate/Internship) [888]
AISLS Dissertation Planning Grants (Graduate/Grant) [929]
AISLS Fellowships Program (Doctorate/Fellowship) [930]
AISLS Grants for Language Instruction (Doctorate/Grant) [931]
Justice John F. Aiso Scholarships (Undergraduate/Scholarship) [5541]
AIST Baltimore Member Chapter Scholarships (Undergraduate/Scholarship) [1989]
AIST Midwest Member Chapter - Engineering Scholarships (Undergraduate/Scholarship) [1990]
AIST Midwest Member Chapter - Non-Engineering Scholarships (Undergraduate/Scholarship) [1991]
AIST Midwest Member Chapter - Western States Scholarships (Undergraduate/Scholarship) [1992]
AIST Northwest Member Chapter Scholarships (Undergraduate/Scholarship) [1993]
AIST Ohio Valley Chapter Scholarships (Undergraduate/Scholarship) [1994]
AIST San Francisco Member Chapter Scholarships (Undergraduate/Scholarship) [1995]
AJL Conference Stipends (Graduate/Grant) [2010]
AJL Scholarship Fund (Graduate/Scholarship) [2011]
Crown Prince Akihito Scholarship Foundation (Graduate/Scholarship) [5535]
Akron Bar Association Foundation Scholarships (Undergraduate/Scholarship) [182]
ALA Allergic Respiratory Diseases Research Award (Doctorate/Grant) [969]
Alabama ARN Scholarship (Professional development/Scholarship) [2054]
Alabama Power Scholarships (Undergraduate/Scholarship) [7529]
Alamo Area Paralegal Association Educational Scholarships (Undergraduate, Professional development/Scholarship) [209]
Alamo IFT Scholarship (Undergraduate/Scholarship) [5175]
Jonathan Alan Scholarship Fund (Undergraduate/Scholarship) [10497]
Albert Einstein Distinguished Educator Fellowships (AEF) (Graduate, Other/Fellowship) [9794]
Bette Lou Albert, New Mexico, Memorial Scholarship Fund (Undergraduate, Graduate/Scholarship) [5689]
Alberta Holstein Association Scholarships (Undergraduate/Scholarship) [246]
Alberta Innovates - Technology Futures Graduate Student Scholarships in ICT (Doctorate, Graduate, Master's/Scholarship) [257]

Alberta Innovates - Technology Futures Graduate Student Scholarships in Nanotechnology (Doctorate, Graduate/Scholarship) [258]
Alberta Innovates - Technology Futures Graduate Student Scholarships in Omics (Doctorate, Graduate/Scholarship) [259]
Bruce and Betty Alberts Endowed Scholarships in Physiology (Undergraduate/Scholarship) [6243]
Albinas Elskus Scholarship (All/Scholarship) [9488]
ALCOA Foundation Corporate Scholarships (Undergraduate, Graduate/Scholarship) [4645]
ALD Graduate Fellowships (Graduate/Fellowship) [6696]
Owen F. Aldis Scholarship Fund (Doctorate/Scholarship) [5420]
Alex Scholarship Funds (Undergraduate/Scholarship) [6280]
Anne L. Alexander and Blaise Robert Alexander Memorial Scholarships (Undergraduate/Scholarship) [4038]
Neil Alexander Scholarships (Undergraduate/Scholarship) [6688]
Alex's Lemonade Stand Foundation Epidemiology Grants (Doctorate, Master's, Professional development/Grant) [318]
Alex's Lemonade Stand Foundation Innovation Grants (Other/Grant) [319]
Alex's Lemonade Stand Foundation Young Investigator Grants (Doctorate, Master's, Professional development/Grant) [320]
ALF Postdoctoral Research Fellowship Award (Postdoctorate, Professional development/Fellowship) [966]
Floyd S. Alford Jr. Scholarships (Undergraduate/Scholarship) [10212]
Horatio Alger National Scholarships (Undergraduate/Scholarship) [4948]
Emma and Meloid Algood Tuition Scholarships (Graduate, Undergraduate/Scholarship) [6718]
Margaret M. Alkek Scholarships (Undergraduate/Scholarship) [3548]
All-American Vector Marketing Scholarship Program (Undergraduate/Scholarship) [10364]
ALL-SIS Conference of Newer Law Librarians Grants (Professional development/Grant) [528]
Robinson G. Allen Athletic Memorial Scholarships (Undergraduate/Scholarship) [8444]
Frances C. Allen Fellowships (Graduate/Fellowship) [7408]
William A. Allen Memorial Metal Shop/Auto Body Scholarships (Undergraduate/Scholarship) [8445]
Dorothea E. Allen Scholarship (Undergraduate/Scholarship) [4427]
Alliance Defending Freedom - Blackstone Legal Fellowships (Undergraduate/Fellowship) [331]
Alliance Francaise of Hartford Harpin/Rohinsky Scholarships (Undergraduate/Scholarship) [4736]
Allman Medical Scholarship (Undergraduate/Scholarship) [6555]
ALOA Scholarship Foundation (Undergraduate/Scholarship) [1816]
Tillie B. Alperin Scholarship (Undergraduate/Scholarship) [10156]
ALPFA Scholarship Programs (Graduate, Undergraduate/Scholarship) [2013]
Alpha Chi Omega Love and Loyalty Grants (Professional development/Grant) [346]
Alpha Chi Sigma Scholarship Awards (Graduate, Undergraduate/Scholarship) [348]
Alpha Delta Gamma Educational Foundation Scholarships (Undergraduate, Graduate/Scholarship) [350]
Alpha Kappa Alpha - Educational Advancement Foundation Financial Need-Based Scholarships (Graduate, Undergraduate/Scholarship) [352]
Alpha Kappa Alpha - Educational Advancement Foundation Merit Scholarships (Graduate, Undergraduate/Scholarship) [353]
Alpha Mu Tau Undergraduate Scholarships (Undergraduate/Scholarship) [1258]
Alpha Tau Omega Graduate Scholarships (Graduate/Scholarship) [359]
Alpha Tau Omega Undergraduate Scholarships (Undergraduate/Scholarship) [360]
Justin Scot Alston Memorial Scholarships (Undergraduate/Scholarship) [5026]

UNITED STATES

Phillip Alston Scholarships *(Undergraduate/Scholarship)* [10213]
Robert E. Altenhofen Memorial Scholarships *(Graduate, Undergraduate/Scholarship)* [1802]
AMA Foundation Minority Scholars Awards *(Graduate/Scholarship)* [989]
AMA Foundation Physicians of Tomorrow Scholarships *(Graduate/Scholarship)* [990]
AMACESP Student Scholarships *(Undergraduate/Scholarship)* [178]
AMBUCS Scholarships for Therapists Program *(Graduate, Undergraduate/Scholarship)* [381]
Lou Amen Legacy Scholarships *(Undergraduate/Scholarship)* [2446]
America Express Travel Scholarships *(Undergraduate/Scholarship)* [1436]
America Responds Memorial Scholarships *(Undergraduate/Scholarship)* [1406]
American Academy of Periodontology Educator Scholarships *(Postdoctorate/Scholarship)* [420]
American Acne and Rosacea Society Mentorship Grant *(Professional development/Grant)* [426]
American Art Therapy Association Anniversary Scholarships *(Graduate/Scholarship)* [448]
American Association of Blacks in Energy Scholarships *(Undergraduate/Scholarship)* [464]
American Association for Cancer Research Minority Scholar Awards *(Graduate/Award)* [472]
American Association of Cereal Chemists Graduate Fellowships *(Graduate/Fellowship)* [12]
American Association of Family and Consumer Sciences Undergraduate Scholarships *(Undergraduate/Scholarship)* [498]
American Association for Hand Surgery Annual Research Awards *(Other/Award)* [500]
American Association of Plastic Surgeons Academic Scholars Program *(Professional development/Scholarship)* [564]
American Association of State Troopers Scholarship Foundation First Scholarships *(Undergraduate/Scholarship)* [577]
American Association of State Troopers Scholarship Foundation Second Scholarships *(Undergraduate/Scholarship)* [578]
American Association of Stratigraphic Palynologists Student Scholarships *(Graduate/Scholarship)* [16]
American Association of University Women American Fellowships *(Doctorate, Postdoctorate/Fellowship)* [599]
American Association of University Women Career Development Grants *(Postgraduate/Grant)* [600]
American Association of University Women Master's and First Professional Awards *(Other/Award)* [602]
American Association of University Women Selected Professions Fellowships *(Other/Fellowship)* [603]
American Association for Women in Community Colleges Regional Scholarships *(Undergraduate/Scholarship)* [605]
American Association for Women in Community Colleges Scholarship LEADERS Institute *(Other/Scholarship)* [606]
American Bus Association Academic Merit Scholarships *(Undergraduate, Graduate/Scholarship)* [639]
American Business Women's Association Sarasota Sunrise Chapter Scholarships *(Undergraduate, Vocational/Occupational/Scholarship)* [3317]
American Cancer Society - Postdoctoral Fellowships *(Doctorate/Fellowship)* [644]
American Cancer Society - Research Scholar Grants *(Doctorate, Professional development/Grant)* [645]
American Conifer Society Scholarships *(Undergraduate/Scholarship)* [714]
American Council of the Blind Scholarships *(Graduate, Undergraduate/Scholarship)* [720]
American Council of Engineering Companies of Illinois Scholarships *(Undergraduate/Scholarship)* [722]
American Council of Independent Laboratories Scholarships *(Undergraduate/Scholarship)* [732]
American Councils for International Education Critical Language Scholarships *(Undergraduate, Graduate/Scholarship)* [746]
American Counsel Association Scholarships *(Undergraduate/Scholarship)* [748]
American Criminal Justice Association - Lambda Alpha Epsilon Student Scholarships - Graduate Level *(Graduate, Master's, Doctorate/Scholarship)* [753]
American Criminal Justice Association - Lambda Alpha Epsilon Student Scholarships - Upper and Lower Division Levels *(Undergraduate/Scholarship)* [754]
American Darts Organization Memorial Scholarship *(Undergraduate/Scholarship)* [767]
American Dental Association Allied Dental Student Scholarships *(Undergraduate/Scholarship)* [769]
American Dental Association Dental Assisting Scholarship Program *(Undergraduate/Scholarship)* [770]
American Dental Association Dental Hygiene Scholarship Program *(Undergraduate/Scholarship)* [771]
American Dental Association Dental Laboratory Technology Scholarship Program *(Undergraduate/Scholarship)* [772]
American Dental Association Minority Dental Student Scholarships *(Undergraduate/Scholarship)* [773]
American Dental Hygienists' Association Institute for Oral Health Research Grants *(Master's/Fellowship)* [776]
American Diabetes Association and Boehringer Ingelheim Research Award: Chronic Kidney Disease and Renal Insufficiency in the Setting of Diabetes *(Doctorate, Professional development/Award)* [780]
American Division Veterans Association Scholarships *(Undergraduate/Scholarship)* [383]
American Enterprise Institute National Research Initiative Fellowships (NRI) *(Graduate/Fellowship)* [786]
American Express Professional Development Scholarships *(Other/Scholarship)* [859]
American Federation of Police and Concerned Citizen Scholarships *(Undergraduate/Scholarship)* [790]
American Foreign Service Association Scholarship Fund *(Undergraduate/Scholarship)* [816]
American Foundation for Suicide and Prevention Pilot Grants *(Postgraduate/Grant)* [834]
American Historical Association Fellowships in Aerospace History *(Doctorate/Fellowship)* [851]
American Indian Fellowship in Business Scholarships *(Graduate, Master's, Undergraduate/Scholarship)* [6844]
American Institute for Economic Research Student Summer Fellowships *(Doctorate, Graduate, Undergraduate/Fellowship)* [911]
American Institute of Physics Congressional Science Fellowships *(Doctorate/Fellowship)* [924]
American Institute of Physics State Department Science Fellowships *(Doctorate/Fellowship)* [925]
American Legion Eagle Scout of the Year Scholarships *(Undergraduate/Scholarship)* [6918]
The American Legion Legacy Scholarships *(Undergraduate/Scholarship)* [954]
American Liver Foundation Liver Scholar Awards *(Doctorate/Award)* [967]
American Lung Association Biomedical Research Grants *(Doctorate/Grant)* [970]
American Lung Association Clinical Patient Care Research Grants *(Doctorate/Grant)* [971]
American Lung Association Dalsemer Research Grants *(Doctorate/Grant)* [972]
American Lung Association DeSousa Awards *(Doctorate/Grant)* [973]
American Lung Association Lung Cancer Discovery Awards *(Doctorate/Grant)* [974]
American Lung Association Scholar Program *(Professional development/Grant)* [979]
American Lung Association Senior Research Training Fellowships *(Doctorate/Fellowship)* [975]
American Lung Association Social-Behavioral Research Grants *(Doctorate/Grant)* [976]
American Nephrology Nurses' Association Evidence-Based Research Grants *(Other/Grant)* [1025]
American Nephrology Nurses' Association Research Grants *(Doctorate, Graduate/Grant)* [1026]

Legal Residence Index

American Nuclear Society Incoming Freshman Scholarships *(Undergraduate/Scholarship)* [1032]
American Nuclear Society Undergraduates Scholarships *(Undergraduate/Scholarship)* [1033]
American Pediatric Surgical Nurses Association Educational Grants *(Other/Grant)* [1076]
American Philological Association Minority Student Summer Fellowships *(Undergraduate/Fellowship)* [9106]
American Planning Association ENRE Student Fellowship Program *(Graduate/Fellowship)* [1103]
American Psychoanalytic Association Fellowships *(Doctorate, Postdoctorate, Other/Fellowship)* [1129]
American Psychology-Law Society Dissertation Awards *(Graduate/Award)* [1155]
American Psychology-Law Society Early Career Professional Grants-In-Aid *(Other/Grant)* [1156]
American Psychology-Law Society Student Grants-In-Aid *(Graduate/Grant)* [1157]
American Quarter Horse Foundation Scholarships *(Undergraduate/Scholarship)* [1171]
American Railway Engineering and Maintenance-of-Way Association Scholarships *(Undergraduate/Scholarship)* [1175]
American Rental Association Foundation Scholarships *(Graduate, Undergraduate, Vocational/Occupational/Scholarship)* [1191]
American Research in the Humanities in China Fellowships *(Doctorate/Fellowship)* [737]
American Roentgen Ray Society Scholarships *(Other/Scholarship)* [1221]
American-Scandinavian Foundation Fellowships to Study in Scandinavia *(Graduate/Fellowship)* [1231]
American-Scandinavian Foundation Grants to Study in Scandinavia *(Graduate/Grant)* [1232]
American-Scandinavian Foundation Translation Prize *(Other/Prize)* [1233]
American Society of Colon and Rectal Surgeons International Fellowships *(Other/Fellowship)* [1265]
American Society of Colon and Rectal Surgeons Travel Scholarships *(Other/Scholarship)* [1266]
American Society of Crime Laboratory Directors Scholarships *(Graduate, Undergraduate, Master's, Doctorate/Scholarship)* [1278]
American Society of Electroneurodiagnostic Technologists Student Education Grants (ASET) *(Undergraduate/Grant)* [1300]
American Society for Enology and Viticulture Scholarships *(Graduate, Undergraduate/Scholarship)* [1307]
American Society of Heating, Refrigerating, and Air-Conditioning Memorial Scholarships *(Undergraduate/Scholarship)* [1327]
American Society for Horticultural Science Student Travel Grants *(Graduate, Undergraduate/Grant)* [1336]
American Society of Mammalogists - Fellowships in Mammalogy *(Graduate/Fellowship)* [1356]
American Society of Mammalogists Grants-in-Aid of Research *(Graduate, Undergraduate/Grant)* [1357]
American Society for Microbiology Undergraduate Research Fellowships *(Undergraduate/Fellowship)* [1368]
American Society of Military Comptrollers National Scholarship Program *(Undergraduate/Scholarship)* [1375]
American Society of Mining and Reclamation Memorial Scholarships *(Undergraduate/Scholarship, Recognition)* [1377]
American Society of Naval Engineers Scholarships (ASNE) *(Graduate, Undergraduate/Scholarship)* [1379]
American Society of Safety Engineers Construction Safety Scholarships *(Undergraduate/Scholarship)* [1407]
American Sokol Merit Awards *(Undergraduate/Scholarship, Recognition)* [1448]
American Speech Language Hearing Foundation Clinical Research Grants *(Doctorate/Grant)* [1450]
American Speech Language Hearing Foundation Endowed Scholarships *(Graduate, Master's, Doc-*

torate/Scholarship) [1451]
American Speech Language Hearing Foundation General Scholarships (Graduate, Master's, Doctorate/Scholarship) [1452]
American Speech Language Hearing Foundation Scholarships for International Students (Graduate, Master's, Doctorate/Scholarship) [1453]
American Speech Language Hearing Foundation Scholarships for Minority Students (Graduate, Master's, Doctorate/Scholarship) [1454]
American Water Ski Educational Foundation Scholarships (Undergraduate/Scholarship) [10351]
American Watercolor Society Scholarship Program for Art Teachers (Other/Scholarship) [1500]
American Welding Society District Scholarships (Undergraduate/Scholarship) [1503]
American Welding Society Graduate Research Fellowships (Graduate/Fellowship) [1504]
American Welding Society National Scholarships (Undergraduate/Scholarship) [1506]
American Welding Society Past Presidents Scholarships (Undergraduate, Graduate/Scholarship) [1507]
Americans for Informed Democracy Global Scholar Program (Undergraduate/Scholarship) [1532]
AmeriGlide Achiever Scholarships (Undergraduate/Scholarship) [1534]
Anna Ames Clinical Excellence Student Grants (Undergraduate/Grant) [2481]
Arsham Amirikian Engineering Scholarships (Undergraduate/Scholarship) [1508]
AMLN Scholarships for Arab American Students (Graduate, Undergraduate/Scholarship) [1003]
AMS Centennial Fellowships (Postdoctorate/Fellowship) [985]
AMS Freshman Undergraduate Scholarships (Undergraduate/Scholarship) [997]
AMS Graduate Fellowships in the History of Science (Graduate/Fellowship) [998]
AMS/Industry/Government Graduate Fellowships (Graduate/Fellowship) [999]
AMS/Industry Minority Scholarships (Undergraduate/Scholarship) [1000]
AMS Teacher Education Scholarships (Undergraduate/Scholarship) [1007]
AMS Undergraduate Named Scholarships (Undergraduate/Scholarship) [1001]
AMSA Graduate Student Research Poster Competition Award (Undergraduate, Doctorate, Master's/Award) [987]
AMSN Career Mobility Scholarship Awards (Undergraduate, Doctorate/Scholarship) [37]
AMSSM-ACSM Clinical Research Grants (Professional development/Grant) [993]
AMSUS Dentist Awards (Professional development/Recognition) [1538]
AMSUS Nursing Awards (Advanced Professional/Recognition) [1539]
AMSUS Physician Awards (Advanced Professional/Recognition) [1540]
AMTA Past Presidents' Conference Scholar Awards (Professional development/Award) [1010]
AMTA Student Conference Scholar Awards (Undergraduate, Graduate/Award) [1011]
AMTF Graduate Scholarships (Graduate/Scholarship) [1259]
AMVETS National Scholarships - Entering College Freshmen (Undergraduate/Scholarship) [1545]
AMVETS National Scholarships - For Veterans (Undergraduate/Scholarship) [1546]
AMVETS National Scholarships - JROTC (Undergraduate/Scholarship) [1547]
ANA Multicultural Excellence Scholarship Fund (MAIP) (Graduate, Undergraduate/Internship) [456]
Anaheim Police Survivors and Scholarship Fund (Undergraduate/Scholarship) [1549]
ANCA Scholarships (Undergraduate/Scholarship) [1712]
Anchor Plastics Scholarships (Graduate, Undergraduate/Scholarship) [8072]
Anchor QEA Environmental Scholarships (Graduate/Scholarship) [1551]
Anchor Scholarship Foundation Scholarships (Undergraduate/Scholarship) [9616]
Andersen Nontraditional Scholarships for Women's Education and Retraining (ANSWER) (Undergraduate/Scholarship) [4176]
Mary Louise Andersen Scholarship (Undergraduate/Scholarship) [1574]
William G. Anderson, DO, Minority Scholarships (Undergraduate/Scholarship) [1063]
The Anderson Group Summer Institute Scholarships (Other/Scholarship) [1553]
Henry H. Anderson, Jr. Sail Training Scholarship (Professional development/Scholarship) [9640]
Judge Isaac Anderson, Jr. Scholarships (Undergraduate/Scholarship) [9418]
A.T. Anderson Memorial Scholarships (Graduate, Undergraduate/Scholarship) [889]
Charles Lee Anderson Memorial Scholarships (Undergraduate/Scholarship) [3275]
Gladys C. Anderson Memorial Scholarships (Graduate, Undergraduate/Scholarship) [818]
Earl I. Anderson Scholarships (Undergraduate/Scholarship) [1722]
Kathy D. and Stephen J. Anderson Scholarships (Undergraduate/Scholarship) [3210]
Redlands Rotary Club - Donald C. Anderson Scholarships (Undergraduate/Scholarship) [8446]
Michael P. Anderson Scholarships in Space Science (Undergraduate/Scholarship) [7137]
Grace Andow Memorial Scholarships (Undergraduate, Graduate/Scholarship) [5548]
Margaret J. Andrew Memorial Scholarships (Undergraduate, Graduate/Scholarship) [8909]
Cindy Andrews Educational Scholarships (Undergraduate/Scholarship) [8447]
William H. Andrews/HAWS Scholarships (Undergraduate/Scholarship) [10569]
Richard E. Andrews Memorial Scholarships (Undergraduate/Scholarship) [627]
Androscoggin County Chamber of Commerce Adult Scholarships (Professional development/Scholarship) [1555]
ANF/ANN-FNRE Nursing Research Grants (Professional development/Grant) [1042]
ANF/ENRS Nursing Research Grants (Professional development/Grant) [1043]
ANF/STTI Nursing Research Grants (Master's, Doctorate/Grant) [1044]
Angus Foundation General Undergraduate Student Scholarships (Undergraduate/Scholarship) [1557]
Angus Foundation Graduate Student Degree Scholarship Program (Graduate/Scholarship) [1558]
Angus Foundation Scholarships (Undergraduate/Scholarship) [7032]
Angus/Talon Youth Educational Learning Program Endowment Fund (Graduate, Undergraduate/Scholarship) [1559]
Anheuser-Busch NAPABA Law Foundation Presidential Scholarships (Undergraduate/Scholarship) [6703]
Animal Compassion Undergraduate Scholarships (Undergraduate/Scholarship) [8015]
ANNA Nephrology Nurse Researcher Awards (Doctorate, Graduate/Award) [1027]
Anne Friedberg Innovative Scholarship Awards (Other/Scholarship) [9104]
Leonore Annenberg Teaching Fellowships (Graduate/Fellowship) [10677]
Annette Urso Rickel Foundation Dissertation Award for Public Policy (Graduate/Scholarship) [1137]
Annual Research Doctoral and Postgraduate Fellowship Grant Program (Doctorate, Postdoctorate, Postgraduate, Advanced Professional/Fellowship, Grant) [2586]
Annuity.org Scholarships (Undergraduate, Graduate/Scholarship) [1565]
ANS Research Grants (Professional development/Grant) [1030]
Hettie Margaret Anthony Fellowship (Doctorate/Fellowship) [5779]
Hettie M. Anthony Fellowships (Doctorate/Fellowship) [5787]
Antimicrobial Stewardship Fellowship Award (Professional development/Award, Fellowship) [7929]
AOF/Johnson & Johnson Vision Care - Innovation in Education Grants (Advanced Professional, Professional development/Grant) [414]
AOFAS Research Grants Program (Graduate/Grant) [1060]
AORN Academic Scholarships (Undergraduate, Master's, Doctorate/Scholarship) [2035]
AORN Administrator Skills Course (Professional development/Recognition, Grant) [2036]
AORN Foundation Scholarship Program (Undergraduate, Doctorate, Master's/Scholarship) [2037]
AOS Research Training Fellowships (Graduate/Fellowship) [1067]
AOSA Research Grants (Undergraduate/Grant) [1053]
AOSA Research Partnership Grants (Professional development/Grant) [1054]
APA Society Convention Research Awards (Undergraduate, Graduate/Award) [8317]
APABA-SV Scholarships (Advanced Professional/Scholarship) [1786]
APAGS-CLGBTC Grant Program (Graduate/Grant) [1131]
APALA Scholarship Award (Doctorate, Master's/Scholarship) [1788]
APC High School Scholarship Awards (Undergraduate/Scholarship) [78]
APDA Medical Students Summer Fellowships (Graduate, Professional development/Fellowship) [1071]
APDA Postdoctoral Research Fellowships (Other/Fellowship) [1072]
APDA Research Grants (Other/Grant) [1073]
APF/COGDOP Graduate Research Scholarships (Doctorate, Graduate/Scholarship) [1138]
APF High School Psychology Teacher Network Grants (Advanced Professional, Professional development/Grant) [1139]
APF Professional Development Awards for High School Psychology Teachers (Advanced Professional, Professional development/Grant) [1140]
APF Visionary Grants (Graduate/Grant) [1141]
APhA Auxilliary Scholarship (Undergraduate/Scholarship) [1575]
APHF Academic Scholarships (Undergraduate/Scholarship) [1069]
APHL Emerging Infectious Diseases Fellowships (Doctorate/Fellowship) [2048]
Appalachian School of Law Merit Scholarship Program (Undergraduate/Scholarship) [1590]
Appraisal Institute Education Trust Undergraduate Scholarships (Undergraduate/Scholarship) [1596]
APS Scholarships for Minority Undergraduate Physics Majors (Undergraduate/Scholarship) [7138]
APS Society Convention Research Awards (Undergraduate, Graduate/Award) [8318]
APS Student Research Award (Undergraduate, Graduate/Award) [2045]
APSA Congressional Fellowship for Communications Scholars and Journalists (Advanced Professional, Professional development/Fellowship) [1108]
APSA Congressional Fellowships for Journalists (Advanced Professional, Professional development/Fellowship) [1109]
APSA Congressional Fellowships for Political Scientists (Advanced Professional, Professional development/Fellowship) [1110]
APSA Fund for Latino Scholarship (Undergraduate, Graduate/Scholarship) [1111]
APSA/Health and Aging Policy Fellowships (Graduate, Advanced Professional, Professional development/Fellowship) [1112]
APSA Minority Fellows Program (Doctorate/Fellowship) [1113]
APSA Presidency Research Group Fellowships (Graduate, Postdoctorate/Fellowship) [1118]
APSA Small Research Grant Program (Doctorate/Grant) [1114]
APSA U.S. Federal Executives Fellowships (Advanced Professional, Professional development/Fellowship) [1115]
APT US&C Scholarships (Advanced Professional/Scholarship) [2050]
APTA Minority Scholarships - Faculty Development Scholarships (Postdoctorate/Scholarship) [1096]
APTA Minority Scholarships - Physical Therapist Assistant Students (Undergraduate/Scholarship) [1097]
APTA Minority Scholarships - Physical Therapist Students (Undergraduate/Scholarship) [1098]

ARA Scholarship Awards *(Undergraduate/Scholarship)* [2136]
Frank G. Araujo Memorial Scholarships *(Undergraduate/Scholarship)* [8449]
ARCADIS Scholarships *(Master's, Doctorate/Scholarship)* [1482]
ARCE Funded Fellowships *(Doctorate, Postdoctorate/Fellowship)* [1195]
ARCE Research Associates Fellowships *(Doctorate, Postdoctorate, Professional development/Fellowship)* [1196]
Archaeological Institute of America Fellowships for Study in the U.S. *(Postdoctorate/Fellowship)* [1604]
Archaeology of Portugal Fellowships *(Professional development/Fellowship)* [1605]
George F. Archambault Scholarship *(Undergraduate/Scholarship)* [1576]
NHCGNE Patricia G. Archbold Predoctoral Scholar Award *(Doctorate/Scholarship)* [6982]
Arctic Physical Therapy Scholarship *(Undergraduate/Scholarship)* [1619]
AREMA Committee 12 - Rail Transit Scholarships *(Undergraduate/Scholarship)* [1176]
AREMA Committee 18 - Light Density and Short Line Railways Scholarships *(Undergraduate/Scholarship)* [1177]
AREMA Committee 24 - Education and Training Scholarships *(Undergraduate/Scholarship)* [1178]
AREMA Committee 27 - Maintenance-of-Way Work Equipment Scholarships *(Undergraduate/Scholarship)* [1179]
AREMA Committee 33 - Electric Energy Utilization Scholarships *(Undergraduate/Scholarship)* [1180]
AREMA Michigan Tech Alumni Scholarships *(Graduate, Undergraduate/Scholarship)* [1181]
AREMA Presidential Spouse Scholarships *(Undergraduate/Scholarship)* [1182]
Arent Fox Diversity Scholarships *(Graduate, Juris Doctorate/Scholarship)* [1621]
A.R.F.O.R.A. Undergraduate Scholarships for Women *(Undergraduate/Scholarship)* [1224]
ARIT Fellowships in the Humanities and Social Sciences in Turkey *(Postdoctorate, Graduate/Fellowship)* [1201]
ARIT National Endowment for the Humanities Advanced Fellowships for Research in Turkey *(Postdoctorate/Fellowship)* [1202]
ARIT Summer Fellowships for Intensive Advanced Turkish Language Study *(Graduate, Undergraduate/Fellowship)* [1203]
Arizona Hydrological Society Scholarships *(Graduate, Undergraduate/Scholarship)* [1635]
Arizona Nurses Foundation Scholarships *(Doctorate, Graduate, Undergraduate/Scholarship)* [1639]
Rick Arkans Eagle Scout Scholarships *(Undergraduate/Scholarship)* [6919]
Arkansas Green Industry Association Professional Grants *(Professional development, Undergraduate/Grant)* [1651]
Armenian American Citizen's League Scholarships *(Undergraduate/Scholarship)* [1682]
Armenian American Medical Association Scholarships *(Undergraduate/Scholarship)* [1683]
Armenian American Pharmacists' Association Scholarships *(Graduate/Scholarship)* [1684]
Armenian Bar Association Graduate Scholarships in Law *(Graduate/Scholarship)* [1669]
Armenian General Athletic Union Scholarships *(Undergraduate/Scholarship)* [1685]
Armenian Professional Society Graduate Student Scholarships *(Graduate/Scholarship)* [1675]
Armenian Relief Society Scholarships *(Graduate, Undergraduate/Scholarship)* [1686]
Ethel Louise Armstrong Foundation Scholarships *(Graduate/Scholarship)* [8750]
Louis Armstrong Scholarships *(Undergraduate/Scholarship)* [1268]
Army Health Professions Scholarships Program *(Professional development/Scholarship)* [9878]
Norma Arnold Clerical Scholarships *(Undergraduate/Scholarship)* [6221]
ARNOVA Emerging Scholar Awards *(Graduate/Award)* [2056]

Jane B. Aron Doctoral Fellowships *(Doctorate/Fellowship)* [6787]
Don Aron Scholarships *(Undergraduate/Scholarship)* [6875]
Judge Sidney M. Aronovitz Memorial Scholarships *(Undergraduate/Scholarship)* [6451]
ARRL Foundation General Fund Scholarships *(Undergraduate/Scholarship)* [1723]
ARS of Eastern USA Lazarian Graduate Scholarship *(Master's, Doctorate/Scholarship)* [1680]
ARS Undergraduate Scholarships *(Undergraduate/Scholarship)* [1677]
Arthritis Foundation Doctoral Dissertation Awards for Arthritis Health Professionals *(Doctorate/Fellowship)* [1769]
Arthritis Foundation Innovative Research Grants *(Doctorate/Grant)* [1770]
Arthritis Foundation Investigator Awards *(Doctorate/Award)* [1771]
Arthritis Foundation Postdoctoral Fellowships *(Doctorate/Fellowship)* [1772]
Artist-in-Residence Workspace Grant *(Professional development/Grant)* [2843]
The Artist in Landscape Design Scholarship by Fullmer's Landscaping *(Undergraduate/Scholarship)* [7581]
David Arver Memorial Scholarships *(Undergraduate/Scholarship)* [155]
Dutch and Ginger Arver Scholarships *(Undergraduate/Scholarship)* [156]
Chester Arzell and Helen Miller Montgomery Scholarships *(Undergraduate/Scholarship)* [10570]
ASA Graduate Scholarships *(Graduate/Scholarship)* [1243]
ASA Minority Fellowship Program (ASA MFP) *(Graduate, Doctorate, Professional development/Fellowship)* [1445]
ASA/NSF/BLS Fellowships *(Graduate/Fellowship)* [1463]
ASA Student Forum Travel Awards *(Undergraduate, Graduate/Grant)* [1446]
ASBA College Scholarship Grant Program *(Postgraduate/Scholarship)* [1239]
ASBC Foundation Graduate Scholarships *(Graduate/Scholarship)* [1247]
ASBC Foundation Undergraduate Scholarships *(Undergraduate/Scholarship)* [1248]
ASBPE Young Leaders Scholarships *(Professional development/Scholarship)* [1250]
ASC Graduate Fellowships for Ethnic Minorities *(Doctorate/Fellowship)* [1280]
Elizabeth and Sherman Asche Memorial Scholarships *(Graduate, Undergraduate/Scholarship)* [1832]
ASCO/CCF Young Investigator Awards *(Professional development, Advanced Professional/Grant)* [3369]
ASCP Phlebotomy Scholarships *(Undergraduate/Scholarship)* [1262]
ASECS Graduate Student Research Paper Awards *(Graduate/Award)* [1283]
ASECS Innovative Course Design Competition *(Undergraduate/Award)* [1284]
ASECS Women's Caucus Editing and Translation Fellowships *(Doctorate/Fellowship)* [1285]
ASEE/NSF Small Business Postdoctoral Research Diversity Fellowships *(Postdoctorate/Fellowship)* [1303]
ASEH Minority Travel Grants *(Graduate, Other/Grant)* [1309]
Officer Brian A. Aselton Memorial Scholarships *(Undergraduate/Scholarship)* [4737]
ASET Scholarships *(Other/Scholarship)* [1301]
ASG Scholar Awards *(Professional development/Scholarship)* [1321]
ASGP Graduate Research Fellowships *(Graduate/Fellowship)* [223]
ASHARE Undergraduate Engineering Scholarships *(Undergraduate/Scholarship)* [1328]
ASHFoundation New Century Scholars Doctoral Scholarships *(Doctorate/Scholarship)* [1455]
ASHFoundation New Century Scholars Research Grants *(Doctorate/Grant)* [1456]
ASHFoundation New Investigators Research Grants *(Doctorate/Grant)* [1457]
ASHFoundation Scholarships for NSSLHA Members

(Graduate/Scholarship) [1458]
ASHFoundation Speech Science Research Grants *(Doctorate/Grant)* [1459]
ASHFoundation Student Research Grants in Audiology *(Doctorate/Grant)* [1460]
ASHFoundation Student Research Grants in Early Childhood Language Development *(Doctorate, Master's/Grant)* [1461]
ASHP Student Research Awards *(Doctorate/Award)* [1323]
ASHS Industry Division Student Travel Grants *(Graduate, Undergraduate/Grant)* [1337]
ASHS Scholars Awards *(Undergraduate/Scholarship)* [1338]
ASI Sheep Heritage Foundation Memorial Scholarship *(Graduate/Scholarship)* [1241]
Asian Development Bank - Japan Scholarships *(Graduate/Scholarship)* [3759]
ASID Foundation Legacy Scholarships for Graduate Students *(Graduate/Scholarship)* [1341]
ASIS Foundation Chapter Matching Scholarships *(Undergraduate/Scholarship)* [1794]
ASLA Council of Fellow Scholarships *(Undergraduate/Scholarship)* [1346]
ASLA Council of Fellows Scholarships *(Undergraduate/Scholarship)* [5913]
ASLMS Research Grants *(Postdoctorate/Grant)* [1349]
ASLMS Student Research Grants *(Undergraduate, Graduate, Professional development/Grant)* [1350]
ASM/CDC Program in Infectious Disease and Public Health Microbiology *(Postdoctorate/Fellowship)* [1369]
ASM Congressional Science Fellowships *(Postdoctorate/Fellowship)* [1370]
ASM Science Teaching Fellowships - Student *(Undergraduate/Fellowship)* [1371]
ASM Undergraduate Research Capstone Program *(Undergraduate/Fellowship)* [1372]
ASMS Research Awards *(Other/Grant)* [1363]
ASNT Fellowship Award *(Graduate/Fellowship, Award)* [1384]
ASPIRE Rheumatology and Dermatology Research Awards *(Postdoctorate/Award)* [8023]
Myron "Ted" Asplin Foundation Scholarships *(Undergraduate/Scholarship)* [5097]
ASPPH/CDC Public Health Fellowship Program *(Doctorate, Graduate/Fellowship)* [2060]
ASPPH/EPA Environmental Health Fellowship Program *(Doctorate, Postdoctorate/Fellowship)* [2061]
ASPPH/NHTSA Public Health Fellowship Program *(Postdoctorate/Fellowship)* [2062]
ASPPH Public Health Policy Fellowship Program *(Doctorate, Postdoctorate/Fellowship)* [2063]
ASPPH Public Health Preparedness Fellowship Program *(Postdoctorate/Fellowship)* [2064]
Len Assante Scholarship Fund *(Undergraduate/Scholarship)* [6976]
Michael M. Assarian Scholarships *(Undergraduate/Scholarship)* [1687]
ASSE Diversity Committee Scholarships *(Graduate, Undergraduate/Scholarship)* [1408]
Associated Women for Pepperdine Scholarships *(Undergraduate/Scholarship)* [7962]
Association for the Advancement of Baltic Studies Dissertation Grants for Graduate Students *(Doctorate/Grant)* [1823]
Association of American Indian Physicians Scholarships *(Graduate, Undergraduate/Scholarship)* [1838]
Association for Compensatory Educators of Texas Paraprofessionals Scholarships *(Other/Scholarship)* [1928]
Association for Compensatory Educators of Texas Scholarships *(Undergraduate/Scholarship)* [1929]
Association of Desk and Derrick Clubs Education Trust Scholarships *(Undergraduate/Scholarship)* [1931]
Association of Donor Recruitment Professionals Hughes Scholarships *(Other/Scholarship)* [1937]
Association of Donor Recruitment Professionals Presidential Scholarships *(Other/Scholarship)* [1938]
Association of Energy Engineers Foundation Schol-

Legal Residence Index   UNITED STATES

arship Program *(Graduate, Undergraduate/Scholarship)* [1946]
Association of Flight Attendants Scholarship Fund *(Undergraduate/Scholarship)* [1963]
Association of Government Accountants Undergraduate/Graduate Scholarships for Community Service Accomplishments *(Graduate, Undergraduate/Scholarship)* [1971]
Association of Government Accountants Undergraduate/Graduate Scholarships for Full-time study *(Graduate, Undergraduate/Scholarship)* [1972]
Association of Government Accountants Undergraduate/Graduate Scholarships for Part-time study *(Graduate, Undergraduate/Scholarship)* [1973]
Association for Preservation Technology International Student Scholarships *(Graduate, Undergraduate/Scholarship)* [2041]
Association for Psychological Science Student Grants (APS) *(Graduate, Undergraduate/Grant)* [2046]
Association of State Dam Safety Officials Undergraduate Scholarships *(Undergraduate/Scholarship)* [2074]
Association of the United States Navy Scholarships *(Undergraduate/Scholarship)* [2083]
Association for Women in Sports Media Internship/Scholarship Program *(Undergraduate/Scholarship, Internship)* [2101]
ASTA Alaska Airlines Scholarships *(Undergraduate/Scholarship)* [1437]
ASTA Holland America Line Graduate Research Scholarships *(Graduate/Scholarship)* [1438]
ASTA Rigby, Healy, Simmons Scholarships *(Graduate/Scholarship)* [1439]
ASTR Research Fellowships *(Other/Fellowship)* [1433]
ASTRO Junior Faculty Career Research Training Awards *(Advanced Professional, Professional development/Grant)* [1392]
ASTRO Minority Summer Fellowship Awards *(Postgraduate, Professional development/Fellowship)* [1393]
ASTRO Residents/Fellows in Radiation Oncology Research Seed Grants *(Advanced Professional, Professional development/Grant)* [1394]
ASTRO/ROI Comparative Effectiveness Research Awards *(Professional development/Grant)* [1395]
Astronaut Scholarship Foundation Scholarships *(Undergraduate/Scholarship)* [2105]
AT&T Business Internship Awards *(Undergraduate/Internship)* [10214]
Martha and Robert Atherton Ministerial Scholarships *(Master's/Scholarship)* [9831]
ISA Aerospace Industries Division - William H. Atkinson Scholarships *(Graduate, Undergraduate/Scholarship)* [5396]
Atlantic Salmon Federation Olin Fellowships *(Graduate/Fellowship)* [2120]
Atlas Shrugged Essay Contest *(Graduate, Undergraduate, High School/Prize)* [2163]
ATS Abstract Scholarships *(Undergraduate, Graduate, Doctorate/Scholarship)* [1473]
Attorney-CPA Foundation Scholarships *(Postgraduate/Scholarship)* [391]
AUA Foundation Urology Research Bridge Awards *(Postgraduate/Award)* [10346]
Aubespin Scholarships *(Undergraduate/Scholarship)* [718]
A. B. and Hazel Augenstein Scholarship Funds *(Undergraduate/Scholarship)* [6281]
Herzog August Bibliothek Wolfenbüttel Fellowships *(Postdoctorate/Fellowship)* [7409]
H. Thomas Austern Memorial Writing Competition *(Doctorate/Award, Prize)* [4127]
Austin Alumnae Association Beta Xi Scholarship *(Undergraduate/Scholarship)* [5690]
Australian-American Health Policy Fellowships *(Doctorate, Graduate/Fellowship)* [3159]
Auto Accident Law Firm Survivor Scholarships *(Graduate/Scholarship)* [1592]
Auto-Pets "Out-of-the-Box Thinking" Scholarships *(All/Award)* [2129]
Automotive Technician Scholarship Program *(Undergraduate/Scholarship)* [6344]

Automotive Women's Alliance Foundation Scholarships *(Undergraduate/Scholarship)* [2138]
Auxiliary Undergraduate Scholarships *(Undergraduate/Scholarship)* [1796]
AvaCare Medical Scholarships *(Undergraduate/Scholarship)* [2142]
Avis Budget Group Scholarships *(Graduate/Scholarship)* [1440]
AVMA Fellowship Program *(Professional development/Fellowship)* [1478]
AVS Applied Surface Science Division Awards *(Graduate/Award)* [2146]
AVS Biomaterial Interfaces Division - Early Career Researchers Awards *(Graduate/Monetary)* [2147]
AVS Electronic Materials and Photonic Division Postdoctoral Award *(Postdoctorate/Award)* [2148]
AVS Manufacturing Science and Technology Group Awards *(Graduate/Award)* [2149]
AVS MEMS and NEMS Technical Group Best Paper Awards *(Undergraduate, Graduate/Monetary)* [2150]
AVS Nanometer-Scale Science and Technology Division Graduate Award *(Graduate/Monetary)* [2151]
AVS Spectroscopic Ellipsometry Focus Topic Graduate Student Awards *(Graduate/Award)* [2152]
AVS Thin Film Division James Harper Awards *(Graduate/Monetary)* [2153]
Award for Outstanding Doctoral Dissertation in Laser Science *(Doctorate/Award)* [1086]
Award for Outstanding Doctoral Thesis Research in Biological Physics *(Doctorate/Award)* [1087]
AWG Minority Scholarships *(Undergraduate/Scholarship)* [2093]
AWM Mathematics Travel Grants *(Doctorate/Grant)* [2098]
AWMA Niagara Frontier Section College Scholarships *(Graduate, Undergraduate/Scholarship)* [149]
AWSCPA National Scholarships *(Graduate/Scholarship)* [1530]
AWWA American Water Scholarships *(Master's, Doctorate/Scholarship)* [1483]
AWWA Illinois Section Safe Water Scholarship Awards *(Undergraduate, Master's, Doctorate/Scholarship)* [1496]
AXA Achievement Scholarships *(Undergraduate/Scholarship)* [2161]
Susan Ayers Memorial Scholarships *(Undergraduate/Scholarship)* [8332]
Ayn Rand Institute Anthem Essay Contest *(High School, Undergraduate/Prize)* [2164]
Ayn Rand Institute Fountainhead Essay Contest *(High School, Undergraduate/Prize)* [2165]
William Stone Ayres Scholarship *(Undergraduate/Scholarship)* [3661]
John M. Azarian Memorial Armenian Youth Scholarship Fund *(Undergraduate/Scholarship)* [1688]
B-Brave McMahon/Stratton Scholarship Fund *(Undergraduate/Scholarship)* [4039]
Tom Babcox Memorial Scholarships *(Professional development/Scholarship)* [2124]
Bachelor of Science in Nursing Academic Scholarships *(Graduate/Scholarship)* [6656]
Paula Backscheider Archival Fellowships *(Other/Fellowship)* [1286]
BACUS Scholarships *(Graduate, Undergraduate/Scholarship)* [9467]
Leo Baeck Institute - DAAD Fellowships *(Doctorate/Fellowship)* [3602]
BAFTX Early Starters Awards *(Undergraduate/Scholarship)* [2365]
Morton Bahr Scholarships *(Undergraduate/Scholarship)* [3165]
Marian Breland Bailey Award *(Graduate, Undergraduate/Award)* [1860]
The Bailey Family Foundation High School Scholarships Program *(Undergraduate/Scholarship)* [2168]
Lincoln C. Bailey Memorial Scholarship Fund *(Undergraduate/Scholarship)* [5390]
Esther Tuttle Bailey Memorial Scholarships *(Undergraduate/Scholarship)* [5691]
Bambi Bailey Scholarships *(Undergraduate/Scholarship)* [3197]

Sandra Sebrell Bailey Scholarships *(Undergraduate/Scholarship)* [3579]
Mark B. Bain Graduate Fellowship *(Doctorate, Master's, Graduate/Fellowship)* [4980]
Marian Wood Baird Scholarships *(Undergraduate/Scholarship)* [9973]
Michael Baker Corp. Scholarship for Diversity in Engineering *(Undergraduate/Scholarship)* [1976]
Baker Donelson Diversity Scholarships *(Undergraduate/Scholarship)* [2170]
Baker and Hostetler Diversity Fellowships *(Undergraduate/Fellowship)* [2172]
Baker and McKenzie Diversity Fellowships *(Postgraduate, Professional development/Fellowship)* [2175]
Francis Warren Baker Memorial Scholarships *(Undergraduate/Scholarship)* [8910]
Airgas - Jerry Baker Scholarships *(Undergraduate/Scholarship)* [1509]
ACI Elmer Baker Student Fellowships *(Undergraduate, Graduate/Fellowship)* [707]
ACI Baker Student Fellowships *(Undergraduate, Graduate/Fellowship)* [706]
George C. Balch Scholarships *(Graduate, Undergraduate/Scholarship)* [9958]
Bernt Balchen, Jr. and Olav Jorgen Hegge Hardingfele Scholarships *(Other/Scholarship)* [4717]
Birgit Baldwin Fellowships *(Graduate/Fellowship)* [6395]
Norman S. Baldwin Fishery Science Scholarship *(Doctorate, Graduate/Scholarship)* [5260]
Donald A. Baldwin Sr. Business Aviation Management Scholarships *(Professional development/Scholarship)* [6829]
Balestreri/Cutino Scholarships *(Undergraduate/Scholarship)* [757]
Ball Horticultural Company Scholarships *(Undergraduate/Scholarship)* [798]
Vic and Margaret Ball Student Intern Scholarships *(Undergraduate/Internship)* [799]
Ballantyne Resident Research Grants *(Other/Grant)* [847]
G. Thomas Balsbaugh Memorial Scholarship Fund *(Undergraduate/Scholarship)* [4231]
B&W Y-12 Scholarship Fund *(Undergraduate/Scholarship)* [3752]
Bank of America Junior Achievement Scholarship Fund *(Undergraduate/Scholarship)* [4177]
Brenda S. Bank Educational Workshop Scholarships *(Undergraduate/Scholarship)* [9123]
Harvey Washington Banks Scholarships in Astronomy *(Undergraduate/Scholarship)* [7139]
Sharon D. Banks Undergraduate Memorial Scholarships *(Undergraduate/Scholarship)* [10674]
Banner Bank Business Scholarships *(Undergraduate/Scholarship)* [6057]
Donald W. Banner Diversity Scholarships for Law Students *(Graduate/Scholarship)* [2190]
Mark T. Banner Scholarships for Law Students *(Postgraduate/Scholarship)* [6093]
Barakat Trust and Barakat Foundation Scholarships *(Graduate, Postdoctorate/Scholarship)* [1598]
Cynthia and Alan Baran Fine Arts and Music Scholarships *(Undergraduate/Scholarship)* [3211]
Leslie Baranowski Scholarships for Professional Excellence *(Professional development/Scholarship)* [5144]
Barbara Jordan Memorial Scholarships *(Undergraduate, Graduate/Scholarship)* [2078]
Lewis B. Barber Memorial Scholarships *(Undergraduate/Scholarship)* [9419]
Jack R. Barckhoff Welding Management Scholarships *(Undergraduate/Scholarship)* [1510]
Thomas J. Bardos Science Education Awards for Undergraduate Students *(Undergraduate/Award)* [473]
Edgar Barge Memorial Scholarships *(Undergraduate/Scholarship)* [4559]
TCDA Carroll Barnes Student Scholarships *(Undergraduate/Scholarship)* [668]
Marguerite Ross Barnett Research Grant *(Graduate, Postdoctorate/Grant)* [1119]
Gina L. Barnhart Memorial Scholarship Fund *(Undergraduate/Scholarship)* [4040]
Robbie Barron Memorial Scholarships *(Undergraduate/Scholarship)* [4232]

Gloria Barron Wilderness Society Scholarship (Graduate/Scholarship) [10557]
Eivind H. Barth, Jr. Memorial Scholarships (Undergraduate/Scholarship) [2508]
Elsa Barton Educational Scholarship Fund (Undergraduate, Vocational/Occupational/Scholarship) [1127]
Bascom Hill Society Scholarships (Undergraduate/Scholarship) [10316]
Basic Research Fellowship Program (Postdoctorate/Fellowship) [634]
Bat Conservation International Student Research Scholarships (Graduate, Undergraduate/Scholarship) [2201]
H. Burton Bates Jr. Scholarships (Graduate, Undergraduate/Scholarship) [10402]
Jim Batten Community Newspaper Internships (Undergraduate/Internship) [10215]
Raymond B. Bauer Research Award (Professional development/Grant) [6479]
Marian Sims Baughn Scholarships (Undergraduate/Scholarship) [5692]
Hazel Reed Baumeister Scholarship Program (Undergraduate/Scholarship) [8947]
Bob Baxter Scholarships (Graduate, Undergraduate/Scholarship) [7106]
Timothy Baylink Good Fellowship Awards (Undergraduate/Fellowship) [8452]
John Bayliss Broadcast Foundation Internship Programs (Undergraduate/Internship) [2203]
John Bayliss Broadcast Foundation Radio Scholarships (Undergraduate/Scholarship) [2204]
BDC Visiting Fellowships (Advanced Professional, Professional development/Fellowship) [2382]
Beatitudes Fellowships (Professional development/Fellowship) [2208]
Catherine H. Beattie Fellowships (Graduate/Fellowship) [2867]
Jane Beattie Memorial Scholarships (Graduate, Professional development/Scholarship) [9160]
Beaver Medical Clinic-Glen Adams Scholarship Awards (Undergraduate/Scholarship) [8453]
Beaver Medical Clinic-H.E.A.R.T. Scholarship Awards (Undergraduate/Scholarship) [8454]
Beaver Medical Clinic-Premed Scholarship Awards (Undergraduate/Scholarship) [8455]
Don C. Beaver Memorial Scholarships (Undergraduate/Scholarship) [2447]
BECA Foundation General Scholarships Fund (Undergraduate/Scholarship) [2210]
Beca #Traductor Scholarships (All/Scholarship) [9458]
Becas Univision Scholarship Program (Undergraduate, Graduate/Scholarship) [4902]
Bechtel Engineering and Science Scholarships (Undergraduate/Scholarship) [6278]
Bechtel Group Foundation Scholarships for Safety & Health (Undergraduate/Scholarship) [1409]
Beck-Pfann Memorial Scholarships (Undergraduate/Scholarship) [7964]
Garvin L. Beck Scholarships (Undergraduate/Scholarship) [8456]
Dr. Joyce Beckett Scholarships (Graduate, Undergraduate/Scholarship) [6719]
Clifford L. Bedford Scholarship Award (Undergraduate/Scholarship) [5177]
BedwettingStore.com Design a Mascot Scholarships (Undergraduate, Graduate/Scholarship) [5635]
Raymond and Donald Beeler Memorial Scholarships (Undergraduate/Scholarship) [8457]
BEF Scholarships of the Arts (Graduate, Undergraduate/Scholarship) [2337]
Beinecke Rare Book and Manuscript Library Visiting Postdoctoral Scholar Fellowships (Postdoctorate/Fellowship) [2214]
N.S. Beinstock Fellowships (Other/Fellowship) [8402]
Hannah Beiter Graduate Student Research Grants (Doctorate, Graduate/Grant) [2909]
Bel Canto Vocal Scholarship Foundation Vocal Competition (Graduate/Award, Scholarship) [2217]
Belfer-Aptman Dissertation Research Awards (Doctorate/Grant) [6409]
AG Bell College Scholarship Awards (Undergraduate, Graduate/Scholarship) [314]

Alfred D. Bell, Jr. Travel Grants (Graduate/Grant) [4137]
John Bell and Lawrence Thornton Scholarship Fund (Undergraduate/Scholarship) [4738]
A.G. Bell School Age Financial Aid Program (Undergraduate/Scholarship) [315]
Bradley Stuart Beller Special Merit Award (Doctorate, Postdoctorate/Award) [3370]
Belmont University Commercial Music Showcase Scholarships (Undergraduate/Scholarship) [3212]
David Beltran Memorial Scholarships (Undergraduate/Scholarship) [8458]
Samuel Flagg Bemis Dissertation Research Grants (Doctorate, Graduate/Grant) [9133]
Reckitt Benckiser Student Scholarships (Graduate/Scholarship) [6771]
Richard W. Bendicksen Memorial Scholarships (Undergraduate/Scholarship) [1726]
H. Y. Benedict Fellowships (Graduate/Fellowship) [340]
George Benes, MD & Michael Mallee, EdD Point Scholarships (Undergraduate, Graduate, Doctorate/Scholarship) [8170]
Arthur Lockwood Beneventi Law Scholarships (Undergraduate/Scholarship) [7149]
Dave Benferado Scholarships (Graduate/Scholarship) [140]
Benign Essential Blepharospasm Research Foundation Research Grants (Doctorate, Postdoctorate/Grant) [2224]
HDR/Henry "Bud" Benjes Scholarships (Master's/Scholarship) [1484]
Jean Bennett Memorial Student Travel Grants (Graduate, Undergraduate/Grant) [7671]
Casey Bennett Scholarships (Undergraduate/Scholarship) [4007]
Price Benowitz Social Justice Scholarships (Undergraduate/Scholarship) [8228]
Elizabeth Benson Scholarship Awards (Undergraduate/Scholarship) [8542]
Benton-Meier Neuropsychology Graduate Scholarships (Graduate/Scholarship) [1142]
Linn-Benton County Scholarships (Undergraduate/Scholarship) [7709]
Rosalie Bentzinger Scholarships (Doctorate/Scholarship) [9849]
Lester G. Benz Memorial Scholarships for College Journalism Study (Other/Scholarship) [8396]
Fred Berg Awards (Undergraduate/Award) [3796]
Charlotte V. Bergen Scholarships (Undergraduate/Scholarship) [1269]
Bergman Scholarships (Undergraduate/Scholarship) [7487]
Bergmann Family Scholarship Funds (Undergraduate/Scholarship) [6282]
The Joseph Berkman, and Michael and Sarah Chipkin Holocaust/Genocide Studies Award (Graduate/Scholarship) [9581]
Berkowitz Fellowships (Professional development/Fellowship) [9743]
ARRS/Leonard Berlin Scholarships in Medical Professionalism (Other/Scholarship) [1222]
Louise Berman Fellows Award (Graduate, Master's, Doctorate/Fellowship, Award) [5667]
Richard L. Bernardi Memorial Scholarships (Undergraduate/Scholarship) [3276]
Stuart L. Bernath Dissertation Grants (Doctorate, Graduate/Grant) [9134]
Myrna F. Bernath Fellowships (Doctorate, Graduate/Fellowship) [9135]
Bill Bernbach Diversity Scholarships (Undergraduate/Scholarship) [457]
Hon. Peggy Bernheim Memorial Scholarships (Undergraduate/Scholarship) [2377]
Donald H. Bernstein/John B. Talbert, Jr. Scholarships (Undergraduate/Scholarship) [4179]
Thomas M. Berry Jr. Scholarships (Graduate, Undergraduate/Scholarship) [10403]
Jean Clark Berry Scholarships (Graduate, Undergraduate/Scholarship) [5693]
Best Price Nutrition and Health Scholarships (Undergraduate/Scholarship) [2237]
Beta Mu Project 2000 Scholarships (Undergraduate/Scholarship) [5695]
Beta Omega Scholarships (Undergraduate/Scholarship) [8911]

Beta Pi Project 2000 Scholarship in Memory of Kristy LeMond (Undergraduate/Scholarship) [5696]
Beta Pi Sigma Sorority Scholarships (BPSSS) (Undergraduate/Scholarship) [2244]
Beta Province Project 2000 Scholarships (Undergraduate/Scholarship) [5697]
Beta Sigma Scholarships (Undergraduate/Scholarship) [8912]
Beta Tau Scholarship Fund (Undergraduate/Scholarship) [5698]
Beta Theta Memorial Scholarships (Graduate, Undergraduate/Scholarship) [5699]
Beta Xi Project 2000 Scholarships (Undergraduate/Scholarship) [5700]
Beta Zeta Project 2000 Scholarships (Undergraduate/Scholarship) [5701]
Bethune-Cookman University Excelsior Scholarship Level 1 (Undergraduate/Scholarship) [2250]
Bethune-Cookman University Presidential Scholarships (Undergraduate/Scholarship) [2251]
Harold Bettinger Scholarships (Undergraduate, Graduate/Scholarship) [800]
Leonard Bettinger Vocational Scholarships (Undergraduate, Vocational/Occupational/Scholarship) [801]
William and Dorothy Bevan Scholarship (Graduate, Master's, Doctorate/Scholarship) [1143]
Albert J. Beveridge Grants for Research in the Western Hemisphere (Doctorate/Grant) [852]
Beverly Estate Scholarship (Undergraduate/Scholarship) [3662]
Leo Biaggi de Blasys Bogliasco Fellowships (Professional development/Fellowship) [2326]
BIE-Loan for Service for Graduates (Graduate/Loan) [882]
James L. Biggane Fellowships in Finance (Graduate/Fellowship) [7367]
Pierre and Patricia Bikai Fellowships (Graduate/Fellowship) [655]
Jan Bingle Scholarships (Master's, Doctorate/Scholarship) [3055]
Helen & Bob Bintz Scholarship Funds (Undergraduate/Scholarship) [6283]
Biogen Idec Hemophilia Scholarship Program (Undergraduate, Graduate, Doctorate/Scholarship) [2310]
BioRx/Hemophilia of North Carolina Educational Scholarships (Undergraduate/Scholarship) [6985]
Birmingham-Southern College Eagle Scout Scholarships (Undergraduate/Scholarship) [6920]
Graduate Student Honoraria - Elmer C. Birney Awards (Master's, Doctorate/Award) [1358]
Bisexual Foundation Scholarships (Graduate/Scholarship) [9284]
The Bishop James C. Baker Award (Doctorate/Scholarship) [9850]
Lebbeus F. Bissell Scholarships (Undergraduate/Scholarship) [4739]
Dr. Richard E. Bjork Memorial Graduate Study Award (Graduate/Scholarship) [9582]
Ted Bjornn University of Idaho Graduate Student Scholarships (Graduate/Scholarship) [5033]
Ted Bjornn University of Idaho Undergraduate Student Scholarships (Undergraduate/Scholarship) [5034]
Law Offices of David A. Black Annual Hearing Impaired Scholarships (All/Scholarship) [5957]
Reid Blackburn Scholarships (Undergraduate/Scholarship) [7107]
Eileen Blackey Doctoral Fellowships (Doctorate/Fellowship) [6788]
William T. Blackwell Scholarship Fund (Undergraduate/Scholarship) [7019]
Beatrice K. Blair Scholarships (Undergraduate/Scholarship) [2305]
Blakemore Freeman Fellowships (Undergraduate, Advanced Professional/Fellowship) [2307]
Blakemore Refresher Grants (Professional development/Grant) [2308]
Margaret Blanchard Dissertation Support Fund (Graduate/Grant) [10216]
Joan Blend Scholarship Fund (Graduate/Scholarship) [9493]
M. Hildred Blewett Fellowships (Postdoctorate/Fellowship) [1088]

Everitt P. Blizard Scholarships *(Graduate/Scholarship)* [1034]
Ellin Bloch and Pierre Ritchie Diversity Dissertation Grant *(Graduate/Grant)* [1132]
Jeanne Humphrey Block Dissertation Award *(Postdoctorate/Award)* [4784]
Ellen Blodgett Memorial Scholarships *(Undergraduate/Scholarship)* [7375]
BMES Graduate and Undergraduate Student Awards *(Graduate, Undergraduate/Award)* [2271]
BMO Capital Markets Lime Connect Equity through Education Scholarships *(Undergraduate, Graduate/Scholarship)* [6087]
Board of Certification for Emergency Nursing (BCEN) Undergraduate Scholarships *(Undergraduate/Scholarship)* [3860]
David and Camille Boatwright Endowed Scholarships *(Undergraduate/Scholarship)* [7965]
Sandra Bobbitt Continuing Education Scholarship *(Undergraduate/Scholarship)* [2032]
Edith and Arnold N. Bodtker Grants *(Undergraduate, Graduate/Grant, Internship)* [3522]
B.O.G. Pest Control Scholarship Funds *(Undergraduate, Graduate/Scholarship)* [2323]
Hagop Bogigian Scholarship Fund *(Undergraduate/Scholarship)* [1689]
Bogliasco Fellowships *(Professional development/Fellowship)* [2327]
Bohemian Lawyers Association of Chicago Scholarships *(Graduate/Scholarship)* [2333]
Brian Bolton Graduate/Mature Student Essay Awards *(Undergraduate, Graduate/Award)* [4301]
Friends of Megan Bolton Memorial Fund *(Undergraduate/Scholarship)* [4233]
BOMA/NY Scholarships *(Undergraduate/Scholarship)* [2404]
Carol Bond Community College Scholarships *(Undergraduate/Scholarship)* [7479]
Carol Bond University Scholarships *(Undergraduate/Scholarship)* [7480]
Barbara Bonnema Memorial Scholarships *(Undergraduate/Scholarship)* [8459]
Ellis J. Bonner Scholarships *(Graduate/Scholarship)* [6754]
Sam L. Booke, Sr. Scholarships *(Undergraduate/Scholarship)* [10572]
Boomer Benefits Scholarships *(Undergraduate/Scholarship)* [2335]
Admiral Mike Boorda Loans Program *(Undergraduate/Loan)* [7234]
David L. Boren Fellowships *(Graduate/Fellowship)* [5199]
David L. Boren Scholarships *(Undergraduate, College/Scholarship)* [5200]
David L. Boren Undergraduate Scholarships *(Graduate, Undergraduate/Scholarship)* [1968]
Dr. Anita Borg Memorial Scholarships - USA *(Graduate, Undergraduate/Scholarship)* [4493]
Maria Gonzales Borrero Scholarships *(Undergraduate/Scholarship)* [4740]
Tom Bost Scholarships *(Undergraduate/Scholarship)* [10217]
Boston Intercollegiate Alumnae Association Adelphe Scholarship *(Undergraduate/Scholarship)* [5702]
Stephen Botein Fellowships *(Doctorate/Fellowship)* [433]
Dr. George T. Bottomley Scholarships *(Undergraduate/Scholarship)* [6350]
Richard J. Bouchard AECOM Scholarships *(Undergraduate, Graduate/Scholarship)* [1162]
Bound to Stay Bound Books Scholarships *(Graduate/Scholarship)* [2017]
Rev. Andrew L. Bouwhuis Memorial Scholarship Program *(Undergraduate/Scholarship)* [2814]
Billy Bowling Memorial Scholarship *(Undergraduate/Scholarship)* [7530]
Boy Scouts of America Troop 3 Scholarships - Art Till/Nathan E. Smith Memorial Scholarships *(Undergraduate, Vocational/Occupational/Scholarship)* [8460]
Dr. Betty J. Boyd-Beu and Edwin G. Beu, Jr. Scholarships *(Undergraduate/Scholarship)* [10011]
W. Scott Boyd Group Grants *(Advanced Professional/Grant)* [5282]
Corris Boyd Scholarships *(Master's/Scholarship)* [2085]
Dody Boyd Scholarships *(Undergraduate/Scholarship)* [3214]
Boyle Family Scholarship *(Undergraduate/Scholarship)* [1577]
BPW Foundation Career Advancement Scholarships *(Undergraduate/Scholarship)* [2422]
Mildred Cater Bradham Social Work Fellowships *(Graduate, Professional development/Fellowship)* [10814]
Carol June Bradley Awards *(Professional development/Grant)* [6625]
Charles Bradley Memorial Scholarships *(Undergraduate/Scholarship)* [4723]
Paul W. Bradley Scholarships *(Undergraduate/Scholarship)* [7377]
Edward J. Brady Memorial Scholarships *(Undergraduate/Scholarship)* [1511]
W. Philip Braender and Nancy Coleman Braender Scholarships *(Undergraduate/Scholarship)* [4741]
BRAF Grants *(Graduate/Grant)* [2301]
TACS/A. Bragas and Associates Student Scholarships *(Undergraduate/Scholarship)* [9686]
Susan Brager Occupational Education Scholarships *(Undergraduate/Scholarship)* [8333]
Byard Braley Scholarship *(Undergraduate/Scholarship)* [5462]
George and Mary Brammer Scholarship *(Undergraduate/Scholarship)* [3663]
The Helen and Edward Brancati Teacher Development Scholarships *(Other/Scholarship)* [2783]
Linda Brandt Research Awards *(Postgraduate/Award)* [2039]
Farella Braun + Martel LLP 1L Diversity Scholarship Program *(Undergraduate/Scholarship)* [3968]
Theodore E.D. Braun Research Travel Fellowships *(Other/Fellowship)* [1287]
Breakthrough to Nursing Scholarships *(Undergraduate/Scholarship)* [4268]
Ann Marie Bredefeld Scholarships *(Undergraduate/Scholarship)* [7966]
Kenneth H. Breeden Scholarships *(Undergraduate/Scholarship)* [5924]
William J. Brennan Graduate Assistant Fellowships *(Graduate/Fellowship)* [7678]
Hilda E. Bretzlaff Foundation Scholarships *(Undergraduate/Scholarship, Grant)* [2363]
Rick Brewer Scholarships *(Undergraduate/Scholarship)* [10218]
Mary Ann Brichta Scholarships *(Undergraduate/Scholarship)* [10317]
James Bridenbaugh Memorial Scholarships *(Undergraduate/Scholarship)* [802]
Lloyd Bridges Scholarships *(Graduate, Other/Scholarship)* [2835]
Parsons Brinckerhoff-Jim Lammie Scholarships *(Undergraduate/Scholarship)* [1163]
Wade O. Brinker Resident Research Award *(Undergraduate/Award)* [10378]
Cathy L. Brock Memorial Scholarships *(Graduate/Scholarship)* [5167]
Margaret Martin Brock Scholarships in Law *(Undergraduate/Scholarship)* [7967]
Houston Alumnae Association, Doris Krikham Brokaw Memorial Adelphe Scholarship *(Undergraduate, Graduate/Scholarship)* [5703]
John G. Brokaw Scholarships *(Undergraduate/Scholarship)* [7227]
Brookdale Leadership in Aging Fellowships *(Other/Fellowship)* [2380]
Shirley J. Brooke Endowed Scholarships *(Undergraduate/Scholarship)* [7969]
George M. Brooker, CPM Diversity Collegiate Scholarship *(Graduate, Undergraduate/Scholarship)* [5215]
Seth R. and Corrine H. Brooks Memorial Scholarships *(Undergraduate/Scholarship)* [2246]
Carl E. Brooks Scholarships *(Undergraduate/Scholarship)* [9421]
Dorothy B. Brothers Executive Scholarship Program *(Undergraduate/Scholarship)* [10656]
William A. and Ann M. Brothers Scholarships *(Undergraduate/Scholarship)* [1512]
Selena Danette Brown Book Scholarships *(Graduate, Undergraduate/Scholarship)* [6720]
Marjorie M. Brown Dissertation Fellowship *(Doctorate/Fellowship)* [5780]
Diana Brown Endowed Scholarships *(Undergraduate/Scholarship)* [6018]
Marjorie M. Brown Fellowship Program *(Postdoctorate/Fellowship)* [5788]
John Carter Brown Library Long-Term Fellowships *(Graduate, Doctorate/Fellowship)* [2384]
John Carter Brown Library Short-Term Fellowships *(Doctorate, Postdoctorate/Fellowship)* [2385]
Olympia Brown and Max Kapp Awards *(Master's/Scholarship)* [9832]
Catherine Amelia Thew Brown Memorial Scholarship Funds *(Undergraduate/Scholarship)* [6284]
Quincy Brown Memorial Scholarships *(Undergraduate/Scholarship)* [8461]
Jesse Brown Memorial Youth Scholarship Program *(Advanced Professional/Scholarship)* [3632]
JoAhn Brown-Nash Memorial Scholarships *(Undergraduate/Scholarship)* [3215]
Ron Brown Scholars Program *(Undergraduate/Scholarship)* [2387]
D.C. and Virginia Brown Scholarships *(Undergraduate/Scholarship)* [3090]
Jack H. Brown Scholarships *(Undergraduate/Scholarship)* [2448]
Mary L. Brown Scholarships *(Undergraduate/Scholarship)* [5467]
Charles S. Brown Scholarships in Physics *(Graduate, Undergraduate/Scholarship)* [7140]
VPPPA Stephen Brown Scholarships *(Graduate, Undergraduate/Scholarship)* [10417]
Warren K. Brown Scholarships *(Undergraduate/Scholarship)* [1410]
Richard A. Brown Student Scholarships *(Undergraduate/Scholarship)* [9691]
Regina Brown Undergraduate Student Fellowships *(Undergraduate/Fellowship)* [6879]
Peggy Browning Fund - Chicago School-Year Fellowships *(Graduate, Undergraduate/Fellowship)* [2394]
Hollis Brownstein Research Grants *(Professional development/Grant)* [6011]
Sheriff W. Bruce Umpleby Law Enforcement Scholarship Fund *(Undergraduate/Scholarship)* [9494]
Robert W. Brunsman Memorial Scholarship *(Professional development/Scholarship)* [5360]
Katie Brush Memorial Scholarships *(Master's, Doctorate/Scholarship)* [3056]
Bryant Essay Scholarships *(Undergraduate, Graduate/Scholarship)* [2396]
Edward C. Bryant Scholarship for an Outstanding Graduate Student in Survey Statistics *(Graduate/Scholarship)* [1464]
Bryant Visual Content Scholarships *(Undergraduate, Graduate/Scholarship)* [2397]
BSA Educational Scholarships *(Undergraduate/Scholarship)* [2426]
BSF General Scholarship Awards *(Undergraduate, Vocational/Occupational/Scholarship)* [2197]
BSF Science and Medicine Research Grants *(Professional development/Grant)* [2199]
Patricia Buchanan Memorial Scholarships *(Undergraduate/Scholarship)* [10318]
Lt. General Douglas D. Buchholz Memorial Scholarship *(Undergraduate/Scholarship)* [89]
John and Elisabeth Buck Endowed Scholarships *(Graduate, Postdoctorate/Scholarship)* [6244]
Peter Buck Fellowships Program - Graduate *(Graduate/Fellowship)* [9030]
Peter Buck Fellowships Program - Postdoctoral *(Postdoctorate/Fellowship)* [9031]
Buckfire & Buckfire, P.C. Law School Diversity Scholarships *(Graduate/Scholarship)* [2399]
Buckfire & Buckfire, P.C. Medical Diversity Scholarships *(Advanced Professional/Scholarship)* [2400]
Buder Scholarships for American Indian Law Students *(Juris Doctorate/Scholarship)* [10474]
Gary L. Buffington Memorial Scholarships *(Undergraduate/Scholarship)* [5138]
Tien Bui Memorial Scholarships *(Undergraduate/Scholarship)* [10573]
Buick Achievers Scholarship Program *(Undergraduate/Scholarship)* [4359]
Pamfil and Maria Bujea Family Orthodox Christian Seminarian Scholarships *(Undergraduate/Scholarship)* [1225]

William S. Bullinger Scholarships (Doctorate/Scholarship) [3983]
Mike Buoncristiano Memorial Scholarship Fund (Undergraduate/Scholarship) [6287]
C. Lalor Burdick Scholarships (Graduate, Master's, Doctorate/Scholarship) [6245]
George M. Burditt Scholarships (Undergraduate/Scholarship) [1965]
Max M. Burger Endowed Scholarships in Embryology (Graduate, Master's, Doctorate/Scholarship) [6246]
Graduate Fellowship Program - Robert M. Burger Fellowships (Doctorate, Graduate/Fellowship) [8832]
Burger King Employee Scholars Program (Undergraduate/Scholarship) [2410]
Burger King Scholars Program (Undergraduate/Scholarship) [2411]
Richard J. Burk, Jr. Fellowships (Graduate/Fellowship) [4808]
ACLS Frederick Burkhardt Residential Fellowships (Other/Fellowship) [434]
Frederick Burkhardt Residential Fellowships for Recently Tenured Scholars (Advanced Professional, Professional development/Fellowship) [738]
John Burroughs Bogliasco Fellowships (Professional development/Fellowship) [2328]
Burroughs Wellcome Fund Collaborative Research Travel Grants (CRTG) (Doctorate, Postdoctorate, Professional development/Grant) [2413]
Burroughs Wellcome Travel Fellowships (Undergraduate, Graduate/Fellowship, Grant) [9305]
Wes Burton Memorial Scholarships (Undergraduate/Scholarship) [10574]
Bush Artist Fellowships (Professional development/Fellowship) [2419]
Bush Fellowship Program (Other/Fellowship) [2420]
Lindsay Buster Memorial Scholarships (Undergraduate/Scholarship) [3277]
Walter Byers Postgraduate Scholarships (Graduate, Postgraduate/Scholarship) [6861]
byourself Scholarship Fund (Undergraduate, Vocational/Occupational/Scholarship) [3318]
Dr. F. Ross Byrd Scholarships (Graduate, Vocational/Occupational, Postgraduate/Scholarship) [10463]
George J. Bysiewicz Scholarship Fund (Undergraduate/Scholarship) [3198]
C200 Scholar Awards (Graduate/Scholarship) [3156]
CAAO Scholarship (Professional development/Scholarship) [3356]
Cadmus Communications Corporation Graphics Scholarship Endowment Fund (Undergraduate/Scholarship) [4181]
Edwin Anthony and Adelaide Boudreaux Cadogan Scholarships (Graduate/Fellowship) [8747]
Cal State San Macros Alumna Scholarships (Undergraduate/Scholarship) [2486]
Tese Caldarelli Memorial Scholarships (Graduate, Undergraduate/Scholarship) [6723]
Dave Caldwell Scholarships (Graduate/Scholarship) [1485]
Caledonia Alumni Association Scholarship Funds (Undergraduate/Scholarship) [6285]
Calgary USAEE/IAEE North American Conference Registration Fee Scholarships (Undergraduate/Scholarship) [9883]
Calhoun County Auburn University Scholarships (Undergraduate/Scholarship) [3260]
Calhoun Valedictorian, Salutatorian/Top 5 Scholarships (Undergraduate/Scholarship) [2432]
California Bar Foundation 1L Diversity Scholarships (Graduate/Scholarship) [2442]
California Bar Foundation 3L Diversity Scholarships (Undergraduate/Scholarship) [2443]
California Council of the Blind Scholarships (Undergraduate, Graduate/Scholarship) [8751]
California Sea Grant State Fellowship (Graduate/Fellowship) [2479]
Calihan Academic Fellowships (Graduate, Professional development/Fellowship, Grant) [56]
Calihan Travel Grants (Graduate/Grant) [57]
Calista Education and Culture Scholarships (Graduate, Undergraduate, Vocational/Occupational/Scholarship) [2490]

Captain Jodi Callahan Memorial Scholarships (Graduate, Master's/Scholarship) [122]
W.L. Calvert Memorial Scholarships (Graduate/Scholarship) [4966]
Calvin Alumni Association-Washington, D.C. Scholarships (Undergraduate/Scholarship) [2504]
Camden County College Foundation Scholarships (Undergraduate/Scholarship) [2522]
Stuart Cameron and Margaret McLeod Memorial Scholarships (SCMS) (Graduate, Undergraduate/Scholarship) [5205]
Wesley C. Cameron Scholarships (Undergraduate/Scholarship) [7228]
Camille and Henry Dreyfus Foundation - Senior Scientist Mentor Program (Professional development/Grant) [3695]
Camp Network Counselor Appreciation Scholarships (Undergraduate/Scholarship) [2528]
Thomas R. Camp Scholarships (Graduate/Scholarship) [1486]
Campus Discovery Scholarships (Undergraduate/Scholarship) [2532]
Cancer for College Scholarships (Graduate, Undergraduate/Scholarship) [2770]
Cancer Survivors' Fund Scholarships (Undergraduate/Scholarship) [2779]
CANFIT Nutrition, Physical Education and Culinary Arts Scholarships (Graduate, Undergraduate/Scholarship) [3167]
Annie J. Cannon Award in Astronomy (Doctorate/Award, Recognition) [613]
Therese A. Cannon Educational Scholarships (Other/Scholarship) [5372]
CANS/SNRS Dissertation Research Grants (Doctorate/Grant) [9405]
Commander Ronald J. Cantin Scholarships (Undergraduate/Scholarship) [3075]
CAODC Occupational Health and Safety Scholarships (Professional development/Scholarship) [2570]
CAODC Scholarship Program (Undergraduate/Scholarship) [2571]
John Caoile Memorial Scholarships (Undergraduate/Scholarship) [8335]
CAPAL Public Service Scholarships (Graduate, Undergraduate/Scholarship) [3341]
Cape Fear Community College Merit Scholarships (Undergraduate/Scholarship) [2786]
Lester J. Cappon Fellowships in Documentary Editing (Postdoctorate/Fellowship) [7410]
Daniel Cardillo Charitable Fund (Professional development/Scholarship) [6192]
Career Awards for Medical Scientists (CAMS) (Postdoctorate, Advanced Professional, Professional development/Grant) [2414]
Career Awards for Science and Mathematics Teachers (Other/Award) [2415]
Career Awards at the Scientific Interface (CASI) (Doctorate, Postdoctorate, Advanced Professional, Professional development/Grant) [2416]
Career Development Scholarships (Postdoctorate, Postgraduate/Scholarship) [4129]
Career Mobility Scholarships (Graduate, Undergraduate, Vocational/Occupational/Scholarship) [4269]
CareerFitter Scholarships (Undergraduate, Graduate/Scholarship) [2795]
CareFusion Fellowships for Neonatal and Pediatric Therapists (Professional development/Fellowship) [1209]
Beth Carew Memorial Scholarships (Undergraduate/Scholarship) [6986]
John Carew Memorial Scholarships (Graduate/Scholarship) [803]
John L. Carey Scholarship Awards (Graduate/Scholarship) [901]
Caribbean Actuarial Scholarship (Undergraduate/Scholarship) [61]
AABA Read Carlock Memorial Scholarship Fund (Other/Scholarship) [1625]
Glen and Babs Carlson Endowed Scholarships (Undergraduate/Scholarship) [6019]
Dan Carman Attorney at Law Criminal Defense Scholarships (Advanced Professional/Scholarship) [3520]
Walta Wilkinson Carmichael Scholarships (Undergraduate/Scholarship) [8913]
Carnegie Observatories Graduate Research Fellowships (Graduate, Doctorate/Fellowship) [2799]
Carollo Engineers Scholarships (Master's/Scholarship) [1487]
Pete Carpenter Fellowship (Professional development/Fellowship) [2318]
Carpenters' Company Scholarships (Undergraduate/Scholarship) [2801]
Walter and Elsie Carr Endowed Scholarships (Undergraduate/Scholarship) [6020]
Willis H. Carrier Scholarships (Undergraduate/Scholarship, Award) [1329]
Karen D. Carsel Memorial Scholarships (Graduate/Scholarship) [819]
Rachel Carson Prize (Other/Prize) [1310]
Gene Carte Student Paper Competition Awards (Undergraduate, Graduate/Prize) [1281]
Leigh Carter Scholarships (Undergraduate/Scholarship) [3217]
CAS Trust Scholarship (Undergraduate/Scholarship) [2809]
CASBS Fellowships (Doctorate, Other/Fellowship) [2841]
Cascara Vacation Rentals Hospitality Matters Scholarships (Undergraduate, Graduate/Scholarship) [2805]
TCDA Jim and Glenda Casey Professional Scholarships (Other/Scholarship) [669]
Elton Casey Scholarships (Undergraduate/Scholarship) [10219]
Local 827 Peter J. Casey Scholarships (Undergraduate/Scholarship) [5288]
Carlos M. Castaneda Journalism Scholarships (Graduate/Scholarship) [2807]
The Kerri Castellini Women's Leadership Scholarships (Undergraduate/Scholarship) [8229]
Catholic Aid Association's Post-High School Tuition Scholarships (Undergraduate/Scholarship) [2818]
Catholic Biblical Association of America Scholarships (Undergraduate/Scholarship) [2812]
Catholic Relief Services Summer Internships (Undergraduate, Graduate, Professional development/Internship) [2816]
Robert A. Catlin/David W. Long Memorial Fellowships (Graduate/Fellowship) [1104]
Cave Conservancy Foundation Graduate and Undergraduate Fellowships (Doctorate, Graduate, Undergraduate/Fellowship) [2823]
Christine Kerr Cawthorne Scholarships (Undergraduate/Scholarship) [8914]
Llewellyn L. Cayvan String Instrument Scholarships (Undergraduate/Scholarship) [4580]
CBC Spouses Education Scholarship Fund (Graduate, Undergraduate/Scholarship) [3345]
CBC Spouses Heineken USA Performing Arts Scholarships (Undergraduate/Scholarship) [3346]
CBC Spouses Visual Arts Scholarships (Undergraduate/Scholarship) [3347]
CBCF Congressional Fellows Program (Other/Fellowship) [3348]
CCF Academic Fellowships in Karst Studies - Graduate (Master's, Doctorate/Fellowship) [2820]
CCF Academic Fellowships in Karst Studies - Undegraduate (Undergraduate/Fellowship) [2821]
CCF Career Development Award (Professional development/Grant) [3371]
CCF Improving Cancer Care Grants (Professional development, Doctorate/Grant) [3372]
CCF Merit Award (Professional development, Doctorate/Award) [3373]
CCFA Career Development Awards (Doctorate/Grant) [3476]
CCFA Research Fellowship Awards (Doctorate, Graduate/Fellowship) [3477]
CCFA Student Research Fellowship Awards (Graduate, Undergraduate/Grant) [3478]
CCSD School Counselors' Scholarships (Undergraduate/Scholarship) [8336]
CCU Alumni Endowed Scholarships (Undergraduate/Scholarship) [3136]
CCWH/Berkshire Conference of Women Historians Graduate Student Fellowships (Doctorate/Fellowship) [3418]
CDA Foundation Allied Dental Student Scholarships (Undergraduate/Scholarship) [2828]

CDA Foundation Dental Student Scholarships *(All/Scholarship)* [2829]
CDC Presidential Management Fellows Program *(Graduate/Fellowship)* [9917]
CDC Preventive Medicine Residency and Fellowships *(Other/Fellowship)* [9918]
CDC Public Health Informatics Fellowships *(Professional development, Master's, Graduate/Fellowship)* [9919]
L.B. Cebik, W4RNL, and Jean Cebik, N4TZP, Memorial Scholarships *(Undergraduate/Scholarship)* [1730]
Cedarcrest Farms Scholarships *(Graduate, Undergraduate/Scholarship)* [944]
CEJIL Communications Internships *(Undergraduate, Graduate/Internship)* [2860]
CEJIL Legal Internships *(Graduate, Professional development/Internship)* [2861]
Cengage Learning Scholarships Program *(Undergraduate/Scholarship)* [2839]
Cengage Travel Award for Teachers of Reading at a Community College *(Professional development/Monetary)* [3123]
DAR Centennial Scholarship *(Undergraduate/Scholarship)* [7150]
Center for the Education of Women Scholarships *(Graduate, Undergraduate/Scholarship)* [10195]
Center for the Education of Women Student Research Grants *(Graduate, Undergraduate/Grant)* [10196]
Center for Engineering in Medicine Predoctoral Fellows Program *(Postdoctorate/Fellowship)* [6316]
Center for Lesbian and Gay Studies Fellowships *(Graduate/Fellowship)* [2863]
Centerville-Abington Dollars for Scholars *(Undergraduate/Scholarship)* [10502]
CentraState Band Aid Open Committee Scholarships *(Undergraduate/Scholarship)* [2876]
CERT College Scholarships *(Graduate, Undergraduate/Scholarship)* [3435]
Certified Municipal Clerk Scholarships (CMC) *(Other/Scholarship)* [5350]
Certified Neuroscience Registered Nurse Recertification Grant Program *(Other/Grant)* [545]
Cerutti Group Scholarships *(Undergraduate/Scholarship)* [4646]
Arthur and Gladys Cervenka Scholarships *(Undergraduate/Scholarship)* [9168]
CES Conference Travel Grants *(Graduate, Professional development/Grant)* [3437]
CES First Article Prize *(Professional development/Prize)* [3438]
CES Pre-Dissertation Research Fellowships *(Graduate/Fellowship)* [3439]
CF Abogados Legal Scholarships *(Graduate/Scholarship)* [2781]
CfA Postdoctoral Fellowships *(Postdoctorate/Fellowship)* [4780]
CFNIL Senior Memorial Scholarships *(Undergraduate/Scholarship)* [3279]
CFR Military Fellowships *(Professional development/Fellowship)* [3442]
CFR National Intelligence Fellowships *(Professional development/Fellowship)* [3443]
CFR Stanton Nuclear Security Fellowships *(Doctorate, Postdoctorate, Advanced Professional/Fellowship)* [3444]
CFR Volunteer Internships *(Undergraduate, Graduate/Internship)* [3445]
CH2M Hill/AEESP Outstanding Doctoral Dissertation Award *(Graduate, Doctorate/Award)* [1951]
Rick Chace Foundation Scholarships *(Graduate/Scholarship)* [2024]
Chaîne des Rôtisseurs Scholarships *(Undergraduate/Scholarship)* [758]
ChairScholars National Scholarship Program *(Undergraduate/Scholarship)* [2889]
Jeanne S. Chall Research Fellowship *(Doctorate, Graduate/Fellowship)* [5355]
Challenge Met Scholarships *(Undergraduate/Scholarship)* [1732]
Mariam K. Chamberlain Fellowships in Women and Public Policy *(Graduate/Fellowship)* [5228]
Logan S. Chambers Individual Scholarships *(Other/Scholarship)* [5283]
Chambersburg/Fannett-Metal School District Scholarship Fund *(Undergraduate/Scholarship)* [4234]
Chambliss Astronomy Achievement Student Awards *(Undergraduate, Graduate/Award)* [614]
Bryan A. Champion Memorial Scholarship *(Undergraduate/Scholarship)* [7582]
Jason Chaney Memorial Scholarship Fund *(Undergraduate/Scholarship)* [10503]
Channabasappa Memorial Scholarships *(Graduate, Doctorate/Scholarship)* [5319]
Harry H. and Floy B. Chapin Scholarships *(Undergraduate/Scholarship)* [3280]
Nancy J. Chapman Scholarships *(Other/Scholarship)* [1939]
S. Penny Chappell Scholarships *(Undergraduate/Scholarship)* [8085]
Chapter 1 - Detroit Founding Chapter Undergraduate Scholarships *(Undergraduate/Scholarship)* [9169]
Chapter 31 - Peoria Endowed Scholarships *(Undergraduate/Scholarship)* [9173]
Chapter 52 - Wichita Scholarships *(Graduate, Undergraduate/Scholarship)* [9175]
Chapter 56 - Fort Wayne Scholarships *(Graduate, Undergraduate/Scholarship)* [9176]
Chapter 6 Fairfield County Scholarships *(Undergraduate/Scholarship)* [9177]
Chapter 67 - Phoenix Scholarships *(Undergraduate/Scholarship)* [9178]
Charles A. Lindbergh Fellowships *(Graduate/Fellowship)* [9021]
Charles H. Bussmann Graduate Scholarship *(Graduate, Undergraduate/Scholarship)* [6271]
Charlotte Housing Authority Scholarship Fund (CHASF) *(Undergraduate, Vocational/Occupational/Scholarship)* [4185]
Charlotte-Mecklenburg Schools Scholarship Incentive Program *(Undergraduate/Scholarship)* [4186]
Emilie Du Chatelet Awards *(Doctorate/Award)* [1288]
CCWH Nupur Chaudhuri First Article Prizes *(Professional development/Prize)* [3419]
Chautauqua Scholarships Program *(Undergraduate/Scholarship)* [5367]
Cesar E. Chavez Scholarships *(Undergraduate/Scholarship)* [8463]
CHCI Graduate Fellowships *(Graduate/Fellowship)* [3352]
CHCI Public Policy Fellowships *(Professional development/Fellowship)* [3353]
CHCI Scholarships *(Undergraduate, Graduate/Scholarship)* [3354]
Chemical Heritage Foundation Travel Grants (CHF) *(All/Grant)* [2891]
Cherokee Nation Pell Scholarships *(Undergraduate/Scholarship)* [2894]
Melba Dawn Chiarenza Scholarship Fund *(Undergraduate/Scholarship)* [10504]
Kevin Child Scholarships *(Undergraduate/Scholarship)* [6987]
Childbirth Educator Program Scholarships *(All/Scholarship)* [5909]
John and Ruth Childe Scholarships *(Undergraduate/Scholarship)* [9422]
Children of Evangeline Section Scholarships *(Graduate, Undergraduate/Scholarship)* [9249]
Children of Unitarian Universalist Ministers College Scholarships *(Undergraduate/Scholarship)* [9833]
Jane Coffin Childs Memorial Fund - Medical Research Fellowships *(Postdoctorate/Fellowship)* [2915]
Charline Chilson Scholarships *(Undergraduate/Scholarship)* [3580]
China Google PhD Fellowships *(Doctorate/Fellowship)* [4494]
Chinese American Medical Society Summer Research Fellowships Program *(Undergraduate/Fellowship)* [2917]
Helen Krich Chinoy Dissertation Research Fellowships *(Doctorate/Fellowship)* [1434]
CHOIR MD Post-Residency Fellowship in Health Services Research *(Postdoctorate/Fellowship)* [10376]
Choose Your Future Scholarships *(Undergraduate/Scholarship)* [3219]
Chopin Foundation of the United States Scholarships *(Undergraduate/Scholarship)* [2928]
CHOPR Postdoctoral Fellowships *(Postdoctorate/Fellowship)* [10267]
Chrétien International Research Grants *(Doctorate/Grant)* [615]
Betty Sams Christian Fellowships *(Doctorate/Fellowship)* [10396]
Frances N. Christian Memorial Endowment Nursing Scholarship *(Graduate, Undergraduate/Scholarship)* [9583]
Christian Pharmacists Fellowship International *(Advanced Professional/Fellowship)* [2934]
Irene R. Christman Scholarship *(Undergraduate/Scholarship)* [7939]
Christmas Tree Chapter Scholarship Awards *(Undergraduate/Scholarship)* [7692]
Commander Daniel J. Christovich Scholarship Fund *(Undergraduate/Scholarship)* [3076]
Chronic Lymphocytic Leukemia Collaborative Grants *(Advanced Professional/Grant)* [6157]
Chrysalis Scholarships *(Graduate/Scholarship)* [2094]
The Churchill Scholarships *(Postgraduate/Scholarship)* [2940]
CIA Undergraduate Scholarships *(Undergraduate/Scholarship)* [1969]
CIGNA Healthcare Graduate Scholarships *(Graduate/Scholarship)* [6957]
CIGNA Healthcare Undergraduate Scholarships *(Undergraduate/Scholarship)* [6958]
Cincinnati High School Scholarships *(Undergraduate/Scholarship)* [2949]
Cinestory Fellowship *(Professional development/Fellowship)* [3029]
CISDL Global Research Fellowship - Associate Fellows *(Graduate/Fellowship)* [2880]
CISDL Global Research Fellowship - Legal Research Fellows *(Graduate/Fellowship)* [2881]
CISDL Global Research Fellowships - Senior Research Fellows *(Other/Fellowship)* [2882]
Citi Foundation Scholarship Program *(Undergraduate/Scholarship)* [866]
Citi/TELACU Scholars Mentoring Program *(Undergraduate/Scholarship)* [9659]
City Bar Diversity Fellowships Program *(Undergraduate/Fellowship)* [7343]
City of Sanibel Employee Dependent Scholarships *(Undergraduate/Scholarship)* [9423]
Civil Air Patrol Flight Scholarships *(Undergraduate/Scholarship)* [3039]
Civitan Shropshire Scholarships *(Undergraduate, Vocational/Occupational/Scholarship)* [3041]
CJA Legal Internships *(Professional development/Internship)* [2858]
CJH Graduate Research Fellowships *(Doctorate/Fellowship)* [2851]
CJH Visiting Scholars Program *(Doctorate/Fellowship)* [7343]
CLA/CP Scholarship *(Other/Scholarship)* [8672]
Clackamas Chapter Scholarship Awards *(Undergraduate/Scholarship)* [7693]
Claes Nobel Academic Scholarships for Members *(High School/Scholarship)* [7159]
Clan Ross Foundation Scholarships *(Undergraduate/Scholarship)* [3043]
Cecil Earl Clapp, Sr. Memorial Scholarship *(Undergraduate/Scholarship)* [7531]
Michele Clark Fellowships *(Undergraduate/Fellowship)* [8403]
Vickie Clark-Flaherty Scholarships *(Undergraduate/Scholarship)* [7471]
Howard A. Clark Horticulture Scholarships *(Undergraduate/Scholarship)* [3220]
Robert A. Clark Memorial Educational Scholarships *(Professional development/Scholarship)* [7166]
Thomas Arkle Clark Scholar-Leader of the Year Endowed Scholarships *(Graduate, Undergraduate/Scholarship)* [8061]
Athalie Clarke Endowed Scholarships *(Undergraduate/Scholarship)* [7970]
Lucy and Charles W.E. Clarke Scholarships *(Undergraduate/Scholarship)* [1797]
IADR John Clarkson Fellowship *(Postdoctorate/Fellowship)* [5250]
Classic Wines of California Scholarships *(Undergraduate/Scholarship)* [2449]

Clay Maitland CGF Scholarship (Undergraduate/Scholarship) [3077]
Clay Postdoctoral Fellowships (Postdoctorate/Fellowship) [4781]
CLCA Landscape Educational Advancement Foundation Educational Grant Program (Undergraduate/Grant) [2467]
Brian Dane Cleary Memorial Scholarships (Undergraduate/Scholarship) [7971]
Lula Faye Clegg Memorial Scholarship Fund (Undergraduate/Scholarship) [4188]
Tyler Clementi Point Scholarship (Undergraduate/Scholarship) [8171]
Geraldine Clewell Fellowships - Doctoral Student (Graduate/Fellowship) [8086]
Geraldine Clewell Fellowships - Masteral (Graduate/Fellowship) [8087]
Geraldine Clewell Scholarships - Undergraduate (Undergraduate/Scholarship) [8088]
Justice Robert L. Clifford Fellowships (Undergraduate/Fellowship) [6593]
James L. Clifford Prize (Other/Prize, Monetary) [1289]
David H. Clift Scholarships (Graduate/Scholarship) [961]
Clinical Project Funding for Advanced Practice Oncology Nurses (Advanced Professional, Professional development/Grant) [7616]
Clinical Research Fellowship for Medical Students (Graduate/Fellowship) [3699]
Clinician Scientist Development Awards (Postgraduate/Fellowship) [7883]
Paul W. Clopper Scholarship Grant for Junior Dental Students (Undergraduate/Scholarship) [5068]
Closs/Parnitzke/Clarke Scholarships (Undergraduate/Scholarship) [8089]
The Club Foundation Faculty Research Grants (Professional development/Grant) [3060]
The Clubs of America Scholarships Award for Career Success (Undergraduate/Scholarship) [3065]
CMA Private Lesson Program: Instrumental Scholarships for Elementary and Middle School Students (Undergraduate/Scholarship) [3037]
CMAA Student Conference Travel Grants (Undergraduate/Grant) [3061]
CMC-KLI Leadership Research Fellowship (Undergraduate/Fellowship) [3045]
CMC-KLI Social Sector Internship Program (Undergraduate/Internship) [3046]
CMC-KLI Social Sector Research Fellowship (Undergraduate/Fellowship) [3047]
CME Beef Industry Scholarships (Undergraduate/Scholarship) [6841]
CMH Dissertation Fellowships (Graduate/Fellowship) [9876]
CMSF Scholarships (Undergraduate, Graduate/Scholarship) [2932]
CNA Foundation Scholarships (Graduate, Undergraduate/Scholarship) [1411]
CNS-UCSB Graduate Fellowships for Science and Engineering (Postdoctorate/Fellowship) [10127]
Coast Guard Foundation Enlisted Education Grants (Advanced Professional/Grant) [3078]
The Helena B. Cobb Annual Scholarships (Undergraduate, Vocational/Occupational/Scholarship) [10665]
The Helena B. Cobb Four-Year Higher Education Grants (Undergraduate, Vocational/Occupational/Scholarship) [10666]
J.C. and Rheba Cobb Memorial Scholarships (Undergraduate/Scholarship) [6867]
Gordon W. and Agnes P. Cobb Scholarships (Undergraduate/Scholarship) [3754]
John Coburn and Harold Winters Student Award in Plasma Science and Technology (Graduate/Award) [2154]
Coca-Cola First Generation Scholarships (Undergraduate/Scholarship) [867]
Coca-Cola Scholars Program Scholarships (Undergraduate/Scholarship) [3115]
Cocke, Szpanka and Taylor Scholarships (Undergraduate/Scholarship) [10404]
The April Cockerham DREAM Act Scholarships (Undergraduate, Graduate/Scholarship) [8230]
Frank M. Coda Scholarships (Undergraduate/Scholarship) [1330]

CODY Foundation Fund (Undergraduate/Scholarship) [4235]
Coeur d'Alene Alumni Scholarships (Undergraduate/Scholarship) [6021]
Thomas D. Coffield Scholarships (Undergraduate/Scholarship) [4582]
Claude T. Coffman Memorial Scholarships (Undergraduate/Scholarship) [10157]
COHEAO Scholarships (Undergraduate/Scholarship) [3071]
American Academy of Periodontology Dr. D. Walter Cohen Teaching Fellowships (Postdoctorate/Fellowship) [421]
Ardis Cohoon Scholarships (Undergraduate/Scholarship) [10220]
Anna C. and Oliver C. Colburn Fellowships (Doctorate/Fellowship) [1606]
Warren E. "Whitey" Cole American Society of Highway Engineers Scholarships (Undergraduate/Scholarship) [4042]
Arthur H. Cole Grants in Aid (Doctorate/Grant, Award) [3779]
Paul Cole Scholarships (Undergraduate/Scholarship) [9221]
Coleopterists Society - Youth Incentive Award (Undergraduate/Award) [3117]
Colgate-Palmolive/HDA Foundation Scholarships (Master's, Postgraduate/Scholarship) [4892]
College Art Association Wyeth Publication Grants (Other/Grant) [3119]
College of Engineering and Physical Sciences Industry Scholarships (Undergraduate/Scholarship) [10208]
Captain Winifred Quick Collins Scholarships (Undergraduate/Scholarship) [7229]
Lloyd E. and Rachel S. Collins Scholarships (Undergraduate/Scholarship) [10576]
ColorMasters Scholarships (Undergraduate/Scholarship) [4333]
Columbus Citizens Foundation College Scholarships (Undergraduate/Scholarship) [3151]
Columbus Citizens Foundation High School Scholarships (Undergraduate/Scholarship) [3152]
John R. Colvin Legal Scholarships (Graduate/Scholarship) [3154]
Robert N. Colwell Memorial Fellowships (Doctorate, Graduate/Fellowship) [1803]
Commonwealth "Good Citizen" Scholarships (Undergraduate/Scholarship) [1977]
Communal Studies Association Research Fellowships (Graduate/Fellowship) [3163]
Community-based Natural Resource Management Assistantships (Undergraduate, Advanced Professional/Internship) [3169]
The Community Foundation Student Education Loan Funds for Gay and Lesbians (Undergraduate/Loan) [3221]
Community Legal Services of Philadelphia Fellowships (Postgraduate/Fellowship) [3337]
Comparative Effectiveness Research Professorship (CERP) (Professional development, Doctorate/Grant) [3374]
Comparative Perspectives on Chinese Culture and Society Grants (Doctorate/Grant) [739]
Alan Compton and Bob Stanley Professional Scholarships (Professional development/Scholarship) [2192]
Condon Prize for Best Student Essay in Psychological Anthropology (Graduate, Undergraduate/Prize, Recognition) [9281]
Maridell Braham Condon Scholarships (Undergraduate/Scholarship) [8915]
Conduct and Utilization of Research in Nursing (CURN) Awards (Professional development/Award) [6476]
Conference of State Bank Supervisors Graduate School Scholarships (Graduate/Award) [3343]
Congressional Fellows on Women and Public Policy (Doctorate, Graduate, Master's/Fellowship) [10672]
Congressional Research Awards (Graduate/Award) [3626]
Al Conklin and Bill de Decker Business Aviation Management Scholarships (Undergraduate/Scholarship) [6830]
Connecticut Mortgage Bankers Social Affairs Committee Scholarships (Undergraduate/Scholarship) [4745]
Connecticut Space Grant College Consortium Undergraduate Research Fellowships (Undergraduate/Fellowship) [3367]
Cecelia Connelly Memorial Scholarships in Underwater Archaeology (Graduate, Undergraduate/Scholarship) [10638]
Karen Connick Memorial Scholarships (Undergraduate/Scholarship) [4560]
Louis M. Connor Jr. Scholarships (Undergraduate/Scholarship) [10221]
Conservation Department Program Fellowships (Graduate/Fellowship) [9028]
Constancy, Brooks and Smith Diversity Scholars Awards (Undergraduate/Award) [3407]
Consumer Law Public Service Fellowships (Undergraduate/Fellowship) [8433]
Contemporary Club Scholarships (Undergraduate/Scholarship) [8465]
Continuing Education Awards (Undergraduate/Scholarship, Award) [6778]
Jorge Espejel Contreras IALEIA Scholarship Award (Undergraduate/Scholarship) [5266]
Convergence Assistantship Grants (Undergraduate/Grant) [4708]
Jack Kent Cooke Dissertation Fellowship Award (Doctorate/Fellowship) [5492]
Jack Kent Cooke Foundation College Scholarships (Undergraduate/Scholarship) [3411]
Jack Kent Cooke Foundation Graduate Scholarships (Graduate/Scholarship) [3412]
Jack Kent Cooke Foundation Undergraduate Transfer Scholarships (Undergraduate/Scholarship) [3413]
Jack Kent Cooke Foundation Young Scholars (Undergraduate/Scholarship) [3414]
Jack Kent Cooke Graduate Arts Awards (Graduate/Award) [5493]
Cooley Diversity Fellowship (Graduate, Undergraduate/Fellowship) [3416]
Cope Middle School PTSA Scholarships (Undergraduate/Scholarship) [8466]
Rob Copeland Memorial Scholarships (Undergraduate/Scholarship) [6022]
Copper and Brass Servicenter Association Inc. Scholarship Program (Undergraduate/Scholarship) [3421]
Beta Nu/Caryl Cordis D'hondt Scholarships (Undergraduate/Scholarship) [8916]
Theta/Caryl Cordis D'hondt Scholarships (Undergraduate/Scholarship) [8917]
Valdemar A. Cordova Scholarships (Undergraduate/Award) [6110]
Bill Cormack Scholarships (Undergraduate/Scholarship) [9706]
Cornaro Scholarships for Graduate Studies (Graduate/Scholarship) [5686]
D.C. Cornelius Memorial Scholarships (Undergraduate/Scholarship) [10577]
Holly Cornell Scholarship (Master's/Scholarship) [1488]
Corning Outstanding Student Paper Competition (Graduate, Undergraduate/Award) [7672]
Coro Fellows Program in Public Affairs (Postgraduate/Fellowship) [3423]
The Corp - More Uncommon Grounds Scholarships (Undergraduate/Scholarship) [9604]
The Corp - Students of Georgetown Inc. Coke Scholarships (Undergraduate/Scholarship) [9605]
The Corp - Students of Georgetown Inc. Textbook Scholarships (Undergraduate/Scholarship) [9606]
Correctional Education Association Scholarships (Graduate, Undergraduate/Scholarship) [3427]
NSS Sara Corrie Memorial Grants (Professional development/Grant) [7181]
Tom Cory Memorial Scholarships (Undergraduate/Scholarship) [1614]
COTA Scholarships for Occupational Therapy Assistants (Undergraduate/Scholarship) [7762]
Cottrell Scholar Awards (CSA) (Graduate, Advanced Professional, Professional development/Grant) [8555]
Dr. George C. Cotzias Memorial Fellowship (Other/Fellowship) [1074]

SRC NRI Hans J. Coufal Fellowships *(Graduate/Fellowship)* [8838]
Council on Social Work Education Minority Fellowship Program for Doctoral Students *(Postdoctorate/Fellowship)* [3454]
Council on Social Work Education Scholars Program *(Doctorate/Scholarship)* [3455]
Courage to Grow Scholarships *(Undergraduate/Scholarship)* [3461]
Pfizer Soozie Courter Hemophilia Scholarship Program *(Undergraduate/Scholarship)* [6988]
Richard P. Covert, Ph.D./FHIMSS Scholarships for Management Systems *(Graduate, Postgraduate, Undergraduate/Scholarship)* [4830]
The Joe E. Covington Awards for Research on Bar Admissions Testing *(Doctorate, Graduate/Award)* [6873]
Justin Forrest Cox "Beat the Odds" Memorial Scholarships *(Undergraduate/Scholarship)* [3093]
Gertrude M. Cox Scholarships *(Graduate, Master's, Doctorate/Scholarship)* [1465]
CPA Foundation Minority Scholarships *(Graduate/Scholarship)* [2471]
Craft Research Fund Grants *(Other/Grant)* [2845]
Crafton Elementary School PTA Scholarships *(Undergraduate/Scholarship)* [8467]
Crain Educational Grant Program *(Undergraduate/Scholarship)* [8948]
Robert E. Cramer Product Design and Development Scholarship *(Undergraduate/Scholarship)* [9259]
Rick Crane Group Real Estate Scholarship Fund *(Undergraduate/Scholarship)* [6023]
Meredith P. Crawford Fellowships in I/O Psychology *(Doctorate/Fellowship)* [4990]
AWG Maria Luisa Crawford Field Camp Scholarships *(Undergraduate/Scholarship)* [2095]
Creative Glass Center of America Fellowships *(Advanced Professional/Fellowship)* [3467]
CRI Clinic and Laboratory Integration Program Grants (CLIP) *(Professional development/Grant)* [2772]
CRI Irvington Postdoctoral Fellowship Program *(Postdoctorate/Fellowship)* [2773]
CRI Irvington Postdoctoral Fellowships *(Postdoctorate, Doctorate/Fellowship)* [2774]
Critical Language Scholarships for Intensive Summer Institutes *(Graduate, Undergraduate/Scholarship)* [1204]
CRMA Scholarships *(Graduate, Undergraduate/Scholarship)* [2899]
Crohn's and Colitis Foundation of America Senior Research Awards *(Doctorate, Graduate/Grant)* [3479]
Cromwell Fellowships *(Graduate/Fellowship)* [1354]
Kathryn M. Cronin Scholarships *(Undergraduate/Scholarship)* [10222]
CrossLites Scholarships *(Undergraduate, Graduate/Scholarship)* [3481]
R.G. and Ruth Crossno Memorial Scholarships *(Undergraduate/Scholarship)* [3756]
CROW Fellowships *(All/Fellowship)* [3053]
Crowder Scholarships *(Undergraduate/Scholarship)* [4192]
Howard A. Crum Student Scholarships *(Undergraduate/Scholarship)* [10179]
Lydia Cruz and Sandra Maria Ramos Scholarships *(Undergraduate/Scholarship)* [3577]
CSA Fraternal Life Scholarships *(Undergraduate/Scholarship)* [3483]
CSCPA College Scholarships *(Graduate, Undergraduate/Scholarship)* [3147]
CSCPA High School Scholarships *(Undergraduate/Scholarship)* [3148]
CSCPA Sophomore Scholarships *(Undergraduate/Scholarship)* [3149]
CSF Graduate Fellowships *(Graduate/Fellowship)* [2936]
CSF Scripps Headliners Scholarships *(Undergraduate/Scholarship)* [2979]
CSSA Research Grants *(Undergraduate, Graduate, Advanced Professional/Grant)* [2428]
CSX Scholarships *(Undergraduate/Scholarship)* [1183]
CTEC Internships *(Undergraduate/Internship)* [1567]
CTF Young Investigator Awards (CTF-YIA) *(Graduate, Postdoctorate, Doctorate/Award)* [2911]
CTFS-ForestGEO Research Grants Program *(Graduate, Postdoctorate, Advanced Professional/Grant)* [9041]
CTFS Research Grants Program *(Graduate, Postdoctorate, Professional development/Grant)* [9036]
CTP Scholarship Program *(Other/Scholarship)* [7113]
Cuban American Bar Association Scholarships *(All/Scholarship)* [3485]
John P. Culhane Professional Pilot Scholarships *(Undergraduate/Scholarship)* [215]
Linda Cullen Memorial Scholarships *(Undergraduate/Scholarship)* [759]
Murtha Cullina LLP Scholarships Fund *(Undergraduate/Scholarship)* [3199]
Esther Cummings Memorial Scholarships *(Undergraduate/Scholarship)* [7378]
Brian Cummins Memorial Scholarships *(Undergraduate/Scholarship)* [4746]
John J. Cunningham Memorial Scholarships *(Undergraduate/Scholarship)* [1184]
The Cure Starts Now Foundation Grants *(Graduate, Doctorate/Grant)* [3492]
Nancy Curry Scholarships *(Vocational/Occupational/Scholarship)* [8804]
John J. Curtin, Jr. Fellowships *(Undergraduate/Fellowship)* [620]
Michael D. Curtin Renaissance Student Memorial Scholarships *(Undergraduate/Scholarship)* [3757]
Jennifer Curtis Byler Scholarships *(Undergraduate/Scholarship)* [7188]
Don and Barbara Curtis Excellence Fund for Extracurricular Student Activities *(Undergraduate/Grant)* [10223]
Dewey Lee Curtis Scholarships *(Advanced Professional/Scholarship)* [3541]
Cystic Fibrosis Scholarship Foundation *(Undergraduate/Scholarship)* [3494]
DA Davidson Presidential Scholarships *(Undergraduate/Scholarship)* [10436]
DAAD Learn German in Germany Grants *(Doctorate/Grant)* [3603]
DAAD Study Scholarship Awards *(Graduate/Scholarship)* [3604]
DAAD Undergraduate Scholarship Program *(Undergraduate/Scholarship)* [3605]
DACOR Graduate Fellowships for Study of International Affairs *(Graduate, Master's/Fellowship)* [3496]
Daedalian Foundation Matching Scholarships Program *(Undergraduate/Scholarship)* [3499]
Daggy Youth/Student Scholarships *(Undergraduate, Professional development/Scholarship)* [5444]
DAI Fellowships for Study in Berlin *(Doctorate/Fellowship)* [1607]
Detroit Section/Robert G. Dailey Scholarship *(Undergraduate/Scholarship)* [9260]
Daily Lineups Scholarship Awards *(Undergraduate, Master's/Award, Scholarship)* [3504]
Dairy Farmers of America Scholarships *(Undergraduate/Scholarship)* [3506]
Dalai Lama Trust Graduate Scholarships *(Graduate/Scholarship)* [3508]
Daland Fellowships in Clinical Investigation *(Doctorate, Postgraduate/Fellowship)* [1079]
Dalcroze Society of America Memorial Scholarships *(Graduate/Scholarship)* [3510]
Chester Dale Fellowships *(Doctorate/Fellowship)* [6429]
John L. Dales Standard Scholarship *(Undergraduate/Scholarship)* [8827]
Dallas Alumnae Association Adelphe Scholarships *(Undergraduate/Scholarship)* [5704]
Dallas Alumnae Association Gamma Phi Chapter Scholarships *(Undergraduate/Scholarship)* [5705]
Serena D. Dalton Scholarships *(Undergraduate/Scholarship)* [10578]
Marvin E. Daly Memorial Scholarship *(Undergraduate/Scholarship)* [7532]
Damon Runyon Cancer Research Foundation Fellowships *(Doctorate, Graduate, Postdoctorate/Fellowship)* [3514]
Damon Runyon Physician-Scientist Training Awards *(Postdoctorate, Professional development/Award)* [3515]
Damon Runyon-Rachleff Innovation Awards *(Postdoctorate/Award)* [3516]
Damon Runyon-Sohn Pediatric Cancer Fellowship Awards *(Master's, Doctorate/Fellowship)* [3517]
Arthur H. Daniels Scholarships *(Undergraduate/Scholarship)* [8470]
DAPA Student Member Scholarships *(Undergraduate/Scholarship)* [3512]
Mary Mouzon Darby Undergraduate Scholarships *(Undergraduate/Scholarship)* [4985]
Darden Restaurants Point Scholarships *(Undergraduate, Graduate, Doctorate/Scholarship)* [8172]
The Hugh and Hazel Darling Dean Scholarships *(Undergraduate/Scholarship)* [7972]
Darling Foundation Endowed School of Law Scholarships *(Undergraduate/Scholarship)* [7973]
The Dave Family "Humor Studies" Scholarships *(Undergraduate, Graduate/Scholarship)* [1848]
David Library Fellowships *(Doctorate, Postdoctorate/Fellowship)* [3527]
David Meador Foundation - Hospitality-Food Service Scholarships *(Undergraduate/Scholarship)* [7294]
Lucile Caswell Davids Memorial Adelphe Scholarships *(Undergraduate, Graduate/Scholarship)* [5706]
Davis Foundation Postdoctoral Fellowships *(Doctorate, Master's/Fellowship)* [4814]
Davis Memorial Foundation Scholarships *(Graduate, Undergraduate/Scholarship)* [3533]
Dwight F. Davis Memorial Scholarships *(Undergraduate/Scholarship)* [9974]
Johnny Davis Memorial Scholarships *(Undergraduate/Scholarship)* [157]
Davis-Putter Scholarships Fund *(Undergraduate, Graduate/Scholarship)* [8659]
Arlene Davis Scholarships *(Undergraduate/Scholarship)* [3581]
Fran Morgenstern Davis Scholarships *(Undergraduate/Scholarship)* [1270]
James H. Davis Scholarships *(Undergraduate/Scholarship)* [4100]
Raymond Davis Scholarships *(Undergraduate, Graduate/Scholarship)* [9150]
Colonel Richard M. Dawson Highway Patrol Scholarship Fund *(Undergraduate/Scholarship)* [3222]
Dayton Amateur Radio Association Scholarships *(Undergraduate/Scholarship)* [1737]
DBA Student Scholarships *(Undergraduate/Scholarship)* [3653]
DBI Scholarships Fund *(Undergraduate/Scholarship)* [3223]
DCH Freehold Toyota Scholarships *(Undergraduate/Scholarship)* [2878]
Edilia and François Auguste de Montêquin Fellowships *(Doctorate/Fellowship)* [9083]
Bert and Sally de Vries Fellowships *(Undergraduate, Graduate/Fellowship)* [656]
Kenneth J. De Witt NASA/OSGC Scholarship at The University of Toledo *(Undergraduate/Scholarship)* [7592]
Alphonso Deal Scholarship Awards *(Undergraduate/Scholarship)* [6825]
Derek Lee Dean Soccer Scholarships *(Undergraduate/Scholarship)* [3094]
Don Debolt Franchising Scholarship Program *(Undergraduate/Scholarship)* [5335]
Matthew Debono Memorial Scholarship Funds *(Undergraduate, Graduate/Scholarship)* [1588]
Debt.com Scholarships *(All/Scholarship)* [3539]
Walter M. Decker Point Scholarships *(Graduate, Undergraduate/Scholarship)* [8173]
Decommissioning, Decontamination and Reutilization Scholarships *(Graduate, Master's/Scholarship)* [1035]
Earl Dedman Memorial Scholarships *(Undergraduate/Scholarship)* [804]
DEED Student Research Grant/Internships *(Undergraduate, Graduate/Grant, Scholarship, Internship)* [1160]
Anthony R. Dees Educational Workshop Scholarships *(Undergraduate/Scholarship)* [9124]
DefensiveDriving.com Scholarships *(Undergraduate/Scholarship)* [3543]

Edward Delaney Scholarships (Professional development/Scholarship) [1982]
Jane Delano Student Nurse Scholarships (Undergraduate, Graduate/Scholarship) [1023]
Jan DiMartino Delany Memorial Scholarships (Undergraduate/Scholarship) [4236]
Martha Delman and Milton Arthur Krug Endowed Scholarships (Undergraduate/Scholarship) [7974]
Vine Deloria Jr. Memorial Scholarships (Graduate, Professional development/Scholarship) [868]
Delta Chi Alumnae Memorial Scholarships (Undergraduate/Scholarship) [8918]
Delta Epsilon Sigma Graduate Fellowships (Graduate/Fellowship) [3566]
Delta Epsilon Sigma Undergraduate Scholarships (Undergraduate/Scholarship) [3567]
Delta Faucet Scholarships (Undergraduate/Scholarship) [8160]
Delta Gamma Undergraduate Merit-Based Scholarships (Undergraduate/Scholarship) [3569]
Delta Iota Alumni Scholarships (Undergraduate/Scholarship) [8967]
Delta Kappa Project 2000 Scholarships (Undergraduate/Scholarship) [5707]
Delta Nu Alpha Foundation Scholarships (Undergraduate/Scholarship) [3573]
Delta Nu Project 2000 Scholarships (Undergraduate/Scholarship) [5708]
Delta Phi Epsilon Educational Foundation Scholarships (Undergraduate, Graduate/Scholarship) [3575]
Delta Project 2000 Scholarships (Undergraduate/Scholarship) [5709]
Delta Tau Project 2000 Scholarships (Undergraduate/Scholarship) [5710]
Delta Upsilon Project 2000 Nowell Memorial Scholarships (Undergraduate/Scholarship) [5711]
Delta Zeta Undergraduate Scholarships (Undergraduate/Scholarship) [3582]
Law Offices of Michael A. DeMayo Scholarships (Undergraduate/Scholarship) [5963]
DEMCO New Leaders Travel Grants (Professional development/Grant) [8372]
Christopher Demetris Memorial Scholarships (Undergraduate/Scholarship) [4845]
Inez Demonet Scholarship (Graduate/Scholarship) [10373]
Albert W. Dent Graduate Student Scholarships (Undergraduate/Scholarship) [687]
Michael Denton Scholarship (Undergraduate/Scholarship) [7533]
Denton Scholarships (Graduate/Scholarship) [8897]
John Denver Music Scholarships (Undergraduate/Scholarship) [1271]
Denver Scholarship Foundation Scholarships (Undergraduate/Scholarship) [3600]
Dick Depaolis Memorial Scholarships (Undergraduate/Scholarship) [3325]
Depression and ADHD Fellowships (Postdoctorate/Fellowship) [5840]
DEPS Graduate Scholarship Program (Graduate/Scholarship) [3624]
Karekin DerAvedision Memorial Endowment Fund (Undergraduate/Scholarship) [1692]
Pat Dermargosian Memorial Scholarships (Undergraduate/Scholarship) [8471]
Descendant Scholarships (Undergraduate/Scholarship) [3500]
Libby Deschenes Prize for Applied Research (Undergraduate/Prize) [10537]
Design and Multimedia Internships - New York (Undergraduate, Graduate/Internship) [4430]
APTRA-Clete Roberts/Kathryn Dettman Memorial Journalism Scholarship (Undergraduate/Scholarship) [1818]
Development Fund for Black Students in Science and Technology Scholarships (Undergraduate/Scholarship) [3612]
Albert and Jane Dewey Scholarships (Undergraduate/Scholarship) [4748]
Dezao Legal Awards (Advanced Professional/Scholarship) [5959]
Edward D. Di Loreto-Odell S. McConnell Scholarships (Undergraduate/Scholarship) [7975]
Diabetes Scholars Foundation College Scholarships (Undergraduate/Scholarship) [3616]

Julio C. Diaz Academic Scholarship (Undergraduate/Scholarship) [9498]
Edwina Eustis Dick Scholarship for Music Therapy Interns (Graduate/Scholarship) [1012]
Jean Dearth Dickerscheid Fellowships (Graduate/Fellowship) [8090]
Dickey Rural Networks College Scholarship Program (Undergraduate, Vocational/Occupational/Scholarship) [3618]
Bill Dickey Scholarship Association Scholarships (Undergraduate/Scholarship) [3620]
Diffuse Large B-Cell Lymphoma Explorations Grants (Advanced Professional/Grant) [6158]
Rudolph Dillman Memorial Scholarships (Graduate, Undergraduate/Scholarship) [820]
Carol DiMaiti Scholarship Awards (Undergraduate/Scholarship) [6308]
Gretchen Dimico Memorial Scholarships (Undergraduate/Scholarship) [6025]
The E.R. and Lilian B. Dimmette Scholarship Fund (Undergraduate/Scholarship) [4193]
Raymond DiPaglia Endowment Scholarship (Undergraduate/Scholarship) [3664]
The Angie Dipietro Women in Business Scholarships (Undergraduate/Scholarship) [8231]
Disability Care Center Disabled Student Scholarships (Undergraduate/Scholarship) [3629]
Disability Care Center Special Education Scholarships (Undergraduate/Scholarship) [3630]
Disabled War Veterans Scholarships (Undergraduate/Scholarship) [90]
Discover Bar Exam Loans (Graduate/Loan) [3634]
Discover Graduate Loans (Graduate, Master's, Doctorate/Loan) [3635]
Discover Health Professions Loans (Graduate/Loan) [3636]
Discover Law Loans (Graduate/Loan) [3637]
Discover MBA Loans (Graduate/Loan) [3638]
Discover Residency Loans (Graduate/Loan) [3639]
Dissertation Award in Hadronic Physics (Doctorate/Award) [1089]
Dissertation Fellowships in East European Studies (Doctorate/Fellowship) [740]
Dissertation Proposal Development Fellowships (Doctorate/Fellowship) [9053]
Distinguished Flying Cross Society Scholarships (Undergraduate/Scholarship) [3641]
Distinguished Young Women Scholarships (Undergraduate/Scholarship) [3643]
LaRue A. Ditmore Music Scholarships (Undergraduate/Scholarship) [10650]
Diversity Executive Leadership Program Scholarships (Other/Scholarship) [1778]
Diversity Fellowship Program (DFP) (Graduate/Fellowship) [6589]
Robert A. and Barbara Divine Graduate Student Travel Grants (Graduate/Grant) [9136]
Dixon Hughes Goodman LLP Annual Scholarship (Undergraduate/Scholarship) [3645]
Daniel B. Dixon Scholarships (Undergraduate/Scholarship) [324]
Peggy Dixon Two-Year Scholarships (Undergraduate/Scholarship) [9254]
Mychajlo Dmytrenko Fine Arts Foundation Scholarships (Undergraduate/Scholarship) [9980]
Charles Dobbins FTA Scholarships (Undergraduate, Vocational/Occupational/Scholarship) [4316]
Dr. Mac Scholarships (Undergraduate/Scholarship) [3225]
Doctoral Dissertation Grants (Doctorate/Grant) [5386]
Document Management and Graphic Communications Industry Scholarships (Undergraduate/Scholarship) [3852]
F. Atlee Dodge Maintenance Scholarships (Undergraduate/Scholarship) [216]
Robert Winchester Dodson Scholarships (Undergraduate/Scholarship) [10225]
DOE Computational Science Graduate Fellowships (DOE CSGF) (Doctorate, Graduate/Fellowship) [5887]
Emmett J. Doerr Memorial Distinguished Scout Scholarships (Undergraduate/Scholarship) [6921]
Dofflemyer Scholarships (Undergraduate/Scholarship) [6922]
Dollar-A-Day Academic Scholarships (Graduate, Undergraduate/Scholarship) [3649]
Dolphin Scholarships (Undergraduate/Scholarship) [3651]
Scott Dominguez - Craters of the Moon Chapter Scholarships (Graduate, Undergraduate/Scholarship) [1412]
Marion Jones Donaldson Scholarship Fund (Undergraduate/Scholarship) [4043]
Hon. Ralph W.E. Donges Memorial Scholarships (Undergraduate/Scholarship) [2510]
Doniphan Community Foundation Scholarships (Undergraduate/Scholarship) [4561]
Mike and Gail Donley Spouse Scholarships (Undergraduate, Graduate, Postgraduate/Scholarship) [123]
Harry A. Donn Scholarships (Undergraduate/Scholarship) [4749]
Jim Doogan Memorial Scholarships (Undergraduate/Scholarship) [10096]
Joseph M. Dorgan Scholarship (Undergraduate/Scholarship) [3666]
Pauly D'Orlando Memorial Art Scholarships (Graduate, Undergraduate/Scholarship) [9834]
Father Connie Dougherty Scholarships (Undergraduate, Vocational/Occupational/Scholarship) [3320]
Douglass Foundation Fellowship in American Art (Doctorate/Fellowship) [9001]
Douglass Foundation Fellowships in American Art (Graduate/Fellowship) [6430]
Dow Chemical Company Fellowships (Graduate/Fellowship) [7085]
Margaret Dowell-Gravatt, M.D. Scholarships (Undergraduate/Scholarship) [2226]
Downeast Energy Scholarships (Undergraduate/Scholarship) [3659]
Jay and Rheba Downes Memorial Scholarships (Undergraduate/Scholarship) [3095]
W.B.H. Dowse Fellowships (Professional development/Fellowship) [6326]
Rodger Doxsey Travel Prizes (Graduate, Postdoctorate/Prize) [616]
Helen Cashatt Drais Memorial Adelphe Scholarships (Undergraduate/Scholarship) [5712]
Drake University Law School Law Opportunity Scholarships - Disadvantage (Undergraduate/Scholarship) [3667]
Drake University Law School Law Opportunity Scholarships - Diversity (Undergraduate/Scholarship) [3668]
Drake University Law School Public Service Scholarships (Undergraduate/Scholarship) [3669]
The "Drawn to Art" Fellowships (Doctorate/Fellowship) [436]
C. Cleveland Drennon, Jr. Memorial Scholarships (Undergraduate/Scholarship) [10158]
Wilma Sackett Dressel Scholarships (Undergraduate/Scholarship) [8919]
Margaret Drew Alpha Fellowships (Graduate/Fellowship) [8091]
Charles Drew Scholarships (Other/Scholarship) [1940]
Louis Dreyfus Warner-Chappell City College Scholarships (Undergraduate/Scholarship) [1272]
Thomas J. Drinan Memorial Fellowships (Undergraduate/Fellowship) [8434]
Drug Development Research Professorship (Professional development/Internship) [3375]
Richard Drukker Memorial Scholarships (Undergraduate/Scholarship) [7326]
Sergeant Major Douglas R. Drum Memorial Scholarship Fund (Undergraduate/Scholarship) [1005]
Harold D. Drummond Scholarships (Undergraduate, Graduate/Scholarship) [5668]
Dry Defender Protect Your Bed Scholarships (Undergraduate, Graduate/Scholarship) [5636]
DSA Dante Prizes (Undergraduate/Prize, Monetary) [3524]
Henry Belin du Pont Dissertation Fellowships (Doctorate, Graduate/Fellowship) [4688]
Henry Belin du Pont Research Grants (Graduate/Fellowship) [4689]
Martin Duberman Fellowships (Other/Fellowship) [2864]
John W. Duckett Jr., AFUD Pediatric Research Scholarships (Undergraduate/Scholarship) [9246]

The Steve Duckett Local Conservation Scholarships (Undergraduate, Postgraduate/Scholarship) [8232]
Julia M. Duckwall Scholarships (Professional development/Scholarship) [1983]
Mark Duda Scholarship Fund (Graduate, Undergraduate/Scholarship) [6288]
Doris Duke Conservation Fellows Program (Master's/Fellowship) [10678]
Duluth Building and Construction Trades Council Scholarships (Undergraduate/Scholarship) [3707]
Dumbarton Oaks Fellowships (Doctorate, Graduate/Fellowship) [3728]
Dumbarton Oaks Junior Fellowships (Graduate/Fellowship) [3729]
Dumbarton Oaks Research Library and Collection Bliss Symposium Awards (Undergraduate, Graduate/Award) [3730]
Dumbarton Oaks Research Library and Collection Graduate Research Workshops (Undergraduate, Graduate/Fellowship) [3731]
Dumbarton Oaks Research Library and Collection One-Month Research Stipends (Doctorate/Monetary) [3732]
Dumbarton Oaks Research Library and Collection Post-Baccalaureate Media Fellowships (Graduate/Fellowship) [3733]
Dumbarton Oaks Research Library and Collection Project Grants (Doctorate/Grant) [3734]
Dumbarton Oaks Research Library and Collection Short-Term Predoctoral Residencies Grants (Doctorate/Grant) [3735]
Dumbarton Oaks Research Library and Collection Summer Fellowships (Graduate/Fellowship) [3736]
Dumbarton Oaks Research Library and Collection Summer Internships for Harvard Students (Undergraduate, Graduate/Internship) [3737]
Dumbarton Oaks Research Library and Collection Post-Doctoral Teaching Fellowships (Postdoctorate/Fellowship) [3738]
Duncan Aviation Scholarships (Undergraduate/Scholarship) [158]
Wade and Marcelene Duncan Scholarships (Undergraduate/Scholarship) [10579]
Ed Dunkelblau Scholarships (All/Scholarship, Award) [1849]
Durning Sisters Scholarships (Graduate/Scholarship) [3549]
Joe Durso, Jr. Memorial Scholarship (Undergraduate/Scholarship) [6576]
Sue and Ken Dyer Foundation Travel Scholarships (Undergraduate/Scholarship) [4238]
Marvin and Joanell Dyrstad Scholarship (Undergraduate/Scholarship) [1578]
Dystonia Medical Research Foundation Clinical Fellowships (Postdoctorate/Fellowship) [3746]
Josephine P. White Eagle Scholarships (Undergraduate, Graduate/Scholarship) [4911]
Eagles Fly for Leukemia Scholarships (Undergraduate/Scholarship) [2906]
EAIA Research Grants (Other/Grant) [3748]
Howard G. and Gladys A. Eakes Memorial Scholarships (Undergraduate/Scholarship) [4562]
EAPSI Fellowships (Doctorate, Graduate/Fellowship) [7124]
Amelia Earhart Memorial Academic Scholarships (Undergraduate/Scholarship) [7439]
Earl Warren Civil Rights Training Scholarships (Graduate/Scholarship) [6645]
Early-Career Patient-Oriented Diabetes Research Awards (Professional development/Award) [5640]
Early Career Postdoctoral Fellowships in East European Studies (Postdoctorate/Fellowship) [741]
Robert E. Early Memorial Scholarship (Undergraduate/Scholarship) [3670]
Bob East Scholarships (Graduate, Undergraduate/Scholarship) [7108]
East-West Center Graduate Degree Fellowships (Master's, Doctorate, Graduate/Fellowship) [3760]
Eastern Orthodox Scouting Scholarships (Undergraduate/Scholarship) [6923]
David Eaton Scholarships (Master's/Scholarship) [9835]
ECA Applied Urban Communication Research Grants (Professional development/Grant) [3768]

ECA Centennial Scholarships (Master's, Doctorate/Scholarship) [3769]
Echoing Green Black Male Achievement Fellowships (Professional development/Fellowship) [3773]
Echoing Green Climate Fellowships (Professional development/Fellowship) [3774]
Echoing Green Global Fellowships (Professional development/Fellowship) [3775]
W. Wesley Eckenfelder Gradute Research Award (Graduate, Master's, Doctorate/Award) [1952]
ECMS Scholarships (Undergraduate/Scholarship) [3771]
Ed Bradley Scholarships (Undergraduate/Scholarship) [8404]
Margaret Eddy Scholarships (Graduate/Scholarship) [7379]
Edgecliff Alumni Awards (Undergraduate/Scholarship) [10718]
Edgecliff McAuley Art Scholarships (Undergraduate/Scholarship) [10719]
Edgecliff McAuley Music Scholarships (Undergraduate/Scholarship) [10720]
S. Randolph Edmonds Young Scholars Competition (Graduate, Undergraduate/Scholarship) [2303]
Melanie and Todd Edmonson Memorial Scholarships (Undergraduate/Scholarship) [3261]
Edon Farmers Cooperative Scholarships (Undergraduate/Scholarship) [3794]
Education Advancement Scholarships (Graduate, Master's, Doctorate/Scholarship) [548]
Education Factor Scholarships (Graduate, Undergraduate/Scholarship) [6378]
"Education is Power" Scholarships (Undergraduate/Scholarship) [6989]
Educational Audiology Association Doctoral Scholarships (Doctorate/Scholarship) [3797]
Educational and Cultural Affairs Alumni Small Grants Program (ECA) (Other/Grant) [5380]
The Educational Foundation of KyCPA Scholarships (Undergraduate/Scholarship) [5821]
EDvestinU(r) National Monthly Scholarships (Undergraduate/Scholarship) [7309]
Edward R. Murrow Press Fellowships (Professional development/Fellowship) [3446]
The Edwards Annual College Scholarships (Undergraduate/Scholarship) [3810]
Esther Edwards Graduate Scholarships (Doctorate, Professional development/Scholarship) [9851]
Carli Edwards Memorial Scholarships (Undergraduate/Scholarship) [8871]
Jimmy Edwards Scholarships (Undergraduate/Scholarship) [3226]
EERI/FEMA Graduate Fellowship in Earthquake Hazard Reduction (Graduate/Fellowship) [3750]
John and Alice Egan Multi-Year Mentioning Scholarships (Undergraduate/Scholarship) [3501]
Bill Egan Scholarship Program (Undergraduate/Scholarship) [7694]
EHA Exploratory Travel and Data Grants (Doctorate/Grant) [3780]
EHA Graduate Dissertation Fellowships (Doctorate/Fellowship) [3781]
E.I. DuPont Graduate Fellowship (Graduate/Fellowship) [7086]
John R. Eidson Jr., Scholarships (Undergraduate/Scholarship) [3096]
Mike Eidson Scholarships (Graduate, Undergraduate/Scholarship) [516]
Eight and Forty Lung and Respiratory Disease Nursing Scholarships (Other/Scholarship) [955]
Hillel Einhorn New Investigator Award (Doctorate/Award) [9161]
Eisbrouch & Marsh Scholarship Awards (Undergraduate, Graduate/Scholarship) [3814]
Harold E. Eisenberg Foundation Scholarships (Other/Scholarship) [5304]
Jeri Eiserman, RRT Professional Education Research Fellowships (Professional development/Fellowship) [1210]
EJI Justice Fellowship (Graduate, Postgraduate, Professional development/Fellowship) [3916]
Farouk El-Baz Student Research Grants (Graduate, Undergraduate/Grant) [4363]
El Dorado County Mineral and Gem Society Scholarships (Undergraduate/Scholarship) [3816]

George and Isabelle Elanjian Scholarships (Undergraduate/Scholarship) [10198]
W. Eldridge and Emily Lowe Scholarships (Undergraduate/Scholarship) [8968]
Herman E. Elgar Memorial Scholarships (Undergraduate/Scholarship) [3671]
Eli Lilly and Company/Black Data Processing Associates Scholarships (Undergraduate/Scholarship) [2206]
Elie Wiesel Prize in Ethics (Undergraduate/Prize, Award) [10553]
Dr. Robert Elliott Memorial Scholarships (Undergraduate/Scholarship) [6351]
Pauline Elliott Scholarships (Undergraduate/Scholarship) [6352]
Robert A. Ellis Scholarships in Physics (Undergraduate/Scholarship) [7141]
William P. Elrod Memorial Scholarships (Undergraduate/Scholarship) [9656]
Emerald Empire Chapter Scholarship Awards (Undergraduate/Scholarship) [7695]
Emergency Medicine Physician Scholarships for Health Information Management Program (Undergraduate/Scholarship) [9500]
EMLF Law Student Scholarships (Undergraduate/Scholarship) [3869]
Emmanuel Bible College Scholarships (Undergraduate/Scholarship) [1693]
EMS Scholarship Awards (All/Award) [8150]
ENA Foundation Annual Conference Scholarships (Advanced Professional, Professional development/Scholarship) [3861]
ENA Foundation Seed Research Grants (Master's, Advanced Professional/Grant) [3862]
ENA Foundation State Challenge Undergraduate Scholarship (Undergraduate/Scholarship) [3858]
Thomas O. Enders Graduate Fellowships (Graduate/Fellowship) [1876]
Endocrine Society Summer Research Fellowships (Graduate, Undergraduate/Fellowship) [3864]
Endodontic Educator Fellowship Award (Graduate/Fellowship) [492]
Endodontic Research Grants (Graduate/Grant) [493]
Endourological Society Fellowships (Professional development/Fellowship) [3867]
Endowment Fund for Education Grants (Undergraduate/Grant) [2264]
Endowment Fund for Education, Loans/Grants for Educational Materials (Undergraduate/Grant) [2266]
Endowment Fund for Education, Loans/Grants for Equipment (Undergraduate/Grant) [2267]
Endowment Fund for Education, Loans (Undergraduate/Loan) [2265]
ENF Most Valuable Student Scholarships (Undergraduate/Scholarship) [3854]
Engaged Anthropology Grants (Doctorate, Postdoctorate/Grant) [10515]
Jane Engelberg Memorial Fellowship (Professional development/Fellowship) [7156]
Enhanced Insurance Scholarships Program (Undergraduate/Scholarship) [10340]
Harold E. Ennes Scholarships (Graduate, Other/Award, Scholarship) [9092]
Irene Winifred Eno Grants (Professional development/Grant) [1342]
Ensurify Safe Driving Scholarships (Undergraduate/Scholarship) [3876]
Enterprise Rent-A-Car Scholarships (Graduate, Undergraduate/Scholarship) [8073]
Entertainment Media Internships - Los Angeles (Undergraduate, Graduate/Internship) [4431]
Lindsay M. Entz Memorial Scholarships (Undergraduate/Scholarship) [4044]
Environmental Research and Education Foundation Scholarships (Master's, Doctorate, Postdoctorate/Scholarship) [3900]
EPA Science to Achieve Results Fellowships (STAR) (Graduate/Fellowship) [9932]
Epilepsy Foundation Behavioral Sciences Post-Doctoral Fellowships (Postdoctorate/Fellowship) [3902]
Epilepsy Foundation Behavioral Sciences Student Fellowships (Graduate, Undergraduate/Fellowship) [3903]

Epilepsy Foundation Health Sciences Student Fellowships *(Doctorate, Graduate/Fellowship)* [3904]
Epilepsy Foundation Post-doctoral Research and Training Fellowships *(Postdoctorate/Fellowship)* [3905]
Epilepsy Foundation Pre-doctoral Research Training Fellowships *(Graduate/Fellowship)* [3906]
Epilepsy Foundation Research Grants *(Doctorate/Grant)* [3907]
Epilepsy Foundation Research and Training Fellowships for Clinicians *(Doctorate, Other/Grant)* [3908]
Epsilon Delta Project 2000 Scholarships *(Undergraduate/Scholarship)* [5713]
Epsilon Epsilon Scholarships *(Undergraduate/Scholarship)* [8920]
Epsilon Mu Scholarships *(Graduate, Undergraduate/Scholarship)* [5714]
Epsilon Tau Pi's Soaring Eagle Scholarships *(Undergraduate/Scholarship)* [6924]
Epsilon Tau Scholarships *(Undergraduate/Scholarship)* [8921]
Dena Epstein Awards for Archival and Library Research in American Music *(Professional development/Grant)* [6626]
Alan R. Epstein "Reach for the Stars" Scholarships *(Undergraduate/Scholarship)* [6452]
Lee Epstein Scholarship Fund *(Graduate, Undergraduate/Scholarship)* [6289]
Equal Justice Works Fellowship Program *(Graduate, Undergraduate/Fellowship)* [3918]
Robert C. Erb Sr. Scholarships *(Undergraduate/Scholarship)* [6353]
ERCA Community Contribution Scholarships *(Undergraduate/Scholarship)* [3804]
ERDAS Internship *(Graduate/Internship, Award)* [1804]
Harriet Erich Graduate Fellowships *(Graduate/Fellowship, Scholarship)* [3550]
Bruce T. and Jackie Mahi Erickson Grant *(Graduate, Undergraduate/Grant)* [7907]
Erickson-Zoellers Point Scholarships *(Undergraduate, Graduate, Doctorate/Scholarship)* [8174]
Ernest Hemingway Research Grants *(Other/Grant)* [4855]
Ernst and Young Scholarships *(Undergraduate/Scholarship)* [1780]
Judge Samuel J. Ervin, III Fellowships *(Graduate/Fellowship)* [6004]
Extrusion Division/Lew Erwin Memorial Scholarship *(Graduate, Postgraduate/Scholarship)* [9261]
ESA Foundation Life Grants *(Undergraduate/Grant)* [3914]
ESA Foundation Scholarship Program *(Undergraduate/Scholarship)* [3878]
Boomer Esiason Foundation General Academic Scholarships *(Undergraduate, Graduate/Scholarship)* [2338]
Charles A. Esser Memorial Scholarships *(Graduate/Scholarship)* [1631]
NSPF Ray B. Essick Scholarship Awards *(Other/Scholarship)* [7192]
R. Wayne Estes Endowed Scholarships *(Undergraduate/Scholarship)* [7976]
Larry L. Etherton Scholarships *(Graduate, Undergraduate/Scholarship)* [1185]
Ethnic Minority and Women's Enhancement Postgraduate Scholarships *(Graduate/Scholarship)* [6862]
ETS Postdoctoral Fellowships *(Postdoctorate/Fellowship)* [3806]
Alex J. Ettl Grants *(Other/Grant)* [7127]
European College of Liberal Arts Scholarships *(Undergraduate/Scholarship)* [9981]
Chick Evans Caddie Scholarships *(Undergraduate/Scholarship)* [10531]
Lee S. Evans/National Housing Endowment Scholarships *(Undergraduate, Graduate/Scholarship)* [7003]
Evans and Petree Law Firm Scholarship *(Undergraduate/Scholarship)* [10159]
J. Everett and Louise Light Scholarships *(Undergraduate, Graduate/Scholarship)* [5669]
Clifton W. Everett, Sr. Community Lawyer Fellowships *(Graduate/Fellowship)* [6005]
Everglades Foundation Fellowship *(Graduate, Doctorate, Master's/Fellowship)* [3931]
Everglades Foundation Internship *(Postgraduate, Postdoctorate/Internship)* [3932]
Everglades Foundation Scholarships *(Graduate, Master's, Doctorate/Scholarship)* [3933]
Executive Women International Scholarship Program (EWISP) *(Undergraduate/Scholarship)* [3936]
ExeptionalNurse.com Scholarships *(Undergraduate, Graduate/Scholarship)* [3940]
Exercise For Life Athletic Scholarships Program *(Undergraduate/Scholarship)* [3942]
The Expert Institute Legal Blog Post Writing Contest *(Graduate/Award)* [3942]
Experts Exchange Scholarships Contest *(Undergraduate, Graduate/Scholarship)* [3944]
Express Medical Supply Scholarships *(Undergraduate/Scholarship)* [3948]
William C. Ezell Fellowships *(Postdoctorate/Fellowship)* [415]
Facebook Fellowships Program *(Doctorate/Fellowship)* [3950]
FACS Graduate Fellowships *(Graduate/Fellowship)* [6798]
FACT "Second Chance" Scholarship Program *(Undergraduate/Scholarship)* [3999]
Faculty Research Visit Grants *(Doctorate/Grant, Award)* [3606]
Faegre Baker Daniels Diversity & Inclusion Fellowships *(Graduate/Fellowship)* [3954]
FAER Mentored Research Training Grants *(Professional development/Grant)* [4163]
FAER Research in Education Grants *(Advanced Professional/Grant)* [4164]
FAER Research Fellowship Grants *(Postdoctorate, Postgraduate, Graduate/Grant)* [4165]
Claire M. Fagin Fellow Award *(Doctorate/Fellowship)* [6983]
Fahs-Beck Fund for Research and Experimentation - Doctoral Dissertation Grants *(Doctorate/Grant)* [7347]
Fahs-Beck Fund for Research and Experimentation - Postdoctoral Grants *(Postdoctorate/Grant)* [7348]
FAIC Latin American and Caribbean Scholars Program *(Other/Scholarship)* [908]
Wayne G. Failor Scholarships *(Undergraduate/Scholarship)* [7947]
Fairbanks Chapter Legacy Scholarships *(Undergraduate/Scholarship)* [10097]
Sherman Fairchild Post Graduate Fellowships in Conservation *(Postgraduate/Fellowship)* [6591]
D.J. Fairgrave Education Trust *(Undergraduate/Scholarship)* [3672]
AIST Benjamin F. Fairless Scholarships *(Undergraduate/Scholarship)* [1996]
Faith Initiatives Internships - New York *(Undergraduate, Graduate/Internship)* [4432]
Falcon Achievement Scholarships *(Undergraduate/Scholarship)* [8200]
Magnetic Interfaces and Nanostructures Division - The Leo M. Falicov Student Award *(Graduate/Grant)* [2155]
Fall Fellowships in Korean Studies *(Other/Fellowship)* [5870]
The Fallen Heroes Scholarships *(Undergraduate/Scholarship)* [3079]
Families of Freedom Scholarship Fund - America Scholarships *(Undergraduate, Vocational/Occupational/Scholarship)* [3956]
Family and Children's Services of Lebanon County Fund *(Undergraduate/Scholarship)* [4239]
FAMU Presidential Scholarship - Florida Community College Scholarships *(Undergraduate/Scholarship)* [4076]
Fanconi Anemia Research Grants *(Postdoctorate/Grant)* [3964]
William M. Fanning Maintenance Scholarships *(Undergraduate/Scholarship)* [6831]
The Fantasy Sports Daily Scholarship Program - General Scholarship for Advanced Education *(Undergraduate, Graduate, Master's/Scholarship)* [3966]
John S.W. Fargher, Jr. Scholarships *(Graduate/Scholarship)* [5185]
Judge McIntyre Faries Scholarships *(Undergraduate/Scholarship)* [7977]
Palmer Farley Memorial Scholarships *(Graduate/Scholarship)* [4696]
Walter Moran Farmer Scholarships *(Juris Doctorate/Scholarship)* [10475]
Farmington UNICO Scholarships *(Undergraduate/Scholarship)* [4751]
W.D. Farr Scholarships *(Graduate/Scholarship)* [6842]
Bertha M. Fase Memorial Scholarship Fund *(Undergraduate/Scholarship)* [4515]
FASEB MARC Travel Awards *(Undergraduate, Graduate, Postdoctorate/Award)* [9306]
Anne M. Fassett Scholarships *(Undergraduate, Graduate/Scholarship)* [9428]
Miklos Faust International Travel Awards *(Doctorate/Grant)* [1339]
James R. Favor Risk Management Scholarship Fund *(Undergraduate/Scholarship)* [5715]
FCA Grants to Artists *(Advanced Professional/Grant)* [4227]
FCBA Foundation Internship Stipends for Law Students *(Professional development/Internship)* [3973]
FCBA Foundation Law School Scholarships *(Postgraduate/Scholarship)* [3974]
FCIL Schaffer Grants for Foreign Law Librarians *(Professional development/Grant)* [529]
Fecon Scholarships *(Undergraduate/Scholarship)* [4088]
Federated Insurance Scholarships *(Graduate, Undergraduate/Scholarship)* [8074]
Adrienne Zoe Fedok Art and Music Scholarships *(Undergraduate/Scholarship)* [4240]
FEEA-NTEU Scholarships *(Graduate, Postgraduate, Undergraduate/Scholarship)* [3989]
Nolan W. Feeser Scholarship Fund *(Undergraduate/Scholarship)* [4045]
FEF Scholarships *(Undergraduate/Scholarship)* [3952]
Ruth B. Fein Prize *(Graduate/Prize)* [949]
Symee Ruth Feinberg Memorial Scholarships *(Undergraduate/Scholarship)* [4752]
Lillian and Alex Feir Graduate Student Travel Awards *(Master's, Doctorate/Award)* [3880]
Fejos Postdoctoral Fellowships in Ethnographic Film *(Postdoctorate/Fellowship)* [10516]
Feldman Law Firm Disabled Veterans Scholarships *(All/Scholarship)* [4009]
Feldman & Royle, Attorneys at Law Autism Scholarships *(All/Scholarship)* [4011]
Milton Feldstein Memorial Scholarships *(Graduate/Scholarship)* [141]
Fellowship on Women & Public Policy *(Graduate/Fellowship)* [10102]
The Judy Felt Memorial Volunteerism Scholarship *(College, Undergraduate/Scholarship)* [1821]
Reese Felts Scholarships *(Undergraduate/Scholarship)* [10226]
Diane Ross Fennekohl Endowment Fund for Education *(Undergraduate/Scholarship)* [5716]
John E. Fenton, Jr. Public Service Awards *(Postgraduate/Fellowship)* [8435]
Dr. James A. Ferguson Emerging Infectious Diseases Fellowships *(Graduate/Fellowship)* [5815]
Fermilab Science Undergraduate Laboratory Internship *(Undergraduate/Internship)* [9900]
Fermilab Summer Internships in Science and Technology *(Undergraduate/Internship)* [9901]
Lt. Colonel Romeo and Josephine Bass Ferretti Scholarships *(Undergraduate/Scholarship)* [124]
FFA Scholarship *(Undergraduate/Scholarship)* [7583]
FHSMAI Scholarship Program *(Graduate/Scholarship)* [4264]
Mary Lou Fiala Fellowships *(Other/Fellowship)* [5305]
FICE Scholarships *(Undergraduate/Scholarship)* [4089]
Field Aviation Co., Inc. Scholarships *(Undergraduate/Scholarship)* [159]
Carole Fielding Student Grant *(Undergraduate, Graduate/Grant)* [10131]
Beth K. Fields Scholarships *(Undergraduate/Scholarship)* [10144]

Fieldwork Fellowships *(Undergraduate/Award, Fellowship)* [3927]
Filipino Bar Association of Northern California Scholarships (FBANC) *(Advanced Professional/Scholarship)* [4022]
Christine Filipovich Scholarships *(Master's, Doctorate/Scholarship)* [3057]
Alan R. and Barbara D. Finberg Fellowships *(Graduate/Fellowship)* [4998]
Fred Finch Scholarships *(Undergraduate/Scholarship)* [9816]
Herb and Anne Fincher Memorial Scholarships *(Undergraduate/Scholarship)* [3176]
William Robert Findley Graduate Chemistry Scholarship *(Graduate/Scholarship)* [7151]
Sakura Finetek Student Scholarships *(Undergraduate/Scholarship)* [7167]
Helen R. Finley-Loescher and Stephen Loescher Scholarships *(Undergraduate/Scholarship)* [3283]
Finnegan Diversity Scholarships *(Juris Doctorate/Scholarship)* [4030]
Firland Foundation Graduate Pulmonary Nursing Fellowships *(Professional development/Fellowship)* [4034]
FIRST Operator Certification Awards *(Professional development/Internship)* [4074]
Eugenia Vellner Fischer Award for the Performing Arts *(Undergraduate/Scholarship)* [6556]
William A. Fischer Memorial Scholarships *(Graduate/Scholarship)* [1805]
Fish & Richardson 1L Diversity Fellowships *(Undergraduate/Scholarship)* [4066]
The Fisher-Clark Memorial Endowed Scholarships *(Undergraduate/Scholarship)* [6026]
Joseph L. Fisher Doctoral Dissertation Fellowships *(Graduate/Fellowship)* [8561]
Arthur and Juna Fisher Memorial Track Scholarships *(Undergraduate/Scholarship)* [8475]
Jack B. Fisher Scholarship Fund *(Undergraduate/Scholarship)* [9501]
Allison E. Fisher Scholarships *(Undergraduate, Graduate/Scholarship)* [4068]
Ameel J. Fisher Scholarships *(Undergraduate/Scholarship)* [10227]
Marjorie Gosselin Fitzgerald, Upsilon, Permanently Restricted Scholarship Fund *(Undergraduate/Scholarship)* [5717]
Dr. Joseph Fitzsimmons Scholarships *(Doctorate/Scholarship)* [9959]
Gloria Flaherty Scholarships *(Graduate/Scholarship)* [4466]
FLASH Social Science Scholarships *(Graduate/Scholarship)* [3976]
Albert Flegenheimer Memorial Scholarships *(Undergraduate/Scholarship)* [6494]
Fleming/Blaszcak Scholarships *(Undergraduate, Graduate/Scholarship)* [9262]
Charlie Fleming Education Fund Scholarships *(Undergraduate/Scholarship)* [7195]
Laura M. Fleming Scholarships *(Undergraduate, Vocational/Occupational/Scholarship)* [4194]
FLEOA Foundation Scholarship Program *(Undergraduate/Scholarship)* [3991]
Flight Attendants/Flight Technician Scholarships *(Other/Scholarship)* [6832]
Grant H. Flint International Scholarships - Category I *(Undergraduate/Scholarship)* [9337]
Grant H. Flint International Scholarships - Category II *(Undergraduate/Scholarship)* [9338]
Dave Florence Scholarship Fund *(Undergraduate/Scholarship)* [6290]
Florence Young Memorial Scholarships *(Master's/Scholarship)* [1833]
Brendan Flores Alumni Leadership Circle Scholarship - Clark High School *(Undergraduate/Scholarship)* [8344]
Florida Automotive Industry Scholarships *(Undergraduate/Scholarship)* [2125]
Florida Education Fund McKnight Doctoral Fellowships *(Graduate/Fellowship)* [4085]
Florida Fertilizer and Agrichemical Association Scholarships *(Undergraduate/Scholarship)* [4096]
Florida Outdoor Writers Association Scholarships *(Undergraduate/Scholarship)* [4104]
Florida Public Health Association Public Health Graduate Scholarships *(Graduate/Scholarship)* [4108]
Florida Public Health Association Public Health Undergraduate Scholarships *(Undergraduate/Scholarship)* [4109]
Barney Flynn Memorial Scholarships *(Undergraduate/Scholarship)* [3097]
John Flynn Memorial Scholarships *(Undergraduate/Scholarship)* [3284]
Paul B. and Aline Flynn Scholarships *(Undergraduate/Scholarship)* [9429]
FMA-FEEA Scholarship Program *(Undergraduate/Scholarship)* [3993]
Follicular Lymphoma Research Grants *(Advanced Professional/Grant)* [6159]
Frank Fong Scholarships *(Undergraduate/Scholarship)* [9076]
Foot Locker Scholar Athletes *(Undergraduate/Scholarship)* [4131]
For the Love of Chocolate Foundation Scholarships *(Undergraduate, Graduate, Professional development/Scholarship)* [4133]
Ford Foundation Dissertation Fellowships *(Graduate, Doctorate/Fellowship)* [6675]
Ford Foundation Diversity Fellowships *(Graduate, Doctorate, Postdoctorate, Postgraduate/Fellowship)* [6676]
Ford Foundation Postdoctoral Fellowships *(Postdoctorate/Fellowship)* [6677]
Ford Foundation Predoctoral Fellowships *(Graduate, Doctorate/Fellowship)* [6678]
A. Ward Ford Memorial Research Grants *(Postdoctorate, Professional development/Grant)* [1351]
Anne Ford Scholarships *(Undergraduate/Scholarship)* [6850]
Nancy B. Forest and L. Michael Honaker Master's Grant for Research in Psychology *(Graduate/Grant)* [1133]
The FormsBirds Scholarships *(Undergraduate/Scholarship)* [4140]
Leland Stanford Forrest Scholarship *(Undergraduate/Scholarship)* [3673]
Forté Fellowships *(Master's/Fellowship)* [4151]
Stephen J. Fortgang/University of Northern Iowa Chapter Scholarship *(Undergraduate/Scholarship)* [5670]
Genevieve Forthun Scholarships *(Undergraduate/Scholarship)* [8092]
Dr. Nancy Foster Scholarship Program *(Postgraduate, Graduate/Scholarship)* [7077]
Andrew Foster Scholarships *(Undergraduate/Scholarship)* [6815]
Dr. Nancy Foster Scholarships *(Graduate/Scholarship)* [4159]
Foundation of American Institute for Conservation Lecture Grants *(Other/Grant)* [909]
Foundation for the Carolinas Rotary Scholarship Fund *(Undergraduate/Scholarship)* [4195]
Foundation of the Federal Bar Association Public Service Scholarship Award *(Undergraduate/Scholarship)* [4260]
The Foundation of the National Student Nurses' Association Scholarships *(Graduate, Undergraduate/Scholarship)* [7190]
Foundation for Neonatal Research and Education Scholarships *(Doctorate, Graduate, Postgraduate, Undergraduate/Scholarship)* [4272]
Foundation for the Preservation of Honey Bees Graduate Scholarships *(Graduate/Scholarship)* [4281]
Foundation Relations Internships - Los Angeles *(Undergraduate, Graduate/Internship)* [4433]
Foundation for Surgical Technology Scholarships *(Graduate/Scholarship)* [2076]
Founding Fathers Leadership Scholarships *(Undergraduate/Scholarship)* [10617]
Founding Mothers' Student Scholarships - Graduate *(Graduate/Scholarship)* [2015]
Mary Metzger Fouse Memorial Scholarship Fund *(Undergraduate/Scholarship)* [5718]
Don Fox Memorial Scholarship *(Undergraduate/Scholarship)* [211]
Captain Ernest Fox Perpetual Scholarships *(Undergraduate/Scholarship)* [3080]
FPA Summer Internships Program *(Undergraduate/Internship)* [4072]
William A. Fraker Student Heritage Awards *(Graduate, Undergraduate/Award)* [1256]
Frame My Future Scholarships Contest *(Undergraduate, Graduate/Scholarship)* [2938]
Franchise Law Diversity Scholarship Awards *(Undergraduate/Scholarship)* [5336]
Joe Francis Haircare Scholarships *(Undergraduate/Scholarship)* [4289]
Parker B. Francis Respiratory Research Grants *(Advanced Professional, Professional development/Grant)* [1211]
Gloria Francke Scholarship *(Undergraduate/Scholarship)* [1579]
Joe Francomano Scholarships *(Undergraduate/Scholarship)* [5630]
Mayme and Herb Frank Scholarship Program *(Graduate, Undergraduate/Scholarship)* [1782]
Michael W. and Jean D. Franke Family Foundation Scholarships *(Graduate, Undergraduate/Scholarship)* [1186]
Loren Frankel Memorial Scholarships *(Undergraduate, Graduate/Scholarship)* [995]
Mary Weiking Franken Scholarships *(Undergraduate/Scholarship)* [8093]
The Ginny Frankenthaler Memorial Scholarships *(Undergraduate/Scholarship)* [9385]
John Hope Franklin Dissertation Fellowships *(Doctorate/Fellowship)* [1080]
Franklin Elementary School PTA Scholarships *(Undergraduate/Scholarship)* [8476]
John Hope Franklin Prize *(Other/Prize)* [5971]
Franklin Research Grants *(Doctorate/Grant)* [1081]
Benjamin Franklin Trust Fund *(Undergraduate, Vocational/Occupational/Scholarship)* [4046]
Violet and Cyril Franks Scholarship *(Graduate/Scholarship)* [1144]
Joseph Frasca Excellence in Aviation Scholarships *(Undergraduate/Scholarship)* [10104]
Fraser Stryker Diversity Scholarships *(Undergraduate/Scholarship)* [4293]
FRAXA Postdoctoral Fellowships *(Postdoctorate, Master's/Fellowship)* [4295]
FREA Scholarship *(Undergraduate/Scholarship)* [4111]
Fred and Avery Test Scholarships *(Undergraduate/Scholarship)* [10180]
Fredrikson and Byron Foundation Minority Scholarships *(Undergraduate/Scholarship)* [4297]
Emanuel R. Freedman Scholarships *(Graduate, Undergraduate/Scholarship)* [7772]
Freedom Alliance Scholarships *(Undergraduate/Scholarship)* [4299]
Kevin Freeman Travel Grants *(Graduate, Other/Grant)* [6627]
Don Freeman Work-in-Progress Grants *(Advanced Professional/Grant)* [9096]
Malcolm and Mildred Freidberg Fellowships *(Professional development/Fellowship)* [6327]
The French Culinary Institute Classic Pastry Arts Scholarships *(Other, Undergraduate/Scholarship)* [3487]
Richard A. Freund International Scholarships *(Graduate/Scholarship)* [1389]
Ludo Frevel Crystallography Scholarships *(Graduate/Scholarship)* [5294]
Carleton A. Friday Scholarship *(Undergraduate/Scholarship)* [6527]
Dale E. Fridell Memorial Scholarships *(Undergraduate, Vocational/Occupational/Scholarship)* [9593]
Fried, Frank, Harris, Shriver and Jacobson Fellowships *(Graduate/Fellowship)* [4303]
MHS Marc Friedlaender Fellowships *(Professional development/Fellowship)* [6328]
A.E. Robert Friedman Scholarships *(Undergraduate/Scholarship)* [7795]
Phil Friel Scholarships *(Undergraduate/Scholarship)* [6354]
Kennedy T. Friend Scholarships *(Graduate, Undergraduate/Scholarship)* [325]
Friends of Coal Scholarships *(Undergraduate/Scholarship)* [10523]
Friends of Mary Automotive Scholarships *(Undergraduate/Scholarship)* [8872]
Friends of Project 10 Models of Excellence Scholarships *(Undergraduate/Scholarship)* [4307]

Froberg-Suess JD/MBA Scholarships *(Undergraduate/Scholarship)* [7978]
Dean A. Froehlich Endowed Scholarships *(Undergraduate/Scholarship)* [6027]
Patricia and Phillip Frost Fellowships *(Doctorate, Postdoctorate/Fellowship)* [9002]
"Frugal Student" Scholarships *(Undergraduate/Scholarship)* [7950]
Fruits and Vegetable Industries Scholarships *(Undergraduate/Scholarship)* [6487]
Marian Johnson Frutiger Scholarships *(Undergraduate/Scholarship)* [8922]
William and Francis Fry Honorary Fellowships for Contributions to Therapeutic Ultrasound *(Professional development/Fellowship)* [5431]
Mary Alice Fry Memorial Scholarships *(Undergraduate, Graduate/Scholarship)* [5719]
FSF Student Travel Grant *(Undergraduate, Graduate/Grant)* [4135]
FTE Dissertation Fellowships *(Graduate, Doctorate/Fellowship)* [4153]
FTE Doctoral Fellowships *(Doctorate, Graduate/Fellowship)* [4154]
FTE North American Doctoral Fellowships *(Doctorate, Graduate/Fellowship)* [4155]
Gerard Swartz Fudge Memorial Scholarships *(Undergraduate/Scholarship)* [5027]
Keiko Fukuda Scholarships *(Undergraduate/Scholarship)* [9960]
Kathryn Fuller Science for Nature Post-Doctoral Fellowships *(Graduate, Postdoctorate/Fellowship)* [10707]
Arthur Flagler Fultz Research Awards *(Professional development/Grant)* [1013]
Daniel G. and Helen I. Fultz Scholarship Fund *(Undergraduate/Scholarship)* [4047]
Arkansas Nursing Foundation - Dorothea Fund Scholarships *(Other/Scholarship)* [1656]
Donald M. Furbush Professional Development Grants *(Other/Grant)* [5216]
Dr. Horace Furumoto Innovations Professional Development - Young Investigator Awards *(Professional development/Award)* [1352]
Future Leader Initial NCTM Annual Meeting Attendance Awards *(Advanced Professional/Award, Monetary)* [6888]
Future Leaders of Manufacturing Scholarships *(Graduate, Undergraduate/Scholarship)* [9181]
Future STEM Teacher Scholarship *(Undergraduate/Scholarship)* [9657]
Mearl K. Gable II Memorial Grants *(Other/Grant)* [4709]
Gaddy Student Scholarships *(Undergraduate/Scholarship)* [10582]
Gaebe Eagle Scout Awards *(Undergraduate/Scholarship)* [6925]
Farley Moody Galbraith Scholarship Fund *(Undergraduate/Scholarship)* [3262]
Thomas W. Gallagher Scholarships Fund *(Undergraduate/Scholarship)* [9503]
Louise Bales Gallagher Scholarships *(Undergraduate/Scholarship)* [3551]
Whitney Laine Gallahar Memorial Scholarship Fund *(Undergraduate/Scholarship)* [3263]
Sam Gallant Memorial Scholarships *(Graduate, Undergraduate/Scholarship)* [1643]
The Gallery Collection's Create-A-Greeting Card Scholarships *(Undergraduate/Scholarship)* [4318]
Gamewarden Scholarship program *(High School, Undergraduate, Vocational/Occupational/Scholarship)* [4320]
Gamma Chi Project 2000 Scholarships *(Undergraduate/Scholarship)* [5720]
Gamma Iota Scholarships - Gamma Tau *(Undergraduate/Scholarship)* [8923]
Gamma Iota Scholarships - Kappa Eta *(Undergraduate/Scholarship)* [8924]
Gamma Iota Scholarships - Zeta Kappa *(Undergraduate/Scholarship)* [8925]
Gamma Iota Scholarships - Zeta Nu *(Undergraduate/Scholarship)* [8926]
Gamma Mu Project 2000 Scholarships *(Undergraduate/Scholarship)* [5721]
Gamma Pi Project 2000 Scholarships *(Undergraduate/Scholarship)* [5722]
Gamma Sigma Alpha Graduate Scholarships *(Graduate/Scholarship)* [4322]
Gamma Theta Project 2000 Scholarships *(Undergraduate/Scholarship)* [5723]
Gamma Zeta Project 2000 Scholarships *(Undergraduate/Scholarship)* [5724]
John A. Gans Scholarship *(Undergraduate/Scholarship)* [1580]
Gantenbein Medical Fund Fellowship *(Graduate/Fellowship)* [3497]
GAPA Scholarships *(Undergraduate/Scholarship)* [4327]
Michael and Gina Garcia Rail Engineering Scholarships *(Undergraduate, Graduate/Scholarship)* [1187]
William R. Gard Memorial Scholarships *(Undergraduate/Scholarship)* [6654]
Garden Club of America Awards in Tropical Botany (GCA) *(Doctorate/Award)* [4324]
Jewell Gardiner Scholarships *(Undergraduate/Scholarship)* [2473]
IGS John Gardner Fellowship *(Undergraduate/Fellowship)* [10108]
Gardner Foundation Infusion Nurses Society Education Scholarships *(Professional development/Scholarship)* [5145]
Robert Gardner Memorial Fellowships *(Graduate/Fellowship)* [4809]
Dwight D. Gardner Scholarships *(Undergraduate/Scholarship)* [5186]
Victoria M. Gardner Scholarships *(Undergraduate/Scholarship)* [10228]
Eugene Garfield Doctoral Dissertation Fellowship *(Doctorate/Fellowship)* [2239]
Peter M. Gargano Scholarship Fund *(Undergraduate/Scholarship)* [3709]
Garikian Scholarship Fund *(Undergraduate/Scholarship)* [1694]
Garmin Scholarships *(Undergraduate/Scholarship)* [160]
Gerald Garner Memorial Scholarships *(Undergraduate/Scholarship)* [7979]
Gail Garner R.I.S.E. Memorial Scholarships *(Undergraduate/Scholarship)* [8477]
Kays Gary Scholarships *(Undergraduate/Scholarship)* [10229]
Ethel Mae Gaston Memorial Scholarships *(Undergraduate/Scholarship)* [7380]
Edwin W. Gaston Scholarships *(Undergraduate/Scholarship)* [341]
Gates Cambridge Scholarships *(Graduate, Master's, Doctorate, Postgraduate, Postdoctorate/Scholarship)* [6746]
The Gates Millennium Scholars *(Undergraduate/Scholarship)* [4903]
Marian P. and David M. Gates Scholarship for Non-Residents *(Undergraduate/Scholarship)* [10181]
Kappa Kappa Gamma Foundation - Mary Maxwell Gates Scholarships *(Undergraduate, Graduate/Scholarship)* [5725]
Stephen Gates Scholarships *(Undergraduate/Scholarship)* [10230]
Frank Caleb & Margaret Thompson Gates Student Scholarships *(Undergraduate/Scholarship)* [10182]
A.R.F.O.R.A. Martha Gavrila Scholarships for Women *(Postgraduate/Scholarship)* [1226]
GAWP Graduate Scholarships *(Graduate/Scholarship)* [4377]
Lowell Gaylor Memorial Scholarships *(Undergraduate/Scholarship)* [161]
Florence S. Gaynor Scholarships *(Graduate/Scholarship)* [6755]
GCSAA Scholars Competition *(Undergraduate/Scholarship)* [4483]
GCSAA Student Essay Contest *(Graduate, Undergraduate/Prize)* [4484]
GED Jump Start Scholarships *(Professional development/Scholarship)* [8805]
GEF Scholarship Program *(Undergraduate, Graduate/Scholarship)* [4647]
Lawrence Gelfand - Armin Rappaport - Walter LaFeber Dissertation Fellowships *(Doctorate, Graduate/Scholarship)* [9137]
Elaine Gelman Scholarship Awards *(Undergraduate/Scholarship)* [6772]
The Gene and John Athletic Scholarships *(Undergraduate/Scholarship)* [9589]
General Falcon Scholarships *(Undergraduate/Scholarship)* [8201]
General Mills Foundation Scholarships *(Undergraduate/Scholarship)* [869]
General Scholarships for Higher Learning *(Undergraduate, Graduate, Master's/Scholarship)* [4960]
Geological Society of America Graduate Student Research Grants *(Doctorate, Graduate/Grant)* [4364]
George Foreman Tribute to Lyndon B. Johnson Scholarships *(Undergraduate/Scholarship)* [8405]
George W. and Ethel B. Hoefler Fund *(Undergraduate/Scholarship)* [3322]
Doris Y. and John J. Gerber Scholarships *(Undergraduate/Scholarship)* [10464]
Walter Gerboth Awards *(Other/Award)* [6628]
German Historical Institute Doctoral and Postdoctoral Fellowships *(Doctorate, Postgraduate/Fellowship)* [4395]
German Historical Institute Fellowships at the Horner Library *(Doctorate/Fellowship)* [4396]
German Studies Research Grants *(Undergraduate/Grant, Award)* [3607]
Bunny Kline Gerner and Robin Gerner Doty Memorial Adelphe Scholarships *(Undergraduate/Scholarship)* [5726]
Eloise Gerry Fellowships *(Graduate, Postdoctorate/Fellowship)* [8904]
Elizabeth Tucker Gessley Scholarship *(Undergraduate/Scholarship)* [5727]
Getty Conservation Guest Scholar Grants *(Professional development/Grant)* [4406]
Getty GRI-NEH Postdoctoral Fellowships *(Postdoctorate/Fellowship)* [4408]
Getty Postdoctoral Fellowships in Conservation Science *(Postdoctorate/Fellowship)* [4410]
Getty Postdoctoral Fellowships *(Postdoctorate/Fellowship)* [4409]
Getty Predoctoral Fellowships *(Doctorate/Fellowship)* [4411]
Getty Scholar Grants *(Professional development/Grant)* [4412]
GFLC AWMA Scholarships *(Undergraduate, Graduate/Scholarship)* [4361]
GFOA Minorities in Government Finance Scholarship *(Graduate, Undergraduate/Scholarship)* [4502]
GIA Scholarship- Distance Education eLearning *(Graduate/Scholarship)* [4334]
GIA Scholarships - On Campus *(Graduate/Scholarship)* [4335]
IDSA Gianninoto Graduate Scholarships *(Graduate, Undergraduate/Scholarship)* [5136]
Emily V. Gibbes Scholarships *(Undergraduate/Scholarship)* [7381]
John J. Gibbons Fellowships in Public Interest and Constitutional Law *(Professional development/Fellowship)* [4421]
Robert D. Gibson Scholarship *(Undergraduate/Scholarship)* [1581]
Joy Gibson Scholarships *(Undergraduate/Scholarship)* [10231]
Margaret S. Gilbert Scholarship Fund *(Undergraduate/Scholarship)* [9505]
Gilbreth Memorial Fellowships *(Graduate/Scholarship, Fellowship)* [5187]
Terry M. Giles Honor Scholar Program *(Undergraduate/Scholarship)* [7980]
Composites Division/Harold Giles Scholarship *(Undergraduate, Graduate/Scholarship)* [9263]
William Harrison Gill Education Fund *(Undergraduate/Scholarship)* [2228]
AIST Midwest Member Chapter - Jack Gill Scholarships *(Undergraduate/Scholarship)* [1997]
R.L. Gillette Scholarships *(Undergraduate/Scholarship)* [821]
Gilliam Fellowships for Advanced Study *(Doctorate/Fellowship)* [4974]
Benjamin A. Gilman International Scholarship *(Undergraduate/Scholarship)* [10060]
Leo Gilmartin Scholarships *(Undergraduate/Scholarship)* [8167]
Susan Kay Munson Gilmore Memorial Scholarships *(Undergraduate, Vocational/Occupational/Scholarship)* [3285]

Allan Gilmour & Eric Jirgens Point Scholarships *(Undergraduate, Graduate, Doctorate/Scholarship)* [8175]
Jack R. Gilstrap Scholarships *(Undergraduate, Graduate/Scholarship)* [1165]
Lawrence Ginocchio Aviation Scholarships *(Undergraduate/Scholarship)* [6833]
Alex Gissler Memorial Scholarships *(Undergraduate/Scholarship)* [6355]
GJEC Dissertation Completion Fellowships *(Postdoctorate/Fellowship)* [6490]
GLA Beard Scholarships *(Master's/Scholarship)* [4384]
GLA Hubbard Scholarships *(Master's/Scholarship)* [4385]
GLAAD Communications/PR Internships - New York *(Undergraduate, Graduate/Internship)* [4434]
GLAAD News Internships - New York *(Undergraduate, Graduate/Internship)* [4435]
GLAAD Spanish-Language and Latino Media Internships - Los Angeles *(Undergraduate, Graduate/Internship)* [4436]
GLAAD Youth Issues Internships - New York *(Undergraduate, Graduate/Internship)* [4437]
J. Robert Gladden Orthopaedic Society International Traveling Fellowship *(Undergraduate/Fellowship)* [4443]
Jane R. Glaser Scholarships *(Undergraduate/Scholarship)* [1476]
John Glaser Scholarships *(Undergraduate/Scholarship)* [3121]
GLATA Living Memorial Doctorate Scholarships *(Doctorate, Graduate/Fellowship)* [4653]
GLATA Living Memorial Graduate Scholarships *(Graduate/Fellowship, Scholarship)* [4654]
Herman and Bess Glazer Scholarship Fund *(Undergraduate/Scholarship)* [4662]
Gleaner Life Insurance Society Scholarships *(Undergraduate/Scholarship)* [4447]
Glendale Latino Association Scholarships *(Undergraduate/Scholarship)* [4449]
Glenn/AFAR Scholarships for Research in the Biology of Aging *(Graduate, Doctorate/Scholarship)* [788]
Glenn Miller Scholarships *(Undergraduate/Scholarship)* [4451]
Global Volcanism Program for Visiting Scientist/Postdoctoral Fellowships *(Postdoctorate/Fellowship)* [9032]
Globe-Trotters Member Chapter Scholarships *(Undergraduate, Postgraduate/Scholarship)* [1998]
Alfred B. Glossbrenner Scholarships *(Undergraduate/Scholarship)* [1999]
Bud Glover Memorial Scholarships *(Undergraduate/Scholarship)* [162]
Irene Carlson Gnaedinger Memorial Scholarships *(Undergraduate/Scholarship)* [6028]
Dr. Robert H. Goddard Memorial Scholarships *(Graduate, Undergraduate/Scholarship)* [7179]
Glenn Godfrey Memorial Scholarships *(Undergraduate, Graduate/Scholarship)* [5864]
Rosen Goertz Point Scholarship *(Undergraduate, Graduate, Doctorate/Scholarship)* [8176]
Shirley J. Gold Scholarship *(Undergraduate/Scholarship)* [793]
William Goldberg Diamond Corp. Scholarships *(Undergraduate/Scholarship)* [4336]
Daniel B. Goldberg Scholarship *(Graduate/Scholarship)* [4503]
Golden Eagle Coins Scholarships *(Undergraduate/Scholarship)* [4470]
Golden Key Graduate Scholar Awards *(Graduate, Master's, Doctorate/Scholarship)* [6747]
Golden Key Study Abroad Scholarships *(Undergraduate/Scholarship)* [4472]
William R. Goldfarb Memorial Scholarships *(Undergraduate/Scholarship)* [1739]
Goldia.com Jewelry Scholarships *(Undergraduate, Graduate/Scholarship)* [4474]
Dr. Guido Goldman Fellowships *(Doctorate, Postdoctorate/Scholarship)* [724]
Alois and Marie Goldmann Scholarship Fund *(Undergraduate/Scholarship)* [5041]
Barry M. Goldwater Scholarships *(Undergraduate/Scholarship)* [10319]
Joshua Gomes Memorial Scholarship Fund *(Undergraduate, Graduate/Scholarship)* [6990]
Millie Gonzalez Memorial Scholarships *(Undergraduate/Scholarship)* [4859]
Goodman Acker Scholarships *(Graduate/Scholarship)* [4489]
Victor and Ruth N. Goodman Memorial Scholarships *(Graduate/Scholarship)* [4697]
James L. and Genevieve H. Goodwin Scholarships *(Undergraduate/Scholarship)* [4753]
Google-American Indian Science and Engineering Society Scholarships *(Graduate, Undergraduate/Scholarship)* [4495]
Google European Doctoral Fellowships *(Doctorate/Fellowship)* [4496]
Google Hispanic College Fund Scholarships *(Graduate, Undergraduate/Scholarship)* [4497]
Google Lime Scholarships for Students with Disabilities *(Undergraduate, Graduate, Doctorate/Scholarship)* [6089]
Google US/Canada PhD Fellowships *(Graduate, Doctorate/Fellowship)* [4498]
Richard Goolsby Scholarship Fund *(Graduate, Undergraduate/Scholarship)* [4196]
FAMU Presidential Scholarship - George W. Gore Assistantship Scholarship *(Undergraduate/Scholarship)* [4077]
Sarah "Sally" Ives Gore Gamma Kappa Sapphire Scholarships *(Graduate, Undergraduate/Scholarship)* [5728]
Richard C. Gorecki Scholarships *(Undergraduate/Scholarship)* [8202]
TCDA Bill Gorham Student Scholarships *(Undergraduate/Scholarship)* [670]
Nettie and Jesse Gorov Scholarships *(Undergraduate/Scholarship)* [3286]
Consuelo W. Gosnell Memorial Scholarships *(Graduate/Fellowship)* [6789]
Louis Gottschalk Prize *(Other/Prize)* [1291]
Carl W. Gottschalk Research Scholar Grants *(Professional development/Grant)* [1381]
Norma Gotwalt Scholarship Fund *(Undergraduate/Scholarship)* [4241]
Government Documents Special Interest Section - Veronica Maclay Student Grants *(Master's/Grant)* [530]
Wilford Hayes Gowen Scholarship Fund *(Undergraduate/Scholarship)* [10161]
Goya Scholarships *(Graduate/Scholarship)* [8852]
Graduate Fellowship Program - Research Fellowships (GFP) *(Doctorate, Graduate/Fellowship)* [8833]
Graduate Fellowships in Alternatives in Scientific Research *(Doctorate, Graduate/Fellowship)* [5333]
Graduate Student Travel Grants *(Doctorate, Master's/Grant)* [462]
Graduate Student Travel Grants *(Graduate, Other/Grant)* [9111]
A. Allen Grafftham Research Grants *(Advanced Professional, Professional development/Grant)* [1842]
Graham and Dunn 1L Diversity Fellowships *(Graduate/Fellowship)* [4506]
Rachel Graham Memorial Scholarships *(Undergraduate/Scholarship)* [8478]
Grand Canyon Historical Society Scholarships *(Graduate/Scholarship)* [4508]
Charles Hall Grandgent Awards *(Graduate/Award, Monetary)* [3525]
AMA/Charles H. Grant Scholarships *(Undergraduate/Scholarship)* [39]
Grass Fellowships at the Marine Biological Laboratory *(Doctorate, Postdoctorate/Fellowship)* [4643]
Lucille Cheever Graubart/Lambda Scholarships *(Undergraduate/Scholarship)* [8927]
Thomas B. Grave and Elizabeth F. Grave Scholarships *(Undergraduate, Graduate/Scholarship)* [6247]
Caswell Grave Scholarships *(Undergraduate, Graduate/Scholarship)* [6248]
Camille F. Gravel, Jr. Scholarships *(Professional development/Scholarship)* [6114]
Gravure Publishing Council Scholarships *(Undergraduate, Graduate/Scholarship)* [4648]
IADR John Gray Fellowship *(Other/Fellowship)* [5251]
Alexander G. Gray, Jr. Scholarships *(Graduate/Scholarship)* [6340]
Arkansas Nursing Foundation - Mary Gray Scholarships *(Other/Scholarship)* [1657]
Great Falls Broadcasters Association Scholarships *(Undergraduate/Scholarship)* [6577]
Great Lakes Commission Sea Grant Fellowships *(Graduate/Scholarship)* [4656]
Great Lakes Section Diversity Scholarship *(Graduate, Undergraduate/Scholarship)* [5178]
GREAT MINDS Collegiate Scholarship Program *(Undergraduate/Scholarship)* [338]
Greater Research Opportunities (GRO) Undergraduate Fellowships *(Undergraduate/Fellowship)* [9933]
Frank L. Greathouse Government Accounting Scholarship *(Graduate, Undergraduate/Scholarship)* [4504]
Bishop Charles P. Greco Graduate Fellowships *(Graduate, Master's/Fellowship)* [5853]
Philip F. Greco Memorial Scholarships *(Undergraduate/Scholarship)* [6170]
Greek Orthodox Archdiocese of America Paleologos Graduate Scholarships *(Graduate/Scholarship)* [4666]
Crystal Green Memorial Scholarship *(Undergraduate/Scholarship)* [2314]
Howard L. Green Scholarships *(Undergraduate/Scholarship)* [7317]
Priscilla Green Scholarships *(Undergraduate/Scholarship)* [3465]
William G. and Mayme J. Green Scholarships *(Undergraduate/Scholarship)* [4754]
K2TEO Martin J. Green, Sr. Memorial Scholarships *(Undergraduate/Scholarship)* [1741]
Robert D. Greenberg Scholarships *(Graduate, Other/Scholarship)* [9093]
Michael Greenberg Student Writing Competition *(Graduate/Monetary, Scholarship)* [7052]
Richard L. Greene Dissertation Award *(Doctorate/Award)* [1090]
Curt Greene Memorial Scholarships *(Undergraduate/Scholarship)* [4725]
Elizabeth Greenhalgh Memorial Scholarships in Journalism, Graphic Arts, or Photography *(Undergraduate/Scholarship)* [10639]
Greenlining Institute Fellowships *(Graduate/Fellowship)* [4670]
Guy P. Greenwald Jr. Endowed Scholarships *(Undergraduate/Scholarship)* [7981]
Greenwich Scholarship Association Scholarships (GSA) *(Undergraduate/Scholarship)* [4672]
Anna Munger Greenwood Memorial Adelphe Scholarship *(Undergraduate/Scholarship)* [5729]
Lily H. Gridley Memorial Scholarships *(Undergraduate/Scholarship)* [10651]
Griffin Foundation Scholarships *(Undergraduate/Scholarship)* [4674]
Homajean Grisham Memorial Scholarship *(Undergraduate/Scholarship)* [7534]
Enid Hall Griswold Memorial Scholarships *(Undergraduate/Scholarship)* [7152]
Andrew Gronholdt Arts Scholarship Awards *(Undergraduate, Vocational/Occupational, Graduate, Master's/Scholarship)* [310]
Jennifer C. Groot Memorial Fellowships *(Undergraduate, Graduate/Fellowship)* [657]
Caroline L. Gross Fellowships *(Professional development/Fellowship)* [7304]
Charles Grossman Graduate Scholarships *(Graduate/Scholarship)* [5306]
F.C. Grote Fund Scholarships *(Graduate, Undergraduate/Scholarship)* [326]
Kathern F. Gruber Scholarship Program *(Undergraduate/Scholarship)* [2312]
Elizabeth M. Gruber Scholarships *(Graduate/Scholarship)* [3583]
Jack M. and Mary Lou Gruber Scholarships *(Undergraduate/Scholarship)* [6029]
GSA Scholarships for International Nurses *(Undergraduate, Master's/Scholarship)* [4458]
Guajardo & Marks Law School Scholarships *(Graduate/Scholarship)* [4676]
Guelph Caribbean Canadian Association Graduate Scholarships *(Undergraduate/Scholarship)* [4678]
Eleanor Guetzloe Undergraduate Scholarship *(Un-*

dergraduate/Scholarship) [3433]
Harry Frank Guggenheim Dissertation Fellowships (Doctorate/Fellowship) [4681]
Guggenheim Fellowships (Doctorate/Fellowship) [9022]
Harry Frank Guggenheim Foundation Research Grants (Professional development/Grant) [4682]
John Simon Guggenheim Memorial Fellowships - U.S. and Canadian Competition (Advanced Professional/Fellowship) [4684]
Bobette Bibo Gugliotta Memorial Scholarships for Creative Writing (Undergraduate/Scholarship) [8951]
Jimmy Guild Memorial Scholarships (Undergraduate/Scholarship) [6030]
GuildScholar Awards (Undergraduate/Scholarship) [5596]
Guin-Stanford Scholarships (Advanced Professional/Scholarship) [3264]
Calouste Gulbenkian Foundation Scholarships (Undergraduate/Scholarship) [1696]
Gulf Coast Past President's Scholarships (Undergraduate/Scholarship) [1413]
Larry Gulley Scholarships (Undergraduate/Scholarship) [9125]
Harold Gulliksen Psychometric Research Fellowships (Doctorate, Graduate/Fellowship) [3807]
Warren and Rosalie Gummow Endowed Scholarships (Undergraduate/Scholarship) [7982]
SME Education Foundation Connie & Robert T. Gunter Scholarships (Undergraduate/Scholarship) [9182]
George Gurney Fellowships (Doctorate, Postdoctorate/Fellowship) [9003]
Mary Ewing Guthrey/Mary Keller Moyer Memorial Scholarship (Undergraduate, Graduate/Scholarship) [5730]
Guzkowski Family Scholarships (Undergraduate/Scholarship) [8479]
GWS Scholarships (Undergraduate, Graduate/Scholarship) [145]
GWSCPA Scholarships (Undergraduate/Scholarship) [4664]
Wesley R. Habley NACADA Summer Institute Scholarships (Other/Scholarship) [6672]
Louise Wallace Hackney Fellowships for the Study of Chinese Art (Doctorate, Postdoctorate/Fellowship) [1058]
HACU/Denny's Hungry for Education Scholarships (Undergraduate, Graduate/Scholarship) [4883]
HACU/Empacadora Fruticola Santa Ines S.A. de C.V. Scholarships (Undergraduate, Graduate/Scholarship) [4884]
HACU/JCPenny Leadership Excellence Scholarships (Undergraduate, Graduate/Scholarship) [4886]
HACU/KIA Motors America, Inc. Scholarships (Undergraduate, Graduate/Scholarship) [4887]
HACU/NASCAR Scholarships (Graduate, Undergraduate/Scholarship) [4888]
Perry F. Hadlock Memorial Scholarships (Undergraduate/Scholarship) [1742]
Suzanne Lovell Hadsell Memorial Scholarship (Undergraduate/Scholarship) [5731]
Joseph E. Hagan Memorial Scholarships (Undergraduate/Scholarship) [4312]
Lee Hakel Graduate Student Scholarship (Doctorate/Scholarship) [9152]
Hall of Achievement Scholarships (Undergraduate/Scholarship) [2450]
Stephen K. Hall ACWA Water Law and Policy Scholarships (Graduate/Scholarship) [1872]
Joyce C. Hall College Scholarships (Undergraduate/Scholarship) [7960]
Hall County Medical Society Scholarships (Undergraduate/Scholarship) [4563]
Anna E. Hall Memorial Scholarships (Undergraduate, Graduate/Scholarship) [8055]
Chappie Hall Scholarship Program (Undergraduate/Scholarship) [2]
David J. Hallissey Memorial Internships (Graduate, Undergraduate/Internship) [1441]
Alice Hamilton Prize (Other/Prize) [1311]
TIAA-CREF Ruth Simms Hamilton Research Fellowships (Graduate/Fellowship) [9737]
Dwight A. Hamilton Scottish Rite Foundation of

Colorado Graduate Scholarships (Graduate/Scholarship) [8821]
Caitlin Hammaren Memorial Scholarship (Undergraduate/Scholarship) [5732]
Richard A. Hammill Scholarship Fund (Undergraduate/Scholarship) [981]
Jay Hammond Memorial Scholarships (Undergraduate/Scholarship) [10098]
Tommie J. Hamner Scholarships (Undergraduate/Scholarship) [8094]
HANA Scholarships (Undergraduate, Graduate, Doctorate/Scholarship) [9852]
Morris Hanauer Scholarships (Undergraduate/Scholarship) [4337]
Robert Hancock Memorial Scholarship Awards (Undergraduate/Scholarship) [6498]
Handweavers Guild of America and Dendel Scholarships (Graduate, Undergraduate/Scholarship) [4710]
Byron Hanke Fellowships (Doctorate, Graduate, Undergraduate/Fellowship) [4225]
Zenon C.R. Hansen Leadership Scholarships (Undergraduate/Scholarship) [6926]
Clement T. Hanson Scholarships (Undergraduate/Scholarship) [6569]
Duane Hanson Scholarships (Undergraduate/Scholarship) [1331]
Haraldson Foundation Scholarships (Undergraduate, Graduate/Scholarship) [4713]
Isaac and Mary Harbottle Scholarships (Graduate, Undergraduate/Scholarship) [7909]
Dolores Ruth Heady Hardy Memorial Scholarship (Undergraduate/Scholarship) [5733]
Hardy, Wolf & Downing Scholarships (Undergraduate, Graduate/Scholarship) [4719]
Bryce Harlow Fellowship Program (Graduate/Fellowship) [4721]
Matt Harmon Memorial Scholarships (Undergraduate/Scholarship) [9434]
North Las Vegas Firefighters William J. Harnedy Memorial Scholarships (Undergraduate/Scholarship) [8348]
Harness Tracks of America Scholarship Fund (Undergraduate/Scholarship) [4727]
Walter and Lucille Harper Scholarships (Undergraduate/Scholarship) [5806]
Harrell Family Fellowships (Graduate/Fellowship) [658]
H.H. Harris Foundation Scholarships (Professional development, Undergraduate/Scholarship) [836]
Leon Harris/Les Nichols Memorial Scholarships to Spartan College of Aeronautics & Technology (Undergraduate/Scholarship) [163]
William H. Harris Memorial Scholarships (Graduate, Undergraduate/Scholarship) [8075]
Frank and Charlene Harris Scholarships (Undergraduate/Scholarship) [3228]
Peg Hart Harrison Memorial Scholarships (Undergraduate/Scholarship) [3552]
Morton and Beatrice Harrison Scholarship Fund (Undergraduate/Scholarship) [4048]
Lullelia W. Harrison Scholarships in Counseling (Graduate, Undergraduate/Scholarship) [10815]
Harry S. Truman Scholarships (Postgraduate/Scholarship) [9803]
Claude B. Hart Memorial Scholarships (Undergraduate/Scholarship) [10584]
Carroll Hart Scholarship (Graduate/Scholarship) [9126]
Ida L. Hartenberg Charitable Scholarships (Undergraduate/Scholarship) [4755]
Hartford Grammar School Scholarships (Undergraduate/Scholarship) [4756]
Hartford Whalers Booster Club Scholarships (Undergraduate/Scholarship) [4778]
Gabe A. Hartl Scholarships (Undergraduate/Scholarship) [137]
Gail L. Hartshorn Memorial Fund (Undergraduate/Scholarship) [7838]
William T. Hartzell Memorial Scholarships (Undergraduate/Scholarship) [8480]
Harvey Fellows Program (Graduate/Fellowship) [6632]
Delta Gamma Foundation Florence Margaret Harvey Memorial Scholarships (Graduate, Undergraduate/Scholarship) [822]

Donald F. Hastings Scholarships (Undergraduate/Scholarship) [1513]
Donald and Shirley Hastings Scholarships (Undergraduate/Scholarship) [1514]
Charles Hauser Scholarships (Undergraduate/Scholarship) [10232]
AISC Education Foundation - Fred R. Havens Fund (Undergraduate, Graduate/Scholarship) [937]
Lex and Scott Hawkins Endowed Scholarship (Undergraduate/Scholarship) [3674]
Don C. Hawkins Memorial Scholarships (Undergraduate/Scholarship) [164]
Thomas T. Hayashi Memorial Scholarships (Graduate/Scholarship) [5550]
R. Garn Haycock Memorial Scholarships (Undergraduate/Scholarship) [8481]
Edward and Cora Hayes Scholarship (Undergraduate/Scholarship) [3675]
Samuel P. Hays Research Fellowships (Other/Fellowship) [1312]
Hazen and Sawyer Scholarships (Master's/Scholarship) [1489]
HBI-BGI Scholar-in-Residence Program (Undergraduate/Scholarship) [2359]
HBO Point Scholarships (Graduate, Undergraduate/Scholarship) [8177]
HDSA Research Grants (Graduate/Grant) [5019]
Edith Head Scholarships (Undergraduate/Scholarship) [3584]
Health Policy Scholarship for General Surgeons (Professional development/Scholarship) [697]
Health Services Research Dissertation Awards (Doctorate/Award) [9914]
Healthcare Information Management Systems Scholarships (Graduate, Postgraduate, Undergraduate/Scholarship) [4831]
Annamae Heaps Law Scholarship (Undergraduate/Scholarship) [3676]
William Randolph Hearst Endowed Scholarships (Undergraduate/Scholarship) [7382]
HECUA Scholarship for Community Engagement (Undergraduate/Scholarship) [4878]
HECUA Scholarship for Social Justice (Undergraduate/Scholarship) [4879]
Professor Ulla Hedner Scholarships (Undergraduate/Scholarship) [6991]
Howell Heflin Memorial Scholarship (Undergraduate/Scholarship) [7535]
Lavonne Heghinian Scholarships (Undergraduate/Scholarship) [3585]
Dale O. Heimberger CRNA Memorial Scholarship Fund (Graduate/Scholarship) [9509]
Joel T. Heinen Undergraduate Support Scholarships (Undergraduate/Scholarship) [10183]
Steven H. Heisler Law Scholarships (Graduate/Scholarship) [4836]
Helicopter Foundation International Commercial Helicopter Rating Scholarships (Other/Scholarship) [4838]
Helicopter Foundation International Maintenance Technician Certificate Scholarships (Other/Scholarship) [4839]
Hellenic Times Scholarships (Undergraduate, Graduate/Scholarship) [4843]
Joan Heller-Diane Bernard Fellowships (Graduate, Undergraduate/Fellowship) [2865]
Joseph T. Helling Scholarship Fund (Undergraduate/Scholarship) [5106]
Helm Family Scholarships (Undergraduate/Scholarship) [8706]
ASIL Arthur C. Helton Fellowship Program (Professional development/Fellowship) [1344]
Arthur Helton Fellowships (Graduate/Fellowship) [7401]
Clinton J. Helton Manufacturing Scholarships (Undergraduate/Scholarship) [9183]
Hemlow Prize in Burney Studies (Graduate/Prize) [1292]
Hemophilia Federation of America Educational Scholarships (Undergraduate/Scholarship) [4860]
Hench Post-Dissertation Fellowship (Postdoctorate/Fellowship) [438]
Douglas B. Henderson Leadership Scholarships (Doctorate/Scholarship) [3984]
The Henderson Memorial Endowed Scholarships (Undergraduate/Scholarship) [6031]

Gerald V. Henderson Memorial Scholarships *(Undergraduate, Graduate/Scholarship)* [9210]
Doris Hendren Memorial Scholarships *(Undergraduate/Scholarship)* [8707]
Henigson Human Rights Fellowships *(Graduate, Master's, Juris Doctorate/Fellowship)* [4786]
SNMMI Robert E. Henkin, MD, Government Relations Fellowship *(Professional development/Fellowship)* [9222]
Henley-Putnam University Scholarships *(Other/Scholarship)* [5267]
Allan F. Henry/Paul A. Greebler Scholarships *(Graduate/Scholarship)* [1036]
Gene Henson Scholarships *(Undergraduate/Scholarship)* [2113]
Richard A. Herbert Memorial Scholarships *(Undergraduate/Scholarship)* [1480]
Robert N. Herbert Undergraduate Scholarships *(Undergraduate/Scholarship)* [9216]
Hereditary Disease Foundation Basic Research Grants *(Advanced Professional/Grant)* [4869]
Herbert Herff Presidential Law Scholarships *(Undergraduate/Scholarship)* [10162]
Manuel Hernandez, Jr. Foundation Scholarships *(Undergraduate/Scholarship)* [3099]
Catarino and Evangelina Hernández Research Fellowships in Latino History *(Advanced Professional/Fellowship)* [9713]
The Herpetologists' League Graduate Research Award *(Graduate/Award)* [4871]
Purdue University Ray W. Herrick Laboratories Research Fellowship *(Graduate/Fellowship)* [8388]
Jessica M. Herron, Epsilon Nu, Memorial Scholarship *(Undergraduate/Scholarship)* [5734]
Herschede Engineering Scholarships *(Graduate/Scholarship)* [8898]
Isabel M. Herson Scholarships in Education *(Graduate, Undergraduate/Scholarship)* [10816]
Hertz Foundation Graduate Fellowship Award *(Graduate/Fellowship)* [4875]
Hertz Foundation Graduate Fellowships *(Graduate, Master's, Doctorate/Fellowship)* [6748]
Hertz Foundation Thesis Prize *(Graduate/Prize)* [4876]
Wayne E. Hesch Memorial Scholarship *(Undergraduate, Graduate/Scholarship)* [1543]
Darrel Hess Community College Geography Scholarships *(Undergraduate/Scholarship)* [1830]
Beth B. Hess Memorial Scholarships *(Doctorate, Graduate/Fellowship, Award)* [9331]
Melvyn F. Hester Scholarships *(Master's, Professional development/Scholarship)* [7383]
Caroline M. Hewins Scholarships *(Graduate/Scholarship)* [4776]
HFMA Connecticut Chapter Scholarships *(Undergraduate, Graduate/Scholarship)* [4827]
HFMH Bilingual Scholarships for Mental Health Workforce Diversity *(Graduate/Scholarship)* [4913]
HGS Foundation Undergraduate Scholarships *(Undergraduate/Scholarship)* [4967]
HHMI Medical Research Fellowships *(Undergraduate/Fellowship)* [4976]
HIAA Graduate Student Travel Grants *(Graduate/Grant)* [4908]
Mark and Michelle Hiepler Endowed Scholarships *(Undergraduate/Scholarship)* [7983]
Regina Higdon Scholarships *(Undergraduate/Scholarship)* [3229]
John Higham Travel Grants *(Graduate/Grant)* [5087, 7716]
Robert S. Hilbert Memorial Student Travel Grants *(Graduate, Undergraduate/Grant)* [7673]
Hill Country Master Gardeners Horticulture Scholarships *(Undergraduate/Scholarship)* [4881]
Judge Delmas C. Hill Scholarships *(Undergraduate/Scholarship)* [10429]
Conrad N. Hilton Scholarships *(Undergraduate/Scholarship)* [4414]
D. Glenn Hilts Scholarships *(Graduate, Undergraduate/Scholarship)* [2069]
Lucy Hilty Research Grants *(Graduate/Grant)* [1173]
Brooke Hindle Postdoctoral Fellowships *(Postdoctorate/Fellowship)* [9142]

Jim and Nancy Hinkle Travel Grants *(Graduate/Grant)* [4856]
Hinman-Jensen Endowed Scholarships *(Undergraduate/Scholarship)* [6032]
HIPLA Judicial Fellowships *(Undergraduate/Fellowship)* [4969]
HIPLA Scholarships for University of Houston Law Center Students *(Graduate, Undergraduate/Scholarship)* [4970]
Hispanic Association of Colleges and Universities Scholarships *(Undergraduate/Scholarship)* [4890]
Hispanic Scholarship Fund General College Scholarship Program (HSF) *(Undergraduate/Scholarship)* [4904]
Hispanic Serving Institution Scholarships (HSIS) *(Undergraduate/Scholarship)* [9870]
Historically Black College or University Scholarships (HBCUS) *(Undergraduate/Scholarship)* [9871]
HIV Prevention Research Advocacy Fellowships *(Professional development/Fellowship)* [2140]
Albert H. Hix, W8AH Memorial Scholarships *(Undergraduate/Scholarship)* [1743]
HLS/MLA Professional Development Grants *(Other/Grant)* [6386]
Lou Hochberg Awards - University/College Essay Awards *(Undergraduate/Award)* [7747]
Lou Hochberg Awards - University Thesis/Dissertation Awards *(Undergraduate, Graduate/Scholarship)* [7748]
Hochschulsommerkurse *(Undergraduate/Grant, Award)* [3608]
James E. Hoff, S.J. Scholars *(Undergraduate/Scholarship)* [10721]
Dorothy M. and Earl S. Hoffman Award *(Graduate/Award)* [2156]
Henry Hoffman Memorial Scholarship Fund *(Undergraduate/Scholarship)* [6740]
Robert and Elaine Hoffman Memorial Scholarships *(Undergraduate/Scholarship)* [10163]
Electronics Division Lewis C. Hoffman Scholarships *(Undergraduate/Scholarship)* [664]
Miriam Hoffman Scholarships *(Undergraduate, Graduate/Scholarship)* [9853]
Zelle Hofmann Diversity in Law Scholarships *(Undergraduate/Scholarship)* [10812]
Michael J. Hogan Language Fellowships *(Graduate/Fellowship)* [9138]
The Thelma S. Hoge Memorial Scholarship Fund *(Undergraduate/Scholarship)* [3205]
Houston/Nancy Holliman Scholarships *(Undergraduate/Scholarship)* [3586]
Cleve Holloway Memorial Scholarship Fund *(Undergraduate/Scholarship)* [3265]
Joseph A. Holmes Safety Association Scholarships *(Undergraduate, Graduate/Scholarship)* [4918]
Alan Holoch Memorial Grants *(Professional development/Grant)* [531]
W. Stull Holt Dissertation Fellowships *(Doctorate, Graduate/Fellowship)* [9139]
Arthur and Janet Holzheimer Fellowship in the History of Cartography *(Postdoctorate, Doctorate/Fellowship)* [7411]
Holzheimer Memorial Student Scholarship for Economic Development Planning *(Graduate, Master's/Scholarship)* [1105]
HomeCity Real Estate Scholarships *(Undergraduate/Scholarship)* [4925]
Honeywell Avionics Scholarships *(Undergraduate/Scholarship)* [165]
Kathryn Hookanson Law Fellowship *(Undergraduate/Scholarship)* [10164]
Lillie Hope-McGarvey Health Scholarship Awards *(Undergraduate, Vocational/Occupational, Graduate, Master's/Scholarship)* [311]
Hope for the Warriors Spouse/Caregiver Scholarships *(Undergraduate, Graduate/Scholarship)* [4933]
Johns Hopkins Department of Emergency Medicine Administration Fellowships *(Advanced Professional, Professional development/Fellowship)* [5607]
Seth Horen, K1LOM Memorial Scholarships *(Undergraduate/Scholarship)* [1744]
Brenda Renee Horn Memorial Scholarship *(Undergraduate/Scholarship)* [4313]
Edward L. Horne, Jr. Scholarships *(Advanced Professional/Scholarship)* [7732]
Sandra Jo Hornick Scholarships *(Undergraduate/Scholarship)* [5671]
Judge and Mrs. Robert D. Horowitz Legal Scholarship Fund *(Graduate/Scholarship)* [9512]
J. Jay Hostetler Scholarships *(Undergraduate/Scholarship)* [5672]
John C. "Jack" Hough Memorial Law Scholarship *(Undergraduate/Scholarship)* [10165]
Alston S. Householder Fellowships *(Doctorate/Fellowship)* [9907]
Houston Alumnae Association, Eunice "Scotty" Scott Siverson Memorial Adelphe Scholarship *(Undergraduate, Graduate/Scholarship)* [5735]
Paul Green Houston Scholarships *(Undergraduate/Scholarship)* [10233]
Sarah Jane Houston Scholarships *(Undergraduate/Scholarship)* [3587]
Houtan Scholarships *(Graduate/Scholarship)* [4972]
Kaspar Hovannisian Memorial Scholarships *(Graduate/Scholarship)* [1697]
Hirair and Anna Hovnanian Foundation Presidential Scholarships *(Undergraduate/Scholarship)* [1698]
Hirair and Anna Hovnanian Foundation Scholarships *(Undergraduate/Scholarship)* [1699]
Barbara J. and M. William Howard Jr. Scholarships *(Undergraduate/Scholarship)* [7384]
C.D. Howard Scholarships *(Undergraduate/Scholarship)* [5298]
Graduate Student Honoraria - A. Brazier Howell Awards *(Master's, Doctorate/Award)* [1359]
William C. Howell Scholarship *(Graduate, Master's, Doctorate/Scholarship)* [1145]
William B. Howell Scholarships *(Undergraduate/Scholarship)* [1515]
Christopher Hoy/ERT Scholarships *(Graduate/Scholarship)* [962]
Carol Hoy Scholarship Fund *(Undergraduate/Scholarship)* [4243]
HRH Prince Alwaleed Bin Talal ISNA Fellowships *(Graduate/Fellowship)* [5486]
HRSA Scholarships for Disadvantaged Students *(Undergraduate/Scholarship)* [9923]
HSF/Marathon Oil College Scholarship Program *(Undergraduate/Scholarship)* [4905]
HSF/Wells Fargo Scholarship Program *(Undergraduate/Scholarship)* [4906]
Chun-tu Hsueh Fellowship for International Scholars *(Graduate, Postdoctorate/Grant)* [1120]
Huber Engineered Woods Product Evaluation Scholarships *(Graduate/Scholarship)* [3977]
Amber Huber Memorial Scholarships *(Undergraduate/Scholarship)* [3287]
Huenefeld/Denton Scholarships *(Undergraduate/Scholarship)* [3588]
A. Joseph Huerta "Puedo" Scholarships *(Undergraduate/Scholarship)* [3100]
Dixon Hughes Goodman Scholarships *(Undergraduate, Graduate/Scholarship)* [10405]
Roger K. Hughes Legacy Scholarships *(Undergraduate/Scholarship)* [2451]
Paul A. Hughes Memorial Scholarships *(Undergraduate/Scholarship)* [2452]
Mary M. Hughes Research Fellowships in Texas History *(Professional development/Fellowship)* [9714]
Huguenot Society of South Carolina Graduate Scholarships *(Graduate/Scholarship)* [4986]
Humane Studies Fellowships *(Graduate/Fellowship, Scholarship)* [5183]
Humanism in Medicine Scholarships *(Undergraduate/Scholarship)* [9600]
Anna C. Hume Scholarship *(Undergraduate/Scholarship)* [4428]
Kevin Hummer Point Scholarships *(Graduate, Undergraduate/Scholarship)* [8178]
Cecil C. Humphreys Law Fellowships *(Undergraduate/Fellowship, Internship)* [10166]
Betty Jo Creighton Hunkele Adelphe Scholarship *(Undergraduate/Scholarship)* [5736]
Dr. Richard M. Hunt Fellowships *(Doctorate, Postdoctorate/Fellowship)* [725]
Hunt Postdoctoral Fellowships *(Postdoctorate/Fellowship)* [10517]
Frederick V. Hunt Postdoctoral Research Fellowships in Acoustics *(Postdoctorate/Fellowship)* [53]

Michael A. Hunter Memorial Scholarships *(Undergraduate/Scholarship)* [2907]
Carrie Hunter-Tate Award *(Undergraduate, Graduate/Grant)* [6794]
Curtis E. Huntington Memorial Scholarship *(Undergraduate/Scholarship)* [62]
Huntington's Disease Society of America Research Fellowships *(Postdoctorate/Fellowship)* [5020]
Sang Ok Hur Scholarships *(Undergraduate/Scholarship)* [7385]
James F. Hurley III Bicentennial Merit Scholarships *(Undergraduate/Scholarship)* [10234]
Walter Doc Hurley Scholarship *(Undergraduate/Scholarship)* [4757]
Zora Neale Hurston Scholarships *(Graduate/Scholarship)* [10817]
Norman E. and Mary-Belle Huston Scholarships *(Graduate, Undergraduate/Scholarship)* [5397]
Dr. James L. Hutchinson and Evelyn Ribbs Hutchinson Medical School Scholarship Fund *(Undergraduate/Scholarship)* [8952]
The Hyatt Hotels Fund For Minority Lodging Management Students *(Undergraduate/Scholarship)* [860]
Hydro Research Foundation Fellowships *(Advanced Professional/Fellowship)* [5023]
Mike Hylton and Ron Niederman Memorial Scholarships *(Undergraduate/Scholarship)* [4861]
Libbie H. Hyman Memorial Scholarships *(Graduate, Undergraduate/Scholarship)* [9156]
The Steve Hymans Extended Stay Scholarship Program *(Undergraduate/Scholarship)* [861]
Hypertherm International HyTech Leadership Scholarships *(Graduate/Scholarship)* [1516]
IAAP Wings Chapter Scholarships *(Undergraduate/Scholarship)* [5244]
IABA Scholarships *(Graduate/Scholarship)* [5476]
IAEM Scholarship Program *(Undergraduate/Scholarship)* [5256]
IAESTE United States Internships *(Undergraduate/Internship)* [3489]
IAF Fellowships *(Doctorate/Fellowship)* [5232]
IAHCSMM-Purdue University Scholarship Awards *(Other/Scholarship)* [5263]
IALD Education Trust Scholarship Program *(Graduate, Undergraduate/Scholarship)* [5271]
IALL Regular Bursaries *(Other/Scholarship)* [5269]
IARS Mentored Research Awards (IMRA) *(Professional development/Grant)* [5242]
IARSLCE Graduate Student Scholarships *(Graduate/Scholarship)* [5273]
IASC Associate Fellowships *(Doctorate/Fellowship)* [10308]
IASC Doctoral Fellowships - Dissertation *(Doctorate/Fellowship)* [10309]
IASC Doctoral Fellowships - Pre-Dissertation *(Doctorate/Fellowship)* [10310]
IASC Postdoctoral Fellowships *(Postdoctorate/Fellowship)* [10311]
IASC Visiting Fellowships *(Professional development/Fellowship)* [10312]
IASP Visiting Professor Grants *(Professional development/Grant)* [5275]
IAWP International Scholarship Award *(Other/Scholarship)* [5280]
IBEA Undergraduate Scholarships *(Undergraduate/Scholarship)* [5057]
ICAFS Idaho Graduate Student Scholarships *(Graduate/Scholarship)* [5035]
ICAFS Idaho High School Student Scholarships *(Undergraduate/Scholarship)* [5036]
ICAFS Idaho Undergraduate Student Scholarships *(Undergraduate/Scholarship)* [5037]
ICDA Graduate Scholarships *(Graduate/Scholarship)* [5464]
ICDA Research Grants *(Graduate/Grant)* [5465]
Ice Skating Institute of America Education Foundation Scholarships *(Undergraduate/Scholarship)* [5031]
ICJS Short-Term Fellowships *(Doctorate, Postdoctorate, Advanced Professional/Fellowship)* [8997]
ICMA Local Government Management Fellowships *(Master's/Fellowship)* [5296]
IDA Fellowship Awards *(Other/Fellowship)* [5320]
Idaho Nursing and Health Professions Scholarships *(Undergraduate/Scholarship)* [5042]

David Iden Memorial Safety Scholarships *(Undergraduate/Scholarship)* [1415]
IDTA Freestyle Scholarships *(Undergraduate/Scholarship)* [5317]
IFDA Student Member Scholarships *(Undergraduate/Scholarship)* [5338]
IFMA Foundation Scholarships *(Undergraduate, Graduate/Scholarship)* [5327]
IFSEA Worthy Goal Scholarships *(Two Year College, Undergraduate, Vocational/Occupational/Scholarship)* [5329]
IIE Council of Fellows Undergraduate Scholarships *(Undergraduate/Scholarship)* [5188]
IILJ Scholarships *(Doctorate/Scholarship)* [5202]
IILJ Visiting Fellowships and Research *(Postdoctorate/Fellowship)* [5203]
IISE Presidents Scholarships *(Undergraduate/Scholarship)* [5189]
Illinois Association of Chamber of Commerce Executives Scholarships *(Professional development/Scholarship)* [5054]
Illinois Division Scholarships *(Undergraduate/Scholarship)* [6519]
Illuminator Educational Foundation Scholarships *(Undergraduate/Scholarship)* [2453]
ILSA Internships *(Graduate/Internship)* [5353]
IMA Memorial Education Fund Scholarships (MEF) *(Graduate, Undergraduate/Scholarship)* [5206]
Imagine America College Scholarships for High School Students *(Undergraduate/Scholarship)* [5083]
Imagine America Military Awards Program *(Undergraduate/Scholarship, Grant)* [5084]
Imagine America Scholarships for Adult Students *(Undergraduate/Scholarship)* [5085]
Elmer S. Imes Scholarships in Physics *(Undergraduate/Scholarship)* [7142]
John L. Imhoff Scholarships *(Graduate, Undergraduate/Scholarship)* [5190]
David G. Imig Awards for Distinguished Achievement in Teacher Education *(Other/Recognition)* [486]
IMS AWWA Graduate Science and Engineering Scholarships *(Graduate/Scholarship)* [5239]
Independent Professional Seed Association Student Recognition Awards *(Undergraduate/Scholarship)* [5098]
Indian Health Service Professionals Program *(Undergraduate/Scholarship)* [875]
Indiana FFA Association State Fair Scholarship *(Undergraduate/Scholarship)* [5110]
Indiana State University Academic Excellence Scholarships *(Undergraduate/Scholarship)* [5116]
Indiana State University Academic Promise Scholarships *(Undergraduate/Scholarship)* [5126]
Indiana State University Creative and Performing Arts Awards *(Undergraduate/Scholarship)* [5127]
Indiana State University Incentive Scholarships *(Undergraduate/Scholarship)* [5117]
Indiana State University Transfer Student Scholarships *(Undergraduate/Scholarship)* [5120]
Individual Advanced Research Opportunities Program For Master's Students *(Graduate, Master's/Fellowship)* [5381]
Individual K-Grants *(All/Grant)* [5823]
Individual Professional Development Scholarship *(Professional development/Scholarship)* [4161]
INF Scholarships *(Undergraduate/Scholarship)* [5472]
Influenster Code Like a Girl Scholarships *(Undergraduate, Graduate/Scholarship)* [5140]
Informatics Post Doctoral Fellowships *(Doctorate/Fellowship)* [8027]
Informatics Pre Doctoral Fellowships *(Doctorate/Fellowship)* [8028]
Informatics Sabbatical Fellowships *(Doctorate, Postdoctorate/Fellowship)* [8029]
Information Age Publishing Graduate Student Book Scholarships *(Doctorate, Graduate/Scholarship)* [5142]
Terrance N. Ingraham Pediatric Optometry Residency Support *(Graduate/Fellowship)* [416]
Jennifer Ingrum Scholarships *(Undergraduate/Scholarship)* [3230]
INIA Scholarship Program *(Undergraduate/Scholarship)* [5363]

Injury Scholarships *(Undergraduate/Scholarship)* [4731]
Innovations in Software Scholarships *(Undergraduate, Graduate/Scholarship)* [10758]
Innovative Grants-Pilot and Research Tool Grants *(Postdoctorate/Grant)* [5641]
Institute for Anarchist Studies Grants for Radical Writers and Translators *(Professional development/Grant)* [5165]
Institute of Food Technologists Graduate Scholarships *(Graduate/Scholarship)* [5171]
Institute of Food Technologists Junior/Senior Scholarships *(Undergraduate/Scholarship)* [5172]
Institute of Food Technologists Sophomore Scholarships *(Undergraduate/Scholarship)* [5173]
Institute for Health Metrics and Evaluation Post Bachelor Fellowships *(Graduate/Fellowship)* [5180]
Institute for Health Metrics and Evaluation Post Graduate Fellowships *(Doctorate, Postdoctorate/Fellowship)* [5181]
Institute for the International Education of Students Faculty Fellowships *(Other/Fellowship)* [7412]
Institute of Management Accountants FAR Doctoral Student Grants Program *(Doctorate/Grant)* [5207]
Institute-NEH Postdoctoral Fellowships *(Doctorate, Other/Fellowship)* [7613]
Institute of Turkish Studies Dissertation Writing Grants *(Graduate/Grant)* [5223]
Institute of Turkish Studies Post-Doctoral Summer Travel-Research Grants *(Postdoctorate/Grant)* [5224]
Institute of Turkish Studies Sabbatical Research Grants *(Other/Grant)* [5225]
Institute of Turkish Studies Summer Language Study Grants in Turkey *(Graduate/Grant)* [5226]
Instructional Design & Learning Technologies Scholarships *(Undergraduate, Graduate/Scholarship)* [3820]
Intensive Language Course Grants *(Doctorate/Grant)* [3609]
Inter American Press Association Scholarships *(Undergraduate/Scholarship)* [9061]
Intermediaries and Reinsurance Underwriters Association Summer Intern Scholarships Program *(Undergraduate/Scholarship)* [5237]
International Affairs Fellowships in Japan (IAF-J) *(Professional development/Fellowship)* [3447]
International Affairs Fellowships in Nuclear Security (IAF-NS) *(Professional development/Fellowship)* [3448]
International Association of Black Actuaries Scholarships *(Undergraduate/Scholarship)* [5248]
International Association for Food Protection - Student Travel Scholarship Program *(Undergraduate, Graduate/Scholarship)* [5258]
International Association of Foundation Drilling Scholarships for Civil Engineering Students *(Graduate/Scholarship)* [75]
International Association of Foundation Drilling Scholarships for Part-time Civil Engineering Graduate School Students *(Graduate/Scholarship)* [76]
International Association of Wildland Fire Graduate-Level Scholarships *(Doctorate, Graduate/Scholarship)* [5278]
International Code Council Foundation General Scholarship Fund *(Undergraduate/Scholarship)* [5299]
International Code Council Scholarships *(Graduate/Scholarship)* [3978]
International Dairy-Deli-Bakery Association Undergraduate/Graduate Scholarships *(Graduate, Undergraduate/Scholarship)* [5314]
International Development and Education Award in Palliative Care *(Professional development/Award)* [3376]
International Development and Education Awards *(Professional development, Doctorate/Grant)* [3377]
International Dissertation Research Fellowship (IDRF) *(Graduate, Doctorate/Fellowship)* [9054]
International Doctoral Scholarships for Studies Specializing in Jewish Fields *(Doctorate/Scholarship, Award)* [6411]
International Door Association Scholarship Founda-

tion Program *(Undergraduate, Vocational/Occupational/Scholarship)* [5322]
International Executive Housekeepers Association Education Foundation Scholarship Awards *(Undergraduate/Scholarship)* [5324]
International Executive Housekeepers Association Spartan Scholarship Awards *(Undergraduate/Scholarship)* [5325]
International Fellowships in Jewish Studies and Jewish Culture *(Professional development/Fellowship)* [6412]
International Foodservice Editorial Council Scholarships *(Graduate, Undergraduate/Scholarship)* [5331]
International Furnishings and Design Association Part-time Student Scholarships *(Undergraduate/Scholarship)* [5339]
International GI Training Grant Award *(Professional development/Grant)* [685]
International Innovation Grants *(Professional development/Grant)* [3378]
International Operators Scholarship *(Professional development/Scholarship)* [6834]
International Order of the King's Daughters and Sons North American Indian Scholarship Program *(Undergraduate/Scholarship)* [876]
International Radio and Television Society Foundation Summer Fellowships Program *(Undergraduate, Graduate/Fellowship)* [5378]
International Sanitary Supply Association Foundation Scholarships *(Undergraduate/Scholarship)* [5392]
International Scholarship Programs for Community Service *(Undergraduate/Scholarship)* [6413]
International Society Annual Meeting Travel Grant *(Professional development/Grant)* [408]
International Society for Humor Studies Graduate Student Awards (GSA) *(Graduate/Award, Scholarship)* [5422]
International Society for Humor Studies Scholarly Contribution Awards (SCA) *(Other/Award)* [5423]
International Trademark Association-Ladas Memorial Awards *(Other, Undergraduate/Award)* [5447]
International Trainee Scholarships (ITS) *(Doctorate/Scholarship)* [1474]
International Women's Fishing Association Scholarship Trust *(Graduate/Scholarship)* [5456]
Internet Society Fellowships to the IETF *(Doctorate, Master's/Fellowship)* [5460]
Interracial Scholarship Fund of Greater Hartford *(Undergraduate/Scholarship)* [4758]
Investigators in the Pathogenesis of Infectious Disease Awards *(Doctorate, Postdoctorate, Professional development/Grant)* [2417]
Iowa Association of Electric Cooperatives - Electric Cooperative Pioneer Trust Fund Scholarship *(Undergraduate/Scholarship)* [3678]
Iowa Division Scholarships *(Undergraduate/Scholarship)* [6520]
Iowa Journalism Institute Scholarships *(Undergraduate/Scholarship)* [5473]
Iowa Library Association Foundation Scholarships *(Graduate/Scholarship)* [5469]
Susan K. Ipacs Nursing Legacy Scholarships *(Undergraduate, High School/Scholarship)* [4169]
IPMA-HR Graduate Study Fellowships *(Graduate, Master's/Fellowship)* [5376]
IPPR Events Internships *(Undergraduate/Internship)* [5209]
IPR Pathfinder Award *(Advanced Professional/Recognition, Grant)* [5212]
IREX Individual Advanced Research Opportunities Program For Pre-doctoral Students *(Doctorate/Fellowship)* [5382]
IREX Individual Advanced Research Opportunities Program For Professionals *(Other/Fellowship)* [5383]
IREX Individual Advanced Research Opportunities Program for Postdoctoral Scholars *(Postdoctorate/Fellowship)* [5384]
Harriet Irsay Scholarships *(Graduate, Undergraduate/Scholarship)* [927]
IRSF Mentored Training Fellowships *(Advanced Professional, Postdoctorate/Fellowship)* [5388]
ISA Educational Foundation Scholarships *(Undergraduate/Scholarship)* [5398]

ISA Executive Board Scholarships *(Graduate, Undergraduate/Scholarship)* [5399]
ISA Section and District Scholarships - Houston *(Graduate, Undergraduate/Scholarship)* [5400]
ISA Section and District Scholarships - Lehigh Valley *(Graduate, Undergraduate/Scholarship)* [5401]
ISA Section and District Scholarships - Richmond Hopewell *(Graduate, Undergraduate/Scholarship)* [5402]
ISA Section and District Scholarships - Southwestern Wyoming *(Graduate, Undergraduate/Scholarship)* [5403]
ISA Section and District Scholarships - Texas, Louisiana and Mississippi *(Graduate, Undergraduate/Scholarship)* [5404]
ISA Section and District Scholarships - Wilmington *(Graduate, Undergraduate/Scholarship)* [5405]
ISA Technical Division Scholarships - Analysis Division *(Graduate, Undergraduate/Scholarship)* [5406]
ISA Technical Division Scholarships - Chemical and Petroleum Industries Division *(Graduate, Undergraduate/Scholarship)* [5407]
ISA Technical Division Scholarships - Food and Pharmaceutical Industries Division *(Graduate, Undergraduate/Scholarship)* [5408]
ISA Technical Division Scholarships - Power Industry Division *(Graduate, Undergraduate/Scholarship)* [5409]
ISA Technical Division Scholarships - Process Measurement and Control Division *(Graduate, Undergraduate/Scholarship)* [5410]
ISA Technical Division Scholarships - Pulp and Paper Industry Division *(Graduate, Undergraduate/Scholarship)* [5411]
ISA Technical Division Scholarships - Test Measurement Division *(Graduate, Undergraduate/Scholarship)* [5412]
ISA Technical Division Scholarships - Water and Wastewater Industries Division *(Graduate, Undergraduate/Scholarship)* [5413]
ISBA General Scholarships *(Graduate, Undergraduate/Scholarship)* [5052]
Hazel D. Isbell Fellowships *(Graduate/Fellowship, Scholarship)* [3553]
(ISC)2 Foundation Information Security Scholarships *(Graduate, Undergraduate/Scholarship)* [5348]
ISCALC International Scholarship Fund *(Undergraduate/Scholarship)* [4049]
ISDS Graduate Student Scholarships *(Doctorate, Graduate/Scholarship)* [5416]
ISF Excellence in Community Service Scholarships *(Undergraduate/Scholarship)* [5478]
ISF Undergraduate Scholarships *(Undergraduate/Scholarship)* [5479]
ISID Small Grant *(Postdoctorate, Professional development/Grant)* [5425]
Islamic Scholarship Fund Scholarships (ISF) *(Postgraduate, Undergraduate/Scholarship)* [5484]
Broughton Isom Memorial Scholarship *(Undergraduate/Scholarship)* [7536]
ISOPE Offshore Mechanics Scholarships for Outstanding Students *(Graduate/Scholarship)* [5427]
ISPE Foundation Scholarships *(Undergraduate/Scholarship)* [5066]
ISRS Graduate Fellowships *(Doctorate, Graduate/Fellowship)* [5429]
ISTTE Scholarships *(Graduate, Undergraduate/Scholarship)* [5435]
ISTU Student Prize *(Undergraduate/Prize)* [5432]
ISU Child of Alumni Book Voucher Awards *(Undergraduate/Scholarship)* [5128]
ISU Gongaware Scholarships *(Undergraduate/Scholarship)* [5121]
ISU Networks Scholarships College of Business *(Undergraduate/Scholarship)* [5122]
ITAA Graduate Student Best Paper Award *(Graduate/Monetary)* [5442]
Italian Language Scholarships *(Undergraduate/Scholarship)* [7682]
ITEEA Greer/FTE Grants *(Other/Grant)* [5437]
ITNS Research Grants *(Other/Grant)* [5449]
ITW Welding Companies Scholarships *(Undergraduate/Scholarship)* [1517]

Ivanhoe Foundation Fellowships *(Master's/Fellowship)* [5488]
Bob and Mary Ives Scholarships *(Graduate, Undergraduate/Scholarship)* [5414]
Jack and Jill of America National Scholarships Program *(Undergraduate/Scholarship)* [5490]
Jackie Robinson Scholarships *(Undergraduate/Scholarship)* [5495]
Jackman Scholarships *(Undergraduate/Scholarship)* [8095]
Graduate Student Honoraria - Anna M. Jackson Awards *(Master's, Doctorate/Award)* [1360]
Ruth K. Jacobs Memorial Scholarships *(Graduate, Undergraduate/Scholarship)* [2930]
Freddy L. Jacobs Scholarships *(Undergraduate/Scholarship)* [5284]
Eric L. Jacobson Memorial Scholarships *(Undergraduate/Scholarship)* [8482]
Jacque Placette Chapman Master's Fellowships *(Graduate, Master's/Fellowship)* [7679]
Louis I. Jaffe Memorial Scholarships-ODU *(Graduate/Scholarship)* [4701]
Jagiellonian University Summer Program Scholarship *(Professional development/Scholarship)* [8204]
Jain Foundation Merit-Based Scholarships *(All/Scholarship)* [5518]
Jain Foundation Social-Media Scholarships *(All/Scholarship)* [5519]
Jamail/Long Challenge Grant Scholarships *(Undergraduate/Scholarship)* [4896]
Peter and Malina James and Dr. Louis P. James Legacy Scholarships *(Graduate, Master's, Doctorate/Scholarship)* [1146]
Olivia James Traveling Fellowships *(Professional development/Fellowship)* [1608]
J. Franklin Jameson Fellowships in American History *(Professional development/Fellowship)* [853]
Jan Jancin Competition Awards *(Undergraduate/Award)* [941]
Janelia Farm Graduate Program *(Graduate/Award)* [4978]
Janssen Therapeutics Point Scholarships *(Undergraduate, Graduate, Doctorate/Scholarship)* [8179]
Japan Foundation, New York Doctoral Fellowship Program *(Doctorate/Fellowship)* [5537]
Japan Foundation, New York Long-Term Research Fellowship Program *(Professional development/Fellowship)* [5538]
Japan Foundation, New York Short-Term Fellowship Program *(Professional development/Fellowship)* [5539]
Japan Society for the Promotion of Science Fellowship Program *(Doctorate/Fellowship)* [9055]
Dr. Ali Jarrahi Merit Scholarships *(Undergraduate/Scholarship)* [5480]
Carl and Lucille Jarrett Scholarship Fund *(Undergraduate/Scholarship)* [4050]
Airgas - Terry Jarvis Memorial Scholarships *(Undergraduate/Scholarship)* [1518]
Jacob K. Javits Fellowships Program *(Master's, Doctorate/Fellowship)* [9894]
JCC Association Graduate Education Scholarships *(Graduate/Scholarship)* [5562]
JCCF Equal Voice Journalism Scholarship *(Professional development/Scholarship)* [10152]
JDRF Advanced Postdoctoral Fellowships *(Postdoctorate/Fellowship)* [5642]
JDRF Career Development Awards *(Professional development, Postdoctorate/Grant)* [5643]
JDRF Postdoctoral Fellowships *(Postdoctorate/Fellowship)* [5644]
JEA Future Teacher Scholarships *(Undergraduate, Master's/Scholarship)* [5625]
Sister Rita Jeanne Scholarships *(Undergraduate/Monetary, Scholarship)* [5626]
Jefferson Graduate Fellowships *(Doctorate, Graduate/Fellowship)* [5564]
Jeffress Trust Awards Program in Interdisciplinary Research *(Professional development/Award)* [4816]
John Jeffries Meteorology Scholarships *(Graduate/Scholarship)* [3979]
Elise Reed Jenkins Memorial Scholarships -

UNITED STATES   Legal Residence Index

Gamma Lambda *(Undergraduate/Scholarship)* [8928]
Elise Reed Jenkins Memorial Scholarships - Gamma Psi *(Undergraduate/Scholarship)* [8929]
John H. Jenkins Research Fellowships in Texas History *(Professional development/Fellowship)* [9715]
Martha Combs Jenkins Scholarships *(Undergraduate/Scholarship)* [8096]
Gaynold Jensen Education Stipends *(Postdoctorate, Other/Scholarship)* [3622]
Walter J. Jensen Fellowships *(Other/Fellowship)* [8052]
Nancy Lorraine Jensen Memorial Scholarships *(Undergraduate/Scholarship)* [9345]
Stanley "Doc" Jensen Scholarships *(Undergraduate/Scholarship)* [760]
Jerman-Cahoon Student Scholarship *(Undergraduate/Scholarship)* [1397]
Kenneth Jernigan Scholarships *(Undergraduate/Scholarship)* [6947]
Jerome Fellowships *(Other/Fellowship)* [8152]
Jerome Robbins Bogliasco Fellowships in Dance *(Professional development/Fellowship)* [2329]
Brian Jimenez Memorial Scholarships *(Undergraduate/Scholarship)* [8483]
Rev. and Mrs. A.K. Jizmejian Educational Fund *(Undergraduate/Scholarship)* [1700]
JLTLA Judge's Scholarships *(Undergraduate/Scholarship)* [9817]
Reverend H. John and Asako Yamashita Memorial Scholarships *(Graduate/Scholarship)* [5551]
Johns Hopkins Medicine Disaster Fellowships *(Professional development/Fellowship)* [5608]
Johns Hopkins Medicine Emergency Medical Services Fellowship *(Professional development/Fellowship)* [5609]
Johns Hopkins Medicine International Emergency and Public Health Fellowships *(Graduate/Fellowship)* [5610]
Johns Hopkins Medicine Medical Education Fellowships *(Professional development/Fellowship)* [5611]
Johns Hopkins Medicine Observation Medicine Fellowships *(Professional development/Fellowship)* [5612]
Johns Hopkins Medicine Research Fellowships *(Professional development/Fellowship)* [5613]
Johns Hopkins University/Applied Physics Laboratory Alexander Kossiakoff Scholarships *(Doctorate, Graduate, Master's/Scholarship)* [5310]
Wilma Winberg Johnson Adelphe Scholarship for Chapter Consultants *(Undergraduate/Scholarship)* [5738]
Alvin H. Johnson AMS 50 Dissertation Fellowships *(Doctorate/Fellowship)* [1020]
Sylvia Taylor Johnson Fellowships in Educational Measurement *(Doctorate/Fellowship)* [3808]
Robert Wood Johnson Foundation Health Policy Fellows Program *(Advanced Professional, Professional development/Fellowship)* [8629]
Johnson and Johnson/AACN Minority Nurse Faculty Scholars *(Graduate/Scholarship)* [480]
MCCA Lloyd M. Johnson, Jr. Scholarships *(Graduate/Scholarship)* [6553]
Joseph C. Johnson Memorial Grants *(Undergraduate/Grant, Scholarship)* [1252]
Gregory D. Johnson Memorial Scholarships *(Doctorate, Graduate, Master's/Scholarship)* [7036]
Professor Emeritus Dr. Bill Johnson Memorial Scholarships *(Undergraduate/Scholarship)* [8874]
Camilla C. Johnson Scholarships *(Undergraduate/Scholarship)* [4602]
The Johnson & Wales Scholarships *(Undergraduate/Scholarship)* [5631]
Nancy Johnston Memorial Scholarships *(Graduate, Undergraduate/Scholarship)* [9675]
OOIDA Mary Johnston Scholarships *(Undergraduate/Scholarship)* [7785]
Joint Japan/World Bank Graduate Scholarship Program for Developing Country National (JJ/WB-GSP) *(Graduate/Scholarship)* [10696]
Joint Japan/World Bank Graduate Scholarship Program for Japanese National (JJ/WBGSP) *(Graduate, Master's, Doctorate/Scholarship)* [10697]
Redlands Council PTA - Dorathy Jolley Memorial Scholarships *(Undergraduate/Scholarship)* [8484]
George E. Jonas Scholarships *(Graduate, Undergraduate/Scholarship)* [5616]
Greater Baton Rouge Chapter - Don Jones Excellence in Safety Scholarships *(Undergraduate/Scholarship)* [1416]
Jones-Lovich Grants in Southwestern Herpetology *(Master's, Doctorate/Grant)* [4872]
Annabel Lambeth Jones Scholarships *(Undergraduate/Scholarship)* [4200]
Barbara Jordan Scholarships *(Undergraduate/Scholarship)* [9819]
Joseph H. Fichter Research Grants *(Other/Grant)* [2071]
E.J. Josey Scholarships *(Graduate/Scholarship, Award)* [2296]
Journey Toward Ordained Ministry Scholarships *(Undergraduate, Graduate/Scholarship)* [9854]
Journyx Scholarships *(Undergraduate, Graduate/Scholarship)* [5628]
Leslie W. Joyce and Paul W. Thayer Graduate Fellowship in I-O Psychology *(Doctorate/Fellowship)* [9153]
JSA/Jefferson Lab Graduate Fellowships *(Doctorate, Graduate/Fellowship)* [5566]
JSR Foundation Endowed School of Law Scholarships *(Undergraduate/Scholarship)* [7984]
George E. Judd Scholarships *(Undergraduate/Scholarship)* [9436]
Woodrow Judkins Endowed Scholarships *(Undergraduate/Scholarship)* [7985]
Martha Julian Memorial Scholarship *(Undergraduate/Scholarship)* [212]
Junior Firefighter Scholarships *(Undergraduate/Scholarship)* [7211]
George W. Juno Memorial Scholarships *(Undergraduate/Scholarship)* [4339]
JustNebulizers.com Respiratory Care Scholarships *(Undergraduate, Graduate/Scholarship)* [5637]
JustWalkers.com Mobility Scholarships *(Undergraduate, Graduate/Scholarship)* [5638]
JW Surety Bonds Scholarships *(Undergraduate, Graduate/Scholarship)* [5646]
Mike Kabo Global Scholarships *(Other/Scholarship)* [4456]
Annette Kade Fellowships *(Graduate/Scholarship)* [6431]
Daniel Kahikina and Millie Akaka Scholarships *(Graduate, Undergraduate/Scholarship)* [7910]
Kaiser Media Fellowships in Health Reporting *(Advanced Professional, Professional development/Fellowship)* [5648]
Kaiser Permanente Northern California Delivery Science Fellowships Program *(Postgraduate/Fellowship)* [5650]
Judge Edward Y. Kakita Memorial Scholarships *(Undergraduate/Scholarship)* [5542]
Sam Kalman Scholarship *(Undergraduate/Scholarship)* [1582]
Shripat Kamble Urban Entomology Graduate Student Awards for Innovative Research *(Doctorate/Recognition, Grant)* [3881]
Kamehameha Schools Class of 1968 "Ka Poli O Kaiona" Scholarships *(Graduate, Undergraduate/Scholarship)* [7912]
Kamehameha Schools Class of 1972 Scholarships *(Graduate, Undergraduate/Scholarship)* [7913]
Benjamin Kaminer Endowed Scholarships in Physiology *(Graduate, Master's, Doctorate/Scholarship)* [6249]
WLALA Fran Kandel Public Interest Grants *(Postgraduate/Grant)* [10646]
Kansas City Division Scholarships *(Undergraduate/Scholarship)* [6521]
Walter Kapala Scholarships *(Undergraduate/Scholarship)* [4759]
Kaplan Lawyers PC Legal Scholarships *(Graduate/Scholarship)* [5665]
Don Kaplan Legacy Scholarships *(Undergraduate/Scholarship)* [2454]
Kaplan Scholarships *(Graduate/Scholarship)* [4898]
Steve Kaplan TV and Film Studies Scholarships *(Other/Scholarship)* [1273]
Kappa Kappa Gamma Foundation Project 2000 Scholarships *(Undergraduate/Scholarship)* [5739]
Kappa Kappa Gamma Graduate Scholarships *(Graduate/Scholarship)* [5740]
Kappa Kappa Gamma Undergraduate Scholarships *(Undergraduate/Scholarship)* [5741]
Kappa Omicron Nu Leadership Undergraduate Scholarships *(Undergraduate/Scholarship)* [5781]
Kappa Omicron Nu National Alumni Fellowships *(Graduate/Fellowship)* [5782]
Kappa Project 2000 Scholarships *(Undergraduate/Scholarship)* [5742]
Kappa Sigma Scholarship/Leadership Awards *(Undergraduate/Scholarship)* [5792]
Kappa Zeta Scholarships *(Undergraduate/Scholarship)* [8930]
The ISASI Rudolf Kapustin Memorial Scholarships *(Undergraduate/Scholarship)* [5394]
Josephine de Karman Fellowships *(Graduate, Undergraduate/Fellowship)* [5796]
KASF Chair Scholarships *(Graduate, Undergraduate/Scholarship)* [5873]
KASF Designated Scholarships *(Graduate, Undergraduate/Scholarship)* [5874]
KASF General Scholarships *(Undergraduate, Graduate, Professional development/Scholarship)* [5875]
Ken Kashiwahara Scholarships *(Undergraduate/Scholarship)* [8399]
Magoichi and Shizuko Kato Memorial Scholarships *(Graduate, Master's, Doctorate/Scholarship)* [5552]
Lucile B. Kaufman Women's Scholarships *(Undergraduate/Scholarship)* [9184]
N.G. Kaul Memorial Scholarships *(Doctorate, Graduate/Scholarship)* [7403]
E. Wayne Kay Co-op Scholarships *(Undergraduate/Scholarship)* [9185]
E. Wayne Kay Community College Scholarships *(Undergraduate/Scholarship)* [9186]
E. Wayne Kay High School Scholarships *(Undergraduate/Scholarship)* [9187]
KCC Foundation Gold Key Scholarships *(Undergraduate/Scholarship)* [5807]
KCC Foundation Scholarships *(Undergraduate/Scholarship)* [5808]
KCC-JEE Graduate Fellowships *(Graduate/Fellowship)* [5855]
KCC Trustee Scholarships *(Undergraduate/Scholarship)* [5809]
KDP International Scholarship Program - President Scholarship *(Undergraduate, Graduate, Doctorate/Scholarship)* [5674]
KDP MBNA Scholarships *(Undergraduate, Graduate/Scholarship)* [5675]
Keepers Preservation Education Fund *(Undergraduate/Award)* [6202]
KEF Academic Scholarships *(Undergraduate, Graduate/Scholarship)* [5865]
KEF College/University Basic Scholarships *(Undergraduate/Scholarship)* [5866]
KEF Vocational Education Scholarship *(Undergraduate/Scholarship)* [5867]
Kegler Brown Diversity Scholarship *(Graduate/Scholarship)* [5804]
Annette and Ernest Keith Scholarships *(Undergraduate/Scholarship)* [8485]
Rita Mae Kelly Fund *(Graduate, Doctorate/Fellowship)* [1121]
Kelly Law Team Annual Down Syndrome Scholarships *(All/Scholarship)* [5811]
Robert E. Kelsey Annual Scholarship *(Undergraduate/Scholarship)* [7933]
Willmoore H. Kendall Scholarships *(Professional development/Scholarship)* [3062]
Alexander Kendrick Memorial Scholarships *(Graduate, Undergraduate/Scholarship)* [7773]
Southwest Ohio Environmental Horticulture Association (SOEHA) Lloyd W. Kennedy Scholarship *(Undergraduate/Scholarship)* [7584]
Oscar Kenshur Book Prize *(Other/Prize)* [1293]
Raymond A. Kent-Navy V-12/ROTC Scholarships *(Undergraduate/Scholarship)* [10145]
Kentucky Paralegal Association Student Scholarships *(Undergraduate/Scholarship)* [5819]
Kerrigan Scholarships *(Undergraduate/Scholarship)* [7986]
Ashley E. Ketcher Memorial Scholarships *(Undergraduate/Scholarship)* [3289]

Ketchum Excellence in Public Relations Research Award *(Graduate/Fellowship, Internship)* [5213]
Debbie Khalil Memorial Scholarships *(Graduate, Undergraduate/Scholarship)* [8076]
Graduate Fellowship Program - Mahboob Khan/Advanced Micro Devices Fellowships *(Doctorate, Graduate/Fellowship)* [8834]
KHIMA Graduate Scholarships *(Graduate/Scholarship)* [5661]
Michael Kidger Memorial Scholarships in Optical Design *(Undergraduate/Scholarship)* [9468]
The Michael Kiely Strong Roots Scholarships *(Undergraduate/Scholarship)* [8233]
Julia Kiene Fellowships in Electrical Energy *(Graduate/Fellowship)* [10660]
Kilbuck Family Native American Scholarships *(Undergraduate/Scholarship)* [2230]
Bernard Kilgore Memorial Scholarships *(Undergraduate/Scholarship)* [7327]
Killam Fellowships *(Undergraduate/Fellowship)* [4229]
Kimberly Elementary School PTA Scholarships *(Undergraduate/Scholarship)* [8486]
Kimmel Scholars Award *(Doctorate/Grant)* [5832]
Arthur M. and Berdena King Eagle Scout Scholarships *(Undergraduate/Scholarship)* [6927]
Kit C. King Graduate Scholarships *(Graduate/Scholarship)* [7109]
King Ice Scholarships *(Undergraduate, Graduate/Scholarship)* [5834]
Larry King/Jeffrey Fashion Cares Point Scholarship *(Undergraduate, Graduate, Doctorate/Scholarship)* [8180]
Martin Luther King Jr. Scholarships *(Undergraduate/Scholarship)* [5836]
Martin Luther King Law Scholarship *(Undergraduate/Scholarship)* [3680]
Steven G. King Play Environments Scholarships *(Undergraduate/Scholarship)* [5914]
Forest A. King Scholarship *(Undergraduate/Scholarship)* [3681]
Jessica King Scholarships *(Other/Scholarship)* [3490]
Don King Student Fellowships *(Undergraduate/Fellowship)* [5021]
Charles A. King Trust Postdoctoral Research Fellowships *(Postdoctorate/Fellowship)* [4817]
Kingsbury Elementary School PTA Scholarships *(Undergraduate/Scholarship)* [8487]
Southwest Chapter Roy Kinslow Scholarships *(Undergraduate/Scholarship)* [1417]
Treva C. Kintner Scholarships *(Undergraduate/Scholarship)* [8097]
Kiplinger Fellowship *(Professional development/Fellowship)* [7599]
Ruth L. Kirschstein NRSA Individual Pre-Doctoral Fellowships *(Doctorate/Fellowship)* [9926]
Kislak Fellowships in American Studies *(Graduate, Postdoctorate/Fellowship)* [5844]
Kislak Short Term Fellowships Opportunities in American Studies *(Undergraduate, Graduate/Fellowship)* [5845]
Tamo Kitaura Scholarships *(Other/Scholarship)* [9961]
AACT John Kitt Memorial Scholarships *(Undergraduate/Scholarship)* [477]
Kiwanis Club of Redlands Foundation Academic Excellence Scholarships *(Undergraduate/Scholarship)* [8488]
Klarman Family Foundation Grants Program in Eating Disorders Research *(Professional development/Grant)* [4818]
Louis T. Klauder Scholarships *(Undergraduate, Graduate/Scholarship)* [1166]
Jane M. Klausman Women in Business Scholarships *(Graduate, Undergraduate/Scholarship)* [10826]
The Margie Klein "Paper Plate" Scholarships *(Undergraduate/Scholarship)* [1850]
Gerda and Kurt Klein Scholarships *(Undergraduate/Scholarship)* [4962]
Dr. Eva Kleinpeter Scholarship *(Undergraduate/Scholarship)* [5676]
Klingenstein Fellowships in the Neurosciences *(Doctorate, Other/Fellowship)* [5838]
Arthur Klorfein Scholarship and Fellowship Fund *(Undergraduate, Graduate/Scholarship)* [6250]
Kluge Fellowships *(Doctorate, Graduate/Fellowship)* [5846]
American Marketing Association-Connecticut Chapter, Anna C. Klune Memorial Scholarships *(Graduate/Scholarship)* [4760]
Joseph H. Klupenger Scholarship Awards *(Undergraduate/Scholarship)* [7696]
AALL/Wolters Kluwer Law & Business Grants *(Professional development/Grant)* [532]
John A. Knauss Marine Policy Fellowship *(Graduate/Fellowship)* [9890]
John S. Knight Fellowships *(Other/Fellowship)* [5849]
Robert E. Knight Professional Scholarships *(Graduate/Scholarship)* [9692]
Elva Knight Research Grants *(Professional development/Grant)* [5356]
Knight-Wallace Fellowship *(Professional development/Fellowship)* [5851]
Knights of Vartan, Fresno Lodge No. 9 Scholarships *(Undergraduate/Scholarship)* [1701]
Knox-Hume Scholarships *(Undergraduate/Scholarship)* [3232]
Glenn Knudsvig Memorial Scholarships *(Graduate, Undergraduate/Scholarship)* [679]
Ina Knutsen Scholarships *(Undergraduate/Scholarship)* [8875]
Koch Scholars Program *(Undergraduate/Scholarship)* [10430]
Kodak Fellowships in Film Preservation *(Graduate/Fellowship)* [2025]
Herb Kohl Educational Foundation Excellence Scholarships *(Undergraduate/Scholarship)* [5857]
Herb Kohl Educational Foundation Initiative Scholarships *(Undergraduate/Scholarship)* [5858]
James P. Kohn Memorial Scholarships *(Graduate/Scholarship)* [1418]
DSRSD James B. Kohnen Scholarships *(Undergraduate, High School/Scholarship)* [3697]
P. Johnson and C. Kolb Memorial Scholarships *(Undergraduate, Graduate, Master's, Doctorate/Scholarship)* [8752]
Gwin J. and Ruth Kolb Research Travel Fellowships *(Doctorate, Other/Fellowship)* [1294]
Susan G. Komen for the Cure College Scholarship Awards *(Two Year College/Award, Scholarship)* [5861]
Susan G. Komen for the Cure Post-doctoral Fellowships - Clinical Research Grants *(Postdoctorate/Grant, Fellowship)* [5862]
KON/GEICO LeaderShape Undergraduate Scholarship *(Undergraduate/Scholarship)* [5789]
KON National Alumni Chapter Grant *(Professional development/Grant)* [5783]
KON New Initiatives Grant *(Professional development/Grant)* [5784]
Emily Day Koppell Memorial Adelphe Scholarship *(Undergraduate, Graduate/Scholarship)* [5743]
Elizabeth Munsterberg Koppitz Child Psychology Graduate Fellowships *(Graduate, Doctorate/Fellowship)* [1147]
Herman P. Kopplemann Scholarships *(Undergraduate/Scholarship)* [4761]
Kor Memorial Scholarships *(Undergraduate, Graduate/Scholarship)* [5842]
Korean Language Study Awards *(Graduate/Scholarship)* [5871]
Korean Studies Dissertation Workshop Funds *(Graduate/Fellowship)* [9056]
AIST Willy Korf Memorial Fund *(Undergraduate/Scholarship)* [2000]
Kosciuszko Foundation Graduate Study and Research in Poland Scholarships *(Graduate/Scholarship)* [5877]
Kosciuszko Foundation Tuition Scholarships *(Graduate/Scholarship)* [5878]
Kosciuszko Foundation Year Abroad Scholarships *(Graduate, Undergraduate/Scholarship)* [5879]
Marcia J. Koslov Scholarship *(Professional development/Scholarship)* [533]
Eugene and Elinor Kotur Scholarship Trust Fund *(Undergraduate, Graduate/Scholarship)* [10443]
Kovaluk Scholarship Fund *(Undergraduate/Scholarship)* [9984]
Marjorie Kovler Research Fellowships *(Professional development/Fellowship)* [5602]
ONLA Phil Kozel Memorial Scholarship *(Undergraduate/Scholarship)* [7585]
KPMG Foundation Minority Accounting Doctoral Scholarships *(Doctorate/Scholarship)* [5885]
KPMG Point Scholarship *(Undergraduate, Graduate, Doctorate/Scholarship)* [8181]
Eve Kraft Education and College Scholarships *(Undergraduate/Scholarship)* [9975]
William D. Krahling Excellence in Journalism Scholarships *(Undergraduate/Scholarship)* [361]
Norman Kramer Scholarship Awards *(Undergraduate/Scholarship)* [6499]
Melvin Kranzberg Dissertation Fellowships *(Doctorate/Fellowship)* [9143]
Michael Kraus Research Grants *(Doctorate/Grant)* [854]
Sharon Kreikemeier Memorial Scholarships *(Undergraduate/Scholarship)* [7242]
Kress/AAR Fellowships *(Professional development/Fellowship)* [1855]
Kress Conservation Fellowships *(Postgraduate/Fellowship)* [5889]
Kress Fellowships in Art History at Foreign Institutions *(Graduate/Fellowship)* [5890]
Samuel H. Kress Foundation Dissertation Fellowships *(Doctorate/Fellowship)* [9084]
Samuel H. Kress Grants for Research and Publication in Classical Art and Architecture *(Professional development/Grant)* [1609]
Mathilde Krim Fellowships in Basic Biomedical Research *(Doctorate/Fellowship)* [1536]
Krist-Reavley Minority Scholarships *(Undergraduate/Scholarship)* [7987]
David A. Kronick Travelling Fellowships *(Doctorate, Graduate/Fellowship)* [6387]
Eugene S. Kropf Scholarships *(Undergraduate/Scholarship)* [10105]
Kristin Bjurstrom Krueger Student Scholarship Program *(Undergraduate/Scholarship)* [6404]
Melvin Kruger Endowed Scholarship Program *(Undergraduate, Vocational/Occupational/Scholarship)* [7122]
Melvin Kruger Endowed Scholarships *(Graduate, Undergraduate/Scholarship)* [8644]
KTA Chapter Adviser Research Grant Award *(Professional development/Grant)* [5794]
George F. Kugler, Jr. Scholarships *(Undergraduate/Scholarship)* [2512]
Don Kuhn Memorial Scholarship Fund *(Graduate/Scholarship)* [6291]
Irene Corbally Kuhn Scholarships *(Graduate, Undergraduate/Scholarship)* [7774]
Kumin Scholars Program *(Undergraduate/Scholarship)* [8953]
Chris Kurzweil Scholarship *(Undergraduate/Scholarship)* [3329]
Sam and Florice Kuwahara Memorial Scholarship *(Undergraduate, Graduate/Scholarship)* [5553]
Henry and Chiyo Kuwahara Memorial Scholarships *(Undergraduate, Graduate/Scholarship)* [5554]
Julia Kwan Endowed Scholarships *(Graduate/Scholarship)* [7988]
Anne Emery Kyllo Professional Scholarships *(Professional development/Scholarship)* [1014]
L-3 Communications Avionics Systems Scholarships *(Undergraduate/Scholarship)* [166]
LA Tutors Innovation in Education Scholarships *(All/Scholarship)* [5896]
Gretchen Laatsch Scholarships *(Graduate/Scholarship)* [1926]
Ladah Law Firm, PLLC Injury Scholarships *(Undergraduate, Graduate/Scholarship)* [5898]
LAF Landscape Forms Design for People Scholarships *(Undergraduate/Scholarship)* [5915]
Jeffery P. LaFage Graduate Student Research Award *(Master's, Doctorate/Grant)* [3882]
Ken LaFountaine First Nations Scholarships *(Undergraduate/Scholarship)* [8876]
Ron LaFreniere Business Administration Scholarship *(Undergraduate/Scholarship)* [8877]
LAFS - Cal State University San Marcos General Scholarships *(Undergraduate/Scholarship)* [2212]
The Lagrant Foundation - Graduate Students Scholarships *(Graduate/Scholarship)* [5900]
The Lagrant Foundation - Undergraduate Students

Scholarships *(Undergraduate/Scholarship)* [5901]
Ray and Kathy LaHood Scholarships for the Study of American Government *(Undergraduate/Scholarship)* [3627]
Casey Laine Armed Forces Scholarships *(Undergraduate/Scholarship)* [3101]
Douglas Lake Improvement Association Scholarships *(Undergraduate/Scholarship)* [10184]
Lakselaget Foundation Scholarships *(Graduate, Undergraduate/Scholarship)* [5903]
Lalor Foundation Merit Awards *(Postdoctorate/Award)* [9307]
Lalor Foundation Post-Doctoral Fellowships *(Postdoctorate/Fellowship)* [5905]
Paul C. K. Lam Memorial Scholarship at The University of Akron *(Undergraduate/Scholarship)* [7593]
LAM Pilot Project Awards *(Master's, Postdoctorate/Grant)* [5907]
Lamar University College of Engineering Scholarships *(Undergraduate/Scholarship)* [6928]
Lambda Project 2000 Scholarship *(Undergraduate/Scholarship)* [5744]
Elaine Johnson Lampert Journalism Memorial Adelphe Scholarship *(Graduate/Award)* [5745]
Lance Surety College Scholarships *(Undergraduate, Graduate/Scholarship)* [5911]
Harold Lancour Scholarship for Foreign Study *(Professional development/Scholarship)* [2240]
Frank S. Land Scholarships *(Undergraduate/Scholarship)* [3598]
Robert S. Landauer, Sr. Memorial Fellowships *(Graduate/Fellowship)* [4810]
The Lanford Family Highway Worker Memorial Scholarship Program *(Undergraduate/Scholarship)* [1219]
Frank H. Lang Merit Scholarships *(Undergraduate/Scholarship)* [5922]
Lansdale Public Policy Fellowship *(Advanced Professional, Professional development/Fellowship)* [1245]
The Otis and Florence Lapham Memorial Scholarships *(Undergraduate/Scholarship)* [5508]
Lapides Fellowships in Pre-1865 Juvenile Literature and Ephemera *(Graduate, Postdoctorate/Fellowship)* [439]
Katherine Roberts LaPorte Memorial Adelphe Scholarship *(Undergraduate/Scholarship)* [5746]
Christian Larew Memorial Scholarships *(Graduate/Scholarship)* [6071]
Peter and Jody Larkin Legacy Scholarships *(Undergraduate/Scholarship)* [2455]
Arnold "Les" Larsen, FAIA, Memorial Scholarships *(Graduate/Scholarship)* [896]
Larson Aquatic Research Support Scholarships (LARS) *(Graduate/Scholarship)* [1490]
David B. Larson Fellowships in Health and Spirituality *(Doctorate/Fellowship)* [5847]
Las Vegas Chinatown Scholarships *(Undergraduate/Scholarship)* [8352]
Laser Technology, Engineering and Applications Scholarships *(Graduate, Undergraduate/Scholarship)* [9469]
Daniel Lasky Scholarship Fund *(Undergraduate/Scholarship)* [7081]
Jay and Deborah Last Fellowships *(Doctorate/Fellowship)* [440]
Latham Diversity Scholars *(Undergraduate/Scholarship)* [5935]
Latinos for Dental Careers Scholarships *(Undergraduate/Scholarship)* [2830]
Estée Lauder Point Scholarships *(Undergraduate, Graduate, Doctorate/Scholarship)* [8182]
Candia Baker Laughlin Certification Scholarships *(Undergraduate/Scholarship)* [389]
Robert J. Lavidge Nonprofit Marketing Research Scholarships *(Other/Scholarship)* [982]
Law Enforcement Memorial Scholarship Fund *(Undergraduate/Scholarship)* [4202]
Law Fellows Program *(Undergraduate/Fellowship)* [6710]
Law Foundation of Ontario Community Leadership in Justice Fellowships *(Other/Fellowship)* [5945]
Law and Society Association Article Prize *(Other/Prize)* [5972]

Law and Society Association Dissertation Prize *(Other/Prize)* [5973]
Law and Society Association Undergraduate Student Paper Prize *(Undergraduate/Prize)* [5975]
Willie D. Lawson, Jr. Memorial Scholarships *(Doctorate, Graduate, Other/Scholarship)* [6819]
Lawsuit Legal American Nursing Support Scholarships *(Undergraduate/Scholarship)* [5983]
Verne Lawyer Scholarship *(Undergraduate/Scholarship)* [3682]
Sue Kay Lay Memorial Scholarships *(Undergraduate/Scholarship)* [3102]
Lazarian Graduate Scholarships *(Graduate/Scholarship)* [1678]
LCRF Grants *(Advanced Professional, Professional development/Grant)* [6141]
LCSC Presidential Out-of-State Tuition Scholarships *(Undergraduate/Scholarship)* [6035]
LCSC Welding Club Scholarships *(Undergraduate/Scholarship)* [6036]
Betsy B. and Garold A. Leach Scholarships for Museum Studies *(Undergraduate/Scholarship)* [3589]
Leadership Conference Scholarship *(Other/Scholarship)* [6835]
Leadership Development Online Course Scholarships *(Professional development/Scholarship)* [7617]
LEAGUE Foundation Scholarships *(Undergraduate/Scholarship)* [8660]
League of Latin American Citizens General Electric Scholarships *(Undergraduate/Scholarship)* [5987]
Steven A. Leahy Law Office Marine Service/Law School Scholarships *(Postgraduate/Scholarship)* [5955]
Leakey Foundation Research Grants *(Doctorate, Advanced Professional/Grant)* [5992]
William C. Leary Memorial Emergency Services Scholarships *(Undergraduate/Scholarship)* [9822]
LeClairRyan Diversity Scholarships *(Undergraduate/Scholarship)* [6000]
Hwain Chang Lee scholarships *(Undergraduate/Scholarship)* [7386]
Albert J. and Mae Lee Memorial Scholarships *(Undergraduate/Scholarship)* [7989]
William K. Lee Scholarships *(Undergraduate/Scholarship)* [7387]
Lee Womack Scholarship Fund *(Undergraduate/Scholarship)* [6570]
The Leesfield/AAJ Law Student Scholarships *(Undergraduate/Scholarship)* [517]
Robert E. Leet and Clara Guthrie Patterson Trust Awards Program in Clinical Research *(Professional development/Grant)* [4819]
Judge William B. Leffler Scholarships *(Undergraduate/Scholarship)* [10167]
The Legacy Fellowships *(Doctorate/Fellowship)* [441]
Doreen Legg Memorial Scholarships *(Undergraduate/Scholarship)* [8490]
Jay C. and B. Nadine Leggett Charitable Scholarship Fund *(Undergraduate/Scholarship)* [9519]
Herbert Lehman Education Scholarships *(Undergraduate/Scholarship)* [6646]
PCH Architects/Steven J. Lehnhof Memorial Architectural Scholarships *(Undergraduate/Scholarship)* [8491]
Gilder Lehrman Short-Term Fellowships *(Graduate, Postdoctorate/Fellowship)* [6007]
Leiber and Stoller Music Scholarships *(Undergraduate/Scholarship)* [1274]
Colonel Theodore A. Leisen Memorial and Training Endowment Funds *(Graduate, Professional development/Grant, Scholarship)* [7249]
Lemelson Center Travel to Collections Awards *(Graduate, Professional development/Award)* [9026]
Lemelson Student Fellowships *(Graduate/Award)* [9282]
Stan Lencki Scholarships *(Undergraduate/Scholarship)* [6356]
Franklin A. Lenfesty Memorial Scholarship *(Undergraduate/Scholarship)* [7537]
John Lennon Scholarships *(Undergraduate/Scholarship)* [2319]

Craig Lensch Memorial Scholarships *(Undergraduate/Scholarship)* [2378]
V.A. Leonard Scholarships *(Graduate, Undergraduate/Scholarship)* [356]
Leopold Education Project Scholarships *(Undergraduate/Scholarship)* [3291]
Lerner-Scott Prize *(Doctorate/Prize)* [7717]
Irwin S. Lerner Student Scholarships *(Undergraduate/Scholarship)* [7168]
Brigid Leventhal Special Merit Award *(Postdoctorate, Professional development/Award)* [3379]
Myra Levick Scholarships *(Graduate/Scholarship)* [449]
Jack A. and Louise S. Levine Memorial Scholarships *(Undergraduate/Scholarship)* [8492]
Saul Levine Memorial Scholarships *(Graduate/Scholarship)* [1037]
Harry and Miriam Levinson Scholarship *(Graduate, Master's, Doctorate/Scholarship)* [1148]
Herbert Levy Memorial Scholarship *(Undergraduate/Scholarship)* [9255]
William J. Levy Point Scholarship *(Undergraduate, Graduate, Doctorate/Scholarship)* [8183]
Lewis-Clark Coin Club Endowed Scholarships *(Undergraduate/Scholarship)* [6037]
Lewis and Clark Fund for Exploration and Field Research *(Graduate, Postdoctorate/Grant)* [1082]
Lewis-Clark State College - Military Order of the Purple Heart Scholarships *(Undergraduate/Scholarship)* [6041]
Lewis-Clark State College Transfer Scholarships *(Undergraduate/Scholarship)* [6058]
Lloyd Lewis Fellowships in American History *(Postdoctorate/Fellowship)* [7413]
George T. Lewis, Jr. Academic Scholarship Fund *(Undergraduate/Scholarship)* [4203]
Frederick D. Lewis Jr. Scholarships *(Undergraduate/Scholarship)* [3683]
Ted Lewis Memorial Scholarship *(Undergraduate/Scholarship)* [213]
Flora Lewis Memorial Scholarships *(Graduate, Undergraduate/Scholarship)* [7775]
S. Evelyn Lewis Memorial Scholarships in Medical Health Sciences *(Graduate, Undergraduate/Scholarship)* [10818]
Jonathan D. Lewis Point Scholarships *(Graduate, Undergraduate/Scholarship)* [8184]
Lewis-Reynolds-Smith Founders Fellowship *(Graduate/Fellowship)* [4857]
Marvin Lewis Scholarships *(Undergraduate/Scholarship)* [6060]
Lewiston Service League Memorial Scholarships *(Undergraduate/Scholarship)* [6043]
Lexington Alumni Scholarships *(Undergraduate/Scholarship)* [6062]
Lexington Community Foundation Annual Scholarships *(Undergraduate/Scholarship)* [6063]
Lexington Community Foundation/CCC Scholarships *(Undergraduate/Scholarship)* [6064]
Ta Liang Memorial Awards *(Graduate/Grant, Award)* [1806]
Liberty Mutual Scholarships *(Undergraduate/Scholarship)* [1420]
Richard T. Liddicoat Scholarships *(Graduate/Scholarship)* [4340]
Dolores Zohrab Liebmann Fund - Graduate School Fellowships *(Graduate/Fellowship)* [6075]
Dolores Zohrab Liebmann Fund - Independent Research/Study Grants *(Graduate/Grant)* [6076]
Dolores Zohrab Liebmann Fund - Publication Grants *(Graduate/Grant)* [6077]
LIFE Lessons Scholarship Program *(Undergraduate/Scholarship)* [6079]
Life Sciences Research Foundation Postdoctoral Fellowship Program *(Postdoctorate/Fellowship)* [6081]
Frank R. Lillie Fellowships and Scholarships *(Undergraduate, Graduate/Scholarship)* [6251]
Lilly Endocrine Scholars Fellowship Awards *(Doctorate, Other/Fellowship)* [3865]
Lilly Scholarships in Religion for Journalists *(Other/Scholarship)* [8549]
Esther Lim Memorial Scholarships *(Undergraduate/Scholarship)* [2918]
Lim, Ruger & Kim Scholarships *(Undergraduate/Scholarship)* [6704]

AIST Ronald E. Lincoln Memorial Scholarships (Undergraduate/Scholarship) [2001]
John C. Lincoln Memorial Scholarships (Undergraduate/Scholarship) [1519]
Donald A.B. Lindberg Research Fellowships (Doctorate, Graduate/Fellowship) [6388]
Lindenwood University Scouting Scholarships (Undergraduate/Scholarship) [6929]
George N. Lindsay Civil Rights Legal Fellowships (Graduate/Fellowship) [5985]
Margaret B. Lindsey Award for Distinguished Research in Teacher Education (Other/Award, Recognition) [487]
Johnny Lineberry Memorial Scholarships (Undergraduate, Vocational/Occupational/Scholarship) [10588]
Link Foundation/Smithsonian Graduate Fellowships in Marine Science (Graduate/Fellowship) [9033]
Ronald B. Linsky Fellowships for Outstanding Water Research (Graduate, Master's, Doctorate/Fellowship) [7213]
Linsley Scholarship Fund (Undergraduate/Scholarship) [2913]
LionsDeal Scholarships (Undergraduate/Scholarship) [6095]
F. Maynard Lipe Scholarship Award (Master's, Postgraduate/Scholarship) [683]
Lawrence Lipking Fellowships at the Newberry Library (Graduate/Fellowship) [7414]
LITA/LSSI Minority Scholarships (Graduate/Scholarship) [6072]
LITA/OCLC Minority Scholarships (Graduate/Scholarship) [6073]
Litherland/FTEE Scholarships (Undergraduate/Scholarship) [5438]
Littleton-Griswold Research Grants (Doctorate/Grant) [855]
Ruth Liu Memorial Scholarships (Undergraduate/Scholarship) [2919]
LiveCareer Scholarships (Undergraduate/Scholarship) [6099]
Lawrence Livermore National Laboratory Fellowships (Doctorate/Fellowship) [9905]
Davis Levin Livingston Public Interest Law Scholarships (Postgraduate/Scholarship) [3531]
David C. Lizárraga Graduate Fellowships (Graduate/Fellowship) [9660]
LLN Student Scholarships (Undergraduate/Scholarship) [5939]
E.C. Lloyd and J.C.U. Johnson Scholarship Fund (Undergraduate/Scholarship) [3266]
Loan Forgiveness Scholarships (Graduate, Undergraduate/Loan, Scholarship) [9463]
Virgil K. Lobring Scholarship (Undergraduate/Scholarship) [3331]
Local 564 Scholarship Award (High School/Scholarship) [5454]
Local Internet Service Scholarships (Undergraduate/Scholarship) [6103]
Leon I. Lock and Barbara R. Lock Scholarship Fund (Undergraduate/Scholarship) [4246]
Miriam "Doc" Locke Memorial Adelphe Scholarships (Graduate/Scholarship) [5747]
Mary Elizabeth Lockwood Beneventi MBA Scholarship (Graduate/Scholarship) [7153]
Loewenstein-Wiener Fellowship Award (Professional development/Fellowship) [947]
Audrey Loftus Memorial Scholarships (Undergraduate/Scholarship) [10099]
Stephen Logan Memorial Scholarships (Undergraduate/Scholarship) [4330]
Abram D. and Maxine H. Londa Scholarships (Undergraduate/Scholarship) [7334]
Lone Star GIA Associate and Alumni Scholarships (Undergraduate/Scholarship) [4341]
Lawrence A. Long Memorial Law Scholarships (Undergraduate/Scholarship) [362]
James E. Long Memorial Post Doctoral Fellowships (Postdoctorate/Fellowship) [5311]
Long-term International Fellowships (Professional development/Fellowship) [3380]
Kay Longcope Scholarships (Graduate, Undergraduate/Scholarship) [7047]
Louise Loomis Memorial Adelphe Scholarships (Undergraduate/Scholarship) [5748]
Suzanne and Caleb Loring Research Fellowships (Professional development/Fellowship) [6329]
Barbara Lotze Scholarships for Future Teachers (Undergraduate/Scholarship) [562]
Lou Hochberg Awards - University Thesis/Dissertation Research Improvement and Implementation Grants (Graduate/Award, Grant) [7749]
CH2M - Willie T. Loud Scholarships (Undergraduate, Graduate/Scholarship) [6959]
Louisiana Agricultural Consultants Association Scholarships (Graduate, Undergraduate/Scholarship) [6112]
Louisville Institute Dissertation Fellowships (Doctorate/Fellowship) [6128]
Louisville Institute First Book Grants for Minority Scholars (Doctorate/Grant) [6129]
Louisville Institute Project Grant for Researchers (Doctorate/Grant) [6130]
Louisville Institute Sabbatical Grants for Researchers (Doctorate/Grant) [6131]
Louthian Law School Scholarships (Advanced Professional/Scholarship) [6133]
First Lieutenant Scott McClean Love Memorial Scholarship - Children of Soldiers (Undergraduate, Vocational/Occupational/Scholarship) [1714]
First Lieutenant Scott McClean Love Memorial Scholarship - Spouses of Soldiers (Undergraduate, Vocational/Occupational/Scholarship) [1715]
D.J. Lovell Scholarships (Graduate, Undergraduate/Scholarship) [9470]
Lowe Family First Summer Student Scholarships (Undergraduate/Scholarship) [10185]
Gertie S. Lowe Nursing Scholarship Awards (Undergraduate/Scholarship) [3267]
LPHA Scholarships (Graduate, Undergraduate/Scholarship) [6126]
LSU Eye Center Clinical Retina Fellowships (Undergraduate/Fellowship) [6126]
Henry Luce Foundation/ACLS Dissertation Fellowships in American Art (Graduate, Doctorate/Fellowship) [742]
Elsa Ludeke Graduate Scholarships (Graduate/Scholarship) [3590]
David F. Ludovici Scholarships (Undergraduate/Scholarship) [4091]
Lugonia Alumni/Harrison Lightfoot Scholarships (Undergraduate/Scholarship) [8493]
LULAC GM Scholarships (Graduate, High School, Undergraduate, Vocational/Occupational/Award) [5988]
LULAC National Scholarship Fund (LNSF) (Graduate, Undergraduate/Scholarship) [5989]
Audrey Lumsden-Kouvel Fellowships (Postdoctorate/Fellowship) [7415]
Juan and Esperanza Luna Scholarship (Undergraduate/Scholarship) [1583]
Lung Health Dissertation Grants (Graduate/Grant) [977]
Ann & Robert H. Lurie Children's Memorial Hospital Postgraduate Administrative Fellowships (Postgraduate/Fellowship) [6143]
Luso-American Education Foundation C-1 General Scholarships (Undergraduate/Scholarship) [6145]
Luso-American Fraternal Federation B-2 Scholarships (Postgraduate/Scholarship) [6149]
Luso-American Fraternal Federation B-3 Scholarships (Professional development/Scholarship) [6150]
Luso-American Fraternal Federation B-4 Scholarships (Professional development/Scholarship) [6151]
Lutheran Student Scholastic and Service Scholarships - College and University Students (Undergraduate/Scholarship) [2248]
Lymphatic Research Foundation Additional Support for NIH-funded F32 Postdoctoral Fellows Awards (Postdoctorate/Award) [4820]
Lymphatic Research Foundation Postdoctoral Fellowship Awards Program (Postdoctorate/Fellowship) [4821]
Boyd N. Lyon Scholarships (Doctorate, Graduate, Master's/Scholarship) [6162]
The C. Lyons Fellowship Program (Advanced Professional/Fellowship) [7050]
Verne LaMarr Lyons Memorial Scholarships (Graduate, Master's/Fellowship) [6790]
Carie and George Lyter Scholarship Fund (Undergraduate/Scholarship) [4247]
Margaret Smith Maase Scholarships (Undergraduate/Scholarship) [7388]
MABF Scholarships (Postgraduate/Scholarship) [6442]
John Mabry Forestry Scholarships (Undergraduate/Scholarship) [8423]
MAC Emeritus Scholarships for First-Time Meeting Attendees (Professional development/Scholarship) [6516]
Bill MacAloney Legacy Scholarships (Undergraduate/Scholarship) [2456]
MacArthur Fellows Program (Professional development/Fellowship) [6164]
Catharine Macaulay Prize (Graduate/Prize) [1295]
MACC Scholarships (Other/Scholarship) [6444]
Katie MacDonald Memorial Scholarships (Graduate, Undergraduate/Scholarship) [9865]
Warren Mack Scholarship (Undergraduate/Scholarship) [5622]
Robert Mack Scholarships (Graduate, Undergraduate/Scholarship) [6166]
Thermoset Division/James I. Mackenzie and James H. Cunningham Scholarships (Undergraduate, Graduate/Scholarship) [9264]
Mackey-Byars Scholarships for Communication Excellence (Undergraduate/Scholarship) [10237]
MACPA Scholarships (Undergraduate, Graduate/Scholarship) [6298]
Carol E. Macpherson Memorial Scholarship (Graduate, Undergraduate/Scholarship) [10203]
Andrew Macrina Scholarships (Graduate/Scholarship) [761]
Eileen C. Maddex Fellowships (Graduate/Fellowship) [5785]
Dorothy L. Maddy Workshop/Seminar Scholarship (All/Scholarship) [9489]
Lawrence Madeiros Scholarships (Undergraduate/Scholarship) [6992]
James Madison Foundation - Junior Fellowships (Advanced Professional/Fellowship) [6174]
James Madison Foundation - Senior Fellowships (Graduate/Fellowship) [6175]
James Madison Graduate Fellowships (Graduate/Fellowship) [6176]
Madson Graduate Scholarships (Graduate/Scholarship) [8899]
Gordon and Delores Madson Scholarship (Undergraduate/Scholarship) [3684]
MAES Founders Scholarships (Graduate, Undergraduate/Scholarship) [6178]
MAES General Scholarships (Graduate, Undergraduate/Scholarship) [6179]
MAES Graduate Scholarships (Graduate/Scholarship) [6180]
MAES Padrino/Madrina Scholarships (Graduate, Undergraduate/Scholarship) [6181]
MAES Pipeline Scholarships (Graduate, Undergraduate/Scholarship) [6182]
MAES Presidential Scholarships (Graduate, Undergraduate/Scholarship) [6183]
Keith Maffioli Scholarships (Undergraduate/Scholarship) [3292]
Dr. Edward May Magruder Medical Scholarships (Undergraduate/Scholarship) [677]
Sonia S. Maguire Outstanding Scholastic Achievement Awards (Graduate, Undergraduate/Scholarship) [9618]
Dan and Rachel Mahi Educational Scholarships (Graduate, Undergraduate/Scholarship) [7914]
Maiman Student Paper Competition (Graduate, Undergraduate/Award) [7674]
Maine Community College Scholarships (Undergraduate/Scholarship) [6222]
Maine Graphic Arts Association Scholarships (Undergraduate/Scholarship) [6215]
Maintenance Technical Reward and Career Scholarships (Undergraduate/Scholarship) [6836]
The Make It Move Scholarships (Undergraduate/Scholarship) [1594]
Make Us Proud Scholarships (Undergraduate/Scholarship) [4793]
Malayalee Engineers Association Scholarships (Undergraduate/Fellowship) [6225]
MALDEF Dream Act Student Activist Scholarships (Undergraduate, Graduate/Scholarship) [6446]

Maley/FTE Scholarships *(Graduate/Scholarship)* [5439]

Maley/FTEE Teacher Scholarships *(Professional development/Scholarship)* [5440]

Margaret Mallett Nursing Scholarship *(Undergraduate/Scholarship)* [8878]

NBCFAE Mamie W. Mallory National Scholarship Program *(Undergraduate/Scholarship)* [6813]

Ann M. Mallouk Scholarships *(Master's/Scholarship)* [7389]

Malmberg Scholarships *(Undergraduate/Scholarship)* [1471]

Joseph J. Malone Fellowships in Arab and Islamic Studies *(Professional development/Fellowship)* [6895]

Reba Malone Scholarships *(Undergraduate, Graduate/Scholarship)* [1167]

Sue A. Malone Scholarships *(Doctorate, Graduate, Professional development/Scholarship)* [5662]

David C. Maloney Scholarships *(Undergraduate/Scholarship)* [7079]

Optimist Club Of Redlands - Ralph Maloof Scholarships *(Undergraduate/Scholarship)* [8494]

Dr. Julianne Malveaux Scholarships *(Undergraduate/Scholarship)* [6762]

Malyon-Smith Scholarship Award *(Graduate/Scholarship)* [9285]

Lyle Mamer Fellowships *(Graduate/Fellowship, Award)* [10661]

MANAA Media Scholarships *(Graduate, Undergraduate/Scholarship)* [6382]

Manchester Scholarship Foundation - Adult Learners Scholarships *(Undergraduate/Scholarship)* [4763]

Mangasar M. Mangasarian Scholarship Fund *(Graduate/Scholarship)* [1702]

Manhattan Street Capital Annual National Scholarships *(Undergraduate, Graduate, Doctorate/Scholarship)* [6227]

Mann Law Firm Scholarships *(Advanced Professional/Scholarship)* [3529]

Raleigh Mann Scholarships *(Undergraduate/Scholarship)* [10238]

Mansfield Soccer Association Scholarships *(Undergraduate/Scholarship)* [6229]

Honorable Carol Los Mansmann Memorial Scholarships *(Graduate, Undergraduate/Scholarship)* [327]

Paul Mansur Scholarships *(Undergraduate/Scholarship)* [5345]

Mantle Cell Lymphoma Research Grants *(Advanced Professional/Grant)* [6160]

March of Dimes General Research Grants *(Professional development/Grant)* [6233]

March of Dimes Graduate Nursing Scholarships *(Graduate/Scholarship)* [6234]

Harold and Inge Marcus Scholarships *(Undergraduate/Scholarship)* [5191]

American Turkish Society Arif Mardin Music Fellowships *(Other/Fellowship)* [9811]

Margaret Mead Award *(Other/Award)* [9081]

The Margarian Scholarships *(Undergraduate, Graduate/Scholarship)* [6239]

Art Margosian Scholarship *(Undergraduate/Scholarship)* [5623]

Marine Biological Laboratory Pioneers Fund *(Undergraduate, Graduate/Scholarship)* [6252]

Marine Corps League National Scholarships *(Undergraduate/Scholarship)* [6269]

Marine Technology Society ROV Scholarships (MTS ROV) *(Undergraduate, Graduate/Scholarship)* [6272]

Shirley Stone Marinkovich Memorial Scholarships *(Undergraduate/Scholarship)* [5749]

Dr. Frank and Florence Marino Scholarships *(Undergraduate/Scholarship)* [4764]

Mariposa Elementary School PTA Scholarships *(Undergraduate/Scholarship)* [8495]

Marisol Scholarship *(Undergraduate/Scholarship)* [5750]

Howard T. Markey Memorial Scholarship *(Undergraduate/Scholarship)* [3985]

Markham-Colegrave International Scholarships *(Undergraduate/Scholarship)* [805]

Markley Family Scholarship Fund *(Undergraduate/Scholarship)* [9522]

Markley Scholarships *(Undergraduate/Scholarship)* [6724]

Kaia Lynn Markwalter Endowed Scholarships *(Undergraduate/Scholarship)* [6044]

Abby Marlatt Scholarship *(Undergraduate/Scholarship)* [10322]

Marliave Scholarship Fund *(Undergraduate/Scholarship, Grant)* [1948]

Abraham Lincoln Marovitz Public Interest Law Scholarships *(Undergraduate/Scholarship)* [2897]

George Perkins Marsh Prize *(Other/Prize)* [1313]

Marsh Risk Consulting Scholarships *(Undergraduate/Scholarship)* [1421]

Marsh Writing/Research Scholarship Awards *(Undergraduate, Graduate/Scholarship, Award)* [5677]

Marshall-Baruch Fellowships *(Doctorate/Fellowship)* [6295]

Marshall Memorial Fellowships *(Other/Fellowship)* [4399]

Ray and Gertrude Marshall Scholarships *(Undergraduate/Scholarship)* [762]

Ron Marshall Scholarships *(Undergraduate/Scholarship)* [1192]

Sarah Shinn Marshall Scholarships *(Undergraduate/Scholarship)* [3554]

Martha Weston Grant *(Advanced Professional/Grant)* [9097]

William B. Martin East Carolina University Scholarships *(Undergraduate/Scholarship)* [5678]

Susan B. Martin Memorial Scholarships *(Graduate/Scholarship)* [5038]

Edna L. Martin Scholarships *(Undergraduate/Scholarship)* [3237]

Martin Sisters Scholarships *(Undergraduate/Scholarship)* [3555]

Dottie Martin Teacher Scholarships *(Graduate, Undergraduate/Scholarship)* [7464]

John S. Martinez and Family Scholarship Fund *(Undergraduate/Scholarship)* [3200]

Eric Martinez Memorial Scholarships *(Graduate, Undergraduate/Scholarship)* [9866]

Anthony A. Martino Memorial Scholarships *(Undergraduate/Scholarship)* [4462]

Maryland Poison Center Clinical Toxicology Fellowships *(Doctorate, Graduate/Fellowship)* [6300]

Maryland Speech Language Hearing Association Graduate Scholarships *(Graduate/Scholarship)* [6302]

Mas Family Scholarships *(Graduate, Undergraduate/Scholarship)* [6304]

The Maschhoffs Pork Production Scholarships *(Undergraduate/Scholarship)* [7037]

MASNA Student Scholarships *(Undergraduate, Graduate/Scholarship)* [6241]

Margaret Edwards Mason Adelphe Scholarship *(Undergraduate, Graduate/Scholarship)* [5751]

Masonic-Range Science Scholarships *(Undergraduate/Scholarship)* [9298]

Massachusetts Bar Foundation Legal Intern Fellowship Program (LIFP) *(Undergraduate/Fellowship)* [6310]

Massachusetts General Hospital Clinical Translational Fellowships at Pfizer *(Advanced Professional/Fellowship)* [6318]

Massachusetts General Hospital/Harvard Medical School Internships *(Doctorate/Internship)* [6319]

S.O. Mast Founder's Scholarships *(Undergraduate, Graduate/Scholarship)* [6325]

Master Municipal Clerks Academy Scholarships *(Other/Scholarship)* [5351]

Master's Degree with a Major in Nursing Academic Scholarships *(Graduate/Scholarship)* [6657]

Ruth G. and Joseph D. Matarazzo Scholarship *(Graduate, Master's, Doctorate/Scholarship)* [1149]

Material Handling Education Foundation Scholarships *(Doctorate, Graduate, Undergraduate/Scholarship)* [6346]

Mathematics Mentoring Travel Grants for Women *(Doctorate/Scholarship)* [2099]

Katharine & Bryant Mather Scholarship *(Graduate/Scholarship)* [708]

AILA Virginia Mathews Memorial Scholarships *(Graduate/Scholarship)* [885]

Noel D. Matkin Awards *(Undergraduate/Award)* [3798]

Rene Matos Memorial Scholarships *(Undergraduate, Vocational/Occupational/Scholarship)* [6996]

The Renardo A. Matteucci Scholarship Fund *(Undergraduate/Scholarship)* [3206]

Greg Matthews Memorial Scholarships *(Undergraduate/Scholarship)* [7990]

Antonio Mattos Memorial Scholarships *(Undergraduate/Scholarship)* [6152]

Donald Mauer Scholarships *(Undergraduate/Scholarship)* [10239]

Elizabeth M. Mauro Reimbursement Awards *(Advanced Professional/Award)* [63]

Maxwell Graduate Scholarships in Medical Journalism *(Graduate/Scholarship)* [10240]

Juliann and Joe Maxwell Scholarships *(Undergraduate/Scholarship)* [3238]

Juliann King Maxwell Scholarships for Riverview High School *(Undergraduate, Vocational/Occupational/Scholarship)* [3239]

May-Cassioppi Scholarships *(Undergraduate/Scholarship)* [3293]

Howard Mayer Brown Fellowship *(Graduate/Fellowship)* [1021]

John E. Mayfield ABLE Scholarships *(Undergraduate/Scholarship)* [3240]

Clara Mayo Grants Program *(Graduate/Grant)* [9290]

Giuliano Mazzetti Scholarships *(Undergraduate/Scholarship)* [9188]

Charles "Chuck" McAdams Memorial Scholarships *(Graduate, Undergraduate/Scholarship)* [9644]

Walter Samuel McAfee Scholarships in Space Physics *(Undergraduate/Scholarship)* [7143]

McAllister Fellowships *(Professional development/Fellowship)* [1867]

MCBA Scholarship *(Undergraduate/Scholarship)* [6465]

McBurney General Scholarships *(Undergraduate/Scholarship)* [10323]

Rev. Richard S. McCarroll and Mrs. E. Allison McCarroll Scholarships *(Undergraduate, Graduate/Scholarship)* [7390]

Doreen McMullan McCarthy Memorial Academic Scholarship for Women with Bleeding Disorders *(Undergraduate/Scholarship)* [6993]

Bill McCarthy Scout Scholarship Fund *(Undergraduate/Scholarship)* [9523]

McCaughan Heritage Scholarships *(Undergraduate/Scholarship)* [1064]

McClatchy Minority Scholarship and Fellowship *(Undergraduate/Scholarship)* [9369]

McCleary Law Fellows Program *(Graduate, Undergraduate/Fellowship)* [4992]

McCloy Fellowships in Agriculture *(Professional development/Fellowship)* [727]

McCloy Fellowships in Environmental Policy *(Professional development/Fellowship)* [728]

McCloy Fellowships in Journalism *(Professional development/Fellowship)* [729]

McCloy Fellowships in Urban Affairs *(Professional development/Fellowship)* [730]

Anne O'Hare McCormick Scholarship Fund *(Graduate/Scholarship)* [7429]

Niqui McCown Honor and Memorial Scholarship Fund *(Undergraduate/Scholarship)* [10505]

McDaniel College Eagle Scout Scholarships *(Undergraduate/Scholarship)* [6930]

J. McDonald and Judy Williams School of Law Scholarships *(Undergraduate/Scholarship)* [7991]

Michele L. McDonald Scholarships *(Undergraduate/Scholarship)* [3801]

Bodie McDowell Scholarships *(Graduate, Undergraduate/Scholarship)* [7770]

MCEA Financial Assistance Award *(Undergraduate/Scholarship)* [6267]

Foster G. McGaw Graduate Student Scholarships *(Graduate/Scholarship)* [688]

Foster G. McGaw Scholarships *(Undergraduate, Graduate/Scholarship)* [2086]

Nancy B. Woolridge McGee Graduate Fellowships *(Graduate/Fellowship)* [10819]

Senator Patricia K. McGee Nursing Faculty Scholarships *(Doctorate, Graduate/Scholarship)* [7365]

Lucille E. McGee Scholarships *(Undergraduate/Scholarship)* [5509]
Thomas R. McGetchin Memorial Scholarship Awards *(Undergraduate/Scholarship)* [9997]
Richard McGrath Memorial Fund Awards *(Undergraduate/Award)* [755]
Linda and Vincent McGrath Scholarship *(Undergraduate/Scholarship)* [5679]
William P. McHugh Memorial Fund Award *(Doctorate, Graduate/Fellowship)* [1197]
Mary Bowles McInnis Adelphe Scholarship *(Undergraduate/Scholarship)* [5752]
McJulien Minority Graduate Scholarships *(Graduate/Scholarship)* [1944]
Molly McKay Scholarships *(Undergraduate/Scholarship)* [10241]
J.B. and Marilyn McKenzie Graduate Student Fellowships *(Graduate/Fellowship)* [10186]
AIST Midwest Member Chapter - Betty McKern Scholarships *(Undergraduate/Scholarship)* [2002]
John J. McKetta Undergraduate Scholarships *(Undergraduate/Scholarship)* [905]
Arthur Patch McKinlay Scholarships *(Graduate, Undergraduate/Scholarship)* [680]
McKinley Elementary School PTA Scholarships *(Undergraduate/Scholarship)* [8496]
John L. and Eleanore I. Mckinley Scholarships *(Undergraduate/Scholarship)* [3591]
Elizabeth McKissick Memorial Scholarships *(Undergraduate/Scholarship)* [6045]
H. H. McKnight Memorial Scholarships *(Undergraduate/Scholarship)* [10168]
C.A. "Pete" McKnight Scholarships *(Undergraduate/Scholarship)* [10242]
Paul R. McLaughlin Fellowship *(Undergraduate/Fellowship)* [8436]
McLean Scholarships *(Undergraduate/Scholarship)* [1978]
John McLendon Memorial Minority Postgraduate Scholarships *(Postdoctorate/Scholarship)* [6738]
Ruth McMillan Student Grants *(Undergraduate/Grant)* [2482]
Ronald E. McNair Scholarships in Space and Optical Physics *(Undergraduate/Scholarship)* [7144]
McNeely Stephenson of New Albany Community Involvement Scholarships *(Undergraduate/Scholarship)* [6372]
National Association of Pediatric Nurse Practitioners McNeil Annual Scholarships *(Undergraduate/Scholarship)* [6773]
National Association of Pediatric Nurse Practitioners McNeil Rural and Underserved Scholarships *(Graduate/Scholarship)* [6774]
Joan Reagin McNeill Scholarships - Alpha Theta *(Undergraduate/Scholarship)* [8931]
Joan Reagin McNeill Scholarships - Theta Phi *(Undergraduate/Scholarship)* [8932]
O. Ruth McQuown Scholarship - Graduate Award for Current Students *(Graduate/Scholarship)* [10135]
MCRTA Book Scholarships *(Undergraduate/Scholarship)* [6449]
MDA Development Grants *(Doctorate/Grant)* [6622]
MDA Research Grants *(Advanced Professional/Grant)* [6623]
MDF Post-Doctoral Fellowships *(Postdoctorate/Fellowship)* [6643]
MDI Biological Laboratory High school Student Summer Research Fellowships *(Undergraduate/Fellowship)* [6606]
David Meador Foundation - Club Management Student Scholarships *(Undergraduate/Scholarship)* [7295]
Ben Meadows Natural Resource Scholarships - Academic Achievement Scholarships *(Undergraduate/Scholarship)* [2221]
Ben Meadows Natural Resource Scholarships - Leadership Scholarships *(Undergraduate/Scholarship)* [2222]
Med Technology and Clinical Lab Science Scholarships *(Undergraduate/Scholarship)* [104]
Medford Rogue Rotary Scholarship *(Undergraduate/Scholarship)* [6380]
Medical Library Association Scholarships for Minority Students *(Graduate/Scholarship)* [6389]
Medical Student Rotation for Underrepresented Populations *(Graduate/Grant)* [3381]
Medicus Student Exchange Scholarships *(Graduate, Undergraduate/Scholarship)* [9619]
Medieval Academy Dissertation Grants *(Graduate/Grant)* [6396]
Rixio Medina and Associates Hispanics in Safety Scholarships *(Graduate, Undergraduate/Scholarship)* [1422]
Medina County Retired Teachers Association Scholarship *(Undergraduate/Scholarship)* [6400]
Edward Heywood Megson Scholarships *(Undergraduate/Scholarship)* [10243]
Karl Mehlmann Scholarships *(Undergraduate/Scholarship)* [3138]
Kumar Mehta Scholarship *(Graduate/Scholarship)* [709]
Susan R. Meisinger Fellowship for Graduate Study in HR *(Graduate, Master's, Advanced Professional/Fellowship)* [9146]
Dr. Roger E. Meisner Veterinary Medicine Educational Scholarship Fund *(Undergraduate/Scholarship)* [7501]
Carl J. Mejel Scholarship *(Undergraduate/Scholarship)* [794]
Philip H. Melanson Memorial Scholarships *(Undergraduate, Graduate/Scholarship)* [10154]
Frederic G. Melcher Scholarships *(Graduate/Scholarship)* [2018]
Mellon/ACLS Dissertation Completion Fellowships *(Graduate, Doctorate/Fellowship)* [743]
Mellon-CES Dissertation Completion Fellowships *(Graduate/Fellowship)* [3440]
Mellon Fellowships for Dissertation Research in the Humanities *(Doctorate, Graduate/Fellowship, Scholarship)* [3450]
Mellon Fellowships for Dissertation Research in Original Sources *(Doctorate/Fellowship)* [3451]
MHS Andrew W. Mellon Fellowships *(Professional development/Fellowship)* [6330]
Mellon Fellowships in Urban Landscape Studies *(Graduate, Master's, Doctorate/Fellowship)* [3739]
Andrew W. Mellon Foundation Fellowships *(Graduate/Fellowship)* [7740]
Institute Andrew W. Mellon Postdoctoral Research Fellowships *(Doctorate/Fellowship)* [7614]
Terry Mellor Continuing Education Grant *(Undergraduate/Grant)* [9480]
MELNA Scholarship *(Undergraduate, Graduate/Scholarship)* [6217]
E.V. and Nancy Melosi Travel Grants *(Graduate, Other/Grant)* [1314]
The Tatiana Mendez Future Resources Scholarships *(Undergraduate/Scholarship)* [8234]
Joseph C. Menezes Scholarship *(Undergraduate/Scholarship)* [6189]
Mensa Education and Research Foundation U.S. Scholarships *(Undergraduate/Scholarship)* [6424]
Mentored Clinical Scientist Development Awards *(Doctorate/Award)* [9915]
Mentored Research Scholar Grant in Applied and Clinical Research *(Doctorate, Professional development/Grant)* [646]
Benchwarmers of Redlands-Jess Mercado Football Scholarships *(Undergraduate/Scholarship)* [8497]
Erickson Merkel Foundation Scholarships *(Undergraduate/Scholarship)* [3925]
John Merrick Law Scholarships *(Undergraduate/Scholarship)* [7992]
MESA Student Travel Fund *(Undergraduate/Grant)* [6511]
Scott Mesh Honorary Grant for Research in Psychology *(Graduate/Grant)* [1134]
Christopher Mesi Memorial Music Scholarships *(Undergraduate/Scholarship)* [2803]
Mesothelioma Memorial Scholarships *(Undergraduate, Vocational/Occupational/Scholarship)* [9594]
Nicholas Metropolis Award for Outstanding Doctoral Thesis Work in Computational Physics *(Doctorate/Award)* [1091]
Metropolitan Museum of Art Bothmer Fellowship *(Doctorate/Fellowship)* [6432]
Metropolitan Museum of Art Conservation and Scientific Research Fellowships *(Graduate/Fellowship)* [6433]
Metropolitan Museum of Art Research Scholarship in Photograph Conservation *(Graduate/Scholarship)* [6434]
Mexican American Alumni Association Scholarships *(Graduate, Undergraduate/Scholarship)* [10356]
Mexican American Legal Defense and Educational Fund Law School Scholarships *(Undergraduate/Scholarship)* [6447]
Theodore Meyer Scholarships *(Undergraduate, Graduate/Scholarship)* [1015]
MFJC International Fellowships in Jewish Studies *(Other/Fellowship)* [6414]
MGH Department of Psychiatry Behavioral Neurology and Neuropsychiatry Fellowships *(Advanced Professional, Professional development/Fellowship)* [6320]
MGH Department of Psychiatry Eating Disorders Summer Research Fellowships *(Advanced Professional, Professional development/Fellowship)* [6321]
MGH Department of Psychiatry Forensic Psychiatry Fellowships *(Professional development/Fellowship)* [6322]
MGH Department of Psychiatry Global Psychiatric Clinical Research Training Program *(Advanced Professional/Fellowship)* [6323]
MHS African American Studies Fellowships *(Professional development/Fellowship)* [6331]
MHS/Cushing Academy Fellowships on Environmental History *(Professional development/Fellowship)* [6332]
MHS Long-Term Research Fellowships *(Professional development/Fellowship)* [6333]
MHS/Massachusetts Society of the Cincinnati Fellowships *(Professional development/Fellowship)* [6334]
MICA Scholarships *(Undergraduate/Scholarship)* [6532]
Michigan Accountancy Foundation Final Year Accounting Scholarship *(Graduate/Scholarship)* [6457]
Michigan Council of Women in Technology High School Scholarship Program *(Undergraduate/Scholarship)* [6467]
Michigan Education Association Scholarships *(Undergraduate/Scholarship)* [6470]
Michigan League for Nursing Scholarships *(Undergraduate/Scholarship)* [6472]
Michigan Realtors Scholarship Trust *(Graduate, Undergraduate/Scholarship)* [6461]
Michigan Society of Fellows Three-Year Fellowships *(Postdoctorate/Fellowship)* [6481]
Michigan Stormwater-Floodplain Association Scholarships *(Graduate, Undergraduate/Scholarship)* [6492]
Michigan Sugar Company Hotel Restaurant/Resort Management Scholarships *(Undergraduate/Scholarship)* [6495]
Michigan Sugar Queen Scholarships *(Undergraduate/Scholarship)* [6496]
John G. and Betty J. Mick Scholarship Fund *(Undergraduate/Scholarship)* [9526]
Microsoft Research Graduate Women's Scholarships *(Graduate/Scholarship)* [6506]
Microsoft Research PhD Fellowships *(Doctorate/Fellowship)* [6507]
Mid-Continent Instrument Scholarships *(Undergraduate/Scholarship)* [167]
Beth Middleton Memorial Scholarships *(Undergraduate/Scholarship)* [3961]
Midlothian Rotary Club "Service Above Self" Scholarship *(Undergraduate/Scholarship)* [6513]
Ella and Harold Midtbo Scholarships *(Undergraduate/Scholarship)* [7391]
Midwest Modern Language Association Fellowships *(Doctorate, Postdoctorate/Fellowship)* [7416]
Albert and Eloise Midyette Memorial Scholarship Fund *(Undergraduate/Scholarship)* [4204]
Migrant Health Scholarships *(Other/Scholarship)* [6846]
Mihaly Russin Scholarship Awards *(Graduate/Scholarship)* [8656]
Mikimoto Scholarships *(Graduate/Scholarship)* [4342]
Mary Ann Mikulic Scholarships *(Other/Scholarship)* [2052]

Milan Getting Scholarships *(Undergraduate/Scholarship)* [9335]
Milbank Diversity Scholars Program *(Undergraduate/Scholarship)* [6530]
Mildred Colodny Diversity Scholarships for Graduate Study in Historic Preservation *(Graduate/Scholarship)* [7202]
Eunice Miles Scholarships *(Undergraduate/Scholarship)* [4343]
William F. Miles Scholarships *(Undergraduate/Scholarship)* [4702]
Military Service Scholarships *(Graduate, Undergraduate/Scholarship)* [8900]
Cheryl Allyn Miller Award *(Doctorate, Graduate/Monetary)* [9332]
Miller Electric International WorldSkills Competition Scholarships *(Undergraduate/Scholarship)* [1520]
Warren E. Miller Fellowship in Electoral Politics *(Advanced Professional, Graduate, Postdoctorate/Fellowship)* [1122]
Ruth R. and Alyson R. Miller Fellowships *(Professional development/Fellowship)* [6335]
Robbie Miller Memorial Scholarships *(Undergraduate/Scholarship)* [6046]
Raymond W. Miller, PE and Alice E. Miller Scholarships *(Undergraduate/Scholarship)* [4092]
Raymond W. Miller, PE Scholarships *(Undergraduate/Scholarship)* [4093]
MillerCoors Engineering and Sciences Scholarships *(Undergraduate/Scholarship)* [68]
MillerCoors National Scholarships *(Undergraduate/Scholarship)* [69]
Dolphus E. Milligan Graduate Fellowships *(Graduate/Fellowship)* [7087]
Carolina Panthers Players Sam Mills Memorial Scholarship Fund *(Undergraduate/Scholarship)* [4205]
Carolina Panthers Players Sam Mills Memorial Scholarships *(Graduate/Scholarship)* [4206]
Quincy Sharpe Mills Memorial Scholarships *(Undergraduate/Scholarship)* [10244]
George Hi'ilani Mills Perpetual Fellowships *(Graduate/Fellowship)* [7915]
J. Clawson Mills Scholarships *(Doctorate/Scholarship)* [6435]
Abby and Howard Milstein Innovation Award in Reproductive Medicine *(Advanced Professional, Professional development/Award, Grant)* [5618]
Abby and Howard Milstein Reproductive Medicine Research Award *(Advanced Professional, Professional development/Award, Grant)* [5619]
Milton Postgraduate Fellowships *(Postgraduate/Fellowship)* [5080]
Mineral & Metallurgical Processing Division Scholarships and Richard Klimpel Memorial Scholarships *(Undergraduate, Graduate/Scholarship)* [9211]
Mary Minglen Scholarship Program *(Postgraduate/Scholarship)* [1047]
Minnesota Association County Probation Officers Scholarships *(Undergraduate/Scholarship)* [6541]
Minnesota Association of Township Scholarships *(Undergraduate, Vocational/Occupational/Scholarship)* [6545]
Minnesota Division Scholarships *(Undergraduate/Scholarship)* [6522]
Minnesota GLBT Educational Fund *(Undergraduate/Scholarship)* [8661]
Minnesota State Archery Association Scholarships Program *(Undergraduate/Scholarship)* [6551]
Jacque I. Minnotte Health Reporting Fellowships *(Other/Fellowship)* [8406]
Minority-Serving Institution Faculty Scholar Awards *(Doctorate/Award)* [474]
Minority Visiting Students Awards *(Undergraduate, Graduate/Award, Internship)* [9011]
Minton-Spidell Point Scholarship *(Undergraduate, Graduate, Doctorate/Scholarship)* [8185]
Christine Mirzayan Science and Technology Policy Graduate Fellowships *(Graduate/Fellowship)* [6679]
Molly Ann Mishler Memorial Scholarships *(Undergraduate/Scholarship)* [10030]
Miss America Community Service Scholarship *(Undergraduate/Scholarship)* [6557]
Miss America Quality of Life Awards *(Undergraduate/Scholarship)* [6558]

Joseph and Catherine Missigman Memorial Nursing Scholarships *(Undergraduate/Scholarship)* [4051]
Missigman Scholarship Fund *(Undergraduate/Scholarship)* [4052]
Joshua Esch Mitchell Aviation Scholarships *(Undergraduate/Scholarship)* [4611]
George J. Mitchell Postgraduate Scholarships *(Postgraduate/Scholarship)* [6749]
Dorothy Mitchell Scholarships *(Undergraduate/Scholarship)* [8498]
George J. Mitchell Scholarships *(Postgraduate/Scholarship)* [10349]
Sam Mizrahi Memorial Scholarships *(Undergraduate/Scholarship)* [4248]
MJSA Education Foundation Scholarship Fund *(Undergraduate/Scholarship)* [6231]
MLA Continuing Education Awards (CE) *(Graduate/Grant)* [6390]
MLA Financial Assistance *(Graduate, Advanced Professional/Grant)* [6567]
MLA/NLM Spectrum Scholarship Program *(Undergraduate/Scholarship)* [6391]
MLA Research, Development, and Demonstration Project Grants *(Graduate/Grant)* [6392]
MMJGA Scholarships *(Undergraduate/Scholarship)* [6549]
MMRF Research Fellow Awards *(Postdoctorate, Professional development/Grant)* [6612]
MMUF Dissertation Grants *(Graduate/Grant)* [10679]
MMUF Travel and Research Grants *(Graduate/Grant)* [10680]
MNLA Academic Scholarships *(Undergraduate/Scholarship)* [6474]
MOAA American Patriot Scholarships *(Undergraduate/Scholarship)* [6534]
Ralph Modjeski Scholarships *(Graduate, Undergraduate/Scholarship)* [8198]
MODNA Nursing Education Scholarships *(Doctorate, Graduate/Fellowship)* [6509]
Francis H. Moffitt Memorial Scholarships *(Graduate, Undergraduate/Scholarship)* [1807]
Molecular Evolution Fellowships *(Doctorate/Fellowship)* [9012]
Antoinette M. Molinari Memorial Scholarships *(Doctorate/Scholarship)* [417]
Momeni Foundation Scholastic Achievement Scholarships *(Undergraduate/Scholarship)* [7021]
Monaghan/Trudell Fellowships for Aerosol Technique Development *(Professional development/Fellowship)* [1212]
Nell I. Mondy Fellowships *(Graduate, Doctorate/Fellowship)* [8905]
Mongan Commonwealth Fund Fellowship in Minority Health Policy *(Other/Fellowship)* [3161]
Monsanto Commitment To Agriculture Scholarships *(Undergraduate/Scholarship)* [6574]
Montana Broadcasters Association Broadcast Engineering Scholarships *(Undergraduate/Scholarship)* [6578]
Pearl Moore Career Development Awards *(Professional development/Grant)* [7618]
Letitia Moore Charitable Trust Scholarship *(Undergraduate/Scholarship)* [10739]
Moore Middle School PTA Scholarships *(Undergraduate/Scholarship)* [8499]
Annabelle Moore Scholarship *(Undergraduate/Scholarship)* [2408]
Farmers Union Industries Foundation Stanley Moore Scholarships *(Undergraduate/Scholarship)* [7488]
NFU Foundation Stanley Moore Scholarships *(Undergraduate/Scholarship)* [7489]
Willie Hobbs Moore Scholarships *(Undergraduate/Scholarship)* [7145]
Dan Mordecai Educational Scholarships *(Graduate, Undergraduate/Scholarship)* [7265]
Robert E. and Judy More Scholarship Fund *(Undergraduate/Scholarship)* [4053]
Jake S. More Scholarship *(Undergraduate/Scholarship)* [3685]
Thomas More Scholarships *(Undergraduate/Scholarship)* [4487]
Thomas S. Morgan Memorial Scholarship *(Graduate, Master's/Scholarship)* [8044]
Sonia Morgan Scholarships *(Undergraduate/Scholarship)* [7335]

Morgan Stanley Pediatrics Fellowships *(Doctorate, Postdoctorate, Postgraduate, Graduate/Fellowship)* [618]
Morgan Stanley Tribal Scholars Program *(Undergraduate/Scholarship)* [870]
Robert L. Morlan Redlands Area Interfaith Council Scholarships *(Undergraduate/Scholarship)* [8500]
Leo F. Moro Baseball Memorial Scholarships *(Undergraduate/Scholarship)* [4249]
Frank Morrell Endowed Memorial Scholarships *(Graduate, Master's, Doctorate/Scholarship)* [6254]
June Morrison Scholarship Fund *(Undergraduate/Scholarship)* [10538]
Harry L. Morrison Scholarships *(Undergraduate/Scholarship)* [7146]
Dorothy Morrison Undergraduate Scholarships *(Undergraduate/Scholarship)* [1260]
Mortar Board National Foundation Fellowships *(Postdoctorate/Fellowship)* [6600]
Morton Cure Paralysis Fund Research Grants *(Professional development, Postdoctorate/Grant)* [6602]
William Howard Morton Scholarships *(Undergraduate, Graduate/Scholarship)* [7392]
Dwight Mosley Scholarships *(Undergraduate/Scholarship)* [9976]
Motorola Solutions Point Scholarship *(Undergraduate, Graduate, Doctorate/Scholarship)* [8186]
John R. Mott Scholarships *(Undergraduate/Scholarship)* [6604]
Mt. Hood Chapter Scholarship Awards *(Undergraduate/Scholarship)* [7697]
Mountain Memorial Funds *(Graduate, Master's, Doctorate/Award)* [6255]
Dorothy Mountain Memorial Scholarships *(Graduate/Scholarship)* [6135]
Burton J. Moyer Memorial Fellowships *(Fellowship)* [4811]
MPAC-DC Graduate Policy Fellowships *(Graduate/Fellowship)* [6630]
MPI CRV Scholarships *(Other/Scholarship)* [6402]
MPI-WI Founders Grant Program *(Professional development/Grant)* [6405]
MSEA/SEIU Part-time Student Members Scholarships *(Undergraduate/Scholarship)* [6223]
MSGC Undergraduate-Under-Represented Minority Fellowship Program *(Undergraduate/Fellowship)* [6485]
The MTS Student Scholarship for Graduate Students *(Graduate/Scholarship)* [6273]
The MTS Student Scholarship for Graduating High School Seniors *(Undergraduate/Scholarship)* [6274]
The MTS Student Scholarship for Two-Year, Technical, Engineering and Community College Students *(Undergraduate/Scholarship)* [6275]
Mu Alpha Theta Summer Grants *(Undergraduate, Graduate/Grant)* [6610]
Muddy Waters Scholarships *(Undergraduate/Scholarship)* [2316]
Mueller Undergraduate Scholarships *(Undergraduate/Scholarship)* [10618]
Multi-Country Research Fellowships *(Doctorate/Fellowship)* [3431]
Multicultural Work-in-Progress Grant *(Advanced Professional/Grant)* [9098]
Muncy Rotary Club Scholarship Fund *(Undergraduate/Scholarship)* [4054]
Muncy Scholars Award Fund *(Undergraduate/Scholarship)* [4055]
Marvin Mundel Memorial Scholarships *(Undergraduate/Scholarship)* [5192]
Rick Munoz Memorial Scholarships *(Undergraduate/Scholarship)* [8502]
Kiwanis Club of Redlands Foundation - Martin and Dorothy Munz Scholarships *(Undergraduate/Scholarship)* [8503]
Jack K. and Gertrude Murphy Fellowships *(Graduate/Fellowship)* [8748]
Linda J. Murphy Scholarships *(Undergraduate/Scholarship)* [10644]
NACCED Annual John C. Murphy Scholarships *(Graduate, Undergraduate/Scholarship)* [6742]
Muscle Shoals Kiwanis/Wal-Mart Scholarship *(Un-*

dergraduate/Scholarship) [7538]
Mutual of Omaha Finance Careers Scholarships (Undergraduate, Graduate/Scholarship) [105]
Mutual of Omaha Sales and Marketing Student Scholarships (Undergraduate, Graduate/Scholarship) [106]
MWH Scholarships (Master's/Scholarship) [1491]
My Life As A Lawyer Scholarships (Graduate, Undergraduate/Scholarship) [3425]
MyApartmentMap Housing Scholarships (Undergraduate/Scholarship) [6634]
Sam A. Myar Jr. Law Scholarship (Undergraduate/Scholarship) [10170]
Myasthenia Gravis Foundation of America Nursing Research Fellowships (Undergraduate/Fellowship) [6636]
Myasthenia Gravis Foundation of America Student Research Fellowships (Graduate, Undergraduate/Fellowship) [6637]
Mary Fran Myers Scholarships (Professional development, Undergraduate/Scholarship) [10129]
NAAE Upper Division Scholarships (Undergraduate/Scholarship) [6712]
NAAMA Scholarships (Undergraduate/Scholarship) [6701]
NABA National Scholarship Program (Graduate, Undergraduate/Scholarship) [6716]
NACA Foundation Graduate Scholarships (Graduate, Master's, Postdoctorate/Scholarship) [6725]
NACA Multicultural Professional Development Grant (Undergraduate, Graduate, Professional development/Grant) [6729]
NACA Northern Plains Regional Student Leadership Scholarships (Undergraduate/Scholarship) [6730]
NACA South Student Leadership Scholarships (Undergraduate/Scholarship) [6731]
NACADA Scholarships (Graduate/Scholarship) [6673]
NACDS Foundation Merit-Based Scholarships (All/Scholarship) [6736]
James B. Nachman ASCO Junior Faculty Award in Pediatric Oncology (Doctorate, Professional development/Grant) [3382]
NAED/Spencer Dissertation Fellowship Program (Graduate, Doctorate/Fellowship) [6681]
NAFA Corporate Aviation Business Scholarship (Undergraduate, Graduate/Scholarship) [6692]
NAFA International Dissertation Research Fellowships (Graduate, Doctorate/Fellowship) [6750]
NAFA Scholarship Programs (Undergraduate/Scholarship) [6690]
NAGAP Graduate Student Enrollment Management Research Grants (Graduate/Grant) [6752]
Jack Nagasaka Memorial Scholarships (Undergraduate/Scholarship) [8504]
IADR Toshio Nakao Fellowship (Other/Fellowship) [5252]
NANBPWC National Scholarships (Undergraduate/Scholarship) [6764]
Robyn Nance Memorial Scholarships (Undergraduate/Scholarship) [8505]
NAPABA Law Foundation Scholarships (Undergraduate/Scholarship) [6705]
NAPC FORUM Scholarships (Undergraduate/Scholarship) [6694]
NAPRHSW Scholarships (Undergraduate, Graduate/Scholarship) [6776]
NARAL Pro-Choice America Development Internships (Undergraduate, Graduate, Professional development/Internship) [6659]
NARAL Pro-Choice America Policy Internships (Professional development/Internship) [6660]
NARAL Pro-Choice America Political Internships (Undergraduate, Graduate, Professional development/Internship) [6661]
NARFE-FEEA Scholarship Awards Program (Undergraduate/Scholarship) [6686]
NASA RISGC Graduate Fellowships (Master's, Postdoctorate, Graduate/Fellowship) [8613]
NASA WVSGC Undergraduate Research Fellowship (Undergraduate/Fellowship) [10527]
NASCOE Scholarships (Undergraduate/Scholarship) [6744]
NASE Future Entrepreneur (Undergraduate/Scholarship) [6784]
Kermit B. Nash Academic Scholarships (Undergraduate/Scholarship) [8891]
Elizabeth Nash Foundation Scholarships (Undergraduate, Graduate/Scholarship) [6663]
Archie Hartwell Nash Memorial Scholarships (Graduate, Undergraduate/Scholarship) [3245]
NASLR Mined Land Reclamation Educational Grant (Undergraduate/Scholarship, Grant) [6792]
NASP-ERT Minority Scholarships for Graduate Training in School Psychology (Graduate/Scholarship) [6780]
National AAHAM Scholarships (Undergraduate/Scholarship) [504]
National American Arab Nurses Association Scholarships (Undergraduate, Master's/Scholarship) [6699]
National Association of Abandoned Mine Land Programs Scholarships (Undergraduate/Scholarship) [6708]
National Association for Armenian Studies and Research Scholarships (Graduate, Postgraduate/Scholarship) [1703]
National Association of Biology Teachers BioClub Student Awards (Undergraduate/Scholarship) [6714]
National Association of Campus Activities Scholarships for Student Leaders (Undergraduate/Scholarship) [6732]
National Association for the Self-Employed Scholarships (Professional development/Scholarship) [6785]
National Association of Women in Construction Construction Trades Scholarships (Undergraduate/Scholarship) [6800]
National Association of Women in Construction Founders Undergraduate Scholarships (Undergraduate/Scholarship) [6801]
National Ataxia Foundation Research Fellowships (Other/Fellowship) [6806]
National Ataxia Foundation Research Grants (Other/Grant) [6807]
National Beta Club Scholarships (Undergraduate/Scholarship) [6809]
National Biosafety and Biocontainment Training Program Fellowships (Graduate, Postgraduate/Fellowship) [6811]
National Black Deaf Advocate Scholarships (Graduate, Undergraduate/Scholarship) [6816]
National Black Nurses Association Scholarships (Undergraduate/Scholarship) [6823]
National Board Technical Scholarships (Undergraduate/Scholarship) [6827]
National Center for Health Statistics Postdoctoral Research Awards (Postdoctorate/Fellowship) [9920]
National Collegiate Athletic Association Postgraduate Scholarships (Postgraduate/Scholarship) [6863]
National Community Pharmacists Association Summer Internship Programs (Undergraduate/Internship) [6868]
National Costumers Association Scholarships (Undergraduate/Scholarship) [6877]
National Council on Public History Graduate Student Travel Awards (Doctorate, Graduate/Grant) [6882]
National Council on Public History Student Project Awards (Undergraduate/Grant) [6883]
National Court Reporters Association Student Intern Scholarship (Undergraduate/Scholarship) [6897]
National Dairy Herd Information Association Scholarship Program (Undergraduate/Scholarship) [6903]
National Dental Hygienists' Association Scholarships (Undergraduate/Scholarship) [6916]
The National Endowment for the Humanities Fellowships (Graduate/Fellowship) [1198]
National Endowment for the Humanities Research Fellowships (Doctorate/Fellowship) [660]
National GEM Consortium - MS Engineering Fellowships (Graduate/Fellowship) [6967]
National GEM Consortium - PhD Engineering Fellowships (Doctorate, Graduate/Fellowship) [6968]
National GEM Consortium - PhD Science Fellowships (Doctorate, Graduate/Fellowship) [6969]
National Geographic Conservation Trust Grants (Doctorate, Advanced Professional/Grant) [6971]
National Geographic Expedition Council Grants (Advanced Professional/Grant) [6972]
National Geographic Society/Waitt Grants (Advanced Professional/Grant) [6973]
National Geographic Young Explorers Grants (Advanced Professional/Grant) [6974]
National Greenhouse Manufacturers Association Scholarships (Undergraduate/Scholarship) [806]
National Guard Association of Rhode Island Scholarship (Undergraduate/Scholarship) [6978]
National High School Oratorical Contest Scholarship (Undergraduate/Scholarship) [956]
National Huguenot Society College and Postgraduate Student Scholarships (Undergraduate, Postgraduate/Scholarship) [7006]
National Humanities Center Fellowships (Doctorate, Postdoctorate/Fellowship) [7008]
National Institute of Health Undergraduate Scholarship Program (NIH UGSP) (Undergraduate/Scholarship) [9930]
National Iranian American Council Fellowships (Graduate, Undergraduate/Fellowship) [7022]
National Judges Association Scholarships (Other/Scholarship) [7030]
National Junior Horticultural Association Alumni Scholarships (Undergraduate/Scholarship) [7034]
National Junior Swine Association Outstanding Member Scholarships (Graduate/Scholarship) [7038]
National Medical Fellowships Need-Based Scholarships (Undergraduate/Scholarship) [7061]
National Merit Harris Corporation Scholarship Program (Undergraduate/Scholarship) [4729]
National Merit Scholarship Program (Undergraduate/Scholarship) [7063]
National Organization of Italian-American Women Scholarships (Undergraduate, Graduate/Scholarship) [7083]
National Pathfinder Scholarships (Graduate, Master's, Undergraduate/Scholarship) [6954]
National Poultry and Food Distributors Association Scholarships (Undergraduate/Scholarship) [7102]
National Preservation Institute Scholarships (Professional development/Scholarship) [7104]
National Recreation and Park Association Diversity Scholarships (Undergraduate/Scholarship) [7118]
National Science Foundation Graduate Research Fellowship Program (NSF-GRFP) (Graduate/Fellowship) [7125]
National Sculpture Society Scholarships (Undergraduate/Scholarship) [7128]
National Security Education Program - David L. Boren Fellowships (Graduate/Fellowship) [10137]
National Sheriffs' Association Scholarship Program (Graduate, Undergraduate/Scholarship) [7130]
National Slovak Society Senior Scholarships (Undergraduate, Vocational/Occupational/Scholarship) [7132]
National Society of Accountants Scholarship Program (Undergraduate/Scholarship) [7134]
National Space Biomedical Research Institute Postdoctoral Fellowships (Postdoctorate/Fellowship) [7177]
National Swimming Pool Foundation Scholarship Awards (Other/Scholarship) [7193]
National Technical Honor Society Scholarships (Professional development/Scholarship) [2424]
National Technical Honor Society Scholarships (Undergraduate/Scholarship) [3962]
Native American Community Scholars Awards (Graduate/Fellowship) [9013]
Native American Education Grants (Graduate, Undergraduate/Grant) [877]
Native American Visiting Student Awards (Graduate/Fellowship) [9014]
Native Hawaiian Chamber of Commerce Scholarships (Graduate, Undergraduate/Scholarship) [7916]
Native Hawaiian Visual Arts Scholarships (Graduate, Undergraduate/Scholarship) [7917]
Naval Helicopter Association Scholarships (Undergraduate, Graduate/Scholarship) [7223]
Naval Research Enterprise Internship Program (NREIP) (Undergraduate, Graduate, Professional development/Internship) [1304]
Naval Weather Service Association Scholarships

(Undergraduate/Scholarship) [7225]
Navy, Army or Air Force ROTC Scholarship Program (Undergraduate/Scholarship) [3502]
NAWJ Equal Access to Justice Scholarships (Graduate/Scholarship) [6803]
The Nazareth Scholarships (Undergraduate/Scholarship) [7238]
NBCUniversal Point Scholarship (Undergraduate, Graduate, Doctorate/Scholarship) [8187]
NBCUniversal Tony Coelho Media Scholarships (Undergraduate, Graduate/Scholarship) [555]
NBMBAA Graduate Scholarships Program (Graduate/Scholarship) [6821]
NBRC/AMP H. Frederic Helmholz, Jr., MD Educational Research Funds (Master's, Doctorate/Grant) [1213]
NCBWL Scholarships (Undergraduate/Scholarship) [6666]
NCCF Survivor Scholarships (Undergraduate/Scholarship) [6865]
NCCT Postdoctoral Research Program (Postdoctorate, Advanced Professional, Professional development/Fellowship) [9941]
NCEA Postdoctoral Research Program (Postdoctorate, Advanced Professional, Professional development/Fellowship) [9943]
NCECA Graduate Student Fellowships (Graduate/Fellowship) [6880]
NCPA Foundation Presidential Scholarships (Undergraduate/Scholarship) [6869]
NCRF New Professional Reporter Grant (Other/Grant) [6898]
NCSEA New Leader Scholarships (Professional development/Scholarship) [6859]
NCSGC Undergraduate Research Scholarships (Undergraduate/Scholarship) [7484]
NCSGC Undergraduate Scholarships (Undergraduate/Scholarship) [7485]
NCTE Research Foundation Grants (Other/Grant) [6885]
NCTM Emerging Teacher-Leaders in Elementary School Mathematics Grants for Grades K-5 Teachers (Other/Grant) [6889]
NCTM Prospective 7-12 Secondary Teacher Course Work Scholarships (Professional development/Scholarship) [6890]
NCTM School In-Service Training Grants for Grades 6-8 Teachers (Undergraduate/Grant) [6891]
NCTM School In-Service Training Grants for Grades 9-12 Teachers (Undergraduate/Grant) [6892]
NCTM School In-Service Training Grants for Grades K-5 Teachers (Undergraduate/Grant) [6893]
NDIA Picatinny Chapter Scholarships (Undergraduate/Scholarship) [6909]
NDSEG Fellowships (Graduate/Fellowship) [6911]
NDSGC American Indian Scholarships (Undergraduate/Scholarship) [7494]
NDSGC Graduate Fellowships (Graduate, Master's, Doctorate/Scholarship, Fellowship) [7495]
NDSGC Summer Faculty Fellowships (Professional development/Scholarship, Fellowship) [7496]
NDSGC Undergraduate Fellowships (Undergraduate/Scholarship, Fellowship) [7497]
NDSGC Undergraduate Scholarships (Undergraduate/Scholarship) [7498]
NDTA Academic Scholarship Program A (Undergraduate/Scholarship) [6913]
NDTA Academic Scholarship Program B (Undergraduate/Scholarship) [6914]
NEDA Eating Recovery Center Foundation Early Career Investigator Grants (Professional development/Grant) [6938]
NEDA Feeding Hope Fund for Clinical Research Grants (Professional development/Grant) [6939]
Need-Based Scholarships (Doctorate/Scholarship) [3986]
J.W. "Bill" Neese Scholarships (Undergraduate/Scholarship) [5300]
NEH Fellowships for Senior Scholars (Doctorate/Fellowship) [2853]
NEHA/AAS Scholarship (Graduate, Undergraduate/Scholarship) [6943]
Paul and Ruth Neidhold Business Scholarships (Undergraduate/Scholarship) [3294]
Neilsen Psychosocial Research Grants - Pilot Psychosocial Research Grants (Professional development/Grant) [7254]
Neilsen Psychosocial Research Grants - Postdoctoral Psychosocial Fellowships (Postdoctorate/Fellowship) [7255]
Neilsen Psychosocial Research Grants - Proof of Concept Research Grants (Professional development/Grant) [7256]
Edward J. Nell Memorial Scholarships in Journalism (Undergraduate/Scholarship) [8397]
Dave Nelsen Scholarships (Undergraduate/Scholarship) [6766]
Charles I. Nelson Endowed Scholarships (Undergraduate/Scholarship) [7993]
Carol Nelson Scholarship (Undergraduate/Scholarship) [5753]
Bill Nelson Scholarship Endowment (BNSE) (Undergraduate, Graduate/Scholarship) [7768]
AIST Midwest Member Chapter - Don Nelson Scholarships (Undergraduate/Scholarship) [2003]
Law Offices of Judd S. Nemiro Dyslexia Scholarships (All/Scholarship) [5961]
NEMLA Summer Fellowships (Graduate, Other/Fellowship) [7511]
NEMRA Educational Scholarship Foundation (Undergraduate, Vocational/Occupational/Scholarship) [6941]
NERL Postdoctoral Research Program (Postdoctorate, Advanced Professional, Professional development/Fellowship) [9935]
NERRS Graduate Research Fellowships (GRF) (Graduate/Fellowship) [6945]
NESCPA Fifth-Year Scholarships (Graduate/Scholarship) [7251]
NESCPA General Scholarships (Graduate, Undergraduate/Scholarship) [7252]
Netfloor USA Access Flooring College Scholarships (Undergraduate/Scholarship) [7261]
Reverend John S. Nettles Scholarships (Undergraduate/Scholarship) [3268]
Elizabeth Neuffer Fellowships (Other/Fellowship) [5458]
New Hampshire Snowmobile Association Book Scholarships (Undergraduate/Scholarship) [7313]
New Investigator Research Grant (Doctorate/Grant) [393]
New Investigator Research Grant (Postdoctorate/Grant) [374]
New Mexico Association for Bilingual Education Scholarships (Undergraduate/Scholarship) [7339]
New Museum Bogliasco Fellowship in Visual Art (Professional development/Fellowship) [2330]
New Orleans Ghost Tours Scholarships (Undergraduate/Scholarship) [7341]
New York Financial Writers' Associations Scholarships (Graduate, Undergraduate/Scholarship) [7354]
New York Point Honors Point Scholarship (Undergraduate, Graduate, Doctorate/Scholarship) [8188]
New York State Senate - Legislative Fellowships (Graduate, Postgraduate/Fellowship) [7368]
New York Water Environment Association Scholarships (Undergraduate/Scholarship) [7404]
Ted and Ruth Neward Scholarships (Undergraduate, Graduate/Scholarship) [9265]
Newberry Consortium on American Indian Studies Faculty Fellowships (Other/Fellowship) [7417]
Newberry Consortium on American Indian Studies Graduate Student Fellowships (Doctorate/Fellowship) [7418]
Newberry Library ACM/GLCA Faculty Fellowships (Other/Fellowship) [7419]
Newberry Library/Ecole Nationale des Chartes Exchange Fellowships (Graduate/Fellowship) [7420]
Newberry Library National Endowment for the Humanities Fellowships (Postdoctorate/Fellowship) [7421]
Newberry Library Short-Term Resident Fellowships for Individual Research (Postdoctorate, Doctorate/Fellowship) [7422]
The Shanon Newberry Physical Therapy Scholarship Endowment (Doctorate/Scholarship) [9584]
Newcomer Supply Student Scholarships (Undergraduate/Scholarship) [7169]
Caroline H. Newhouse Scholarship Fund (Professional development/Scholarship, Grant) [2793]
Newkirk Center for Science and Society Graduate Student Fellowships (Doctorate, Graduate/Fellowship) [7427]
Newman Civic Fellows Awards (Undergraduate/Award) [2530]
Edsel Newman Scholarships (Undergraduate/Scholarship) [6065]
Newman University Scouting Scholarships (Undergraduate/Scholarship) [6931]
Alwin B. Newton Scholarships (Undergraduate/Scholarship) [1332]
NFDA Professional Women's Conference Scholarships (Undergraduate/Scholarship) [4314]
NFPA/PACE Scholarships (Other/Scholarship) [6951]
NFPA Youth Scholarships (Undergraduate, Vocational/Occupational/Scholarship) [6961]
NGA Conservation Fellowships (Graduate/Award) [6963]
NGAT Educational Scholarships (Graduate, Undergraduate/Scholarship) [6980]
NGC College Scholarships (Graduate, Undergraduate/Scholarship) [6965]
NHAEOP Member Scholarships (Undergraduate/Scholarship) [7299]
NHEERL Postdoctoral Research Program (Postdoctorate, Advanced Professional, Professional development/Fellowship) [9937]
NHFA Scholarships (Graduate/Scholarship) [6998]
NHPGA Apprentice Scholarships (Undergraduate/Scholarship) [6358]
NHS National Scholarships (Undergraduate/Scholarship) [7000]
NHS Regional Scholarships (Undergraduate/Scholarship) [7001]
NIABA/NIAF Scholarships (Graduate/Scholarship) [7025]
NIAC Iranian-American Scholarship Fund (Undergraduate, Graduate/Scholarship) [7023]
NIAF Scholarships - General Category I (Undergraduate, Graduate, Postgraduate/Scholarship) [7027]
NIAF Scholarships - General Category II (Undergraduate, Graduate, Postgraduate/Scholarship) [7028]
NIBA Presidential Scholarships (Undergraduate/Scholarship) [7010]
Donald E. Nichols Scholarships (Undergraduate/Scholarship) [1333]
George E. Nichols Undergradute Scholarships (Undergraduate/Scholarship) [10187]
Gunnar Nicholson Endowed Scholarships (Undergraduate/Scholarship) [7994]
AIST Midwest Member Chapter - Mel Nickel Scholarships (Undergraduate/Scholarship) [2004]
Herbert W. Nickens Medical Student Scholarships (Advanced Professional/Scholarship) [1840]
Mike Niemeyer Memorial Football Scholarships (Undergraduate/Scholarship) [8506]
Eva Nieminski Honorary Graduate Science and Engineering Scholarships (Graduate/Scholarship) [5240]
Helen W. Nies Memorial Scholarship (Postgraduate/Scholarship) [3987]
NIJ Visiting Fellowships (Other/Fellowship) [7012]
Nikko Cosmetic Surgery Center Annual Breast Cancer Survivor Scholarships (All/Scholarship) [7434]
NINR Mentored Patient-Oriented Research Career Development Award (Doctorate/Grant) [7015]
NINR Midcareer Investigator Award in Patient-Oriented Research (Doctorate/Grant) [7016]
NINR Pathway to Independence Award (Doctorate/Grant) [7017]
Evelyn S. Nish Scholarships (Undergraduate/Scholarship) [8933]
Nissan North America, Inc. Scholarships (Undergraduate/Scholarship) [871]
NIU-CSEAS Foreign Language and Area Studies (FLAS) Fellowships (Undergraduate, Graduate/Fellowship) [7518]
NJCBIR Individual Research Grants (Other/Grant) [9549]
NJCBIR Pilot Research Grants (Other/Grant) [9550]
NJCBIR Postdoctoral and Graduate Student Fellow-

ships *(Graduate, Postdoctorate/Fellowship)* [9551]
NJPA Foundation Scholarship for Research on Diversity Issues *(Graduate/Scholarship)* [7329]
NJSA Visionary Leader Scholarships *(Graduate/Scholarship)* [7039]
NJSBF Labor Law Scholarships *(Undergraduate/Scholarship)* [7336]
NLBRA National Royalty Scholarships *(Undergraduate/Scholarship)* [7054]
NLBRA Rainwater Scholarships *(Undergraduate/Scholarship)* [7055]
NLBRA World All Around Scholarships *(Undergraduate/Scholarship)* [7056]
NLBRA World Event Scholarships *(Undergraduate/Scholarship)* [7057]
NLBRA/Wrangler Academic Scholarships *(Undergraduate/Scholarship)* [7058]
NLBRA Youth Board Officer Scholarships *(Undergraduate/Scholarship)* [7059]
NLM Associate Fellowships *(Postgraduate/Fellowship)* [9928]
NMCRS Gold Star Scholarship Program *(Undergraduate/Scholarship)* [7235]
NMIA Scholarship Program *(Undergraduate, Graduate/Scholarship)* [7071]
NMNH American Indian Program Fellowships *(Graduate/Fellowship)* [9034]
NMPF National Dairy Leadership Scholarships *(Graduate, Master's, Doctorate/Scholarship)* [7073]
NMSC College and University Sponsorship of Merit Scholarship Awards *(Undergraduate/Scholarship)* [7064]
NMSC Corporate-Sponsored Achievement Scholarship Awards *(Undergraduate/Scholarship)* [7065]
NMSC National Achievement Scholarship Program *(Undergraduate/Scholarship)* [7066]
NMSC Special Scholarships *(Undergraduate/Scholarship)* [7067]
NOAA EPP Undergraduate Scholarships (USP) *(Undergraduate/Scholarship)* [9891]
NOAA Graduate Sciences Scholarships *(Graduate/Scholarship)* [9892]
NOBCChE Procter and Gamble Fellowships *(Graduate/Fellowship)* [7088]
Leonard Noble Educational Scholarships *(Professional development/Scholarship)* [7170]
George H. Nofer Scholarships for Law and Public Policy *(Graduate/Scholarship)* [316]
NOHIMSS Student Scholarship Program *(Undergraduate, Master's, Doctorate/Scholarship)* [7523]
Alfred H. Nolle Scholarships *(Undergraduate/Scholarship)* [342]
Helen Woodruff Nolop Scholarships in Audiology and Allied Fields *(Graduate/Scholarship)* [3592]
Non Commissioned Officers Association Scholarships *(Undergraduate/Scholarship)* [7441]
Deborah Munroe Noonan Memorial Research Awards *(Professional development/Grant)* [4822]
Nor' Easters Scholarships - Four-year Program *(Undergraduate/Scholarship)* [4915]
Nor' Easters Scholarships - Two-year Program *(Undergraduate/Scholarship)* [4916]
Norall Scholarship Trust *(Undergraduate/Scholarship)* [6066]
Marian Norby Scholarships *(Other/Scholarship)* [9310]
Norfolk Southern Foundation Scholarships *(Undergraduate/Scholarship)* [1188]
North American Conference on British Studies Dissertation Year Fellowships *(Doctorate, Postdoctorate/Fellowship)* [7443]
North American Conference on British Studies-Huntington Library Fellowships *(Doctorate, Postdoctorate/Fellowship)* [7444]
North American Van Lines Military Scholarship Competition *(Undergraduate/Scholarship)* [7449]
North Carolina Commercial Flower Growers Association Floriculture Scholarships *(Graduate, Undergraduate/Scholarship)* [7456]
North Carolina Council of Epsilon Sigma Alpha Scholarships *(Graduate, Other, Undergraduate/Scholarship)* [7458]
North Carolina Nursery and Landscape Association Horticulture Scholarships *(Undergraduate/Scholarship)* [7468]
North Central, Region 9 Scholarships *(Undergraduate/Scholarship)* [9191]
North Dakota Division Scholarships *(Undergraduate/Scholarship)* [6523]
North Dakota Farmers Union Co-op House Scholarships *(Undergraduate/Scholarship)* [7490]
North Dakota Farmers Union Scholarships *(Undergraduate/Scholarship)* [7491]
North Florida Chapter Safety Education Scholarships *(Graduate, Undergraduate/Scholarship)* [1423]
North Mecklenburg Teachers' Memorial Scholarships *(Undergraduate/Scholarship)* [4208]
Michelle North Scholarships for Safety *(Other/Scholarship)* [4840]
North Texas Relocation Professionals Scholarships *(Undergraduate/Scholarship)* [7505]
NorthCoast Medical Scholarship Program *(Postgraduate/Scholarship)* [1048]
Northeastern Illinois Chapter Scholarships *(Graduate, Undergraduate/Scholarship)* [1424]
Northern Arizona Native-American Foundation Scholarships *(Undergraduate, Vocational/Occupational/Scholarship)* [7516]
Northern California Chapter of HIMSS Scholarships *(Graduate, Postgraduate, Undergraduate/Scholarship)* [4832]
Northern California DX Foundation Scholarships *(Undergraduate/Scholarship)* [1749]
Northern Trust Point Scholarship *(Undergraduate, Graduate, Doctorate/Scholarship)* [8189]
Cedric Northrop Fellowships *(Professional development/Fellowship)* [4035]
Northrop Grumman Engineering Scholarships *(Undergraduate/Scholarship)* [7527]
Northwest Community Center Scholarships *(Undergraduate/Scholarship)* [3295]
Northwest-Shoals Community College Academic Scholarships *(Undergraduate/Scholarship)* [7539]
Northwest-Shoals Community College Applied Technology Scholarships *(Undergraduate/Scholarship)* [7540]
Northwest-Shoals Community College Athletic Scholarships *(Undergraduate/Scholarship)* [7541]
Northwest-Shoals Community College Bank Independent Scholarships *(Undergraduate/Scholarship)* [7542]
Northwest-Shoals Community College Fine Arts Scholarships - Art *(Undergraduate/Scholarship)* [7543]
Northwest-Shoals Community College Fine Arts Scholarships - Drama *(Undergraduate/Scholarship)* [7544]
Northwest-Shoals Community College Fine Arts Scholarships - Music *(Undergraduate/Scholarship)* [7545]
Northwest-Shoals Community College High School Academic Scholarships *(Undergraduate/Scholarship)* [7546]
Northwest-Shoals Community College Independent Computer Scholarships *(Undergraduate/Scholarship)* [7547]
Northwest-Shoals Community College Student Activities Scholarships *(Undergraduate/Scholarship)* [7548]
Northwestern Mutual Financial Network Scholarships *(Graduate, Undergraduate/Scholarship)* [8077]
Vessa Notchev Fellowships *(Doctorate, Graduate/Fellowship)* [8906]
Notre Dame Club of Canton Scholarships *(Undergraduate/Scholarship)* [9528]
NOVA Foundation Scholarships *(Doctorate, Graduate, Master's/Scholarship)* [7560]
Novak Awards *(Doctorate/Monetary)* [58]
Mike and Flo Novovesky Scholarships *(Undergraduate/Scholarship)* [807]
Noyce Scholarships for Secondary Math and Science Education *(Undergraduate/Scholarship)* [5123]
NPC Scholarships *(Graduate/Scholarship)* [7100]
NPM Academic Scholarships *(Graduate, Undergraduate/Scholarship)* [6768]
NPM Program Scholarships *(Undergraduate/Scholarship)* [6769]
NPPF Still and Multimedia Scholarships *(Undergraduate/Scholarship)* [7110]
NPPF TV News Scholarships *(Undergraduate/Scholarship)* [7111]
NPSC Fellowships *(Graduate/Fellowship)* [7098]
NRL-ASEE Postdoctoral Fellowships *(Postdoctorate/Fellowship)* [9966]
NRMRL Postdoctoral Research Program *(Postdoctorate, Advanced Professional, Professional development/Fellowship)* [9939]
NSA Electrical Engineering Student Scholarships *(Undergraduate, Graduate, Doctorate/Scholarship)* [107]
NSA Mathematics and Computer Science Student Scholarships *(Undergraduate, Graduate, Doctorate/Scholarship)* [108]
NSHMBA Scholarships *(Graduate/Scholarship)* [7164]
NSHSS Academic Paper Awards *(High School/Scholarship)* [7160]
NSHSS National Scholar Awards *(High School/Scholarship)* [7161]
NSPS Scholarships *(Undergraduate/Scholarship)* [7175]
NSS Conservation Grants *(Advanced Professional/Grant)* [7182]
NSS Education Grants *(Undergraduate/Grant)* [7183]
NSSA/NSCA Collegiate Scholarships *(Undergraduate/Scholarship)* [7186]
NTHS/HOSA Scholarships *(Undergraduate/Scholarship)* [7197]
Nuclear Criticality Safety Pioneers Scholarships *(Graduate/Scholarship)* [1038]
NUF Fellowships *(Graduate, Postgraduate, Other/Fellowship)* [7209]
NURSE Corps Scholarship Program *(Professional development/Scholarship)* [9924]
Nurseries Foundation Scholarship Awards *(Undergraduate/Scholarship)* [7698]
Nurseries Memorial Scholarship Awards *(Graduate/Scholarship)* [7699]
Nuts, Bolts and Thingamajigs Scholarships *(Undergraduate, Vocational/Occupational/Scholarship)* [7562]
The Nuts.com Healthy Eating Scholarships *(Undergraduate, Graduate/Scholarship)* [7564]
NVIDIA Graduate Fellowships *(Graduate/Fellowship)* [7566]
NWF Campus Ecology Fellowships *(Graduate, Undergraduate/Fellowship)* [7216]
NWRI Fellowships *(Graduate, Master's, Doctorate/Fellowship)* [7214]
NWSA Graduate Scholarships *(Graduate/Scholarship)* [7219]
NYCT Paid Graduate Student Philanthropy Fellowships - Arts and Historic Preservation *(Graduate/Fellowship)* [7349]
NYCT Paid Graduate Student Philanthropy Fellowships - Children, Youth, Families, Education, Human Justice and Workforce *(Graduate/Fellowship)* [7350]
NYCT Paid Graduate Student Philanthropy Fellowships - Community Development and the Environment *(Graduate/Fellowship)* [7351]
NYCT Paid Graduate Student Philanthropy Fellowships - Health and People with Special Needs *(Graduate/Fellowship)* [7352]
NYLA-Dewey Scholarship *(Master's, Undergraduate/Scholarship)* [7357]
NYU Langone Medical Center Science Student Scholarships *(Undergraduate, Graduate/Scholarship)* [109]
NYU School of Law Fellowships at HRW *(Graduate/Fellowship)* [4999]
OAH-IEHS Huggins-Quarles Dissertation Awards *(Doctorate, Graduate/Grant)* [7718]
OAS Academic Scholarships - Graduate *(Graduate/Scholarship)* [7722]
Dennis J. O'Brien USAEE/IAEE Best Student Paper Award *(Undergraduate/Award)* [9884]
Oceanic Research Group Scholarships *(Graduate, Undergraduate/Scholarship)* [7570]
Edward A. O'Connor Founder's Scholarships *(Un-*

dergraduate/Scholarship) [83]
Justice Sandra Day O'Connor Scholarship (Undergraduate/Scholarship) [6804]
Basil O'Connor Starter Scholar Research Awards (Professional development/Grant) [6235]
Odd Fellows Lodge No. 8 Endowed Scholarships (Undergraduate/Scholarship) [6048]
Captain Jennifer Shafer Odom Memorial Scholarships - Children of Soldiers (Undergraduate, Vocational/Occupational/Scholarship) [1716]
Captain Jennifer Shafer Odom Memorial Scholarships - Spouses of Soldiers (Undergraduate/Scholarship) [1717]
Office of Science Graduate Fellowships (Graduate/Fellowship) [9912]
Ohio Association of Broadcaster's Kids Scholarships (Undergraduate/Scholarship) [7572]
Ohio Newspaper Association University Journalism Scholarships (Undergraduate/Scholarship) [7578]
Ohio Space Grant Consortium Graduate Fellowships (Graduate, Doctorate, Master's/Fellowship) [7594]
Ohio Space Grant Consortium Special Minority Fellowships (Doctorate, Graduate, Master's/Fellowship) [7595]
Lawrence "Bud" Ohlman Memorial Scholarships (Undergraduate/Scholarship) [808]
The Seth Okin Good Deeds Scholarships (Undergraduate/Scholarship) [8235]
Oklahoma City University Full-Time Merit Scholarships (Graduate/Scholarship) [7601]
Oklahoma Restaurant Association Scholarships (Graduate, Undergraduate/Scholarship) [7604]
Rhonda J.B. O'Leary Memorial Scholarship (Undergraduate, Graduate/Scholarship) [3802]
Olin/Searle Fellows in Law (Other/Fellowship) [3995]
Jeff Oliphant Memorial Post-Graduate Scholarships (Postgraduate/Scholarship) [10619]
Robert B. Oliver ASNT Scholarships (Undergraduate/Scholarship) [1385]
MHS Andrew Oliver Research Fellowships (Professional development/Fellowship) [6336]
Frank del Olmo Memorial Scholarships (Undergraduate/Scholarship) [2826]
Roy C. and Dorothy Jean Olson Memorial Scholarships (Undergraduate/Scholarship) [5361]
Charlie O'Meilia Scholarships (Undergraduate/Scholarship) [5301]
Omicron Delta Kappa Foundation Scholarships (Graduate/Scholarship) [7611]
Omicron Nu Research Fellowships (Postdoctorate/Fellowship) [5790]
Eloise Pitts O'More Scholarships (Undergraduate/Scholarship) [3247]
Oncology Nursing Society Foundation - Bachelor's Scholarships (Undergraduate/Scholarship) [7619]
Oncology Nursing Society Foundation - Doctoral Scholarships (Doctorate, Professional/Scholarship) [7620]
Oncology Nursing Society Foundation - Master's Scholarships (Graduate, Master's/Scholarship) [7621]
Oncology Trainee Travel Awards (Professional development/Grant) [3383]
ONLA President's Scholarship (Undergraduate/Scholarship) [7586]
ONS Foundation Congress Scholarships (Professional development/Scholarship) [7622]
ONS Foundation Dissertation Research Grants (Doctorate, Professional development/Grant) [7623]
ONS Foundation Research Grants (Advanced Professional/Grant) [7624]
ONWA Annual Scholarships (Undergraduate/Scholarship) [7579]
Open Society Baltimore Community Fellowships (Advanced Professional/Fellowship) [7661]
Open Society Fellowships (Other/Fellowship) [7662]
Open Society Presidential Fellowships (Advanced Professional/Fellowship) [7663]
Opera Foundation Scholarships (Other/Scholarship) [7669]
Operation JumpStart Scholarships (Graduate/Scholarship) [458]
OPERF/ABC Resident Travel Award (Professional development/Grant) [7755]
OPERF Educator and Student Awards (Professional development/Grant) [7756]
OPERF Fellowships (Graduate, Master's, Doctorate/Fellowship) [7757]
OPERF Small Grants (Doctorate/Grant) [7758]
Frank Oppenheimer Scholarship Program (Postgraduate/Scholarship) [1049]
Dwight D. Opperman Scholarships (Undergraduate/Scholarship) [3686]
Optical Design and Engineering Scholarships (Graduate, Undergraduate/Scholarship) [9471]
Order of Omega Doctoral Fellowships (Doctorate, Graduate/Fellowship) [7680]
Order Sons of Italy Foundation General Scholarships (Graduate, Undergraduate/Scholarship) [7683]
L'Oreal USA Fellowships for Women in Science (Postdoctorate/Fellowship) [6107]
Oregon Association of Nurseries Scholarship Program (Undergraduate/Scholarship) [7700]
Oregon Farm Bureau Memorial Scholarships (Undergraduate/Scholarship) [7706]
Organization of American States AOS-Placed Scholarships (Graduate, Undergraduate/Scholarship) [7727]
Organization of American States Graduate Scholarships (Doctorate, Graduate/Scholarship) [7728]
Organization of American States Self-Placed Scholarships (Doctorate, Graduate/Scholarship) [7729]
Organization of Black Aerospace Professionals General Scholarships (All/Scholarship) [7733]
Organization of Chinese Americans Scholarships (Undergraduate/Scholarship) [1784]
Louisa Anne Oriente Scholarships (Graduate/Scholarship) [5681]
Original Tax Credit Scholarship (Undergraduate/Scholarship) [1627]
Oronzio de Nora Industrial Electrochemistry Fellowships (Postdoctorate/Fellowship) [3850]
Orthopaedic Foot and Ankle Fellowships (Graduate, Professional development/Fellowship) [1061]
Orthopaedic Specialists Nursing Scholarships (Undergraduate/Scholarship) [10590]
Orthopaedic Trauma Association Research Grants (Other/Grant) [7753]
Mary Reiko Osaka Memorial Scholarships (Undergraduate, Graduate/Scholarship) [5555]
The Kenneth J. Osborn Memorial Scholarships (Undergraduate/Scholarship) [1808]
Royce Osborn Minority Scholarship (Undergraduate/Scholarship) [1398]
OSCA Graduate Student Scholarship Program (Graduate/Scholarship) [7590]
OSGC Community College Scholarships (Undergraduate/Scholarship) [7596]
OSGC Education Scholarships (Undergraduate/Scholarship) [7597]
OSHA Graduate Scholarships (Graduate/Scholarship) [7606]
M. Dick Osumi Civil Rights and Public Interest Scholarship (Graduate, Undergraduate/Scholarship) [5543]
Donald F. and Mildred Topp Othmer National Scholarship Awards (Undergraduate/Scholarship) [906]
Ellis R. Ott Scholarships (Graduate, Master's/Scholarship) [1390]
Ottawa Police 150th Anniversary Scholarships (Undergraduate/Scholarship) [2347]
Ted H. Ousley Scholarship Fund (Undergraduate/Scholarship) [4209]
Outlaw Student's Medical Professions Scholarships (Undergraduate/Scholarship) [9595]
Outlaw Student's Minority Scholarships (Undergraduate/Scholarship) [9596]
Outlaw Student's Nursing School Scholarships (Undergraduate/Scholarship) [9597]
Outlaw Student's Teacher Scholarships (Undergraduate/Scholarship) [9598]
Outstanding Doctoral Thesis in Astrophysics (Doctorate/Award) [1092]
Overflow/PLUS Tax Credit Scholarships (Undergraduate/Scholarship) [1628]
Helene M. Overly Memorial Scholarships (Undergraduate/Scholarship) [10675]
Overseas Press Club Foundation Harper's Magazine Scholarships (Graduate, Undergraduate/Scholarship) [7776]
Overseas Press Club Foundation Reuters Scholarships (Graduate, Undergraduate/Scholarship) [7777]
Elvina Jane Owen Awards (Graduate, Undergraduate/Scholarship) [9855]
Charles and Melva T. Owen Memorial Scholarships (Undergraduate/Scholarship) [6948]
Abraham A. Oyedeji Scholarships (Undergraduate/Scholarship) [7393]
Ozarks Division Scholarships (Undergraduate/Scholarship) [6524]
The Pac-10 Postgraduate Scholarships (Graduate/Scholarship) [7787]
Packard Fellowships for Science and Engineering (Professional development/Fellowship) [7793]
The Arthur J. Packard Memorial Scholarship Competition (Undergraduate/Scholarship) [862]
Barbara L. Packer Fellowships (Doctorate, Postdoctorate/Fellowship) [442]
Laurie Page-Peck Scholarship Fund (Undergraduate/Scholarship) [2103]
The Pain Special Merit Award (Postdoctorate, Professional development/Award) [3384]
Paleontological Society Student Research Grants (Graduate, Undergraduate/Grant) [17]
Robert R. Palmer Research Travel Fellowships (Other/Fellowship) [1296]
Pan Pacific Law Enforcement Scholarships (Undergraduate/Scholarship) [8745]
The PanHellenic Scholarships (Undergraduate/Scholarship) [7797]
ACI Charles Pankow Foundation ACI Student Fellowships (Graduate, Undergraduate/Fellowship) [710]
Katharine Pantzer Fellowships in the British Book Trades (Other/Fellowship) [2256]
Arthur and Barbara Pape Endowments (Graduate/Grant) [10269]
Paper Stock Industries Chapter ISRI RRF Scholarship (Undergraduate/Scholarship) [7801]
Pappaioanou Veterinary Public Health and Applied Epidemiology Fellowships (Undergraduate/Fellowship) [2833]
Parapsychological Association Research Endowments (All/Grant) [7805]
Pardee Community Building Scholarships (Undergraduate/Scholarship) [8359]
Joseph M. Parish Memorial Grants (Undergraduate/Scholarship, Grant) [1253]
Cissy McDaniel Parker Scholarships (Undergraduate/Scholarship) [3557]
E.U. and Gene Parker Scholarships (Undergraduate/Scholarship) [6949]
Parking Industry Institute Scholarship Program (Undergraduate/Scholarship) [7094]
Sylvia Parkinson Scholarships (Undergraduate/Scholarship) [4766]
Parkinson's Disease Foundation International Research Grants Program (Postdoctorate/Grant) [7884]
PARMA Scholarships (Undergraduate/Scholarship) [8325]
The Paros-Digiquartz Scholarships (Graduate, Undergraduate/Scholarship) [6276]
William E. Parrish Scholarships (Graduate, Master's/Scholarship) [8045]
Elisabeth M. and Winchell M. Parsons Scholarships (Graduate/Scholarship) [1798]
Part the Cloud Translational Research Funds (Postgraduate/Grant) [375]
Partners HealthCare Geriatric Psychiatry Fellowships (Professional development/Fellowship) [6324]
Pasteur Foundation Postdoctoral Fellowships (Postdoctorate/Fellowship) [7899]
PATCH Early Childhood Education Scholarships (Other/Scholarship) [7903]
Patient Advocate Scholarship Program (Professional development/Scholarship) [3385]
James H. Patrenos Memorial Scholarships (Undergraduate/Scholarship) [8969]
Gail Patrick Charitable Trust Scholarships (Undergraduate/Scholarship) [3593]
Patterson Belknap Webb & Tyler LLP Diversity Fel-

lowships *(Doctorate/Fellowship)* [7905]
Alice Conger Patterson Scholarships *(Undergraduate/Scholarship)* [10591]
Walter S. Patterson Scholarships *(Graduate/Scholarship)* [2370]
Joanne Holbrook Patton Military Spouse Scholarships *(Graduate, Undergraduate/Scholarship)* [7069]
Kenyon T. Payne Outstanding Student Awards *(Undergraduate/Award)* [6500]
PCCE Scholarship *(Undergraduate/Scholarship)* [6952]
PCF Challenge Awards *(Professional development/Grant)* [8312]
PCF Young Investigator Awards *(Professional development/Grant)* [8313]
PDC Scholarships *(Undergraduate/Scholarship)* [1425]
PDF-APDA Summer Student Fellowships *(Undergraduate, Graduate/Scholarship)* [7885]
PDF-PSG Mentored Clinical Research Awards *(Professional development/Award)* [7886]
PDF Student Travel Award *(Graduate, Undergraduate/Scholarship)* [7887]
Chuck Peacock Memorial Scholarships *(Undergraduate/Scholarship)* [169]
Peale Scholarship Grant *(Professional development/Scholarship)* [8058]
Scott Pearlman Field Awards for Science and Exploration *(Other/Award)* [3946]
Robert L. Peaslee-Detroit Brazing and Soldering Division Scholarships *(Undergraduate/Scholarship)* [1521]
Laura Ann Peck Memorial Endowed Scholarships *(Undergraduate/Scholarship)* [6049]
Pediatric Endocrinology Nursing Society Academic Education Scholarships *(Undergraduate/Scholarship)* [7926]
Pediatric Endocrinology Nursing Society Convention Reimbursement Awards *(Undergraduate/Award)* [7927]
Peermusic Latin Scholarship *(Undergraduate/Scholarship)* [2320]
Melissa Pellegrin Memorial Scholarships *(Undergraduate, Graduate/Scholarship)* [7751]
Louis Pelzer Memorial Awards *(Graduate/Award)* [7719]
Pembroke Center Faculty Fellowships *(Professional development/Fellowship)* [2389]
Pembroke Center Faculty Seed Grants *(Professional development/Grant)* [2390]
Pembroke Center Graduate Fellowships *(Graduate/Fellowship)* [2391]
Pembroke Center for Teaching and Research on Women Postdoctoral Fellowships *(Postdoctorate/Fellowship)* [2392]
Pension Real Estate Association Scholarships *(Undergraduate, Graduate/Scholarship)* [7952]
PEO Educational Loan Funds *(Undergraduate, Master's, Doctorate/Loan)* [7954]
PEO Scholars Awards *(Doctorate/Award, Scholarship)* [7956]
Pepperdine University Diversity Scholarships *(Doctorate, Graduate/Scholarship)* [7995]
Pepperdine University School of Law Armenian Student Scholarships *(Undergraduate/Scholarship)* [7996]
Pepperdine University School of Law Dean's Merit Scholarships *(Doctorate, Graduate/Scholarship)* [7997]
Pepperdine University School of Law Faculty Scholars Award *(Doctorate, Graduate/Scholarship)* [7998]
Pepperdine University School of Law JD/MBA Endowed Scholarships *(Undergraduate/Scholarship)* [7999]
Pepperdine University School of Law Special Law School Scholarships *(Undergraduate/Scholarship)* [8000]
Pepsi Scholarships *(Undergraduate/Scholarship)* [863]
Joe Perdue Scholarships *(Undergraduate/Scholarship)* [3063]
Joaquim Pereira Memorial Scholarships *(Undergraduate/Scholarship)* [6153]

Rudy Perez Songwriting Scholarships *(Undergraduate/Scholarship)* [1275]
Perkins Coie 1L Diversity Fellowships *(Postgraduate/Fellowship)* [8011]
Perkins Coie 1L Patent Litigation and Patent Fellowships *(Postgraduate/Fellowship)* [8012]
Perkins Coie 1L Political Law Fellowships *(Postgraduate/Fellowship)* [8013]
Eleanor Perry Memorial Endowed Scholarships *(Undergraduate/Scholarship)* [6050]
Chet and Jannett Perry Rotary Club of Fort Myers Scholarship Fund *(Undergraduate/Scholarship)* [9444]
Jim Perry Vocational Scholarships *(Undergraduate, Vocational/Occupational/Scholarship)* [809]
Gilberto and Lennetta Pesquera Medical School Scholarships *(Graduate, Doctorate/Scholarship, Grant)* [4453]
PETA Foundation Law Internships *(Graduate/Internship)* [7958]
Pete Wilson Graduate Scholarships *(Graduate, Undergraduate/Scholarship)* [8407]
Pete Wilson Journalism Scholarships *(Graduate, Undergraduate/Scholarship)* [8408]
Paul Evan Peters Fellowship *(Master's, Doctorate/Fellowship)* [3073]
Kate B. and Hall J. Peterson Fellowships *(Doctorate/Fellowship)* [443]
Lizette Peterson Homer Injury Prevention Grant Awards *(Other, Undergraduate, Graduate/Grant)* [1571]
Captain James H. Peterson Memorial Scholarships *(Undergraduate/Scholarship)* [4715]
Charles E. Peterson Senior Fellowships *(Other/Fellowship)* [2107]
Silvio and Eugenia Petrini Grants *(Other/Grant)* [4711]
Petroleum Engineering Scholarships *(Undergraduate/Scholarship)* [9250]
Petroleum Packaging Council Scholarships *(Undergraduate/Scholarship)* [8019]
Chuck Pezzano Scholarships *(Undergraduate/Scholarship)* [5286]
Pfafftown Jaycees/Lynn Canada Memorial Scholarships *(Undergraduate/Scholarship)* [10593]
Dr. Harry V. Pfautz Memorial Scholarship Fund *(Undergraduate/Scholarship)* [4250]
Ruth Cook Pfautz Memorial Scholarship Fund *(Undergraduate/Scholarship)* [4251]
L. Gordon, Jr. and June D. Pfefferkorn Scholarships *(Undergraduate/Scholarship)* [10594]
Pfizer Scholarship Funds *(Undergraduate, Graduate/Scholarship)* [6256]
PFLAG Columbia-Howard County Scholarship *(Undergraduate/Scholarship)* [8025]
Carl H. Pforzheimer, Jr. Research Grants *(Graduate, Other/Grant)* [5800]
PGSF Scholarships *(Undergraduate/Scholarship)* [8284]
Pharmaceutics Post Doctoral Fellowships *(Postdoctorate/Fellowship)* [8030]
Pharmaceutics Research Starter Grants *(Doctorate/Grant)* [8031]
Pharmaceutics Sabbatical Fellowships *(Postdoctorate/Fellowship)* [8032]
Pharmacology/Toxicology Pre Doctoral Fellowships *(Doctorate/Fellowship)* [8033]
Marshall Phelps Athletic Memorial Scholarships *(Undergraduate/Scholarship)* [8507]
Phi Alpha Theta Doctoral Scholarships *(Doctorate/Scholarship)* [8046]
Phi Alpha Theta Faculty Advisor Research Grant *(Other/Grant)* [8047]
Phi Delta Gamma Academic Achievement Awards *(Undergraduate/Scholarship)* [8059]
Phi Eta Sigma Distinguished Member Scholarships - Graduate or Professional *(Graduate, Other/Scholarship)* [8062]
Phi Eta Sigma Distinguished Member Scholarships - Undergraduate *(Undergraduate/Scholarship)* [8063]
Phi Eta Sigma Undergraduate Scholarship Awards *(Undergraduate/Scholarship)* [8064]
Phi Kappa Phi Fellowships *(Graduate, Undergraduate/Fellowship)* [8066]
Phi Kappa Sigma Foundation Scholarship *(Undergraduate/Scholarship)* [8068]
Phi Kappa Sigma Need-Based Scholarships *(Undergraduate/Scholarship)* [8069]
Phi Kappa Sigma Participation-Based Scholarships *(Undergraduate/Scholarship)* [8070]
Phi Sigma Epsilon Past National President Scholarships *(Graduate, Undergraduate/Scholarship)* [8078]
Phi Theta Kappa Scholarships *(Undergraduate/Scholarship)* [5124]
Phi Upsilon Omicron Candle Fellowships *(Graduate/Fellowship)* [8098]
Phi Upsilon Omicron Challenge Scholarships *(Undergraduate/Scholarship)* [8099]
Phi Upsilon Omicron Diamond Anniversary Fellowships *(Graduate/Fellowship)* [8100]
Phi Upsilon Omicron Founders Fellowships *(Graduate/Fellowship)* [8101]
Phi Upsilon Omicron Golden Anniversary Scholarships *(Undergraduate/Scholarship)* [8102]
Phi Upsilon Omicron Past Presidents Scholarships *(Undergraduate/Scholarship)* [8103]
Phi Upsilon Omicron Presidents Research Fellowships *(Graduate/Fellowship)* [8104]
Philadelphia Public Interest Fellowships *(Undergraduate/Fellowship)* [8111]
Walter T. Philippy Scholarships *(Undergraduate/Scholarship)* [6359]
Philips Respironics Fellowships in Mechanical Ventilation *(Professional development/Award)* [1214]
Philips Respironics Fellowships in Non-Invasive Respiratory Care *(Professional development/Fellowship)* [1215]
Jamie Phillips Endowed Scholarships *(Undergraduate/Scholarship)* [8001]
Phillips Fund Grants for Native American Research *(Doctorate, Master's/Grant)* [1083]
Margaret E. Phillips Scholarships *(Graduate/Scholarship)* [10305]
William Philpott Scholarships *(Undergraduate/Scholarship)* [2269]
Ed Phinney Commemorative Scholarships *(Graduate, Undergraduate/Scholarship)* [681]
PhRMA Foundation Health Outcomes Post Doctoral Fellowships *(Postdoctorate/Fellowship)* [8034]
PhRMA Foundation Health Outcomes Pre Doctoral Fellowships *(Doctorate/Fellowship)* [8035]
PhRMA Foundation Health Outcomes Research Starter Grants *(Doctorate/Grant)* [8036]
PhRMA Foundation Health Outcomes Sabbatical Fellowships *(Postdoctorate/Fellowship)* [8037]
PhRMA Foundation Informatics Research Starter Grants *(Doctorate/Grant)* [8038]
PhRMA Foundation Pharmaceutics Pre Doctoral Fellowships *(Doctorate/Fellowship)* [8039]
PhRMA Foundation Pharmacology/Toxicology Research Starter Grants *(Doctorate/Grant)* [8040]
PhRMA Foundation Pharmacology/Toxicology Sabbatical Fellowships *(Postdoctorate/Fellowship)* [8041]
PhRMA Foundaton Pharmacology/Toxicology Post Doctoral Fellowships *(Postdoctorate/Fellowship)* [8042]
The Physical Therapy Faculty Scholarship Endowment *(Graduate/Scholarship)* [9585]
Pi Gamma Mu Scholarships *(Graduate/Scholarship)* [8133]
Pi Project 2000 Tali James Memorial Scholarships *(Undergraduate/Scholarship)* [5756]
Thomas R. Pickering Graduate Foreign Affairs Fellowships *(Graduate, Undergraduate/Fellowship)* [10681]
Mary Pickford Scholarships *(Graduate/Scholarship)* [2026]
Peter L. Picknelly Honorary Scholarships *(Undergraduate/Scholarship)* [640]
Ronald C. and Joyce Pierce - Mobile Section Named Scholarships *(Undergraduate/Scholarship)* [1522]
Nicholas J. Piergrossi Scholarships *(Undergraduate/Scholarship)* [4768]
William Pigott Memorial Scholarships *(Undergraduate/Scholarship)* [3296]
David Pilon Scholarships for Training in Professional Psychology *(Graduate/Scholarship)* [1135]

Pilot Project Award *(Professional development/ Award, Grant)* [9239]
John Pine Memorial Scholarships *(Doctorate, Graduate/Scholarship)* [8048]
Julia T. Pingree Student Scholarship *(Undergraduate/Scholarship)* [7300]
Stephen D. Pisinski Memorial Scholarships *(Undergraduate/Scholarship)* [8376]
Christopher Mark Pitkin Memorial Scholarships *(Undergraduate/Scholarship)* [6994]
Day Pitney LLP Scholarships *(Undergraduate/Scholarship)* [4769]
Pitsenbarger Awards *(Undergraduate/Grant, Award)* [125]
Dr. Aura-Lee A. and James Hobbs Pittenger American History Scholarships *(Undergraduate/Scholarship)* [7154]
Robert Pittman Scholarships-Internships *(Undergraduate/Scholarship, Internship)* [10245]
Carter Pitts Scholarships *(Undergraduate/Scholarship)* [5474]
PKD Foundation Fellowships *(Doctorate, Graduate/ Fellowship)* [8144]
Wayne F. Placek Grants *(Graduate, Doctorate/ Grant)* [1150]
James L. Plafkin Memorial Scholarships *(Undergraduate/Scholarship)* [10188]
Al Plamann Legacy Scholarships *(Undergraduate/ Scholarship)* [2457]
Betsy Plank/PRSSA Scholarships *(Undergraduate/ Scholarship)* [8377]
PlasticPlace Young Entrepreneurs Scholarships *(Undergraduate/Scholarship)* [8148]
Plastics Pioneers Association Scholarships *(Undergraduate/Scholarship)* [9266]
Katherine Barton Platt Excavation Fellowships *(Other, Undergraduate/Fellowship)* [1237]
Platt Family Scholarship Prize Essay Contest *(Graduate, Undergraduate/Scholarship, Monetary)* [6091]
Pleasantview Public Schools Fund *(Undergraduate/ Scholarship)* [4564]
PLSCA Scholarships *(Undergraduate/Scholarship)* [6101]
Harold and Harriet Plum Memorial Scholarships *(Undergraduate/Scholarship)* [2513]
Plumbing-Heating-Cooling Contractors Association Educational Foundation Need-Based Scholarships *(Undergraduate/Scholarship)* [8162]
Plumbing-Heating-Cooling Contractors Association Educational Foundation Scholarships *(Undergraduate/Scholarship)* [8163]
PLUS Foundation Financial Aid Scholarships *(Undergraduate/Scholarship)* [8168]
PMCA/Penn State Fellowship in Confectionery Research *(Graduate/Fellowship)* [8293]
PNAA Nursing Scholarship Award *(Master's, Doctorate/Scholarship)* [8113]
David Pohl Scholarships *(Master's/Scholarship)* [9836]
Point Foundation Scholarships *(Undergraduate/ Scholarship)* [8662]
Daniel H. Pokorny Memorial Scholarship Awards *(Undergraduate/Scholarship)* [8543]
Pokross/Curhan Family Fund Prize *(Graduate, Undergraduate/Prize)* [950]
Donald and Susie Polden Dean's Scholarships *(Undergraduate/Scholarship)* [10171]
Tibor T. Polgar Fellowships *(Graduate, Undergraduate/Fellowship)* [4981]
Police Explorer Scholarships Program *(Undergraduate/Scholarship)* [4106]
Polish American Club of North Jersey Scholarships *(Graduate, Undergraduate/Scholarship)* [5881]
Polish National Alliance of Brooklyn, USA Scholarships *(Undergraduate/Scholarship)* [5882]
Roy H. Pollack Scholarships *(Graduate, Master's/ Scholarship)* [9837]
A. H. Pollard Travelling PhD Scholarships *(Postdoctorate/Scholarship)* [5163]
Harvey M. Pollicove Memorial Scholarships *(Undergraduate/Scholarship)* [7675]
David J. Pollini Scholarships *(Undergraduate/Scholarship)* [6360]
Justice Stewart G. Pollock Fellowships *(Undergraduate/Fellowship)* [6594]

Harold F. Polston Scholarships *(Graduate, Undergraduate/Scholarship)* [1426]
Polymer Modifiers and Additives Division Scholarships *(Undergraduate/Scholarship)* [9267]
Harriet and Leon Pomerance Fellowships *(Professional development/Fellowship)* [1610]
Edward C. Pomeroy Awards for Outstanding Contributions to Teacher Education *(Other/Recognition)* [488]
PON Graduate Student Grants *(Graduate/Grant)* [4789]
PON Next Generation Grants *(Doctorate, Postdoctorate/Grant)* [4790]
PON Summer Fellowships *(Graduate/Fellowship)* [4791]
Pope Scholarship Awards *(Undergraduate/Scholarship)* [6361]
Portable Sanitation Association International Scholarship Fund *(Undergraduate/Scholarship)* [8207]
Karin Riley Porter Good Works Scholarships *(Undergraduate, Graduate/Scholarship)* [8236]
Porter Physiology Development Fellowship Awards *(Doctorate/Fellowship)* [1100]
AFT Robert Porter Scholarship Program *(Undergraduate/Scholarship)* [795]
Portland Area Business Association Scholarships *(Undergraduate/Scholarship)* [3921]
Portland Cement Association Scholarships *(Graduate/Scholarship)* [3980]
Portuguese-American Scholarship Foundation *(Undergraduate/Scholarship)* [8209]
Postdoctoral Fellowships for Clinical Neurologists *(Postdoctorate/Fellowship)* [7888]
Poteet Strawberry Festival Association Scholarships *(Graduate, Undergraduate/Scholarship)* [8213]
Barbara Potter Scholarships *(Professional development/Scholarship)* [1055]
Erwin Potts Scholarships *(Undergraduate/Scholarship)* [10246]
George V. Powell Diversity Scholarships *(Graduate/ Scholarship)* [5920]
Gerald Powell Scholarships *(Undergraduate/Scholarship)* [3269]
Susan Kelly Power and Helen Hornbeck Tanner Fellowships *(Doctorate, Postdoctorate/Fellowship)* [7423]
Powers-Knapp Scholarships *(Undergraduate/Scholarship)* [10326]
Practising Law Institute Law Student Scholarships *(Advanced Professional, Professional development/Scholarship)* [8215]
Lou and Carole Prato Sports Reporting Scholarships *(Undergraduate/Scholarship)* [8409]
Praxair International Scholarships *(Undergraduate/ Scholarship)* [1523]
Presbyterian Association of Musicians Scholarships *(All/Scholarship)* [8217]
Prevent Cancer Foundation Fellowships *(Postdoctorate/Fellowship)* [8225]
Peridian International, Inc./Rae L. Price, FASLA Scholarship *(Undergraduate/Scholarship)* [1347]
Peridian International, Inc./Rae L. Price, FASLA Scholarships *(Undergraduate/Scholarship)* [5916]
Jim and Dee Price Scholarships *(Undergraduate/ Scholarship)* [4565]
Judith McManus Price Scholarships *(Undergraduate, Graduate/Scholarship)* [1106]
Lendon N. Pridgen, GlaxoSmithKline - NOBCChE Fellowships *(Graduate/Fellowship)* [7089]
Dean Prim Scholarships *(Undergraduate/Scholarship)* [10595]
Primate Conservation Grants *(Graduate, Professional development/Grant)* [8276]
Eric Primavera Memorial Scholarships *(Undergraduate/Scholarship)* [4094]
Josef Princ Memorial Scholarships *(Undergraduate/ Scholarship)* [8360]
Print and Graphics Scholarship Foundation Awards (PGSF-GATF) *(Graduate, Undergraduate/Scholarship, Fellowship)* [8282]
Miguel Pro Scholarships *(Undergraduate/Scholarship)* [10724]
Procter & Gamble Professional Oral Health/HDA Foundation Scholarships *(Undergraduate/Scholarship)* [4893]
Professional Development and Education Fund

(PDEF) Professional Development Scholarships *(Professional development/Scholarship)* [9223]
Professional Research Grants *(Professional development/Grant)* [1399]
Professional Women in Pest Management Scholarships *(Graduate, Other/Scholarship)* [7096]
Professional Women of Redlands, PoWeR to Continue Learning Scholarships *(Undergraduate/ Scholarship)* [8508]
Progressive Dairy Producer Awards *(All/Grant)* [6905]
Property and Environment Research Center Graduate Fellowships *(Graduate/Fellowship)* [8297]
Property and Environment Research Center Lone Mountain Fellowships *(Other/Fellowship)* [8298]
Property and Environment Research Center Media Fellowships *(Other/Fellowship)* [8299]
Proven Data Recovery Technology Scholarships *(All/Scholarship)* [8315]
Barbara F. Prowant Nursing Research Grants *(Graduate/Grant)* [1028]
PRSA Diversity Multicultural Scholarships *(Undergraduate/Scholarship)* [8378]
Prudential 1L Summer Internships *(Postgraduate/ Internship)* [6706]
Neil Pruitt, Sr. Memorial Scholarships *(Undergraduate/Scholarship)* [6870]
Joseph E. Pryor Graduate Fellowships *(Graduate/ Fellowship, Scholarship)* [343]
Cheryl White Pryor Memorial Scholarships *(Undergraduate/Scholarship)* [3558]
Phillis Brinton Pryor Panhellenic Scholarship *(Undergraduate/Scholarship)* [5757]
PSGC/NASA Space Grant Fellowships at the PSGC Affiliate Institutions *(Graduate/Fellowship)* [7945]
PSHF Good Idea Grants *(Other/Grant)* [8381]
Public Interest Environmental Law Fellowships *(Graduate/Fellowship)* [3898]
Public Interest Fellowships for Law Students of Color *(Undergraduate/Fellowship)* [4491]
Public Service Fellows Internship Program - Center for Government Leadership *(Undergraduate, Graduate/Internship)* [7890]
Public Service Fellows Internship Program - Communications *(Undergraduate, Graduate, Professional development/Internship)* [7891]
Public Service Fellows Internship Program - Development *(Undergraduate, Graduate, Professional development/Internship)* [7892]
Public Service Fellows Internship Program - Education and Outreach *(Undergraduate, Graduate, Professional development/Internship)* [7893]
Public Service Fellows Internship Program - Government Affairs *(Undergraduate, Graduate, Professional development/Internship)* [7894]
Public Service Fellows Internship Program - Government Transformation and Agency Partnerships *(Undergraduate, Graduate, Professional development/Internship)* [7895]
Public Service Fellows Internship Program - Human Resources *(Undergraduate, Graduate, Professional development/Internship)* [7896]
Public Service Fellows Internship Program - Research *(Undergraduate, Graduate, Professional development/Internship)* [7897]
Eugene C. Pulliam Fellowships for Editorial Writing *(Other/Fellowship)* [8902]
Pulliam/Kilgore Freedom of Information Internships *(Undergraduate/Internship)* [9279]
Paul Pumpian Scholarship *(Undergraduate/Scholarship)* [1584]
John Purfield Endowed Scholarships *(Undergraduate/Scholarship)* [8002]
A.O. Putnam Memorial Scholarships *(Undergraduate/Scholarship)* [5193]
PVA Research Foundation Fellowships *(Postdoctorate/Fellowship)* [7803]
PWC Internships *(Undergraduate, Graduate/Internship)* [8156]
Harry V. Quadracci Memorial Scholarships *(Undergraduate, Graduate/Scholarship)* [4649]
Quarter Century Wireless Association Scholarships *(Undergraduate/Scholarship)* [8390]
Queer Foundation Effective Writing and Scholarships *(Undergraduate/Prize, Scholarship)* [8394]

Michael J. Quill Scholarships *(Undergraduate/Scholarship)* [9766]
Bob Quincy Scholarships *(Undergraduate/Scholarship)* [10248]
AIST Judith A. Quinn Detroit Member Chapter Scholarship *(Undergraduate/Scholarship)* [2005]
Dr. Sidney Rafal Memorial Scholarships *(Undergraduate/Scholarship)* [4770]
The Raffin-Gathercole Scholarships *(Undergraduate/Scholarship)* [4331]
Marjorie Usher Ragan Scholarships *(Undergraduate/Scholarship)* [10249]
Railroad and Mine Workers Memorial Scholarships *(Graduate/Scholarship)* [5556]
Rain Bird Intelligent Use of Water Scholarships *(Undergraduate/Scholarship)* [5917]
J.J. Rains Memorial Scholarships *(Undergraduate/Scholarship)* [3104]
Tom D. Ralls Memorial Scholarship *(Professional development/Scholarship)* [4285]
The NASSCO Jeffrey D. Ralston Memorial Scholarship *(Undergraduate/Scholarship)* [6668]
Rama Scholarships for the American Dream *(Graduate, Undergraduate/Scholarship)* [864]
A. Stanley Rand Fellowships Program *(Undergraduate, Doctorate, Postdoctorate/Fellowship)* [9037]
Herbert W. Rand Fellowships and Scholarships *(Undergraduate, Graduate/Scholarship)* [6257]
Commander Newell S. Rand Jr. Scholarship Program *(Undergraduate/Scholarship)* [7809]
Helen F. "Jerri" Rand Memorial Scholarships *(Undergraduate, Vocational/Occupational/Scholarship)* [3323]
R&E Foundation Education Scholarships *(Graduate, Other/Scholarship)* [8416]
James Randi Educational Foundation Scholarships *(Graduate, Undergraduate/Scholarship)* [8427]
Jennings Randolph Peace Scholarship Dissertation Program *(Doctorate/Scholarship)* [9990]
United States Institute of Peace Jennings Randolph Senior Fellowship Program *(Advanced Professional/Fellowship)* [9991]
Rangel Graduate Fellowship *(Graduate/Fellowship)* [8429]
Jeannette Rankin Scholarships *(Undergraduate, Vocational/Occupational/Scholarship)* [8431]
Rappaport Fellows Program in Law and Public Policy *(Undergraduate/Fellowship)* [8437]
Geeta Rastogi Memorial Scholarships *(Undergraduate/Scholarship)* [10338]
General John Paul Ratay Educational Grants *(Undergraduate/Grant)* [6535]
James K. Rathmell Jr. Memorial Scholarships *(Undergraduate, Graduate/Scholarship)* [810]
Ratner and Sugarmon Scholarship *(Undergraduate/Scholarship)* [10172]
Dennis Raveling Scholarships *(Undergraduate/Scholarship)* [2488]
Lenny Ravich "Shalom" Scholarships *(Advanced Professional/Scholarship)* [1851]
Rawley Silver Awards for Excellence *(Graduate/Scholarship)* [450]
Rawley Silver Research Award *(Postgraduate, Postdoctorate/Award)* [451]
William C. Ray, CIH, CSP Arizona Scholarships *(Graduate, Undergraduate/Scholarship)* [1427]
W.B. Ray HS Class of '56 Averill Johnson Scholarships *(Undergraduate/Scholarship)* [3105]
Raytheon Scholarship Program *(Undergraduate/Scholarship)* [8440]
RBPA Scholarships *(All/Scholarship)* [8425]
Carl C. and Abbie Rebman Trust Scholarships *(Undergraduate/Scholarship)* [4566]
Redlands Baseball/Softball for Youth Scholarship *(Undergraduate/Scholarship)* [8509]
Redlands High School Academic Decathlon Scholarships *(Undergraduate/Scholarship)* [8511]
Redlands High School Boy's Varsity Volleyball Scholarships *(Undergraduate/Scholarship)* [8512]
Redlands High School Girls' Volleyball Boosters Scholarship Awards *(Undergraduate/Scholarship)* [8513]
Redlands High School Mock Trial Scholarships *(Undergraduate/Scholarship)* [8514]
Redlands High School-PTSA Scholarships *(Undergraduate/Scholarship)* [8515]

Redlands High School Softball Booster Scholarship Awards *(Undergraduate/Scholarship)* [8516]
Redlands High School Spiritleaders Scholarships *(Undergraduate/Scholarship)* [8517]
Redlands High School Terrier Band Boosters Club Scholarships *(Undergraduate/Scholarship)* [8518]
Redlands High School Vocal Music Boosters Scholarship Awards *(Undergraduate/Scholarship)* [8519]
Redlands Morning Kiwanis Club Foundation Scholarships *(Undergraduate/Scholarship)* [8520]
The Reese Fellowships *(Doctorate/Fellowship)* [444]
Bob Reeve Aviation Management Scholarships *(Undergraduate/Scholarship)* [217]
REFORMA Scholarship Program *(Doctorate, Graduate, Other/Scholarship)* [8534]
Rehabmart.com Scholarships *(Undergraduate/Scholarship)* [8545]
Dan M. Reichard, Jr. Scholarships *(Undergraduate, Graduate/Scholarship)* [1168]
Mark A. Reid Memorial Scholarship Grants *(Undergraduate/Scholarship)* [3297]
George Reinke Scholarships *(Other/Scholarship)* [1442]
Remkus-Sochaki Academmic Achievement Scholarships *(Undergraduate/Scholarship)* [8205]
REMSA Scholarships *(Undergraduate/Scholarship)* [1189]
Betty Rendel Scholarships *(Undergraduate/Scholarship)* [6955]
James Renwick Fellowship in American Craft *(Doctorate, Postdoctorate/Fellowship)* [9004]
Bertha and Byron L. Reppert Scholarship Fund *(Undergraduate/Scholarship)* [4252]
Research Career Development Awards *(Professional development/Fellowship, Grant)* [7625]
Research Resident/Fellow Grants *(Professional development/Grant)* [8417]
Reservation Counter College Scholarships *(Undergraduate, Graduate, Advanced Professional/Scholarship)* [8559]
Resident Travel Award for Underrepresented Populations *(Professional development/Award)* [3386]
Resilience Action Fund Scholarships *(Graduate/Scholarship)* [3981]
Resistance Welder Manufacturers' Association Scholarships *(Undergraduate/Scholarship)* [1524]
Resume Template Design Scholarships *(Undergraduate, Graduate/Scholarship)* [10369]
Retail Chapter Scholarship Awards *(Undergraduate/Scholarship)* [7701]
Retired League Postmasters Scholarship Program *(Undergraduate/Scholarship)* [8569]
Reuters Institute Visiting Fellowships *(Professional development/Fellowship)* [10265]
Thomson Reuters/MLA Doctoral Fellowships *(Doctorate, Graduate/Fellowship)* [6393]
Mike Reynolds Journalism Scholarships *(Undergraduate/Scholarship)* [8410]
Reynoldsburg-Pickerington Rotary Club High School Scholarship *(Undergraduate/Scholarship)* [8595]
Janet Reynoldson Memorial Scholarship *(Undergraduate/Scholarship)* [3687]
RFDF MBA Preparation Fellowships *(Graduate, Undergraduate/Fellowship)* [8619]
RFDF Pre-MBA Fellowships *(Graduate/Fellowship)* [8620]
Lori Rhett Memorial Scholarships *(Graduate, Undergraduate/Scholarship)* [6733]
Rho Chi, AFPE First Year Graduate Fellowships *(Doctorate, Graduate/Fellowship)* [8597]
Rho Chi Society Clinical Research Scholarships *(Postdoctorate/Scholarship)* [8598]
Haynes Rice Scholarships *(Graduate/Scholarship)* [6756]
Barbara Hagan Richards Scholarships *(Undergraduate/Scholarship)* [3249]
James Edward "Bill" Richards Scholarships *(Undergraduate/Scholarship)* [3250]
Ellen Swallow Richards Travel Grants *(Graduate, Other/Grant)* [1315]
Henry and Sylvia Richardson Research Grant *(Postdoctorate/Grant)* [3883]
J. Milton Richardson Theological Fellowships *(Graduate/Fellowship)* [363]

Frank J. Richter Scholarships *(Graduate, Undergraduate/Scholarship)* [570]
John Riddick Student Grants *(Graduate/Grant)* [7446]
Honorable Joseph H. Ridge Memorial Scholarships *(Undergraduate/Scholarship)* [328]
Jasper Ridge Restoration Fellowships Jasper Ridge Biological Preserve *(Graduate, Postdoctorate/Fellowship)* [3777]
ANN Ingrid Josefin Ridky Academic Scholarships *(Undergraduate, Graduate/Scholarship)* [45]
Donald Riebhoff Memorial Scholarships *(Undergraduate/Scholarship)* [1753]
Bryon Riesch Paralysis Foundation Research Grants *(Professional development/Grant)* [8617]
Rieser Fellowships *(Undergraduate/Fellowship)* [2406]
Dan Rigel Memorial Educational Grants *(Professional development, Advanced Professional/Grant)* [1843]
Ameen Rihani Scholarship Program *(Undergraduate/Scholarship)* [1599]
Rim-Freeman Point Scholarship *(Undergraduate/Scholarship)* [8190]
Rimington Trophy Scholarships *(Undergraduate, Graduate/Scholarship)* [2340]
Lois McDonald Rinehart Adelphe Scholarship *(Undergraduate, Graduate/Scholarship)* [5759]
Fauneil J. Rinn Scholarships *(Undergraduate/Scholarship)* [8954]
John T. Riordan Professional Education Scholarships *(Other/Scholarship)* [5307]
Ritchie-Jennings Memorial Scholarships *(Undergraduate, Graduate/Scholarship)* [1923]
Paul H. Rittle Sr. Professional Development Grants *(Other/Grant)* [5217]
Thomas and Ruth River International Scholarships *(Undergraduate, Graduate/Scholarship)* [10704]
Riverside Sheriffs Association Member Scholarship Program *(Graduate, Undergraduate/Scholarship)* [8622]
Anthony Rizzo Scholarship Award *(Professional development/Scholarship)* [7514]
RMNP Research Fellowship *(Graduate/Fellowship)* [8635]
Jerry Robbins Scholarship *(Undergraduate/Scholarship)* [5682]
Robert J. McNamara Student Paper Awards *(Graduate/Award)* [2072]
Robert S. McNamara Fellowships Program (RSMFP) *(Doctorate/Fellowship)* [10698]
Robert Wood Johnson Clinical Scholarships *(Graduate, Professional development/Fellowship)* [8630]
Paul V. Roberts/AEESP Outstanding Doctoral Dissertation Award *(Graduate, Doctorate/Prize, Monetary)* [1953]
Clifford Roberts Graduate Fellowships *(Doctorate/Fellowship)* [4415]
Eugene L. Roberts Jr. Prize *(Undergraduate/Prize)* [10250]
Elliott C. Roberts Scholarships *(Graduate/Scholarship)* [5168]
Actuary of Tomorrow - Stuart A. Robertson Memorial Scholarship *(Undergraduate/Scholarship)* [64]
Lola Ellis Robertson Scholarships *(Graduate, Master's, Doctorate/Scholarship)* [6258]
Ben Robinette Scholarship Endowment Fund *(Undergraduate/Scholarship)* [4211]
Samuel Robinson Awards *(Undergraduate/Award)* [8219]
Helen M. Robinson Grants *(Doctorate/Award, Monetary, Grant)* [5357]
NKA Dr. Violet B. Robinson Memorial Graduate Scholarship *(Advanced Professional/Scholarship)* [7043]
Claude Robinson Scholarships *(Undergraduate/Scholarship)* [7040]
Nell Bryant Robinson Scholarships *(Undergraduate/Scholarship)* [8105]
Paul S. Robinson Scholarships *(Undergraduate/Scholarship)* [9115]
Sara Roby Fellowship in Twentieth-Century American Realism *(Doctorate, Postdoctorate/Fellowship)* [9005]
August M. Rocco Scholarship Fund *(Undergraduate/Scholarship)* [9531]

Rochelle Scholarship *(College/Scholarship)* [6124]
Rockford Area Habitat for Humanity College Scholarships *(Undergraduate/Scholarship)* [3298]
Rockwell Collins Scholarships *(Undergraduate/Scholarship)* [170]
Paul W. Rodgers Scholarship *(Undergraduate, Master's, Doctorate/Scholarship)* [5261]
R.O.E.A. Dumitru Golea Goldy-Gemu Scholarships *(Undergraduate/Scholarship)* [1227]
Kimberly Marie Rogers Memorial Scholarship Fund *(Undergraduate, Vocational/Occupational/Scholarship)* [4057]
Mister Rogers Memorial Scholarship *(Graduate, Master's, Doctorate/Scholarship)* [47]
Joseph Wood Rogers Memorial Scholarships *(Undergraduate/Scholarship)* [8880]
Kenneth Rogers Memorial Scholarships *(Undergraduate/Scholarship)* [6051]
Mary Stuart Rogers Scholarships *(Undergraduate/Scholarship)* [10561]
Sandra Journey Rolf Scholarship Fund *(Undergraduate, Graduate/Scholarship)* [5760]
Rome Prize *(Doctorate, Graduate/Prize, Award)* [424]
Ronald McDonald House Charities African American Future Achievers Scholarships *(Undergraduate/Scholarship)* [8639]
Ronald McDonald House Charities/HACER Scholarships *(Undergraduate/Scholarship)* [8640]
Ronald McDonald House Charities Scholarships in Asia *(Undergraduate/Scholarship)* [8642]
Ronald McDonald House Charities Scholarships *(Undergraduate/Scholarship)* [8641]
Dorothy Worden Ronken Scholarships *(Graduate/Scholarship)* [3594]
Susanna Stover Root Memorial Scholarship *(Undergraduate/Scholarship)* [5761]
Roothbert Fund Scholarships *(Undergraduate/Scholarship)* [8646]
Florence C. Rose and S. Meryl Rose Scholarships *(Graduate, Master's, Doctorate/Scholarship)* [6259]
Dr. Wayne F. Rose Scholarship Fund *(Undergraduate/Scholarship)* [4058]
Betty Rose Scholarships *(Undergraduate/Scholarship)* [1276]
Clarence J. Rosecrans Scholarship *(Graduate, Master's, Doctorate/Scholarship)* [1151]
Rosemary Quigley Memorial Scholarships *(Undergraduate, Graduate/Scholarship)* [2341]
Esther Katz Rosen Fund Grants *(Graduate, Doctorate/Grant)* [1152]
Jack Rosen Scholarship *(Undergraduate/Scholarship)* [5683]
Ollie Rosenberg Educational Trust *(Undergraduate/Scholarship)* [4253]
Mandell and Lester Rosenblatt Undergraduate Scholarships *(Undergraduate/Scholarship)* [9217]
Walter A. Rosenblith New Investigator Award *(Postdoctorate/Award)* [4806]
Barbara Rosenblum Cancer Dissertation Scholarships *(Doctorate/Fellowship, Scholarship)* [9333]
Marshall N. Rosenbluth Outstanding Doctoral Thesis Award *(Doctorate/Award)* [1093]
ASPPH/CDC Allan Rosenfield Global Health Fellowship Program *(Postdoctorate, Postgraduate/Fellowship)* [2065]
Rosenthal Bar Exam Scholarship Fund *(Advanced Professional/Scholarship)* [2444]
Harold W. Rosenthal Fellowships in International Relations *(Professional development/Fellowship, Internship)* [2043]
Marty Rosness Student Scholarships *(Undergraduate/Scholarship)* [1623]
IADR Norton Ross Fellowship *(Postgraduate/Fellowship)* [5253]
Colonel Jerry W. Ross Scholarship *(Undergraduate/Scholarship)* [1585]
The Bea and Harry Ross Scholarship Endowment *(Graduate/Scholarship)* [9586]
Ross Trust Future School Counselors Essay Competition *(Master's, Doctorate/Award, Prize)* [750]
Hon. Rudolph J. Rossetti Memorial Scholarships *(Undergraduate/Scholarship)* [2515]
Rotary Club of Corpus Christi Scholarships *(Undergraduate/Scholarship)* [3106]

Rotary Foundation Global Grant Scholarships *(Graduate/Scholarship)* [8648]
Rotary Peace Fellowship Program *(Graduate, Master's/Fellowship)* [3701]
Rotary Public Safety Scholarships *(Undergraduate/Scholarship)* [4212]
Richard J. Roth Journalism Fellowships *(Graduate/Fellowship)* [7369]
Edward S. Roth Manufacturing Engineering Scholarships *(Graduate, Undergraduate/Scholarship)* [9192]
Marjorie Roy Rothermel Scholarships *(Master's/Scholarship)* [1800]
Hal Rothman Dissertation Fellowships *(Doctorate, Graduate/Fellowship)* [1316]
Theodore Rousseau Fellowships *(Graduate/Fellowship)* [6436]
Marion and Donald Routh Student Research Grants *(Undergraduate/Grant)* [1572]
Rove Pest Control Scholarships *(Undergraduate/Scholarship)* [8650]
Rovelstad Scholarship in International Librarianship *(Undergraduate, Graduate/Award, Scholarship)* [3452]
Roy Rowan Scholarships *(Graduate, Undergraduate/Scholarship)* [7778]
Rowe Family Fellowships *(Graduate/Fellowship)* [7742]
Leo S. Rowe Pan American Fund *(Graduate, Undergraduate/Loan)* [7730]
Travis Roy Foundation Individual Grants *(All/Grant)* [8652]
Lucille and Edward R. Roybal Foundation Public Health Scholarships *(Graduate, Undergraduate/Scholarship)* [8654]
RSDSA Research Grants *(Other/Grant)* [8532]
RSNA/AAPM Fellowships for Graduate Study in Medical Physics *(Graduate/Fellowship)* [560]
RSNA/AUR/APDR/SCARD Radiology Education Research Development Grant *(Professional development/Grant)* [8418]
RSNA Education Scholar Grant *(Professional development/Grant)* [8419]
RSNA Research Scholar Grants *(Professional development/Grant)* [8420]
RSNA Research Seed Grants *(Professional development/Grant)* [8421]
RTDNA Presidents Scholarships *(Undergraduate/Scholarship)* [8411]
IPMI Richard Rubin Memorial Scholarship Award *(Graduate/Award)* [5374]
Paul and Ellen Ruckes Scholarships *(Graduate, Undergraduate/Scholarship)* [823]
Joe Rudd Scholarships *(Master's, Juris Doctorate/Scholarship)* [8637]
Lim Ruger Foundation Scholarships *(Undergraduate/Scholarship)* [5544]
Damon Runyon Clinical Investigator Awards *(Doctorate, Graduate, Postdoctorate/Fellowship, Award)* [3518]
Ruppert Educational Grant Program *(Undergraduate/Grant)* [8955]
Hermann L. Rusch Scholarships *(Other/Scholarship, Grant)* [763]
Russell Athletics Scholarship *(Undergraduate/Scholarship)* [2109]
Liane B. Russell Fellowships *(Postdoctorate/Fellowship)* [9908]
Norman K. Russell Scholarships *(Graduate, Doctorate/Scholarship)* [7092]
The Anthony C. Russo Scholarships *(Graduate/Scholarship)* [7115]
NPELRA Foundation - Anthony C. Russo Scholarships *(Graduate/Scholarship)* [7116]
Lucile Rust Scholarships *(Undergraduate/Scholarship)* [8106]
Deborah Jean Rydberg Memorial Scholarships *(Undergraduate/Scholarship)* [3299]
Charles A. Ryskamp Research Fellowships *(Postgraduate, Postdoctorate, Professional development/Fellowship)* [744]
SAA Native American Scholarships *(Undergraduate, Graduate, Professional development/Scholarship)* [9079]
SABA NC - Organizational Fellowships *(Undergraduate/Fellowship)* [9352]

SABA NC - Pro Bono Fellowships *(Undergraduate/Fellowship)* [9353]
SABA NC - Public Interest Fellowships *(Undergraduate/Fellowship)* [9354]
Sacks For CF Scholarships *(Professional development/Scholarship)* [2342]
SAEMS Environmental Scholarships *(Undergraduate, Graduate/Scholarship)* [9396]
Safer Athletic Field Environments Scholarships (SAFE) *(Graduate, Undergraduate/Scholarship)* [9481]
Russell Sage Foundation Visiting Scholars *(Postdoctorate/Fellowship)* [8668]
Ruth Sager Scholarships *(Undergraduate, Graduate/Scholarship)* [6260]
SAH Study Tour Fellowships *(Graduate/Fellowship)* [9085]
Don Sahli-Kathy Woodall Graduate Scholarships *(Graduate/Scholarship)* [9677]
Sons and Daughters Don Sahli-Kathy Woodall Scholarships *(Graduate, Undergraduate/Scholarship)* [9678]
St. Francis Xavier Scholarships *(Undergraduate/Scholarship)* [10725]
St. James Armenian Church Memorial Scholarships *(Undergraduate/Scholarship)* [1704]
St. Louis Paralegal Association Student Scholarships *(Undergraduate/Scholarship)* [8673]
Saints Cyril and Methodius Scholarships *(Undergraduate/Scholarship)* [8657]
SAJA Journalism Scholarships *(Undergraduate, Graduate/Scholarship)* [9356]
Joseph and Amelia Saks Scholarship Fund *(Undergraduate/Scholarship)* [3270]
The Bill, W2ONV, and Ann Salerno Memorial Scholarship *(Undergraduate/Scholarship)* [1755]
Eugene Gene Sallee, W4YFR Memorial Scholarships *(Undergraduate/Scholarship)* [1756]
Sally Beauty Scholarships for High School Graduates *(Undergraduate/Scholarship)* [8286]
Salon Supply Store Cosmetology Scholarships *(Undergraduate/Scholarship)* [8678]
Salvatori Fellowships *(Graduate/Fellowship)* [5234]
Henry Salvatori Scholarships *(Undergraduate/Scholarship)* [7684]
The Walter Samek III Memorial Scholarship Fund *(Undergraduate/Scholarship)* [3207]
SAMFund Grants *(Advanced Professional/Grant)* [8682]
Margaret Jerome Sampson Scholarships *(Undergraduate/Scholarship)* [8107]
Ray and Pearl Sams Scholarships *(Undergraduate/Scholarship)* [10597]
Samsung American Legion Scholarships *(Undergraduate/Scholarship)* [957]
Sand Hill Scholars Program *(Undergraduate/Scholarship)* [8957]
Bill Sanderson Aviation Maintenance Technician Scholarships *(Postgraduate/Scholarship)* [4841]
Leonard H. Sandler Fellowships *(Graduate/Fellowship)* [5000]
The Amato Sanita Brighter Future Scholarships *(Undergraduate, Graduate, Advanced Professional/Scholarship)* [379]
SANS Inc./Mead Leadership Fellows Program *(Professional development/Fellowship)* [7509]
SAO (Smithsonian Astrophysical Observatory) Predoctoral Fellowships *(Graduate/Fellowship)* [4782]
Bert Saperstein Communication Scholarships *(Undergraduate/Scholarship)* [8758]
Saratoga County Bar Association Law Student Scholarships *(Undergraduate/Scholarship)* [8760]
Frank Sarli Memorial Scholarship *(Undergraduate/Scholarship)* [6899]
Saskatchewan Trucking Association Scholarships *(Undergraduate/Scholarship)* [8784]
Sho Sato Memorial Scholarships *(Undergraduate, Graduate/Scholarship)* [5557]
Satter Human Rights Fellowships *(Graduate, Master's, Juris Doctorate/Fellowship)* [4787]
Dave Sauer Memorial College Scholarships *(Undergraduate/Scholarship)* [150]
James A. Sauer Memorial Fellowships *(Graduate/Fellowship)* [662]

Curtis M. Saulsbury Scholarship Fund *(Undergraduate/Scholarship)* [3201]
Save Mart Legacy Scholarships *(Undergraduate/Scholarship)* [2458]
John A. Savoy Scholarship Fund *(Undergraduate/Scholarship)* [4059]
Bill Sawyer Memorial Scholarships *(Undergraduate/Scholarship)* [6052]
Herbert M. Saylor Memorial Scholarship *(Graduate/Scholarship)* [9341]
SBE/Ennes Youth Scholarships *(Undergraduate/Scholarship)* [9094]
SC and R Foundation Scholarships *(Undergraduate/Scholarship)* [9460]
Leslie and Mary Ella Scales Memorial Scholarships *(Undergraduate/Scholarship)* [3271]
SC&R Foundation Grant Program *(Undergraduate/Grant)* [9461]
SCBWI Student Illustrator Scholarship *(Undergraduate, Graduate/Grant, Scholarship)* [9099]
SCBWI Student Writer Scholarship *(Graduate, Doctorate, Undergraduate/Grant, Scholarship)* [9100]
SCBWI Work-in-Progress Awards *(Advanced Professional/Grant, Award)* [9101]
SCCLA Fellowships *(Graduate/Fellowship)* [9398]
SCCLA Scholarships *(Graduate/Scholarship)* [9399]
SCDAA Post-Doctoral Research Fellowships *(Doctorate/Fellowship)* [8892]
Mary Turnbull Schacht Memorial Scholarships *(Undergraduate/Scholarship)* [8934]
David W. Schacht Native American Student Scholarships *(Undergraduate/Scholarship)* [2231]
Schallek Awards *(Graduate/Award)* [6397]
Schallek Fellowships *(Graduate/Fellowship)* [6398]
Schatz Energy Fellowships for Graduate Studies *(Graduate/Fellowship)* [5004]
Abe Schechter Graduate Scholarships *(Graduate/Scholarship)* [8400]
Schedulers and Dispatchers Monetary Scholarships *(Other/Scholarship)* [6837]
Leopold Schepp Foundation Scholarships *(Undergraduate, Graduate/Scholarship)* [8788]
Justin G. Schiller Fellowships *(Doctorate, Postdoctorate/Fellowship)* [445]
Arthur M. Schlesinger, Jr. Fellowships *(Professional development/Fellowship)* [5603]
Harold W. Schloss Memorial Scholarship Fund *(Undergraduate/Scholarship)* [2810]
Esther Schlundt Memorial Scholarships *(Graduate/Scholarship)* [5112]
Julie Schmid Research Scholarship *(Advanced Professional/Scholarship)* [2033]
Ronald L. Schmied Scholarships *(Other, Undergraduate/Scholarship)* [4686]
Bernadotte E. Schmitt Grants *(Doctorate/Grant)* [856]
Prof. George Schneider, Jr. Manufacturing Technology Education Scholarships *(Undergraduate/Scholarship)* [9193]
Richard J. Schnell Memorial Scholarships *(Postdoctorate/Scholarship)* [3300]
Stanley M. Schoenfeld Memorial Scholarship *(Postgraduate/Scholarship)* [7363]
Lillian P. Schoephoerster Scholarships *(Undergraduate/Scholarship)* [8108]
Dale M. Schoettler Scholarships *(Undergraduate, Graduate/Scholarship)* [8753]
The Scholarship Foundation of St. Louis Scholarships *(Graduate, Undergraduate/Scholarship)* [8796]
Scholarship Foundation of Santa Barbara General Undergraduate,Vocational and Graduate/Medical Scholarships and Loans Program *(Undergraduate, Graduate/Scholarship)* [8799]
Scholarship for Junior PHS Commissioned Officers *(Undergraduate/Scholarship)* [8115]
Scholarships of the Morris Radio Club of New Jersey *(Undergraduate/Scholarship)* [1757]
Scholarships for Veterans with Post-Traumatic Stress Disorder *(All/Scholarship)* [8624]
School Nutrition Association of Kansas Education Scholarship *(Undergraduate/Scholarship)* [8810]
Schoolsfirst Federal Credit Union Scholarships *(Undergraduate/Scholarship)* [8526]
Schrank Family Scholarships *(Undergraduate/Scholarship)* [10189]

Kurt H. and Donna M. Schuler Cash Grants *(Undergraduate/Scholarship, Grant)* [1254]
Alice Southworth Schulman, Class of 1954, Simmons Scholarships for Unitarian Universalist Women *(Undergraduate/Scholarship)* [9838]
Richard E. Schultes Research Awards *(Graduate/Grant, Award)* [9113]
Al Schuman/Ecolab Undergraduate Entrepreneurial Scholarships *(Undergraduate/Scholarship)* [7120]
James F. Schumar Scholarships *(Graduate/Fellowship)* [1039]
Schurgin Family Foundation Scholarships *(Undergraduate/Scholarship)* [5308]
Karen Schuvie Scholarships *(Undergraduate/Scholarship, Loan)* [5663]
AIST William E. Schwabe Memorial Scholarships *(Undergraduate/Scholarship)* [2007]
Schwan's Food Service Scholarships *(Vocational/Occupational/Scholarship)* [8806]
Marla Schwartz Education Grant *(Graduate, Professional development/Grant)* [534]
Marla Schwartz Grants *(Professional development, Graduate/Grant)* [535]
Abba P. Schwartz Research Fellowships *(Professional development/Fellowship)* [5604]
Fritz Schwartz Serials Education Scholarships *(Graduate, Other/Scholarship)* [7447]
Evalee C. Schwarz Educational Loans *(Undergraduate, Graduate/Loan)* [8812]
David R. Schweisberg Memorial Scholarships *(Graduate, Undergraduate/Scholarship)* [7779]
Science Foundation Arizona Graduate Research Fellowships (GRF) *(Graduate/Fellowship)* [8814]
Science, Mathematics And Research for Transformation Scholarship for Service Program (SMART) *(Undergraduate, Graduate/Scholarship)* [1305]
SCIRTS (Spinal Cord Injury Research on the Translational Spectrum) Pilot Research Grants *(Professional development/Grant)* [7257]
SCIRTS (Spinal Cord Injury Research on the Translational Spectrum) Postdoctoral Fellowships *(Postdoctorate/Fellowship)* [7258]
SCIRTS (Spinal Cord Injury Research on the Translational Spectrum) Senior Research Grants *(Professional development/Grant)* [7259]
Scleroderma Foundation Established Investigator Grants *(Doctorate/Grant)* [8816]
Scleroderma Foundation New Investigator Grants *(Doctorate/Grant)* [8817]
Carl A. Scott Book Scholarships *(Undergraduate/Scholarship)* [3456]
IADR David B. Scott Fellowship *(Professional development/Fellowship, Award)* [5254]
Herbert Scoville Jr. Peace Fellowships *(Graduate/Fellowship)* [8825]
Bonnie Sorenson Scudder Scholarships *(Undergraduate/Scholarship)* [3301]
Seabee Memorial Scholarship Association Scholarships *(Undergraduate/Scholarship)* [9043]
Glenn T. Seaborg Congressional Science and Engineering Fellowships *(Professional development/Fellowship)* [1040]
Seaman Family Scholarships *(Undergraduate/Scholarship)* [3108]
Lewis L. Seaman Junior Enlisted Awards for Outstanding Operational Support *(Professional development/Recognition)* [1541]
SEE Education Foundation Scholarships *(Undergraduate, Graduate, Doctorate/Scholarship)* [5418]
Seed Companies Scholarships *(Undergraduate, Graduate/Scholarship)* [811]
Aaron Seesan Memorial Scholarship Fund *(Undergraduate/Scholarship)* [9532]
Dr. Eugene M. Seidner Student Scholarship Program *(Undergraduate, Graduate/Scholarship)* [35]
D. Mitchell Self Memorial Scholarship *(Undergraduate/Scholarship)* [7549]
Walter and Rita Selvy Scholarship *(Undergraduate/Scholarship)* [3688]
SEMA Memorial Scholarships *(Graduate, Undergraduate/Scholarship)* [9464]
Senior Innovation Scholarships *(Undergraduate, Graduate/Scholarship)* [8146]
SeniorAdvice Caregiver Scholarships *(Undergraduate/Scholarship)* [8840]

SeniorAdvice Volunteer Scholarships *(Undergraduate/Scholarship)* [8841]
Sentinels of Freedom Scholarships *(Advanced Professional/Scholarship)* [8843]
William "Buddy" Sentner Scholarship Awards *(Undergraduate/Scholarship)* [566]
Senyk Memorial Scholarships *(Undergraduate, Master's/Scholarship)* [10801]
SEO Optimizers Scholarships *(All/Scholarship)* [8845]
Sequoyah Graduate Scholarships *(Master's/Scholarship)* [1834]
Serbian Bar Association of America Scholarships *(Graduate/Scholarship)* [8847]
Charles W. Serby COPD Research Fellowships *(Professional development/Fellowship)* [1216]
Sertoma Communicative Disorders Scholarship *(Undergraduate/Scholarship)* [8849]
Sertoma Hard of Hearing and Deaf Scholarships *(Undergraduate/Scholarship)* [8850]
Frank B. Sessa Scholarship *(Professional development/Scholarship)* [2241]
Roger Sessions Memorial Bogliasco Fellowships in Music *(Professional development/Fellowship)* [2331]
Seton Hall Law Merit Scholarships *(Graduate/Scholarship)* [8855]
Margaret B. Ševčenko Prize in Islamic Art and Culture *(Doctorate/Prize)* [4909]
John R. Sevier Memorial Scholarship Award *(Undergraduate/Scholarship)* [9998]
Hubert K. and JoAnn Seymour Scholarships *(Undergraduate/Scholarship)* [7492]
SFP Junior Investigator's Career Development Awards *(Other/Grant)* [9119]
SFP Mid-Career/Mentor Awards for Family Planning *(Other/Grant)* [9120]
SFP Student Research Grants *(Graduate/Grant)* [9121]
Al Shackleford and Dan Martin Professional Scholarships *(Professional development/Scholarship)* [2193]
Barbara A. Shacochis Scholarships *(Undergraduate/Scholarship)* [8003]
Albert R. and Alma Shadle Fellowships *(Graduate/Fellowship)* [1361]
Charles Shafae Scholarships *(Undergraduate/Scholarship)* [7799]
Elizabeth Shafer Memorial Scholarships *(Undergraduate/Scholarship)* [8362]
SHAFR Dissertation Completion Fellowships *(Doctorate/Fellowship)* [9140]
Saleem Shah Early Career Award *(Doctorate/Recognition)* [1158]
Shamberg Scholarships *(Undergraduate/Scholarship)* [10431]
Albert F. Shanker Scholarship *(Undergraduate/Scholarship)* [796]
William H. Shannon Fellowships *(Graduate, Undergraduate/Fellowship)* [5445]
Law Office of David P. Shapiro Annual Leukemia Scholarships *(All/Scholarship)* [5949]
Benjamin G. Shatz Scholarships *(Undergraduate/Scholarship)* [8004]
Luci Shaw Fellowship *(Undergraduate/Fellowship)* [5081]
Anne Shaw Fellowships *(Graduate/Fellowship)* [9727]
Josephine Kerbey Shaw Memorial Undergraduate Scholarship *(Undergraduate/Scholarship)* [5763]
Donna Gail Shaw Scholarship for Chapter Service *(Undergraduate, Graduate, Doctorate/Scholarship)* [5684]
Shear-Miles Agricultural Fellowship *(Graduate, Doctorate/Fellowship)* [10205]
Shear-Miles Agricultural Scholarship *(Graduate, Doctorate/Scholarship)* [10206]
Regina B. Shearn Scholarships *(Graduate, Undergraduate/Scholarship)* [357]
Jim Sheerin Scholarships *(Undergraduate/Scholarship)* [6362]
Sheet Metal And Air Conditioning Contractors' National Association College of Fellows Scholarships *(Undergraduate/Scholarship)* [8859]
Shell Incentive Scholarship Fund *(Undergraduate/Scholarship)* [8861]

Shell Oil Company Technical Scholarships (Undergraduate/Scholarship) [8862]
Shell Process Technology Scholarships (Undergraduate/Scholarship) [8863]
Susan Goldsmith Shelley Scholarship (Undergraduate/Scholarship) [5764]
Bruce Shelton Scholarships (Undergraduate/Scholarship) [10598]
Bill and Ann Sheperd Legal Scholarship Fund (Undergraduate/Scholarship) [3923]
Joseph Henry Shepherd Scholarship (Undergraduate/Scholarship) [10173]
Robert P. Sheppard Leadership Awards (High School/Scholarship) [7162]
Marion A. and Ruth Sherwood Family Fund Education Scholarships (Undergraduate/Scholarship) [4546]
Marion A. and Ruth K. Sherwood Family Fund Engineering Scholarships (Undergraduate/Scholarship) [4547]
Morgan and Jeanie Sherwood Travel Grants (Graduate, Other/Grant) [1317]
Shields-Gillespie Scholarships (Other/Scholarship) [1056]
Jacqueline Shields Memorial Scholarships (Graduate/Scholarship) [142]
Milton L. Shifman Endowed Scholarships (Undergraduate, Graduate/Scholarship) [6261]
Chiyoko and Thomas Shimazaki Scholarships (Graduate/Scholarship) [5558]
The Shincho Graduate Fellowships for Study in Japan (Graduate/Fellowship) [5802]
Shinn Family Scholarships (Undergraduate/Scholarship) [6054]
Joseph Shinoda Memorial Scholarships (Undergraduate/Scholarship) [8867]
Jason Shipley Memorial Scholarships (Undergraduate/Scholarship) [7041]
Shohet Scholars Program (Professional development/Grant) [5290]
Shoreline Community College Part-Time Students Scholarships (Undergraduate/Scholarship) [8882]
Short-term Senior Fellowships in Iranian Studies (Professional development/Fellowship) [914]
SHOT-NASA Fellowships (Doctorate, Postdoctorate/Fellowship) [9144]
Thomas E. Shown, M.D. Memorial Scholarships (Undergraduate/Scholarship) [10599]
SHPE Dissertation Scholarship (Doctorate/Scholarship) [9130]
SHPE Professional Scholarship (Master's, Doctorate/Scholarship) [9131]
Ralph W. Shrader Diversity Scholarship (Graduate/Scholarship) [91]
SHRM Certification Scholarships - Individual (Professional development/Scholarship) [9147]
SHRM Foundation Academic Scholarships (Graduate, Undergraduate/Scholarship) [9148]
Law Office of Matthew Shrum Annual Scholarships for Single Mothers (Undergraduate/Scholarship) [5953]
Clifford G. Shull Fellowships (Postdoctorate/Fellowship) [9909]
Mary Isabel Sibley Fellowships (Doctorate/Fellowship) [8053]
SICB Fellowships of Graduate Student Travel (FGST) (Graduate/Fellowship) [9157]
SICB Grants-in-Aid of Research Program (GIAR) (Graduate/Grant) [9158]
Sidley Diversity and Inclusion Scholarships (Undergraduate/Scholarship) [8894]
Sidley Prelaw Scholars Initiative (Undergraduate/Scholarship) [8895]
Norman Siegel Research Scholar Grants (Doctorate/Grant) [1382]
Jeff Siegel Scholarships (Undergraduate/Scholarship) [7359]
Siemens-ASCP Scholarship (Undergraduate/Scholarship) [1263]
Siemens Clinical Advancement Scholarship (Undergraduate, Master's/Scholarship) [1400]
E.J. Sierleja Memorial Fellowships (Graduate/Fellowship) [5194]
Sigma Delta Epsilon Fellowships (Graduate, Postdoctorate/Fellowship) [8907]
Sigma Diagnostics Student Scholarships (Undergraduate/Scholarship) [7171]
Sigma Kappa Foundation Alumnae Continuing Education Scholarships (Undergraduate/Scholarship) [8935]
Sigma Kappa Foundation Alzheimer's/Gerontology Scholarships (Graduate/Scholarship) [8936]
Sigma Kappa Foundation Founders' Scholarships (Undergraduate/Scholarship) [8937]
Sigma Kappa Foundation Gerontology Scholarships (Undergraduate/Scholarship) [8938]
Sigma Kappa Foundation Michigan Scholarships (Undergraduate/Scholarship) [8939]
Meyer D. and Dorothy C. Silverman Scholarship (Undergraduate/Scholarship) [3251]
Stuart Silverman Scholarships (Undergraduate/Scholarship) [8005]
Willard B. Simmons Sr. Memorial Scholarships (Undergraduate/Scholarship) [6871]
Julian Simon Fellowships (Other/Fellowship) [8300]
Simon Youth Foundation Community Scholarships (Undergraduate/Scholarship) [8959]
Simonton Windows Scholarships (Undergraduate/Scholarship) [7864]
DW Simpson Actuarial Science Scholarship Program (Undergraduate/Scholarship) [8963]
Carole Simpson Scholarships (Undergraduate/Scholarship) [8412]
Aaron B. Singleton Memorial Scholarship (Undergraduate/Scholarship) [7550]
Sino-American Pharmaceutical Professionals Association Scholarships (Undergraduate/Scholarship) [8971]
Helen J. Sioussat/Fay Wells Scholarships (Graduate/Scholarship) [2371]
Sixt Rent a Car Scholarships (Undergraduate/Scholarship) [8973]
Leif and Inger Sjöberg Awards (Advanced Professional, Professional development/Award, Grant, Prize) [1235]
Skadden Fellowships (Graduate/Fellowship) [8978]
Francelene Skinner Memorial Scholarships (Undergraduate/Scholarship) [6067]
Rand Skolnick Point Scholarship (Undergraduate, Graduate, Doctorate/Scholarship) [8191]
Skooblie Scholarships (Undergraduate/Scholarship) [8984]
Allogan Slagle Memorial Scholarships (Undergraduate, Graduate/Scholarship) [1835]
Robert W. Sledge Fellowships (Graduate/Fellowship) [344]
Sleeping Angels Co. Scholarships (All/Scholarship) [8986]
Slifka Foundation Interdisciplinary Fellowships (Doctorate, Master's/Fellowship) [6437]
Alfred P. Sloan Foundation Graduate Scholarships - Sloan Indigenous Graduate Partnership (Master's, Doctorate/Scholarship) [6683]
Alfred P. Sloan Foundation Graduate Scholarships - Sloan Minority Ph.D. Program (Doctorate/Scholarship) [6684]
Sloan Northwood University Heavy-Duty Scholarships (Undergraduate/Scholarship) [2127]
Sloan Research Fellowships (Doctorate/Fellowship) [8988]
Thomas J. Slocum Memorial Scholarships to Redstone College (Undergraduate/Scholarship) [171]
The Aaron and Rita Slom Scholarships (Undergraduate/Scholarship) [9762]
Ann Kelsay Small Scholarship (Undergraduate/Scholarship) [5766]
SME Coal and Energy Division Scholarships (Undergraduate/Scholarship) [9212]
SME Directors Scholarships (Undergraduate/Scholarship) [9194]
SME Education Foundation Family Scholarships (Undergraduate/Scholarship) [9195]
SME Environmental Division Scholarships (Undergraduate, Graduate/Scholarship) [9213]
Dr. George M. Smerk Scholarships (Undergraduate, Graduate/Scholarship) [1169]
SMFM/AAOGF Scholarship Awards (Graduate/Scholarship) [9206]
SmileMarketing Dental Scholarships (Doctorate/Scholarship) [8990]
James I. Smith, III Notre Dame Law School Scholarship Fund (Graduate, Undergraduate/Scholarship) [329]
David H. Smith Conservation Research Fellowships (Postdoctorate/Fellowship) [9109]
Hy Smith Endowment Fund (Undergraduate/Scholarship) [4704]
Ryan and Jamie Smith Essay Contest (Graduate, Postgraduate/Scholarship) [8992]
Smith Family Awards Program for Excellence in Biomedical Research (Advanced Professional, Professional development/Grant) [4823]
Henry DeWitt Smith Graduate Scholarships (Graduate/Scholarship) [9214]
Stanley Smith Horticultural Fellowships (Graduate, Undergraduate/Fellowship) [7744]
Brian and Cathy Smith Memorial Fund (Graduate/Scholarship) [1016]
Colonel Nate Smith Memorial Scholarships (Graduate, Undergraduate/Scholarship) [6374]
Tacy Anna Smith Memorial Scholarships (Undergraduate/Scholarship) [4213]
Ralph and Josephine Smith Scholarship Fund (Undergraduate/Scholarship) [4060]
A.O. Smith Scholarships (Undergraduate/Scholarship) [8164]
C. Bainbridge Smith Scholarships (Undergraduate/Scholarship) [7344]
Helen J. and Harold Gilman Smith Scholarships (Graduate, Undergraduate/Scholarship) [2232]
Joseph Sumner Smith Scholarships (Undergraduate/Scholarship) [9839]
Richard S. Smith Scholarships (Undergraduate/Scholarship) [9858]
William E. Smith Scholarships (Graduate/Scholarship) [199]
Nadine Barrie Smith Student Awards (Undergraduate/Award) [5433]
Smithsonian Institution Graduate Student Fellowships (Graduate/Fellowship) [9015]
Smithsonian Institution Postdoctoral Fellowships (Doctorate/Fellowship) [9016]
Smithsonian Institution Predoctoral Fellowships (Doctorate/Fellowship) [9017]
Smithsonian Institution Senior Fellowships (Doctorate/Fellowship) [9018]
Smithsonian Postgraduate Fellowships in Conservation of Museum Collection Program (Postgraduate/Fellowship) [9019]
Virginia M. Smyth Scholarships (Graduate/Scholarship) [4382]
Gladys Snauble Scholarships (Undergraduate/Scholarship) [4622]
SNF Professional Growth Scholarships (Graduate, Undergraduate/Scholarship) [8807]
SNMMI-TS Advanced Practitioner Program Scholarship (Professional development/Scholarship) [9224]
SNMMI-TS Bachelor's Degree Completion Scholarships (Undergraduate/Scholarship) [9225]
William Brewster Snow Award (Graduate/Award, Monetary) [1954]
A.C. Snow and Katherine Snow Smith Scholarship (Undergraduate/Scholarship) [10251]
Helen D. Snow Memorial Scholarships (Undergraduate/Scholarship) [8056]
Snowmobile Association of Massachusetts Scholarships (Undergraduate/Scholarship) [9045]
SNRS Research Grants (Professional development/Grant) [9407]
SNRS/STTI Research Grants (Professional development/Grant) [9408]
SOAP/Kybele International Outreach Grant (Advanced Professional, Professional development/Grant) [9231]
Arnold Sobel Scholarships (Undergraduate/Scholarship) [3081]
SOBP Travel Fellowship Award-Early Career Investigator(International) (Postdoctorate/Award) [9090]
Society of Allied Weight Engineers Scholarships (Undergraduate/Scholarship) [9077]
Society for the Arts in Healthcare Student Scholarships (Doctorate, Graduate, Undergraduate/Scholarship) [9088]
Society of Exploration Geophysicists Foundation Scholarships (Graduate, Undergraduate/Scholarship) [9117]

Society for Linguistic Anthropology Student Essay Prize *(Graduate, Undergraduate/Prize)* [9163]
Society of Manufacturing Engineers Ford PAS Scholarships (SME) *(Undergraduate/Scholarship)* [9197]
Society of Marine Port Engineers Scholarship Loans *(Undergraduate/Scholarship loan)* [9204]
Society of Pediatric Nurses Educational Scholarships *(Graduate, Other/Scholarship)* [9241]
Society for Pediatric Radiology Research Fellows *(Graduate, Other/Fellowship)* [9243]
Society for Pediatric Radiology Seed Grants *(Graduate, Other/Grant)* [9244]
Society for Pediatric Urology Research Grant Program *(Undergraduate/Grant)* [9247]
Society for the Scientific Study of Sexuality Student Research Grants *(Undergraduate/Grant)* [9302]
Society of Vacuum Coaters Foundation Scholarships *(Vocational/Occupational, Two Year College, Undergraduate, Graduate/Scholarship)* [9323]
SOHN Allied Health to BSN Degree Scholarship *(Undergraduate/Scholarship)* [9233]
Louis B. Sohn Fellowships in Human Rights and Environment *(Graduate/Fellowship)* [2849]
SOHN Graduate Degree Scholarship *(Undergraduate/Scholarship)* [9234]
SOHN RN to BSN Degree Scholarship *(Undergraduate/Scholarship)* [9235]
The Thomas Soldan Healthy Communities Scholarships *(Undergraduate, Graduate/Scholarship)* [8237]
Carrie Fox Solin Blow Molding Division Memorial Scholarships *(Undergraduate/Scholarship)* [9268]
SOM Foundation Architecture, Design and Urban Design Prize *(Graduate, Undergraduate/Prize)* [8980]
SOM Foundation Structural Engineering Travel Fellowships *(Doctorate, Graduate, Master's, Undergraduate/Fellowship)* [8981]
SOM Foundation Travel Fellowships in Architecture, Design and Urban Design *(Graduate, Undergraduate/Fellowship)* [8982]
SOMA Student Research Fellowships *(Undergraduate/Fellowship)* [9601]
Dr. Kiyoshi Sonoda Memorial Scholarships *(Graduate, Master's, Doctorate/Scholarship)* [5559]
Sons of Norway Foundation Scholarships to Oslo International Summer School *(Undergraduate/Scholarship)* [9346]
Sons of Union Veterans of the Civil War Scholarships *(Undergraduate/Scholarship)* [9348]
Sony Pictures Scholarships *(Graduate/Scholarship)* [2027]
SOPHE/ATSDR Student Fellowships in Environmental Health or Emergency Preparedness *(Doctorate, Graduate, Master's/Fellowship)* [9292]
SOPHE/CDC Student Fellowships in Child, Adolescent and School Health *(Doctorate, Graduate, Master's/Fellowship)* [9293]
SOPHE/CDC Student Fellowships in Injury Prevention *(Graduate/Fellowship)* [9294]
Theodore C. Sorensen Research Fellowships *(Professional development/Fellowship)* [5605]
Soroptimist International of Chambersburg Scholarship Fund *(Undergraduate/Scholarship)* [4255]
Paul & Daisy Soros Fellowships *(Graduate/Fellowship)* [9350]
Soros Justice Advocacy Fellowships - Track I *(Professional development/Fellowship)* [7664]
Soros Justice Advocacy Fellowships - Track II *(Professional development/Fellowship)* [7665]
Soros Justice Media Fellowships - Track I *(Professional development/Fellowship)* [7666]
Soros Justice Media Fellowships - Track II *(Professional development/Fellowship)* [7667]
SORP Student Conference Scholarship *(Graduate, Undergraduate/Scholarship)* [9237]
Eastman Kodak Dr. Theophilus Sorrell Fellowships *(Graduate/Fellowship)* [7090]
South Carolina Association for Financial Professionals Certified Treasury Professional Scholarships *(Other/Scholarship)* [9358]
South Carolina Scholastic Press Association Scholarships *(Undergraduate/Scholarship)* [9370]
South Carolina Scholastic Press Association Yearbook Scholarships *(Undergraduate/Scholarship)* [9371]
South Carolina Tourism and Hospitality Educational Foundation Scholarships *(Undergraduate/Scholarship)* [9366]
South Carolina Undergraduate Scholarships *(Undergraduate/Scholarship)* [9367]
South Central Modern Language Association Fellowships *(Doctorate, Postdoctorate/Fellowship)* [7424]
South Central Power Scholarships *(Undergraduate/Scholarship)* [9373]
South Dakota Division Scholarships *(Undergraduate/Scholarship)* [6525]
South Jersey Golf Association Scholarships *(Undergraduate/Scholarship)* [9379]
Southern Nevada Sports Hall of Fame Scholarships *(Undergraduate/Scholarship)* [8364]
Southern Scholarship Foundation Scholarships *(Undergraduate/Scholarship)* [9413]
Southwest Movers Association Scholarships *(Undergraduate/Scholarship)* [9454]
Sovereign Nations Scholarships *(Undergraduate/Scholarship)* [872]
Iwalani Carpenter Sowa Scholarships *(Graduate/Scholarship)* [7919]
Master Sergeant William Sowers Memorial Scholarships *(Undergraduate/Scholarship)* [133]
Michael P. Spadafora Medical Toxicology Travel Awards *(Professional development/Grant)* [690]
Amy E. Spain Memorial Scholarships *(Undergraduate/Scholarship)* [10174]
Spangenberg Shibley & Liber Video PSA Scholarship Awards *(Undergraduate/Scholarship)* [9456]
Nathan Sparks Memorial Scholarships *(Undergraduate/Scholarship)* [3272]
SPE Foundation General Scholarships *(Undergraduate, Graduate/Scholarship)* [9269]
SPE Injection Molding Division Scholarships *(Undergraduate, Graduate/Scholarship)* [9271]
SPE Student Awards for Innovations in Imaging *(Undergraduate, Graduate/Scholarship)* [9252]
SPE Thermoforming Division Memorial Scholarships *(Undergraduate, Graduate/Scholarship)* [9272]
SPE Thermoplastic Elastomers Special Interest Group Scholarship *(Undergraduate, Graduate/Scholarship)* [9273]
SPE Thermoplastic Materials and Foams Division Scholarships *(Undergraduate/Scholarship)* [9274]
SPE Vinyl Plastics Division Educational Grants *(Undergraduate/Grant)* [9275]
Special Events Internships - Los Angeles *(Undergraduate, Graduate/Internship)* [4438]
Special Events Internships - New York *(Undergraduate, Graduate/Internship)* [4439]
Special Fund for the Study of Women and Politics *(Graduate, Postdoctorate/Grant)* [1123]
Specialty Equipment Market Association Scholarships *(Graduate, Undergraduate, Vocational/Occupational/Scholarship)* [9465]
Specialty Nursing Scholarships *(Undergraduate/Scholarship)* [4270]
Spice Box Grants *(Advanced Professional/Grant)* [764]
SPIE Student Author Travel Grants *(Graduate, Undergraduate/Grant)* [9472]
Phillip A. Spiegel IASP Congress Trainee Scholarship *(College, Graduate, Undergraduate/Scholarship)* [5276]
Charles and Carol Spielberger Scholarships *(Graduate, Master's, Doctorate/Scholarship)* [1153]
Spirit of Anne Frank Outstanding Scholarship Award *(Undergraduate/Scholarship)* [1563]
The Spirit Square Center for Arts and Education Scholarship Fund *(Undergraduate/Scholarship)* [4214]
Spokeo Connections Scholarships *(Undergraduate/Scholarship)* [9478]
SPOOM Research Grants *(Graduate/Grant)* [9277]
Sports Internships - Los Angeles *(Undergraduate, Graduate/Internship)* [4440]
Sporty's/Cincinnati Avionics Scholarships *(Undergraduate, Vocational/Occupational/Scholarship)* [172]
Spotlight on Nursing Graduate Nursing Student Scholarships *(Graduate/Scholarship)* [9484]
Spouse Tuition Aid Loan Program (STAP) *(Undergraduate, Graduate/Loan)* [7236]
The Springfield Family Scholarships *(Undergraduate/Scholarship)* [10175]
SPS Future Teacher Scholarships *(Undergraduate/Scholarship)* [9256]
SPS Leadership Scholarships *(Undergraduate/Scholarship)* [9257]
SPSmedical CS Scholarships *(Other/Scholarship)* [5264]
SPSSI Grants-In-Aid Program *(Graduate, Postdoctorate/Grant)* [9287]
SRC Master's Scholarships Program (MSP) *(Graduate, Master's/Scholarship)* [8835]
SREB-State Doctoral Scholars Program - Dissertation Awards *(Doctorate/Scholarship, Award)* [9410]
SREB-State Doctoral Scholars Program - Doctoral Awards *(Doctorate, Graduate/Scholarship)* [9411]
SRF Post-doctoral Fellowships *(Postdoctorate/Fellowship)* [8819]
SSF Research Grants *(Other/Grant)* [8975]
SSF Student Fellowships *(Doctorate, Undergraduate/Fellowship)* [8976]
The SSPI Mid-Atlantic Chapter Scholarships *(Graduate, Undergraduate/Scholarship)* [9300]
John F. and Anna Lee Stacey Scholarships *(All/Scholarship)* [6901]
Ernest and Charlene Stachowiak Memorial Scholarships *(Undergraduate/Scholarship)* [3302]
Stafford Loan for Graduate Students - Unsubsidized Stafford Loans *(Graduate/Loan)* [9486]
Matt Stager Memorial Scholarship Fund *(Undergraduate/Scholarship)* [10482]
Steven A. Stahl Research Grants *(Graduate/Grant)* [5358]
Standard and Poor's Award for Economic and Business Reporting - S&P Scholarships *(Graduate, Undergraduate/Scholarship)* [7780]
Marion Barr Stanfield Art Scholarships *(Graduate, Undergraduate/Scholarship)* [9840]
Otto M. Stanfield Law Scholarships *(Graduate/Scholarship)* [9841]
A.R.O.Y. Stanitz Scholarships *(Undergraduate/Scholarship)* [1228]
J. Newell Stannard Fellowships *(Graduate/Fellowship)* [4812]
Thomas J. Stanton, Jr. Scholarships *(Graduate/Scholarship)* [8853]
Star-Ledger Scholarships for the Performing Arts *(Undergraduate/Scholarship)* [7324]
Kenneth and Barbara Starks Plant Resistance to Insects Graduate Student Research Awards *(Graduate/Grant)* [3884]
STC-PSC Scholarships *(Undergraduate, Graduate/Scholarship)* [9315]
STC Scholarships *(Graduate, Undergraduate/Scholarship)* [9311]
The Stanley H. Stearman Awards *(Undergraduate/Scholarship)* [7135]
Robert P. Stearns/SCS Engineers Scholarships *(Graduate/Scholarship)* [9339]
Tom Steel Post-Graduate Fellowships *(Postgraduate, Other/Fellowship)* [8274]
Joseph S. Steinberg Emerging Jewish Filmmaker Fellowships *(Undergraduate, Graduate/Fellowship)* [2856]
Cecilia Steinfeldt Fellowships for Research in the Arts and Material Culture *(Professional development/Fellowship)* [9717]
Peter T. Steinwedell Scholarships *(Undergraduate/Scholarship)* [4772]
Elin J. Stene/Xi Scholarships *(Undergraduate/Scholarship)* [8940]
Gabe Stepetin Business Scholarship Awards *(Undergraduate, Vocational/Occupational, Graduate, Master's/Scholarship)* [312]
Mike Stephenson Legal Scholarships *(Graduate/Scholarship)* [6370]
Elizabeth Coulter Stephenson Scholarships *(Undergraduate/Scholarship, Grant)* [3595]
Charles Sternberg Scholarship *(Graduate/Scholarship)* [1844]
Richard Stessel Memorial Scholarships *(Graduate/Scholarship)* [143]
AGWT Thomas M. Stetson Scholarships *(Under-

graduate/Scholarship) [841]
Raymond H. Stetson Scholarships in Phonetics and Speech Science (Graduate/Scholarship) [54]
Christine K. Stevens Development Scholarships (Undergraduate, Graduate/Scholarship) [1017]
Stevens Doctoral Awards (Doctorate/Award) [5312]
Benjamin F. Stevens Fellowships (Professional development/Fellowship) [6337]
H.L. Stevenson Scholarships (Graduate, Undergraduate/Scholarship) [7781]
Richie Stevenson Scholarships (Undergraduate, Vocational/Occupational/Scholarship) [3253]
Allegheny Branch of Mid-America Chapter - Nancy Stewart Professional Development Scholarships (Professional development/Scholarship) [1443]
Dr. Gunnar B. Stickler Scholarships (Undergraduate, Vocational/Occupational/Scholarship) [9578]
Dell Chenoweth Stifel Scholarship (Graduate/Scholarship) [5767]
The Richard Stockton College of New Jersey Foundation Alumni Association Graduate Awards (Graduate/Scholarship) [9587]
Louis Stokes Health Scholars Program (Undergraduate/Scholarship) [3349]
Louis Stokes Urban Health Policy Fellows Program (Other/Fellowship) [3350]
Ralph W. Stone Graduate Fellowships (Graduate/Fellowship, Grant) [7184]
Stop Hunger Scholarships (Undergraduate/Scholarship) [573]
Stop-Painting.com Scholarships (Undergraduate/Scholarship) [5147]
Martin L. Stout Scholarships (Undergraduate, Graduate/Scholarship) [1949]
George A. Strait Minority Scholarship (Graduate/Scholarship) [536]
Bonnie Strangio Education Scholarships (Graduate, Undergraduate/Scholarship) [2343]
Carole J. Streeter, KB9JBR Scholarships (Undergraduate/Scholarship) [1760]
John Streiff Memorial Scholarships (Undergraduate/Scholarship) [6055]
Stanley W. Strew Educational Fund Scholarships (Undergraduate/Scholarship) [2438]
STRI Short-Term Fellowships (Undergraduate, Graduate, Postdoctorate/Fellowship) [9038]
Robby Strong Cancer Survivor Scholarships (Graduate/Scholarship) [6596]
Student Investigator Research Grant - General Audiology/Hearing Science (Graduate, Doctorate/Grant) [394]
Student Investigator Research Grant - Hearing Aids, Clinical Protocols and Patient Outcomes (Graduate, Doctorate/Grant) [395]
Student Investigator Research Grant - Vestibular (Graduate, Doctorate/Grant) [396]
Student Research Awards from the Behavioral Gerontology SIG (Undergraduate, Graduate/Award, Monetary) [1861]
Student Summer Research Fellowship (Undergraduate, Graduate/Fellowship) [397]
Student Training and Research in Tumor Immunology Grants (Graduate/Grant) [2775]
Study Scholarships for Artists or Musicians (Graduate/Scholarship) [3610]
Stultz Scholarships (Undergraduate/Scholarship) [10600]
Horace W. Stunkard Scholarships (Undergraduate, Graduate/Scholarship) [6262]
AIST Southeast Member Chapter Gene Suave Scholarships (Undergraduate/Scholarship) [2008]
Subic Bay-Cubi Point Scholarships (Undergraduate/Scholarship) [7231]
Caroline tum Suden/Frances Hellebrandt Professional Opportunity Awards (Postdoctorate, Other/Award) [1101]
Suffolk Public Interest Law Group Summer Fellowships (SPILG) (Undergraduate/Fellowship) [8438]
Jerome M. Sullivan Research Funds (Professional development/Grant) [1217]
John A. and Jean Quinn Sullivan Scholarship Funds (Undergraduate/Scholarship) [3725]
Phil Sullivan Scholarships (Undergraduate/Scholarship) [8265]
VPPPA William Sullivan Scholarships (Graduate, Undergraduate/Scholarship) [10418]

William A. Sullivan Scholarships (Undergraduate/Scholarship) [7232]
Lee Summer Student Fellowship (Undergraduate, Master's/Fellowship) [8553]
Roger K. Summit Scholarships for North America (Graduate/Scholarship) [8302]
Hatton W. Sumners Endowed Law Schools Scholarships (Undergraduate, Graduate/Scholarship) [9608]
Hatton W. Sumners Endowed Undergraduate School Scholarships (Undergraduate/Scholarship) [9609]
Hatton W. Sumners Non-Endowed Undergraduate and Graduate Scholarships (Undergraduate, Graduate/Scholarship) [9610]
Superior District Legislative Mentoring Student Grants RT to DC (Undergraduate/Grant) [2484]
Superior District Legislative Mentoring Student Grants (Undergraduate/Grant) [2483]
Surety and Fidelity Industry Intern and Scholarship Program for Minority Students (Undergraduate/Scholarship) [9614]
SUS Foundation Junior Faculty Grants (Other/Grant) [9320]
Sussman-Miller Educational Assistance Award Program (Undergraduate/Scholarship) [305]
SUT Houston Graduate Scholarships (Graduate/Scholarship) [9317]
SUT Houston Undergraduate Scholarships (Undergraduate/Scholarship) [9318]
Sutherland/Purdy Scholarships (Undergraduate/Scholarship) [8109]
Margaret Svec Scholarships (Undergraduate/Scholarship) [8884]
Lorraine E. Swain Scholarships (Undergraduate/Scholarship) [8941]
Swede Swanson Memorial Scholarships (Undergraduate/Scholarship) [7243]
Daniel Swarovski and Company Scholarships (Graduate/Scholarship) [4345]
Hanns Swarzenski and Brigitte Horney Swarzenski Fellowship (Graduate/Fellowship) [6438]
SWE Scholarships (Undergraduate, Graduate/Scholarship) [9329]
Swensrud Teacher Fellowships at MHS (Massachusetts Historical Society) (Professional development/Fellowship) [6338]
Stan Swinton Scholarships (Graduate, Undergraduate/Scholarship) [7782]
Switzer Environmental Fellowships (Graduate/Fellowship) [9623]
Mary Switzer Research Fellowships - Distinguished Fellowships (Doctorate/Fellowship) [9896]
Mary Switzer Research Fellowships - Merit Fellowships (Professional development/Fellowship) [9897]
Symantec Research Labs Graduate Fellowships (Doctorate, Graduate/Fellowship) [9625]
Harry Taback 9/11 Memorial Scholarships (Undergraduate/Scholarship) [1429]
Hazaros Tabakoglu Scholarship Fund (Undergraduate/Scholarship) [1705]
The Tabat Scholarship Fund (Graduate/Scholarship) [4005]
TAC Foundation-Stantec Consulting Scholarships (Graduate/Scholarship) [9790]
TACS/Texas Tech University ISD Scholarships (Undergraduate/Scholarship) [9687]
Tag and Label Manufacturers Institute Scholarships - Four-Year Colleges (Undergraduate/Scholarship) [9629]
Tag and Label Manufacturers Institute Scholarships - Two-Year Colleges (Undergraduate/Scholarship) [9630]
Tailhook Educational Foundation Scholarship Program (Undergraduate/Scholarship) [9632]
Taiwanese American Community Scholarships (Undergraduate/Scholarship) [9634]
Robert M. Takasugi Public Interest Fellowships (Postgraduate/Fellowship) [9636]
Kei Takemoto Memorial Scholarships (Undergraduate/Scholarship) [173]
Tall Clubs International Student Scholarships (Undergraduate/Scholarship) [9638]
Justice Stephen K. Tamura Scholarships (Undergraduate/Scholarship) [5545]

Mitsuyoshi Tanaka Dissertation Award in Experimental Particle Physics (Doctorate/Award) [1094]
Janet Cullen Tanaka Scholarships (Undergraduate/Scholarship) [2096]
Alexander M. Tanger Scholarships (Graduate/Scholarship) [2372]
William J. Tangye Scholarships (Undergraduate/Scholarship) [5302]
Hal Tanner Sr. Scholarships (Undergraduate/Scholarship) [10252]
Alex Tanous Scholarship Award (Undergraduate/Scholarship) [9642]
Frederick A. Tarantino Memorial Scholarship Award (Undergraduate/Scholarship) [9999]
Lee Tarbox Memorial Scholarships (Undergraduate/Scholarship) [174]
Targeted Research Initiative for Health Outcomes (Doctorate/Grant) [3909]
Bud and Linda Tarrson Fellowships (Professional development/Fellowship) [422]
TaskEasy Scholarships for Future Entrepreneurs (Undergraduate/Scholarship) [9646]
Jack Tate/ThinkCOLLEGE Scholarship Fund (Undergraduate/Scholarship) [4216]
Jordan B. Tatter Scholarships (Undergraduate/Scholarship) [6488]
Taylor/Blakeslee University Fellowships (Other, Undergraduate/Fellowship) [3429]
Joshua C. Taylor Fellowships (Doctorate, Postdoctorate/Fellowship) [9006]
Ryan "Munchie" Taylor Memorial Scholarships (Undergraduate/Scholarship) [6154]
Tom Taylor Memorial Scholarships to Spartan College of Aeronautics and Technology (Undergraduate/Scholarship) [175]
Charles "Buck" and Dora Taylor Scholarship (Undergraduate/Scholarship) [3689]
The Ed Tayter Outstanding Citizen Scholarships (Undergraduate/Scholarship) [8238]
TCA-ACBH Scholarships (Undergraduate/Scholarship) [9812]
TCA Outstanding Graduate Student Awards (Graduate/Award) [9695]
TCA Scholarship (Undergraduate/Scholarship) [9800]
TCA-UMD Scholarships (Undergraduate/Scholarship) [9813]
TCAdvance Scholarships (Undergraduate/Scholarship) [9814]
TCATA College Scholarship Program (Undergraduate/Scholarship) [9721]
TCDA Abbott IPCO Professional Scholarships (Other/Scholarship) [671]
TCDA Gandy Ink Professional Scholarships (Professional development/Scholarship) [672]
TCDA General Fund Scholarships (Undergraduate/Scholarship) [673]
TCDA Past Presidents Student Scholarships (Undergraduate/Scholarship) [674]
Teacher Education Scholarships (Advanced Professional/Scholarship) [1008]
Teacher of the Visually Impaired Loans (Undergraduate, Graduate/Loan) [9556]
Teammates Mentoring Scholarship Program (Undergraduate/Scholarship) [4567]
Tech Mastery Scholarships (Undergraduate/Scholarship) [8551]
TechChecks Business Leadership Scholarships (Undergraduate/Scholarship) [9650]
Technical Women's Organization Education Scholarships (TWO) (Undergraduate/Scholarship) [9652]
Dwight Teed Scholarships (Undergraduate/Scholarship) [9612]
Marvin H. and Kathleen G. Teget Leadership Scholarships (Undergraduate/Scholarship) [9602]
Telecommunications Association of Michigan Scholarship Fund (Undergraduate/Scholarship) [9663]
Telford Scholarships (Undergraduate/Scholarship) [40]
Tell Us Your Story Scholarships (Undergraduate/Scholarship) [10495]
Telluride Association Summer Program Scholarships (Undergraduate/Scholarship) [9665]
Mary L. Tenopyr Graduate Student Scholarships (Doctorate/Scholarship) [9154]
The Terra Foundation Fellowships in American Art

(Undergraduate, Doctorate, Postdoctorate/Fellowship) [9007]
Terra Foundation Fellowships at the Smithsonian American Art Museum (Postdoctorate/Fellowship) [9680]
Terra Foundation Postdoctoral Teaching Fellowships at the Courtauld Institute of Art, London (Postdoctorate/Fellowship) [9681]
Terra Foundation Postdoctoral Teaching Fellowships at the Institut National d'Histoire de l'Art, Paris (Postdoctorate/Fellowship) [9682]
Terra Summer Residency Fellowships (Master's, Doctorate/Fellowship) [9684]
Marc Tetalman, MD, Memorial Award (Professional development, Doctorate/Recognition) [9227]
Steven M. Teutsch Prevention Effectiveness Fellowships (Doctorate/Fellowship) [9921]
Texas Computer Education Association Professional Educator Grants (Other/Grant) [9693]
Texas Elks State Association Eagle Scout Scholarships (Undergraduate/Scholarship) [9697]
Texas Elks State Association Girl Scout Gold Award Scholarships (Undergraduate/Scholarship) [9698]
Texas Music Educators Association Past-Presidents Memorial Scholarships (Undergraduate/Scholarship) [9707]
Texas Mutual Scholarship Program (Undergraduate, Vocational/Occupational/Scholarship) [9709]
Texas Scholarships of Academic Excellence (Undergraduate, Graduate/Scholarship) [9559]
Texas Society of Professional Engineers Scholarships (Undergraduate/Scholarship) [9711]
Texas State Technical College Scholarships (Undergraduate/Scholarship) [176]
Texas Telephone Association Foundation Scholarships (Undergraduate/Scholarship) [9719]
TFAS Congressional Scholarship Awards (Undergraduate/Award, Scholarship) [4309]
Jim and Pat Thacker Sports Communication Internships (Undergraduate/Grant) [10253]
Anil and Neema Thakrar Family Fund No. 1 (Undergraduate/Scholarship) [4257]
ThanksUSA Scholarships (Undergraduate, Vocational/Occupational/Scholarship) [9723]
The Cover Guy Annual Scholarships (Undergraduate, Graduate/Scholarship) [3463]
Theatre Guild Scholarship (Undergraduate/Scholarship) [9725]
Thermo Scientific Educational Scholarships (Professional development/Scholarship) [7172]
Thesaurus Linguae Latinae Fellowships (TTL) (Doctorate/Fellowship) [9107]
Elizabeth R. Thomas Alumni Nursing Scholarship (Undergraduate/Scholarship) [8885]
Charles C. Thomas Scholarship (Undergraduate/Scholarship) [1586]
Barber Owen Thomas Scholarships (Undergraduate/Scholarship) [8942]
Rev. Chuck and Nancy Thomas Scholarships (Professional development/Scholarship) [9842]
Thome Foundation Awards Program in Age-Related Macular Degeneration Research (Professional development/Grant) [4824]
Thome Foundation Awards Program in Alzheimer's Disease Drug Discovery Research (Professional development/Grant) [4825]
The Honorable Raymond Thompson Endowed Scholarships (Undergraduate/Scholarship) [8006]
Matilda B. Thompson Scholarship (Undergraduate/Scholarship) [4929]
Thompson Scholarships for Women in Safety (Graduate/Scholarship) [1430]
Thornberg/Havens Scholarships (Undergraduate/Scholarship) [3596]
Thomas P. Thornton Scholarships (Undergraduate/Scholarship) [5089]
Thurgood Marshall Fellowships Program (Undergraduate/Fellowship) [7345]
Tiftickjian Law Firm, P.C. Juvenile Justice Law School Scholarships (Postgraduate/Scholarship) [9741]
Tikvah Fellowships (Graduate, Professional development/Fellowship) [9745]
Tillman Scholars Program (Undergraduate, Graduate/Scholarship) [7901]

Jack E. Tillson Scholarships (Graduate/Scholarship) [5470]
Eben Tisdale Fellowships (Undergraduate/Fellowship) [4310]
TMA Research Fellowships (Postdoctorate/Grant, Fellowship) [6641]
TMCF Scholarships (Undergraduate/Scholarship) [9735]
Mario J. Tocco Hydrocephalus Foundation Scholarships (Undergraduate/Scholarship) [5028]
Richard Cecil Todd and Clauda Pennock Todd Tripod Scholarships (Graduate, Undergraduate/Scholarship) [8082]
Robert Toigo Foundation Fellowships (Master's/Fellowship) [9747]
William Tomar Memorial Scholarships (Undergraduate/Scholarship) [2519]
The Adelle and Erwin Tomash Fellowship in the History of Information Technology (Doctorate, Graduate/Fellowship) [10201]
John L. Tomasovic, Sr. Scholarships (Undergraduate/Scholarship) [812]
Took Trust Point Scholarship (Undergraduate, Graduate, Doctorate/Scholarship) [8192]
George Torkildsen Literary Awards (Professional development/Award, Trophy) [10705]
Aram Torossian Memorial Scholarships (Undergraduate/Scholarship) [1706]
Ferdinand Torres Scholarships (Graduate, Undergraduate/Scholarship) [824]
Tortuga Backpacks Study Abroad Scholarships (Undergraduate/Scholarship) [9756]
Touchstone Special Achievement Scholarships (Undergraduate/Scholarship) [7588]
Tourette Association of America Research Grant Awards (Master's, Doctorate/Grant) [9758]
Town and County Club Scholarships (Undergraduate/Scholarship) [4773]
Toyota Financial Services Point Scholarship (Undergraduate, Graduate, Doctorate/Scholarship) [8193]
Toyota/TELACU Scholarships (Undergraduate/Scholarship) [9661]
The Joyce Tracy Fellowships (Doctorate/Fellowship) [446]
TRALA Industry Scholarship Awards (Undergraduate/Scholarship) [9798]
Vera Tran Memorial Scholarships (Undergraduate/Scholarship) [10388]
Reuben Trane Scholarships (Undergraduate/Scholarship) [1334]
Trans Issues Internships - New York (Undergraduate, Graduate/Internship) [4441]
Transamerica Retirement Solutions Leaders in Health Care Scholarships (Graduate/Scholarship) [5169]
Transatlantic Fellows Program (Other/Fellowship) [4400]
Translational Research Professorship (Professional development/Internship) [3387]
Transoft Solutions, Inc. Ahead of the Curve Scholarships (AOTC) (Graduate, Undergraduate/Scholarship) [5221]
Traub-Dicker Rainbow Scholarships (Undergraduate/Scholarship) [9590]
Morton M. Traum Surface Science Student Awards (Graduate, Doctorate/Prize) [2157]
Trelut Family Legacy Scholarships (Undergraduate/Scholarship) [2459]
Tri Delta Alpha Eta Scholarships (Undergraduate/Scholarship) [3559]
Tri Delta Alpha Rho Leadership Scholarships (Undergraduate/Scholarship) [3560]
Tri Delta Atlanta Alumnae Achievement Scholarships (Undergraduate/Scholarship) [3561]
Tri Delta Beta Gamma Memorial Scholarships (Undergraduate/Scholarship) [3562]
Tri Delta Northern Virginia Alumnae Chapter Scholarships (Undergraduate/Scholarship) [3564]
Tribute Fund Community Grant (Professional development/Grant) [9102]
Thomas and Glenna Trimble Endowed Scholarships (Undergraduate/Scholarship) [8007]
Tim Triner Letter Carriers Scholarship Fund (Undergraduate/Scholarship) [9539]
J.P. and Madeline Trinkaus Endowed Scholarships

in Embryology (Graduate, Master's, Doctorate/Scholarship) [6263]
Charlie Trotters's Culinary Education Foundation Scholarships (Other, Undergraduate/Scholarship) [765]
Jo Anne J. Trow Scholarships (Undergraduate/Scholarship) [6697]
Truckload Carriers Association Scholarships (Undergraduate/Scholarship) [9801]
William H. Truettner Fellowships (Undergraduate, Doctorate, Postdoctorate/Scholarship) [9008]
TrustedPros Scholarships (Undergraduate/Scholarship) [9805]
Trustees College Scholarships (Undergraduate/Scholarship) [6171]
Trustees Law School Scholarships (Undergraduate/Scholarship) [6172]
Norman J. Tschantz/Walter C. Deuble Scholarships (Undergraduate/Scholarship) [9540]
TSHP R&E Foundation Scholarship Program (Undergraduate, Graduate/Scholarship) [9807]
Tucker Family Scholarships (Undergraduate/Scholarship) [10254]
Barry Tuckwell Scholarships (All/Scholarship) [5346]
Richard R. Tufenkian Memorial Scholarships (Undergraduate/Scholarship) [1671]
Edward Tuinier Memorial Scholarships (Undergraduate/Scholarship) [813]
Graydon A. Tunstall Undergraduate Student Scholarships (Undergraduate/Scholarship) [8049]
Earl S. Tupper 3-year Postdoctoral Fellowships in Tropical Biology (Postdoctorate/Fellowship) [9039]
Turf and Ornamental Communicators Association Scholarship Program (Undergraduate/Scholarship) [9809]
Hans Turley Prize in Queer Eighteenth-Century Studies (Graduate, Other/Prize) [1297]
Jeff Turner-Forsyth Audubon Society Scholarships (Undergraduate/Scholarship) [10601]
James A. Turner, Jr. Memorial Scholarships (Undergraduate/Scholarship) [1525]
Mark and Vera Turner Memorial Scholarships (Undergraduate/Scholarship) [6068]
Emmett H. Turner Scholarships (Undergraduate/Scholarship) [3255]
Ira G. Turpin Scholars Fund (Undergraduate/Scholarship) [9541]
Tuscumbia Kiwanis Scholarship (Undergraduate/Scholarship) [7551]
Lydia Donaldson Tutt-Jones Memorial Research Grant (Graduate, Other, Master's/Grant) [93]
Two Year/Community Broadcast Education Association Scholarship Awards (Graduate/Scholarship) [2373]
TxHIMA Outstanding Student Scholarship (Undergraduate/Scholarship) [9704]
William R. Tyler Fellowships (Graduate/Fellowship) [3740]
Florence Tyson Grants to Study Music Pyschotherapy (Professional development/Grant) [1018]
UAA Janice K. Barden Aviation Scholarships (Undergraduate/Scholarship) [6838]
UAB Health Policy Fellowship (Graduate, Master's, Doctorate/Scholarship) [10002]
UAF Alumni Association Scholarships (Undergraduate/Scholarship) [10100]
UAF Community and Technical College Culinary Arts Scholarships (Undergraduate/Scholarship) [9823]
UC MEXUS-CICESE Graduate Student Short-Term Research and Training Program (Master's, Doctorate, Postdoctorate/Grant) [10110]
UC MEXUS-CICESE Short-term Research & Training Program (Graduate/Award, Grant) [10115]
UC MEXUS-CONACYT Collaborative Grants (Professional development/Grant) [10116]
UC MEXUS-CONACYT Postdoctoral Research Fellowships (Postdoctorate/Fellowship) [10118]
UC MEXUS Dissertation Research Grants (Graduate/Grant) [10119]
UC MEXUS Grants for Dissertation Research (Graduate/Grant) [10111]
UC MEXUS Scholars in Residence Program - Graduate (Graduate/Scholarship) [10120]

UNITED STATES

UC MEXUS Scholars in Residence Program - Recent University Graduates *(Postgraduate/Scholarship)* [10121]
UC MEXUS Scholars in Residence Program - Visiting Faculty *(Professional development/Scholarship)* [10122]
UC MEXUS Small Grants for UC Faculty *(Graduate/Grant)* [10123]
UC MEXUS Small Grants for UC Postdocs *(Postdoctorate/Grant)* [10124]
UC MEXUS Small Grants for UC Students *(Graduate, Postdoctorate/Grant)* [10125]
The UCSD Black Alumni Scholarships for Engineering, Mathematics and Science *(Undergraduate/Scholarship)* [8737]
UCT Scholarships *(Graduate, Other, Undergraduate/Scholarship)* [7686]
Morris K. Udall Scholarships *(Undergraduate/Scholarship)* [9825]
UF Center for Latin American Studies FLAS Summer Fellowships *(Master's, Graduate, Undergraduate/Award, Fellowship)* [10133]
UFCW Local Union Scholarships *(Undergraduate/Scholarship)* [9847]
UH Manoa Starr Foundation Graduate Fellowships in Asian Studies *(Graduate/Grant)* [10138]
Sandy Ulm Scholarships *(Undergraduate/Scholarship)* [4081]
UMBS Istock Family Scholarships *(Undergraduate/Scholarship)* [10190]
UMBS Returning Student Award *(Undergraduate/Scholarship)* [10191]
UMDF Clinical Research Fellowship Training Awards *(Professional development/Fellowship)* [9860]
UNCF/Merck Graduate Science Research Dissertation Fellowships *(Graduate/Fellowship)* [6426, 9862]
UNCF/Merck Postdoctoral Science Research Fellowships *(Postdoctorate/Fellowship)* [6427, 9863]
Undergraduate/Graduate Scholarships *(Undergraduate, Graduate/Scholarship)* [5315]
Undergraduate Session Assistants Program *(Undergraduate/Other)* [7370]
Bettie Underwood Dental Assisting Scholarships *(Undergraduate/Scholarship)* [2831]
UNESCO-L'Oreal for Women in Science International Fellowships *(Doctorate, Postdoctorate/Fellowship)* [6108]
UNH Alumni Association Legacy Scholarships *(Undergraduate/Scholarship)* [10209]
UNH Parents Association Endowment Scholarship Fund *(Undergraduate/Scholarship)* [10210]
Union of Marash Armenian Scholarships *(Undergraduate, Graduate/Scholarship)* [1707]
Union Plus Scholarship Program *(Undergraduate/Scholarship)* [5451]
United Engineering Foundation Grants *(All/Grant)* [9845]
United Health Foundation National Association of Hispanic Nurses Scholarships *(Graduate, Undergraduate/Scholarship)* [6758]
United Methodist General Scholarships *(Undergraduate, Graduate/Scholarship)* [9856]
United Parcel Service Scholarships for Female Students *(Undergraduate/Scholarship)* [5195]
United Parcel Service Scholarships for Minority Students *(Undergraduate/Scholarship)* [5196]
United South and Eastern Tribes Scholarship Fund *(Undergraduate/Scholarship)* [9868]
U.S. Air Force ROTC Express Scholarships *(Undergraduate/Scholarship)* [9872]
U.S. Air Force ROTC High School Scholarships *(Undergraduate/Scholarship)* [9873]
U.S. Air Force ROTC In-College Scholarships *(Undergraduate/Scholarship)* [9874]
U.S. Aircraft Insurance Group Professional Development Program (USAIG PDP) Scholarships *(Undergraduate/Scholarship)* [6839]
U.S. Bates Scholarship Program *(Undergraduate/Scholarship)* [5452]
U.S. BIA Indian Higher Education Grants *(Undergraduate/Grant)* [878]
United States Capitol Historical Society Fellowships *(Graduate/Fellowship)* [9886]
The United States Department of State, Bureau of Educational & Cultural Affairs Fellowships *(Graduate/Fellowship)* [1199]
United States Geospatial Intelligence Foundation Graduate Scholarships *(Graduate/Scholarship)* [9945]
United States Geospatial Intelligence Foundation High School Scholarships *(Undergraduate/Scholarship)* [9946]
United States Geospatial Intelligence Foundation Undergraduate Scholarships *(Undergraduate/Scholarship)* [9947]
U.S. Medical Supplies' Medical Professionals of Tomorrow Scholarships *(Undergraduate, Graduate/Scholarship)* [9964]
United States Society on Dams Scholarships *(Graduate, Undergraduate/Scholarship)* [9971]
U.S.-U.K. Young Investigator Exchange Fellowship *(Postdoctorate/Fellowship)* [376]
UnitedAg Scholarship Program *(Undergraduate/Scholarship)* [9988]
Universal Studios Preservation Scholarships *(Graduate/Scholarship)* [2028]
University of Hawaii at Manoa East-West Center Graduate Fellowships *(Graduate, Postdoctorate/Fellowship)* [10139]
University of Hawaii at Manoa Graduate Assistantship Awards *(Graduate/Award)* [10140]
University of Hawaii at Manoa Graduate Student Organization Travel Funds *(Graduate/Grant)* [10141]
University of Hawaii at Manoa Japan Travel Bureau Scholarships *(Graduate, Undergraduate/Scholarship)* [10142]
University of Oregon Dean's Scholarships *(Undergraduate/Scholarship)* [10260]
University of Oregon Diversity Excellence Scholarships *(Undergraduate/Scholarship)* [10261]
University of Oregon General University Scholarships *(Undergraduate/Scholarship)* [10262]
University of Puget Sound LGBT Leadership Scholarships Fund *(Undergraduate/Scholarship)* [8664]
University Senior and Master's Program Scholarships *(Graduate/Scholarship)* [1644]
University of Texas at Austin Special Research Grants *(Professional development/Grant)* [10276]
University of Wisconsin-Madison/CALS Minority Scholarships *(Undergraduate/Scholarship)* [10327]
University of Wisconsin-Madison Chancellor's Scholarships *(Undergraduate/Scholarship)* [10328]
University of Wisconsin-Madison National Merit Scholarships *(Undergraduate/Scholarship)* [10329]
University of Wisconsin-Madison Single Parent Scholarships *(Undergraduate/Scholarship)* [10330]
UPE Scholarship Awards *(Graduate, Undergraduate/Scholarship)* [10342]
UPS Diversity Scholarships *(Undergraduate/Scholarship)* [1431]
Urban and Regional Policy (Comparative Domestic Policy) Fellowships *(Other/Fellowship)* [4401]
The Urban Scholarship Fund *(Undergraduate/Scholarship)* [9689]
CASFM-Ben Urbonas Scholarships *(Graduate/Scholarship)* [3132]
Urology Care Foundation/Astellas Rising Star in Urology Research Awards *(Postdoctorate, Other/Award)* [10347]
USA Funds Access to Education Scholarships *(Graduate, Undergraduate/Scholarship)* [9986]
USAttorneys.com Immigration Scholarships Essay Contest *(Undergraduate/Scholarship)* [10353]
USAttorneys.com National Scholarships Essay Contest *(Undergraduate/Scholarship)* [10354]
USAWOASF/Grantham University On-Line Scholarships *(Graduate, Undergraduate/Scholarship)* [9880]
USAWOASF Regular Scholarships *(Undergraduate/Scholarship)* [9881]
USDA-NIFA-AFRI Merit Awards *(Postdoctorate/Award)* [9308]
USGA/Chevron STEM Scholarship Program *(Undergraduate/Scholarship)* [9954]
USGLC Internships - Communications *(Undergraduate, Doctorate/Internship)* [9949]
USGLC Internships - Government Relations *(Undergraduate, Graduate/Internship)* [9950]
USGLC Internships - Outreach *(Undergraduate, Graduate/Internship)* [9951]
USGLC Internships - Policy *(Undergraduate, Graduate/Internship)* [9952]
USHJA General Scholarships *(Undergraduate/Scholarship)* [9956]
USPAACC Ampcus Hallmark Scholarships *(Undergraduate/Scholarship)* [9968]
USPAACC Denny's Hungry for Education Scholarship *(Undergraduate/Scholarship)* [9969]
USS Coral Sea Remembrance Scholarships *(Undergraduate/Scholarship)* [10358]
USTA Serves College Education Scholarships *(Undergraduate/Scholarship)* [9977]
USTA Serves College Textbook Scholarship *(Undergraduate/Scholarship)* [9978]
Utility Workers Union of America Scholarship Program *(Undergraduate/Scholarship)* [10360]
John D. Utterback Scholarship Program *(Undergraduate/Scholarship)* [322]
U.V.A. Faculty Fellowships *(Professional development/Fellowship)* [10313]
UW-Madison Engineering Diversity Scholarships *(Undergraduate/Scholarship)* [10331]
UW-Madison GLBT Alumni Council Scholarships *(Undergraduate, Graduate/Scholarship)* [10332]
UW-Madison Reserve Officers Training Corps Scholarships *(Undergraduate/Scholarship)* [10333]
UW-Madison School of Education Minority Scholarships *(Undergraduate/Scholarship)* [10334]
VA AWWA Graduate Student Scholarships *(Graduate/Scholarship)* [1498]
VABANC Scholarships *(Graduate, Undergraduate/Scholarship)* [10383]
Wallace Vail Scholarships *(Undergraduate/Scholarship)* [7337]
ValuePenguin Scholarships *(Undergraduate/Scholarship)* [10362]
Valuing Diversity PhD Scholarships *(Doctorate/Scholarship)* [983]
Jacob and Rita Van Namen Marketing Scholarships *(Undergraduate/Scholarship)* [814]
Adolph Van Pelt Special Fund for Indians Scholarships *(Undergraduate/Scholarship)* [1836]
William P. Van Wagenen Fellowships *(Undergraduate/Fellowship)* [543]
Gary Vanden Berg Internship Grant *(Undergraduate/Grant)* [9482]
The Vander Putten Family Scholarships *(Advanced Professional/Scholarship)* [3082]
René M. Vandervelde Research Grants *(Undergraduate, Professional development/Grant)* [1845]
Russell and Sigurd Varian Award *(Graduate/Recognition)* [2158]
Varian Radiation Therapy Advancement Scholarship *(Undergraduate, Master's, Doctorate/Scholarship)* [1401]
Vascular Surgery Trainee Advocacy Travel Scholarship *(Advanced Professional, Professional development/Scholarship, Grant)* [9326]
Vector Marketing Canadian Scholarship Awards *(Undergraduate/Scholarship)* [10365]
Vector Marketing Scholarships *(Graduate, Undergraduate/Scholarship)* [8079]
Vectorworks Design Scholarships *(Undergraduate, Graduate/Scholarship, Prize)* [10367]
Ventana Medical Systems In Situ Hybridization Awards *(Other/Award)* [7173]
Helen Veress-Mitchell Scholarship Fund *(Undergraduate/Scholarship)* [2788]
Graduate Fellowship Program - Peter Verhofstadt Fellowships *(Graduate/Fellowship)* [8836]
Vermont Paralegal Organization Scholarships *(Undergraduate/Scholarship)* [10371]
Vern Parish *(Graduate, Undergraduate/Scholarship)* [964]
Chester M. Vernon Memorial Eagle Scout Scholarships *(Undergraduate/Scholarship)* [6934]
A. Verville Fellowships *(Professional development/Fellowship)* [9023]
Vesalius Trust Student Research Scholarships

(Graduate, Undergraduate/Scholarship) [10374]
Veterans of Foreign Wars Scout of the Year (Undergraduate/Scholarship) [6935]
Veterinary and Pre-Veterinary Academic Scholarships (Undergraduate/Scholarship) [3647]
Zelda Walling Vicha Memorial Scholarships (Undergraduate/Scholarship) [1387]
William F. Vilas Scholarships (Undergraduate/Scholarship) [10335]
Dr. Juan D. Villarreal/HDA Foundation Scholarships (Undergraduate/Scholarship) [4894]
Villers Fellowships for Health Care Justice (Graduate/Fellowship) [3958]
Violin Society of America Scholarships (Undergraduate/Scholarship) [10390]
Virginia Tech Doctoral Scholarship (Doctorate/Scholarship) [10406]
Virginia Tech Student Travel Award (Undergraduate, Graduate/Award) [1955]
Vision Zero Auto Accident Prevention Scholarships (Postgraduate/Scholarship) [5951]
Vista Health Solutions' Scholarships (Undergraduate/Scholarship) [10413]
John D. Voelker Foundation Native American Scholarships (Undergraduate/Scholarship) [10415]
Von Ogden Vogt Scholarships (Master's/Scholarship) [9843]
Miki Vohryzek-Bolden Student Paper Competition (Undergraduate/Prize) [10539]
Voices On Point Scholarship (Undergraduate, Graduate, Doctorate/Scholarship) [8194]
Irma E. Voigt Memorial Scholarships (Undergraduate/Scholarship) [8943]
Paul A. Volcker Endowment for Public Service Research and Education (Doctorate/Grant) [1116]
The Sybil Jennings Vorheis Memorial Undergraduate Scholarships (Undergraduate/Scholarship) [4218]
Vorobek Point Scholarship (Undergraduate, Graduate, Doctorate/Scholarship) [8195]
Abe Voron Scholarships (Graduate/Scholarship) [2374]
Dr. Edward G. Voss Memorial Scholarships (Undergraduate/Scholarship) [10192]
VPPPA June Brothers Scholarships (Graduate, Undergraduate/Scholarship) [10419]
VSCPA Educational Foundation Graduate Scholarships (Graduate/Scholarship) [10407]
VSCPA Educational Foundation Minority Scholarships (Graduate, Undergraduate/Scholarship) [10408]
VSCPA Educational Foundation Undergraduate Scholarships (Undergraduate/Scholarship) [10409]
VSCPA PhD Accounting Scholarships (Doctorate, Graduate/Scholarship) [10410]
WACE National Co-op Scholarship Program (Undergraduate/Scholarship) [10693]
Jane and Gregg Waddill Memorial Adelphe Scholarship (Undergraduate/Scholarship) [5768]
Robert & Barbara Wade Scholarships (Undergraduate/Scholarship) [6069]
Wadsworth International Fellowships (Graduate/Fellowship) [10519]
WAEPA Scholarship Program (Undergraduate/Scholarship) [10711]
Jack H. Wagner Scholarships (Graduate, Undergraduate/Scholarship) [6504]
Selman A. Waksman Endowed Scholarships in Microbial Diversity (Graduate, Master's, Doctorate/Scholarship) [6264]
Jane C. Waldbaum Archaeological Field School Scholarships (Undergraduate/Scholarship) [1611]
Laramie Walden Memorial Fund (Undergraduate/Scholarship) [4219]
Margaret E. Waldron Scholarship Fund (Undergraduate/Scholarship) [4061]
Helen Zick Walker Adelphe Scholarship (Undergraduate/Scholarship) [5769]
Gary Walker Memorial Scholarships (Other/Scholarship) [4266]
Arthur BC Walker Scholarships (Undergraduate/Scholarship) [7147]
Myrtle & Earl Walker Scholarships (Undergraduate/Scholarship) [9199]

Walmart Associate Scholarships (Undergraduate/Scholarship) [10425]
Harry Walts Memorial Graduate Scholarships (Graduate/Scholarship) [6136]
Imogene Ward Nursing Scholarships (Undergraduate/Scholarship) [4079]
Judith Warner Memorial Scholarships (Undergraduate/Scholarship) [8369]
Earl Warren Scholarships (Graduate/Scholarship) [6648]
Washburn University School of Law Business and Transactional Law Center Scholarships (Undergraduate/Scholarship) [10432]
Washburn University School of Law Child and Family Advocacy Fellowships (Undergraduate/Fellowship) [10433]
Washington College Bound Scholarships (Undergraduate/Scholarship) [10471]
Washington University Law School Chancellor's Graduate Fellowships (Advanced Professional/Fellowship) [10476]
Washington University Law School Olin Fellowships for Women (Advanced Professional/Fellowship) [10477]
Vincent T. Wasilewski Scholarships (Graduate/Scholarship) [2375]
Stand Watie Scholarships (Undergraduate/Scholarship) [9343]
ASM Robert D. Watkins Graduate Research Fellowships (Postdoctorate/Fellowship) [1373]
Dr. James Watson Fellowship Program (Doctorate, Graduate/Fellowship) [4485]
Jeannette K. Watson Fellowships (Undergraduate/Fellowship, Internship) [10491]
Thomas J. Watson Fellowships (Undergraduate/Fellowship) [10493]
George Watt Prize (Undergraduate, Graduate/Prize) [26]
Wayne County Bank Scholarships (Undergraduate/Scholarship) [7552]
Wayne County Foundation Anonymous Scholarship Fund (Graduate/Scholarship) [10508]
Kurt Wayne Scholarships (Graduate/Scholarship) [4346]
WDHOF Undergraduate Scholarships in Marine Conservation (Undergraduate/Scholarship) [10640]
Richard M. Weaver Fellowships (Graduate/Fellowship) [5235]
W.E.B. Du Bois Fellowships (Doctorate/Fellowship) [7013]
John W. Webb Lecture Awards (Other/Recognition) [1324]
Faye and Rendell Webb Scholarships (Undergraduate/Scholarship) [3112]
TCDA Cloys Webb Student Scholarships (Undergraduate/Scholarship) [675]
Allen and Loureena Weber Scholarships (Undergraduate/Scholarship) [9200]
Art and Dannie Weber Scholarships (Undergraduate/Scholarship) [10603]
Webster Society Scholarships (Juris Doctorate/Scholarship) [10478]
Sheldon Wechsler and George Mertz Contact Lens Residency Awards (Professional development, Advanced Professional/Award) [418]
Kenneth G. Weckel Scholarships (Graduate/Scholarship) [6528]
WEF Canham Graduate Studies Scholarships (Graduate/Scholarship) [10480]
Frank L. Weil Memorial Eagle Scout Scholarships (Undergraduate/Scholarship) [6936]
Arthur and Lila Weinberg Fellowship for Independent Scholars and Researchers (Other/Fellowship) [7425]
Alvin M. Weinberg Fellowships (Doctorate/Fellowship) [9910]
Bertold E. Weinberg Scholarships (Graduate/Scholarship) [711]
Edith Weingarten Scholarship Program (Postgraduate/Scholarship) [1050]
The Bee Winkler Weinstein Scholarship Fund (Undergraduate, Vocational/Occupational/Scholarship) [9591]
William E. Weisel Scholarships (Undergraduate/Scholarship) [9201]

Susan C. Weiss Clinical Advancement Scholarships (Other/Scholarship) [9229]
Polaire Weissman Funds (Graduate/Fellowship) [6439]
Edward Kent Welch Memorial Scholarships (Undergraduate/Scholarship) [10604]
Welch Scholars Grants (Undergraduate/Grant) [1065]
James R. Welch Scholarship (Graduate/Scholarship) [1846]
Welder Wildlife Foundation Fellowships (Graduate, Master's, Doctorate/Fellowship) [10510]
Wells Fargo American Indian Scholarships - Graduate (Graduate/Scholarship) [883]
Wells Fargo Point Scholarship (Undergraduate/Scholarship) [8196]
Wells Fargo Veterans Scholarships Program (Undergraduate/Scholarship) [10512]
Jean Hess Wells Memorial Adelphe Graduate Scholarship (Graduate/Scholarship) [5771]
Jean Hess Wells Memorial Adelphe Scholarship (Undergraduate/Scholarship) [5772]
Donald M. Wells Scholarships (Undergraduate/Scholarship) [4632]
Wellstone Fellowships for Social Justice (Graduate/Fellowship) [3959]
Peter R. Weitz Prize (Other/Prize) [4402]
Francis X. Weninger Scholarships (Undergraduate/Scholarship) [10726]
Wenner-Gren Foundation Dissertation Fieldwork Grants (Doctorate/Grant) [10520]
Wenner-Gren Foundation Post-PhD Research Grants (Doctorate/Grant) [10521]
John R. and Joan F. Werren Scholarships Fund (Undergraduate/Scholarship) [9543]
Redlands Evening Lions Club - Barbara Westen Memorial Scholarships (Undergraduate/Scholarship) [8529]
Robert B. Westover Scholarships (Undergraduate/Scholarship) [4347]
Mary Elizabeth Westpheling - Long Beach Alumnae Association Memorial Scholarhips (Undergraduate/Scholarship) [5773]
Frederick K. Weyerhaeuser Forest History Fellowships (Graduate/Fellowship) [4138]
WFI International Fellowships (Undergraduate/Fellowship) [10702]
Whan Memorial Scholarships (Graduate, Undergraduate/Scholarship) [8080]
Edwyna Wheadon Postgraduate Training Scholarship Fund (Postgraduate/Scholarship) [6886]
Haemer Wheatcraft Scholarship (Undergraduate/Scholarship) [3690]
Stan Wheeler Mentorship Awards (Other/Award) [5976]
Paul A. Whelan Aviation Scholarships (Undergraduate, Graduate/Scholarship) [10106]
Nellie Yeoh Whetten Award (Graduate/Recognition) [2159]
Law Office of David D. White Annual Traumatic Brain Injury Scholarships (All/Scholarship) [5947]
White Collar Defense Diversity Scholarships (Undergraduate, Advanced Professional/Scholarship) [8239]
Bradford White Corporation Scholarships (Undergraduate/Scholarship) [8165]
The Brian J. White Endowed Law Scholarships (Undergraduate/Scholarship) [8008]
Howard A. White Endowed Scholarships (Undergraduate/Scholarship) [8009]
Richard S. White Fellowships (Undergraduate/Fellowship) [4853]
White House Fellows (Other/Fellowship) [8223]
Paul D. White Scholarship (Undergraduate/Scholarship) [2173]
ACI Richard N. White Student Fellowships (Master's/Fellowship) [712]
Ann Cook Whitman Scholarships for Perry High School (Undergraduate/Scholarship) [4416]
Ann Cook Whitman Washington, DC Scholarships (Undergraduate/Scholarship) [4417]
Jane and Morgan Whitney Fellowships (Graduate/Fellowship) [6440]
Helen Hay Whitney Foundation Fellowships (Postdoctorate/Fellowship) [10551]
Why Get Your Blue On? Video Scholarships (Gradu-

ate, Undergraduate/Award, Scholarship) [10543]
Alice Hersey Wick Scholarships (Undergraduate/Scholarship) [8944]
Tom Wicker Scholarships (Graduate/Scholarship) [10256]
Larry B. Wickham Memorial Scholarship for Graduate Studies (Graduate/Scholarship) [6608]
Lois Widley Student Scholarships (Graduate, Undergraduate/Scholarship) [5365]
Richard A. Wiebe Public Service Fellowships (Graduate/Fellowship) [7371]
Ethyl and Armin Wiebke Memorial Scholarships (Undergraduate/Scholarship) [10652]
Barbara Wiedner and Dorothy Vandercook Memorial Peace Scholarships (Undergraduate/Scholarship) [4639]
Timothy Wiese Memorial Scholarships (Undergraduate, Graduate/Scholarship) [8754]
Fred Wiesner Educational Excellence Scholarships (Undergraduate, Graduate/Scholarship) [2079]
WIFLE Regular Scholarship Program (Graduate, Postdoctorate, Undergraduate/Scholarship) [10642]
Fred C. Wikoff, Jr. Scholarships (Undergraduate, Vocational/Occupational/Scholarship) [4220]
Teddy Wilburn Scholarships (Undergraduate/Scholarship) [3256]
Wild Felid Legacy Scholarships (Graduate/Scholarship) [10555]
Wilder Dimension Scholarships for Advanced Study in Theatre Arts (Graduate/Scholarship) [3693]
Samuel S. Wilks Awards (Advanced Professional/Award, Monetary) [1466]
Andrea Will Memorial Scholarships (Undergraduate/Scholarship) [8945]
Willamette Chapter Scholarship Awards (Undergraduate/Scholarship) [7702]
Willard & Spackman Scholarship Program (Postgraduate/Scholarship) [1051]
James B. Willett Educational Memorial Scholarship Award (Undergraduate/Scholarship) [10000]
William Randolph Hearst Educational Endowments (Undergraduate, Graduate/Scholarship) [6265]
Williams Chorale Bacardi Fallon Performing Arts Scholarships (Undergraduate/Award, Scholarship) [10563]
Sidney B. Williams, Jr. Scholarships (Undergraduate/Scholarship) [942]
Rodney Williams Legacy Scholarships (Undergraduate/Scholarship) [10150]
BM1 James Elliott Williams Memorial Scholarship Fund (Undergraduate/Scholarship) [7922]
E. E. Williams Research Grants (Master's, Doctorate/Grant) [4873]
T. Franklin Williams Research Scholars Award Program (Other/Grant) [4804]
CSM Virgil R. Williams Scholarships (Undergraduate/Scholarship) [3871]
Gary and Gussie Williams Scholarships (Undergraduate/Scholarship) [10193]
Maxine Williams Scholarships (Undergraduate/Scholarship) [540]
Cenie Jomo Williams Tuition Scholarships (Graduate, Undergraduate/Scholarship) [6721]
Lippincott Williams and Wilkins Scholarships (Master's, Doctorate/Scholarship) [3058]
Beverly Willis Architecture Foundation Travel Fellowship (Doctorate/Fellowship) [9086]
Gary S. Wilmer/RAMI Music Scholarships (Undergraduate/Scholarship) [3303]
The Edgar C. Wilson Fellowship (Graduate/Fellowship) [10274]
Saul T. Wilson, Jr. Scholarships (Graduate, Undergraduate/Scholarship) [9888]
Bob Wilson Legacy Scholarships (Undergraduate/Scholarship) [2460]
John Charles Wilson and Robert Doran Sr. Scholarships (Undergraduate/Scholarship) [5246]
Michael Wilson Scholarships (Undergraduate/Scholarship) [126]
Theo Wilson Scholarships (Graduate, Undergraduate/Scholarship) [7783]
Winston Build Your Future Scholarship (Graduate, Undergraduate, Vocational/Occupational/Scholarship) [8808]

David A. Winston Health Policy Scholarship (Graduate/Scholarship) [2087]
Winterhoff Scholarships (Undergraduate, Graduate/Scholarship) [1774]
Winterthur Research Fellowships (Graduate/Fellowship) [10609]
Wisconsin Laboratory Association Graduate Student Scholarships (Graduate/Scholarship) [10627]
Wisconsin Laboratory Association Technical Student Scholarships (Undergraduate, Graduate/Scholarship) [10628]
Wisconsin Laboratory Association Undergraduate University Student Scholarships (Undergraduate/Scholarship) [10629]
Wisconsin Lawton Minority Retention Grants (Undergraduate/Grant) [10336]
William B. Wisdom Grant in Aid of Research (Professional development/Grant) [10634]
WLALA Scholarships (Postgraduate/Scholarship) [10647]
WNBA Eastman Grants (Other/Grant) [10668]
WOCN Accredited Nursing Education Scholarships (Graduate, Undergraduate/Scholarship) [10715]
WOCN Advanced Education Scholarships (Graduate/Scholarship) [10716]
Woksape Oyate: "Wisdom of the People" Distinguished Scholars Awards (Undergraduate/Scholarship) [873]
Paul R. Wolf Memorial Scholarships (Graduate/Scholarship) [1809]
Emil Wolf Outstanding Student Paper Competition (Graduate, Undergraduate/Award) [7676]
Wolf Trap Grants for High School Performing Arts Teachers (Other/Grant) [10631]
The Wolf Trap Internship Program (Graduate, Other, Undergraduate/Internship) [10632]
Deborah Partridge Wolfe International Fellowships (Graduate, Undergraduate/Fellowship) [10820]
Nona Hobbs Wolfe Memorial Scholarship (Undergraduate/Scholarship) [5774]
Eleanor M. Wolfson Memorial Scholarship Fund (Undergraduate/Scholarship) [4063]
Wendy Y. Wolfson Memorial Scholarship Fund (Undergraduate/Scholarship) [4064]
Abel Wolman Fellowships (Doctorate/Fellowship) [1492]
Woman In Rural Electrification Scholarships (Undergraduate/Scholarship) [9383]
Women in Cancer Research Scholar Awards (Graduate, Postdoctorate/Award) [475]
Women In Defense HORIZONS Scholarships (Graduate, Undergraduate/Scholarship) [10636]
Women on Par Scholarships (Undergraduate/Scholarship) [3938]
Women of Today's Manufacturing Scholarships (Undergraduate/Scholarship) [3304]
Women of WSAJ Bar Preparation Scholarships (Undergraduate/Scholarship) [10458]
Women's Army Corps Veterans Association Scholarships (Undergraduate/Scholarship) [10654]
Women's Jewelry Association Member Grants (Professional development/Grant) [10663]
Women's Leadership in Agriculture Scholarship Program (Undergraduate/Scholarship) [7574]
Women's Leadership Training Grant (Advanced Professional, Professional development/Grant) [9327]
Women's Overseas and Service League Scholarships for Women (Undergraduate/Scholarship) [10670]
Carolyn Wones Recruitment Scholarship Grants (Undergraduate/Scholarship) [3305]
Denis Wong and Associates Scholarships (Graduate, Undergraduate/Scholarship) [7920]
Dr. Harold S. Wood Awards for Excellence (Undergraduate/Award) [4349]
Wood County Bar Association Memorial Scholarships (Graduate/Scholarship) [7874]
Mary and Elliot Wood Foundation Graduate Scholarship Fund (Graduate/Scholarship) [4222]
Mary and Elliot Wood Foundation Undergraduate Scholarship Fund (Undergraduate/Scholarship) [4223]
Wood Fruitticher Grocery Company, Inc. Scholarships (Graduate, Undergraduate/Scholarship) [201]

Rolla F. Wood Graduate Scholarships (Graduate/Scholarship) [8083]
Ed Wood Memorial Scholarship Awards (Undergraduate/Scholarship) [7703]
Irene Woodall Graduate Scholarships (Master's/Scholarship) [778]
Woodrow Wilson International Center for Scholars Fellowships (Doctorate/Fellowship) [10567]
Woodrow Wilson-Rockefeller Brothers Fund Fellowships for Aspiring Teachers of Color (Undergraduate/Fellowship) [10682]
Helen M. Woodruff Fellowships (Professional development/Fellowship) [1612]
Carter G. Woodson Institute Post-doctoral Residential Research and Teaching Fellowships (Postdoctorate/Fellowship) [10684]
Carter G. Woodson Institute Pre-doctoral Residential Research Fellowships (Doctorate/Fellowship) [10685]
Betsy B. Woodward Scholarships (Undergraduate/Scholarship) [1966]
Woody Guthrie Fellowship (Professional development/Fellowship) [2321]
Woodyard Family Scholarships (Undergraduate/Scholarship) [4568]
Blanche E. Woolls Scholarships (Graduate/Scholarship) [2242]
Patty Wooten Scholarships (Professional development/Scholarship, Award, Recognition) [1852]
John W. Work III Memorial Foundation Scholarships (Undergraduate/Scholarship) [3258]
Working for Farmers' Success Scholarships (Undergraduate/Scholarship) [10691]
World Book Graduate Scholarships in Library and Information Science (Graduate/Scholarship) [2680]
Worldstudio AIGA Scholarships (Graduate, Undergraduate/Scholarship) [10709]
Donald Worster Travel Grants (Graduate, Other/Grant) [1319]
Worthy Gemological Scholarships (Undergraduate/Scholarship) [10713]
WRI Education Foundation Scholarships - Graduate (Graduate/Scholarship) [10611]
WRI Education Foundation Scholarships - High School Seniors (Undergraduate/Scholarship) [10612]
WRI Education Foundation Scholarships - Undergraduate (Undergraduate/Scholarship) [10613]
Davis Wright Tremaine 1L Diversity Scholarships (Undergraduate/Scholarship) [3535]
WSAJ Diversity Bar Preparation Scholarships (Undergraduate/Scholarship) [10460]
WSGC Scholarships for Incoming Freshmen (Undergraduate/Scholarship) [10456]
WSSA Student Paper Competition (Undergraduate, Graduate/Award) [10535]
WYCUP Scholarships (Other/Scholarship) [10700]
Wyeth Foundation Predoctoral Fellowship (Postdoctorate/Fellowship) [9009]
Margaret Wyeth Scholarships (Undergraduate/Scholarship) [3306]
Wyeth-SUS Clinical Scholar Awards (Other/Award) [9321]
Xavier Community-Engaged Fellowships (Undergraduate/Fellowship) [10727]
Xavier University Chancellor Scholarships (Undergraduate/Scholarship) [10728]
Xavier University Departmental Scholarships (Undergraduate/Scholarship) [10729]
Xavier University Honors Bachelor of Arts Scholarships (Undergraduate/Scholarship) [10730]
Xavier University Legacy Scholarships (Undergraduate/Scholarship) [10731]
Xavier University Presidential Scholarships (Undergraduate/Scholarship) [10732]
Xavier University ROTC Scholarships - Air Force ROTC (Undergraduate/Scholarship) [10733]
Xavier University ROTC Scholarships - Army ROTC (Undergraduate/Scholarship) [10734]
Xavier University Williams Scholarships (Undergraduate/Scholarship) [10735]
Xerox Technical Minority Scholarships (Graduate, Undergraduate/Scholarship) [10737]
Yale Graduate and Professional Students Research

Fellowships *(Graduate, Professional development/Fellowship)* [2215]
Yamhill County Farm Bureau Scholarships *(Undergraduate/Scholarship)* [7707]
William J. Yankee Memorial Scholarships *(Undergraduate/Scholarship)* [1125]
Gwen Yarnell Theatre Scholarships *(Undergraduate/Scholarship)* [4028]
Yasme Foundation Scholarships *(Undergraduate/Scholarship)* [1765]
Minoru Yasui Memorial Scholarships *(Graduate, Master's, Doctorate/Scholarship)* [5560]
Willa Yeck Memorial Scholarship Fund *(Undergraduate/Scholarship)* [6292]
Marilyn Yetso Memorial Scholarships *(Graduate/Scholarship)* [9829]
The YFU Americas Scholarships *(Undergraduate/Scholarship)* [10770]
Gary Yoshimura Scholarships *(Undergraduate/Scholarship)* [8379]
Jack and Edna May Yost Scholarships *(Undergraduate/Scholarship)* [4258]
Alma H. Young Emerging Scholar Awards *(Doctorate/Award, Monetary)* [10344]
Young Investigators Achievement Award *(Advanced Professional, Professional development/Award, Grant)* [5620]
Young People For Fellowships *(Professional development/Fellowship)* [10764]
Donnell B. Young Scholarships *(Undergraduate/Scholarship)* [308]
Pearl I. Young Scholarships *(Undergraduate/Scholarship)* [7499]
Elmer Cooke Young - Taylor Young Scholarships *(Undergraduate/Scholarship)* [4774]
George D. Younger Scholarships *(Undergraduate/Scholarship)* [7394]
Yount, Hyde & Barbour Scholarships *(Undergraduate/Scholarship)* [10411]
Your Skin Is In College Ambassador Scholarships *(Undergraduate/Scholarship)* [6407]
Youth Empowerment Summit Scholarships *(Undergraduate/Scholarship)* [6817]
Youth Partners Accessing Capital (PAC) *(Undergraduate/Scholarship)* [354]
The Youth Scholarship Program *(Undergraduate/Scholarship)* [2871]
YWA Foundation Scholarships *(Graduate, Undergraduate/Scholarship)* [10766]
Z/I Imaging Scholarships *(Graduate/Scholarship)* [1810]
Zagunis Student Leader Scholarships *(Graduate, Undergraduate/Scholarship)* [6734]
Lisa Zaken Awards For Excellence *(Graduate, Undergraduate/Award, Monetary)* [5197]
James and Joy Zana Memorial Scholarships *(Undergraduate/Scholarship)* [4569]
Zarley, McKee, Thomte, Voorhees, Sease Law Scholarship *(Undergraduate/Scholarship)* [3691]
The Zebra Safe Driver Scholarships *(Undergraduate, Graduate/Scholarship)* [10810]
Urashi Zen Scholarships *(Undergraduate/Scholarship)* [8272]
The Zenith Fellows Award Program (Zenith) *(Postdoctorate/Fellowship)* [377]
Harry and Angel Zerigian Scholarships *(Undergraduate/Scholarship)* [1708]
Zeta Chapter Memorial Scholarship Awards *(Undergraduate/Scholarship)* [3307]
Zeta Phi Beta Sorority General Graduate Scholarships *(Graduate/Scholarship)* [10821]
Zeta Phi Beta Sorority General Undergraduate Scholarships *(Undergraduate/Scholarship)* [10822]
Zeta Sigma Project 2000 Scholarships *(Undergraduate/Scholarship)* [5775]
A.F. Zimmerman Scholarships *(Graduate, Master's/Scholarship)* [8050]
Morris L. and Rebecca Ziskind Memorial Scholarships *(Undergraduate/Scholarship)* [5029]
Amelia Zollner IPPR/UCL Internship Award *(Undergraduate/Internship)* [5210]
Ruth and Sherman Zudekoff Scholarships *(Undergraduate/Scholarship)* [3202]
Leo Zupin Memorial Scholarship Fund *(Undergraduate, Vocational/Occupational/Scholarship)* [4556]

Francis Sylvia Zverina Scholarships *(Undergraduate/Scholarship)* [4867]

UNITED STATES (BY REGION)

Long Island
H.J. "Duke" Ellington Memorial Scholarship Award *(Undergraduate/Scholarship)* [7513]

Mid Atlantic Region
NACA Mid Atlantic Graduate Student Scholarships *(Graduate, Master's, Doctorate/Scholarship)* [6726]
NACA Mid Atlantic Higher Education Research Scholarships *(Master's/Scholarship)* [6727]
NACA Mid Atlantic Undergraduate Scholarships for Student Leaders *(Undergraduate/Scholarship)* [6728]

Midwestern States
Archie Motley Memorial Scholarships for Minority Students *(Graduate/Scholarship)* [6517]

New England States
Dvora Brodie Scholarships *(Graduate, Postgraduate, Undergraduate/Scholarship)* [4829]
Charles H. Hood Foundation Child Health Research Awards Program *(Doctorate/Grant)* [4815]
NELA Conference Scholarships *(All/Scholarship)* [7297]
Shaw-Worth Memorial Scholarship *(Undergraduate/Scholarship)* [5002]

Northwestern States
William Bennett W7PHO Memorial Scholarships *(Undergraduate/Scholarship)* [1727]
Clair Shirey Scholarships *(Undergraduate/Scholarship)* [10037]

Pacific States
William Bennett W7PHO Memorial Scholarships *(Undergraduate/Scholarship)* [1727]

Southeastern States
Leighton M. Ballew Directing Scholarships *(Undergraduate/Scholarship)* [9387]
Polly Holliday Scholarships *(Undergraduate/Scholarship)* [9388]
Robert Porterfield Graduate Scholarships *(Graduate/Scholarship)* [9389]
Marian A. Smith Scholarships *(Graduate/Scholarship)* [9390]
Southeastern Theatre Conference Secondary School Scholarships *(Undergraduate/Scholarship)* [9391]
William E. Wilson Scholarships *(Graduate/Scholarship)* [9392]

Southern States
SNRS Dissertation Research Grants *(Doctorate/Grant)* [9406]

Southwestern States
William Bennett W7PHO Memorial Scholarships *(Undergraduate/Scholarship)* [1727]

Western States
Institute of Transportation Engineers - Western District Fellowships *(Graduate/Fellowship)* [5220]
Western Society of Weed Science Outstanding Student Scholarship Program *(Graduate, Undergraduate/Scholarship)* [10541]

UNITED STATES (BY STATE)

Alabama
ACHE/American Legion Auxiliary Scholarships *(Undergraduate/Scholarship)* [184]
ACHE Police Officers and Firefighters Survivors' Educational Assistance Programs *(Undergraduate/Scholarship)* [187]
ACHE Senior Adult Scholarships *(Undergraduate/Scholarship)* [188]
Alabama Gi Dependents' Educational Benefit Program *(Undergraduate/Scholarship)* [190]
Alabama Horse Council Scholarships *(Undergraduate/Scholarship)* [203]
Alabama National Guard Educational Assistance Program *(Undergraduate/Scholarship)* [191]
Alabama Scholarships for Dependents of Blind Parents *(Undergraduate/Scholarship)* [192]
Alabama Student Assistance Programs *(Undergraduate/Scholarship)* [193]
Alabama Student Grant Programs *(Undergraduate, Vocational/Occupational/Grant)* [194]
Birmingham District Alabama Dietetic Association Scholarships *(Graduate, Undergraduate/Scholarship)* [196]
Birmingham Student Scholarships *(Undergraduate/Scholarship)* [2273]
William Verbon Black Scholarships *(Undergraduate/Scholarship)* [205]
Leon Bradley Scholarship Program *(Undergraduate/Scholarship)* [575]
Johnston Cabaniss Scholarships *(Graduate/Scholarship)* [206]
Charles Clarke Cordle Memorial Scholarships *(Undergraduate/Scholarship)* [1736]
J. Craig and Page T. Smith Scholarships *(Undergraduate/Scholarship)* [8999]
Legacy Inc. College Undergraduate and Graduate Scholarships *(Graduate, Undergraduate/Scholarship)* [6002]
McFarffels Scholarships *(Undergraduate/Scholarship)* [8256]
The Medalist Club Post Graduate Scholarships *(Postgraduate/Scholarship)* [6376]
NAJA Scholarships *(Graduate/Scholarship)* [6760]
North Alabama Dietetic Association Scholarships *(Graduate, Undergraduate/Scholarship)* [197]
Northeast Alabama District Dietetic Association Scholarships *(Graduate, Undergraduate/Scholarship)* [198]
Regions Riding Forward Scholarships Essay Contest *(Undergraduate/Scholarship)* [8536]
Justice Janie L. Shores Scholarships *(Undergraduate/Scholarship)* [207]
Southeast Alabama Dietetic Association Scholarships *(Graduate, Undergraduate/Scholarship)* [200]
SPE Gulf Coast Hurricane Scholarships *(Undergraduate/Scholarship)* [9270]
SSAWMA Scholarships *(Graduate/Scholarship)* [9415]
Mary Katherine "Kathy" Williamson Scholarship Fund *(Undergraduate/Scholarship)* [3273]

Alaska
AIA Alaska Scholarships *(Graduate, Undergraduate/Scholarship)* [893]
Alaska Aerospace Development Corporation Scholarships *(Undergraduate/Scholarship)* [10004]
Alaska Native Medical Center Auxiliary Scholarships *(Undergraduate/Scholarship)* [10005]
Alaska Press Club Scholarships *(Undergraduate/Scholarship)* [10006]
Mike Ardaw Scholarships *(Undergraduate/Scholarship)* [10007]
Paul Arnold Memorial Scholarships *(Undergraduate/Scholarship)* [8241]
Asian and Pacific Islander Queers Sisters Scholarships *(Undergraduate/Scholarship)* [8242]
Associates in Behavioral Health Scholarships *(Graduate/Scholarship)* [8243]
Elaine Atwood Scholarship *(Undergraduate/Scholarship)* [10049]
Dr. Jon Baker Memorial Scholarship *(Graduate, Un-*

dergraduate/Scholarship) [10050]
UAA Michael Baring-Gould Memorial Scholarship (Graduate, Undergraduate/Scholarship) [10051]
Lawrence Bayer Business Administration Scholarships (Undergraduate/Scholarship) [10008]
Charles E. Behlke Engineering Memorial Scholarships (Undergraduate/Scholarship) [10009]
Mark A. Beltz Scholarship (Graduate, Undergraduate/Scholarship) [10052]
Bill Bendiner and Doug Morgenson Scholarships (Undergraduate/Scholarship) [8246]
Bill and Nell Biggs Scholarships (Undergraduate/Scholarship) [10088]
Bolick Foreign Student Scholarships (Undergraduate/Scholarship) [10010]
Pat Brakke Political Science Scholarship (Undergraduate/Scholarship) [10053]
Mary Lou Brown Scholarships (Undergraduate/Scholarship) [1729]
Bunnell Scholarships (Undergraduate/Scholarship) [10012]
Loyal D. Burkett Memorial Scholarships (Undergraduate/Scholarship) [10013]
Lyle Carlson Wildlife Management Scholarships (Undergraduate/Scholarship) [10014]
Deloris Carter Hampton Scholarships (Undergraduate/Scholarship) [8247]
Emi Chance for Aspiring Artists Scholarship (Undergraduate/Scholarship) [10054]
Edward Rollin Clinton Memorial for Music (Undergraduate/Scholarship) [10055]
Donald O. Coffman Scholarships (Undergraduate/Scholarship) [8248]
Dennis Coleman Choral Conducting Scholarships (Undergraduate/Scholarship) [8250]
Dennis Coleman Memorial Scholarships (Undergraduate/Scholarship) [8251]
Mable B. Crawford Memorial Scholarships (Undergraduate/Scholarship) [10015]
Brian M. Day Scholarships (Undergraduate/Scholarship) [8252]
Patricia Hughes Eastaugh Teaching Scholarship (Undergraduate/Scholarship) [10016]
UAA Governor William A. Egan Scholarship (Undergraduate/Scholarship) [10056]
Excellence in Geographic Information Systems Scholarships (Undergraduate/Scholarship) [10017]
Lydia Fohn-Hansen/Lola Hill Memorial Scholarships (Undergraduate, Graduate/Scholarship) [10018]
Michael D. Ford Memorial Scholarship (Graduate, Undergraduate/Scholarship) [10057]
Johnny & Sarah Frank Scholarships (Undergraduate/Scholarship) [10019]
Jan and Glenn Fredericks Scholarship (Graduate, Undergraduate/Scholarship) [10058]
Ardell French Memorial Scholarship (Undergraduate/Scholarship) [10059]
Charles F. Gould Endowment Scholarships (Undergraduate/Scholarship) [10020]
Ken Gray Endowment Scholarship (Undergraduate/Scholarship) [10061]
Patty Hamilton Early Childhood Development Scholarships (Undergraduate/Scholarship) [10021]
Muriel Hannah Scholarships in Art (Undergraduate, Graduate/Scholarship) [10062]
Lenore and George Hedla Accounting Scholarship (Undergraduate/Scholarship) [10063]
John Henderson Endowment Scholarships (Undergraduate/Scholarship) [10022]
Donald Wills Jacobs Scholarships (Undergraduate/Scholarship) [10023]
Chris L. Kleinke Scholarship (Graduate/Scholarship) [10064]
Iver and Cora Knapstad Scholarships (Undergraduate/Scholarship) [10024]
Kris Knudson Memorial Scholarship (Graduate, Undergraduate/Scholarship) [10065]
Robert W. Korn Scholarships (Undergraduate/Scholarship) [10025]
Arlene Kuhner Memorial Scholarship (Undergraduate/Scholarship) [10066]
Austin E. Lathrop Scholarships (Undergraduate/Scholarship) [10026]
Franklin M. Leach Scholarships (Undergraduate/Scholarship) [10027]

Obrzut Ling Scholarships (Undergraduate/Scholarship) [8255]
Matanuska-Susitna College Regent's Scholarships (Undergraduate/Scholarship) [10089]
Larry Matfay Cultural Heritage Scholarships (Undergraduate, Graduate/Scholarship) [5868]
Dave McCloud Aviation Memorial Scholarships (Undergraduate/Scholarship) [10028]
Richard Mellon Scholarships (Undergraduate/Scholarship) [10029]
Jack D. Motteler Scholarships (Undergraduate/Scholarship) [8257]
Andrew Nerland Scholarships (Undergraduate/Scholarship) [10031]
Maureen E. Nolan-Cahill Memorial Scholarships (Undergraduate/Scholarship) [10032]
Nordic Ski Association of Anchorage Scholarships (Undergraduate/Scholarship) [221]
Don and Jan O'Dowd/SAA Statewide Scholarships (Undergraduate/Scholarship) [10033]
Diane Olsen Memorial Scholarship (Undergraduate/Scholarship) [10067]
Alvin G. Ott Fish and Wildlife Scholarships (Undergraduate/Scholarship) [10034]
Pignalberi Public Policy Scholarship (Graduate/Scholarship) [10068]
Pride Foundation Political Leadership Scholarships (Undergraduate/Scholarship) [8258]
Pride Foundation Regional Scholarships (Undergraduate/Scholarship) [8259]
Pride Foundation Scholarships (Undergraduate/Scholarship) [8663]
Pride Foundation Social Work Scholarships (Undergraduate/Scholarship) [8260]
Pt. Lay Memorial Scholarships (Undergraduate/Scholarship) [10035]
April Relyea Scholarship (Graduate, Undergraduate/Scholarship) [10069]
Robert Browning Scholarships (Undergraduate/Scholarship) [8262]
A.D. Al and Maxine Robertson Memorial Scholarship (Undergraduate/Scholarship) [10036]
Pat and Cliff Rogers Nursing Scholarships (Undergraduate/Scholarship) [10090]
Dr. Orrin Rongstad Wildlife Scholarship (Undergraduate/Scholarship) [10091]
Rosenberg-Ibarra Scholarships (Undergraduate/Scholarship) [8263]
Brown Schoenheit Memorial Scholarship (Undergraduate/Scholarship) [10070]
Eveline Schuster Memorial Award/Scholarship (Graduate, Undergraduate/Scholarship) [10071]
Seldovia Native Association Achievement Scholarships (Undergraduate, Graduate/Scholarship) [8829]
Seldovia Native Association General Scholarships (Undergraduate, Graduate/Scholarship) [8830]
Clair Shirey Scholarships (Undergraduate/Scholarship) [10037]
Linda Simmons Memorial Scholarships (Undergraduate/Scholarship) [219]
Ward Sims Memorial Scholarships (Undergraduate/Scholarship) [10038]
Lillian Smith Scholarship for Teaching Students (Graduate, Undergraduate/Scholarship) [10072]
Snodgrass Scholarships (Undergraduate/Scholarship) [10039]
Sourdough Reunion Memorial Endowment Scholarships (Undergraduate/Scholarship) [10040]
Kathy Spadoni Memorial Scholarship (Undergraduate/Scholarship) [8264]
Sheri Stears Education Scholarship (Undergraduate/Scholarship) [10073]
Sturgulewski Family Scholarship (Graduate, Undergraduate/Scholarship) [10074]
UAA Accounting Club Scholarship (Undergraduate/Scholarship) [10075]
UAA Alaska Kidney Foundation Scholarship (Graduate, Undergraduate/Scholarship) [10076]
UAA Alumni Association Scholarship (Undergraduate/Scholarship) [10077]
UAA College of Business and Public Policy Scholarships (Graduate, Undergraduate/Scholarship) [10078]
UAA Friends of the Performing Arts Scholarship (Undergraduate/Scholarship) [10079]

UAA GCI, Inc. Scholarship (Undergraduate/Scholarship) [10080]
UAA Kimura Scholarship Fund for Illustration (Undergraduate/Scholarship) [10081]
UAA Kimura Scholarship Fund for Photography (Undergraduate/Scholarship) [10082]
UAA Quanterra Scholarship (Graduate/Scholarship) [10083]
UAA RRANN Program Scholarships (Undergraduate/Scholarship) [10084]
UAF College of Liberal Arts - Anchorage Daily News Journalism Awards (Undergraduate/Scholarship) [10094]
Ric Ulrich and Chuck Pischke Scholarships (Undergraduate/Scholarship) [8266]
Umialik Scholarships (Undergraduate/Scholarship) [10041]
University of Alaska Scholars Program (Undergraduate/Scholarship) [10042]
Patricia Van Kirk Scholarships (Undergraduate/Scholarship) [8267]
Wells Fargo Career Scholarship (Undergraduate/Scholarship) [10085]
Wells Fargo Scholarships (Undergraduate/Scholarship) [8268]
Arthur N. Wilson, MD, Scholarships (Undergraduate/Scholarship) [991]
William S. Wilson Memorial Scholarships (Undergraduate/Scholarship) [10043]
Melissa J. Wolf Scholarship (Undergraduate/Scholarship) [10086]
Guy A. Woodings Scholarships (Undergraduate/Scholarship) [10044]
Wozumi Family Scholarships (Undergraduate/Scholarship) [8270]
Ralph Yetka Memorial Scholarships (Undergraduate/Scholarship) [10045]
Joan C. Yoder Memorial Nursing Scholarships (Undergraduate/Scholarship) [10046]
You Go Girl! Scholarships (Undergraduate/Scholarship) [8271]
Yukon Delta Fisheries Development Association Scholarships (Undergraduate, Graduate/Scholarship) [10047]
Urashi Zen Scholarships (Undergraduate/Scholarship) [8272]

Arizona

ACSO Scholarships (Undergraduate/Scholarship) [1633]
Marvin A. Andrews Scholarships/Internships (Graduate/Internship, Scholarship) [1630]
APS/ASU Scholarships (Undergraduate/Scholarship) [8139]
APS/Maricopa County Community Colleges Scholarships (Undergraduate/Scholarship) [8140]
Arizona Nursery Association Scholarships (Undergraduate/Scholarship) [1637]
ASCPA High School Scholarships (Undergraduate/Scholarship, Monetary) [1641]
Walt Bartram Memorial Education Award, Region 12 and Chapter 119 (Undergraduate/Scholarship) [9167]
Central Arizona DX Association Scholarships (Undergraduate/Scholarship) [1731]
Charles N. Fisher Memorial Scholarships (Undergraduate/Scholarship) [1738]
Gail Goodell Folsom Memorial Scholarships (Undergraduate/Scholarship) [6650]
Future CPA Scholarships (Undergraduate/Scholarship) [1642]
HACU/Gilberto Salazar Escoboza Scholarships (Undergraduate, Graduate/Scholarship) [4885]
HACU/Videxport S.A. de C.V. Scholarships (Undergraduate, Graduate/Scholarship) [4889]
Kappa Delta Phi Scholarship Program (Postgraduate/Scholarship) [1046]
Prescott Fine Arts Association Scholarship Program (Undergraduate/Scholarship) [8221]
Region II Scholarships (Graduate, Undergraduate/Scholarship) [1428]
Rocky Mountain Coal Mining Institute Engineering/Geology Scholarships (Undergraduate/Scholarship) [8632]
Rocky Mountain Coal Mining Institute Technical

Scholarships *(Undergraduate/Scholarship)* [8633]

Arkansas

ARAFCS Doctoral Scholarships *(Doctorate/Scholarship)* [1646]
ARAFCS Masters Scholarships *(Graduate/Scholarship)* [1647]
Arkansas Green Industry Association Student Scholarships *(Undergraduate/Scholarship)* [1652]
Arkansas Public Health Association Scholarships *(Undergraduate/Scholarship)* [1659]
Arkansas Single Parent Scholarships *(Undergraduate, Graduate/Scholarship)* [1661]
Arkansas State University Mountain Home Scholarships *(Undergraduate/Scholarship)* [1663]
ArLA Scholarships *(Graduate/Scholarship)* [1654]
Cherokee Nation Graduate Scholarships *(Graduate/Scholarship)* [2893]
Cherokee Nation Scholarships *(Undergraduate/Scholarship)* [2895]
Lone Star GIA Associate and Alumni Scholarships *(Undergraduate/Scholarship)* [4341]
Randall Matthis for Environmental Studies Scholarships *(Graduate, Undergraduate/Scholarship)* [1649]
Fred R. McDaniel Memorial Scholarships *(Undergraduate/Scholarship)* [1746]
NAJA Scholarships *(Graduate/Scholarship)* [6760]
WillEtta Long Oates, Gamma Nu, Memorial Scholarship *(Undergraduate, Graduate/Scholarship)* [5754]
Regions Riding Forward Scholarships Essay Contest *(Undergraduate/Scholarship)* [8536]
Hatton W. Sumners Scholarships *(Undergraduate/Scholarship)* [7602]

California

American GI Forum of San Jose Scholarships *(Undergraduate/Scholarship)* [8756]
Aquatics Booster Club Scholarships *(Undergraduate/Scholarship)* [8448]
Connie "Chelo" Armendariz Memorial Scholarships *(Undergraduate/Scholarship)* [8450]
Richard E. Arnason Court Scholarships *(Undergraduate/Scholarship)* [3409]
Luis Arreola Memorial Scholarships *(Undergraduate/Scholarship)* [8686]
Asian/Pacific Bar Association of Sacramento Law Foundation Scholarship *(Graduate, Postgraduate/Scholarship)* [1790]
Association of California Water Agencies Scholarships *(Undergraduate/Scholarship)* [1871]
Association for Women in Architecture Scholarships *(Undergraduate/Scholarship)* [2089]
Frank H. Ault Scholarships *(Undergraduate/Scholarship)* [8687]
Baha'i Faith Scholarships for Racial Harmony *(Undergraduate/Scholarship)* [8451]
Ballard Family Foundation Scholarships *(Undergraduate/Scholarship)* [8688]
Barta-Lehman Musical Scholarships *(Undergraduate/Scholarship)* [8689]
Walt Bartram Memorial Education Award, Region 12 and Chapter 119 *(Undergraduate/Scholarship)* [9167]
Bay Area Minority Law Student Scholarships *(Graduate, Undergraduate/Scholarship)* [2195]
Ray and Mary Bell Memorial Scholarships *(Undergraduate/Scholarship)* [8690]
James R. and Geraldine F. Bertelsen Scholarships *(Undergraduate/Scholarship)* [8691]
Dorothy M. Bolyard Memorial Scholarships *(Undergraduate/Scholarship)* [8692]
AFCEA San Diego Buck Bragunier Leadership Scholarship *(Undergraduate/Scholarship)* [1667]
Breslauer Family Scholarships *(Undergraduate/Scholarship)* [8693]
Louise A. Broderick San Diego County Scholarships *(Undergraduate/Scholarship)* [8694]
California Association of Family and Consumer Sciences - San Diego Chapter Scholarships (CAFCS) *(Undergraduate, Graduate/Scholarship)* [8695]
California Groundwater Association Scholarships *(Undergraduate/Scholarship)* [2462]
California Scottish Rite Foundation Scholarships *(Undergraduate/Scholarship)* [2477]
Calvin Alumni Association California- Bay Area Scholarships *(Undergraduate/Scholarship)* [2493]
Calvin Alumni Association Southern California Chapter Scholarships *(Undergraduate/Scholarship)* [2502]
Robert G. Campbell Scholarships *(Undergraduate/Scholarship)* [8462]
CHEA Undergraduate Scholarship Program for Students with Disabilities *(Undergraduate/Scholarship)* [2464]
CHEA Vocational Grants *(Undergraduate/Grant)* [2465]
Cheerful Giver Scholarships *(Undergraduate/Scholarship)* [8696]
Chicana Latina Scholarship Fund *(Graduate, Undergraduate/Scholarship)* [2901]
Willis W. and Ethel M. Clark Foundation Fellowships *(Graduate/Fellowship)* [3049]
The Club at Morningside Scholarships *(Undergraduate, Graduate/Scholarship)* [8697]
Community Bank - Lee Guggisberg Foundation Memorial Scholarships *(Undergraduate/Scholarship)* [8464]
Madison and Edith Cooper Scholarships *(Undergraduate/Scholarship)* [8698]
Crafton Hills College Foundation Scholarships *(Undergraduate/Scholarship)* [8468]
Crawford Scholarships *(Undergraduate/Scholarship)* [8699]
Redlands Rotary Club - Ernest L. Cronemeyer Memorial Scholarships *(Undergraduate/Scholarship)* [8469]
Rebecca Lee Crumpler, M.D. Scholarships *(Advanced Professional/Scholarship)* [1865]
Curry Awards for Girls and Young Women *(Undergraduate/Scholarship)* [8949]
Davis Family Scholarships *(Undergraduate/Scholarship)* [8700]
Death Valley '49ers Scholarships *(Undergraduate/Scholarship)* [3537]
Ruth DeMoss Scholarships *(Undergraduate/Scholarship)* [8701]
Herman H. Derksen Scholarships *(Undergraduate/Scholarship)* [8702]
Drinkwater Family Scholarships *(Undergraduate/Scholarship)* [8703]
James Echols Scholarship Award *(Undergraduate/Scholarship)* [2434]
Eustace-Kwan Family Foundation Scholarships *(Undergraduate/Scholarship)* [8950]
James Mackenzie Fallows Scholarships Honoring Gertrude Baccus *(Undergraduate/Scholarship)* [8473]
James Mackenzie Fallows Scholarships Honoring William Cunningham *(Undergraduate/Scholarship)* [8474]
Charles N. Fisher Memorial Scholarships *(Undergraduate/Scholarship)* [1738]
Reuben H. Fleet Memorial Scholarships *(Undergraduate/Scholarship)* [8704]
Sue Fleming Memorial Scholarships *(Undergraduate/Scholarship)* [2440]
Joel Garcia Memorial Scholarship *(Undergraduate/Scholarship)* [2825]
Getty Foundation Library Research Grants *(Professional development/Grant)* [4407]
HACU/Gilberto Salazar Escoboza Scholarships *(Undergraduate, Graduate/Scholarship)* [4885]
HACU/Videxport S.A. de C.V. Scholarships *(Undergraduate, Graduate/Scholarship)* [4889]
Leslie Jane Hahn Memorial Scholarships *(Undergraduate/Scholarship)* [8705]
Peter Hess Scholarships *(Undergraduate/Scholarship)* [4338]
Clair A. Hill Scholarships *(Undergraduate/Scholarship)* [1873]
Albert W. and Mildred Hubbard Scholarships *(Undergraduate/Scholarship)* [8708]
Ruth E. Jenkins Scholarships *(Undergraduate/Scholarship)* [8709]
John F. Kennedy Scholarship Award *(Undergraduate/Scholarship)* [2435]
Napoleon A. Jones, III Memorial Scholarships *(Undergraduate/Scholarship)* [8710]
Alice Newell Joslyn Medical Fund *(Undergraduate/Scholarship)* [2211]
Kappa Delta Phi Scholarship Program *(Postgraduate/Scholarship)* [1046]
Kawano Family Scholarships *(Undergraduate/Scholarship)* [8711]
Kiwanis Club of Escondido Scholarships *(Undergraduate/Scholarship)* [8712]
Friends and Family of Christopher J. Kohlmeier Scholarships *(Undergraduate/Scholarship)* [8489]
Judith Keller Marx Krumholz Scholarships *(Undergraduate/Scholarship)* [8713]
Patrick Ledden Honorary Scholarships *(Undergraduate/Scholarship)* [8714]
Lehman Family Scholarships *(Undergraduate/Scholarship)* [8715]
The Lemon Grove Education Foundation Scholarships *(Undergraduate/Scholarship)* [8716]
Luso-American Education Foundation G-1 Grants *(Other/Grant)* [6146]
Luso-American Education Foundation G-2 Grants *(Other/Grant)* [6147]
Luso-American Education Foundation G-3 Grants *(Postgraduate/Grant)* [6148]
McKinley Elementary School PTA Scholarships *(Undergraduate/Scholarship)* [8496]
Mission Bay Hospital Auxiliary Scholarships *(Undergraduate/Scholarship)* [8717]
MKC/Preuss Scholarship Fund *(Undergraduate/Scholarship)* [8718]
Wilma Motley Memorial California Merit Scholarships *(Undergraduate/Scholarship)* [777]
Harry Munoz Memorial Scholarships *(Undergraduate/Scholarship)* [8501]
Stuart L. Noderer Memorial Scholarships *(Undergraduate/Scholarship)* [8719]
Casilda Pagan Educational/Vocational Scholarships *(Graduate, Undergraduate, Postgraduate/Scholarship)* [4964]
Ben Palacio Scholarships *(Undergraduate/Scholarship)* [9962]
Pearman Family Scholarships *(Undergraduate/Scholarship)* [8720]
Mario Pedrozzi Scholarships *(Undergraduate, Graduate/Scholarship)* [7931]
Steve Petix Journalism Scholarships *(Undergraduate/Scholarship)* [8721]
Pollard-Bailey Scholarships *(Undergraduate/Scholarship)* [8722]
Qualcomm San Diego Science, Technology, Engineering and Mathematics Scholarships *(Undergraduate/Scholarship)* [8723]
Rancho Bernardo/Smith Scholarships *(Undergraduate/Scholarship)* [8724]
Redlands Community Scholarship Foundation Awards *(Undergraduate/Scholarship)* [8510]
Redlands Rotary Club Foundation Discretionary Scholarships *(Undergraduate/Scholarship)* [8521]
Redlands Teachers Association Scholarships *(Undergraduate/Scholarship)* [8522]
Smiley Elementary School PTA - Beverly Roberts Memorial Scholarships *(Undergraduate/Scholarship)* [8523]
Charles and Ruth Ronin Memorial Scholarships *(Undergraduate/Scholarship)* [8524]
The Rotary Club of Rancho Bernardo Sunrise Community Service Scholarships *(Undergraduate/Scholarship)* [8725]
Michael A. Russo Memorial Scholarships *(Undergraduate/Scholarship)* [8525]
SALEF Health Career Scholarships *(Undergraduate, Graduate/Scholarship)* [8680]
The San Diego Foundation Community Scholarships I *(Undergraduate/Scholarship)* [8726]
The San Diego Foundation Community Scholarships II *(Undergraduate/Scholarship)* [8727]
San Pasqual Academy Scholarships *(Undergraduate/Scholarship)* [8728]
Leo and Trinidad Sanchez Scholarships *(Undergraduate/Scholarship)* [8956]
Santa Clara La Raza Lawyers Scholarships *(Graduate/Scholarship)* [5894]
Malini E. Sathyadev Memorial Scholarships *(Undergraduate/Scholarship)* [8729]
Scholarship Foundation of Santa Barbara Art Schol-

arship Program *(Undergraduate/Scholarship)* [8798]
School Library Paraprofessional Scholarships - Southern Region *(Advanced Professional/Scholarship)* [2474]
SCLMA Medical Student Scholarships *(Undergraduate, Graduate/Scholarship)* [9401]
Felix R. Sepulveda Memorial Scholarships - Northside Booster Club *(Undergraduate/Scholarship)* [8527]
Service League Volunteer Scholarships *(Undergraduate/Scholarship)* [10447]
Harvey L. Simmons Memorial Scholarships *(Undergraduate/Scholarship)* [8730]
Gladys Ann Smith Greater Los Angeles Women's Council Scholarships *(Undergraduate/Scholarship)* [7230]
Soroptimist International of Redlands Scholarships *(Undergraduate/Scholarship)* [8528]
South Coast Area High School Senior Honors Scholarship Program *(Undergraduate/Scholarship)* [8800]
Step Up Scholarships *(Undergraduate, Graduate/Scholarship)* [8731]
Mark and Karla Stuart Family Scholarship *(Undergraduate/Scholarship)* [8732]
Teacher Librarian Scholarships *(Master's/Scholarship)* [2475]
Raymond A. Tice Scholarships I *(Undergraduate/Scholarship)* [8733]
Raymond A. Tice Scholarships II *(Undergraduate/Scholarship)* [8734]
Vincent Trotter Health Care Scholarships *(Undergraduate/Scholarship)* [8735]
The UCSD Black Alumni Scholarship for Arts and Humanities *(Undergraduate/Scholarship)* [8736]
U.S. Bank Scholarships *(Undergraduate/Scholarship)* [8738]
USA Freestyle Martial Arts Scholarships *(Undergraduate/Scholarship)* [8739]
Winifred Van Hagen/Rosalind Cassidy Scholarship Award *(Undergraduate/Scholarship)* [2436]
Weissbuch Family Scholarships *(Undergraduate/Scholarship)* [8740]
WHHS Medical Staff Scholarships *(Undergraduate/Scholarship)* [10448]
Leon Williams Scholarships *(Undergraduate/Scholarship)* [8741]
Randy Williams Scholarships *(Undergraduate/Scholarship)* [8742]
Redlands Footlighters, Inc. - Merle and Peggy Williams Scholarships *(Undergraduate/Scholarship)* [8530]
Jean Wright-Elson Scholarships *(Doctorate, Graduate, Undergraduate/Scholarship)* [8743]
Youth Leadership Scholarships *(Undergraduate/Scholarship)* [2469]

Colorado

Roy Anderson Memorial Scholarships *(Graduate, Undergraduate/Scholarship)* [3140]
Broadcast Education and Development Program *(Other/Scholarship)* [3134]
Colorado Nurses Foundation Nightingale Scholarships *(Graduate, Undergraduate/Scholarship)* [3141]
El Pomar Fellowships *(Graduate/Fellowship)* [3818]
Lola Fehr: Nightingale Scholarships *(Graduate, Undergraduate/Scholarship)* [3142]
Iris Scholarship *(Undergraduate/Scholarship)* [5737]
LAEF Scholarships *(Undergraduate/Scholarship)* [5937]
Stephen T. Marchello Scholarships *(Undergraduate/Scholarship)* [6237]
H.M. Muffly Memorial Scholarships *(Graduate, Undergraduate/Scholarship)* [3143]
Colorado Nurses Association: Virginia Paulson Memorial Scholarships *(Graduate, Undergraduate/Scholarship)* [3144]
Region II Scholarships *(Graduate, Undergraduate/Scholarship)* [1428]
Rocky Mountain Coal Mining Institute Engineering/Geology Scholarships *(Undergraduate/Scholarship)* [8632]
Rocky Mountain Coal Mining Institute Technical Scholarships *(Undergraduate/Scholarship)* [8633]
Patty Walter Memorial Scholarships *(Graduate, Undergraduate/Scholarship)* [3145]

Connecticut

Frederick G. Adams Scholarships *(Undergraduate/Scholarship)* [4735]
Associated General Contractors of Connecticut Scholarships *(Undergraduate/Scholarship)* [3365]
Thomas M. Blake Memorial Scholarships *(Undergraduate/Scholarship)* [3360]
Gerald J. and Helen Bogen Fund *(Undergraduate/Scholarship)* [4660]
Rhea Sourifman Caplin Memorial Scholarships *(Undergraduate/Scholarship)* [4742]
Casey Family Services Alumni Scholarships *(Graduate, Undergraduate, Vocational/Occupational/Scholarship)* [4157]
The College Club of Hartford Scholarships *(Undergraduate/Scholarship)* [4743]
Connecticut Association of Land Surveyors Memorial Scholarships *(Undergraduate/Scholarship)* [3358]
Connecticut Association of Latinos in Higher Education Scholarships *(Undergraduate/Scholarship)* [4744]
Julia B. DeCapua Fund *(Undergraduate/Scholarship)* [4661]
C. Rodney Demarest Memorial Scholarships *(Undergraduate/Scholarship)* [4747]
Charles Dubose Scholarships *(Undergraduate/Scholarship)* [4750]
H.J. "Duke" Ellington Memorial Scholarship Award *(Undergraduate/Scholarship)* [7513]
Herman and Bess Glazer Scholarship Fund *(Undergraduate/Scholarship)* [4662]
Killingworth Foundation Scholarships *(Undergraduate/Scholarship)* [5830]
Dr. James L. Lawson Memorial Scholarships *(Undergraduate/Scholarship)* [1745]
Les Dames D'Escoffier New York Scholarships *(Undergraduate/Scholarship)* [6009]
Lighthouse International Scholarships - Collegebound Awards *(High School, Undergraduate/Scholarship)* [6083]
Lighthouse International Scholarships - Graduate Awards *(Graduate/Scholarship)* [6084]
Lighthouse International Scholarships - Undergraduate Awards *(Undergraduate/Scholarship)* [6085]
Mary Main Memorial Scholarships *(Undergraduate/Scholarship)* [4762]
ARTC Glenn Moon Scholarships *(Undergraduate/Scholarship)* [4765]
NASSLEO Scholarships - Region I *(Undergraduate/Scholarship)* [6782]
New England FEMARA Scholarships *(Undergraduate/Scholarship)* [1748]
New York Women in Communications, Inc. Foundation Scholarships *(Graduate, Undergraduate/Scholarship)* [7406]
Pellegrini Scholarships *(Undergraduate, Graduate/Scholarship)* [9620]
Dorothy E. Hofmann Pembroke Scholarships *(Undergraduate/Scholarship)* [4767]
Rosa Quezada Memorial Education Scholarships *(Undergraduate/Scholarship)* [3361]
Mary C. Rawlins Scholarships *(Undergraduate/Scholarship)* [4771]
John Soto Scholarships *(Undergraduate/Scholarship)* [3362]
Edward Traurig Scholarships *(Undergraduate/Scholarship)* [10484]
Marta Vallin Memorial Scholarships *(Undergraduate/Scholarship)* [3363]
Waterbury Bar Association Scholarships *(Undergraduate/Scholarship)* [10485]
WBA Bar President's Scholarships *(Undergraduate/Scholarship)* [10486]
WBA Paralegal/Legal Assistant Scholarships *(Undergraduate/Scholarship)* [10487]
Yankee Clipper Contest Club, Inc. Youth Scholarships *(Undergraduate/Scholarship)* [1764]
Young Christian Leaders Scholarships *(Undergraduate/Scholarship)* [10760]
Zimmermann Scholarships *(Graduate/Scholarship)* [9621]

Delaware

Horatio Alger Delaware Scholarships *(Undergraduate/Scholarship)* [4936]
Chrysler Technical Scholarship Fund *(Undergraduate/Scholarship)* [3545]
Generation III Scholarships *(Undergraduate/Scholarship)* [3783]
German Society Scholarships *(Undergraduate/Scholarship)* [4404]
Gruwell Scholarships *(Undergraduate/Scholarship)* [3178]
Dick and Pat Hazel Minority Scholarships *(Undergraduate/Scholarship)* [3180]
Lighthouse International Scholarships - Collegebound Awards *(High School, Undergraduate/Scholarship)* [6083]
Lighthouse International Scholarships - Graduate Awards *(Graduate/Scholarship)* [6084]
Lighthouse International Scholarships - Undergraduate Awards *(Undergraduate/Scholarship)* [6085]
NASSLEO Scholarships - Region I *(Undergraduate/Scholarship)* [6782]
Pellegrini Scholarships *(Undergraduate, Graduate/Scholarship)* [9620]
Drew Smith Memorial Scholarships *(Undergraduate/Scholarship)* [3187]
Zimmermann Scholarships *(Graduate/Scholarship)* [9621]

District of Columbia

Frederick B. Abramson Memorial Foundation Scholarships *(Undergraduate/Scholarship)* [28]
Horatio Alger District of Columbia, Maryland and Virginia Scholarships *(Undergraduate/Scholarship)* [4937]
Dr. Johnella Banks Memorial Scholarships *(Undergraduate/Scholarship)* [2298]
Board of Young Adult Advisors Scholarships *(Graduate/Scholarship)* [9827]
Alice Yuriko Endo Memorial Scholarships *(Undergraduate/Scholarship)* [5549]
FCBA Foundation College Scholarship Program *(Undergraduate/Scholarship)* [3972]
Dwight P. Jacobus Scholarships *(Undergraduate/Scholarship)* [2058]
Lighthouse International Scholarships - Collegebound Awards *(High School, Undergraduate/Scholarship)* [6083]
Lighthouse International Scholarships - Graduate Awards *(Graduate/Scholarship)* [6084]
Lighthouse International Scholarships - Undergraduate Awards *(Undergraduate/Scholarship)* [6085]
MyMozaic.com Annual Scholarships *(Undergraduate/Scholarship)* [6639]
NASSLEO Scholarships - Region I *(Undergraduate/Scholarship)* [6782]
Margaret Pemberton Scholarships *(Undergraduate/Scholarship)* [2299]

Florida

Jordan Abdo Memorial Scholarship *(Undergraduate/Scholarship)* [9417]
Emily and Roland Abraham Educational Funds *(Undergraduate/Scholarship)* [3316]
Horatio Alger Florida Scholarships *(Undergraduate/Scholarship)* [4938]
Judge Isaac Anderson, Jr. Scholarships *(Undergraduate/Scholarship)* [9418]
The Bailey Family Foundation College Scholarship Program *(Undergraduate/Scholarship)* [2167]
Lewis B. Barber Memorial Scholarships *(Undergraduate/Scholarship)* [9419]
James Bilder Scholarships *(Undergraduate/Scholarship)* [9420]
Leon Bradley Scholarship Program *(Undergraduate/Scholarship)* [575]
Cesar A. Calas/FES Miami Chapter Scholarships *(Undergraduate/Scholarship)* [4087]
Calvin Alumni Association Florida-Gulf Coast Scholarships *(Undergraduate/Scholarship)* [2494]
Calvin Alumni Association-South Florida Scholar-

Legal Residence Index

ships *(Undergraduate/Scholarship)* [2499]
Celler Legal P.A. Employment Skills Scholarship Program *(Undergraduate/Scholarship)* [2837]
Central Florida Jazz Society Scholarships *(Undergraduate/Award, Scholarship)* [2869]
ChairScholars Florida Scholarship Program *(Undergraduate/Scholarship)* [2888]
COUSE-Gram Scholarships *(Undergraduate/Scholarship)* [9424]
Reuben R. Cowles Youth Awards *(Undergraduate/Award)* [945]
D&A Florida Scholarships *(Undergraduate/Scholarship)* [9425]
Doctors Ira and Udaya Dash Nursing Scholarships *(Undergraduate, Graduate/Scholarship)* [9426]
Clifford W. and Doris E. Davis Educational Scholarship Fund *(Undergraduate, Vocational/Occupational/Scholarship)* [3319]
Jim Dodson Law Scholarships *(Undergraduate/Scholarship)* [5600]
Dunbar Heritage Scholarships *(Undergraduate/Scholarship)* [9427]
FICPA Educational Foundation 1040K Race Scholarships *(Undergraduate/Scholarship)* [4098]
Florida Engineering Society University Scholarships *(Undergraduate/Scholarship)* [4090]
Florida Nurses Foundation Scholarships *(Undergraduate, Master's, Doctorate/Scholarship)* [4102]
Florida Public Transportation Association Scholarships (FPTA) *(Undergraduate, Graduate/Scholarship)* [1164]
Clay Ford Florida Board of Accountancy Minority Scholarships *(Undergraduate/Scholarship)* [4083]
James Franklin and Dorothy J. Warnell Scholarship Fund *(Undergraduate, Vocational/Occupational/Scholarship)* [3321]
Doris W. Frey Memorial Scholarships *(Undergraduate, Graduate/Scholarship)* [9430]
American Association of University Women Sue Gottcent Memorial Scholarship Fund *(Undergraduate, Graduate/Scholarship)* [9431]
William L. Graddy Law School Scholarships *(Graduate/Scholarship)* [9432]
Francis Harris Gresham Scholarships *(Undergraduate/Scholarship)* [9433]
V.J. Johnson Memorial Scholarships *(Undergraduate/Scholarship)* [579]
Chip Johnson Scholarships *(Undergraduate/Scholarship)* [9435]
Kappa Delta Phi Scholarship Program *(Postgraduate/Scholarship)* [1046]
Doc Keen Memorial Scholarships *(Undergraduate/Scholarship)* [9437]
Isabel Mayer Kirkpatrick Scholarships *(Undergraduate/Scholarship)* [9438]
Robert A. Kleckner Scholarships *(Undergraduate, Graduate/Scholarship)* [9439]
Lighthouse International Scholarships - Collegebound Awards *(High School, Undergraduate/Scholarship)* [6083]
Lighthouse International Scholarships - Graduate Awards *(Graduate/Scholarship)* [6084]
Lighthouse International Scholarships - Undergraduate Awards *(Undergraduate/Scholarship)* [6085]
Roy W. Likins Scholarships *(Undergraduate, Graduate/Scholarship)* [1494]
Love of Bonita Empowerment Scholarships *(Undergraduate/Scholarship)* [9440]
Robert V. McKenna Scholarships *(Undergraduate/Scholarship)* [9654]
Ruth Messmer Memorial Scholarships *(Undergraduate/Scholarship)* [9441]
NAJA Scholarships *(Graduate/Scholarship)* [6760]
Judge William J. Nelson Scholarships *(Undergraduate/Scholarship)* [9442]
Robert B. and Dorothy Pence Scholarships *(Undergraduate/Scholarship)* [9443]
Regions Riding Forward Scholarships Essay Contest *(Undergraduate/Scholarship)* [8536]
Faye Lynn Roberts Educational Scholarships *(Undergraduate, Graduate/Scholarship)* [9445]
David G. Robinson Arts Scholarships *(Undergraduate/Scholarship)* [9446]
The Rotary Club of Cape Coral Goldcoast Scholarship Fund *(Undergraduate/Scholarship)* [2784]
IRARC Memorial Joseph P. Rubino WA4MMD Scholarships *(Undergraduate/Scholarship)* [1754]
Robert C. and Margaret A. Schikora Scholarships *(Undergraduate/Scholarship)* [9447]
John M. and Mary A. Shanley Memorial Scholarships *(Undergraduate, Graduate/Scholarship)* [9448]
Southwest Florida Community Foundation College Assistance Scholarships *(Undergraduate/Scholarship)* [9449]
Southwest Florida Deputy Sheriffs Association Fund Scholarships *(Undergraduate/Scholarship)* [9450]
SPE Gulf Coast Hurricane Scholarships *(Undergraduate/Scholarship)* [9270]
Anne Sturrock Nursing Scholarships *(Undergraduate, Graduate/Scholarship)* [9451]
John I. and Madeleine R. Taeni Scholarships *(Undergraduate/Scholarship)* [9452]
Jacki Tuckfield Memorial Graduate Business Scholarship Fund *(Doctorate, Graduate, Master's/Scholarship)* [6453]
Ted G. Wilson Memorial Scholarships *(Undergraduate/Scholarship)* [8288]

Georgia

Horatio Alger Georgia Scholarships *(Undergraduate/Scholarship)* [4939]
Leon Bradley Scholarship Program *(Undergraduate/Scholarship)* [575]
Charles Clarke Cordle Memorial Scholarships *(Undergraduate/Scholarship)* [1736]
Reuben R. Cowles Youth Awards *(Undergraduate/Award)* [945]
Larry Dean Davis Scholarship Program *(Undergraduate/Scholarship)* [7924]
Steve Dearduff Scholarships *(Graduate, Undergraduate/Scholarship)* [3194]
E. Lanier Finch Scholarships *(Undergraduate/Scholarship)* [4375]
Forsyth County United Way Scholarships *(Undergraduate/Scholarship)* [5925]
Georgia Engineering Foundation Scholarships *(Graduate/Scholarship)* [4380]
Philip R. Karr, III Scholarship Fund *(Graduate/Scholarship)* [4378]
Lighthouse International Scholarships - Collegebound Awards *(High School, Undergraduate/Scholarship)* [6083]
Lighthouse International Scholarships - Graduate Awards *(Graduate/Scholarship)* [6084]
Lighthouse International Scholarships - Undergraduate Awards *(Undergraduate/Scholarship)* [6085]
Mollie Lukken Memorial Scholarships *(Graduate, Other/Scholarship)* [5633]
Durwood McAlister Scholarships *(Undergraduate/Scholarship)* [4387]
Morris Newspaper Corp. Scholarships *(Undergraduate/Scholarship)* [4388]
Edna A. Noblin Dawsonville Lions Club Scholarships *(Undergraduate/Scholarship)* [5926]
NWAG Georgia, USA Scholarships *(Undergraduate/Scholarship)* [7431]
Regions Riding Forward Scholarships Essay Contest *(Undergraduate/Scholarship)* [8536]
John S. and Jacqueline P. Rider Scholarships *(Undergraduate/Scholarship)* [10596]
William C. Rogers Scholarships *(Undergraduate/Scholarship)* [4389]
Scholarships for an Education Towards Law *(Graduate/Scholarship)* [3812]
Eric E. Smoker Memorial Scholarships *(Undergraduate/Scholarship)* [7521]
SSAWMA Scholarships *(Graduate/Scholarship)* [9415]
George and Pearl Strickland Scholarships *(Graduate, Undergraduate/Scholarship)* [3195]
Kirk Sutlive Scholarships *(Undergraduate/Scholarship)* [4390]
Watson-Brown Scholarships *(Undergraduate/Scholarship)* [10489]
Ted G. Wilson Memorial Scholarships *(Undergraduate/Scholarship)* [8288]

Hawaii

CHEA Undergraduate Scholarship Program for Students with Disabilities *(Undergraduate/Scholarship)* [2464]
CHEA Vocational Grants *(Undergraduate/Grant)* [2465]
Victoria S. and Bradley L. Geist Scholarships *(Undergraduate/Scholarship)* [4795]
Goldman Sachs/Matsuo Takabuki Commemorative Scholarships *(Graduate/Scholarship)* [7908]
HCF Community Scholarships Fund *(Undergraduate, Graduate/Scholarship)* [4796]
R.W. "Bob" Holden Memorial Scholarships *(Undergraduate/Scholarship)* [4798]
HPGS/ALOH Graduate Scholarships *(Graduate/Scholarship)* [4801]
HPGS Undergraduate Scholarships *(Undergraduate/Scholarship)* [4802]
Clem Judd Jr. Memorial Scholarships *(Undergraduate/Scholarship)* [4799]
Gladys Kamakaküokalani 'Ainoa Brandt Scholarships *(Graduate, Undergraduate/Scholarship)* [7911]
Ka'u Chamber of Commerce College Scholarships *(Undergraduate/Scholarship)* [5798]
William S. Richardson Commemorative Scholarships *(Graduate/Scholarship)* [7918]
Hawaii Chapter/David T. Woolsey Scholarships *(Undergraduate, Graduate, Professional development/Scholarship)* [5918]
The Frank Der Yuen Aviation Scholarship *(Undergraduate/Scholarship)* [7789]

Idaho

The "21" Endowed Scholarships *(Undergraduate/Scholarship)* [6015]
Horatio Alger Lola and Duane Hagadone Idaho Scholarships *(Undergraduate/Scholarship)* [4943]
American Legion Boys/Girls State Scholarships *(Undergraduate/Scholarship)* [6017]
Paul Arnold Memorial Scholarships *(Undergraduate/Scholarship)* [8241]
Asian and Pacific Islander Queers Sisters Scholarships *(Undergraduate/Scholarship)* [8242]
Associates in Behavioral Health Scholarships *(Graduate/Scholarship)* [8243]
Bill Bendiner and Doug Morgenson Scholarships *(Undergraduate/Scholarship)* [8246]
Mary Lou Brown Scholarships *(Undergraduate/Scholarship)* [1729]
Deloris Carter Hampton Scholarships *(Undergraduate/Scholarship)* [8247]
Donald O. Coffman Scholarships *(Undergraduate/Scholarship)* [8248]
Dennis Coleman Choral Conducting Scholarships *(Undergraduate/Scholarship)* [8250]
Dennis Coleman Memorial Scholarships *(Undergraduate/Scholarship)* [8251]
Mike Crapo Math and Science Scholarship Fund *(Undergraduate/Scholarship)* [5040]
Laura Moore Cunningham Foundation General Scholarships *(Undergraduate/Scholarship)* [6024]
Brian M. Day Scholarships *(Undergraduate/Scholarship)* [8252]
Frank and Gladys Hopkins Endowed Scholarships *(Undergraduate/Scholarship)* [6033]
Horatio Alger Idaho University Scholarships *(Undergraduate/Scholarship)* [4958]
Idaho Nursery and Landscape Association Scholarships *(Undergraduate/Scholarship)* [5048]
Idaho Opportunity Scholarships *(Undergraduate/Scholarship)* [9547]
Idaho Society of CPA's Scholarships *(Undergraduate/Scholarship)* [5043]
Inland Northwest Business Alliance Scholarships (INBA) *(Undergraduate/Scholarship)* [8254]
Margaret G. Johnson and Marge J. Stout Scholarships *(Undergraduate/Scholarship)* [6034]
Lewis-Clark State College Foundation Scholars Scholarships *(Undergraduate/Scholarship)* [6038]
Lewis-Clark State College Governor's Cup Scholarships *(Undergraduate/Scholarship)* [6039]
Lewis-Clark State College In-State Non-Traditional Student Scholarships *(Undergraduate/Scholarship)* [6040]

Lewis-Clark State College Provost Scholarships *(Undergraduate/Scholarship)* [6042]
Obrzut Ling Scholarships *(Undergraduate/Scholarship)* [8255]
McFarffels Scholarships *(Undergraduate/Scholarship)* [8256]
Jack D. Motteler Scholarships *(Undergraduate/Scholarship)* [8257]
Eugene Northrup Scholarships *(Undergraduate/Scholarship)* [6047]
Jim Poore Memorial Scholarships *(Undergraduate/Scholarship)* [5044]
Pride Foundation Political Leadership Scholarships *(Undergraduate/Scholarship)* [8258]
Pride Foundation Regional Scholarships *(Undergraduate/Scholarship)* [8259]
Pride Foundation Scholarships *(Undergraduate/Scholarship)* [8663]
Pride Foundation Social Work Scholarships *(Undergraduate/Scholarship)* [8260]
Region II Scholarships *(Graduate, Undergraduate/Scholarship)* [1428]
Robert Browning Scholarships *(Undergraduate/Scholarship)* [8262]
Rosenberg-Ibarra Scholarships *(Undergraduate/Scholarship)* [8263]
Safelink Internet Scholarships *(Undergraduate/Scholarship)* [8666]
Roger C. Sathre Memorial Scholarship Fund *(Undergraduate/Scholarship)* [5045]
Susan P. Schroeder Memorial Scholarships *(Undergraduate/Scholarship)* [6053]
W.L. Shattuck Scholarships *(Undergraduate/Scholarship)* [5046]
Kathy Spadoni Memorial Scholarships *(Undergraduate/Scholarship)* [8264]
Tschudy Family Scholarships *(Undergraduate/Scholarship)* [5050]
Ric Ulrich and Chuck Pischke Scholarships *(Undergraduate/Scholarship)* [8266]
Patricia Van Kirk Scholarships *(Undergraduate/Scholarship)* [8267]
Wells Fargo Scholarships *(Undergraduate/Scholarship)* [8268]
Wozumi Family Scholarships *(Undergraduate/Scholarship)* [8270]
You Go Girl! Scholarships *(Undergraduate/Scholarship)* [8271]
Urashi Zen Scholarships *(Undergraduate/Scholarship)* [8272]

Illinois

AIA Northeast Illinois Student Scholarships *(Undergraduate, Graduate/Scholarship)* [895]
Horatio Alger Illinois Scholarships *(Undergraduate/Scholarship)* [4940]
Allied Health Care Professional Scholarships *(Undergraduate/Scholarship)* [5070]
James M. Banovetz Illinois Local Government Fellowships *(Graduate, Master's/Fellowship)* [5059]
Beta Lambda Project 2000 Scholarship *(Undergraduate/Scholarship)* [5694]
MAC Louisa Bowen Memorial Scholarships for Graduate Students in Archival Administration *(Graduate/Scholarship)* [6515]
Robert C. Byrd Honors Scholarships *(Undergraduate/Scholarship)* [5071]
Calvin Alumni Association-Illinois Scholarships *(Undergraduate/Scholarship)* [2495]
CFNIL Community Foundation Scholarships *(Undergraduate/Scholarship)* [3278]
Chapter 23 - Quad Cities Iowa/Illinois Scholarships *(Undergraduate/Scholarship)* [9172]
Chicago FM Club Scholarships *(Undergraduate/Scholarship)* [1733]
Community Foundation of the Fox River Valley Scholarships *(Undergraduate/Scholarship)* [3192]
Margaret T. Craig Community Service Scholarships *(Undergraduate/Scholarship)* [3281]
William R. Durham/Theater Scholarships *(Undergraduate/Scholarship)* [3282]
Robert Esser Student Achievement Scholarships *(Graduate, Undergraduate/Scholarship)* [5061]
Field Museum Graduate Student Fellowships *(Graduate/Fellowship)* [4017]
Sergeant Paul Fisher Scholarships *(Undergraduate/Scholarship)* [6907]
Harold B. Halter Memorial Scholarship *(Undergraduate/Scholarship)* [3970]
IAAI Scholarship Foundation Accounting Scholarships *(Undergraduate/Scholarship)* [5091]
IBEA Graduate Scholarships *(Graduate/Scholarship)* [5056]
Illinois Future Teacher Corps Scholarships *(Undergraduate/Scholarship)* [5072]
Illinois Lake Management Association Undergraduate/Graduate Scholarships *(Graduate, Undergraduate/Scholarship)* [5062]
Illinois Landscape Contractors Association Scholarships *(Undergraduate/Scholarship)* [5064]
Illinois Special Education Teacher Tuition Waiver Scholarships (SETTW) *(Undergraduate/Scholarship)* [5073]
Illinois Student Assistance Commission Medical Student Scholarships *(Undergraduate/Scholarship)* [5074]
Illinois Student Assistance Commission Merit Recognition Scholarships (MRS) *(Undergraduate/Scholarship)* [5075]
Illinois Student Assistance Commission Nurse Educator Scholarships (NESP) *(Undergraduate/Scholarship)* [5076]
Illinois Student Assistance Commission Nursing Education Scholarships *(Undergraduate/Scholarship)* [5077]
International Management Council Scholarships (IMC) *(Undergraduate/Scholarship)* [3288]
Jewish Federation Academic Scholarships *(Graduate, Undergraduate/Scholarship)* [5598]
La Voz Latina Scholarships *(Undergraduate/Scholarship)* [3290]
Edmond A. Metzger Scholarships *(Undergraduate/Scholarship)* [1747]
Minority Teachers of Illinois Scholarships (MTI) *(Undergraduate/Scholarship)* [5078]
Daniel Murphy Scholarships *(High School/Scholarship)* [6620]
Peoria Area Amateur Radio Club Scholarships *(Undergraduate/Scholarship)* [1751]
Regions Riding Forward Scholarships Essay Contest *(Undergraduate/Scholarship)* [8536]
APSAIL's Ralph Silverman Memorial Scholarships *(Undergraduate/Scholarship)* [2126]
Six Meter Club of Chicago Scholarships *(Undergraduate/Scholarship)* [1758]

Indiana

Clifford V. Abbott Memorial Scholarships *(Undergraduate/Scholarship)* [9561]
Horatio Alger Indiana Scholarships *(Undergraduate/Scholarship)* [4941]
Warren M. Anderson Scholarships *(Undergraduate/Scholarship)* [5115]
Tara Lynn Arnold Scholarships *(Undergraduate/Scholarship)* [9562]
Richard L. Baker Memorial Scholarships *(Undergraduate/Scholarship)* [9563]
MAC Louisa Bowen Memorial Scholarships for Graduate Students in Archival Administration *(Graduate/Scholarship)* [6515]
Verna Curry Boyer Scholarships *(Undergraduate/Scholarship)* [9564]
Erika A. and George E. Brattain Sr. Scholarship Fund *(Undergraduate, High School/Scholarship)* [10498]
Ralph Burkhardt Scholarship Fund *(Undergraduate, High School/Scholarship)* [10499]
Lucille Campbell Scholarship Fund *(Undergraduate, High School/Scholarship)* [10500]
Betty J. Cecere Memorial Scholarship Endowment Fund *(Undergraduate, High School/Scholarship)* [10501]
Chicago FM Club Scholarships *(Undergraduate/Scholarship)* [1733]
Ellen Eberhardt Memorial Scholarships *(Undergraduate/Scholarship)* [9565]
Don and Eileen Fulton Nursing Scholarships *(Undergraduate/Scholarship)* [9566]
Granger Business Association College Scholarships *(Undergraduate/Scholarship)* [4641]
Helen R. Greenamyer Memorial Scholarships *(Undergraduate/Scholarship)* [9567]
Katherine M. Grosscup Scholarships *(Undergraduate, Graduate/Scholarship)* [4325]
Ed Haas Memorial Scholarships *(Undergraduate/Scholarship)* [9568]
Pauline Hand Memorial Scholarships *(Undergraduate/Scholarship)* [9569]
M.G. "Doc" Headley Scholarships *(Undergraduate/Scholarship)* [9570]
Dale Hughes, Jr. Memorial Scholarships *(Undergraduate/Scholarship)* [9571]
Indiana Alumni Scholarships *(Undergraduate/Scholarship)* [10722]
Indiana Broadcasters Association College Scholarship Program *(Undergraduate/Scholarship)* [5108]
Indiana State University Academic Excellence Scholarships *(Undergraduate/Scholarship)* [5116]
Indiana State University Creative and Performing Arts Awards *(Undergraduate/Scholarship)* [5127]
Indiana State University President's Scholarships *(Undergraduate/Scholarship)* [5118]
Indiana State University Rural Health Scholarships *(Graduate/Scholarship)* [5119]
ISU Gongaware Scholarships *(Undergraduate/Scholarship)* [5121]
Jewish Federation Academic Scholarships *(Graduate, Undergraduate/Scholarship)* [5598]
Kappa Delta Phi Scholarship Program *(Postgraduate/Scholarship)* [1046]
KDP Huntington Bank Scholarship *(Undergraduate/Scholarship)* [5673]
John W. Kelley Memorial Scholarships *(Undergraduate/Scholarship)* [9572]
Kendrick Foundation, Inc. Scholarships *(Undergraduate/Scholarship)* [5813]
Central Indiana ASSE Jim Kriner Memorial Scholarships *(Graduate, Undergraduate/Scholarship)* [1419]
Mandel and Lauretta Abrahamer Scholarships *(Undergraduate/Scholarship)* [9573]
Edmond A. Metzger Scholarships *(Undergraduate/Scholarship)* [1747]
Anthony Munoz Scholarships *(Undergraduate/Scholarship)* [6618]
Clarence & Josephine Myers Undergraduate Scholarships *(Graduate, Undergraduate/Scholarship)* [9190]
Nixon Family Scholarship Fund *(Undergraduate, High School/Scholarship)* [10506]
Nicholas H. Noyes, Jr. Scholarship *(Undergraduate/Scholarship)* [5680]
Paul and Inger Friend 4-H Scholarships *(Undergraduate/Scholarship)* [9574]
Phi Theta Kappa Scholarships *(Undergraduate/Scholarship)* [5124]
Dr. J. Glenn Radcliffe Memorial Scholarships *(Undergraduate/Scholarship)* [9575]
Frederick Rakestraw Law Scholarships *(Graduate/Scholarship)* [7520]
Regions Riding Forward Scholarships Essay Contest *(Undergraduate/Scholarship)* [8536]
Reid Hospital Graduate Student Scholarships *(Graduate/Scholarship)* [10507]
Nettie and Edward Shelah Scholarships *(Undergraduate/Scholarship)* [9576]
Lynn Brower Shonk Memorial Scholarship *(Undergraduate/Scholarship)* [5765]
Six Meter Club of Chicago Scholarships *(Undergraduate/Scholarship)* [1758]
University of Louisville Eagle Scout Scholarships *(Undergraduate/Scholarship)* [6932]
Sue Marsh Weller Memorial Scholarships *(Graduate/Scholarship)* [5113]

Iowa

Ak-Sar-Ben Scholarships *(Undergraduate/Scholarship)* [4935]
ARRL Foundation PHD Scholarships *(Undergraduate/Scholarship)* [1724]
MAC Louisa Bowen Memorial Scholarships for Graduate Students in Archival Administration *(Graduate/Scholarship)* [6515]
Chapter 23 - Quad Cities Iowa/Illinois Scholarships *(Undergraduate/Scholarship)* [9172]

Grace O. Doane Scholarship (Undergraduate/Scholarship) [3665]
Sergeant Paul Fisher Scholarships (Undergraduate/Scholarship) [6907]
Paul and Helen L. Grauer Scholarships (Undergraduate/Scholarship) [1740]
John M. Helmick Law Scholarship (Undergraduate/Scholarship) [3677]
Herbert Hoover Uncommon Student Awards (Undergraduate/Scholarship) [4931]
Horatio Alger Ak-Sar-Ben Scholarships (Undergraduate/Scholarship) [4957]
James P. Irish Scholarship (Undergraduate/Scholarship) [3679]
Kappa Delta Phi Scholarship Program (Postgraduate/Scholarship) [1046]
James B. Morris Scholarships (Undergraduate/Scholarship) [6598]
Ray, NORP and Katie, WOKTE Pautz Scholarships (Undergraduate/Scholarship) [1750]
Regions Riding Forward Scholarships Essay Contest (Undergraduate/Scholarship) [8536]

Kansas

ARRL Foundation PHD Scholarships (Undergraduate/Scholarship) [1724]
MAC Louisa Bowen Memorial Scholarships for Graduate Students in Archival Administration (Graduate/Scholarship) [6515]
Cherokee Nation Graduate Scholarships (Graduate/Scholarship) [2893]
Cherokee Nation Scholarships (Undergraduate/Scholarship) [2895]
Irving W. Cook WA0CGS Scholarships (Undergraduate/Scholarship) [1735]
Paul and Helen L. Grauer Scholarships (Undergraduate/Scholarship) [1740]
Kansas Association of Broadcasters Scholarships (Undergraduate/Scholarship) [5652]
Kansas Dental Education Opportunities Program (Graduate/Scholarship) [5654]
Kansas Distinguished Scholarship Program (Graduate/Scholarship) [5655]
Kansas Nurse Educator Service Scholarships (Graduate/Scholarship) [5656]
Kansas Optometry Service Scholarships (Graduate, Undergraduate/Scholarship) [5657]
Kansas Osteopathic Medical Service Scholarships (Graduate, Other/Scholarship) [5658]
The Floyd Lietz Memorial Scholarship (Undergraduate/Scholarship) [8323]
John J. Mingenback Memorial Scholarships (Graduate, Undergraduate/Scholarship) [4468]
WillEtta Long Oates, Gamma Nu, Memorial Scholarship (Undergraduate, Graduate/Scholarship) [5754]
Ray, NORP and Katie, WOKTE Pautz Scholarships (Undergraduate/Scholarship) [1750]
James B. Pearson Fellowships (Graduate/Scholarship) [5659]
Martha Mitchell Pearson Memorial Scholarship (Undergraduate, Graduate/Scholarship) [5755]
A.J. and Lynda Hare Scribante Scholarship Fund (Undergraduate/Scholarship) [5762]
Hatton W. Sumners Scholarships (Undergraduate/Scholarship) [7602]
Lynn McNabb Walton Adelphe Scholarhship (Undergraduate/Scholarship) [5770]
J.L. Weigand, Jr. Legal Education Trust Scholarships (Undergraduate/Scholarship) [10434]

Kentucky

Horatio Alger Kentucky Scholarships (Undergraduate/Scholarship) [4942]
Betty Bell Scholarship Fund (Undergraduate/Scholarship) [4922]
MAC Louisa Bowen Memorial Scholarships for Graduate Students in Archival Administration (Graduate/Scholarship) [6515]
Leon Bradley Scholarship Program (Undergraduate/Scholarship) [575]
Tommy Bright Scholarship Fund (Undergraduate/Scholarship) [4923]
Graduate Realtor Institute Scholarships (Graduate/Scholarship) [5817]
Katherine M. Grosscup Scholarships (Undergraduate, Graduate/Scholarship) [4325]
Sam J. Hord Memorial Scholarships (Undergraduate/Scholarship) [9381]
Kappa Delta Phi Scholarship Program (Postgraduate/Scholarship) [1046]
Kentucky Alumni Club Scholarships - Frankfort/Capital Region Alumni Club (Undergraduate/Scholarship) [10146]
Kentucky Alumni Club Scholarships - Lexington/Central Kentucky Alumni Club (Undergraduate/Scholarship) [10147]
Kentucky Alumni Club Scholarships - Somerset/Lake Cumberland Area Alumni Club (Undergraduate/Scholarship) [10148]
Kentucky Educational Excellence Scholarships (Undergraduate/Scholarship) [2261]
KHEAA Teacher Scholarship (Undergraduate/Scholarship) [2262]
Anthony Munoz Scholarships (Undergraduate/Scholarship) [6618]
Regions Riding Forward Scholarships Essay Contest (Undergraduate/Scholarship) [8536]
South Kentucky RECC High School Senior Scholarships (Undergraduate/Scholarship) [9382]
IRFI Dr. Mubin I. Syed Scholarship and Mohtarama Afshan J. Syed Scholarship (Undergraduate/Scholarship) [5482]
University of Louisville Eagle Scout Scholarships (Undergraduate/Scholarship) [6932]
Covington-Cincinnati/Northern Kentucky Alumni Club - Dane Wagge Scholarships (Undergraduate/Scholarship) [10149]

Louisiana

Horatio Alger Louisiana Scholarships (Undergraduate/Scholarship) [4944]
American Radio Relay League Louisiana Memorial Scholarships (Undergraduate/Scholarship) [1721]
AWMA Louisiana Section Scholarships (Undergraduate, Graduate/Scholarship) [147]
Frank L. Dautriel Memorial Scholarships for Graduates (Graduate/Scholarship) [6116]
Frank L. Dautriel Memorial Scholarships for Undergraduates (Undergraduate/Scholarship) [6117]
Lone Star GIA Associate and Alumni Scholarships (Undergraduate/Scholarship) [4341]
Louisiana Library Association Scholarships (Graduate/Scholarship) [6119]
Fred R. McDaniel Memorial Scholarships (Undergraduate/Scholarship) [1746]
Mary Moore Mitchell Scholarships (Graduate/Scholarship) [6120]
NAJA Scholarships (Graduate/Scholarship) [6760]
Regions Riding Forward Scholarships Essay Contest (Undergraduate/Scholarship) [8536]
Scholarships for a Higher Education in Law (Graduate/Scholarship) [2361]
Society of Louisiana Certified Public Accountants Scholarships (Undergraduate, Graduate/Scholarship) [9165]
SPE Gulf Coast Hurricane Scholarships (Undergraduate/Scholarship) [9270]
Hatton W. Sumners Scholarships (Undergraduate/Scholarship) [7602]

Maine

Brent R. Churchill Memorial Scholarships (Undergraduate/Scholarship) [6191]
Casey Family Services Alumni Scholarships (Graduate, Undergraduate, Vocational/Occupational/Scholarship) [4157]
John S. and Marjoria R. Cunningham Camp Scholarships (Professional development/Scholarship) [6193]
Downeast Feline Scholarships (Graduate/Scholarship) [6194]
Foundation for Seacoast Health Scholarships (Undergraduate, Graduate/Scholarship) [4283]
Guy P. Gannett Scholarships (Undergraduate/Scholarship) [6195]
Georgetown Working League Scholarships (Undergraduate/Scholarship) [4368]
Ronald P. Guerrette Future Farmers of America Scholarship Fund (Undergraduate/Scholarship) [6196]
Catharine Wilder Guiles Scholarships (Graduate/Scholarship) [6197]
Iberdrola USA Scholarships (Undergraduate/Scholarship) [6198]
Ella R. Ifill Fund (Undergraduate/Scholarship) [6199]
Island Institute Scholarship Fund (Undergraduate/Scholarship) [6200]
Edward G. Kaelber Scholarships (Undergraduate/Scholarship) [6201]
Dr. James L. Lawson Memorial Scholarships (Undergraduate/Scholarship) [1745]
Lighthouse International Scholarships - College-bound Awards (High School, Undergraduate/Scholarship) [6083]
Lighthouse International Scholarships - Graduate Awards (Graduate/Scholarship) [6084]
Lighthouse International Scholarships - Undergraduate Awards (Undergraduate/Scholarship) [6085]
Maine Community Foundation - Rice Scholarships (Undergraduate/Scholarship) [6203]
Maine Nutrition Council Scholarships (Undergraduate/Scholarship) [6219]
Maine Vietnam Veterans Scholarships (Advanced Professional/Scholarship) [6204]
Joseph W. Mayo ALS Scholarships (Undergraduate/Scholarship) [6205]
Gary Merrill Memorial Scholarships (Undergraduate/Scholarship) [6206]
Ruth Milan-Altrusa Scholarships (Undergraduate/Scholarship) [6207]
Hugh and Elizabeth Montgomery Scholarships (Undergraduate/Scholarship) [6208]
NASSLEO Scholarships - Region I (Undergraduate/Scholarship) [6782]
New England FEMARA Scholarships (Undergraduate/Scholarship) [1748]
Patriot Education Scholarships (Undergraduate/Scholarship) [6209]
Jerome Peters Family Scholarships (Undergraduate/Scholarship) [6210]
Riggs Cove Foundation Scholarships (Undergraduate/Scholarship) [4369]
Benjamin Riggs Scholarships (Undergraduate/Scholarship) [4370]
Lawrence and Louise Robbins Scholarships (Undergraduate/Scholarship) [6211]
Robinhood Marine Center Scholarships (Undergraduate/Scholarship) [4371]
James and Marilyn Rockefeller Scholarships (Undergraduate/Scholarship) [6212]
Henry L.P. Schmelzer College Transitions Scholarships (Undergraduate/Scholarship) [6213]
Josephine Hooker Shain Scholarships (Undergraduate/Scholarship) [4372]
Southern Maine Women's Golf Association Scholarships (Professional development/Scholarship) [9403]
Lawrence Alan Spiegel Remembrance Scholarships (Undergraduate/Scholarship) [4920]
Susan Vincent Memorial Scholarship (Undergraduate/Scholarship) [6187]
Woodex Bearing Company Scholarships (Undergraduate/Scholarship) [4373]
Yankee Clipper Contest Club, Inc. Youth Scholarships (Undergraduate/Scholarship) [1764]

Maryland

Horatio Alger District of Columbia, Maryland and Virginia Scholarships (Undergraduate/Scholarship) [4937]
BCCC Foundation General Scholarship Fund (Undergraduate/Scholarship) [2178]
BCCC Workforce Creation Scholarships (Undergraduate/Scholarship) [2179]
Board of Young Adult Advisors Scholarships (Graduate/Scholarship) [9827]
William R. Bowen Scholarships (Undergraduate/Scholarship) [3171]
William T. Burbage Family Memorial Scholarships (Undergraduate/Scholarship) [3172]

Letitia B. Carter Scholarships *(Undergraduate, Advanced Professional/Scholarship)* [8563]
Casey Family Services Alumni Scholarships *(Graduate, Undergraduate, Vocational/Occupational/Scholarship)* [4157]
Irene Culver Collins and Louis Franklin Collins Scholarships *(Undergraduate/Scholarship)* [3173]
Eastern Shore Building Industry Association Scholarships *(Undergraduate/Scholarship)* [3174]
Federalsburg Rotary Club Scholarships *(Undergraduate/Scholarship)* [3175]
Green Hill Yacht and Country Club Scholarships *(Undergraduate/Scholarship)* [3177]
Hancock Family Snow Hill High School Scholarships *(Undergraduate/Scholarship)* [3179]
Marcia S. Harris Legacy Fund Scholarships *(Undergraduate, Advanced Professional/Scholarship)* [8564]
Dick and Pat Hazel Minority Scholarships *(Undergraduate/Scholarship)* [3180]
Dwight P. Jacobus Scholarships *(Undergraduate/Scholarship)* [2058]
Martin S. Kane Memorial Community Service Award Scholarships *(Undergraduate/Scholarship)* [3181]
Kathleen Kelly Undergraduate Scholarship Award *(Undergraduate/Scholarship)* [8374]
Lighthouse International Scholarships - Collegebound Awards *(High School, Undergraduate/Scholarship)* [6083]
Lighthouse International Scholarships - Graduate Awards *(Graduate/Scholarship)* [6084]
Lighthouse International Scholarships - Undergraduate Awards *(Undergraduate/Scholarship)* [6085]
NASSLEO Scholarships - Region I *(Undergraduate/Scholarship)* [6782]
PFLAG Columbia-Howard County Scholarship *(Undergraduate/Scholarship)* [8025]
TFC Edward A. Plank, Jr. Memorial Scholarships *(Undergraduate/Scholarship)* [3182]
Progress Lane Scholarships *(Undergraduate/Scholarship)* [3183]
Duane V. Puerde Memorial Scholarships *(Undergraduate/Scholarship)* [3184]
Elizabeth Pusey Scholarships *(Undergraduate/Scholarship)* [3185]
RAMEF/NRAEF Co-Branded Scholarships *(Undergraduate/Scholarship)* [8565]
Lana K. Rinehart Scholarships *(Undergraduate/Scholarship)* [3186]
Rotary Club of Annapolis Scholarship *(Undergraduate/Scholarship)* [1561]
Drew Smith Memorial Scholarships *(Undergraduate/Scholarship)* [3187]
Esther M. Smith Scholarships *(Undergraduate/Scholarship)* [3188]
Gary Wagner, K3OMI Scholarships *(Undergraduate/Scholarship)* [1762]
Wi-Hi Class of '55 Scholarship *(Undergraduate/Scholarship)* [3189]
M. William and Frances J. Tilghman Scholarships *(Undergraduate/Scholarship)* [3190]

Massachusetts

Adler Pollock & Sheehan Diversity Scholarships *(Undergraduate/Scholarship)* [71]
Boston City Federation "Return to School" Scholarships *(Undergraduate, Graduate/Scholarship)* [4351]
Casey Family Services Alumni Scholarships *(Graduate, Undergraduate, Vocational/Occupational/Scholarship)* [4157]
Sgt. Cherven Scholarship *(Undergraduate/Scholarship)* [6312]
Community Foundation of Western Massachusetts Community Scholarship Program *(Undergraduate/Scholarship)* [3335]
Dorchester Woman's Club Music Scholarship - Voice *(Undergraduate/Scholarship)* [4352]
Early Childhood Educators Scholarship Program *(Undergraduate/Scholarship)* [6342]
Gehring Memorial Foundation Scholarships *(Graduate, Undergraduate/Scholarship)* [5100]
GFWCMA Communication Disorder/Speech Therapy Scholarships *(Graduate/Scholarship)* [4353]
Barnett D. Gordon Scholarships *(Graduate, Undergraduate/Scholarship)* [5101]
Hai Guin Scholarships Association *(Undergraduate/Scholarship)* [1695]
Independent University Alumni Association Scholarships *(Graduate, Undergraduate/Scholarship)* [5102]
Joseph Kaplan Fund *(Graduate, Undergraduate/Scholarship)* [5103]
Dr. James L. Lawson Memorial Scholarships *(Undergraduate/Scholarship)* [1745]
Lighthouse International Scholarships - Collegebound Awards *(High School, Undergraduate/Scholarship)* [6083]
Lighthouse International Scholarships - Graduate Awards *(Graduate/Scholarship)* [6084]
Lighthouse International Scholarships - Undergraduate Awards *(Undergraduate/Scholarship)* [6085]
MALSCE Memorial Scholarships *(Undergraduate/Scholarship)* [6306]
Massachusetts Federation of Polish Women's Clubs Scholarships *(Undergraduate/Scholarship)* [5880]
MEFA Graduate Loans *(Graduate/Loan)* [6314]
NASSLEO Scholarships - Region I *(Undergraduate/Scholarship)* [6782]
Nickels for Notes Music Scholarship *(Undergraduate/Scholarship)* [4354]
Pennies for Art Scholarships *(Undergraduate/Scholarship)* [4355]
Catherine E. Philbin Scholarships *(Undergraduate, Graduate/Scholarship)* [4356]
Plumbing-Heating-Cooling Contractors Association Educational Foundation Massachusetts Auxiliary Scholarships *(Undergraduate/Scholarship)* [8161]
Portuguese American Police Association Scholarships *(Undergraduate/Scholarship)* [8211]
Prince Henry Society Scholarships *(Undergraduate/Scholarship)* [8278]
The Scholarship Foundation of Wakefield Scholarships *(All/Scholarship)* [8802]
Percy W. Wadman, M.D. Scholarship *(Postgraduate/Scholarship)* [4291]
Women's Italian Club of Boston Scholarships *(Undergraduate/Scholarship)* [4357]
Worcester County Conservation District Annual Scholarships Program *(Undergraduate/Scholarship)* [10687]
Worcester District Medical Society Scholarship Fund *(Undergraduate/Scholarship)* [10689]
Yankee Clipper Contest Club, Inc. Youth Scholarships *(Undergraduate/Scholarship)* [1764]
Dr. Marie E. Zakrzewski Medical Scholarships *(Doctorate/Scholarship)* [5883]
Jacob Ziskind Memorial Fund for Upperclassmen *(Graduate, Undergraduate/Scholarship)* [5104]

Michigan

The Clarke B. Adams Memorial Foundation Lapeer County Community Foundation Fund *(Undergraduate/Scholarship)* [5928]
Altrusa International of Grand Rapids Scholarships *(Undergraduate/Scholarship)* [4573]
Arts Council of Greater Grand Rapids Minority Scholarships *(Undergraduate/Scholarship)* [4574]
Dr. Noyes L. Avery, Jr. and Ann E. Avery Scholarships *(Undergraduate, Graduate/Scholarship)* [4575]
Bernice Barabash Sports Scholarships *(Undergraduate/Scholarship)* [5497]
Charles A. Bassett Endowed Memorial Scholarship Fund *(Undergraduate/Scholarship)* [4510]
Dennis J. Beck Memorial Scholarships *(Undergraduate/Scholarship)* [5498]
Black Men Building Resources Scholarships *(Undergraduate/Scholarship)* [4576]
Geraldine Geistert Boss Scholarships *(Undergraduate/Scholarship)* [4577]
MAC Louisa Bowen Memorial Scholarships for Graduate Students in Archival Administration *(Graduate/Scholarship)* [6515]
Ross P. Broesamle Educational Scholarship Fund *(Undergraduate/Scholarship)* [5929]
Harry and Lucille Brown Scholarships *(Undergraduate/Scholarship)* [4578]
Dorothy and Dick Burgess Scholarships *(Undergraduate/Scholarship)* [5499]
Calvin Alumni Association-Michigan Lakeshore Scholarships *(Undergraduate/Scholarship)* [2496]
Calvin Alumni Association-Michigan, Lansing Scholarships *(Undergraduate/Scholarship)* [2497]
Calvin Alumni Association-Southeast Michigan Scholarships *(Undergraduate/Scholarship)* [2500]
Calvin Alumni Association-Southwest Michigan, Kalamazoo Scholarships *(Undergraduate/Scholarship)* [2503]
Orrie and Dorothy Cassada Scholarships *(Undergraduate/Scholarship)* [4579]
Chapter 198 - Downriver Detroit Scholarships *(Graduate, Undergraduate/Scholarship)* [9171]
Chapter 311 - Tri City Scholarships *(Undergraduate/Scholarship)* [9174]
Aim High Jerry Clay Scholarships *(Undergraduate/Scholarship)* [4581]
Geri Coccodrilli Culinary Scholarship Fund *(Undergraduate/Scholarship)* [4511]
Paul Collins Scholarships *(Undergraduate/Scholarship)* [4583]
Rosemary Cook Education Scholarships *(Undergraduate/Scholarship)* [4584]
Gerald M. Crane Music Award Scholarships *(Undergraduate/Scholarship)* [4585]
Dake Community Manufacturing Scholarships *(Undergraduate/Scholarship)* [4512]
June Danby and Pat Pearse Education Scholarships *(Undergraduate/Scholarship)* [5500]
Darooge Family Scholarships *(Undergraduate/Scholarship)* [4586]
Antenore C. "Butch" Davanzo Scholarships *(Graduate, Undergraduate/Scholarship)* [6502]
Antonia Dellas Memorial Scholarships *(Undergraduate/Scholarship)* [5501]
Achille and Irene Despres, William and Andre Scholarships *(Undergraduate/Scholarship)* [4587]
Detroit Economic Club Scholarship *(Undergraduate/Scholarship)* [3326]
Donald J. DeYoung Scholarships *(Undergraduate/Scholarship)* [4588]
Chapter 116 - Kalamazoo - Roscoe Douglas Scholarships *(Undergraduate/Scholarship)* [9180]
Economic Club Business Study Abroad Scholarships *(Undergraduate/Scholarship)* [4589]
Economic Club of Grand Rapids Scholarships *(Undergraduate/Scholarship)* [4590]
Erickson Education Scholarships *(Undergraduate/Scholarship)* [4513]
The Eleonor A. Ernest Scholarships *(Undergraduate/Scholarship)* [5502]
Melissa Eleanor Ernest Scholarships *(Undergraduate/Scholarship)* [5503]
Robert P. Ernest Scholarships *(Undergraduate/Scholarship)* [5504]
Kevin Ernst Memorial Scholarship Fund *(Undergraduate/Scholarship)* [4514]
Virginia Valk Fehsenfeld Scholarships *(Undergraduate/Scholarship)* [4591]
Scott A. Flahive Memorial Scholarship Fund *(Undergraduate/Scholarship)* [4516]
Floto-Peel Family Scholarship Fund *(Undergraduate, Vocational/Occupational/Scholarship)* [4517]
John L. and Victory E. Frantz Scholarship *(Undergraduate/Scholarship)* [4518]
Melbourne and Alice E. Frontjes Scholarships *(Undergraduate/Scholarship)* [4592]
Carolyn Gallmeyer Scholarships *(Undergraduate/Scholarship)* [4593]
Mathilda and Carolyn Gallmeyer Scholarships *(Undergraduate/Scholarship)* [4594]
Gauthier Family Scholarship Fund *(Undergraduate/Scholarship)* [4519]
Irma Gelhausen Scholarship Fund *(Undergraduate/Scholarship)* [5930]
Gerber Foundation Merit Scholarships *(Undergraduate/Scholarship)* [4392]
Daniel Gerber, Sr. Medallion Scholarships *(Undergraduate/Scholarship)* [4393]
Tom Gifford Scholarships *(Undergraduate/Scholarship)* [4520]
Grand Haven Offshore Challenge Scholarship Fund *(Undergraduate/Scholarship)* [4521]
Grand Rapids Scholarship Association *(Undergraduate/Scholarship)* [4595]
Grand Rapids University Prep Founder's Scholar-

ships *(Undergraduate/Scholarship)* [4596]
Katherine M. Grosscup Scholarships *(Undergraduate, Graduate/Scholarship)* [4325]
Hackett Family Scholarships *(Undergraduate/Scholarship)* [4597]
Guy D. and Mary Edith Halladay Graduate Scholarships *(Undergraduate/Scholarship)* [4598]
Guy D. and Mary Edith Halladay Music Scholarships *(Graduate, Undergraduate/Scholarship)* [4599]
Martha and Oliver Hansen Memorial Scholarships *(Undergraduate/Scholarship)* [5505]
Bob and Dawn Hardy Automotive Scholarships *(Undergraduate/Scholarship)* [5506]
Barbara and Nicole Heacox Foreign Travel and Study Scholarship Fund *(Undergraduate/Scholarship)* [4522]
Marjorie M. Hendricks Environmental Education Scholarship Fund *(Undergraduate/Scholarship)* [4523]
John P. Hennessey Scholarships *(Graduate, Undergraduate/Scholarship)* [6503]
Michael Herman Scholarships *(Undergraduate, Vocational/Occupational/Scholarship)* [4524]
Hierholzer-Fojtik Scholarship Fund *(Undergraduate/Scholarship)* [4525]
Wayne Hildebrant Police Scholarship Fund *(Undergraduate/Scholarship)* [5931]
Hoffman Family Scholarship Fund *(Undergraduate/Scholarship)* [4526]
Robert Holmes Scholarship *(Undergraduate/Scholarship)* [3327]
Detroit Tigers Willie Horton Scholarship *(Undergraduate/Scholarship)* [3328]
Donald and Florence Hunting Scholarships *(Undergraduate/Scholarship)* [4600]
Jack Family Scholarships *(Undergraduate/Scholarship)* [4601]
James W. Junior and Jane T. Brown Scholarships *(Undergraduate, Vocational/Occupational/Scholarship)* [4527]
William and Beatrice Kavanaugh Scholarships *(Undergraduate/Scholarship)* [5507]
Seth Koehler Central High School Scholarship Fund *(Undergraduate, Vocational/Occupational/Scholarship)* [4528]
Vivian M. Kommer Scholarships *(Undergraduate/Scholarship)* [4603]
Roger and Jacquelyn Vander Laan Family Scholarships *(Undergraduate/Scholarship)* [4604]
Ladies Literary Club Scholarships *(Undergraduate/Scholarship)* [4605]
Lavina Laible Scholarships *(Undergraduate/Scholarship)* [4606]
Paul J. Laninga Memorial Scholarship Fund *(Undergraduate/Scholarship)* [4529]
Stephen Lankester Scholarships *(Undergraduate/Scholarship)* [4607]
Lapeer County Medical Scholarship Fund *(Undergraduate/Scholarship)* [5932]
Rick and Beverly Lattin Education Scholarship Fund *(Undergraduate/Scholarship)* [4530]
Jack W. Leatherman Family Scholarship Fund *(Undergraduate, Vocational/Occupational/Scholarship)* [4531]
Imelda "Mel" and Ralph LeMar Scholarship *(Undergraduate/Scholarship)* [3330]
Sherman L. and Mabel C. Lepard Scholarships *(Undergraduate/Scholarship)* [4608]
Pat and John MacTavish Scholarship Fund *(Undergraduate/Scholarship)* [4532]
John T. and Frances J. Maghielse Scholarships *(Undergraduate/Scholarship)* [4609]
MCBA Scholarship *(Undergraduate/Scholarship)* [6465]
Fred & Lena Meijer Scholarships *(Undergraduate/Scholarship)* [4610]
Michigan Auto Law Student Diversity Scholarships *(Undergraduate/Scholarship)* [6463]
Michigan Council of Women in Technology Undergraduate Scholarship Program *(Undergraduate/Scholarship)* [6468]
Michigan Nurses Foundation Scholarships *(Undergraduate, Graduate/Scholarship)* [6477]
Michigan Society of Professional Engineers Scholarships *(Undergraduate/Scholarship)* [6483]

Robert L. and Hilda Treasure Mitchell Scholarships *(Undergraduate/Scholarship)* [4612]
Kyle R. Moreland Memorial Scholarships *(Undergraduate/Scholarship)* [4533]
Harry J. Morris, Jr. Emergency Services Scholarships *(Undergraduate/Scholarship)* [4613]
NAIFA West Michigan Scholarships *(Undergraduate/Scholarship)* [4614]
NALS of Michigan Scholarships *(Undergraduate/Scholarship)* [6652]
North Ottawa Hospital Auxiliary Scholarship Fund *(Undergraduate/Scholarship)* [4534]
Peggy Kommer Novosad Scholarships *(Graduate, Postgraduate/Scholarship)* [4615]
Patricia and Armen Oumedian Scholarships *(Undergraduate/Scholarship)* [4616]
Carl Parsell Scholarship Fund *(Undergraduate/Scholarship)* [6459]
Marvin R. and Pearl E. Patterson Family Scholarships Fund *(Undergraduate/Scholarship)* [4535]
P.E.O. Chapter DS Scholarships *(Undergraduate, Vocational/Occupational/Scholarship)* [4536]
Terry Linda Potter Scholarship Fund *(Undergraduate/Scholarship)* [4537]
Reach for Your Goal Scholarships *(Undergraduate/Scholarship)* [4617]
Jacob L. Reinecke Memorial Scholarship Fund *(Undergraduate/Scholarship)* [4538]
Daniel L. Reiss Memorial Scholarship Fund *(Undergraduate/Scholarship)* [4539]
Phillip Guy Richardson Memorial Scholarships *(Undergraduate/Scholarship)* [5510]
Harold and Eleanor Ringelberg Scholarships *(Undergraduate/Scholarship)* [4540]
Josephine Ringold Scholarships *(Undergraduate/Scholarship)* [4618]
Jean and Tom Rosenthal Scholarship Program *(Undergraduate/Scholarship)* [3332]
Dave & Laurie Russell Family Scholarships for Habitat for Humanity of Kent County Families *(Undergraduate/Scholarship)* [4619]
Charles and Eleanor Rycenga Education Scholarship Fund *(Undergraduate/Scholarship)* [4541]
Dr. William A. and Marceleine J. Sautter Hanover-Horton High School Youth of Promise Scholarships *(Undergraduate/Scholarship)* [5511]
Millicent M. Schaffner Endowed Memorial Scholarships *(Undergraduate/Scholarship)* [4542]
David and Jinny Schultz Family Scholarship *(Undergraduate/Scholarship)* [4543]
Jeptha Wade Schureman Scholarship Program *(Undergraduate/Scholarship)* [3333]
David and Sharon Seaver Family Scholarship Fund *(Undergraduate/Scholarship)* [4544]
Margery J. Seeger Scholarships *(Undergraduate/Scholarship)* [4620]
Ken and Sandy Sharkey Family Scholarship Fund *(Undergraduate/Scholarship)* [4545]
Miller G. Sherwood Family Scholarship Fund *(Undergraduate/Scholarship)* [4548]
Hazel Simms Nursing Scholarships *(Other/Scholarship)* [5933]
Ronald T. Smith Family Scholarships *(Undergraduate, Graduate/Scholarship)* [4621]
The Eileen J. Smith, R.N. Memorial Scholarships *(Undergraduate/Scholarship)* [5512]
Christine Soper Scholarships *(Undergraduate/Scholarship)* [4623]
Faith Speckhard Scholarships *(Undergraduate/Scholarship)* [5513]
Dr. William E. and Norma Sprague Scholarships *(Undergraduate, Graduate/Scholarship)* [4624]
Zachary Taylor Stevens Memorial Scholarships *(Undergraduate/Scholarship)* [1759]
Edward P. Suchecki Family Scholarship Fund *(Undergraduate/Scholarship)* [4549]
Henry D. and Ruth G. Swartz Family Scholarship Fund *(Undergraduate/Scholarship)* [4550]
Paul Tejada Memorial Scholarships *(Undergraduate/Scholarship)* [5514]
Dorothy B. and Charles E. Thomas Scholarships *(Undergraduate/Scholarship)* [4625]
Barbara and Howard Thompson Scholarships *(Undergraduate/Scholarship)* [5515]
Dorothy J. Thurston Graduate Scholarships *(Undergraduate/Scholarship)* [4626]

Mildred E. Troske Music Scholarships *(Undergraduate/Scholarship)* [4627]
U-M Alumnae Club (University of Michigan) Scholarships *(Undergraduate/Scholarship)* [4628]
H. Wayne Van Agtmael Cosmetology Scholarship Fund *(Undergraduate/Scholarship)* [4551]
Keith C. Vanderhyde Scholarships *(Undergraduate/Scholarship)* [4629]
Jacob R. and Mary M. VanLoo and Lenore K. VanLoo Scholarships *(Undergraduate/Scholarship)* [4630]
Chad Vollmer Scholarships *(Undergraduate/Scholarship)* [4631]
Sue Walicki Nursing Scholarships *(Undergraduate/Scholarship)* [5516]
Warner Norcross & Judd Minority Scholarships *(Undergraduate/Scholarship)* [10427]
West Michigan Nursery and Landscape Association Scholarship Fund *(Undergraduate/Scholarship)* [4552]
Western Michigan Society of Health-System Pharmacists Scholarships *(Undergraduate/Scholarship)* [10533]
Louise Wachter Wickham Scholarships *(Undergraduate/Scholarship)* [4553]
Elmo Wierenga Alumni Scholarships *(Undergraduate/Scholarship)* [4633]
Walter C. Winchester Scholarships *(Undergraduate/Scholarship)* [4634]
Amos and Marilyn Winsand - Detroit Section Named Scholarships *(Undergraduate/Scholarship)* [1526]
Michael J. Wolf Scholarships *(Undergraduate/Scholarship)* [4635]
Women's Club of Grand Haven Scholarships *(Undergraduate/Scholarship)* [4554]
Violet Wondergem Health Science Scholarships *(Undergraduate/Scholarship)* [4636]
Audrey L. Wright Scholarships *(Undergraduate/Scholarship)* [4637]
Zenko Family Scholarship Fund *(Undergraduate/Scholarship)* [4555]

Minnesota

Horatio Alger Minnesota Scholarships *(Undergraduate/Scholarship)* [4945]
Darrell and Palchie Asselin Scholarships *(Undergraduate/Scholarship)* [3703]
William E. Barto Scholarships *(Undergraduate/Scholarship)* [3704]
MAC Louisa Bowen Memorial Scholarships for Graduate Students in Archival Administration *(Graduate/Scholarship)* [6515]
Bernard B. and Mary L. Brusin Scholarships *(Undergraduate/Scholarship)* [3705]
DSACF Modern Woodmen of America Scholarships *(Undergraduate/Scholarship)* [3706]
Duluth Central High School Alumni Scholarships *(Undergraduate/Scholarship)* [3708]
Patricia S. Gustafson '56 Memorial Scholarships *(Undergraduate/Scholarship)* [3710]
Jeanne H. Hemmingway Scholarships *(Undergraduate/Scholarship)* [3711]
Gus and Henrietta Hill Scholarships *(Undergraduate/Scholarship)* [3712]
Max and Julia Houghton Duluth Central Scholarships *(Undergraduate/Scholarship)* [3713]
Greg Irons Award Fund *(Undergraduate/Scholarship)* [3714]
The Jackson Club Scholarships *(Undergraduate/Scholarship)* [3715]
Cory Jam Memorial Award Fund *(Undergraduate/Scholarship)* [3716]
Lilly Lorenzen Scholarships *(Undergraduate/Scholarship)* [1470]
Many Voices Fellowships *(Other/Fellowship)* [8153]
McKnight Advancement Grants *(Other/Grant)* [8154]
McKnight Theater Artist Fellowships *(Other/Fellowship)* [8155]
Minneapolis Jewish Federation Camp Scholarships *(Undergraduate/Scholarship)* [6539]
Minnesota Association of Public Accountant Scholarships *(Undergraduate/Scholarship)* [6543]
Minnesota Health Information Management Associa-

tion Scholarships *(Undergraduate/Scholarship)* [6547]
Minnesota Power Community Involvement Scholarships *(Undergraduate/Scholarship)* [3717]
Hubert A. Nelson Scholarships *(Undergraduate/Scholarship)* [3718]
Amelia and Emanuel Nessell Scholarships *(Undergraduate/Scholarship)* [3719]
Anderson Niskanen Scholarships *(Undergraduate/Scholarship)* [3720]
Arthur L. Norberg Travel Fund *(Advanced Professional/Grant)* [10200]
Dr. Mark Rathke Family Scholarships *(Undergraduate/Scholarship)* [3721]
Lawrence E. and Mabel Jackson Rudberg Scholarships *(Undergraduate/Scholarship)* [3722]
Phil Shykes Memorial Scholarships *(Undergraduate/Scholarship)* [3723]
Dale and Betty George Sola Scholarships *(Undergraduate/Scholarship)* [3724]
Upper Midwest Human Rights Fellowship Program *(Graduate/Scholarship, Fellowship)* [4996]
Robert B. and Sophia Whiteside Scholarships *(Undergraduate/Scholarship)* [3726]

Mississippi

ARRLF Mississippi Scholarships *(Undergraduate/Scholarship)* [1725]
Fred R. McDaniel Memorial Scholarships *(Undergraduate/Scholarship)* [1746]
MSCPA Undergraduate Scholarships *(Undergraduate/Scholarship)* [6562]
NAJA Scholarships *(Graduate/Scholarship)* [6760]
Buster Pool Memorial Scholarships *(Undergraduate/Scholarship)* [3248]
Regions Riding Forward Scholarships Essay Contest *(Undergraduate/Scholarship)* [8536]
Ross/Nickey Scholarships *(Graduate/Scholarship)* [6563]
SPE Gulf Coast Hurricane Scholarships *(Undergraduate/Scholarship)* [9270]
SSAWMA Scholarships *(Graduate/Scholarship)* [9415]
University of Southern Mississippi Eagle Scout/Gold Award Scholarship *(Undergraduate/Scholarship)* [6933]

Missouri

Horatio Alger Missouri Scholarships *(Undergraduate/Scholarship)* [4946]
ARRL Foundation PHD Scholarships *(Undergraduate/Scholarship)* [1724]
MAC Louisa Bowen Memorial Scholarships for Graduate Students in Archival Administration *(Graduate/Scholarship)* [6515]
Chapter 17 - St. Louis Scholarships *(Undergraduate/Scholarship)* [9170]
Cherokee Nation Graduate Scholarships *(Graduate/Scholarship)* [2893]
Cherokee Nation Scholarships *(Undergraduate/Scholarship)* [2895]
Paul and Helen L. Grauer Scholarships *(Undergraduate/Scholarship)* [1740]
Health Professional Nursing Student Loans *(Undergraduate, Graduate/Loan)* [6565]
Kappa Delta Phi Scholarship Program *(Postgraduate/Scholarship)* [1046]
John Allen Love Scholarships *(Graduate, Undergraduate/Scholarship)* [10304]
NAJA Scholarships *(Graduate/Scholarship)* [6760]
Ray, NORP and Katie, WOKTE Pautz Scholarships *(Undergraduate/Scholarship)* [1750]
Martha Mitchell Pearson Memorial Scholarship *(Undergraduate, Graduate/Scholarship)* [5755]
Regions Riding Forward Scholarships Essay Contest *(Undergraduate/Scholarship)* [8536]
Hatton W. Sumners Scholarships *(Undergraduate/Scholarship)* [7602]

Montana

Horatio Alger Montana Scholarships *(Undergraduate/Scholarship)* [4947]
Paul Arnold Memorial Scholarships *(Undergraduate/Scholarship)* [8241]
Asian and Pacific Islander Queers Sisters Scholarships *(Undergraduate/Scholarship)* [8242]
Associates in Behavioral Health Scholarships *(Graduate/Scholarship)* [8243]
Bill Bendiner and Doug Morgenson Scholarships *(Undergraduate/Scholarship)* [8246]
Mary Lou Brown Scholarships *(Undergraduate/Scholarship)* [1729]
Scott Brownlee Memorial Scholarships *(Undergraduate, Graduate/Scholarship)* [6582]
Deloris Carter Hampton Scholarships *(Undergraduate/Scholarship)* [8247]
Donald O. Coffman Scholarships *(Undergraduate/Scholarship)* [8248]
Dennis Coleman Choral Conducting Scholarships *(Undergraduate/Scholarship)* [8250]
Dennis Coleman Memorial Scholarships *(Undergraduate/Scholarship)* [8251]
Brian M. Day Scholarships *(Undergraduate/Scholarship)* [8252]
EAA Tuition Scholarships *(Undergraduate/Scholarship)* [3873]
EAA Workshop Scholarships *(Undergraduate/Scholarship)* [3874]
Anthony Gerharz Scholarships *(Undergraduate, Graduate/Scholarship)* [6583]
Eldon E. and JoAnn C. Kuhns Family Scholarships *(Undergraduate, Graduate/Scholarship)* [6584]
Obrzut Ling Scholarships *(Undergraduate/Scholarship)* [8255]
Stephen T. Marchello Scholarships *(Undergraduate/Scholarship)* [6237]
McFarfels Scholarships *(Undergraduate/Scholarship)* [8256]
Jack D. Motteler Scholarships *(Undergraduate/Scholarship)* [8257]
MSCPA Scholarship - Montana Tech *(Undergraduate, Graduate/Scholarship)* [6585]
MSCPA Scholarship - MSU Bozeman *(Undergraduate, Graduate/Scholarship)* [6586]
MSCPA Scholarship - University of Montana *(Undergraduate, Graduate/Scholarship)* [6587]
Donald E. Pizzini Memorial Nurse Scholarships *(Undergraduate, Professional development/Scholarship)* [6580]
Pride Foundation Political Leadership Scholarships *(Undergraduate/Scholarship)* [8258]
Pride Foundation Regional Scholarships *(Undergraduate/Scholarship)* [8259]
Pride Foundation Scholarships *(Undergraduate/Scholarship)* [8663]
Pride Foundation Social Work Scholarships *(Undergraduate/Scholarship)* [8260]
Region II Scholarships *(Graduate, Undergraduate/Scholarship)* [1428]
Robert Browning Scholarships *(Undergraduate/Scholarship)* [8262]
Rocky Mountain Coal Mining Institute Engineering/Geology Scholarships *(Undergraduate/Scholarship)* [8632]
Rocky Mountain Coal Mining Institute Technical Scholarships *(Undergraduate/Scholarship)* [8633]
Rosenberg-Ibarra Scholarships *(Undergraduate/Scholarship)* [8263]
Kathy Spadoni Memorial Scholarships *(Undergraduate/Scholarship)* [8264]
Ric Ulrich and Chuck Pischke Scholarships *(Undergraduate/Scholarship)* [8266]
Upper Midwest Human Rights Fellowship Program *(Graduate/Scholarship, Fellowship)* [4996]
Patricia Van Kirk Scholarships *(Undergraduate/Scholarship)* [8267]
Wells Fargo Scholarships *(Undergraduate/Scholarship)* [8268]
Wozumi Family Scholarships *(Undergraduate/Scholarship)* [8270]
You Go Girl! Scholarships *(Undergraduate/Scholarship)* [8271]
Urashi Zen Scholarships *(Undergraduate/Scholarship)* [8272]

Nebraska

ARRL Foundation PHD Scholarships *(Undergraduate/Scholarship)* [1724]
MAC Louisa Bowen Memorial Scholarships for Graduate Students in Archival Administration *(Graduate/Scholarship)* [6515]
Susan Thompson Buffett Foundation Scholarships *(Undergraduate/Scholarship)* [2402]
Paul and Helen L. Grauer Scholarships *(Undergraduate/Scholarship)* [1740]
Horatio Alger Ak-Sar-Ben Scholarships *(Undergraduate/Scholarship)* [4957]
Nebraska Farm Bureau Greater Horizon Scholarships *(Undergraduate/Scholarship)* [7240]
Nebraska Paralegal Association Student Scholarships *(Undergraduate/Scholarship)* [7247]
Louise A. Nixon Scholarships *(Graduate/Scholarship)* [7245]
Ray, NORP and Katie, WOKTE Pautz Scholarships *(Undergraduate/Scholarship)* [1750]
Hatton W. Sumners Scholarships *(Undergraduate/Scholarship)* [7602]

Nevada

Adelson Family Scholarships *(Undergraduate/Scholarship)* [8328]
Alliance of Black Culinarians Scholarships *(Undergraduate/Scholarship)* [8330]
American Nuclear Society Nevada Section Scholarships *(Undergraduate/Scholarship)* [8331]
Aaron Edward Arnoldsen Memorial Scholarships *(Undergraduate/Scholarship)* [1719]
Agustin C. Cano Memorial Scholarships *(Undergraduate/Scholarship)* [8334]
Cheyenne High School Desert Shields Scholarship *(Undergraduate/Scholarship)* [8337]
Clark High School Academy of Finance Scholarships *(Undergraduate/Scholarship)* [8338]
Tsutako Curo Scholarships *(Undergraduate/Scholarship)* [8339]
Mickey Donnelly Memorial Scholarships *(Undergraduate/Scholarship)* [8340]
Travis Dunning Memorial Scholarships *(Undergraduate/Scholarship)* [8341]
Palo Verde High School - Barbara Edwards Memorial Scholarships *(Undergraduate/Scholarship)* [8342]
Gordy Fink Memorial Scholarships *(Undergraduate/Scholarship)* [8343]
Brendan Flores Alumni Leadership Circle Scholarship - Clark High School *(Undergraduate/Scholarship)* [8344]
Fraser Family Scholarships *(Undergraduate/Scholarship)* [8345]
Veronica Gantt Memorial Scholarships *(Undergraduate/Scholarship)* [8346]
Glazing Industry Scholarships *(Undergraduate/Scholarship)* [8347]
Gretchen Hauff Memorial Scholarships *(Undergraduate/Scholarship)* [8349]
Michael J. Hoggard Memorial Scholarships *(Undergraduate/Scholarship)* [8350]
JMA Architecture Studios Scholarships *(Undergraduate/Scholarship)* [8351]
Michael Koizumi APWA Scholarships *(Undergraduate/Scholarship, Internship)* [7263]
Nate Mack/Cindi Turner Scholarships *(Undergraduate/Scholarship)* [8353]
Corporal Joseph Martinez U.S. Army/Durango High School AFJROTC *(Undergraduate/Scholarship)* [8354]
Mesquite Club Evening Chapter Inc. Scholarships *(Undergraduate/Scholarship)* [8355]
National Security Technologies Engineering and Science Scholarships *(Undergraduate/Scholarship, Internship)* [8356]
Palo Verde High School Faculty Follies Scholarships *(Undergraduate/Scholarship)* [8357]
Panther Cafe Scholarships *(Undergraduate/Scholarship)* [8358]
R.M. Princ Scholarships *(Undergraduate/Scholarship)* [8361]
Region II Scholarships *(Graduate, Undergraduate/Scholarship)* [1428]
Smith's Personal Best Scholarships *(Undergraduate/Scholarship)* [8363]
Spartan Staff Scholarships *(Undergraduate/Scholarship)* [8365]

Legal Residence Index

Tall Awareness Scholarships *(Undergraduate/Scholarship)* [8366]
Tarkanian Teacher Education Academy at Clark High School Scholarships *(Undergraduate/Scholarship)* [8367]
Sheila Tarr-Smith Memorial Scholarships *(Undergraduate/Scholarship)* [8368]
Edwin F. Wiegand Science and Technology Scholarships *(Undergraduate/Scholarship)* [8370]

New Hampshire

Casey Family Services Alumni Scholarships *(Graduate, Undergraduate, Vocational/Occupational/Scholarship)* [4157]
Bruce Clement Post-Secondary Education Scholarships *(Undergraduate/Scholarship)* [7311]
Foundation for Seacoast Health Scholarships *(Undergraduate, Graduate/Scholarship)* [4283]
Dr. James L. Lawson Memorial Scholarships *(Undergraduate/Scholarship)* [1745]
Lighthouse International Scholarships - Collegebound Awards *(High School, Undergraduate/Scholarship)* [6083]
Lighthouse International Scholarships - Graduate Awards *(Graduate/Scholarship)* [6084]
Lighthouse International Scholarships - Undergraduate Awards *(Undergraduate/Scholarship)* [6085]
Rick Mahoney Scholarships *(Undergraduate/Scholarship)* [6357]
The Medallion Fund Scholarships *(Undergraduate/Scholarship)* [7302]
NASSLEO Scholarships - Region I *(Undergraduate/Scholarship)* [6782]
New England FEMARA Scholarships *(Undergraduate/Scholarship)* [1748]
Piscataqua Region Artist Advancement Grants *(Professional development/Grant)* [7305]
Louise Tillotson Teaching Fellowships *(Professional development/Fellowship)* [7306]
Louise Tillotson Teaching Professional Development Scholarships *(Professional development/Scholarship)* [7307]
Johnny Trombly Scholarships *(Undergraduate/Scholarship)* [6572]
Yankee Clipper Contest Club, Inc. Youth Scholarships *(Undergraduate/Scholarship)* [1764]

New Jersey

Benjamin Asbell Memorial Scholarships *(Undergraduate/Scholarship)* [2507]
Armen H. Bululian Scholarships *(Undergraduate/Scholarship)* [1690]
Calvin Alumni Association-New Jersey Scholarships *(Undergraduate/Scholarship)* [2498]
Jeffrey Carollo Music Scholarships *(Undergraduate/Scholarship)* [7323]
CentraState Associated Auxiliaries Scholarships *(Undergraduate/Scholarship)* [2875]
CentraState Healthcare Foundation Health Professions Scholarships *(Undergraduate/Scholarship)* [2877]
Constantinople Armenian Relief Society Scholarships (CARS) *(Undergraduate/Scholarship)* [1691]
Hon. Joseph W. Cowgill Memorial Scholarships *(Undergraduate/Scholarship)* [2509]
George Dale Scholarship Fund *(Undergraduate/Scholarship)* [1776]
DuBois Brothers Scholarships *(Undergraduate/Scholarship)* [2511]
H.J. "Duke" Ellington Memorial Scholarship Award *(Undergraduate/Scholarship)* [7513]
Gallo Blue Chip Scholarships *(Undergraduate/Scholarship)* [4724]
Vincent S. Haneman-Joseph B. Perskie Memorial Foundation Scholarships *(Graduate, Undergraduate/Scholarship)* [2115]
HRET Health Career Scholarships *(Postgraduate, Undergraduate/Scholarship)* [7319]
Bernadine Johnson-Marshall and Martha Bell Williams Scholarships *(Undergraduate/Scholarship)* [1863]
Les Dames D'Escoffier New York Scholarships *(Undergraduate/Scholarship)* [6009]
Lighthouse International Scholarships - Collegebound Awards *(High School, Undergraduate/Scholarship)* [6083]
Lighthouse International Scholarships - Graduate Awards *(Graduate/Scholarship)* [6084]
Lighthouse International Scholarships - Undergraduate Awards *(Undergraduate/Scholarship)* [6085]
NASSLEO Scholarships - Region I *(Undergraduate/Scholarship)* [6782]
NCNJ-AWMA Undergraduate Scholarship *(Undergraduate/Scholarship)* [152]
New York Women in Communications, Inc. Foundation Scholarships *(Graduate, Undergraduate/Scholarship)* [7406]
NJCBIR Programmatic Multi-Investigator Project Grants *(Other/Grant)* [9552]
NJLA Scholarships *(Graduate, Postgraduate/Scholarship)* [7321]
NJOEF Scholarships *(Undergraduate/Scholarship)* [7315]
NJSCPA College Scholarships *(Graduate, Undergraduate/Scholarship)* [7331]
NJSCPA High School Scholarships *(Undergraduate/Scholarship)* [7332]
Pellegrini Scholarships *(Undergraduate, Graduate/Scholarship)* [9620]
Louis C. Portella Memorial Scholarships *(Graduate/Scholarship)* [2514]
Ann S. Salsberg Scholarship Awards *(Undergraduate/Award, Scholarship)* [2516]
Jay A. Strassberg Memorial Scholarships *(Undergraduate/Scholarship)* [2517]
Daniel B. Toll Memorial Scholarships *(Undergraduate/Scholarship)* [2518]
Bruce A. Wallace Memorial Scholarships *(Undergraduate/Scholarship)* [2520]
Yankee Clipper Contest Club, Inc. Youth Scholarships *(Undergraduate/Scholarship)* [1764]
Young Christian Leaders Scholarships *(Undergraduate/Scholarship)* [10760]
Zimmermann Scholarships *(Graduate/Scholarship)* [9621]

New Mexico

Robby Baker Memorial Scholarships *(Undergraduate/Scholarship)* [299]
Walt Bartram Memorial Education Award, Region 12 and Chapter 119 *(Undergraduate/Scholarship)* [9167]
Notah Begay III Scholarship Program *(Undergraduate/Scholarship)* [300]
Chapter 93 - Albuquerque Scholarships *(Undergraduate/Scholarship)* [9179]
Bryan Cline Memorial Soccer Scholarship Program *(Undergraduate/Scholarship)* [301]
Excel Staffing Companies Scholarships for Excellence in Continuing Education *(Undergraduate/Scholarship)* [302]
Lone Star GIA Associate and Alumni Scholarships *(Undergraduate/Scholarship)* [4341]
Fred R. McDaniel Memorial Scholarships *(Undergraduate/Scholarship)* [1746]
New Mexico Manufactured Housing Association Scholarship Program *(Undergraduate/Scholarship)* [303]
Region II Scholarships *(Graduate, Undergraduate/Scholarship)* [1428]
Rocky Mountain Coal Mining Institute Engineering/Geology Scholarships *(Undergraduate/Scholarship)* [8632]
Rocky Mountain Coal Mining Institute Technical Scholarships *(Undergraduate/Scholarship)* [8633]
Barnes W. Rose, Jr. and Eva Rose Nichol Scholarship Fund *(Undergraduate/Scholarship)* [304]
Hatton W. Sumners Scholarships *(Undergraduate/Scholarship)* [7602]
Woodcock Family Education Scholarship Program *(Undergraduate/Scholarship)* [306]

New York

Arlyn Scales Awards for Science and Technology *(Undergraduate/Scholarship)* [3035]
Robert L. Bernstein Fellowships in International Human Rights *(Graduate/Fellowship)* [4994]
Henry Broughton, K2AE Memorial Scholarships *(Undergraduate/Scholarship)* [1728]
Calvin Alumni Association-New Jersey Scholarships *(Undergraduate/Scholarship)* [2498]
CHRGJ Emerging Human Rights Scholarship Conference *(Graduate/Scholarship)* [7398]
CHRGJ International Human Rights Fellowships *(Doctorate, Professional development/Fellowship, Internship)* [7399]
CHRGJ Students Human Rights Scholars Program *(Graduate, Advanced Professional, Professional development/Scholarship)* [7400]
Colombian Education Fund Scholarships *(Undergraduate/Scholarship)* [3130]
Constantinople Armenian Relief Society Scholarships (CARS) *(Undergraduate/Scholarship)* [1691]
H.J. "Duke" Ellington Memorial Scholarship Award *(Undergraduate/Scholarship)* [7513]
Gallo Blue Chip Scholarships *(Undergraduate/Scholarship)* [4724]
Joseph H. Gellert/Dutchess County Bar Association Scholarships *(Undergraduate/Scholarship)* [3744]
Les Dames D'Escoffier New York Scholarships *(Undergraduate/Scholarship)* [6009]
Lighthouse International Scholarships - Collegebound Awards *(High School, Undergraduate/Scholarship)* [6083]
Lighthouse International Scholarships - Graduate Awards *(Graduate/Scholarship)* [6084]
Lighthouse International Scholarships - Undergraduate Awards *(Undergraduate/Scholarship)* [6085]
David J. Moynihan Scholarships *(Undergraduate/Scholarship)* [7373]
NASSLEO Scholarships - Region I *(Undergraduate/Scholarship)* [6782]
New York State Association of Agricultural Fairs Scholarships *(Undergraduate/Scholarship)* [7361]
The New York Times College Scholarships *(Undergraduate/Scholarship, Internship)* [7396]
New York Women in Communications, Inc. Foundation Scholarships *(Graduate, Undergraduate/Scholarship)* [7406]
NYFWA Scholarships *(Undergraduate, Graduate/Scholarship)* [7355]
Faith E. O'Neal Scholarships *(Undergraduate/Scholarship)* [8392]
Victoria Ovis Memorial Scholarships *(Undergraduate/Scholarship)* [7045]
Pellegrini Scholarships *(Undergraduate, Graduate/Scholarship)* [9620]
Harry B. Pulver Scholarships *(Undergraduate/Scholarship)* [4454]
Saint Andrews Scholarships *(Undergraduate/Scholarship)* [8670]
Stanley M. Schoenfeld Memorial Scholarship *(Postgraduate/Scholarship)* [7363]
Norman E. Strohmeier, W2VRS Memorial Scholarships *(Undergraduate/Scholarship)* [1761]
Albert E. Wischmeyer Memorial Scholarships *(Undergraduate/Scholarship)* [9202]
Yankee Clipper Contest Club, Inc. Youth Scholarships *(Undergraduate/Scholarship)* [1764]
Young Christian Leaders Scholarships *(Undergraduate/Scholarship)* [10760]
Zimmermann Scholarships *(Graduate/Scholarship)* [9621]
Lorraine Zitone Memorial Scholarship Fund *(Undergraduate/Scholarship)* [6293]

North Carolina

Henry S. and Carolyn Adams Scholarship Fund *(Undergraduate/Scholarship)* [4172]
African American Network - Carolinas Scholarship Fund *(Undergraduate/Scholarship)* [4174]
William Tasse Alexander Scholarship Fund *(Undergraduate/Scholarship)* [4175]
Pete and Ellen Bensley Memorial Scholarship Fund *(Undergraduate/Scholarship)* [4178]
F.A. and Charlotte Blount Scholarships *(Undergraduate/Scholarship)* [10571]
T. Frank Booth Memorial Scholarship Fund *(Undergraduate/Scholarship)* [4180]
Leon Bradley Scholarship Program *(Undergraduate/Scholarship)* [575]

Kasie Ford Capling Memorial Scholarship Endowment Fund *(Undergraduate/Scholarship)* [4182]
William F. Carl Scholarships *(Undergraduate/Scholarship)* [7470]
Julian E. Carnes Scholarship Fund *(Undergraduate/Scholarship)* [4183]
Carolinas-Virginias Retail Hardware Scholarships *(Undergraduate/Scholarship)* [4184]
Children's Scholarship Fund of Charlotte *(Undergraduate/Scholarship)* [4187]
Cole Foundation Undergraduate Scholarship Program *(Undergraduate/Scholarship)* [4189]
Sally Cole Visual Arts Scholarship Fund *(Undergraduate/Scholarship)* [4190]
Elmer and Rosa Lee Collins Scholarships *(Undergraduate/Scholarship)* [10575]
Reuben R. Cowles Youth Awards *(Undergraduate/Award)* [945]
James Davis Scholarships *(Undergraduate/Scholarship)* [10224]
Virginia Elizabeth and Alma Vane Taylor Nursing Scholarship *(Undergraduate/Scholarship)* [10580]
Jack Ervin EDI Scholarships *(Other/Scholarship)* [7460]
Forsyth County Nursing Scholarships *(Undergraduate/Scholarship)* [10581]
Garden Club Council of Winston-Salem and Forsyth County Council Scholarships *(Undergraduate/Scholarship)* [10583]
Jim Graham Scholarships *(Undergraduate/Scholarship)* [7482]
Governor James E. Holshouser Professional Development Scholarships *(Other/Scholarship)* [7461]
Hughes Memorial Foundation Scholarships *(Graduate/Scholarship)* [4983]
Edward Jackson International Scholarships *(Undergraduate/Scholarship)* [10235]
Oliver Joel and Ellen Pell Denny Healthcare Scholarship Fund *(Undergraduate/Scholarship)* [10585]
James V. Johnson Scholarship Fund *(Undergraduate/Scholarship)* [4199]
Stella B. Johnson Scholarships *(Undergraduate/Scholarship)* [10586]
K & W Cafeterias Scholarships *(Undergraduate/Scholarship)* [7472]
Glenn Keever Scholarships *(Undergraduate/Scholarship)* [10236]
Mary and Millard Kiker Scholarships *(Undergraduate/Scholarship)* [4201]
Douglas Gray Kimel Scholarships *(Undergraduate/Scholarship)* [10587]
Lighthouse International Scholarships - College-bound Awards *(High School, Undergraduate/Scholarship)* [6083]
Lighthouse International Scholarships - Graduate Awards *(Graduate/Scholarship)* [6084]
Lighthouse International Scholarships - Undergraduate Awards *(Undergraduate/Scholarship)* [6085]
L.D. and Elsie Long Memorial Scholarships *(Graduate/Scholarship)* [10589]
Dr. Blanca Moore-Velez Woman of Substance Scholarships *(Undergraduate/Scholarship)* [6763]
NC Hospitality Education Foundation Scholarships - Four Year College or University *(Undergraduate/Scholarship)* [7473]
NC Hospitality Education Foundation Scholarships - Graduate *(Graduate/Scholarship)* [7474]
NC Hospitality Education Foundation Scholarships - High School *(Undergraduate/Scholarship)* [7475]
NC Hospitality Education Foundation Scholarships - Two Year Community or Junior College *(Undergraduate/Scholarship)* [7476]
NCACPA Outstanding Minority Accounting Student Scholarships *(Undergraduate/Scholarship)* [7451]
NCRLA Golden Corral Scholarships *(Undergraduate/Scholarship)* [7477]
North Carolina Association of Health Care Recruiters Scholarships *(Undergraduate/Scholarship)* [7454]
North Carolina CPA Foundation Scholarships *(Undergraduate/Scholarship)* [7452]
North Carolina Heroes Financial Hardship Grant *(All/Grant)* [7466]
North Carolina League for Nursing Academic Scholarships *(Graduate/Scholarship)* [4207]
William H. and Lena M. Petree Scholarships *(Undergraduate/Scholarship)* [10592]
Peter DeWitt Pruden and Phyliss Harrill Pruden Scholarships *(Undergraduate/Scholarship)* [10247]
Regions Riding Forward Scholarships Essay Contest *(Undergraduate/Scholarship)* [8536]
Dan Stewart Scholarships *(Other/Scholarship)* [7462]
Mary Stewart and William T. Covington, Jr. Scholarship Fund *(Undergraduate/Scholarship)* [4215]
Charles H. Stone Scholarships *(Undergraduate/Scholarship)* [2081]
Turner Family Scholarships *(Undergraduate, Vocational/Occupational/Scholarship)* [4217]
Nell and Spencer Waggoner Scholarships *(Undergraduate/Scholarship)* [10602]
Gary Wagner, K3OMI Scholarships *(Undergraduate/Scholarship)* [1762]
David Julian Wichard Scholarships *(Undergraduate/Scholarship)* [10255]
The L. Phil and Alice J. Wicker Scholarship *(Undergraduate/Scholarship)* [1763]
Edwin H. and Louise N. Williamson Endowed Scholarships *(Undergraduate/Scholarship)* [10605]
Harriet Glen Wilmore Scholarship *(Undergraduate, Vocational/Occupational/Scholarship)* [4221]
Ted G. Wilson Memorial Scholarships *(Undergraduate/Scholarship)* [8288]
Winston-Salem Foundation Scholarships *(Undergraduate/Scholarship)* [10606]
WTVD Endowment Scholarships *(Undergraduate/Scholarship)* [10257]
Blanche Raper Zimmerman Scholarships *(Other/Scholarship)* [10607]

North Dakota

Horatio Alger North Dakota Scholarships *(Undergraduate/Scholarship)* [4949]
MAC Louisa Bowen Memorial Scholarships for Graduate Students in Archival Administration *(Graduate/Scholarship)* [6515]
North Dakota Veterinary Medical Association Scholarships *(Undergraduate/Scholarship)* [7502]
Rocky Mountain Coal Mining Institute Engineering/Geology Scholarships *(Undergraduate/Scholarship)* [8632]
Rocky Mountain Coal Mining Institute Technical Scholarships *(Undergraduate/Scholarship)* [8633]
Upper Midwest Human Rights Fellowship Program *(Graduate/Scholarship, Fellowship)* [4996]
Dr. William "Tim" Whalen Memorial Scholarships *(Undergraduate/Scholarship)* [7503]

Ohio

AISC/Ohio Structural Steel Association Scholarships *(Graduate/Scholarship)* [934]
American Guild of Organists, Canton Chapter Charitable Fund *(Undergraduate/Scholarship)* [9492]
Ora E. Anderson Scholarships *(Undergraduate, High School/Scholarship)* [4167]
Michael Bany Memorial Scholarships *(Undergraduate/Scholarship)* [2944]
Walter and Marilyn Bartlett Scholarships *(Undergraduate/Scholarship)* [2945]
MAC Louisa Bowen Memorial Scholarships for Graduate Students in Archival Administration *(Graduate/Scholarship)* [6515]
Milton and Edith Brown Memorial Scholarships *(Undergraduate/Scholarship)* [2946]
Harry D. Callahan Educational Trust *(Undergraduate/Scholarship)* [9495]
Eugene Carroll Scholarships *(Undergraduate/Scholarship)* [2947]
George H. and Anna Casper Fund *(Undergraduate/Scholarship)* [9496]
CFT/ACPSOP Scholarships *(Undergraduate/Scholarship)* [2948]
Cleveland Executive Fellowships (CEF) *(Other/Fellowship)* [3051]
Ruth M. Cogan Scholarship Fund *(Undergraduate/Scholarship)* [9497]
T.L. Conlan Scholarships *(Undergraduate/Scholarship)* [2950]
Dave Couch Memorial Scholarships *(Undergraduate/Scholarship)* [7820]
CSF Ach Family Scholarships *(Undergraduate/Scholarship)* [2951]
CSF Barr Foundation Scholarships *(Undergraduate/Scholarship)* [2952]
CSF Barrett Family Scholarships *(Undergraduate/Scholarship)* [2953]
CSF Borden Inc. Scholarships *(Undergraduate/Scholarship)* [2954]
CSF Castellini Foundation Scholarships *(Undergraduate/Scholarship)* [2955]
CSF Cincinnati Bell Scholarships *(Undergraduate/Scholarship)* [2956]
CSF Cincinnati Financial Corporation Scholarships *(Undergraduate/Scholarship)* [2957]
CSF Crosset Family Scholarships *(Undergraduate/Scholarship)* [2958]
CSF Dater Foundation Scholarships *(Undergraduate/Scholarship)* [2959]
CSF Duke Energy Scholarships *(Undergraduate/Scholarship)* [2960]
CSF Farmer Family Foundation Scholarships *(Undergraduate/Scholarship)* [2961]
CSF Fifth Third Bank Combined Scholarships *(Undergraduate/Scholarship)* [2962]
CSF Fletemeyer Family Scholarships *(Undergraduate/Scholarship)* [2963]
CSF Gardner Foundation Scholarships *(Undergraduate/Scholarship)* [2964]
CSF Goldman, Sachs and Company Scholarships *(Undergraduate/Scholarship)* [2965]
CSF H.C. Schott Foundation Scholarships *(Undergraduate/Scholarship)* [2966]
CSF Heidelberg Distributing Co. Scholarships *(Undergraduate/Scholarship)* [2967]
CSF Heinz Pet Products Scholarships *(Undergraduate/Scholarship)* [2968]
CSF Juilfs Foundation Scholarships *(Undergraduate/Scholarship)* [2969]
CSF Kroger Cincinnati/Dayton Scholarships *(Undergraduate/Scholarship)* [2970]
CSF McCall Educational Scholarships *(Undergraduate/Scholarship)* [2971]
CSF Midland Company Scholarships *(Undergraduate/Scholarship)* [2972]
CSF Nethercott Family Scholarships *(Undergraduate/Scholarship)* [2973]
CSF Ohio National Foundation Scholarships *(Undergraduate/Scholarship)* [2974]
CSF Pepper Family Scholarships *(Undergraduate/Scholarship)* [2975]
CSF Pichler Family Scholarships *(Undergraduate/Scholarship)* [2976]
CSF PNC Bank Scholarships *(Undergraduate/Scholarship)* [2977]
CSF Procter and Gamble Scholarships *(Undergraduate/Scholarship)* [2978]
CSF Semple Foundation Scholarships *(Undergraduate/Scholarship)* [2980]
CSF Union Central 135th Anniversary Scholarships *(Undergraduate/Scholarship)* [2981]
CSF U.S. Bank N.A. Scholarships *(Undergraduate/Scholarship)* [2982]
CSF Western-Southern Foundation Scholarships *(Undergraduate/Scholarship)* [2983]
CSF Woodward Trustees Scholarships *(Undergraduate/Scholarship)* [2984]
CSF Wynne Family Memorial Scholarships *(Undergraduate/Scholarship)* [2985]
Curtis/Breeden Scholarships *(Doctorate/Scholarship)* [2986]
Estelle Davis Memorial Scholarships *(Undergraduate/Scholarship)* [2987]
Robert Martz DiGiacomo Memorial Scholarship Fund *(Undergraduate/Scholarship)* [9499]
Harold K. Douthit Regional Scholarships *(Undergraduate/Scholarship)* [7576]
Thomas J. Emery Memorial Scholarships *(Undergraduate/Scholarship)* [2988]
Lyle and Rlene Everingham Family Scholarships *(Undergraduate/Scholarship)* [2989]
Lyle Everingham Scholarships *(Undergraduate/Scholarship)* [2990]
Fine Arts Association Minority Scholarships *(Undergraduate/Scholarship)* [4026]

Fine Arts Association United Way Scholarships (Undergraduate/Scholarship) [4027]
Alice J. Foit Scholarships (Undergraduate/Scholarship) [9502]
William A. Friedlander Scholarships (Undergraduate/Scholarship) [2991]
Priscilla Gamble Scholarships (Undergraduate/Scholarship) [2992]
David A. and Pamela A. Gault Charitable Fund (Undergraduate/Scholarship) [9504]
G.E. Aviation Scholarships (Undergraduate/Scholarship) [2993]
Milacron Geier Scholarships (Undergraduate/Scholarship) [2994]
Laverne L. Gibson Memorial Scholarships (Undergraduate/Scholarship) [7830]
Zelma Gray Medical School Scholarships (Graduate, Doctorate/Fellowship) [4168]
Greater Cincinnati Scholarships Association (Undergraduate/Scholarship) [2995]
James H. and Shirley L. Green Scholarship Fund (Undergraduate/Scholarship) [9506]
Velma Shotwell Griffin Memorial Scholarship Fund (Undergraduate/Scholarship) [9507]
Katherine M. Grosscup Scholarships (Undergraduate, Graduate/Scholarship) [4325]
Dr. James H. Heckman Memorial Scholarship Fund (Undergraduate/Scholarship) [9508]
Richard Heekin Scholarships (Undergraduate/Scholarship) [2996]
Helen Steiner Rice Scholarships (Undergraduate/Scholarship) [2997]
Dwight Hibbard Scholarships (Undergraduate/Scholarship) [2998]
Florette B. Hoffheimer Scholarships (Undergraduate/Scholarship) [2999]
Raymond T. Hoge Scholarship Fund (Undergraduate/Scholarship) [9510]
Minnie Hopkins Memorial Scholarship Fund of Lathrop/Compton School (Undergraduate/Scholarship) [9511]
Roger and Joyce Howe Scholarships (Undergraduate/Scholarship) [3000]
Virginia C. Jack and Ralph L. Jack Scholarships (Undergraduate/Scholarship) [9513]
Jackson High School Alumni Scholarship Fund (Undergraduate/Scholarship) [9514]
Johnny Bench Scholarships (Undergraduate/Scholarship) [3001]
Ella Wilson Johnson Scholarships (Undergraduate/Scholarship) [3002]
David J. Joseph Company Scholarships (Undergraduate/Scholarship) [3003]
Junior Achievement of East Central Ohio, Inc. Scholarship Fund (Undergraduate/Scholarship) [9515]
David A. Kaiser Memorial Scholarship Fund (Undergraduate/Scholarship) [9516]
Kappa Delta Phi Scholarship Program (Postgraduate/Scholarship) [1046]
KDP Huntington Bank Scholarship (Undergraduate/Scholarship) [5673]
Raymond and Augusta Klink Scholarships (Undergraduate/Scholarship) [3004]
Bob and Linda Kohlhepp Scholarships (Undergraduate/Scholarship) [3005]
Samuel Krugliak Legal Scholarship Fund (Undergraduate/Scholarship) [9517]
Lake Dollars for Scholars Endowment Fund (Undergraduate/Scholarship) [9518]
Carl H. Lindner Family Scholarships (Undergraduate/Scholarship) [3006]
Lillian Grace Mahan Scholarship Fund (Graduate/Scholarship) [9520]
Manzer-Keener-Wefler Scholarships (Undergraduate/Scholarship) [9521]
Sanders J. Mestel Legal Scholarship Fund (Undergraduate/Scholarship) [9524]
Harry Mestel Memorial Accounting Scholarship Fund (Undergraduate/Scholarship) [9525]
Lt. Colonel Robert G. Moreland Vocational/Technical Fund (Undergraduate/Scholarship) [9527]
Anthony Munoz Scholarships (Undergraduate/Scholarship) [6618]
Corwin Nixon Scholarships (Undergraduate/Scholarship) [3007]
Ohio Newspaper Association Minority Scholarships (Undergraduate/Scholarship) [7577]
Ohio War Orphan Scholarships (Undergraduate/Scholarship) [10723]
O'Jays Scholarship Fund (Undergraduate/Scholarship) [9529]
Perry Township School Memorial Scholarship Fund (Undergraduate/Scholarship) [9530]
CSF Charles and Claire Phillips Scholarships (Undergraduate/Scholarship) [3008]
Thomas W. Porter, W8KYZ Scholarships Honoring Michael Daugherty, W8LSE (Undergraduate/Scholarship) [1752]
Marvin Rammelsberg Scholarships (Undergraduate/Scholarship) [3009]
Robert H. Reakirt Scholarships (Undergraduate/Scholarship) [3010]
Reid Hospital Graduate Student Scholarships (Graduate/Scholarship) [10507]
Reynoldsburg-Pickerington Rotary Club High School Scholarship (Undergraduate/Scholarship) [8595]
William J. Rielly/MCURC Scholarships (Undergraduate/Scholarship) [3011]
Mary Roberts Scholarships (Undergraduate/Scholarship) [3012]
Thomas Warren Roberts Scholarships (Undergraduate/Scholarship) [7856]
St. Joseph's Hospital School of Nursing Alumnae Scholarship (Undergraduate/Scholarship) [7861]
S.C. Johnson, A Family Company Scholarships (Undergraduate/Scholarship) [3013]
CSF Charlotte R. Schmidlapp Scholarships (Undergraduate/Scholarship) [3014]
Nelson Schwab Jr. Scholarships (Undergraduate/Scholarship) [3015]
Stephen Schwartz Musical Theatre Scholarships (Undergraduate/Scholarship) [4988]
Judge Benjamin Schwartz Scholarships (Undergraduate/Scholarship) [3016]
CSF E.W. Scripps Foundation Scholarship Fund (Undergraduate/Scholarship) [3017]
S. David Shor Scholarships (Undergraduate/Scholarship) [3018]
Don and Madalyn Sickafoose Educational Trust (Undergraduate/Scholarship) [9533]
Lowe Simpson Scholarships (Undergraduate/Scholarship) [3019]
Ruth Skeeles Memorial Scholarship Fund (Undergraduate/Scholarship) [9534]
Frank Foster Skillman Scholarships (Undergraduate/Scholarship) [3020]
Stark County Bar Association Fund (Undergraduate/Scholarship) [9535]
Stark County Dairy Promoters Scholarships (Undergraduate/Scholarship) [9536]
Joseph S. Stern, Jr. Scholarships (Undergraduate/Scholarship) [3021]
Zachary Taylor Stevens Memorial Scholarships (Undergraduate/Scholarship) [1759]
Jeffrey Tyler Sweitzer Wrestling Memorial Scholarship Fund (Undergraduate/Scholarship) [9537]
Timothy S. Sweterlitsch Memorial Scholarship Fund (Undergraduate/Scholarship) [9538]
Martha W. Tanner Memorial Scholarships (Undergraduate/Scholarship) [3022]
CSF Christopher Todd Grant Memorial Scholarships (Undergraduate/Scholarship) [3023]
Dee Wacksman Scholarships (Undergraduate/Scholarship) [3024]
Covington-Cincinnati/Northern Kentucky Alumni Club - Dane Wagge Scholarships (Undergraduate/Scholarship) [10149]
Lester and Eleanor Webster Foundation Scholarships (Undergraduate/Scholarship) [9542]
Western Reserve Herb Society Scholarships (Undergraduate/Scholarship) [4866]
Whitaker-Minard Memorial Scholarships (Undergraduate/Scholarship) [7871]
Wayne F. White and Bob Evans Legacy Scholarships (Undergraduate, High School/Scholarship) [4170]
Mary Kean White Memorial Scholarship Fund (Undergraduate/Scholarship) [9544]
Glenn Wilson Broadcast Journalism Scholarships (Undergraduate/Scholarship) [7873]
HCRTA/Glen O. and Wyllabeth Wise Scholarships (Undergraduate/Scholarship) [3025]
L and T Woolfolk Memorial Scholarships (Undergraduate/Scholarship) [3026]
Workshops, Inc. and Stark MRDD Fostering Diversity Through Special Needs Scholarship Fund (Undergraduate/Scholarship) [9545]
Louis B. Zapoleon Memorial Scholarships (Undergraduate/Scholarship) [3027]

Oklahoma

Cherokee Nation Graduate Scholarships (Graduate/Scholarship) [2893]
Cherokee Nation Scholarships (Undergraduate/Scholarship) [2895]
Tom and Judith Comstock Scholarships (Undergraduate/Scholarship) [1734]
Lone Star GIA Associate and Alumni Scholarships (Undergraduate/Scholarship) [4341]
The Brandon Magalassi Memorial Scholarship Foundation Scholarships (Undergraduate/Scholarship) [6185]
Fred R. McDaniel Memorial Scholarships (Undergraduate/Scholarship) [1746]
Hatton W. Sumners Scholarships (Undergraduate/Scholarship) [7602]
Lynn McNabb Walton Adelphe Scholarhship (Undergraduate/Scholarship) [5770]

Oregon

Paul Arnold Memorial Scholarships (Undergraduate/Scholarship) [8241]
Asian and Pacific Islander Queers Sisters Scholarships (Undergraduate/Scholarship) [8242]
Associates in Behavioral Health Scholarships (Graduate/Scholarship) [8243]
Bill Bendiner and Doug Morgenson Scholarships (Undergraduate/Scholarship) [8246]
Mary Lou Brown Scholarships (Undergraduate/Scholarship) [1729]
Deloris Carter Hampton Scholarships (Undergraduate/Scholarship) [8247]
Clackamas County Farm Bureau Scholarships (Undergraduate/Scholarship) [7705]
Donald O. Coffman Scholarships (Undergraduate/Scholarship) [8248]
Dennis Coleman Choral Conducting Scholarships (Undergraduate/Scholarship) [8250]
Dennis Coleman Memorial Scholarships (Undergraduate/Scholarship) [8251]
Brian M. Day Scholarships (Undergraduate/Scholarship) [8252]
Hispanic Metropolitan Chamber Scholarships (Graduate, Undergraduate/Scholarship) [4900]
Gregori Jakovina Endowment Scholarships (Undergraduate/Scholarship) [3920]
Obrzut Ling Scholarships (Undergraduate/Scholarship) [8255]
McFarffels Scholarships (Undergraduate/Scholarship) [8256]
Chapter 63 - Portland James E. Morrow Scholarships (Graduate, Undergraduate/Scholarship) [9189]
Jack D. Motteler Scholarships (Undergraduate/Scholarship) [8257]
OAIA Scholarships (Undergraduate, Graduate/Scholarship) [7690]
Oregon Association of Broadcasters Scholarships (Undergraduate/Scholarship) [7688]
Oregon Literary Fellowships (Advanced Professional/Fellowship) [6097]
OSCPA Educational Foundation College Scholarships (Undergraduate/Scholarship) [7711]
OSCPA Educational Foundation High School Scholarships (Undergraduate/Scholarship) [7712]
Pride Foundation Political Leadership Scholarships (Undergraduate/Scholarship) [8258]
Pride Foundation Regional Scholarships (Undergraduate/Scholarship) [8259]
Pride Foundation Scholarships (Undergraduate/Scholarship) [8663]
Pride Foundation Social Work Scholarships (Undergraduate/Scholarship) [8260]
Pride of the Rose Scholarship Fund (Undergraduate/Scholarship) [3922]

UNITED STATES   Legal Residence Index

Robert Browning Scholarships *(Undergraduate/Scholarship)* [8262]
Rosenberg-Ibarra Scholarships *(Undergraduate/Scholarship)* [8263]
Chapter 63 - Portland Uncle Bud Smith Scholarships *(Undergraduate/Scholarship)* [9196]
Kathy Spadoni Memorial Scholarships *(Undergraduate/Scholarship)* [8264]
Robert W. and Bernice Ingalls Staton Scholarships *(Undergraduate/Scholarship)* [10259]
Ric Ulrich and Chuck Pischke Scholarships *(Undergraduate/Scholarship)* [8266]
University of Oregon Presidential Scholarships *(Undergraduate/Scholarship)* [10263]
Patricia Van Kirk Scholarships *(Undergraduate/Scholarship)* [8267]
Wells Fargo Scholarships *(Undergraduate/Scholarship)* [8268]
Wozumi Family Scholarships *(Undergraduate/Scholarship)* [8270]
You Go Girl! Scholarships *(Undergraduate/Scholarship)* [8271]
Urashi Zen Scholarships *(Undergraduate/Scholarship)* [8272]

Pennsylvania

Horatio Alger Pennsylvania Scholarships *(Undergraduate/Scholarship)* [4950]
Allegheny County Medical Society Medical Student Scholarships (ACMS) *(Undergraduate/Scholarship)* [4274]
Alliance Medical Education Scholarship Fund (AMES) *(Undergraduate/Scholarship)* [4275]
American Philosophical Society Library Resident Research Fellowships *(Doctorate/Fellowship)* [1078]
Bailey/Hollister Scholarships *(Graduate, Professional development/Scholarship)* [7935]
Joseph R. Calder, Jr., MD Scholarship Fund *(Undergraduate/Scholarship)* [4041]
Malcolm U. Dantzler Scholarships *(Other/Scholarship)* [9363]
The William H. Davis, Jr. Scholarship Fund *(Undergraduate/Scholarship)* [3204]
Dr. Michael Dorizas Memorial Scholarships *(Undergraduate/Scholarship)* [4846]
Lou Drane Music Scholarships *(Undergraduate/Scholarship)* [4237]
H.J. "Duke" Ellington Memorial Scholarship Award *(Undergraduate/Scholarship)* [7513]
Howard Fox Memorial Law Scholarships *(Graduate/Scholarship)* [2235]
Gallo Blue Chip Scholarships *(Undergraduate/Scholarship)* [4724]
Generation III Scholarships *(Undergraduate/Scholarship)* [3783]
Green Knight Economic Development Corporation Scholarships *(Undergraduate/Scholarship)* [4668]
Katherine M. Grosscup Scholarships *(Undergraduate, Graduate/Scholarship)* [4325]
Scott A. Gunder, MD, DCMS Presidential Scholarships *(Undergraduate/Scholarship)* [4276]
Hellenic University Club of Philadelphia Founders Scholarships *(Undergraduate/Scholarship)* [4847]
Nicholas S. Hetos, DDS, Memorial Graduate Scholarships *(Graduate, Doctorate/Scholarship)* [4848]
Hope Through Learning Awards *(Undergraduate/Scholarship)* [4927]
Roberta L. Houpt Scholarship Fund *(Undergraduate/Scholarship)* [4242]
Erin L. Jenkins Memorial Scholarship Fund *(Undergraduate/Scholarship)* [4244]
Ken and Romaine Kauffman Scholarship Fund *(Undergraduate/Scholarship)* [4245]
Schmidt Kramer Scholarships for Academic Excellence *(Undergraduate/Scholarship)* [8792]
Lighthouse International Scholarships - College-bound Awards *(High School, Undergraduate/Scholarship)* [6083]
Lighthouse International Scholarships - Graduate Awards *(Graduate/Scholarship)* [6084]
Lighthouse International Scholarships - Undergraduate Awards *(Undergraduate/Scholarship)* [6085]
Lycoming County Medical Society Scholarships (LCMS) *(Undergraduate/Scholarship)* [4277]

Olivia M. Marquart Scholarships *(Graduate, Master's, Doctorate/Scholarship)* [9828]
Montgomery County Medical Society Scholarships (MCMS) *(Undergraduate/Scholarship)* [4278]
Albert and Alice Nacinovich Music Scholarships *(Undergraduate/Scholarship)* [4056]
NASSLEO Scholarships - Region I *(Undergraduate/Scholarship)* [6782]
New York Women in Communications, Inc. Foundation Scholarships *(Graduate, Undergraduate/Scholarship)* [7406]
Northampton County Medical Society Alliance Scholarships *(Undergraduate/Scholarship)* [7507]
NTHA Forest Resources Scholarships for College Students *(Undergraduate/Scholarship)* [7525]
Dr. Nicholas Padis Memorial Graduate Scholarships *(Graduate/Scholarship)* [4849]
Pellegrini Scholarships *(Undergraduate, Graduate/Scholarship)* [9620]
Pennsylvania Engineering Foundation Undergradaute Scholarships *(Undergraduate/Scholarship)* [7943]
Pennsylvania Heartland Unit Scholarships *(Undergraduate/Scholarship)* [4864]
Pennsylvania Land Surveyors Foundation Scholarships *(Undergraduate/Scholarship)* [7941]
Pennsylvania Library Association MLS Scholarships *(Graduate/Scholarship)* [7937]
Myrtle Siegfried, MD and Michael Vigilante, MD Scholarships *(Undergraduate/Scholarship)* [4279]
J. Ward Sleichter and Frances F. Sleichter Memorial Scholarship Fund *(Undergraduate/Scholarship)* [4254]
South Carolina Public Health Association Scholarships *(Undergraduate/Scholarship)* [9364]
Minnie Patton Stayman Scholarships *(Undergraduate/Scholarship)* [7948]
Joseph L. and Vivian E. Steele Music Scholarship Fund *(Undergraduate/Scholarship)* [4256]
Dr. Peter A. Theodos Memorial Graduate Scholarships *(Undergraduate, Graduate/Scholarship)* [4850]
Dimitri J. Ververelli Memorial Scholarship for Architecture and/or Engineering *(Undergraduate/Scholarship)* [4851]
Monica M. Weaver Memorial Fund *(Undergraduate/Scholarship)* [4062]
John G. Williams Scholarship Fund *(Undergraduate/Scholarship)* [10565]
Yankee Clipper Contest Club, Inc. Youth Scholarships *(Undergraduate/Scholarship)* [1764]
Young Christian Leaders Scholarships *(Undergraduate/Scholarship)* [10760]
Zimmermann Scholarships *(Graduate/Scholarship)* [9621]

Rhode Island

Adler Pollock & Sheehan Diversity Scholarships *(Undergraduate/Scholarship)* [71]
Bach Organ Scholarship *(Undergraduate/Scholarship)* [8602]
Thomas F. Black, Jr. Memorial Scholarships *(Undergraduate/Scholarship)* [8600]
Casey Family Services Alumni Scholarships *(Graduate, Undergraduate, Vocational/Occupational/Scholarship)* [4157]
Antonio Cirino Memorial Art Education Fellowships *(Graduate/Fellowship)* [8603]
Constant Memorial Scholarship *(Undergraduate/Scholarship)* [8604]
Edward Leon Duhamel Scholarship Fund *(Undergraduate/Scholarship)* [8605]
GFWC Women's Club of South County Scholarships *(Undergraduate/Scholarship)* [8606]
Rhode Island Commission on Women/Freda H. Goldman Education Awards *(Undergraduate/Award, Scholarship)* [8607]
Dr. James L. Lawson Memorial Scholarships *(Undergraduate/Scholarship)* [1745]
Lighthouse International Scholarships - College-bound Awards *(High School, Undergraduate/Scholarship)* [6083]
Lighthouse International Scholarships - Graduate Awards *(Graduate/Scholarship)* [6084]
Lighthouse International Scholarships - Undergraduate Awards *(Undergraduate/Scholarship)* [6085]
NASSLEO Scholarships - Region I *(Undergraduate/Scholarship)* [6782]
New England FEMARA Scholarships *(Undergraduate/Scholarship)* [1748]
Rhode Island Association of Former Legislators Scholarships *(Undergraduate/Scholarship)* [8608]
RISLA Student Loans *(Undergraduate, Graduate/Loan)* [8615]
Lily and Catello Sorrentino Memorial Scholarships *(Undergraduate/Scholarship)* [8609]
Bruce and Marjorie Sundlun Scholarships *(Undergraduate/Scholarship)* [8610]
The AIWF/Patricia Tillinghast Memorial Scholarships *(Graduate, Undergraduate/Scholarship)* [939]
Marilynne Graboys Wool Scholarships *(Graduate/Scholarship)* [8611]
Yankee Clipper Contest Club, Inc. Youth Scholarships *(Undergraduate/Scholarship)* [1764]

South Carolina

African American Network - Carolinas Scholarship Fund *(Undergraduate/Scholarship)* [4174]
Leon Bradley Scholarship Program *(Undergraduate/Scholarship)* [575]
Julian E. Carnes Scholarship Fund *(Undergraduate/Scholarship)* [4183]
Carolinas-Virginias Retail Hardware Scholarships *(Undergraduate/Scholarship)* [4184]
Reuben R. Cowles Youth Awards *(Undergraduate/Award)* [945]
Judy Crocker Memorial Scholarship Fund *(Undergraduate/Scholarship)* [4191]
Harry Hampton Fund Scholarship *(Undergraduate/Scholarship)* [4733]
Howard B. Higgins South Carolina Dental Scholarships *(Undergraduate/Scholarship)* [4197]
Wilbert L. and Zora F. Holmes Scholarship Endowment Fund *(Undergraduate/Scholarship)* [4198]
Lighthouse International Scholarships - College-bound Awards *(High School, Undergraduate/Scholarship)* [6083]
Lighthouse International Scholarships - Graduate Awards *(Graduate/Scholarship)* [6084]
Lighthouse International Scholarships - Undergraduate Awards *(Undergraduate/Scholarship)* [6085]
Henry DeWitt Plyler Scholarship Fund *(Undergraduate/Scholarship)* [4210]
Regions Riding Forward Scholarships Essay Contest *(Undergraduate/Scholarship)* [8536]
SCLEOA Scholarships *(Undergraduate/Scholarship)* [9361]
South Carolina Association for Financial Professionals College Education Scholarships *(Undergraduate/Scholarship)* [9359]
Charles H. Stone Scholarships *(Undergraduate/Scholarship)* [2081]
Watson-Brown Scholarships *(Undergraduate/Scholarship)* [10489]
The L. Phil and Alice J. Wicker Scholarship *(Undergraduate/Scholarship)* [1763]
Ted G. Wilson Memorial Scholarships *(Undergraduate/Scholarship)* [8288]
YMF Scholarships *(Undergraduate/Scholarship)* [10762]

South Dakota

Horatio Alger South Dakota Scholarships *(Undergraduate/Scholarship)* [4951]
MAC Louisa Bowen Memorial Scholarships for Graduate Students in Archival Administration *(Graduate/Scholarship)* [6515]
Marianne M. Stenvig Scholarships *(Master's, Doctorate/Scholarship)* [9375]
Upper Midwest Human Rights Fellowship Program *(Graduate/Scholarship, Fellowship)* [4996]
Jerry Wheeler Scholarships *(Undergraduate/Scholarship)* [9377]

Tennessee

George Oliver Benton Memorial Scholarships *(Undergraduate/Scholarship)* [3213]
Leon Bradley Scholarship Program *(Undergraduate/Scholarship)* [575]

Ruby A. Brown Memorial Scholarships *(Undergraduate/Scholarship)* [3753]
William and Clara Bryan Scholarships *(Undergraduate/Scholarship)* [3216]
Cheatham County Community Foundation Scholarships *(Undergraduate/Scholarship)* [3218]
Steven L. Coffey Memorial Scholarships *(Undergraduate/Scholarship)* [3755]
Reuben R. Cowles Youth Awards *(Undergraduate/Award)* [945]
B.J. Dean Scholarships *(Undergraduate/Scholarship)* [3224]
Federal Court Bench and Bar Scholarships *(Undergraduate/Scholarship)* [10160]
Pauline LaFon Gore Scholarships *(Undergraduate/Scholarship)* [3227]
Maude Keisling/Cumberland County Extension Homemakers Scholarships *(Undergraduate/Scholarship)* [3231]
Senator Carl O. Koella, Jr. Memorial Scholarships *(Undergraduate/Scholarship)* [3233]
Michael B. Kruse Scholarships *(Graduate, Undergraduate/Scholarship)* [3234]
Heloise Werthan Kuhn Scholarships *(Undergraduate/Scholarship)* [3235]
Diane G. Lowe and John Gomez, IV Scholarships *(Undergraduate/Scholarship)* [3236]
Aurella Varallo Mariani Scholarship Program *(Undergraduate/Scholarship)* [6665]
John E. Mayfield Scholarship Fund for Cheatham County Central High School *(Undergraduate/Scholarship)* [3241]
John E. Mayfield Scholarship Fund for Harpeth High School *(Undergraduate/Scholarship)* [3242]
John E. Mayfield Scholarship Fund for Pleasant View Christian High School *(Undergraduate/Scholarship)* [3243]
John E. Mayfield Scholarship Fund for Sycamore High School *(Undergraduate/Scholarship)* [3244]
Memphis Access and Diversity Scholarships *(Undergraduate/Scholarship)* [10169]
NAJA Scholarships *(Graduate/Scholarship)* [6760]
Nashville Unit Scholarships *(Undergraduate/Scholarship)* [4863]
Jerry Newson Scholarships *(Undergraduate/Scholarship)* [3246]
Peter DeWitt Pruden and Phyliss Harrill Pruden Scholarships *(Undergraduate/Scholarship)* [10247]
Regions Riding Forward Scholarships Essay Contest *(Undergraduate/Scholarship)* [8536]
Drue Smith/Society of Professional Journalists Scholarships *(Undergraduate/Scholarship)* [3252]
SSAWMA Scholarships *(Graduate/Scholarship)* [9415]
Tennessee Bar Foundation IOLTA Law School Scholarships *(Undergraduate/Scholarship)* [10176]
Tennessee Trucking Foundation Scholarships *(Undergraduate/Scholarship)* [3254]
Gary Wagner, K3OMI Scholarships *(Undergraduate/Scholarship)* [1762]
The Woman's Club of Nashville Scholarship Endowment Fund *(Undergraduate/Scholarship)* [3257]
Wyatt, Tarrant & Combs, LLP, Dr. Benjamin L. Hooks Scholarship *(Undergraduate/Scholarship)* [10177]

Texas

Horatio Alger Texas - Fort Worth Scholarships *(Undergraduate/Scholarship)* [4952]
Horatio Alger Texas Scholarships *(Undergraduate/Scholarship)* [4953]
Allen - Marty Allen Scholarships *(Undergraduate/Scholarship)* [3085]
AWMA Louisiana Section Scholarships *(Undergraduate, Graduate/Scholarship)* [147]
BAFTX Graduate Awards *(Undergraduate/Scholarship)* [2366]
BAFTX Junior Achievers Awards *(Undergraduate/Scholarship)* [2367]
BAFTX Undergraduate Awards *(Undergraduate/Scholarship)* [2368]
Zachary Barriger Memorial Scholarships *(Undergraduate/Scholarship)* [3086]
Willa Beach-Porter Music Scholarships *(Undergraduate/Scholarship)* [2873]
O.J. Beck, Jr. Memorial Scholarships *(Undergraduate/Scholarship)* [3087]
Reverend E.F. Bennett Scholarships *(Undergraduate/Scholarship)* [3088]
Mary E. Bivins Foundation Religious Scholarship Program *(Graduate, Undergraduate/Scholarship)* [2275]
Kathi Bowles Scholarships for Women in Technology *(Undergraduate, Graduate/Scholarship)* [2091]
Marion Luna Brem/Pat McNeil Health and Education Scholarships *(Undergraduate/Scholarship)* [3089]
Kae and Kay Brockermeyer Endowed Scholarships *(Undergraduate/Scholarship)* [7968]
Cecil E. Burney Scholarships *(Undergraduate/Scholarship)* [3091]
C.C.H.R.M.A. Scholarships *(Undergraduate/Scholarship)* [3092]
Evelyn L. Cockrell Memorial Scholarship Award *(Undergraduate/Scholarship)* [9701]
Tom and Judith Comstock Scholarships *(Undergraduate/Scholarship)* [1734]
B.J. Dean Scholarships *(Undergraduate/Scholarship)* [3224]
Melissa Ann Guerra Scholarships *(Undergraduate/Scholarship)* [3098]
George Gustafson HSE Memorial Scholarships *(Graduate, Undergraduate/Scholarship)* [1414]
George and Mary Josephine Hamman Foundation Scholarships *(Undergraduate/Scholarship)* [4693]
Institute of Transportation Engineers - Texas District Fellowships *(Graduate/Fellowship)* [5219]
JLTLA Minority Law Student Scholarships *(Undergraduate/Scholarship)* [9818]
Mary Jon and J. P. Bryan Leadership in Education Awards *(Advanced Professional/Award)* [9716]
Danny T. Le Memorial Scholarships *(Undergraduate/Scholarship)* [10385]
Lone Star GIA Associate and Alumni Scholarships *(Undergraduate/Scholarship)* [4341]
Fred R. McDaniel Memorial Scholarships *(Undergraduate/Scholarship)* [1746]
McKinney Sisters Undergraduate Scholarships *(Undergraduate/Scholarship)* [3556]
Brian and Colleen Miller Math and Science Scholarships *(Undergraduate/Scholarship)* [3103]
Tad Nelson Law Firm Scholarships *(Undergraduate/Scholarship)* [5965]
Le Hoang Nguyen College Scholarships (LHN) *(Undergraduate/Scholarship)* [10386]
The Thuy Nguyen Scholarships *(High School/Scholarship)* [10387]
North Texas GIA Alumni Association Scholarships *(Undergraduate/Scholarship)* [4344]
WillEtta Long Oates, Gamma Nu, Memorial Scholarship *(Undergraduate, Graduate/Scholarship)* [5754]
Regions Riding Forward Scholarships Essay Contest *(Undergraduate/Scholarship)* [8536]
Rocky Mountain Coal Mining Institute Engineering/Geology Scholarships *(Undergraduate/Scholarship)* [8632]
Rocky Mountain Coal Mining Institute Technical Scholarships *(Undergraduate/Scholarship)* [8633]
SAC Scholarships for Higher Education *(Undergraduate/Scholarship)* [9558]
San Angelo Area Foundation Scholarships *(All/Scholarship)* [8684]
Kevin Saunders Wheelchair Success Scholarships *(Undergraduate/Scholarship)* [3107]
Judge Terry Shamsie Scholarships *(Undergraduate/Scholarship)* [3109]
SLEAMC Scholarships *(Graduate, Undergraduate/Scholarship)* [8865]
Herman J. Smith Scholarships *(Undergraduate, Graduate/Scholarship)* [7004]
South Texas Unit Scholarships *(Undergraduate/Scholarship)* [4865]
SPE Gulf Coast Hurricane Scholarships *(Undergraduate/Scholarship)* [9270]
Jim Springer Memorial Scholarships *(Undergraduate/Scholarship)* [3110]
Peggy P. Starks Scholarship *(Postgraduate/Scholarship)* [9702]
STC-Lone Star Chapter Traditional Education Scholarships *(Graduate, Undergraduate/Scholarship)* [9313]
Hatton W. Sumners Scholarships *(Undergraduate/Scholarship)* [7602]
Talbert Family Memorial Scholarships *(Undergraduate/Scholarship)* [3111]
Texas Elks State Association Scholarships *(Undergraduate/Scholarship)* [9699]
Marie Trahan/Susman Godfrey Scholarships *(Undergraduate/Scholarship)* [9820]
Tri Delta Houston Alumnae Chapter Graduate Fellowships *(Graduate/Fellowship, Scholarship)* [3563]
TSHP R&E Foundation Scholarship Program *(Undergraduate, Graduate/Scholarship)* [9807]
TxHIMA HIA-HIT Scholarship *(Undergraduate/Scholarship)* [9703]
Dr. Dana Williams Scholarships *(Undergraduate/Scholarship)* [3113]

Utah

Horatio Alger Utah Scholarships *(Undergraduate/Scholarship)* [4954]
Region II Scholarships *(Graduate, Undergraduate/Scholarship)* [1428]
Rocky Mountain Coal Mining Institute Engineering/Geology Scholarships *(Undergraduate/Scholarship)* [8632]
Rocky Mountain Coal Mining Institute Technical Scholarships *(Undergraduate/Scholarship)* [8633]

Vermont

American Legion Department of Vermont Scholarships *(Undergraduate, High School/Scholarship)* [959]
Casey Family Services Alumni Scholarships *(Graduate, Undergraduate, Vocational/Occupational/Scholarship)* [4157]
Dr. James L. Lawson Memorial Scholarships *(Undergraduate/Scholarship)* [1745]
Lighthouse International Scholarships - College-bound Awards *(High School, Undergraduate/Scholarship)* [6083]
Lighthouse International Scholarships - Graduate Awards *(Graduate/Scholarship)* [6084]
Lighthouse International Scholarships - Undergraduate Awards *(Undergraduate/Scholarship)* [6085]
NASSLEO Scholarships - Region I *(Undergraduate/Scholarship)* [6782]
New England FEMARA Scholarships *(Undergraduate/Scholarship)* [1748]
Johnny Trombly Scholarships *(Undergraduate/Scholarship)* [6572]
Yankee Clipper Contest Club, Inc. Youth Scholarships *(Undergraduate/Scholarship)* [1764]

Virginia

Horatio Alger District of Columbia, Maryland and Virginia Scholarships *(Undergraduate/Scholarship)* [4937]
Bayly-Tiffany Scholarships *(Undergraduate/Scholarship)* [10301]
Leo Bourassa Scholarships *(Undergraduate, Graduate/Scholarship)* [10398]
Leon Bradley Scholarship Program *(Undergraduate/Scholarship)* [575]
Carolinas-Virginias Retail Hardware Scholarships *(Undergraduate/Scholarship)* [4184]
Richard D. and Sheppard R. Cooke Memorial Scholarships *(Graduate/Scholarship)* [4695]
Reuben R. Cowles Youth Awards *(Undergraduate/Award)* [945]
V. Thomas Forehand, Jr. Scholarships *(Undergraduate/Scholarship)* [10302]
Jane S. Glenn Memorial Endowed Scholarships *(Undergraduate/Scholarship)* [8626]
Hampton Roads Association of Social Workers Scholarships *(Graduate/Scholarship)* [4698]
Hampton Roads Sanitation District Environmental Scholarships *(Graduate/Scholarship)* [4699]
Hughes Memorial Foundation Scholarships *(Graduate/Scholarship)* [4983]
Louis I. Jaffe Memorial Scholarships-NSU Alumni

(Graduate/Scholarship) [4700]
Kaprielian Memorial Scholarships (Undergraduate/Scholarship) [10303]
James N. Kincanon Scholarships (Undergraduate/Scholarship) [8627]
Lighthouse International Scholarships - College-bound Awards (High School, Undergraduate/Scholarship) [6083]
Lighthouse International Scholarships - Graduate Awards (Graduate/Scholarship) [6084]
Lighthouse International Scholarships - Undergraduate Awards (Undergraduate/Scholarship) [6085]
Marshall Undergraduate Scholars Program (Undergraduate/Award) [6296]
Thomas W. Porter, W8KYZ Scholarships Honoring Michael Daugherty, W8LSE (Undergraduate/Scholarship) [1752]
Peter DeWitt Pruden and Phyliss Harrill Pruden Scholarships (Undergraduate/Scholarship) [10247]
Regions Riding Forward Scholarships Essay Contest (Undergraduate/Scholarship) [8536]
Ellis W. Rowe Scholarships (Undergraduate/Scholarship) [4703]
Florence L. Smith Medical Scholarships (Graduate/Scholarship) [4705]
Drew Smith Memorial Scholarships (Undergraduate/Scholarship) [3187]
Enid W. and Bernard B. Spigel Architectural Scholarships (Graduate, Undergraduate/Scholarship) [4706]
Charles H. Stone Scholarships (Undergraduate/Scholarship) [2081]
Tidewater Builders Association Scholarships (Undergraduate/Scholarship) [9739]
Virginia Museum of Fine Arts Visual Arts Fellowships (Graduate, Other, Undergraduate/Fellowship) [10400]
Gary Wagner, K3OMI Scholarships (Undergraduate/Scholarship) [1762]
The L. Phil and Alice J. Wicker Scholarship (Undergraduate/Scholarship) [1763]
Alice Hinchcliffe Williams, RDH, MS Graduate Scholarships (Graduate/Scholarship) [10394]
Ted G. Wilson Memorial Scholarships (Undergraduate/Scholarship) [8288]
Charles Fred Wonson Scholarships (Undergraduate/Scholarship) [10306]

Washington

Horatio Alger Washington Scholarships (Undergraduate/Scholarship) [4955]
American Indian Endowed Scholarships (Graduate, Undergraduate/Scholarship) [10470]
Paul Arnold Memorial Scholarships (Undergraduate/Scholarship) [8241]
Asian and Pacific Islander Queers Sisters Scholarships (Undergraduate/Scholarship) [8242]
Associates in Behavioral Health Scholarships (Graduate/Scholarship) [8243]
Barbara Bailey Scholarships (Undergraduate/Scholarship) [8244]
Bellevue PFLAG Scholarships (Undergraduate/Scholarship) [8245]
Bill Bendiner and Doug Morgenson Scholarships (Undergraduate/Scholarship) [8246]
Beta Sigma Phi Visual Arts Scholarship (Undergraduate/Scholarship) [8869]
Boeing Company Scholarships (Undergraduate/Scholarship) [8870]
Mary Lou Brown Scholarships (Undergraduate/Scholarship) [1729]
Calvin Alumni Association-Washington, Lynden Scholarships (Undergraduate/Scholarship) [2505]
Deloris Carter Hampton Scholarships (Undergraduate/Scholarship) [8247]
Donald O. Coffman Scholarships (Undergraduate/Scholarship) [8248]
Cole Family Scholarships (Undergraduate/Scholarship) [8249]
Dennis Coleman Choral Conducting Scholarships (Undergraduate/Scholarship) [8250]
Dennis Coleman Memorial Scholarships (Undergraduate/Scholarship) [8251]
College Success Foundation Chateau Ste. Michelle Scholarship Fund (Undergraduate/Scholarship) [3125]
College Success Foundation Leadership 1000 Scholarships (Undergraduate/Scholarship) [3126]
College Success Foundation Realize the Dream Scholarships (Undergraduate/Scholarship) [3127]
College Success Foundation Washington State Governors' Scholarship for Foster Youth (Undergraduate/Scholarship) [3128]
Brian M. Day Scholarships (Undergraduate/Scholarship) [8252]
Derivative Duo Scholarships (Undergraduate/Scholarship) [8253]
Grays Harbor Community Foundation Scholarships (Undergraduate, Graduate/Scholarship) [4651]
Greater Seattle Business Association Scholarships (GSBA Scholarships) (Undergraduate/Scholarship) [4658]
High School Academic Scholarship (Undergraduate/Scholarship) [8873]
Inland Northwest Business Alliance Scholarships (INBA) (Undergraduate/Scholarship) [8254]
Gregori Jakovina Endowment Scholarships (Undergraduate/Scholarship) [3920]
Lemelson Center Fellowships (Doctorate, Postdoctorate, Professional development/Fellowship) [9025]
Obrzut Ling Scholarships (Undergraduate/Scholarship) [8255]
Norm Manly Maritime Educational Scholarships (Undergraduate/Scholarship) [10768]
Edmund F. Maxwell Scholarships (Undergraduate/Scholarship) [6348]
McFarffels Scholarships (Undergraduate/Scholarship) [8256]
Mill Creek Business Association Scholarships (Undergraduate/Scholarship) [6537]
Chapter 63 - Portland James E. Morrow Scholarships (Graduate, Undergraduate/Scholarship) [9189]
Jack D. Motteler Scholarships (Undergraduate/Scholarship) [8257]
Eric Niemitalo Scholarships in Earth and Environmental Science (Undergraduate/Scholarship) [8879]
Olympia Tumwater Foundation Traditional Scholarships (Undergraduate/Scholarship) [7608]
Olympia Tumwater Foundation Transitional (non-traditional) Scholarships (Undergraduate/Scholarship) [7609]
Pride Foundation Political Leadership Scholarships (Undergraduate/Scholarship) [8258]
Pride Foundation Regional Scholarships (Undergraduate/Scholarship) [8259]
Pride Foundation Scholarships (Undergraduate/Scholarship) [8663]
Pride Foundation Social Work Scholarships (Undergraduate/Scholarship) [8260]
Pride of the Rose Scholarship Fund (Undergraduate/Scholarship) [3922]
Don Renschler Scholarships (Graduate/Scholarship) [8261]
Robert Browning Scholarships (Undergraduate/Scholarship) [8262]
Rosenberg-Ibarra Scholarships (Undergraduate/Scholarship) [8263]
Shoreline Community College Full-Time Continuing Students Scholarships (Undergraduate/Scholarship) [8881]
Shoreline - Lake Forest Park High School Scholarship (Undergraduate/Scholarship) [8883]
Chapter 63 - Portland Uncle Bud Smith Scholarships (Undergraduate/Scholarship) [9196]
Kathy Spadoni Memorial Scholarships (Undergraduate/Scholarship) [8264]
Ric Ulrich and Chuck Pischke Scholarships (Undergraduate/Scholarship) [8266]
Patricia Van Kirk Scholarships (Undergraduate/Scholarship) [8267]
WALPA Lake Student Scholarships (Undergraduate, Graduate/Scholarship) [10466]
Washington City/County Management Association Scholarships (Graduate/Scholarship) [10438]
Washington CPA Foundation Scholarships (Undergraduate/Scholarship) [10452]
Washington Higher Education Coordinating Board - State Need Grants (SNG) (Undergraduate/Grant) [10472]
Washington State Nurses Association Foundation Scholarships (WSNF) (Graduate, Undergraduate/Scholarship) [10468]
George Waterman Memorial Scholarships (Undergraduate/Scholarship) [10453]
Wells Fargo Scholarships (Undergraduate/Scholarship) [8268]
Whidbey Island Giving Circle Scholarships (Undergraduate/Scholarship) [8269]
WIGA Scholarships (Postgraduate, Other, Undergraduate/Scholarship) [10450]
Wozumi Family Scholarships (Undergraduate/Scholarship) [8270]
WSAJ American Justice Essay Scholarships (Undergraduate/Scholarship) [10459]
WSAJ Presidents' Scholarships (Undergraduate/Scholarship) [10461]
WSGC Community College Transfer Scholarships (Undergraduate/Scholarship) [10455]
You Go Girl! Scholarships (Undergraduate/Scholarship) [8271]
Urashi Zen Scholarships (Undergraduate/Scholarship) [8272]

West Virginia

Martin K. Alsup Scholarships (Undergraduate/Scholarship) [7811]
The Ambrose-Ramsey Trust (Undergraduate/Scholarship) [7812]
Joe Barbarow Memorial Scholarships (Undergraduate/Scholarship) [7813]
Lewis and Gurry Batten/Sand Plains Educational Trust Scholarships (Undergraduate/Scholarship) [7814]
William (Billbo) Boston/Harold Knopp Scholarship (Undergraduate/Scholarship) [7815]
Chester H. Bruce Memorial Scholarships (Undergraduate/Scholarship) [7816]
Freda Burge Scholarships (Undergraduate/Scholarship) [7817]
Carolinas-Virginias Retail Hardware Scholarships (Undergraduate/Scholarship) [4184]
George H. Clinton Scholarship Fund (Undergraduate/Scholarship) [7818]
Dwight O. Conner and Ellen Conner Lepp/Danhart Scholarships (Undergraduate/Scholarship) [7819]
Dave Couch Memorial Scholarships (Undergraduate/Scholarship) [7820]
Jennifer Coulter Memorial Scholarships (Undergraduate/Scholarship) [7821]
Cindy Curry Memorial Scholarships (Undergraduate/Scholarship) [7822]
Kenneth D. and Katherine D. Davis Scholarships (Undergraduate/Scholarship) [7823]
Lawrence E. and Jean L. Davis Scholarships (Undergraduate/Scholarship) [7824]
Doddridge County Promise Scholarships (Undergraduate/Scholarship) [7825]
Deborah Gandee Dudding Memorial Scholarships (Undergraduate/Scholarship) [7826]
David Edward Farson Scholarships (Undergraduate/Scholarship) [7827]
Fostering Hope Scholarships Fund (Undergraduate/Scholarship) [7828]
William E. "Bill" Gallagher Scholarships (Undergraduate/Scholarship) [7829]
Laverne L. Gibson Memorial Scholarships (Undergraduate/Scholarship) [7830]
Shane Gilbert Memorial Scholarships (Undergraduate/Scholarship) [7831]
Russ Grant Memorial Scholarship for Tennis (Undergraduate/Scholarship) [7832]
Katherine M. Grosscup Scholarships (Undergraduate, Graduate/Scholarship) [4325]
Sara Gwisdalla Memorial Scholarships (Undergraduate/Scholarship) [7833]
Clayburn and Garnet R. Hanna Scholarships (Undergraduate/Scholarship) [7834]
H.G. Hardbarger Science and Mathematics Awards (Undergraduate/Award) [7835]
Harrisville Lions Club Scholarships (Undergraduate/Scholarship) [7836]

Harry Hartleben Scholarships (Undergraduate/Scholarship) [7837]
Gail L. Hartshorn Memorial Fund (Undergraduate/Scholarship) [7838]
Gregory Linn Haught Citizenship Awards (Undergraduate/Award, Scholarship) [7839]
Dorcas Edmonson Haught Scholarships (Undergraduate/Scholarship) [7840]
Ella Beren Hersch Scholarships (Undergraduate/Scholarship) [7841]
Holly Jackson-Wuller Memorial Scholarships (Undergraduate/Scholarship) [7842]
K.A.S.A Memorial Scholarships (Undergraduate/Scholarship) [7843]
Dr. Charles Kelly Memorial Scholarships (Undergraduate/Scholarship) [7844]
Judge Oliver Kessel Memorial Scholarships - Ripley Rotary (Undergraduate/Scholarship) [7845]
The Langfitt-Ambrose Trust Scholarship (Undergraduate/Scholarship) [7846]
Lighthouse International Scholarships - College-bound Awards (High School, Undergraduate/Scholarship) [6083]
Lighthouse International Scholarships - Graduate Awards (Graduate/Scholarship) [6084]
Lighthouse International Scholarships - Undergraduate Awards (Undergraduate/Scholarship) [6085]
Megan Nicole Longwell Scholarships (Undergraduate/Scholarship) [7847]
Bryce-Lietzke Martin Scholarships (Undergraduate/Scholarship) [7848]
Dudley Mullins/Cabot Corporation Scholarships (Undergraduate/Scholarship) [7849]
NASSLEO Scholarships - Region I (Undergraduate/Scholarship) [6782]
Pennsboro Alumni Scholarship Fund (Undergraduate/Scholarship) [7850]
Pepsi Wood County Technical/Caperton Center Scholarship Fund (Undergraduate/Scholarship) [7851]
William R. Pfalzgraf Scholarships (Undergraduate/Scholarship) [7852]
Herschel Pifer Memorial Scholarships (Undergraduate/Scholarship) [7853]
William Reaser Scholarships (Undergraduate/Scholarship) [7854]
James H. Roberts Athletic Scholarships (Undergraduate/Scholarship) [7855]
James Robinson Memorial Scholarship - Ripley Rotary (Undergraduate/Scholarship) [7857]
Carl Rose Memorial Scholarships (Undergraduate/Scholarship) [7858]
S. Byrl Ross Memorial Scholarship Fund (Undergraduate/Scholarship) [7859]
The Viking Voices - Mike Ruben Honorarium and John Rice Memorial Scholarship (Undergraduate/Scholarship) [7860]
St. Joseph's Hospital School of Nursing Alumnae Scholarship (Undergraduate/Scholarship) [7861]
Everett Oscar Shimp Memorial Scholarships (Undergraduate/Scholarship) [7862]
Pat Shimp Memorial Scholarships (Undergraduate/Scholarship) [7863]
Bill Six Memorial Scholarship Fund (Undergraduate/Scholarship) [7865]
Mary K. Smith Rector Scholarships (Undergraduate/Scholarship) [7866]
Zachary Taylor Stevens Memorial Scholarships (Undergraduate/Scholarship) [1759]
Charles H. Stone Scholarships (Undergraduate/Scholarship) [2081]
C.R. Thomas Scholarships (Undergraduate/Scholarship) [7867]
Charles A. Townsend Scholarships (Undergraduate/Scholarship) [7868]
Gary Wagner, K3OMI Scholarships (Undergraduate/Scholarship) [1762]
Wayne-Meador-Elliott Scholarships (Undergraduate/Scholarship) [7869]
West Virginia Nurses Association District No. 3 Scholarships (Undergraduate/Scholarship) [7870]
West Virginia PTA Scholarships (Undergraduate/Scholarship) [10525]
Whitaker-Minard Memorial Scholarships (Undergraduate/Scholarship) [7871]
The L. Phil and Alice J. Wicker Scholarship (Undergraduate/Scholarship) [1763]
S. William and Martha R. Goff Educational Scholarships (Undergraduate/Scholarship) [7872]
Glenn Wilson Broadcast Journalism Scholarships (Undergraduate/Scholarship) [7873]

Wisconsin

MAC Louisa Bowen Memorial Scholarships for Graduate Students in Archival Administration (Graduate/Scholarship) [6515]
Walter and Louise Buell Graduate Scholarships (Graduate/Scholarship) [4142]
Calvin Alumni Association-Southeastern Wisconsin Scholarships (Undergraduate/Scholarship) [2501]
Chicago FM Club Scholarships (Undergraduate/Scholarship) [1733]
Jason Dahnert Memorial Scholarships (Undergraduate/Scholarship) [4143]
Jerome Hake Engineering Scholarships (Undergraduate/Scholarship) [4144]
Gene Halker Memorial Scholarships (Graduate, Undergraduate/Scholarship) [4145]
Eileen Harrison Education Scholarships (Graduate, Undergraduate/Scholarship) [4146]
Kemper K. Knapp Scholarships (Undergraduate/Scholarship) [10320]
Robert C. and Judith L. Knapp Scholarships (Graduate, Undergraduate/Scholarship) [4147]
Jane Shaw Knox Graduate Scholarships (Graduate/Scholarship) [4148]
George Koeppel Scholarships/All School (Undergraduate/Scholarship) [10321]
Herb Kohl Educational Foundation Teacher Fellowships (Professional development/Fellowship) [5859]
E.H. Marth Food and Environmental Scholarships (Undergraduate/Scholarship) [10615]
Menominee Tribal Scholarships (Undergraduate, Graduate/Scholarship) [6418]
Edmond A. Metzger Scholarships (Undergraduate/Scholarship) [1747]
Minority Teacher Loans (Undergraduate, Graduate/Loan) [9554]
John P. and Tashia F. Morgridge Scholarships (Undergraduate/Scholarship) [10324]
NCSEA Judge Ross Leadership Scholarships (Professional development/Scholarship) [6858]
Nursing Student Loans (Graduate/Loan) [9555]
Pi Lambda Theta Scholarships (Undergraduate/Scholarship) [10325]
Ralph and Clara Rutledge Memorial Scholarships (Graduate/Scholarship) [4149]
Six Meter Club of Chicago Scholarships (Undergraduate/Scholarship) [1758]
Upper Midwest Human Rights Fellowship Program (Graduate/Scholarship, Fellowship) [4996]
Chapter 4 - Lawrence A. Wacker Memorial Scholarships (Undergraduate/Scholarship) [9198]
WHIMA Established Professional Scholarship (Graduate/Scholarship) [10623]
WIEA Scholarships (Doctorate, Graduate, Undergraduate/Scholarship) [10625]
Wisconsin Broadcasters Association Foundation Student Scholarships (Undergraduate/Scholarship) [10621]

Wyoming

Horatio Alger Wyoming Scholarships (Undergraduate/Scholarship) [4956]
Iris Scholarship (Undergraduate/Scholarship) [5737]
Marie Mathew Rask-Gamma Omicron Educational Endowment (Undergraduate/Scholarship) [5758]
Region II Scholarships (Graduate, Undergraduate/Scholarship) [1428]
Rocky Mountain Coal Mining Institute Engineering/Geology Scholarships (Undergraduate/Scholarship) [8632]
Rocky Mountain Coal Mining Institute Technical Scholarships (Undergraduate/Scholarship) [8633]

CANADA

AABP Amstutz Scholarships (Undergraduate/Scholarship) [466]
AACE International Competitive Scholarships (Undergraduate/Scholarship) [14]
AAN Medical Student Summer Research Scholarships (Graduate/Scholarship) [412]
AANS Medical Student Summer Research Fellowships (MSSRF) (Undergraduate/Fellowship) [542]
AAPM Summer Undergraduate Fellowships (Undergraduate/Fellowship) [559]
AASLD Autoimmune Liver Diseases Pilot Research Awards (Graduate, Doctorate, Postdoctorate, Professional development/Award, Grant) [582]
AASLD Clinical and Translational Research Awards (Professional development/Grant) [584]
The AASSC Gurli Aagaard Woods Undergraduate Publication Awards (Undergraduate/Award) [1825]
The AASSC Marna Feldt Graduate Publication Awards (Graduate/Award) [1826]
AASSC Norwegian Travel Grants (Professional development/Grant) [1827]
AATS Resident Critical Care Scholarships (Professional development/Scholarship) [596]
Dr. Anderson Abbott Awards (Undergraduate/Scholarship) [10278]
Aboriginal Canadians Scholarship (Undergraduate/Scholarship) [7204]
ACI-NA Scholarships (Graduate, Undergraduate/Scholarship) [180]
Jack Ackroyd Scholarships (Other/Scholarship) [1878]
Acoustical Society of America Minority Fellowships (Graduate/Fellowship) [52]
ADAC Foundation Scholarships (Undergraduate/Scholarship) [1767]
AEF Educational Scholarship (Undergraduate/Scholarship) [234]
Affiliated Distributors Electrical Industry Scholarship Awards (Undergraduate/Scholarship) [3822]
AFT-Oregon Union Plus Credit Card Scholarship (Undergraduate/Scholarship) [792]
AGE-WELL Graduate Student and Postdoctoral Awards in Technology and Aging (Master's, Doctorate, Postdoctorate/Award) [111]
AHNS Pilot Research Grants (Other/Grant) [846]
AIHS Graduate Studentships (Master's, Doctorate, Professional development/Fellowship) [251]
AIHS Media Fellowships - CBC Radio (Undergraduate, Graduate/Fellowship) [252]
AIHS Postgraduate Fellowships (Postgraduate, Advanced Professional/Fellowship) [253]
Alberta Association of Gerontology Student Awards - Edmonton Chapter (Graduate, Undergraduate/Award) [226]
Alberta Association of Gerontology Student Awards (Graduate/Award) [225]
Alberta Award for the Study of Canadian Human Rights and Multiculturalism (Doctorate, Graduate/Award) [261]
Alberta Child Care Association Professional Development Grants (Professional development/Grant) [232]
Alberta Innovates - Technology Futures Graduate Student Scholarships in ICT (Doctorate, Graduate, Master's/Scholarship) [257]
Alberta Innovates - Technology Futures Graduate Student Scholarships in Nanotechnology (Doctorate, Graduate/Scholarship) [258]
Alberta Innovates - Technology Futures Graduate Student Scholarships in Omics (Doctorate, Graduate/Scholarship) [259]
Alberta Teachers Association Doctoral Fellowships in Education (Doctorate/Fellowship) [294]
Alberta Teachers Association Educational Research Award (Other/Scholarship) [295]
Dulemba Aleksander and Stefania Scholarship (Undergraduate/Scholarship) [8571]
Alexander Graham Bell Canada Graduate Scholarship Program (Doctorate, Master's/Scholarship) [3401]
Hon. Lincoln Alexander Scholarships (Undergraduate, Graduate/Scholarship) [2277]
Stephanie Ali Memorial Scholarships (Undergraduate/Scholarship) [10279]
ALIS Graduate Student Scholarships (Graduate/Scholarship) [264]
ALIS International Education Awards - Ukraine (Un-

CANADA

dergraduate/Scholarship) [265]
Lorraine Allison Scholarship (Graduate/Scholarship) [1616]
Marjorie Almstrom Scholarships (Undergraduate, Master's/Scholarship) [10774]
ALS Canada Bridge Grants (Professional development/Grant) [365]
ALS Canada Doctoral Research Awards (Doctorate, Professional development/Fellowship) [366]
ALS Canada and Tim E. Noel Postdoctoral Fellowships (Postdoctorate, Professional development/Fellowship) [367]
Jaedyn Amann Memorial Scholarships (Undergraduate, Master's/Scholarship) [10775]
America Express Travel Scholarships (Undergraduate/Scholarship) [1436]
American Association for Cancer Research Minority Scholar Awards (Graduate/Award) [472]
American Judges Association Law Student Essay Competition (Undergraduate/Prize) [952]
Bernard Amtmann Fellowships (Postgraduate, Other/Fellowship) [2258]
Dr. Andy Anderson Young Professional Awards (Professional development/Award) [8117]
Annette Urso Rickel Foundation Dissertation Award for Public Policy (Graduate/Scholarship) [1137]
Annual Research Doctoral and Postgraduate Fellowship Grant Program (Doctorate, Postdoctorate, Postgraduate, Advanced Professional/Fellowship, Grant) [2586]
ANS Research Grants (Professional development/Grant) [1030]
ANSER Graduate Student Awards for Research on Nonprofits and the Social Economy (Graduate/Award) [2030]
APALA Scholarship Award (Doctorate, Master's/Scholarship) [1788]
Aplastic Anemia and Myelodysplasia Association of Canada Scholarships (Graduate/Scholarship) [2694]
Applied Hospitality Degree Scholarships (Undergraduate/Scholarship) [2657]
Architects Association of PEI Scholarships (Undergraduate/Scholarship) [3309]
Arctic Physical Therapy Scholarship (Undergraduate/Scholarship) [1619]
ARIT Fellowships in the Humanities and Social Sciences in Turkey (Postdoctorate, Graduate/Fellowship) [1201]
Robin P. Armstrong Memorial Prize for Excellence in Native Studies Awards (Graduate/Award) [1880]
Robert Armstrong Memorial Scholarships (Undergraduate, Graduate/Scholarship) [10776]
ASA Graduate Scholarships (Graduate/Scholarship) [1243]
ASAC-CJAS PhD Research Grant Awards (Doctorate/Grant) [73]
Asia Pacific Foundation of Canada Junior Research Fellowships (Undergraduate, Master's/Fellowship) [4113]
Asia Pacific Foundation of Canada Media Fellowships (Professional development/Fellowship) [4114]
Asia Pacific Foundation of Canada Post-Graduate Research Fellowships (Master's, Doctorate/Fellowship) [4115]
Association of Desk and Derrick Clubs Education Trust Scholarships (Undergraduate/Scholarship) [1931]
ASTA Alaska Airlines Scholarships (Undergraduate/Scholarship) [1437]
ASTA Holland America Line Graduate Research Scholarships (Graduate/Scholarship) [1438]
ASTA Rigby, Healy, Simmons Scholarships (Graduate/Scholarship) [1439]
AstraZeneca Scholarships (Doctorate/Scholarship) [2695]
Martha and Robert Atherton Ministerial Scholarships (Master's/Scholarship) [9831]
Atkinson Fellowships in Public Policy (Professional development/Fellowship) [2111]
Atlantic Provinces Library Association Memorial Awards (Undergraduate/Scholarship) [2117]
Atlantic Salmon Federation Olin Fellowships (Graduate/Fellowship) [2120]
Auto Body Technician Certificate Scholarships (Un-

dergraduate/Scholarship) [8765]
Avis Budget Group Scholarships (Graduate/Scholarship) [1440]
Awards for Judaic Studies and/or Studies in Israel (Undergraduate, Postgraduate/Scholarship) [5591]
Azrieli Neurodevelopmental Research Program (Advanced Professional/Grant) [2350]
Airgas - Jerry Baker Scholarships (Undergraduate/Scholarship) [1509]
Victoria Baldwin Memorial Scholarships (Undergraduate, Master's/Award) [10777]
Lynn Ann Baldwin Scholarships (Graduate/Scholarship) [1888]
Ball Horticultural Company Scholarships (Undergraduate/Scholarship) [798]
Ballantyne Resident Research Grants (Other/Grant) [847]
Bank of Canada Fellowship Award (Doctorate, Other/Fellowship, Grant) [2187]
Bank of Canada Governor's Awards (Doctorate, Other/Award, Grant) [2188]
Banting Postdoctoral Fellowships (Postdoctorate/Fellowship) [3402]
Helen Bassett Commemorative Student Award (Undergraduate, Graduate/Scholarship) [7221]
Baxter Corporation Canadian Research Awards in Anesthesia (Other/Award, Monetary) [2538]
BCPF Bursaries (Undergraduate/Scholarship) [9476]
BCSF Scholarships (Undergraduate/Scholarship) [2294]
Suzanne Beauregard Scholarships (Undergraduate/Scholarship) [4476]
Beaverbrook Media at McGill Student Paper Prize (Graduate/Prize) [2615]
Ed Becker Conference Travel Awards (Undergraduate, Graduate/Award) [3886]
Ann C. Beckingham Scholarships (Graduate, Other/Scholarship) [2645]
Dr. Ann C. Beckingham Scholarships (Doctorate/Scholarship) [2696]
Jenny Panitch Beckow Memorial Scholarships Israel (Graduate/Scholarship) [5570]
Harvey Bell Memorial Prize (Graduate/Award) [10271]
Beverlee Bell Scholarships in Human Rights and Democracy (Graduate/Scholarship) [3655]
A.G. Bell School Age Financial Aid Program (Undergraduate/Scholarship) [315]
Max Bell Senior Fellow Grants (Advanced Professional/Grant) [2219]
Viscount Bennett Fellowships (Graduate/Fellowship) [2581]
The Bentley Cropping Systems Fellowship (Graduate/Fellowship) [2886]
Henry Besner Memorial Scholarships (Undergraduate, Master's/Scholarship) [10778]
Harold Bettinger Scholarships (Undergraduate, Graduate/Scholarship) [800]
Leonard Bettinger Vocational Scholarships (Undergraduate, Vocational/Occupational/Scholarship) [801]
Dr. Noorali and Sabiya Bharwani Endowment (Undergraduate/Scholarship) [2253]
Hussein Jina Bharwani Memorial Endowment (Undergraduate/Scholarship) [2254]
BHCRI Bridge Funds (Advanced Professional, Professional development/Grant) [5012]
BHCRI Cancer Research Training Program Awards (Graduate, Postdoctorate, Advanced Professional, Professional development/Grant) [5013]
BHCRI Matching Funds (Advanced Professional, Professional development/Grant) [5014]
BHCRI Miscellaneous Funds (Advanced Professional, Professional development/Grant) [5015]
BHCRI Seed Funds (Advanced Professional, Professional development/Grant) [5016]
BHCRI Studentship Awards (Undergraduate, Graduate, Advanced Professional/Grant) [5017]
Biological Survey of Canada Scholarships (Postgraduate/Scholarship) [3887]
Lucie and Thornton Blackburn Scholarships (Graduate, Juris Doctorate/Scholarship) [2544]
Alex Blaski Memorial Scholarships (Undergraduate/Scholarship) [8572]

M. Hildred Blewett Fellowships (Postdoctorate/Fellowship) [1088]
Lawrence Bloomberg Entrance Awards (Postgraduate/Award) [10741]
BMO Capital Markets Lime Connect Equity through Education Scholarships (Undergraduate, Graduate/Scholarship) [6087]
BMO Financial Group Lime Connect Canada Scholarship Program for Students with Disabilities (Undergraduate, Graduate/Scholarship) [6088]
Edith and Arnold N. Bodtker Grants (Undergraduate, Graduate/Grant, Internship) [3522]
Yvonne L. Bombardier Visual Arts Scholarships (Master's, Doctorate/Scholarship) [1665]
Steve Bonk Scholarships (Postgraduate/Scholarship) [2766]
Lorne and Ruby Bonnell Scholarships (Undergraduate/Scholarship) [3311]
John H. Borden Scholarships (Postgraduate/Scholarship) [3888]
Maria and Czeslaw Borek Scholarships (Undergraduate/Scholarship) [8573]
Bound to Stay Bound Books Scholarships (Graduate/Scholarship) [2017]
Jim Bourque Scholarship (Undergraduate/Scholarship) [1617]
Herbie Bouwman Memorial Scholarships (Undergraduate, Master's/Scholarship) [10779]
CAG Margery Boyce Bursary Awards (Undergraduate/Award, Scholarship) [2553]
Eugene Boyko Memorial Scholarships (Undergraduate/Scholarship) [228]
Geoffrey Bradshaw Memorial Scholarships (Graduate/Scholarship) [10780]
Brain Canada-ALS Canada Career Transition Awards (Postdoctorate, Advanced Professional, Professional development/Grant) [2351]
Brain Canada-ALS Canada Discovery Grants (Advanced Professional, Professional development/Grant) [2352]
Brain Canada-ALS Canada Hudson Translational Team Grants (Advanced Professional, Professional development/Grant) [2353]
Brain Canada/CQDM "Focus on Brain" Partnership Program (Advanced Professional/Grant) [2354]
Brain Canada/NeuroDevNet Developmental Neurosciences Research Training Awards (Postdoctorate, Advanced Professional, Professional development/Grant) [2355]
Brain Canada/RBC Research Partnership in Mental Health Services for Children and Youth Funds (Advanced Professional/Grant) [2356]
James Bridenbaugh Memorial Scholarships (Undergraduate/Scholarship) [802]
Margaret Brine Graduate Scholarships (Graduate/Scholarship) [2634]
Louis J. Brody Q.C. Entrance Scholarships (Graduate/Scholarship) [10742]
Norm Bromberger Research Bursaries (Undergraduate, Graduate/Scholarship) [3469]
Peter F. Bronfman Entrance Awards (Postgraduate/Award) [10743]
Peter F. Bronfman Scholarships of Merit (Postgraduate/Scholarship) [10744]
Brooks Scholarships (Graduate/Scholarship) [3894]
CFSA Randal Brown & Associates Awards (Undergraduate/Award) [1911]
Brown Dental Scholarships (Undergraduate/Scholarship) [5521]
Olympia Brown and Max Kapp Awards (Master's/Scholarship) [9832]
Robert K. Brown Scholarships (Undergraduate, Master's/Scholarship) [2278]
Pamfil and Maria Bujea Family Orthodox Christian Seminarian Scholarships (Undergraduate/Scholarship) [1225]
Burger King Scholars Program (Undergraduate/Scholarship) [2411]
Burndy Canada Inc. Academic Achievement Awards (Undergraduate/Scholarship) [3823]
Business, Education and Technology Scholarships (Graduate, Undergraduate/Scholarship) [334]
Leon C. Bynoe Memorial Scholarships (Undergraduate/Scholarship) [10280]
CADE Bursary (Undergraduate/Scholarship) [2550]

CADE Scholarships (Undergraduate/Scholarship) [2551]
CAG Health and Health Care Study Group Awards (Graduate/Award) [1881]
CAHR Master's Level Scholarships (Master's/Scholarship) [2557]
CALL/ACBD Education Reserve Fund Grants (Professional development/Grant) [2561]
CALL/ACBD Research Grants (Graduate/Grant) [2562]
Cameco Corporation Scholarships in the Geological Sciences - Continuing Students (Undergraduate/Scholarship) [2524]
Cameco Corporation Scholarships in the Geological Sciences - Entering Students (Undergraduate/Scholarship) [2525]
Dalton Camp Awards (Undergraduate/Award, Monetary) [4305]
Canadian Anesthesiologists' Society Research Awards (Other/Award) [2539]
Canadian Association of Cardiac Rehabilitation Graduate Scholarship Awards (Graduate/Scholarship) [2548]
Canadian Association of Geographers Historical Geography Study Group Awards (Master's, Graduate, Undergraduate/Award) [1882]
Canadian Association of Law Teachers Award for Academic Excellence (Other/Award) [2566]
Canadian Association for the Practical Study of Law in Education Fellowships (Graduate/Fellowship) [2573]
Canadian Association for Studies in Co-operation Scholarships Lemaire Co-operative Studies Awards (CASC) (Graduate, Undergraduate/Scholarship) [2611]
Canadian Blood Services Graduate Fellowship (Graduate/Fellowship) [2583]
Canadian Blood Services Postdoctoral Fellowship (Postdoctorate/Fellowship) [2584]
Canadian Cancer Society Travel Awards (Doctorate, Master's, Postdoctorate/Award) [2605]
Canadian Council of Technicians and Technologists Scholarships for Technology Students (Undergraduate/Scholarship) [3392]
The Canadian Derivatives Exchange Scholars Program (Graduate, Postgraduate/Scholarship) [2345]
Canadian Energy Law Foundation Graduate Scholarships in Law (Advanced Professional/Scholarship) [2620]
Canadian Evaluation Society Educational Fund Scholarships (Graduate/Scholarship) [4125]
Canadian Federation of Independent Grocers National Scholarships (Undergraduate/Scholarship) [4003]
Canadian Federation of University Women Etobicoke Bursary (Undergraduate/Scholarship) [10281]
Canadian Hard of Hearing Association Scholarship Programs (Undergraduate/Scholarship) [2651]
Canadian Home Economics Association Fellowships (Master's, Doctorate/Fellowship) [2629]
Canadian Hospitality Foundation College Entrance Scholarships (Undergraduate/Scholarship) [2658]
Canadian Hospitality Foundation University Entrance Scholarships (Undergraduate/Scholarship) [2659]
Canadian Hydrographic Association Student Awards (Undergraduate/Award, Monetary, Medal) [2662]
Canadian Identification Society Essay/Scholarship Awards (Advanced Professional, Professional development/Prize) [2664]
Canadian Institute for Advanced Legal Studies French Language Scholarships (Graduate, Advanced Professional/Scholarship) [5149]
Canadian Iranian Foundation Scholarships (Undergraduate/Scholarship) [2677]
Canadian IT Law Association Student Writing Contest (Undergraduate/Prize) [2020]
Canadian Japanese-Mennonite Scholarships (Graduate/Scholarship) [6416]
Canadian Nurses Foundation Northern Award (Undergraduate/Scholarship) [2697]
Canadian Nurses Foundation Scholarships (Undergraduate, Master's, Doctorate/Scholarship) [2698]
Canadian Occupational Therapy Foundation Graduate Scholarships (Doctorate, Master's/Scholarship) [2717]
Canadian Occupational Therapy Foundation Invacare Master's Scholarships (Master's/Scholarship) [2718]
Canadian Pain Society Post-Doctoral Fellowship Awards (Postdoctorate/Fellowship) [2724]
Canadian Parking Association Scholarships (Undergraduate/Scholarship) [1921]
Canadian Picture Pioneers Scholarships (Undergraduate/Scholarship) [2734]
Canadian Polar Commission Scholarships (Doctorate, Graduate/Scholarship) [1933]
Canadian Poultry Research Council Postgraduate Scholarships (Postgraduate/Scholarship) [2736]
Canadian Sanitation Supply Association Scholarships (Undergraduate/Scholarship) [2738]
Canadian Seniors' Golf Association Scholarships (Undergraduate/Scholarship) [4477]
Canadian Society for the Study of Education Mentorship Awards (Other/Award) [9067]
Canadian Society for the Study of Education New Scholar Fellowships (CSSE) (Professional development/Fellowship) [9068]
Canadian Studies Postdoctoral Fellowships (Postdoctorate/Fellowship) [3398]
Canadian Technical Asphalt Association Scholarships (Undergraduate/Scholarship) [2762]
Canadian Water Resources Association Scholarships (Undergraduate/Scholarship) [1905]
CAPE Scholarships (Undergraduate, Postdoctorate/Scholarship) [2768]
Cardiac Health Foundation of Canada Scholarships (Graduate/Scholarship) [2790]
Thelma Cardwell Scholarships (Graduate/Scholarship) [2719]
Career Awards for Medical Scientists (CAMS) (Postdoctorate, Advanced Professional, Professional development/Grant) [2414]
Career Awards at the Scientific Interface (CASI) (Doctorate, Postdoctorate, Advanced Professional, Professional development/Grant) [2416]
Career Development Scholarships (Postdoctorate, Postgraduate/Scholarship) [4129]
John Carew Memorial Scholarships (Graduate/Scholarship) [803]
Herb Carnegie Scholarships (Undergraduate/Scholarship) [2279]
CARO-ELEKTA Research Fellowship Program (Professional development/Fellowship) [1900]
Orin Carver Scholarships (Undergraduate/Scholarship) [3312]
CAS/GE Healthcare Canada Inc. Research Awards (Other/Award) [2540]
CAS Trust Scholarship (Undergraduate/Scholarship) [2809]
CAS/Vitaid-LMA Residents' Research Grant Competition (Other/Award) [2541]
Fraser Milner Casgrain LLP Scholarships (Graduate, Juris Doctorate/Scholarship) [2280]
Fraser Milner Casgrain Scholarships (Other/Scholarship) [2182]
Catzman Awards for Professionalism and Civility (Advanced Professional, Professional development/Award) [80]
CBCF - Ontario Nurse and Allied Health Professional Fellowships (Advanced Professional, Professional development/Fellowship) [2592]
CBCF - Ontario Physician Fellowships (Doctorate, Professional development/Fellowship) [2593]
CBCF - Ontario Research Fellowships (Doctorate, Postdoctorate, Professional development/Fellowship) [2594]
CBCF - Ontario Research Project Grants (Advanced Professional, Professional development/Grant) [2595]
CC Times Scholarships (Undergraduate/Scholarship) [2921]
CCFF Clinical Fellowships (Doctorate, Graduate/Fellowship) [4013]
CCFF Fellowships (Doctorate, Graduate/Fellowship) [4014]
CCFF (Doctorate, Graduate/Fellowship) [4015]
CCLA Summer Legal Internships (Graduate/Internship) [1892]
CEMF Undergraduate Engineering Scholarships (Undergraduate/Scholarship) [2622]
CFN Interdisciplinary Fellowships Program (Graduate, Postdoctorate, Advanced Professional/Fellowship) [2638]
CFSA Aon Fire Protection Engineering Award (Undergraduate/Scholarship) [1912]
CFSA City of Markham, Buildings Standards Department Award (Undergraduate/Scholarship) [1913]
CFSA Fire Safety Awards (Postgraduate/Award, Monetary) [1914]
CFSA Leber Rubes Inc. Awards (Postgraduate/Award, Monetary) [1915]
CFSA LRI Engineering Award (Undergraduate/Scholarship) [1916]
CFSA Nadine International Inc. Awards (Undergraduate/Award) [1917]
CFSA Siemens Canada Award (Undergraduate/Scholarship) [1918]
CFSA Underwriters' Laboratories of Canada Awards (Undergraduate/Award) [1919]
CGNA Memorial Scholarship (Graduate, Other/Scholarship) [2646]
CGPF Endowments Conference Scholarships (Undergraduate/Scholarship) [2648]
Mary Anne Chambers Scholarships (Undergraduate/Scholarship) [5522]
Chapter 6 Fairfield County Scholarships (Undergraduate/Scholarship) [9177]
Chechahko Consumers Co-Op Ltd. Scholarships (Undergraduate, Master's/Scholarship) [10782]
Bernard Chernos Essay Competition (Undergraduate/Prize) [1893]
Shirley Cheshire Memorial Scholarship Awards (Undergraduate/Scholarship) [6853]
Chevalier Award Scholarship (Undergraduate/Scholarship) [2618]
Childhood Cancer Survivor Scholarships (Undergraduate/Scholarship) [2903]
Chinese Professionals Association of Canada BMO Diversity Scholarships (Undergraduate/Scholarship) [2922]
Chinese Professionals Association of Canada Education Foundation Awards (High School/Award) [2923]
Chinese Professionals Association of Canada Journalism Scholarships (Undergraduate/Scholarship) [2924]
Chinese Professionals Association of Canada Professional Achievement Awards (Other/Award) [2925]
CHS - Bursary Program Scholarships (Undergraduate/Scholarship) [2653]
CHS - Mature Student Bursary Program Scholarships (Undergraduate/Scholarship) [2654]
CHS Scholarships (Undergraduate/Scholarship) [2655]
CIBC Scholarships (Undergraduate, Graduate/Scholarship) [2281]
CIFAR Global Scholars Program (Advanced Professional, Professional development/Scholarship) [2670]
CIHR Health Law, Ethics and Policy Fellowships (Graduate/Fellowship) [2942]
CIP Fellow's Travel Scholarships (Undergraduate/Scholarship) [2672]
CISDL Global Research Fellowship - Associate Fellows (Graduate/Fellowship) [2880]
CISDL Global Research Fellowship - Legal Research Fellows (Graduate/Fellowship) [2881]
CISDL Global Research Fellowships - Senior Research Fellows (Other/Fellowship) [2882]
City of Toronto Graduate Scholarships for Women in Mathematics (Master's, Doctorate/Scholarship) [10282]
City of Toronto Queen Elizabeth II Sesquicentennial Scholarships in Community Health Nursing for Graduates (Graduate/Scholarship) [10283]
City of Toronto Queen Elizabeth II Sesquicentennial Scholarships in Community Health Nursing for Undergraduates (Undergraduate/Scholarship) [10284]
City of Toronto Scholarships for Aboriginal Students (Graduate, Undergraduate/Scholarship) [10285]
City of Toronto Women's Studies Scholarships

(Graduate, Undergraduate/Scholarship) [10286]
CJF Canadian Journalism Fellowships *(Graduate, Other, Undergraduate/Fellowship)* [4117]
CLA/ACB Dafoe Scholarships *(Graduate/Scholarship)* [2679]
CLA-ACE Internship Program *(Graduate, Juris Doctorate/Internship)* [6013]
Greg Clerk Awards *(Advanced Professional, Professional development/Award)* [4118]
David H. Clift Scholarships *(Graduate/Scholarship)* [961]
CMOS-SCMO President's Prize *(Professional development/Prize)* [2682]
CN Scholarships for Women *(Undergraduate/Scholarship)* [2692]
CNIB Master's Scholarships *(Master's/Scholarship)* [2688]
CNST Scholarships *(Doctorate, Graduate/Scholarship)* [1934]
Marshall A. Cohen Entrance Awards *(Postgraduate/Award)* [10745]
Anna C. and Oliver C. Colburn Fellowships *(Doctorate/Fellowship)* [1606]
Desmond Conacher Scholarships *(Graduate/Scholarship)* [9071]
Connor/Spafford Scholarships *(Undergraduate/Scholarship)* [4478]
Convectair Sustainable Development Scholarship Awards *(Undergraduate/Scholarship)* [3824]
Roy Cooper Memorial Scholarships *(Undergraduate/Scholarship)* [5998]
COPA Scholarship Fund *(Undergraduate/Scholarship)* [2722]
Helen & Orval Couch Memorial Scholarships *(Undergraduate, Master's/Scholarship)* [10783]
Steve Cowan Memorial Scholarships *(Undergraduate/Scholarship)* [3471]
Gertrude M. Cox Scholarships *(Graduate, Master's, Doctorate/Scholarship)* [1465]
CPS Clinical Pain Management Fellowship Awards *(Postgraduate/Fellowship)* [2725]
CPS Excellence in Interprofessional Pain Education Awards *(Other/Award)* [2726]
CPS Interprofessional Nursing Project Awards *(Other/Award)* [2727]
CPS Knowledge Translation Research Awards *(Other/Grant)* [2728]
CPS Nursing Excellence in Pain Management Awards *(Other/Award)* [2729]
CPS Nursing Research and Education Awards *(Other/Grant)* [2730]
CPS Outstanding Pain Mentorship Awards *(Other/Award)* [2731]
CPS Trainee Research Awards *(Doctorate/Grant, Award)* [2732]
CRM-ISM Postdoctoral Fellowships *(Postdoctorate/Fellowship)* [9993]
Crohn's and Colitis Canada Grants in Aid of Research *(Advanced Professional, Professional development/Grant)* [3473]
Crohn's and Colitis Canada Innovations in IBD Research Grants *(Advanced Professional, Professional development/Grant)* [3474]
CSBS Student Prize Competition *(Graduate/Prize)* [2744]
CSCI Distinguished Scientist Lectures and Awards *(Advanced Professional/Award)* [9073]
CSEG Scholarship Trust Fund *(Graduate, Undergraduate/Scholarship)* [2748]
CSLA Leaders of Distinction Award *(Professional development/Recognition)* [2759]
CSLA Leadership Scholarships *(Undergraduate/Scholarship)* [2760]
CSMLS Student Scholarship Awards *(Postgraduate/Scholarship)* [2750]
CSOHNS Fellowships *(Graduate/Fellowship)* [2752]
CSSE ARTS Graduate Research Awards *(Graduate/Award)* [9069]
CSSHE Masters Thesis/Project Awards *(Master's/Award)* [2756]
CSSHE Research Awards *(Professional development/Award)* [2757]
CTRF Scholarships for Graduate Study in Transportation *(Graduate/Scholarship)* [2764]
Culinary (1-Year Program) Scholarships *(Undergraduate/Scholarship)* [2660]

DAAD Learn German in Germany Grants *(Doctorate/Grant)* [3603]
DAAD Study Scholarship Awards *(Graduate/Scholarship)* [3604]
DAAD Undergraduate Scholarship Program *(Undergraduate/Scholarship)* [3605]
Roger Daley Postdoctoral Publication Awards *(Postdoctorate/Monetary)* [2683]
D&R Sobey Scholarships *(Undergraduate/Scholarship)* [9047]
Mark & Dorothy Danzker Scholarships *(Postgraduate/Scholarship)* [5592]
Amy and Tim Dauphinee Scholarships *(Graduate/Scholarship)* [2575]
Canadian Association for Studies in Co-operation Scholarships - Amy and Tim Dauphinee Scholarships (CASC) *(Graduate/Scholarship)* [2612]
Jim Davie Memorial Scholarships *(Undergraduate, Master's/Scholarship)* [10784]
Laurence Decore Awards for Student Leadership *(Undergraduate/Scholarship)* [271]
Earl Dedman Memorial Scholarships *(Undergraduate/Scholarship)* [804]
Delta Faucet Scholarships *(Undergraduate/Scholarship)* [8160]
Albert W. Dent Graduate Student Scholarships *(Undergraduate/Scholarship)* [687]
Helen L. Dewar Scholarships *(Undergraduate/Scholarship)* [9729]
Diabetes Hope Foundation Scholarships *(Undergraduate/Scholarship)* [3614]
Dr. Allan A. Dixon Memorial Scholarships *(Postgraduate/Scholarship)* [2742]
William Donald Dixon Research Grants *(Graduate, Undergraduate, Advanced Professional/Grant)* [2665]
Julian Dobranowski Memorial Scholarships *(Undergraduate/Scholarship)* [8574]
Dr. Biljan Memorial Awards *(Advanced Professional/Award, Grant)* [2636]
Dominio of Canada Insurance Scholarships *(Graduate/Scholarship)* [8128]
Lloyd M. Dosdall Memorial Scholarships *(Postgraduate/Scholarship)* [3889]
Douglas-Coldwell Foundation Scholarships in Social Affairs *(Graduate/Scholarship)* [3656]
Tommy Douglas Memorial Scholarship *(Undergraduate/Scholarship)* [7205]
DSA Dante Prizes *(Undergraduate/Prize, Monetary)* [3524]
Lise M. Duchesneau Scholarship *(Undergraduate/Scholarship)* [1895]
Dr. Allan Duncan Memorial Scholarships *(Undergraduate, Master's/Scholarship)* [10785]
Bob Dyer/OEL Apprenticeship Scholarships *(Undergraduate/Scholarship)* [3825]
Joshua Dyke Family Scholarships *(Undergraduate/Scholarship)* [9730]
e8 Sustainable Energy Development Post-Doctoral Scholarship Programme (ESED) *(Postdoctorate/Scholarship)* [4460]
Eaton Awards of Academic Achievement *(Undergraduate/Scholarship)* [3826]
David Eaton Scholarships *(Master's/Scholarship)* [9835]
École Polytechnique Commemorative Awards *(Master's, Doctorate, Graduate/Award, Fellowship)* [2630]
EDC International Business Scholarships *(Undergraduate/Scholarship)* [2603]
The Edit My Paper Proofreading Scholarships *(Undergraduate/Scholarship)* [3785]
Edmonton Epilepsy Continuing Education Scholarships *(Undergraduate/Scholarship)* [3792]
EFC Atlantic Region Scholarships *(Undergraduate/Scholarship)* [3827]
EFC University and College Scholarships *(Undergraduate/Scholarship)* [3828]
Eli Lilly Graduate Scholarship *(Graduate, Postgraduate/Scholarship)* [1886]
Clay Elliott Scholarship Foundation Scholarships *(Undergraduate/Scholarship)* [3856]
endMS Doctoral Studentship Awards *(Doctorate/Internship)* [6614]
endMS Master's Studentship Awards *(Master's/Internship)* [6615]

endMS Postdoctoral Fellowships *(Postdoctorate/Fellowship)* [6616]
Entomological Society of Canada Postgraduate Awards *(Postgraduate/Award)* [3890]
Entomological Society of Saskatchewan Student Presentation Awards *(Undergraduate/Award)* [3895]
Entomological Society of Saskatchewan Travel Awards *(Professional development/Award)* [3896]
Extendicare Scholarships in Gerontology *(Master's/Scholarship)* [2699]
Faculty Research Visit Grants *(Doctorate/Grant, Award)* [3606]
Fahs-Beck Fund for Research and Experimentation - Doctoral Dissertation Grants *(Doctorate/Grant)* [7347]
Fahs-Beck Fund for Research and Experimentation - Postdoctoral Grants *(Postdoctorate/Grant)* [7348]
Fellowships in the PMAC-AGPC *(Professional development/Fellowship)* [8295]
FFB-C Postdoctoral Fellowships *(Postdoctorate/Fellowship)* [4262]
Fields Institute - Fields Research Immersion Fellowships *(Postdoctorate/Fellowship)* [4019]
Fieldwork Fellowships *(Undergraduate/Award, Fellowship)* [3927]
FINCAD Women in Finance Scholarships *(Graduate/Scholarship)* [4024]
Firefly Foundation/ASRP Spark Award *(Postdoctorate, Advanced Professional/Grant)* [371, 4032]
Martin Fischer Awards *(Undergraduate/Award)* [2649]
Flamenco Student Scholarships *(Undergraduate, Professional development/Scholarship)* [4070]
Follicular Lymphoma Research Grants *(Advanced Professional/Grant)* [6159]
Foresters Scholarships *(Undergraduate/Scholarship)* [5095]
Edward Foster Awards *(Advanced Professional/Award)* [2666]
Foundation for the Advancement of Aboriginal Youth Bursary Program *(Undergraduate/Scholarship)* [3389]
Foundation for the Advancement of Aboriginal Youth Scholarships *(Undergraduate/Scholarship)* [3390]
Terry Fox Memorial Scholarship *(Undergraduate/Scholarship)* [7206]
AIHS Cy Frank Fellowships: Impact Assessment *(Doctorate, Professional development/Fellowship)* [254]
Franklin Empire Scholarship Awards *(Undergraduate/Scholarship)* [3829]
Henry Friesen Awards and Lectures *(Doctorate/Award)* [9074]
FTE Doctoral Fellowships *(Doctorate, Graduate/Fellowship)* [4154]
FTE North American Doctoral Fellowships *(Doctorate, Graduate/Fellowship)* [4155]
Future Leader in Radiocommunications Scholarships *(Undergraduate/Scholarship)* [3394]
FXRFC Medical Research Postdoctoral Fellowships *(Postdoctorate/Fellowship)* [4287]
GAAC Project Grants *(Undergraduate, Professional development/Grant)* [4445]
Gabriel Dumont College Graduate Student Bursary *(Postgraduate, Master's, Doctorate/Scholarship)* [3742]
Franciszek Gadzala Memorial Scholarships *(Undergraduate/Scholarship)* [8575]
Harry Gairey Scholarships *(Undergraduate/Scholarship)* [2282]
GCABC Youth Scholarship Awards *(Undergraduate/Scholarship)* [4419]
G.E. Lighting Canada Community Leadership Awards *(Undergraduate/Award)* [3830]
Geological Society of America Graduate Student Research Grants *(Doctorate, Graduate/Grant)* [4364]
Gerrie Electric Memorial Scholarship Awards *(Undergraduate/Scholarship)* [3831]
GFOA Minorities in Government Finance Scholarship *(Graduate, Undergraduate/Scholarship)* [4502]
Keith Gilmore Foundation - Diploma Scholarships *(Other/Scholarship)* [4423]

Keith Gilmore Foundation - Postgraduate Scholarships *(Postgraduate/Scholarship)* [4424]
Keith Gilmore Foundation - Undergraduate Scholarships *(Undergraduate/Scholarship)* [4425]
Dr. Helen Preston Glass Fellowships *(Doctorate/Fellowship)* [2700]
Jane Glassco Northern Fellowships *(Professional development/Fellowship)* [4500]
Franciszek Glogowski Memorial Scholarships *(Undergraduate/Scholarship)* [8576]
Daniel B. Goldberg Scholarship *(Graduate/Scholarship)* [4503]
Goldia.com Jewelry Scholarships *(Undergraduate, Graduate/Scholarship)* [4474]
Charles D. Gonthier Research Fellowships *(Graduate, Advanced Professional/Fellowship)* [2668]
Baxter Corporation - Jean Goodwill Scholarships *(Graduate/Scholarship)* [24]
Google Lime Scholarships for Students with Disabilities *(Undergraduate, Graduate, Doctorate/Scholarship)* [6089]
Lucille May Gopie Scholarships *(Undergraduate, Graduate/Scholarship)* [2283]
Wilhelmina Gordon Foundation Scholarships *(Undergraduate/Scholarship)* [6854]
Carl W. Gottschalk Research Scholar Grants *(Professional development/Grant)* [1381]
Graduate Fellowship Program - Research Fellowships (GFP) *(Doctorate, Graduate/Fellowship)* [8833]
Graduate Research Awards for Disarmament, Arms Control and Non-Proliferation *(Master's, Doctorate/Award)* [8961]
Graduate Research-Travel Scholarships *(Graduate/Scholarship)* [3891]
Charles Hall Grandgent Awards *(Graduate/Award, Monetary)* [3525]
Grant Assistance Program for Autism Professionals - College Programs *(Undergraduate/Grant)* [7650]
Grant Assistance Program for Autism Professionals - Doctoral Programs *(Doctorate/Grant)* [7651]
Grant Assistance Program for Autism Professionals - Institutional Standards *(Undergraduate, Graduate/Grant)* [7652]
Grant Assistance Program for Autism Professionals - Masters Programs *(Master's/Grant)* [7653]
Grant Assistance Program for Autism Professionals - Professional Certification Programs *(Undergraduate, Professional development/Grant)* [7654]
Grant Assistance Program for Autism Professionals - Retroactive Assistance *(Advanced Professional, Professional development/Grant)* [7655]
Grant Assistance Program for Autism Professionals - Undergraduate Programs *(Undergraduate/Grant)* [7656]
Mona Gray Creative Arts Scholarships *(Graduate, Undergraduate/Scholarship)* [5593]
Graybar Canada Award of Excellence Scholarships *(Undergraduate/Scholarship)* [3832]
Frank L. Greathouse Government Accounting Scholarship *(Graduate, Undergraduate/Scholarship)* [4504]
Leslie C. Green Veterans Scholarships *(Juris Doctorate, Advanced Professional/Scholarship)* [3458]
Reginald K. Groome Memorial Scholarships *(Undergraduate/Scholarship)* [8823]
Jennifer C. Groot Memorial Fellowships *(Undergraduate, Graduate/Fellowship)* [657]
John Simon Guggenheim Memorial Fellowships - U.S. and Canadian Competition *(Advanced Professional/Fellowship)* [4684]
Guntley-Lorimer Science and Arts Scholarships *(Undergraduate/Scholarship)* [2284]
David J. Hallissey Memorial Internships *(Graduate, Undergraduate/Internship)* [1441]
Hamilton Industrial Environmental Association Bursaries-Mohawk College *(Undergraduate/Scholarship)* [4691]
Al Hamilton Scholarships *(Undergraduate/Scholarship)* [8766]
Stan Hamilton Scholarships *(Undergraduate/Scholarship)* [8766]
Hammond Power Solutions Inc. Outstanding Electrical Scholar Awards *(Undergraduate/Award)* [3833]
Handweavers Guild of America and Dendel Scholarships *(Graduate, Undergraduate/Scholarship)* [4710]
Tom Hanson Photojournalism Awards *(All/Internship)* [4119]
Harkness Fellowships in Health Care Policy and Practice *(Graduate, Doctorate/Fellowship)* [3160]
Father J. Harold Conway Memorial Scholarships *(Postgraduate/Fellowship)* [7632]
B. Harper Bull Conservation Fellowships *(Graduate/Fellowship)* [9749]
Nicky & Ted Harrison Memorial Scholarships *(Undergraduate, Master's/Scholarship)* [10786]
Rona Hatt Master's Scholarships in Chemical Engineering *(Master's/Scholarship)* [2623]
Mary Jane Hendrie Memorial Scholarships *(Graduate, Undergraduate/Scholarship)* [10287]
Herb Stovel Scholarship Funds - Conference Bursaries *(Undergraduate, Graduate, Professional development/Scholarship)* [7199]
Herb Stovel Scholarship Funds - Project Bursaries *(Undergraduate, Graduate, Professional development/Scholarship)* [7200]
Robert N. Herbert Undergraduate Scholarships *(Undergraduate/Scholarship)* [9216]
Judy Hill Memorial Scholarships *(Undergraduate/Scholarship)* [2701]
Geordie Hilton Academic Scholarships *(Undergraduate/Scholarship)* [4480]
D. Glenn Hilts Scholarships *(Graduate, Undergraduate/Scholarship)* [2069]
Hispanic Serving Institution Scholarships (HSIS) *(Undergraduate/Scholarship)* [9870]
Hochschulsommerkurse *(Undergraduate/Grant, Award)* [3608]
C.H.(Chuck) Hodgson Scholarships *(Undergraduate/Scholarship)* [10547]
Irving J. Hoffman Memorial Scholarships *(Undergraduate/Scholarship)* [10288]
Lois Hole Humanities and Social Sciences Scholarships *(Undergraduate/Scholarship)* [273]
Norm Hollend Fellowships in Oncology *(Postdoctorate/Fellowship)* [6138]
E.B. Horsman & Son Scholarships *(Undergraduate/Scholarship)* [3834]
Hosinec Family Scholarships *(Graduate, Undergraduate/Scholarship)* [10289]
Lloyd Houlden Memorial Research Fellowships *(Advanced Professional, Professional development/Fellowship)* [2559]
Goldwin Howland Scholarships *(Graduate/Scholarship)* [2720]
Christopher Hoy/ERT Scholarships *(Graduate/Scholarship)* [962]
Donald Hoy Memorial Scholarships *(Undergraduate, Master's/Scholarship)* [10787]
John Hoyt Memorial Scholarships *(Undergraduate, Master's/Scholarship)* [10788]
Hubbell Canada LP "Electrical Industry Leadership" Scholarship Awards *(Undergraduate/Scholarship)* [3835]
Steven Huesing Scholarships *(Graduate, Undergraduate/Scholarship)* [3067]
Kathryn Huget Leadership Awards *(Master's, Doctorate/Award)* [2430]
Tertia M.C. Hughes Memorial Graduate Student Prize *(Graduate/Award, Prize)* [2684]
Humber College Institute of Technology and Advanced Learning Scholarships *(Undergraduate/Scholarship)* [5524]
John Peters Humphrey Student Fellowships *(Graduate/Fellowship)* [3459]
I Have a Dream Scholarships *(Undergraduate/Scholarship)* [5525]
IBA Law Student Scholarship Foundation Scholarships *(Undergraduate/Scholarship)* [5130]
ICJS Short-Term Fellowships *(Doctorate, Postdoctorate, Advanced Professional/Fellowship)* [8997]
Ideal Supply Scholarship Awards *(Undergraduate/Scholarship)* [3836]
In-course Scholarships - Chinese Dance Workshop Scholarships *(Undergraduate/Scholarship)* [10290]
Indspire Health Careers Bursary and Scholarships *(Graduate, Undergraduate/Scholarship)* [5132]
Indspire Post-Secondary Education Scholarships *(Graduate, Undergraduate/Scholarship)* [5133]
Industrial R&D Fellowships *(Postdoctorate/Fellowship)* [3403]
Institute Community Support Program ICR Publication Prizes *(Undergraduate, Graduate, Postgraduate, Postdoctorate/Prize)* [5230]
Intensive Language Course Grants *(Doctorate/Grant)* [3609]
Inter American Press Association Scholarships *(Undergraduate/Scholarship)* [9061]
International Association of Black Actuaries Scholarships *(Undergraduate/Scholarship)* [5248]
International Association of Foundation Drilling Scholarships for Civil Engineering Students *(Graduate/Scholarship)* [75]
International Association of Foundation Drilling Scholarships for Part-time Civil Engineering Graduate School Students *(Graduate/Scholarship)* [76]
International Council for Canadian Studies Graduate Student Scholarships *(Graduate/Scholarship)* [3399]
International GI Training Grant Award *(Professional development/Grant)* [685]
International Grenfell Association Bursary *(Undergraduate/Scholarship)* [5341]
International Grenfell Association Post-Secondary Bursaries *(Undergraduate/Scholarship)* [5342]
International Grenfell Association Secondary/High School Bursaries *(Undergraduate/Scholarship)* [5343]
International Law Research Program Fellowships *(Advanced Professional, Professional development/Fellowship)* [2884]
International Society Annual Meeting Travel Grant *(Professional development/Grant)* [408]
Investigators in the Pathogenesis of Infectious Disease Awards *(Doctorate, Postdoctorate, Professional development/Grant)* [2417]
Investors Group Scholarships for Not-For-Profit Leaders *(Other/Scholarship)* [2183]
IODE Canada Labrador Bursary *(Undergraduate/Scholarship)* [6855]
ISM Doctoral Fellowships *(Doctorate/Fellowship)* [5160]
ISM Scholarships for Graduate Studies *(Graduate/Scholarship)* [5161]
Dr. Karl C. Ivarson Scholarships *(Master's, Doctorate/Scholarship)* [113]
Jamaican Canadian Association Alberta Scholarship Program *(Undergraduate/Scholarship)* [5533]
Helen Janko Memorial Scholarships *(Undergraduate, Master's/Scholarship)* [10789]
Drzymala Janusz and Roma Scholarship *(Undergraduate/Scholarship)* [8577]
Airgas - Terry Jarvis Memorial Scholarships *(Undergraduate/Scholarship)* [1518]
Herbert H. Jasper Fellowships in Neurosciences *(Postdoctorate/Fellowship)* [2568]
Hon. Michaelle Jean Scholarships *(Undergraduate/Scholarship)* [2286]
Harry Jerome Legacy Scholarships *(Undergraduate, Graduate/Scholarship)* [2287]
Harry Johannes Scholarships *(Undergraduate, Graduate/Scholarship)* [10790]
Johnson & Johnson Scholarships *(Undergraduate/Scholarship)* [2702]
Douglas Johnson Memorial Scholarships *(Undergraduate, Master's/Scholarship)* [10791]
E.J. Josey Scholarships *(Graduate/Scholarship, Award)* [2296]
Kazimiera Juchniewicz Memorial Scholarships *(Undergraduate/Scholarship)* [8578]
Stefan and Weronika Kacperski Memorial Scholarships *(Undergraduate/Scholarship)* [8579]
Kalmen Kaplansky Scholarships in Economic and Social Rights *(Graduate/Scholarship)* [3657]
Kappa Kappa Gamma Foundation of Canada Graduate Scholarships *(Graduate, Doctorate/Scholarship)* [5777]
Lucile B. Kaufman Women's Scholarships *(Undergraduate/Scholarship)* [9184]
Dr. Terry Kavanagh Fellowships *(Graduate/Fellowship)* [2791]

CANADA   Legal Residence Index

E. Wayne Kay Community College Scholarships *(Undergraduate/Scholarship)* [9186]
Gunild Keetman Scholarships *(Other, Undergraduate/Scholarship)* [7714]
Dr. Dorothy J. Kergin Fellowships *(Doctorate, Master's/Fellowship)* [2703]
Kerrwil's J.W. Kerr Continuing Education Scholarship Awards *(Undergraduate/Scholarship)* [3837]
Edgar Kerstan Memorial Scholarships *(Undergraduate/Scholarship)* [6420]
Keith Kevan Award *(Postgraduate/Award)* [3892]
KFOC Allied Health Doctoral Fellowship *(Doctorate/Fellowship)* [5825]
KFOC Allied Health Scholarships *(Graduate/Scholarship)* [5826]
KFOC Biomedical Fellowships *(Postdoctorate/Fellowship)* [5827]
KFOC Biomedical Scholarships *(Doctorate/Scholarship)* [5828]
Khaki University and Y.M.C.A. Memorial Scholarships *(Undergraduate/Scholarship)* [10291]
Killam Fellowships *(Undergraduate/Fellowship)* [4229]
Mackenzie King Open Scholarships *(Graduate/Scholarship)* [6366]
Mackenzie King Travelling Scholarships *(Graduate/Scholarship)* [6367]
Annie Kirshenblatt Memorial Scholarships *(Graduate, Undergraduate/Scholarship)* [9751]
Flo Kitz Memorial Scholarships *(Undergraduate, Master's/Scholarship)* [10792]
Klarman Family Foundation Grants Program in Eating Disorders Research *(Professional development/Grant)* [4818]
Stefan and Janina Klimt Scholarships *(Undergraduate/Scholarship)* [8580]
George Kokociński Memorial Scholarships *(Undergraduate/Scholarship)* [8581]
Bernie Kom Memorial Awards *(Postgraduate/Award)* [10746]
Korean Studies Dissertation Workshop Funds *(Graduate/Fellowship)* [9056]
Krawczyk-Krane Family Scholarships *(Undergraduate/Scholarship)* [8582]
Robert Krembil Scholarships of Merit *(Doctorate/Scholarship)* [10747]
David A. Kronick Travelling Fellowships *(Doctorate, Graduate/Fellowship)* [6387]
Canadian Zionist Federation - Dr. Leon Aryeh Kronitz Scholarships *(Undergraduate, Graduate/Scholarship)* [2640]
Leo J. Krysa Family Undergraduate Scholarships *(Undergraduate/Scholarship)* [2674]
Jan Kuropas Memorial Scholarships *(Undergraduate/Scholarship)* [8583]
Lafarge Community Leaders Scholarships *(Other/Scholarship)* [2184]
Alexander Fraser Laidlaw Fellowships *(Graduate/Fellowship, Scholarship)* [2576]
Canadian Association for Studies in Co-operation Scholarships - Alexander Fraser Laidlaw Fellowships *(Graduate/Fellowship)* [2613]
Allen T. Lambert Scholarships *(Postgraduate/Scholarship)* [10748]
John and Lois Lamont Graduate Scholarship *(Graduate/Scholarship)* [2627]
James D. Lang Memorial Scholarships *(Graduate/Scholarship)* [2563]
Karen E. Latt Memorial Scholarships *(Graduate/Scholarship)* [5584]
Kenneth Laundy Entrance Scholarships *(Graduate/Scholarship)* [10749]
Law Foundation of British Columbia Graduate Fellowships *(Graduate/Fellowship)* [5941]
Law Society of British Columbia Scholarships *(Graduate, Undergraduate/Scholarship)* [5978]
Robert G. Lawrence Prize *(Doctorate, Other, Graduate/Prize, Award)* [1902]
Queenie Leader Memorial Scholarships *(Undergraduate, Master's/Scholarship)* [10793]
The Leaders of Tomorrow Scholarships *(Undergraduate, Vocational/Occupational/Scholarship)* [3765]
Lemaire Co-operative Studies Awards *(Undergraduate, Graduate/Scholarship)* [2577]
Carol Anne Letheren Entrance Awards *(Postgraduate/Award, Scholarship)* [10750]
Lilly Scholarships in Religion for Journalists *(Other/Scholarship)* [8549]
Tecla Lin & Nelia Laroza Memorial Scholarships *(Undergraduate/Scholarship)* [2704]
Donald A.B. Lindberg Research Fellowships *(Doctorate, Graduate/Fellowship)* [6388]
LionsDeal Scholarships *(Undergraduate/Scholarship)* [6095]
Hushy Lipton Memorial Scholarship Funds *(Undergraduate, Graduate, Postgraduate/Scholarship)* [2641]
LITA/LSSI Minority Scholarships *(Graduate/Scholarship)* [6072]
LITA/OCLC Minority Scholarships *(Graduate/Scholarship)* [6073]
Ian Lithgow Memorial Awards *(Master's/Award)* [10751]
Grant Livingston Memorial Scholarships *(Undergraduate, Master's/Scholarship)* [10794]
London Goodenough Association of Canada Scholarships *(Graduate/Scholarship)* [6105]
Long-term International Fellowships *(Professional development/Fellowship)* [3380]
Charles Luttman Scholarship *(Undergraduate/Scholarship)* [2536]
Burton MacDonald and Rosemarie Sampson Fellowships *(Undergraduate, Graduate/Fellowship)* [659]
Dr. Sally Macdonald Scholarships *(Undergraduate, Master's/Scholarship)* [10795]
Dr. Arlene MacIntyre Medical Student Bursaries *(Undergraduate/Grant)* [7640]
CEMF Claudette MacKay-Lassonde Graduate Scholarships *(Doctorate, Postdoctorate/Scholarship)* [2624]
MAF Canada Scholarship Fund *(Undergraduate/Scholarship)* [6560]
Manhattan Street Capital Annual National Scholarships *(Undergraduate, Graduate, Doctorate/Scholarship)* [6227]
Markham-Colegrave International Scholarships *(Undergraduate/Scholarship)* [805]
Eleanor Jean Martin Award *(Master's/Scholarship)* [2705]
Dick Martin Scholarships *(Postgraduate/Scholarship)* [2609]
Right Honourable Paul Martin Sr. Scholarships *(Graduate/Scholarship)* [5150]
Beverley Mascoll Scholarships *(Undergraduate/Scholarship)* [2288]
Val Mason Scholarships *(Postgraduate/Scholarship)* [2746]
Elizabeth Massey Award *(Postgraduate/Award)* [2631]
Norman Matechuk Memorial Scholarships *(Undergraduate, Master's/Scholarship)* [10796]
Tadeusz Maziarz Scholarships *(Undergraduate/Scholarship)* [8584]
John Mazurek Memorial-Morgex Insurance Scholarship *(Other/Scholarship)* [296]
Heather McCallum Scholarships *(Doctorate, Other/Scholarship)* [1903]
Hans McCorriston Motive Power Machinist Grant Programs *(Undergraduate/Scholarship)* [2132]
Joseph McCulley Educational Scholarships *(Graduate, Undergraduate/Scholarship)* [10292]
William H. McGannon Foundation Scholarships *(Graduate, Undergraduate/Scholarship)* [6364]
Foster G. McGaw Graduate Student Scholarships *(Graduate/Scholarship)* [688]
R. Tait Mckenzie Awards *(Professional development/Award)* [8118]
John J. McKetta Undergraduate Scholarships *(Undergraduate/Scholarship)* [905]
John Alexander McLean Scholarships *(Undergraduate/Scholarship)* [9731]
R. Roy McMurtry Fellowships in Legal History *(Doctorate, Graduate/Fellowship)* [7760]
Douglas McRorie Memorial Scholarships *(Doctorate, Master's/Scholarship)* [114]
Medical Library Association Scholarships for Minority Students *(Graduate/Scholarship)* [6389]
Dr. Ernest and Minnie Mehl Scholarships *(Undergraduate/Scholarship)* [281]
Frederic G. Melcher Scholarships *(Graduate/Scholarship)* [2018]
Mensa Canada General Scholarships *(Undergraduate/Scholarship)* [6421]
CAG Donald Menzies Bursary Awards *(Postgraduate/Scholarship, Award)* [2554]
Merck Frosst Canada Ltd. Postgraduate Pharmacy Fellowships *(Graduate/Fellowship)* [1957]
Al Mercury Scholarships *(Undergraduate/Scholarship)* [10293]
Metcalf Innovation Fellowships *(Advanced Professional, Professional development/Fellowship)* [4366]
Bernard Michel Scholarships *(Undergraduate/Scholarship)* [2526]
Michener-Deacon Fellowship for Journalism Education *(Professional development/Fellowship)* [4121]
Bronislaw Michno Memorial Scholarships *(Undergraduate/Scholarship)* [8585]
Military Nurses Association Scholarships *(Master's/Scholarship)* [2706]
Mineralogical Association of Canada Scholarships *(Doctorate, Graduate/Scholarship)* [2022]
Minerva Scholarships *(Undergraduate/Scholarship)* [2289]
Minnesota GLBT Educational Fund *(Undergraduate/Scholarship)* [8661]
Minority-Serving Institution Faculty Scholar Awards *(Doctorate/Award)* [474]
MLA Research, Development, and Demonstration Project Grants *(Graduate/Grant)* [6392]
Murray Montague Memorial Scholarships *(Undergraduate/Scholarship)* [4571]
Thomas More Scholarships *(Undergraduate/Scholarship)* [4487]
John H. Moss Scholarships *(Undergraduate/Scholarship)* [10294]
Movember Clinical Trials *(Advanced Professional/Grant)* [8304]
Movember Discovery Grants *(Advanced Professional, Professional development/Grant)* [8305]
Movember Rising Star in Prostate Cancer Research Awards *(Advanced Professional, Professional development/Grant)* [8306]
Movember Team Grants *(Advanced Professional, Professional development/Grant)* [8307]
Marvin Mundel Memorial Scholarships *(Undergraduate/Scholarship)* [5192]
Margaret Munro Award *(Undergraduate/Scholarship)* [2707]
Dr. Helen K. Mussallem Fellowships *(Master's/Scholarship)* [2708]
NAAMA Scholarships *(Undergraduate/Scholarship)* [6701]
Irwin Allen Nadal Entrance Awards *(Master's/Award)* [10752]
Miles Spencer Nadal Entrance Awards *(Master's/Award)* [10753]
National Board Technical Scholarships *(Undergraduate/Scholarship)* [6827]
National Greenhouse Manufacturers Association Scholarships *(Undergraduate/Scholarship)* [806]
National Society of Accountants Scholarship Program *(Undergraduate/Scholarship)* [7134]
Natural Sciences and Engineering Research Council Postgraduate Scholarships *(Doctorate/Scholarship)* [3404]
Marek Nawrot Memorial Scholarships *(Undergraduate/Scholarship)* [8586]
NBHRF/ASRP Doctoral Training Awards *(Doctorate/Grant)* [372, 7267]
NBHRF Doctoral Studentships *(Doctorate/Grant)* [7269]
NBHRF Master's Studentships *(Master's/Grant)* [7272]
NBHRF Postdoctoral Fellowships *(Postdoctorate/Fellowship)* [7273]
NBMBAA Graduate Scholarships Program *(Graduate/Scholarship)* [6821]
NCLEJ Law School Graduate Fellows and Volunteers *(Graduate/Fellowship)* [6848]
Nedien Hoganson Memorial Scholarships *(Undergraduate, Master's/Scholarship)* [10797]
Dr. Ezra Nesbeth Scholarships *(Undergraduate/Scholarship)* [5526]

Neuroscience Certification Bursary Awards *(Other/Award)* [1889]
Alan H. Neville Memorial Scholarships *(Undergraduate/Scholarship)* [335]
Newberry Library/Ecole Nationale des Chartes Exchange Fellowships *(Graduate/Fellowship)* [7420]
Norman Nicholson Scholarships *(Undergraduate/Scholarship)* [2607]
Sharon Nield Memorial Scholarships *(Undergraduate/Scholarship)* [2710]
Erik Nielsen Memorial Scholarships *(Undergraduate, Master's/Scholarship)* [10798]
NLM Associate Fellowships *(Postgraduate/Fellowship)* [9928]
Norfolk Southern Foundation Scholarships *(Undergraduate/Scholarship)* [1188]
North American Conference on British Studies Dissertation Year Fellowships *(Doctorate, Postdoctorate/Fellowship)* [7443]
North American Conference on British Studies-Huntington Library Fellowships *(Doctorate, Postdoctorate/Fellowship)* [7444]
North American Society Fellowships *(Professional development/Fellowship)* [8119]
Northern Resident Scholarships *(Doctorate, Graduate/Scholarship)* [1935]
Nova Scotia Salmon Association Scholarships *(Undergraduate/Scholarship)* [7556]
Mike and Flo Novovesky Scholarships *(Undergraduate/Scholarship)* [807]
Nuffield Canada Farming Scholarships *(Undergraduate/Scholarship)* [7558]
AEBC Rick Oakes Scholarships for the Arts *(Undergraduate/Scholarship)* [336]
OAS Academic Scholarships - Graduate *(Graduate/Scholarship)* [7722]
O'Brien Foundation Fellowships *(Postgraduate, Master's, Doctorate/Fellowship)* [7568]
Lawrence "Bud" Ohlman Memorial Scholarships *(Undergraduate/Scholarship)* [808]
OHTN Postdoctoral Fellowships *(Doctorate/Fellowship)* [7637]
Omatsu FACL Scholarships *(Juris Doctorate, Advanced Professional/Scholarship)* [4001]
OMHF Postdoctoral Fellowships *(Postdoctorate/Fellowship)* [7648]
OMSBF Sun Life Financial Medical Student Bursaries *(Undergraduate/Grant)* [7644]
ONECA Four Directions Scholarship *(Undergraduate/Scholarship)* [7658]
OOBS Student Leadership Scholarships *(Undergraduate/Scholarship)* [7766]
Osram Sylvania Scholastic Achievement Awards *(Undergraduate/Scholarship)* [3838]
Michael Oykhman Criminal Law and Evidence Scholarships *(Juris Doctorate, Advanced Professional/Scholarship)* [6455]
Parkinson Canada Basic Research Fellowships *(Advanced Professional/Fellowship)* [7876]
Parkinson Canada Clinical Movement Disorder Fellowships *(Advanced Professional, Professional development/Fellowship)* [7877]
Parkinson Canada Clinical Research Fellowships *(Professional development/Fellowship)* [7878]
Parkinson Canada Graduate Student Awards *(Graduate, Advanced Professional/Grant)* [7879]
Parkinson Canada New Investigator Award Grants *(Professional development/Grant)* [7880]
Parkinson Canada Pilot Project Grants *(Advanced Professional/Grant)* [7881]
Ted Parnell Scholarship *(Undergraduate/Scholarship)* [10772]
Senator Norman Paterson Fellowships *(Doctorate/Scholarship)* [2711]
Q. O. (Quint) Patrick Scholarships *(Undergraduate/Scholarship)* [10548]
Arthur Paulin Automotive Aftermarket Scholarship Awards *(Postgraduate, Undergraduate/Scholarship)* [2133]
PEA Bursaries *(Undergraduate/Scholarship)* [8290]
PEA Scholarships *(Undergraduate/Scholarship)* [8291]
Robert L. Peaslee-Detroit Brazing and Soldiering Division Scholarships *(Undergraduate/Scholarship)* [1521]
PEO Educational Loan Funds *(Undergraduate, Master's, Doctorate/Loan)* [7954]
PEO Scholars Awards *(Doctorate/Award, Scholarship)* [7956]
Nalini Perera Little Lotus Bud Master's Scholarships *(Master's/Scholarship)* [2689]
Jim Perry Vocational Scholarships *(Undergraduate, Vocational/Occupational/Scholarship)* [809]
Persons Case Scholarships *(Undergraduate, Graduate/Scholarship)* [285]
Petroleum History Society Graduate Scholarships *(Graduate/Scholarship)* [8017]
PHE Canada National Award for Teaching Excellence in Physical Education *(Professional development/Recognition)* [8120]
PHE Canada Student Awards *(Undergraduate/Award)* [8121]
Shoshana Philipp (Kirshenblatt) R.N. Memorial Scholarships *(Graduate, Undergraduate/Scholarship)* [9752]
Philips Lighting Continuing Education Awards *(Undergraduate/Scholarship)* [3839]
Physiotherapy Foundation of Canada Research Grant *(Other/Grant)* [8129]
Eleonora Pidperyhora Scholarship *(Undergraduate/Scholarship)* [8587]
PIMS Postdoctoral Fellowships *(Doctorate/Fellowship)* [7791]
Dr. Adolph Piotrowski Memorial Art Scholarships *(Undergraduate/Scholarship)* [8588]
Pipe Line Contractors Association of Canada Student Bursary *(Undergraduate, Postgraduate/Scholarship)* [8142]
Platform Support Grants *(Advanced Professional/Grant)* [2357]
D.F. Plett Graduate Fellowships *(Graduate/Fellowship)* [8158]
Plumbing-Heating-Cooling Contractors Association Educational Foundation Need-Based Scholarships *(Undergraduate/Scholarship)* [8162]
Plumbing-Heating-Cooling Contractors Association Educational Foundation Scholarships *(Undergraduate/Scholarship)* [8163]
David Pohl Scholarships *(Master's/Scholarship)* [9836]
Roy H. Pollack Scholarships *(Graduate, Master's/Scholarship)* [9837]
Harriet and Leon Pomerance Fellowships *(Professional development/Fellowship)* [1610]
Gail Posluns Fellowships in Hematology *(Postdoctorate/Fellowship)* [6139]
Postdoctoral Fellowships at the Fields Institute *(Postdoctorate/Fellowship)* [4020]
J.R. (Joe) Power National Scholarships *(Postgraduate/Scholarship)* [8383]
Prairie Baseball Academy Scholarships *(Undergraduate/Scholarship)* [286]
Gerald Pratley Award *(Doctorate, Graduate/Award)* [1884]
Diana M. Priestly Memorial Scholarships *(Undergraduate/Scholarship)* [2564]
Prince Edward Island Law Student Scholarships *(Undergraduate/Scholarship)* [5980]
Alexander Pringle Criminal Law Scholarships *(Advanced Professional/Scholarship)* [8280]
Prostate Cancer Canada Clinical Research Fellowships *(Advanced Professional/Fellowship)* [8308]
Prostate Cancer Canada Graduate Studentships *(Graduate, Doctorate/Grant)* [8309]
Prostate Cancer Canada Postdoctoral Research Fellowships *(Postdoctorate, Advanced Professional/Fellowship)* [8310]
Provincial and Regional 4-H Scholarships *(Undergraduate/Scholarship)* [9]
PSAC-AGR National Scholarships *(Postgraduate/Scholarship)* [8384]
PSAC - Coughlin National Scholarships *(Postgraduate/Scholarship)* [8385]
PSAC Regional Scholarships *(Postgraduate/Scholarship)* [8386]
Psychology Association of Saskatchewan Student Scholarships - Academic Achievement *(Master's, Doctorate/Scholarship)* [8320]
Psychology Association of Saskatchewan Student Scholarships - Research Based *(Master's, Doctorate/Scholarship)* [8321]
Morris M. Pulver Scholarship Funds *(Undergraduate, Graduate, Postgraduate/Scholarship)* [2642]
Doug Purvis Prize *(Other/Prize)* [2546]
Queen Elizabeth II Graduate Scholarship Program *(Doctorate, Graduate/Scholarship)* [287]
Diamond & James Quong Memorial Scholarships *(Undergraduate, Master's/Scholarship)* [10799]
RAB Design Lighting Award of Excellence *(Undergraduate/Scholarship)* [3840]
James K. Rathmell Jr. Memorial Scholarships *(Undergraduate, Graduate/Scholarship)* [810]
Registered Apprenticeship Program/CTS Scholarships (RAP) *(Undergraduate/Scholarship)* [288]
J.H. Stewart Reid Memorial Fellowship Trust *(Doctorate/Fellowship, Award)* [8547]
Siobhan Isabella Reid Memorial Scholarships *(Graduate, Undergraduate/Scholarship)* [5994]
George Reinke Scholarships *(Other/Scholarship)* [1442]
Thomson Reuters/MLA Doctoral Fellowships *(Doctorate, Graduate/Fellowship)* [6393]
W. Reymont Scholarships *(Undergraduate/Scholarship)* [8589]
Marion Roberts Memorial Scholarships *(Undergraduate/Scholarship)* [2134]
Gertrude J. Robinson Book Prize *(Professional development/Prize)* [2616]
R.O.E.A. Dumitru Golea Goldy-Gemu Scholarships *(Undergraduate/Scholarship)* [1227]
Roy Seymour Rogers and Geraldine Ruth Rogers Scholarships *(Undergraduate/Scholarship)* [9732]
Red Rogers Memorial Scholarships *(Undergraduate, Master's/Scholarship)* [10800]
Mandell and Lester Rosenblatt Undergraduate Scholarships *(Undergraduate/Scholarship)* [9217]
Rothberg International School Graduate Merit Scholarships *(Graduate, Master's/Scholarship)* [2643]
Robert Roy Awards *(Advanced Professional/Award, Recognition)* [1897]
Royal Bank Scholarships *(Undergraduate, Master's/Scholarship)* [2290]
RPNAS Baccalaureate Level Program Scholarships *(Undergraduate/Scholarship)* [8538]
RPNAS Doctorate Level Program Scholarship *(Doctorate/Scholarship)* [8539]
RPNAS Master's Level Program Scholarship *(Master's/Scholarship)* [8540]
RTDNF Scholarships *(Undergraduate, Graduate/Scholarship)* [8414]
Glen Ruby Memorial Scholarships *(Undergraduate/Scholarship)* [2754]
Rutherford Scholars *(Undergraduate/Scholarship)* [289]
Ryerson Scholarships *(Undergraduate/Scholarship)* [5527]
Chester & Maria Sadowski Memorial Scholarships *(Undergraduate/Scholarship)* [8590]
Saint Paul University Excellence Scholarships *(Undergraduate/Scholarship, Medal)* [8675]
Saint Paul University Financial Aid Bursaries *(Undergraduate, Graduate/Scholarship)* [8676]
AIST David H. Samson Canadian Scholarships *(Undergraduate/Scholarship)* [2006]
Sanofi Pasteur Scholarships *(Master's/Scholarship)* [2712]
SARP Education Assistance Grants *(Professional development/Grant)* [8762]
SARP Professional Development Grants *(Professional development/Grant)* [8763]
Saskatchewan Government Insurance Actuarial Science Scholarships *(Undergraduate/Scholarship)* [8769]
Saskatchewan Government Insurance Anniversary Scholarships *(Undergraduate/Scholarship)* [8770]
Saskatchewan Hockey Association Scholarships *(Undergraduate/Scholarship)* [8775]
Saskatchewan Pulse Growers Undergraduate Scholarships *(Undergraduate/Scholarship)* [8778]
Saskatchewan School Boards Association Graduate Student Awards *(Graduate/Monetary)* [8782]
François J. Saucier Prize in Applied Oceanography *(Professional development/Award, Prize)* [2685]
James A. Sauer Memorial Fellowships *(Graduate/Fellowship)* [662]
Savoy Foundation Postdoctoral and Clinical Re-

CANADA

search Fellowships *(Postdoctorate/Fellowship)* [4123]
Meta M. Sawyer Bursary Fund *(Undergraduate/Grant)* [7645]
Schlegel-UW RIA Scholarships *(Doctorate/Scholarship)* [2555]
Richard J. Schmeelk Fellowships *(Graduate/Fellowship)* [8790]
Schneider Electric Student Merit Awards *(Undergraduate/Scholarship)* [3841]
B.E. Schnurr Memorial Fund Research Grants *(Other/Grant)* [8130]
Scholarships for the Next Generation of Scientists *(Postdoctorate/Scholarship)* [2777]
Tanna H. Schulich MBA Entrance Scholarships *(Graduate/Scholarship)* [10754]
Fritz Schwartz Serials Education Scholarships *(Graduate, Other/Scholarship)* [7447]
Scotiabank Scholarships *(Undergraduate/Scholarship)* [2291]
Seed Companies Scholarships *(Undergraduate, Graduate/Scholarship)* [811]
Senior Innovation Scholarships *(Undergraduate, Graduate/Scholarship)* [8146]
SFP Undergraduate Scholarships *(Undergraduate/Scholarship)* [8794]
SGI Business Insurance Diploma Scholarships *(Undergraduate/Scholarship)* [8772]
SGI Research Grants *(Graduate/Grant)* [8773]
Shastri Scholar Travel Subsidy Grants (SSTSG) *(Graduate, Professional development/Grant)* [8857]
David S. Sheridan Canadian Research Awards *(Other/Award)* [2542]
Siemens Canada Academic Awards *(Undergraduate/Award)* [3842]
Sigma Theta Tau International Scholarships *(Doctorate/Scholarship)* [2713]
Sloan Research Fellowships *(Doctorate/Fellowship)* [8988]
SME Education Foundation Family Scholarships *(Undergraduate/Scholarship)* [9195]
Donald Smiley Prize *(Advanced Professional/Prize, Award, Recognition)* [1908]
Eva Smith Bursary *(Undergraduate/Scholarship)* [5528]
Brian Smith Memorial Scholarships *(Undergraduate/Scholarship)* [2348]
A.O. Smith Scholarships *(Undergraduate/Scholarship)* [8164]
Bolesław & Irena Sobczak Scholarships *(Undergraduate/Scholarship)* [8591]
Frank H. Sobey Awards for Excellence in Business Studies *(Undergraduate/Award)* [9048]
Sobeys & Empire Work Experience & Scholarship Program - Future Leaders Awards *(Other/Scholarship)* [9049]
Society of Graphic Designers of Canada Adobe Scholarships *(Undergraduate/Scholarship)* [9063]
Society of Graphic Designers of Canada Applied Arts Scholarships *(Undergraduate/Scholarship)* [9064]
Society of Graphic Designers of Canada Veer Scholarships *(Undergraduate/Scholarship)* [9065]
Carin Alma E. Somers Scholarship Trust *(Undergraduate/Scholarship)* [2118]
Sonepar Canada Scholarship Awards *(Undergraduate/Scholarship)* [3843]
SPEATBC Scholarships *(Undergraduate, High School/Scholarship)* [9296]
Jean and Manny Spinner Scholarships *(Undergraduate/Scholarship)* [5587]
SSHRC Doctoral Fellowship Program *(Doctorate/Fellowship, Scholarship)* [3396]
Standard Recognition of Excellence Awards *(Undergraduate/Scholarship)* [3844]
Lasek Stanisław and Aniela Scholarship *(Undergraduate/Scholarship)* [8592]
Taylor Statten Memorial Fellowships *(Graduate/Scholarship)* [10295]
The Stanley H. Stearman Awards *(Undergraduate/Scholarship)* [7135]
Harry Steele Entrance Awards *(Postgraduate/Award)* [10755]
Evelyn Steele Memorial Scholarships *(Undergraduate, Master's/Scholarship)* [10802]

H.H. Stern Grant Awards *(Advanced Professional, Professional development/Award, Grant)* [1898]
David Stockwood Memorial Prize *(Advanced Professional, Professional development/Prize)* [81]
Marlene Streit Golf Scholarships *(Undergraduate/Scholarship)* [4481]
Study Scholarships for Artists or Musicians *(Graduate/Scholarship)* [3610]
Summerside-Natick International Friendship Hockey Scholarships *(Undergraduate/Scholarship)* [3314]
SuperKutz Scholarships *(Undergraduate/Scholarship)* [5892]
TAC Foundation-3M Canada Company Scholarships *(Graduate, Undergraduate/Scholarship)* [9768]
TAC Foundation-407 ETR Scholarships *(Undergraduate, Graduate/Scholarship)* [9769]
TAC Foundation-Amec Foster Wheeler Scholarships *(Undergraduate, Graduate/Scholarship)* [9770]
TAC Foundation-ATS Traffic Group of Companies Scholarships *(Undergraduate, Graduate/Scholarship)* [9771]
TAC Foundation-Canadian Council of Independent Laboratories Graduate Student Scholarships *(Graduate/Scholarship)* [9772]
TAC Foundation-CCMTA Road Safety Scholarships *(Undergraduate, Graduate/Scholarship)* [9773]
TAC Foundation-Cement Association of Canada Scholarships *(Graduate, Undergraduate/Scholarship)* [9774]
TAC Foundation-Dillon Consulting Scholarships *(Undergraduate, Graduate/Scholarship)* [9775]
TAC Foundation-Dr. Ralph Haas Graduate Student Scholarships *(Graduate/Scholarship)* [9776]
TAC Foundation-EllisDon Community College/CEGEP Scholarships *(Undergraduate/Scholarship)* [9777]
TAC Foundation-exp Scholarships *(Undergraduate, Graduate/Scholarship)* [9778]
TAC Foundation-Golder Associates Ltd. Scholarships *(Undergraduate, Graduate/Scholarship)* [9779]
TAC Foundation-HDR Corporation Graduate Student Scholarships *(Graduate/Scholarship)* [9780]
TAC Foundation-IBI Group Scholarships *(Undergraduate, Graduate/Scholarship)* [9781]
TAC Foundation-ISL Engineering Scholarships *(Undergraduate, Graduate/Scholarship)* [9782]
TAC Foundation-LEA Consulting Ltd. Scholarships *(Undergraduate, Graduate/Scholarship)* [9783]
TAC Foundation-MMM Group Limited Scholarships *(Undergraduate, Graduate/Scholarship)* [9784]
TAC Foundation-Municipalities Scholarships *(Undergraduate, Graduate/Scholarship)* [9785]
TAC Foundation-Parsons Scholarships *(Undergraduate, Graduate/Scholarship)* [9786]
TAC Foundation-Peto MacCallum Undergraduate & College Scholarships *(Undergraduate/Scholarship)* [9787]
TAC Foundation-Provinces and Territories Scholarships *(Undergraduate, Graduate/Scholarship)* [9788]
TAC Foundation-SNC Lavalin Scholarships *(Undergraduate, Graduate/Scholarship)* [9789]
TAC Foundation-Stantec Consulting Scholarships *(Graduate/Scholarship)* [9790]
TAC Foundation-Tetra Tech EBA Inc. Scholarships *(Undergraduate, Graduate/Scholarship)* [9791]
Katharine Whiteside Taylor Bursary *(Professional development/Scholarship)* [7807]
Betty & Charles Taylor Scholarships *(Advanced Professional/Scholarship)* [10803]
RABC William Taylor Scholarships *(Undergraduate/Scholarship)* [3846]
TD Meloche-Monnex Scholarships *(Doctorate/Scholarship)* [2714]
Tell Us Your Story Scholarships *(Undergraduate/Scholarship)* [10495]
TEVA Canada Scholarship *(Undergraduate/Scholarship)* [2904]
The Cover Guy Annual Scholarships *(Undergraduate, Graduate/Scholarship)* [3463]
THFC Medical Research Grants *(Professional development/Grant)* [4834]
Thomas & Betts Scholarship Awards *(Undergraduate/Scholarship)* [3847]

Legal Residence Index

Barbara Thomas Bursary *(Undergraduate/Scholarship)* [5529]
Nadene M. Thomas Graduate Research Scholarships *(Graduate/Scholarship)* [297]
Rev. Chuck and Nancy Thomas Scholarships *(Professional development/Scholarship)* [9842]
Dr. Andrew Thomson Prize in Applied Meteorology *(Professional development/Award, Prize)* [2686]
Ken Thomson Scholarships *(Undergraduate/Scholarship)* [1906]
TIAC / Parks Canada Sustainable Tourism Scholarships *(Undergraduate, Master's/Scholarship)* [9760]
John L. Tomasovic, Sr. Scholarships *(Undergraduate/Scholarship)* [812]
Evald Torokvei Foundation Scholarships *(Graduate/Scholarship)* [10296]
Toronto Rehab Scholarships in Rehabilitation-Related Research *(Graduate/Scholarship)* [9753]
Toronto Rehabilitation Institute Graduate Student Scholarships - Ontario Student Opportunities Trust Fund (OSOTF) *(Graduate/Scholarship)* [9754]
Toyota Earth Day Scholarships *(Undergraduate/Scholarship)* [9764]
Transoft Solutions, Inc. Ahead of the Curve Scholarships (AOTC) *(Graduate, Undergraduate/Scholarship)* [5221]
Transportation Association of Canada Foundation Scholarships *(Graduate, Undergraduate/Scholarship)* [9792]
Marie Tremaine Fellowships *(Postgraduate, Other/Fellowship)* [2259]
Trudeau Fellowships - Regular *(Advanced Professional, Professional development/Fellowship)* [8135]
Trudeau Fellowships - Visiting *(Advanced Professional, Professional development/Fellowship)* [8136]
Trudeau Foundation Doctoral Scholarships *(Doctorate/Scholarship)* [8137]
Sam Tughan Scholarships *(Undergraduate/Scholarship)* [2739]
Ukrainian Canadian Professional and Business Club Scholarships in Education *(Undergraduate/Scholarship)* [2675]
United Parcel Service Scholarships for Female Students *(Undergraduate/Scholarship)* [5195]
United Parcel Service Scholarships for Minority Students *(Undergraduate/Scholarship)* [5196]
University of Toronto Accenture Scholarships *(Undergraduate/Scholarship)* [10297]
University of Toronto SAC Undergraduate Grants *(Undergraduate/Grant)* [10299]
Claudette Upton Scholarships *(Undergraduate/Scholarship)* [3787]
Vale Manitoba Operations Scholarships *(Undergraduate/Scholarship, Internship)* [9995]
Vale Master's in Engineering Scholarships *(Master's/Scholarship)* [2625]
Jacob and Rita Van Namen Marketing Scholarships *(Undergraduate/Scholarship)* [814]
John Vanderlee Award *(Undergraduate/Scholarship)* [2715]
Vanier Canada Graduate Scholarships *(Graduate/Scholarship)* [3405]
Dr. Csaba Oliver Vargha Medical Student Bursaries *(Undergraduate/Grant)* [7646]
Vectorworks Design Scholarships *(Undergraduate, Graduate/Scholarship, Prize)* [10367]
Jill Vickers Prize *(Other/Award)* [1909]
Philip F. Vineberg Travelling Fellowships in the Humanities *(Undergraduate/Scholarship)* [6368]
Visible Minorities Scholarship *(Undergraduate/Scholarship)* [7207]
Von Ogden Vogt Scholarships *(Master's/Scholarship)* [9843]
Jane C. Waldbaum Archaeological Field School Scholarships *(Undergraduate/Scholarship)* [1611]
Martin Walmsley Fellowships for Technological Entrepreneurship *(Graduate/Fellowship)* [7627]
Flis Walter and Anna Memorial Scholarship *(Undergraduate/Scholarship)* [8593]
War Memorial Doctoral Scholarships *(Postgraduate/Scholarship)* [6856]
Colin Wasacase Scholarship *(Undergraduate/Scholarship)* [7659]

Glenn Watson Scholarships *(Undergraduate/Scholarship)* [9394]
WEDA Scholarship Program *(Professional development/Scholarship)* [10529]
John V. Wehausen Graduate Scholarships for Advanced Study in Ship Hydrodynamics and Wave Theory *(Graduate/Scholarship)* [9218]
Joel A. Weinstein Memorial Scholarships *(Postgraduate, Undergraduate/Scholarship)* [5594]
William E. Weisel Scholarships *(Undergraduate/Scholarship)* [9201]
Dorothy Wellnitz Canadian Scholarships *(Undergraduate, Vocational/Occupational/Scholarship)* [1193]
WESCO Student Achievement Awards *(Undergraduate/Scholarship)* [3848]
W. Garfield Weston Awards for Northern Research *(Graduate, Postdoctorate/Fellowship)* [10421]
Weston Brain Institute International Fellowships in Neuroscience Program *(Graduate/Fellowship)* [10422]
Weston Brain Institute Rapid Response Program *(Postdoctorate, Advanced Professional, Professional development/Grant)* [10423]
Bradford White Corporation Scholarships *(Undergraduate/Scholarship)* [8165]
Portia White Scholarships *(Undergraduate/Scholarship)* [2292]
Whitehorse Shotokan Karate Club Scholarships *(Undergraduate, Master's/Scholarship)* [10804]
Ann Collins Whitmore Memorial Scholarship (ACWMS) *(Graduate/Scholarship)* [8131]
RS Williamson and Eliford Mott Memorial Scholarships *(Undergraduate/Scholarship)* [10549]
Dr. Alice E. Wilson Awards *(Graduate, Doctorate/Award, Fellowship)* [2632]
Ross A. Wilson Science Scholarships *(Undergraduate/Scholarship)* [9733]
Abel Wolman Fellowships *(Doctorate/Fellowship)* [1492]
Women in Coaching National Coaching Institute Scholarships *(Undergraduate/Scholarship)* [3069]
Women on Par Scholarships *(Undergraduate/Scholarship)* [3938]
Women's Health Research Foundation of Canada Scholarship Program *(Graduate/Scholarship)* [10658]
Geoffrey H. Wood Scholarships *(Undergraduate/Scholarship)* [2740]
Frank and Betty Woodhams Memorial Scholarships *(Undergraduate/Scholarship)* [6422]
World Book Graduate Scholarships in Library and Information Science *(Graduate/Scholarship)* [2680]
Pang Xiaoyan Scholarships *(Undergraduate/Scholarship)* [2926]
Marusia Yaworska Entrance Scholarships *(Graduate/Scholarship)* [10445]
York Graduate Scholarships *(Graduate/Scholarship)* [10756]
York Regional Police Scholarships *(Undergraduate/Scholarship)* [5530]
Jessie Young Bursary Awards *(Other/Award)* [1890]
Jeff Young Memorial Scholarships *(Undergraduate, Master's/Scholarship)* [10805]
Youth Affairs Committee Rising Star Scholarships *(Undergraduate/Scholarship)* [5531]
Youth or the Environment Scholarships *(Other/Scholarship)* [2185]
The Yukon Foundation Medical Laboratory Scholarships *(Undergraduate, Master's/Award)* [10806]
Yukon Law Foundation Scholarships *(Undergraduate/Scholarship)* [10808]

CANADA (BY PROVINCE)

Alberta

AFA Aboriginal Traditional Arts Individual Project Grants *(Professional development/Grant)* [236]
AFA Art Acquisition by Application Grants *(Professional development/Grant)* [237]
AFA Cultural Relations Project Grants *(Professional development/Grant)* [238]
AFA Dance Project Grants *(Professional development/Grant)* [239]
AFA Film and Video Arts Project Grants *(Professional development/Grant)* [240]
AFA Literary Arts Project Grants *(Professional development/Grant)* [241]
AFA Music Project Grants *(Professional development/Grant)* [242]
AFA Theatre & Performance Art Project Grants *(Professional development/Grant)* [243]
AFA Visual Arts and New Media Project Grants *(Professional development/Grant)* [244]
Alberta Blue Cross Scholarships for Aboriginal Students *(Undergraduate/Scholarship)* [230]
Alberta Centennial Scholarships - Alberta *(Undergraduate/Scholarship)* [262]
Alberta Innovates Graduate Student Scholarships *(Graduate/Scholarship)* [256]
Alberta Ukrainian Centennial Commemorative Scholarships *(Graduate/Scholarship)* [10440]
ALIS Fellowships for Full-time Studies in French *(Undergraduate/Fellowship)* [263]
Janet and Horace Allen Scholarships *(Undergraduate/Scholarship)* [266]
Alliance Pipeline Scholarships *(Other/Scholarship)* [2181]
Arts Graduate Scholarships *(Graduate/Scholarship)* [267]
Sam Bull Memorial Scholarships *(Undergraduate/Scholarship)* [248]
Theodore R. Campbell Scholarships *(Undergraduate/Scholarship)* [268]
Carmangay Home and School Association Scholarships *(Undergraduate/Scholarship)* [269]
Robert C. Carson Memorial Bursary *(Undergraduate/Scholarship)* [270]
CBCF - Prairies/NWT Grants in Basic Biomedical Research *(Advanced Professional, Professional development/Grant)* [2597]
CBCF - Prairies/NWT Grants in Clinical Research *(Advanced Professional, Professional development/Grant)* [2598]
CBCF - Prairies/NWT Grants in Health Services and Policy Research *(Advanced Professional, Professional development/Grant)* [2599]
CBCF - Prairies/NWT Postdoctoral Fellowships *(Postdoctorate, Professional development/Fellowship)* [2600]
CBCF - Prairies/NWT Research Grants in Psychosocial, Cultural and Environmental Determinants of Health *(Advanced Professional, Professional development/Grant)* [2601]
Earl and Countess of Wessex - World Championships in Athletics Scholarships *(Undergraduate/Scholarship)* [272]
Senator James Gladstone Memorial Scholarships *(Graduate, Undergraduate/Scholarship)* [249]
Grande Prairie 4-H District Scholarships *(Undergraduate/Scholarship)* [8]
Helen and George Kilik Scholarships *(Undergraduate/Scholarship)* [274]
Anna and John Kolesay Memorial Scholarships *(Undergraduate/Scholarship)* [275]
Jason Lang Scholarships *(Undergraduate/Scholarship)* [276]
Language Teacher Bursary Program Awards *(Other/Award)* [277]
Languages In Teacher Education Scholarships *(Undergraduate/Scholarship)* [278]
Sir James Lougheed Awards of Distinction *(Doctorate, Graduate/Award)* [279]
Lowry Awards for Women of Excellence *(Undergraduate, Graduate, Advanced Professional/Award, Scholarship)* [3789]
Al Maurer Awards *(Undergraduate, Graduate, Advanced Professional/Award, Scholarship)* [3790]
Louise McKinney Post-secondary Scholarships *(Undergraduate/Scholarship)* [280]
Charles S. Noble Scholarships for Study at Harvard *(Undergraduate/Scholarship)* [282]
Northern Alberta Development Council Bursary Awards *(Undergraduate/Award)* [283]
Northern Alberta Development Council Bursary Partnership Program *(Undergraduate/Award)* [284]
Oil & Gas, Trades & Technology (OGTT) Bursary and Scholarship Awards (OGTT) *(Undergraduate/Scholarship)* [5134]
Risk Management and Insurance Scholarships - University of Calgary *(Undergraduate/Scholarship)* [8768]
Risk Management and Insurance Scholarships *(Undergraduate/Scholarship)* [8767]
Alexander Rutherford Scholarships for High School Achievement *(Undergraduate/Scholarship)* [290]
Saskatchewan Government Insurance Corporate Scholarships *(Undergraduate/Scholarship)* [8771]
Servus Credit Union 4-H Scholarships *(Undergraduate/Scholarship)* [10]
Dr. Robert and Anna Shaw Scholarships *(Undergraduate/Scholarship)* [291]
Dr. Robert Norman Shaw Scholarships *(Undergraduate/Scholarship)* [292]
Syncrude/Athabasca University Aboriginal Scholarships *(Undergraduate/Scholarship)* [9627]
Viscount Bennett Scholarships *(Postgraduate, Advanced Professional/Scholarship)* [5969]
Robert E. Walter Memorial Scholarship *(Undergraduate/Scholarship)* [6168]

British Columbia

Alliance Pipeline Scholarships *(Other/Scholarship)* [2181]
Calvin Alumni Association British Columbia Scholarships *(Undergraduate/Scholarship)* [2492]
CBCF - BC/Yukon Region Breast Cancer Research Grants Competition *(Advanced Professional/Grant)* [2587]
CBCF - BC/Yukon Region Breast Cancer Survivor Dragon Boat Grants *(Professional development/Grant)* [2588]
CBCF - BC/Yukon Region Community Health Grants *(Professional development/Grant)* [2589]
CBCF - BC/Yukon Region Small Initiative Funds *(Professional development/Grant)* [2590]
MSFHR Scholar Awards *(Advanced Professional, Professional development/Grant)* [8994]
MSFHR Trainee Awards *(Postdoctorate, Professional development/Grant)* [8995]

Manitoba

CBCF - Prairies/NWT Grants in Basic Biomedical Research *(Advanced Professional, Professional development/Grant)* [2597]
CBCF - Prairies/NWT Grants in Clinical Research *(Advanced Professional, Professional development/Grant)* [2598]
CBCF - Prairies/NWT Grants in Health Services and Policy Research *(Advanced Professional, Professional development/Grant)* [2599]
CBCF - Prairies/NWT Postdoctoral Fellowships *(Postdoctorate, Professional development/Fellowship)* [2600]
CBCF - Prairies/NWT Research Grants in Psychosocial, Cultural and Environmental Determinants of Health *(Advanced Professional, Professional development/Grant)* [2601]
Risk Management and Insurance Scholarships - University of Calgary *(Undergraduate/Scholarship)* [8768]
Risk Management and Insurance Scholarships *(Undergraduate/Scholarship)* [8767]
Saskatchewan Government Insurance Corporate Scholarships *(Undergraduate/Scholarship)* [8771]

New Brunswick

Astra Zeneca Medical Scholarships *(Advanced Professional/Scholarship)* [7275]
Bell Aliant Medical Education Scholarships *(Advanced Professional/Scholarship)* [7276]
BMO Harris Scholarships *(Advanced Professional/Scholarship)* [7277]
CIBC Medical Education Scholarships *(Advanced Professional/Scholarship)* [7278]
Mary Ellen Driscoll Scholarships *(Undergraduate/Scholarship)* [4479]
Dr. Isaac Keillor Farrer, Advanced Medical Education Scholarships *(Advanced Professional/Scholarship)* [7279]
Friends of the Christofor Foundation Scholarships

CANADA

(Advanced Professional/Scholarship) [7280]
Horizon Health Network Scholarships *(Advanced Professional/Scholarship)* [7281]
Berton W. Huestis Memorial Scholarships *(Advanced Professional/Scholarship)* [7282]
Robert R. McCain Memorial Scholarships *(Advanced Professional/Scholarship)* [7283]
G. William McQuade Memorial Scholarships *(Advanced Professional/Scholarship)* [7284]
NB College of Physicians and Surgeons Medical Education Scholarships *(Advanced Professional/Scholarship)* [7285]
NBHRF Bridge Grants *(Professional development/Grant)* [7268]
NBHRF Establishment Grants *(Professional development/Grant)* [7270]
NBHRF Health Research Strategic Initiative Grants *(Professional development/Grant)* [7271]
New Brunswick Nurses Association Scholarships *(Master's/Scholarship)* [7709]
RBC Medical Education Scholarships *(Advanced Professional/Scholarship)* [7286]
Regional Development Corporation Scholarships *(Advanced Professional/Scholarship)* [7287]
Scotiabank Medical Education Scholarships *(Advanced Professional/Scholarship)* [7288]
Dr. Paul and Gayle Sohi Medical Education Scholarships *(Advanced Professional/Scholarship)* [7289]
TD Bank Medical Education Scholarships *(Advanced Professional/Scholarship)* [7290]
Dr. Henrik and Wanda Tonning Memorial Scholarships *(Advanced Professional/Scholarship)* [7291]
Dr. Frank and Audrey Wanamaker Medical Scholarships *(Advanced Professional/Scholarship)* [7292]

Newfoundland and Labrador

Jim Hierlihy Memorial Scholarship *(Undergraduate/Scholarship)* [3911]
Law Foundation of Newfoundland and Labrador Law School Scholarships *(Advanced Professional/Scholarship)* [5943]
Mature Student Scholarship *(Undergraduate/Scholarship)* [3912]
Ocean Industries Student Research Awards *(Undergraduate, Graduate, Postdoctorate/Award)* [8557]

Northwest Territories

CBCF - Prairies/NWT Grants in Basic Biomedical Research *(Advanced Professional, Professional development/Grant)* [2597]
CBCF - Prairies/NWT Grants in Clinical Research *(Advanced Professional, Professional development/Grant)* [2598]
CBCF - Prairies/NWT Grants in Health Services and Policy Research *(Advanced Professional, Professional development/Grant)* [2599]
CBCF - Prairies/NWT Postdoctoral Fellowships *(Postdoctorate, Professional development/Fellowship)* [2600]
CBCF - Prairies/NWT Research Grants in Psychosocial, Cultural and Environmental Determinants of Health *(Advanced Professional, Professional development/Grant)* [2601]
NWT Law Foundation/Graeme Garson Scholarships *(Advanced Professional/Scholarship)* [7554]

Nova Scotia

Scholarship Award of the Bell Aliant Pioneer Volunteers *(Undergraduate/Scholarship)* [2690]

Nunavut

CBCF - Prairies/NWT Grants in Basic Biomedical Research *(Advanced Professional, Professional development/Grant)* [2597]
CBCF - Prairies/NWT Grants in Clinical Research *(Advanced Professional, Professional development/Grant)* [2598]
CBCF - Prairies/NWT Grants in Health Services and Policy Research *(Advanced Professional, Professional development/Grant)* [2599]
CBCF - Prairies/NWT Postdoctoral Fellowships *(Postdoctorate, Professional development/Fellowship)* [2600]
CBCF - Prairies/NWT Research Grants in Psychosocial, Cultural and Environmental Determinants of Health *(Advanced Professional, Professional development/Grant)* [2601]

Ontario

AEBC Toronto Chapter Scholarships *(Undergraduate/Scholarship)* [333]
Mary Babcock Fellowships for Labour Studies Application *(Graduate/Fellowship)* [7629]
Doreen Brady Memorial Scholarships *(Postgraduate/Scholarship)* [7630]
CAA National Capital Region Writing Contests *(All/Award, Prize, Monetary)* [2579]
Rose Cassin Memorial Scholarships *(Postgraduate/Scholarship)* [7631]
Educational Fellowships for Practicing Physicians *(Advanced Professional, Professional development/Fellowship)* [8123]
PSI Graham Farquharson Knowledge Translation Fellowships *(Advanced Professional, Professional development/Fellowship)* [8124]
Guelph Caribbean Canadian Association Undergraduate Scholarships *(Undergraduate/Scholarship)* [4679]
Dr. E. Bruce Hendrick Scholarships *(All/Scholarship)* [9474]
Dr. Gilbert Hopson Medical Student Bursaries *(Undergraduate/Grant)* [7639]
Joan Kamps Memorial Bursaries *(Undergraduate, Graduate, Postgraduate, Professional development/Scholarship)* [7633]
Margaret Lynch Religious Study Fellowships *(Graduate/Scholarship)* [7634]
OMSBF Burlington Medical Student Bursaries *(Undergraduate/Grant)* [7641]
OMSBF District Four - Physician Care Bursaries *(Undergraduate/Grant)* [7642]
OMSBF Durham Medical Society Medical Student Bursaries *(Undergraduate/Grant)* [7643]
Ontario Women's Institute Scholarships *(Undergraduate/Scholarship)* [3997]
PSI Healthcare Research by Community Physicians Grants *(Advanced Professional, Professional development/Grant)* [8125]
Resident Research Grants *(Postgraduate, Professional development/Grant)* [8126]
Cecilia Rowan Religious Study Fellowships *(Graduate/Fellowship)* [7635]
Beatrice Drinnan Spence Scholarships *(Undergraduate, Vocational/Occupational/Scholarship)* [3766]
Tristin Memorial Scholarships *(Undergraduate, Vocational/Occupational/Scholarship)* [5996]
University of Toronto Nortel Institute Undergraduate Scholarships *(Undergraduate/Scholarship)* [10298]
Wilkinson and Company LLP Scholarships *(Undergraduate/Scholarship)* [10559]

Prince Edward Island

Joan Auld Scholarships *(Undergraduate/Scholarship)* [3310]
Lowell Phillips Scholarships *(Undergraduate/Scholarship)* [3313]
Scholarship Award of the Bell Aliant Pioneer Volunteers *(Undergraduate/Scholarship)* [2690]

Quebec

Evelyn Joy Abramowicz Memorial Scholarships *(Undergraduate/Scholarship)* [5568]
Therese and David Bohbot Scholarships *(Undergraduate/Scholarship)* [5571]
Stephen Bronfman Scholarship Funds in Environmental Studies *(Graduate/Scholarship)* [5572]
Bernice and Gordon Brown Scholarships *(Undergraduate/Scholarship)* [5573]
CAA National Capital Region Writing Contests *(All/Award, Prize, Monetary)* [2579]
Hadar Chemtob Memorial Scholarships *(Undergraduate/Scholarship)* [5574]
Ruth and Victor David Scholarships *(Undergraduate, Graduate/Scholarship)* [5575]
Harry Feldman Memorial Scholarships *(Undergraduate/Scholarship)* [5576]
Jack Gitlitz CA Memorial Scholarships for Study in Israel *(Undergraduate/Scholarship)* [5577]
Harry Hopmeyer Memorial Scholarships *(Undergraduate/Scholarship)* [5578]
IRSST Doctoral Scholarship *(Doctorate/Fellowship)* [5152]
IRSST Doctoral Scholarships Abroad *(Doctorate/Fellowship)* [5153]
IRSST Doctoral Scholarships Supplement *(Doctorate/Fellowship)* [5154]
IRSST Masters Scholarships Supplement *(Master's/Fellowship)* [5156]
IRSST Masters Scholarships *(Master's/Scholarship)* [5155]
IRSST Postdoctoral Scholarships Abroad *(Postdoctorate/Fellowship)* [5158]
IRSST Postdoctoral Scholarships *(Postdoctorate/Fellowship)* [5157]
Mitchell Karper Memorial Scholarships *(Undergraduate/Scholarship)* [5579]
Joseph Katz Memorial Scholarships *(Undergraduate/Scholarship)* [5580]
Micki and Norm Keesal Scholarships *(Undergraduate/Scholarship)* [5581]
Henriette and Marcel Korner Scholarships *(Undergraduate/Scholarship)* [5582]
Liela Klinger Kurztman Memorial Scholarships *(Undergraduate/Scholarship)* [5583]
Irene Brand Lieberman Memorial Scholarships *(Graduate, Postgraduate/Scholarship)* [5585]
Musia and Leon Schwartz Scholarships *(Undergraduate, Graduate/Scholarship)* [5586]
Stelpro Scholarships 360: Energizing Potential *(Undergraduate/Scholarship)* [3845]
Bernard Michael Tarshis Memorial Scholarships for Jewish Studies *(Undergraduate/Scholarship)* [5588]
Dr. Steven S. Zalcman Memorial Scholarships *(Graduate, Postgraduate/Scholarship)* [5589]

Saskatchewan

Alliance Pipeline Scholarships *(Other/Scholarship)* [2181]
CBCF - Prairies/NWT Grants in Basic Biomedical Research *(Advanced Professional, Professional development/Grant)* [2597]
CBCF - Prairies/NWT Grants in Clinical Research *(Advanced Professional, Professional development/Grant)* [2598]
CBCF - Prairies/NWT Grants in Health Services and Policy Research *(Advanced Professional, Professional development/Grant)* [2599]
CBCF - Prairies/NWT Postdoctoral Fellowships *(Postdoctorate, Professional development/Fellowship)* [2600]
CBCF - Prairies/NWT Research Grants in Psychosocial, Cultural and Environmental Determinants of Health *(Advanced Professional, Professional development/Grant)* [2601]
Don Jaques Memorial Fellowships *(Graduate/Fellowship)* [8777]
Poundmaker Memorial Scholarships *(Undergraduate/Scholarship)* [10272]
Risk Management and Insurance Scholarships - University of Calgary *(Undergraduate/Scholarship)* [8768]
Risk Management and Insurance Scholarships *(Undergraduate/Scholarship)* [8767]
Saskatchewan Government Insurance Corporate Scholarships *(Undergraduate/Scholarship)* [8771]
Saskatchewan School Boards Association Education Scholarships *(Undergraduate/Scholarship)* [8781]
Dr. Alfred E. Slinkard Scholarships *(Graduate/Scholarship)* [8779]

Yukon Territory

Brian Campion Scholarship Scholarships *(Advanced Professional/Scholarship)* [10781]
CBCF - BC/Yukon Region Breast Cancer Research Grants Competition *(Advanced Professional/Grant)* [2587]

Legal Residence Index

CBCF - BC/Yukon Region Breast Cancer Survivor Dragon Boat Grants *(Professional development/Grant)* [2588]
CBCF - BC/Yukon Region Community Health Grants *(Professional development/Grant)* [2589]
CBCF - BC/Yukon Region Small Initiative Funds *(Professional development/Grant)* [2590]
Ted Parnell Scholarship *(Undergraduate/Scholarship)* [10772]

INTERNATIONAL

AACE International Competitive Scholarships *(Undergraduate/Scholarship)* [14]
AAMC Foundation Engagement Program for International Curators Grants *(Advanced Professional, Professional development/Grant)* [1854]
AAN International Scholarship Award *(Professional development/Scholarship)* [411]
AATS Cardiothoracic Surgery Resident Poster Competition *(Professional development/Award)* [593]
Afdhal/McHutchison LIFER Awards *(Postdoctorate, Professional development/Grant)* [587]
Amelia Earhart Fellowship Program *(Doctorate, Postgraduate/Fellowship)* [10824]
American Association of University Women International Fellowships *(Graduate, Postgraduate/Fellowship)* [601]
American Welding Society International Scholarships *(Undergraduate, Graduate/Scholarship)* [1505]
The Bentley Cropping Systems Fellowship *(Graduate/Fellowship)* [2886]
Franklin Mosher Baldwin Memorial Fellowships *(Master's, Doctorate/Fellowship)* [5991]
Conference and Workshop Grants *(Professional development/Grant)* [10514]
Amy and Tim Dauphinee Scholarships *(Graduate/Scholarship)* [2575]
Delta Kappa Gamma Society International World Fellowships *(Professional development/Fellowship)* [3571]
Fermilab Internships for Physics Majors *(Undergraduate/Internship)* [9899]
HHMI International Student Research Fellowships *(Doctorate/Fellowship)* [4975]
IOIA Organic Community Initiative Scholarships *(Other/Scholarship)* [5369]
Alexander Fraser Laidlaw Fellowships *(Graduate/Fellowship, Scholarship)* [2576]
Law and Society Association International Prize *(Other/Prize)* [5974]
Lemaire Co-operative Studies Awards *(Undergraduate, Graduate/Scholarship)* [2577]
LSAC Research Grant Program *(Professional development/Grant)* [5967]
Lee Kimche McGrath Worldwide Fellowships *(Other/Fellowship)* [2067]
National Geographic Expedition Council Grants *(Advanced Professional/Grant)* [6972]
National Geographic Young Explorers Grants *(Advanced Professional/Grant)* [6974]
PEO International Peace Scholarships *(Graduate, Master's, Doctorate/Scholarship)* [7955]
Resume Template Design Scholarships *(Undergraduate, Graduate/Scholarship)* [10369]
Rice-Cullimore Scholarships *(Graduate/Scholarship)* [1799]
IOIA Andrew Rutherford Scholarships *(Other/Scholarship)* [5370]
Ryan and Jamie Smith Essay Contest *(Graduate, Postgraduate/Scholarship)* [8992]
Lee Teng Undergraduate Fellowships in Accelerator Science and Engineering *(Undergraduate/Fellowship)* [9903]
Terra Foundation Fellowships at the Smithsonian American Art Museum *(Postdoctorate/Fellowship)* [9680]
Terra Foundation Research Travel Grants *(Doctorate, Undergraduate/Grant)* [9683]
Tikvah Fellowships *(Graduate, Professional development/Fellowship)* [9745]
Tourette Association of America Research Grant Awards *(Master's, Doctorate/Grant)* [9758]
UNC-CGI C.V. Starr Scholarships *(Undergraduate, Graduate/Scholarship)* [2847]
John D. Wirth Travel Grants for International Scholars *(Graduate, Other/Grant)* [1318]
Deborah Partridge Wolfe International Fellowships *(Graduate, Undergraduate/Fellowship)* [10820]

INTERNATIONAL (BY REGION)

Africa

American Society for Microbiology International Fellowships for Africa *(Postdoctorate/Fellowship)* [1365]
Baker and McKenzie Graduate Legal Studies Scholarships *(Graduate, Professional development/Scholarship)* [2176]
Documentary Film Grants *(Professional development/Grant)* [369]
ICNL Research Fellowships *(Advanced Professional, Professional development/Fellowship)* [5292]
Wadsworth African Fellowships *(Doctorate/Fellowship)* [10518]

Asia and Pacific

Baker and McKenzie Graduate Legal Studies Scholarships *(Graduate, Professional development/Scholarship)* [2176]
East-West Center Graduate Degree Fellowships *(Master's, Doctorate, Graduate/Fellowship)* [3760]

Asia

American Society for Microbiology International Fellowships for Asia *(Postdoctorate/Fellowship)* [1366]
Documentary Film Grants *(Professional development/Grant)* [369]
ICNL Research Fellowships *(Advanced Professional, Professional development/Fellowship)* [5292]
University of Hawaii at Manoa East-West Center Graduate Fellowships *(Graduate, Postdoctorate/Fellowship)* [10139]

Australasia

Our World Underwater Scholarship Society North American Rolex Scholarships *(Undergraduate, Professional development/Scholarship)* [7764]

Caribbean

Caribbean Hotel and Tourism Association Academic Scholarships *(Graduate, Undergraduate/Scholarship)* [2797]
IAF Fellowships *(Doctorate/Fellowship)* [5232]
ICNL Research Fellowships *(Advanced Professional, Professional development/Fellowship)* [5292]
OAS Academic Scholarship for Undergraduate Studies *(Undergraduate/Scholarship)* [7721]
Leo S. Rowe Pan American Fund *(Graduate, Undergraduate/Loan)* [7730]
TFI Latin America Media Arts Fund *(Professional development/Grant)* [9796]

Central America

OAS Scholarships for Professional Development - Disaster Communications Management *(Professional development/Scholarship)* [7723]
OAS Scholarships for Professional Development - Radio Spectrum Monitoring Techniques and Procedures *(Professional development/Scholarship)* [7724]
OAS Scholarships for Professional Development - Satellite Communications *(Professional development/Scholarship)* [7725]

Eastern Europe

Prins Foundation Fellowship for Senior Scholars *(Doctorate/Fellowship)* [2854]
Prins Foundation Post-Doctoral and Early Career Fellowship for Emigrating Scholars *(Professional development, Postdoctorate/Fellowship)* [2855]

Eurasia

ICNL Research Fellowships *(Advanced Professional, Professional development/Fellowship)* [5292]
Bill Maynes Fellowships *(Professional development/Fellowship)* [3929]

Europe

Baker and McKenzie Graduate Legal Studies Scholarships *(Graduate, Professional development/Scholarship)* [2176]
Fieldwork Fellowships *(Undergraduate/Award, Fellowship)* [3927]
HAESF Graduate Scholarships *(Graduate/Scholarship)* [5008]
HAESF Professional Internship Program *(Doctorate/Internship)* [5009]
HAESF Senior Leaders and Scholars Fellowships *(Other/Fellowship)* [5010]
ICNL Research Fellowships *(Advanced Professional, Professional development/Fellowship)* [5292]
Monte R. Mitchell Global Scholarships *(Undergraduate/Scholarship)* [168]
Our World Underwater Scholarship Society North American Rolex Scholarships *(Undergraduate, Professional development/Scholarship)* [7764]
Physics of Accelerators and Related Technology for International Students *(Undergraduate/Internship)* [9902]

Latin America and the Caribbean

American Society for Microbiology International Fellowships for Latin America and the Caribbean *(Postdoctorate/Fellowship)* [1367]

Latin America

Baker and McKenzie Graduate Legal Studies Scholarships *(Graduate, Professional development/Scholarship)* [2176]
Documentary Film Grants *(Professional development/Grant)* [369]
IAF Fellowships *(Doctorate/Fellowship)* [5232]
ICNL Research Fellowships *(Advanced Professional, Professional development/Fellowship)* [5292]
Pew Latin American Fellows Program in the Biomedical Sciences *(Other/Fellowship)* [8021]
Leo S. Rowe Pan American Fund *(Graduate, Undergraduate/Loan)* [7730]

Middle East

Baker and McKenzie Graduate Legal Studies Scholarships *(Graduate, Professional development/Scholarship)* [2176]
ICNL Research Fellowships *(Advanced Professional, Professional development/Fellowship)* [5292]

North America

Afdhal/McHutchison LIFER Awards *(Postdoctorate, Professional development/Grant)* [587]
American Association of Professional Apiculturists Research Scholarships *(Graduate, Undergraduate/Scholarship)* [568]
American Wine Society Educational Foundation Scholarships *(Graduate/Scholarship)* [1528]
Baker and McKenzie Graduate Legal Studies Scholarships *(Graduate, Professional development/Scholarship)* [2176]
Chronic Pain Medicine Research Grants *(Professional development/Grant)* [1403]
Robert E. Dougherty Scholarships *(Undergraduate, Postgraduate/Scholarship)* [3339]
A.C. Elias, Jr. Irish-American Research Travel Fellowships *(Other/Fellowship)* [1290]

Independent Lubricant Manufacturers Association Scholarships *(Undergraduate/Scholarship)* [5093]
Integra Foundation NNF Research Grant Awards *(Other/Grant)* [546]
International Scholars Program for Young Vascular Surgeons *(Graduate/Scholarship)* [9325]
J. Merrill Knapp Research Fellowship *(Undergraduate/Fellowship)* [843]
Carl Koller Memorial Research Grants *(Professional development/Grant)* [1404]
OAS Scholarships for Professional Development - Disaster Communications Management *(Professional development/Scholarship)* [7723]
OAS Scholarships for Professional Development - Radio Spectrum Monitoring Techniques and Procedures *(Professional development/Scholarship)* [7724]
OAS Scholarships for Professional Development - Satellite Communications *(Professional development/Scholarship)* [7725]
Our World Underwater Scholarship Society North American Rolex Scholarships *(Undergraduate, Professional development/Scholarship)* [7764]
Galvanize the Future: Edgar K. Schutz Scholarships *(Undergraduate, Graduate/Scholarship)* [838]
Wexner Graduate Fellowships/Davidson Scholars *(Graduate/Fellowship)* [10545]
Aubrey L. Williams Research Travel Fellowships *(Doctorate/Fellowship)* [1298]

Pacific Islands

APIASF Scholarships *(Undergraduate/Scholarship)* [1792]

Scandinavia

ASF/Annika Teig/Skidmore, Owings and Merrill Fellowships *(Postgraduate/Fellowship)* [1234]

South America

OAS Scholarships for Professional Development - Disaster Communications Management *(Professional development/Scholarship)* [7723]
OAS Scholarships for Professional Development - Radio Spectrum Monitoring Techniques and Procedures *(Professional development/Scholarship)* [7724]
OAS Scholarships for Professional Development - Satellite Communications *(Professional development/Scholarship)* [7725]
TFI Latin America Media Arts Fund *(Professional development/Grant)* [9796]

Southeast Asia

William L. Bradley Memorial Scholarships *(Undergraduate/Scholarship)* [7376]

Soviet Union (former)

Prins Foundation Fellowship for Senior Scholars *(Doctorate/Fellowship)* [2854]
Prins Foundation Post-Doctoral and Early Career Fellowship for Emigrating Scholars *(Professional development, Postdoctorate/Fellowship)* [2855]

U.S. Territories

APIASF Scholarships *(Undergraduate/Scholarship)* [1792]
A.G. Bell School Age Financial Aid Program *(Undergraduate/Scholarship)* [315]
HRSA Scholarships for Disadvantaged Students *(Undergraduate/Scholarship)* [9923]
Inspire our Future Scholarships *(All/Scholarship)* [9648]
National MS Society New Jersey Metro Chapter Scholarship Program *(Undergraduate/Scholarship)* [7075]
OAS Scholarships for Professional Development -

The ABC of Telecommunications *(Professional development/Scholarship)* [7726]

INTERNATIONAL (BY COUNTRY)

Argentina

CEJIL Communications Internships *(Undergraduate, Graduate/Internship)* [2860]
CEJIL Legal Internships *(Graduate, Professional development/Internship)* [2861]
OAS Academic Scholarships - Graduate *(Graduate/Scholarship)* [7722]

Australia

Goldia.com Jewelry Scholarships *(Undergraduate, Graduate/Scholarship)* [4474]
Harkness Fellowships in Health Care Policy and Practice *(Doctorate, Graduate/Fellowship)* [3160]
Morgan Stanley Pediatrics Fellowships *(Doctorate, Postdoctorate, Postgraduate, Graduate/Fellowship)* [618]

Barbados

OAS Academic Scholarships - Graduate *(Graduate/Scholarship)* [7722]

Bolivia

OAS Academic Scholarships - Graduate *(Graduate/Scholarship)* [7722]

Brazil

CEJIL Communications Internships *(Undergraduate, Graduate/Internship)* [2860]
CEJIL Legal Internships *(Graduate, Professional development/Internship)* [2861]
Goldia.com Jewelry Scholarships *(Undergraduate, Graduate/Scholarship)* [4474]
OAS Academic Scholarships - Graduate *(Graduate/Scholarship)* [7722]

Chile

OAS Academic Scholarships - Graduate *(Graduate/Scholarship)* [7722]

China

Lucy Hsu Ho Scholarships *(Undergraduate/Scholarship)* [2229]

Colombia

OAS Academic Scholarships - Graduate *(Graduate/Scholarship)* [7722]

Costa Rica

CEJIL Communications Internships *(Undergraduate, Graduate/Internship)* [2860]
CEJIL Legal Internships *(Graduate, Professional development/Internship)* [2861]
OAS Academic Scholarships - Graduate *(Graduate/Scholarship)* [7722]

Cuba

Cintas Foundation Fellowships in Architecture *(Professional development/Fellowship)* [3031]
Cintas Foundation Fellowships in Visual Arts *(Professional development/Fellowship)* [3032]
Brandon Fradd Fellowship *(Professional development/Fellowship)* [3033]

Denmark

American-Scandinavian Foundation Fellowships and Grants to Study in America *(Graduate, Professional development/Fellowship, Grant)* [1230]
Edith and Arnold N. Bodtker Grants *(Undergraduate,

Graduate/Grant, Internship)* [3522]
SSOC Scholarships *(Undergraduate/Scholarship)* [8786]

Dominican Republic

OAS Academic Scholarships - Graduate *(Graduate/Scholarship)* [7722]

Ecuador

OAS Academic Scholarships - Graduate *(Graduate/Scholarship)* [7722]

El Salvador

OAS Academic Scholarships - Graduate *(Graduate/Scholarship)* [7722]

Finland

American-Scandinavian Foundation Fellowships and Grants to Study in America *(Graduate, Professional development/Fellowship, Grant)* [1230]
SSOC Scholarships *(Undergraduate/Scholarship)* [8786]

France

Jenny d'Héricourt Fellowships *(Doctorate/Fellowship)* [435]

Germany

APSA Congressional Fellowships *(Other/Fellowship)* [4398]
DAI Fellowships for Study in Berlin *(Doctorate/Fellowship)* [1607]
The Christoph Daniel Ebeling Fellowships *(Postdoctorate, Postgraduate/Fellowship)* [437]
Harkness Fellowships in Health Care Policy and Practice *(Doctorate, Graduate/Fellowship)* [3160]
Anna-Maria and Stephen M. Kellen Fellowships *(Professional development/Fellowship)* [726]
McCloy Fellowships in Agriculture *(Professional development/Fellowship)* [727]
McCloy Fellowships in Environmental Policy *(Professional development/Fellowship)* [728]
McCloy Fellowships in Journalism *(Professional development/Fellowship)* [729]
McCloy Fellowships in Urban Affairs *(Professional development/Fellowship)* [730]

Ghana

ACLS African Humanities Fellowships *(Postdoctorate/Fellowship)* [734]
GCABC Youth Scholarship Awards *(Undergraduate/Scholarship)* [4419]
Next Generation Social Sciences in Africa: Doctoral Dissertation Completion Fellowships *(Doctorate/Fellowship)* [9057]
Next Generation Social Sciences in Africa: Doctoral Dissertation Proposal Fellowships *(Doctorate/Fellowship)* [9058]
Next Generation Social Sciences in Africa: Doctoral Dissertation Research Fellowship *(Doctorate/Fellowship)* [9059]

Greenland

Fritz Schwartz Serials Education Scholarships *(Graduate, Other/Scholarship)* [7447]

Grenada

OAS Academic Scholarships - Graduate *(Graduate/Scholarship)* [7722]

Guam

AFT-Oregon Union Plus Credit Card Scholarship *(Undergraduate/Scholarship)* [792]

Hungary
Dr. Elemér and Éva Kiss Scholarship Fund (Undergraduate/Scholarship) [5006]

Iceland
American-Scandinavian Foundation Fellowships and Grants to Study in America (Graduate, Professional development/Fellowship, Grant) [1230]
SSOC Scholarships (Undergraduate/Scholarship) [8786]

India
Guthikonda BasavapunnaRao and Umadevi Scholarships (Graduate/Scholarship) [9667]
Goldia.com Jewelry Scholarships (Undergraduate, Graduate/Scholarship) [4474]
Chereddi NarayanaRao and Radhamanohari Scholarships (Graduate/Scholarship) [9668]
Guthikonda Ramabrahmam and Balamani (Graduate/Scholarship) [9669]
Shastri Scholar Travel Subsidy Grants (SSTSG) (Graduate, Professional development/Grant) [8857]
Gadde Sitaramamma and Tirupataiah Scholarships (Graduate/Scholarship) [9670]
Vallabhaneni Sukundamma and Lakshmaiah Scholarships (Graduate/Scholarship) [9671]
TANA Foundation Graduate Scholarships (Graduate/Scholarship) [9672]
Kodali Veeraiah and Sarojini Scholarships (Graduate/Scholarship) [9673]

Indonesia
William L. Bradley Memorial Scholarships (Undergraduate/Scholarship) [7376]
Indonesian Directorate General of Higher Education Scholarships (Graduate/Scholarship) [3761]
Japan Indonesia Presidential Scholarship Program (Doctorate/Scholarship) [10695]

Ireland
A.C. Elias, Jr. Irish-American Research Travel Fellowships (Other/Fellowship) [1290]

Israel
Jenny Panitch Beckow Memorial Scholarships Canada (Undergraduate, Graduate/Scholarship) [5569]
Ruth and Victor David Scholarships (Undergraduate, Graduate/Scholarship) [5575]
Klarman Family Foundation Grants Program in Eating Disorders Research (Professional development/Grant) [4818]
Tikvah Fellowships (Graduate, Professional development/Fellowship) [9745]

Italy
John R. Mott Scholarships (Undergraduate/Scholarship) [6604]

Jamaica
Marcus Mosiah Garvey Scholarships (Undergraduate/Scholarship) [5523]
OAS Academic Scholarships - Graduate (Graduate/Scholarship) [7722]

Japan
Abe Fellowship Program (Professional development/Fellowship) [9051]
Abe Fellowships for Journalists (Professional development/Fellowship) [9052]
Crown Prince Akihito Scholarship Foundation (Graduate/Scholarship) [5535]
Goldia.com Jewelry Scholarships (Undergraduate, Graduate/Scholarship) [4474]
Japan Indonesia Presidential Scholarship Program (Doctorate/Scholarship) [10695]
Obuchi Student Scholarships (Graduate/Scholarship) [3762]
Wagner-Torizuka Fellowships (Professional development/Fellowship) [9228]

Jordan
Kenneth W. Russell Memorial Fellowships (Undergraduate, Graduate/Fellowship) [661]

Kazakhstan
Russian/Central Asian Student Scholarships (Undergraduate/Scholarship) [10092]

Kyrgyzstan
Russian/Central Asian Student Scholarships (Undergraduate/Scholarship) [10092]

Mexico
AASLD Autoimmune Liver Diseases Pilot Research Awards (Graduate, Doctorate, Postdoctorate, Professional development/Award, Grant) [582]
AASLD Clinical and Translational Research Awards (Professional development/Grant) [584]
Geological Society of America Graduate Student Research Grants (Doctorate, Graduate/Grant) [4364]
John J. McKetta Undergraduate Scholarships (Undergraduate/Scholarship) [905]
Marvin Mundel Memorial Scholarships (Undergraduate/Scholarship) [5192]
OAS Academic Scholarships - Graduate (Graduate/Scholarship) [7722]
Ronald L. Schmied Scholarships (Other, Undergraduate/Scholarship) [4686]
Fritz Schwartz Serials Education Scholarships (Graduate, Other/Scholarship) [7447]
TFI Latin America Media Arts Fund (Professional development/Grant) [9796]
UC MEXUS-CICESE Graduate Student Short-Term Research and Training Program (Master's, Doctorate, Postdoctorate/Grant) [10110]
UC MEXUS-CONACYT Collaborative Grants (Professional development/Grant) [10116]
UC MEXUS-CONACYT Doctoral Fellowships (Doctorate/Fellowship) [10117]
UC MEXUS-CONACYT Postdoctoral Research Fellowships (Postdoctorate/Fellowship) [10118]
UC MEXUS Dissertation Research Grants (Graduate/Grant) [10119]
UC MEXUS Grants for Dissertation Research (Graduate/Grant) [10111]
UC MEXUS Scholars in Residence Program - Graduate (Graduate/Scholarship) [10120]
UC MEXUS Scholars in Residence Program - Recent University Graduates (Postgraduate/Scholarship) [10121]
UC MEXUS Scholars in Residence Program - Visiting Faculty (Professional development/Scholarship) [10122]
UC MEXUS Small Grants for UC Faculty (Graduate/Grant) [10123]
UC MEXUS Small Grants for UC Postdocs (Postdoctorate/Grant) [10124]
UC MEXUS Small Grants for UC Students (Graduate, Postdoctorate/Grant) [10125]
United Parcel Service Scholarships for Female Students (Undergraduate/Scholarship) [5195]
United Parcel Service Scholarships for Minority Students (Undergraduate/Scholarship) [5196]
Abel Wolman Fellowships (Doctorate/Fellowship) [1492]

Mongolia
Enkhbaatar Demchig Field Research Fellowship Program (Undergraduate/Fellowship) [651]

Nepal
Hugh and Helen Wood Nepales Scholarships (Undergraduate/Scholarship) [2233]

Netherlands
Harkness Fellowships in Health Care Policy and Practice (Doctorate, Graduate/Fellowship) [3160]

New Zealand
Harkness Fellowships in Health Care Policy and Practice (Doctorate, Graduate/Fellowship) [3160]

Nigeria
ACLS African Humanities Fellowships (Postdoctorate/Fellowship) [734]
Next Generation Social Sciences in Africa: Doctoral Dissertation Completion Fellowships (Doctorate/Fellowship) [9057]
Next Generation Social Sciences in Africa: Doctoral Dissertation Proposal Fellowships (Doctorate/Fellowship) [9058]
Next Generation Social Sciences in Africa: Doctoral Dissertation Research Fellowship (Doctorate/Fellowship) [9059]
NWAG Nigeria Scholarships (Undergraduate/Scholarship) [7432]

North Korea
Asia-Pacific Biomedical Research Foundation Merit Awards (Postdoctorate/Award) [9304]

Norway
American-Scandinavian Foundation Fellowships and Grants to Study in America (Graduate, Professional development/Fellowship, Grant) [1230]
Harkness Fellowships in Health Care Policy and Practice (Doctorate, Graduate/Fellowship) [3160]
SSOC Scholarships (Undergraduate/Scholarship) [8786]

Pakistan
AIPS Post-Doctoral Fellowships (Postdoctorate/Fellowship) [920]
AIPS Pre-Doctoral Fellowships (Doctorate, Graduate/Fellowship) [921]

Panama
OAS Academic Scholarships - Graduate (Graduate/Scholarship) [7722]

Peru
William L. Brown Fellowships (Graduate/Fellowship) [7735]
David and Deborah Clark Fellowships (Graduate/Fellowship) [7736]
Rexford Daubenmire Fellowships (Graduate/Fellowship) [7737]
Dole Food Fellowships (Graduate/Fellowship) [7738]
Emily P. Foster Fellowships (Graduate/Fellowship) [7739]
OAS Academic Scholarships - Graduate (Graduate/Scholarship) [7722]
Peace Frogs Fellowships (Graduate/Fellowship) [7741]
Lillian and Murray Slatkin Fellowships (Graduate/Fellowship) [7743]
F. Christian and Betty Thompson Fellowships (Graduate/Fellowship) [7745]

Philippines
William L. Bradley Memorial Scholarships (Undergraduate/Scholarship) [7376]
PNAA Nursing Scholarship Award (Master's, Doctorate/Scholarship) [8113]

Puerto Rico
AFT-Oregon Union Plus Credit Card Scholarship (Undergraduate/Scholarship) [792]
Army Health Professions Scholarships Program (Professional development/Scholarship) [9878]

INTERNATIONAL

HACU/JCPenny Leadership Excellence Scholarships *(Undergraduate, Graduate/Scholarship)* [4886]
HACU/KIA Motors America, Inc. Scholarships *(Undergraduate, Graduate/Scholarship)* [4887]
Hispanic Association of Colleges and Universities Scholarships *(Undergraduate/Scholarship)* [4890]
HRSA Scholarships for Disadvantaged Students *(Undergraduate/Scholarship)* [9923]
Imagine America College Scholarships for High School Students *(Undergraduate/Scholarship)* [5083]

Russia

East-West Center Graduate Degree Fellowships *(Master's, Doctorate, Graduate/Fellowship)* [3760]
HBI-BGI Scholar-in-Residence Program *(Undergraduate/Scholarship)* [2359]
Russian/Central Asian Student Scholarships *(Undergraduate/Scholarship)* [10092]

Serbia

Dr. Elemér and Éva Kiss Scholarship Fund *(Undergraduate/Scholarship)* [5006]

Slovakia

Dr. Elemér and Éva Kiss Scholarship Fund *(Undergraduate/Scholarship)* [5006]

South Africa

ACLS African Humanities Fellowships *(Postdoctorate/Fellowship)* [734]
Next Generation Social Sciences in Africa: Doctoral Dissertation Completion Fellowships *(Doctorate/Fellowship)* [9057]
Next Generation Social Sciences in Africa: Doctoral Dissertation Proposal Fellowships *(Doctorate/Fellowship)* [9058]
Next Generation Social Sciences in Africa: Doctoral Dissertation Research Fellowship *(Doctorate/Fellowship)* [9059]

South Korea

Asia-Pacific Biomedical Research Foundation Merit Awards *(Postdoctorate/Award)* [9304]
Goldia.com Jewelry Scholarships *(Undergraduate, Graduate/Scholarship)* [4474]

Suriname

OAS Academic Scholarship for Undergraduate Studies *(Undergraduate/Scholarship)* [7721]

Sweden

American-Scandinavian Foundation Fellowships and Grants to Study in America *(Graduate, Professional development/Fellowship, Grant)* [1230]
Harkness Fellowships in Health Care Policy and Practice *(Doctorate, Graduate/Fellowship)* [3160]
SSOC Scholarships *(Undergraduate/Scholarship)* [8786]

Switzerland

Harkness Fellowships in Health Care Policy and Practice *(Doctorate, Graduate/Fellowship)* [3160]

Taiwan

Joel R. Friend Scholarships *(Undergraduate/Scholarship)* [2227]

Tanzania

ACLS African Humanities Fellowships *(Postdoctorate/Fellowship)* [734]
Godparents for Tanzania Scholarship *(Undergraduate/Scholarship)* [4464]
Next Generation Social Sciences in Africa: Doctoral Dissertation Completion Fellowships *(Doctorate/Fellowship)* [9057]
Next Generation Social Sciences in Africa: Doctoral Dissertation Proposal Fellowships *(Doctorate/Fellowship)* [9058]
Next Generation Social Sciences in Africa: Doctoral Dissertation Research Fellowship *(Doctorate/Fellowship)* [9059]

Thailand

Joel R. Friend Scholarships *(Undergraduate/Scholarship)* [2227]

Trinidad and Tobago

OAS Academic Scholarships - Graduate *(Graduate/Scholarship)* [7722]

Turkey

Getty Research Exchange Fellowship Program for Cultural Heritage Preservation *(Doctorate/Fellowship)* [1205]
Ilse Hanfmann, George Hanfmann and Machteld Mellink Fellowships *(Doctorate/Fellowship)* [1206]

Turkmenistan

Russian/Central Asian Student Scholarships *(Undergraduate/Scholarship)* [10092]

Uganda

ACLS African Humanities Fellowships *(Postdoctorate/Fellowship)* [734]
Next Generation Social Sciences in Africa: Doctoral Dissertation Completion Fellowships *(Doctorate/Fellowship)* [9057]
Next Generation Social Sciences in Africa: Doctoral Dissertation Proposal Fellowships *(Doctorate/Fellowship)* [9058]
Next Generation Social Sciences in Africa: Doctoral Dissertation Research Fellowship *(Doctorate/Fellowship)* [9059]

Ukraine

Alberta Ukrainian Centennial Commemorative Scholarships *(Graduate/Scholarship)* [10440]
ALIS International Education Awards - Ukraine *(Undergraduate/Scholarship)* [265]
Canada-Ukraine Parliamentary Program Internship Scholarships (CUPP) *(Undergraduate/Scholarship, Internship)* [10441]
Chopivsky Fellowships *(Graduate/Fellowship)* [10442]
Dr. Elemér and Éva Kiss Scholarship Fund *(Undergraduate/Scholarship)* [5006]
The Ivan Shandor Memorial Ukrainian American Bar Association Scholarships *(Graduate, Master's/Scholarship)* [10444]
USA/USA-Ukramerazha Scholarships *(Undergraduate/Scholarship)* [9982]
Marusia Yaworska Entrance Scholarships *(Graduate/Scholarship)* [10445]

United Kingdom

Hilda E. Bretzlaff Foundation Scholarships *(Undergraduate/Scholarship, Grant)* [2363]
Goldia.com Jewelry Scholarships *(Undergraduate, Graduate/Scholarship)* [4474]
Harkness Fellowships in Health Care Policy and Practice *(Doctorate, Graduate/Fellowship)* [3160]
Saint Andrews Scholarships *(Undergraduate/Scholarship)* [8670]
U.S.-U.K. Young Investigator Exchange Fellowship *(Postdoctorate/Fellowship)* [376]

United States Virgin Islands

AFT-Oregon Union Plus Credit Card Scholarship *(Undergraduate/Scholarship)* [792]
Almeric Christian Memorial Scholarships *(Graduate/Scholarship)* [10392]

Uruguay

OAS Academic Scholarships - Graduate *(Graduate/Scholarship)* [7722]

Uzbekistan

Russian/Central Asian Student Scholarships *(Undergraduate/Scholarship)* [10092]

Vietnam

Southeast Asian Ministers of Education Organization-Vietnam Scholarship Program *(Graduate/Scholarship)* [3763]
VEF Fellowship Program *(Doctorate, Master's/Fellowship)* [10380]
VEF Visiting Scholars Program *(Doctorate/Fellowship)* [10381]

Place of Study Index

This index lists awards that carry restrictions on where study may take place. Award citations are arranged alphabetically under the following geographic headings: United States, United States (by region), United States (by state), Canada, Canada (by province), International, International (by region), and International (by country). Each citation is followed by the study level and award type, which appear in parentheses. Numbers following the parenthetical information indicate book entry numbers for particular awards, not page numbers.

UNITED STATES

180 Medical College Scholarship Program *(Undergraduate, Graduate/Scholarship)* [4]
1Dental Dentistry Scholarships *(Undergraduate/Scholarship)* [6]
4th Infantry Division Association Memorial Scholarships *(All/Scholarship)* [6670]
AAA Postdoctoral Fellowship Program *(Postdoctorate/Fellowship)* [460]
AAAA Scholarship Program *(Undergraduate, Graduate/Scholarship)* [1710]
AAACN Conference Scholarships for Nursing Students *(Undergraduate/Scholarship)* [385]
AAACN Education Scholarships *(Undergraduate/Scholarship)* [386]
AAACN Research Grants *(Undergraduate/Grant)* [387]
AAACN Scholarships *(Undergraduate/Scholarship)* [388]
AAAS Mass Media Science and Engineering Fellowship *(Undergraduate, Graduate, Postdoctorate/Fellowship, Award)* [453]
AAAS Science and Technology Policy Fellowships *(Professional development/Fellowship)* [454]
AABP Amstutz Scholarships *(Undergraduate/Scholarship)* [466]
AABP Bovine Veterinary Student Recognition Awards *(Undergraduate/Scholarship)* [467]
AABP Education Grants *(Undergraduate/Grant)* [468]
AABP Student Externship Program *(Undergraduate/Scholarship)* [469]
AACD Dentist Fellowships *(Professional development/Fellowship)* [405]
AACD Laboratory Fellowships *(Professional development/Fellowship)* [406]
AACE International Competitive Scholarships *(Undergraduate/Scholarship)* [14]
AACN Continuing Professional Development Scholarships *(Advanced Professional, Other/Scholarship)* [490]
AACOM Scholar in Residence Program *(Professional development/Scholarship)* [482]
AACPDM Student Scholarships *(Professional development/Scholarship)* [399]
AACPDM Transformative Practice Grants *(Professional development/Grant)* [400]
AACR Scholar-in-Training Awards: Other Conferences and Meetings *(Graduate, Postdoctorate, Professional development/Grant)* [471]
AACT Junior Investigator Research Grants *(Professional development/Grant)* [402]
AACT Toxicology Trainee Research Grants *(Professional development/Grant)* [403]
AACTE Outstanding Book Awards *(Other/Recognition)* [484]
AACTE Outstanding Dissertation Awards *(Doctorate/Award)* [485]
AAEP/ALSIC Scholarships *(Undergraduate/Scholarship)* [495]
AAEP Foundation Past Presidents' Research Fellowships *(Graduate, Professional development/Scholarship)* [496]

AAFPE LEX Scholarships *(Undergraduate/Scholarship)* [553]
AAFSW College Merit Scholarship *(College, Undergraduate/Scholarship)* [1820]
AAG Dissertation Research Grants *(Doctorate/Grant)* [1829]
AAHD Scholarships *(Graduate, Undergraduate/Scholarship)* [502]
AAI Careers in Immunology Fellowship Program *(Graduate, Doctorate, Postdoctorate/Fellowship)* [506]
AAI Public Policy Fellows Program (PPFP) *(Doctorate, Postdoctorate/Fellowship)* [507]
AAIB Scholarships *(Undergraduate/Scholarship)* [509]
AAIDD Fellowship *(Advanced Professional, Professional development/Fellowship)* [511]
AAJ Trial Advocacy Scholarships *(Undergraduate/Scholarship)* [515]
AALL Leadership Academy Grants *(Professional development/Grant)* [519]
AALL Minority Leadership Development Award *(Graduate/Award)* [520]
AALL Research Funds *(Professional development/Grant)* [521]
AALL Scholarships for Continuing Education Classes *(Postgraduate/Scholarship)* [522]
AALL Technical Services SIS Active Member Grant *(Professional development/Grant)* [523]
AALL Technical Services SIS Experienced Member General Grant *(Professional development/Grant)* [524]
AALL Technical Services SIS Leadership Academy Grant *(Professional development/Grant)* [525]
AALL Technical Services SIS Management Institute Grant *(Professional development/Grant)* [526]
AALL Technical Services SIS New Member General Grant *(Professional development/Grant)* [527]
AAMC Foundation Engagement Program for International Curators Grants *(Advanced Professional, Professional development/Grant)* [1854]
AAMFT Minority Fellowships *(Doctorate, Graduate/Fellowship)* [538]
AAN Clinical Research Training Fellowships *(Other/Fellowship)* [410]
AAN International Scholarship Award *(Professional development/Scholarship)* [411]
AAN Medical Student Summer Research Scholarships *(Graduate/Scholarship)* [412]
A&WMA Scholarships *(Graduate/Scholarship)* [139]
AANS Medical Student Summer Research Fellowships (MSSRF) *(Undergraduate/Fellowship)* [542]
AAOHN Professional Development Scholarships - Academic Study *(Graduate, Undergraduate/Scholarship)* [550]
AAOHN Professional Development Scholarships - Continuing Education *(Other/Scholarship)* [551]
AAPM Diversity Recruitment through Education and Mentoring Program (MUSE) *(Undergraduate/Fellowship)* [557]
AAPM Fellowships for Graduate Study in Medical Physics *(Graduate/Fellowship)* [558]
AAPM Summer Undergraduate Fellowships *(Undergraduate/Fellowship)* [559]

Leroy F. Aarons Scholarships *(Graduate, Undergraduate/Scholarship)* [7049]
AAS-American Historical Print Collectors Society Fellowships *(Doctorate/Fellowship)* [428]
AAS-American Society for Eighteenth Century Studies Fellowships *(Postdoctorate/Fellowship)* [429]
AAS CIAC Small Grants *(Graduate/Grant)* [1857]
AAS Fellowships for Creative and Performing Artists and Writers *(Professional development/Fellowship, Award)* [430]
AAS Korean Studies Scholarship Program *(Graduate/Scholarship)* [1858]
AAS National Endowment for the Humanities Long-Term Fellowships *(Postdoctorate/Fellowship)* [431]
AAS-Northeast Modern Language Association Fellowships *(Undergraduate/Fellowship)* [432]
AASA Educational Administration Scholarship Awards *(Postgraduate/Scholarship)* [572]
AASLD Advanced/Transplant Hepatology Fellowships *(Professional development/Fellowship)* [581]
AASLD Autoimmune Liver Diseases Pilot Research Awards *(Graduate, Doctorate, Postdoctorate, Professional development/Award, Grant)* [582]
AASLD Career Development Awards in Liver Transplantation *(Professional development/Grant)* [583]
AASLD Clinical and Translational Research Awards *(Professional development/Grant)* [584]
AASLD NP/PA Clinical Hepatology Fellowships *(Professional development/Fellowship)* [585]
AASLD Pinnacle Research Awards in Liver Disease *(Professional development/Grant)* [586]
AAST/ETHICON Research Grants in Local Wound Haemostatics and Hemorrhage Control Scholarships *(Graduate, Postgraduate/Grant)* [589]
AAST/KCI Research Grant *(Doctorate/Grant)* [590]
AAST Medical Student, Resident and In-Training Fellow Scholarships *(Advanced Professional/Scholarship)* [591]
AATS Cardiothoracic Surgery Resident Poster Competition *(Professional development/Award)* [593]
AATS Medical Students Summer Intern Scholarships *(Undergraduate/Scholarship, Internship)* [594]
AATS Perioperative/Team-Based Care Poster Competition *(Professional development/Award)* [595]
AATS Resident Critical Care Scholarships *(Professional development/Scholarship)* [596]
AATS/STS Cardiothoracic Ethics Forum Scholarships *(Professional development/Scholarship)* [597]
AAUW American Fellowships *(Doctorate, Postdoctorate/Fellowship)* [19]
AAUW Career Development Grants *(Graduate, Advanced Professional, Professional development/Grant)* [20]
AAUW International Fellowships *(Master's, Doctorate, Postdoctorate/Fellowship)* [21]
AAUW Selected Professions Fellowships *(Graduate, Master's, Doctorate/Fellowship)* [22]
AAZK/AZA Advances in Animal Keeping Course Grants *(Professional development/Grant)* [608]
AAZK Conservation, Preservation and Restoration Grants *(Professional development/Grant)* [609]
AAZK Professional Development Grants *(Profes-

sional development/Grant) [610]
AAZK Research Grants (Professional development/Grant) [611]
ABA Diversity Scholarships (Undergraduate/Scholarship) [636]
ABA Members Scholarships for ABA Bus and Tour Operators Only (Undergraduate/Scholarship) [637]
ABA Members Scholarships for All ABA Member Companies (Undergraduate, Graduate/Scholarship) [638]
ABA Scholarships (Undergraduate/Scholarship) [626]
Anthony Abbene Scholarships (Undergraduate/Scholarship) [5025]
Clifford V. Abbott Memorial Scholarships (Undergraduate/Scholarship) [9561]
ABC-Clio Research Grants (Graduate/Grant) [9208]
Jordan Abdo Memorial Scholarship (Undergraduate/Scholarship) [9417]
Abe Fellowship Program (Professional development/Fellowship) [9051]
Abe Fellowships for Journalists (Professional development/Fellowship) [9052]
Ruth Abernathy Presidential Scholarships (Graduate, Undergraduate/Scholarship) [9128]
ABF Doctoral/Post-Doctoral Fellowships (Doctorate, Graduate/Fellowship) [622]
ABF Law and Social Science Dissertation Fellowship and Mentoring Program (Graduate/Fellowship) [623]
ABF Montgomery Summer Research Diversity Fellowships in Law and Social Science (Undergraduate/Fellowship) [624]
ABFSE National Scholarship Program (Undergraduate/Scholarship) [629]
Kyutaro and Yasuo Abiko Memorial Scholarships (Undergraduate/Scholarship) [5547]
Evelyn Abrams Memorial Scholarships (Undergraduate/Scholarship) [8327]
ABTA Discovery Grant Program (Professional development/Grant) [631]
ABTA Medical Student Summer Fellowship Program (Undergraduate/Grant, Fellowship) [632]
ABTA Translational Grant Program (Postdoctorate/Grant) [633]
Academy of Motion Picture Arts and Sciences Student Academy Awards (Undergraduate/Award) [42]
Academy of Neonatal Nursing Conference Scholarships (Professional development/Scholarship) [44]
Accenture American Indian Scholarship Program (Graduate, Undergraduate/Scholarship) [880]
The Achieve Physical Therapy and Fitness Scholarship (Doctorate/Scholarship) [9580]
ACI BASF Construction Chemicals Student Fellowships (Graduate, Undergraduate/Fellowship) [701]
ACI Cagley ACI Student Fellowships (Graduate, Master's, Undergraduate/Fellowship) [702]
ACI Foundation Scholarships (Graduate/Scholarship) [703]
ACI-NA Scholarships (Graduate, Undergraduate/Scholarship) [180]
ACI President's Fellowships (Doctorate, Master's/Fellowship) [704]
ACI W.R. Grace Scholarships (Graduate/Scholarship) [705]
ACJA-LAE Student Paper Competitions (Undergraduate, Graduate/Scholarship) [752]
ACLS Collaborative Research Fellowships (Doctorate/Fellowship) [735]
ACLS Fellowships (Advanced Professional, Professional development/Fellowship) [736]
ACMPE Scholarship Fund Program (Graduate, Undergraduate/Scholarship) [6384]
ACMS Intensive Mongolian Language Fellowship Program (Undergraduate/Fellowship) [648]
ACNL Research Scholarships (Graduate/Scholarship) [1869]
ACNM Foundation, Inc. Fellowships for Graduate Education (Doctorate, Postdoctorate/Fellowship, Grant) [692]
ACNM Foundation Midwives of Color-Watson Midwifery Student Scholarship (Undergraduate/Scholarship) [693]
ACOR-CAORC Post-Graduate Fellowships (Doctorate, Postdoctorate/Award) [653]

Acoustical Society of America Minority Fellowships (Graduate/Fellowship) [52]
ACPA Foundation Annual Fund (Professional development/Grant) [695]
Andreas Acrivos Dissertation Award in Fluid Dynamics (Graduate, Doctorate/Award) [1085]
ACS/ASA Health Policy and Management Scholarships (Professional development/Scholarship) [1468]
ACS Doctoral Degree Scholarships in Cancer Nursing (Doctorate, Graduate/Scholarship) [642]
ACS Graduate Scholarships in Cancer Nursing Practice (Graduate, Master's, Doctorate/Scholarship) [643]
ACS Law Fellowships (Graduate/Fellowship) [716]
ACS Rubber Division Undergraduate Scholarships (Undergraduate/Scholarship) [666]
ACSO Scholarships (Undergraduate/Scholarship) [1633]
ACSUS Distinguished Dissertation Awards (Doctorate/Award) [1875]
Actuarial Diversity Scholarship (Undergraduate/Scholarship) [60]
ACUI Research and Education Grant (Undergraduate, Graduate, Professional development/Grant) [1925]
ACVO Best Resident Manuscript Awards (Undergraduate/Recognition) [699]
ADAA Career Development Travel Awards (Other/Award) [1569]
Nancy Ashley Adams/Ashley Adams Koetje Scholarships (Undergraduate/Scholarship) [3547]
EFWA Moss Adams Foundation Scholarships (Undergraduate/Scholarship) [3800]
Ruth D. Adams Fund (Undergraduate/Scholarship) [4037]
The Clarke B. Adams Memorial Foundation Lapeer County Community Foundation Fund (Undergraduate/Scholarship) [5928]
Lt. Holly Adams Memorial Scholarships (Undergraduate/Scholarship) [3209]
RPMDA/Ed Adams Memorial Scholarships (Other/Scholarship) [8567]
Ruth Adams Memorial Scholarships (Undergraduate/Scholarship) [8442]
Henry S. and Carolyn Adams Scholarship Fund (Undergraduate/Scholarship) [4172]
Henry Adams Scholarships (Undergraduate/Scholarship) [1326]
Gladys Ross Carlson Adelphe Scholarship Fund (Undergraduate, Graduate/Award) [5688]
Adelson Family Scholarships (Undergraduate/Scholarship) [8328]
Adelson Scholarships (Undergraduate/Scholarship) [8329]
ADHA IOH Sigma Phi Alpha Graduate Scholarships (Graduate/Scholarship) [775]
Howard E. and Wilma J. Adkins Memorial Scholarships (Undergraduate/Scholarship) [1502]
Adler Pollock & Sheehan Diversity Scholarships (Undergraduate/Scholarship) [71]
ADMA International Scholarship (Undergraduate/Scholarship) [2144]
Adolescent/Young Adult Lymphoma Cooperative Groups Correlative Studies Grants (Advanced Professional/Grant) [6156]
Herb Adrian Memorial Scholarship Fund (Undergraduate/Scholarship) [4173]
Adult Students in Scholastic Transition Scholarships (ASIST) (Professional development/Scholarship) [3935]
Advance Degree and Clinical Research Training Grants in Alpha-1 Antitrypsin Deficiency (Master's/Grant) [1208]
Advance Prevention Lawsuit Legal Scholarships (Undergraduate/Scholarship) [5982]
"Advice to Your High School Self" Scholarships (Undergraduate/Scholarship) [2534]
AE Flight Training Scholarships (Other/Scholarship) [7436]
AE Jet Type Rating Scholarships (Other/Scholarship) [7437]
AE Technical Training Scholarships (Other/Scholarship) [7438]
AECT Foundation Mentor Endowment Scholarships (Doctorate, Graduate/Scholarship) [1942]

AECT Legacy Scholarship (Master's, Graduate, Professional development/Scholarship) [1943]
AED Student Early Career Investigator Travel Fellowships (Undergraduate, Graduate, Postdoctorate, Postgraduate/Fellowship) [32]
AED Student Research Grants (Undergraduate, Graduate, Postgraduate/Grant) [33]
AERA-AIR Fellows Program (Postdoctorate/Fellowship) [782]
AERA-ETS Fellowship Program in Measurement and Education Research (Doctorate/Fellowship) [783]
AERA Minority Fellowship Program in Education Research (Doctorate/Fellowship) [784]
Aerospace Corporation Science and Engineering Student Scholarships (Undergraduate, Graduate/Scholarship) [95]
AES Educational Foundation Grants (Graduate/Grant, Award) [2122]
AESF Foundation Scholarships (Undergraduate, Graduate/Scholarship) [6796]
AFCEA Cyber Studies and Intelligence Scholarships (Undergraduate, Graduate/Scholarship) [85]
AFCEA Scholarship for Working Professionals (Undergraduate, Graduate/Scholarship) [86]
AFCEA Science, Technology, Engineering and Math Teachers Scholarships (Graduate/Scholarship, Grant) [87]
Afdhal/McHutchison LIFER Awards (Postdoctorate, Professional development/Grant) [587]
AFFIRM University Scholarships (Undergraduate/Scholarship) [1961]
Affirmative Action Student Scholarship Mini-Grant Travel Awards (Undergraduate, Master's, Doctorate/Grant) [30]
Afghanistan and Iraq War Veterans Scholarship (Undergraduate/Scholarship) [88]
AFPE Gateway Research Scholarships (Doctorate/Scholarship) [826]
AFPE Pre-Doctoral Fellowships in Pharmaceutical Sciences for Underrepresented Minorities (Doctorate, Graduate/Fellowship) [828]
AFPE Pre-Doctoral Fellowships in Pharmaceutical Sciences (Doctorate/Fellowship) [827]
AFPPA Student Scholarships (Undergraduate/Scholarship) [1959]
AFSA Chapter 155 Division 1 Scholarships - Category 1 (Undergraduate/Scholarship) [130]
AFSA Chapter 155 Division 1 Scholarships - Category 2 (Undergraduate/Scholarship) [131]
AFSA Chapter 155 Division 1 Scholarships - Category 3 (Undergraduate/Scholarship) [132]
AFSP - Distinguished Investigator Grants (Postgraduate/Award) [830]
AFSP Postdoctoral Research Fellowships (Postgraduate/Fellowship) [831]
AFSP Standard Research Grants (Postgraduate/Grant) [832]
AFSP Young Investigator Grants (Postgraduate/Grant) [833]
AFT-Oregon Union Plus Credit Card Scholarship (Undergraduate/Scholarship) [792]
AfterCollege/AACN Nursing Scholarships (Graduate, Undergraduate/Scholarship) [479]
AfterCollege-AACN Scholarships (Undergraduate, Master's, Doctorate/Scholarship) [96]
AfterCollege Business Student Scholarships (Undergraduate, Graduate, Doctorate/Scholarship) [97]
AfterCollege Engineering Student Scholarships (Undergraduate, Graduate, Doctorate, Master's/Scholarship) [98]
AfterCollege Occupational Therapy Scholarships (Master's, Doctorate/Scholarship) [99]
AfterCollege Physical Therapist Student Scholarships (Undergraduate, Master's, Doctorate/Scholarship) [100]
AfterCollege Science Student Scholarships (Undergraduate, Graduate, Doctorate/Scholarship) [101]
AfterCollege STEM Inclusion Scholarships (Undergraduate, Graduate/Scholarship) [102]
AfterCollege Succurro Scholarships (Undergraduate, Graduate, Doctorate/Scholarship) [103]
AFWA Masters Degree Scholarships (Undergraduate, Master's/Scholarship) [49]
AFWA Undergraduate Scholarships (Undergraduate/Scholarship) [50]

Place of Study Index

UNITED STATES

AGBU Heritage Scholar Grant *(Undergraduate/Scholarship, Grant)* [1673]
AGC Foundation Outstanding Educator Awards *(Other/Award)* [1812]
AGC New York State Chapter Scholarship Program *(Undergraduate/Scholarship)* [1814]
The Agnes Sopcak Memorial Scholarship *(Undergraduate/Scholarship)* [10649]
Agriculture Future of America Community Scholarships *(Undergraduate/Scholarship)* [116]
Agriculture Future of America Scholarships *(Undergraduate/Scholarship)* [117]
AGWT Baroid Scholarships *(Undergraduate/Scholarship)* [840]
AH&LEF American Express Scholarship *(Undergraduate/Scholarship)* [858]
AHCJ Reporting Fellowships on Health Care Performance *(Other/Fellowship)* [3158]
Patty Ahearn Victoria Elementary Scholarships *(Undergraduate/Scholarship)* [8443]
Ahepa Buckeye Scholarship Awards *(Undergraduate/Scholarship)* [119]
AHEPA Family District No. 1 Scholarships *(Graduate, Undergraduate/Scholarship)* [849]
AHETEMS/ExxonMobil Scholarships *(Undergraduate/Scholarship)* [8887]
AHETEMS General Scholarships *(Undergraduate, Graduate/Scholarship)* [8888]
AHETEMS Professional Scholarships *(Graduate/Scholarship)* [8889]
AHNS/AAO-HNS Young Investigator Award *(Other/Grant)* [845]
AHNS Pilot Research Grants *(Other/Grant)* [846]
AIA Alaska Scholarships *(Graduate, Undergraduate/Scholarship)* [893]
AIA and the Global Automotive Aftermarket Symposium Scholarships *(Undergraduate/Scholarship)* [2131]
AIA Graduate Student Travel Awards *(Graduate/Grant)* [1603]
AIA Northeast Illinois Student Scholarships *(Undergraduate, Graduate/Scholarship)* [895]
AIAA Foundation Scholarship Program *(Graduate, Undergraduate/Scholarship)* [891]
AIChE Minority Scholarship Awards for College Students *(Undergraduate/Scholarship)* [903]
AIChE Minority Scholarship Awards for Incoming College Freshmen *(Undergraduate/Scholarship)* [904]
AIEA Presidential Fellows Program *(Undergraduate/Fellowship)* [1985]
AIGC Fellowships - Graduate *(Graduate/Fellowship)* [881]
AIPN Student Scholarships *(All/Scholarship)* [1987]
AIPS Post-Doctoral Fellowships *(Postdoctorate/Fellowship)* [920]
AIPS Pre-Doctoral Fellowships *(Doctorate, Graduate/Fellowship)* [921]
AIR Dissertation Grants *(Doctorate/Grant)* [1980]
Air Force Association/Grantham Scholarships *(Undergraduate/Scholarship)* [121]
Air Force Sergeants Association Scholarship Program *(Undergraduate/Scholarship)* [128]
Air Products and Chemicals, Inc. Scholarships *(Undergraduate/Scholarship)* [1975]
AIR Research Grants *(Professional development/Grant)* [1981]
Air Traffic Control Association Full-time Employee Student Scholarships *(Other/Scholarship)* [135]
Air Traffic Control Association Non-employee Student Scholarships *(Undergraduate/Scholarship)* [136]
Aircraft Owners and Pilots Association Scholarships *(Undergraduate/Scholarship)* [154]
AISES Intel Scholarships *(Graduate, Undergraduate/Scholarship)* [887]
AISLS Dissertation Planning Grants *(Graduate/Grant)* [929]
AISLS Grants for Language Instruction *(Doctorate/Grant)* [931]
Justice John F. Aiso Scholarships *(Undergraduate/Scholarship)* [5541]
AIST Baltimore Member Chapter Scholarships *(Undergraduate/Scholarship)* [1989]
AIST Midwest Member Chapter - Engineering Scholarships *(Undergraduate/Scholarship)* [1990]

AIST Midwest Member Chapter - Non-Engineering Scholarships *(Undergraduate/Scholarship)* [1991]
AIST Midwest Member Chapter - Western States Scholarships *(Undergraduate/Scholarship)* [1992]
AIST Northwest Member Chapter Scholarships *(Undergraduate/Scholarship)* [1993]
AIST Ohio Valley Chapter Scholarships *(Undergraduate/Scholarship)* [1994]
AIST San Francisco Member Chapter Scholarships *(Undergraduate/Scholarship)* [1995]
AJL Conference Stipends *(Graduate/Grant)* [2010]
AJL Scholarship Fund *(Graduate/Scholarship)* [2011]
Ak-Sar-Ben Scholarships *(Undergraduate/Scholarship)* [4935]
Crown Prince Akihito Scholarship Foundation *(Graduate/Scholarship)* [5535]
ALA Allergic Respiratory Diseases Research Award *(Doctorate/Grant)* [969]
Alabama ARN Scholarship *(Professional development/Scholarship)* [2054]
Alabama Horse Council Scholarships *(Undergraduate/Scholarship)* [203]
Alamo Area Paralegal Association Educational Scholarships *(Undergraduate, Professional development/Scholarship)* [209]
Alamo IFT Scholarship *(Undergraduate/Scholarship)* [5175]
Jonathan Alan Scholarship Fund *(Undergraduate/Scholarship)* [10497]
Albert Einstein Distinguished Educator Fellowships (AEF) *(Graduate, Other/Fellowship)* [9794]
Bette Lou Albert, New Mexico, Memorial Scholarship Fund *(Undergraduate, Graduate/Scholarship)* [5689]
Alberta Holstein Association Scholarships *(Undergraduate/Scholarship)* [246]
Bruce and Betty Alberts Endowed Scholarships in Physiology *(Undergraduate/Scholarship)* [6243]
Albinas Elskus Scholarship *(All/Scholarship)* [9488]
ALCOA Foundation Corporate Scholarships *(Undergraduate, Graduate/Scholarship)* [4645]
ALD Graduate Fellowships *(Graduate/Fellowship)* [6696]
Owen F. Aldis Scholarship Fund *(Doctorate/Scholarship)* [5420]
Alex Scholarship Funds *(Undergraduate/Scholarship)* [6280]
Anne L. Alexander and Blaise Robert Alexander Memorial Scholarships *(Undergraduate/Scholarship)* [4038]
William Tasse Alexander Scholarship Fund *(Undergraduate/Scholarship)* [4175]
Neil Alexander Scholarships *(Undergraduate/Scholarship)* [6688]
Alex's Lemonade Stand Foundation Epidemiology Grants *(Doctorate, Master's, Professional development/Grant)* [318]
Alex's Lemonade Stand Foundation Innovation Grants *(Other/Grant)* [319]
Alex's Lemonade Stand Foundation Young Investigator Grants *(Doctorate, Master's, Professional development/Grant)* [320]
ALF Postdoctoral Research Fellowship Award *(Postdoctorate, Professional development/Fellowship)* [966]
Floyd S. Alford Jr. Scholarships *(Undergraduate/Scholarship)* [10212]
Horatio Alger Delaware Scholarships *(Undergraduate/Scholarship)* [4936]
Horatio Alger District of Columbia, Maryland and Virginia Scholarships *(Undergraduate/Scholarship)* [4937]
Horatio Alger Florida Scholarships *(Undergraduate/Scholarship)* [4938]
Horatio Alger Georgia Scholarships *(Undergraduate/Scholarship)* [4939]
Horatio Alger Illinois Scholarships *(Undergraduate/Scholarship)* [4940]
Horatio Alger Indiana Scholarships *(Undergraduate/Scholarship)* [4941]
Horatio Alger Kentucky Scholarships *(Undergraduate/Scholarship)* [4942]
Horatio Alger Minnesota Scholarships *(Undergraduate/Scholarship)* [4945]

Horatio Alger Missouri Scholarships *(Undergraduate/Scholarship)* [4946]
Horatio Alger National Scholarships *(Undergraduate/Scholarship)* [4948]
Horatio Alger North Dakota Scholarships *(Undergraduate/Scholarship)* [4949]
Horatio Alger Pennsylvania Scholarships *(Undergraduate/Scholarship)* [4950]
Horatio Alger South Dakota Scholarships *(Undergraduate/Scholarship)* [4951]
Horatio Alger Texas - Fort Worth Scholarships *(Undergraduate/Scholarship)* [4952]
Horatio Alger Texas Scholarships *(Undergraduate/Scholarship)* [4953]
Horatio Alger Utah Scholarships *(Undergraduate/Scholarship)* [4954]
Horatio Alger Washington Scholarships *(Undergraduate/Scholarship)* [4955]
Horatio Alger Wyoming Scholarships *(Undergraduate/Scholarship)* [4956]
Emma and Meloid Algood Tuition Scholarships *(Graduate, Undergraduate/Scholarship)* [6718]
Margaret M. Alkek Scholarships *(Undergraduate/Scholarship)* [3548]
All-American Vector Marketing Scholarship Program *(Undergraduate/Scholarship)* [10364]
ALL-SIS Conference of Newer Law Librarians Grants *(Professional development/Grant)* [528]
Robinson G. Allen Athletic Memorial Scholarships *(Undergraduate/Scholarship)* [8444]
Frances C. Allen Fellowships *(Graduate/Fellowship)* [7408]
William A. Allen Memorial Metal Shop/Auto Body Scholarships *(Undergraduate/Scholarship)* [8445]
Dorothea E. Allen Scholarship *(Undergraduate/Scholarship)* [4427]
Alliance of Black Culinarians Scholarships *(Undergraduate/Scholarship)* [8330]
Alliance Defending Freedom - Blackstone Legal Fellowships *(Undergraduate/Fellowship)* [331]
Alliance Francaise of Hartford Harpin/Rohinsky Scholarships *(Undergraduate/Scholarship)* [4736]
Allman Medical Scholarship *(Undergraduate/Scholarship)* [6555]
ALOA Scholarship Foundation *(Undergraduate/Scholarship)* [1816]
Tillie B. Alperin Scholarship *(Undergraduate/Scholarship)* [10156]
ALPFA Scholarship Programs *(Graduate, Undergraduate/Scholarship)* [2013]
Alpha Chi Omega Love and Loyalty Grants *(Professional development/Grant)* [346]
Alpha Chi Sigma Scholarship Awards *(Graduate, Undergraduate/Scholarship)* [348]
Alpha Delta Gamma Educational Foundation Scholarships *(Undergraduate, Graduate/Scholarship)* [350]
Alpha Kappa Alpha - Educational Advancement Foundation Financial Need-Based Scholarships *(Graduate, Undergraduate/Scholarship)* [352]
Alpha Kappa Alpha - Educational Advancement Foundation Merit Scholarships *(Graduate, Undergraduate/Scholarship)* [353]
Alpha Mu Tau Undergraduate Scholarships *(Undergraduate/Scholarship)* [1258]
Alpha Tau Omega Graduate Scholarships *(Graduate/Scholarship)* [359]
Alpha Tau Omega Undergraduate Scholarships *(Undergraduate/Scholarship)* [360]
Justin Scot Alston Memorial Scholarships *(Undergraduate/Scholarship)* [5026]
Phillip Alston Scholarships *(Undergraduate/Scholarship)* [10213]
Martin K. Alsup Scholarships *(Undergraduate/Scholarship)* [7811]
Robert E. Altenhofen Memorial Scholarships *(Graduate, Undergraduate/Scholarship)* [1802]
AMA Foundation Minority Scholars Awards *(Graduate/Scholarship)* [989]
AMA Foundation Physicians of Tomorrow Scholarships *(Graduate/Scholarship)* [990]
AMACESP Student Scholarships *(Undergraduate/Scholarship)* [178]
The Ambrose-Ramsey Trust *(Undergraduate/Scholarship)* [7812]
AMBUCS Scholarships for Therapists Program

Scholarships, Fellowships and Loans, 34th Ed.

UNITED STATES

(Graduate, Undergraduate/Scholarship) [381]
Amelia Earhart Fellowship Program (Doctorate, Postgraduate/Fellowship) [10824]
Lou Amen Legacy Scholarships (Undergraduate/Scholarship) [2446]
America Express Travel Scholarships (Undergraduate/Scholarship) [1436]
America Responds Memorial Scholarships (Undergraduate/Scholarship) [1406]
American Academy of Periodontology Educator Scholarships (Postdoctorate/Scholarship) [420]
American Acne and Rosacea Society Mentorship Grant (Professional development/Grant) [426]
American Art Therapy Association Anniversary Scholarships (Graduate/Scholarship) [448]
American Association of Blacks in Energy Scholarships (Undergraduate/Scholarship) [464]
American Association for Cancer Research Minority Scholar Awards (Graduate/Award) [472]
American Association of Cereal Chemists Graduate Fellowships (Graduate/Fellowship) [12]
American Association of Family and Consumer Sciences Undergraduate Scholarships (Undergraduate/Scholarship) [498]
American Association for Hand Surgery Annual Research Awards (Other/Award) [500]
American Association of Plastic Surgeons Academic Scholars Program (Professional development/Scholarship) [564]
American Association of State Troopers Scholarship Foundation First Scholarships (Undergraduate/Scholarship) [577]
American Association of State Troopers Scholarship Foundation Second Scholarships (Undergraduate/Scholarship) [578]
American Association of Stratigraphic Palynologists Student Scholarships (Graduate/Scholarship) [16]
American Association of University Women American Fellowships (Doctorate, Postdoctorate/Fellowship) [599]
American Association of University Women Career Development Grants (Postgraduate/Grant) [600]
American Association of University Women International Fellowships (Graduate, Postgraduate/Fellowship) [601]
American Association of University Women Master's and First Professional Awards (Other/Award) [602]
American Association of University Women Selected Professions Fellowships (Other/Fellowship) [603]
American Association for Women in Community Colleges Regional Scholarships (Undergraduate/Scholarship) [605]
American Association for Women in Community Colleges Scholarship LEADERS Institute (Other/Scholarship) [606]
American Bus Association Academic Merit Scholarships (Undergraduate, Graduate/Scholarship) [639]
American Business Women's Association Sarasota Sunrise Chapter Scholarships (Undergraduate, Vocational/Occupational/Scholarship) [3317]
American Cancer Society - Postdoctoral Fellowships (Doctorate/Fellowship) [644]
American Cancer Society - Research Scholar Grants (Doctorate, Professional development/Grant) [645]
American Conifer Society Scholarships (Undergraduate/Scholarship) [714]
American Council of the Blind Scholarships (Graduate, Undergraduate/Scholarship) [720]
American Council of Independent Laboratories Scholarships (Undergraduate/Scholarship) [732]
American Councils for International Education Critical Language Scholarships (Undergraduate, Graduate/Scholarship) [746]
American Counsel Association Scholarships (Undergraduate/Scholarship) [748]
American Criminal Justice Association - Lambda Alpha Epsilon Student Scholarships - Graduate Level (Graduate, Master's, Doctorate/Scholarship) [753]
American Criminal Justice Association - Lambda Alpha Epsilon Student Scholarships - Upper and Lower Division Levels (Undergraduate/Scholarship) [754]
American Darts Organization Memorial Scholarship

(Undergraduate/Scholarship) [767]
American Dental Association Allied Dental Student Scholarships (Undergraduate/Scholarship) [769]
American Dental Association Dental Assisting Scholarship Program (Undergraduate/Scholarship) [770]
American Dental Association Dental Hygiene Scholarship Program (Undergraduate/Scholarship) [771]
American Dental Association Dental Laboratory Technology Scholarship Program (Undergraduate/Scholarship) [772]
American Dental Association Minority Dental Student Scholarships (Undergraduate/Scholarship) [773]
American Dental Hygienists' Association Institute for Oral Health Research Grants (Master's/Fellowship) [776]
American Diabetes Association and Boehringer Ingelheim Research Award: Chronic Kidney Disease and Renal Insufficiency in the Setting of Diabetes (Doctorate, Professional development/Award) [780]
American Division Veterans Association Scholarships (Undergraduate/Scholarship) [383]
American Express Professional Development Scholarships (Other/Scholarship) [859]
American Federation of Police and Concerned Citizen Scholarships (Undergraduate/Scholarship) [790]
American Foreign Service Association Scholarship Fund (Undergraduate/Scholarship) [816]
American Foundation for Suicide and Prevention Pilot Grants (Postgraduate/Grant) [834]
American GI Forum of San Jose Scholarships (Undergraduate/Scholarship) [8756]
American Guild of Organists, Canton Chapter Charitable Fund (Undergraduate/Scholarship) [9492]
American Historical Association Fellowships in Aerospace History (Doctorate/Fellowship) [851]
American Indian Endowed Scholarships (Graduate, Undergraduate/Scholarship) [10470]
American Indian Fellowship in Business Scholarships (Graduate, Master's, Undergraduate/Scholarship) [6844]
American Institute for Economic Research Student Summer Fellowships (Doctorate, Graduate, Undergraduate/Fellowship) [911]
American Institute of Physics Congressional Science Fellowships (Doctorate/Fellowship) [924]
American Institute of Physics State Department Science Fellowships (Doctorate/Fellowship) [925]
American Judges Association Law Student Essay Competition (Undergraduate/Prize) [952]
American Legion Eagle Scout of the Year Scholarships (Undergraduate/Scholarship) [6918]
The American Legion Legacy Scholarships (Undergraduate/Scholarship) [954]
American Liver Foundation Liver Scholar Awards (Doctorate/Award) [967]
American Lung Association Biomedical Research Grants (Doctorate/Grant) [970]
American Lung Association Clinical Patient Care Research Grants (Doctorate/Grant) [971]
American Lung Association Dalsemer Research Grants (Doctorate/Grant) [972]
American Lung Association DeSousa Awards (Doctorate/Grant) [973]
American Lung Association Lung Cancer Discovery Awards (Doctorate/Grant) [974]
American Lung Association Scholar Program (Professional development/Grant) [979]
American Lung Association Senior Research Training Fellowships (Doctorate/Fellowship) [975]
American Lung Association Social-Behavioral Research Grants (Doctorate/Grant) [976]
American Nephrology Nurses' Association Evidence-Based Research Grants (Other/Grant) [1025]
American Nephrology Nurses' Association Research Grants (Doctorate, Graduate/Grant) [1026]
American Nuclear Society Incoming Freshman Scholarships (Undergraduate/Scholarship) [1032]
American Nuclear Society Undergraduates Scholarships (Undergraduate/Scholarship) [1033]
American Pediatric Surgical Nurses Association Educational Grants (Other/Grant) [1076]
American Philological Association Minority Student

Summer Fellowships (Undergraduate/Fellowship) [9106]
American Philosophical Society Library Resident Research Fellowships (Doctorate/Fellowship) [1078]
American Planning Association ENRE Student Fellowship Program (Graduate/Fellowship) [1103]
American Psychoanalytic Association Fellowships (Doctorate, Postdoctorate, Other/Fellowship) [1129]
American Psychology-Law Society Dissertation Awards (Graduate/Award) [1155]
American Psychology-Law Society Early Career Professional Grants-In-Aid (Other/Grant) [1156]
American Psychology-Law Society Student Grants-In-Aid (Graduate/Grant) [1157]
American Quarter Horse Foundation Scholarships (Undergraduate/Scholarship) [1171]
American Railway Engineering and Maintenance-of-Way Association Scholarships (Undergraduate/Scholarship) [1175]
American Rental Association Foundation Scholarships (Graduate, Undergraduate, Vocational/Occupational/Scholarship) [1191]
American Research in the Humanities in China Fellowships (Doctorate/Fellowship) [737]
American Roentgen Ray Society Scholarships (Other/Scholarship) [1221]
American-Scandinavian Foundation Fellowships and Grants to Study in America (Graduate, Professional development/Fellowship, Grant) [1230]
American-Scandinavian Foundation Translation Prize (Other/Prize) [1233]
American Society of Colon and Rectal Surgeons International Fellowships (Other/Fellowship) [1265]
American Society of Colon and Rectal Surgeons Travel Scholarships (Other/Scholarship) [1266]
American Society of Crime Laboratory Directors Scholarships (Graduate, Undergraduate, Master's, Doctorate/Scholarship) [1278]
American Society of Electroneurodiagnostic Technologists Student Education Grants (ASET) (Undergraduate/Grant) [1300]
American Society for Enology and Viticulture Scholarships (Graduate, Undergraduate/Scholarship) [1307]
American Society of Heating, Refrigerating, and Air-Conditioning Memorial Scholarships (Undergraduate/Scholarship) [1327]
American Society for Horticultural Science Student Travel Grants (Graduate, Undergraduate/Grant) [1336]
American Society of Mammalogists - Fellowships in Mammalogy (Graduate/Fellowship) [1356]
American Society of Mammalogists Grants-in-Aid of Research (Graduate, Undergraduate/Grant) [1357]
American Society for Microbiology International Fellowships for Africa (Postdoctorate/Fellowship) [1365]
American Society for Microbiology International Fellowships for Asia (Postdoctorate/Fellowship) [1366]
American Society for Microbiology International Fellowships for Latin America and the Caribbean (Postdoctorate/Fellowship) [1367]
American Society for Microbiology Undergraduate Research Fellowships (Undergraduate/Fellowship) [1368]
American Society of Military Comptrollers National Scholarship Program (Undergraduate/Scholarship) [1375]
American Society of Mining and Reclamation Memorial Scholarships (Undergraduate/Scholarship, Recognition) [1377]
American Society of Naval Engineers Scholarships (ASNE) (Graduate, Undergraduate/Scholarship) [1379]
American Society of Safety Engineers Construction Safety Scholarships (Undergraduate/Scholarship) [1407]
American Sokol Merit Awards (Undergraduate/Scholarship, Recognition) [1448]
American Speech Language Hearing Foundation Clinical Research Grants (Doctorate/Grant) [1450]
American Speech Language Hearing Foundation

Endowed Scholarships *(Graduate, Master's, Doctorate/Scholarship)* [1451]
American Speech Language Hearing Foundation General Scholarships *(Graduate, Master's, Doctorate/Scholarship)* [1452]
American Speech Language Hearing Foundation Scholarships for International Students *(Graduate, Master's, Doctorate/Scholarship)* [1453]
American Speech Language Hearing Foundation Scholarships for Minority Students *(Graduate, Master's, Doctorate/Scholarship)* [1454]
American Water Ski Educational Foundation Scholarships *(Undergraduate/Scholarship)* [10351]
American Watercolor Society Scholarship Program for Art Teachers *(Other/Scholarship)* [1500]
American Welding Society District Scholarships *(Undergraduate/Scholarship)* [1503]
American Welding Society Graduate Research Fellowships *(Graduate/Fellowship)* [1504]
American Welding Society National Scholarships *(Undergraduate/Scholarship)* [1506]
American Welding Society Past Presidents Scholarships *(Undergraduate, Graduate/Scholarship)* [1507]
Americans for Informed Democracy Global Scholar Program *(Undergraduate/Scholarship)* [1532]
AmeriGlide Achiever Scholarships *(Undergraduate/Scholarship)* [1534]
Arsham Amirikian Engineering Scholarships *(Undergraduate/Scholarship)* [1508]
AMS Centennial Fellowships *(Postdoctorate/Fellowship)* [985]
AMS Freshman Undergraduate Scholarships *(Undergraduate/Scholarship)* [997]
AMS Graduate Fellowships in the History of Science *(Graduate/Fellowship)* [998]
AMS/Industry/Government Graduate Fellowships *(Graduate/Fellowship)* [999]
AMS/Industry Minority Scholarships *(Undergraduate/Scholarship)* [1000]
AMS Teacher Education Scholarships *(Undergraduate/Scholarship)* [1007]
AMS Undergraduate Named Scholarships *(Undergraduate/Scholarship)* [1001]
AMSA Graduate Student Research Poster Competition Award *(Undergraduate, Doctorate, Master's/Award)* [987]
AMSN Career Mobility Scholarship Awards *(Undergraduate, Doctorate/Scholarship)* [37]
AMSSM-ACSM Clinical Research Grants *(Professional development/Grant)* [993]
AMSUS Dentist Awards *(Professional development/Recognition)* [1538]
AMSUS Nursing Awards *(Advanced Professional/Recognition)* [1539]
AMSUS Physician Awards *(Advanced Professional/Recognition)* [1540]
AMTA Past Presidents' Conference Scholar Awards *(Professional development/Award)* [1010]
AMTA Student Conference Scholar Awards *(Undergraduate, Graduate/Award)* [1011]
AMTF Graduate Scholarships *(Graduate/Scholarship)* [1259]
AMVETS National Scholarships - Entering College Freshmen *(Undergraduate/Scholarship)* [1545]
AMVETS National Scholarships - For Veterans *(Undergraduate/Scholarship)* [1546]
AMVETS National Scholarships - JROTC *(Undergraduate/Scholarship)* [1547]
ANA Multicultural Excellence Scholarship Fund (MAIP) *(Graduate, Undergraduate/Internship)* [456]
Anaheim Police Survivors and Scholarship Fund *(Undergraduate/Scholarship)* [1549]
ANCA Scholarships *(Undergraduate/Scholarship)* [1712]
Anchor Plastics Scholarships *(Graduate, Undergraduate/Scholarship)* [8072]
Anchor QEA Environmental Scholarships *(Graduate/Scholarship)* [1551]
Anchor Scholarship Foundation Scholarships *(Undergraduate/Scholarship)* [9616]
Andersen Nontraditional Scholarships for Women's Education and Retraining (ANSWER) *(Undergraduate/Scholarship)* [4176]

Mary Louise Andersen Scholarship *(Undergraduate/Scholarship)* [1574]
William G. Anderson, DO, Minority Scholarships *(Undergraduate/Scholarship)* [1063]
The Anderson Group Summer Institute Scholarships *(Other/Scholarship)* [1553]
Henry H. Anderson, Jr. Sail Training Scholarship *(Professional development/Scholarship)* [9640]
Judge Isaac Anderson, Jr. Scholarships *(Undergraduate/Scholarship)* [9418]
A.T. Anderson Memorial Scholarships *(Graduate, Undergraduate/Scholarship)* [889]
Charles Lee Anderson Memorial Scholarships *(Undergraduate/Scholarship)* [3275]
Gladys C. Anderson Memorial Scholarships *(Graduate, Undergraduate/Scholarship)* [818]
Earl I. Anderson Scholarships *(Undergraduate/Scholarship)* [1722]
Kathy D. and Stephen J. Anderson Scholarships *(Undergraduate/Scholarship)* [3210]
Redlands Rotary Club - Donald C. Anderson Scholarships *(Undergraduate/Scholarship)* [8446]
Michael P. Anderson Scholarships in Space Science *(Undergraduate/Scholarship)* [7137]
Grace Andow Memorial Scholarships *(Undergraduate, Graduate/Scholarship)* [5548]
Margaret J. Andrew Memorial Scholarships *(Undergraduate, Graduate/Scholarship)* [8909]
Cindy Andrews Educational Scholarships *(Undergraduate/Scholarship)* [8447]
William H. Andrews/HAWS Scholarships *(Undergraduate/Scholarship)* [10569]
Richard E. Andrews Memorial Scholarships *(Undergraduate/Scholarship)* [627]
Androscoggin County Chamber of Commerce Adult Scholarships *(Professional development/Scholarship)* [1555]
ANF/ANN-FNRE Nursing Research Grants *(Professional development/Grant)* [1042]
ANF/ENRS Nursing Research Grants *(Professional development/Grant)* [1043]
ANF/STTI Nursing Research Grants *(Master's, Doctorate/Grant)* [1044]
Angus Foundation General Undergraduate Student Scholarships *(Undergraduate/Scholarship)* [1557]
Angus Foundation Graduate Student Degree Scholarship Program *(Graduate/Scholarship)* [1558]
Angus Foundation Scholarships *(Undergraduate/Scholarship)* [7032]
Angus/Talon Youth Educational Learning Program Endowment Fund *(Graduate, Undergraduate/Scholarship)* [1559]
Anheuser-Busch NAPABA Law Foundation Presidential Scholarships *(Undergraduate/Scholarship)* [6703]
Animal Compassion Undergraduate Scholarships *(Undergraduate/Scholarship)* [8015]
ANNA Nephrology Nurse Researcher Awards *(Doctorate, Graduate/Award)* [1027]
Anne Friedberg Innovative Scholarship Awards *(Other/Scholarship)* [9104]
Leonore Annenberg Teaching Fellowships *(Graduate/Fellowship)* [10677]
Annette Urso Rickel Foundation Dissertation Award for Public Policy *(Graduate/Scholarship)* [1137]
Annual Research Doctoral and Postgraduate Fellowship Grant Program *(Doctorate, Postdoctorate, Postgraduate, Advanced Professional/Fellowship, Grant)* [2586]
Annuity.org Scholarships *(Undergraduate, Graduate/Scholarship)* [1565]
ANS Research Grants *(Professional development/Grant)* [1030]
Hettie Margaret Anthony Fellowship *(Doctorate/Fellowship)* [5779]
Hettie M. Anthony Fellowships *(Doctorate/Fellowship)* [5787]
Antimicrobial Stewardship Fellowship Award *(Professional development/Award, Fellowship)* [1138]
AOF/Johnson & Johnson Vision Care - Innovation in Education Grants *(Advanced Professional, Professional development/Grant)* [414]
AOFAS Research Grants Program *(Graduate/Grant)* [1060]
AORN Academic Scholarships *(Undergraduate, Master's, Doctorate/Scholarship)* [2035]

AORN Administrator Skills Course *(Professional development/Recognition, Grant)* [2036]
AORN Foundation Scholarship Program *(Undergraduate, Doctorate, Master's/Scholarship)* [2037]
AOS Research Training Fellowships *(Graduate/Fellowship)* [1067]
AOSA Research Grants *(Undergraduate/Grant)* [1053]
AOSA Research Partnership Grants *(Professional development/Grant)* [1054]
APA Society Convention Research Awards *(Undergraduate, Graduate/Award)* [8317]
APABA-SV Scholarships *(Advanced Professional/Scholarship)* [1786]
APAGS-CLGBTC Grant Program *(Graduate/Grant)* [1131]
APALA Scholarship Award *(Doctorate, Master's/Scholarship)* [1788]
APC High School Scholarship Awards *(Undergraduate/Scholarship)* [78]
APDA Medical Students Summer Fellowships *(Graduate, Professional development/Fellowship)* [1071]
APDA Postdoctoral Research Fellowships *(Other/Fellowship)* [1072]
APDA Research Grants *(Other/Grant)* [1073]
APF/COGDOP Graduate Research Scholarships *(Doctorate, Graduate/Scholarship)* [1138]
APF High School Psychology Teacher Network Grants *(Advanced Professional, Professional development/Grant)* [1139]
APF Professional Development Awards for High School Psychology Teachers *(Advanced Professional, Professional development/Grant)* [1140]
APF Visionary Grants *(Graduate/Grant)* [1141]
APhA Auxilliary Scholarship *(Undergraduate/Scholarship)* [1575]
APHF Academic Scholarships *(Undergraduate/Scholarship)* [1069]
APHL Emerging Infectious Diseases Fellowships *(Doctorate/Fellowship)* [2048]
APIASF Scholarships *(Undergraduate/Scholarship)* [1792]
Appalachian School of Law Merit Scholarship Program *(Undergraduate/Scholarship)* [1590]
Appraisal Institute Education Trust Undergraduate Scholarships *(Undergraduate/Scholarship)* [1596]
APS/ASU Scholarships *(Undergraduate/Scholarship)* [8139]
APS/Maricopa County Community Colleges Scholarships *(Undergraduate/Scholarship)* [8140]
APS Scholarships for Minority Undergraduate Physics Majors *(Undergraduate/Scholarship)* [7138]
APS Society Convention Research Awards *(Undergraduate, Graduate/Award)* [8318]
APS Student Research Award *(Undergraduate, Graduate/Award)* [2045]
APSA Congressional Fellowship for Communications Scholars and Journalists *(Advanced Professional, Professional development/Fellowship)* [1108]
APSA Congressional Fellowships for Journalists *(Advanced Professional, Professional development/Fellowship)* [1109]
APSA Congressional Fellowships for Political Scientists *(Advanced Professional, Professional development/Fellowship)* [1110]
APSA Congressional Fellowships *(Other/Fellowship)* [4398]
APSA Fund for Latino Scholarship *(Undergraduate, Graduate/Scholarship)* [1111]
APSA/Health and Aging Policy Fellowships *(Graduate, Advanced Professional, Professional development/Fellowship)* [1112]
APSA Minority Fellows Program *(Doctorate/Fellowship)* [1113]
APSA Presidency Research Group Fellowships *(Graduate, Postdoctorate/Fellowship)* [1118]
APSA Small Research Grant Program *(Doctorate/Grant)* [1114]
APSA U.S. Federal Executives Fellowships *(Advanced Professional, Professional development/Fellowship)* [1115]
APT US&C Scholarships *(Advanced Professional/Scholarship)* [2050]
APTA Minority Scholarships - Faculty Development

UNITED STATES

Scholarships *(Postdoctorate/Scholarship)* [1096]
APTA Minority Scholarships - Physical Therapist Assistant Students *(Undergraduate/Scholarship)* [1097]
APTA Minority Scholarships - Physical Therapist Students *(Undergraduate/Scholarship)* [1098]
Aquatics Booster Club Scholarships *(Undergraduate/Scholarship)* [8448]
ARA Scholarship Awards *(Undergraduate/Scholarship)* [2136]
Frank G. Araujo Memorial Scholarships *(Undergraduate/Scholarship)* [8449]
ARCADIS Scholarships *(Master's, Doctorate/Scholarship)* [1482]
ARCE Funded Fellowships *(Doctorate, Postdoctorate/Fellowship)* [1195]
ARCE Research Associates Fellowships *(Doctorate, Postdoctorate, Professional development/Fellowship)* [1196]
Archaeological Institute of America Fellowships for Study in the U.S. *(Postdoctorate/Fellowship)* [1604]
George F. Archambault Scholarship *(Undergraduate/Scholarship)* [1576]
NHCGNE Patricia G. Archbold Predoctoral Scholar Award *(Doctorate/Scholarship)* [6982]
Arctic Physical Therapy Scholarship *(Undergraduate/Scholarship)* [1619]
AREMA Committee 12 - Rail Transit Scholarships *(Undergraduate/Scholarship)* [1176]
AREMA Committee 18 - Light Density and Short Line Railways Scholarships *(Undergraduate/Scholarship)* [1177]
AREMA Committee 24 - Education and Training Scholarships *(Undergraduate/Scholarship)* [1178]
AREMA Committee 27 - Maintenance-of-Way Work Equipment Scholarships *(Undergraduate/Scholarship)* [1179]
AREMA Committee 33 - Electric Energy Utilization Scholarships *(Undergraduate/Scholarship)* [1180]
AREMA Presidential Spouse Scholarships *(Undergraduate/Scholarship)* [1182]
Arent Fox Diversity Scholarships *(Graduate, Juris Doctorate/Scholarship)* [1621]
A.R.F.O.R.A. Undergraduate Scholarships for Women *(Undergraduate/Scholarship)* [1224]
Arizona Nursery Association Scholarships *(Undergraduate/Scholarship)* [1637]
Arizona Nurses Foundation Scholarships *(Doctorate, Graduate, Undergraduate/Scholarship)* [1639]
Rick Arkans Eagle Scout Scholarships *(Undergraduate/Scholarship)* [6919]
Arkansas Green Industry Association Professional Grants *(Professional development, Undergraduate/Grant)* [1651]
Arkansas Green Industry Association Student Scholarships *(Undergraduate/Scholarship)* [1652]
Arkansas Public Health Association Scholarships *(Undergraduate/Scholarship)* [1659]
Arkansas Single Parent Scholarships *(Undergraduate, Graduate/Scholarship)* [1661]
ArLA Scholarships *(Graduate/Scholarship)* [1654]
Connie "Chelo" Armendariz Memorial Scholarships *(Undergraduate/Scholarship)* [8450]
Armenian American Citizen's League Scholarships *(Undergraduate/Scholarship)* [1682]
Armenian American Medical Association Scholarships *(Undergraduate/Scholarship)* [1683]
Armenian Bar Association Graduate Scholarships in Law *(Graduate/Scholarship)* [1669]
Armenian General Athletic Union Scholarships *(Undergraduate/Scholarship)* [1685]
Armenian Professional Society Graduate Student Scholarships *(Graduate/Scholarship)* [1675]
Armenian Relief Society Scholarships *(Graduate, Undergraduate/Scholarship)* [1686]
Ethel Louise Armstrong Foundation Scholarships *(Graduate/Scholarship)* [8750]
Louis Armstrong Scholarships *(Undergraduate/Scholarship)* [1268]
Army Health Professions Scholarships Program *(Professional development/Scholarship)* [9878]
Richard E. Arnason Court Scholarships *(Undergraduate/Scholarship)* [3409]
Norma Arnold Clerical Scholarships *(Undergraduate/Scholarship)* [6221]

Paul Arnold Memorial Scholarships *(Undergraduate/Scholarship)* [8241]
Tara Lynn Arnold Scholarships *(Undergraduate/Scholarship)* [9562]
ARNOVA Emerging Scholar Awards *(Graduate/Award)* [2056]
Jane B. Aron Doctoral Fellowships *(Doctorate/Fellowship)* [6787]
Don Aron Scholarships *(Undergraduate/Scholarship)* [6875]
Judge Sidney M. Aronovitz Memorial Scholarships *(Undergraduate/Scholarship)* [6451]
Kush Arora Federal Criminal Justice Reform Scholarships *(Undergraduate, Graduate/Scholarship)* [8227]
Luis Arreola Memorial Scholarships *(Undergraduate/Scholarship)* [8686]
ARRL Foundation General Fund Scholarships *(Undergraduate/Scholarship)* [1723]
ARRL Foundation PHD Scholarships *(Undergraduate/Scholarship)* [1724]
ARS of Eastern USA Lazarian Graduate Scholarship *(Master's, Doctorate/Scholarship)* [1680]
ARS Undergraduate Scholarships *(Undergraduate/Scholarship)* [1677]
Arthritis Foundation Doctoral Dissertation Awards for Arthritis Health Professionals *(Doctorate/Fellowship)* [1769]
Arthritis Foundation Innovative Research Grants *(Doctorate/Grant)* [1770]
Arthritis Foundation Investigator Awards *(Doctorate/Award)* [1771]
Arthritis Foundation Postdoctoral Fellowships *(Doctorate/Fellowship)* [1772]
Artist-in-Residence Workspace Grant *(Professional development/Grant)* [2843]
The Artist in Landscape Design Scholarship by Fullmer's Landscaping *(Undergraduate/Scholarship)* [7581]
Arts Council of Greater Grand Rapids Minority Scholarships *(Undergraduate/Scholarship)* [4574]
David Arver Memorial Scholarships *(Undergraduate/Scholarship)* [155]
Dutch and Ginger Arver Scholarships *(Undergraduate/Scholarship)* [156]
ASA Graduate Scholarships *(Graduate/Scholarship)* [1243]
ASA Minority Fellowship Program (ASA MFP) *(Graduate, Doctorate, Professional development/Fellowship)* [1445]
ASA/NSF/BLS Fellowships *(Graduate/Fellowship)* [1463]
ASA Student Forum Travel Awards *(Undergraduate, Graduate/Grant)* [1446]
ASBA College Scholarship Grant Program *(Postgraduate/Scholarship)* [1239]
ASBC Foundation Graduate Scholarships *(Graduate/Scholarship)* [1247]
ASBC Foundation Undergraduate Scholarships *(Undergraduate/Scholarship)* [1248]
ASBPE Young Leaders Scholarships *(Professional development/Scholarship)* [1250]
ASC Graduate Fellowships for Ethnic Minorities *(Doctorate/Fellowship)* [1280]
Elizabeth and Sherman Asche Memorial Scholarships *(Graduate, Undergraduate/Scholarship)* [1832]
ASCO/CCF Young Investigator Awards *(Professional development, Advanced Professional/Grant)* [3369]
ASCP Phlebotomy Scholarships *(Undergraduate/Scholarship)* [1262]
ASECS Graduate Student Research Paper Awards *(Graduate/Award)* [1283]
ASECS Innovative Course Design Competition *(Undergraduate/Award)* [1284]
ASECS Women's Caucus Editing and Translation Fellowships *(Doctorate/Fellowship)* [1285]
ASEE/NSF Small Business Postdoctoral Research Diversity Fellowships *(Postdoctorate/Fellowship)* [1303]
ASEH Minority Travel Grants *(Graduate, Other/Grant)* [1309]
Officer Brian A. Aselton Memorial Scholarships *(Undergraduate/Scholarship)* [4737]
ASET Scholarships *(Other/Scholarship)* [1301]

ASF/Annika Teig/Skidmore, Owings and Merrill Fellowships *(Postgraduate/Fellowship)* [1234]
ASG Scholar Awards *(Professional development/Scholarship)* [1321]
ASGP Graduate Research Fellowships *(Graduate/Fellowship)* [223]
ASHARE Undergraduate Engineering Scholarships *(Undergraduate/Scholarship)* [1328]
ASHFoundation New Century Scholars Doctoral Scholarships *(Doctorate/Scholarship)* [1455]
ASHFoundation New Century Scholars Research Grants *(Doctorate/Grant)* [1456]
ASHFoundation New Investigators Research Grants *(Doctorate/Grant)* [1457]
ASHFoundation Scholarships for NSSLHA Members *(Graduate/Scholarship)* [1458]
ASHFoundation Speech Science Research Grants *(Doctorate/Grant)* [1459]
ASHFoundation Student Research Grants in Audiology *(Doctorate/Grant)* [1460]
ASHFoundation Student Research Grants in Early Childhood Language Development *(Doctorate, Master's/Grant)* [1461]
ASHP Student Research Awards *(Doctorate/Award)* [1323]
ASHS Industry Division Student Travel Grants *(Graduate, Undergraduate/Grant)* [1337]
ASHS Scholars Awards *(Undergraduate/Scholarship)* [1338]
ASI Sheep Heritage Foundation Memorial Scholarship *(Graduate/Scholarship)* [1241]
Asia-Pacific Biomedical Research Foundation Merit Awards *(Postdoctorate/Award)* [9304]
Asian and Pacific Islander Queers Sisters Scholarships *(Undergraduate/Scholarship)* [8242]
ASID Foundation Legacy Scholarships for Graduate Students *(Graduate/Scholarship)* [1341]
ASIS Foundation Chapter Matching Scholarships *(Undergraduate/Scholarship)* [1794]
ASLA Council of Fellow Scholarships *(Undergraduate/Scholarship)* [1346]
ASLA Council of Fellows Scholarships *(Undergraduate/Scholarship)* [5913]
ASLMS Research Grants *(Postdoctorate/Grant)* [1349]
ASLMS Student Research Grants *(Undergraduate, Graduate, Professional development/Grant)* [1350]
ASM/CDC Program in Infectious Disease and Public Health Microbiology *(Postdoctorate/Fellowship)* [1369]
ASM Congressional Science Fellowships *(Postdoctorate/Fellowship)* [1370]
ASM Science Teaching Fellowships - Student *(Undergraduate/Fellowship)* [1371]
ASM Undergraduate Research Capstone Program *(Undergraduate/Fellowship)* [1372]
ASMS Research Awards *(Other/Grant)* [1363]
ASNT Fellowship Award *(Graduate/Fellowship, Award)* [1384]
ASPIRE Rheumatology and Dermatology Research Awards *(Postdoctorate/Award)* [8023]
Myron "Ted" Asplin Foundation Scholarships *(Undergraduate/Scholarship)* [5097]
ASPPH/CDC Public Health Fellowship Program *(Doctorate, Graduate/Fellowship)* [2060]
ASPPH/EPA Environmental Health Fellowship Program *(Doctorate, Postdoctorate/Fellowship)* [2061]
ASPPH/NHTSA Public Health Fellowship Program *(Postdoctorate/Fellowship)* [2062]
ASPPH Public Health Policy Fellowship Program *(Doctorate, Postdoctorate/Fellowship)* [2063]
ASPPH Public Health Preparedness Fellowship Program *(Postdoctorate/Fellowship)* [2064]
Len Assante Scholarship Fund *(Undergraduate/Scholarship)* [6976]
Michael M. Assarian Scholarships *(Undergraduate/Scholarship)* [1687]
ASSE Diversity Committee Scholarships *(Graduate, Undergraduate/Scholarship)* [1408]
Darrell and Palchie Asselin Scholarships *(Undergraduate/Scholarship)* [3703]
Associated General Contractors of Connecticut Scholarships *(Undergraduate/Scholarship)* [3365]
Associates in Behavioral Health Scholarships *(Graduate/Scholarship)* [8243]
Association for the Advancement of Baltic Studies

Dissertation Grants for Graduate Students *(Doctorate/Grant)* [1823]
Association of American Indian Physicians Scholarships *(Graduate, Undergraduate/Scholarship)* [1838]
Association for Compensatory Educators of Texas Paraprofessionals Scholarships *(Other/Scholarship)* [1928]
Association for Compensatory Educators of Texas Scholarships *(Undergraduate/Scholarship)* [1929]
Association of Desk and Derrick Clubs Education Trust Scholarships *(Undergraduate/Scholarship)* [1931]
Association of Donor Recruitment Professionals Hughes Scholarships *(Other/Scholarship)* [1937]
Association of Donor Recruitment Professionals Presidential Scholarships *(Other/Scholarship)* [1938]
Association of Energy Engineers Foundation Scholarship Program *(Graduate, Undergraduate/Scholarship)* [1946]
Association of Flight Attendants Scholarship Fund *(Undergraduate/Scholarship)* [1963]
Association of Government Accountants Undergraduate/Graduate Scholarships for Community Service Accomplishments *(Graduate, Undergraduate/Scholarship)* [1971]
Association of Government Accountants Undergraduate/Graduate Scholarships for Full-time study *(Graduate, Undergraduate/Scholarship)* [1972]
Association of Government Accountants Undergraduate/Graduate Scholarships for Part-time study *(Graduate, Undergraduate/Scholarship)* [1973]
Association for Preservation Technology International Student Scholarships *(Graduate, Undergraduate/Scholarship)* [2041]
Association for Psychological Science Student Grants (APS) *(Graduate, Undergraduate/Grant)* [2046]
Association of State Dam Safety Officials Undergraduate Scholarships *(Undergraduate/Scholarship)* [2074]
Association of the United States Navy Scholarships *(Undergraduate/Scholarship)* [2083]
Association for Women in Sports Media Internship/Scholarship Program *(Undergraduate/Scholarship, Internship)* [2101]
ASTA Alaska Airlines Scholarships *(Undergraduate/Scholarship)* [1437]
ASTA Holland America Line Graduate Research Scholarships *(Graduate/Scholarship)* [1438]
ASTA Rigby, Healy, Simmons Scholarships *(Graduate/Scholarship)* [1439]
ASTR Research Fellowships *(Other/Fellowship)* [1433]
ASTRO Junior Faculty Career Research Training Awards *(Advanced Professional, Professional development/Grant)* [1392]
ASTRO Minority Summer Fellowship Awards *(Postgraduate, Professional development/Fellowship)* [1393]
ASTRO Residents/Fellows in Radiation Oncology Research Seed Grants *(Advanced Professional, Professional development/Grant)* [1394]
ASTRO/ROI Comparative Effectiveness Research Awards *(Professional development/Grant)* [1395]
Astronaut Scholarship Foundation Scholarships *(Undergraduate/Scholarship)* [2105]
AT&T Business Internship Awards *(Undergraduate/Internship)* [10214]
Martha and Robert Atherton Ministerial Scholarships *(Master's/Scholarship)* [9831]
ISA Aerospace Industries Division - William H. Atkinson Scholarships *(Graduate, Undergraduate/Scholarship)* [5396]
Atlantic Salmon Federation Olin Fellowships *(Graduate/Fellowship)* [2120]
Atlas Shrugged Essay Contest *(Graduate, Undergraduate, High School/Prize)* [2163]
ATS Abstract Scholarships *(Undergraduate, Graduate, Doctorate/Scholarship)* [1473]
Attorney-CPA Foundation Scholarships *(Postgraduate/Scholarship)* [391]
AUA Foundation Urology Research Bridge Awards *(Postgraduate/Award)* [10346]
Aubespin Scholarships *(Undergraduate/Scholarship)* [718]
A. B. and Hazel Augenstein Scholarship Funds *(Undergraduate/Scholarship)* [6281]
Frank H. Ault Scholarships *(Undergraduate/Scholarship)* [8687]
H. Thomas Austern Memorial Writing Competition *(Doctorate/Award, Prize)* [4127]
Austin Alumnae Association Beta Xi Scholarship *(Undergraduate/Scholarship)* [5690]
Auto Accident Law Firm Survivor Scholarships *(Graduate/Scholarship)* [1592]
Auto-Pets "Out-of-the-Box Thinking" Scholarships *(All/Award, Scholarship)* [2129]
Automotive Technician Scholarship Program *(Undergraduate/Scholarship)* [6344]
Automotive Women's Alliance Foundation Scholarships *(Undergraduate/Scholarship)* [2138]
Auxiliary Undergraduate Scholarships *(Undergraduate/Scholarship)* [1796]
AvaCare Medical Scholarships *(Undergraduate/Scholarship)* [2142]
Avis Budget Group Scholarships *(Graduate/Scholarship)* [1440]
AVMA Fellowship Program *(Professional development/Fellowship)* [1478]
AVS Applied Surface Science Division Awards *(Graduate/Award)* [2146]
AVS Biomaterial Interfaces Division - Early Career Researchers Awards *(Graduate/Monetary)* [2147]
AVS Electronic Materials and Photonic Division Postdoctoral Award *(Postdoctorate/Award)* [2148]
AVS Manufacturing Science and Technology Group Awards *(Graduate/Award)* [2149]
AVS MEMS and NEMS Technical Group Best Paper Awards *(Undergraduate, Graduate/Monetary)* [2150]
AVS Nanometer-Scale Science and Technology Division Graduate Award *(Graduate/Monetary)* [2151]
AVS Spectroscopic Ellipsometry Focus Topic Graduate Student Awards *(Graduate/Award)* [2152]
AVS Thin Film Division James Harper Awards *(Graduate/Monetary)* [2153]
Award for Outstanding Doctoral Dissertation in Laser Science *(Doctorate/Award)* [1086]
Award for Outstanding Doctoral Thesis Research in Biological Physics *(Doctorate/Award)* [1087]
AWG Minority Scholarships *(Undergraduate/Scholarship)* [2093]
AWM Mathematics Travel Grants *(Doctorate/Grant)* [2098]
AWMA Louisiana Section Scholarships *(Undergraduate, Graduate/Scholarship)* [147]
AWSCPA National Scholarships *(Graduate/Scholarship)* [1530]
AWWA American Water Scholarships *(Master's, Doctorate/Scholarship)* [1483]
AWWA Illinois Section Safe Water Scholarship Awards *(Undergraduate, Master's, Doctorate/Scholarship)* [1496]
AXA Achievement Scholarships *(Undergraduate/Scholarship)* [2161]
Susan Ayers Memorial Scholarships *(Undergraduate/Scholarship)* [8332]
Ayn Rand Institute Anthem Essay Contest *(High School, Undergraduate/Prize)* [2164]
Ayn Rand Institute Fountainhead Essay Contest *(High School, Undergraduate/Prize)* [2165]
John M. Azarian Memorial Armenian Youth Scholarship Fund *(Undergraduate/Scholarship)* [1688]
Tom Babcox Memorial Scholarships *(Professional development/Scholarship)* [2124]
Bach Organ Scholarship *(Undergraduate/Scholarship)* [8602]
Bachelor of Science in Nursing Academic Scholarships *(Graduate/Scholarship)* [6656]
Paula Backscheider Archival Fellowships *(Other/Fellowship)* [1286]
BACUS Scholarships *(Graduate, Undergraduate/Scholarship)* [9467]
BAFTX Early Starters Awards *(Undergraduate/Scholarship)* [2365]
Baha'i Faith Scholarships for Racial Harmony *(Undergraduate/Scholarship)* [8451]
Morton Bahr Scholarships *(Undergraduate/Scholarship)* [3165]
Marian Breland Bailey Award *(Graduate, Undergraduate/Award)* [1860]
The Bailey Family Foundation College Scholarship Program *(Undergraduate/Scholarship)* [2167]
The Bailey Family Foundation High School Scholarships Program *(Undergraduate/Scholarship)* [2168]
Bailey/Hollister Scholarships *(Graduate, Professional development/Scholarship)* [7935]
Lincoln C. Bailey Memorial Scholarship Fund *(Undergraduate/Scholarship)* [5390]
Esther Tuttle Bailey Memorial Scholarships *(Undergraduate/Scholarship)* [5691]
Bambi Bailey Scholarships *(Undergraduate/Scholarship)* [3197]
Barbara Bailey Scholarships *(Undergraduate/Scholarship)* [8244]
Sandra Sebrell Bailey Scholarships *(Undergraduate/Scholarship)* [3579]
Marian Wood Baird Scholarships *(Undergraduate/Scholarship)* [9973]
Baker Donelson Diversity Scholarships *(Undergraduate/Scholarship)* [2170]
Baker and Hostetler Diversity Fellowships *(Undergraduate/Fellowship)* [2172]
Baker and McKenzie Diversity Fellowships *(Postgraduate, Professional development/Fellowship)* [2175]
Baker and McKenzie Graduate Legal Studies Scholarships *(Graduate, Professional development/Scholarship)* [2176]
Francis Warren Baker Memorial Scholarships *(Undergraduate/Scholarship)* [8910]
Richard L. Baker Memorial Scholarships *(Undergraduate/Scholarship)* [9563]
Robby Baker Memorial Scholarships *(Undergraduate/Scholarship)* [299]
Airgas - Jerry Baker Scholarships *(Undergraduate/Scholarship)* [1509]
ACI Elmer Baker Student Fellowships *(Undergraduate, Graduate/Fellowship)* [707]
ACI Baker Student Fellowships *(Undergraduate, Graduate/Fellowship)* [706]
George C. Balch Scholarships *(Graduate, Undergraduate/Scholarship)* [9958]
Bernt Balchen, Jr. and Olav Jorgen Hegge Hardingfele Scholarships *(Other/Scholarship)* [4717]
Birgit Baldwin Fellowships *(Graduate/Fellowship)* [6395]
Norman S. Baldwin Fishery Science Scholarship *(Doctorate, Graduate/Scholarship)* [5260]
Donald A. Baldwin Sr. Business Aviation Management Scholarships *(Professional development/Scholarship)* [6829]
Balestreri/Cutino Scholarships *(Undergraduate/Scholarship)* [757]
Ball Horticultural Company Scholarships *(Undergraduate/Scholarship)* [798]
Vic and Margaret Ball Student Intern Scholarships *(Undergraduate/Internship)* [799]
Ballantyne Resident Research Grants *(Other/Grant)* [847]
Ballard Family Foundation Scholarships *(Undergraduate/Scholarship)* [8688]
G. Thomas Balsbaugh Memorial Scholarship Fund *(Undergraduate/Scholarship)* [4231]
Bank of America Junior Achievement Scholarship Fund *(Undergraduate/Scholarship)* [4177]
Dr. Johnella Banks Memorial Scholarships *(Undergraduate/Scholarship)* [2298]
Harvey Washington Banks Scholarships in Astronomy *(Undergraduate/Scholarship)* [7139]
Sharon D. Banks Undergraduate Memorial Scholarships *(Undergraduate/Scholarship)* [10674]
Donald W. Banner Diversity Scholarships for Law Students *(Graduate/Scholarship)* [2190]
Mark T. Banner Scholarships for Law Students *(Postgraduate/Scholarship)* [6093]
James M. Banovetz Illinois Local Government Fellowships *(Graduate, Master's/Fellowship)* [5059]
Michael Bany Memorial Scholarships *(Undergraduate/Scholarship)* [2944]
Bernice Barabash Sports Scholarships *(Undergraduate/Scholarship)* [5497]

UNITED STATES

Barakat Trust and Barakat Foundation Scholarships *(Graduate, Postdoctorate/Scholarship)* [1598]
Cynthia and Alan Baran Fine Arts and Music Scholarships *(Undergraduate/Scholarship)* [3211]
Leslie Baranowski Scholarships for Professional Excellence *(Professional development/Scholarship)* [5144]
Barbara Jordan Memorial Scholarships *(Undergraduate, Graduate/Scholarship)* [2078]
Joe Barbarow Memorial Scholarships *(Undergraduate/Scholarship)* [7813]
Lewis B. Barber Memorial Scholarships *(Undergraduate/Scholarship)* [9419]
Thomas J. Bardos Science Education Awards for Undergraduate Students *(Undergraduate/Award)* [473]
Marguerite Ross Barnett Research Grant *(Graduate, Postdoctorate/Grant)* [1119]
Gina L. Barnhart Memorial Scholarship Fund *(Undergraduate/Scholarship)* [4040]
Robbie Barron Memorial Scholarships *(Undergraduate/Scholarship)* [4232]
Barta-Lehman Musical Scholarships *(Undergraduate/Scholarship)* [8689]
Walter and Marilyn Bartlett Scholarships *(Undergraduate/Scholarship)* [2945]
Elsa Barton Educational Scholarship Fund *(Undergraduate, Vocational/Occupational/Scholarship)* [1127]
Guthikonda BasavapunnaRao and Umadevi Scholarships *(Graduate/Scholarship)* [9667]
Bascom Hill Society Scholarships *(Undergraduate/Scholarship)* [10316]
Basic Research Fellowship Program *(Postdoctorate/Fellowship)* [634]
Charles A. Bassett Endowed Memorial Scholarship Fund *(Undergraduate/Scholarship)* [4510]
Bat Conservation International Student Research Scholarships *(Graduate, Undergraduate/Scholarship)* [2201]
Jim Batten Community Newspaper Internships *(Undergraduate/Internship)* [10215]
Lewis and Gurry Batten/Sand Plains Educational Trust Scholarships *(Undergraduate/Scholarship)* [7814]
Marian Sims Baughn Scholarships *(Undergraduate/Scholarship)* [5692]
Bob Baxter Scholarships *(Graduate, Undergraduate/Scholarship)* [7106]
Timothy Baylink Good Fellowship Awards *(Undergraduate/Fellowship)* [8452]
John Bayliss Broadcast Foundation Internship Programs *(Undergraduate/Internship)* [2203]
John Bayliss Broadcast Foundation Radio Scholarships *(Undergraduate/Scholarship)* [2204]
BCCC Workforce Creation Scholarships *(Undergraduate/Scholarship)* [2179]
BDC Visiting Fellowships *(Advanced Professional, Professional development/Fellowship)* [2382]
Willa Beach-Porter Music Scholarships *(Undergraduate/Scholarship)* [2873]
Beatitudes Fellowships *(Professional development/Fellowship)* [2208]
Catherine H. Beattie Fellowships *(Graduate/Fellowship)* [2867]
Jane Beattie Memorial Scholarships *(Graduate, Professional development/Scholarship)* [9160]
Beaver Medical Clinic-Glen Adams Scholarship Awards *(Undergraduate/Scholarship)* [8453]
Beaver Medical Clinic-H.E.A.R.T. Scholarship Awards *(Undergraduate/Scholarship)* [8454]
Beaver Medical Clinic-Premed Scholarship Awards *(Undergraduate/Scholarship)* [8455]
Don C. Beaver Memorial Scholarships *(Undergraduate/Scholarship)* [2447]
Beca #Traductor Scholarships *(All/Scholarship)* [9458]
Becas Univision Scholarship Program *(Undergraduate, Graduate/Scholarship)* [4902]
Bechtel Engineering and Science Scholarships *(Undergraduate/Scholarship)* [6278]
O.J. Beck, Jr. Memorial Scholarships *(Undergraduate/Scholarship)* [3087]
Dennis J. Beck Memorial Scholarships *(Undergraduate/Scholarship)* [5498]

Beck-Pfann Memorial Scholarships *(Undergraduate/Scholarship)* [7964]
Garvin L. Beck Scholarships *(Undergraduate/Scholarship)* [8456]
Dr. Joyce Beckett Scholarships *(Graduate, Undergraduate/Scholarship)* [6719]
Clifford L. Bedford Scholarship Award *(Undergraduate/Scholarship)* [5177]
BedwettingStore.com Design a Mascot Scholarships *(Undergraduate, Graduate/Scholarship)* [5635]
Raymond and Donald Beeler Memorial Scholarships *(Undergraduate/Scholarship)* [8457]
BEF Scholarships of the Arts *(Graduate, Undergraduate/Scholarship)* [2337]
Notah Begay III Scholarship Program *(Undergraduate/Scholarship)* [300]
N.S. Beinstock Fellowships *(Other/Fellowship)* [8402]
Hannah Beiter Graduate Student Research Grants *(Doctorate, Graduate/Grant)* [2909]
Bel Canto Vocal Scholarship Foundation Vocal Competition *(Graduate/Award, Scholarship)* [2217]
Belfer-Aptman Dissertation Research Awards *(Doctorate/Grant)* [6409]
AG Bell College Scholarship Awards *(Undergraduate, Graduate/Scholarship)* [314]
Alfred D. Bell, Jr. Travel Grants *(Graduate/Grant)* [4137]
John Bell and Lawrence Thornton Scholarship Fund *(Undergraduate/Scholarship)* [4738]
Ray and Mary Bell Memorial Scholarships *(Undergraduate/Scholarship)* [8690]
Betty Bell Scholarship Fund *(Undergraduate/Scholarship)* [4922]
A.G. Bell School Age Financial Aid Program *(Undergraduate/Scholarship)* [315]
Bradley Stuart Beller Special Merit Award *(Doctorate, Postdoctorate/Award)* [3370]
Bellevue PFLAG Scholarships *(Undergraduate/Scholarship)* [8245]
David Beltran Memorial Scholarships *(Undergraduate/Scholarship)* [8458]
Samuel Flagg Bemis Dissertation Research Grants *(Doctorate, Graduate/Grant)* [9133]
Reckitt Benckiser Student Scholarships *(Graduate/Scholarship)* [6771]
Richard W. Bendicksen Memorial Scholarships *(Undergraduate/Scholarship)* [1726]
Bill Bendiner and Doug Morgenson Scholarships *(Undergraduate/Scholarship)* [8246]
H. Y. Benedict Fellowships *(Graduate/Fellowship)* [340]
George Benes, MD & Michael Mallee, EdD Point Scholarships *(Undergraduate, Graduate, Doctorate/Scholarship)* [8170]
Arthur Lockwood Beneventi Law Scholarships *(Undergraduate/Scholarship)* [7149]
Dave Benferado Scholarships *(Graduate/Scholarship)* [140]
Benign Essential Blepharospasm Research Foundation Research Grants *(Doctorate, Postdoctorate/Grant)* [2224]
HDR/Henry "Bud" Benjes Scholarships *(Master's/Scholarship)* [1484]
Jean Bennett Memorial Student Travel Grants *(Graduate, Undergraduate/Grant)* [7671]
Casey Bennett Scholarships *(Undergraduate/Scholarship)* [4007]
William Bennett W7PHO Memorial Scholarships *(Undergraduate/Scholarship)* [1727]
Price Benowitz Social Justice Scholarships *(Undergraduate/Scholarship)* [8228]
Elizabeth Benson Scholarship Awards *(Undergraduate/Scholarship)* [8542]
Benton-Meier Neuropsychology Graduate Scholarships *(Graduate/Scholarship)* [1142]
Linn-Benton County Scholarships *(Undergraduate/Scholarship)* [7709]
Rosalie Bentzinger Scholarships *(Doctorate/Scholarship)* [9849]
Lester G. Benz Memorial Scholarships for College Journalism Study *(Other/Scholarship)* [8396]
Fred Berg Awards *(Undergraduate/Award)* [3796]
Charlotte V. Bergen Scholarships *(Undergraduate/Scholarship)* [1269]

Bergman Scholarships *(Undergraduate/Scholarship)* [7487]
Bergmann Family Scholarship Funds *(Undergraduate/Scholarship)* [6282]
The Joseph Berkman, and Michael and Sarah Chipkin Holocaust/Genocide Studies Award *(Graduate/Scholarship)* [9581]
ARRS/Leonard Berlin Scholarships in Medical Professionalism *(Other/Scholarship)* [1222]
Louise Berman Fellows Award *(Graduate, Master's, Doctorate/Fellowship, Award)* [5667]
Richard L. Bernardi Memorial Scholarships *(Undergraduate/Scholarship)* [3276]
Stuart L. Bernath Dissertation Grants *(Doctorate, Graduate/Grant)* [9134]
Myrna F. Bernath Fellowships *(Doctorate, Graduate/Fellowship)* [9135]
Hon. Peggy Bernheim Memorial Scholarships *(Undergraduate/Scholarship)* [2377]
Donald H. Bernstein/John B. Talbert, Jr. Scholarships *(Undergraduate/Scholarship)* [4179]
Jean Clark Berry Scholarships *(Graduate, Undergraduate/Scholarship)* [5693]
Best Price Nutrition and Health Scholarships *(Undergraduate/Scholarship)* [2237]
Beta Lambda Project 2000 Scholarship *(Undergraduate/Scholarship)* [5694]
Beta Mu Project 2000 Scholarships *(Undergraduate/Scholarship)* [5695]
Beta Pi Project 2000 Scholarship in Memory of Kristy LeMond *(Undergraduate/Scholarship)* [5696]
Beta Pi Sigma Sorority Scholarships (BPSSS) *(Undergraduate/Scholarship)* [2244]
Beta Province Project 2000 Scholarships *(Undergraduate/Scholarship)* [5697]
Beta Sigma Scholarships *(Undergraduate/Scholarship)* [8912]
Beta Tau Scholarship Fund *(Undergraduate/Scholarship)* [5698]
Beta Theta Memorial Scholarships *(Graduate, Undergraduate/Scholarship)* [5699]
Beta Xi Project 2000 Scholarships *(Undergraduate/Scholarship)* [5700]
Beta Zeta Project 2000 Scholarships *(Undergraduate/Scholarship)* [5701]
Harold Bettinger Scholarships *(Undergraduate, Graduate/Scholarship)* [800]
Leonard Bettinger Vocational Scholarships *(Undergraduate, Vocational/Occupational/Scholarship)* [801]
William and Dorothy Bevan Scholarship *(Graduate, Master's, Doctorate/Scholarship)* [1143]
Albert J. Beveridge Grants for Research in the Western Hemisphere *(Doctorate/Grant)* [852]
BIE-Loan for Service for Graduates *(Graduate/Loan)* [882]
James L. Biggane Fellowships in Finance *(Graduate/Fellowship)* [7367]
James Bilder Scholarships *(Undergraduate/Scholarship)* [9420]
Jan Bingle Scholarships *(Master's, Doctorate/Scholarship)* [3055]
Helen & Bob Bintz Scholarship Funds *(Undergraduate/Scholarship)* [6283]
Biogen Idec Hemophilia Scholarship Program *(Undergraduate, Graduate, Doctorate/Scholarship)* [2310]
BioRx/Hemophilia of North Carolina Educational Scholarships *(Undergraduate/Scholarship)* [6985]
Birmingham District Alabama Dietetic Association Scholarships *(Graduate, Undergraduate/Scholarship)* [196]
Birmingham Student Scholarships *(Undergraduate/Scholarship)* [2273]
Graduate Student Honoraria - Elmer C. Birney Awards *(Master's, Doctorate/Award)* [1358]
Bisexual Foundation Scholarships *(Graduate/Scholarship)* [9284]
The Bishop James C. Baker Award *(Doctorate/Scholarship)* [9850]
Lebbeus F. Bissell Scholarships *(Undergraduate/Scholarship)* [4739]
Mary E. Bivins Foundation Religious Scholarship Program *(Graduate, Undergraduate/Scholarship)* [2275]

Dr. Richard E. Bjork Memorial Graduate Study Award *(Graduate/Scholarship)* [9582]
Law Offices of David A. Black Annual Hearing Impaired Scholarships *(All/Scholarship)* [5957]
Thomas F. Black, Jr. Memorial Scholarships *(Undergraduate/Scholarship)* [8600]
Black Men Building Resources Scholarships *(Undergraduate/Scholarship)* [4576]
Reid Blackburn Scholarships *(Undergraduate/Scholarship)* [7107]
Eileen Blackey Doctoral Fellowships *(Doctorate/Fellowship)* [6788]
William T. Blackwell Scholarship Fund *(Undergraduate/Scholarship)* [7019]
Beatrice K. Blair Scholarships *(Undergraduate/Scholarship)* [2305]
Thomas M. Blake Memorial Scholarships *(Undergraduate/Scholarship)* [3360]
Blakemore Freeman Fellowships *(Undergraduate, Advanced Professional/Fellowship)* [2307]
Blakemore Refresher Grants *(Professional development/Grant)* [2308]
Margaret Blanchard Dissertation Support Fund *(Graduate/Grant)* [10216]
Joan Blend Scholarship Fund *(Undergraduate/Scholarship)* [9493]
M. Hildred Blewett Fellowships *(Postdoctorate/Fellowship)* [1088]
Everitt P. Blizard Scholarships *(Graduate/Scholarship)* [1034]
Ellin Bloch and Pierre Ritchie Diversity Dissertation Grant *(Graduate/Grant)* [1132]
Jeanne Humphrey Block Dissertation Award *(Postdoctorate/Award)* [4784]
Ellen Blodgett Memorial Scholarships *(Undergraduate/Scholarship)* [7375]
F.A. and Charlotte Blount Scholarships *(Undergraduate/Scholarship)* [10571]
BMES Graduate and Undergraduate Student Awards *(Graduate, Undergraduate/Award)* [2271]
BMO Capital Markets Lime Connect Equity through Education Scholarships *(Undergraduate, Graduate/Scholarship)* [6087]
BMO Financial Group Lime Connect Canada Scholarship Program for Students with Disabilities *(Undergraduate, Graduate/Scholarship)* [6088]
Board of Certification for Emergency Nursing (BCEN) Undergraduate Scholarships *(Undergraduate/Scholarship)* [3860]
Board of Young Adult Advisors Scholarships *(Graduate/Scholarship)* [9827]
Sandra Bobbitt Continuing Education Scholarship *(Undergraduate/Scholarship)* [2032]
Edith and Arnold N. Bodtker Grants *(Undergraduate, Graduate/Grant, Internship)* [3522]
B.O.G. Pest Control Scholarship Funds *(Undergraduate, Graduate/Scholarship)* [2323]
Gerald J. and Helen Bogen Fund *(Undergraduate/Scholarship)* [4660]
Hagop Bogigian Scholarship Fund *(Undergraduate/Scholarship)* [1689]
Bogliasco Fellowships *(Professional development/Fellowship)* [2327]
Bohemian Lawyers Association of Chicago Scholarships *(Graduate/Scholarship)* [2333]
Brian Bolton Graduate/Mature Student Essay Awards *(Undergraduate, Graduate/Award)* [4301]
Friends of Megan Bolton Memorial Fund *(Undergraduate/Scholarship)* [4233]
BOMA/NY Scholarships *(Undergraduate/Scholarship)* [2404]
Barbara Bonnema Memorial Scholarships *(Undergraduate/Scholarship)* [8459]
Ellis J. Bonner Scholarships *(Graduate/Scholarship)* [6754]
Sam L. Booke, Sr. Scholarships *(Undergraduate/Scholarship)* [10572]
Boomer Benefits Scholarships *(Undergraduate/Scholarship)* [2335]
Admiral Mike Boorda Loans Program *(Undergraduate/Loan)* [7234]
T. Frank Booth Memorial Scholarship Fund *(Undergraduate/Scholarship)* [4180]
David L. Boren Undergraduate Scholarships *(Graduate, Undergraduate/Scholarship)* [1968]
Dr. Anita Borg Memorial Scholarships - USA *(Graduate, Undergraduate/Scholarship)* [4493]
Maria Gonzales Borrero Scholarships *(Undergraduate/Scholarship)* [4740]
Tom Bost Scholarships *(Undergraduate/Scholarship)* [10217]
Boston City Federation "Return to School" Scholarships *(Undergraduate, Graduate/Scholarship)* [4351]
Boston Intercollegiate Alumnae Association Adelphe Scholarship *(Undergraduate/Scholarship)* [5702]
Stephen Botein Fellowships *(Doctorate/Fellowship)* [433]
Dr. George T. Bottomley Scholarships *(Undergraduate/Scholarship)* [6350]
Richard J. Bouchard AECOM Scholarships *(Undergraduate, Graduate/Scholarship)* [1162]
Bound to Stay Bound Books Scholarships *(Graduate/Scholarship)* [2017]
Rev. Andrew L. Bouwhuis Memorial Scholarship Program *(Graduate/Scholarship)* [2814]
MAC Louisa Bowen Memorial Scholarships for Graduate Students in Archival Administration *(Graduate/Scholarship)* [6515]
William R. Bowen Scholarships *(Undergraduate/Scholarship)* [3171]
Boy Scouts of America Troop 3 Scholarships - Art Till/Nathan E. Smith Memorial Scholarships *(Undergraduate, Vocational/Occupational/Scholarship)* [8460]
W. Scott Boyd Group Grants *(Advanced Professional/Grant)* [5282]
Corris Boyd Scholarships *(Master's/Scholarship)* [2085]
Dody Boyd Scholarships *(Undergraduate/Scholarship)* [3214]
Verna Curry Boyer Scholarships *(Undergraduate/Scholarship)* [9564]
Boyle Family Scholarship *(Undergraduate/Scholarship)* [1577]
Mildred Cater Bradham Social Work Fellowships *(Graduate, Professional development/Fellowship)* [10814]
Carol June Bradley Awards *(Professional development/Grant)* [6625]
Charles Bradley Memorial Scholarships *(Undergraduate/Scholarship)* [4723]
William L. Bradley Memorial Scholarships *(Undergraduate/Scholarship)* [7376]
Paul W. Bradley Scholarships *(Undergraduate/Scholarship)* [7377]
Edward J. Brady Memorial Scholarships *(Undergraduate/Scholarship)* [1511]
W. Philip Braender and Nancy Coleman Braender Scholarships *(Undergraduate/Scholarship)* [4741]
BRAF Grants *(Graduate/Grant)* [2301]
TACS/A. Bragas and Associates Student Scholarships *(Undergraduate/Scholarship)* [9686]
AFCEA San Diego Buck Bragunier Leadership Scholarship *(Undergraduate/Scholarship)* [1667]
Byard Braley Scholarship *(Undergraduate/Scholarship)* [5462]
The Helen and Edward Brancati Teacher Development Scholarships *(Other/Scholarship)* [2783]
Linda Brandt Research Awards *(Postgraduate/Award)* [2039]
Erika A. and George E. Brattain Sr. Scholarship Fund *(Undergraduate, High School/Scholarship)* [10498]
Theodore E.D. Braun Research Travel Fellowships *(Other/Fellowship)* [1287]
Breakthrough to Nursing Scholarships *(Undergraduate/Scholarship)* [4268]
Ann Marie Bredefeld Scholarships *(Undergraduate/Scholarship)* [7966]
William J. Brennan Graduate Assistant Fellowships *(Graduate/Fellowship)* [7678]
Brent R. Churchill Memorial Scholarships *(Undergraduate/Scholarship)* [6191]
Breslauer Family Scholarships *(Undergraduate/Scholarship)* [8693]
Hilda E. Bretzlaff Foundation Scholarships *(Undergraduate, Graduate, Grant)* [2363]
Rick Brewer Scholarships *(Undergraduate/Scholarship)* [10218]
James Bridenbaugh Memorial Scholarships *(Undergraduate/Scholarship)* [802]
Lloyd Bridges Scholarships *(Graduate, Other/Scholarship)* [2835]
Tommy Bright Scholarship Fund *(Undergraduate/Scholarship)* [4923]
Parsons Brinckerhoff-Jim Lammie Scholarships *(Undergraduate, Graduate/Scholarship)* [1163]
Wade O. Brinker Resident Research Award *(Undergraduate/Award)* [10378]
Broadcast Education and Development Program *(Other/Scholarship)* [3134]
Cathy L. Brock Memorial Scholarships *(Graduate/Scholarship)* [5167]
Kae and Kay Brockermeyer Endowed Scholarships *(Undergraduate/Scholarship)* [7968]
Louise A. Broderick San Diego County Scholarships *(Undergraduate/Scholarship)* [8694]
Ross P. Broesamle Educational Scholarship Fund *(Undergraduate/Scholarship)* [5929]
Houston Alumnae Association, Doris Krikham Brokaw Memorial Adelphe Scholarship *(Undergraduate, Graduate/Scholarship)* [5703]
John G. Brokaw Scholarships *(Undergraduate/Scholarship)* [7227]
Brookdale Leadership in Aging Fellowships *(Other/Fellowship)* [2380]
Shirley J. Brooke Endowed Scholarships *(Undergraduate/Scholarship)* [7969]
George M. Brooker, CPM Diversity Collegiate Scholarship *(Graduate, Undergraduate/Scholarship)* [5215]
Seth R. and Corrine H. Brooks Memorial Scholarships *(Undergraduate/Scholarship)* [2246]
Carl E. Brooks Scholarships *(Undergraduate/Scholarship)* [9421]
Dorothy B. Brothers Executive Scholarship Program *(Undergraduate/Scholarship)* [10656]
William A. and Ann M. Brothers Scholarships *(Undergraduate/Scholarship)* [1512]
Henry Broughton, K2AE Memorial Scholarships *(Undergraduate/Scholarship)* [1728]
Selena Danette Brown Book Scholarships *(Graduate, Undergraduate/Scholarship)* [6720]
Marjorie M. Brown Dissertation Fellowship *(Doctorate/Fellowship)* [5780]
Marjorie M. Brown Fellowship Program *(Postdoctorate/Fellowship)* [5788]
John Carter Brown Library Long-Term Fellowships *(Graduate, Doctorate/Fellowship)* [2384]
John Carter Brown Library Short-Term Fellowships *(Doctorate, Postdoctorate/Fellowship)* [2385]
Olympia Brown and Max Kapp Awards *(Master's/Scholarship)* [9832]
Catherine Amelia Thew Brown Memorial Scholarship Funds *(Undergraduate/Scholarship)* [6284]
Milton and Edith Brown Memorial Scholarships *(Undergraduate/Scholarship)* [2946]
Quincy Brown Memorial Scholarships *(Undergraduate/Scholarship)* [8461]
Ruby A. Brown Memorial Scholarships *(Undergraduate/Scholarship)* [3753]
Jesse Brown Memorial Youth Scholarship Program *(Advanced Professional/Scholarship)* [3632]
Ron Brown Scholars Program *(Undergraduate/Scholarship)* [2387]
Harry and Lucille Brown Scholarships *(Undergraduate/Scholarship)* [4578]
Jack H. Brown Scholarships *(Undergraduate/Scholarship)* [2448]
Mary L. Brown Scholarships *(Undergraduate/Scholarship)* [5467]
Mary Lou Brown Scholarships *(Undergraduate/Scholarship)* [1729]
Charles S. Brown Scholarships in Physics *(Graduate, Undergraduate/Scholarship)* [7140]
VPPPA Stephen Brown Scholarships *(Graduate, Undergraduate/Scholarship)* [10417]
Richard A. Brown Student Scholarships *(Undergraduate/Scholarship)* [9691]
Regina Brown Undergraduate Student Fellowships *(Undergraduate/Fellowship)* [6879]
Peggy Browning Fund - Chicago School-Year Fellowships *(Graduate, Undergraduate/Fellowship)* [2394]
Hollis Brownstein Research Grants *(Professional development/Grant)* [6011]
Chester H. Bruce Memorial Scholarships *(Under-

graduate/Scholarship) [7816]
Sheriff W. Bruce Umpleby Law Enforcement Scholarship Fund (Undergraduate/Scholarship) [9494]
Robert W. Brunsman Memorial Scholarship (Professional development/Scholarship) [5360]
Katie Brush Memorial Scholarships (Master's, Doctorate/Scholarship) [3056]
Bernard B. and Mary L. Brusin Scholarships (Undergraduate/Scholarship) [3705]
William and Clara Bryan Scholarships (Undergraduate/Scholarship) [3216]
Bryant Essay Scholarships (Undergraduate, Graduate/Scholarship) [2396]
Edward C. Bryant Scholarship for an Outstanding Graduate Student in Survey Statistics (Graduate/Scholarship) [1464]
Bryant Visual Content Scholarships (Undergraduate, Graduate/Scholarship) [2397]
BSA Educational Scholarships (Undergraduate/Scholarship) [2426]
BSF Science and Medicine Research Grants (Professional development/Grant) [2199]
Lt. General Douglas D. Buchholz Memorial Scholarship (Undergraduate/Scholarship) [89]
John and Elisabeth Buck Endowed Scholarships (Graduate, Postdoctorate/Scholarship) [6244]
Peter Buck Fellowships Program - Graduate (Graduate/Fellowship) [9030]
Peter Buck Fellowships Program - Postdoctoral (Postdoctorate/Fellowship) [9031]
Buckfire & Buckfire, P.C. Law School Diversity Scholarships (Graduate/Scholarship) [2399]
Buckfire & Buckfire, P.C. Medical Diversity Scholarships (Advanced Professional/Scholarship) [2400]
Walter and Louise Buell Graduate Scholarships (Graduate/Scholarship) [4142]
Gary L. Buffington Memorial Scholarships (Undergraduate/Scholarship) [5138]
Buick Achievers Scholarship Program (Undergraduate/Scholarship) [4359]
Pamfil and Maria Bujea Family Orthodox Christian Seminarian Scholarships (Undergraduate/Scholarship) [1225]
William S. Bullinger Scholarships (Doctorate/Scholarship) [3983]
Armen H. Bululian Scholarships (Undergraduate/Scholarship) [1690]
Mike Buoncristiano Memorial Scholarship Fund (Undergraduate/Scholarship) [6287]
William T. Burbage Family Memorial Scholarships (Undergraduate/Scholarship) [3172]
C. Lalor Burdick Scholarships (Graduate, Master's, Doctorate/Scholarship) [6245]
George M. Burditt Scholarships (Undergraduate/Scholarship) [1965]
Max M. Burger Endowed Scholarships in Embryology (Graduate, Master's, Doctorate/Scholarship) [6246]
Graduate Fellowship Program - Robert M. Burger Fellowships (Doctorate, Graduate/Fellowship) [8832]
Burger King Employee Scholars Program (Undergraduate/Scholarship) [2410]
Burger King Scholars Program (Undergraduate/Scholarship) [2411]
Richard J. Burk, Jr. Fellowships (Graduate/Fellowship) [4808]
ACLS Frederick Burkhardt Residential Fellowships (Other/Fellowship) [434]
Frederick Burkhardt Residential Fellowships for Recently Tenured Scholars (Advanced Professional, Professional development/Fellowship) [738]
Ralph Burkhardt Scholarship Fund (Undergraduate, High School/Scholarship) [10499]
Cecil E. Burney Scholarships (Undergraduate/Scholarship) [3091]
Burroughs Wellcome Fund Collaborative Research Travel Grants (CRTG) (Doctorate, Postdoctorate, Professional development/Grant) [2413]
Burroughs Wellcome Travel Fellowships (Undergraduate, Graduate/Fellowship, Grant) [9305]
Wes Burton Memorial Scholarships (Undergraduate/Scholarship) [10574]
Bush Artist Fellowships (Professional development/Fellowship) [2419]
Bush Fellowship Program (Other/Fellowship) [2420]

Lindsay Buster Memorial Scholarships (Undergraduate/Scholarship) [3277]
Walter Byers Postgraduate Scholarships (Graduate, Postgraduate/Scholarship) [6861]
byourself Scholarship Fund (Undergraduate, Vocational/Occupational/Scholarship) [3318]
Robert C. Byrd Honors Scholarships (Undergraduate/Scholarship) [5071]
Dr. F. Ross Byrd Scholarships (Graduate, Vocational/Occupational, Postgraduate/Scholarship) [10463]
George J. Bysiewicz Scholarship Fund (Undergraduate/Scholarship) [3198]
C200 Scholar Awards (Graduate/Scholarship) [3156]
CAAO Scholarship (Professional development/Scholarship) [3356]
Johnston Cabaniss Scholarships (Graduate/Scholarship) [206]
Cal State San Macros Alumna Scholarships (Undergraduate/Scholarship) [2486]
Joseph R. Calder, Jr., MD Scholarship Fund (Undergraduate/Scholarship) [4041]
Dave Caldwell Scholarships (Graduate/Scholarship) [1485]
Caledonia Alumni Association Scholarship Funds (Undergraduate/Scholarship) [6285]
Calgary USAEE/IAEE North American Conference Registration Fee Scholarships (Undergraduate/Scholarship) [9883]
Calhoun County Auburn University Scholarships (Undergraduate/Scholarship) [3260]
California Association of Family and Consumer Sciences - San Diego Chapter Scholarships (CAFCS) (Undergraduate, Graduate/Scholarship) [8695]
California Bar Foundation 1L Diversity Scholarships (Graduate/Scholarship) [2442]
California Council of the Blind Scholarships (Undergraduate, Graduate/Scholarship) [8751]
California Groundwater Association Scholarships (Undergraduate/Scholarship) [2462]
California Scottish Rite Foundation Scholarships (Undergraduate/Scholarship) [2477]
California Sea Grant State Fellowship (Graduate/Fellowship) [2479]
Calihan Academic Fellowships (Graduate, Professional development/Fellowship, Grant) [56]
Calihan Travel Grants (Graduate/Grant) [57]
Calista Education and Culture Scholarships (Graduate, Undergraduate, Vocational/Occupational/Scholarship) [2490]
Captain Jodi Callahan Memorial Scholarships (Graduate, Master's/Scholarship) [122]
W.L. Calvert Memorial Scholarships (Graduate/Scholarship) [4966]
Calvin Alumni Association British Columbia Scholarships (Undergraduate/Scholarship) [2492]
Calvin Alumni Association Southern California Chapter Scholarships (Undergraduate/Scholarship) [2502]
Camden County College Foundation Scholarships (Undergraduate/Scholarship) [2522]
Stuart Cameron and Margaret McLeod Memorial Scholarships (SCMS) (Graduate, Undergraduate/Scholarship) [5205]
Wesley C. Cameron Scholarships (Undergraduate/Scholarship) [7228]
Camille and Henry Dreyfus Foundation - Senior Scientist Mentor Program (Professional development/Grant) [3695]
Camp Network Counselor Appreciation Scholarships (Undergraduate/Scholarship) [2528]
Thomas R. Camp Scholarships (Graduate/Scholarship) [1486]
Lucille Campbell Scholarship Fund (Undergraduate, High School/Scholarship) [10500]
Robert G. Campbell Scholarships (Undergraduate/Scholarship) [8462]
Campus Discovery Scholarships (Undergraduate/Scholarship) [2532]
Cancer for College Scholarships (Graduate, Undergraduate/Scholarship) [2770]
Cancer Survivors' Fund Scholarships (Undergraduate/Scholarship) [2779]
Annie J. Cannon Award in Astronomy (Doctorate/Award, Recognition) [613]

Therese A. Cannon Educational Scholarships (Other/Scholarship) [5372]
Agustin C. Cano Memorial Scholarships (Undergraduate/Scholarship) [8334]
Commander Ronald J. Cantin Scholarships (Undergraduate/Scholarship) [3075]
CAODC Occupational Health and Safety Scholarships (Professional development/Scholarship) [2570]
CAODC Scholarship Program (Undergraduate/Scholarship) [2571]
Cape Fear Community College Merit Scholarships (Undergraduate/Scholarship) [2786]
Rhea Sourifman Caplin Memorial Scholarships (Undergraduate/Scholarship) [4742]
Lester J. Cappon Fellowships in Documentary Editing (Postdoctorate/Fellowship) [7410]
Daniel Cardillo Charitable Fund (Professional development/Scholarship) [6192]
Career Awards for Medical Scientists (CAMS) (Postdoctorate, Advanced Professional, Professional development/Grant) [2414]
Career Awards at the Scientific Interface (CASI) (Doctorate, Postdoctorate, Advanced Professional, Professional development/Grant) [2416]
Career Development Scholarships (Postdoctorate, Postgraduate/Scholarship) [4129]
Career Mobility Scholarships (Graduate, Undergraduate, Vocational/Occupational/Scholarship) [4269]
CareerFitter Scholarships (Undergraduate, Graduate/Scholarship) [2795]
CareFusion Fellowships for Neonatal and Pediatric Therapists (Professional development/Fellowship) [1209]
Beth Carew Memorial Scholarships (Undergraduate/Scholarship) [6986]
John Carew Memorial Scholarships (Graduate/Scholarship) [803]
John L. Carey Scholarship Awards (Graduate/Scholarship) [901]
Caribbean Actuarial Scholarship (Undergraduate/Scholarship) [61]
AABA Read Carlock Memorial Scholarship Fund (Other/Scholarship) [1625]
Dan Carman Attorney at Law Criminal Defense Scholarships (Advanced Professional/Scholarship) [3520]
Walta Wilkinson Carmichael Scholarships (Undergraduate/Scholarship) [8913]
Carnegie Observatories Graduate Research Fellowships (Graduate, Doctorate/Fellowship) [2799]
Julian E. Carnes Scholarship Fund (Undergraduate/Scholarship) [4183]
Carolinas-Virginias Retail Hardware Scholarships (Undergraduate/Scholarship) [4184]
Carollo Engineers Scholarships (Master's/Scholarship) [1487]
Jeffrey Carollo Music Scholarships (Undergraduate/Scholarship) [7323]
Carpenters' Company Scholarships (Undergraduate/Scholarship) [2801]
Willis H. Carrier Scholarships (Undergraduate/Scholarship, Award) [1329]
Eugene Carroll Scholarships (Undergraduate/Scholarship) [2947]
Karen D. Carsel Memorial Scholarships (Graduate/Scholarship) [819]
Rachel Carson Prize (Other/Prize) [1310]
Gene Carte Student Paper Competition Awards (Undergraduate, Graduate/Prize) [1281]
Deloris Carter Hampton Scholarships (Undergraduate/Scholarship) [8247]
Letitia B. Carter Scholarships (Undergraduate, Advanced Professional/Scholarship) [8563]
CAS Trust Scholarship (Undergraduate/Scholarship) [2809]
CASBS Fellowships (Doctorate, Other/Fellowship) [2841]
Cascara Vacation Rentals Hospitality Matters Scholarships (Undergraduate, Graduate/Scholarship) [2805]
Casey Family Services Alumni Scholarships (Graduate, Undergraduate, Vocational/Occupational/Scholarship) [4157]

Elton Casey Scholarships *(Undergraduate/Scholarship)* [10219]
Local 827 Peter J. Casey Scholarships *(Undergraduate/Scholarship)* [5288]
George H. and Anna Casper Fund *(Undergraduate/Scholarship)* [9496]
Carlos M. Castaneda Journalism Scholarships *(Graduate/Scholarship)* [2807]
The Kerri Castellini Women's Leadership Scholarships *(Undergraduate/Scholarship)* [8229]
Catholic Aid Association's Post-High School Tuition Scholarships *(Undergraduate/Scholarship)* [2818]
Catholic Biblical Association of America Scholarships *(Undergraduate/Scholarship)* [2812]
Catholic Relief Services Summer Internships *(Undergraduate, Graduate, Professional development/Internship)* [2816]
Robert A. Catlin/David W. Long Memorial Fellowships *(Graduate/Fellowship)* [1104]
Cave Conservancy Foundation Graduate and Undergraduate Fellowships *(Doctorate, Graduate, Undergraduate/Fellowship)* [2823]
Christine Kerr Cawthorne Scholarships *(Undergraduate/Scholarship)* [8914]
Llewellyn L. Cayvan String Instrument Scholarships *(Undergraduate/Scholarship)* [4580]
CBC Spouses Education Scholarship Fund *(Graduate, Undergraduate/Scholarship)* [3345]
CBC Spouses Heineken USA Performing Arts Scholarships *(Undergraduate/Scholarship)* [3346]
CBC Spouses Visual Arts Scholarships *(Undergraduate/Scholarship)* [3347]
CBCF Congressional Fellows Program *(Other/Fellowship)* [3348]
CCF Academic Fellowships in Karst Studies - Graduate *(Master's, Doctorate/Fellowship)* [2820]
CCF Academic Fellowships in Karst Studies - Undegraduate *(Undergraduate/Fellowship)* [2821]
CCF Career Development Award *(Professional development/Grant)* [3371]
CCF Improving Cancer Care Grants *(Professional development, Doctorate/Grant)* [3372]
CCF Merit Award *(Professional development, Doctorate/Award)* [3373]
CCFA Career Development Awards *(Doctorate/Grant)* [3476]
CCFA Research Fellowship Awards *(Doctorate, Graduate/Fellowship)* [3477]
CCFA Student Research Fellowship Awards *(Graduate, Undergraduate/Grant)* [3478]
CCSD School Counselors' Scholarships *(Undergraduate/Scholarship)* [8336]
CCWH/Berkshire Conference of Women Historians Graduate Student Fellowships *(Doctorate/Fellowship)* [3418]
CDC Presidential Management Fellows Program *(Graduate/Fellowship)* [9917]
CDC Preventive Medicine Residency and Fellowships *(Other/Fellowship)* [9918]
L.B. Cebik, W4RNL, and Jean Cebik, N4TZP, Memorial Scholarships *(Undergraduate/Scholarship)* [1730]
Betty J. Cecere Memorial Scholarship Endowment Fund *(Undergraduate, High School/Scholarship)* [10501]
Cedarcrest Farms Scholarships *(Graduate, Undergraduate/Scholarship)* [944]
CEJIL Communications Internships *(Undergraduate, Graduate/Internship)* [2860]
CEJIL Legal Internships *(Graduate, Professional development/Internship)* [2861]
Cengage Learning Scholarships Program *(Undergraduate/Scholarship)* [2839]
Cengage Travel Award for Teachers of Reading at a Community College *(Professional development/Monetary)* [3123]
DAR Centennial Scholarship *(Undergraduate/Scholarship)* [7150]
Center for Engineering in Medicine Predoctoral Fellows Program *(Postdoctorate/Fellowship)* [6316]
Center for Lesbian and Gay Studies Fellowships *(Graduate/Fellowship)* [2863]
Centerville-Abington Dollars for Scholars *(Undergraduate/Scholarship)* [10502]
Central Arizona DX Association Scholarships *(Undergraduate/Scholarship)* [1731]

CentraState Associated Auxiliaries Scholarships *(Undergraduate/Scholarship)* [2875]
CentraState Healthcare Foundation Health Professions Scholarships *(Undergraduate/Scholarship)* [2877]
CERT College Scholarships *(Graduate, Undergraduate/Scholarship)* [3435]
Certified Municipal Clerk Scholarships (CMC) *(Other/Scholarship)* [5350]
Certified Neuroscience Registered Nurse Recertification Grant Program *(Other/Grant)* [545]
Cerutti Group Scholarships *(Undergraduate/Scholarship)* [4646]
Arthur and Gladys Cervenka Scholarships *(Undergraduate/Scholarship)* [9168]
CES Conference Travel Grants *(Graduate, Professional development/Grant)* [3437]
CES First Article Prize *(Professional development/Prize)* [3438]
CF Abogados Legal Scholarships *(Graduate/Scholarship)* [2781]
CfA Postdoctoral Fellowships *(Postdoctorate/Fellowship)* [4780]
CFNIL Community Foundation Scholarships *(Undergraduate/Scholarship)* [3278]
CFNIL Senior Memorial Scholarships *(Undergraduate/Scholarship)* [3279]
CFR National Intelligence Fellowships *(Professional development/Fellowship)* [3443]
CFT/ACPSOP Scholarships *(Undergraduate/Scholarship)* [2948]
CH2M Hill/AEESP Outstanding Doctoral Dissertation Award *(Graduate, Doctorate/Award)* [1951]
Rick Chace Foundation Scholarships *(Graduate/Scholarship)* [2024]
Chaîne des Rôtisseurs Scholarships *(Undergraduate/Scholarship)* [758]
ChairScholars National Scholarship Program *(Undergraduate/Scholarship)* [2889]
Jeanne S. Chall Research Fellowship *(Doctorate, Graduate/Fellowship)* [5355]
Challenge Met Scholarships *(Undergraduate/Scholarship)* [1732]
Mariam K. Chamberlain Fellowships in Women and Public Policy *(Graduate/Fellowship)* [5228]
Logan S. Chambers Individual Scholarships *(Other/Scholarship)* [5283]
Chambliss Astronomy Achievement Student Awards *(Undergraduate, Graduate/Award)* [614]
Bryan A. Champion Memorial Scholarship *(Undergraduate/Scholarship)* [7582]
Jason Chaney Memorial Scholarship Fund *(Undergraduate/Scholarship)* [10503]
Channabasappa Memorial Scholarships *(Graduate, Doctorate/Scholarship)* [5319]
Harry H. and Floy B. Chapin Scholarships *(Undergraduate/Scholarship)* [3280]
Nancy J. Chapman Scholarships *(Other/Scholarship)* [1939]
S. Penny Chappell Scholarships *(Undergraduate/Scholarship)* [8085]
Chapter 17 - St. Louis Scholarships *(Undergraduate/Scholarship)* [9170]
Chapter 6 Fairfield County Scholarships *(Undergraduate/Scholarship)* [9177]
Charles H. Bussmann Graduate Scholarship *(Graduate, Undergraduate/Scholarship)* [6271]
Charlotte Housing Authority Scholarship Fund (CHASF) *(Undergraduate, Vocational/Occupational/Scholarship)* [4185]
Emilie Du Chatelet Awards *(Doctorate/Award)* [1288]
CCWH Nupur Chaudhuri First Article Prizes *(Professional development/Prize)* [3419]
Cesar E. Chavez Scholarships *(Undergraduate/Scholarship)* [8463]
CHCI Scholarships *(Undergraduate, Graduate/Scholarship)* [3354]
CHEA Undergraduate Scholarship Program for Students with Disabilities *(Undergraduate/Scholarship)* [2464]
CHEA Vocational Grants *(Undergraduate/Grant)* [2465]
Cheatham County Community Foundation Scholarships *(Undergraduate/Scholarship)* [3218]
Cheerful Giver Scholarships *(Undergraduate/Scholarship)* [8696]

Chemical Heritage Foundation Travel Grants (CHF) *(All/Grant)* [2891]
Cherokee Nation Graduate Scholarships *(Graduate/Scholarship)* [2893]
Cherokee Nation Pell Scholarships *(Graduate/Scholarship)* [2894]
Cherokee Nation Scholarships *(Undergraduate/Scholarship)* [2895]
Sgt. Cherven Scholarship *(Undergraduate/Scholarship)* [6312]
Cheyenne High School Desert Shields Scholarship *(Undergraduate/Scholarship)* [8337]
Melba Dawn Chiarenza Scholarship Fund *(Undergraduate/Scholarship)* [10504]
Chicago FM Club Scholarships *(Undergraduate/Scholarship)* [1733]
Kevin Child Scholarships *(Undergraduate/Scholarship)* [6987]
Childbirth Educator Program Scholarships *(All/Scholarship)* [5909]
John and Ruth Childe Scholarships *(Undergraduate/Scholarship)* [9422]
Children of Evangeline Section Scholarships *(Graduate, Undergraduate/Scholarship)* [9249]
Children of Unitarian Universalist Ministers College Scholarships *(Undergraduate/Scholarship)* [9833]
Children's Scholarship Fund of Charlotte *(Undergraduate/Scholarship)* [4187]
Jane Coffin Childs Memorial Fund - Medical Research Fellowships *(Postdoctorate/Fellowship)* [2915]
Charline Chilson Scholarships *(Undergraduate/Scholarship)* [3580]
Chinese American Medical Society Summer Research Fellowships Program *(Undergraduate/Fellowship)* [2917]
Helen Krich Chinoy Dissertation Research Fellowships *(Doctorate/Fellowship)* [1434]
CHOIR MD Post-Residency Fellowship in Health Services Research *(Postdoctorate/Fellowship)* [10376]
Choose Your Future Scholarships *(Undergraduate/Scholarship)* [3219]
Chopin Foundation of the United States Scholarships *(Undergraduate/Scholarship)* [2928]
Chrétien International Research Grants *(Doctorate/Grant)* [615]
Frances N. Christian Memorial Endowment Nursing Scholarship *(Graduate, Undergraduate/Scholarship)* [9583]
Almeric Christian Memorial Scholarships *(Graduate/Scholarship)* [10392]
Christian Pharmacists Fellowship International *(Advanced Professional/Fellowship)* [2934]
Irene R. Christman Scholarship *(Undergraduate/Scholarship)* [7939]
Christmas Tree Chapter Scholarship Awards *(Undergraduate/Scholarship)* [7692]
Commander Daniel J. Christovich Scholarship Fund *(Undergraduate/Scholarship)* [3076]
Chronic Lymphocytic Leukemia Collaborative Grants *(Advanced Professional/Grant)* [6157]
Chrysalis Scholarships *(Graduate/Scholarship)* [2094]
Chrysler Technical Scholarship Fund *(Undergraduate/Scholarship)* [3545]
The Churchill Scholarships *(Postgraduate/Scholarship)* [2940]
CIA Undergraduate Scholarships *(Undergraduate/Scholarship)* [1969]
CIGNA Healthcare Graduate Scholarships *(Graduate/Scholarship)* [6957]
CIGNA Healthcare Undergraduate Scholarships *(Undergraduate/Scholarship)* [6958]
Cincinnati High School Scholarships *(Undergraduate/Scholarship)* [2949]
Cinestory Fellowship *(Professional development/Fellowship)* [3029]
Cintas Foundation Fellowships in Architecture *(Professional development/Fellowship)* [3031]
Cintas Foundation Fellowships in Visual Arts *(Professional development/Fellowship)* [3032]
Antonio Cirino Memorial Art Education Fellowships *(Graduate/Fellowship)* [8603]
CISDL Global Research Fellowship - Associate Fellows *(Graduate/Fellowship)* [2880]

UNITED STATES   Place of Study Index

CISDL Global Research Fellowship - Legal Research Fellows *(Graduate/Fellowship)* [2881]
CISDL Global Research Fellowships - Senior Research Fellows *(Other/Fellowship)* [2882]
Citi Foundation Scholarship Program *(Undergraduate/Scholarship)* [866]
Citi/TELACU Scholars Mentoring Program *(Undergraduate/Scholarship)* [9659]
City Bar Diversity Fellowships Program *(Undergraduate/Fellowship)* [7343]
City of Sanibel Employee Dependent Scholarships *(Undergraduate/Scholarship)* [9423]
Civil Air Patrol Flight Scholarships *(Undergraduate/Scholarship)* [3039]
Civitan Shropshire Scholarships *(Undergraduate, Vocational/Occupational/Scholarship)* [3041]
CJH Graduate Research Fellowships *(Doctorate/Fellowship)* [2851]
CJH Visiting Scholars Program *(Doctorate/Fellowship)* [2852]
CLA/CP Scholarship *(Other/Scholarship)* [8672]
Clackamas Chapter Scholarship Awards *(Undergraduate/Scholarship)* [7693]
Claes Nobel Academic Scholarships for Members *(High School/Scholarship)* [7159]
Clan Ross Foundation Scholarships *(Undergraduate/Scholarship)* [3043]
Michele Clark Fellowships *(Undergraduate/Fellowship)* [8403]
Vickie Clark-Flaherty Scholarships *(Undergraduate/Scholarship)* [7471]
Willis W. and Ethel M. Clark Foundation Fellowships *(Graduate/Fellowship)* [3049]
Clark High School Academy of Finance Scholarships *(Undergraduate/Scholarship)* [8338]
Howard A. Clark Horticulture Scholarships *(Undergraduate/Scholarship)* [3220]
Robert A. Clark Memorial Educational Scholarships *(Professional development/Scholarship)* [7166]
Thomas Arkle Clark Scholar-Leader of the Year Endowed Scholarships *(Graduate, Undergraduate/Scholarship)* [8061]
Lucy and Charles W.E. Clarke Scholarships *(Undergraduate/Scholarship)* [1797]
IADR John Clarkson Fellowship *(Postdoctorate/Fellowship)* [5250]
Classic Wines of California Scholarships *(Undergraduate/Scholarship)* [2449]
Clay Maitland CGF Scholarship *(Undergraduate/Scholarship)* [3077]
Clay Postdoctoral Fellowships *(Postdoctorate/Fellowship)* [4781]
Aim High Jerry Clay Scholarships *(Undergraduate/Scholarship)* [4581]
Bruce Clement Post-Secondary Education Scholarships *(Undergraduate/Scholarship)* [7311]
Tyler Clementi Point Scholarship *(Undergraduate/Scholarship)* [8171]
Cleveland Executive Fellowships (CEF) *(Other/Fellowship)* [3051]
Geraldine Clewell Fellowships - Doctoral Student *(Graduate/Fellowship)* [8086]
Geraldine Clewell Fellowships - Masteral *(Graduate/Fellowship)* [8087]
Geraldine Clewell Scholarships - Undergraduate *(Undergraduate/Scholarship)* [8088]
Justice Robert L. Clifford Fellowships *(Undergraduate/Fellowship)* [6593]
James L. Clifford Prize *(Other/Prize, Monetary)* [1289]
David H. Clift Scholarships *(Graduate/Scholarship)* [961]
Bryan Cline Memorial Soccer Scholarship Program *(Undergraduate/Scholarship)* [301]
Clinical Project Funding for Advanced Practice Oncology Nurses *(Advanced Professional, Professional development/Grant)* [7616]
Clinical Research Fellowship for Medical Students *(Graduate/Fellowship)* [3699]
Clinician Scientist Development Awards *(Postgraduate/Fellowship)* [7883]
George H. Clinton Scholarship Fund *(Undergraduate/Scholarship)* [7818]
Paul W. Clopper Scholarship Grant for Junior Dental Students *(Undergraduate/Scholarship)* [5068]

Closs/Parnitzke/Clarke Scholarships *(Undergraduate/Scholarship)* [8089]
The Club Foundation Faculty Research Grants *(Professional development/Grant)* [3060]
The Club at Morningside Scholarships *(Undergraduate, Graduate/Scholarship)* [8697]
The Clubs of America Scholarships Award for Career Success *(Undergraduate/Scholarship)* [3065]
CMA Private Lesson Program: Instrumental Scholarships for Elementary and Middle School Students *(Undergraduate/Scholarship)* [3037]
CMAA Student Conference Travel Grants *(Undergraduate/Grant)* [3061]
CMC-KLI Leadership Research Fellowship *(Undergraduate/Fellowship)* [3045]
CMC-KLI Social Sector Internship Program *(Undergraduate/Internship)* [3046]
CMC-KLI Social Sector Research Fellowship *(Undergraduate/Fellowship)* [3047]
CME Beef Industry Scholarships *(Undergraduate/Scholarship)* [6841]
CMH Dissertation Fellowships *(Graduate/Fellowship)* [9876]
CNA Foundation Scholarships *(Graduate, Undergraduate/Scholarship)* [1411]
CNS-UCSB Graduate Fellowships for Science and Engineering *(Postdoctorate/Fellowship)* [10127]
Coast Guard Foundation Enlisted Education Grants *(Advanced Professional/Grant)* [3078]
The Helena B. Cobb Annual Scholarships *(Undergraduate, Vocational/Occupational/Scholarship)* [10665]
The Helena B. Cobb Four-Year Higher Education Grants *(Undergraduate, Vocational/Occupational/Scholarship)* [10666]
J.C. and Rheba Cobb Memorial Scholarships *(Undergraduate/Scholarship)* [6867]
Gordon W. and Agnes P. Cobb Scholarships *(Undergraduate/Scholarship)* [3754]
John Coburn and Harold Winters Student Award in Plasma Science and Technology *(Graduate/Award)* [2154]
Coca-Cola First Generation Scholarships *(Undergraduate/Scholarship)* [867]
Coca-Cola Scholars Program Scholarships *(Undergraduate/Scholarship)* [3115]
Geri Coccodrilli Culinary Scholarship Fund *(Undergraduate/Scholarship)* [4511]
The April Cockerham DREAM Act Scholarships *(Undergraduate, Graduate/Scholarship)* [8230]
Evelyn L. Cockrell Memorial Scholarship Award *(Undergraduate/Scholarship)* [9701]
Frank M. Coda Scholarships *(Undergraduate/Scholarship)* [1330]
Donald O. Coffman Scholarships *(Undergraduate/Scholarship)* [8248]
COHEAO Scholarships *(Undergraduate/Scholarship)* [3071]
American Academy of Periodontology Dr. D. Walter Cohen Teaching Fellowships *(Postdoctorate/Fellowship)* [421]
Ardis Cohoon Scholarships *(Undergraduate/Scholarship)* [10220]
Anna C. and Oliver C. Colburn Fellowships *(Doctorate/Fellowship)* [1606]
Cole Family Scholarships *(Undergraduate/Scholarship)* [8249]
Cole Foundation Undergraduate Scholarship Program *(Undergraduate/Scholarship)* [4189]
Arthur H. Cole Grants in Aid *(Doctorate/Grant, Award)* [3779]
Paul Cole Scholarships *(Undergraduate/Scholarship)* [9221]
Dennis Coleman Choral Conducting Scholarships *(Undergraduate/Scholarship)* [8250]
Dennis Coleman Memorial Scholarships *(Undergraduate/Scholarship)* [8251]
Coleopterists Society - Youth Incentive Award *(Undergraduate/Award)* [3117]
Colgate-Palmolive/HDA Foundation Scholarships *(Master's, Postgraduate/Scholarship)* [4892]
College Art Association Wyeth Publication Grants *(Other/Grant)* [3119]
Irene Culver Collins and Louis Franklin Collins Scholarships *(Undergraduate/Scholarship)* [3173]
Captain Winifred Quick Collins Scholarships *(Undergraduate/Scholarship)* [7229]
Elmer and Rosa Lee Collins Scholarships *(Undergraduate/Scholarship)* [10575]
Colombian Education Fund Scholarships *(Undergraduate/Scholarship)* [3130]
ColorMasters Scholarships *(Undergraduate/Scholarship)* [4333]
Columbus Citizens Foundation College Scholarships *(Undergraduate/Scholarship)* [3151]
Columbus Citizens Foundation High School Scholarships *(Undergraduate/Scholarship)* [3152]
John R. Colvin Legal Scholarships *(Graduate/Scholarship)* [3154]
Robert N. Colwell Memorial Fellowships *(Doctorate, Graduate/Fellowship)* [1803]
Commonwealth "Good Citizen" Scholarships *(Undergraduate/Scholarship)* [1977]
Communal Studies Association Research Fellowships *(Graduate/Fellowship)* [3163]
Community Bank - Lee Guggisberg Foundation Memorial Scholarships *(Undergraduate/Scholarship)* [8464]
Community-based Natural Resource Management Assistantships *(Undergraduate, Advanced Professional/Internship)* [3169]
Community Foundation of the Fox River Valley Scholarships *(Undergraduate/Scholarship)* [3192]
The Community Foundation Student Education Loan Funds for Gay and Lesbians *(Undergraduate/Loan)* [3221]
Community Foundation of Western Massachusetts Community Scholarship Program *(Undergraduate/Scholarship)* [3335]
Community Legal Services of Philadelphia Fellowships *(Postgraduate/Fellowship)* [3337]
Comparative Effectiveness Research Professorship (CERP) *(Professional development, Doctorate/Grant)* [3374]
Comparative Perspectives on Chinese Culture and Society Grants *(Doctorate/Grant)* [739]
Alan Compton and Bob Stanley Professional Scholarships *(Professional development/Scholarship)* [2192]
Tom and Judith Comstock Scholarships *(Undergraduate/Scholarship)* [1734]
Condon Prize for Best Student Essay in Psychological Anthropology *(Graduate, Undergraduate/Prize, Recognition)* [9281]
Maridell Braham Condon Scholarships *(Undergraduate/Scholarship)* [8915]
Conduct and Utilization of Research in Nursing (CURN) Awards *(Professional development/Award)* [6476]
Conference and Workshop Grants *(Professional development/Grant)* [10514]
Congressional Fellows on Women and Public Policy *(Doctorate, Graduate, Master's/Fellowship)* [10672]
Congressional Research Awards *(Graduate/Award)* [3626]
Al Conklin and Bill de Decker Business Aviation Management Scholarships *(Undergraduate/Scholarship)* [6830]
T.L. Conlan Scholarships *(Undergraduate/Scholarship)* [2950]
Connecticut Association of Land Surveyors Memorial Scholarships *(Undergraduate/Scholarship)* [3358]
Connecticut Association of Latinos in Higher Education Scholarships *(Undergraduate/Scholarship)* [4744]
Connecticut Mortgage Bankers Social Affairs Committee Scholarships *(Undergraduate/Scholarship)* [4745]
Connecticut Space Grant College Consortium Undergraduate Research Fellowships *(Undergraduate/Fellowship)* [3367]
Cecelia Connelly Memorial Scholarships in Underwater Archaeology *(Graduate, Undergraduate/Scholarship)* [10638]
Dwight O. Conner and Ellen Conner Lepp/Danhart Scholarships *(Undergraduate/Scholarship)* [7819]
Louis M. Connor Jr. Scholarships *(Undergraduate/Scholarship)* [10221]
Conservation Department Program Fellowships *(Graduate/Fellowship)* [9028]

Constant Memorial Scholarship *(Undergraduate/Scholarship)* [8604]
Constantinople Armenian Relief Society Scholarships (CARS) *(Undergraduate/Scholarship)* [1691]
Consumer Law Public Service Fellowships *(Undergraduate/Fellowship)* [8433]
Contemporary Club Scholarships *(Undergraduate/Scholarship)* [8465]
Continuing Education Awards *(Undergraduate/Scholarship, Award)* [6778]
Jorge Espejel Contreras IALEIA Scholarship Award *(Undergraduate/Scholarship)* [5266]
Convergence Assistantship Grants *(Undergraduate/Grant)* [4708]
Irving W. Cook WA0CGS Scholarships *(Undergraduate/Scholarship)* [1735]
Jack Kent Cooke Dissertation Fellowship Award *(Doctorate/Fellowship)* [5492]
Jack Kent Cooke Foundation College Scholarships *(Undergraduate/Scholarship)* [3411]
Jack Kent Cooke Foundation Graduate Scholarships *(Graduate/Scholarship)* [3412]
Jack Kent Cooke Foundation Undergraduate Transfer Scholarships *(Undergraduate/Scholarship)* [3413]
Jack Kent Cooke Foundation Young Scholars *(Undergraduate/Scholarship)* [3414]
Jack Kent Cooke Graduate Arts Awards *(Graduate/Award)* [5493]
Cooley Diversity Fellowship *(Graduate, Undergraduate/Fellowship)* [3416]
Madison and Edith Cooper Scholarships *(Undergraduate/Scholarship)* [8698]
Cope Middle School PTSA Scholarships *(Undergraduate/Scholarship)* [8466]
Copper and Brass Servicenter Association Inc. Scholarship Program *(Undergraduate/Scholarship)* [3421]
Beta Nu/Caryl Cordis D'hondt Scholarships *(Undergraduate/Scholarship)* [8916]
Theta/Caryl Cordis D'hondt Scholarships *(Undergraduate/Scholarship)* [8917]
Charles Clarke Cordle Memorial Scholarships *(Undergraduate/Scholarship)* [1736]
Cornaro Scholarships for Graduate Studies *(Graduate/Scholarship)* [5686]
D.C. Cornelius Memorial Scholarships *(Undergraduate/Scholarship)* [10577]
Holly Cornell Scholarship *(Master's/Scholarship)* [1488]
Corning Outstanding Student Paper Competition *(Graduate, Undergraduate/Award)* [7672]
Correctional Education Association Scholarships *(Graduate, Undergraduate/Scholarship)* [3427]
NSS Sara Corrie Memorial Grants *(Professional development/Grant)* [7181]
Tom Cory Memorial Scholarships *(Undergraduate/Scholarship)* [1614]
COTA Scholarships for Occupational Therapy Assistants *(Undergraduate/Scholarship)* [7762]
Cottrell Scholar Awards (CSA) *(Graduate, Advanced Professional, Professional development/Grant)* [8555]
Dr. George C. Cotzias Memorial Fellowship *(Other/Fellowship)* [1074]
Dave Couch Memorial Scholarships *(Undergraduate/Scholarship)* [7820]
SRC NRI Hans J. Coufal Fellowships *(Graduate/Fellowship)* [8838]
Jennifer Coulter Memorial Scholarships *(Undergraduate/Scholarship)* [7821]
Council on Social Work Education Minority Fellowship Program for Doctoral Students *(Postdoctorate/Fellowship)* [3454]
Council on Social Work Education Scholars Program *(Doctorate/Scholarship)* [3455]
Courage to Grow Scholarships *(Undergraduate/Scholarship)* [3461]
Pfizer Soozie Courter Hemophilia Scholarship Program *(Undergraduate/Scholarship)* [6988]
COUSE-Gram Scholarships *(Undergraduate/Scholarship)* [9424]
Richard P. Covert, Ph.D./FHIMSS Scholarships for Management Systems *(Graduate, Postgraduate, Undergraduate/Scholarship)* [4830]
The Joe E. Covington Awards for Research on Bar Admissions Testing *(Doctorate, Graduate/Award)* [6873]
Reuben R. Cowles Youth Awards *(Undergraduate/Award)* [945]
Justin Forrest Cox "Beat the Odds" Memorial Scholarships *(Undergraduate/Scholarship)* [3093]
Gertrude M. Cox Scholarships *(Graduate, Master's, Doctorate/Scholarship)* [1465]
Craft Research Fund Grants *(Other/Grant)* [2845]
Crafton Elementary School PTA Scholarships *(Undergraduate/Scholarship)* [8467]
Margaret T. Craig Community Service Scholarships *(Undergraduate/Scholarship)* [3281]
Robert E. Cramer Product Design and Development Scholarship *(Undergraduate/Scholarship)* [9259]
Meredith P. Crawford Fellowships in I/O Psychology *(Doctorate/Fellowship)* [4990]
AWG Maria Luisa Crawford Field Camp Scholarships *(Undergraduate/Scholarship)* [2095]
Crawford Scholarships *(Undergraduate/Scholarship)* [8699]
Creative Glass Center of America Fellowships *(Advanced Professional/Fellowship)* [3467]
CRI Clinic and Laboratory Integration Program Grants (CLIP) *(Professional development/Grant)* [2772]
CRI Irvington Postdoctoral Fellowship Program *(Postdoctorate/Fellowship)* [2773]
CRI Irvington Postdoctoral Fellowships *(Postdoctorate, Doctorate/Fellowship)* [2774]
Critical Language Scholarships for Intensive Summer Institutes *(Graduate, Undergraduate/Scholarship)* [1204]
CRMA Scholarships *(Graduate, Undergraduate/Scholarship)* [2899]
Crohn's and Colitis Foundation of America Senior Research Awards *(Doctorate, Graduate/Grant)* [3479]
Cromwell Fellowships *(Graduate/Fellowship)* [1354]
Redlands Rotary Club - Ernest L. Cronemeyer Memorial Scholarships *(Undergraduate/Scholarship)* [8469]
Kathryn M. Cronin Scholarships *(Undergraduate/Scholarship)* [10222]
CrossLites Scholarships *(Undergraduate, Graduate/Scholarship)* [3481]
R.G. and Ruth Crossno Memorial Scholarships *(Undergraduate/Scholarship)* [3756]
CROW Fellowships *(All/Fellowship)* [3053]
Crowder Scholarships *(Undergraduate/Scholarship)* [4192]
Howard A. Crum Student Scholarships *(Undergraduate/Scholarship)* [10179]
Lydia Cruz and Sandra Maria Ramos Scholarships *(Undergraduate/Scholarship)* [3577]
CSA Fraternal Life Scholarships *(Undergraduate/Scholarship)* [3483]
CSF Ach Family Scholarships *(Undergraduate/Scholarship)* [2951]
CSF Barr Foundation Scholarships *(Undergraduate/Scholarship)* [2952]
CSF Barrett Family Scholarships *(Undergraduate/Scholarship)* [2953]
CSF Borden Inc. Scholarships *(Undergraduate/Scholarship)* [2954]
CSF Castellini Foundation Scholarships *(Undergraduate/Scholarship)* [2955]
CSF Cincinnati Bell Scholarships *(Undergraduate/Scholarship)* [2956]
CSF Cincinnati Financial Corporation Scholarships *(Undergraduate/Scholarship)* [2957]
CSF Crosset Family Scholarships *(Undergraduate/Scholarship)* [2958]
CSF Dater Foundation Scholarships *(Undergraduate/Scholarship)* [2959]
CSF Duke Energy Scholarships *(Undergraduate/Scholarship)* [2960]
CSF Farmer Family Foundation Scholarships *(Undergraduate/Scholarship)* [2961]
CSF Fifth Third Bank Combined Scholarships *(Undergraduate/Scholarship)* [2962]
CSF Fletemeyer Family Scholarships *(Undergraduate/Scholarship)* [2963]
CSF Gardner Foundation Scholarships *(Undergraduate/Scholarship)* [2964]
CSF Goldman, Sachs and Company Scholarships *(Undergraduate/Scholarship)* [2965]
CSF Graduate Fellowships *(Graduate/Fellowship)* [2936]
CSF H.C. Schott Foundation Scholarships *(Undergraduate/Scholarship)* [2966]
CSF Heidelberg Distributing Co. Scholarships *(Undergraduate/Scholarship)* [2967]
CSF Heinz Pet Products Scholarships *(Undergraduate/Scholarship)* [2968]
CSF Juilfs Foundation Scholarships *(Undergraduate/Scholarship)* [2969]
CSF Kroger Cincinnati/Dayton Scholarships *(Undergraduate/Scholarship)* [2970]
CSF McCall Educational Scholarships *(Undergraduate/Scholarship)* [2971]
CSF Midland Company Scholarships *(Undergraduate/Scholarship)* [2972]
CSF Nethercott Family Scholarships *(Undergraduate/Scholarship)* [2973]
CSF Ohio National Foundation Scholarships *(Undergraduate/Scholarship)* [2974]
CSF Pepper Family Scholarships *(Undergraduate/Scholarship)* [2975]
CSF Pichler Family Scholarships *(Undergraduate/Scholarship)* [2976]
CSF PNC Bank Scholarships *(Undergraduate/Scholarship)* [2977]
CSF Procter and Gamble Scholarships *(Undergraduate/Scholarship)* [2978]
CSF Scripps Headliners Scholarships *(Undergraduate/Scholarship)* [2979]
CSF Semple Foundation Scholarships *(Undergraduate/Scholarship)* [2980]
CSF Union Central 135th Anniversary Scholarships *(Undergraduate/Scholarship)* [2981]
CSF U.S. Bank N.A. Scholarships *(Undergraduate/Scholarship)* [2982]
CSF Western-Southern Foundation Scholarships *(Undergraduate/Scholarship)* [2983]
CSF Woodward Trustees Scholarships *(Undergraduate/Scholarship)* [2984]
CSF Wynne Family Memorial Scholarships *(Undergraduate/Scholarship)* [2985]
CSSA Research Grants *(Undergraduate, Graduate, Advanced Professional/Grant)* [2428]
CSX Scholarships *(Undergraduate/Scholarship)* [1183]
CTEC Internships *(Undergraduate/Internship)* [1567]
CTF Young Investigator Awards (CTF-YIA) *(Graduate, Postdoctorate, Doctorate/Award)* [2911]
CTFS-ForestGEO Research Grants Program *(Graduate, Postdoctorate, Advanced Professional/Grant)* [9041]
CTFS Research Grants Program *(Graduate, Postdoctorate, Professional development/Grant)* [9036]
CTP Scholarship Program *(Other/Scholarship)* [7113]
John P. Culhane Professional Pilot Scholarships *(Undergraduate/Scholarship)* [215]
Linda Cullen Memorial Scholarships *(Undergraduate/Scholarship)* [759]
Murtha Cullina LLP Scholarships Fund *(Undergraduate/Scholarship)* [3199]
Esther Cummings Memorial Scholarships *(Undergraduate/Scholarship)* [7378]
Brian Cummins Memorial Scholarships *(Undergraduate/Scholarship)* [4746]
John S. and Marjoria R. Cunningham Camp Scholarships *(Professional development/Scholarship)* [6193]
John J. Cunningham Memorial Scholarships *(Undergraduate/Scholarship)* [1184]
The Cure Starts Now Foundation Grants *(Graduate, Doctorate/Grant)* [3492]
Tsutako Curo Scholarships *(Undergraduate/Scholarship)* [8339]
Curry Awards for Girls and Young Women *(Undergraduate/Scholarship)* [8949]
Nancy Curry Scholarships *(Vocational/Occupational/Scholarship)* [8804]
John J. Curtin, Jr. Fellowships *(Undergraduate/Fellowship)* [620]
Michael D. Curtin Renaissance Student Memorial Scholarships *(Undergraduate/Scholarship)* [3757]
Curtis/Breeden Scholarships *(Doctorate/Scholarship)* [2986]

UNITED STATES

Jennifer Curtis Byler Scholarships *(Undergraduate/Scholarship)* [7188]
Don and Barbara Curtis Excellence Fund for Extracurricular Student Activities *(Undergraduate/Grant)* [10223]
Dewey Lee Curtis Scholarships *(Advanced Professional/Scholarship)* [3541]
Cystic Fibrosis Scholarship Foundation *(Undergraduate/Scholarship)* [3494]
DA Davidson Presidential Scholarships *(Undergraduate/Scholarship)* [10436]
DACOR Graduate Fellowships for Study of International Affairs *(Graduate, Master's/Fellowship)* [3496]
Daedalian Foundation Matching Scholarships Program *(Undergraduate/Scholarship)* [3499]
Daggy Youth/Student Scholarships *(Undergraduate, Professional development/Scholarship)* [5444]
Jason Dahnert Memorial Scholarships *(Undergraduate/Scholarship)* [4143]
DAI Fellowships for Study in Berlin *(Doctorate/Fellowship)* [1607]
Detroit Section/Robert G. Dailey Scholarship *(Undergraduate/Scholarship)* [9260]
Daily Lineups Scholarship Awards *(Undergraduate, Master's/Award, Scholarship)* [3504]
Dairy Farmers of America Scholarships *(Undergraduate/Scholarship)* [3506]
Dake Community Manufacturing Scholarships *(Undergraduate/Scholarship)* [4512]
Daland Fellowships in Clinical Investigation *(Doctorate, Postgraduate/Fellowship)* [1079]
Dalcroze Society of America Memorial Scholarships *(Graduate/Scholarship)* [3510]
Chester Dale Fellowships *(Doctorate/Fellowship)* [6429]
John L. Dales Standard Scholarship *(Undergraduate/Scholarship)* [8827]
Dallas Alumnae Association Adelphe Scholarships *(Undergraduate/Scholarship)* [5704]
Dallas Alumnae Association Gamma Phi Chapter Scholarships *(Undergraduate/Scholarship)* [5705]
Serena D. Dalton Scholarships *(Undergraduate/Scholarship)* [10578]
Damon Runyon Cancer Research Foundation Fellowships *(Doctorate, Graduate, Postdoctorate/Fellowship)* [3514]
Damon Runyon Physician-Scientist Training Awards *(Postdoctorate, Professional development/Award)* [3515]
Damon Runyon-Rachleff Innovation Awards *(Postdoctorate/Fellowship)* [3516]
Damon Runyon-Sohn Pediatric Cancer Fellowship Awards *(Master's, Doctorate/Fellowship)* [3517]
June Danby and Pat Pearse Education Scholarships *(Undergraduate/Scholarship)* [5500]
Arthur H. Daniels Scholarships *(Undergraduate/Scholarship)* [8470]
DAPA Student Member Scholarships *(Undergraduate/Scholarship)* [3512]
Mary Mouzon Darby Undergraduate Scholarships *(Undergraduate/Scholarship)* [4985]
Darden Restaurants Point Scholarships *(Undergraduate, Graduate, Doctorate/Scholarship)* [8172]
Frank L. Dautriel Memorial Scholarships for Graduates *(Graduate/Scholarship)* [6116]
Frank L. Dautriel Memorial Scholarships for Undergraduates *(Undergraduate/Scholarship)* [6117]
The Dave Family "Humor Studies" Scholarships *(Undergraduate, Graduate/Scholarship)* [1848]
David Library Fellowships *(Doctorate, Postdoctorate/Fellowship)* [3527]
David Meador Foundation - Hospitality-Food Service Scholarships *(Undergraduate/Scholarship)* [7294]
Lucile Caswell Davids Memorial Adelphe Scholarships *(Undergraduate, Graduate/Scholarship)* [5706]
Clifford W. and Doris E. Davis Educational Scholarship Fund *(Undergraduate, Vocational/Occupational/Scholarship)* [3319]
Davis Family Scholarships *(Undergraduate/Scholarship)* [8700]
Davis Foundation Postdoctoral Fellowships *(Doctorate, Master's/Fellowship)* [4814]
Davis Memorial Foundation Scholarships *(Graduate, Undergraduate/Scholarship)* [3533]

Dwight F. Davis Memorial Scholarships *(Undergraduate/Scholarship)* [9974]
Estelle Davis Memorial Scholarships *(Undergraduate/Scholarship)* [2987]
Johnny Davis Memorial Scholarships *(Undergraduate/Scholarship)* [157]
Davis-Putter Scholarships Fund *(Undergraduate, Graduate/Scholarship)* [8659]
Larry Dean Davis Scholarship Program *(Undergraduate/Scholarship)* [7924]
Arlene Davis Scholarships *(Undergraduate/Scholarship)* [3581]
Fran Morgenstern Davis Scholarships *(Undergraduate/Scholarship)* [1270]
James Davis Scholarships *(Undergraduate/Scholarship)* [10224]
Kenneth D. and Katherine D. Davis Scholarships *(Undergraduate/Scholarship)* [7823]
Raymond Davis Scholarships *(Undergraduate, Graduate/Scholarship)* [9150]
Colonel Richard M. Dawson Highway Patrol Scholarship Fund *(Undergraduate/Scholarship)* [3222]
Brian M. Day Scholarships *(Undergraduate/Scholarship)* [8252]
Dayton Amateur Radio Association Scholarships *(Undergraduate/Scholarship)* [1737]
DBA Student Scholarships *(Undergraduate/Scholarship)* [3653]
DBI Scholarships Fund *(Undergraduate/Scholarship)* [3223]
Edilia and François Auguste de Montêquin Fellowships *(Doctorate/Fellowship)* [9083]
Kenneth J. De Witt NASA/OSGC Scholarship at The University of Toledo *(Undergraduate/Scholarship)* [7592]
Alphonso Deal Scholarship Awards *(Undergraduate/Scholarship)* [6825]
Steve Dearduff Scholarships *(Graduate, Undergraduate/Scholarship)* [3194]
Don Debolt Franchising Scholarship Program *(Undergraduate/Scholarship)* [5335]
Matthew Debono Memorial Scholarship Funds *(Undergraduate, Graduate/Scholarship)* [1588]
Debt.com Scholarships *(All/Scholarship)* [3539]
Julia B. DeCapua Fund *(Undergraduate/Scholarship)* [4661]
Walter M. Decker Point Scholarships *(Graduate, Undergraduate/Scholarship)* [8173]
Decommissioning, Decontamination and Reutilization Scholarships *(Graduate, Master's/Scholarship)* [1035]
Earl Dedman Memorial Scholarships *(Undergraduate/Scholarship)* [804]
DEED Student Research Grant/Internships *(Undergraduate, Graduate/Grant, Scholarship, Internship)* [1160]
DefensiveDriving.com Scholarships *(Undergraduate/Scholarship)* [3543]
Edward Delaney Scholarships *(Professional development/Scholarship)* [1982]
Jane Delano Student Nurse Scholarships *(Undergraduate, Graduate/Scholarship)* [1023]
Vine Deloria Jr. Memorial Scholarships *(Graduate, Professional development/Scholarship)* [868]
Delta Chi Alumnae Memorial Scholarships *(Undergraduate/Scholarship)* [8918]
Delta Epsilon Sigma Graduate Fellowships *(Graduate/Fellowship)* [3566]
Delta Epsilon Sigma Undergraduate Scholarships *(Undergraduate/Scholarship)* [3567]
Delta Faucet Scholarships *(Undergraduate/Scholarship)* [8160]
Delta Gamma Undergraduate Merit-Based Scholarships *(Undergraduate/Scholarship)* [3569]
Delta Iota Alumni Scholarships *(Undergraduate/Scholarship)* [8967]
Delta Kappa Gamma Society International World Fellowships *(Professional development/Fellowship)* [3571]
Delta Kappa Project 2000 Scholarships *(Undergraduate/Scholarship)* [5707]
Delta Nu Alpha Foundation Scholarships *(Undergraduate/Scholarship)* [3573]
Delta Nu Project 2000 Scholarships *(Undergraduate/Scholarship)* [5708]
Delta Phi Epsilon Educational Foundation Scholarships *(Undergraduate, Graduate/Scholarship)* [3575]
Delta Project 2000 Scholarships *(Undergraduate/Scholarship)* [5709]
Delta Tau Project 2000 Scholarships *(Undergraduate/Scholarship)* [5710]
Delta Upsilon Project 2000 Nowell Memorial Scholarships *(Undergraduate/Scholarship)* [5711]
Delta Zeta Undergraduate Scholarships *(Undergraduate/Scholarship)* [3582]
Law Offices of Michael A. DeMayo Scholarships *(Undergraduate/Scholarship)* [5963]
DEMCO New Leaders Travel Grants *(Professional development/Grant)* [8372]
Christopher Demetris Memorial Scholarships *(Undergraduate/Scholarship)* [4845]
Inez Demonet Scholarship *(Graduate/Scholarship)* [10373]
Albert W. Dent Graduate Student Scholarships *(Undergraduate/Scholarship)* [687]
Denton Scholarships *(Graduate/Scholarship)* [8897]
John Denver Music Scholarships *(Undergraduate/Scholarship)* [1271]
Denver Scholarship Foundation Scholarships *(Undergraduate/Scholarship)* [3600]
Dick Depaolis Memorial Scholarships *(Undergraduate/Scholarship)* [3325]
Depression and ADHD Fellowships *(Postdoctorate/Fellowship)* [5840]
DEPS Graduate Scholarship Program *(Graduate/Scholarship)* [3624]
Karekin DerAvedision Memorial Endowment Fund *(Undergraduate/Scholarship)* [1692]
Derivative Duo Scholarships *(Undergraduate/Scholarship)* [8253]
Pat Dermargosian Memorial Scholarships *(Undergraduate/Scholarship)* [8471]
Descendant Scholarships *(Undergraduate/Scholarship)* [3500]
Libby Deschenes Prize for Applied Research *(Undergraduate/Prize)* [10537]
Achille and Irene Despres, William and Andre Scholarships *(Undergraduate/Scholarship)* [4587]
Detroit Economic Club Scholarship *(Undergraduate/Scholarship)* [3326]
Development Fund for Black Students in Science and Technology Scholarships *(Undergraduate/Scholarship)* [3612]
Albert and Jane Dewey Scholarships *(Undergraduate/Scholarship)* [4748]
Donald J. DeYoung Scholarships *(Undergraduate/Scholarship)* [4588]
Dezao Legal Awards *(Advanced Professional/Scholarship)* [5959]
Jenny d'Héricourt Fellowships *(Doctorate/Fellowship)* [435]
Diabetes Scholars Foundation College Scholarships *(Undergraduate/Scholarship)* [3616]
Edwina Eustis Dick Scholarship for Music Therapy Interns *(Graduate/Scholarship)* [1012]
Jean Dearth Dickerscheid Fellowships *(Graduate/Fellowship)* [8090]
Dickey Rural Networks College Scholarship Program *(Undergraduate, Vocational/Occupational/Scholarship)* [3618]
Bill Dickey Scholarship Association Scholarships *(Undergraduate/Scholarship)* [3620]
Diffuse Large B-Cell Lymphoma Explorations Grants *(Advanced Professional/Grant)* [6158]
Robert Martz DiGiacomo Memorial Scholarship Fund *(Undergraduate/Scholarship)* [9499]
Rudolph Dillman Memorial Scholarships *(Graduate, Undergraduate/Scholarship)* [820]
Carol DiMaiti Scholarship Awards *(Undergraduate/Scholarship)* [6308]
The E.R. and Lilian B. Dimmette Scholarship Fund *(Undergraduate/Scholarship)* [4193]
The Angie Dipietro Women in Business Scholarships *(Undergraduate/Scholarship)* [8231]
Disability Care Center Disabled Student Scholarships *(Undergraduate/Scholarship)* [3629]
Disability Care Center Special Education Scholarships *(Undergraduate/Scholarship)* [3630]
Disabled War Veterans Scholarships *(Undergraduate/Scholarship)* [90]
Discover Bar Exam Loans *(Graduate/Loan)* [3634]

Discover Graduate Loans *(Graduate, Master's, Doctorate/Loan)* [3635]
Discover Health Professions Loans *(Graduate/Loan)* [3636]
Discover Law Loans *(Graduate/Loan)* [3637]
Discover MBA Loans *(Graduate/Loan)* [3638]
Discover Residency Loans *(Graduate/Loan)* [3639]
Dissertation Award in Hadronic Physics *(Doctorate/Award)* [1089]
Dissertation Fellowships in East European Studies *(Doctorate/Fellowship)* [740]
Dissertation Proposal Development Fellowships *(Doctorate/Fellowship)* [9053]
Distinguished Flying Cross Society Scholarships *(Undergraduate/Scholarship)* [3641]
Distinguished Young Women Scholarships *(Undergraduate/Scholarship)* [3643]
LaRue A. Ditmore Music Scholarships *(Undergraduate/Scholarship)* [10650]
Diversity Executive Leadership Program Scholarships *(Other/Scholarship)* [1778]
Diversity Fellowship Program (DFP) *(Undergraduate/Fellowship)* [6589]
Robert A. and Barbara Divine Graduate Student Travel Grants *(Graduate/Grant)* [9136]
Dixon Hughes Goodman LLP Annual Scholarship *(Undergraduate/Scholarship)* [3645]
Peggy Dixon Two-Year Scholarships *(Undergraduate/Scholarship)* [9254]
Grace O. Doane Scholarship *(Undergraduate/Scholarship)* [3665]
Charles Dobbins FTA Scholarships *(Undergraduate, Vocational/Occupational/Scholarship)* [4316]
Doctoral Dissertation Grants *(Doctorate/Grant)* [5386]
Document Management and Graphic Communications Industry Scholarships *(Undergraduate/Scholarship)* [3852]
Documentary Film Grants *(Professional development/Grant)* [369]
Doddridge County Promise Scholarships *(Undergraduate/Scholarship)* [7825]
F. Atlee Dodge Maintenance Scholarships *(Undergraduate/Scholarship)* [216]
Jim Dodson Law Scholarships *(Undergraduate/Scholarship)* [5600]
Robert Winchester Dodson Scholarships *(Undergraduate/Scholarship)* [10225]
DOE Computational Science Graduate Fellowships (DOE CSGF) *(Doctorate, Graduate/Fellowship)* [5887]
Emmett J. Doerr Memorial Distinguished Scout Scholarships *(Undergraduate/Scholarship)* [6921]
Dofflemyer Scholarships *(Undergraduate/Scholarship)* [6922]
Dollar-A-Day Academic Scholarships *(Graduate, Undergraduate/Scholarship)* [3649]
Dolphin Scholarships *(Undergraduate/Scholarship)* [3651]
Scott Dominguez - Craters of the Moon Chapter Scholarships *(Graduate, Undergraduate/Scholarship)* [1412]
Marion Jones Donaldson Scholarship Fund *(Undergraduate/Scholarship)* [4043]
Mike and Gail Donley Spouse Scholarships *(Undergraduate, Graduate, Postgraduate/Scholarship)* [123]
Harry A. Donn Scholarships *(Undergraduate/Scholarship)* [4749]
Dorchester Woman's Club Music Scholarship - Voice *(Undergraduate/Scholarship)* [4352]
Joseph M. Dorgan Scholarship *(Undergraduate/Scholarship)* [3666]
Pauly D'Orlando Memorial Art Scholarships *(Graduate, Undergraduate/Scholarship)* [9834]
Father Connie Dougherty Scholarships *(Undergraduate, Vocational/Occupational/Scholarship)* [3320]
Robert E. Dougherty Scholarships *(Undergraduate, Postgraduate/Scholarship)* [3339]
Douglass Foundation Fellowship in American Art *(Doctorate/Fellowship)* [9001]
Douglass Foundation Fellowships in American Art *(Graduate/Fellowship)* [6430]
Dow Chemical Company Fellowships *(Graduate/Fellowship)* [7085]

Margaret Dowell-Gravatt, M.D. Scholarships *(Undergraduate/Scholarship)* [2226]
Downeast Energy Scholarships *(Undergraduate/Scholarship)* [3659]
Downeast Feline Scholarships *(Graduate/Scholarship)* [6194]
W.B.H. Dowse Fellowships *(Professional development/Fellowship)* [6326]
Rodger Doxsey Travel Prizes *(Graduate, Postdoctorate/Prize)* [616]
Helen Cashatt Drais Memorial Adelphe Scholarships *(Undergraduate/Scholarship)* [5712]
Drake University Law School Law Opportunity Scholarships - Diversity *(Undergraduate/Scholarship)* [3668]
Lou Drane Music Scholarships *(Undergraduate/Scholarship)* [4237]
The "Drawn to Art" Fellowships *(Doctorate/Fellowship)* [436]
Wilma Sackett Dressel Scholarships *(Undergraduate/Scholarship)* [8919]
Margaret Drew Alpha Fellowships *(Graduate/Fellowship)* [8091]
Charles Drew Scholarships *(Other/Scholarship)* [1940]
Louis Dreyfus Warner-Chappell City College Scholarships *(Undergraduate/Scholarship)* [1272]
Thomas J. Drinan Memorial Fellowships *(Undergraduate/Fellowship)* [8434]
Drinkwater Family Scholarships *(Undergraduate/Scholarship)* [8703]
Drug Development Research Professorship *(Professional development/Internship)* [3375]
Richard Drukker Memorial Scholarships *(Undergraduate/Scholarship)* [7326]
Sergeant Major Douglas R. Drum Memorial Scholarship Fund *(Undergraduate/Scholarship)* [1005]
Harold D. Drummond Scholarships *(Undergraduate, Graduate/Scholarship)* [5668]
Dry Defender Protect Your Bed Scholarships *(Undergraduate, Graduate/Scholarship)* [5636]
DSA Dante Prizes *(Undergraduate/Prize, Monetary)* [3524]
DSACF Modern Woodmen of America Scholarships *(Undergraduate/Scholarship)* [3706]
Henry Belin du Pont Dissertation Fellowships *(Doctorate, Graduate/Fellowship)* [4688]
Henry Belin du Pont Research Grants *(Graduate/Fellowship)* [4689]
Martin Duberman Fellowships *(Other/Fellowship)* [2864]
Charles Dubose Scholarships *(Undergraduate/Scholarship)* [4750]
John W. Duckett Jr., AFUD Pediatric Research Scholarships *(Undergraduate/Scholarship)* [9246]
The Steve Duckett Local Conservation Scholarships *(Undergraduate, Postgraduate/Scholarship)* [8232]
Julia M. Duckwall Scholarships *(Professional development/Scholarship)* [1983]
Mark Duda Scholarship Fund *(Graduate, Undergraduate/Scholarship)* [6288]
Deborah Gandee Dudding Memorial Scholarships *(Undergraduate/Scholarship)* [7826]
Edward Leon Duhamel Scholarship Fund *(Undergraduate/Scholarship)* [8605]
Doris Duke Conservation Fellows Program *(Master's/Fellowship)* [10678]
Duluth Building and Construction Trades Council Scholarships *(Undergraduate/Scholarship)* [3707]
Duluth Central High School Alumni Scholarships *(Undergraduate/Scholarship)* [3708]
Dumbarton Oaks Research Library and Collection Bliss Symposium Awards *(Undergraduate, Graduate/Award)* [3730]
Dumbarton Oaks Research Library and Collection Graduate Research Workshops *(Undergraduate, Graduate/Fellowship)* [3731]
Dumbarton Oaks Research Library and Collection One-Month Research Stipends *(Doctorate/Monetary)* [3732]
Dumbarton Oaks Research Library and Collection Post-Baccalaureate Media Fellowships *(Graduate/Fellowship)* [3733]
Dumbarton Oaks Research Library and Collection Project Grants *(Doctorate/Grant)* [3734]
Dumbarton Oaks Research Library and Collection Short-Term Predoctoral Residencies Grants *(Doctorate/Grant)* [3735]
Dumbarton Oaks Research Library and Collection Summer Fellowships *(Graduate/Fellowship)* [3736]
Dumbarton Oaks Research Library and Collection Summer Internships for Harvard Students *(Undergraduate, Graduate/Internship)* [3737]
Dunbar Heritage Scholarships *(Undergraduate/Scholarship)* [9427]
Duncan Aviation Scholarships *(Undergraduate/Scholarship)* [158]
Wade and Marcelene Duncan Scholarships *(Undergraduate/Scholarship)* [10579]
Ed Dunkelblau Scholarships *(All/Scholarship, Award)* [1849]
Travis Dunning Memorial Scholarships *(Undergraduate/Scholarship)* [8341]
William R. Durham/Theater Scholarships *(Undergraduate/Scholarship)* [3282]
Durning Sisters Scholarships *(Graduate/Scholarship)* [3549]
Joe Durso, Jr. Memorial Scholarship *(Undergraduate/Scholarship)* [6576]
Marvin and Joanell Dyrstad Scholarship *(Undergraduate/Scholarship)* [1578]
Dystonia Medical Research Foundation Clinical Fellowships *(Postdoctorate/Fellowship)* [3746]
EAA Tuition Scholarships *(Undergraduate/Scholarship)* [3873]
EAA Workshop Scholarships *(Undergraduate/Scholarship)* [3874]
Josephine P. White Eagle Scholarships *(Undergraduate, Graduate/Scholarship)* [4911]
Eagles Fly for Leukemia Scholarships *(Undergraduate/Scholarship)* [2906]
EAIA Research Grants *(Other/Grant)* [3748]
Amelia Earhart Memorial Academic Scholarships *(Undergraduate/Scholarship)* [7439]
Earl Warren Civil Rights Training Scholarships *(Graduate/Scholarship)* [6645]
Early-Career Patient-Oriented Diabetes Research Awards *(Professional development/Award)* [5640]
Early Career Postdoctoral Fellowships in East European Studies *(Postdoctorate/Fellowship)* [741]
Early Childhood Educators Scholarship Program *(Undergraduate/Scholarship)* [6342]
Robert E. Early Memorial Scholarship *(Undergraduate/Scholarship)* [3670]
Bob East Scholarships *(Graduate, Undergraduate/Scholarship)* [7108]
Eastern Orthodox Scouting Scholarships *(Undergraduate/Scholarship)* [6923]
Eastern Shore Building Industry Association Scholarships *(Undergraduate/Scholarship)* [3174]
David Eaton Scholarships *(Master's/Scholarship)* [9835]
Ellen Eberhardt Memorial Scholarships *(Undergraduate/Scholarship)* [9565]
ECA Applied Urban Communication Research Grants *(Professional development/Grant)* [3768]
ECA Centennial Scholarships *(Master's, Doctorate/Scholarship)* [3769]
Echoing Green Black Male Achievement Fellowships *(Professional development/Fellowship)* [3773]
Echoing Green Climate Fellowships *(Professional development/Fellowship)* [3774]
Echoing Green Global Fellowships *(Professional development/Fellowship)* [3775]
James Echols Scholarship Award *(Undergraduate/Scholarship)* [2434]
W. Wesley Eckenfelder Gradute Research Award *(Graduate, Master's, Doctorate/Award)* [1952]
ECMS Scholarships *(Undergraduate/Scholarship)* [3771]
Economic Club of Grand Rapids Scholarships *(Undergraduate/Scholarship)* [4590]
Ed Bradley Scholarships *(Undergraduate/Scholarship)* [8404]
Margaret Eddy Scholarships *(Graduate/Scholarship)* [7379]
Edgecliff Alumni Awards *(Undergraduate/Scholarship)* [10718]
Edgecliff McAuley Art Scholarships *(Undergraduate/Scholarship)* [10719]

Edgecliff McAuley Music Scholarships *(Undergraduate/Scholarship)* [10720]
S. Randolph Edmonds Young Scholars Competition *(Graduate, Undergraduate/Scholarship)* [2303]
Melanie and Todd Edmonson Memorial Scholarships *(Undergraduate/Scholarship)* [3261]
Edon Farmers Cooperative Scholarships *(Undergraduate/Scholarship)* [3794]
Education Advancement Scholarships *(Graduate, Master's, Doctorate/Scholarship)* [548]
Education Factor Scholarships *(Graduate, Undergraduate/Scholarship)* [6378]
"Education is Power" Scholarships *(Undergraduate/Scholarship)* [6989]
Educational Audiology Association Doctoral Scholarships *(Doctorate/Scholarship)* [3797]
Educational and Cultural Affairs Alumni Small Grants Program (ECA) *(Other/Grant)* [5380]
EDvestinU(r) National Monthly Scholarships *(Undergraduate/Scholarship)* [7309]
The Edwards Annual College Scholarships *(Undergraduate/Scholarship)* [3810]
Esther Edwards Graduate Scholarships *(Doctorate, Professional development/Scholarship)* [9851]
Carli Edwards Memorial Scholarships *(Undergraduate/Scholarship)* [8871]
Jimmy Edwards Scholarships *(Undergraduate/Scholarship)* [3226]
EERI/FEMA Graduate Fellowship in Earthquake Hazard Reduction *(Graduate/Fellowship)* [3750]
John and Alice Egan Multi-Year Mentioning Scholarships *(Undergraduate/Scholarship)* [3501]
Bill Egan Scholarship Program *(Undergraduate/Scholarship)* [7694]
EHA Exploratory Travel and Data Grants *(Doctorate/Grant)* [3780]
EHA Graduate Dissertation Fellowships *(Doctorate/Fellowship)* [3781]
E.I. DuPont Graduate Fellowship *(Graduate/Fellowship)* [7086]
Mike Eidson Scholarships *(Graduate, Undergraduate/Scholarship)* [516]
Eight and Forty Lung and Respiratory Disease Nursing Scholarships *(Other/Scholarship)* [955]
Hillel Einhorn New Investigator Award *(Doctorate/Award)* [9161]
Eisbrouch & Marsh Scholarship Awards *(Undergraduate, Graduate/Scholarship)* [3814]
Harold E. Eisenberg Foundation Scholarships *(Other/Scholarship)* [5304]
Jeri Eiserman, RRT Professional Education Research Fellowships *(Professional development/Fellowship)* [1210]
Farouk El-Baz Student Research Grants *(Graduate, Undergraduate/Grant)* [4363]
El Dorado County Mineral and Gem Society Scholarships *(Undergraduate/Scholarship)* [3816]
George and Isabelle Elanjian Scholarships *(Undergraduate/Scholarship)* [10198]
W. Eldridge and Emily Lowe Scholarships *(Undergraduate/Scholarship)* [8968]
Eli Lilly and Company/Black Data Processing Associates Scholarships *(Undergraduate/Scholarship)* [2206]
Elie Wiesel Prize in Ethics *(Undergraduate/Prize, Award)* [10553]
Dr. Robert Elliott Memorial Scholarships *(Undergraduate/Scholarship)* [6351]
Optimist Club of Redlands - Virginia Elliott Scholarships *(Undergraduate/Scholarship)* [8472]
Pauline Elliott Scholarships *(Undergraduate/Scholarship)* [6352]
Robert A. Ellis Scholarships in Physics *(Undergraduate/Scholarship)* [7141]
William P. Elrod Memorial Scholarships *(Undergraduate/Scholarship)* [9656]
Thomas J. Emery Memorial Scholarships *(Undergraduate/Scholarship)* [2988]
EMLF Law Student Scholarships *(Undergraduate/Scholarship)* [3869]
Emmanuel Bible College Scholarships *(Undergraduate/Scholarship)* [1693]
EMS Scholarship Awards *(All/Award)* [8150]
ENA Foundation Annual Conference Scholarships *(Advanced Professional, Professional development/Scholarship)* [3861]

ENA Foundation Seed Research Grants *(Master's, Advanced Professional/Grant)* [3862]
ENA Foundation State Challenge Undergraduate Scholarship *(Undergraduate/Scholarship)* [3858]
Thomas O. Enders Graduate Fellowships *(Graduate/Fellowship)* [1876]
Alice Yuriko Endo Memorial Scholarships *(Undergraduate/Scholarship)* [5549]
Endocrine Society Summer Research Fellowships *(Graduate, Undergraduate/Fellowship)* [3864]
Endodontic Educator Fellowship Award *(Graduate/Fellowship)* [492]
Endodontic Research Grants *(Graduate/Grant)* [493]
Endourological Society Fellowships *(Professional development/Fellowship)* [3867]
Endowment Fund for Education Grants *(Undergraduate/Grant)* [2264]
Endowment Fund for Education, Loans/Grants for Educational Materials *(Undergraduate/Grant)* [2266]
Endowment Fund for Education, Loans/Grants for Equipment *(Undergraduate/Grant)* [2267]
Endowment Fund for Education, Loans *(Undergraduate/Loan)* [2265]
ENF Most Valuable Student Scholarships *(Undergraduate/Scholarship)* [3854]
Engaged Anthropology Grants *(Doctorate, Postdoctorate/Grant)* [10515]
Jane Engelberg Memorial Fellowship *(Professional development/Fellowship)* [7156]
Enhanced Insurance Scholarships Program *(Undergraduate/Scholarship)* [10340]
Harold E. Ennes Scholarships *(Graduate, Other/Award, Scholarship)* [9092]
Irene Winifred Eno Grants *(Professional development/Grant)* [1342]
Ensurify Safe Driving Scholarships *(Undergraduate/Scholarship)* [3876]
Enterprise Rent-A-Car Scholarships *(Graduate, Undergraduate/Scholarship)* [8073]
Environmental Research and Education Foundation Scholarships *(Master's, Doctorate, Postdoctorate/Scholarship)* [3900]
EPA Science to Achieve Results Fellowships (STAR) *(Graduate/Fellowship)* [9932]
Epilepsy Foundation Behavioral Sciences Post-Doctoral Fellowships *(Postdoctorate/Fellowship)* [3902]
Epilepsy Foundation Behavioral Sciences Student Fellowships *(Graduate, Undergraduate/Fellowship)* [3903]
Epilepsy Foundation Health Sciences Student Fellowships *(Doctorate, Graduate/Fellowship)* [3904]
Epilepsy Foundation Post-doctoral Research and Training Fellowships *(Postdoctorate/Fellowship)* [3905]
Epilepsy Foundation Pre-doctoral Research Training Fellowships *(Graduate/Fellowship)* [3906]
Epilepsy Foundation Research Grants *(Doctorate/Grant)* [3907]
Epilepsy Foundation Research and Training Fellowships for Clinicians *(Doctorate, Other/Grant)* [3908]
Epsilon Delta Project 2000 Scholarships *(Undergraduate/Scholarship)* [5713]
Epsilon Epsilon Scholarships *(Undergraduate/Scholarship)* [8920]
Epsilon Mu Scholarships *(Graduate, Undergraduate/Scholarship)* [5714]
Epsilon Tau Scholarships *(Undergraduate/Scholarship)* [8921]
Dena Epstein Awards for Archival and Library Research in American Music *(Professional development/Grant)* [6626]
Alan R. Epstein "Reach for the Stars" Scholarships *(Undergraduate/Scholarship)* [6452]
Lee Epstein Scholarship Fund *(Graduate, Undergraduate/Scholarship)* [6289]
Equal Justice Works Fellowship Program *(Graduate, Undergraduate/Fellowship)* [3918]
Robert C. Erb Sr. Scholarships *(Undergraduate/Scholarship)* [6353]
ERCA Community Contribution Scholarships *(Undergraduate/Scholarship)* [3804]
ERDAS Internship *(Graduate/Internship, Award)* [1804]

Bruce T. and Jackie Mahi Erickson Grant *(Graduate, Undergraduate/Grant)* [7907]
Erickson-Zoellers Point Scholarships *(Undergraduate, Graduate, Doctorate/Scholarship)* [8174]
Ernest Hemingway Research Grants *(Other/Grant)* [4855]
The Eleanor A. Ernest Scholarships *(Undergraduate/Scholarship)* [5502]
Melissa Eleanor Ernest Scholarships *(Undergraduate/Scholarship)* [5503]
Robert P. Ernest Scholarships *(Undergraduate/Scholarship)* [5504]
Kevin Ernst Memorial Scholarship Fund *(Undergraduate/Scholarship)* [4514]
Ernst and Young Scholarships *(Undergraduate/Scholarship)* [1780]
Extrusion Division/Lew Erwin Memorial Scholarship *(Graduate, Postgraduate/Scholarship)* [9261]
ESA Foundation Life Grants *(Undergraduate/Grant)* [3914]
ESA Foundation Scholarship Program *(Undergraduate/Scholarship)* [3878]
Boomer Esiason Foundation General Academic Scholarships *(Undergraduate, Graduate/Scholarship)* [2338]
NSPF Ray B. Essick Scholarship Awards *(Other/Scholarship)* [7192]
Ethnic Minority and Women's Enhancement Postgraduate Scholarships *(Graduate/Scholarship)* [6862]
ETS Postdoctoral Fellowships *(Postdoctorate/Fellowship)* [3806]
Alex J. Ettl Grants *(Other/Grant)* [7127]
Eustace-Kwan Family Foundation Scholarships *(Undergraduate/Scholarship)* [8950]
Chick Evans Caddie Scholarships *(Undergraduate/Scholarship)* [10531]
Lee S. Evans/National Housing Endowment Scholarships *(Undergraduate, Graduate/Scholarship)* [7003]
Evans and Petree Law Firm Scholarship *(Undergraduate/Scholarship)* [10159]
J. Everett and Louise Light Scholarships *(Undergraduate, Graduate/Scholarship)* [5669]
Everglades Foundation Fellowship *(Graduate, Doctorate, Master's/Fellowship)* [3931]
Everglades Foundation Internship *(Postgraduate, Postdoctorate/Internship)* [3932]
Everglades Foundation Scholarships *(Graduate, Master's, Doctorate/Scholarship)* [3933]
Lyle and Rlene Everingham Family Scholarships *(Undergraduate/Scholarship)* [2989]
Lyle Everingham Scholarships *(Undergraduate/Scholarship)* [2990]
Excel Staffing Companies Scholarships for Excellence in Continuing Education *(Undergraduate/Scholarship)* [302]
Executive Women International Scholarship Program (EWISP) *(Undergraduate/Scholarship)* [3936]
ExeptionalNurse.com Scholarships *(Undergraduate, Graduate/Scholarship)* [3940]
Exercise For Life Athletic Scholarships Program *(Undergraduate/Scholarship)* [2339]
The Expert Institute Legal Blog Post Writing Contest *(Graduate/Award)* [3942]
Experts Exchange Scholarships Contest *(Undergraduate, Graduate/Scholarship)* [3944]
Express Medical Supply Scholarships *(Undergraduate/Scholarship)* [3948]
William C. Ezell Fellowships *(Postdoctorate/Fellowship)* [415]
Facebook Fellowships Program *(Doctorate/Fellowship)* [3950]
FACS Graduate Fellowships *(Graduate/Fellowship)* [6798]
FACT "Second Chance" Scholarship Program *(Undergraduate/Scholarship)* [3999]
Faegre Baker Daniels Diversity & Inclusion Fellowships *(Graduate/Fellowship)* [3954]
FAER Mentored Research Training Grants *(Professional development/Grant)* [4163]
FAER Research in Education Grants *(Advanced Professional/Grant)* [4164]
FAER Research Fellowship Grants *(Postdoctorate, Postgraduate, Graduate/Grant)* [4165]

UNITED STATES

Claire M. Fagin Fellow Award *(Doctorate/Fellowship)* [6983]
Fahs-Beck Fund for Research and Experimentation - Doctoral Dissertation Grants *(Doctorate/Grant)* [7347]
Fahs-Beck Fund for Research and Experimentation - Postdoctoral Grants *(Postdoctorate/Grant)* [7348]
FAIC Latin American and Caribbean Scholars Program *(Other/Scholarship)* [908]
Wayne G. Failor Scholarships *(Undergraduate/Scholarship)* [7947]
Sherman Fairchild Post Graduate Fellowships in Conservation *(Postgraduate/Fellowship)* [6591]
AIST Benjamin F. Fairless Scholarships *(Undergraduate/Scholarship)* [1996]
Falcon Achievement Scholarships *(Undergraduate/Scholarship)* [8200]
Magnetic Interfaces and Nanostructures Division - The Leo M. Falicov Student Award *(Graduate/Grant)* [2155]
Fall Fellowships in Korean Studies *(Other/Fellowship)* [5870]
The Fallen Heroes Scholarships *(Undergraduate/Scholarship)* [3079]
James Mackenzie Fallows Scholarships Honoring Gertrude Baccus *(Undergraduate/Scholarship)* [8473]
James Mackenzie Fallows Scholarships Honoring William Cunningham *(Undergraduate/Scholarship)* [8474]
Families of Freedom Scholarship Fund - America Scholarships *(Undergraduate, Vocational/Occupational/Scholarship)* [3956]
Family and Children's Services of Lebanon County Fund *(Undergraduate/Scholarship)* [4239]
FAMU Presidential Scholarship - Florida Community College Scholarships *(Undergraduate/Scholarship)* [4076]
Fanconi Anemia Research Grants *(Postdoctorate/Grant)* [3964]
William M. Fanning Maintenance Scholarships *(Undergraduate/Scholarship)* [6831]
The Fantasy Sports Daily Scholarship Program - General Scholarship for Advanced Education *(Undergraduate, Graduate, Master's/Scholarship)* [3966]
John S.W. Fargher, Jr. Scholarships *(Graduate/Scholarship)* [5185]
Farmington UNICO Scholarships *(Undergraduate/Scholarship)* [4751]
W.D. Farr Scholarships *(Graduate/Scholarship)* [6842]
FASEB MARC Travel Awards *(Undergraduate, Graduate, Postdoctorate/Award)* [9306]
Anne M. Fassett Scholarships *(Undergraduate, Graduate/Scholarship)* [9428]
Miklos Faust International Travel Awards *(Doctorate/Grant)* [1339]
James R. Favor Risk Management Scholarship Fund *(Undergraduate/Scholarship)* [5715]
FCA Grants to Artists *(Advanced Professional/Grant)* [4227]
FCBA Foundation College Scholarship Program *(Undergraduate/Scholarship)* [3972]
FCBA Foundation Internship Stipends for Law Students *(Professional development/Internship)* [3973]
FCBA Foundation Law School Scholarships *(Postgraduate/Scholarship)* [3974]
FCIL Schaffer Grants for Foreign Law Librarians *(Professional development/Grant)* [529]
Federalsburg Rotary Club Scholarships *(Undergraduate/Scholarship)* [3175]
Federated Insurance Scholarships *(Graduate, Undergraduate/Scholarship)* [8074]
Adrienne Zoe Fedok Art and Music Scholarships *(Undergraduate/Scholarship)* [4240]
FEEA-NTEU Scholarships *(Graduate, Postgraduate, Undergraduate/Scholarship)* [3989]
FEF Scholarships *(Undergraduate/Scholarship)* [3952]
Ruth B. Fein Prize *(Graduate/Prize)* [949]
Symee Ruth Feinberg Memorial Scholarships *(Undergraduate/Scholarship)* [4752]
Lillian and Alex Feir Graduate Student Travel Awards *(Master's, Doctorate/Award)* [3880]

Fejos Postdoctoral Fellowships in Ethnographic Film *(Postdoctorate/Fellowship)* [10516]
Feldman Law Firm Disabled Veterans Scholarships *(All/Scholarship)* [4009]
Feldman & Royle, Attorneys at Law Autism Scholarships *(All/Scholarship)* [4011]
Milton Feldstein Memorial Scholarships *(Graduate/Scholarship)* [141]
The Judy Felt Memorial Volunteerism Scholarship *(College, Undergraduate/Scholarship)* [1821]
Reese Felts Scholarships *(Undergraduate/Scholarship)* [10226]
Diane Ross Fennekohl Endowment Fund for Education *(Undergraduate/Scholarship)* [5716]
John E. Fenton, Jr. Public Service Awards *(Postgraduate/Fellowship)* [8435]
Dr. James A. Ferguson Emerging Infectious Diseases Fellowships *(Graduate/Fellowship)* [5815]
Fermilab Internships for Physics Majors *(Undergraduate/Internship)* [9899]
Fermilab Science Undergraduate Laboratory Internship *(Undergraduate/Internship)* [9900]
Fermilab Summer Internships in Science and Technology *(Undergraduate/Internship)* [9901]
Lt. Colonel Romeo and Josephine Bass Ferretti Scholarships *(Undergraduate/Scholarship)* [124]
FFA Scholarship *(Undergraduate/Scholarship)* [7583]
FHSMAI Scholarship Program *(Graduate/Scholarship)* [4264]
Mary Lou Fiala Fellowships *(Other/Fellowship)* [5305]
FICE Scholarships *(Undergraduate/Scholarship)* [4089]
Field Museum Graduate Student Fellowships *(Graduate/Fellowship)* [4017]
Carole Fielding Student Grant *(Undergraduate, Graduate/Grant)* [10131]
Fieldwork Fellowships *(Undergraduate/Award, Fellowship)* [3927]
Filipino Bar Association of Northern California Scholarships (FBANC) *(Advanced Professional/Scholarship)* [4022]
Christine Filipovich Scholarships *(Master's, Doctorate/Scholarship)* [3057]
Alan R. and Barbara D. Finberg Fellowships *(Graduate/Fellowship)* [4998]
E. Lanier Finch Scholarships *(Undergraduate/Scholarship)* [4375]
Fred Finch Scholarships *(Undergraduate/Scholarship)* [9816]
Herb and Anne Fincher Memorial Scholarships *(Undergraduate/Scholarship)* [3176]
William Robert Findley Graduate Chemistry Scholarship *(Graduate/Scholarship)* [7151]
Fine Arts Association Minority Scholarships *(Undergraduate/Scholarship)* [4026]
Fine Arts Association United Way Scholarships *(Undergraduate/Scholarship)* [4027]
Sakura Finetek Student Scholarships *(Undergraduate/Scholarship)* [7167]
Helen R. Finley-Loescher and Stephen Loescher Scholarships *(Undergraduate/Scholarship)* [3283]
Finnegan Diversity Scholarships *(Juris Doctorate/Scholarship)* [4030]
FIRST Operator Certification Awards *(Professional development/Internship)* [4074]
Eugenia Vellner Fischer Award for the Performing Arts *(Undergraduate/Scholarship)* [6556]
William A. Fischer Memorial Scholarships *(Graduate/Scholarship)* [1805]
Fish & Richardson 1L Diversity Fellowships *(Undergraduate/Scholarship)* [4066]
Joseph L. Fisher Doctoral Dissertation Fellowships *(Graduate/Fellowship)* [8561]
Charles N. Fisher Memorial Scholarships *(Undergraduate/Scholarship)* [1738]
Arthur and Juna Fisher Memorial Track Scholarships *(Undergraduate/Scholarship)* [8475]
Jack B. Fisher Scholarship Fund *(Undergraduate/Scholarship)* [9501]
Allison E. Fisher Scholarships *(Undergraduate, Graduate/Scholarship)* [4068]
Ameel J. Fisher Scholarships *(Undergraduate/Scholarship)* [10227]

Sergeant Paul Fisher Scholarships *(Undergraduate/Scholarship)* [6907]
Marjorie Gosselin Fitzgerald, Upsilon, Permanently Restricted Scholarship Fund *(Undergraduate/Scholarship)* [5717]
Dr. Joseph Fitzsimmons Scholarships *(Doctorate/Scholarship)* [9959]
Gloria Flaherty Scholarships *(Graduate/Scholarship)* [4466]
Scott A. Flahive Memorial Scholarship Fund *(Undergraduate/Scholarship)* [4516]
FLASH Social Science Scholarships *(Graduate/Scholarship)* [3976]
Albert Flegenheimer Memorial Scholarships *(Undergraduate/Scholarship)* [6494]
Fleming/Blaszcak Scholarships *(Undergraduate, Graduate/Scholarship)* [9262]
Charlie Fleming Education Fund Scholarships *(Undergraduate/Scholarship)* [7195]
Laura M. Fleming Scholarships *(Undergraduate, Vocational/Occupational/Scholarship)* [4194]
FLEOA Foundation Scholarship Program *(Undergraduate/Scholarship)* [3991]
Flight Attendants/Flight Technician Scholarships *(Other/Scholarship)* [6832]
Grant H. Flint International Scholarships - Category I *(Undergraduate/Scholarship)* [9337]
Grant H. Flint International Scholarships - Category II *(Undergraduate/Scholarship)* [9338]
Dave Florence Scholarship Fund *(Undergraduate/Scholarship)* [6290]
Florence Young Memorial Scholarships *(Master's/Scholarship)* [1833]
Brendan Flores Alumni Leadership Circle Scholarship - Clark High School *(Undergraduate/Scholarship)* [8344]
Florida Automotive Industry Scholarships *(Undergraduate/Scholarship)* [2125]
Florida Fertilizer and Agrichemical Association Scholarships *(Undergraduate/Scholarship)* [4096]
Florida Nurses Foundation Scholarships *(Undergraduate, Master's, Doctorate/Scholarship)* [4102]
Florida Public Health Association Public Health Graduate Scholarships *(Graduate/Scholarship)* [4108]
Florida Public Health Association Public Health Undergraduate Scholarships *(Undergraduate/Scholarship)* [4109]
Florida Public Transportation Association Scholarships (FPTA) *(Undergraduate, Graduate/Scholarship)* [1164]
Floto-Peel Family Scholarship Fund *(Undergraduate, Vocational/Occupational/Scholarship)* [4517]
John Flynn Memorial Scholarships *(Undergraduate/Scholarship)* [3284]
Paul B. and Aline Flynn Scholarships *(Undergraduate/Scholarship)* [9429]
FMA-FEEA Scholarship Program *(Undergraduate/Scholarship)* [3993]
Alice J. Foit Scholarships *(Undergraduate/Scholarship)* [9502]
Follicular Lymphoma Research Grants *(Advanced Professional/Grant)* [6159]
Frank Fong Scholarships *(Undergraduate/Scholarship)* [9076]
Foot Locker Scholar Athletes *(Undergraduate/Scholarship)* [4131]
For the Love of Chocolate Foundation Scholarships *(Undergraduate, Graduate, Professional development/Scholarship)* [4133]
Ford Foundation Dissertation Fellowships *(Graduate, Doctorate/Fellowship)* [6675]
Ford Foundation Diversity Fellowships *(Graduate, Doctorate, Postdoctorate, Postgraduate/Fellowship)* [6676]
Ford Foundation Postdoctoral Fellowships *(Postdoctorate/Fellowship)* [6677]
Ford Foundation Predoctoral Fellowships *(Graduate, Doctorate/Fellowship)* [6678]
A. Ward Ford Memorial Research Grants *(Postdoctorate, Professional development/Grant)* [1351]
Anne Ford Scholarships *(Undergraduate/Scholarship)* [6850]
Nancy B. Forest and L. Michael Honaker Master's Grant for Research in Psychology *(Graduate/Grant)* [1133]

The FormsBirds Scholarships *(Undergraduate/Scholarship)* [4140]
Forsyth County Nursing Scholarships *(Undergraduate/Scholarship)* [10581]
Forté Fellowships *(Master's/Fellowship)* [4151]
Stephen J. Fortgang/University of Northern Iowa Chapter Scholarship *(Undergraduate/Scholarship)* [5670]
Genevieve Forthun Scholarships *(Undergraduate/Scholarship)* [8092]
Dr. Nancy Foster Scholarship Program *(Postgraduate, Graduate/Scholarship)* [7077]
Dr. Nancy Foster Scholarships *(Graduate/Scholarship)* [4159]
Fostering Hope Scholarships Fund *(Undergraduate/Scholarship)* [7828]
Foundation of American Institute for Conservation Lecture Grants *(Other/Grant)* [909]
Foundation of the Federal Bar Association Public Service Scholarship Award *(Undergraduate/Scholarship)* [4260]
The Foundation of the National Student Nurses' Association Scholarships *(Graduate, Undergraduate/Scholarship)* [7190]
Foundation for Neonatal Research and Education Scholarships *(Doctorate, Graduate, Postgraduate, Undergraduate/Scholarship)* [4272]
Foundation for Seacoast Health Scholarships *(Undergraduate, Graduate/Scholarship)* [4283]
Foundation for Surgical Technology Scholarships *(Graduate/Scholarship)* [2076]
Founding Mothers' Student Scholarships - Graduate *(Graduate/Scholarship)* [2015]
Mary Metzger Fouse Memorial Scholarship Fund *(Undergraduate/Scholarship)* [5718]
Howard Fox Memorial Law Scholarships *(Graduate/Scholarship)* [2235]
Don Fox Memorial Scholarship *(Undergraduate/Scholarship)* [211]
Captain Ernest Fox Perpetual Scholarships *(Undergraduate/Scholarship)* [3080]
FPA Summer Internships Program *(Undergraduate/Internship)* [4072]
Brandon Fradd Fellowship *(Professional development/Fellowship)* [3033]
William A. Fraker Student Heritage Awards *(Graduate, Undergraduate/Award)* [1256]
Frame My Future Scholarships Contest *(Undergraduate, Graduate/Scholarship)* [2938]
Franchise Law Diversity Scholarship Awards *(Undergraduate/Scholarship)* [5336]
Joe Francis Haircare Scholarships *(Undergraduate/Scholarship)* [4289]
Parker B. Francis Respiratory Research Grants *(Advanced Professional, Professional development/Grant)* [1211]
Gloria Francke Scholarship *(Undergraduate/Scholarship)* [1579]
Joe Francomano Scholarships *(Undergraduate/Scholarship)* [5630]
Mayme and Herb Frank Scholarship Program *(Graduate, Undergraduate/Scholarship)* [1782]
Loren Frankel Memorial Scholarships *(Undergraduate, Graduate/Scholarship)* [995]
Mary Weiking Franken Scholarships *(Undergraduate/Scholarship)* [8093]
The Ginny Frankenthaler Memorial Scholarships *(Undergraduate/Scholarship)* [9385]
John Hope Franklin Dissertation Fellowships *(Doctorate/Fellowship)* [1080]
James Franklin and Dorothy J. Warnell Scholarship Fund *(Undergraduate, Vocational/Occupational/Scholarship)* [3321]
Franklin Elementary School PTA Scholarships *(Undergraduate/Scholarship)* [8476]
John Hope Franklin Prize *(Other/Prize)* [5971]
Franklin Research Grants *(Doctorate/Grant)* [1081]
Violet and Cyril Franks Scholarship *(Graduate/Scholarship)* [1144]
John L. and Victory E. Frantz Scholarship *(Undergraduate/Scholarship)* [4518]
Joseph Frasca Excellence in Aviation Scholarships *(Undergraduate/Scholarship)* [10104]
Fraser Family Scholarships *(Undergraduate/Scholarship)* [8345]

Fraser Stryker Diversity Scholarships *(Undergraduate/Scholarship)* [4293]
FRAXA Postdoctoral Fellowships *(Postdoctorate, Master's/Fellowship)* [4295]
FREA Scholarship *(Undergraduate/Scholarship)* [4111]
Fred and Avery Test Scholarships *(Undergraduate/Scholarship)* [10180]
Fredrikson and Byron Foundation Minority Scholarships *(Undergraduate/Scholarship)* [4297]
Emanuel R. Freedman Scholarships *(Graduate, Undergraduate/Scholarship)* [7772]
Freedom Alliance Scholarships *(Undergraduate/Scholarship)* [4299]
Kevin Freeman Travel Grants *(Graduate, Other/Grant)* [6627]
Don Freeman Work-in-Progress Grants *(Advanced Professional/Grant)* [9096]
Malcolm and Mildred Freidberg Fellowships *(Professional development/Fellowship)* [6327]
The French Culinary Institute Classic Pastry Arts Scholarships *(Other, Undergraduate/Scholarship)* [3487]
Richard A. Freund International Scholarships *(Graduate/Scholarship)* [1389]
Ludo Frevel Crystallography Scholarships *(Graduate/Scholarship)* [5294]
Doris W. Frey Memorial Scholarships *(Undergraduate, Graduate/Scholarship)* [9430]
Dale E. Fridell Memorial Scholarships *(Undergraduate, Vocational/Occupational/Scholarship)* [9593]
Fried, Frank, Harris, Shriver and Jacobson Fellowships *(Graduate/Fellowship)* [4303]
MHS Marc Friedlaender Fellowships *(Professional development/Fellowship)* [6328]
William A. Friedlander Scholarships *(Undergraduate/Scholarship)* [2991]
A.E. Robert Friedman Scholarships *(Undergraduate/Scholarship)* [7795]
Phil Friel Scholarships *(Undergraduate/Scholarship)* [6354]
Joel R. Friend Scholarships *(Undergraduate/Scholarship)* [2227]
Kennedy T. Friend Scholarships *(Graduate, Undergraduate/Scholarship)* [325]
Friends of Coal Scholarships *(Undergraduate/Scholarship)* [10523]
Friends of Mary Automotive Scholarships *(Undergraduate/Scholarship)* [8872]
Friends of Project 10 Models of Excellence Scholarships *(Undergraduate/Scholarship)* [4307]
Froberg-Suess JD/MBA Scholarships *(Undergraduate/Scholarship)* [7978]
Patricia and Phillip Frost Fellowships *(Doctorate, Postdoctorate/Fellowship)* [9002]
"Frugal Student" Scholarships *(Undergraduate/Scholarship)* [7950]
Fruits and Vegetable Industries Scholarships *(Undergraduate/Scholarship)* [6487]
Marian Johnson Frutiger Scholarships *(Undergraduate/Scholarship)* [8922]
William and Francis Fry Honorary Fellowships for Contributions to Therapeutic Ultrasound *(Professional development/Fellowship)* [5431]
Mary Alice Fry Memorial Scholarships *(Undergraduate, Graduate/Scholarship)* [5719]
FSF Student Travel Grant *(Undergraduate, Graduate/Grant)* [4135]
FTE Dissertation Fellowships *(Graduate, Doctorate/Fellowship)* [4153]
FTE Doctoral Fellowships *(Doctorate, Graduate/Fellowship)* [4154]
FTE North American Doctoral Fellowships *(Doctorate, Graduate/Fellowship)* [4155]
Gerard Swartz Fudge Memorial Scholarships *(Undergraduate/Scholarship)* [5027]
Keiko Fukuda Scholarships *(Undergraduate/Scholarship)* [9960]
Kathryn Fuller Science for Nature Post-Doctoral Fellowships *(Graduate, Postdoctorate/Fellowship)* [10707]
Don and Eileen Fulton Nursing Scholarships *(Undergraduate/Scholarship)* [9566]
Arthur Flagler Fultz Research Awards *(Professional development/Grant)* [1013]
Donald M. Furbush Professional Development Grants *(Other/Grant)* [5216]
Dr. Horace Furumoto Innovations Professional Development - Young Investigator Awards *(Professional development/Award)* [1352]
Future Leader Initial NCTM Annual Meeting Attendance Awards *(Advanced Professional/Award, Monetary)* [6888]
Future Leaders of Manufacturing Scholarships *(Graduate, Undergraduate/Scholarship)* [9181]
Future STEM Teacher Scholarship *(Undergraduate/Scholarship)* [9657]
Mearl K. Gable II Memorial Grants *(Other/Grant)* [4709]
Gaddy Student Scholarships *(Undergraduate/Scholarship)* [10582]
Gaebe Eagle Scout Awards *(Undergraduate/Scholarship)* [6925]
Farley Moody Galbraith Scholarship Fund *(Undergraduate/Scholarship)* [3262]
Louise Bales Gallagher Scholarships *(Undergraduate/Scholarship)* [3551]
Whitney Laine Gallahar Memorial Scholarship Fund *(Undergraduate/Scholarship)* [3263]
The Gallery Collection's Create-A-Greeting Card Scholarships *(Undergraduate/Scholarship)* [4318]
Carolyn Gallmeyer Scholarships *(Undergraduate/Scholarship)* [4593]
Gallo Blue Chip Scholarships *(Undergraduate/Scholarship)* [4724]
Priscilla Gamble Scholarships *(Undergraduate/Scholarship)* [2992]
Gamewarden Scholarship program *(High School, Undergraduate, Vocational/Occupational/Scholarship)* [4320]
Gamma Chi Project 2000 Scholarships *(Undergraduate/Scholarship)* [5720]
Gamma Iota Scholarships - Gamma Tau *(Undergraduate/Scholarship)* [8923]
Gamma Iota Scholarships - Kappa Eta *(Undergraduate/Scholarship)* [8924]
Gamma Iota Scholarships - Zeta Kappa *(Undergraduate/Scholarship)* [8925]
Gamma Iota Scholarships - Zeta Nu *(Undergraduate/Scholarship)* [8926]
Gamma Mu Project 2000 Scholarships *(Undergraduate/Scholarship)* [5721]
Gamma Pi Project 2000 Scholarships *(Undergraduate/Scholarship)* [5722]
Gamma Sigma Alpha Graduate Scholarships *(Graduate/Scholarship)* [4322]
Gamma Theta Project 2000 Scholarships *(Undergraduate/Scholarship)* [5723]
Gamma Zeta Project 2000 Scholarships *(Undergraduate/Scholarship)* [5724]
Guy P. Gannett Scholarships *(Undergraduate/Scholarship)* [6195]
John A. Gans Scholarship *(Undergraduate/Scholarship)* [1580]
Gantenbein Medical Fund Fellowship *(Graduate/Fellowship)* [3497]
Veronica Gantt Memorial Scholarships *(Undergraduate/Scholarship)* [8346]
Michael and Gina Garcia Rail Engineering Scholarships *(Undergraduate, Graduate/Scholarship)* [1187]
William R. Gard Memorial Scholarships *(Undergraduate/Scholarship)* [6654]
Garden Club of America Awards in Tropical Botany (GCA) *(Doctorate/Award)* [4324]
Garden Club Council of Winston-Salem and Forsyth County Council Scholarships *(Undergraduate/Scholarship)* [10583]
Jewell Gardiner Scholarships *(Undergraduate/Scholarship)* [2473]
Gardner Foundation Infusion Nurses Society Education Scholarships *(Professional development/Scholarship)* [5145]
Robert Gardner Memorial Fellowships *(Graduate/Fellowship)* [4809]
Dwight D. Gardner Scholarships *(Undergraduate/Scholarship)* [5186]
Victoria M. Gardner Scholarships *(Undergraduate/Scholarship)* [10228]
Eugene Garfield Doctoral Dissertation Fellowship *(Doctorate/Fellowship)* [2239]

Peter M. Gargano Scholarship Fund *(Undergraduate/Scholarship)* [3709]
Garikian Scholarship Fund *(Undergraduate/Scholarship)* [1694]
Garmin Scholarships *(Undergraduate/Scholarship)* [160]
Gail Garner R.I.S.E. Memorial Scholarships *(Undergraduate/Scholarship)* [8477]
Kays Gary Scholarships *(Undergraduate/Scholarship)* [10229]
Ethel Mae Gaston Memorial Scholarships *(Undergraduate/Scholarship)* [7380]
Edwin W. Gaston Scholarships *(Undergraduate/Scholarship)* [341]
The Gates Millennium Scholars *(Undergraduate/Scholarship)* [4903]
Marian P. and David M. Gates Scholarship for Non-Residents *(Undergraduate/Scholarship)* [10181]
Kappa Kappa Gamma Foundation - Mary Maxwell Gates Scholarships *(Undergraduate, Graduate/Scholarship)* [5725]
Stephen Gates Scholarships *(Undergraduate/Scholarship)* [10230]
Frank Caleb & Margaret Thompson Gates Student Scholarships *(Undergraduate/Scholarship)* [10182]
A.R.F.O.R.A. Martha Gavrila Scholarships for Women *(Postgraduate/Scholarship)* [1226]
GAWP Graduate Scholarships *(Graduate/Scholarship)* [4377]
Lowell Gaylor Memorial Scholarships *(Undergraduate/Scholarship)* [161]
Florence S. Gaynor Scholarships *(Graduate/Scholarship)* [6755]
GCSAA Scholars Competition *(Undergraduate/Scholarship)* [4483]
GCSAA Student Essay Contest *(Graduate, Undergraduate/Prize)* [4484]
G.E. Aviation Scholarships *(Undergraduate/Scholarship)* [2993]
GED Jump Start Scholarships *(Professional development/Scholarship)* [8805]
GEF Scholarship Program *(Undergraduate, Graduate/Scholarship)* [4647]
Gehring Memorial Foundation Scholarships *(Graduate, Undergraduate/Scholarship)* [5100]
Milacron Geier Scholarships *(Undergraduate/Scholarship)* [2994]
Victoria S. and Bradley L. Geist Scholarships *(Undergraduate/Scholarship)* [4795]
Lawrence Gelfand - Armin Rappaport - Walter LaFeber Dissertation Fellowships *(Doctorate, Graduate/Fellowship)* [9137]
Irma Gelhausen Scholarship Fund *(Undergraduate/Scholarship)* [5930]
Joseph H. Gellert/Dutchess County Bar Association Scholarships *(Undergraduate/Scholarship)* [3744]
Elaine Gelman Scholarship Awards *(Undergraduate/Scholarship)* [6772]
The Gene and John Athletic Scholarships *(Undergraduate/Scholarship)* [9589]
General Falcon Scholarships *(Undergraduate/Scholarship)* [8201]
General Scholarships for Higher Learning *(Undergraduate, Graduate, Master's/Scholarship)* [4960]
Generation III Scholarships *(Undergraduate/Scholarship)* [3783]
Geological Society of America Graduate Student Research Grants *(Doctorate, Graduate/Grant)* [4364]
George W. and Ethel B. Hoefler Fund *(Undergraduate/Scholarship)* [3322]
Georgetown Working League Scholarships *(Undergraduate/Scholarship)* [4368]
Gerber Foundation Merit Scholarships *(Undergraduate/Scholarship)* [4392]
Doris Y. and John J. Gerber Scholarships *(Undergraduate/Scholarship)* [10464]
Daniel Gerber, Sr. Medallion Scholarships *(Undergraduate/Scholarship)* [4393]
Walter Gerboth Awards *(Other/Award)* [6628]
German Historical Institute Doctoral and Postdoctoral Fellowships *(Doctorate, Postgraduate/Fellowship)* [4395]
German Historical Institute Fellowships at the Horner Library *(Doctorate/Fellowship)* [4396]

German Society Scholarships *(Undergraduate/Scholarship)* [4404]
German Studies Research Grants *(Undergraduate, Grant, Award)* [3607]
Bunny Kline Gerner and Robin Gerner Doty Memorial Adelphe Scholarships *(Undergraduate/Scholarship)* [5726]
Eloise Gerry Fellowships *(Graduate, Postdoctorate/Fellowship)* [8904]
Elizabeth Tucker Gessley Scholarship *(Undergraduate/Scholarship)* [5727]
Getty GRI-NEH Postdoctoral Fellowships *(Postdoctorate/Fellowship)* [4408]
Getty Research Exchange Fellowship Program for Cultural Heritage Preservation *(Doctorate/Fellowship)* [1205]
GFOA Minorities in Government Finance Scholarship *(Graduate, Undergraduate/Scholarship)* [4502]
GFWC Women's Club of South County Scholarships *(Undergraduate/Scholarship)* [8606]
GFWCMA Communication Disorder/Speech Therapy Scholarships *(Graduate/Scholarship)* [4353]
GIA Scholarship- Distance Education eLearning *(Graduate/Scholarship)* [4334]
GIA Scholarships - On Campus *(Graduate/Scholarship)* [4335]
IDSA Gianninoto Graduate Scholarships *(Graduate, Undergraduate/Scholarship)* [5136]
Emily V. Gibbes Scholarships *(Undergraduate/Scholarship)* [7381]
John J. Gibbons Fellowships in Public Interest and Constitutional Law *(Professional development/Fellowship)* [4421]
Laverne L. Gibson Memorial Scholarships *(Undergraduate/Scholarship)* [7830]
Robert D. Gibson Scholarship *(Undergraduate/Scholarship)* [1581]
Joy Gibson Scholarships *(Undergraduate/Scholarship)* [10231]
Shane Gilbert Memorial Scholarships *(Undergraduate/Scholarship)* [7831]
Gilbreth Memorial Fellowships *(Graduate, Scholarship, Fellowship)* [5187]
Terry M. Giles Honor Scholar Program *(Undergraduate/Scholarship)* [7980]
Composites Division/Harold Giles Scholarship *(Undergraduate, Graduate/Scholarship)* [9263]
AIST Midwest Member Chapter - Jack Gill Scholarships *(Undergraduate/Scholarship)* [1997]
R.L. Gillette Scholarships *(Undergraduate/Scholarship)* [821]
Gilliam Fellowships for Advanced Study *(Doctorate/Fellowship)* [4974]
Benjamin A. Gilman International Scholarship *(Undergraduate/Scholarship)* [10060]
Leo Gilmartin Scholarships *(Undergraduate/Scholarship)* [8167]
Susan Kay Munson Gilmore Memorial Scholarships *(Undergraduate, Vocational/Occupational/Scholarship)* [3285]
Allan Gilmour & Eric Jirgens Point Scholarships *(Undergraduate, Graduate, Doctorate/Scholarship)* [8175]
Jack R. Gilstrap Scholarships *(Undergraduate, Graduate/Scholarship)* [1165]
Lawrence Ginocchio Aviation Scholarships *(Undergraduate/Scholarship)* [6833]
Alex Gissler Memorial Scholarships *(Undergraduate/Scholarship)* [6355]
GJEC Dissertation Completion Fellowships *(Postdoctorate/Fellowship)* [6490]
GLA Beard Scholarships *(Master's/Scholarship)* [4384]
GLA Hubbard Scholarships *(Master's/Scholarship)* [4385]
J. Robert Gladden Orthopaedic Society International Traveling Fellowship *(Undergraduate/Fellowship)* [4443]
John Glaser Scholarships *(Undergraduate/Scholarship)* [3121]
GLATA Living Memorial Doctorate Scholarships *(Doctorate, Graduate/Scholarship)* [4653]
GLATA Living Memorial Graduate Scholarships *(Graduate/Fellowship, Scholarship)* [4654]
Herman and Bess Glazer Scholarship Fund *(Undergraduate/Scholarship)* [4662]
Glazing Industry Scholarships *(Undergraduate/Scholarship)* [8347]
Gleaner Life Insurance Society Scholarships *(Undergraduate/Scholarship)* [4447]
Glendale Latino Association Scholarships *(Undergraduate/Scholarship)* [4449]
Glenn/AFAR Scholarships for Research in the Biology of Aging *(Graduate, Doctorate/Scholarship)* [788]
Glenn Miller Scholarships *(Undergraduate/Scholarship)* [4451]
Global Volcanism Program for Visiting Scientist/Postdoctoral Fellowships *(Postdoctorate/Fellowship)* [9032]
Globe-Trotters Member Chapter Scholarships *(Undergraduate, Postgraduate/Scholarship)* [1998]
Alfred B. Glossbrenner Scholarships *(Undergraduate/Scholarship)* [1999]
Bud Glover Memorial Scholarships *(Undergraduate/Scholarship)* [162]
Dr. Robert H. Goddard Memorial Scholarships *(Graduate, Undergraduate/Scholarship)* [7179]
Glenn Godfrey Memorial Scholarships *(Undergraduate, Graduate/Scholarship)* [5864]
Rosen Goertz Point Scholarship *(Undergraduate, Graduate, Doctorate/Scholarship)* [8176]
Shirley J. Gold Scholarship *(Undergraduate/Scholarship)* [793]
William Goldberg Diamond Corp. Scholarships *(Undergraduate/Scholarship)* [4336]
Daniel B. Goldberg Scholarship *(Graduate/Scholarship)* [4503]
Golden Eagle Coins Scholarships *(Undergraduate/Scholarship)* [4470]
Golden Key Graduate Scholar Awards *(Graduate, Master's, Doctorate/Scholarship)* [6747]
Golden Key Study Abroad Scholarships *(Undergraduate/Scholarship)* [4472]
William R. Goldfarb Memorial Scholarships *(Undergraduate/Scholarship)* [1739]
Goldia.com Jewelry Scholarships *(Undergraduate, Graduate/Scholarship)* [4474]
Rhode Island Commission on Women/Freda H. Goldman Education Awards *(Undergraduate/Award, Scholarship)* [8607]
Dr. Guido Goldman Fellowships *(Doctorate, Postdoctorate/Fellowship)* [724]
Goldman Sachs/Matsuo Takabuki Commemorative Scholarships *(Graduate/Scholarship)* [7908]
Joshua Gomes Memorial Scholarship Fund *(Undergraduate, Graduate/Scholarship)* [6990]
Millie Gonzalez Memorial Scholarships *(Undergraduate/Scholarship)* [4859]
Goodman Acker Scholarships *(Graduate/Scholarship)* [4489]
Victor and Ruth N. Goodman Memorial Scholarships *(Graduate/Scholarship)* [4697]
James L. and Genevieve H. Goodwin Scholarships *(Undergraduate/Scholarship)* [4753]
Google-American Indian Science and Engineering Society Scholarships *(Graduate, Undergraduate/Scholarship)* [4495]
Google Hispanic College Fund Scholarships *(Graduate, Undergraduate/Scholarship)* [4497]
Google Lime Scholarships for Students with Disabilities *(Undergraduate, Graduate, Doctorate/Scholarship)* [6089]
Google US/Canada PhD Fellowships *(Graduate, Doctorate/Fellowship)* [4498]
Richard Goolsby Scholarship Fund *(Graduate, Undergraduate/Scholarship)* [4196]
Barnett D. Gordon Scholarships *(Graduate, Undergraduate/Scholarship)* [5101]
FAMU Presidential Scholarship - George W. Gore Assistantship Scholarship *(Undergraduate/Scholarship)* [4077]
Sarah "Sally" Ives Gore Gamma Kappa Sapphire Scholarships *(Graduate, Undergraduate/Scholarship)* [5728]
Richard C. Gorecki Scholarships *(Undergraduate/Scholarship)* [8202]
Nettie and Jesse Gorov Scholarships *(Undergraduate/Scholarship)* [3286]
Consuelo W. Gosnell Memorial Scholarships *(Graduate/Fellowship)* [6789]

American Association of University Women Sue Gottcent Memorial Scholarship Fund *(Undergraduate, Graduate/Scholarship)* [9431]
Louis Gottschalk Prize *(Other/Prize)* [1291]
Carl W. Gottschalk Research Scholar Grants *(Professional development/Grant)* [1381]
Government Documents Special Interest Section - Veronica Maclay Student Grants *(Master's/Grant)* [530]
Wilford Hayes Gowen Scholarship Fund *(Undergraduate/Scholarship)* [10161]
Goya Scholarships *(Graduate/Scholarship)* [8852]
William L. Graddy Law School Scholarships *(Graduate/Scholarship)* [9432]
Graduate Fellowship Program - Research Fellowships (GFP) *(Doctorate, Graduate/Fellowship)* [8833]
Graduate Fellowships in Alternatives in Scientific Research *(Doctorate, Graduate/Fellowship)* [5333]
Graduate Realtor Institute Scholarships *(Graduate/Scholarship)* [5817]
Graduate Student Travel Grants *(Doctorate, Master's/Grant)* [462]
Graduate Student Travel Grants *(Graduate, Other/Grant)* [9111]
A. Allen Graffham Research Grants *(Advanced Professional, Professional development/Grant)* [1842]
Graham and Dunn 1L Diversity Fellowships *(Graduate/Fellowship)* [4506]
Rachel Graham Memorial Scholarships *(Undergraduate/Scholarship)* [8478]
Jim Graham Scholarships *(Undergraduate/Scholarship)* [7482]
Grand Canyon Historical Society Scholarships *(Graduate/Scholarship)* [4508]
Grand Rapids University Prep Founder's Scholarships *(Undergraduate/Scholarship)* [4596]
Charles Hall Grandgent Awards *(Graduate/Award, Monetary)* [3525]
Granger Business Association College Scholarships *(Undergraduate/Scholarship)* [4641]
Russ Grant Memorial Scholarship for Tennis *(Undergraduate/Scholarship)* [7832]
AMA/Charles H. Grant Scholarships *(Undergraduate/Scholarship)* [39]
Lucille Cheever Graubart/Lambda Scholarships *(Undergraduate/Scholarship)* [8927]
Paul and Helen L. Grauer Scholarships *(Undergraduate/Scholarship)* [1740]
Thomas B. Grave and Elizabeth F. Grave Scholarships *(Undergraduate, Graduate/Scholarship)* [6247]
Caswell Grave Scholarships *(Undergraduate, Graduate/Scholarship)* [6248]
Camille F. Gravel, Jr. Scholarships *(Professional development/Scholarship)* [6114]
Gravure Publishing Council Scholarships *(Undergraduate, Graduate/Scholarship)* [4648]
IADR John Gray Fellowship *(Other/Fellowship)* [5251]
Alexander G. Gray, Jr. Scholarships *(Graduate/Scholarship)* [6340]
Grays Harbor Community Foundation Scholarships *(Undergraduate, Graduate/Scholarship)* [4651]
Great Lakes Commission Sea Grant Fellowships *(Graduate/Scholarship)* [4656]
Great Lakes Section Diversity Scholarship *(Graduate, Undergraduate/Scholarship)* [5178]
GREAT MINDS Collegiate Scholarship Program *(Undergraduate/Scholarship)* [338]
Greater Cincinnati Scholarships Association *(Undergraduate/Scholarship)* [2995]
Greater Research Opportunities (GRO) Undergraduate Fellowships *(Undergraduate/Fellowship)* [9933]
Greater Seattle Business Association Scholarships (GSBA Scholarships) *(Undergraduate/Scholarship)* [4658]
Frank L. Greathouse Government Accounting Scholarship *(Graduate, Undergraduate/Scholarship)* [4504]
Bishop Charles P. Greco Graduate Fellowships *(Graduate, Master's/Scholarship)* [5853]
Greek Orthodox Archdiocese of America Paleologos Graduate Scholarships *(Graduate/Scholarship)* [4666]

Green Hill Yacht and Country Club Scholarships *(Undergraduate/Scholarship)* [3177]
Green Knight Economic Development Corporation Scholarships *(Undergraduate/Scholarship)* [4668]
Crystal Green Memorial Scholarship *(Undergraduate/Scholarship)* [2314]
James H. and Shirley L. Green Scholarship Fund *(Undergraduate/Scholarship)* [9506]
Howard L. Green Scholarships *(Undergraduate/Scholarship)* [7317]
William G. and Mayme J. Green Scholarships *(Undergraduate/Scholarship)* [4754]
K2TEO Martin J. Green, Sr. Memorial Scholarships *(Undergraduate/Scholarship)* [1741]
Helen R. Greenamyer Memorial Scholarships *(Undergraduate/Scholarship)* [9567]
Robert D. Greenberg Scholarships *(Graduate, Other/Scholarship)* [9093]
Michael Greenberg Student Writing Competition *(Graduate/Monetary, Scholarship)* [7052]
Richard L. Greene Dissertation Award *(Doctorate/Award)* [1090]
Curt Greene Memorial Scholarships *(Undergraduate/Scholarship)* [4725]
Elizabeth Greenhalgh Memorial Scholarships in Journalism, Graphic Arts, or Photography *(Undergraduate/Scholarship)* [10639]
Greenlining Institute Fellowships *(Graduate/Fellowship)* [4670]
Greenwich Scholarship Association Scholarships (GSA) *(Undergraduate/Scholarship)* [4672]
Anna Munger Greenwood Memorial Adelphe Scholarship *(Undergraduate/Scholarship)* [5729]
Francis Harris Gresham Scholarships *(Undergraduate/Scholarship)* [9433]
Lily H. Gridley Memorial Scholarships *(Undergraduate/Scholarship)* [10651]
Velma Shotwell Griffin Memorial Scholarship Fund *(Undergraduate/Scholarship)* [9507]
Enid Hall Griswold Memorial Scholarships *(Undergraduate/Scholarship)* [7152]
Andrew Gronholdt Arts Scholarship Awards *(Undergraduate, Vocational/Occupational, Graduate, Master's/Scholarship)* [310]
Caroline L. Gross Fellowships *(Professional development/Fellowship)* [7304]
Katherine M. Grosscup Scholarships *(Undergraduate, Graduate/Scholarship)* [4325]
Charles Grossman Graduate Scholarships *(Graduate/Scholarship)* [5306]
Kathern F. Gruber Scholarship Program *(Undergraduate/Scholarship)* [2312]
Elizabeth M. Gruber Scholarships *(Graduate/Scholarship)* [3583]
Gruwell Scholarships *(Undergraduate/Scholarship)* [3178]
GSA Scholarships for International Nurses *(Undergraduate, Master's/Scholarship)* [4458]
Guajardo & Marks Law School Scholarships *(Graduate/Scholarship)* [4676]
Guelph Caribbean Canadian Association Graduate Scholarships *(Undergraduate/Scholarship)* [4678]
Ronald P. Guerrette Future Farmers of America Scholarship Fund *(Undergraduate/Scholarship)* [6196]
Eleanor Guetzloe Undergraduate Scholarship *(Undergraduate/Scholarship)* [3433]
Harry Frank Guggenheim Dissertation Fellowships *(Doctorate/Fellowship)* [4681]
Harry Frank Guggenheim Foundation Research Grants *(Professional development/Grant)* [4682]
John Simon Guggenheim Memorial Fellowships - U.S. and Canadian Competition *(Advanced Professional/Fellowship)* [4684]
GuildScholar Awards *(Undergraduate/Scholarship)* [5596]
Guin-Stanford Scholarships *(Advanced Professional/Scholarship)* [3264]
Calouste Gulbenkian Foundation Scholarships *(Undergraduate/Scholarship)* [1696]
Gulf Coast Past President's Scholarships *(Undergraduate/Scholarship)* [1413]
Harold Gulliksen Psychometric Research Fellowships *(Doctorate, Graduate/Fellowship)* [3807]
SME Education Foundation Connie & Robert T.

Gunter Scholarships *(Undergraduate/Scholarship)* [9182]
George Gurney Fellowships *(Doctorate, Postdoctorate/Fellowship)* [9003]
Patricia S. Gustafson '56 Memorial Scholarships *(Undergraduate/Scholarship)* [3710]
Mary Ewing Guthrey/Mary Keller Moyer Memorial Scholarship *(Undergraduate, Graduate/Scholarship)* [5730]
Guzkowski Family Scholarships *(Undergraduate/Scholarship)* [8479]
Sara Gwisdalla Memorial Scholarships *(Undergraduate/Scholarship)* [7833]
GWS Scholarships *(Undergraduate, Graduate/Scholarship)* [145]
GWSCPA Scholarships *(Undergraduate/Scholarship)* [4664]
Ed Haas Memorial Scholarships *(Undergraduate/Scholarship)* [9568]
Wesley R. Habley NACADA Summer Institute Scholarships *(Other/Scholarship)* [6672]
Hackett Family Scholarships *(Undergraduate/Scholarship)* [4597]
Louise Wallace Hackney Fellowships for the Study of Chinese Art *(Doctorate, Postdoctorate/Fellowship)* [1058]
HACU/Empacadora Fruticola Santa Ines S.A. de C.V. Scholarships *(Undergraduate, Graduate/Scholarship)* [4884]
HACU/Gilberto Salazar Escoboza Scholarships *(Undergraduate, Graduate/Scholarship)* [4885]
HACU/JCPenny Leadership Excellence Scholarships *(Undergraduate, Graduate/Scholarship)* [4886]
HACU/KIA Motors America, Inc. Scholarships *(Undergraduate, Graduate/Scholarship)* [4887]
HACU/Videxport S.A. de C.V. Scholarships *(Undergraduate, Graduate/Scholarship)* [4889]
Perry F. Hadlock Memorial Scholarships *(Undergraduate/Scholarship)* [1742]
Suzanne Lovell Hadsell Memorial Scholarship *(Undergraduate, Graduate/Scholarship)* [5731]
HAESF Graduate Scholarships *(Graduate/Scholarship)* [5008]
HAESF Senior Leaders and Scholars Fellowships *(Other/Fellowship)* [5010]
Joseph E. Hagan Memorial Scholarships *(Undergraduate/Scholarship)* [4312]
Leslie Jane Hahn Memorial Scholarships *(Undergraduate/Scholarship)* [8705]
Jerome Hake Engineering Scholarships *(Undergraduate/Scholarship)* [4144]
Lee Hakel Graduate Student Scholarship *(Doctorate/Scholarship)* [9152]
Gene Halker Memorial Scholarships *(Graduate, Undergraduate/Scholarship)* [4145]
Hall of Achievement Scholarships *(Undergraduate/Scholarship)* [2450]
Stephen K. Hall ACWA Water Law and Policy Scholarships *(Graduate/Scholarship)* [1872]
Joyce C. Hall College Scholarships *(Undergraduate/Scholarship)* [7960]
Anna E. Hall Memorial Scholarships *(Undergraduate, Graduate/Scholarship)* [8055]
Chappie Hall Scholarship Program *(Undergraduate/Scholarship)* [2]
Guy D. and Mary Edith Halladay Music Scholarships *(Graduate, Undergraduate/Scholarship)* [4599]
David J. Hallissey Memorial Internships *(Graduate, Undergraduate/Internship)* [1441]
Harold B. Halter Memorial Scholarship *(Undergraduate/Scholarship)* [3970]
Alice Hamilton Prize *(Other/Prize)* [1311]
TIAA-CREF Ruth Simms Hamilton Research Fellowships *(Graduate/Fellowship)* [9737]
Dwight A. Hamilton Scottish Rite Foundation of Colorado Graduate Scholarships *(Graduate/Scholarship)* [8821]
Caitlin Hammaren Memorial Scholarship *(Undergraduate/Scholarship)* [5732]
Tommie J. Hamner Scholarships *(Undergraduate/Scholarship)* [8094]
Hampton Roads Association of Social Workers Scholarships *(Graduate/Scholarship)* [4698]
HANA Scholarships *(Undergraduate, Graduate,

Doctorate/Scholarship) [9852]
Morris Hanauer Scholarships *(Undergraduate/Scholarship)* [4337]
Hancock Family Snow Hill High School Scholarships *(Undergraduate/Scholarship)* [3179]
Robert Hancock Memorial Scholarship Awards *(Undergraduate/Scholarship)* [6498]
Pauline Hand Memorial Scholarships *(Undergraduate/Scholarship)* [9569]
Handweavers Guild of America and Dendel Scholarships *(Graduate, Undergraduate/Scholarship)* [4710]
Vincent S. Haneman-Joseph B. Perskie Memorial Foundation Scholarships *(Graduate, Undergraduate/Scholarship)* [2115]
Byron Hanke Fellowships *(Doctorate, Graduate, Undergraduate/Fellowship)* [4225]
Clayburn and Garnet R. Hanna Scholarships *(Undergraduate/Scholarship)* [7834]
Zenon C.R. Hansen Leadership Scholarships *(Undergraduate/Scholarship)* [6926]
Clement T. Hanson Scholarships *(Undergraduate/Scholarship)* [6569]
Duane Hanson Scholarships *(Undergraduate/Scholarship)* [1331]
Isaac and Mary Harbottle Scholarships *(Graduate, Undergraduate/Scholarship)* [7909]
Dolores Ruth Heady Hardy Memorial Scholarship *(Undergraduate/Scholarship)* [5733]
Hardy, Wolf & Downing Scholarships *(Undergraduate, Graduate/Scholarship)* [4719]
Harkness Fellowships in Health Care Policy and Practice *(Doctorate, Graduate/Fellowship)* [3160]
Bryce Harlow Fellowship Program *(Graduate/Fellowship)* [4721]
Matt Harmon Memorial Scholarships *(Undergraduate/Scholarship)* [9434]
Harness Tracks of America Scholarship Fund *(Undergraduate/Scholarship)* [4727]
Walter and Lucille Harper Scholarships *(Undergraduate/Scholarship)* [5806]
H.H. Harris Foundation Scholarships *(Professional development, Undergraduate/Scholarship)* [836]
Marcia S. Harris Legacy Fund Scholarships *(Undergraduate, Advanced Professional/Scholarship)* [8564]
William H. Harris Memorial Scholarships *(Graduate, Undergraduate/Scholarship)* [8075]
Frank and Charlene Harris Scholarships *(Undergraduate/Scholarship)* [3228]
Eileen Harrison Education Scholarships *(Graduate, Undergraduate/Scholarship)* [4146]
Peg Hart Harrison Memorial Scholarships *(Undergraduate/Scholarship)* [3552]
Lullelia W. Harrison Scholarships in Counseling *(Graduate, Undergraduate/Scholarship)* [10815]
Harrisville Lions Club Scholarships *(Undergraduate/Scholarship)* [7836]
Harry S. Truman Scholarships *(Postgraduate/Scholarship)* [9803]
Claude B. Hart Memorial Scholarships *(Undergraduate/Scholarship)* [10584]
Ida L. Hartenberg Charitable Scholarships *(Undergraduate/Scholarship)* [4755]
Hartford Grammar School Scholarships *(Undergraduate/Scholarship)* [4756]
Hartford Whalers Booster Club Scholarships *(Undergraduate/Scholarship)* [4778]
Gabe A. Hartl Scholarships *(Undergraduate/Scholarship)* [137]
Harry Hartleben Scholarships *(Undergraduate/Scholarship)* [7837]
Gail L. Hartshorn Memorial Fund *(Undergraduate/Scholarship)* [7838]
William T. Hartzell Memorial Scholarships *(Undergraduate/Scholarship)* [8480]
Harvey Fellows Program *(Graduate/Fellowship)* [6632]
Delta Gamma Foundation Florence Margaret Harvey Memorial Scholarships *(Graduate, Undergraduate/Scholarship)* [822]
Donald F. Hastings Scholarships *(Undergraduate/Scholarship)* [1513]
Donald and Shirley Hastings Scholarships *(Undergraduate/Scholarship)* [1514]
Gretchen Hauff Memorial Scholarships *(Undergraduate/Scholarship)* [8349]
Gregory Linn Haught Citizenship Awards *(Undergraduate/Award, Scholarship)* [7839]
Charles Hauser Scholarships *(Undergraduate/Scholarship)* [10232]
Don C. Hawkins Memorial Scholarships *(Undergraduate/Scholarship)* [164]
Thomas T. Hayashi Memorial Scholarships *(Graduate/Scholarship)* [5550]
R. Garn Haycock Memorial Scholarships *(Undergraduate/Scholarship)* [8481]
Samuel P. Hays Research Fellowships *(Other/Fellowship)* [1312]
Hazen and Sawyer Scholarships *(Master's/Scholarship)* [1489]
HBI-BGI Scholar-in-Residence Program *(Undergraduate/Scholarship)* [2359]
HBO Point Scholarships *(Graduate, Undergraduate/Scholarship)* [8177]
HCF Community Scholarships Fund *(Undergraduate, Graduate/Scholarship)* [4796]
HDSA Research Grants *(Graduate/Grant)* [5019]
Edith Head Scholarships *(Undergraduate/Scholarship)* [3584]
M.G. "Doc" Headley Scholarships *(Undergraduate/Scholarship)* [9570]
Health Policy Scholarship for General Surgeons *(Professional development/Scholarship)* [697]
Health Services Research Dissertation Awards *(Doctorate/Award)* [9914]
Healthcare Information Management Systems Scholarships *(Graduate, Postgraduate, Undergraduate/Scholarship)* [4831]
William Randolph Hearst Endowed Scholarships *(Undergraduate/Scholarship)* [7382]
Dr. James H. Heckman Memorial Scholarship Fund *(Undergraduate/Scholarship)* [9508]
HECUA Scholarship for Community Engagement *(Undergraduate/Scholarship)* [4878]
HECUA Scholarship for Social Justice *(Undergraduate/Scholarship)* [4879]
Professor Ulla Hedner Scholarships *(Undergraduate/Scholarship)* [6991]
Richard Heekin Scholarships *(Undergraduate/Scholarship)* [2996]
Lavonne Heghinian Scholarships *(Undergraduate/Scholarship)* [3585]
Joel T. Heinen Undergraduate Support Scholarships *(Undergraduate/Scholarship)* [10183]
Steven H. Heisler Law Scholarships *(Graduate/Scholarship)* [4836]
Helen Steiner Rice Scholarships *(Undergraduate/Scholarship)* [2997]
Helicopter Foundation International Commercial Helicopter Rating Scholarships *(Other/Scholarship)* [4838]
Helicopter Foundation International Maintenance Technician Certificate Scholarships *(Other/Scholarship)* [4839]
Hellenic Times Scholarships *(Undergraduate, Graduate/Scholarship)* [4843]
Joan Heller-Diane Bernard Fellowships *(Graduate, Undergraduate/Fellowship)* [2865]
Joseph T. Helling Scholarship Fund *(Undergraduate/Scholarship)* [5106]
ASIL Arthur C. Helton Fellowship Program *(Professional development/Fellowship)* [1344]
Hemlow Prize in Burney Studies *(Graduate/Prize)* [1292]
Hemophilia Federation of America Educational Scholarships *(Undergraduate/Scholarship)* [4860]
Hench Post-Dissertation Fellowship *(Postdoctorate/Fellowship)* [438]
Douglas B. Henderson Leadership Scholarships *(Doctorate/Scholarship)* [3984]
Gerald V. Henderson Memorial Scholarships *(Undergraduate, Graduate/Scholarship)* [9210]
Henigson Human Rights Fellowships *(Graduate, Master's, Juris Doctorate/Fellowship)* [4786]
SNMMI Robert E. Henkin, MD, Government Relations Fellowship *(Professional development/Fellowship)* [9222]
Henley-Putnam University Scholarships *(Other/Scholarship)* [5267]
Allan F. Henry/Paul A. Greebler Scholarships *(Graduate/Scholarship)* [1036]
Robert N. Herbert Undergraduate Scholarships *(Undergraduate/Scholarship)* [9216]
Hereditary Disease Foundation Basic Research Grants *(Advanced Professional/Grant)* [4869]
Michael Herman Scholarships *(Undergraduate, Vocational/Occupational/Scholarship)* [4524]
Manuel Hernandez, Jr. Foundation Scholarships *(Undergraduate/Scholarship)* [3099]
The Herpetologists' League Graduate Research Award *(Graduate/Award)* [4871]
Purdue University Ray W. Herrick Laboratories Research Fellowship *(Graduate/Fellowship)* [8388]
Jessica M. Herron, Epsilon Nu, Memorial Scholarship *(Undergraduate/Scholarship)* [5734]
Ella Beren Hersch Scholarships *(Undergraduate/Scholarship)* [7841]
Herschede Engineering Scholarships *(Graduate/Scholarship)* [8898]
Isabel M. Herson Scholarships in Education *(Graduate, Undergraduate/Scholarship)* [10816]
Hertz Foundation Graduate Fellowship Award *(Graduate/Fellowship)* [4875]
Hertz Foundation Graduate Fellowships *(Graduate, Master's, Doctorate/Fellowship)* [6748]
Hertz Foundation Thesis Prize *(Graduate/Prize)* [4876]
Wayne E. Hesch Memorial Scholarship *(Undergraduate, Graduate/Scholarship)* [1543]
Darrel Hess Community College Geography Scholarships *(Undergraduate/Scholarship)* [1830]
Beth B. Hess Memorial Scholarships *(Doctorate, Graduate/Fellowship, Award)* [9331]
Peter Hess Scholarships *(Undergraduate/Scholarship)* [4338]
Melvyn F. Hester Scholarships *(Master's, Professional development/Scholarship)* [7383]
Caroline M. Hewins Scholarships *(Graduate/Scholarship)* [4776]
HFMA Connecticut Chapter Scholarships *(Undergraduate, Graduate/Scholarship)* [4827]
HFMH Bilingual Scholarships for Mental Health Workforce Diversity *(Graduate/Scholarship)* [4913]
HGS Foundation Undergraduate Scholarships *(Undergraduate/Scholarship)* [4967]
HHMI International Student Research Fellowships *(Doctorate/Fellowship)* [4975]
HHMI Medical Research Fellowships *(Undergraduate/Fellowship)* [4976]
HIAA Graduate Student Travel Grants *(Graduate/Grant)* [4908]
Dwight Hibbard Scholarships *(Undergraduate/Scholarship)* [2998]
Jim Hierlihy Memorial Scholarship *(Undergraduate/Scholarship)* [3911]
Howard B. Higgins South Carolina Dental Scholarships *(Undergraduate/Scholarship)* [4197]
John Higham Travel Grants *(Graduate/Grant)* [5087, 7716]
Robert S. Hilbert Memorial Student Travel Grants *(Graduate, Undergraduate/Grant)* [7673]
Wayne Hildebrant Police Scholarship Fund *(Undergraduate/Scholarship)* [5931]
Gus and Henrietta Hill Scholarships *(Undergraduate/Scholarship)* [3712]
D. Glenn Hilts Scholarships *(Graduate, Undergraduate/Scholarship)* [2069]
Lucy Hilty Research Grants *(Graduate/Grant)* [1173]
Brooke Hindle Postdoctoral Fellowships *(Postdoctorate/Fellowship)* [9142]
Jim and Nancy Hinkle Travel Grants *(Graduate/Grant)* [4856]
HIPLA Judicial Fellowships *(Undergraduate/Fellowship)* [4969]
HIPLA Scholarships for University of Houston Law Center Students *(Graduate, Undergraduate/Scholarship)* [4970]
Hispanic Association of Colleges and Universities Scholarships *(Undergraduate/Scholarship)* [4890]
Hispanic Metropolitan Chamber Scholarships *(Graduate, Undergraduate/Scholarship)* [4900]
Hispanic Scholarship Fund General College Scholarship Program (HSF) *(Undergraduate/Scholarship)* [4904]
Hispanic Serving Institution Scholarships (HSIS) *(Undergraduate/Scholarship)* [9870]
Historically Black College or University Scholarships

UNITED STATES

(HBCUS) *(Undergraduate/Scholarship)* [9871]
HIV Prevention Research Advocacy Fellowships *(Professional development/Fellowship)* [2140]
Albert H. Hix, W8AH Memorial Scholarships *(Undergraduate/Scholarship)* [1743]
HLS/MLA Professional Development Grants *(Other/Grant)* [6386]
Lucy Hsu Ho Scholarships *(Undergraduate/Scholarship)* [2229]
Lou Hochberg Awards - University/College Essay Awards *(Undergraduate/Award)* [7747]
Lou Hochberg Awards - University Thesis/Dissertation Awards *(Undergraduate, Graduate/Scholarship)* [7748]
James E. Hoff, S.J. Scholars *(Undergraduate/Scholarship)* [10721]
Florette B. Hoffheimer Scholarships *(Undergraduate/Scholarship)* [2999]
Dorothy M. and Earl S. Hoffman Award *(Graduate/Award)* [2156]
Hoffman Family Scholarship Fund *(Undergraduate/Scholarship)* [4526]
Henry Hoffman Memorial Scholarship Fund *(Undergraduate/Scholarship)* [6740]
Electronics Division Lewis C. Hoffman Scholarships *(Undergraduate/Scholarship)* [664]
Miriam Hoffman Scholarships *(Undergraduate, Graduate/Scholarship)* [9853]
Zelle Hofmann Diversity in Law Scholarships *(Undergraduate/Scholarship)* [10812]
Michael J. Hogan Language Fellowships *(Graduate/Fellowship)* [9138]
The Thelma S. Hoge Memorial Scholarship Fund *(Undergraduate/Scholarship)* [3205]
Raymond T. Hoge Scholarship Fund *(Undergraduate/Scholarship)* [9510]
Michael J. Hoggard Memorial Scholarships *(Undergraduate/Scholarship)* [8350]
R.W. "Bob" Holden Memorial Scholarships *(Undergraduate/Scholarship)* [4798]
Houston/Nancy Holliman Scholarships *(Undergraduate/Scholarship)* [3586]
Cleve Holloway Memorial Scholarship Fund *(Undergraduate/Scholarship)* [3265]
Joseph A. Holmes Safety Association Scholarships *(Undergraduate, Graduate/Scholarship)* [4918]
Robert Holmes Scholarship *(Undergraduate/Scholarship)* [3327]
Alan Holoch Memorial Grants *(Professional development/Grant)* [531]
W. Stull Holt Dissertation Fellowships *(Doctorate, Graduate/Fellowship)* [9139]
Arthur and Janet Holzheimer Fellowship in the History of Cartography *(Postdoctorate, Doctorate/Fellowship)* [7411]
Holzheimer Memorial Student Scholarship for Economic Development Planning *(Graduate, Master's/Scholarship)* [1105]
HomeCity Real Estate Scholarships *(Undergraduate/Scholarship)* [4925]
Honeywell Avionics Scholarships *(Undergraduate/Scholarship)* [165]
Charles H. Hood Foundation Child Health Research Awards Program *(Doctorate/Grant)* [4815]
Lillie Hope-McGarvey Health Scholarship Awards *(Undergraduate, Vocational/Occupational, Graduate, Master's/Scholarship)* [311]
Hope Through Learning Awards *(Undergraduate/Scholarship)* [4927]
Hope for the Warriors Spouse/Caregiver Scholarships *(Undergraduate, Graduate/Scholarship)* [4933]
Johns Hopkins Department of Emergency Medicine Administration Fellowships *(Advanced Professional, Professional development/Fellowship)* [5607]
Minnie Hopkins Memorial Scholarship Fund of Lathrop/Compton School *(Undergraduate/Scholarship)* [9511]
Horatio Alger Ak-Sar-Ben Scholarships *(Undergraduate/Scholarship)* [4957]
Seth Horen, K1LOM Memorial Scholarships *(Undergraduate/Scholarship)* [1744]
Brenda Renee Horn Memorial Scholarship *(Undergraduate/Scholarship)* [4313]
Edward L. Horne, Jr. Scholarships *(Advanced Professional/Scholarship)* [7732]
Sandra Jo Hornick Scholarships *(Undergraduate/Scholarship)* [5671]
Judge and Mrs. Robert D. Horowitz Legal Scholarship Fund *(Graduate/Scholarship)* [9512]
Detroit Tigers Willie Horton Scholarship *(Undergraduate/Scholarship)* [3328]
J. Jay Hostetler Scholarships *(Undergraduate/Scholarship)* [5672]
Max and Julia Houghton Duluth Central Scholarships *(Undergraduate/Scholarship)* [3713]
Roberta L. Houpt Scholarship Fund *(Undergraduate/Scholarship)* [4242]
Alston S. Householder Fellowships *(Doctorate/Fellowship)* [9907]
Houston Alumnae Association, Eunice "Scotty" Scott Siverson Memorial Adelphe Scholarship *(Undergraduate, Graduate/Scholarship)* [5735]
Paul Green Houston Scholarships *(Undergraduate/Scholarship)* [10233]
Sarah Jane Houston Scholarships *(Undergraduate/Scholarship)* [3587]
Houtan Scholarships *(Graduate/Scholarship)* [4972]
Kaspar Hovannisian Memorial Scholarships *(Graduate/Scholarship)* [1697]
Hirair and Anna Hovnanian Foundation Presidential Scholarships *(Undergraduate/Scholarship)* [1698]
Hirair and Anna Hovnanian Foundation Scholarships *(Undergraduate/Scholarship)* [1699]
Barbara J. and M. William Howard Jr. Scholarships *(Undergraduate/Scholarship)* [7384]
C.D. Howard Scholarships *(Undergraduate/Scholarship)* [5298]
Roger and Joyce Howe Scholarships *(Undergraduate/Scholarship)* [3000]
Graduate Student Honoraria - A. Brazier Howell Awards *(Master's, Doctorate/Award)* [1359]
William C. Howell Scholarship *(Graduate, Master's, Doctorate/Scholarship)* [1145]
William B. Howell Scholarships *(Undergraduate/Scholarship)* [1515]
Christopher Hoy/ERT Scholarships *(Graduate/Scholarship)* [962]
Carol Hoy Scholarship Fund *(Undergraduate/Scholarship)* [4243]
HRET Health Career Scholarships *(Postgraduate, Undergraduate/Scholarship)* [7319]
HRH Prince Alwaleed Bin Talal ISNA Fellowships *(Graduate/Fellowship)* [5486]
HRSA Scholarships for Disadvantaged Students *(Undergraduate/Scholarship)* [9923]
HSF/Marathon Oil College Scholarship Program *(Undergraduate/Scholarship)* [4905]
HSF/Wells Fargo Scholarship Program *(Undergraduate/Scholarship)* [4906]
Chun-tu Hsueh Fellowship for International Scholars *(Graduate, Postdoctorate/Grant)* [1120]
Albert W. and Mildred Hubbard Scholarships *(Undergraduate/Scholarship)* [8708]
Huber Engineered Woods Product Evaluation Scholarships *(Graduate/Scholarship)* [3977]
Amber Huber Memorial Scholarships *(Undergraduate/Scholarship)* [3287]
Huenefeld/Denton Scholarships *(Undergraduate/Scholarship)* [3588]
Dale Hughes, Jr. Memorial Scholarships *(Undergraduate/Scholarship)* [9571]
Roger K. Hughes Legacy Scholarships *(Undergraduate/Scholarship)* [2451]
Hughes Memorial Foundation Scholarships *(Graduate/Scholarship)* [4983]
Paul A. Hughes Memorial Scholarships *(Undergraduate/Scholarship)* [2452]
Mary M. Hughes Research Fellowships in Texas History *(Professional development/Fellowship)* [9714]
Huguenot Society of South Carolina Graduate Scholarships *(Graduate/Scholarship)* [4986]
Humane Studies Fellowships *(Graduate/Fellowship, Scholarship)* [5183]
Humanism in Medicine Scholarships *(Undergraduate/Scholarship)* [9600]
Anna C. Hume Scholarship *(Undergraduate/Scholarship)* [4428]
Kevin Hummer Point Scholarships *(Graduate, Undergraduate/Scholarship)* [8178]
Betty Jo Creighton Hunkele Adelphe Scholarship *(Undergraduate/Scholarship)* [5736]
Dr. Richard M. Hunt Fellowships *(Doctorate, Postdoctorate/Fellowship)* [725]
Hunt Postdoctoral Fellowships *(Postdoctorate/Fellowship)* [10517]
Frederick V. Hunt Postdoctoral Research Fellowships in Acoustics *(Postdoctorate/Fellowship)* [53]
Michael A. Hunter Memorial Scholarships *(Undergraduate/Scholarship)* [2907]
Carrie Hunter-Tate Award *(Undergraduate, Graduate/Grant)* [6794]
Curtis E. Huntington Memorial Scholarship *(Undergraduate/Scholarship)* [62]
Huntington's Disease Society of America Research Fellowships *(Postdoctorate/Fellowship)* [5020]
Sang Ok Hur Scholarships *(Undergraduate/Scholarship)* [7385]
James F. Hurley III Bicentennial Merit Scholarships *(Undergraduate/Scholarship)* [10234]
Walter Doc Hurley Scholarship *(Undergraduate/Scholarship)* [4757]
Zora Neale Hurston Scholarships *(Graduate/Scholarship)* [10817]
Norman E. and Mary-Belle Huston Scholarships *(Graduate, Undergraduate/Scholarship)* [5397]
Dr. James L. Hutchinson and Evelyn Ribbs Hutchinson Medical School Scholarship Fund *(Undergraduate/Scholarship)* [8952]
The Hyatt Hotels Fund For Minority Lodging Management Students *(Undergraduate/Scholarship)* [860]
Hydro Research Foundation Fellowships *(Advanced Professional/Fellowship)* [5023]
Mike Hylton and Ron Niederman Memorial Scholarships *(Undergraduate/Scholarship)* [4861]
Libbie H. Hyman Memorial Scholarships *(Graduate, Undergraduate/Scholarship)* [9156]
The Steve Hymans Extended Stay Scholarship Program *(Undergraduate/Scholarship)* [861]
Hypertherm International HyTech Leadership Scholarships *(Graduate/Scholarship)* [1516]
IAAP Wings Chapter Scholarships *(Undergraduate/Scholarship)* [5244]
IABA Scholarships *(Graduate/Scholarship)* [5476]
IAEM Scholarship Program *(Undergraduate/Scholarship)* [5256]
IAESTE United States Internships *(Undergraduate/Internship)* [3489]
IAHCSMM-Purdue University Scholarship Awards *(Other/Scholarship)* [5263]
IALD Education Trust Scholarship Program *(Graduate, Undergraduate/Scholarship)* [5271]
IALL Regular Bursaries *(Other/Scholarship)* [5269]
IARS Mentored Research Awards (IMRA) *(Professional development/Grant)* [5242]
IARSLCE Graduate Student Scholarships *(Graduate/Scholarship)* [5273]
IASC Associate Fellowships *(Doctorate/Fellowship)* [10308]
IASC Doctoral Fellowships - Dissertation *(Doctorate/Fellowship)* [10309]
IASC Doctoral Fellowships - Pre-Dissertation *(Doctorate/Fellowship)* [10310]
IASC Postdoctoral Fellowships *(Postdoctorate/Fellowship)* [10311]
IASC Visiting Fellowships *(Professional development/Fellowship)* [10312]
IASP Visiting Professor Grants *(Professional development/Grant)* [5275]
IAWP International Scholarship Award *(Other/Scholarship)* [5280]
Iberdrola USA Scholarships *(Undergraduate/Scholarship)* [6198]
ICDA Graduate Scholarships *(Graduate/Scholarship)* [5464]
ICDA Research Grants *(Graduate/Grant)* [5465]
Ice Skating Institute of America Education Foundation Scholarships *(Undergraduate/Scholarship)* [5031]
ICJS Short-Term Fellowships *(Doctorate, Postdoctorate, Advanced Professional/Fellowship)* [8997]
ICMA Local Government Management Fellowships *(Master's/Fellowship)* [5296]
IDA Fellowship Awards *(Other/Fellowship)* [5320]

Idaho Opportunity Scholarships *(Undergraduate/Scholarship)* [9547]
David Iden Memorial Safety Scholarships *(Undergraduate/Scholarship)* [1415]
IDTA Freestyle Scholarships *(Undergraduate/Scholarship)* [5317]
IFDA Student Member Scholarships *(Undergraduate/Scholarship)* [5338]
Ella R. Ifill Fund *(Undergraduate/Scholarship)* [6199]
IFMA Foundation Scholarships *(Undergraduate, Graduate/Scholarship)* [5327]
IFSEA Worthy Goal Scholarships *(Two Year College, Undergraduate, Vocational/Occupational/Scholarship)* [5329]
IIE Council of Fellows Undergraduate Scholarships *(Undergraduate/Scholarship)* [5188]
IILJ Scholarships *(Doctorate/Scholarship)* [5202]
IILJ Visiting Fellowships and Research *(Postdoctorate/Fellowship)* [5203]
IISE Presidents Scholarships *(Undergraduate/Scholarship)* [5189]
Illinois Association of Chamber of Commerce Executives Scholarships *(Professional development/Scholarship)* [5054]
Illinois Division Scholarships *(Undergraduate/Scholarship)* [6519]
Illuminator Educational Foundation Scholarships *(Undergraduate/Scholarship)* [2453]
IMA Memorial Education Fund Scholarships (MEF) *(Graduate, Undergraduate/Scholarship)* [5206]
Imagine America College Scholarships for High School Students *(Undergraduate/Scholarship)* [5083]
Imagine America Military Awards Program *(Undergraduate/Scholarship, Grant)* [5084]
Imagine America Scholarships for Adult Students *(Undergraduate/Scholarship)* [5085]
Elmer S. Imes Scholarships in Physics *(Undergraduate/Scholarship)* [7142]
John L. Imhoff Scholarships *(Graduate, Undergraduate/Scholarship)* [5190]
David G. Imig Awards for Distinguished Achievement in Teacher Education *(Other/Recognition)* [486]
Independent Professional Seed Association Student Recognition Awards *(Undergraduate/Scholarship)* [5098]
Independent University Alumni Association Scholarships *(Graduate, Undergraduate/Scholarship)* [5102]
Indian Health Service Professionals Program *(Undergraduate/Scholarship)* [875]
Indiana Alumni Scholarships *(Undergraduate/Scholarship)* [10722]
Indiana FFA Association State Fair Scholarship *(Undergraduate/Scholarship)* [5110]
Individual K-Grants *(All/Grant)* [5823]
Individual Professional Development Scholarship *(Professional development/Scholarship)* [4161]
INF Scholarships *(Undergraduate/Scholarship)* [5472]
Influenster Code Like a Girl Scholarships *(Undergraduate, Graduate/Scholarship)* [5140]
Informatics Post Doctoral Fellowships *(Doctorate/Fellowship)* [8027]
Informatics Pre Doctoral Fellowships *(Doctorate/Fellowship)* [8028]
Informatics Sabbatical Fellowships *(Doctorate, Postdoctorate/Fellowship)* [8029]
Information Age Publishing Graduate Student Book Scholarships *(Doctorate, Graduate/Scholarship)* [5142]
Terrance N. Ingraham Pediatric Optometry Residency Support *(Graduate/Fellowship)* [416]
Jennifer Ingrum Scholarships *(Undergraduate/Scholarship)* [3230]
INIA Scholarship Program *(Undergraduate/Scholarship)* [5363]
Injury Scholarships *(Undergraduate/Scholarship)* [4731]
Inland Northwest Business Alliance Scholarships (INBA) *(Undergraduate/Scholarship)* [8254]
Innovations in Software Scholarships *(Undergraduate, Graduate/Scholarship)* [10758]
Innovative Grants-Pilot and Research Tool Grants *(Postdoctorate/Grant)* [5641]

Inspire our Future Scholarships *(All/Scholarship)* [9648]
Institute for Anarchist Studies Grants for Radical Writers and Translators *(Professional development/Grant)* [5165]
Institute of Food Technologists Graduate Scholarships *(Graduate/Scholarship)* [5171]
Institute of Food Technologists Junior/Senior Scholarships *(Undergraduate/Scholarship)* [5172]
Institute of Food Technologists Sophomore Scholarships *(Undergraduate/Scholarship)* [5173]
Institute for Health Metrics and Evaluation Post Bachelor Fellowships *(Graduate/Fellowship)* [5180]
Institute for Health Metrics and Evaluation Post Graduate Fellowships *(Doctorate, Postdoctorate/Fellowship)* [5181]
Institute for the International Education of Students Faculty Fellowships *(Other/Fellowship)* [7412]
Institute of Management Accountants FAR Doctoral Student Grants Program *(Doctorate/Grant)* [5207]
Institute-NEH Postdoctoral Fellowships *(Doctorate, Other/Fellowship)* [7613]
Institute of Turkish Studies Dissertation Writing Grants *(Graduate/Grant)* [5223]
Instructional Design & Learning Technologies Scholarships *(Undergraduate, Graduate/Scholarship)* [3820]
Integra Foundation NNF Research Grant Awards *(Other/Grant)* [546]
Inter American Press Association Scholarships *(Undergraduate/Scholarship)* [9061]
Intermediaries and Reinsurance Underwriters Association Summer Intern Scholarships Program *(Undergraduate/Scholarship)* [5237]
International Affairs Fellowships in Nuclear Security (IAF-NS) *(Professional development/Fellowship)* [3448]
International Association of Black Actuaries Scholarships *(Undergraduate/Scholarship)* [5248]
International Association for Food Protection - Student Travel Scholarship Program *(Undergraduate, Graduate/Scholarship)* [5258]
International Association of Foundation Drilling Scholarships for Civil Engineering Students *(Graduate/Scholarship)* [75]
International Association of Foundation Drilling Scholarships for Part-time Civil Engineering Graduate School Students *(Graduate/Scholarship)* [76]
International Association of Wildland Fire Graduate-Level Scholarships *(Doctorate, Graduate/Scholarship)* [5278]
International Code Council Foundation General Scholarship Fund *(Undergraduate/Scholarship)* [5299]
International Code Council Scholarships *(Graduate/Scholarship)* [3978]
International Dairy-Deli-Bakery Association Undergraduate/Graduate Scholarships *(Graduate, Undergraduate/Scholarship)* [5314]
International Development and Education Award in Palliative Care *(Professional development/Award)* [3376]
International Development and Education Awards *(Professional development, Doctorate/Grant)* [3377]
International Dissertation Research Fellowship (IDRF) *(Graduate, Doctorate/Fellowship)* [9054]
International Doctoral Scholarships for Studies Specializing in Jewish Fields *(Doctorate/Scholarship, Award)* [6411]
International Door Association Scholarship Foundation Program *(Undergraduate, Vocational/Occupational/Scholarship)* [5322]
International Executive Housekeepers Association Education Foundation Scholarship Awards *(Undergraduate/Scholarship)* [5324]
International Executive Housekeepers Association Spartan Scholarship Awards *(Undergraduate/Scholarship)* [5325]
International Fellowships in Jewish Studies and Jewish Culture *(Professional development/Fellowship)* [6412]
International Foodservice Editorial Council Scholarships *(Graduate, Undergraduate/Scholarship)* [5331]
International Furnishings and Design Association Part-time Student Scholarships *(Undergraduate/Scholarship)* [5339]
International GI Training Grant Award *(Professional development/Grant)* [685]
International Innovation Grants *(Professional development/Grant)* [3378]
International Management Council Scholarships (IMC) *(Undergraduate/Scholarship)* [3288]
International Operators Scholarship *(Professional development/Scholarship)* [6834]
International Order of the King's Daughters and Sons North American Indian Scholarship Program *(Undergraduate/Scholarship)* [876]
International Radio and Television Society Foundation Summer Fellowships Program *(Undergraduate, Graduate/Scholarship)* [5378]
International Sanitary Supply Association Foundation Scholarships *(Undergraduate/Scholarship)* [5392]
International Scholars Program for Young Vascular Surgeons *(Graduate/Scholarship)* [9325]
International Scholarship Programs for Community Service *(Undergraduate/Scholarship)* [6413]
International Society for Humor Studies Graduate Student Awards (GSA) *(Graduate/Award, Scholarship)* [5422]
International Society for Humor Studies Scholarly Contribution Awards (SCA) *(Other/Award)* [5423]
International Trademark Association-Ladas Memorial Awards *(Other, Undergraduate/Award)* [5447]
International Trainee Scholarships (ITS) *(Doctorate/Scholarship)* [1474]
International Women's Fishing Association Scholarship Trust *(Graduate/Scholarship)* [5456]
Internet Society Fellowships to the IETF *(Doctorate, Master's/Fellowship)* [5460]
Interracial Scholarship Fund of Greater Hartford *(Undergraduate/Scholarship)* [4758]
Investigators in the Pathogenesis of Infectious Disease Awards *(Doctorate, Postdoctorate, Professional development/Grant)* [2417]
IOIA Organic Community Initiative Scholarships *(Other/Scholarship)* [5369]
Iowa Division Scholarships *(Undergraduate/Scholarship)* [6520]
IPMA-HR Graduate Study Fellowships *(Graduate, Master's/Fellowship)* [5376]
IPPR Events Internships *(Undergraduate/Internship)* [5209]
IPR Pathfinder Award *(Advanced Professional/Recognition, Grant)* [5212]
Iris Scholarship *(Undergraduate/Scholarship)* [5737]
Greg Irons Award Fund *(Undergraduate/Scholarship)* [3714]
Harriet Irsay Scholarships *(Graduate, Undergraduate/Scholarship)* [927]
IRSF Mentored Training Fellowships *(Advanced Professional, Postdoctorate/Fellowship)* [5388]
ISA Educational Foundation Scholarships *(Undergraduate/Scholarship)* [5398]
ISA Executive Board Scholarships *(Graduate, Undergraduate/Scholarship)* [5399]
ISA Section and District Scholarships - Houston *(Graduate, Undergraduate/Scholarship)* [5400]
ISA Section and District Scholarships - Lehigh Valley *(Graduate, Undergraduate/Scholarship)* [5401]
ISA Section and District Scholarships - Richmond Hopewell *(Graduate, Undergraduate/Scholarship)* [5402]
ISA Section and District Scholarships - Southwestern Wyoming *(Graduate, Undergraduate/Scholarship)* [5403]
ISA Section and District Scholarships - Texas, Louisiana and Mississippi *(Graduate, Undergraduate/Scholarship)* [5404]
ISA Section and District Scholarships - Wilmington *(Graduate, Undergraduate/Scholarship)* [5405]
ISA Technical Division Scholarships - Analysis Division *(Graduate, Undergraduate/Scholarship)* [5406]
ISA Technical Division Scholarships - Chemical and Petroleum Industries Division *(Graduate, Undergraduate/Scholarship)* [5407]

ISA Technical Division Scholarships - Food and Pharmaceutical Industries Division *(Graduate, Undergraduate/Scholarship)* [5408]
ISA Technical Division Scholarships - Power Industry Division *(Graduate, Undergraduate/Scholarship)* [5409]
ISA Technical Division Scholarships - Process Measurement and Control Division *(Graduate, Undergraduate/Scholarship)* [5410]
ISA Technical Division Scholarships - Pulp and Paper Industry Division *(Graduate, Undergraduate/Scholarship)* [5411]
ISA Technical Division Scholarships - Test Measurement Division *(Graduate, Undergraduate/Scholarship)* [5412]
ISA Technical Division Scholarships - Water and Wastewater Industries Division *(Graduate, Undergraduate/Scholarship)* [5413]
ISBA General Scholarships *(Undergraduate/Scholarship)* [5052]
Hazel D. Isbell Fellowships *(Graduate/Fellowship, Scholarship)* [3553]
(ISC)2 Foundation Information Security Scholarships *(Graduate, Undergraduate/Scholarship)* [5348]
ISCALC International Scholarship Fund *(Undergraduate/Scholarship)* [4049]
ISDS Graduate Student Scholarships *(Doctorate, Graduate/Scholarship)* [5416]
ISF Excellence in Community Service Scholarships *(Undergraduate/Scholarship)* [5478]
ISF Undergraduate Scholarships *(Undergraduate/Scholarship)* [5479]
ISID Small Grant *(Postdoctorate, Professional development/Grant)* [5425]
Islamic Scholarship Fund Scholarships (ISF) *(Postgraduate, Undergraduate/Scholarship)* [5484]
Island Institute Scholarship Fund *(Undergraduate/Scholarship)* [6200]
ISOPE Offshore Mechanics Scholarships for Outstanding Students *(Graduate/Scholarship)* [5427]
ISRS Graduate Fellowships *(Doctorate, Graduate/Fellowship)* [5429]
ISTTE Scholarships *(Graduate, Undergraduate/Scholarship)* [5435]
ISTU Student Prize *(Undergraduate/Prize)* [5432]
ITAA Graduate Student Best Paper Award *(Graduate/Monetary)* [5442]
Italian Language Scholarships *(Undergraduate/Scholarship)* [7682]
ITEEA Greer/FTE Grants *(Other/Grant)* [5437]
ITNS Research Grants *(Other/Grant)* [5449]
ITW Welding Companies Scholarships *(Undergraduate/Scholarship)* [1517]
Ivanhoe Foundation Fellowships *(Master's/Fellowship)* [5488]
Bob and Mary Ives Scholarships *(Graduate, Undergraduate/Scholarship)* [5414]
Jack and Jill of America National Scholarships Program *(Undergraduate/Scholarship)* [5490]
Virginia C. Jack and Ralph L. Jack Scholarships *(Undergraduate/Scholarship)* [9513]
Jackie Robinson Scholarships *(Undergraduate/Scholarship)* [5495]
Jackman Scholarships *(Undergraduate/Scholarship)* [8095]
Graduate Student Honoraria - Anna M. Jackson Awards *(Master's, Doctorate/Award)* [1360]
The Jackson Club Scholarships *(Undergraduate/Scholarship)* [3715]
Jackson High School Alumni Scholarship Fund *(Undergraduate/Scholarship)* [9514]
Edward Jackson International Scholarships *(Undergraduate/Scholarship)* [10235]
Ruth K. Jacobs Memorial Scholarships *(Graduate, Undergraduate/Scholarship)* [2930]
Freddy L. Jacobs Scholarships *(Undergraduate/Scholarship)* [5284]
Eric L. Jacobson Memorial Scholarships *(Undergraduate/Scholarship)* [8482]
Dwight P. Jacobus Scholarships *(Undergraduate/Scholarship)* [2058]
Jacque Placette Chapman Master's Fellowships *(Graduate, Master's/Fellowship)* [7679]
Louis I. Jaffe Memorial Scholarships-NSU Alumni *(Graduate/Scholarship)* [4700]

Jagiellonian University Summer Program Scholarship *(Professional development/Scholarship)* [8204]
Jain Foundation Merit-Based Scholarships *(All/Scholarship)* [5518]
Jain Foundation Social-Media Scholarships *(All/Scholarship)* [5519]
Gregori Jakovina Endowment Scholarships *(Undergraduate/Scholarship)* [3920]
Cory Jam Memorial Award Fund *(Undergraduate/Scholarship)* [3716]
Peter and Malina James and Dr. Louis P. James Legacy Scholarships *(Graduate, Master's, Doctorate/Scholarship)* [1146]
J. Franklin Jameson Fellowships in American History *(Professional development/Fellowship)* [853]
Jan Jancin Competition Awards *(Undergraduate/Award)* [941]
Janelia Farm Graduate Program *(Graduate/Award)* [4978]
Janssen Therapeutics Point Scholarships *(Undergraduate, Graduate, Doctorate/Scholarship)* [8179]
Japan Indonesia Presidential Scholarship Program *(Doctorate/Scholarship)* [10695]
Dr. Ali Jarrahi Merit Scholarships *(Undergraduate/Scholarship)* [5480]
Carl and Lucille Jarrett Scholarship Fund *(Undergraduate/Scholarship)* [4050]
Airgas - Terry Jarvis Memorial Scholarships *(Undergraduate/Scholarship)* [1518]
Jacob K. Javits Fellowships Program *(Master's, Doctorate/Fellowship)* [9894]
JCC Association Graduate Education Scholarships *(Graduate/Scholarship)* [5562]
JCCF Equal Voice Journalism Scholarship *(Professional development/Scholarship)* [10152]
JDRF Advanced Postdoctoral Fellowships *(Postdoctorate/Fellowship)* [5642]
JDRF Career Development Awards *(Professional development, Postdoctorate/Grant)* [5643]
JDRF Postdoctoral Fellowships *(Postdoctorate/Fellowship)* [5644]
JEA Future Teacher Scholarships *(Undergraduate, Master's/Scholarship)* [5625]
Sister Rita Jeanne Scholarships *(Undergraduate/Monetary, Scholarship)* [5626]
Jeffress Trust Awards Program in Interdisciplinary Research *(Professional development/Award)* [4816]
John Jeffries Meteorology Scholarships *(Graduate/Scholarship)* [3979]
Erin L. Jenkins Memorial Scholarship Fund *(Undergraduate/Scholarship)* [4244]
Elise Reed Jenkins Memorial Scholarships - Gamma Lambda *(Undergraduate/Scholarship)* [8928]
Elise Reed Jenkins Memorial Scholarships - Gamma Psi *(Undergraduate/Scholarship)* [8929]
John H. Jenkins Research Fellowships in Texas History *(Professional development/Fellowship)* [9715]
Martha Combs Jenkins Scholarships *(Undergraduate/Scholarship)* [8096]
Ruth E. Jenkins Scholarships *(Undergraduate/Scholarship)* [8709]
Gaynold Jensen Education Stipends *(Postdoctorate, Other/Scholarship)* [3622]
Walter J. Jensen Fellowships *(Other/Fellowship)* [8052]
Nancy Lorraine Jensen Memorial Scholarships *(Undergraduate/Scholarship)* [9345]
Stanley "Doc" Jensen Scholarships *(Undergraduate/Scholarship)* [760]
Jerman-Cahoon Student Scholarship *(Undergraduate/Scholarship)* [1397]
Kenneth Jernigan Scholarships *(Undergraduate/Scholarship)* [6947]
Brian Jimenez Memorial Scholarships *(Undergraduate/Scholarship)* [8483]
Rev. and Mrs. A.K. Jizmejian Educational Fund *(Undergraduate/Scholarship)* [1700]
JLTLA Judge's Scholarships *(Undergraduate/Scholarship)* [9817]
JMA Architecture Studios Scholarships *(Undergraduate/Scholarship)* [8351]
Reverend H. John and Asako Yamashita Memorial Scholarships *(Graduate/Scholarship)* [5551]

John F. Kennedy Scholarship Award *(Undergraduate/Scholarship)* [2435]
Johnny Bench Scholarships *(Undergraduate/Scholarship)* [3001]
Johns Hopkins Medicine Disaster Fellowships *(Professional development/Fellowship)* [5608]
Johns Hopkins Medicine Emergency Medical Services Fellowship *(Professional development/Fellowship)* [5609]
Johns Hopkins Medicine International Emergency and Public Health Fellowships *(Graduate/Fellowship)* [5610]
Johns Hopkins Medicine Medical Education Fellowships *(Professional development/Fellowship)* [5611]
Johns Hopkins Medicine Observation Medicine Fellowships *(Professional development/Fellowship)* [5612]
Johns Hopkins Medicine Research Fellowships *(Professional development/Fellowship)* [5613]
Johns Hopkins University/Applied Physics Laboratory Alexander Kossiakoff Scholarships *(Doctorate, Graduate, Master's/Scholarship)* [5310]
Wilma Winberg Johnson Adelphe Scholarship for Chapter Consultants *(Undergraduate/Scholarship)* [5738]
Alvin H. Johnson AMS 50 Dissertation Fellowships *(Doctorate/Fellowship)* [1020]
Sylvia Taylor Johnson Fellowships in Educational Measurement *(Doctorate/Fellowship)* [3808]
Robert Wood Johnson Foundation Health Policy Fellows Program *(Advanced Professional, Professional development/Fellowship)* [8629]
Johnson and Johnson/AACN Minority Nurse Faculty Scholars *(Graduate/Scholarship)* [480]
MCCA Lloyd M. Johnson, Jr. Scholarships *(Graduate/Scholarship)* [6553]
Joseph C. Johnson Memorial Grants *(Undergraduate/Grant, Scholarship)* [1252]
Gregory D. Johnson Memorial Scholarships *(Doctorate, Graduate, Master's/Scholarship)* [7036]
Professor Emeritus Dr. Bill Johnson Memorial Scholarships *(Undergraduate/Scholarship)* [8874]
V.J. Johnson Memorial Scholarships *(Undergraduate/Scholarship)* [579]
Ella Wilson Johnson Scholarships *(Undergraduate/Scholarship)* [3002]
Stella B. Johnson Scholarships *(Undergraduate/Scholarship)* [10586]
The Johnson & Wales Scholarships *(Undergraduate/Scholarship)* [5631]
OOIDA Mary Johnston Scholarships *(Undergraduate/Scholarship)* [7785]
Joint Japan/World Bank Graduate Scholarship Program for Developing Country National (JJ/WB-GSP) *(Graduate/Scholarship)* [10696]
Joint Japan/World Bank Graduate Scholarship Program for Japanese National (JJ/WBGSP) *(Graduate, Master's, Doctorate/Scholarship)* [10697]
Redlands Council PTA - Dorathy Jolley Memorial Scholarships *(Undergraduate/Scholarship)* [8484]
George E. Jonas Scholarships *(Graduate, Undergraduate/Scholarship)* [5616]
Napoleon A. Jones, III Memorial Scholarships *(Undergraduate/Scholarship)* [8710]
Barbara Jordan Scholarships *(Undergraduate/Scholarship)* [9819]
David J. Joseph Company Scholarships *(Undergraduate/Scholarship)* [3003]
Joseph H. Fichter Research Grants *(Other/Grant)* [2071]
E.J. Josey Scholarships *(Graduate/Scholarship, Award)* [2296]
Journey Toward Ordained Ministry Scholarships *(Undergraduate, Graduate/Scholarship)* [9854]
Journyx Scholarships *(Undergraduate, Graduate/Scholarship)* [5628]
Leslie W. Joyce and Paul W. Thayer Graduate Fellowship in I-O Psychology *(Doctorate/Fellowship)* [9153]
JSA/Jefferson Lab Graduate Fellowships *(Doctorate, Graduate/Scholarship)* [5566]
Clem Judd Jr. Memorial Scholarships *(Undergraduate/Scholarship)* [4799]
George E. Judd Scholarships *(Undergraduate/Scholarship)* [9436]

Martha Julian Memorial Scholarship *(Undergraduate/Scholarship)* [212]
Junior Achievement of East Central Ohio, Inc. Scholarship Fund *(Undergraduate/Scholarship)* [9515]
Junior Firefighter Scholarships *(Undergraduate/Scholarship)* [7211]
James W. Junior and Jane T. Brown Scholarships *(Undergraduate, Vocational/Occupational/Scholarship)* [4527]
George W. Juno Memorial Scholarships *(Undergraduate/Scholarship)* [4339]
JustNebulizers.com Respiratory Care Scholarships *(Undergraduate, Graduate/Scholarship)* [5637]
JustWalkers.com Mobility Scholarships *(Undergraduate, Graduate/Scholarship)* [5638]
JW Surety Bonds Scholarships *(Undergraduate, Graduate/Scholarship)* [5646]
Mike Kabo Global Scholarships *(Other/Scholarship)* [4456]
Annette Kade Fellowships *(Graduate/Fellowship)* [6431]
Edward G. Kaelber Scholarships *(Undergraduate/Scholarship)* [6201]
Daniel Kahikina and Millie Akaka Scholarships *(Graduate, Undergraduate/Scholarship)* [7910]
Kaiser Media Fellowships in Health Reporting *(Advanced Professional, Professional development/Fellowship)* [5648]
David A. Kaiser Memorial Scholarship Fund *(Undergraduate/Scholarship)* [9516]
Judge Edward Y. Kakita Memorial Scholarships *(Undergraduate/Scholarship)* [5542]
Sam Kalman Scholarship *(Undergraduate/Scholarship)* [1582]
Gladys Kamakakńokalani 'Ainoa Brandt Scholarships *(Graduate, Undergraduate/Scholarship)* [7911]
Shripat Kamble Urban Entomology Graduate Student Awards for Innovative Research *(Doctorate/Recognition, Grant)* [3881]
Kamehameha Schools Class of 1968 "Ka Poli O Kaiona" Scholarships *(Graduate, Undergraduate/Scholarship)* [7912]
Kamehameha Schools Class of 1972 Scholarships *(Graduate, Undergraduate/Scholarship)* [7913]
Benjamin Kaminer Endowed Scholarships in Physiology *(Graduate, Master's, Doctorate/Scholarship)* [6249]
Martin S. Kane Memorial Community Service Award Scholarships *(Undergraduate/Scholarship)* [3181]
Kansas Association of Broadcasters Scholarships *(Undergraduate/Scholarship)* [5652]
Kansas City Division Scholarships *(Undergraduate/Scholarship)* [6521]
Kansas Osteopathic Medical Service Scholarships *(Graduate, Other/Scholarship)* [5658]
Walter Kapala Scholarships *(Undergraduate/Scholarship)* [4759]
Joseph Kaplan Fund *(Graduate, Undergraduate/Scholarship)* [5103]
Kaplan Lawyers PC Legal Scholarships *(Graduate/Scholarship)* [5665]
Don Kaplan Legacy Scholarships *(Undergraduate/Scholarship)* [2454]
Kaplan Scholarships *(Graduate/Scholarship)* [4898]
Steve Kaplan TV and Film Studies Scholarships *(Other/Scholarship)* [1273]
Kappa Delta Phi Scholarship Program *(Postgraduate/Scholarship)* [1046]
Kappa Kappa Gamma Foundation Project 2000 Scholarships *(Undergraduate/Scholarship)* [5739]
Kappa Kappa Gamma Graduate Scholarships *(Graduate/Scholarship)* [5740]
Kappa Kappa Gamma Undergraduate Scholarships *(Undergraduate/Scholarship)* [5741]
Kappa Omicron Nu Leadership Undergraduate Scholarships *(Undergraduate/Scholarship)* [5781]
Kappa Omicron Nu National Alumni Fellowships *(Graduate/Fellowship)* [5782]
Kappa Project 2000 Scholarships *(Undergraduate/Scholarship)* [5742]
Kappa Sigma Scholarship/Leadership Awards *(Undergraduate/Scholarship)* [5792]
Kappa Zeta Scholarships *(Undergraduate/Scholarship)* [8930]

The ISASI Rudolf Kapustin Memorial Scholarships *(Undergraduate/Scholarship)* [5394]
Josephine de Karman Fellowships *(Graduate, Undergraduate/Fellowship)* [5796]
Philip R. Karr, III Scholarship Fund *(Graduate/Scholarship)* [4378]
K.A.S.A Memorial Scholarships *(Undergraduate/Scholarship)* [7843]
KASF Chair Scholarships *(Graduate, Undergraduate/Scholarship)* [5873]
KASF Designated Scholarships *(Graduate, Undergraduate/Scholarship)* [5874]
KASF General Scholarships *(Undergraduate, Graduate, Professional development/Scholarship)* [5875]
Ken Kashiwahara Scholarships *(Undergraduate/Scholarship)* [8399]
Magoichi and Shizuko Kato Memorial Scholarships *(Graduate, Master's, Doctorate/Scholarship)* [5552]
Ka'u Chamber of Commerce College Scholarships *(Undergraduate/Scholarship)* [5798]
Lucile B. Kaufman Women's Scholarships *(Undergraduate/Scholarship)* [9184]
N.G. Kaul Memorial Scholarships *(Doctorate, Graduate/Scholarship)* [7403]
William and Beatrice Kavanaugh Scholarships *(Undergraduate/Scholarship)* [5507]
Kawano Family Scholarships *(Undergraduate/Scholarship)* [8711]
E. Wayne Kay Co-op Scholarships *(Undergraduate/Scholarship)* [9185]
E. Wayne Kay Community College Scholarships *(Undergraduate/Scholarship)* [9186]
E. Wayne Kay High School Scholarships *(Undergraduate/Scholarship)* [9187]
KCC Foundation Gold Key Scholarships *(Undergraduate/Scholarship)* [5807]
KCC Foundation Scholarships *(Undergraduate/Scholarship)* [5808]
KCC Trustee Scholarships *(Undergraduate/Scholarship)* [5809]
KDP Huntington Bank Scholarship *(Undergraduate/Scholarship)* [5673]
KDP International Scholarship Program - President Scholarship *(Undergraduate, Graduate, Doctorate/Scholarship)* [5674]
KDP MBNA Scholarships *(Undergraduate, Graduate/Scholarship)* [5675]
Doc Keen Memorial Scholarships *(Undergraduate/Scholarship)* [9437]
Keepers Preservation Education Fund *(Undergraduate/Award)* [6202]
Glenn Keever Scholarships *(Undergraduate/Scholarship)* [10236]
KEF Academic Scholarships *(Undergraduate, Graduate/Scholarship)* [5865]
KEF College/University Basic Scholarships *(Undergraduate/Scholarship)* [5866]
KEF Vocational Education Scholarship *(Undergraduate/Scholarship)* [5867]
Kegler Brown Diversity Scholarship *(Graduate/Scholarship)* [5804]
Maude Keisling/Cumberland County Extension Homemakers Scholarships *(Undergraduate/Scholarship)* [3231]
Annette and Ernest Keith Scholarships *(Undergraduate/Scholarship)* [8485]
Anna-Maria and Stephen M. Kellen Fellowships *(Professional development/Fellowship)* [726]
John W. Kelley Memorial Scholarships *(Undergraduate/Scholarship)* [9572]
Rita Mae Kelly Fund *(Graduate, Doctorate/Fellowship)* [1121]
Kelly Law Team Annual Down Syndrome Scholarships *(All/Scholarship)* [5811]
Robert E. Kelsey Annual Scholarship *(Undergraduate/Scholarship)* [7933]
Willmoore H. Kendall Scholarships *(Professional development/Scholarship)* [3062]
Kendrick Foundation, Inc. Scholarships *(Undergraduate/Scholarship)* [5813]
Alexander Kendrick Memorial Scholarships *(Graduate, Undergraduate/Scholarship)* [7773]
Southwest Ohio Environmental Horticulture Association (SOEHA) Lloyd W. Kennedy Scholarship *(Undergraduate/Scholarship)* [7584]
Oscar Kenshur Book Prize *(Other/Prize)* [1293]
Raymond A. Kent-Navy V-12/ROTC Scholarships *(Undergraduate/Scholarship)* [10145]
Kerrigan Scholarships *(Undergraduate/Scholarship)* [7986]
Judge Oliver Kessel Memorial Scholarships - Ripley Rotary *(Undergraduate/Scholarship)* [7845]
Ashley E. Ketcher Memorial Scholarships *(Undergraduate/Scholarship)* [3289]
Debbie Khalil Memorial Scholarships *(Graduate, Undergraduate/Scholarship)* [8076]
Graduate Fellowship Program - Mahboob Khan/Advanced Micro Devices Fellowships *(Doctorate, Graduate/Fellowship)* [8834]
Michael Kidger Memorial Scholarships in Optical Design *(Undergraduate/Scholarship)* [9468]
The Michael Kiely Strong Roots Scholarships *(Undergraduate/Scholarship)* [8233]
Julia Kiene Fellowships in Electrical Energy *(Graduate/Fellowship)* [10660]
Mary and Millard Kiker Scholarships *(Undergraduate/Scholarship)* [4201]
Bernard Kilgore Memorial Scholarships *(Undergraduate/Scholarship)* [7327]
Killam Fellowships *(Undergraduate/Fellowship)* [4229]
Killingworth Foundation Scholarships *(Undergraduate/Scholarship)* [5830]
Kimberly Elementary School PTA Scholarships *(Undergraduate/Scholarship)* [8486]
Douglas Gray Kimel Scholarships *(Undergraduate/Scholarship)* [10587]
Kimmel Scholars Award *(Doctorate/Grant)* [5832]
James N. Kincanon Scholarships *(Undergraduate/Scholarship)* [8627]
Arthur M. and Berdena King Eagle Scout Scholarships *(Undergraduate/Scholarship)* [6927]
Kit C. King Graduate Scholarships *(Graduate/Scholarship)* [7109]
King Ice Scholarships *(Undergraduate, Graduate/Scholarship)* [5834]
Larry King/Jeffrey Fashion Cares Point Scholarship *(Undergraduate, Graduate, Doctorate/Scholarship)* [8180]
Martin Luther King Jr. Scholarships *(Undergraduate/Scholarship)* [5836]
Martin Luther King Law Scholarship *(Undergraduate/Scholarship)* [3680]
Steven G. King Play Environments Scholarships *(Undergraduate/Scholarship)* [5914]
Jessica King Scholarships *(Other/Scholarship)* [3490]
Don King Student Fellowships *(Undergraduate/Fellowship)* [5021]
Mackenzie King Travelling Scholarships *(Graduate/Scholarship)* [6367]
Kingsbury Elementary School PTA Scholarships *(Undergraduate/Scholarship)* [8487]
Treva C. Kintner Scholarships *(Undergraduate/Scholarship)* [8097]
Kiplinger Fellowship *(Professional development/Fellowship)* [7599]
Isabel Mayer Kirkpatrick Scholarships *(Undergraduate/Scholarship)* [9438]
Ruth L. Kirschstein NRSA Individual Pre-Doctoral Fellowships *(Doctorate/Fellowship)* [9926]
Dr. Elemér and Éva Kiss Scholarship Fund *(Undergraduate/Scholarship)* [5006]
Tamo Kitaura Scholarships *(Other/Scholarship)* [9961]
AACT John Kitt Memorial Scholarship *(Undergraduate/Scholarship)* [477]
Kiwanis Club of Escondido Scholarships *(Undergraduate/Scholarship)* [8712]
Kiwanis Club of Redlands Foundation Academic Excellence Scholarships *(Undergraduate/Scholarship)* [8488]
Klarman Family Foundation Grants Program in Eating Disorders Research *(Professional development/Grant)* [4818]
Louis T. Klauder Scholarships *(Undergraduate, Graduate/Scholarship)* [1166]
Jane M. Klausman Women in Business Scholarships *(Graduate, Undergraduate/Scholarship)* [10826]

Robert A. Kleckner Scholarships *(Undergraduate, Graduate/Scholarship)* [9439]
The Margie Klein "Paper Plate" Scholarships *(Undergraduate/Scholarship)* [1850]
Gerda and Kurt Klein Scholarships *(Undergraduate/Scholarship)* [4962]
Dr. Eva Kleinpeter Scholarship *(Undergraduate/Scholarship)* [5676]
Raymond and Augusta Klink Scholarships *(Undergraduate/Scholarship)* [3004]
Arthur Klorfein Scholarship and Fellowship Fund *(Undergraduate, Graduate/Scholarship)* [6250]
American Marketing Association-Connecticut Chapter, Anna C. Klune Memorial Scholarships *(Graduate/Scholarship)* [4760]
Joseph H. Klupenger Scholarship Awards *(Undergraduate/Scholarship)* [7696]
AALL/Wolters Kluwer Law & Business Grants *(Professional development/Grant)* [532]
Robert C. and Judith L. Knapp Scholarships *(Graduate, Undergraduate/Scholarship)* [4147]
John A. Knauss Marine Policy Fellowship *(Graduate/Fellowship)* [9890]
John S. Knight Fellowships *(Other/Fellowship)* [5849]
Robert E. Knight Professional Scholarships *(Graduate/Scholarship)* [9692]
Elva Knight Research Grants *(Professional development/Grant)* [5356]
Knight-Wallace Fellowship *(Professional development/Fellowship)* [5851]
Knights of Vartan, Fresno Lodge No. 9 Scholarships *(Undergraduate/Scholarship)* [1701]
Jane Shaw Knox Graduate Scholarships *(Graduate/Scholarship)* [4148]
Knox-Hume Scholarships *(Undergraduate/Scholarship)* [3232]
Glenn Knudsvig Memorial Scholarships *(Graduate, Undergraduate/Scholarship)* [679]
Ina Knutsen Scholarships *(Undergraduate/Scholarship)* [8875]
Kodak Fellowships in Film Preservation *(Graduate/Fellowship)* [2025]
Seth Koehler Central High School Scholarship Fund *(Undergraduate, Vocational/Occupational/Scholarship)* [4528]
Senator Carl O. Koella, Jr. Memorial Scholarships *(Undergraduate/Scholarship)* [3233]
Herb Kohl Educational Foundation Excellence Scholarships *(Undergraduate/Scholarship)* [5857]
Herb Kohl Educational Foundation Initiative Scholarships *(Undergraduate/Scholarship)* [5858]
Herb Kohl Educational Foundation Teacher Fellowships *(Professional development/Fellowship)* [5859]
Bob and Linda Kohlhepp Scholarships *(Undergraduate/Scholarship)* [3005]
Friends and Family of Christopher J. Kohlmeier Scholarships *(Undergraduate/Scholarship)* [8489]
James P. Kohn Memorial Scholarships *(Graduate/Scholarship)* [1418]
DSRSD James B. Kohnen Scholarships *(Undergraduate, High School/Scholarship)* [3697]
P. Johnson and C. Kolb Memorial Scholarships *(Undergraduate, Graduate, Master's, Doctorate/Scholarship)* [8752]
Gwin J. and Ruth Kolb Research Travel Fellowships *(Doctorate, Other/Fellowship)* [1294]
Susan G. Komen for the Cure College Scholarship Awards *(Two Year College/Award, Scholarship)* [5861]
Susan G. Komen for the Cure Post-doctoral Fellowships - Clinical Research Grants *(Postdoctorate/Grant, Fellowship)* [5862]
Vivian M. Kommer Scholarships *(Undergraduate/Scholarship)* [4603]
KON/GEICO LeaderShape Undergraduate Scholarship *(Undergraduate/Scholarship)* [5789]
KON National Alumni Chapter Grant *(Professional development/Grant)* [5783]
KON New Initiatives Grant *(Professional development/Grant)* [5784]
Emily Day Koppell Memorial Adelphe Scholarship *(Undergraduate, Graduate/Scholarship)* [5743]
Elizabeth Munsterberg Koppitz Child Psychology Graduate Fellowships *(Graduate, Doctorate/Fellowship)* [1147]
Herman P. Kopplemann Scholarships *(Undergraduate/Scholarship)* [4761]
Kor Memorial Scholarships *(Undergraduate, Graduate/Scholarship)* [5842]
Korean Language Study Awards *(Graduate/Scholarship)* [5871]
Korean Studies Dissertation Workshop Funds *(Graduate/Fellowship)* [9056]
AIST Willy Korf Memorial Fund *(Undergraduate/Scholarship)* [2000]
Kosciuszko Foundation Graduate Study and Research in Poland Scholarships *(Graduate/Scholarship)* [5877]
Kosciuszko Foundation Tuition Scholarships *(Graduate/Scholarship)* [5878]
Kosciuszko Foundation Year Abroad Scholarships *(Graduate, Undergraduate/Scholarship)* [5879]
Marcia J. Koslov Scholarship *(Professional development/Scholarship)* [533]
Eugene and Elinor Kotur Scholarship Trust Fund *(Undergraduate, Graduate/Scholarship)* [10443]
Kovaluk Scholarship Fund *(Undergraduate/Scholarship)* [9984]
Marjorie Kovler Research Fellowships *(Professional development/Fellowship)* [5602]
ONLA Phil Kozel Memorial Scholarship *(Undergraduate/Scholarship)* [7585]
KPMG Foundation Minority Accounting Doctoral Scholarships *(Doctorate/Scholarship)* [5885]
KPMG Point Scholarship *(Undergraduate, Graduate, Doctorate/Scholarship)* [8181]
Eve Kraft Education and College Scholarships *(Undergraduate/Scholarship)* [9975]
William D. Krahling Excellence in Journalism Scholarships *(Undergraduate/Scholarship)* [361]
Norman Kramer Scholarship Awards *(Undergraduate/Scholarship)* [6499]
Schmidt Kramer Scholarships for Academic Excellence *(Undergraduate/Scholarship)* [8792]
Melvin Kranzberg Dissertation Fellowships *(Doctorate/Fellowship)* [9143]
Michael Kraus Research Grants *(Doctorate/Grant)* [854]
Sharon Kreikemeier Memorial Scholarships *(Undergraduate/Scholarship)* [7242]
Kress Conservation Fellowships *(Postgraduate/Fellowship)* [5889]
Kress Fellowships in Art History at Foreign Institutions *(Graduate/Fellowship)* [5890]
Samuel H. Kress Foundation Dissertation Fellowships *(Doctorate/Fellowship)* [9084]
Samuel H. Kress Grants for Research and Publication in Classical Art and Architecture *(Professional development/Grant)* [1609]
Mathilde Krim Fellowships in Basic Biomedical Research *(Doctorate/Fellowship)* [1536]
Krist-Reavley Minority Scholarships *(Undergraduate/Scholarship)* [7987]
David A. Kronick Travelling Fellowships *(Doctorate, Graduate/Fellowship)* [6387]
Eugene S. Kropf Scholarships *(Undergraduate/Scholarship)* [10105]
Kristin Bjurstrom Krueger Student Scholarship Program *(Undergraduate/Scholarship)* [6404]
Melvin Kruger Endowed Scholarship Program *(Undergraduate, Vocational/Occupational/Scholarship)* [7122]
Melvin Kruger Endowed Scholarships *(Graduate, Undergraduate/Scholarship)* [8644]
Samuel Krugliak Legal Scholarship Fund *(Undergraduate/Scholarship)* [9517]
KTA Chapter Adviser Research Grant Award *(Professional development/Grant)* [5794]
Don Kuhn Memorial Scholarship Fund *(Graduate/Scholarship)* [6291]
Heloise Werthan Kuhn Scholarships *(Undergraduate/Scholarship)* [3235]
Irene Corbally Kuhn Scholarships *(Graduate, Undergraduate/Scholarship)* [7774]
Kumin Scholars Program *(Undergraduate/Scholarship)* [8953]
Chris Kurzweil Scholarship *(Undergraduate/Scholarship)* [3329]
Sam and Florice Kuwahara Memorial Scholarship *(Undergraduate/Scholarship)* [5553]
Henry and Chiyo Kuwahara Memorial Scholarships *(Undergraduate, Graduate/Scholarship)* [5554]
Anne Emery Kyllo Professional Scholarships *(Professional development/Scholarship)* [1014]
LA Tutors Innovation in Education Scholarships *(All/Scholarship)* [5896]
La Voz Latina Scholarships *(Undergraduate/Scholarship)* [3290]
Roger and Jacquelyn Vander Laan Family Scholarships *(Undergraduate/Scholarship)* [4604]
Gretchen Laatsch Scholarships *(Graduate/Scholarship)* [1926]
Ladah Law Firm, PLLC Injury Scholarships *(Undergraduate, Graduate/Scholarship)* [5898]
LAEF Scholarships *(Undergraduate/Scholarship)* [5937]
LAF Landscape Forms Design for People Scholarships *(Undergraduate/Scholarship)* [5915]
Jeffery P. LaFage Graduate Student Research Award *(Master's, Doctorate/Grant)* [3882]
Ken LaFountaine First Nations Scholarships *(Undergraduate/Scholarship)* [8876]
Ron LaFreniere Business Administration Scholarship *(Undergraduate/Scholarship)* [8877]
The Lagrant Foundation - Graduate Students Scholarships *(Graduate/Scholarship)* [5900]
The Lagrant Foundation - Undergraduate Students Scholarships *(Undergraduate/Scholarship)* [5901]
Lake Dollars for Scholars Endowment Fund *(Undergraduate/Scholarship)* [9518]
Douglas Lake Improvement Association Scholarships *(Undergraduate/Scholarship)* [10184]
Lakselaget Foundation Scholarships *(Graduate, Undergraduate/Scholarship)* [5903]
Lalor Foundation Merit Awards *(Postdoctorate/Award)* [9307]
Lalor Foundation Post-Doctoral Fellowships *(Postdoctorate/Fellowship)* [5905]
Paul C. K. Lam Memorial Scholarship at The University of Akron *(Undergraduate/Scholarship)* [7593]
LAM Pilot Project Awards *(Master's, Postdoctorate/Grant)* [5907]
Lamar University College of Engineering Scholarships *(Undergraduate/Scholarship)* [6928]
Lambda Project 2000 Scholarship *(Undergraduate/Scholarship)* [5744]
Elaine Johnson Lampert Journalism Memorial Adelphe Scholarship *(Graduate/Award)* [5745]
Lance Surety College Scholarships *(Undergraduate, Graduate/Scholarship)* [5911]
Frank S. Land Scholarships *(Undergraduate/Scholarship)* [3598]
Robert S. Landauer, Sr. Memorial Fellowships *(Graduate/Fellowship)* [4810]
The Lanford Family Highway Worker Memorial Scholarship Program *(Undergraduate/Scholarship)* [1219]
The Langfitt-Ambrose Trust Scholarship *(Undergraduate/Scholarship)* [7846]
Paul J. Laninga Memorial Scholarship Fund *(Undergraduate/Scholarship)* [4529]
Lansdale Public Policy Fellowship *(Advanced Professional, Professional development/Fellowship)* [1245]
Lapeer County Medical Scholarship Fund *(Undergraduate/Scholarship)* [5932]
The Otis and Florence Lapham Memorial Scholarships *(Undergraduate/Scholarship)* [5508]
Lapides Fellowships in Pre-1865 Juvenile Literature and Ephemera *(Graduate, Postdoctorate/Fellowship)* [439]
Katherine Roberts LaPorte Memorial Adelphe Scholarship *(Undergraduate/Scholarship)* [5746]
Christian Larew Memorial Scholarships *(Graduate/Scholarship)* [6071]
Peter and Jody Larkin Legacy Scholarships *(Undergraduate/Scholarship)* [2455]
Larson Aquatic Research Support Scholarships (LARS) *(Graduate/Scholarship)* [1490]
Laser Technology, Engineering and Applications Scholarships *(Graduate, Undergraduate/Scholarship)* [9469]
Daniel Lasky Scholarship Fund *(Undergraduate/Scholarship)* [7081]

Jay and Deborah Last Fellowships *(Doctorate/Fellowship)* [440]
Latham Diversity Scholars *(Undergraduate/Scholarship)* [5935]
Rick and Beverly Lattin Education Scholarship Fund *(Undergraduate/Scholarship)* [4530]
Estée Lauder Point Scholarships *(Undergraduate, Graduate, Doctorate/Scholarship)* [8182]
Candia Baker Laughlin Certification Scholarships *(Undergraduate/Scholarship)* [389]
Mandel and Lauretta Abrahamer Scholarships *(Undergraduate/Scholarship)* [9573]
Robert J. Lavidge Nonprofit Marketing Research Scholarships *(Other/Scholarship)* [982]
Law Fellows Program *(Undergraduate/Fellowship)* [6710]
Law Foundation of Ontario Community Leadership in Justice Fellowships *(Other/Fellowship)* [5945]
Law and Society Association Article Prize *(Other/Prize)* [5972]
Law and Society Association Dissertation Prize *(Other/Prize)* [5973]
Law and Society Association International Prize *(Other/Prize)* [5974]
Law and Society Association Undergraduate Student Paper Prize *(Undergraduate/Prize)* [5975]
Willie D. Lawson, Jr. Memorial Scholarships *(Doctorate, Graduate, Other/Scholarship)* [6819]
Dr. James L. Lawson Memorial Scholarships *(Undergraduate/Scholarship)* [1745]
Lawsuit Legal American Nursing Support Scholarships *(Undergraduate/Scholarship)* [5983]
Lazarian Graduate Scholarships *(Graduate/Scholarship)* [1678]
LCRF Grants *(Advanced Professional, Professional development/Grant)* [6141]
Betsy B. and Garold A. Leach Scholarships for Museum Studies *(Undergraduate/Scholarship)* [3589]
Leadership Conference Scholarship *(Other/Scholarship)* [6835]
Leadership Development Online Course Scholarships *(Professional development/Scholarship)* [7617]
LEAGUE Foundation Scholarships *(Undergraduate/Scholarship)* [8660]
League of Latin American Citizens General Electric Scholarships *(Undergraduate/Scholarship)* [5987]
Steven A. Leahy Law Office Marine Service/Law School Scholarships *(Postgraduate/Scholarship)* [5955]
Leakey Foundation Research Grants *(Doctorate, Advanced Professional/Grant)* [5992]
Jack W. Leatherman Family Scholarship Fund *(Undergraduate, Vocational/Occupational/Scholarship)* [4531]
LeClairRyan Diversity Scholarships *(Undergraduate/Scholarship)* [6000]
Hwain Chang Lee scholarships *(Undergraduate/Scholarship)* [7386]
William K. Lee Scholarships *(Undergraduate/Scholarship)* [7387]
Lee Womack Scholarship Fund *(Undergraduate/Scholarship)* [6570]
The Leesfield/AAJ Law Student Scholarships *(Undergraduate/Scholarship)* [517]
Robert E. Leet and Clara Guthrie Patterson Trust Awards Program in Clinical Research *(Professional development/Grant)* [4819]
The Legacy Fellowships *(Doctorate/Fellowship)* [441]
Doreen Legg Memorial Scholarships *(Undergraduate/Scholarship)* [8490]
Jay C. and B. Nadine Leggett Charitable Scholarship Fund *(Undergraduate/Scholarship)* [9519]
Herbert Lehman Education Scholarships *(Undergraduate/Scholarship)* [6646]
Lehman Family Scholarships *(Undergraduate/Scholarship)* [8715]
PCH Architects/Steven J. Lehnhof Memorial Architectural Scholarships *(Undergraduate/Scholarship)* [8491]
Gilder Lehrman Short-Term Fellowships *(Graduate, Postdoctorate/Fellowship)* [6007]
Leiber and Stoller Music Scholarships *(Undergraduate/Scholarship)* [1274]
Colonel Theodore A. Leisen Memorial and Training Endowment Funds *(Graduate, Professional development/Grant, Scholarship)* [7249]
Imelda "Mel" and Ralph LeMar Scholarship *(Undergraduate/Scholarship)* [3330]
Lemelson Center Fellowships *(Doctorate, Postdoctorate, Professional development/Fellowship)* [9025]
Lemelson Center Travel to Collections Awards *(Graduate, Professional development/Award)* [9026]
Lemelson Student Fellowships *(Graduate/Award)* [9282]
Stan Lencki Scholarships *(Undergraduate/Scholarship)* [6356]
John Lennon Scholarships *(Undergraduate/Scholarship)* [2319]
Craig Lensch Memorial Scholarships *(Undergraduate/Scholarship)* [2378]
V.A. Leonard Scholarships *(Graduate, Undergraduate/Scholarship)* [356]
Leopold Education Project Scholarships *(Undergraduate/Scholarship)* [3291]
Sherman L. and Mabel C. Lepard Scholarships *(Undergraduate/Scholarship)* [4608]
Lerner-Scott Prize *(Doctorate/Prize)* [7717]
Irwin S. Lerner Student Scholarships *(Undergraduate/Scholarship)* [7168]
Les Dames D'Escoffier New York Scholarships *(Undergraduate/Scholarship)* [6009]
Brigid Leventhal Special Merit Award *(Postdoctorate, Professional development/Award)* [3379]
Myra Levick Scholarships *(Graduate/Scholarship)* [449]
Jack A. and Louise S. Levine Memorial Scholarships *(Undergraduate/Scholarship)* [8492]
Saul Levine Memorial Scholarship *(Graduate/Scholarship)* [1037]
Harry and Miriam Levinson Scholarship *(Graduate, Master's, Doctorate/Scholarship)* [1148]
Herbert Levy Memorial Scholarship *(Undergraduate/Scholarship)* [9255]
William J. Levy Point Scholarship *(Undergraduate, Graduate, Doctorate/Scholarship)* [8183]
Lewis and Clark Fund for Exploration and Field Research *(Graduate, Postdoctorate/Grant)* [1082]
Lloyd Lewis Fellowships in American History *(Postdoctorate/Fellowship)* [7413]
George T. Lewis, Jr. Academic Scholarship Fund *(Undergraduate/Scholarship)* [4203]
Ted Lewis Memorial Scholarship *(Undergraduate/Scholarship)* [213]
Flora Lewis Memorial Scholarships *(Graduate, Undergraduate/Scholarship)* [7775]
S. Evelyn Lewis Memorial Scholarships in Medical Health Sciences *(Graduate, Undergraduate/Scholarship)* [10818]
Jonathan D. Lewis Point Scholarships *(Graduate, Undergraduate/Scholarship)* [8184]
Lewis-Reynolds-Smith Founders Fellowship *(Graduate/Fellowship)* [4857]
Lexington Alumni Scholarships *(Undergraduate/Scholarship)* [6062]
Lexington Community Foundation Annual Scholarships *(Undergraduate/Scholarship)* [6063]
Lexington Community Foundation/CCC Scholarships *(Undergraduate/Scholarship)* [6064]
Ta Liang Memorial Awards *(Graduate/Grant, Award)* [1806]
Liberty Mutual Scholarships *(Undergraduate/Scholarship)* [1420]
Richard T. Liddicoat Scholarships *(Graduate/Scholarship)* [4340]
Dolores Zohrab Liebmann Fund - Graduate School Fellowships *(Graduate/Fellowship)* [6075]
Dolores Zohrab Liebmann Fund - Independent Research/Study Grants *(Graduate/Grant)* [6076]
Dolores Zohrab Liebmann Fund - Publication Grants *(Graduate/Grant)* [6077]
LIFE Lessons Scholarship Program *(Undergraduate/Scholarship)* [6079]
Life Sciences Research Foundation Postdoctoral Fellowship Program *(Postdoctorate/Fellowship)* [6081]
Lighthouse International Scholarships - College-bound Awards *(High School, Undergraduate/Scholarship)* [6083]
Lighthouse International Scholarships - Graduate Awards *(Graduate/Scholarship)* [6084]
Lighthouse International Scholarships - Undergraduate Awards *(Undergraduate/Scholarship)* [6085]
Roy W. Likins Scholarships *(Undergraduate, Graduate/Scholarship)* [1494]
Frank R. Lillie Fellowships and Scholarships *(Undergraduate, Graduate/Scholarship)* [6251]
Lilly Endocrine Scholars Fellowship Awards *(Doctorate, Other/Fellowship)* [3865]
Lilly Scholarships in Religion for Journalists *(Other/Scholarship)* [8549]
Esther Lim Memorial Scholarships *(Undergraduate/Scholarship)* [2918]
Lim, Ruger & Kim Scholarships *(Undergraduate/Scholarship)* [6704]
AIST Ronald E. Lincoln Memorial Scholarships *(Undergraduate/Scholarship)* [2001]
John C. Lincoln Memorial Scholarships *(Undergraduate/Scholarship)* [1519]
Donald A.B. Lindberg Research Fellowships *(Doctorate, Graduate/Fellowship)* [6388]
Lindenwood University Scouting Scholarships *(Undergraduate/Scholarship)* [6929]
Carl H. Lindner Family Scholarships *(Undergraduate/Scholarship)* [3006]
George N. Lindsay Civil Rights Legal Fellowships *(Graduate/Fellowship)* [5985]
Margaret B. Lindsey Award for Distinguished Research in Teacher Education *(Other/Award, Recognition)* [487]
Johnny Lineberry Memorial Scholarships *(Undergraduate, Vocational/Occupational/Scholarship)* [10588]
Obrzut Ling Scholarships *(Undergraduate/Scholarship)* [8255]
Link Foundation/Smithsonian Graduate Fellowships in Marine Science *(Graduate/Fellowship)* [9033]
Ronald B. Linsky Fellowships for Outstanding Water Research *(Graduate, Master's, Doctorate/Fellowship)* [7213]
Linsley Scholarship Fund *(Undergraduate/Scholarship)* [2913]
LionsDeal Scholarships *(Undergraduate/Scholarship)* [6095]
F. Maynard Lipe Scholarship Award *(Master's, Postgraduate/Scholarship)* [683]
Lawrence Lipking Fellowships at the Newberry Library *(Graduate/Fellowship)* [7414]
LITA/LSSI Minority Scholarships *(Graduate/Scholarship)* [6072]
LITA/OCLC Minority Scholarships *(Graduate/Scholarship)* [6073]
Litherland/FTEE Scholarships *(Undergraduate/Scholarship)* [5438]
Littleton-Griswold Research Grants *(Doctorate/Grant)* [855]
Ruth Liu Memorial Scholarships *(Undergraduate/Scholarship)* [2919]
LiveCareer Scholarships *(Undergraduate/Scholarship)* [6099]
Lawrence Livermore National Laboratory Fellowships *(Doctorate/Fellowship)* [9905]
Davis Levin Livingston Public Interest Law Scholarships *(Postgraduate/Scholarship)* [3531]
David C. Lizárraga Graduate Fellowships *(Graduate/Fellowship)* [9660]
LLN Student Scholarships *(Undergraduate/Scholarship)* [5939]
E.C. Lloyd and J.C.U. Johnson Scholarship Fund *(Undergraduate/Scholarship)* [3266]
Loan Forgiveness Scholarships *(Graduate, Undergraduate/Loan, Scholarship)* [9463]
Virgil K. Lobring Scholarship *(Undergraduate/Scholarship)* [3331]
Local 564 Scholarship Award *(High School/Scholarship)* [5454]
Local Internet Service Scholarships *(Undergraduate/Scholarship)* [6103]
Miriam "Doc" Locke Memorial Adelphe Scholarships *(Graduate/Scholarship)* [5747]
Mary Elizabeth Lockwood Beneventi MBA Scholarship *(Graduate/Scholarship)* [7153]
Loewenstein-Wiener Fellowship Award *(Professional development/Fellowship)* [947]
Lone Star GIA Associate and Alumni Scholarships

UNITED STATES

(Undergraduate/Scholarship) [4341]
Lawrence A. Long Memorial Law Scholarships *(Undergraduate/Scholarship)* [362]
James E. Long Memorial Post Doctoral Fellowships *(Postdoctorate/Fellowship)* [5311]
L.D. and Elsie Long Memorial Scholarships *(Graduate/Scholarship)* [10589]
Long-term International Fellowships *(Professional development/Fellowship)* [3380]
Kay Longcope Scholarships *(Graduate, Undergraduate/Scholarship)* [7050]
Megan Nicole Longwell Scholarships *(Undergraduate/Scholarship)* [7847]
Louise Loomis Memorial Adelphe Scholarships *(Undergraduate/Scholarship)* [5748]
Suzanne and Caleb Loring Research Fellowships *(Professional development/Fellowship)* [6329]
Barbara Lotze Scholarships for Future Teachers *(Undergraduate/Scholarship)* [562]
Lou Hochberg Awards - University Thesis/Dissertation Research Improvement and Implementation Grants *(Graduate/Award, Grant)* [7749]
CH2M - Willie T. Loud Scholarships *(Undergraduate, Graduate/Scholarship)* [6959]
Louisiana Agricultural Consultants Association Scholarships *(Graduate, Undergraduate/Scholarship)* [6112]
Louisiana Library Association Scholarships *(Graduate/Scholarship)* [6119]
Louisville Institute Dissertation Fellowships *(Doctorate/Fellowship)* [6128]
Louisville Institute First Book Grants for Minority Scholars *(Doctorate/Grant)* [6129]
Louisville Institute Project Grant for Researchers *(Doctorate/Grant)* [6130]
Louisville Institute Sabbatical Grants for Researchers *(Doctorate/Grant)* [6131]
Louthian Law School Scholarships *(Advanced Professional/Fellowship)* [6133]
Love of Bonita Empowerment Scholarships *(Undergraduate/Scholarship)* [9440]
First Lieutenant Scott McClean Love Memorial Scholarship - Children of Soldiers *(Undergraduate, Vocational/Occupational/Scholarship)* [1714]
First Lieutenant Scott McClean Love Memorial Scholarship - Spouses of Soldiers *(Undergraduate, Vocational/Occupational/Scholarship)* [1715]
D.J. Lovell Scholarships *(Graduate, Undergraduate/Scholarship)* [9470]
Lowe Family First Summer Student Scholarships *(Undergraduate/Scholarship)* [10185]
Diane G. Lowe and John Gomez, IV Scholarships *(Undergraduate/Scholarship)* [3236]
LPHA Scholarships *(Graduate, Undergraduate/Scholarship)* [6122]
LSAC Research Grant Program *(Professional development/Grant)* [5967]
LSU Eye Center Clinical Retina Fellowships *(Undergraduate/Fellowship)* [6126]
Henry Luce Foundation/ACLS Dissertation Fellowships in American Art *(Graduate, Doctorate/Fellowship)* [742]
Elsa Ludeke Graduate Scholarships *(Graduate/Scholarship)* [3590]
Lugonia Alumni/Harrison Lightfoot Scholarships *(Undergraduate/Scholarship)* [8493]
Mollie Lukken Memorial Scholarships *(Graduate, Other/Scholarship)* [5633]
LULAC GM Scholarships *(Graduate, High School, Undergraduate, Vocational/Occupational/Award)* [5988]
LULAC National Scholarship Fund (LNSF) *(Graduate, Undergraduate/Scholarship)* [5989]
Audrey Lumsden-Kouvel Fellowships *(Postdoctorate/Fellowship)* [7415]
Juan and Esperanza Luna Scholarship *(Undergraduate/Scholarship)* [1583]
Lung Health Dissertation Grants *(Graduate/Grant)* [977]
Ann & Robert H. Lurie Children's Memorial Hospital Postgraduate Administrative Fellowships *(Postgraduate/Fellowship)* [6143]
Luso-American Education Foundation C-1 General Scholarships *(Undergraduate/Scholarship)* [6145]
Luso-American Education Foundation G-1 Grants *(Other/Grant)* [6146]

Luso-American Education Foundation G-2 Grants *(Other/Grant)* [6147]
Luso-American Education Foundation G-3 Grants *(Postgraduate/Grant)* [6148]
Luso-American Fraternal Federation B-2 Scholarships *(Postgraduate/Scholarship)* [6149]
Luso-American Fraternal Federation B-3 Scholarships *(Professional development/Scholarship)* [6150]
Luso-American Fraternal Federation B-4 Scholarships *(Professional development/Scholarship)* [6151]
Lutheran Student Scholastic and Service Scholarships - College and University Students *(Undergraduate/Scholarship)* [2248]
Lycoming County Medical Society Scholarships (LCMS) *(Undergraduate/Scholarship)* [4277]
Lymphatic Research Foundation Additional Support for NIH-funded F32 Postdoctoral Fellows Awards *(Postdoctorate/Award)* [4820]
Lymphatic Research Foundation Postdoctoral Fellowship Awards Program *(Postdoctorate/Fellowship)* [4821]
Boyd N. Lyon Scholarships *(Doctorate, Graduate, Master's/Scholarship)* [6162]
The C. Lyons Fellowship Program *(Advanced Professional/Fellowship)* [7047]
Verne LaMarr Lyons Memorial Scholarships *(Graduate, Master's/Fellowship)* [6790]
Margaret Smith Maase Scholarships *(Undergraduate/Scholarship)* [7388]
John Mabry Forestry Scholarships *(Undergraduate/Scholarship)* [8423]
MAC Emeritus Scholarships for First-Time Meeting Attendees *(Professional development/Scholarship)* [6516]
Bill MacAloney Legacy Scholarships *(Undergraduate/Scholarship)* [2456]
MacArthur Fellows Program *(Professional development/Fellowship)* [6164]
Catharine Macaulay Prize *(Graduate/Prize)* [1295]
MACC Scholarships *(Other/Scholarship)* [6444]
Katie MacDonald Memorial Scholarships *(Graduate, Undergraduate/Scholarship)* [9865]
Nate Mack/Cindi Turner Scholarships *(Undergraduate/Scholarship)* [8353]
Warren Mack Scholarship *(Undergraduate/Scholarship)* [5622]
Robert Mack Scholarships *(Graduate, Undergraduate/Scholarship)* [6166]
Thermoset Division/James I. Mackenzie and James H. Cunningham Scholarships *(Undergraduate, Graduate/Scholarship)* [9264]
Mackey-Byars Scholarships for Communication Excellence *(Undergraduate/Scholarship)* [10237]
Andrew Macrina Scholarships *(Undergraduate/Scholarship)* [761]
Pat and John MacTavish Scholarship Fund *(Undergraduate/Scholarship)* [4532]
Eileen C. Maddex Fellowships *(Graduate/Fellowship)* [5785]
Dorothy L. Maddy Workshop/Seminar Scholarship *(All/Scholarship)* [9489]
Lawrence Madeiros Scholarships *(Undergraduate/Scholarship)* [6992]
James Madison Foundation - Junior Fellowships *(Advanced Professional/Fellowship)* [6174]
James Madison Foundation - Senior Fellowships *(Graduate/Fellowship)* [6175]
James Madison Graduate Fellowships *(Graduate/Fellowship)* [6176]
Madson Graduate Scholarships *(Graduate/Scholarship)* [8899]
MAES Founders Scholarships *(Graduate, Undergraduate/Scholarship)* [6178]
MAES General Scholarships *(Graduate, Undergraduate/Scholarship)* [6179]
MAES Graduate Scholarships *(Graduate/Scholarship)* [6180]
MAES Padrino/Madrina Scholarships *(Graduate, Undergraduate/Scholarship)* [6181]
MAES Pipeline Scholarships *(Graduate, Undergraduate/Scholarship)* [6182]
MAES Presidential Scholarships *(Graduate, Undergraduate/Scholarship)* [6183]

Keith Maffioli Scholarships *(Undergraduate/Scholarship)* [3292]
The Brandon Magalassi Memorial Scholarship Foundation Scholarships *(Undergraduate/Scholarship)* [6185]
Dr. Edward May Magruder Medical Scholarships *(Undergraduate/Scholarship)* [677]
Sonia S. Maguire Outstanding Scholastic Achievement Awards *(Graduate, Undergraduate/Scholarship)* [9618]
Lillian Grace Mahan Scholarship Fund *(Graduate/Scholarship)* [9520]
Dan and Rachel Mahi Educational Scholarships *(Graduate, Undergraduate/Scholarship)* [7914]
Rick Mahoney Scholarships *(Undergraduate/Scholarship)* [6357]
Maiman Student Paper Competition *(Graduate, Undergraduate/Award)* [7674]
Maine Community College Scholarships *(Undergraduate/Scholarship)* [6222]
Maine Community Foundation - Rice Scholarships *(Undergraduate/Scholarship)* [6203]
Maine Graphic Arts Association Scholarships *(Undergraduate/Scholarship)* [6215]
Maine Nutrition Council Scholarships *(Undergraduate/Scholarship)* [6219]
Maine Vietnam Veterans Scholarships *(Advanced Professional/Scholarship)* [6204]
Maintenance Technical Reward and Career Scholarships *(Undergraduate/Scholarship)* [6836]
The Make It Move Scholarships *(Undergraduate/Scholarship)* [1594]
Make Us Proud Scholarships *(Undergraduate/Scholarship)* [4793]
MALDEF Dream Act Student Activist Scholarships *(Undergraduate, Graduate/Scholarship)* [6446]
Maley/FTE Scholarships *(Graduate/Scholarship)* [5439]
Maley/FTEE Teacher Scholarships *(Professional development/Scholarship)* [5440]
NBCFAE Mamie W. Mallory National Scholarship Program *(Undergraduate/Scholarship)* [6813]
Ann M. Mallouk Scholarships *(Master's/Scholarship)* [7389]
Joseph J. Malone Fellowships in Arab and Islamic Studies *(Professional development/Fellowship)* [6895]
Reba Malone Scholarships *(Undergraduate, Graduate/Scholarship)* [1167]
David C. Maloney Scholarships *(Undergraduate/Scholarship)* [7079]
Optimist Club Of Redlands - Ralph Maloof Scholarships *(Undergraduate/Scholarship)* [8494]
MALSCE Memorial Scholarships *(Undergraduate/Scholarship)* [6306]
Dr. Julianne Malveaux Scholarships *(Undergraduate/Scholarship)* [6762]
Malyon-Smith Scholarship Award *(Graduate/Scholarship)* [9285]
Lyle Mamer Fellowships *(Graduate/Fellowship, Award)* [10661]
MANAA Media Scholarships *(Graduate, Undergraduate/Scholarship)* [6382]
Manchester Scholarship Foundation - Adult Learners Scholarships *(Undergraduate/Scholarship)* [4763]
Mangasar M. Mangasarian Scholarship Fund *(Graduate/Scholarship)* [1702]
Manhattan Street Capital Annual National Scholarships *(Undergraduate, Graduate, Doctorate/Scholarship)* [6227]
Norm Manly Maritime Educational Scholarships *(Undergraduate/Scholarship)* [10768]
Mann Law Firm Scholarships *(Advanced Professional/Scholarship)* [3529]
Raleigh Mann Scholarships *(Undergraduate/Scholarship)* [10238]
Mansfield Soccer Association Scholarships *(Undergraduate/Scholarship)* [6229]
Honorable Carol Los Mansmann Memorial Scholarships *(Graduate, Undergraduate/Scholarship)* [327]
Paul Mansur Scholarships *(Undergraduate/Scholarship)* [5345]
Mantle Cell Lymphoma Research Grants *(Advanced Professional/Grant)* [6160]

Many Voices Fellowships *(Other/Fellowship)* [8153]
Manzer-Keener-Wefler Scholarships *(Undergraduate/Scholarship)* [9521]
March of Dimes General Research Grants *(Professional development/Grant)* [6233]
March of Dimes Graduate Nursing Scholarships *(Graduate/Scholarship)* [6234]
Stephen T. Marchello Scholarships *(Undergraduate/Scholarship)* [6237]
Harold and Inge Marcus Scholarships *(Undergraduate/Scholarship)* [5191]
American Turkish Society Arif Mardin Music Fellowships *(Other/Fellowship)* [9811]
Margaret Mead Award *(Other/Award)* [9081]
The Margarian Scholarships *(Undergraduate, Graduate/Scholarship)* [6239]
Art Margosian Scholarship *(Undergraduate/Scholarship)* [5623]
Aurella Varallo Mariani Scholarship Program *(Undergraduate/Scholarship)* [6665]
Marine Biological Laboratory Pioneers Fund *(Undergraduate, Graduate/Scholarship)* [6252]
Marine Corps League National Scholarships *(Undergraduate/Scholarship)* [6269]
Marine Technology Society ROV Scholarships (MTS ROV) *(Undergraduate, Graduate/Scholarship)* [6272]
Shirley Stone Marinkovich Memorial Scholarships *(Undergraduate/Scholarship)* [5749]
Dr. Frank and Florence Marino Scholarships *(Undergraduate/Scholarship)* [4764]
Mariposa Elementary School PTA Scholarships *(Undergraduate/Scholarship)* [8495]
Marisol Scholarship *(Undergraduate/Scholarship)* [5750]
Howard T. Markey Memorial Scholarship *(Undergraduate/Scholarship)* [3985]
Markham-Colegrave International Scholarships *(Undergraduate/Scholarship)* [805]
Marliave Scholarship Fund *(Undergraduate/Scholarship, Grant)* [1948]
Olivia M. Marquart Scholarships *(Graduate, Master's, Doctorate/Scholarship)* [9828]
George Perkins Marsh Prize *(Other/Prize)* [1313]
Marsh Risk Consulting Scholarships *(Undergraduate/Scholarship)* [1421]
Marsh Writing/Research Scholarship Awards *(Undergraduate, Graduate/Scholarship, Award)* [5677]
Marshall-Baruch Fellowships *(Doctorate/Fellowship)* [6295]
Marshall Memorial Fellowships *(Other/Fellowship)* [4399]
Ray and Gertrude Marshall Scholarships *(Undergraduate/Scholarship)* [762]
Ron Marshall Scholarships *(Undergraduate/Scholarship)* [1192]
Sarah Shinn Marshall Scholarships *(Undergraduate/Scholarship)* [3554]
Marshall Undergraduate Scholars Program *(Undergraduate/Award)* [6296]
E.H. Marth Food and Environmental Scholarships *(Undergraduate/Scholarship)* [10615]
Martha Weston Grant *(Advanced Professional/Grant)* [9097]
William B. Martin East Carolina University Scholarships *(Undergraduate/Scholarship)* [5678]
Bryce-Lietzke Martin Scholarships *(Undergraduate/Scholarship)* [7848]
Edna L. Martin Scholarships *(Undergraduate/Scholarship)* [3237]
Martin Sisters Scholarships *(Undergraduate/Scholarship)* [3555]
Dottie Martin Teacher Scholarships *(Graduate, Undergraduate/Scholarship)* [7464]
John S. Martinez and Family Scholarship Fund *(Undergraduate/Scholarship)* [3200]
Eric Martinez Memorial Scholarships *(Graduate, Undergraduate/Scholarship)* [9866]
Corporal Joseph Martinez U.S. Army/Durango High School AFJROTC *(Undergraduate/Scholarship)* [8354]
Anthony A. Martino Memorial Scholarships *(Undergraduate/Scholarship)* [4462]
Maryland Poison Center Clinical Toxicology Fellowships *(Doctorate, Graduate/Fellowship)* [6300]
Maryland Speech Language Hearing Association Graduate Scholarships *(Graduate/Scholarship)* [6302]
Mas Family Scholarships *(Graduate, Undergraduate/Scholarship)* [6304]
The Maschhoffs Pork Production Scholarships *(Undergraduate/Scholarship)* [7037]
MASNA Student Scholarships *(Undergraduate, Graduate/Scholarship)* [6241]
Margaret Edwards Mason Adelphe Scholarship *(Undergraduate, Graduate/Scholarship)* [5751]
Masonic-Range Science Scholarships *(Undergraduate/Scholarship)* [9298]
Massachusetts Bar Foundation Legal Intern Fellowship Program (LIFP) *(Undergraduate/Fellowship)* [6310]
Massachusetts Federation of Polish Women's Clubs Scholarships *(Undergraduate/Scholarship)* [5880]
S.O. Mast Founder's Scholarships *(Undergraduate, Graduate/Scholarship)* [6253]
Master Municipal Clerks Academy Scholarships *(Other/Scholarship)* [5351]
Master's Degree with a Major in Nursing Academic Scholarships *(Graduate/Scholarship)* [6657]
Ruth G. and Joseph D. Matarazzo Scholarship *(Graduate, Master's, Doctorate/Scholarship)* [1149]
Material Handling Education Foundation Scholarships *(Doctorate, Graduate, Undergraduate/Scholarship)* [6346]
Larry Matfay Cultural Heritage Scholarships *(Undergraduate, Graduate/Scholarship)* [5868]
Mathematics Mentoring Travel Grants for Women *(Doctorate/Scholarship)* [2099]
Katharine & Bryant Mather Scholarship *(Graduate/Scholarship)* [708]
AILA Virginia Mathews Memorial Scholarships *(Graduate/Scholarship)* [885]
Noel D. Matkin Awards *(Undergraduate/Award)* [3798]
Rene Matos Memorial Scholarships *(Undergraduate, Vocational/Occupational/Scholarship)* [6996]
The Renardo A. Matteucci Scholarship Fund *(Undergraduate/Scholarship)* [3206]
Antonio Mattos Memorial Scholarships *(Undergraduate/Scholarship)* [6152]
Mature Student Scholarship *(Undergraduate/Scholarship)* [3912]
Donald Mauer Scholarships *(Undergraduate/Scholarship)* [10239]
Elizabeth M. Mauro Reimbursement Awards *(Advanced Professional/Award)* [63]
Maxwell Graduate Scholarships in Medical Journalism *(Graduate/Scholarship)* [10240]
Edmund F. Maxwell Scholarships *(Undergraduate/Scholarship)* [6348]
Juliann and Joe Maxwell Scholarships *(Undergraduate/Scholarship)* [3238]
Juliann King Maxwell Scholarships for Riverview High School *(Undergraduate, Vocational/Occupational/Scholarship)* [3239]
May-Cassioppi Scholarships *(Undergraduate/Scholarship)* [3293]
Howard Mayer Brown Fellowship *(Graduate/Fellowship)* [1021]
John E. Mayfield ABLE Scholarships *(Undergraduate/Scholarship)* [3240]
John E. Mayfield Scholarship Fund for Cheatham County Central High School *(Undergraduate/Scholarship)* [3241]
John E. Mayfield Scholarship Fund for Harpeth High School *(Undergraduate/Scholarship)* [3242]
John E. Mayfield Scholarship Fund for Pleasant View Christian High School *(Undergraduate/Scholarship)* [3243]
John E. Mayfield Scholarship Fund for Sycamore High School *(Undergraduate/Scholarship)* [3244]
Bill Maynes Fellowships *(Professional development/Fellowship)* [3929]
Joseph W. Mayo ALS Scholarships *(Undergraduate/Scholarship)* [6205]
Clara Mayo Grants Program *(Graduate/Grant)* [9290]
Giuliano Mazzetti Scholarships *(Undergraduate/Scholarship)* [9188]
Charles "Chuck" McAdams Memorial Scholarships *(Graduate, Undergraduate/Scholarship)* [9644]
Walter Samuel McAfee Scholarships in Space Physics *(Undergraduate/Scholarship)* [7143]
McAllister Fellowships *(Professional development/Fellowship)* [1867]
MCBA Scholarship *(Undergraduate/Scholarship)* [6465]
Rev. Richard S. McCarroll and Mrs. E. Allison McCarroll Scholarships *(Undergraduate, Graduate/Scholarship)* [7390]
Doreen McMullan McCarthy Memorial Academic Scholarship for Women with Bleeding Disorders *(Undergraduate/Scholarship)* [6993]
Bill McCarthy Scout Scholarship Fund *(Undergraduate/Scholarship)* [9523]
McCaughan Heritage Scholarships *(Undergraduate/Scholarship)* [1064]
McClatchy Minority Scholarship and Fellowship *(Undergraduate/Scholarship)* [9369]
McCleary Law Fellows Program *(Graduate, Undergraduate/Fellowship)* [4992]
McCloy Fellowships in Agriculture *(Professional development/Fellowship)* [727]
McCloy Fellowships in Environmental Policy *(Professional development/Fellowship)* [728]
McCloy Fellowships in Journalism *(Professional development/Fellowship)* [729]
McCloy Fellowships in Urban Affairs *(Professional development/Fellowship)* [730]
Niqui McCown Honor and Memorial Scholarship Fund *(Undergraduate/Scholarship)* [10505]
McDaniel College Eagle Scout Scholarships *(Undergraduate/Scholarship)* [6930]
Fred R. McDaniel Memorial Scholarships *(Undergraduate/Scholarship)* [1746]
Michele L. McDonald Scholarships *(Undergraduate/Scholarship)* [3801]
Bodie McDowell Scholarships *(Graduate, Undergraduate/Scholarship)* [7770]
MCEA Financial Assistance Award *(Undergraduate/Scholarship)* [6267]
McFarffels Scholarships *(Undergraduate/Scholarship)* [8256]
Foster G. McGaw Graduate Student Scholarships *(Graduate/Scholarship)* [688]
Foster G. McGaw Scholarships *(Undergraduate, Graduate/Scholarship)* [2086]
Nancy B. Woolridge McGee Graduate Fellowships *(Graduate/Fellowship)* [10819]
Lucille E. McGee Scholarships *(Undergraduate/Scholarship)* [5509]
Thomas R. McGetchin Memorial Scholarship Awards *(Undergraduate/Scholarship)* [9997]
Richard McGrath Memorial Fund Awards *(Undergraduate/Award)* [755]
Linda and Vincent McGrath Scholarship *(Undergraduate/Scholarship)* [5679]
Lee Kimche McGrath Worldwide Fellowships *(Other/Fellowship)* [2067]
William P. McHugh Memorial Fund Award *(Doctorate, Graduate/Fellowship)* [1197]
Mary Bowles McInnis Adelphe Scholarship *(Undergraduate/Scholarship)* [5752]
McJulien Minority Graduate Scholarships *(Graduate/Scholarship)* [1944]
Molly McKay Scholarships *(Undergraduate/Scholarship)* [10241]
J.B. and Marilyn McKenzie Graduate Student Fellowships *(Graduate/Fellowship)* [10186]
AIST Midwest Member Chapter - Betty McKern Scholarships *(Undergraduate/Scholarship)* [2002]
John J. McKetta Undergraduate Scholarships *(Undergraduate/Scholarship)* [905]
Arthur Patch McKinlay Scholarships *(Graduate, Undergraduate/Scholarship)* [680]
McKinley Elementary School PTA Scholarships *(Undergraduate/Scholarship)* [8496]
John L. and Eleanore I. Mckinley Scholarships *(Undergraduate/Scholarship)* [3591]
McKinney Sisters Undergraduate Scholarships *(Undergraduate/Scholarship)* [3556]
McKnight Advancement Grants *(Other/Grant)* [8154]
C.A. "Pete" McKnight Scholarships *(Undergraduate/Scholarship)* [10242]
McKnight Theater Artist Fellowships *(Other/Fellowship)* [8155]

UNITED STATES

Paul R. McLaughlin Fellowship *(Undergraduate/Fellowship)* [8436]
McLean Scholarships *(Undergraduate/Scholarship)* [1978]
John McLendon Memorial Minority Postgraduate Scholarships *(Postdoctorate/Scholarship)* [6738]
Ronald E. McNair Scholarships in Space and Optical Physics *(Undergraduate/Scholarship)* [7144]
McNeely Stephenson of New Albany Community Involvement Scholarships *(Undergraduate/Scholarship)* [6372]
National Association of Pediatric Nurse Practitioners McNeil Annual Scholarships *(Undergraduate/Scholarship)* [6773]
National Association of Pediatric Nurse Practitioners McNeil Rural and Underserved Scholarships *(Graduate/Scholarship)* [6774]
Joan Reagin McNeill Scholarships - Alpha Theta *(Undergraduate/Scholarship)* [8931]
Joan Reagin McNeill Scholarships - Theta Phi *(Undergraduate/Scholarship)* [8932]
O. Ruth McQuown Scholarship - Graduate Award for Current Students *(Graduate/Scholarship)* [10135]
MCRTA Book Scholarships *(Undergraduate/Scholarship)* [6449]
MDA Development Grants *(Doctorate/Grant)* [6622]
MDA Research Grants *(Advanced Professional/Grant)* [6623]
MDF Post-Doctoral Fellowships *(Postdoctorate/Fellowship)* [6643]
MDI Biological Laboratory High school Student Summer Research Fellowships *(Undergraduate/Fellowship)* [6606]
David Meador Foundation - Club Management Student Scholarships *(Undergraduate/Scholarship)* [7295]
Ben Meadows Natural Resource Scholarships - Academic Achievement Scholarships *(Undergraduate/Scholarship)* [2221]
Ben Meadows Natural Resource Scholarships - Leadership Scholarships *(Undergraduate/Scholarship)* [2222]
Med Technology and Clinical Lab Science Scholarships *(Undergraduate/Scholarship)* [104]
The Medallion Fund Scholarships *(Undergraduate/Scholarship)* [7302]
Medford Rogue Rotary Scholarship *(Undergraduate/Scholarship)* [6380]
Medical Library Association Scholarships for Minority Students *(Graduate/Scholarship)* [6389]
Medical Student Rotation for Underrepresented Populations *(Graduate/Grant)* [3381]
Medieval Academy Dissertation Grants *(Graduate/Grant)* [6396]
Rixio Medina and Associates Hispanics in Safety Scholarships *(Graduate, Undergraduate/Scholarship)* [1422]
Medina County Retired Teachers Association Scholarship *(Undergraduate/Scholarship)* [6400]
Edward Heywood Megson Scholarships *(Undergraduate/Scholarship)* [10243]
Karl Mehlmann Scholarships *(Undergraduate/Scholarship)* [3138]
Kumar Mehta Scholarship *(Graduate/Scholarship)* [709]
Fred & Lena Meijer Scholarships *(Undergraduate/Scholarship)* [4610]
Susan R. Meisinger Fellowship for Graduate Study in HR *(Graduate, Master's, Advanced Professional/Fellowship)* [9146]
Dr. Roger E. Meisner Veterinary Medicine Educational Scholarship Fund *(Undergraduate/Scholarship)* [7501]
Carl J. Mejel Scholarship *(Undergraduate/Scholarship)* [794]
Frederic G. Melcher Scholarships *(Graduate/Scholarship)* [2018]
Mellon/ACLS Dissertation Completion Fellowships *(Graduate, Doctorate/Fellowship)* [743]
Mellon-CES Dissertation Completion Fellowships *(Graduate/Fellowship)* [3440]
Mellon Fellowships for Dissertation Research in the Humanities *(Doctorate, Graduate/Fellowship, Scholarship)* [3450]
Mellon Fellowships for Dissertation Research in Original Sources *(Doctorate/Fellowship)* [3451]
MHS Andrew W. Mellon Fellowships *(Professional development/Fellowship)* [6330]
Mellon Fellowships in Urban Landscape Studies *(Graduate, Master's, Doctorate/Fellowship)* [3739]
Andrew W. Mellon Foundation Fellowships *(Graduate/Fellowship)* [7740]
Institute Andrew W. Mellon Postdoctoral Research Fellowships *(Doctorate/Fellowship)* [7614]
Terry Mellor Continuing Education Grant *(Undergraduate/Grant)* [9480]
MELNA Scholarship *(Undergraduate, Graduate/Scholarship)* [6217]
E.V. and Nancy Melosi Travel Grants *(Graduate, Other/Grant)* [1314]
Memphis Access and Diversity Scholarships *(Undergraduate/Scholarship)* [10169]
The Tatiana Mendez Future Resources Scholarships *(Undergraduate/Scholarship)* [8234]
Joseph C. Menezes Scholarship *(Undergraduate/Scholarship)* [6189]
Menominee Tribal Scholarships *(Undergraduate, Graduate/Scholarship)* [6418]
Mensa Education and Research Foundation U.S. Scholarships *(Undergraduate/Scholarship)* [6424]
Mentored Clinical Scientist Development Awards *(Doctorate/Award)* [9915]
Mentored Research Scholar Grant in Applied and Clinical Research *(Doctorate, Professional development/Grant)* [646]
Benchwarmers of Redlands-Jess Mercado Football Scholarships *(Undergraduate/Scholarship)* [8497]
Erickson Merkel Foundation Scholarships *(Undergraduate/Scholarship)* [3925]
Gary Merrill Memorial Scholarships *(Undergraduate/Scholarship)* [6206]
MESA Student Travel Fund *(Undergraduate/Grant)* [6511]
Scott Mesh Honorary Grant for Research in Psychology *(Graduate/Grant)* [1134]
Mesothelioma Memorial Scholarships *(Undergraduate, Vocational/Occupational/Scholarship)* [9594]
Ruth Messmer Memorial Scholarships *(Undergraduate/Scholarship)* [9441]
Sanders J. Mestel Legal Scholarship Fund *(Undergraduate/Scholarship)* [9524]
Nicholas Metropolis Award for Outstanding Doctoral Thesis Work in Computational Physics *(Doctorate/Award)* [1091]
Metropolitan Museum of Art Bothmer Fellowship *(Doctorate/Fellowship)* [6432]
Metropolitan Museum of Art Conservation and Scientific Research Fellowships *(Graduate/Fellowship)* [6433]
Metropolitan Museum of Art Research Scholarship in Photograph Conservation *(Graduate/Scholarship)* [6434]
Edmond A. Metzger Scholarships *(Undergraduate/Scholarship)* [1747]
Mexican American Alumni Association Scholarships *(Graduate, Undergraduate/Scholarship)* [10356]
Mexican American Legal Defense and Educational Fund Law School Scholarships *(Undergraduate/Scholarship)* [6447]
Theodore Meyer Scholarships *(Undergraduate, Graduate/Scholarship)* [1015]
MFJC International Fellowships in Jewish Studies *(Other/Fellowship)* [6414]
MHS African American Studies Fellowships *(Professional development/Fellowship)* [6331]
MHS/Cushing Academy Fellowships on Environmental History *(Professional development/Fellowship)* [6332]
MHS Long-Term Research Fellowships *(Professional development/Fellowship)* [6333]
MHS/Massachusetts Society of the Cincinnati Fellowships *(Professional development/Fellowship)* [6334]
MICA Scholarships *(Undergraduate/Scholarship)* [6532]
Michigan Council of Women in Technology High School Scholarship Program *(Undergraduate/Scholarship)* [6467]
Michigan Council of Women in Technology Undergraduate Scholarship Program *(Undergraduate/Scholarship)* [6468]
Michigan Education Association Scholarships *(Undergraduate/Scholarship)* [6470]
Michigan League for Nursing Scholarships *(Undergraduate/Scholarship)* [6472]
Michigan Realtors Scholarship Trust *(Graduate, Undergraduate/Scholarship)* [6461]
Michigan Society of Fellows Three-Year Fellowships *(Postdoctorate/Fellowship)* [6481]
Michigan Stormwater-Floodplain Association Scholarships *(Graduate, Undergraduate/Scholarship)* [6492]
Michigan Sugar Company Hotel Restaurant/Resort Management Scholarships *(Undergraduate/Scholarship)* [6495]
Michigan Sugar Queen Scholarships *(Undergraduate/Scholarship)* [6496]
Microsoft Research Graduate Women's Scholarships *(Graduate/Scholarship)* [6506]
Microsoft Research PhD Fellowships *(Doctorate/Fellowship)* [6507]
Mid-Continent Instrument Scholarships *(Undergraduate/Scholarship)* [167]
Beth Middleton Memorial Scholarships *(Undergraduate/Scholarship)* [3961]
Midlothian Rotary Club "Service Above Self" Scholarship *(Undergraduate/Scholarship)* [6513]
Ella and Harold Midtbo Scholarships *(Undergraduate/Scholarship)* [7391]
Midwest Modern Language Association Fellowships *(Doctorate, Postdoctorate/Fellowship)* [7416]
Migrant Health Scholarships *(Other/Scholarship)* [6846]
Mihaly Russin Scholarship Awards *(Graduate/Scholarship)* [8656]
Mikimoto Scholarships *(Graduate/Scholarship)* [4342]
Mary Ann Mikulic Scholarships *(Other/Scholarship)* [2052]
Milan Getting Scholarships *(Undergraduate/Scholarship)* [9335]
Milbank Diversity Scholars Program *(Undergraduate/Scholarship)* [6530]
Mildred Colodny Diversity Scholarships for Graduate Study in Historic Preservation *(Graduate/Scholarship)* [7202]
Eunice Miles Scholarships *(Undergraduate/Scholarship)* [4343]
William F. Miles Scholarships *(Undergraduate/Scholarship)* [4702]
Military Service Scholarships *(Graduate, Undergraduate/Scholarship)* [8900]
Cheryl Allyn Miller Award *(Doctorate, Graduate/Monetary)* [9332]
Miller Electric International WorldSkills Competition Scholarships *(Undergraduate/Scholarship)* [1520]
Warren E. Miller Fellowship in Electoral Politics *(Advanced Professional, Graduate, Postdoctorate/Fellowship)* [1122]
Ruth R. and Alyson R. Miller Fellowships *(Professional development/Fellowship)* [6335]
MillerCoors Engineering and Sciences Scholarships *(Undergraduate/Scholarship)* [68]
MillerCoors National Scholarships *(Undergraduate/Scholarship)* [69]
Quincy Sharpe Mills Memorial Scholarships *(Undergraduate/Scholarship)* [10244]
George Hi'ilani Mills Perpetual Fellowships *(Graduate/Fellowship)* [7915]
J. Clawson Mills Scholarships *(Doctorate/Scholarship)* [6435]
Abby and Howard Milstein Innovation Award in Reproductive Medicine *(Advanced Professional, Professional development/Award, Grant)* [5618]
Abby and Howard Milstein Reproductive Medicine Research Award *(Advanced Professional, Professional development/Award, Grant)* [5619]
Milton Postgraduate Fellowships *(Postgraduate/Fellowship)* [5080]
Mineral & Metallurgical Processing Division Scholarships and Richard Klimpel Memorial Scholarships *(Undergraduate, Graduate/Scholarship)* [9211]
Mary Minglen Scholarship Program *(Postgraduate/Scholarship)* [1047]
Minneapolis Jewish Federation Camp Scholarships *(Undergraduate/Scholarship)* [6539]
Minnesota Association County Probation Officers

Place of Study Index

UNITED STATES

Scholarships *(Undergraduate/Scholarship)* [6541]
Minnesota Association of Public Accountant Scholarships *(Undergraduate/Scholarship)* [6543]
Minnesota Association of Township Scholarships *(Undergraduate, Vocational/Occupational/Scholarship)* [6545]
Minnesota GLBT Educational Fund *(Undergraduate/Scholarship)* [8661]
Minnesota Power Community Involvement Scholarships *(Undergraduate/Scholarship)* [3717]
Minnesota State Archery Association Scholarships Program *(Undergraduate/Scholarship)* [6551]
Jacque I. Minnotte Health Reporting Fellowships *(Other/Fellowship)* [8406]
Minority-Serving Institution Faculty Scholar Awards *(Doctorate/Award)* [474]
Minority Visiting Students Awards *(Undergraduate, Graduate/Award, Internship)* [9011]
Minton-Spidell Point Scholarship *(Undergraduate, Graduate, Doctorate/Scholarship)* [8185]
Christine Mirzayan Science and Technology Policy Graduate Fellowships *(Graduate/Fellowship)* [6679]
Miss America Community Service Scholarship *(Undergraduate/Scholarship)* [6557]
Miss America Quality of Life Awards *(Undergraduate/Scholarship)* [6558]
Mission Bay Hospital Auxiliary Scholarships *(Undergraduate/Scholarship)* [8717]
Joshua Esch Mitchell Aviation Scholarships *(Undergraduate/Scholarship)* [4611]
Monte R. Mitchell Global Scholarships *(Undergraduate/Scholarship)* [168]
Dorothy Mitchell Scholarships *(Undergraduate/Scholarship)* [8498]
Mary Moore Mitchell Scholarships *(Graduate/Scholarship)* [6120]
Robert L. and Hilda Treasure Mitchell Scholarships *(Undergraduate/Scholarship)* [4612]
MJSA Education Foundation Scholarship Fund *(Undergraduate/Scholarship)* [6231]
MKC/Preuss Scholarship Fund *(Undergraduate/Scholarship)* [8718]
MLA Financial Assistance *(Graduate, Advanced Professional/Grant)* [6567]
MLA/NLM Spectrum Scholarship Program *(Undergraduate/Scholarship)* [6391]
MLA Research, Development, and Demonstration Project Grants *(Graduate/Grant)* [6392]
MMJGA Scholarships *(Undergraduate/Scholarship)* [6549]
MMRF Research Fellow Awards *(Postdoctorate, Professional development/Grant)* [6612]
MMUF Dissertation Grants *(Graduate/Grant)* [10679]
MMUF Travel and Research Grants *(Graduate/Grant)* [10680]
MNLA Academic Scholarships *(Undergraduate/Scholarship)* [6474]
MOAA American Patriot Scholarships *(Undergraduate/Scholarship)* [6534]
Ralph Modjeski Scholarships *(Graduate, Undergraduate/Scholarship)* [8198]
MODNA Nursing Education Scholarships *(Doctorate, Graduate/Fellowship)* [6509]
Francis H. Moffitt Memorial Scholarships *(Graduate, Undergraduate/Scholarship)* [1807]
Molecular Evolution Fellowships *(Doctorate/Fellowship)* [9012]
Antoinette M. Molinari Memorial Scholarships *(Doctorate/Scholarship)* [417]
Momeni Foundation Scholastic Achievement Scholarships *(Undergraduate/Scholarship)* [7021]
Monaghan/Trudell Fellowships for Aerosol Technique Development *(Professional development/Fellowship)* [1212]
Nell I. Mondy Fellowships *(Graduate, Doctorate/Fellowship)* [8905]
Mongan Commonwealth Fund Fellowship in Minority Health Policy *(Other/Fellowship)* [3161]
Monsanto Commitment To Agriculture Scholarships *(Undergraduate/Scholarship)* [6574]
Montana Broadcasters Association Broadcast Engineering Scholarships *(Undergraduate/Scholarship)* [6578]
Montgomery County Medical Society Scholarships (MCMS) *(Undergraduate/Scholarship)* [4278]
Hugh and Elizabeth Montgomery Scholarships *(Undergraduate/Scholarship)* [6208]
ARTC Glenn Moon Scholarships *(Undergraduate/Scholarship)* [4765]
Pearl Moore Career Development Awards *(Professional development/Grant)* [7618]
Letitia Moore Charitable Trust Scholarship *(Undergraduate/Scholarship)* [10739]
Moore Middle School PTA Scholarships *(Undergraduate/Scholarship)* [8499]
Annabelle Moore Scholarship *(Undergraduate/Scholarship)* [2408]
Farmers Union Industries Foundation Stanley Moore Scholarships *(Undergraduate/Scholarship)* [7488]
NFU Foundation Stanley Moore Scholarships *(Undergraduate/Scholarship)* [7489]
Willie Hobbs Moore Scholarships *(Undergraduate/Scholarship)* [7145]
Dr. Blanca Moore-Velez Woman of Substance Scholarships *(Undergraduate/Scholarship)* [6763]
Dan Mordecai Educational Scholarships *(Graduate, Undergraduate/Scholarship)* [7265]
Thomas More Scholarships *(Undergraduate/Scholarship)* [4487]
Kyle R. Moreland Memorial Scholarships *(Undergraduate/Scholarship)* [4533]
Thomas S. Morgan Memorial Scholarship *(Graduate, Master's/Scholarship)* [8044]
Morgan Stanley Pediatrics Fellowships *(Doctorate, Postdoctorate, Postgraduate, Graduate/Fellowship)* [618]
Morgan Stanley Tribal Scholars Program *(Undergraduate/Scholarship)* [870]
Robert L. Morlan Redlands Area Interfaith Council Scholarships *(Undergraduate/Scholarship)* [8500]
Frank Morrell Endowed Memorial Scholarships *(Graduate, Master's, Doctorate/Scholarship)* [6254]
June Morrison Scholarship Fund *(Undergraduate/Scholarship)* [10538]
Harry L. Morrison Scholarships *(Undergraduate/Scholarship)* [7146]
Dorothy Morrison Undergraduate Scholarships *(Undergraduate/Scholarship)* [1260]
Mortar Board National Foundation Fellowships *(Postdoctorate/Fellowship)* [6600]
Morton Cure Paralysis Fund Research Grants *(Professional development, Postdoctorate/Grant)* [6602]
William Howard Morton Scholarships *(Undergraduate, Graduate/Scholarship)* [7392]
Dwight Mosley Scholarships *(Undergraduate/Scholarship)* [9976]
Archie Motley Memorial Scholarships for Minority Students *(Graduate/Scholarship)* [6517]
Motorola Solutions Point Scholarship *(Undergraduate, Graduate, Doctorate/Scholarship)* [8186]
John R. Mott Scholarships *(Undergraduate/Scholarship)* [6604]
Jack D. Motteler Scholarships *(Undergraduate/Scholarship)* [8257]
Mt. Hood Chapter Scholarship Awards *(Undergraduate/Scholarship)* [7697]
Mountain Memorial Funds *(Graduate, Master's, Doctorate/Award)* [6255]
Burton J. Moyer Memorial Fellowships *(Graduate/Fellowship)* [4811]
David J. Moynihan Scholarships *(Undergraduate/Scholarship)* [7373]
MPI CRV Scholarships *(Other/Scholarship)* [6402]
MPI-WI Founders Grant Program *(Professional development/Grant)* [6405]
MSEA/SEIU Part-time Student Members Scholarships *(Undergraduate/Scholarship)* [6223]
The MTS Student Scholarship for Graduate Students *(Graduate/Scholarship)* [6273]
The MTS Student Scholarship for Graduating High School Seniors *(Undergraduate/Scholarship)* [6274]
The MTS Student Scholarship for Two-Year, Technical, Engineering and Community College Students *(Undergraduate/Scholarship)* [6275]
Mu Alpha Theta Summer Grants *(Undergraduate, Graduate/Grant)* [6610]
Mueller Undergraduate Scholarships *(Undergraduate/Scholarship)* [10618]
Dudley Mullins/Cabot Corporation Scholarships *(Undergraduate/Scholarship)* [7849]
Multicultural Work-in-Progress Grant *(Advanced Professional/Grant)* [9098]
Muncy Rotary Club Scholarship Fund *(Undergraduate/Scholarship)* [4054]
Muncy Scholars Award Fund *(Undergraduate/Scholarship)* [4055]
Marvin Mundel Memorial Scholarships *(Undergraduate/Scholarship)* [5192]
Harry Munoz Memorial Scholarships *(Undergraduate/Scholarship)* [8501]
Rick Munoz Memorial Scholarships *(Undergraduate/Scholarship)* [8502]
Anthony Munoz Scholarships *(Undergraduate/Scholarship)* [6618]
Kiwanis Club of Redlands Foundation - Martin and Dorothy Munz Scholarships *(Undergraduate/Scholarship)* [8503]
Daniel Murphy Scholarships *(High School/Scholarship)* [6620]
Linda J. Murphy Scholarships *(Undergraduate/Scholarship)* [10644]
NACCED Annual John C. Murphy Scholarships *(Graduate, Undergraduate/Scholarship)* [6742]
Mutual of Omaha Finance Careers Scholarships *(Undergraduate, Graduate/Scholarship)* [105]
Mutual of Omaha Sales and Marketing Student Scholarships *(Undergraduate, Graduate/Scholarship)* [106]
MWH Scholarships *(Master's/Scholarship)* [1491]
My Life As A Lawyer Scholarships *(Graduate, Undergraduate/Scholarship)* [3425]
MyApartmentMap Housing Scholarships *(Undergraduate/Scholarship)* [6634]
Myasthenia Gravis Foundation of America Nursing Research Fellowships *(Undergraduate/Fellowship)* [6636]
Myasthenia Gravis Foundation of America Student Research Fellowships *(Graduate, Undergraduate/Fellowship)* [6637]
Mary Fran Myers Scholarships *(Professional development, Undergraduate/Scholarship)* [10129]
NAAE Upper Division Scholarships *(Undergraduate/Scholarship)* [6712]
NAAMA Scholarships *(Undergraduate/Scholarship)* [6701]
NABA National Scholarship Program *(Graduate, Undergraduate/Scholarship)* [6716]
NACA Multicultural Professional Development Grant *(Undergraduate, Graduate, Professional development/Grant)* [6729]
NACADA Scholarships *(Graduate/Scholarship)* [6673]
NACDS Foundation Merit-Based Scholarships *(All/Scholarship)* [6736]
James B. Nachman ASCO Junior Faculty Award in Pediatric Oncology *(Doctorate, Professional development/Grant)* [3382]
Albert and Alice Nacinovich Music Scholarships *(Undergraduate/Scholarship)* [4056]
NAED/Spencer Dissertation Fellowship Program *(Graduate, Doctorate/Fellowship)* [6681]
NAFA Corporate Aviation Business Scholarship *(Undergraduate, Graduate/Scholarship)* [6692]
NAFA International Dissertation Research Fellowships *(Graduate, Doctorate/Fellowship)* [6750]
NAFA Scholarship Programs *(Undergraduate/Scholarship)* [6690]
NAGAP Graduate Student Enrollment Management Research Grants *(Graduate/Grant)* [6752]
Jack Nagasaka Memorial Scholarships *(Undergraduate/Scholarship)* [8504]
NAJA Scholarships *(Graduate/Scholarship)* [6760]
IADR Toshio Nakao Fellowship *(Other/Fellowship)* [5252]
NANBPWC National Scholarships *(Undergraduate/Scholarship)* [6764]
Robyn Nance Memorial Scholarships *(Undergraduate/Scholarship)* [8505]
NAPABA Law Foundation Scholarships *(Undergraduate/Scholarship)* [6705]
NAPC FORUM Scholarships *(Undergraduate/Scholarship)* [6694]

Scholarships, Fellowships and Loans, 34th Ed. 1677

UNITED STATES

NAPRHSW Scholarships *(Undergraduate, Graduate/Scholarship)* [6776]
Chereddi NarayanaRao and Radhamanohari Scholarships *(Graduate/Scholarship)* [9668]
NARFE-FEEA Scholarship Awards Program *(Undergraduate/Scholarship)* [6686]
NASA RISGC Graduate Fellowships *(Master's, Postdoctorate, Graduate/Fellowship)* [8613]
NASA WVSGC Undergraduate Research Fellowship *(Undergraduate/Fellowship)* [10527]
NASCOE Scholarships *(Undergraduate/Scholarship)* [6744]
NASE Future Entrepreneur *(Undergraduate/Scholarship)* [6784]
Kermit B. Nash Academic Scholarships *(Undergraduate/Scholarship)* [8891]
Elizabeth Nash Foundation Scholarships *(Undergraduate, Graduate/Scholarship)* [6663]
Nashville Unit Scholarships *(Undergraduate/Scholarship)* [4863]
NASLR Mined Land Reclamation Educational Grant *(Undergraduate/Scholarship, Grant)* [6792]
NASP-ERT Minority Scholarships for Graduate Training in School Psychology *(Graduate/Scholarship)* [6780]
NASSLEO Scholarships - Region I *(Undergraduate/Scholarship)* [6782]
National AAHAM Scholarships *(Undergraduate/Scholarship)* [504]
National American Arab Nurses Association Scholarships *(Undergraduate, Master's/Scholarship)* [6699]
National Association of Abandoned Mine Land Programs Scholarships *(Undergraduate/Scholarship)* [6708]
National Association for Armenian Studies and Research Scholarships *(Graduate, Postgraduate/Scholarship)* [1703]
National Association of Biology Teachers BioClub Student Awards *(Undergraduate/Scholarship)* [6714]
National Association of Campus Activities Scholarships for Student Leaders *(Undergraduate/Scholarship)* [6732]
National Association for the Self-Employed Scholarships *(Professional development/Scholarship)* [6785]
National Association of Women in Construction Construction Trades Scholarships *(Undergraduate/Scholarship)* [6800]
National Association of Women in Construction Founders Undergraduate Scholarships *(Undergraduate/Scholarship)* [6801]
National Ataxia Foundation Research Fellowships *(Other/Fellowship)* [6806]
National Ataxia Foundation Research Grants *(Other/Grant)* [6807]
National Beta Club Scholarships *(Undergraduate/Scholarship)* [6809]
National Biosafety and Biocontainment Training Program Fellowships *(Graduate, Postgraduate/Fellowship)* [6811]
National Black Deaf Advocate Scholarships *(Graduate, Undergraduate/Scholarship)* [6816]
National Black Nurses Association Scholarships *(Undergraduate/Scholarship)* [6823]
National Board Technical Scholarships *(Undergraduate/Scholarship)* [6827]
National Center for Health Statistics Postdoctoral Research Awards *(Postdoctorate/Fellowship)* [9920]
National Collegiate Athletic Association Postgraduate Scholarships *(Postgraduate/Scholarship)* [6863]
National Community Pharmacists Association Summer Internship Programs *(Undergraduate/Internship)* [6868]
National Costumers Association Scholarships *(Undergraduate/Scholarship)* [6877]
National Council on Public History Graduate Student Travel Awards *(Doctorate, Graduate/Grant)* [6882]
National Council on Public History Student Project Awards *(Undergraduate/Grant)* [6883]
National Court Reporters Association Student Intern Scholarship *(Undergraduate/Scholarship)* [6897]

National Dairy Herd Information Association Scholarship Program *(Undergraduate/Scholarship)* [6903]
National Dental Hygienists' Association Scholarships *(Undergraduate/Scholarship)* [6916]
The National Endowment for the Humanities Fellowships *(Graduate/Fellowship)* [1198]
National Endowment for the Humanities Research Fellowships *(Doctorate/Fellowship)* [660]
National GEM Consortium - MS Engineering Fellowships *(Graduate/Fellowship)* [6967]
National GEM Consortium - PhD Engineering Fellowships *(Doctorate, Graduate/Fellowship)* [6968]
National GEM Consortium - PhD Science Fellowships *(Doctorate, Graduate/Fellowship)* [6969]
National Geographic Conservation Trust Grants *(Doctorate, Advanced Professional/Grant)* [6971]
National Geographic Expedition Council Grants *(Advanced Professional/Grant)* [6972]
National Geographic Society/Waitt Grants *(Advanced Professional/Grant)* [6973]
National Geographic Young Explorers Grants *(Advanced Professional/Grant)* [6974]
National Greenhouse Manufacturers Association Scholarships *(Undergraduate/Scholarship)* [806]
National Guard Association of Rhode Island Scholarship *(Undergraduate/Scholarship)* [6978]
National High School Oratorical Contest Scholarship *(Undergraduate/Scholarship)* [956]
National Huguenot Society College and Postgraduate Student Scholarships *(Undergraduate, Postgraduate/Scholarship)* [7006]
National Humanities Center Fellowships *(Doctorate, Postdoctorate/Fellowship)* [7008]
National Institute of Health Undergraduate Scholarship Program (NIH UGSP) *(Undergraduate/Scholarship)* [9930]
National Iranian American Council Fellowships *(Graduate, Undergraduate/Fellowship)* [7022]
National Judges Association Scholarships *(Other/Scholarship)* [7030]
National Junior Horticultural Association Alumni Scholarships *(Undergraduate/Scholarship)* [7034]
National Junior Swine Association Outstanding Member Scholarships *(Graduate/Scholarship)* [7038]
National Medical Fellowships Need-Based Scholarships *(Undergraduate/Scholarship)* [7061]
National Merit Harris Corporation Scholarship Program *(Undergraduate/Scholarship)* [4729]
National Merit Scholarship Program *(Undergraduate/Scholarship)* [7063]
National Organization of Italian-American Women Scholarships *(Undergraduate, Graduate/Scholarship)* [7083]
National Pathfinder Scholarships *(Graduate, Master's, Undergraduate/Scholarship)* [6954]
National Poultry and Food Distributors Association Scholarships *(Undergraduate/Scholarship)* [7102]
National Preservation Institute Scholarships *(Professional development/Scholarship)* [7104]
National Recreation and Park Association Diversity Scholarships *(Undergraduate/Scholarship)* [7118]
National Science Foundation Graduate Research Fellowship Program (NSF-GRFP) *(Graduate/Fellowship)* [7125]
National Sculpture Society Scholarships *(Undergraduate/Scholarship)* [7128]
National Security Education Program - David L. Boren Fellowships *(Graduate/Fellowship)* [10137]
National Security Technologies Engineering and Science Scholarships *(Undergraduate/Scholarship, Internship)* [8356]
National Sheriffs' Association Scholarship Program *(Graduate, Undergraduate/Scholarship)* [7130]
National Slovak Society Senior Scholarships *(Undergraduate, Vocational/Occupational/Scholarship)* [7132]
National Society of Accountants Scholarship Program *(Undergraduate/Scholarship)* [7134]
National Space Biomedical Research Institute Postdoctoral Fellowships *(Postdoctorate/Fellowship)* [7177]
National Swimming Pool Foundation Scholarship Awards *(Other/Scholarship)* [7193]
National Technical Honor Society Scholarships *(Professional development/Scholarship)* [2424]
National Technical Honor Society Scholarships *(Undergraduate/Scholarship)* [3962]
Native American Community Scholars Awards *(Graduate/Fellowship)* [9013]
Native American Education Grants *(Graduate, Undergraduate/Grant)* [877]
Native American Visiting Student Awards *(Graduate/Fellowship)* [9014]
Native Hawaiian Chamber of Commerce Scholarships *(Graduate, Undergraduate/Scholarship)* [7916]
Native Hawaiian Visual Arts Scholarships *(Graduate, Undergraduate/Scholarship)* [7917]
Naval Helicopter Association Scholarships *(Undergraduate, Graduate/Scholarship)* [7223]
Naval Research Enterprise Internship Program (NREIP) *(Undergraduate, Graduate, Professional development/Internship)* [1304]
Naval Weather Service Association Scholarships *(Undergraduate/Scholarship)* [7225]
Navy, Army or Air Force ROTC Scholarship Program *(Undergraduate/Scholarship)* [3502]
NAWJ Equal Access to Justice Scholarships *(Graduate/Scholarship)* [6803]
The Nazareth Scholarships *(Undergraduate/Scholarship)* [7238]
NBCUniversal Point Scholarship *(Undergraduate, Graduate, Doctorate/Scholarship)* [8187]
NBCUniversal Tony Coelho Media Scholarships *(Undergraduate, Graduate/Scholarship)* [555]
NBMBAA Graduate Scholarships Program *(Graduate/Scholarship)* [6821]
NBRC/AMP H. Frederic Helmholz, Jr., MD Educational Research Funds *(Master's, Doctorate/Grant)* [1213]
NCCF Survivor Scholarships *(Undergraduate/Scholarship)* [6865]
NCCT Postdoctoral Research Program *(Postdoctorate, Advanced Professional, Professional development/Fellowship)* [9941]
NCEA Postdoctoral Research Program *(Postdoctorate, Advanced Professional, Professional development/Fellowship)* [9943]
NCECA Graduate Student Fellowships *(Graduate/Fellowship)* [6880]
NCPA Foundation Presidential Scholarships *(Undergraduate/Scholarship)* [6869]
NCRF New Professional Reporter Grant *(Other/Grant)* [6898]
NCSEA Judge Ross Leadership Scholarships *(Professional development/Scholarship)* [6858]
NCSEA New Leader Scholarships *(Professional development/Scholarship)* [6859]
NCSGC Undergraduate Research Scholarships *(Undergraduate/Scholarship)* [7484]
NCSGC Undergraduate Scholarships *(Undergraduate/Scholarship)* [7485]
NCTE Research Foundation Grants *(Other/Grant)* [6885]
NCTM Emerging Teacher-Leaders in Elementary School Mathematics Grants for Grades K-5 Teachers *(Other/Grant)* [6889]
NCTM Prospective 7-12 Secondary Teacher Course Work Scholarships *(Professional development/Scholarship)* [6890]
NCTM School In-Service Training Grants for Grades 6-8 Teachers *(Undergraduate/Grant)* [6891]
NCTM School In-Service Training Grants for Grades 9-12 Teachers *(Undergraduate/Grant)* [6892]
NCTM School In-Service Training Grants for Grades K-5 Teachers *(Undergraduate/Grant)* [6893]
NDIA Picatinny Chapter Scholarships *(Undergraduate/Scholarship)* [6909]
NDSEG Fellowships *(Graduate/Fellowship)* [6911]
NDSGC American Indian Scholarships *(Undergraduate/Scholarship)* [7494]
NDSGC Graduate Fellowships *(Graduate, Master's, Doctorate/Scholarship, Fellowship)* [7495]
NDSGC Summer Faculty Fellowships *(Professional development/Scholarship, Fellowship)* [7496]
NDSGC Undergraduate Fellowships *(Undergraduate/Scholarship, Fellowship)* [7497]
NDSGC Undergraduate Scholarships *(Undergraduate/Scholarship)* [7498]
NDTA Academic Scholarship Program A *(Under-*

graduate/Scholarship) [6913]
NDTA Academic Scholarship Program B (Undergraduate/Scholarship) [6914]
Nebraska Farm Bureau Greater Horizon Scholarships (Undergraduate/Scholarship) [7240]
NEDA Eating Recovery Center Foundation Early Career Investigator Grants (Professional development/Grant) [6938]
NEDA Feeding Hope Fund for Clinical Research Grants (Professional development/Grant) [6939]
Need-Based Scholarships (Doctorate/Scholarship) [3986]
J.W. "Bill" Neese Scholarships (Undergraduate/Scholarship) [5300]
NEH Fellowships for Senior Scholars (Doctorate/Fellowship) [2853]
NEHA/AAS Scholarship (Graduate, Undergraduate/Scholarship) [6943]
Paul and Ruth Neidhold Business Scholarships (Undergraduate/Scholarship) [3294]
Neilsen Psychosocial Research Grants - Pilot Psychosocial Research Grants (Professional development/Grant) [7254]
Neilsen Psychosocial Research Grants - Postdoctoral Psychosocial Fellowships (Postdoctorate/Fellowship) [7255]
Neilsen Psychosocial Research Grants - Proof of Concept Research Grants (Professional development/Grant) [7256]
Edward J. Nell Memorial Scholarships in Journalism (Undergraduate/Scholarship) [8397]
Dave Nelsen Scholarships (Undergraduate/Scholarship) [6766]
Tad Nelson Law Firm Scholarships (Undergraduate/Scholarship) [5965]
Carol Nelson Scholarship (Undergraduate/Scholarship) [5753]
Bill Nelson Scholarship Endowment (BNSE) (Undergraduate, Graduate/Scholarship) [7768]
AIST Midwest Member Chapter - Don Nelson Scholarships (Undergraduate/Scholarship) [2003]
Law Offices of Judd S. Nemiro Dyslexia Scholarships (All/Scholarship) [5961]
NEMLA Summer Fellowships (Graduate, Other/Fellowship) [7511]
NEMRA Educational Scholarship Foundation (Undergraduate, Vocational/Occupational/Scholarship) [6941]
NERRS Graduate Research Fellowships (GRF) (Graduate/Fellowship) [6945]
Amelia and Emanuel Nessell Scholarships (Undergraduate/Scholarship) [3719]
Netfloor USA Access Flooring College Scholarships (Undergraduate/Scholarship) [7261]
Reverend John S. Nettles Scholarships (Undergraduate/Scholarship) [3268]
Elizabeth Neuffer Fellowships (Other/Fellowship) [5458]
New England FEMARA Scholarships (Undergraduate/Scholarship) [1748]
New Hampshire Snowmobile Association Book Scholarships (Undergraduate/Scholarship) [7313]
New Investigator Research Grant (Doctorate/Grant) [393]
New Investigator Research Grant (Postdoctorate/Grant) [374]
New Mexico Manufactured Housing Association Scholarship Program (Undergraduate/Scholarship) [303]
New Orleans Ghost Tours Scholarships (Undergraduate/Scholarship) [7341]
New York Point Honors Point Scholarship (Undergraduate, Graduate, Doctorate/Scholarship) [8188]
New York State Senate - Legislative Fellowships (Graduate, Postgraduate/Fellowship) [7368]
The New York Times College Scholarships (Undergraduate/Scholarship, Internship) [7396]
New York Water Environment Association Scholarships (Undergraduate/Scholarship) [7404]
New York Women in Communications, Inc. Foundation Scholarships (Graduate, Undergraduate/Scholarship) [7406]
Ted and Ruth Neward Scholarships (Undergraduate, Graduate/Scholarship) [9265]
Newberry Consortium on American Indian Studies Faculty Fellowships (Other/Fellowship) [7417]

Newberry Consortium on American Indian Studies Graduate Student Fellowships (Doctorate/Fellowship) [7418]
Newberry Library ACM/GLCA Faculty Fellowships (Other/Fellowship) [7419]
Newberry Library National Endowment for the Humanities Fellowships (Postdoctorate/Fellowship) [7421]
Newberry Library Short-Term Resident Fellowships for Individual Research (Postdoctorate, Doctorate/Fellowship) [7422]
The Shanon Newberry Physical Therapy Scholarship Endowment (Doctorate/Scholarship) [9584]
Newcomer Supply Student Scholarships (Undergraduate/Scholarship) [7169]
Caroline H. Newhouse Scholarship Fund (Professional development/Scholarship, Grant) [2793]
Newman Civic Fellows Awards (Undergraduate/Award) [2530]
Edsel Newman Scholarships (Undergraduate/Scholarship) [6065]
Newman University Scouting Scholarships (Undergraduate/Scholarship) [6931]
Jerry Newson Scholarships (Undergraduate/Scholarship) [3246]
Alwin B. Newton Scholarships (Undergraduate/Scholarship) [1332]
NFDA Professional Women's Conference Scholarships (Undergraduate/Scholarship) [4314]
NFPA/PACE Scholarships (Other/Scholarship) [6951]
NFPA Youth Scholarships (Undergraduate, Vocational/Occupational/Scholarship) [6961]
NGA Conservation Fellowships (Graduate/Award) [6963]
NGAT Educational Scholarships (Graduate, Undergraduate/Scholarship) [6980]
NGC College Scholarships (Graduate, Undergraduate/Scholarship) [6965]
NHAEOP Member Scholarships (Undergraduate/Scholarship) [7299]
NHEERL Postdoctoral Research Program (Postdoctorate, Advanced Professional, Professional development/Fellowship) [9937]
NHFA Scholarships (Graduate/Scholarship) [6998]
NHS National Scholarships (Undergraduate/Scholarship) [7000]
NHS Regional Scholarships (Undergraduate/Scholarship) [7001]
NIABA/NIAF Scholarships (Graduate/Scholarship) [7025]
NIAC Iranian-American Scholarship Fund (Undergraduate, Graduate/Scholarship) [7023]
NIAF Scholarships - General Category I (Undergraduate, Graduate, Postgraduate/Scholarship) [7027]
NIAF Scholarships - General Category II (Undergraduate, Graduate, Postgraduate/Scholarship) [7028]
NIBA Presidential Scholarships (Undergraduate/Scholarship) [7010]
George E. Nichols Undergradute Scholarships (Undergraduate/Scholarship) [10187]
AIST Midwest Member Chapter - Mel Nickel Scholarships (Undergraduate/Scholarship) [2004]
Nickels for Notes Music Scholarship (Undergraduate/Scholarship) [4354]
Herbert W. Nickens Medical Student Scholarships (Advanced Professional/Scholarship) [1840]
Mike Niemeyer Memorial Football Scholarships (Undergraduate/Scholarship) [8506]
Helen W. Nies Memorial Scholarship (Postgraduate/Scholarship) [3987]
NIJ Visiting Fellowships (Other/Fellowship) [7012]
Nikko Cosmetic Surgery Center Annual Breast Cancer Survivor Scholarships (All/Scholarship) [7434]
NINR Mentored Patient-Oriented Research Career Development Award (Doctorate/Grant) [7015]
NINR Midcareer Investigator Award in Patient-Oriented Research (Doctorate/Grant) [7016]
NINR Pathway to Independence Award (Doctorate/Grant) [7017]
Evelyn S. Nish Scholarships (Undergraduate/Scholarship) [8933]
Nissan North America, Inc. Scholarships (Undergraduate/Scholarship) [871]

NIU-CSEAS Foreign Language and Area Studies (FLAS) Fellowships (Undergraduate, Graduate/Fellowship) [7518]
Nixon Family Scholarship Fund (Undergraduate, High School/Scholarship) [10506]
Corwin Nixon Scholarships (Undergraduate/Scholarship) [3007]
Louise A. Nixon Scholarships (Graduate/Scholarship) [7245]
NJLA Scholarships (Graduate, Postgraduate/Scholarship) [7321]
NJOEF Scholarships (Undergraduate/Scholarship) [7315]
NJPA Foundation Scholarship for Research on Diversity Issues (Graduate/Scholarship) [7329]
NJSA Visionary Leader Scholarships (Graduate/Scholarship) [7039]
NJSCPA High School Scholarships (Undergraduate/Scholarship) [7332]
NLBRA National Royalty Scholarships (Undergraduate/Scholarship) [7054]
NLBRA Rainwater Scholarships (Undergraduate/Scholarship) [7055]
NLBRA World All Around Scholarships (Undergraduate/Scholarship) [7056]
NLBRA World Event Scholarships (Undergraduate/Scholarship) [7057]
NLBRA/Wrangler Academic Scholarships (Undergraduate/Scholarship) [7058]
NLBRA Youth Board Officer Scholarships (Undergraduate/Scholarship) [7059]
NLM Associate Fellowships (Postgraduate/Fellowship) [9928]
NMCRS Gold Star Scholarship Program (Undergraduate/Scholarship) [7235]
NMIA Scholarship Program (Undergraduate, Graduate/Scholarship) [7071]
NMNH American Indian Program Fellowships (Graduate/Fellowship) [9034]
NMPF National Dairy Leadership Scholarships (Graduate, Master's, Doctorate/Scholarship) [7073]
NMSC College and University Sponsorship of Merit Scholarship Awards (Undergraduate/Scholarship) [7064]
NMSC Corporate-Sponsored Achievement Scholarship Awards (Undergraduate/Scholarship) [7065]
NMSC National Achievement Scholarship Program (Undergraduate/Scholarship) [7066]
NMSC Special Scholarships (Undergraduate/Scholarship) [7067]
NOAA EPP Undergraduate Scholarships (USP) (Undergraduate/Scholarship) [9891]
NOAA Graduate Sciences Scholarships (Graduate/Scholarship) [9892]
NOBCChE Procter and Gamble Fellowships (Graduate/Fellowship) [7088]
Leonard Noble Educational Scholarships (Professional development/Scholarship) [7170]
Charles S. Noble Scholarships for Study at Harvard (Undergraduate/Scholarship) [282]
Stuart L. Noderer Memorial Scholarships (Undergraduate/Scholarship) [8719]
George H. Nofer Scholarships for Law and Public Policy (Graduate/Scholarship) [316]
Alfred H. Nolle Scholarships (Undergraduate/Scholarship) [342]
Helen Woodruff Nolop Scholarships in Audiology and Allied Fields (Graduate/Scholarship) [3592]
Non Commissioned Officers Association Scholarships (Undergraduate/Scholarship) [7441]
Deborah Munroe Noonan Memorial Research Awards (Professional development/Grant) [4822]
Nor' Easters Scholarships - Four-year Program (Undergraduate/Scholarship) [4915]
Nor' Easters Scholarships - Two-year Program (Undergraduate/Scholarship) [4916]
Norall Scholarship Trust (Undergraduate/Scholarship) [6066]
Marian Norby Scholarships (Other/Scholarship) [9310]
Nordic Ski Association of Anchorage Scholarships (Undergraduate/Scholarship) [221]
North Alabama Dietetic Association Scholarships (Graduate, Undergraduate/Scholarship) [197]
North American Conference on British Studies Dis-

UNITED STATES Place of Study Index

sertation Year Fellowships *(Doctorate, Postdoctorate/Fellowship)* [7443]
North American Conference on British Studies-Huntington Library Fellowships *(Doctorate, Postdoctorate/Fellowship)* [7444]
North American Van Lines Military Scholarship Competition *(Undergraduate/Scholarship)* [7449]
North Carolina Association of Health Care Recruiters Scholarships *(Undergraduate/Scholarship)* [7454]
North Carolina Commercial Flower Growers Association Floriculture Scholarships *(Graduate, Undergraduate/Scholarship)* [7456]
North Carolina Council of Epsilon Sigma Alpha Scholarships *(Graduate, Other, Undergraduate/Scholarship)* [7458]
North Carolina Heroes Financial Hardship Grant *(All/Grant)* [7466]
North Carolina League for Nursing Academic Scholarships *(Graduate/Scholarship)* [4207]
North Carolina Nursery and Landscape Association Horticulture Scholarships *(Undergraduate/Scholarship)* [7468]
North Dakota Division Scholarships *(Undergraduate/Scholarship)* [6523]
North Dakota Farmers Union Co-op House Scholarships *(Undergraduate/Scholarship)* [7490]
North Dakota Farmers Union Scholarships *(Undergraduate/Scholarship)* [7491]
North Ottawa Hospital Auxiliary Scholarship Fund *(Undergraduate/Scholarship)* [4534]
Michelle North Scholarships for Safety *(Other/Scholarship)* [4840]
North Texas GIA Alumni Association Scholarships *(Undergraduate/Scholarship)* [4344]
Northampton County Medical Society Alliance Scholarships *(Undergraduate/Scholarship)* [7507]
NorthCoast Medical Scholarship Program *(Postgraduate/Scholarship)* [1048]
Northeast Alabama District Dietetic Association Scholarships *(Graduate, Undergraduate/Scholarship)* [198]
Northern Arizona Native-American Foundation Scholarships *(Undergraduate, Vocational/Occupational/Scholarship)* [7516]
Northern California DX Foundation Scholarships *(Undergraduate/Scholarship)* [1749]
Northern Trust Point Scholarship *(Undergraduate, Graduate, Doctorate/Scholarship)* [8189]
Northrop Grumman Engineering Scholarships *(Undergraduate/Scholarship)* [7527]
Northwest Community Center Scholarships *(Undergraduate/Scholarship)* [3295]
Northwest-Shoals Community College Academic Scholarships *(Undergraduate/Scholarship)* [7539]
Northwest-Shoals Community College Athletic Scholarships *(Undergraduate/Scholarship)* [7541]
Northwest-Shoals Community College High School Academic Scholarships *(Undergraduate/Scholarship)* [7546]
Northwestern Mutual Financial Network Scholarships *(Graduate, Undergraduate/Scholarship)* [8077]
Vessa Notchev Fellowships *(Doctorate, Graduate/Fellowship)* [8906]
NOVA Foundation Scholarships *(Doctorate, Graduate, Master's/Scholarship)* [7560]
Novak Awards *(Doctorate/Monetary)* [58]
Mike and Flo Novovesky Scholarships *(Undergraduate/Scholarship)* [807]
NPC Scholarships *(Graduate/Scholarship)* [7100]
NPM Academic Scholarships *(Graduate, Undergraduate/Scholarship)* [6768]
NPM Program Scholarships *(Undergraduate/Scholarship)* [6769]
NPPF Still and Multimedia Scholarships *(Undergraduate/Scholarship)* [7110]
NPPF TV News Scholarships *(Undergraduate/Scholarship)* [7111]
NPSC Fellowships *(Graduate/Fellowship)* [7098]
NRL-ASEE Postdoctoral Fellowships *(Postdoctorate/Fellowship)* [9966]
NSA Electrical Engineering Student Scholarships *(Undergraduate, Graduate, Doctorate/Scholarship)* [107]
NSA Mathematics and Computer Science Student Scholarships *(Undergraduate, Graduate, Doctorate/Scholarship)* [108]
NSHMBA Scholarships *(Graduate/Scholarship)* [7164]
NSHSS Academic Paper Awards *(High School/Scholarship)* [7160]
NSHSS National Scholar Awards *(High School/Scholarship)* [7161]
NSPS Scholarships *(Undergraduate/Scholarship)* [7175]
NSS Conservation Grants *(Advanced Professional/Grant)* [7182]
NSS Education Grants *(Undergraduate/Grant)* [7183]
NSSA/NSCA Collegiate Scholarships *(Undergraduate/Scholarship)* [7186]
NTHA Forest Resources Scholarships for College Students *(Undergraduate/Scholarship)* [7525]
NTHS/HOSA Scholarships *(Undergraduate/Scholarship)* [7197]
Nuclear Criticality Safety Pioneers Scholarships *(Graduate/Scholarship)* [1038]
NUF Fellowships *(Graduate, Postgraduate, Other/Fellowship)* [7209]
NURSE Corps Scholarship Program *(Professional development/Scholarship)* [9924]
Nurseries Foundation Scholarship Awards *(Undergraduate/Scholarship)* [7698]
Nurseries Memorial Scholarship Awards *(Graduate/Scholarship)* [7699]
Nuts, Bolts and Thingamajigs Scholarships *(Undergraduate, Vocational/Occupational/Scholarship)* [7562]
The Nuts.com Healthy Eating Scholarships *(Undergraduate, Graduate/Scholarship)* [7564]
NVIDIA Graduate Fellowships *(Graduate/Fellowship)* [7566]
NWF Campus Ecology Fellowships *(Graduate, Undergraduate/Fellowship)* [7216]
NWRI Fellowships *(Graduate, Master's, Doctorate/Fellowship)* [7214]
NWSA Graduate Scholarships *(Graduate/Scholarship)* [7219]
NYCT Paid Graduate Student Philanthropy Fellowships - Arts and Historic Preservation *(Graduate/Fellowship)* [7349]
NYCT Paid Graduate Student Philanthropy Fellowships - Children, Youth, Families, Education, Human Justice and Workforce *(Graduate/Fellowship)* [7350]
NYCT Paid Graduate Student Philanthropy Fellowships - Health and People with Special Needs *(Graduate/Fellowship)* [7352]
NYFWA Scholarships *(Undergraduate, Graduate/Scholarship)* [7355]
NYLA-Dewey Scholarship *(Master's, Undergraduate/Scholarship)* [7357]
NYU School of Law Fellowships at HRW *(Graduate/Fellowship)* [4999]
OAH-IEHS Huggins-Quarles Dissertation Awards *(Doctorate, Graduate/Grant)* [7718]
OAIA Scholarships *(Undergraduate, Graduate/Scholarship)* [7690]
OAS Academic Scholarship for Undergraduate Studies *(Undergraduate/Scholarship)* [7721]
OAS Academic Scholarships - Graduate *(Graduate/Scholarship)* [7722]
OAS Scholarships for Professional Development - Disaster Communications Management *(Professional development/Scholarship)* [7723]
OAS Scholarships for Professional Development - Radio Spectrum Monitoring Techniques and Procedures *(Professional development/Scholarship)* [7724]
OAS Scholarships for Professional Development - Satellite Communications *(Professional development/Scholarship)* [7725]
WillEtta Long Oates, Gamma Nu, Memorial Scholarship *(Undergraduate, Graduate/Scholarship)* [5754]
Dennis J. O'Brien USAEE/IAEE Best Student Paper Award *(Undergraduate/Award)* [9884]
Oceanic Research Group Scholarships *(Graduate, Undergraduate/Scholarship)* [7570]
Edward A. O'Connor Founder's Scholarships *(Undergraduate/Scholarship)* [83]
Justice Sandra Day O'Connor Scholarship *(Undergraduate/Scholarship)* [6804]
Basil O'Connor Starter Scholar Research Awards *(Professional development/Grant)* [6235]
Captain Jennifer Shafer Odom Memorial Scholarships - Children of Soldiers *(Undergraduate, Vocational/Occupational/Scholarship)* [1716]
Captain Jennifer Shafer Odom Memorial Scholarships - Spouses of Soldiers *(Undergraduate/Scholarship)* [1717]
Office of Science Graduate Fellowships *(Graduate/Fellowship)* [9912]
Ohio Association of Broadcaster's Kids Scholarships *(Undergraduate/Scholarship)* [7572]
Ohio Space Grant Consortium Graduate Fellowships *(Graduate, Doctorate, Master's/Fellowship)* [7594]
Ohio Space Grant Consortium Special Minority Fellowships *(Doctorate, Graduate, Master's/Fellowship)* [7595]
Ohio War Orphan Scholarships *(Undergraduate/Scholarship)* [10723]
Lawrence "Bud" Ohlman Memorial Scholarships *(Undergraduate/Scholarship)* [808]
O'Jays Scholarship Fund *(Undergraduate/Scholarship)* [9529]
The Seth Okin Good Deeds Scholarships *(Undergraduate/Scholarship)* [8235]
Oklahoma Restaurant Association Scholarships *(Graduate, Undergraduate/Scholarship)* [7604]
Olin/Searle Fellows in Law *(Other/Fellowship)* [3995]
Jeff Oliphant Memorial Post-Graduate Scholarships *(Postgraduate/Scholarship)* [10619]
Robert B. Oliver ASNT Scholarships *(Undergraduate/Scholarship)* [1385]
MHS Andrew Oliver Research Fellowships *(Professional development/Fellowship)* [6336]
Roy C. and Dorothy Jean Olson Memorial Scholarships *(Undergraduate/Scholarship)* [5361]
Charlie O'Meilia Scholarships *(Undergraduate/Scholarship)* [5301]
Omicron Delta Kappa Foundation Scholarships *(Graduate/Scholarship)* [7611]
Omicron Nu Research Fellowships *(Postdoctorate/Fellowship)* [5790]
Oncology Nursing Society Foundation - Bachelor's Scholarships *(Undergraduate/Scholarship)* [7619]
Oncology Nursing Society Foundation - Doctoral Scholarships *(Doctorate/Scholarship)* [7620]
Oncology Nursing Society Foundation - Master's Scholarships *(Graduate, Master's/Scholarship)* [7621]
Oncology Trainee Travel Awards *(Professional development/Grant)* [3383]
ONLA President's Scholarship *(Undergraduate/Scholarship)* [7586]
ONS Foundation Congress Scholarships *(Professional development/Scholarship)* [7622]
ONS Foundation Dissertation Research Grants *(Doctorate, Professional development/Grant)* [7623]
ONS Foundation Research Grants *(Advanced Professional/Grant)* [7624]
Open Society Fellowships *(Other/Fellowship)* [7662]
Opera Foundation Scholarships *(Other/Scholarship)* [7669]
OPERF/ABC Resident Travel Award *(Professional development/Grant)* [7755]
OPERF Educator and Student Awards *(Professional development/Grant)* [7756]
OPERF Fellowships *(Graduate, Master's, Doctorate/Fellowship)* [7757]
OPERF Small Grants *(Doctorate/Grant)* [7758]
Frank Oppenheimer Scholarship Program *(Postgraduate/Scholarship)* [1049]
Optical Design and Engineering Scholarships *(Graduate, Undergraduate/Scholarship)* [9471]
Order of Omega Doctoral Fellowships *(Doctorate, Graduate/Fellowship)* [7680]
Order Sons of Italy Foundation General Scholarships *(Graduate, Undergraduate/Scholarship)* [7683]
L'Oreal USA Fellowships for Women in Science *(Postdoctorate/Fellowship)* [6107]
Oregon Association of Nurseries Scholarship Pro-

gram *(Undergraduate/Scholarship)* [7700]
Oregon Farm Bureau Memorial Scholarships *(Undergraduate/Scholarship)* [7706]
Oregon Literary Fellowships *(Advanced Professional/Fellowship)* [6097]
Organization of American States AOS-Placed Scholarships *(Graduate, Undergraduate/Scholarship)* [7727]
Organization of American States Graduate Scholarships *(Doctorate, Graduate/Scholarship)* [7728]
Organization of American States Self-Placed Scholarships *(Doctorate, Graduate/Scholarship)* [7729]
Organization of Black Aerospace Professionals General Scholarships *(All/Scholarship)* [7733]
Organization of Chinese Americans Scholarships *(Undergraduate/Scholarship)* [1784]
Louisa Anne Oriente Scholarships *(Graduate/Scholarship)* [5681]
Original Tax Credit Scholarship *(Undergraduate/Scholarship)* [1627]
Oronzio de Nora Industrial Electrochemistry Fellowships *(Postdoctorate/Fellowship)* [3850]
Orthopaedic Foot and Ankle Fellowships *(Graduate, Professional development/Fellowship)* [1061]
Orthopaedic Specialists Nursing Scholarships *(Undergraduate/Scholarship)* [10590]
Mary Reiko Osaka Memorial Scholarships *(Undergraduate, Graduate/Scholarship)* [5555]
The Kenneth J. Osborn Memorial Scholarships *(Undergraduate/Scholarship)* [1808]
Royce Osborn Minority Scholarship *(Undergraduate/Scholarship)* [1398]
OSGC Community College Scholarships *(Undergraduate/Scholarship)* [7596]
OSGC Education Scholarships *(Undergraduate/Scholarship)* [7597]
M. Dick Osumi Civil Rights and Public Interest Scholarship *(Graduate, Undergraduate/Scholarship)* [5543]
Donald F. and Mildred Topp Othmer National Scholarship Awards *(Undergraduate/Scholarship)* [906]
Ellis R. Ott Scholarships *(Graduate, Master's/Scholarship)* [1390]
Ottawa Police 150th Anniversary Scholarships *(Undergraduate/Scholarship)* [2347]
Outlaw Student's Medical Professions Scholarships *(Undergraduate/Scholarship)* [9595]
Outlaw Student's Minority Scholarships *(Undergraduate/Scholarship)* [9596]
Outlaw Student's Nursing School Scholarships *(Undergraduate/Scholarship)* [9597]
Outlaw Student's Teacher Scholarships *(Undergraduate/Scholarship)* [9598]
Outstanding Doctoral Thesis in Astrophysics *(Doctorate/Award)* [1092]
Overflow/PLUS Tax Credit Scholarships *(Undergraduate/Scholarship)* [1628]
Helene M. Overly Memorial Scholarships *(Undergraduate/Scholarship)* [10675]
Overseas Press Club Foundation Harper's Magazine Scholarships *(Graduate, Undergraduate/Scholarship)* [7776]
Overseas Press Club Foundation Reuters Scholarships *(Graduate, Undergraduate/Scholarship)* [7777]
Elvina Jane Owen Awards *(Graduate, Undergraduate/Award)* [9855]
Charles and Melva T. Owen Memorial Scholarships *(Undergraduate/Scholarship)* [6948]
Abraham A. Oyedeji Scholarships *(Undergraduate/Scholarship)* [7393]
Ozarks Division Scholarships *(Undergraduate/Scholarship)* [6524]
The Pac-10 Postgraduate Scholarships *(Graduate/Scholarship)* [7787]
Packard Fellowships for Science and Engineering *(Professional development/Fellowship)* [7793]
The Arthur J. Packard Memorial Scholarship Competition *(Undergraduate/Scholarship)* [862]
Barbara L. Packer Fellowships *(Doctorate, Postdoctorate/Fellowship)* [442]
Casilda Pagan Educational/Vocational Scholarships *(Graduate, Undergraduate, Postgraduate/Scholarship)* [4964]
Laurie Page-Peck Scholarship Fund *(Undergraduate/Scholarship)* [2103]

The Pain Special Merit Award *(Postdoctorate, Professional development/Award)* [3384]
Ben Palacio Scholarships *(Undergraduate/Scholarship)* [9962]
Paleontological Society Student Research Grants *(Graduate, Undergraduate/Grant)* [17]
Robert R. Palmer Research Travel Fellowships *(Other/Fellowship)* [1296]
The PanHellenic Scholarships *(Undergraduate/Scholarship)* [7797]
ACI Charles Pankow Foundation ACI Student Fellowships *(Graduate, Undergraduate/Fellowship)* [710]
Panther Cafe Scholarships *(Undergraduate/Scholarship)* [8358]
Katharine Pantzer Fellowships in the British Book Trades *(Other/Fellowship)* [2256]
Arthur and Barbara Pape Endowments *(Graduate/Grant)* [10269]
Paper Stock Industries Chapter ISRI RRF Scholarship *(Undergraduate/Scholarship)* [7801]
Pappaioanou Veterinary Public Health and Applied Epidemiology Fellowships *(Undergraduate/Fellowship)* [2833]
Parapsychological Association Research Endowments *(All/Grant)* [7805]
Joseph M. Parish Memorial Grants *(Undergraduate/Scholarship, Grant)* [1253]
Cissy McDaniel Parker Scholarships *(Undergraduate/Scholarship)* [3557]
E.U. and Gene Parker Scholarships *(Undergraduate/Scholarship)* [6949]
Parking Industry Institute Scholarship Program *(Undergraduate/Scholarship)* [7094]
Sylvia Parkinson Scholarships *(Undergraduate/Scholarship)* [4766]
Parkinson's Disease Foundation International Research Grants Program *(Postdoctorate/Grant)* [7884]
PARMA Scholarships *(Undergraduate/Scholarship)* [8325]
Ted Parnell Scholarship *(Undergraduate/Scholarship)* [10772]
The Paros-Digiquartz Scholarships *(Graduate, Undergraduate/Scholarship)* [6276]
William E. Parrish Scholarships *(Graduate, Master's/Scholarship)* [8045]
Carl Parsell Scholarship Fund *(Undergraduate/Scholarship)* [6459]
Elisabeth M. and Winchell M. Parsons Scholarships *(Graduate/Scholarship)* [1798]
Part the Cloud Translational Research Funds *(Postgraduate/Grant)* [375]
Patient Advocate Scholarship Program *(Professional development/Scholarship)* [3385]
James H. Patrenos Memorial Scholarships *(Undergraduate/Scholarship)* [8969]
Gail Patrick Charitable Trust Scholarships *(Undergraduate/Scholarship)* [3593]
Patterson Belknap Webb & Tyler LLP Diversity Fellowships *(Doctorate/Fellowship)* [7905]
Walter S. Patterson Scholarships *(Graduate/Scholarship)* [2370]
Joanne Holbrook Patton Military Spouse Scholarships *(Graduate, Undergraduate/Scholarship)* [7069]
Paul and Inger Friend 4-H Scholarships *(Undergraduate/Scholarship)* [9574]
Ray, NORP and Katie, WOKTE Pautz Scholarships *(Undergraduate/Scholarship)* [1750]
Kenyon T. Payne Outstanding Student Awards *(Undergraduate/Award)* [6500]
PCCE Scholarship *(Undergraduate/Scholarship)* [6952]
PCF Challenge Awards *(Professional development/Grant)* [8312]
PCF Young Investigator Awards *(Professional development/Grant)* [8313]
PDC Scholarships *(Undergraduate/Scholarship)* [1425]
PDF-APDA Summer Student Fellowships *(Undergraduate, Graduate/Fellowship)* [7885]
PDF-PSG Mentored Clinical Research Awards *(Professional development/Award)* [7886]
PDF Student Travel Award *(Graduate, Undergraduate/Scholarship)* [7887]

Chuck Peacock Memorial Scholarships *(Undergraduate/Scholarship)* [169]
Peale Scholarship Grant *(Professional development/Scholarship)* [8058]
Scott Pearlman Field Awards for Science and Exploration *(Other/Award)* [3946]
Pearman Family Scholarships *(Undergraduate/Scholarship)* [8720]
Robert L. Peaslee-Detroit Brazing and Soldiering Division Scholarships *(Undergraduate/Scholarship)* [1521]
Pediatric Endocrinology Nursing Society Academic Education Scholarships *(Undergraduate/Scholarship)* [7926]
Pediatric Endocrinology Nursing Society Convention Reimbursement Awards *(Undergraduate/Award)* [7927]
Mario Pedrozzi Scholarships *(Undergraduate, Graduate/Scholarship)* [7931]
Peermusic Latin Scholarship *(Undergraduate/Scholarship)* [2320]
Pellegrini Scholarships *(Undergraduate, Graduate/Scholarship)* [9620]
Louis Pelzer Memorial Awards *(Graduate/Award)* [7719]
Margaret Pemberton Scholarships *(Undergraduate/Scholarship)* [2299]
Pembroke Center Faculty Fellowships *(Professional development/Fellowship)* [2389]
Pembroke Center Faculty Seed Grants *(Professional development/Grant)* [2390]
Pembroke Center Graduate Fellowships *(Graduate/Fellowship)* [2391]
Robert B. and Dorothy Pence Scholarships *(Undergraduate/Scholarship)* [9443]
Pennies for Art Scholarships *(Undergraduate/Scholarship)* [4355]
Pennsboro Alumni Scholarship Fund *(Undergraduate/Scholarship)* [7850]
Pennsylvania Heartland Unit Scholarships *(Undergraduate/Scholarship)* [4864]
Pennsylvania Land Surveyors Foundation Scholarships *(Undergraduate/Scholarship)* [7941]
Pennsylvania Library Association MLS Scholarships *(Graduate/Scholarship)* [7937]
Pension Real Estate Association Scholarships *(Undergraduate, Graduate/Scholarship)* [7952]
PEO Educational Loan Funds *(Undergraduate, Master's, Doctorate/Loan)* [7954]
PEO International Peace Scholarships *(Graduate, Master's, Doctorate/Scholarship)* [7955]
PEO Scholars Awards *(Doctorate/Award, Scholarship)* [7956]
Peoria Area Amateur Radio Club Scholarships *(Undergraduate/Scholarship)* [1751]
Pepsi Scholarships *(Undergraduate/Scholarship)* [863]
Pepsi Wood County Technical/Caperton Center Scholarship Fund *(Undergraduate/Scholarship)* [7851]
Joe Perdue Scholarships *(Undergraduate/Scholarship)* [3063]
Joaquim Pereira Memorial Scholarships *(Undergraduate/Scholarship)* [6153]
Rudy Perez Songwriting Scholarships *(Undergraduate/Scholarship)* [1275]
Perkins Coie 1L Diversity Fellowships *(Postgraduate/Fellowship)* [8011]
Perkins Coie 1L Patent Litigation and Patent Fellowships *(Postgraduate/Fellowship)* [8012]
Chet and Jannett Perry Rotary Club of Fort Myers Scholarship Fund *(Undergraduate/Scholarship)* [9444]
Perry Township School Memorial Scholarship Fund *(Undergraduate/Scholarship)* [9530]
Jim Perry Vocational Scholarships *(Undergraduate, Vocational/Occupational/Scholarship)* [809]
Gilberto and Lennetta Pesquera Medical School Scholarships *(Graduate, Doctorate/Scholarship, Grant)* [4453]
Pete Wilson Graduate Scholarships *(Graduate, Undergraduate/Scholarship)* [8407]
Pete Wilson Journalism Scholarships *(Graduate, Undergraduate/Scholarship)* [8408]
Jerome Peters Family Scholarships *(Undergraduate/Scholarship)* [6210]

Paul Evan Peters Fellowship *(Master's, Doctorate/Fellowship)* [3073]
Kate B. and Hall J. Peterson Fellowships *(Doctorate/Fellowship)* [443]
Lizette Peterson Homer Injury Prevention Grant Awards *(Other, Undergraduate, Graduate/Grant)* [1571]
Captain James H. Peterson Memorial Scholarships *(Undergraduate/Scholarship)* [4715]
Charles E. Peterson Senior Fellowships *(Other/Fellowship)* [2107]
Steve Petix Journalism Scholarships *(Undergraduate/Scholarship)* [8721]
William H. and Lena M. Petree Scholarships *(Undergraduate/Scholarship)* [10592]
Silvio and Eugenia Petrini Grants *(Other/Grant)* [4711]
Petroleum Packaging Council Scholarships *(Undergraduate/Scholarship)* [8019]
Pew Latin American Fellows Program in the Biomedical Sciences *(Other/Fellowship)* [8021]
Chuck Pezzano Scholarships *(Undergraduate/Scholarship)* [5286]
Pfafftown Jaycees/Lynn Canada Memorial Scholarships *(Undergraduate/Scholarship)* [10593]
William R. Pfalzgraf Scholarships *(Undergraduate/Scholarship)* [7852]
L. Gordon, Jr. and June D. Pfefferkorn Scholarships *(Undergraduate/Scholarship)* [10594]
Pfizer Scholarship Funds *(Undergraduate, Graduate/Scholarship)* [6256]
PFLAG Columbia-Howard County Scholarship *(Undergraduate/Scholarship)* [8025]
Carl H. Pforzheimer, Jr. Research Grants *(Graduate, Other/Grant)* [5800]
PGSF Scholarships *(Undergraduate/Scholarship)* [8284]
Pharmaceutics Post Doctoral Fellowships *(Postdoctorate/Fellowship)* [8030]
Pharmaceutics Research Starter Grants *(Doctorate/Grant)* [8031]
Pharmaceutics Sabbatical Fellowships *(Postdoctorate/Fellowship)* [8032]
Pharmacology/Toxicology Pre Doctoral Fellowships *(Doctorate/Fellowship)* [8033]
Marshall Phelps Athletic Memorial Scholarships *(Undergraduate/Scholarship)* [8507]
Phi Alpha Theta Doctoral Scholarships *(Doctorate/Scholarship)* [8046]
Phi Alpha Theta Faculty Advisor Research Grant *(Other/Grant)* [8047]
Phi Delta Gamma Academic Achievement Awards *(Undergraduate/Scholarship)* [8059]
Phi Eta Sigma Distinguished Member Scholarships - Graduate or Professional *(Graduate, Other/Scholarship)* [8062]
Phi Eta Sigma Distinguished Member Scholarships - Undergraduate *(Undergraduate/Scholarship)* [8063]
Phi Eta Sigma Undergraduate Scholarship Awards *(Undergraduate/Scholarship)* [8064]
Phi Kappa Phi Fellowships *(Graduate, Undergraduate/Fellowship)* [8066]
Phi Kappa Sigma Foundation Scholarship *(Undergraduate/Scholarship)* [8068]
Phi Kappa Sigma Need-Based Scholarships *(Undergraduate/Scholarship)* [8069]
Phi Kappa Sigma Participation-Based Scholarships *(Undergraduate/Scholarship)* [8070]
Phi Sigma Epsilon Past National President Scholarships *(Graduate, Undergraduate/Scholarship)* [8078]
Phi Upsilon Omicron Candle Fellowships *(Graduate/Fellowship)* [8098]
Phi Upsilon Omicron Challenge Scholarships *(Undergraduate/Scholarship)* [8099]
Phi Upsilon Omicron Diamond Anniversary Fellowships *(Graduate/Fellowship)* [8100]
Phi Upsilon Omicron Founders Fellowships *(Graduate/Fellowship)* [8101]
Phi Upsilon Omicron Golden Anniversary Scholarships *(Undergraduate/Scholarship)* [8102]
Phi Upsilon Omicron Past Presidents Scholarships *(Undergraduate/Scholarship)* [8103]
Phi Upsilon Omicron Presidents Research Fellowships *(Graduate/Fellowship)* [8104]

Philadelphia Public Interest Fellowships *(Undergraduate/Fellowship)* [8111]
Catherine E. Philbin Scholarships *(Undergraduate, Graduate/Scholarship)* [4356]
Philips Respironics Fellowships in Mechanical Ventilation *(Professional development/Award)* [1214]
Philips Respironics Fellowships in Non-Invasive Respiratory Care *(Professional development/Fellowship)* [1215]
Phillips Fund Grants for Native American Research *(Doctorate, Master's/Grant)* [1083]
CSF Charles and Claire Phillips Scholarships *(Undergraduate/Scholarship)* [3008]
William Philpott Scholarships *(Undergraduate/Scholarship)* [2269]
Ed Phinney Commemorative Scholarships *(Graduate, Undergraduate/Scholarship)* [681]
PhRMA Foundation Health Outcomes Post Doctoral Fellowships *(Postdoctorate/Fellowship)* [8034]
PhRMA Foundation Health Outcomes Pre Doctoral Fellowships *(Doctorate/Fellowship)* [8035]
PhRMA Foundation Health Outcomes Research Starter Grants *(Doctorate/Grant)* [8036]
PhRMA Foundation Health Outcomes Sabbatical Fellowships *(Postdoctorate/Fellowship)* [8037]
PhRMA Foundation Informatics Research Starter Grants *(Doctorate/Grant)* [8038]
PhRMA Foundation Pharmaceutics Pre Doctoral Fellowships *(Doctorate/Fellowship)* [8039]
PhRMA Foundation Pharmacology/Toxicology Research Starter Grants *(Doctorate/Grant)* [8040]
PhRMA Foundation Pharmacology/Toxicology Sabbatical Fellowships *(Postdoctorate/Fellowship)* [8041]
PhRMA Foundation Pharmacology/Toxicology Post Doctoral Fellowships *(Postdoctorate/Fellowship)* [8042]
The Physical Therapy Faculty Scholarship Endowment *(Graduate/Scholarship)* [9585]
Physics of Accelerators and Related Technology for International Students *(Undergraduate/Internship)* [9902]
Pi Gamma Mu Scholarships *(Graduate/Scholarship)* [8133]
Pi Project 2000 Tali James Memorial Scholarships *(Undergraduate/Scholarship)* [5756]
Thomas R. Pickering Graduate Foreign Affairs Fellowships *(Graduate, Undergraduate/Fellowship)* [10681]
Mary Pickford Scholarships *(Graduate/Scholarship)* [2026]
Peter L. Picknelly Honorary Scholarships *(Undergraduate/Scholarship)* [640]
Ronald C. and Joyce Pierce - Mobile Section Named Scholarships *(Undergraduate/Scholarship)* [1522]
Nicholas J. Piergrossi Scholarships *(Undergraduate/Scholarship)* [4768]
Herschel Pifer Memorial Scholarships *(Undergraduate/Scholarship)* [7853]
William Pigott Memorial Scholarships *(Undergraduate/Scholarship)* [3296]
David Pilon Scholarships for Training in Professional Psychology *(Graduate/Scholarship)* [1135]
Pilot Project Award *(Professional development/Award, Grant)* [9239]
John Pine Memorial Scholarships *(Doctorate, Graduate/Scholarship)* [8048]
Julia T. Pingree Student Scholarship *(Undergraduate/Scholarship)* [7300]
Stephen D. Pisinski Memorial Scholarships *(Undergraduate/Scholarship)* [8376]
Christopher Mark Pitkin Memorial Scholarships *(Undergraduate/Scholarship)* [6994]
Day Pitney LLP Scholarships *(Undergraduate/Scholarship)* [4769]
Pitsenbarger Awards *(Undergraduate/Grant, Award)* [125]
Dr. Aura-Lee A. and James Hobbs Pittenger American History Scholarships *(Undergraduate/Scholarship)* [7154]
Robert Pittman Scholarships-Internships *(Undergraduate/Scholarship, Internship)* [10245]
Carter Pitts Scholarships *(Undergraduate/Scholarship)* [5474]

PKD Foundation Fellowships *(Doctorate, Graduate/Fellowship)* [8144]
Wayne F. Placek Grants *(Graduate, Doctorate/Grant)* [1150]
James L. Plafkin Memorial Scholarships *(Undergraduate/Scholarship)* [10188]
Al Plamann Legacy Scholarships *(Undergraduate/Scholarship)* [2457]
TFC Edward A. Plank, Jr. Memorial Scholarships *(Undergraduate/Scholarship)* [3182]
Betsy Plank/PRSSA Scholarships *(Undergraduate/Scholarship)* [8377]
PlasticPlace Young Entrepreneurs Scholarships *(Undergraduate/Scholarship)* [8148]
Plastics Pioneers Association Scholarships *(Undergraduate/Scholarship)* [9266]
Katherine Barton Platt Excavation Fellowships *(Other, Undergraduate/Fellowship)* [1237]
Platt Family Scholarship Prize Essay Contest *(Graduate, Undergraduate/Scholarship, Monetary)* [6091]
PLSCA Scholarships *(Undergraduate/Scholarship)* [6101]
Harold and Harriet Plum Memorial Scholarships *(Undergraduate/Scholarship)* [2513]
Plumbing-Heating-Cooling Contractors Association Educational Foundation Massachusetts Auxiliary Scholarships *(Undergraduate/Scholarship)* [8161]
Plumbing-Heating-Cooling Contractors Association Educational Foundation Need-Based Scholarships *(Undergraduate/Scholarship)* [8162]
Plumbing-Heating-Cooling Contractors Association Educational Foundation Scholarships *(Undergraduate/Scholarship)* [8163]
PLUS Foundation Financial Aid Scholarships *(Undergraduate/Scholarship)* [8168]
Henry DeWitt Plyler Scholarship Fund *(Undergraduate/Scholarship)* [4210]
PNAA Nursing Scholarship Award *(Master's, Doctorate/Scholarship)* [8113]
David Pohl Scholarships *(Master's/Scholarship)* [9836]
Point Foundation Scholarships *(Undergraduate/Scholarship)* [8662]
Daniel H. Pokorny Memorial Scholarship Awards *(Undergraduate/Scholarship)* [8543]
Pokross/Curhan Family Fund Prize *(Graduate, Undergraduate/Prize)* [950]
Police Explorer Scholarships Program *(Undergraduate/Scholarship)* [4106]
Polish American Club of North Jersey Scholarships *(Graduate, Undergraduate/Scholarship)* [5881]
Polish National Alliance of Brooklyn, USA Scholarships *(Undergraduate/Scholarship)* [5882]
Roy H. Pollack Scholarships *(Graduate, Master's/Scholarship)* [9837]
A. H. Pollard Travelling PhD Scholarships *(Postdoctorate/Scholarship)* [5163]
Harvey M. Pollicove Memorial Scholarships *(Undergraduate/Scholarship)* [7675]
David J. Pollini Scholarships *(Undergraduate/Scholarship)* [6360]
Justice Stewart G. Pollock Fellowships *(Undergraduate/Fellowship)* [6594]
Harold F. Polston Scholarships *(Graduate, Undergraduate/Scholarship)* [1426]
Polymer Modifiers and Additives Division Scholarships *(Undergraduate/Scholarship)* [9267]
Harriet and Leon Pomerance Fellowships *(Professional development/Fellowship)* [1610]
Edward C. Pomeroy Awards for Outstanding Contributions to Teacher Education *(Other/Recognition)* [488]
PON Graduate Student Grants *(Graduate/Grant)* [4789]
PON Next Generation Grants *(Doctorate, Postdoctorate/Grant)* [4790]
PON Summer Fellowships *(Graduate/Fellowship)* [4791]
Buster Pool Memorial Scholarships *(Undergraduate/Scholarship)* [3248]
Jim Poore Memorial Scholarships *(Undergraduate/Scholarship)* [5044]
Pope Scholarship Awards *(Undergraduate/Scholarship)* [6361]
Portable Sanitation Association International Schol-

arship Fund *(Undergraduate/Scholarship)* [8207]
Karin Riley Porter Good Works Scholarships *(Undergraduate, Graduate/Scholarship)* [8236]
Porter Physiology Development Fellowship Awards *(Doctorate/Fellowship)* [1100]
AFT Robert Porter Scholarship Program *(Undergraduate/Scholarship)* [795]
Thomas W. Porter, W8KYZ Scholarships Honoring Michael Daugherty, W8LSE *(Undergraduate/Scholarship)* [1752]
Portland Area Business Association Scholarships *(Undergraduate/Scholarship)* [3921]
Portland Cement Association Scholarships *(Graduate/Scholarship)* [3980]
Portuguese American Police Association Scholarships *(Undergraduate/Scholarship)* [8211]
Portuguese-American Scholarship Foundation *(Undergraduate/Scholarship)* [8209]
Postdoctoral Fellowships for Clinical Neurologists *(Postdoctorate/Fellowship)* [7888]
Poteet Strawberry Festival Association Scholarships *(Graduate, Undergraduate/Scholarship)* [8213]
Terry Linda Potter Scholarship Fund *(Undergraduate/Scholarship)* [4537]
Erwin Potts Scholarships *(Undergraduate/Scholarship)* [10246]
George V. Powell Diversity Scholarships *(Graduate/Scholarship)* [5920]
Gerald Powell Scholarships *(Undergraduate/Scholarship)* [3269]
Susan Kelly Power and Helen Hornbeck Tanner Fellowships *(Doctorate, Postdoctorate/Fellowship)* [7423]
Practising Law Institute Law Student Scholarships *(Advanced Professional, Professional development/Scholarship)* [8215]
Lou and Carole Prato Sports Reporting Scholarships *(Undergraduate/Scholarship)* [8409]
Praxair International Scholarships *(Undergraduate/Scholarship)* [1523]
Presbyterian Association of Musicians Scholarships *(All/Scholarship)* [8217]
Prescott Fine Arts Association Scholarship Program *(Undergraduate/Scholarship)* [8221]
Prevent Cancer Foundation Fellowships *(Postdoctorate/Fellowship)* [8225]
Judith McManus Price Scholarships *(Undergraduate, Graduate/Scholarship)* [1106]
Pride Foundation Political Leadership Scholarships *(Undergraduate/Scholarship)* [8258]
Pride Foundation Regional Scholarships *(Undergraduate/Scholarship)* [8259]
Pride Foundation Scholarships *(Undergraduate/Scholarship)* [8663]
Pride Foundation Social Work Scholarships *(Undergraduate/Scholarship)* [8260]
Pride of the Rose Scholarship Fund *(Undergraduate/Scholarship)* [3922]
Lendon N. Pridgen, GlaxoSmithKline - NOBCChE Fellowships *(Graduate/Fellowship)* [7089]
Dean Prim Scholarships *(Undergraduate/Scholarship)* [10595]
Primate Conservation Grants *(Graduate, Professional development/Grant)* [8276]
Josef Princ Memorial Scholarships *(Undergraduate/Scholarship)* [8360]
R.M. Princ Scholarships *(Undergraduate/Scholarship)* [8361]
Prince Henry Society Scholarships *(Undergraduate/Scholarship)* [8278]
Prins Foundation Fellowship for Senior Scholars *(Doctorate/Fellowship)* [2854]
Prins Foundation Post-Doctoral and Early Career Fellowship for Emigrating Scholars *(Professional development, Postdoctorate/Fellowship)* [2855]
Print and Graphics Scholarship Foundation Awards (PGSF-GATF) *(Graduate, Undergraduate/Scholarship, Fellowship)* [8282]
Miguel Pro Scholarships *(Undergraduate/Scholarship)* [10724]
Procter & Gamble Professional Oral Health/HDA Foundation Scholarships *(Undergraduate/Scholarship)* [4893]
Professional Development and Education Fund (PDEF) Professional Development Scholarships *(Professional development/Scholarship)* [9223]

Professional Research Grants *(Professional development/Grant)* [1399]
Professional Women in Pest Management Scholarships *(Graduate, Other/Scholarship)* [7096]
Professional Women of Redlands, PoWeR to Continue Learning Scholarships *(Undergraduate/Scholarship)* [8508]
Progress Lane Scholarships *(Undergraduate/Scholarship)* [3183]
Progressive Dairy Producer Awards *(All/Grant)* [6905]
Property and Environment Research Center Graduate Fellowships *(Graduate/Fellowship)* [8297]
Property and Environment Research Center Lone Mountain Fellowships *(Other/Fellowship)* [8298]
Property and Environment Research Center Media Fellowships *(Other/Fellowship)* [8299]
Proven Data Recovery Technology Scholarships *(All/Scholarship)* [8315]
Barbara F. Prowant Nursing Research Grants *(Graduate/Grant)* [1028]
PRSA Diversity Multicultural Scholarships *(Undergraduate/Scholarship)* [8378]
Prudential 1L Summer Internships *(Postgraduate/Internship)* [6706]
Neil Pruitt, Sr. Memorial Scholarships *(Undergraduate/Scholarship)* [6870]
Joseph E. Pryor Graduate Fellowships *(Graduate/Fellowship, Scholarship)* [343]
Cheryl White Pryor Memorial Scholarships *(Undergraduate/Scholarship)* [3558]
Phillis Brinton Pryor Panhellenic Scholarship *(Undergraduate/Scholarship)* [5757]
PSGC/NASA Space Grant Fellowships at the PSGC Affiliate Institutions *(Graduate/Fellowship)* [7945]
Public Interest Environmental Law Fellowships *(Graduate/Fellowship)* [3898]
Public Interest Fellowships for Law Students of Color *(Undergraduate/Fellowship)* [4491]
Duane V. Puerde Memorial Scholarships *(Undergraduate/Scholarship)* [3184]
Eugene C. Pulliam Fellowships for Editorial Writing *(Other/Fellowship)* [8902]
Pulliam/Kilgore Freedom of Information Internships *(Undergraduate/Internship)* [9279]
Paul Pumpian Scholarship *(Undergraduate/Scholarship)* [1584]
Elizabeth Pusey Scholarships *(Undergraduate/Scholarship)* [3185]
A.O. Putnam Memorial Scholarships *(Undergraduate/Scholarship)* [5193]
PVA Research Foundation Fellowships *(Postdoctorate/Fellowship)* [7803]
PWC Internships *(Undergraduate, Graduate/Internship)* [8156]
Harry V. Quadracci Memorial Scholarships *(Undergraduate, Graduate/Scholarship)* [4649]
Quarter Century Wireless Association Scholarships *(Undergraduate/Scholarship)* [8390]
Queer Foundation Effective Writing and Scholarships *(Undergraduate/Prize, Scholarship)* [8394]
Rosa Quezada Memorial Education Scholarships *(Undergraduate/Scholarship)* [3361]
Michael J. Quill Scholarships *(Undergraduate/Scholarship)* [9766]
Bob Quincy Scholarships *(Undergraduate/Scholarship)* [10248]
AIST Judith A. Quinn Detroit Member Chapter Scholarship *(Undergraduate/Scholarship)* [2005]
Dr. Sidney Rafal Memorial Scholarships *(Undergraduate/Scholarship)* [4770]
Marjorie Usher Ragan Scholarships *(Undergraduate/Scholarship)* [10249]
Railroad and Mine Workers Memorial Scholarships *(Graduate/Scholarship)* [5556]
Rain Bird Intelligent Use of Water Scholarships *(Undergraduate/Scholarship)* [5917]
J.J. Rains Memorial Scholarships *(Undergraduate/Scholarship)* [3104]
Frederick Rakestraw Law Scholarships *(Graduate/Scholarship)* [7520]
The NASSCO Jeffrey D. Ralston Memorial Scholarship *(Undergraduate/Scholarship)* [6668]
Rama Scholarships for the American Dream *(Graduate, Undergraduate/Scholarship)* [864]

Guthikonda Ramabrahmam and Balamani *(Graduate/Scholarship)* [9669]
RAMEF/NRAEF Co-Branded Scholarships *(Undergraduate/Scholarship)* [8565]
Herbert W. Rand Fellowships and Scholarships *(Undergraduate, Graduate/Scholarship)* [6257]
Commander Newell S. Rand Jr. Scholarship Program *(Undergraduate/Scholarship)* [7809]
Helen F. "Jerri" Rand Memorial Scholarships *(Undergraduate, Vocational/Occupational/Scholarship)* [3323]
R&E Foundation Education Scholarships *(Graduate, Other/Scholarship)* [8416]
James Randi Educational Foundation Scholarships *(Graduate, Undergraduate/Scholarship)* [8427]
Jennings Randolph Peace Scholarship Dissertation Program *(Doctorate/Scholarship)* [8428]
United States Institute of Peace Jennings Randolph Senior Fellowship Program *(Advanced Professional/Fellowship)* [9991]
Rangel Graduate Fellowship *(Graduate/Fellowship)* [8429]
Jeannette Rankin Scholarships *(Undergraduate, Vocational/Occupational/Scholarship)* [8431]
Rappaport Fellows Program in Law and Public Policy *(Undergraduate/Fellowship)* [8437]
Marie Mathew Rask-Gamma Omicron Educational Endowment *(Undergraduate/Scholarship)* [5758]
Geeta Rastogi Memorial Scholarships *(Undergraduate/Scholarship)* [10338]
General John Paul Ratay Educational Grants *(Undergraduate/Grant)* [6535]
Dr. Mark Rathke Family Scholarships *(Undergraduate/Scholarship)* [3721]
James K. Rathmell Jr. Memorial Scholarships *(Undergraduate, Graduate/Scholarship)* [810]
Dennis Raveling Scholarships *(Undergraduate/Scholarship)* [2488]
Lenny Ravich "Shalom" Scholarships *(Advanced Professional/Scholarship)* [1851]
Rawley Silver Awards for Excellence *(Graduate/Scholarship)* [450]
Rawley Silver Research Award *(Postgraduate, Postdoctorate/Award)* [451]
Mary C. Rawlins Scholarships *(Undergraduate/Scholarship)* [4771]
William C. Ray, CIH, CSP Arizona Scholarships *(Graduate, Undergraduate/Scholarship)* [1427]
W.B. Ray HS Class of '56 Averill Johnson Scholarships *(Undergraduate/Scholarship)* [3105]
Raytheon Scholarship Program *(Undergraduate/Scholarship)* [8440]
RBPA Scholarships *(All/Scholarship)* [8425]
Robert H. Reakirt Scholarships *(Undergraduate/Scholarship)* [3010]
William Reaser Scholarships *(Undergraduate/Scholarship)* [7854]
Redlands Baseball/Softball for Youth Scholarship *(Undergraduate/Scholarship)* [8509]
Redlands Community Scholarship Foundation Awards *(Undergraduate/Scholarship)* [8510]
Redlands High School Academic Decathlon Scholarships *(Undergraduate/Scholarship)* [8511]
Redlands High School Boy's Varsity Volleyball Scholarships *(Undergraduate/Scholarship)* [8512]
Redlands High School Girls' Volleyball Boosters Scholarship Awards *(Undergraduate/Scholarship)* [8513]
Redlands High School Mock Trial Scholarships *(Undergraduate/Scholarship)* [8514]
Redlands High School-PTSA Scholarships *(Undergraduate/Scholarship)* [8515]
Redlands High School Softball Booster Scholarship Awards *(Undergraduate/Scholarship)* [8516]
Redlands High School Spiritleaders Scholarships *(Undergraduate/Scholarship)* [8517]
Redlands High School Terrier Band Boosters Club Scholarships *(Undergraduate/Scholarship)* [8518]
Redlands High School Vocal Music Boosters Scholarship Awards *(Undergraduate/Scholarship)* [8519]
Redlands Morning Kiwanis Club Foundation Scholarships *(Undergraduate/Scholarship)* [8520]
Redlands Rotary Club Foundation Discretionary Scholarships *(Undergraduate/Scholarship)* [8521]
Redlands Teachers Association Scholarships *(Undergraduate/Scholarship)* [8522]

The Reese Fellowships *(Doctorate/Fellowship)* [444]
Bob Reeve Aviation Management Scholarships *(Undergraduate/Scholarship)* [217]
REFORMA Scholarship Program *(Doctorate, Graduate, Other/Scholarship)* [8534]
Region II Scholarships *(Graduate, Undergraduate/Scholarship)* [1428]
Rehabmart.com Scholarships *(Undergraduate/Scholarship)* [8545]
Dan M. Reichard, Jr. Scholarships *(Undergraduate, Graduate/Scholarship)* [1168]
Reid Hospital Graduate Student Scholarships *(Graduate/Scholarship)* [10507]
Mark A. Reid Memorial Scholarship Grants *(Undergraduate/Scholarship)* [3297]
Jacob L. Reinecke Memorial Scholarship Fund *(Undergraduate/Scholarship)* [4538]
George Reinke Scholarships *(Other/Scholarship)* [1442]
Remkus-Sochaki Academmic Achievement Scholarships *(Undergraduate/Scholarship)* [8205]
REMSA Scholarships *(Undergraduate/Scholarship)* [1189]
Betty Rendel Scholarships *(Undergraduate/Scholarship)* [6955]
Don Renschler Scholarships *(Graduate/Scholarship)* [8261]
James Renwick Fellowship in American Craft *(Doctorate, Postdoctorate/Fellowship)* [9004]
Research Career Development Awards *(Professional development/Fellowship, Grant)* [7625]
Research Resident/Fellow Grants *(Professional development/Grant)* [8417]
Reservation Counter College Scholarships *(Undergraduate, Graduate, Advanced Professional/Scholarship)* [8559]
Resident Travel Award for Underrepresented Populations *(Professional development/Award)* [3386]
Resilience Action Fund Scholarships *(Graduate/Scholarship)* [3981]
Resistance Welder Manufacturers' Association Scholarships *(Undergraduate/Scholarship)* [1524]
Resume Template Design Scholarships *(Undergraduate, Graduate/Scholarship)* [10369]
Retail Chapter Scholarship Awards *(Undergraduate/Scholarship)* [7701]
Retired League Postmasters Scholarship Program *(Undergraduate/Scholarship)* [8569]
Reuters Institute Visiting Fellowships *(Professional development/Fellowship)* [10265]
Thomson Reuters/MLA Doctoral Fellowships *(Doctorate, Graduate/Fellowship)* [6393]
Mike Reynolds Journalism Scholarships *(Undergraduate/Scholarship)* [8410]
Reynoldsburg-Pickerington Rotary Club High School Scholarship *(Undergraduate/Scholarship)* [8595]
RFDF MBA Preparation Fellowships *(Graduate, Undergraduate/Fellowship)* [8619]
RFDF Pre-MBA Fellowships *(Graduate/Fellowship)* [8620]
Rho Chi, AFPE First Year Graduate Fellowships *(Doctorate, Graduate/Fellowship)* [8597]
Rho Chi Society Clinical Research Scholarships *(Postdoctorate/Scholarship)* [8598]
Rhode Island Association of Former Legislators Scholarships *(Undergraduate/Scholarship)* [8608]
Rice-Cullimore Scholarships *(Graduate/Scholarship)* [1799]
Haynes Rice Scholarships *(Graduate/Scholarship)* [6756]
James Edward "Bill" Richards Scholarships *(Undergraduate/Scholarship)* [3250]
Ellen Swallow Richards Travel Grants *(Graduate, Other/Grant)* [1315]
Phillip Guy Richardson Memorial Scholarships *(Undergraduate/Scholarship)* [5510]
Henry and Sylvia Richardson Research Grant *(Postdoctorate/Grant)* [3883]
J. Milton Richardson Theological Fellowships *(Graduate/Fellowship)* [363]
Frank J. Richter Scholarships *(Graduate, Undergraduate/Scholarship)* [570]
John Riddick Student Grants *(Graduate/Grant)* [7446]
John S. and Jacqueline P. Rider Scholarships *(Undergraduate/Scholarship)* [10596]

Honorable Joseph H. Ridge Memorial Scholarships *(Undergraduate/Scholarship)* [328]
Jasper Ridge Restoration Fellowships Jasper Ridge Biological Preserve *(Graduate, Postdoctorate/Fellowship)* [3777]
ANN Ingrid Josefin Ridky Academic Scholarships *(Undergraduate, Graduate/Scholarship)* [45]
Donald Riebhoff Memorial Scholarships *(Undergraduate/Scholarship)* [1753]
William J. Rielly/MCURC Scholarships *(Undergraduate/Scholarship)* [3011]
Bryon Riesch Paralysis Foundation Research Grants *(Professional development/Grant)* [8617]
Rieser Fellowships *(Undergraduate/Fellowship)* [2406]
Dan Rigel Memorial Educational Grants *(Professional development, Advanced Professional/Grant)* [1843]
Riggs Cove Foundation Scholarships *(Undergraduate/Scholarship)* [4369]
Benjamin Riggs Scholarships *(Undergraduate/Scholarship)* [4370]
Ameen Rihani Scholarship Program *(Undergraduate/Scholarship)* [1599]
Rim-Freeman Point Scholarship *(Undergraduate/Scholarship)* [8190]
Rimington Trophy Scholarships *(Undergraduate, Graduate/Scholarship)* [2340]
Lois McDonald Rinehart Adelphe Scholarship *(Undergraduate, Graduate/Scholarship)* [5759]
John T. Riordan Professional Education Scholarships *(Other/Scholarship)* [5307]
Ritchie-Jennings Memorial Scholarships *(Undergraduate, Graduate/Scholarship)* [1923]
Paul H. Rittle Sr. Professional Development Grants *(Other/Grant)* [5217]
Thomas and Ruth River International Scholarships *(Undergraduate, Graduate/Scholarship)* [10704]
Riverside Sheriffs Association Member Scholarship Program *(Graduate, Undergraduate/Scholarship)* [8622]
Anthony Rizzo Scholarship Award *(Professional development/Scholarship)* [7514]
RMNP Research Fellowship *(Graduate/Fellowship)* [8635]
Jerry Robbins Scholarship *(Undergraduate/Scholarship)* [5682]
Lawrence and Louise Robbins Scholarships *(Undergraduate/Scholarship)* [6211]
Robert Browning Scholarships *(Undergraduate/Scholarship)* [8262]
Robert J. McNamara Student Paper Awards *(Graduate/Award)* [2072]
Robert S. McNamara Fellowships Program (RSMFP) *(Doctorate/Fellowship)* [10698]
Robert Wood Johnson Clinical Scholarships *(Graduate, Professional development/Fellowship)* [8630]
Paul V. Roberts/AEESP Outstanding Doctoral Dissertation Award *(Graduate, Doctorate/Prize, Monetary)* [1953]
Faye Lynn Roberts Educational Scholarships *(Undergraduate, Graduate/Scholarship)* [9445]
Clifford Roberts Graduate Fellowships *(Doctorate/Fellowship)* [4415]
Eugene L. Roberts Jr. Prize *(Undergraduate/Prize)* [10250]
Smiley Elementary School PTA - Beverly Roberts Memorial Scholarships *(Undergraduate/Scholarship)* [8523]
Elliott C. Roberts Scholarships *(Graduate/Scholarship)* [5168]
Mary Roberts Scholarships *(Undergraduate/Scholarship)* [3012]
Thomas Warren Roberts Scholarships *(Undergraduate/Scholarship)* [7856]
Actuary of Tomorrow - Stuart A. Robertson Memorial Scholarship *(Undergraduate/Scholarship)* [64]
Lola Ellis Robertson Scholarships *(Graduate, Master's, Doctorate/Scholarship)* [6258]
Robinhood Marine Center Scholarships *(Undergraduate/Scholarship)* [4371]
David G. Robinson Arts Scholarships *(Undergraduate/Scholarship)* [9446]
Samuel Robinson Awards *(Undergraduate/Award)* [8219]

Helen M. Robinson Grants *(Doctorate/Award, Monetary, Grant)* [5357]
NKA Dr. Violet B. Robinson Memorial Graduate Scholarship *(Advanced Professional/Scholarship)* [7043]
Claude Robinson Scholarships *(Undergraduate/Scholarship)* [7040]
Nell Bryant Robinson Scholarships *(Undergraduate/Scholarship)* [8105]
Paul S. Robinson Scholarships *(Undergraduate/Scholarship)* [9115]
Sara Roby Fellowship in Twentieth-Century American Realism *(Doctorate, Postdoctorate/Fellowship)* [9005]
James and Marilyn Rockefeller Scholarships *(Undergraduate/Scholarship)* [6212]
Rockford Area Habitat for Humanity College Scholarships *(Undergraduate/Scholarship)* [3298]
Rockwell Collins Scholarships *(Undergraduate/Scholarship)* [170]
Rocky Mountain Coal Mining Institute Engineering/Geology Scholarships *(Undergraduate/Scholarship)* [8632]
Rocky Mountain Coal Mining Institute Technical Scholarships *(Undergraduate/Scholarship)* [8633]
Paul W. Rodgers Scholarship *(Undergraduate, Master's, Doctorate/Scholarship)* [5261]
R.O.E.A. Dumitru Golea Goldy-Gemu Scholarships *(Undergraduate/Scholarship)* [1227]
Kimberly Marie Rogers Memorial Scholarship Fund *(Undergraduate, Vocational/Occupational/Scholarship)* [4057]
Mister Rogers Memorial Scholarship *(Graduate, Master's, Doctorate/Scholarship)* [47]
Joseph Wood Rogers Memorial Scholarships *(Undergraduate/Scholarship)* [8880]
Mary Stuart Rogers Scholarships *(Undergraduate/Scholarship)* [10561]
Sandra Journey Rolf Scholarship Fund *(Undergraduate, Graduate/Scholarship)* [5760]
Rome Prize *(Doctorate, Graduate/Prize, Award)* [424]
Ronald McDonald House Charities African American Future Achievers Scholarships *(Undergraduate/Scholarship)* [8639]
Ronald McDonald House Charities/HACER Scholarships *(Undergraduate/Scholarship)* [8640]
Ronald McDonald House Charities Scholarships in Asia *(Undergraduate/Scholarship)* [8642]
Ronald McDonald House Charities Scholarships *(Undergraduate/Scholarship)* [8641]
Charles and Ruth Ronin Memorial Scholarships *(Undergraduate/Scholarship)* [8524]
Dorothy Worden Ronken Scholarships *(Graduate/Scholarship)* [3594]
Susanna Stover Root Memorial Scholarship *(Undergraduate/Scholarship)* [5761]
Roothbert Fund Scholarships *(Undergraduate/Scholarship)* [8646]
Barnes W. Rose, Jr. and Eva Rose Nichol Scholarship Fund *(Undergraduate/Scholarship)* [304]
Carl Rose Memorial Scholarships *(Undergraduate/Scholarship)* [7858]
Florence C. Rose and S. Meryl Rose Scholarships *(Graduate, Master's, Doctorate/Scholarship)* [6259]
Dr. Wayne F. Rose Scholarship Fund *(Undergraduate/Scholarship)* [4058]
Betty Rose Scholarships *(Undergraduate/Scholarship)* [1276]
Clarence J. Rosecrans Scholarship *(Graduate, Master's, Doctorate/Scholarship)* [1151]
Rosemary Quigley Memorial Scholarships *(Undergraduate, Graduate/Scholarship)* [2341]
Esther Katz Rosen Fund Grants *(Graduate, Doctorate/Grant)* [1152]
Jack Rosen Scholarship *(Undergraduate/Scholarship)* [5683]
Mandell and Lester Rosenblatt Undergraduate Scholarships *(Undergraduate/Scholarship)* [9217]
Walter A. Rosenblith New Investigator Award *(Postdoctorate/Award)* [4806]
Barbara Rosenblum Cancer Dissertation Scholarships *(Doctorate/Fellowship, Scholarship)* [9333]
Marshall N. Rosenbluth Outstanding Doctoral Thesis Award *(Doctorate/Award)* [1093]

Place of Study Index — UNITED STATES

ASPPH/CDC Allan Rosenfield Global Health Fellowship Program *(Postdoctorate, Postgraduate/Fellowship)* [2065]
Jean and Tom Rosenthal Scholarship Program *(Undergraduate/Scholarship)* [3332]
IADR Norton Ross Fellowship *(Postdoctorate/Fellowship)* [5253]
S. Byrl Ross Memorial Scholarship Fund *(Undergraduate/Scholarship)* [7859]
Colonel Jerry W. Ross Scholarship *(Undergraduate/Scholarship)* [1585]
The Bea and Harry Ross Scholarship Endowment *(Graduate/Scholarship)* [9586]
Ross Trust Future School Counselors Essay Competition *(Master's, Doctorate/Award, Prize)* [750]
Rotary Club of Annapolis Scholarship *(Undergraduate/Scholarship)* [1561]
The Rotary Club of Cape Coral Goldcoast Scholarship Fund *(Undergraduate/Scholarship)* [2784]
The Rotary Club of Rancho Bernardo Sunrise Community Service Scholarships *(Undergraduate/Scholarship)* [8725]
Rotary Foundation Global Grant Scholarships *(Graduate/Scholarship)* [8648]
Rotary Peace Fellowship Program *(Graduate, Master's/Fellowship)* [3701]
Rotary Public Safety Scholarships *(Undergraduate/Scholarship)* [4212]
Richard J. Roth Journalism Fellowships *(Graduate/Fellowship)* [7369]
Marjorie Roy Rothermel Scholarships *(Master's/Scholarship)* [1800]
Hal Rothman Dissertation Fellowships *(Doctorate, Graduate/Fellowship)* [1316]
Theodore Rousseau Fellowships *(Graduate/Fellowship)* [6436]
Marion and Donald Routh Student Research Grants *(Undergraduate/Grant)* [1572]
Rove Pest Control Scholarships *(Undergraduate/Scholarship)* [8650]
Rovelstad Scholarship in International Librarianship *(Undergraduate, Graduate/Award, Scholarship)* [3452]
Roy Rowan Scholarships *(Graduate, Undergraduate/Scholarship)* [7778]
Leo S. Rowe Pan American Fund *(Graduate, Undergraduate/Loan)* [7730]
Ellis W. Rowe Scholarships *(Undergraduate/Scholarship)* [4703]
Travis Roy Foundation Individual Grants *(All/Grant)* [8652]
Lucille and Edward R. Roybal Foundation Public Health Scholarships *(Graduate, Undergraduate/Scholarship)* [8654]
RSDSA Research Grants *(Other/Grant)* [8532]
RSNA/AAPM Fellowships for Graduate Study in Medical Physics *(Graduate/Fellowship)* [560]
RSNA/AUR/APDR/SCARD Radiology Education Research Development Grant *(Professional development/Grant)* [8418]
RSNA Education Scholar Grant *(Professional development/Grant)* [8419]
RSNA Research Scholar Grants *(Professional development/Grant)* [8420]
RSNA Research Seed Grants *(Professional development/Grant)* [8421]
RTDNA Presidents Scholarships *(Undergraduate/Scholarship)* [8411]
The Viking Voices - Mike Ruben Honorarium and John Rice Memorial Scholarship *(Undergraduate/Scholarship)* [7860]
IPMI Richard Rubin Memorial Scholarship Award *(Graduate/Award)* [5374]
IRARC Memorial Joseph P. Rubino WA4MMD Scholarships *(Undergraduate/Scholarship)* [1754]
Paul and Ellen Ruckes Scholarships *(Graduate, Undergraduate/Scholarship)* [823]
Lawrence E. and Mabel Jackson Rudberg Scholarships *(Undergraduate, Graduate/Scholarship)* [3722]
Joe Rudd Scholarships *(Master's, Juris Doctorate/Scholarship)* [8637]
Lim Ruger Foundation Scholarships *(Undergraduate/Scholarship)* [5544]
Damon Runyon Clinical Investigator Awards *(Doctorate, Graduate, Postdoctorate/Fellowship, Award)* [3518]
Hermann G. Rusch Scholarships *(Other/Scholarship, Grant)* [763]
Russell Athletics Scholarship *(Undergraduate/Scholarship)* [2109]
Dave & Laurie Russell Family Scholarships for Habitat for Humanity of Kent County Families *(Undergraduate/Scholarship)* [4619]
Liane B. Russell Fellowships *(Postdoctorate/Fellowship)* [9908]
Kenneth W. Russell Memorial Fellowships *(Undergraduate, Graduate/Fellowship)* [661]
Norman K. Russell Scholarships *(Graduate, Doctorate/Scholarship)* [7092]
Michael A. Russo Memorial Scholarships *(Undergraduate/Scholarship)* [8525]
The Anthony C. Russo Scholarships *(Graduate/Scholarship)* [7115]
NPELRA Foundation - Anthony C. Russo Scholarships *(Graduate/Scholarship)* [7116]
Lucile Rust Scholarships *(Undergraduate/Scholarship)* [8106]
IOIA Andrew Rutherford Scholarships *(Other/Scholarship)* [5370]
Ralph and Clara Rutledge Memorial Scholarships *(Graduate/Scholarship)* [4149]
Deborah Jean Rydberg Memorial Scholarships *(Undergraduate/Scholarship)* [3299]
Charles A. Ryskamp Research Fellowships *(Postgraduate, Postdoctorate, Professional development/Fellowship)* [744]
SAA Native American Scholarships *(Undergraduate, Graduate, Professional development/Scholarship)* [9079]
SABA NC - Organizational Fellowships *(Undergraduate/Fellowship)* [9352]
SABA NC - Pro Bono Fellowships *(Undergraduate/Fellowship)* [9353]
SABA NC - Public Interest Fellowships *(Undergraduate/Fellowship)* [9354]
SAC Scholarships for Higher Education *(Undergraduate/Scholarship)* [9558]
Sacks For CF Scholarships *(Professional development/Scholarship)* [2342]
SAEMS Environmental Scholarships *(Undergraduate, Graduate/Scholarship)* [9396]
Safelink Internet Scholarships *(Undergraduate/Scholarship)* [8666]
Safer Athletic Field Environments Scholarships (SAFE) *(Graduate, Undergraduate/Scholarship)* [9481]
Russell Sage Foundation Visiting Scholars *(Postdoctorate/Fellowship)* [8668]
Ruth Sager Scholarships *(Undergraduate, Graduate/Scholarship)* [6260]
SAH Study Tour Fellowships *(Graduate/Fellowship)* [9085]
Don Sahli-Kathy Woodall Graduate Scholarships *(Graduate/Scholarship)* [9677]
Sons and Daughters Don Sahli-Kathy Woodall Scholarships *(Graduate, Undergraduate/Scholarship)* [9678]
St. Francis Xavier Scholarships *(Undergraduate/Scholarship)* [10725]
St. James Armenian Church Memorial Scholarships *(Undergraduate/Scholarship)* [1704]
St. Joseph's Hospital School of Nursing Alumnae Scholarship *(Undergraduate/Scholarship)* [7861]
St. Louis Paralegal Association Student Scholarships *(Undergraduate/Scholarship)* [8673]
Saints Cyril and Methodius Scholarships *(Undergraduate/Scholarship)* [8657]
SAJA Journalism Scholarships *(Undergraduate, Graduate/Scholarship)* [9356]
Joseph and Amelia Saks Scholarship Fund *(Undergraduate/Scholarship)* [3270]
The Bill, W2ONV, and Ann Salerno Memorial Scholarship *(Undergraduate/Scholarship)* [1755]
Eugene Gene Sallee, W4YFR Memorial Scholarships *(Undergraduate/Scholarship)* [1756]
Sally Beauty Scholarships for High School Graduates *(Undergraduate/Scholarship)* [8286]
Salon Supply Store Cosmetology Scholarships *(Undergraduate/Scholarship)* [8678]
Ann S. Salsberg Scholarship Awards *(Undergraduate/Award, Scholarship)* [2516]
Salvatori Fellowships *(Graduate/Fellowship)* [5234]
Henry Salvatori Scholarships *(Undergraduate/Scholarship)* [7684]
The Walter Samek III Memorial Scholarship Fund *(Undergraduate/Scholarship)* [3207]
SAMFund Grants *(Advanced Professional/Grant)* [8682]
Margaret Jerome Sampson Scholarships *(Undergraduate/Scholarship)* [8107]
Ray and Pearl Sams Scholarships *(Undergraduate/Scholarship)* [10597]
Samsung American Legion Scholarships *(Undergraduate/Scholarship)* [957]
San Angelo Area Foundation Scholarships *(All/Scholarship)* [8684]
The San Diego Foundation Community Scholarships I *(Undergraduate/Scholarship)* [8726]
San Pasqual Academy Scholarships *(Undergraduate/Scholarship)* [8728]
Bill Sanderson Aviation Maintenance Technician Scholarships *(Postgraduate/Scholarship)* [4841]
Leonard H. Sandler Fellowships *(Graduate/Fellowship)* [5000]
The Amato Sanita Brighter Future Scholarships *(Undergraduate, Graduate, Advanced Professional/Scholarship)* [379]
SANS Inc./Mead Leadership Fellows Program *(Professional development/Fellowship)* [7509]
Santa Clara La Raza Lawyers Scholarships *(Graduate/Scholarship)* [5894]
SAO (Smithsonian Astrophysical Observatory) Predoctoral Fellowships *(Graduate/Fellowship)* [4782]
Bert Saperstein Communication Scholarships *(Undergraduate/Scholarship)* [8758]
Saratoga County Bar Association Law Student Scholarships *(Undergraduate/Scholarship)* [8760]
Frank Sarli Memorial Scholarship *(Undergraduate/Scholarship)* [6899]
Saskatchewan Trucking Association Scholarships *(Undergraduate/Scholarship)* [8784]
Malini E. Sathyadev Memorial Scholarships *(Undergraduate/Scholarship)* [8729]
Sho Sato Memorial Scholarships *(Undergraduate, Graduate/Scholarship)* [5557]
Curtis M. Saulsbury Scholarship Fund *(Undergraduate/Scholarship)* [3201]
Kevin Saunders Wheelchair Success Scholarships *(Undergraduate/Scholarship)* [3107]
Save Mart Legacy Scholarships *(Undergraduate/Scholarship)* [2458]
Herbert M. Saylor Memorial Scholarship *(Graduate/Scholarship)* [9341]
SBE/Ennes Youth Scholarships *(Undergraduate/Scholarship)* [9094]
S.C. Johnson, A Family Company Scholarships *(Undergraduate/Scholarship)* [3013]
SC and R Foundation Scholarships *(Undergraduate/Scholarship)* [9460]
Leslie and Mary Ella Scales Memorial Scholarships *(Undergraduate/Scholarship)* [3271]
SC&R Foundation Grant Program *(Undergraduate/Grant)* [9461]
SCBWI Student Illustrator Scholarship *(Undergraduate, Graduate/Grant, Scholarship)* [9099]
SCBWI Student Writer Scholarship *(Graduate, Doctorate, Undergraduate/Grant, Scholarship)* [9100]
SCBWI Work-in-Progress Awards *(Advanced Professional/Grant, Award)* [9101]
SCCLA Fellowships *(Graduate/Fellowship)* [9398]
SCCLA Scholarships *(Graduate/Scholarship)* [9399]
SCDAA Post-Doctoral Research Fellowships *(Doctorate/Fellowship)* [8892]
Mary Turnbull Schacht Memorial Scholarships *(Undergraduate/Scholarship)* [8934]
David W. Schacht Native American Student Scholarships *(Undergraduate/Scholarship)* [2231]
Millicent M. Schaffner Endowed Memorial Scholarships *(Undergraduate/Scholarship)* [4542]
Schallek Awards *(Graduate/Award)* [6397]
Schallek Fellowships *(Graduate/Fellowship)* [6398]
Abe Schechter Graduate Scholarships *(Graduate/Scholarship)* [8400]
Schedulers and Dispatchers Monetary Scholarships *(Other/Scholarship)* [6837]
Leopold Schepp Foundation Scholarships *(Undergraduate, Graduate/Scholarship)* [8788]
Robert C. and Margaret A. Schikora Scholarships

(Undergraduate/Scholarship) [9447]
Justin G. Schiller Fellowships (Doctorate, Postdoctorate/Fellowship) [445]
Arthur M. Schlesinger, Jr. Fellowships (Professional development/Fellowship) [5603]
Harold W. Schloss Memorial Scholarship Fund (Undergraduate/Scholarship) [2810]
Julie Schmid Research Scholarship (Advanced Professional/Scholarship) [2033]
CSF Charlotte R. Schmidlapp Scholarships (Undergraduate/Scholarship) [3014]
Ronald L. Schmied Scholarships (Other, Undergraduate/Scholarship) [4686]
Bernadotte E. Schmitt Grants (Doctorate/Grant) [856]
Richard J. Schnell Memorial Scholarships (Postdoctorate/Scholarship) [3300]
Stanley M. Schoenfeld Memorial Scholarship (Postgraduate/Scholarship) [7363]
Lillian P. Schoephoerster Scholarships (Undergraduate/Scholarship) [8108]
Dale M. Schoettler Scholarships (Undergraduate, Graduate/Scholarship) [8753]
The Scholarship Foundation of St. Louis Scholarships (Graduate, Undergraduate/Scholarship) [8796]
Scholarship Foundation of Santa Barbara Art Scholarship Program (Undergraduate/Scholarship) [8798]
Scholarship Foundation of Santa Barbara General Undergraduate, Vocational and Graduate/Medical Scholarships and Loans Program (Undergraduate, Graduate/Scholarship) [8799]
The Scholarship Foundation of Wakefield Scholarships (All/Scholarship) [8802]
Scholarship for Junior PHS Commissioned Officers (Undergraduate/Scholarship) [8115]
Scholarships for an Education Towards Law (Graduate/Scholarship) [3812]
Scholarships for a Higher Education in Law (Graduate/Scholarship) [2361]
Scholarships of the Morris Radio Club of New Jersey (Undergraduate/Scholarship) [1757]
Scholarships for Veterans with Post-Traumatic Stress Disorder (All/Scholarship) [8624]
School Library Paraprofessional Scholarships - Southern Region (Advanced Professional/Scholarship) [2474]
School Nutrition Association of Kansas Education Scholarship (Undergraduate/Scholarship) [8810]
Schoolsfirst Federal Credit Union Scholarships (Undergraduate/Scholarship) [8526]
Schrank Family Scholarships (Undergraduate/Scholarship) [10189]
Kurt H. and Donna M. Schuler Cash Grants (Undergraduate/Scholarship, Grant) [1254]
Richard E. Schultes Research Awards (Graduate/Grant, Award) [9113]
David and Jinny Schultz Family Scholarship (Undergraduate/Scholarship) [4543]
Al Schuman/Ecolab Undergraduate Entrepreneurial Scholarships (Undergraduate/Scholarship) [7120]
James F. Schumar Scholarships (Graduate/Fellowship) [1039]
Schurgin Family Foundation Scholarships (Undergraduate/Scholarship) [5308]
Nelson Schwab Jr. Scholarships (Undergraduate/Scholarship) [3015]
AIST William E. Schwabe Memorial Scholarships (Undergraduate/Scholarship) [2007]
Schwan's Food Service Scholarships (Vocational/Occupational/Scholarship) [8806]
Marla Schwartz Education Grant (Graduate, Professional development/Grant) [534]
Marla Schwartz Grants (Professional development, Graduate/Grant) [535]
Stephen Schwartz Musical Theatre Scholarships (Undergraduate/Scholarship) [4988]
Abba P. Schwartz Research Fellowships (Professional development/Fellowship) [5604]
Judge Benjamin Schwartz Scholarships (Undergraduate/Scholarship) [3016]
Fritz Schwartz Serials Education Scholarships (Graduate, Other/Scholarship) [7447]
Evalee C. Schwarz Educational Loans (Undergraduate, Graduate/Loan) [8812]

David R. Schweisberg Memorial Scholarships (Graduate, Undergraduate/Scholarship) [7779]
Science, Mathematics And Research for Transformation Scholarship for Service Program (SMART) (Undergraduate, Graduate/Scholarship) [1305]
SCIRTS (Spinal Cord Injury Research on the Translational Spectrum) Pilot Research Grants (Professional development/Grant) [7257]
SCIRTS (Spinal Cord Injury Research on the Translational Spectrum) Postdoctoral Fellowships (Postdoctorate/Fellowship) [7258]
SCIRTS (Spinal Cord Injury Research on the Translational Spectrum) Senior Research Grants (Professional development/Grant) [7259]
SCLEOA Scholarships (Undergraduate/Scholarship) [9361]
Scleroderma Foundation Established Investigator Grants (Doctorate/Grant) [8816]
Scleroderma Foundation New Investigator Grants (Doctorate/Grant) [8817]
SCLMA Medical Student Scholarships (Undergraduate, Graduate/Scholarship) [9401]
Carl A. Scott Book Scholarships (Undergraduate/Scholarship) [3456]
IADR David B. Scott Fellowship (Professional development/Fellowship, Award) [5254]
Herbert Scoville Jr. Peace Fellowships (Graduate/Fellowship) [8825]
CSF E.W. Scripps Foundation Scholarship Fund (Undergraduate/Scholarship) [3017]
Bonnie Sorenson Scudder Scholarships (Undergraduate/Scholarship) [3301]
Seabee Memorial Scholarship Association Scholarships (Undergraduate/Scholarship) [9043]
Glenn T. Seaborg Congressional Science and Engineering Fellowships (Professional development/Fellowship) [1040]
Lewis L. Seaman Junior Enlisted Awards for Outstanding Operational Support (Professional development/Recognition) [1541]
David and Sharon Seaver Family Scholarship Fund (Undergraduate/Scholarship) [4544]
SEE Education Foundation Scholarships (Undergraduate, Graduate, Doctorate/Scholarship) [5418]
Seed Companies Scholarships (Undergraduate, Graduate/Scholarship) [811]
Margery J. Seeger Scholarships (Undergraduate/Scholarship) [4620]
Dr. Eugene M. Seidner Student Scholarship Program (Undergraduate, Graduate/Scholarship) [35]
Seldovia Native Association Achievement Scholarships (Undergraduate, Graduate/Scholarship) [8829]
Seldovia Native Association General Scholarships (Undergraduate, Graduate/Scholarship) [8830]
SEMA Memorial Scholarships (Graduate, Undergraduate/Scholarship) [9464]
Senior Innovation Scholarships (Undergraduate, Graduate/Scholarship) [8146]
SeniorAdvice Caregiver Scholarships (Undergraduate/Scholarship) [8840]
SeniorAdvice Volunteer Scholarships (Undergraduate/Scholarship) [8841]
Sentinels of Freedom Scholarships (Advanced Professional/Scholarship) [8843]
William "Buddy" Sentner Scholarship Awards (Undergraduate/Scholarship) [566]
Senyk Memorial Scholarships (Undergraduate, Master's/Scholarship) [10801]
SEO Optimizers Scholarships (All/Scholarship) [8845]
Felix R. Sepulveda Memorial Scholarships - Northside Booster Club (Undergraduate/Scholarship) [8527]
Sequoyah Graduate Scholarships (Master's/Scholarship) [1834]
Serbian Bar Association of America Scholarships (Graduate/Scholarship) [8847]
Charles W. Serby COPD Research Fellowships (Professional development/Fellowship) [1216]
Sertoma Communicative Disorders Scholarship (Undergraduate/Scholarship) [8849]
Sertoma Hard of Hearing and Deaf Scholarships (Undergraduate/Scholarship) [8850]
Service League Volunteer Scholarships (Undergraduate/Scholarship) [10447]

Frank B. Sessa Scholarship (Professional development/Scholarship) [2241]
Margaret B. Ševčenko Prize in Islamic Art and Culture (Doctorate/Prize) [4909]
John R. Sevier Memorial Scholarship Award (Undergraduate/Scholarship) [9998]
Hubert K. and JoAnn Seymour Scholarships (Undergraduate/Scholarship) [7492]
SFP Junior Investigator's Career Development Awards (Other/Grant) [9119]
SFP Mid-Career/Mentor Awards for Family Planning (Other/Grant) [9120]
SFP Student Research Grants (Graduate/Grant) [9121]
Al Shackleford and Dan Martin Professional Scholarships (Professional development/Scholarship) [2193]
Albert R. and Alma Shadle Fellowships (Graduate/Fellowship) [1361]
Charles Shafae Scholarships (Undergraduate/Scholarship) [7799]
Elizabeth Shafer Memorial Scholarships (Undergraduate/Scholarship) [8362]
SHAFR Dissertation Completion Fellowships (Doctorate/Fellowship) [9140]
Saleem Shah Early Career Award (Doctorate/Recognition) [1158]
Josephine Hooker Shain Scholarships (Undergraduate/Scholarship) [4372]
Albert F. Shanker Scholarship (Undergraduate/Scholarship) [796]
John M. and Mary A. Shanley Memorial Scholarships (Undergraduate, Graduate/Scholarship) [9448]
William H. Shannon Fellowships (Graduate, Undergraduate/Fellowship) [5445]
Law Office of David P. Shapiro Annual Leukemia Scholarships (All/Scholarship) [5949]
Ken and Sandy Sharkey Family Scholarship Fund (Undergraduate/Scholarship) [4545]
W.L. Shattuck Scholarships (Undergraduate/Scholarship) [5046]
Benjamin G. Shatz Scholarships (Undergraduate/Scholarship) [8004]
Luci Shaw Fellowship (Undergraduate/Fellowship) [5081]
Anne Shaw Fellowships (Graduate/Fellowship) [9727]
Josephine Kerbey Shaw Memorial Undergraduate Scholarship (Undergraduate/Scholarship) [5763]
Donna Gail Shaw Scholarship for Chapter Service (Undergraduate, Graduate, Doctorate/Scholarship) [5684]
Shear-Miles Agricultural Fellowship (Graduate, Doctorate/Fellowship) [10205]
Shear-Miles Agricultural Scholarship (Graduate, Doctorate/Scholarship) [10206]
Regina B. Shearn Scholarships (Graduate, Undergraduate/Scholarship) [357]
Jim Sheerin Scholarships (Undergraduate/Scholarship) [6362]
Sheet Metal And Air Conditioning Contractors' National Association College of Fellows Scholarships (Undergraduate/Scholarship) [8859]
Nettie and Edward Shelah Scholarships (Undergraduate/Scholarship) [9576]
Shell Incentive Scholarship Fund (Undergraduate/Scholarship) [8861]
Shell Oil Company Technical Scholarships (Undergraduate/Scholarship) [8862]
Shell Process Technology Scholarships (Undergraduate/Scholarship) [8863]
Susan Goldsmith Shelley Scholarship (Undergraduate/Scholarship) [5764]
Bruce Shelton Scholarships (Undergraduate/Scholarship) [10598]
Bill and Ann Sheperd Legal Scholarship Fund (Undergraduate/Scholarship) [3923]
Robert P. Sheppard Leadership Awards (High School/Scholarship) [7162]
Morgan and Jeanie Sherwood Travel Grants (Graduate, Other/Grant) [1317]
Shields-Gillespie Scholarships (Other/Scholarship) [1056]
Jacqueline Shields Memorial Scholarships (Graduate/Scholarship) [142]

Milton L. Shifman Endowed Scholarships *(Undergraduate, Graduate/Scholarship)* [6261]
Chiyoko and Thomas Shimazaki Scholarships *(Graduate/Scholarship)* [5558]
Everett Oscar Shimp Memorial Scholarships *(Undergraduate/Scholarship)* [7862]
Pat Shimp Memorial Scholarships *(Undergraduate/Scholarship)* [7863]
The Shincho Graduate Fellowships for Study in Japan *(Graduate/Fellowship)* [5802]
Joseph Shinoda Memorial Scholarships *(Undergraduate/Scholarship)* [8867]
Jason Shipley Memorial Scholarships *(Undergraduate/Scholarship)* [7041]
Shohet Scholars Program *(Professional development/Grant)* [5290]
S. David Shor Scholarships *(Undergraduate/Scholarship)* [3018]
Shoreline Community College Full-Time Continuing Students Scholarships *(Undergraduate/Scholarship)* [8881]
Shoreline Community College Part-Time Students Scholarships *(Undergraduate/Scholarship)* [8882]
Shoreline - Lake Forest Park High School Scholarship *(Undergraduate/Scholarship)* [8883]
SHOT-NASA Fellowships *(Doctorate, Postdoctorate/Fellowship)* [9144]
Thomas E. Shown, M.D. Memorial Scholarships *(Undergraduate/Scholarship)* [10599]
SHPE Dissertation Scholarship *(Doctorate/Scholarship)* [9130]
SHPE Professional Scholarship *(Master's, Doctorate/Scholarship)* [9131]
Ralph W. Shrader Diversity Scholarship *(Graduate/Scholarship)* [91]
SHRM Certification Scholarships - Individual *(Professional development/Scholarship)* [9147]
SHRM Foundation Academic Scholarships *(Graduate, Undergraduate/Scholarship)* [9148]
Law Office of Matthew Shrum Annual Scholarships for Single Mothers *(Undergraduate/Scholarship)* [5953]
Clifford G. Shull Fellowships *(Postdoctorate/Fellowship)* [9909]
Phil Shykes Memorial Scholarships *(Undergraduate/Scholarship)* [3723]
Mary Isabel Sibley Fellowships *(Doctorate/Fellowship)* [8053]
SICB Fellowships of Graduate Student Travel (FGST) *(Graduate/Fellowship)* [9157]
SICB Grants-in-Aid of Research Program (GIAR) *(Graduate/Grant)* [9158]
Don and Madalyn Sickafoose Educational Trust *(Undergraduate/Scholarship)* [9533]
Sidley Diversity and Inclusion Scholarships *(Undergraduate/Scholarship)* [8894]
Sidley Prelaw Scholars Initiative *(Undergraduate/Scholarship)* [8895]
Norman Siegel Research Scholar Grants *(Doctorate/Grant)* [1382]
Jeff Siegel Scholarships *(Undergraduate/Scholarship)* [7359]
Myrtle Siegfried, MD and Michael Vigilante, MD Scholarships *(Undergraduate/Scholarship)* [4279]
Siemens-ASCP Scholarship *(Undergraduate/Scholarship)* [1263]
Siemens Clinical Advancement Scholarship *(Undergraduate, Master's/Scholarship)* [1400]
E.J. Sierleja Memorial Fellowships *(Graduate/Fellowship)* [5194]
Sigma Delta Epsilon Fellowships *(Graduate, Postdoctorate/Fellowship)* [8907]
Sigma Diagnostics Student Scholarships *(Undergraduate/Scholarship)* [7171]
Sigma Kappa Foundation Alumnae Continuing Education Scholarships *(Undergraduate/Scholarship)* [8935]
Sigma Kappa Foundation Alzheimer's/Gerontology Scholarships *(Graduate/Scholarship)* [8936]
Sigma Kappa Foundation Founders' Scholarships *(Undergraduate/Scholarship)* [8937]
Sigma Kappa Foundation Gerontology Scholarships *(Undergraduate/Scholarship)* [8938]
APSAIL's Ralph Silverman Memorial Scholarships *(Undergraduate/Scholarship)* [2126]
Meyer D. and Dorothy C. Silverman Scholarship *(Undergraduate/Scholarship)* [3251]
Harvey L. Simmons Memorial Scholarships *(Undergraduate/Scholarship)* [8730]
Linda Simmons Memorial Scholarships *(Undergraduate/Scholarship)* [219]
Willard B. Simmons Sr. Memorial Scholarships *(Undergraduate/Scholarship)* [6871]
Julian Simon Fellowships *(Other/Fellowship)* [8300]
Simon Youth Foundation Community Scholarships *(Undergraduate/Scholarship)* [8959]
Simonton Windows Scholarships *(Undergraduate/Scholarship)* [7864]
Carole Simpson Scholarships *(Undergraduate/Scholarship)* [8412]
Lowe Simpson Scholarships *(Undergraduate/Scholarship)* [3019]
Sino-American Pharmaceutical Professionals Association Scholarships *(Undergraduate/Scholarship)* [8971]
Helen J. Sioussat/Fay Wells Scholarships *(Graduate/Scholarship)* [2371]
Gadde Sitaramamma and Tirupataiah Scholarships *(Graduate/Scholarship)* [9670]
Bill Six Memorial Scholarship Fund *(Undergraduate/Scholarship)* [7865]
Six Meter Club of Chicago Scholarships *(Undergraduate/Scholarship)* [1758]
Sixt Rent a Car Scholarships *(Undergraduate/Scholarship)* [8973]
Leif and Inger Sjöberg Awards *(Advanced Professional, Professional development/Award, Grant, Prize)* [1235]
Skadden Fellowships *(Graduate/Fellowship)* [8978]
Ruth Skeeles Memorial Scholarship Fund *(Undergraduate/Scholarship)* [9534]
Frank Foster Skillman Scholarships *(Undergraduate/Scholarship)* [3020]
Francelene Skinner Memorial Scholarships *(Undergraduate/Scholarship)* [6067]
Rand Skolnick Point Scholarship *(Undergraduate, Graduate, Doctorate/Scholarship)* [8191]
Skooblie Scholarships *(Undergraduate/Scholarship)* [8984]
Allogan Slagle Memorial Scholarships *(Undergraduate, Graduate/Scholarship)* [1835]
SLEAMC Scholarships *(Graduate, Undergraduate/Scholarship)* [8865]
Robert W. Sledge Fellowships *(Graduate/Fellowship)* [344]
Sleeping Angels Co. Scholarships *(All/Scholarship)* [8986]
J. Ward Sleichter and Frances F. Sleichter Memorial Scholarship Fund *(Undergraduate/Scholarship)* [4254]
Slifka Foundation Interdisciplinary Fellowships *(Doctorate, Master's/Fellowship)* [6437]
Alfred P. Sloan Foundation Graduate Scholarships - Sloan Indigenous Graduate Partnership *(Master's, Doctorate/Scholarship)* [6683]
Alfred P. Sloan Foundation Graduate Scholarships - Sloan Minority Ph.D. Program *(Doctorate/Scholarship)* [6684]
Sloan Northwood University Heavy-Duty Scholarships *(Undergraduate/Scholarship)* [2127]
Sloan Research Fellowships *(Doctorate/Fellowship)* [8988]
The Aaron and Rita Slom Scholarships *(Undergraduate/Scholarship)* [9762]
Ann Kelsay Small Scholarship *(Undergraduate/Scholarship)* [5766]
SME Coal and Energy Division Scholarships *(Undergraduate/Scholarship)* [9212]
SME Directors Scholarships *(Undergraduate/Scholarship)* [9194]
SME Education Foundation Family Scholarships *(Undergraduate/Scholarship)* [9195]
SME Environmental Division Scholarships *(Undergraduate, Graduate/Scholarship)* [9213]
Dr. George M. Smerk Scholarships *(Undergraduate, Graduate/Scholarship)* [1169]
SMFM/AAOGF Scholarship Awards *(Graduate/Scholarship)* [9206]
SmileMarketing Dental Scholarships *(Doctorate/Scholarship)* [8990]
James I. Smith, III Notre Dame Law School Scholarship Fund *(Graduate, Undergraduate/Scholarship)* [329]
David H. Smith Conservation Research Fellowships *(Postdoctorate/Fellowship)* [9109]
Ryan and Jamie Smith Essay Contest *(Graduate, Postgraduate/Scholarship)* [8992]
Ronald T. Smith Family Scholarships *(Undergraduate, Graduate/Scholarship)* [4621]
Henry DeWitt Smith Graduate Scholarships *(Graduate/Scholarship)* [9214]
Gladys Ann Smith Greater Los Angeles Women's Council Scholarships *(Undergraduate/Scholarship)* [7230]
Stanley Smith Horticultural Fellowships *(Graduate, Undergraduate/Fellowship)* [7744]
Brian and Cathy Smith Memorial Fund *(Graduate/Scholarship)* [1016]
Colonel Nate Smith Memorial Scholarships *(Graduate, Undergraduate/Scholarship)* [6374]
Drew Smith Memorial Scholarships *(Undergraduate/Scholarship)* [3187]
The Eileen J. Smith, R.N. Memorial Scholarships *(Undergraduate/Scholarship)* [5512]
Ralph and Josephine Smith Scholarship Fund *(Undergraduate/Scholarship)* [4060]
A.O. Smith Scholarships *(Undergraduate/Scholarship)* [8164]
C. Bainbridge Smith Scholarships *(Undergraduate/Scholarship)* [7344]
Esther M. Smith Scholarships *(Undergraduate/Scholarship)* [3188]
Helen J. and Harold Gilman Smith Scholarships *(Graduate, Undergraduate/Scholarship)* [2232]
Richard S. Smith Scholarships *(Undergraduate/Scholarship)* [9858]
William E. Smith Scholarships *(Graduate/Scholarship)* [199]
Drue Smith/Society of Professional Journalists Scholarships *(Undergraduate/Scholarship)* [3252]
Nadine Barrie Smith Student Awards *(Undergraduate/Award)* [5433]
Smith's Personal Best Scholarships *(Undergraduate/Scholarship)* [8363]
Smithsonian Institution Graduate Student Fellowships *(Graduate/Fellowship)* [9015]
Smithsonian Institution Postdoctoral Fellowships *(Doctorate/Fellowship)* [9016]
Smithsonian Institution Predoctoral Fellowships *(Doctorate/Fellowship)* [9017]
Smithsonian Institution Senior Fellowships *(Doctorate/Fellowship)* [9018]
Smithsonian Postgraduate Fellowships in Conservation of Museum Collection Program *(Postgraduate/Fellowship)* [9019]
Eric E. Smoker Memorial Scholarships *(Undergraduate/Scholarship)* [7521]
Virginia M. Smyth Scholarships *(Graduate/Scholarship)* [4382]
Gladys Snauble Scholarships *(Undergraduate/Scholarship)* [4622]
SNF Professional Growth Scholarships *(Graduate, Undergraduate/Scholarship)* [8807]
SNMMI-TS Advanced Practitioner Program Scholarship *(Professional development/Scholarship)* [9224]
SNMMI-TS Bachelor's Degree Completion Scholarships *(Undergraduate/Scholarship)* [9225]
William Brewster Snow Award *(Graduate/Award, Monetary)* [1954]
A.C. Snow and Katherine Snow Smith Scholarship *(Undergraduate/Scholarship)* [10251]
Helen D. Snow Memorial Scholarships *(Undergraduate/Scholarship)* [8056]
Snowmobile Association of Massachusetts Scholarships *(Undergraduate/Scholarship)* [9045]
SNRS Dissertation Research Grants *(Doctorate/Grant)* [9406]
SNRS Research Grants *(Professional development/Grant)* [9407]
SNRS/STTI Research Grants *(Professional development/Grant)* [9408]
SOAP/Kybele International Outreach Grant *(Advanced Professional, Professional development/Grant)* [9231]
Arnold Sobel Scholarships *(Undergraduate/Scholarship)* [3081]

SOBP Travel Fellowship Award-Early Career Investigator(International) *(Postdoctorate/Award)* [9090]
Society of Allied Weight Engineers Scholarships *(Undergraduate/Scholarship)* [9077]
Society for the Arts in Healthcare Student Scholarships *(Doctorate, Graduate, Undergraduate/Scholarship)* [9088]
Society of Exploration Geophysicists Foundation Scholarships *(Graduate, Undergraduate/Scholarship)* [9117]
Society for Linguistic Anthropology Student Essay Prize *(Graduate, Undergraduate/Prize)* [9163]
Society of Manufacturing Engineers Ford PAS Scholarships (SME) *(Undergraduate/Scholarship)* [9197]
Society of Marine Port Engineers Scholarship Loans *(Undergraduate/Scholarship loan)* [9204]
Society of Pediatric Nurses Educational Scholarships *(Graduate, Other/Scholarship)* [9241]
Society for Pediatric Radiology Research Fellows *(Graduate, Other/Fellowship)* [9243]
Society for Pediatric Radiology Seed Grants *(Graduate, Other/Grant)* [9244]
Society for Pediatric Urology Research Grant Program *(Undergraduate/Grant)* [9247]
Society for the Scientific Study of Sexuality Student Research Grants *(Undergraduate/Grant)* [9302]
Society of Vacuum Coaters Foundation Scholarships *(Vocational/Occupational, Two Year College, Undergraduate, Graduate/Scholarship)* [9323]
SOHN Allied Health to BSN Degree Scholarship *(Undergraduate/Scholarship)* [9233]
Louis B. Sohn Fellowships in Human Rights and Environment *(Graduate/Fellowship)* [2849]
SOHN Graduate Degree Scholarship *(Undergraduate/Scholarship)* [9234]
SOHN RN to BSN Degree Scholarship *(Undergraduate/Scholarship)* [9235]
Dale and Betty George Sola Scholarships *(Undergraduate/Scholarship)* [3724]
The Thomas Soldan Healthy Communities Scholarships *(Undergraduate, Graduate/Scholarship)* [8237]
Carrie Fox Solin Blow Molding Division Memorial Scholarships *(Undergraduate/Scholarship)* [9268]
SOM Foundation Architecture, Design and Urban Design Prize *(Graduate, Undergraduate/Prize)* [8980]
SOM Foundation Structural Engineering Travel Fellowships *(Doctorate, Graduate, Master's, Undergraduate/Fellowship)* [8981]
SOM Foundation Travel Fellowships in Architecture, Design and Urban Design *(Graduate, Undergraduate/Fellowship)* [8982]
SOMA Student Research Fellowships *(Undergraduate/Fellowship)* [9601]
Dr. Kiyoshi Sonoda Memorial Scholarships *(Graduate, Master's, Doctorate/Scholarship)* [5559]
Sons of Union Veterans of the Civil War Scholarships *(Undergraduate/Scholarship)* [9348]
Sony Pictures Scholarships *(Graduate/Scholarship)* [2027]
SOPHE/ATSDR Student Fellowships in Environmental Health or Emergency Preparedness *(Doctorate, Graduate, Master's/Fellowship)* [9292]
SOPHE/CDC Student Fellowships in Child, Adolescent and School Health *(Doctorate, Graduate, Master's/Fellowship)* [9293]
SOPHE/CDC Student Fellowships in Injury Prevention *(Graduate/Fellowship)* [9294]
Theodore C. Sorensen Research Fellowships *(Professional development/Fellowship)* [5605]
Soroptimist International of Redlands Scholarships *(Undergraduate/Scholarship)* [8528]
Paul & Daisy Soros Fellowships *(Graduate/Fellowship)* [9350]
Soros Justice Advocacy Fellowships - Track I *(Professional development/Fellowship)* [7664]
Soros Justice Advocacy Fellowships - Track II *(Professional development/Fellowship)* [7665]
Soros Justice Media Fellowships - Track I *(Professional development/Fellowship)* [7666]
Soros Justice Media Fellowships - Track II *(Professional development/Fellowship)* [7667]
SORP Student Conference Scholarship *(Graduate, Undergraduate/Scholarship)* [9237]

Eastman Kodak Dr. Theophilus Sorrell Fellowships *(Graduate/Fellowship)* [7090]
John Soto Scholarships *(Undergraduate/Scholarship)* [3362]
South Carolina Association for Financial Professionals Certified Treasury Professional Scholarships *(Other/Scholarship)* [9358]
South Carolina Tourism and Hospitality Educational Foundation Scholarships *(Undergraduate/Scholarship)* [9366]
South Central Modern Language Association Fellowships *(Doctorate, Postdoctorate/Fellowship)* [7424]
South Central Power Scholarships *(Undergraduate/Scholarship)* [9373]
South Coast Area High School Senior Honors Scholarship Program *(Undergraduate/Scholarship)* [8800]
South Jersey Golf Association Scholarships *(Undergraduate/Scholarship)* [9379]
South Kentucky RECC High School Senior Scholarships *(Undergraduate/Scholarship)* [9382]
Southeast Alabama Dietetic Association Scholarships *(Graduate, Undergraduate/Scholarship)* [200]
Southern Maine Women's Golf Association Scholarships *(Professional development/Scholarship)* [9403]
Southern Nevada Sports Hall of Fame Scholarships *(Undergraduate/Scholarship)* [8364]
Southwest Florida Community Foundation College Assistance Scholarships *(Undergraduate/Scholarship)* [9449]
Southwest Florida Deputy Sheriffs Association Fund Scholarships *(Undergraduate/Scholarship)* [9450]
Southwest Movers Association Scholarships *(Undergraduate/Scholarship)* [9454]
Sovereign Nations Scholarships *(Undergraduate/Scholarship)* [872]
Iwalani Carpenter Sowa Scholarships *(Graduate/Scholarship)* [7919]
Master Sergeant William Sowers Memorial Scholarships *(Undergraduate/Scholarship)* [133]
Michael P. Spadafora Medical Toxicology Travel Awards *(Professional development/Grant)* [690]
Kathy Spadoni Memorial Scholarships *(Undergraduate/Scholarship)* [8264]
Spangenberg Shibley & Liber Video PSA Scholarship Awards *(Undergraduate/Scholarship)* [9456]
Nathan Sparks Memorial Scholarships *(Undergraduate/Scholarship)* [3272]
Spartan Staff Scholarships *(Undergraduate/Scholarship)* [8365]
SPE Foundation General Scholarships *(Undergraduate, Graduate/Scholarship)* [9269]
SPE Injection Molding Division Scholarships *(Undergraduate, Graduate/Scholarship)* [9271]
SPE Student Awards for Innovations in Imaging *(Undergraduate, Graduate/Scholarship)* [9252]
SPE Thermoforming Division Memorial Scholarships *(Undergraduate, Graduate/Scholarship)* [9272]
SPE Thermoplastic Elastomers Special Interest Group Scholarship *(Undergraduate, Graduate/Scholarship)* [9273]
SPE Thermoplastic Materials and Foams Division Scholarships *(Undergraduate/Scholarship)* [9274]
SPE Vinyl Plastics Division Educational Grants *(Undergraduate/Grant)* [9275]
Special Fund for the Study of Women and Politics *(Graduate, Postdoctorate/Grant)* [1123]
Specialty Equipment Market Association Scholarships *(Graduate, Undergraduate, Vocational/Occupational/Scholarship)* [9465]
Specialty Nursing Scholarships *(Undergraduate/Scholarship)* [4270]
Faith Speckhard Scholarships *(Undergraduate/Scholarship)* [5513]
Spice Box Grants *(Advanced Professional/Grant)* [764]
SPIE Student Author Travel Grants *(Graduate, Undergraduate/Grant)* [9472]
Phillip A. Spiegel IASP Congress Trainee Scholarship *(College, Graduate, Undergraduate/Scholarship)* [5276]
Lawrence Alan Spiegel Remembrance Scholarships *(Undergraduate/Scholarship)* [4920]

Charles and Carol Spielberger Scholarships *(Graduate, Master's, Doctorate/Scholarship)* [1153]
Enid W. and Bernard B. Spigel Architectural Scholarships *(Graduate, Undergraduate/Scholarship)* [4706]
Spirit of Anne Frank Outstanding Scholarship Award *(Undergraduate/Scholarship)* [1563]
The Spirit Square Center for Arts and Education Scholarship Fund *(Undergraduate/Scholarship)* [4214]
Spokeo Connections Scholarships *(Undergraduate/Scholarship)* [9478]
SPOOM Research Grants *(Graduate/Grant)* [9277]
Sporty's/Cincinnati Avionics Scholarships *(Undergraduate, Vocational/Occupational/Scholarship)* [172]
Spouse Tuition Aid Loan Program (STAP) *(Undergraduate, Graduate/Loan)* [7236]
Jim Springer Memorial Scholarships *(Undergraduate/Scholarship)* [3110]
SPS Future Teacher Scholarships *(Undergraduate/Scholarship)* [9256]
SPS Leadership Scholarships *(Undergraduate/Scholarship)* [9257]
SPSmedical CS Scholarships *(Other/Scholarship)* [5264]
SPSSI Grants-In-Aid Program *(Graduate, Postdoctorate/Grant)* [9287]
SRC Master's Scholarships Program (MSP) *(Graduate, Master's/Scholarship)* [8835]
SREB-State Doctoral Scholars Program - Dissertation Awards *(Doctorate/Scholarship, Award)* [9410]
SREB-State Doctoral Scholars Program - Doctoral Awards *(Doctorate, Graduate/Scholarship)* [9411]
SRF Post-doctoral Fellowships *(Postdoctorate/Fellowship)* [8819]
SSF Research Grants *(Other/Grant)* [8975]
SSF Student Fellowships *(Doctorate, Undergraduate/Fellowship)* [8976]
SSOC Scholarships *(Undergraduate/Scholarship)* [8786]
The SSPI Mid-Atlantic Chapter Scholarships *(Graduate, Undergraduate/Scholarship)* [9300]
John F. and Anna Lee Stacey Scholarships *(All/Scholarship)* [6901]
Ernest and Charlene Stachowiak Memorial Scholarships *(Undergraduate/Scholarship)* [3302]
Stafford Loan for Graduate Students - Unsubsidized Stafford Loans *(Graduate/Loan)* [9486]
Matt Stager Memorial Scholarship Fund *(Undergraduate/Scholarship)* [10482]
Steven A. Stahl Research Grants *(Graduate/Grant)* [5358]
Standard and Poor's Award for Economic and Business Reporting - S&P Scholarships *(Graduate, Undergraduate/Scholarship)* [7780]
Marion Barr Stanfield Art Scholarships *(Graduate, Undergraduate/Scholarship)* [9840]
Otto M. Stanfield Law Scholarships *(Graduate/Scholarship)* [9841]
A.R.O.Y. Stanitz Scholarships *(Undergraduate/Scholarship)* [1228]
J. Newell Stannard Fellowships *(Graduate/Fellowship)* [4812]
Thomas J. Stanton, Jr. Scholarships *(Graduate/Scholarship)* [8853]
Star-Ledger Scholarships for the Performing Arts *(Undergraduate/Scholarship)* [7324]
Stark County Bar Association Fund *(Undergraduate/Scholarship)* [9535]
Stark County Dairy Promoters Scholarships *(Undergraduate/Scholarship)* [9536]
Kenneth and Barbara Starks Plant Resistance to Insects Graduate Student Research Awards *(Graduate/Grant)* [3884]
Peggy P. Starks Scholarship *(Postgraduate/Scholarship)* [9702]
STC Scholarships *(Graduate, Undergraduate/Scholarship)* [9311]
The Stanley H. Stearman Awards *(Undergraduate/Scholarship)* [7135]
Robert P. Stearns/SCS Engineers Scholarships *(Graduate/Scholarship)* [9339]
Tom Steel Post-Graduate Fellowships *(Postgraduate, Other/Fellowship)* [8274]
Joseph L. and Vivian E. Steele Music Scholarship

Fund *(Undergraduate/Scholarship)* [4256]
Peter T. Steinwedell Scholarships *(Undergraduate/Scholarship)* [4772]
Elin J. Stene/Xi Scholarships *(Undergraduate/Scholarship)* [8940]
Step Up Scholarships *(Undergraduate, Graduate/Scholarship)* [8731]
Gabe Stepetin Business Scholarship Awards *(Undergraduate, Vocational/Occupational, Graduate, Master's/Scholarship)* [312]
Mike Stephenson Legal Scholarships *(Graduate/Scholarship)* [6370]
Elizabeth Coulter Stephenson Scholarships *(Undergraduate/Scholarship, Grant)* [3595]
Joseph S. Stern, Jr. Scholarships *(Undergraduate/Scholarship)* [3021]
Charles Sternberg Scholarship *(Graduate/Scholarship)* [1844]
Richard Stessel Memorial Scholarships *(Graduate/Scholarship)* [143]
AGWT Thomas M. Stetson Scholarships *(Undergraduate/Scholarship)* [841]
Raymond H. Stetson Scholarships in Phonetics and Speech Science *(Graduate/Scholarship)* [54]
Christine K. Stevens Development Scholarships *(Undergraduate, Graduate/Scholarship)* [1017]
Stevens Doctoral Awards *(Doctorate/Award)* [5312]
Benjamin F. Stevens Fellowships *(Professional development/Fellowship)* [6337]
Zachary Taylor Stevens Memorial Scholarships *(Undergraduate/Scholarship)* [1759]
H.L. Stevenson Scholarships *(Graduate, Undergraduate/Scholarship)* [7781]
Richie Stevenson Scholarships *(Undergraduate, Vocational/Occupational/Scholarship)* [3253]
Allegheny Branch of Mid-America Chapter - Nancy Stewart Professional Development Scholarships *(Professional development/Scholarship)* [1443]
Mary Stewart and William T. Covington, Jr. Scholarship Fund *(Undergraduate/Scholarship)* [4215]
Dr. Gunnar B. Stickler Scholarships *(Undergraduate, Vocational/Occupational/Scholarship)* [9578]
Dell Chenoweth Stifel Scholarship *(Graduate/Scholarship)* [5767]
The Richard Stockton College of New Jersey Foundation Alumni Association Graduate Awards *(Graduate/Scholarship)* [9587]
Louis Stokes Health Scholars Program *(Undergraduate/Scholarship)* [3349]
Louis Stokes Urban Health Policy Fellows Program *(Other/Fellowship)* [3350]
Ralph W. Stone Graduate Fellowships *(Graduate/Fellowship, Grant)* [7184]
Stop Hunger Scholarships *(Undergraduate/Scholarship)* [573]
Stop-Painting.com Scholarships *(Undergraduate/Scholarship)* [5147]
Martin L. Stout Scholarships *(Undergraduate, Graduate/Scholarship)* [1949]
George A. Strait Minority Scholarship *(Graduate/Scholarship)* [536]
Bonnie Strangio Education Scholarships *(Graduate, Undergraduate/Scholarship)* [2343]
Carole J. Streeter, KB9JBR Scholarships *(Undergraduate/Scholarship)* [1760]
Stanley W. Strew Educational Fund Scholarships *(Undergraduate/Scholarship)* [2438]
STRI Short-Term Fellowships *(Undergraduate, Graduate, Postdoctorate/Fellowship)* [9038]
Norman E. Strohmeier, W2VRS Memorial Scholarships *(Undergraduate/Scholarship)* [1761]
Robby Strong Cancer Survivor Scholarships *(Graduate/Scholarship)* [6596]
Mark and Karla Stuart Family Scholarship *(Undergraduate/Scholarship)* [8732]
Student Investigator Research Grant - General Audiology/Hearing Science *(Graduate, Doctorate/Grant)* [394]
Student Investigator Research Grant - Hearing Aids, Clinical Protocols and Patient Outcomes *(Graduate, Doctorate/Grant)* [395]
Student Investigator Research Grant - Vestibular *(Graduate, Doctorate/Grant)* [396]
Student Research Awards from the Behavioral Gerontology SIG *(Undergraduate, Graduate/Award, Monetary)* [1861]

Student Summer Research Fellowship *(Undergraduate, Graduate/Fellowship)* [397]
Student Training and Research in Tumor Immunology Grants *(Graduate/Grant)* [2775]
Stultz Scholarships *(Undergraduate/Scholarship)* [10600]
Horace W. Stunkard Scholarships *(Undergraduate, Graduate/Scholarship)* [6262]
Anne Sturrock Nursing Scholarships *(Undergraduate, Graduate/Scholarship)* [9451]
AIST Southeast Member Chapter Gene Suave Scholarships *(Undergraduate/Scholarship)* [2008]
Subic Bay-Cubi Point Scholarships *(Undergraduate/Scholarship)* [7231]
Edward P. Suchecki Family Scholarship Fund *(Undergraduate/Scholarship)* [4549]
Caroline tum Suden/Frances Hellebrandt Professional Opportunity Awards *(Postdoctorate, Other/Award)* [1101]
Suffolk Public Interest Law Group Summer Fellowships (SPILG) *(Undergraduate/Fellowship)* [8438]
Vallabhaneni Sukundamma and Lakshmaiah Scholarships *(Graduate/Scholarship)* [9671]
Jerome M. Sullivan Research Funds *(Professional development/Grant)* [1217]
Phil Sullivan Scholarships *(Undergraduate/Scholarship)* [8265]
VPPPA William Sullivan Scholarships *(Graduate, Undergraduate/Scholarship)* [10418]
William A. Sullivan Scholarships *(Undergraduate/Scholarship)* [7232]
Roger K. Summit Scholarships for North America *(Graduate/Scholarship)* [8302]
Hatton W. Sumners Endowed Law Schools Scholarships *(Undergraduate, Graduate/Scholarship)* [9608]
Hatton W. Sumners Endowed Undergraduate School Scholarships *(Undergraduate/Scholarship)* [9609]
Hatton W. Sumners Non-Endowed Undergraduate and Graduate Scholarships *(Undergraduate, Graduate/Scholarship)* [9610]
Surety and Fidelity Industry Intern and Scholarship Program for Minority Students *(Undergraduate/Scholarship)* [9614]
SUS Foundation Junior Faculty Grants *(Other/Grant)* [9320]
Sussman-Miller Educational Assistance Award Program *(Undergraduate/Scholarship)* [305]
SUT Houston Graduate Scholarships *(Graduate/Scholarship)* [9317]
SUT Houston Undergraduate Scholarships *(Undergraduate/Scholarship)* [9318]
Sutherland/Purdy Scholarships *(Undergraduate/Scholarship)* [8109]
Margaret Svec Scholarships *(Undergraduate/Scholarship)* [8884]
Lorraine E. Swain Scholarships *(Undergraduate/Scholarship)* [8941]
Swede Swanson Memorial Scholarships *(Undergraduate/Scholarship)* [7243]
Daniel Swarovski and Company Scholarships *(Graduate/Scholarship)* [4345]
Henry D. and Ruth G. Swartz Family Scholarship Fund *(Undergraduate/Scholarship)* [4550]
Hanns Swarzenski and Brigitte Horney Swarzenski Fellowship *(Graduate/Fellowship)* [6438]
SWE Scholarships *(Undergraduate, Graduate/Scholarship)* [9329]
Jeffrey Tyler Sweitzer Wrestling Memorial Scholarship Fund *(Undergraduate/Scholarship)* [9537]
Swensrud Teacher Fellowships at MHS (Massachusetts Historical Society) *(Professional development/Fellowship)* [6338]
Timothy S. Sweterlitsch Memorial Scholarship Fund *(Undergraduate/Scholarship)* [9538]
Stan Swinton Scholarships *(Graduate, Undergraduate/Scholarship)* [7782]
Mary Switzer Research Fellowships - Distinguished Fellowships *(Doctorate/Fellowship)* [9896]
Mary Switzer Research Fellowships - Merit Fellowships *(Professional development/Fellowship)* [9897]
IRFI Dr. Mubin I. Syed Scholarship and Mohtarama Afshan J. Syed Scholarship *(Undergraduate/Scholarship)* [5482]

Symantec Research Labs Graduate Fellowships *(Doctorate, Graduate/Fellowship)* [9625]
Harry Taback 9/11 Memorial Scholarships *(Undergraduate/Scholarship)* [1429]
Hazaros Tabakoglu Scholarship Fund *(Undergraduate/Scholarship)* [1705]
The Tabat Scholarship Fund *(Graduate/Scholarship)* [4005]
TAC Foundation-Stantec Consulting Scholarships *(Graduate/Scholarship)* [9790]
John I. and Madeleine R. Taeni Scholarships *(Undergraduate/Scholarship)* [9452]
Tag and Label Manufacturers Institute Scholarships - Four-Year Colleges *(Undergraduate/Scholarship)* [9629]
Tag and Label Manufacturers Institute Scholarships - Two-Year Colleges *(Undergraduate/Scholarship)* [9630]
Tailhook Educational Foundation Scholarship Program *(Undergraduate/Scholarship)* [9632]
Taiwanese American Community Scholarships *(Undergraduate/Scholarship)* [9634]
Kei Takemoto Memorial Scholarships *(Undergraduate/Scholarship)* [173]
Tall Awareness Scholarships *(Undergraduate/Scholarship)* [8366]
Tall Clubs International Student Scholarships *(Undergraduate/Scholarship)* [9638]
Justice Stephen K. Tamura Scholarships *(Undergraduate/Scholarship)* [5545]
TANA Foundation Graduate Scholarships *(Graduate/Scholarship)* [9672]
Mitsuyoshi Tanaka Dissertation Award in Experimental Particle Physics *(Doctorate/Award)* [1094]
Alexander M. Tanger Scholarships *(Graduate/Scholarship)* [2372]
William J. Tangye Scholarships *(Undergraduate/Scholarship)* [5302]
Martha W. Tanner Memorial Scholarships *(Undergraduate/Scholarship)* [3022]
Hal Tanner Sr. Scholarships *(Undergraduate/Scholarship)* [10252]
Alex Tanous Scholarship Award *(Undergraduate/Scholarship)* [9642]
Frederick A. Tarantino Memorial Scholarship Award *(Undergraduate/Scholarship)* [9999]
Lee Tarbox Memorial Scholarships *(Undergraduate/Scholarship)* [174]
Targeted Research Initiative for Health Outcomes *(Doctorate/Grant)* [3909]
Tarkanian Teacher Education Academy at Clark High School Scholarships *(Undergraduate/Scholarship)* [8367]
Bud and Linda Tarrson Fellowships *(Professional development/Fellowship)* [422]
TaskEasy Scholarships for Future Entrepreneurs *(Undergraduate/Scholarship)* [9646]
Jack Tate/ThinkCOLLEGE Scholarship Fund *(Undergraduate/Scholarship)* [4216]
Jordan B. Tatter Scholarships *(Undergraduate/Scholarship)* [6488]
Taylor/Blakeslee University Fellowships *(Other, Undergraduate/Fellowship)* [3429]
Joshua C. Taylor Fellowships *(Doctorate, Postdoctorate/Fellowship)* [9006]
Ryan "Munchie" Taylor Memorial Scholarships *(Undergraduate/Scholarship)* [6154]
The Ed Tayter Outstanding Citizen Scholarships *(Undergraduate/Scholarship)* [8238]
TCA-ACBH Scholarships *(Undergraduate/Scholarship)* [9712]
TCA Outstanding Graduate Student Awards *(Graduate/Award)* [9695]
TCA Scholarship *(Undergraduate/Scholarship)* [9800]
TCA-UMD Scholarships *(Undergraduate/Scholarship)* [9813]
TCAdvance Scholarships *(Undergraduate/Scholarship)* [9814]
TCATA College Scholarship Program *(Undergraduate/Scholarship)* [9721]
Teacher Education Scholarships *(Advanced Professional/Scholarship)* [1008]
Teacher Librarian Scholarships *(Master's/Scholarship)* [2475]
Teacher of the Visually Impaired Loans *(Under-

UNITED STATES

graduate, Graduate/Loan) [9556]
Tech Mastery Scholarships (Undergraduate/Scholarship) [8551]
TechChecks Business Leadership Scholarships (Undergraduate/Scholarship) [9650]
Technical Women's Organization Education Scholarships (TWO) (Undergraduate/Scholarship) [9652]
Dwight Teed Scholarships (Undergraduate/Scholarship) [9612]
Marvin H. and Kathleen G. Teget Leadership Scholarships (Undergraduate/Scholarship) [9602]
Paul Tejada Memorial Scholarships (Undergraduate/Scholarship) [5514]
Telecommunications Association of Michigan Scholarship Fund (Undergraduate/Scholarship) [9663]
Telford Scholarships (Undergraduate/Scholarship) [40]
Tell Us Your Story Scholarships (Undergraduate/Scholarship) [10495]
Telluride Association Summer Program Scholarships (Undergraduate/Scholarship) [9665]
Lee Teng Undergraduate Fellowships in Accelerator Science and Engineering (Undergraduate/Fellowship) [9903]
Mary L. Tenopyr Graduate Student Scholarships (Doctorate/Scholarship) [9154]
The Terra Foundation Fellowships in American Art (Undergraduate, Doctorate, Postdoctorate/Fellowship) [9007]
Terra Foundation Fellowships at the Smithsonian American Art Museum (Postdoctorate/Fellowship) [9680]
Terra Foundation Research Travel Grants (Doctorate, Undergraduate/Grant) [9683]
Marc Tetalman, MD, Memorial Award (Professional development, Doctorate/Recognition) [9227]
Steven M. Teutsch Prevention Effectiveness Fellowships (Doctorate/Fellowship) [9921]
Texas Computer Education Association Professional Educator Grants (Other/Grant) [9693]
Texas Mutual Scholarship Program (Undergraduate, Vocational/Occupational/Scholarship) [9709]
Texas Scholarships of Academic Excellence (Undergraduate, Graduate/Scholarship) [9559]
Texas Society of Professional Engineers Scholarships (Undergraduate/Scholarship) [9711]
Texas State Technical College Scholarships (Undergraduate/Scholarship) [176]
Jim and Pat Thacker Sports Communication Internships (Undergraduate/Grant) [10253]
ThanksUSA Scholarships (Undergraduate, Vocational/Occupational/Scholarship) [9723]
The Cover Guy Annual Scholarships (Undergraduate, Graduate/Scholarship) [3463]
Theatre Guild Scholarship (Undergraduate/Scholarship) [9725]
Thermo Scientific Educational Scholarships (Professional development/Scholarship) [7172]
Thesaurus Linguae Latinae Fellowships (TTL) (Doctorate/Fellowship) [9107]
Elizabeth R. Thomas Alumni Nursing Scholarship (Undergraduate/Scholarship) [8885]
Charles C. Thomas Scholarship (Undergraduate/Scholarship) [1586]
C.R. Thomas Scholarships (Undergraduate/Scholarship) [7867]
Rev. Chuck and Nancy Thomas Scholarships (Professional development/Scholarship) [9842]
Thome Foundation Awards Program in Age-Related Macular Degeneration Research (Professional development/Grant) [4824]
Thome Foundation Awards Program in Alzheimer's Disease Drug Discovery Research (Professional development/Grant) [4825]
Matilda B. Thompson Scholarship (Undergraduate/Scholarship) [4929]
Barbara and Howard Thompson Scholarships (Undergraduate/Scholarship) [5515]
Thompson Scholarships for Women in Safety (Graduate/Scholarship) [1430]
Thornberg/Havens Scholarships (Undergraduate/Scholarship) [3596]
Thomas P. Thornton Scholarships (Undergraduate/Scholarship) [5089]
Thurgood Marshall Fellowships Program (Undergraduate/Fellowship) [7345]

Tidewater Builders Association Scholarships (Undergraduate/Scholarship) [9739]
Tiftickjian Law Firm, P.C. Juvenile Justice Law School Scholarships (Postgraduate/Scholarship) [9741]
Tikvah Fellowships (Graduate, Professional development/Fellowship) [9745]
The AIWF/Patricia Tillinghast Memorial Scholarships (Graduate, Undergraduate/Scholarship) [939]
Tillman Scholars Program (Undergraduate, Graduate/Scholarship) [7901]
Eben Tisdale Fellowships (Undergraduate/Fellowship) [4310]
TMA Research Fellowships (Postdoctorate/Grant, Fellowship) [6641]
TMCF Scholarships (Undergraduate/Scholarship) [9735]
Mario J. Tocco Hydrocephalus Foundation Scholarships (Undergraduate/Scholarship) [5028]
Richard Cecil Todd and Clauda Pennock Todd Tripod Scholarships (Graduate, Undergraduate/Scholarship) [8082]
CSF Christopher Todd Grant Memorial Scholarships (Undergraduate/Scholarship) [3023]
Robert Toigo Foundation Fellowships (Master's/Fellowship) [9747]
John L. Tomasovic, Sr. Scholarships (Undergraduate/Scholarship) [812]
Took Trust Point Scholarship (Undergraduate, Graduate, Doctorate/Scholarship) [8192]
George Torkildsen Literary Awards (Professional development/Award, Trophy) [10705]
Aram Torossian Memorial Scholarships (Undergraduate/Scholarship) [1706]
Ferdinand Torres Scholarships (Graduate, Undergraduate/Scholarship) [824]
Tortuga Backpacks Study Abroad Scholarships (Undergraduate/Scholarship) [9756]
Touchstone Special Achievement Scholarships (Undergraduate/Scholarship) [7588]
Tourette Association of America Research Grant Awards (Master's, Doctorate/Grant) [9758]
Town and County Club Scholarships (Undergraduate/Scholarship) [4773]
Toyota Financial Services Point Scholarship (Undergraduate, Graduate, Doctorate/Scholarship) [8193]
Toyota/TELACU Scholarships (Undergraduate/Scholarship) [9661]
The Joyce Tracy Fellowships (Doctorate/Fellowship) [446]
Marie Trahan/Susman Godfrey Scholarships (Undergraduate/Scholarship) [9820]
TRALA Industry Scholarship Awards (Undergraduate/Scholarship) [9798]
Vera Tran Memorial Scholarships (Undergraduate/Scholarship) [10388]
Reuben Trane Scholarships (Undergraduate/Scholarship) [1334]
Transamerica Retirement Solutions Leaders in Health Care Scholarships (Graduate/Scholarship) [5169]
Transatlantic Fellows Program (Other/Fellowship) [4400]
Translational Research Professorship (Professional development/Internship) [3387]
Transoft Solutions, Inc. Ahead of the Curve Scholarships (AOTC) (Graduate, Undergraduate/Scholarship) [5221]
Traub-Dicker Rainbow Scholarships (Undergraduate/Scholarship) [9590]
Morton M. Traum Surface Science Student Awards (Graduate, Doctorate/Prize) [2157]
Edward Traurig Scholarships (Undergraduate/Scholarship) [10484]
Trelut Family Legacy Scholarships (Undergraduate/Scholarship) [2459]
Tri Delta Alpha Eta Scholarships (Undergraduate/Scholarship) [3559]
Tri Delta Alpha Rho Leadership Scholarships (Undergraduate/Scholarship) [3560]
Tri Delta Atlanta Alumnae Achievement Scholarships (Undergraduate/Scholarship) [3561]
Tri Delta Houston Alumnae Chapter Graduate Fellowships (Graduate/Fellowship, Scholarship) [3563]
Tri Delta Northern Virginia Alumnae Chapter Scholarships (Undergraduate/Scholarship) [3564]
Tribute Fund Community Grant (Professional development/Grant) [9102]
Tim Triner Letter Carriers Scholarship Fund (Undergraduate/Scholarship) [9539]
J.P. and Madeline Trinkaus Endowed Scholarships in Embryology (Graduate, Master's, Doctorate/Scholarship) [6263]
Johnny Trombly Scholarships (Undergraduate/Scholarship) [6572]
Mildred E. Troske Music Scholarships (Undergraduate/Scholarship) [4627]
Vincent Trotter Health Care Scholarships (Undergraduate/Scholarship) [8735]
Charlie Trotters's Culinary Education Foundation Scholarships (Other, Undergraduate/Scholarship) [765]
Jo Anne J. Trow Scholarships (Undergraduate/Scholarship) [6697]
Truckload Carriers Association Scholarships (Undergraduate/Scholarship) [9801]
William H. Truettner Fellowships (Undergraduate, Doctorate, Postdoctorate/Fellowship) [9008]
TrustedPros Scholarships (Undergraduate/Scholarship) [9805]
Trustees College Scholarships (Undergraduate/Scholarship) [6171]
Norman J. Tschantz/Walter C. Deuble Scholarships (Undergraduate/Scholarship) [9540]
Tucker Family Scholarships (Undergraduate/Scholarship) [10254]
Barry Tuckwell Scholarships (All/Scholarship) [5346]
Richard R. Tufenkian Memorial Scholarships (Undergraduate/Scholarship) [1671]
Graydon A. Tunstall Undergraduate Student Scholarships (Undergraduate/Scholarship) [8049]
Turf and Ornamental Communicators Association Scholarship Program (Undergraduate/Scholarship) [9809]
Hans Turley Prize in Queer Eighteenth-Century Studies (Graduate, Other/Prize) [1297]
Jeff Turner-Forsyth Audubon Society Scholarships (Undergraduate/Scholarship) [10601]
James A. Turner, Jr. Memorial Scholarships (Undergraduate/Scholarship) [1525]
Lydia Donaldson Tutt-Jones Memorial Research Grant (Graduate, Other, Master's/Grant) [93]
Two Year/Community Broadcast Education Association Scholarship Awards (Graduate/Scholarship) [2373]
TxHIMA HIA-HIT Scholarship (Undergraduate/Scholarship) [9703]
TxHIMA Outstanding Student Scholarship (Undergraduate/Scholarship) [9704]
William R. Tyler Fellowships (Graduate/Fellowship) [3740]
Florence Tyson Grants to Study Music Pyschotherapy (Professional development/Grant) [1018]
UAA Janice K. Barden Aviation Scholarships (Undergraduate/Scholarship) [6838]
UC MEXUS-CICESE Short-term Research & Training Program (Graduate/Award, Grant) [10115]
UC MEXUS-CONACYT Collaborative Grants (Professional development/Grant) [10116]
UC MEXUS-CONACYT Doctoral Fellowships (Doctorate/Fellowship) [10117]
UC MEXUS-CONACYT Postdoctoral Research Fellowships (Postdoctorate/Fellowship) [10118]
UC MEXUS Dissertation Research Grants (Graduate/Grant) [10119]
UC MEXUS Scholars in Residence Program - Graduate (Graduate/Scholarship) [10120]
UC MEXUS Scholars in Residence Program - Recent University Graduates (Postgraduate/Scholarship) [10121]
UC MEXUS Scholars in Residence Program - Visiting Faculty (Professional development/Scholarship) [10122]
UC MEXUS Small Grants for UC Faculty (Graduate/Grant) [10123]
UC MEXUS Small Grants for UC Postdocs (Postdoctorate/Grant) [10124]
UC MEXUS Small Grants for UC Students (Graduate, Postdoctorate/Grant) [10125]
UCT Scholarships (Graduate, Other, Undergraduate/Scholarship) [7686]

Morris K. Udall Scholarships *(Undergraduate/Scholarship)* [9825]
UF Center for Latin American Studies FLAS Summer Fellowships *(Master's, Graduate, Undergraduate/Award, Fellowship)* [10133]
UFCW Local Union Scholarships *(Undergraduate/Scholarship)* [9847]
UH Manoa Starr Foundation Graduate Fellowships in Asian Studies *(Graduate/Grant)* [10138]
Sandy Ulm Scholarships *(Undergraduate/Scholarship)* [4081]
Ric Ulrich and Chuck Pischke Scholarships *(Undergraduate/Scholarship)* [8266]
UMBS Istock Family Scholarships *(Undergraduate/Scholarship)* [10190]
UMBS Returning Student Award *(Undergraduate/Scholarship)* [10191]
UMDF Clinical Research Fellowship Training Awards *(Professional development/Fellowship)* [9860]
UNCF/Merck Graduate Science Research Dissertation Fellowships *(Graduate/Fellowship)* [6426, 9862]
UNCF/Merck Postdoctoral Science Research Fellowships *(Postdoctorate/Fellowship)* [6427, 9863]
Undergraduate/Graduate Scholarships *(Undergraduate, Graduate/Scholarship)* [5315]
Union of Marash Armenian Scholarships *(Undergraduate, Graduate/Scholarship)* [1707]
Union Plus Scholarship Program *(Undergraduate/Scholarship)* [5451]
United Engineering Foundation Grants *(All/Grant)* [9845]
United Health Foundation National Association of Hispanic Nurses Scholarships *(Graduate, Undergraduate/Scholarship)* [6758]
United Methodist General Scholarships *(Undergraduate, Graduate/Scholarship)* [9856]
United Parcel Service Scholarships for Female Students *(Undergraduate/Scholarship)* [5195]
United Parcel Service Scholarships for Minority Students *(Undergraduate/Scholarship)* [5196]
United South and Eastern Tribes Scholarship Fund *(Undergraduate/Scholarship)* [9868]
U.S. Air Force ROTC Express Scholarships *(Undergraduate/Scholarship)* [9872]
U.S. Air Force ROTC High School Scholarships *(Undergraduate/Scholarship)* [9873]
U.S. Air Force ROTC In-College Scholarships *(Undergraduate/Scholarship)* [9874]
U.S. Aircraft Insurance Group Professional Development Program (USAIG PDP) Scholarships *(Undergraduate/Scholarship)* [6839]
U.S. Bates Scholarship Program *(Undergraduate/Scholarship)* [5452]
U.S. BIA Indian Higher Education Grants *(Undergraduate/Grant)* [878]
United States Capitol Historical Society Fellowships *(Graduate/Fellowship)* [9886]
The United States Department of State, Bureau of Educational & Cultural Affairs Fellowships *(Graduate/Fellowship)* [1199]
United States Geospatial Intelligence Foundation Graduate Scholarships *(Graduate/Scholarship)* [9945]
United States Geospatial Intelligence Foundation High School Scholarships *(Undergraduate/Scholarship)* [9946]
United States Geospatial Intelligence Foundation Undergraduate Scholarships *(Undergraduate/Scholarship)* [9947]
U.S. Medical Supplies' Medical Professionals of Tomorrow Scholarships *(Undergraduate, Graduate/Scholarship)* [9964]
United States Society on Dams Scholarships *(Graduate, Undergraduate/Scholarship)* [9971]
U.S.-U.K. Young Investigator Exchange Fellowship *(Postdoctorate/Fellowship)* [376]
UnitedAg Scholarship Program *(Undergraduate/Scholarship)* [9988]
Universal Studios Preservation Scholarships *(Graduate/Scholarship)* [2028]
University of Hawaii at Manoa Graduate Assistantship Awards *(Graduate/Award)* [10140]
University of Hawaii at Manoa Graduate Student Organization Travel Funds *(Graduate/Grant)* [10141]
University of Hawaii at Manoa Japan Travel Bureau Scholarships *(Graduate, Undergraduate/Scholarship)* [10142]
University of Louisville Eagle Scout Scholarships *(Undergraduate/Scholarship)* [6932]
University of Puget Sound LGBT Leadership Scholarships Fund *(Undergraduate/Scholarship)* [8664]
University of Southern Mississippi Eagle Scout/Gold Award Scholarship *(Undergraduate/Scholarship)* [6933]
University of Texas at Austin Special Research Grants *(Professional development/Grant)* [10276]
University of Wisconsin-Madison Chancellor's Scholarships *(Undergraduate/Scholarship)* [10328]
UPE Scholarship Awards *(Graduate, Undergraduate/Scholarship)* [10342]
Upper Midwest Human Rights Fellowship Program *(Graduate/Scholarship, Fellowship)* [4996]
UPS Diversity Scholarships *(Undergraduate/Scholarship)* [1431]
Urban and Regional Policy (Comparative Domestic Policy) Fellowships *(Other/Fellowship)* [4401]
The Urban Scholarship Fund *(Undergraduate/Scholarship)* [9689]
Urology Care Foundation/Astellas Rising Star in Urology Research Awards *(Postdoctorate, Other/Award)* [10347]
USA Funds Access to Education Scholarships *(Graduate, Undergraduate/Scholarship)* [9986]
USA/USA-Ukramerazha Scholarships *(Undergraduate/Scholarship)* [9982]
USAttorneys.com Immigration Scholarships Essay Contest *(Undergraduate/Scholarship)* [10353]
USAttorneys.com National Scholarships Essay Contest *(Undergraduate/Scholarship)* [10354]
USAWOASF Regular Scholarships *(Undergraduate/Scholarship)* [9881]
USDA-NIFA-AFRI Merit Awards *(Postdoctorate/Award)* [9308]
USGA/Chevron STEM Scholarship Program *(Undergraduate/Scholarship)* [9954]
USHJA General Scholarships *(Undergraduate/Scholarship)* [9956]
USPAACC Ampcus Hallmark Scholarships *(Undergraduate/Scholarship)* [9968]
USPAACC Denny's Hungry for Education Scholarship *(Undergraduate/Scholarship)* [9969]
USS Coral Sea Remembrance Scholarships *(Undergraduate/Scholarship)* [10358]
USTA Serves College Education Scholarships *(Undergraduate/Scholarship)* [9977]
USTA Serves College Textbook Scholarship *(Undergraduate/Scholarship)* [9978]
Utility Workers Union of America Scholarship Program *(Undergraduate/Scholarship)* [10360]
John D. Utterback Scholarship Program *(Undergraduate/Scholarship)* [322]
U.V.A. Faculty Fellowships *(Professional development/Fellowship)* [10313]
UW-Madison GLBT Alumni Council Scholarships *(Undergraduate, Graduate/Scholarship)* [10332]
VABANC Scholarships *(Graduate, Undergraduate/Scholarship)* [10383]
Marta Vallin Memorial Scholarships *(Undergraduate/Scholarship)* [3363]
ValuePenguin Scholarships *(Undergraduate/Scholarship)* [10362]
Valuing Diversity PhD Scholarships *(Doctorate/Scholarship)* [983]
H. Wayne Van Agtmael Cosmetology Scholarship Fund *(Undergraduate/Scholarship)* [4551]
Winifred Van Hagen/Rosalind Cassidy Scholarship Award *(Undergraduate/Scholarship)* [2436]
Patricia Van Kirk Scholarships *(Undergraduate/Scholarship)* [8267]
Jacob and Rita Van Namen Marketing Scholarships *(Undergraduate/Scholarship)* [814]
Adolph Van Pelt Special Fund for Indians Scholarships *(Undergraduate/Scholarship)* [1836]
William P. Van Wagenen Fellowships *(Undergraduate/Fellowship)* [543]
Gary Vanden Berg Internship Grant *(Undergraduate/Grant)* [9482]
The Vander Putten Family Scholarships *(Advanced Professional/Scholarship)* [3082]
René M. Vandervelde Research Grants *(Undergraduate, Professional development/Grant)* [1845]
Russell and Sigurd Varian Award *(Graduate/Recognition)* [2158]
Varian Radiation Therapy Advancement Scholarship *(Undergraduate, Master's, Doctorate/Scholarship)* [1401]
Vascular Surgery Trainee Advocacy Travel Scholarship *(Advanced Professional, Professional development/Scholarship, Grant)* [9326]
Vector Marketing Canadian Scholarship Awards *(Undergraduate/Scholarship)* [10365]
Vector Marketing Scholarships *(Graduate, Undergraduate/Scholarship)* [8079]
Vectorworks Design Scholarships *(Undergraduate, Graduate/Scholarship, Prize)* [10367]
Kodali Veeraiah and Sarojini Scholarships *(Graduate/Scholarship)* [9673]
VEF Fellowship Program *(Doctorate, Master's/Fellowship)* [10380]
VEF Visiting Scholars Program *(Doctorate/Fellowship)* [10381]
Ventana Medical Systems In Situ Hybridization Awards *(Other/Award)* [7173]
Helen Veress-Mitchell Scholarship Fund *(Undergraduate/Scholarship)* [2788]
Graduate Fellowship Program - Peter Verhofstadt Fellowships *(Graduate/Fellowship)* [8836]
Vermont Paralegal Organization Scholarships *(Undergraduate/Scholarship)* [10371]
Vern Parish *(Graduate, Undergraduate/Scholarship)* [964]
Chester M. Vernon Memorial Eagle Scout Scholarships *(Undergraduate/Scholarship)* [6934]
Vesalius Trust Student Research Scholarships *(Graduate, Undergraduate/Scholarship)* [10374]
Veterans of Foreign Wars Scout of the Year *(Undergraduate/Scholarship)* [6935]
Veterinary and Pre-Veterinary Academic Scholarships *(Undergraduate/Scholarship)* [3647]
Zelda Walling Vicha Memorial Scholarships *(Undergraduate/Scholarship)* [1387]
Villers Fellowships for Health Care Justice *(Graduate/Fellowship)* [3958]
Violin Society of America Scholarships *(Undergraduate/Scholarship)* [10390]
Virginia Museum of Fine Arts Visual Arts Fellowships *(Graduate, Other, Undergraduate/Fellowship)* [10400]
Virginia Tech Student Travel Award *(Undergraduate, Graduate/Award)* [1955]
Vision Zero Auto Accident Prevention Scholarships *(Postgraduate/Scholarship)* [5951]
Vista Health Solutions' Scholarships *(Undergraduate/Scholarship)* [10413]
John D. Voelker Foundation Native American Scholarships *(Undergraduate/Scholarship)* [10415]
Von Ogden Vogt Scholarships *(Master's/Scholarship)* [9843]
Miki Vohryzek-Bolden Student Paper Competition *(Undergraduate/Prize)* [10539]
Voices On Point Scholarship *(Undergraduate, Graduate, Doctorate/Scholarship)* [8194]
Irma E. Voigt Memorial Scholarships *(Undergraduate/Scholarship)* [8943]
Paul A. Volcker Endowment for Public Service Research and Education *(Doctorate/Grant)* [1116]
Vorobek Point Scholarship *(Undergraduate, Graduate, Doctorate/Scholarship)* [8195]
Abe Voron Scholarships *(Graduate/Scholarship)* [2374]
Dr. Edward G. Voss Memorial Scholarships *(Undergraduate/Scholarship)* [10192]
VPPPA June Brothers Scholarships *(Graduate, Undergraduate/Scholarship)* [10419]
WACE National Co-op Scholarship Program *(Undergraduate/Scholarship)* [10693]
Chapter 4 - Lawrence A. Wacker Memorial Scholarships *(Undergraduate/Scholarship)* [9198]
Dee Wacksman Scholarships *(Undergraduate/Scholarship)* [3024]
Jane and Gregg Waddill Memorial Adelphe Scholarship *(Undergraduate/Scholarship)* [5768]
Percy W. Wadman, M.D. Scholarship *(Postgraduate/Scholarship)* [4291]

Wadsworth International Fellowships *(Graduate/Fellowship)* [10519]
WAEPA Scholarship Program *(Undergraduate/Scholarship)* [10711]
Gary Wagner, K3OMI Scholarships *(Undergraduate/Scholarship)* [1762]
Wagner-Torizuka Fellowships *(Professional development/Fellowship)* [9228]
Selman A. Waksman Endowed Scholarships in Microbial Diversity *(Graduate, Master's, Doctorate/Scholarship)* [6264]
Jane C. Waldbaum Archaeological Field School Scholarships *(Undergraduate/Scholarship)* [1611]
Laramie Walden Memorial Fund *(Undergraduate/Scholarship)* [4219]
Margaret E. Waldron Scholarship Fund *(Undergraduate/Scholarship)* [4061]
Helen Zick Walker Adelphe Scholarship *(Undergraduate/Scholarship)* [5769]
Gary Walker Memorial Scholarships *(Other/Scholarship)* [4266]
Arthur BC Walker Scholarships *(Undergraduate/Scholarship)* [7147]
Myrtle & Earl Walker Scholarships *(Undergraduate/Scholarship)* [9199]
Walmart Associate Scholarships *(Undergraduate/Scholarship)* [10425]
Imogene Ward Nursing Scholarships *(Undergraduate/Scholarship)* [4079]
Warner Norcross & Judd Minority Scholarships *(Undergraduate/Scholarship)* [10427]
Earl Warren Scholarships *(Graduate/Scholarship)* [6648]
Washington College Bound Scholarships *(Undergraduate/Scholarship)* [10471]
Washington Higher Education Coordinating Board - State Need Grants (SNG) *(Undergraduate/Grant)* [10472]
Vincent T. Wasilewski Scholarships *(Graduate/Scholarship)* [2375]
Waterbury Bar Association Scholarships *(Undergraduate/Scholarship)* [10485]
Stand Watie Scholarships *(Undergraduate/Scholarship)* [9343]
ASM Robert D. Watkins Graduate Research Fellowships *(Postdoctorate/Fellowship)* [1373]
Watson-Brown Scholarships *(Undergraduate/Scholarship)* [10489]
Dr. James Watson Fellowship Program *(Doctorate, Graduate/Fellowship)* [4485]
George Watt Prize *(Undergraduate, Graduate/Prize)* [26]
Wayne County Foundation Anonymous Scholarship Fund *(Graduate/Scholarship)* [10508]
Wayne-Meador-Elliott Scholarships *(Undergraduate/Scholarship)* [7869]
Kurt Wayne Scholarships *(Graduate/Scholarship)* [4346]
WBA Bar President's Scholarships *(Undergraduate/Scholarship)* [10486]
WBA Paralegal/Legal Assistant Scholarships *(Undergraduate/Scholarship)* [10487]
WDHOF Undergraduate Scholarships in Marine Conservation *(Undergraduate/Scholarship)* [10640]
Richard M. Weaver Fellowships *(Graduate/Fellowship)* [5235]
Monica E. Weaver Memorial Fund *(Undergraduate/Scholarship)* [4062]
W.E.B. Du Bois Fellowships *(Doctorate/Fellowship)* [7013]
John W. Webb Lecture Awards *(Other/Recognition)* [1324]
Art and Dannie Weber Scholarships *(Undergraduate/Scholarship)* [10603]
Sheldon Wechsler and George Mertz Contact Lens Residency Awards *(Professional development, Advanced Professional/Award)* [418]
WEF Canham Graduate Studies Scholarships *(Graduate/Scholarship)* [10480]
Frank L. Weil Memorial Eagle Scout Scholarships *(Undergraduate/Scholarship)* [6936]
Arthur and Lila Weinberg Fellowship for Independent Scholars and Researchers *(Other/Fellowship)* [7425]

Alvin M. Weinberg Fellowships *(Doctorate/Fellowship)* [9910]
Bertold E. Weinberg Scholarship *(Graduate/Scholarship)* [711]
Edith Weingarten Scholarship Program *(Postgraduate/Scholarship)* [1050]
The Bee Winkler Weinstein Scholarship Fund *(Undergraduate, Vocational/Occupational/Scholarship)* [9591]
William E. Weisel Scholarships *(Undergraduate/Scholarship)* [9201]
Susan C. Weiss Clinical Advancement Scholarships *(Other/Scholarship)* [9229]
Polaire Weissman Funds *(Graduate/Fellowship)* [6439]
Edward Kent Welch Memorial Scholarships *(Undergraduate/Scholarship)* [10604]
Welch Scholars Grants *(Undergraduate/Grant)* [1065]
James R. Welch Scholarship *(Graduate/Scholarship)* [1846]
Welder Wildlife Foundation Fellowships *(Graduate, Master's, Doctorate/Fellowship)* [10510]
Sue Marsh Weller Memorial Scholarships *(Graduate/Scholarship)* [5113]
Wells Fargo American Indian Scholarships - Graduate *(Graduate/Scholarship)* [883]
Wells Fargo Point Scholarship *(Undergraduate/Scholarship)* [8196]
Wells Fargo Scholarships *(Undergraduate/Scholarship)* [8268]
Wells Fargo Veterans Scholarships Program *(Undergraduate/Scholarship)* [10512]
Jean Hess Wells Memorial Adelphe Graduate Scholarship *(Graduate/Scholarship)* [5771]
Jean Hess Wells Memorial Adelphe Scholarship *(Undergraduate/Scholarship)* [5772]
Wellstone Fellowships for Social Justice *(Graduate/Fellowship)* [3959]
Peter R. Weitz Prize *(Other/Prize)* [4402]
Francis X. Weninger Scholarships *(Undergraduate/Scholarship)* [10726]
Wenner-Gren Foundation Dissertation Fieldwork Grants *(Doctorate/Grant)* [10520]
Wenner-Gren Foundation Post-PhD Research Grants *(Doctorate/Grant)* [10521]
West Michigan Nursery and Landscape Association Scholarship Fund *(Undergraduate/Scholarship)* [4552]
West Virginia Nurses Association District No. 3 Scholarships *(Undergraduate/Scholarship)* [7870]
West Virginia PTA Scholarships *(Undergraduate/Scholarship)* [10525]
Redlands Evening Lions Club - Barbara Westen Memorial Scholarships *(Undergraduate/Scholarship)* [8529]
Western Michigan Society of Health-System Pharmacists Scholarships *(Undergraduate/Scholarship)* [10533]
Western Reserve Herb Society Scholarships *(Undergraduate/Scholarship)* [4866]
Western Society of Weed Science Outstanding Student Scholarship Program *(Graduate, Undergraduate/Scholarship)* [10541]
Robert B. Westover Scholarships *(Undergraduate/Scholarship)* [4347]
Mary Elizabeth Westpheling - Long Beach Alumnae Association Memorial Scholarhips *(Undergraduate/Scholarship)* [5773]
Dr. William "Tim" Whalen Memorial Scholarships *(Undergraduate/Scholarship)* [7503]
Whan Memorial Scholarships *(Graduate, Undergraduate/Scholarship)* [8080]
Edwyna Wheadon Postgraduate Training Scholarship Fund *(Postgraduate/Scholarship)* [6886]
Stan Wheeler Mentorship Awards *(Other/Award)* [5976]
Paul A. Whelan Aviation Scholarships *(Undergraduate, Graduate/Scholarship)* [10106]
Nellie Yeoh Whetten Award *(Graduate/Recognition)* [2159]
Whidbey Island Giving Circle Scholarships *(Undergraduate/Scholarship)* [8269]
WHIMA Established Professional Scholarship *(Graduate/Scholarship)* [10623]
Whitaker-Minard Memorial Scholarships *(Undergraduate/Scholarship)* [7871]
Law Office of David D. White Annual Traumatic Brain Injury Scholarships *(All/Scholarship)* [5947]
White Collar Defense Diversity Scholarships *(Undergraduate, Advanced Professional/Scholarship)* [8239]
Bradford White Corporation Scholarships *(Undergraduate/Scholarship)* [8165]
The Brian J. White Endowed Law Scholarships *(Undergraduate/Scholarship)* [8008]
Richard S. White Fellowships *(Undergraduate/Fellowship)* [4853]
White House Fellows *(Other/Fellowship)* [8223]
Mary Kean White Memorial Scholarship Fund *(Undergraduate/Scholarship)* [9544]
Paul D. White Scholarship *(Undergraduate/Scholarship)* [2173]
ACI Richard N. White Student Fellowships *(Master's/Fellowship)* [712]
Robert B. and Sophia Whiteside Scholarships *(Undergraduate/Scholarship)* [3726]
Ann Cook Whitman Scholarships for Perry High School *(Undergraduate/Scholarship)* [4416]
Jane and Morgan Whitney Fellowships *(Graduate/Fellowship)* [6440]
Helen Hay Whitney Foundation Fellowships *(Postdoctorate/Fellowship)* [10551]
Wi-Hi Class of '55 Scholarship *(Undergraduate/Scholarship)* [3189]
David Julian Wichard Scholarships *(Undergraduate/Scholarship)* [10255]
Alice Hersey Wick Scholarships *(Undergraduate/Scholarship)* [8944]
Tom Wicker Scholarships *(Graduate/Scholarship)* [10256]
Larry B. Wickham Memorial Scholarship for Graduate Studies *(Graduate/Scholarship)* [6608]
Louise Wachter Wickham Scholarships *(Undergraduate/Scholarship)* [4553]
Lois Widley Student Scholarships *(Graduate, Undergraduate/Scholarship)* [5365]
WIEA Scholarships *(Doctorate, Graduate, Undergraduate/Scholarship)* [10625]
Richard A. Wiebe Public Service Fellowships *(Graduate/Fellowship)* [7371]
Ethyl and Armin Wiebke Memorial Scholarships *(Undergraduate/Scholarship)* [10652]
Barbara Wiedner and Dorothy Vandercook Memorial Peace Scholarships *(Undergraduate/Scholarship)* [4639]
Elmo Wierenga Alumni Scholarships *(Undergraduate/Scholarship)* [4633]
Timothy Wiese Memorial Scholarships *(Undergraduate, Graduate/Scholarship)* [8754]
Fred Wiesner Educational Excellence Scholarships *(Undergraduate, Graduate/Scholarship)* [2079]
WIFLE Regular Scholarship Program *(Graduate, Postdoctorate, Undergraduate/Scholarship)* [10642]
Fred C. Wikoff, Jr. Scholarships *(Undergraduate, Vocational/Occupational/Scholarship)* [4220]
Wild Felid Legacy Scholarships *(Graduate/Scholarship)* [10555]
Wilder Dimension Scholarships for Advanced Study in Theatre Arts *(Graduate/Scholarship)* [3693]
Samuel S. Wilks Awards *(Advanced Professional/Award, Monetary)* [1466]
Andrea Will Memorial Scholarships *(Undergraduate/Scholarship)* [8945]
Willamette Chapter Scholarship Awards *(Undergraduate/Scholarship)* [7702]
Willard & Spackman Scholarship Program *(Postgraduate/Scholarship)* [1051]
James B. Willett Educational Memorial Scholarship Award *(Undergraduate/Scholarship)* [10000]
M. William and Frances J. Tilghman Scholarships *(Undergraduate/Scholarship)* [3190]
S. William and Martha R. Goff Educational Scholarships *(Undergraduate/Scholarship)* [7872]
William Randolph Hearst Educational Endowments *(Undergraduate, Graduate/Scholarship)* [6265]
Williams Chorale Bacardi Fallon Performing Arts Scholarships *(Undergraduate/Award, Scholarship)* [10563]
Sidney B. Williams, Jr. Scholarships *(Undergraduate/Scholarship)* [942]

Rodney Williams Legacy Scholarships *(Undergraduate/Scholarship)* [10150]
BM1 James Elliott Williams Memorial Scholarship Fund *(Undergraduate/Scholarship)* [7922]
Alice Hinchcliffe Williams, RDH, MS Graduate Scholarships *(Graduate/Scholarship)* [10394]
E. E. Williams Research Grants *(Master's, Doctorate/Grant)* [4873]
T. Franklin Williams Research Scholars Award Program *(Other/Grant)* [4804]
Aubrey L. Williams Research Travel Fellowships *(Doctorate/Fellowship)* [1298]
John G. Williams Scholarship Fund *(Undergraduate/Scholarship)* [10565]
CSM Virgil R. Williams Scholarships *(Undergraduate/Scholarship)* [3871]
Dr. Dana Williams Scholarships *(Undergraduate/Scholarship)* [3113]
Gary and Gussie Williams Scholarships *(Undergraduate/Scholarship)* [10193]
Leon Williams Scholarships *(Undergraduate/Scholarship)* [8741]
Maxine Williams Scholarships *(Undergraduate/Scholarship)* [540]
Randy Williams Scholarships *(Undergraduate/Scholarship)* [8742]
Redlands Footlighters, Inc. - Merle and Peggy Williams Scholarships *(Undergraduate/Scholarship)* [8530]
Cenie Jomo Williams Tuition Scholarships *(Graduate, Undergraduate/Scholarship)* [6721]
Lippincott Williams and Wilkins Scholarships *(Master's, Doctorate/Scholarship)* [3058]
Mary Katherine "Kathy" Williamson Scholarship Fund *(Undergraduate/Scholarship)* [3273]
Beverly Willis Architecture Foundation Travel Fellowship *(Doctorate/Fellowship)* [9086]
Gary S. Wilmer/RAMI Music Scholarships *(Undergraduate/Scholarship)* [3303]
Harriet Glen Wilmore Scholarship *(Undergraduate, Vocational/Occupational/Scholarship)* [4221]
Glenn Wilson Broadcast Journalism Scholarships *(Undergraduate/Scholarship)* [7873]
Saul T. Wilson, Jr. Scholarships *(Graduate, Undergraduate/Scholarship)* [9888]
Bob Wilson Legacy Scholarships *(Undergraduate/Scholarship)* [2460]
Arthur N. Wilson, MD, Scholarships *(Undergraduate/Scholarship)* [991]
John Charles Wilson and Robert Doran Sr. Scholarships *(Undergraduate/Scholarship)* [5246]
Michael Wilson Scholarships *(Undergraduate/Scholarship)* [126]
Theo Wilson Scholarships *(Graduate, Undergraduate/Scholarship)* [7783]
Winston Build Your Future Scholarship *(Graduate, Undergraduate, Vocational/Occupational/Scholarship)* [8808]
David A. Winston Health Policy Scholarship *(Graduate/Scholarship)* [2087]
Winston-Salem Foundation Scholarships *(Undergraduate/Scholarship)* [10606]
Winterhoff Scholarships *(Undergraduate, Graduate/Scholarship)* [1774]
Winterthur Research Fellowships *(Graduate/Fellowship)* [10609]
John D. Wirth Travel Grants for International Scholars *(Graduate, Other/Grant)* [1318]
Wisconsin Laboratory Association Graduate Student Scholarships *(Graduate/Scholarship)* [10627]
Wisconsin Laboratory Association Technical Student Scholarships *(Undergraduate, Graduate/Scholarship)* [10628]
Wisconsin Laboratory Association Undergraduate University Student Scholarships *(Undergraduate/Scholarship)* [10629]
William B. Wisdom Grant in Aid of Research *(Professional development/Grant)* [10634]
HCRTA/Glen O. and Wyllabeth Wise Scholarships *(Undergraduate/Scholarship)* [3025]
WNBA Eastman Grants *(Other/Grant)* [10668]
WOCN Accredited Nursing Education Scholarships *(Graduate, Undergraduate/Scholarship)* [10715]
WOCN Advanced Education Scholarships *(Graduate/Scholarship)* [10716]
Woksape Oyate: "Wisdom of the People" Distinguished Scholars Awards *(Undergraduate/Scholarship)* [873]
Paul R. Wolf Memorial Scholarships *(Graduate/Scholarship)* [1809]
Emil Wolf Outstanding Student Paper Competition *(Graduate, Undergraduate/Award)* [7676]
Wolf Trap Grants for High School Performing Arts Teachers *(Other/Grant)* [10631]
The Wolf Trap Internship Program *(Graduate, Other, Undergraduate/Internship)* [10632]
Deborah Partridge Wolfe International Fellowships *(Graduate, Undergraduate/Fellowship)* [10820]
Nona Hobbs Wolfe Memorial Scholarship *(Undergraduate/Scholarship)* [5774]
Eleanor M. Wolfson Memorial Scholarship Fund *(Undergraduate/Scholarship)* [4063]
Wendy Y. Wolfson Memorial Scholarship Fund *(Undergraduate/Scholarship)* [4064]
Abel Wolman Fellowships *(Doctorate/Fellowship)* [1492]
The Woman's Club of Nashville Scholarship Endowment Fund *(Undergraduate/Scholarship)* [3257]
Women in Cancer Research Scholar Awards *(Graduate, Postdoctorate/Award)* [475]
Women In Defense HORIZONS Scholarships *(Graduate, Undergraduate/Scholarship)* [10636]
Women on Par Scholarships *(Undergraduate/Scholarship)* [3938]
Women of Today's Manufacturing Scholarships *(Undergraduate/Scholarship)* [3304]
Women of WSAJ Bar Preparation Scholarships *(Undergraduate/Scholarship)* [10458]
Women's Army Corps Veterans Association Scholarships *(Undergraduate/Scholarship)* [10654]
Women's Club of Grand Haven Scholarships *(Undergraduate/Scholarship)* [4554]
Women's Italian Club of Boston Scholarships *(Undergraduate/Scholarship)* [4357]
Women's Jewelry Association Member Grants *(Professional development/Grant)* [10663]
Women's Leadership in Agriculture Scholarship Program *(Undergraduate/Scholarship)* [7574]
Women's Leadership Training Grant *(Advanced Professional, Professional development/Grant)* [9327]
Women's Overseas and Service League Scholarships for Women *(Undergraduate/Scholarship)* [10670]
Carolyn Wones Recruitment Scholarship Grants *(Undergraduate/Scholarship)* [3305]
Denis Wong and Associates Scholarships *(Graduate, Undergraduate/Scholarship)* [7920]
Dr. Harold S. Wood Awards for Excellence *(Undergraduate/Award)* [4349]
Wood County Bar Association Memorial Scholarships *(Graduate/Scholarship)* [7874]
Mary and Elliot Wood Foundation Graduate Scholarship Fund *(Graduate/Scholarship)* [4222]
Wood Fruitticher Grocery Company, Inc. Scholarships *(Graduate, Undergraduate/Scholarship)* [201]
Rolla F. Wood Graduate Scholarships *(Graduate/Scholarship)* [8083]
Hugh and Helen Wood Nepales Scholarships *(Undergraduate/Scholarship)* [2233]
Irene Woodall Graduate Scholarships *(Master's/Scholarship)* [778]
Woodcock Family Education Scholarship Program *(Undergraduate/Scholarship)* [306]
Woodex Bearing Company Scholarships *(Undergraduate/Scholarship)* [4373]
Woodrow Wilson International Center for Scholars Fellowships *(Doctorate/Fellowship)* [10567]
Woodrow Wilson-Rockefeller Brothers Fund Fellowships for Aspiring Teachers of Color *(Undergraduate/Fellowship)* [10682]
Carter G. Woodson Institute Post-doctoral Residential Research and Teaching Fellowships *(Postdoctorate/Fellowship)* [10684]
Carter G. Woodson Institute Pre-doctoral Residential Research Fellowships *(Doctorate/Fellowship)* [10685]
Betsy B. Woodward Scholarships *(Undergraduate/Scholarship)* [1966]
Marilynne Graboys Wool Scholarships *(Graduate/Scholarship)* [8611]
L and T Woolfolk Memorial Scholarships *(Undergraduate/Scholarship)* [3026]
Blanche E. Woolls Scholarships *(Graduate/Scholarship)* [2242]
Hawaii Chapter/David T. Woolsey Scholarships *(Undergraduate, Graduate, Professional development/Scholarship)* [5918]
Patty Wooten Scholarships *(Professional development/Scholarship, Award, Recognition)* [1852]
Worcester District Medical Society Scholarship Fund *(Undergraduate/Scholarship)* [10689]
John W. Work III Memorial Foundation Scholarships *(Undergraduate/Scholarship)* [3258]
Working for Farmers' Success Scholarships *(Undergraduate/Scholarship)* [10691]
Workshops, Inc. and Stark MRDD Fostering Diversity Through Special Needs Scholarship Fund *(Undergraduate/Scholarship)* [9545]
Worldstudio AIGA Scholarships *(Graduate, Undergraduate/Scholarship)* [10709]
Donald Worster Travel Grants *(Graduate, Other/Grant)* [1319]
Worthy Gemological Scholarships *(Undergraduate/Scholarship)* [10713]
Wozumi Family Scholarships *(Undergraduate/Scholarship)* [8270]
WRI Education Foundation Scholarships - Graduate *(Graduate/Scholarship)* [10611]
WRI Education Foundation Scholarships - High School Seniors *(Undergraduate/Scholarship)* [10612]
WRI Education Foundation Scholarships - Undergraduate *(Undergraduate/Scholarship)* [10613]
Jean Wright-Elson Scholarships *(Doctorate, Graduate, Undergraduate/Scholarship)* [8743]
Audrey L. Wright Scholarships *(Undergraduate/Scholarship)* [4637]
WSAJ American Justice Essay Scholarships *(Undergraduate/Scholarship)* [10459]
WSAJ Diversity Bar Preparation Scholarships *(Undergraduate/Scholarship)* [10460]
WSAJ Presidents' Scholarships *(Undergraduate/Scholarship)* [10461]
WSGC Scholarships for Incoming Freshmen *(Undergraduate/Scholarship)* [10456]
WSSA Student Paper Competition *(Undergraduate, Graduate/Award)* [10535]
WTVD Endowment Scholarships *(Undergraduate/Scholarship)* [10257]
Wyatt, Tarrant & Combs, LLP, Dr. Benjamin L. Hooks Scholarship *(Undergraduate/Scholarship)* [10177]
WYCUP Scholarships *(Other/Scholarship)* [10700]
Wyeth Foundation Predoctoral Fellowship *(Postdoctorate/Fellowship)* [9009]
Margaret Wyeth Scholarships *(Undergraduate/Scholarship)* [3306]
Wyeth-SUS Clinical Scholar Awards *(Other/Award)* [9321]
Xavier Community-Engaged Fellowships *(Undergraduate/Fellowship)* [10727]
Xavier University Chancellor Scholarships *(Undergraduate/Scholarship)* [10728]
Xavier University Departmental Scholarships *(Undergraduate/Scholarship)* [10729]
Xavier University Honors Bachelor of Arts Scholarships *(Undergraduate/Scholarship)* [10730]
Xavier University Legacy Scholarships *(Undergraduate/Scholarship)* [10731]
Xavier University Presidential Scholarships *(Undergraduate/Scholarship)* [10732]
Xavier University ROTC Scholarships - Air Force ROTC *(Undergraduate/Scholarship)* [10733]
Xavier University ROTC Scholarships - Army ROTC *(Undergraduate/Scholarship)* [10734]
Xavier University Williams Scholarships *(Undergraduate/Scholarship)* [10735]
Xerox Technical Minority Scholarships *(Graduate, Undergraduate/Scholarship)* [10737]
Yale Graduate and Professional Students Research Fellowships *(Graduate, Professional development/Fellowship)* [2215]
Yankee Clipper Contest Club, Inc. Youth Scholarships *(Undergraduate/Scholarship)* [1764]
William J. Yankee Memorial Scholarships *(Undergraduate/Scholarship)* [1125]

UNITED STATES

Gwen Yarnell Theatre Scholarships *(Undergraduate/Scholarship)* [4028]
Yasme Foundation Scholarships *(Undergraduate/Scholarship)* [1765]
Minoru Yasui Memorial Scholarships *(Graduate, Master's, Doctorate/Scholarship)* [5560]
Willa Yeck Memorial Scholarship Fund *(Undergraduate/Scholarship)* [6292]
Marilyn Yetso Memorial Scholarships *(Graduate/Scholarship)* [9829]
YMF Scholarships *(Undergraduate/Scholarship)* [10762]
Gary Yoshimura Scholarships *(Undergraduate/Scholarship)* [8379]
You Go Girl! Scholarships *(Undergraduate/Scholarship)* [8271]
Young Christian Leaders Scholarships *(Undergraduate/Scholarship)* [10760]
Alma H. Young Emerging Scholar Awards *(Doctorate/Award, Monetary)* [10344]
Young Investigators Achievement Award *(Advanced Professional, Professional development/Award, Grant)* [5620]
Young People For Fellowships *(Professional development/Fellowship)* [10764]
Donnell B. Young Scholarships *(Undergraduate/Scholarship)* [308]
Pearl I. Young Scholarships *(Undergraduate/Scholarship)* [7499]
Elmer Cooke Young - Taylor Young Scholarships *(Undergraduate/Scholarship)* [4774]
George D. Younger Scholarships *(Undergraduate/Scholarship)* [7394]
Your Skin Is In College Ambassador Scholarships *(Undergraduate/Scholarship)* [6407]
Youth Empowerment Summit Scholarships *(Undergraduate/Scholarship)* [6817]
Youth Leadership Scholarships *(Undergraduate/Scholarship)* [2469]
Youth Partners Accessing Capital (PAC) *(Undergraduate/Scholarship)* [354]
The Youth Scholarship Program *(Undergraduate/Scholarship)* [2871]
The Frank Der Yuen Aviation Scholarship *(Undergraduate/Scholarship)* [7789]
Z/I Imaging Scholarships *(Graduate/Scholarship)* [1810]
Lisa Zaken Awards For Excellence *(Graduate, Undergraduate/Award, Monetary)* [5197]
Dr. Marie E. Zakrzewski Medical Scholarships *(Doctorate/Scholarship)* [5883]
Louis B. Zapoleon Memorial Scholarships *(Undergraduate/Scholarship)* [3027]
The Zebra Safe Driver Scholarships *(Undergraduate, Graduate/Scholarship)* [10810]
Urashi Zen Scholarships *(Undergraduate/Scholarship)* [8272]
The Zenith Fellows Award Program (Zenith) *(Postdoctorate/Fellowship)* [377]
Zenko Family Scholarship Fund *(Undergraduate/Scholarship)* [4555]
Harry and Angel Zerigian Scholarships *(Undergraduate/Scholarship)* [1708]
Zeta Chapter Memorial Scholarship Awards *(Undergraduate/Scholarship)* [3307]
Zeta Phi Beta Sorority General Graduate Scholarships *(Graduate/Scholarship)* [10821]
Zeta Phi Beta Sorority General Undergraduate Scholarships *(Undergraduate/Scholarship)* [10822]
Zeta Sigma Project 2000 Scholarships *(Undergraduate/Scholarship)* [5775]
A.F. Zimmerman Scholarships *(Graduate, Master's/Scholarship)* [8050]
Blanche Raper Zimmerman Scholarships *(Other/Scholarship)* [10607]
Zimmermann Scholarships *(Graduate/Scholarship)* [9621]
Jacob Ziskind Memorial Fund for Upperclassmen *(Graduate, Undergraduate/Scholarship)* [5104]
Morris L. and Rebecca Ziskind Memorial Scholarships *(Undergraduate/Scholarship)* [5029]
Lorraine Zitone Memorial Scholarship Fund *(Undergraduate/Scholarship)* [6293]
Amelia Zollner IPPR/UCL Internship Award *(Undergraduate/Internship)* [5210]
Ruth and Sherman Zudekoff Scholarships *(Undergraduate/Scholarship)* [3202]
Francis Sylvia Zverina Scholarships *(Undergraduate/Scholarship)* [4867]

UNITED STATES (BY REGION)

Central Region
Markley Scholarships *(Undergraduate/Scholarship)* [6724]

Eastern States
Constancy, Brooks and Smith Diversity Scholars Awards *(Undergraduate/Award)* [3407]

Long Island
H.J. "Duke" Ellington Memorial Scholarship Award *(Undergraduate/Scholarship)* [7513]

Mid America Region
Tese Caldarelli Memorial Scholarships *(Graduate, Undergraduate/Scholarship)* [6723]
NACA Foundation Graduate Scholarships *(Graduate, Master's, Postdoctorate/Scholarship)* [6725]
Zagunis Student Leader Scholarships *(Graduate, Undergraduate/Scholarship)* [6734]

Mid Atlantic Region
Tese Caldarelli Memorial Scholarships *(Graduate, Undergraduate/Scholarship)* [6723]
NACA Foundation Graduate Scholarships *(Graduate, Master's, Postdoctorate/Scholarship)* [6725]
NACA Mid Atlantic Graduate Student Scholarships *(Graduate, Master's, Doctorate/Scholarship)* [6726]
NACA Mid Atlantic Higher Education Research Scholarships *(Master's/Scholarship)* [6727]
NACA Mid Atlantic Undergraduate Scholarships for Student Leaders *(Undergraduate/Scholarship)* [6728]
Zagunis Student Leader Scholarships *(Graduate, Undergraduate/Scholarship)* [6734]

Mid-Western States
Constancy, Brooks and Smith Diversity Scholars Awards *(Undergraduate/Award)* [3407]

New England States
Dvora Brodie Scholarships *(Graduate, Postgraduate, Undergraduate/Scholarship)* [4829]
NELA Conference Scholarships *(All/Scholarship)* [7297]
Shaw-Worth Memorial Scholarship *(Undergraduate/Scholarship)* [5002]
Switzer Environmental Fellowships *(Graduate/Fellowship)* [9623]

North Central Region
North Central, Region 9 Scholarships *(Undergraduate/Scholarship)* [9191]

Northeastern States
NACA Foundation Graduate Scholarships *(Graduate, Master's, Postdoctorate/Scholarship)* [6725]

Northwestern States
WFI International Fellowships *(Undergraduate/Fellowship)* [10702]

Pacific Northwest states
AISES Summer Internships *(Undergraduate, Graduate/Internship)* [888]

Pacific Northwest States
Lori Rhett Memorial Scholarships *(Graduate, Undergraduate/Scholarship)* [6733]

Southeastern States
Leighton M. Ballew Directing Scholarships *(Undergraduate/Scholarship)* [9387]
Polly Holliday Scholarships *(Undergraduate/Scholarship)* [9388]
NACA South Student Leadership Scholarships *(Undergraduate/Scholarship)* [6731]
Robert Porterfield Graduate Scholarships *(Graduate/Scholarship)* [9389]
Marian A. Smith Scholarships *(Graduate/Scholarship)* [9390]
Southeastern Theatre Conference Secondary School Scholarships *(Undergraduate/Scholarship)* [9391]
William E. Wilson Scholarships *(Graduate/Scholarship)* [9392]

Southern States
CANS/SNRS Dissertation Research Grants *(Doctorate/Grant)* [9405]
Constancy, Brooks and Smith Diversity Scholars Awards *(Undergraduate/Award)* [3407]

Southwestern States
Jones-Lovich Grants in Southwestern Herpetology *(Master's, Doctorate/Grant)* [4872]

Western states
IMS AWWA Graduate Science and Engineering Scholarships *(Graduate/Scholarship)* [5239]

Western States
Constancy, Brooks and Smith Diversity Scholars Awards *(Undergraduate/Award)* [3407]
Institute of Transportation Engineers - Western District Fellowships *(Graduate/Fellowship)* [5220]
Eva Nieminski Honorary Graduate Science and Engineering Scholarships *(Graduate/Scholarship)* [5240]

UNITED STATES (BY STATE)

Alabama
ACHE/American Legion Auxiliary Scholarships *(Undergraduate/Scholarship)* [184]
ACHE Junior and Community College Athletic Scholarships *(Undergraduate/Scholarship)* [185]
ACHE Junior and Community College Performing Arts Scholarships *(Undergraduate/Scholarship)* [186]
ACHE Police Officers and Firefighters Survivors' Educational Assistance Programs *(Undergraduate/Scholarship)* [187]
ACHE Senior Adult Scholarships *(Undergraduate/Scholarship)* [188]
ACHE Two-Year College Academic Scholarships *(Undergraduate/Scholarship)* [189]
AISC/Southern Association of Steel Fabricators Scholarships *(Graduate/Scholarship)* [936]
Alabama Gi Dependents' Educational Benefit Program *(Undergraduate/Scholarship)* [190]
Alabama National Guard Educational Assistance Program *(Undergraduate/Scholarship)* [191]
Alabama Power Scholarships *(Undergraduate/Scholarship)* [7529]
Alabama Scholarships for Dependents of Blind Parents *(Undergraduate/Scholarship)* [192]
Alabama Student Assistance Programs *(Undergraduate/Scholarship)* [193]
Alabama Student Grant Programs *(Undergraduate, Vocational/Occupational/Grant)* [194]
Birmingham-Southern College Eagle Scout Scholarships *(Undergraduate/Scholarship)* [6920]
William Verbon Black Scholarships *(Undergraduate/Scholarship)* [205]

Place of Study Index

UNITED STATES

Billy Bowling Memorial Scholarship *(Undergraduate/Scholarship)* [7530]
Leon Bradley Scholarship Program *(Undergraduate/Scholarship)* [575]
Calhoun Valedictorian, Salutatorian/Top 5 Scholarships *(Undergraduate/Scholarship)* [2432]
Cecil Earl Clapp, Sr. Memorial Scholarship *(Undergraduate/Scholarship)* [7531]
J. Craig and Page T. Smith Scholarships *(Undergraduate/Scholarship)* [8999]
Marvin E. Daly Memorial Scholarship *(Undergraduate/Scholarship)* [7532]
Michael Denton Scholarship *(Undergraduate/Scholarship)* [7533]
EJI Justice Fellowship *(Graduate, Postgraduate, Professional development/Fellowship)* [3916]
Harriet Erich Graduate Fellowships *(Graduate/Fellowship, Scholarship)* [3550]
Homajean Grisham Memorial Scholarship *(Undergraduate/Scholarship)* [7534]
Howell Heflin Memorial Scholarship *(Undergraduate/Scholarship)* [7535]
Broughton Isom Memorial Scholarship *(Undergraduate/Scholarship)* [7536]
Legacy Inc. College Undergraduate and Graduate Scholarships *(Graduate, Undergraduate/Scholarship)* [6002]
Franklin A. Lenfesty Memorial Scholarship *(Undergraduate/Scholarship)* [7537]
Gertie S. Lowe Nursing Scholarship Awards *(Undergraduate/Scholarship)* [3267]
The Medalist Club Post Graduate Scholarships *(Postgraduate/Scholarship)* [6376]
Muscle Shoals Kiwanis/Wal-Mart Scholarship *(Undergraduate/Scholarship)* [7538]
Norfolk Southern Foundation Scholarships *(Undergraduate/Scholarship)* [1188]
Northwest-Shoals Community College Applied Technology Scholarships *(Undergraduate/Scholarship)* [7540]
Northwest-Shoals Community College Bank Independent Scholarships *(Undergraduate/Scholarship)* [7542]
Northwest-Shoals Community College Fine Arts Scholarships - Art *(Undergraduate/Scholarship)* [7543]
Northwest-Shoals Community College Fine Arts Scholarships - Drama *(Undergraduate/Scholarship)* [7544]
Northwest-Shoals Community College Fine Arts Scholarships - Music *(Undergraduate/Scholarship)* [7545]
Northwest-Shoals Community College Independent Computer Scholarships *(Undergraduate/Scholarship)* [7547]
Northwest-Shoals Community College Student Activities Scholarships *(Undergraduate/Scholarship)* [7548]
Regions Riding Forward Scholarships Essay Contest *(Undergraduate/Scholarship)* [8536]
D. Mitchell Self Memorial Scholarship *(Undergraduate/Scholarship)* [7549]
Justice Janie L. Shores Scholarships *(Undergraduate/Scholarship)* [207]
Aaron B. Singleton Memorial Scholarship *(Undergraduate/Scholarship)* [7550]
SPE Gulf Coast Hurricane Scholarships *(Undergraduate/Scholarship)* [9270]
SSAWMA Scholarships *(Graduate/Scholarship)* [9415]
Tuscumbia Kiwanis Scholarship *(Undergraduate/Scholarship)* [7551]
UAB Health Policy Fellowship *(Graduate, Master's, Doctorate/Scholarship)* [10002]
Wayne County Bank Scholarships *(Undergraduate/Scholarship)* [7552]

Alaska

Alaska Aerospace Development Corporation Scholarships *(Undergraduate/Scholarship)* [10004]
Alaska Native Medical Center Auxiliary Scholarships *(Undergraduate/Scholarship)* [10005]
Alaska Press Club Scholarships *(Undergraduate/Scholarship)* [10006]
Mike Ardaw Scholarships *(Undergraduate/Scholarship)* [10007]
Elaine Atwood Scholarship *(Undergraduate/Scholarship)* [10049]
Dr. Jon Baker Memorial Scholarship *(Graduate, Undergraduate/Scholarship)* [10050]
UAA Michael Baring-Gould Memorial Scholarship *(Graduate, Undergraduate/Scholarship)* [10051]
Lawrence Bayer Business Administration Scholarships *(Undergraduate/Scholarship)* [10008]
Charles E. Behlke Engineering Memorial Scholarships *(Undergraduate/Scholarship)* [10009]
Mark A. Beltz Scholarship *(Graduate, Undergraduate/Scholarship)* [10052]
Bill and Nell Biggs Scholarships *(Undergraduate/Scholarship)* [10088]
Bolick Foreign Student Scholarships *(Undergraduate/Scholarship)* [10010]
Dr. Betty J. Boyd-Beu and Edwin G. Beu, Jr. Scholarships *(Undergraduate/Scholarship)* [10011]
Pat Brakke Political Science Scholarship *(Undergraduate/Scholarship)* [10053]
Bunnell Scholarships *(Undergraduate/Scholarship)* [10012]
Loyal D. Burkett Memorial Scholarships *(Undergraduate/Scholarship)* [10013]
Lyle Carlson Wildlife Management Scholarships *(Undergraduate/Scholarship)* [10014]
Emi Chance for Aspiring Artists Scholarship *(Undergraduate/Scholarship)* [10054]
Edward Rollin Clinton Memorial for Music *(Undergraduate/Scholarship)* [10055]
Mable B. Crawford Memorial Scholarships *(Undergraduate/Scholarship)* [10015]
APTRA-Clete Roberts/Kathryn Dettman Memorial Journalism Scholarship *(Undergraduate/Scholarship)* [1818]
Jim Doogan Memorial Scholarships *(Undergraduate/Scholarship)* [10096]
Patricia Hughes Eastaugh Teaching Scholarship *(Undergraduate/Scholarship)* [10016]
UAA Governor William A. Egan Scholarship *(Undergraduate/Scholarship)* [10056]
Excellence in Geographic Information Systems Scholarships *(Undergraduate/Scholarship)* [10017]
Fairbanks Chapter Legacy Scholarships *(Undergraduate/Scholarship)* [10097]
Lydia Fohn-Hansen/Lola Hill Memorial Scholarships *(Undergraduate, Graduate/Scholarship)* [10018]
Michael D. Ford Memorial Scholarship *(Graduate, Undergraduate/Scholarship)* [10057]
Johnny & Sarah Frank Scholarships *(Undergraduate/Scholarship)* [10019]
Jan and Glenn Fredericks Scholarship *(Graduate, Undergraduate/Scholarship)* [10058]
Ardell French Memorial Scholarship *(Undergraduate/Scholarship)* [10059]
Charles F. Gould Endowment Scholarships *(Undergraduate/Scholarship)* [10020]
Ken Gray Endowment Scholarship *(Undergraduate/Scholarship)* [10061]
Patty Hamilton Early Childhood Development Scholarships *(Undergraduate/Scholarship)* [10021]
Jay Hammond Memorial Scholarships *(Undergraduate/Scholarship)* [10098]
Muriel Hannah Scholarships in Art *(Undergraduate, Graduate/Scholarship)* [10062]
Lenore and George Hedla Accounting Scholarship *(Undergraduate/Scholarship)* [10063]
John Henderson Endowment Scholarships *(Undergraduate/Scholarship)* [10022]
Donald Wills Jacobs Scholarships *(Undergraduate/Scholarship)* [10023]
Chris L. Kleinke Scholarship *(Graduate/Scholarship)* [10064]
Iver and Cora Knapstad Scholarships *(Undergraduate/Scholarship)* [10024]
Kris Knudson Memorial Scholarship *(Graduate, Undergraduate/Scholarship)* [10065]
Robert W. Korn Scholarships *(Undergraduate/Scholarship)* [10025]
Arlene Kuhner Memorial Scholarship *(Undergraduate/Scholarship)* [10066]
Austin E. Lathrop Scholarships *(Undergraduate/Scholarship)* [10026]
Franklin M. Leach Scholarships *(Undergraduate/Scholarship)* [10027]
William C. Leary Memorial Emergency Services Scholarships *(Undergraduate/Scholarship)* [9822]
Audrey Loftus Memorial Scholarships *(Undergraduate/Scholarship)* [10099]
Matanuska-Susitna College Regent's Scholarships *(Undergraduate/Scholarship)* [10089]
Dave McCloud Aviation Memorial Scholarships *(Undergraduate/Scholarship)* [10028]
Richard Mellon Scholarships *(Undergraduate/Scholarship)* [10029]
Molly Ann Mishler Memorial Scholarships *(Undergraduate/Scholarship)* [10030]
Andrew Nerland Scholarships *(Undergraduate/Scholarship)* [10031]
Maureen E. Nolan-Cahill Memorial Scholarships *(Undergraduate/Scholarship)* [10032]
Don and Jan O'Dowd/SAA Statewide Scholarships *(Undergraduate/Scholarship)* [10033]
Diane Olsen Memorial Scholarship *(Undergraduate/Scholarship)* [10067]
Alvin G. Ott Fish and Wildlife Scholarships *(Undergraduate/Scholarship)* [10034]
Pignalberi Public Policy Scholarship *(Graduate/Scholarship)* [10068]
Pt. Lay Memorial Scholarships *(Undergraduate/Scholarship)* [10035]
April Relyea Scholarship *(Graduate, Undergraduate/Scholarship)* [10069]
A.D. Al and Maxine Robertson Memorial Scholarship *(Undergraduate/Scholarship)* [10036]
Pat and Cliff Rogers Nursing Scholarships *(Undergraduate/Scholarship)* [10090]
Dr. Orrin Rongstad Wildlife Scholarship *(Undergraduate/Scholarship)* [10091]
Russian/Central Asian Student Scholarships *(Undergraduate/Scholarship)* [10092]
Brown Schoenheit Memorial Scholarship *(Undergraduate/Scholarship)* [10070]
Eveline Schuster Memorial Award/Scholarship *(Graduate, Undergraduate/Scholarship)* [10071]
Clair Shirey Scholarships *(Undergraduate/Scholarship)* [10037]
Ward Sims Memorial Scholarships *(Undergraduate/Scholarship)* [10038]
Lillian Smith Scholarship for Teaching Students *(Graduate, Undergraduate/Scholarship)* [10072]
Snodgrass Scholarships *(Undergraduate/Scholarship)* [10039]
Sourdough Reunion Memorial Endowment Scholarships *(Undergraduate/Scholarship)* [10040]
Sheri Stears Education Scholarship *(Undergraduate/Scholarship)* [10073]
Sturgulewski Family Scholarship *(Graduate, Undergraduate/Scholarship)* [10074]
UAA Accounting Club Scholarship *(Undergraduate/Scholarship)* [10075]
UAA Alaska Kidney Foundation Scholarship *(Graduate, Undergraduate/Scholarship)* [10076]
UAA Alumni Association Scholarship *(Undergraduate/Scholarship)* [10077]
UAA College of Business and Public Policy Scholarships *(Graduate, Undergraduate/Scholarship)* [10078]
UAA Friends of the Performing Arts Scholarship *(Undergraduate/Scholarship)* [10079]
UAA GCI, Inc. Scholarship *(Undergraduate/Scholarship)* [10080]
UAA Kimura Scholarship Fund for Illustration *(Undergraduate/Scholarship)* [10081]
UAA Kimura Scholarship Fund for Photography *(Undergraduate/Scholarship)* [10082]
UAA Quanterra Scholarship *(Graduate/Scholarship)* [10083]
UAA RRANN Program Scholarships *(Undergraduate/Scholarship)* [10084]
UAF Alumni Association Scholarships *(Undergraduate/Scholarship)* [10100]
UAF College of Liberal Arts - Anchorage Daily News Journalism Awards *(Undergraduate/Scholarship)* [10094]
UAF Community and Technical College Culinary Arts Scholarships *(Undergraduate/Scholarship)* [9823]

UNITED STATES

Umialik Scholarships *(Undergraduate/Scholarship)* [10041]
University of Alaska Scholars Program *(Undergraduate/Scholarship)* [10042]
Wells Fargo Career Scholarship *(Undergraduate/Scholarship)* [10085]
William S. Wilson Memorial Scholarships *(Undergraduate/Scholarship)* [10043]
Melissa J. Wolf Scholarship *(Undergraduate/Scholarship)* [10086]
Guy A. Woodings Scholarships *(Undergraduate/Scholarship)* [10044]
Ralph Yetka Memorial Scholarships *(Undergraduate/Scholarship)* [10045]
Joan C. Yoder Memorial Nursing Scholarships *(Undergraduate/Scholarship)* [10046]
Yukon Delta Fisheries Development Association Scholarships *(Undergraduate, Graduate/Scholarship)* [10047]

Arizona

AISES Summer Internships *(Undergraduate, Graduate/Internship)* [888]
Marvin A. Andrews Scholarships/Internships *(Graduate/Internship, Scholarship)* [1630]
Arizona Hydrological Society Scholarships *(Graduate, Undergraduate/Scholarship)* [1635]
ASCPA High School Scholarships *(Undergraduate/Scholarship, Monetary)* [1641]
Walt Bartram Memorial Education Award, Region 12 and Chapter 119 *(Undergraduate/Scholarship)* [9167]
Chapter 67 - Phoenix Scholarships *(Undergraduate/Scholarship)* [9178]
Valdemar A. Cordova Scholarships *(Undergraduate/Award)* [6110]
APTRA-Clete Roberts/Kathryn Dettman Memorial Journalism Scholarship *(Undergraduate/Scholarship)* [1818]
Charles A. Esser Memorial Scholarships *(Graduate/Scholarship)* [1631]
Gail Goodell Folsom Memorial Scholarships *(Undergraduate/Scholarship)* [6650]
Future CPA Scholarships *(Undergraduate/Scholarship)* [1642]
Sam Gallant Memorial Scholarships *(Graduate, Undergraduate/Scholarship)* [1643]
HACU/Denny's Hungry for Education Scholarships *(Undergraduate, Graduate/Scholarship)* [4883]
Marty Rosness Student Scholarships *(Undergraduate/Scholarship)* [1623]
Science Foundation Arizona Graduate Research Fellowships (GRF) *(Graduate/Fellowship)* [8814]
University Senior and Master's Program Scholarships *(Graduate/Scholarship)* [1644]

Arkansas

AISC/Southern Association of Steel Fabricators Scholarships *(Graduate/Scholarship)* [936]
ARAFCS Doctoral Scholarships *(Doctorate/Scholarship)* [1646]
ARAFCS Masters Scholarships *(Graduate/Scholarship)* [1647]
Arkansas State University Mountain Home Scholarships *(Undergraduate/Scholarship)* [1663]
Arkansas Nursing Foundation - Dorothea Fund Scholarships *(Other/Scholarship)* [1656]
Arkansas Nursing Foundation - Mary Gray Scholarships *(Other/Scholarship)* [1657]
Randall Matthis for Environmental Studies Scholarships *(Graduate, Undergraduate/Scholarship)* [1649]
Regions Riding Forward Scholarships Essay Contest *(Undergraduate/Scholarship)* [8536]

California

AAJUW Scholarships *(Graduate, Undergraduate/Scholarship)* [513]
Carl Joseph Adelhardt Memorial Scholarships *(Undergraduate/Scholarship)* [4329]
Anna Ames Clinical Excellence Student Grants *(Undergraduate/Grant)* [2481]
Asian/Pacific Bar Association of Sacramento Law Foundation Scholarship *(Graduate, Postgraduate/Scholarship)* [1790]
Associated Women for Pepperdine Scholarships *(Undergraduate/Scholarship)* [7962]
Association of California Water Agencies Scholarships *(Undergraduate/Scholarship)* [1871]
Association for Women in Architecture Scholarships *(Undergraduate/Scholarship)* [2089]
Walt Bartram Memorial Education Award, Region 12 and Chapter 119 *(Undergraduate/Scholarship)* [9167]
Hazel Reed Baumeister Scholarship Program *(Undergraduate/Scholarship)* [8947]
Bay Area Minority Law Student Scholarships *(Graduate, Undergraduate/Scholarship)* [2195]
BECA Foundation General Scholarships Fund *(Undergraduate/Scholarship)* [2210]
Bill Bernbach Diversity Scholarships *(Undergraduate/Scholarship)* [457]
James R. and Geraldine F. Bertelsen Scholarships *(Undergraduate/Scholarship)* [8691]
David and Camille Boatwright Endowed Scholarships *(Undergraduate/Scholarship)* [7965]
Dorothy M. Bolyard Memorial Scholarships *(Undergraduate/Scholarship)* [8692]
Farella Braun + Martel LLP 1L Diversity Scholarship Program *(Undergraduate/Scholarship)* [3968]
Margaret Martin Brock Scholarships in Law *(Undergraduate/Scholarship)* [7967]
Edwin Anthony and Adelaide Boudreaux Cadogan Scholarships *(Graduate/Fellowship)* [8747]
California Bar Foundation 3L Diversity Scholarships *(Undergraduate/Scholarship)* [2443]
CANFIT Nutrition, Physical Education and Culinary Arts Scholarships *(Graduate, Undergraduate/Scholarship)* [3167]
Pete Carpenter Fellowship *(Professional development/Fellowship)* [2318]
CDA Foundation Allied Dental Student Scholarships *(Undergraduate/Scholarship)* [2828]
CDA Foundation Dental Student Scholarships *(All/Scholarship)* [2829]
Chicana Latina Scholarship Fund *(Graduate, Undergraduate/Scholarship)* [2901]
CJA Legal Internships *(Professional development/Internship)* [2858]
Athalie Clarke Endowed Scholarships *(Undergraduate/Scholarship)* [7970]
CLCA Landscape Educational Advancement Foundation Educational Grant Program *(Undergraduate/Grant)* [2467]
Brian Dane Cleary Memorial Scholarships *(Undergraduate/Scholarship)* [7971]
Coro Fellows Program in Public Affairs *(Postgraduate/Fellowship)* [3423]
CPA Foundation Minority Scholarships *(Graduate/Scholarship)* [2471]
Crafton Hills College Foundation Scholarships *(Undergraduate/Scholarship)* [8468]
Crain Educational Grant Program *(Undergraduate/Scholarship)* [8948]
Rebecca Lee Crumpler, M.D. Scholarships *(Advanced Professional/Scholarship)* [1865]
The Hugh and Hazel Darling Dean Scholarships *(Undergraduate/Scholarship)* [7972]
Darling Foundation Endowed School of Law Scholarships *(Undergraduate/Scholarship)* [7973]
Death Valley '49ers Scholarships *(Undergraduate/Scholarship)* [3537]
Martha Delman and Milton Arthur Krug Endowed Scholarships *(Undergraduate/Scholarship)* [7974]
Ruth DeMoss Scholarships *(Undergraduate/Scholarship)* [8701]
Herman H. Derksen Scholarships *(Undergraduate/Scholarship)* [8702]
APTRA-Clete Roberts/Kathryn Dettman Memorial Journalism Scholarship *(Undergraduate/Scholarship)* [1818]
Edward D. Di Loreto-Odell S. McConnell Scholarships *(Undergraduate/Scholarship)* [7975]
Entertainment Media Internships - Los Angeles *(Undergraduate, Graduate/Internship)* [4431]
R. Wayne Estes Endowed Scholarships *(Undergraduate/Scholarship)* [7976]
Judge McIntyre Faries Scholarships *(Undergraduate/Scholarship)* [7977]
Reuben H. Fleet Memorial Scholarships *(Undergraduate/Scholarship)* [8704]
Sue Fleming Memorial Scholarships *(Undergraduate/Scholarship)* [2440]
Ford Motor Company Scholarship *(Undergraduate/Scholarship)* [10113]
Foundation Relations Internships - Los Angeles *(Undergraduate, Graduate/Internship)* [4433]
GAPA Scholarships *(Undergraduate/Scholarship)* [4327]
Joel Garcia Memorial Scholarship *(Undergraduate/Scholarship)* [2825]
IGS John Gardner Fellowship *(Undergraduate/Fellowship)* [10108]
Gerald Garner Memorial Scholarships *(Undergraduate/Scholarship)* [7979]
Getty Conservation Guest Scholar Grants *(Professional development/Grant)* [4406]
Getty Foundation Library Research Grants *(Professional development/Grant)* [4407]
Getty Postdoctoral Fellowships in Conservation Science *(Postdoctorate/Fellowship)* [4410]
Getty Postdoctoral Fellowships *(Postdoctorate/Fellowship)* [4409]
Getty Predoctoral Fellowships *(Doctorate/Fellowship)* [4411]
Getty Scholar Grants *(Professional development/Grant)* [4412]
Guy P. Greenwald Jr. Endowed Scholarships *(Undergraduate/Scholarship)* [7981]
Bobette Bibo Gugliotta Memorial Scholarships for Creative Writing *(Undergraduate/Scholarship)* [8951]
Warren and Rosalie Gummow Endowed Scholarships *(Undergraduate/Scholarship)* [7982]
HACU/Denny's Hungry for Education Scholarships *(Undergraduate, Graduate/Scholarship)* [4883]
Helm Family Scholarships *(Undergraduate/Scholarship)* [8706]
Doris Hendren Memorial Scholarships *(Undergraduate/Scholarship)* [8707]
Mark and Michelle Hiepler Endowed Scholarships *(Undergraduate/Scholarship)* [7983]
Clair A. Hill Scholarships *(Undergraduate/Scholarship)* [1873]
Nancy Johnston Memorial Scholarships *(Graduate, Undergraduate/Scholarship)* [9675]
Alice Newell Joslyn Medical Fund *(Undergraduate/Scholarship)* [2211]
JSR Foundation Endowed School of Law Scholarships *(Undergraduate/Scholarship)* [7984]
Woodrow Judkins Endowed Scholarships *(Undergraduate/Scholarship)* [7985]
Kaiser Permanente Northern California Delivery Science Fellowships Program *(Postgraduate/Fellowship)* [5650]
WLALA Fran Kandel Public Interest Grants *(Postgraduate/Grant)* [10646]
Judith Keller Marx Krumholz Scholarships *(Undergraduate/Scholarship)* [8713]
Julia Kwan Endowed Scholarships *(Graduate/Scholarship)* [7988]
LAFS - Cal State University San Marcos General Scholarships *(Undergraduate/Scholarship)* [2212]
Frank H. Lang Merit Scholarships *(Undergraduate/Scholarship)* [5922]
Latinos for Dental Careers Scholarships *(Undergraduate/Scholarship)* [2830]
Patrick Ledden Honorary Scholarships *(Undergraduate/Scholarship)* [8714]
Albert J. and Mae Lee Memorial Scholarships *(Undergraduate/Scholarship)* [7989]
The Lemon Grove Education Foundation Scholarships *(Undergraduate/Scholarship)* [8716]
Stephen Logan Memorial Scholarships *(Undergraduate/Scholarship)* [4330]
MABF Scholarships *(Postgraduate/Scholarship)* [6442]
Mangasar M. Mangasarian Scholarship Fund *(Graduate/Scholarship)* [1702]
Greg Matthews Memorial Scholarships *(Undergraduate/Scholarship)* [7990]
J. McDonald and Judy Williams School of Law Scholarships *(Undergraduate/Scholarship)* [7991]
Ruth McMillan Student Grants *(Undergraduate/Grant)* [2482]

John Merrick Law Scholarships *(Undergraduate/Scholarship)* [7992]
Mexican American Alumni Association Scholarships *(Graduate, Undergraduate/Scholarship)* [10356]
Wilma Motley Memorial California Merit Scholarships *(Undergraduate/Scholarship)* [777]
Jack K. and Gertrude Murphy Fellowships *(Graduate/Fellowship)* [8748]
Charles I. Nelson Endowed Scholarships *(Undergraduate/Scholarship)* [7993]
Newkirk Center for Science and Society Graduate Student Fellowships *(Doctorate, Graduate/Fellowship)* [7427]
Gunnar Nicholson Endowed Scholarships *(Undergraduate/Scholarship)* [7994]
Northern California Chapter of HIMSS Scholarships *(Graduate, Postgraduate, Undergraduate/Scholarship)* [4832]
Frank del Olmo Memorial Scholarships *(Undergraduate/Scholarship)* [2826]
Operation JumpStart Scholarships *(Graduate/Scholarship)* [458]
Pan Pacific Law Enforcement Scholarships *(Undergraduate/Scholarship)* [8745]
Pepperdine University Diversity Scholarships *(Doctorate, Graduate/Scholarship)* [7995]
Pepperdine University School of Law Armenian Student Scholarships *(Undergraduate/Scholarship)* [7996]
Pepperdine University School of Law Dean's Merit Scholarships *(Doctorate, Graduate/Scholarship)* [7997]
Pepperdine University School of Law Faculty Scholars Award *(Doctorate, Graduate/Scholarship)* [7998]
Pepperdine University School of Law JD/MBA Endowed Scholarships *(Undergraduate/Scholarship)* [7999]
Pepperdine University School of Law Special Law School Scholarships *(Undergraduate/Scholarship)* [8000]
Jamie Phillips Endowed Scholarships *(Undergraduate/Scholarship)* [8001]
Pollard-Bailey Scholarships *(Undergraduate/Scholarship)* [8722]
Peridian International, Inc./Rae L. Price, FASLA Scholarship *(Undergraduate/Scholarship)* [1347]
Peridian International, Inc./Rae L. Price, FASLA Scholarships *(Undergraduate/Scholarship)* [5916]
John Purfield Endowed Scholarships *(Undergraduate/Scholarship)* [8002]
Qualcomm San Diego Science, Technology, Engineering and Mathematics Scholarships *(Undergraduate/Scholarship)* [8723]
The Raffin-Gathercole Scholarships *(Undergraduate/Scholarship)* [4331]
Rancho Bernardo/Smith Scholarships *(Undergraduate/Scholarship)* [8724]
Fauneil J. Rinn Scholarships *(Undergraduate/Scholarship)* [8954]
Rosenthal Bar Exam Scholarship Fund *(Advanced Professional/Scholarship)* [2444]
Edward S. Roth Manufacturing Engineering Scholarships *(Graduate, Undergraduate/Scholarship)* [9192]
Ruppert Educational Grant Program *(Undergraduate/Grant)* [8955]
SALEF Health Career Scholarships *(Undergraduate, Graduate/Scholarship)* [8680]
The San Diego Foundation Community Scholarships II *(Undergraduate/Scholarship)* [8727]
Leo and Trinidad Sanchez Scholarships *(Undergraduate/Scholarship)* [8956]
Sand Hill Scholars Program *(Undergraduate/Scholarship)* [8957]
Schatz Energy Fellowships for Graduate Studies *(Graduate/Fellowship)* [5004]
Barbara A. Shacochis Scholarships *(Undergraduate/Scholarship)* [8003]
Stuart Silverman Scholarships *(Undergraduate/Scholarship)* [8005]
Special Events Internships - Los Angeles *(Undergraduate, Graduate/Internship)* [4438]
Lee Summer Student Fellowship *(Undergraduate, Master's/Fellowship)* [8553]
Superior District Legislative Mentoring Student Grants RT to DC *(Undergraduate/Grant)* [2484]
Superior District Legislative Mentoring Student Grants *(Undergraduate/Grant)* [2483]
Switzer Environmental Fellowships *(Graduate/Fellowship)* [9623]
Robert M. Takasugi Public Interest Fellowships *(Postgraduate/Fellowship)* [9636]
The Honorable Raymond Thompson Endowed Scholarships *(Undergraduate/Scholarship)* [8006]
Raymond A. Tice Scholarships I *(Undergraduate/Scholarship)* [8733]
Raymond A. Tice Scholarships II *(Undergraduate/Scholarship)* [8734]
Thomas and Glenna Trimble Endowed Scholarships *(Undergraduate/Scholarship)* [8007]
UC MEXUS-CICESE Graduate Student Short-Term Research and Training Program *(Master's, Doctorate, Postdoctorate/Grant)* [10110]
UC MEXUS Grants for Dissertation Research *(Graduate/Grant)* [10111]
The UCSD Black Alumni Scholarship for Arts and Humanities *(Undergraduate/Scholarship)* [8736]
The UCSD Black Alumni Scholarships for Engineering, Mathematics and Science *(Undergraduate/Scholarship)* [8737]
Bettie Underwood Dental Assisting Scholarships *(Undergraduate/Scholarship)* [2831]
U.S. Bank Scholarships *(Undergraduate/Scholarship)* [8738]
USA Freestyle Martial Arts Scholarships *(Undergraduate/Scholarship)* [8739]
Weissbuch Family Scholarships *(Undergraduate/Scholarship)* [8740]
WHHS Medical Staff Scholarships *(Undergraduate/Scholarship)* [10448]
Howard A. White Endowed Scholarships *(Undergraduate/Scholarship)* [8009]
WLALA Scholarships *(Postgraduate/Scholarship)* [10647]

Colorado

AISC/Rocky Mountain Steel Construction Association Scholarships *(Graduate/Scholarship)* [935]
Roy Anderson Memorial Scholarships *(Graduate, Undergraduate/Scholarship)* [3140]
CCU Alumni Endowed Scholarships *(Undergraduate/Scholarship)* [3136]
Colorado Nurses Foundation Nightingale Scholarships *(Graduate, Undergraduate/Scholarship)* [3141]
Conference of State Bank Supervisors Graduate School Scholarships *(Graduate/Award)* [3343]
CSCPA College Scholarships *(Graduate, Undergraduate/Scholarship)* [3147]
CSCPA High School Scholarships *(Undergraduate/Scholarship)* [3148]
CSCPA Sophomore Scholarships *(Undergraduate/Scholarship)* [3149]
APTRA-Clete Roberts/Kathryn Dettman Memorial Journalism Scholarship *(Undergraduate/Scholarship)* [1818]
El Pomar Fellowships *(Graduate/Fellowship)* [3818]
Lola Fehr: Nightingale Scholarships *(Graduate, Undergraduate/Scholarship)* [3142]
Griffin Foundation Scholarships *(Undergraduate/Scholarship)* [4674]
HACU/Denny's Hungry for Education Scholarships *(Undergraduate, Graduate/Scholarship)* [4883]
Clinton J. Helton Manufacturing Scholarships *(Undergraduate/Scholarship)* [9183]
Richard A. Herbert Memorial Scholarships *(Undergraduate/Scholarship)* [1480]
Dorothy Mountain Memorial Scholarships *(Graduate/Scholarship)* [6135]
H.M. Muffly Memorial Scholarships *(Graduate, Undergraduate/Scholarship)* [3143]
Colorado Nurses Association: Virginia Paulson Memorial Scholarships *(Graduate, Undergraduate/Scholarship)* [3144]
Thomas J. Slocum Memorial Scholarships to Redstone College *(Undergraduate/Scholarship)* [171]
CASFM-Ben Urbonas Scholarships *(Graduate/Scholarship)* [3132]
Patty Walter Memorial Scholarships *(Graduate, Undergraduate/Scholarship)* [3145]

Connecticut

Frederick G. Adams Scholarships *(Undergraduate/Scholarship)* [4735]
AMLN Scholarships for Arab American Students *(Graduate, Undergraduate/Scholarship)* [1003]
Armenian American Pharmacists' Association Scholarships *(Graduate/Scholarship)* [1684]
Beinecke Rare Book and Manuscript Library Visiting Postdoctoral Scholar Fellowships *(Postdoctorate/Fellowship)* [2214]
Chopivsky Fellowships *(Graduate/Fellowship)* [10442]
The College Club of Hartford Scholarships *(Undergraduate/Scholarship)* [4743]
B.J. Dean Scholarships *(Undergraduate/Scholarship)* [3224]
C. Rodney Demarest Memorial Scholarships *(Undergraduate/Scholarship)* [4747]
H.J. "Duke" Ellington Memorial Scholarship Award *(Undergraduate/Scholarship)* [7513]
Kennedy T. Friend Scholarships *(Graduate, Undergraduate/Scholarship)* [325]
Priscilla Green Scholarships *(Undergraduate/Scholarship)* [3465]
Mary Main Memorial Scholarships *(Undergraduate/Scholarship)* [4762]
NYU Langone Medical Center Science Student Scholarships *(Undergraduate, Graduate/Scholarship)* [109]
Sylvia Parkinson Scholarships *(Undergraduate/Scholarship)* [4766]
Dorothy E. Hofmann Pembroke Scholarships *(Undergraduate/Scholarship)* [4767]
DW Simpson Actuarial Science Scholarship Program *(Undergraduate/Scholarship)* [8963]
Smith Family Awards Program for Excellence in Biomedical Research *(Advanced Professional, Professional development/Grant)* [4823]

Delaware

Dick and Pat Hazel Minority Scholarships *(Undergraduate/Scholarship)* [3180]
Norfolk Southern Foundation Scholarships *(Undergraduate/Scholarship)* [1188]
NYU Langone Medical Center Science Student Scholarships *(Undergraduate, Graduate/Scholarship)* [109]

District of Columbia

Frederick B. Abramson Memorial Foundation Scholarships *(Undergraduate/Scholarship)* [28]
AISES Summer Internships *(Undergraduate, Graduate/Internship)* [888]
American Enterprise Institute National Research Initiative Fellowships (NRI) *(Graduate/Fellowship)* [786]
CAPAL Public Service Scholarships *(Graduate, Undergraduate/Scholarship)* [3341]
Charles A. Lindbergh Fellowships *(Graduate/Fellowship)* [9021]
CHCI Graduate Fellowships *(Graduate/Fellowship)* [3352]
CHCI Public Policy Fellowships *(Professional development/Fellowship)* [3353]
The Corp - More Uncommon Grounds Scholarships *(Undergraduate/Scholarship)* [9604]
The Corp - Students of Georgetown Inc. Coke Scholarships *(Undergraduate/Scholarship)* [9605]
The Corp - Students of Georgetown Inc. Textbook Scholarships *(Undergraduate/Scholarship)* [9606]
Dumbarton Oaks Fellowships *(Doctorate, Graduate/Fellowship)* [3728]
Dumbarton Oaks Junior Fellowships *(Graduate/Fellowship)* [3729]
Dumbarton Oaks Research Library and Collection Post-Doctoral Teaching Fellowships *(Postdoctorate/Fellowship)* [3738]
Andrew Foster Scholarships *(Undergraduate/Scholarship)* [6815]
Guggenheim Fellowships *(Doctorate/Fellowship)* [9022]
ILSA Internships *(Graduate/Internship)* [5353]
Kislak Fellowships in American Studies *(Graduate, Postdoctorate/Fellowship)* [5844]

UNITED STATES

Kislak Short Term Fellowships Opportunities in American Studies *(Undergraduate, Graduate/Fellowship)* [5845]
Kluge Fellowships *(Doctorate, Graduate/Fellowship)* [5846]
David B. Larson Fellowships in Health and Spirituality *(Doctorate/Fellowship)* [5847]
MPAC-DC Graduate Policy Fellowships *(Graduate/Fellowship)* [6630]
MyMozaic.com Annual Scholarships *(Undergraduate/Scholarship)* [6639]
NARAL Pro-Choice America Development Internships *(Undergraduate, Graduate, Professional development/Internship)* [6659]
NARAL Pro-Choice America Policy Internships *(Professional development/Internship)* [6660]
NARAL Pro-Choice America Political Internships *(Undergraduate, Graduate, Professional development/Internship)* [6661]
NYU Langone Medical Center Science Student Scholarships *(Undergraduate, Graduate/Scholarship)* [109]
Perkins Coie 1L Political Law Fellowships *(Postgraduate/Fellowship)* [8013]
PETA Foundation Law Internships *(Graduate/Internship)* [7958]
Public Service Fellows Internship Program - Center for Government Leadership *(Undergraduate, Graduate/Internship)* [7890]
Public Service Fellows Internship Program - Communications *(Undergraduate, Graduate, Professional development/Internship)* [7891]
Public Service Fellows Internship Program - Development *(Undergraduate, Graduate, Professional development/Internship)* [7892]
Public Service Fellows Internship Program - Education and Outreach *(Undergraduate, Graduate, Professional development/Internship)* [7893]
Public Service Fellows Internship Program - Government Affairs *(Undergraduate, Graduate, Professional development/Internship)* [7894]
Public Service Fellows Internship Program - Government Transformation and Agency Partnerships *(Undergraduate, Graduate, Professional development/Internship)* [7895]
Public Service Fellows Internship Program - Human Resources *(Undergraduate, Graduate, Professional development/Internship)* [7896]
Public Service Fellows Internship Program - Research *(Undergraduate, Graduate, Professional development/Internship)* [7897]
Harold W. Rosenthal Fellowships in International Relations *(Professional development/Fellowship, Internship)* [2043]
The Ivan Shandor Memorial Ukrainian American Bar Association Scholarships *(Graduate, Master's/Scholarship)* [10444]
TFAS Congressional Scholarship Awards *(Undergraduate/Award, Scholarship)* [4309]
USGLC Internships - Communications *(Undergraduate, Doctorate/Internship)* [9949]
USGLC Internships - Government Relations *(Undergraduate, Graduate/Internship)* [9950]
USGLC Internships - Outreach *(Undergraduate, Graduate/Internship)* [9951]
USGLC Internships - Policy *(Undergraduate, Graduate/Internship)* [9952]
A. Verville Fellowships *(Professional development/Fellowship)* [9023]
Ann Cook Whitman Washington, DC Scholarships *(Undergraduate/Scholarship)* [4417]

Florida

Emily and Roland Abraham Educational Funds *(Undergraduate/Scholarship)* [3316]
AISC/Southern Association of Steel Fabricators Scholarships *(Graduate/Scholarship)* [936]
Bill Bernbach Diversity Scholarships *(Undergraduate/Scholarship)* [457]
Bethune-Cookman University Excelsior Scholarship Level 1 *(Undergraduate/Scholarship)* [2250]
Bethune-Cookman University Presidential Scholarships *(Undergraduate/Scholarship)* [2251]
Leon Bradley Scholarship Program *(Undergraduate/Scholarship)* [575]

Calvin Alumni Association Florida-Gulf Coast Scholarships *(Undergraduate/Scholarship)* [2494]
Celler Legal P.A. Employment Skills Scholarship Program *(Undergraduate/Scholarship)* [2837]
Central Florida Jazz Society Scholarships *(Undergraduate/Award, Scholarship)* [2869]
ChairScholars Florida Scholarship Program *(Undergraduate/Scholarship)* [2888]
Cuban American Bar Association Scholarships *(All/Scholarship)* [3485]
D&A Florida Scholarships *(Undergraduate/Scholarship)* [9425]
Doctors Ira and Udaya Dash Nursing Scholarships *(Undergraduate, Graduate/Scholarship)* [9426]
James H. Davis Scholarships *(Undergraduate/Scholarship)* [4100]
Fecon Scholarships *(Undergraduate/Scholarship)* [4088]
FICPA Educational Foundation 1040K Race Scholarships *(Undergraduate, Graduate/Scholarship)* [4098]
Florida Education Fund McKnight Doctoral Fellowships *(Graduate/Fellowship)* [4085]
Florida Engineering Society University Scholarships *(Undergraduate/Scholarship)* [4090]
Florida Outdoor Writers Association Scholarships *(Undergraduate/Scholarship)* [4104]
Clay Ford Florida Board of Accountancy Minority Scholarships *(Undergraduate/Scholarship)* [4083]
HACU/Denny's Hungry for Education Scholarships *(Undergraduate, Graduate/Scholarship)* [4883]
HACU/NASCAR Scholarships *(Graduate, Undergraduate/Scholarship)* [4888]
Chip Johnson Scholarships *(Undergraduate/Scholarship)* [9435]
David F. Ludovici Scholarships *(Undergraduate/Scholarship)* [4091]
Robert V. McKenna Scholarships *(Undergraduate/Scholarship)* [9654]
Raymond W. Miller, PE and Alice E. Miller Scholarships *(Undergraduate/Scholarship)* [4092]
Raymond W. Miller, PE Scholarships *(Undergraduate/Scholarship)* [4093]
Judge William J. Nelson Scholarships *(Undergraduate/Scholarship)* [9442]
Norfolk Southern Foundation Scholarships *(Undergraduate/Scholarship)* [1188]
North Florida Chapter Safety Education Scholarships *(Graduate, Undergraduate/Scholarship)* [1423]
Operation JumpStart Scholarships *(Graduate/Scholarship)* [458]
Melissa Pellegrin Memorial Scholarships *(Undergraduate, Graduate/Scholarship)* [7751]
Eric Primavera Memorial Scholarships *(Undergraduate/Scholarship)* [4094]
Regions Riding Forward Scholarships Essay Contest *(Undergraduate/Scholarship)* [8536]
Edward S. Roth Manufacturing Engineering Scholarships *(Graduate, Undergraduate/Scholarship)* [9192]
DW Simpson Actuarial Science Scholarship Program *(Undergraduate/Scholarship)* [8963]
Southern Scholarship Foundation Scholarships *(Undergraduate/Scholarship)* [9413]
SPE Gulf Coast Hurricane Scholarships *(Undergraduate/Scholarship)* [9270]
Tri Delta Beta Gamma Memorial Scholarships *(Undergraduate/Scholarship)* [3562]
Jacki Tuckfield Memorial Graduate Business Scholarship Fund *(Doctorate, Graduate, Master's/Scholarship)* [6453]
Ted G. Wilson Memorial Scholarships *(Undergraduate/Scholarship)* [8288]

Georgia

AISC/Southern Association of Steel Fabricators Scholarships *(Graduate/Scholarship)* [936]
Brenda S. Bank Educational Workshop Scholarships *(Undergraduate/Scholarship)* [9123]
Bill Bernbach Diversity Scholarships *(Undergraduate/Scholarship)* [457]
Leon Bradley Scholarship Program *(Undergraduate/Scholarship)* [575]
Kenneth H. Breeden Scholarships *(Undergraduate/Scholarship)* [5924]

CDC Public Health Informatics Fellowships *(Professional development, Master's, Graduate/Fellowship)* [9919]
Anthony R. Dees Educational Workshop Scholarships *(Undergraduate/Scholarship)* [9124]
Forsyth County United Way Scholarships *(Undergraduate/Scholarship)* [5925]
Georgia Engineering Foundation Scholarships *(Graduate/Scholarship)* [4380]
Larry Gulley Scholarships *(Undergraduate/Scholarship)* [9125]
HACU/Denny's Hungry for Education Scholarships *(Undergraduate, Graduate/Scholarship)* [4883]
HACU/NASCAR Scholarships *(Graduate, Undergraduate/Scholarship)* [4888]
Richard A. Hammill Scholarship Fund *(Undergraduate/Scholarship)* [981]
Carroll Hart Scholarship *(Graduate/Scholarship)* [9126]
Gene Henson Scholarships *(Undergraduate/Scholarship)* [2113]
Durwood McAlister Scholarships *(Undergraduate/Scholarship)* [4387]
Morris Newspaper Corp. Scholarships *(Undergraduate/Scholarship)* [4388]
NERL Postdoctoral Research Program *(Postdoctorate, Advanced Professional, Professional development/Fellowship)* [9935]
Edna A. Noblin Dawsonville Lions Club Scholarships *(Undergraduate/Scholarship)* [5926]
Norfolk Southern Foundation Scholarships *(Undergraduate/Scholarship)* [1188]
NWAG Georgia, USA Scholarships *(Undergraduate/Scholarship)* [7431]
Operation JumpStart Scholarships *(Graduate/Scholarship)* [458]
Regions Riding Forward Scholarships Essay Contest *(Undergraduate/Scholarship)* [8536]
William C. Rogers Scholarships *(Undergraduate/Scholarship)* [4389]
DW Simpson Actuarial Science Scholarship Program *(Undergraduate/Scholarship)* [8963]
SSAWMA Scholarships *(Graduate/Scholarship)* [9415]
George and Pearl Strickland Scholarships *(Graduate, Undergraduate/Scholarship)* [3195]
Kirk Sutlive Scholarships *(Undergraduate/Scholarship)* [4390]
Ted G. Wilson Memorial Scholarships *(Undergraduate/Scholarship)* [8288]

Hawaii

Asian Development Bank - Japan Scholarships *(Graduate/Scholarship)* [3759]
APTRA-Clete Roberts/Kathryn Dettman Memorial Journalism Scholarship *(Undergraduate/Scholarship)* [1818]
East-West Center Graduate Degree Fellowships *(Master's, Doctorate, Graduate/Fellowship)* [3760]
HPGS/ALOH Graduate Scholarships *(Graduate/Scholarship)* [4801]
HPGS Undergraduate Scholarships *(Undergraduate/Scholarship)* [4802]
Indonesian Directorate General of Higher Education Scholarships *(Graduate/Scholarship)* [3761]
Obuchi Student Scholarships *(Graduate/Scholarship)* [3762]
PATCH Early Childhood Education Scholarships *(Other/Scholarship)* [7903]
PSHF Good Idea Grants *(Other/Grant)* [8381]
William S. Richardson Commemorative Scholarships *(Graduate/Scholarship)* [7918]
Southeast Asian Ministers of Education Organization-Vietnam Scholarship Program *(Graduate/Scholarship)* [3763]
University of Hawaii at Manoa East-West Center Graduate Fellowships *(Graduate, Postdoctorate/Fellowship)* [10139]

Place of Study Index

UNITED STATES

Idaho

The "21" Endowed Scholarships *(Undergraduate/Scholarship)* [6015]
Mamie Adams Memorial Awards *(Undergraduate/Scholarship)* [6016]
Horatio Alger Lola and Duane Hagadone Idaho Scholarships *(Undergraduate/Scholarship)* [4943]
American Legion Boys/Girls State Scholarships *(Undergraduate/Scholarship)* [6017]
Banner Bank Business Scholarships *(Undergraduate/Scholarship)* [6057]
Ted Bjornn University of Idaho Graduate Student Scholarships *(Graduate/Scholarship)* [5033]
Ted Bjornn University of Idaho Undergraduate Student Scholarships *(Undergraduate/Scholarship)* [5034]
Diana Brown Endowed Scholarships *(Undergraduate/Scholarship)* [6018]
Glen and Babs Carlson Endowed Scholarships *(Undergraduate/Scholarship)* [6019]
Walter and Elsie Carr Endowed Scholarships *(Undergraduate/Scholarship)* [6020]
Coeur d'Alene Alumni Scholarships *(Undergraduate/Scholarship)* [6021]
Rob Copeland Memorial Scholarships *(Undergraduate/Scholarship)* [6022]
Rick Crane Group Real Estate Scholarship Fund *(Undergraduate/Scholarship)* [6023]
Mike Crapo Math and Science Scholarship Fund *(Undergraduate/Scholarship)* [5040]
Laura Moore Cunningham Foundation General Scholarships *(Undergraduate/Scholarship)* [6024]
APTRA-Clete Roberts/Kathryn Dettman Memorial Journalism Scholarship *(Undergraduate/Scholarship)* [1818]
Gretchen Dimico Memorial Scholarships *(Undergraduate/Scholarship)* [6025]
The Fisher-Clark Memorial Endowed Scholarships *(Undergraduate/Scholarship)* [6026]
Dean A. Froehlich Endowed Scholarships *(Undergraduate/Scholarship)* [6027]
Irene Carlson Gnaedinger Memorial Scholarships *(Undergraduate/Scholarship)* [6028]
Alois and Marie Goldmann Scholarship Fund *(Undergraduate/Scholarship)* [5041]
Jack M. and Mary Lou Gruber Scholarships *(Undergraduate/Scholarship)* [6029]
Jimmy Guild Memorial Scholarships *(Undergraduate/Scholarship)* [6030]
The Henderson Memorial Endowed Scholarships *(Undergraduate/Scholarship)* [6031]
Hinman-Jensen Endowed Scholarships *(Undergraduate/Scholarship)* [6032]
Frank and Gladys Hopkins Endowed Scholarships *(Undergraduate/Scholarship)* [6033]
Horatio Alger Idaho University Scholarships *(Undergraduate/Scholarship)* [4958]
ICAFS Idaho Graduate Student Scholarships *(Graduate/Scholarship)* [5035]
ICAFS Idaho High School Student Scholarships *(Undergraduate/Scholarship)* [5036]
ICAFS Idaho Undergraduate Student Scholarships *(Undergraduate/Scholarship)* [5037]
Idaho Nursery and Landscape Association Scholarships *(Undergraduate/Scholarship)* [5048]
Idaho Nursing and Health Professions Scholarships *(Undergraduate/Scholarship)* [5042]
Idaho Society of CPA's Scholarships *(Undergraduate/Scholarship)* [5043]
Margaret G. Johnson and Marge J. Stout Scholarships *(Undergraduate/Scholarship)* [6034]
LCSC Presidential Out-of-State Tuition Scholarships *(Undergraduate/Scholarship)* [6035]
LCSC Welding Club Scholarships *(Undergraduate/Scholarship)* [6036]
Lewis-Clark Coin Club Endowed Scholarships *(Undergraduate/Scholarship)* [6037]
Lewis-Clark State College Foundation Scholars Scholarships *(Undergraduate/Scholarship)* [6038]
Lewis-Clark State College Governor's Cup Scholarships *(Undergraduate/Scholarship)* [6039]
Lewis-Clark State College In-State Non-Traditional Student Scholarships *(Undergraduate/Scholarship)* [6040]
Lewis-Clark State College - Military Order of the Purple Heart Scholarships *(Undergraduate/Scholarship)* [6041]
Lewis-Clark State College Provost Scholarships *(Undergraduate/Scholarship)* [6042]
Lewis-Clark State College Transfer Scholarships *(Undergraduate/Scholarship)* [6058]
Lewiston Service League Memorial Scholarships *(Undergraduate/Scholarship)* [6043]
Kaia Lynn Markwalter Endowed Scholarships *(Undergraduate/Scholarship)* [6044]
Susan B. Martin Memorial Scholarships *(Graduate/Scholarship)* [5038]
Elizabeth McKissick Memorial Scholarships *(Undergraduate/Scholarship)* [6045]
Robbie Miller Memorial Scholarships *(Undergraduate/Scholarship)* [6046]
Eugene Northrup Scholarships *(Undergraduate/Scholarship)* [6047]
Odd Fellows Lodge No. 8 Endowed Scholarships *(Undergraduate/Scholarship)* [6048]
Laura Ann Peck Memorial Endowed Scholarships *(Undergraduate/Scholarship)* [6049]
Eleanor Perry Memorial Endowed Scholarships *(Undergraduate/Scholarship)* [6050]
Kenneth Rogers Memorial Scholarships *(Undergraduate/Scholarship)* [6051]
Rosenberg-Ibarra Scholarships *(Undergraduate/Scholarship)* [8263]
Roger C. Sathre Memorial Scholarship Fund *(Undergraduate/Scholarship)* [5045]
Bill Sawyer Memorial Scholarships *(Undergraduate/Scholarship)* [6052]
Susan P. Schroeder Memorial Scholarships *(Undergraduate/Scholarship)* [6053]
Shinn Family Scholarships *(Undergraduate/Scholarship)* [6054]
John Streiff Memorial Scholarships *(Undergraduate/Scholarship)* [6055]
Tschudy Family Scholarships *(Undergraduate/Scholarship)* [5050]
WALPA Lake Student Scholarships *(Undergraduate, Graduate/Scholarship)* [10466]
Washington City/County Management Association Scholarships *(Graduate/Scholarship)* [10438]

Illinois

Allied Health Care Professional Scholarships *(Undergraduate/Scholarship)* [5070]
American Council of Engineering Companies of Illinois Scholarships *(Undergraduate/Scholarship)* [722]
Calvin Alumni Association-Illinois Scholarships *(Undergraduate/Scholarship)* [2495]
Chapter 23 - Quad Cities Iowa/Illinois Scholarships *(Undergraduate/Scholarship)* [9172]
Chapter 31 - Peoria Endowed Scholarships *(Undergraduate/Scholarship)* [9173]
CMSF Scholarships *(Undergraduate, Graduate/Scholarship)* [2932]
Robert Esser Student Achievement Scholarships *(Graduate, Undergraduate/Scholarship)* [5061]
Larry L. Etherton Scholarships *(Graduate, Undergraduate/Scholarship)* [1185]
Michael W. and Jean D. Franke Family Foundation Scholarships *(Graduate, Undergraduate/Scholarship)* [1186]
HACU/Denny's Hungry for Education Scholarships *(Undergraduate, Graduate/Scholarship)* [4883]
IAAI Scholarship Foundation Accounting Scholarships *(Undergraduate/Scholarship)* [5091]
IBEA Graduate Scholarships *(Graduate/Scholarship)* [5056]
IBEA Undergraduate Scholarships *(Undergraduate/Scholarship)* [5057]
Illinois Future Teacher Corps Scholarships *(Undergraduate/Scholarship)* [5072]
Illinois Landscape Contractors Association Scholarships *(Undergraduate/Scholarship)* [5064]
Illinois Special Education Teacher Tuition Waiver Scholarships (SETTW) *(Undergraduate/Scholarship)* [5073]
Illinois Student Assistance Commission Medical Student Scholarships *(Undergraduate/Scholarship)* [5074]
Illinois Student Assistance Commission Merit Recognition Scholarships (MRS) *(Undergraduate/Scholarship)* [5075]
Illinois Student Assistance Commission Nurse Educator Scholarships (NESP) *(Undergraduate/Scholarship)* [5076]
Illinois Student Assistance Commission Nursing Education Scholarships *(Undergraduate/Scholarship)* [5077]
ISPE Foundation Scholarships *(Undergraduate/Scholarship)* [5066]
Jewish Federation Academic Scholarships *(Graduate, Undergraduate/Scholarship)* [5598]
Ray and Kathy LaHood Scholarships for the Study of American Government *(Undergraduate/Scholarship)* [3627]
Arnold "Les" Larsen, FAIA, Memorial Scholarships *(Graduate/Scholarship)* [896]
Abraham Lincoln Marovitz Public Interest Law Scholarships *(Undergraduate/Scholarship)* [2897]
Minority Teachers of Illinois Scholarships (MTI) *(Undergraduate/Scholarship)* [5078]
Muddy Waters Scholarships *(Undergraduate/Scholarship)* [2316]
Norfolk Southern Foundation Scholarships *(Undergraduate/Scholarship)* [1188]
Northeastern Illinois Chapter Scholarships *(Graduate, Undergraduate/Scholarship)* [1424]
Regions Riding Forward Scholarships Essay Contest *(Undergraduate/Scholarship)* [8536]
Edward S. Roth Manufacturing Engineering Scholarships *(Graduate, Undergraduate/Scholarship)* [9192]
DW Simpson Actuarial Science Scholarship Program *(Undergraduate/Scholarship)* [8963]
Donald M. Wells Scholarships *(Undergraduate/Scholarship)* [4632]
Andrea Will Memorial Scholarships *(Undergraduate/Scholarship)* [8945]

Indiana

Warren M. Anderson Scholarships *(Undergraduate/Scholarship)* [5115]
The Artist in Landscape Design Scholarship by Fullmer's Landscaping *(Undergraduate/Scholarship)* [7581]
Warren K. Brown Scholarships *(Undergraduate/Scholarship)* [1410]
Chapter 56 - Fort Wayne Scholarships *(Graduate, Undergraduate/Scholarship)* [9176]
Robert Esser Student Achievement Scholarships *(Graduate, Undergraduate/Scholarship)* [5061]
Illinois Landscape Contractors Association Scholarships *(Undergraduate/Scholarship)* [5064]
Indiana Broadcasters Association College Scholarship Program *(Undergraduate/Scholarship)* [5108]
Indiana State University Academic Excellence Scholarships *(Undergraduate/Scholarship)* [5116]
Indiana State University Academic Promise Scholarships *(Undergraduate/Scholarship)* [5126]
Indiana State University Creative and Performing Arts Awards *(Undergraduate/Scholarship)* [5127]
Indiana State University Incentive Scholarships *(Undergraduate/Scholarship)* [5117]
Indiana State University President's Scholarships *(Undergraduate/Scholarship)* [5118]
Indiana State University Rural Health Scholarships *(Graduate/Scholarship)* [5119]
Indiana State University Transfer Student Scholarships *(Undergraduate/Scholarship)* [5120]
ISU Child of Alumni Book Voucher Awards *(Undergraduate/Scholarship)* [5128]
ISU Gongaware Scholarships *(Undergraduate/Scholarship)* [5121]
ISU Networks Scholarships College of Business *(Undergraduate/Scholarship)* [5122]
Central Indiana ASSE Jim Kriner Memorial Scholarships *(Graduate, Undergraduate/Scholarship)* [1419]
Marvin Lewis Scholarships *(Undergraduate/Scholarship)* [6060]
Clarence & Josephine Myers Undergraduate Scholarships *(Graduate, Undergraduate/Scholarship)* [9190]
Norfolk Southern Foundation Scholarships *(Undergraduate/Scholarship)* [1188]

UNITED STATES

Noyce Scholarships for Secondary Math and Science Education (Undergraduate/Scholarship) [5123]
Nicholas H. Noyes, Jr. Scholarship (Undergraduate/Scholarship) [5680]
Phi Theta Kappa Scholarships (Undergraduate/Scholarship) [5124]
Dr. J. Glenn Radcliffe Memorial Scholarships (Undergraduate/Scholarship) [9575]
Regions Riding Forward Scholarships Essay Contest (Undergraduate/Scholarship) [8536]
August M. Rocco Scholarship Fund (Undergraduate/Scholarship) [9531]
Esther Schlundt Memorial Scholarships (Graduate/Scholarship) [5112]
Lynn Brower Shonk Memorial Scholarship (Undergraduate/Scholarship) [5765]
DW Simpson Actuarial Science Scholarship Program (Undergraduate/Scholarship) [8963]
Spotlight on Nursing Graduate Nursing Student Scholarships (Graduate/Scholarship) [9484]
Barber Owen Thomas Scholarships (Undergraduate/Scholarship) [8942]

Iowa

William Stone Ayres Scholarship (Undergraduate/Scholarship) [3661]
Beverly Estate Scholarship (Undergraduate/Scholarship) [3662]
George and Mary Brammer Scholarship (Undergraduate/Scholarship) [3663]
Chapter 23 - Quad Cities Iowa/Illinois Scholarships (Undergraduate/Scholarship) [9172]
CMSF Scholarships (Undergraduate, Graduate/Scholarship) [2932]
Raymond DiPaglia Endowment Scholarship (Undergraduate/Scholarship) [3664]
Drake University Law School Law Opportunity Scholarships - Disadvantage (Undergraduate/Scholarship) [3667]
Drake University Law School Public Service Scholarships (Undergraduate/Scholarship) [3669]
Herman E. Elgar Memorial Scholarship (Undergraduate/Scholarship) [3671]
D.J. Fairgrave Education Trust (Undergraduate/Scholarship) [3672]
Leland Stanford Forrest Scholarship (Undergraduate/Scholarship) [3673]
Lex and Scott Hawkins Endowed Scholarship (Undergraduate/Scholarship) [3674]
Edward and Cora Hayes Scholarship (Undergraduate/Scholarship) [3675]
Annamae Heaps Law Scholarship (Undergraduate/Scholarship) [3676]
John M. Helmick Law Scholarship (Undergraduate/Scholarship) [3677]
Herbert Hoover Uncommon Student Awards (Undergraduate/Scholarship) [4931]
Illinois Landscape Contractors Association Scholarships (Undergraduate/Scholarship) [5064]
Iowa Association of Electric Cooperatives - Electric Cooperative Pioneer Trust Fund Scholarship (Undergraduate/Scholarship) [3678]
Iowa Journalism Institute Scholarships (Undergraduate/Scholarship) [5473]
Iowa Library Association Foundation Scholarships (Graduate/Scholarship) [5469]
James P. Irish Scholarship (Undergraduate/Scholarship) [3679]
Forest A. King Scholarship (Undergraduate/Scholarship) [3681]
Verne Lawyer Scholarship (Undergraduate/Scholarship) [3682]
Frederick D. Lewis Jr. Scholarships (Undergraduate/Scholarship) [3683]
Gordon and Delores Madson Scholarship (Undergraduate/Scholarship) [3684]
Jake S. More Scholarship (Undergraduate/Scholarship) [3685]
James B. Morris Scholarships (Undergraduate/Scholarship) [6598]
Norfolk Southern Foundation Scholarships (Undergraduate/Scholarship) [1188]
Dwight D. Opperman Scholarships (Undergraduate/Scholarship) [3686]
Regions Riding Forward Scholarships Essay Contest (Undergraduate/Scholarship) [8536]
Janet Reynoldson Memorial Scholarship (Undergraduate/Scholarship) [3687]
Walter and Rita Selvy Scholarship (Undergraduate/Scholarship) [3688]
DW Simpson Actuarial Science Scholarship Program (Undergraduate/Scholarship) [8963]
Charles "Buck" and Dora Taylor Scholarship (Undergraduate/Scholarship) [3689]
Jack E. Tillson Scholarships (Graduate/Scholarship) [5470]
Haemer Wheatcraft Scholarship (Undergraduate/Scholarship) [3690]
Zarley, McKee, Thomte, Voorhees, Sease Law Scholarship (Undergraduate/Scholarship) [3691]

Kansas

Chapter 52 - Wichita Scholarships (Graduate, Undergraduate/Scholarship) [9175]
AISC Education Foundation - Fred R. Havens Fund (Undergraduate, Graduate/Scholarship) [937]
Judge Delmas C. Hill Scholarships (Undergraduate/Scholarship) [10429]
Kansas Dental Education Opportunities Program (Graduate/Scholarship) [5654]
Kansas Distinguished Scholarship Program (Graduate/Scholarship) [5655]
Kansas Nurse Educator Service Scholarships (Graduate/Scholarship) [5656]
KHIMA Graduate Scholarships (Graduate/Scholarship) [5661]
Koch Scholars Program (Undergraduate/Scholarship) [10430]
The Floyd Lietz Memorial Scholarship (Undergraduate/Scholarship) [8323]
Sue A. Malone Scholarships (Doctorate, Graduate, Professional development/Scholarship) [5662]
John J. Mingenback Memorial Scholarships (Graduate, Undergraduate/Scholarship) [4468]
Martha Mitchell Pearson Memorial Scholarship (Undergraduate, Graduate/Scholarship) [5755]
Karen Schuvie Scholarships (Undergraduate/Scholarship, Loan) [5663]
A.J. and Lynda Hare Scribante Scholarship Fund (Undergraduate/Scholarship) [5762]
Shamberg Scholarships (Undergraduate/Scholarship) [10431]
USAWOASF/Grantham University On-Line Scholarships (Graduate, Undergraduate/Scholarship) [9880]
Lynn McNabb Walton Adelphe Scholarhship (Undergraduate/Scholarship) [5770]
Washburn University School of Law Business and Transactional Law Center Scholarships (Undergraduate/Scholarship) [10432]
Washburn University School of Law Child and Family Advocacy Fellowships (Undergraduate/Fellowship) [10433]
J.L. Weigand, Jr. Legal Education Trust Scholarships (Undergraduate/Scholarship) [10434]

Kentucky

AISC/Southern Association of Steel Fabricators Scholarships (Graduate/Scholarship) [936]
The Artist in Landscape Design Scholarship by Fullmer's Landscaping (Undergraduate/Scholarship) [7581]
Bechtel Group Foundation Scholarships for Safety & Health (Undergraduate/Scholarship) [1409]
Leon Bradley Scholarship Program (Undergraduate/Scholarship) [575]
Warren K. Brown Scholarships (Undergraduate/Scholarship) [1410]
The Educational Foundation of KyCPA Scholarships (Undergraduate/Scholarship) [5821]
Beth K. Fields Scholarships (Undergraduate/Scholarship) [10144]
Sam J. Hord Memorial Scholarships (Undergraduate/Scholarship) [9381]
Kentucky Alumni Club Scholarships - Frankfort/Capital Region Alumni Club (Undergraduate/Scholarship) [10146]
Kentucky Alumni Club Scholarships - Lexington/Central Kentucky Alumni Club (Undergraduate/Scholarship) [10147]
Kentucky Alumni Club Scholarships - Somerset/Lake Cumberland Area Alumni Club (Undergraduate/Scholarship) [10148]
Kentucky Educational Excellence Scholarships (Undergraduate/Scholarship) [2261]
Kentucky Paralegal Association Student Scholarships (Undergraduate/Scholarship) [5819]
KHEAA Teacher Scholarship (Undergraduate/Scholarship) [2262]
Marvin Lewis Scholarships (Undergraduate/Scholarship) [6060]
Norfolk Southern Foundation Scholarships (Undergraduate/Scholarship) [1188]
Marvin Rammelsberg Scholarships (Undergraduate/Scholarship) [3009]
Regions Riding Forward Scholarships Essay Contest (Undergraduate/Scholarship) [8536]
Covington-Cincinnati/Northern Kentucky Alumni Club - Dane Wagge Scholarships (Undergraduate/Scholarship) [10149]
Allen and Loureena Weber Scholarships (Undergraduate/Scholarship) [9200]
Woman In Rural Electrification Scholarships (Undergraduate/Scholarship) [9383]

Louisiana

AISC/Southern Association of Steel Fabricators Scholarships (Graduate/Scholarship) [936]
Horatio Alger Louisiana Scholarships (Undergraduate/Scholarship) [4944]
American Radio Relay League Louisiana Memorial Scholarships (Undergraduate/Scholarship) [1721]
Greater Baton Rouge Chapter - Don Jones Excellence in Safety Scholarships (Undergraduate/Scholarship) [1416]
Norfolk Southern Foundation Scholarships (Undergraduate/Scholarship) [1188]
Petroleum Engineering Scholarships (Undergraduate/Scholarship) [9250]
Regions Riding Forward Scholarships Essay Contest (Undergraduate/Scholarship) [8536]
Rochelle Scholarship (College/Scholarship) [6124]
Society of Louisiana Certified Public Accountants Scholarships (Undergraduate, Graduate/Scholarship) [9165]
SPE Gulf Coast Hurricane Scholarships (Undergraduate/Scholarship) [9270]

Maine

Catharine Wilder Guiles Scholarships (Graduate/Scholarship) [6197]
Ruth Milan-Altrusa Scholarships (Undergraduate/Scholarship) [6207]
NYU Langone Medical Center Science Student Scholarships (Undergraduate, Graduate/Scholarship) [109]
Patriot Education Scholarships (Undergraduate/Scholarship) [6209]
Henry L.P. Schmelzer College Transitions Scholarships (Undergraduate/Scholarship) [6213]
Susan Vincent Memorial Scholarship (Undergraduate/Scholarship) [6187]

Maryland

Dr. Johnella Banks Memorial Scholarships (Undergraduate/Scholarship) [2298]
BCCC Foundation General Scholarship Fund (Undergraduate/Scholarship) [2178]
Dick and Pat Hazel Minority Scholarships (Undergraduate/Scholarship) [3180]
Kathleen Kelly Undergraduate Scholarship Award (Undergraduate/Scholarship) [8374]
MACPA Scholarships (Undergraduate, Graduate/Scholarship) [6298]
Dolphus E. Milligan Graduate Fellowships (Graduate/Fellowship) [7087]
Norfolk Southern Foundation Scholarships (Undergraduate/Scholarship) [1188]
NYU Langone Medical Center Science Student Scholarships (Undergraduate, Graduate/Scholarship) [109]
Open Society Baltimore Community Fellowships

(Advanced Professional/Fellowship) [7661]
Margaret Pemberton Scholarships *(Undergraduate/Scholarship)* [2299]
PFLAG Columbia-Howard County Scholarship *(Undergraduate/Scholarship)* [8025]
Tom D. Ralls Memorial Scholarship *(Professional development/Scholarship)* [4285]
Lana K. Rinehart Scholarships *(Undergraduate/Scholarship)* [3186]
Charles A. Townsend Scholarships *(Undergraduate/Scholarship)* [7868]

Massachusetts

Armenian American Pharmacists' Association Scholarships *(Graduate/Scholarship)* [1684]
Tom Gifford Scholarships *(Undergraduate/Scholarship)* [4520]
Grass Fellowships at the Marine Biological Laboratory *(Doctorate, Postdoctorate/Fellowship)* [4643]
Hai Guin Scholarships Association *(Undergraduate/Scholarship)* [1695]
AISC Education Foundation - Fred R. Havens Fund *(Undergraduate, Graduate/Scholarship)* [937]
Charles A. King Trust Postdoctoral Research Fellowships *(Postdoctorate/Fellowship)* [4817]
Massachusetts General Hospital Clinical Translational Fellowships at Pfizer *(Advanced Professional/Fellowship)* [6318]
Massachusetts General Hospital/Harvard Medical School Internships *(Doctorate/Internship)* [6319]
MEFA Graduate Loans *(Graduate/Loan)* [6314]
Philip H. Melanson Memorial Scholarships *(Undergraduate, Graduate/Scholarship)* [10154]
MGH Department of Psychiatry Behavioral Neurology and Neuropsychiatry Fellowships *(Advanced Professional, Professional development/Fellowship)* [6320]
MGH Department of Psychiatry Eating Disorders Summer Research Fellowships *(Advanced Professional, Professional development/Fellowship)* [6321]
MGH Department of Psychiatry Forensic Psychiatry Fellowships *(Professional development/Fellowship)* [6322]
MGH Department of Psychiatry Global Psychiatric Clinical Research Training Program *(Advanced Professional/Fellowship)* [6323]
Leo F. Moro Baseball Memorial Scholarships *(Undergraduate/Scholarship)* [4249]
NYU Langone Medical Center Science Student Scholarships *(Undergraduate, Graduate/Scholarship)* [109]
Partners HealthCare Geriatric Psychiatry Fellowships *(Professional development/Fellowship)* [6324]
Harry B. Pulver Scholarships *(Undergraduate/Scholarship)* [4454]
Edward S. Roth Manufacturing Engineering Scholarships *(Graduate, Undergraduate/Scholarship)* [9192]
Joseph Sumner Smith Scholarships *(Undergraduate/Scholarship)* [9839]
Worcester County Conservation District Annual Scholarships Program *(Undergraduate/Scholarship)* [10687]

Michigan

AISC/Great Lakes Fabricators and Erectors Association Fellowships *(Graduate/Fellowship)* [933]
Altrusa International of Grand Rapids Scholarships *(Undergraduate/Scholarship)* [4573]
AREMA Michigan Tech Alumni Scholarships *(Graduate, Undergraduate/Scholarship)* [1181]
Dr. Noyes L. Avery, Jr. and Ann E. Avery Scholarships *(Undergraduate, Graduate/Scholarship)* [4575]
Raymond B. Bauer Research Award *(Professional development/Grant)* [6479]
Geraldine Geistert Boss Scholarships *(Undergraduate/Scholarship)* [4577]
Dorothy and Dick Burgess Scholarships *(Undergraduate/Scholarship)* [5499]
Calvin Alumni Association California- Bay Area Scholarships *(Undergraduate/Scholarship)* [2493]
Calvin Alumni Association-Michigan Lakeshore Scholarships *(Undergraduate/Scholarship)* [2496]
Calvin Alumni Association-Michigan, Lansing Scholarships *(Undergraduate/Scholarship)* [2497]
Calvin Alumni Association-New Jersey Scholarships *(Undergraduate/Scholarship)* [2498]
Calvin Alumni Association-South Florida Scholarships *(Undergraduate/Scholarship)* [2499]
Calvin Alumni Association-Southeast Michigan Scholarships *(Undergraduate/Scholarship)* [2500]
Calvin Alumni Association-Southeastern Wisconsin Scholarships *(Undergraduate/Scholarship)* [2501]
Calvin Alumni Association-Southwest Michigan, Kalamazoo Scholarships *(Undergraduate/Scholarship)* [2503]
Calvin Alumni Association-Washington, D.C. Scholarships *(Undergraduate/Scholarship)* [2504]
Calvin Alumni Association-Washington, Lynden Scholarships *(Undergraduate/Scholarship)* [2505]
Orrie and Dorothy Cassada Scholarships *(Undergraduate/Scholarship)* [4579]
Center for the Education of Women Scholarships *(Graduate, Undergraduate/Scholarship)* [10195]
Center for the Education of Women Student Research Grants *(Graduate, Undergraduate/Grant)* [10196]
Chapter 1 - Detroit Founding Chapter Undergraduate Scholarships *(Undergraduate/Scholarship)* [9169]
Chapter 198 - Downriver Detroit Scholarships *(Graduate, Undergraduate/Scholarship)* [9171]
Chapter 311 - Tri City Scholarships *(Undergraduate/Scholarship)* [9174]
CMSF Scholarships *(Undergraduate, Graduate/Scholarship)* [2932]
Thomas D. Coffield Scholarships *(Undergraduate/Scholarship)* [4582]
Paul Collins Scholarships *(Undergraduate/Scholarship)* [4583]
Rosemary Cook Education Scholarships *(Undergraduate/Scholarship)* [4584]
Gerald M. Crane Music Award Scholarships *(Undergraduate/Scholarship)* [4585]
Darooge Family Scholarships *(Undergraduate/Scholarship)* [4586]
Antenore C. "Butch" Davanzo Scholarships *(Graduate, Undergraduate/Scholarship)* [6502]
Antonia Dellas Memorial Scholarships *(Undergraduate/Scholarship)* [5501]
Chapter 116 - Kalamazoo - Roscoe Douglas Scholarships *(Undergraduate/Scholarship)* [9180]
Erickson Education Scholarships *(Undergraduate/Scholarship)* [4513]
Bertha M. Fase Memorial Scholarship Fund *(Undergraduate/Scholarship)* [4515]
Virginia Valk Fehsenfeld Scholarships *(Undergraduate/Scholarship)* [4591]
Melbourne and Alice E. Frontjes Scholarships *(Undergraduate/Scholarship)* [4592]
Mathilda and Carolyn Gallmeyer Scholarships *(Undergraduate/Scholarship)* [4594]
Gauthier Family Scholarship Fund *(Undergraduate/Scholarship)* [4519]
Grand Haven Offshore Challenge Scholarship Fund *(Undergraduate/Scholarship)* [4521]
Grand Rapids Scholarship Association *(Undergraduate/Scholarship)* [4595]
Philip F. Greco Memorial Scholarships *(Undergraduate/Scholarship)* [6170]
Guy D. and Mary Edith Halladay Graduate Scholarships *(Undergraduate/Scholarship)* [4598]
Martha and Oliver Hansen Memorial Scholarships *(Undergraduate/Scholarship)* [5505]
Bob and Dawn Hardy Automotive Scholarships *(Undergraduate/Scholarship)* [5506]
Marjorie M. Hendricks Environmental Education Scholarship Fund *(Undergraduate/Scholarship)* [4523]
John P. Hennessey Scholarships *(Graduate, Undergraduate/Scholarship)* [6503]
Hierholzer-Fojtik Scholarship Fund *(Undergraduate/Scholarship)* [4525]
Donald and Florence Hunting Scholarships *(Undergraduate/Scholarship)* [4600]
Illinois Landscape Contractors Association Scholarships *(Undergraduate/Scholarship)* [5064]
Jack Family Scholarships *(Undergraduate/Scholarship)* [4601]
Camilla C. Johnson Scholarships *(Undergraduate/Scholarship)* [4602]
Ladies Literary Club Scholarships *(Undergraduate/Scholarship)* [4605]
Lavina Laible Scholarships *(Undergraduate/Scholarship)* [4606]
Stephen Lankester Scholarships *(Undergraduate/Scholarship)* [4607]
John T. and Frances J. Maghielse Scholarships *(Undergraduate/Scholarship)* [4609]
Michigan Accountancy Foundation Final Year Accounting Scholarship *(Graduate/Scholarship)* [6457]
Michigan Auto Law Student Diversity Scholarships *(Undergraduate/Scholarship)* [6463]
Michigan Education Association Scholarships *(Undergraduate/Scholarship)* [6470]
Michigan Nurses Foundation Scholarships *(Undergraduate, Graduate/Scholarship)* [6477]
Michigan Society of Professional Engineers Scholarships *(Undergraduate/Scholarship)* [6483]
Harry J. Morris, Jr. Emergency Services Scholarships *(Undergraduate/Scholarship)* [4613]
NACA Northern Plains Regional Student Leadership Scholarships *(Undergraduate/Scholarship)* [6730]
NAIFA West Michigan Scholarships *(Undergraduate/Scholarship)* [4614]
NALS of Michigan Scholarships *(Undergraduate/Scholarship)* [6652]
Norfolk Southern Foundation Scholarships *(Undergraduate/Scholarship)* [1188]
Peggy Kommer Novosad Scholarships *(Graduate, Postgraduate/Scholarship)* [4615]
Patricia and Armen Oumedian Scholarships *(Undergraduate/Scholarship)* [4616]
Marvin R. and Pearl E. Patterson Family Scholarships Fund *(Undergraduate/Scholarship)* [4535]
P.E.O. Chapter DS Scholarships *(Undergraduate, Vocational/Occupational/Scholarship)* [4536]
Reach for Your Goal Scholarships *(Undergraduate/Scholarship)* [4617]
Daniel L. Reiss Memorial Scholarship Fund *(Undergraduate/Scholarship)* [4539]
Harold and Eleanor Ringelberg Scholarships *(Undergraduate/Scholarship)* [4540]
Josephine Ringold Scholarships *(Undergraduate/Scholarship)* [4618]
Charles and Eleanor Rycenga Education Scholarship Fund *(Undergraduate/Scholarship)* [4541]
Dr. William A. and Marceleine J. Sautter Hanover-Horton High School Youth of Promise Scholarships *(Undergraduate/Scholarship)* [5511]
Prof. George Schneider, Jr. Manufacturing Technology Education Scholarships *(Undergraduate/Scholarship)* [9193]
Jeptha Wade Schureman Scholarship Program *(Undergraduate/Scholarship)* [3333]
Marion A. and Ruth Sherwood Family Fund Education Scholarships *(Undergraduate/Scholarship)* [4546]
Marion A. and Ruth K. Sherwood Family Fund Engineering Scholarships *(Undergraduate/Scholarship)* [4547]
Miller G. Sherwood Family Scholarship Fund *(Undergraduate/Scholarship)* [4548]
Sigma Kappa Foundation Michigan Scholarships *(Undergraduate/Scholarship)* [8939]
Hazel Simms Nursing Scholarships *(Other/Scholarship)* [5933]
DW Simpson Actuarial Science Scholarship Program *(Undergraduate/Scholarship)* [8963]
Christine Soper Scholarships *(Undergraduate/Scholarship)* [4623]
Dorothy B. and Charles E. Thomas Scholarships *(Undergraduate/Scholarship)* [4625]
Dorothy J. Thurston Graduate Scholarships *(Undergraduate/Scholarship)* [4626]
Trustees Law School Scholarships *(Undergraduate/Scholarship)* [6172]
Edward Tuinier Memorial Scholarships *(Undergraduate/Scholarship)* [813]
U-M Alumnae Club (University of Michigan) Scholarships *(Undergraduate/Scholarship)* [4628]

UNITED STATES

Keith C. Vanderhyde Scholarships *(Undergraduate/Scholarship)* [4629]
Jacob R. and Mary M. VanLoo and Lenore K. VanLoo Scholarships *(Undergraduate/Scholarship)* [4630]
Chad Vollmer Scholarships *(Undergraduate/Scholarship)* [4631]
Jack H. Wagner Scholarships *(Graduate, Undergraduate/Scholarship)* [6504]
Sue Walicki Nursing Scholarships *(Undergraduate/Scholarship)* [5516]
Donald M. Wells Scholarships *(Undergraduate/Scholarship)* [4632]
Walter C. Winchester Scholarships *(Undergraduate/Scholarship)* [4634]
Amos and Marilyn Winsand - Detroit Section Named Scholarships *(Undergraduate/Scholarship)* [1526]
Michael J. Wolf Scholarships *(Undergraduate/Scholarship)* [4635]
Violet Wondergem Health Science Scholarships *(Undergraduate/Scholarship)* [4636]
Leo Zupin Memorial Scholarship Fund *(Undergraduate, Vocational/Occupational/Scholarship)* [4556]

Minnesota

William E. Barto Scholarships *(Undergraduate/Scholarship)* [3704]
Robert Esser Student Achievement Scholarships *(Graduate, Undergraduate/Scholarship)* [5061]
General Mills Foundation Scholarships *(Undergraduate/Scholarship)* [869]
Jeanne H. Hemmingway Scholarships *(Undergraduate/Scholarship)* [3711]
Illinois Lake Management Association Undergraduate/Graduate Scholarships *(Graduate, Undergraduate/Scholarship)* [5062]
Jerome Fellowships *(Other/Fellowship)* [8152]
Carol E. Macpherson Memorial Scholarship *(Graduate, Undergraduate/Scholarship)* [10203]
Minnesota Division Scholarships *(Undergraduate/Scholarship)* [6522]
Minnesota Health Information Management Association Scholarships *(Undergraduate/Scholarship)* [6547]
Hubert A. Nelson Scholarships *(Undergraduate/Scholarship)* [3718]
Anderson Niskanen Scholarships *(Undergraduate/Scholarship)* [3720]
Arthur L. Norberg Travel Fund *(Advanced Professional/Grant)* [10200]
Edward S. Roth Manufacturing Engineering Scholarships *(Graduate, Undergraduate/Scholarship)* [9192]
The Adelle and Erwin Tomash Fellowship in the History of Information Technology *(Doctorate, Graduate/Fellowship)* [10201]

Mississippi

AISC/Southern Association of Steel Fabricators Scholarships *(Graduate/Scholarship)* [936]
ARRLF Mississippi Scholarships *(Undergraduate/Scholarship)* [1725]
MSCPA Undergraduate Scholarships *(Undergraduate/Scholarship)* [4560]
Norfolk Southern Foundation Scholarships *(Undergraduate/Scholarship)* [1188]
Regions Riding Forward Scholarships Essay Contest *(Undergraduate/Scholarship)* [8536]
Ross/Nickey Scholarships *(Graduate/Scholarship)* [6563]
SPE Gulf Coast Hurricane Scholarships *(Undergraduate/Scholarship)* [9270]
SSAWMA Scholarships *(Graduate/Scholarship)* [9415]

Missouri

Buder Scholarships for American Indian Law Students *(Juris Doctorate/Scholarship)* [10474]
Chapter 52 - Wichita Scholarships *(Graduate, Undergraduate/Scholarship)* [9175]
Coro Fellows Program in Public Affairs *(Postgraduate/Fellowship)* [3423]
Walter Moran Farmer Scholarships *(Juris Doctorate/Scholarship)* [10475]

AISC Education Foundation - Fred R. Havens Fund *(Undergraduate, Graduate/Scholarship)* [937]
Health Professional Nursing Student Loans *(Undergraduate, Graduate/Loan)* [6565]
Illinois Landscape Contractors Association Scholarships *(Undergraduate/Scholarship)* [5064]
Kansas Optometry Service Scholarships *(Graduate, Undergraduate/Scholarship)* [5657]
Norfolk Southern Foundation Scholarships *(Undergraduate/Scholarship)* [1188]
Martha Mitchell Pearson Memorial Scholarship *(Undergraduate, Graduate/Scholarship)* [5755]
Regions Riding Forward Scholarships Essay Contest *(Undergraduate/Scholarship)* [8536]
DW Simpson Actuarial Science Scholarship Program *(Undergraduate/Scholarship)* [8963]
Washington University Law School Chancellor's Graduate Fellowships *(Advanced Professional/Fellowship)* [10476]
Washington University Law School Olin Fellowships for Women *(Advanced Professional/Fellowship)* [10477]
Webster Society Scholarships *(Juris Doctorate/Scholarship)* [10478]

Montana

Horatio Alger Montana Scholarships *(Undergraduate/Scholarship)* [4947]
Bechtel Group Foundation Scholarships for Safety & Health *(Undergraduate/Scholarship)* [1409]
Scott Brownlee Memorial Scholarships *(Undergraduate, Graduate/Scholarship)* [6582]
APTRA-Clete Roberts/Kathryn Dettman Memorial Journalism Scholarship *(Undergraduate/Scholarship)* [1818]
Anthony Gerharz Scholarships *(Undergraduate, Graduate/Scholarship)* [6583]
Great Falls Broadcasters Association Scholarships *(Undergraduate/Scholarship)* [6577]
Eldon E. and JoAnn C. Kuhns Family Scholarships *(Undergraduate, Graduate/Scholarship)* [6584]
MSCPA Scholarship - Montana Tech *(Undergraduate, Graduate/Scholarship)* [6585]
MSCPA Scholarship - MSU Bozeman *(Undergraduate, Graduate/Scholarship)* [6586]
MSCPA Scholarship - University of Montana *(Undergraduate, Graduate/Scholarship)* [6587]
Donald E. Pizzini Memorial Nurse Scholarships *(Undergraduate, Professional development/Scholarship)* [6580]

Nebraska

Ahrens Charitable Trust Scholarship *(Undergraduate/Scholarship)* [4558]
Edgar Barge Memorial Scholarships *(Undergraduate/Scholarship)* [4559]
Beta Omega Scholarships *(Undergraduate/Scholarship)* [8911]
BSF General Scholarship Awards *(Undergraduate, Vocational/Occupational/Scholarship)* [2197]
Susan Thompson Buffett Foundation Scholarships *(Undergraduate/Scholarship)* [2402]
Karen Connick Memorial Scholarships *(Undergraduate/Scholarship)* [4560]
Doniphan Community Foundation Scholarships *(Undergraduate/Scholarship)* [4561]
Howard G. and Gladys A. Eakes Memorial Scholarships *(Undergraduate/Scholarship)* [4562]
Hall County Medical Society Scholarships *(Undergraduate/Scholarship)* [4563]
Nebraska Paralegal Association Student Scholarships *(Undergraduate/Scholarship)* [7247]
NESCPA Fifth-Year Scholarships *(Graduate/Scholarship)* [7251]
NESCPA General Scholarships *(Graduate, Undergraduate/Scholarship)* [7252]
Pleasantview Public Schools Fund *(Undergraduate/Scholarship)* [4564]
Jim and Dee Price Scholarships *(Undergraduate/Scholarship)* [4565]
Carl C. and Abbie Rebman Trust Scholarships *(Undergraduate/Scholarship)* [4566]
Teammates Mentoring Scholarship Program *(Undergraduate/Scholarship)* [4567]

Mark and Vera Turner Memorial Scholarships *(Undergraduate/Scholarship)* [6068]
Robert & Barbara Wade Scholarships *(Undergraduate/Scholarship)* [6069]
Woodyard Family Scholarships *(Undergraduate/Scholarship)* [4568]
James and Joy Zana Memorial Scholarships *(Undergraduate/Scholarship)* [4569]

Nevada

American Nuclear Society Nevada Section Scholarships *(Undergraduate/Scholarship)* [8331]
Aaron Edward Arnoldsen Memorial Scholarships *(Undergraduate/Scholarship)* [1719]
Susan Brager Occupational Education Scholarships *(Undergraduate/Scholarship)* [8333]
John Caoile Memorial Scholarships *(Undergraduate/Scholarship)* [8335]
APTRA-Clete Roberts/Kathryn Dettman Memorial Journalism Scholarship *(Undergraduate/Scholarship)* [1818]
Mickey Donnelly Memorial Scholarships *(Undergraduate/Scholarship)* [8340]
Palo Verde High School - Barbara Edwards Memorial Scholarships *(Undergraduate/Scholarship)* [8342]
Gordy Fink Memorial Scholarships *(Undergraduate/Scholarship)* [8343]
HACU/Denny's Hungry for Education Scholarships *(Undergraduate, Graduate/Scholarship)* [4883]
North Las Vegas Firefighters William J. Harnedy Memorial Scholarships *(Undergraduate/Scholarship)* [8348]
Michael Koizumi APWA Scholarships *(Undergraduate/Scholarship, Internship)* [7263]
Las Vegas Chinatown Scholarships *(Undergraduate/Scholarship)* [8352]
Mesquite Club Evening Chapter Inc. Scholarships *(Undergraduate/Scholarship)* [8355]
NERL Postdoctoral Research Program *(Postdoctorate, Advanced Professional, Professional development/Fellowship)* [9935]
Palo Verde High School Faculty Follies Scholarships *(Undergraduate/Scholarship)* [8357]
Pardee Community Building Scholarships *(Undergraduate/Scholarship)* [8359]
Sheila Tarr-Smith Memorial Scholarships *(Undergraduate/Scholarship)* [8368]
Judith Warner Memorial Scholarships *(Undergraduate/Scholarship)* [8369]
Edwin F. Wiegand Science and Technology Scholarships *(Undergraduate/Scholarship)* [8370]

New Hampshire

College of Engineering and Physical Sciences Industry Scholarships *(Undergraduate/Scholarship)* [10208]
NHPGA Apprentice Scholarships *(Undergraduate/Scholarship)* [6358]
NYU Langone Medical Center Science Student Scholarships *(Undergraduate, Graduate/Scholarship)* [109]
Walter T. Philippy Scholarships *(Undergraduate/Scholarship)* [6359]
Piscataqua Region Artist Advancement Grants *(Professional development/Grant)* [7305]
Harry B. Pulver Scholarships *(Undergraduate/Scholarship)* [4454]
Louise Tillotson Teaching Fellowships *(Professional development/Fellowship)* [7306]
Louise Tillotson Teaching Professional Development Scholarships *(Professional development/Scholarship)* [7307]
UNH Alumni Association Legacy Scholarships *(Undergraduate/Scholarship)* [10209]
UNH Parents Association Endowment Scholarship Fund *(Undergraduate/Scholarship)* [10210]

New Jersey

AMLN Scholarships for Arab American Students *(Graduate, Undergraduate/Scholarship)* [1003]
Benjamin Asbell Memorial Scholarships *(Undergraduate/Scholarship)* [2507]
Eivind H. Barth, Jr. Memorial Scholarships *(Under-*

graduate/Scholarship) [2508]
CentraState Band Aid Open Committee Scholarships (Undergraduate/Scholarship) [2876]
Hon. Joseph W. Cowgill Memorial Scholarships (Undergraduate/Scholarship) [2509]
George Dale Scholarship Fund (Undergraduate/Scholarship) [1776]
DCH Freehold Toyota Scholarships (Undergraduate/Scholarship) [2878]
Hon. Ralph W.E. Donges Memorial Scholarships (Undergraduate/Scholarship) [2510]
DuBois Brothers Scholarships (Undergraduate/Scholarship) [2511]
H.J. "Duke" Ellington Memorial Scholarship Award (Undergraduate/Scholarship) [7513]
Bernadine Johnson-Marshall and Martha Bell Williams Scholarships (Undergraduate/Scholarship) [1863]
George F. Kugler, Jr. Scholarships (Undergraduate/Scholarship) [2512]
Abram D. and Maxine H. Londa Scholarships (Undergraduate/Scholarship) [7334]
Sonia Morgan Scholarships (Undergraduate/Scholarship) [7335]
NCNJ-AWMA Undergraduate Scholarship (Undergraduate/Scholarship) [152]
NJCBIR Individual Research Grants (Other/Grant) [9549]
NJCBIR Pilot Research Grants (Other/Grant) [9550]
NJCBIR Postdoctoral and Graduate Student Fellowships (Graduate, Postdoctorate/Fellowship) [9551]
NJCBIR Programmatic Multi-Investigator Project Grants (Other/Grant) [9552]
NJSBF Labor Law Scholarships (Undergraduate/Scholarship) [7336]
NJSCPA College Scholarships (Graduate, Undergraduate/Scholarship) [7331]
Norfolk Southern Foundation Scholarships (Undergraduate/Scholarship) [1188]
NYU Langone Medical Center Science Student Scholarships (Undergraduate, Graduate/Scholarship) [109]
Louis C. Portella Memorial Scholarships (Graduate/Scholarship) [2514]
Hon. Rudolph J. Rossetti Memorial Scholarships (Undergraduate/Scholarship) [2515]
Seton Hall Law Merit Scholarships (Graduate/Scholarship) [8855]
Jay A. Strassberg Memorial Scholarships (Undergraduate/Scholarship) [2517]
Daniel B. Toll Memorial Scholarships (Undergraduate/Scholarship) [2518]
William Tomar Memorial Scholarships (Undergraduate/Scholarship) [2519]
Wallace Vail Scholarships (Undergraduate/Scholarship) [7337]
Bruce A. Wallace Memorial Scholarships (Undergraduate/Scholarship) [2520]

New Mexico

Walt Bartram Memorial Education Award, Region 12 and Chapter 119 (Undergraduate/Scholarship) [9167]
Chapter 93 - Albuquerque Scholarships (Undergraduate/Scholarship) [9179]
APTRA-Clete Roberts/Kathryn Dettman Memorial Journalism Scholarship (Undergraduate/Scholarship) [1818]
General Mills Foundation Scholarships (Undergraduate/Scholarship) [869]
HACU/Denny's Hungry for Education Scholarships (Undergraduate, Graduate/Scholarship) [4883]
New Mexico Association for Bilingual Education Scholarships (Undergraduate/Scholarship) [7339]
Charles A. Townsend Scholarships (Undergraduate/Scholarship) [7868]

New York

AMLN Scholarships for Arab American Students (Graduate, Undergraduate/Scholarship) [1003]
Arlyn Scales Awards for Science and Technology (Undergraduate/Scholarship) [3035]
AWMA Niagara Frontier Section College Scholarships (Graduate, Undergraduate/Scholarship) [149]
Leo Baeck Institute - DAAD Fellowships (Doctorate/Fellowship) [3602]
Mark B. Bain Graduate Fellowship (Doctorate, Master's, Graduate/Fellowship) [4980]
Berkowitz Fellowships (Professional development/Fellowship) [9743]
Robert L. Bernstein Fellowships in International Human Rights (Graduate/Fellowship) [4994]
CFR Military Fellowships (Professional development/Fellowship) [3442]
CFR Stanton Nuclear Security Fellowships (Doctorate, Postdoctorate, Advanced Professional/Fellowship) [3444]
CFR Volunteer Internships (Undergraduate, Graduate/Internship) [3445]
Chautauqua Scholarships Program (Undergraduate/Scholarship) [5367]
CHRGJ Emerging Human Rights Scholarship Conference (Graduate/Scholarship) [7398]
CHRGJ International Human Rights Fellowships (Doctorate, Professional development/Fellowship, Internship) [7399]
CHRGJ Students Human Rights Scholars Program (Graduate, Advanced Professional, Professional development/Scholarship) [7400]
Coro Fellows Program in Public Affairs (Postgraduate/Fellowship) [3423]
Design and Multimedia Internships - New York (Undergraduate, Graduate/Internship) [4430]
H.J. "Duke" Ellington Memorial Scholarship Award (Undergraduate/Scholarship) [7513]
Edward R. Murrow Press Fellowships (Professional development/Fellowship) [3446]
Faith Initiatives Internships - New York (Undergraduate, Graduate/Internship) [4432]
Fellowship on Women & Public Policy (Graduate/Fellowship) [10102]
GFLC AWMA Scholarships (Undergraduate, Graduate/Scholarship) [4361]
GLAAD Communications/PR Internships - New York (Undergraduate, Graduate/Internship) [4434]
GLAAD News Internships - New York (Undergraduate, Graduate/Internship) [4435]
GLAAD Spanish-Language and Latino Media Internships - Los Angeles (Undergraduate, Graduate/Internship) [4436]
GLAAD Youth Issues Internships - New York (Undergraduate, Graduate/Internship) [4437]
HACU/Denny's Hungry for Education Scholarships (Undergraduate, Graduate/Scholarship) [4883]
Arthur Helton Fellowships (Graduate/Fellowship) [7401]
Ketchum Excellence in Public Relations Research Award (Graduate/Fellowship, Internship) [5213]
Anne O'Hare McCormick Scholarship Fund (Graduate/Scholarship) [7429]
Senator Patricia K. McGee Nursing Faculty Scholarships (Doctorate, Graduate/Scholarship) [7365]
New York Financial Writers' Associations Scholarships (Graduate, Undergraduate/Scholarship) [7354]
New York State Association of Agricultural Fairs Scholarships (Undergraduate/Scholarship) [7361]
Norfolk Southern Foundation Scholarships (Undergraduate/Scholarship) [1188]
NYCT Paid Graduate Student Philanthropy Fellowships - Community Development and the Environment (Graduate/Fellowship) [7351]
NYU Langone Medical Center Science Student Scholarships (Undergraduate, Graduate/Scholarship) [109]
Faith E. O'Neal Scholarships (Undergraduate/Scholarship) [8392]
Open Society Presidential Fellowships (Advanced Professional/Fellowship) [7663]
Operation JumpStart Scholarships (Graduate/Scholarship) [458]
Victoria Ovis Memorial Scholarships (Undergraduate/Scholarship) [7045]
Tibor T. Polgar Fellowships (Graduate, Undergraduate/Fellowship) [4981]
Saint Andrews Scholarships (Undergraduate/Scholarship) [8670]
Dave Sauer Memorial College Scholarships (Undergraduate/Scholarship) [150]
Stanley M. Schoenfeld Memorial Scholarship (Postgraduate/Scholarship) [7363]
Special Events Internships - New York (Undergraduate, Graduate/Internship) [4439]
Sports Internships - Los Angeles (Undergraduate, Graduate/Internship) [4440]
Trans Issues Internships - New York (Undergraduate, Graduate/Internship) [4441]
Undergraduate Session Assistants Program (Undergraduate/Other) [7370]
Jeannette K. Watson Fellowships (Undergraduate/Fellowship, Internship) [10491]
Albert E. Wischmeyer Memorial Scholarships (Undergraduate/Scholarship) [9202]
Woody Guthrie Fellowship (Professional development/Fellowship) [2321]
Davis Wright Tremaine 1L Diversity Scholarships (Undergraduate/Scholarship) [3535]

North Carolina

African American Network - Carolinas Scholarship Fund (Undergraduate/Scholarship) [4174]
Chester Arzell and Helen Miller Montgomery Scholarships (Undergraduate/Scholarship) [10570]
Pete and Ellen Bensley Memorial Scholarship Fund (Undergraduate/Scholarship) [4178]
Carol Bond Community College Scholarships (Undergraduate/Scholarship) [7479]
Carol Bond University Scholarships (Undergraduate/Scholarship) [7480]
Leon Bradley Scholarship Program (Undergraduate/Scholarship) [575]
Tien Bui Memorial Scholarships (Undergraduate/Scholarship) [10573]
Cadmus Communications Corporation Graphics Scholarship Endowment Fund (Undergraduate/Scholarship) [4181]
Kasie Ford Capling Memorial Scholarship Endowment Fund (Undergraduate/Scholarship) [4182]
Career Awards for Science and Mathematics Teachers (Other/Award) [2415]
William F. Carl Scholarships (Undergraduate/Scholarship) [7470]
Charlotte-Mecklenburg Schools Scholarship Incentive Program (Undergraduate/Scholarship) [4186]
Lula Faye Clegg Memorial Scholarship Fund (Undergraduate/Scholarship) [4188]
Sally Cole Visual Arts Scholarship Fund (Undergraduate/Scholarship) [4190]
Lloyd E. and Rachel S. Collins Scholarships (Undergraduate/Scholarship) [10576]
Virginia Elizabeth and Alma Vane Taylor Nursing Scholarship (Undergraduate/Scholarship) [10580]
Judge Samuel J. Ervin, III Fellowships (Graduate/Fellowship) [6004]
Jack Ervin EDI Scholarships (Other/Scholarship) [7460]
Clifton W. Everett, Sr. Community Lawyer Fellowships (Graduate/Fellowship) [6005]
Foundation for the Carolinas Rotary Scholarship Fund (Undergraduate/Scholarship) [4195]
HACU/Denny's Hungry for Education Scholarships (Undergraduate, Graduate/Scholarship) [4883]
HACU/NASCAR Scholarships (Graduate, Undergraduate/Scholarship) [4888]
Governor James E. Holshouser Professional Development Scholarships (Other/Scholarship) [7461]
Oliver Joel and Ellen Pell Denny Healthcare Scholarship Fund (Undergraduate/Scholarship) [10585]
James V. Johnson Scholarship Fund (Undergraduate/Scholarship) [4199]
Annabel Lambeth Jones Scholarships (Undergraduate/Scholarship) [4200]
K & W Cafeterias Scholarships (Undergraduate/Scholarship) [7472]
Law Enforcement Memorial Scholarship Fund (Undergraduate/Scholarship) [4202]
William B. Martin East Carolina University Scholarships (Undergraduate/Scholarship) [5678]
Carolina Panthers Players Sam Mills Memorial Scholarship Fund (Undergraduate/Scholarship) [4205]
Carolina Panthers Players Sam Mills Memorial Scholarships (Graduate/Scholarship) [4206]

UNITED STATES

NC Hospitality Education Foundation Scholarships - Four Year College or University *(Undergraduate/Scholarship)* [7473]
NC Hospitality Education Foundation Scholarships - Graduate *(Graduate/Scholarship)* [7474]
NC Hospitality Education Foundation Scholarships - High School *(Undergraduate/Scholarship)* [7475]
NC Hospitality Education Foundation Scholarships - Two Year Community or Junior College *(Undergraduate/Scholarship)* [7476]
NCACPA Outstanding Minority Accounting Student Scholarships *(Undergraduate/Scholarship)* [7451]
NCRLA Golden Corral Scholarships *(Undergraduate/Scholarship)* [7477]
NERL Postdoctoral Research Program *(Postdoctorate, Advanced Professional, Professional development/Fellowship)* [9935]
Norfolk Southern Foundation Scholarships *(Undergraduate/Scholarship)* [1188]
North Carolina CPA Foundation Scholarships *(Undergraduate/Scholarship)* [7452]
North Mecklenburg Teachers' Memorial Scholarships *(Undergraduate/Scholarship)* [4208]
NRMRL Postdoctoral Research Program *(Postdoctorate, Advanced Professional, Professional development/Fellowship)* [9939]
Ted H. Ousley Scholarship Fund *(Undergraduate/Scholarship)* [4209]
Alice Conger Patterson Scholarships *(Undergraduate/Scholarship)* [10591]
Peter DeWitt Pruden and Phyliss Harrill Pruden Scholarships *(Undergraduate/Scholarship)* [10247]
Regions Riding Forward Scholarships Essay Contest *(Undergraduate/Scholarship)* [8536]
Ben Robinette Scholarship Endowment Fund *(Undergraduate/Scholarship)* [4211]
DW Simpson Actuarial Science Scholarship Program *(Undergraduate/Scholarship)* [8963]
Tacy Anna Smith Memorial Scholarships *(Undergraduate/Scholarship)* [4213]
Dan Stewart Scholarships *(Other/Scholarship)* [7462]
Charles H. Stone Scholarships *(Undergraduate/Scholarship)* [2081]
Turner Family Scholarships *(Undergraduate, Vocational/Occupational/Scholarship)* [4217]
UNC-CGI C.V. Starr Scholarships *(Undergraduate, Graduate/Scholarship)* [2847]
The Sybil Jennings Vorheis Memorial Undergraduate Scholarships *(Undergraduate/Scholarship)* [4218]
Nell and Spencer Waggoner Scholarships *(Undergraduate/Scholarship)* [10602]
Frederick K. Weyerhaeuser Forest History Fellowships *(Graduate/Fellowship)* [4138]
The L. Phil and Alice J. Wicker Scholarship *(Undergraduate/Scholarship)* [1763]
Edwin H. and Louise N. Williamson Endowed Scholarships *(Undergraduate/Scholarship)* [10605]
Ted G. Wilson Memorial Scholarships *(Undergraduate/Scholarship)* [8288]
Mary and Elliot Wood Foundation Undergraduate Scholarship Fund *(Undergraduate/Scholarship)* [4223]

North Dakota

North Dakota Veterinary Medical Association Scholarships *(Undergraduate/Scholarship)* [7502]

Ohio

Wayne D. Ackerman Family Scholarship Fund *(Undergraduate/Scholarship)* [9491]
AISC/Ohio Structural Steel Association Scholarships *(Graduate/Scholarship)* [934]
Akron Bar Association Foundation Scholarships *(Undergraduate/Scholarship)* [182]
Ora E. Anderson Scholarships *(Undergraduate, High School/Scholarship)* [4167]
The Artist in Landscape Design Scholarship by Fullmer's Landscaping *(Undergraduate/Scholarship)* [7581]
Jack R. Barckhoff Welding Management Scholarships *(Undergraduate/Scholarship)* [1510]
William (Billbo) Boston/Harold Knopp Scholarship *(Undergraduate/Scholarship)* [7815]
Harry D. Callahan Educational Trust *(Undergraduate/Scholarship)* [9495]
Ruth M. Cogan Scholarship Fund *(Undergraduate/Scholarship)* [9497]
Lawrence E. and Jean L. Davis Scholarships *(Undergraduate/Scholarship)* [7824]
Julio C. Diaz Academic Scholarship *(Undergraduate/Scholarship)* [9498]
Harold K. Douthit Regional Scholarships *(Undergraduate/Scholarship)* [7576]
Emergency Medicine Physician Scholarships for Health Information Management Program *(Undergraduate/Scholarship)* [9500]
Epsilon Tau Pi's Soaring Eagle Scholarships *(Undergraduate/Scholarship)* [6924]
Robert Esser Student Achievement Scholarships *(Graduate, Undergraduate/Scholarship)* [5061]
Thomas W. Gallagher Scholarships Fund *(Undergraduate/Scholarship)* [9503]
David A. and Pamela A. Gault Charitable Fund *(Undergraduate/Scholarship)* [9504]
Margaret S. Gilbert Scholarship Fund *(Undergraduate/Scholarship)* [9505]
Zelma Gray Medical School Scholarships *(Graduate, Doctorate/Fellowship)* [4168]
Dorcas Edmonson Haught Scholarships *(Undergraduate/Scholarship)* [7840]
Dale O. Heimberger CRNA Memorial Scholarship Fund *(Graduate/Scholarship)* [9509]
Illinois Lake Management Association Undergraduate/Graduate Scholarships *(Graduate, Undergraduate/Scholarship)* [5062]
Susan K. Ipacs Nursing Legacy Scholarships *(Undergraduate, High School/Scholarship)* [4169]
Marvin Lewis Scholarships *(Undergraduate/Scholarship)* [6060]
Markley Family Scholarship Fund *(Undergraduate/Scholarship)* [9522]
Harry Mestel Memorial Accounting Scholarship Fund *(Undergraduate/Scholarship)* [9525]
John G. and Betty J. Mick Scholarship Fund *(Undergraduate/Scholarship)* [9526]
Lt. Colonel Robert G. Moreland Vocational/Technical Fund *(Undergraduate/Scholarship)* [9527]
NERL Postdoctoral Research Program *(Postdoctorate, Advanced Professional, Professional development/Fellowship)* [9935]
NOHIMSS Student Scholarship Program *(Undergraduate, Master's, Doctorate/Scholarship)* [7523]
Norfolk Southern Foundation Scholarships *(Undergraduate/Scholarship)* [1188]
Notre Dame Club of Canton Scholarships *(Undergraduate/Scholarship)* [9528]
NRMRL Postdoctoral Research Program *(Postdoctorate, Advanced Professional, Professional development/Fellowship)* [9939]
Ohio Newspaper Association Minority Scholarships *(Undergraduate/Scholarship)* [7577]
Ohio Newspaper Association University Journalism Scholarships *(Undergraduate/Scholarship)* [7578]
ONWA Annual Scholarships *(Undergraduate/Scholarship)* [7579]
OSCA Graduate Student Scholarship Program *(Graduate/Scholarship)* [7590]
Edward S. Roth Manufacturing Engineering Scholarships *(Graduate, Undergraduate/Scholarship)* [9192]
Aaron Seesan Memorial Scholarship Fund *(Undergraduate/Scholarship)* [9532]
Dr. William E. and Norma Sprague Scholarships *(Undergraduate, Graduate/Scholarship)* [4624]
Ira G. Turpin Scholars Fund *(Undergraduate/Scholarship)* [9541]
Lester and Eleanor Webster Foundation Scholarships *(Undergraduate/Scholarship)* [9542]
Wayne F. White and Bob Evans Legacy Scholarships *(Undergraduate, High School/Scholarship)* [4170]

Oklahoma

Chapter 52 - Wichita Scholarships *(Graduate, Undergraduate/Scholarship)* [9175]
Leon Harris/Les Nichols Memorial Scholarships to Spartan College of Aeronautics & Technology *(Undergraduate/Scholarship)* [163]
Kansas Optometry Service Scholarships *(Graduate, Undergraduate/Scholarship)* [5657]
Southwest Chapter Roy Kinslow Scholarships *(Undergraduate/Scholarship)* [1417]
L-3 Communications Avionics Systems Scholarships *(Undergraduate/Scholarship)* [166]
Oklahoma City University Full-Time Merit Scholarships *(Undergraduate/Scholarship)* [7601]
OSHA Graduate Scholarships *(Graduate/Scholarship)* [7606]
Hatton W. Sumners Scholarships *(Undergraduate/Scholarship)* [7602]
Tom Taylor Memorial Scholarships to Spartan College of Aeronautics and Technology *(Undergraduate/Scholarship)* [175]
Lynn McNabb Walton Adelphe Scholarhship *(Undergraduate/Scholarship)* [5770]

Oregon

Clackamas County Farm Bureau Scholarships *(Undergraduate/Scholarship)* [7705]
APTRA-Clete Roberts/Kathryn Dettman Memorial Journalism Scholarship *(Undergraduate/Scholarship)* [1818]
Emerald Empire Chapter Scholarship Awards *(Undergraduate/Scholarship)* [7695]
William Harrison Gill Education Fund *(Undergraduate/Scholarship)* [2228]
Kilbuck Family Native American Scholarships *(Undergraduate/Scholarship)* [2230]
Christopher Mesi Memorial Music Scholarships *(Undergraduate/Scholarship)* [2803]
Chapter 63 - Portland James E. Morrow Scholarships *(Graduate, Undergraduate/Scholarship)* [9189]
Oregon Association of Broadcasters Scholarships *(Undergraduate/Scholarship)* [7688]
OSCPA Educational Foundation College Scholarships *(Undergraduate/Scholarship)* [7711]
OSCPA Educational Foundation High School Scholarships *(Undergraduate/Scholarship)* [7712]
Chapter 63 - Portland Uncle Bud Smith Scholarships *(Undergraduate/Scholarship)* [9196]
Robert W. and Bernice Ingalls Staton Scholarships *(Undergraduate/Scholarship)* [10259]
Janet Cullen Tanaka Scholarships *(Undergraduate/Scholarship)* [2096]
University of Oregon Dean's Scholarships *(Undergraduate/Scholarship)* [10260]
University of Oregon Diversity Excellence Scholarships *(Undergraduate/Scholarship)* [10261]
University of Oregon General University Scholarships *(Undergraduate/Scholarship)* [10262]
University of Oregon Presidential Scholarships *(Undergraduate/Scholarship)* [10263]
Washington City/County Management Association Scholarships *(Graduate/Scholarship)* [10438]
Ed Wood Memorial Scholarship Awards *(Undergraduate/Scholarship)* [7703]
Davis Wright Tremaine 1L Diversity Scholarships *(Undergraduate/Scholarship)* [3535]
Yamhill County Farm Bureau Scholarships *(Undergraduate/Scholarship)* [7707]

Pennsylvania

Allegheny County Medical Society Medical Student Scholarships (ACMS) *(Undergraduate/Scholarship)* [4274]
Alliance Medical Education Scholarship Fund (AMES) *(Undergraduate/Scholarship)* [4275]
B-Brave McMahon/Stratton Scholarship Fund *(Undergraduate/Scholarship)* [4039]
Michael Baker Corp. Scholarship for Diversity in Engineering *(Undergraduate/Scholarship)* [1976]
Chambersburg/Fannett-Metal School District Scholarship Fund *(Undergraduate/Scholarship)* [4234]
CHOPR Postdoctoral Fellowships *(Postdoctorate/Fellowship)* [10267]
CODY Foundation Fund *(Undergraduate/Scholarship)* [4235]
Warren E. "Whitey" Cole American Society of Highway Engineers Scholarships *(Undergraduate/Scholarship)* [4042]

Coro Fellows Program in Public Affairs *(Postgraduate/Fellowship)* [3423]
Malcolm U. Dantzler Scholarships *(Other/Scholarship)* [9363]
The William H. Davis, Jr. Scholarship Fund *(Undergraduate/Scholarship)* [3204]
Jan DiMartino Delany Memorial Scholarships *(Undergraduate/Scholarship)* [4236]
Daniel B. Dixon Scholarships *(Undergraduate/Scholarship)* [324]
Dr. Michael Dorizas Memorial Scholarships *(Undergraduate/Scholarship)* [4846]
H.J. "Duke" Ellington Memorial Scholarship Award *(Undergraduate/Scholarship)* [7513]
Sue and Ken Dyer Foundation Travel Scholarships *(Undergraduate/Scholarship)* [4238]
Lindsay M. Entz Memorial Scholarships *(Undergraduate/Scholarship)* [4044]
Nolan W. Feeser Scholarship Fund *(Undergraduate/Scholarship)* [4045]
Benjamin Franklin Trust Fund *(Undergraduate, Vocational/Occupational/Scholarship)* [4046]
Daniel G. and Helen I. Fultz Scholarship Fund *(Undergraduate/Scholarship)* [4047]
Norma Gotwalt Scholarship Fund *(Undergraduate/Scholarship)* [4241]
F.C. Grote Fund Scholarships *(Graduate, Undergraduate/Scholarship)* [326]
Scott A. Gunder, MD, DCMS Presidential Scholarships *(Undergraduate/Scholarship)* [4276]
Morton and Beatrice Harrison Scholarship Fund *(Undergraduate/Scholarship)* [4048]
Hellenic University Club of Philadelphia Founders Scholarships *(Undergraduate/Scholarship)* [4847]
Nicholas S. Hetos, DDS, Memorial Graduate Scholarships *(Graduate, Doctorate/Scholarship)* [4848]
Conrad N. Hilton Scholarships *(Undergraduate/Scholarship)* [4414]
Ken and Romaine Kauffman Scholarship Fund *(Undergraduate/Scholarship)* [4245]
Leon I. Lock and Barbara R. Lock Scholarship Fund *(Undergraduate/Scholarship)* [4246]
Carie and George Lyter Scholarship Fund *(Undergraduate/Scholarship)* [4247]
Joseph and Catherine Missigman Memorial Nursing Scholarships *(Undergraduate/Scholarship)* [4051]
Missigman Scholarship Fund *(Undergraduate/Scholarship)* [4052]
Sam Mizrahi Memorial Scholarships *(Undergraduate/Scholarship)* [4248]
Robert E. and Judy More Scholarship Fund *(Undergraduate/Scholarship)* [4053]
Norfolk Southern Foundation Scholarships *(Undergraduate/Scholarship)* [1188]
NYU Langone Medical Center Science Student Scholarships *(Undergraduate, Graduate/Scholarship)* [109]
Dr. Nicholas Padis Memorial Graduate Scholarships *(Graduate/Scholarship)* [4849]
Pennsylvania Engineering Foundation Undergradaute Scholarships *(Undergraduate/Scholarship)* [7943]
Dr. Harry V. Pfautz Memorial Scholarship Fund *(Undergraduate/Scholarship)* [4250]
Ruth Cook Pfautz Memorial Scholarship Fund *(Undergraduate/Scholarship)* [4251]
PMCA/Penn State Fellowship in Confectionery Research *(Graduate/Fellowship)* [8293]
Bertha and Byron L. Reppert Scholarship Fund *(Undergraduate/Scholarship)* [4252]
Ollie Rosenberg Educational Trust *(Undergraduate/Scholarship)* [4253]
John A. Savoy Scholarship Fund *(Undergraduate/Scholarship)* [4059]
DW Simpson Actuarial Science Scholarship Program *(Undergraduate/Scholarship)* [8963]
Soroptimist International of Chambersburg Scholarship Fund *(Undergraduate/Scholarship)* [4255]
South Carolina Public Health Association Scholarships *(Undergraduate/Scholarship)* [9364]
Minnie Patton Stayman Scholarships *(Undergraduate/Scholarship)* [7948]
Anil and Neema Thakrar Family Fund No. 1 *(Undergraduate/Scholarship)* [4257]
Dr. Peter A. Theodos Memorial Graduate Scholarships *(Undergraduate, Graduate/Scholarship)* [4850]
Dimitri J. Ververelli Memorial Scholarship for Architecture and/or Engineering *(Undergraduate/Scholarship)* [4851]
John R. and Joan F. Werren Scholarships Fund *(Undergraduate/Scholarship)* [9543]
Jack and Edna May Yost Scholarships *(Undergraduate/Scholarship)* [4258]

Rhode Island

Armenian American Pharmacists' Association Scholarships *(Graduate/Scholarship)* [1684]
Bach Organ Scholarship *(Undergraduate/Scholarship)* [8602]
NYU Langone Medical Center Science Student Scholarships *(Undergraduate, Graduate/Scholarship)* [109]
Pembroke Center for Teaching and Research on Women Postdoctoral Fellowships *(Postdoctorate/Fellowship)* [2392]
RISLA Student Loans *(Undergraduate, Graduate/Loan)* [8615]
Smith Family Awards Program for Excellence in Biomedical Research *(Advanced Professional, Professional development/Grant)* [4823]
Lily and Catello Sorrentino Memorial Scholarships *(Undergraduate/Scholarship)* [8609]
Bruce and Marjorie Sundlun Scholarships *(Undergraduate/Scholarship)* [8610]

South Carolina

African American Network - Carolinas Scholarship Fund *(Undergraduate/Scholarship)* [4174]
Leon Bradley Scholarship Program *(Undergraduate/Scholarship)* [575]
Judy Crocker Memorial Scholarship Fund *(Undergraduate/Scholarship)* [4191]
HACU/Denny's Hungry for Education Scholarships *(Undergraduate, Graduate/Scholarship)* [4883]
Harry Hampton Fund Scholarship *(Undergraduate/Scholarship)* [4733]
Wilbert L. and Zora F. Holmes Scholarship Endowment Fund *(Undergraduate/Scholarship)* [4198]
Albert and Eloise Midyette Memorial Scholarship Fund *(Undergraduate/Scholarship)* [4204]
Carolina Panthers Players Sam Mills Memorial Scholarship Fund *(Undergraduate/Scholarship)* [4205]
Carolina Panthers Players Sam Mills Memorial Scholarships *(Graduate/Scholarship)* [4206]
Norfolk Southern Foundation Scholarships *(Undergraduate/Scholarship)* [1188]
Regions Riding Forward Scholarships Essay Contest *(Undergraduate/Scholarship)* [8536]
South Carolina Association for Financial Professionals College Education Scholarships *(Undergraduate/Scholarship)* [9359]
South Carolina Scholastic Press Association Scholarships *(Undergraduate/Scholarship)* [9370]
South Carolina Scholastic Press Association Yearbook Scholarships *(Undergraduate/Scholarship)* [9371]
South Carolina Undergraduate Scholarships *(Undergraduate/Scholarship)* [9367]
The L. Phil and Alice J. Wicker Scholarship *(Undergraduate/Scholarship)* [1763]
Ted G. Wilson Memorial Scholarships *(Undergraduate/Scholarship)* [8288]

South Dakota

South Dakota Division Scholarships *(Undergraduate/Scholarship)* [6525]
Marianne M. Stenvig Scholarships *(Master's, Doctorate/Scholarship)* [9375]
Jerry Wheeler Scholarships *(Undergraduate/Scholarship)* [9377]

Tennessee

AISC/Southern Association of Steel Fabricators Scholarships *(Graduate/Scholarship)* [936]
B&W Y-12 Scholarship Fund *(Undergraduate/Scholarship)* [3752]
Belmont University Commercial Music Showcase Scholarships *(Undergraduate/Scholarship)* [3212]
George Oliver Benton Memorial Scholarships *(Undergraduate/Scholarship)* [3213]
Leon Bradley Scholarship Program *(Undergraduate/Scholarship)* [575]
JoAhn Brown-Nash Memorial Scholarships *(Undergraduate/Scholarship)* [3215]
Leigh Carter Scholarships *(Undergraduate/Scholarship)* [3217]
Steven L. Coffey Memorial Scholarships *(Undergraduate/Scholarship)* [3755]
Claude T. Coffman Memorial Scholarships *(Undergraduate/Scholarship)* [10157]
Dr. Mac Scholarships *(Undergraduate/Scholarship)* [3225]
C. Cleveland Drennon, Jr. Memorial Scholarships *(Undergraduate/Scholarship)* [10158]
Federal Court Bench and Bar Scholarships *(Undergraduate/Scholarship)* [10160]
Pauline LaFon Gore Scholarships *(Undergraduate/Scholarship)* [3227]
Herbert Herff Presidential Law Scholarships *(Undergraduate/Scholarship)* [10162]
Regina Higdon Scholarships *(Undergraduate/Scholarship)* [3229]
Robert and Elaine Hoffman Memorial Scholarships *(Undergraduate/Scholarship)* [10163]
Kathryn Hookanson Law Fellowship *(Undergraduate/Scholarship)* [10164]
John C. "Jack" Hough Memorial Law Scholarship *(Undergraduate/Scholarship)* [10165]
Cecil C. Humphreys Law Fellowships *(Undergraduate/Fellowship, Internship)* [10166]
Kansas Optometry Service Scholarships *(Graduate, Undergraduate/Scholarship)* [5657]
Michael B. Kruse Scholarships *(Graduate, Undergraduate/Scholarship)* [3234]
Judge William B. Leffler Scholarships *(Undergraduate/Scholarship)* [10167]
H. H. McKnight Memorial Scholarships *(Undergraduate/Scholarship)* [10168]
Sam A. Myar Jr. Law Scholarship *(Undergraduate/Scholarship)* [10170]
Archie Hartwell Nash Memorial Scholarships *(Graduate, Undergraduate/Scholarship)* [3245]
NCBWL Scholarships *(Undergraduate/Scholarship)* [6666]
Donald E. Nichols Scholarships *(Undergraduate/Scholarship)* [1333]
Norfolk Southern Foundation Scholarships *(Undergraduate/Scholarship)* [1188]
Eloise Pitts O'More Scholarships *(Undergraduate/Scholarship)* [3247]
Donald and Susie Polden Dean's Scholarships *(Undergraduate/Scholarship)* [10171]
Peter DeWitt Pruden and Phyliss Harrill Pruden Scholarships *(Undergraduate/Scholarship)* [10247]
Ratner and Sugarmon Scholarship *(Undergraduate/Scholarship)* [10172]
Regions Riding Forward Scholarships Essay Contest *(Undergraduate/Scholarship)* [8536]
Barbara Hagan Richards Scholarships *(Undergraduate/Scholarship)* [3249]
Joseph Henry Shepherd Scholarship *(Undergraduate/Scholarship)* [10173]
Amy E. Spain Memorial Scholarships *(Undergraduate/Scholarship)* [10174]
The Springfield Family Scholarships *(Undergraduate/Scholarship)* [10175]
SSAWMA Scholarships *(Graduate/Scholarship)* [9415]
Tennessee Bar Foundation IOLTA Law School Scholarships *(Undergraduate/Scholarship)* [10176]
Tennessee Trucking Foundation Scholarships *(Undergraduate/Scholarship)* [3254]
Emmett H. Turner Scholarships *(Undergraduate/Scholarship)* [3255]
Teddy Wilburn Scholarships *(Undergraduate/Scholarship)* [3256]
The Edgar C. Wilson Fellowship *(Graduate/Fellowship)* [10274]

Texas

AAMA Houston Chapter Health Training Scholarships *(Other/Scholarship)* [1601]
Alejandro "Alex" Abecia Reaching High Scholarships *(Undergraduate/Scholarship)* [3084]
Adelante Fund Hope Scholarships, CPS Energy Dependents *(Undergraduate/Scholarship)* [66]
Adelante Fund Hope Scholarships, San Antonio, TX Students *(Undergraduate/Scholarship)* [67]
Allen - Marty Allen Scholarships *(Undergraduate/Scholarship)* [3085]
BAFTX Graduate Awards *(Undergraduate/Scholarship)* [2366]
BAFTX Junior Achievers Awards *(Undergraduate/Scholarship)* [2367]
BAFTX Undergraduate Awards *(Undergraduate/Scholarship)* [2368]
TCDA Carroll Barnes Student Scholarships *(Undergraduate/Scholarship)* [668]
Zachary Barriger Memorial Scholarships *(Undergraduate/Scholarship)* [3086]
Reverend E.F. Bennett Scholarships *(Undergraduate/Scholarship)* [3088]
Bill Bernbach Diversity Scholarships *(Undergraduate/Scholarship)* [457]
Kathi Bowles Scholarships for Women in Technology *(Undergraduate, Graduate/Scholarship)* [2091]
Marion Luna Brem/Pat McNeil Health and Education Scholarships *(Undergraduate/Scholarship)* [3089]
D.C. and Virginia Brown Scholarships *(Undergraduate/Scholarship)* [3090]
TCDA Jim and Glenda Casey Professional Scholarships *(Other/Scholarship)* [669]
C.C.H.R.M.A. Scholarships *(Undergraduate/Scholarship)* [3092]
Bill Cormack Scholarships *(Undergraduate/Scholarship)* [9706]
Derek Lee Dean Soccer Scholarships *(Undergraduate/Scholarship)* [3094]
Jay and Rheba Downes Memorial Scholarships *(Undergraduate/Scholarship)* [3095]
John R. Eidson Jr., Scholarships *(Undergraduate/Scholarship)* [3096]
Barney Flynn Memorial Scholarships *(Undergraduate/Scholarship)* [3097]
George Foreman Tribute to Lyndon B. Johnson Scholarships *(Undergraduate/Scholarship)* [8405]
TCDA Bill Gorham Student Scholarships *(Undergraduate/Scholarship)* [670]
Melissa Ann Guerra Scholarships *(Undergraduate/Scholarship)* [3098]
George Gustafson HSE Memorial Scholarships *(Graduate, Undergraduate/Scholarship)* [1414]
HACU/Denny's Hungry for Education Scholarships *(Undergraduate, Graduate/Scholarship)* [4883]
George and Mary Josephine Hamman Foundation Scholarships *(Undergraduate/Scholarship)* [4693]
Haraldson Foundation Scholarships *(Undergraduate, Graduate/Scholarship)* [4713]
Hill Country Master Gardeners Horticulture Scholarships *(Undergraduate/Scholarship)* [4881]
A. Joseph Huerta "Puedo" Scholarships *(Undergraduate/Scholarship)* [3100]
Institute of Transportation Engineers - Texas District Fellowships *(Graduate/Fellowship)* [5219]
Jamail/Long Challenge Grant Scholarships *(Undergraduate/Scholarship)* [4896]
JLTLA Minority Law Student Scholarships *(Undergraduate/Scholarship)* [9818]
Casey Laine Armed Forces Scholarships *(Undergraduate/Scholarship)* [3101]
Sue Kay Lay Memorial Scholarships *(Undergraduate/Scholarship)* [3102]
Danny T. Le Memorial Scholarships *(Undergraduate/Scholarship)* [10385]
Brian and Colleen Miller Math and Science Scholarships *(Undergraduate/Scholarship)* [3103]
Le Hoang Nguyen College Scholarships (LHN) *(Undergraduate/Scholarship)* [10386]
The Thuy Nguyen Scholarships *(High School/Scholarship)* [10387]
North Texas Relocation Professionals Scholarships *(Undergraduate/Scholarship)* [7505]
Operation JumpStart Scholarships *(Graduate/Scholarship)* [458]
Regions Riding Forward Scholarships Essay Contest *(Undergraduate/Scholarship)* [8536]
Rotary Club of Corpus Christi Scholarships *(Undergraduate/Scholarship)* [3106]
Edward S. Roth Manufacturing Engineering Scholarships *(Graduate, Undergraduate/Scholarship)* [9192]
Seaman Family Scholarships *(Undergraduate/Scholarship)* [3108]
Judge Terry Shamsie Scholarships *(Undergraduate/Scholarship)* [3109]
DW Simpson Actuarial Science Scholarship Program *(Undergraduate/Scholarship)* [8963]
Herman J. Smith Scholarships *(Undergraduate, Graduate/Scholarship)* [7004]
South Texas Unit Scholarships *(Undergraduate/Scholarship)* [4865]
SPE Gulf Coast Hurricane Scholarships *(Undergraduate/Scholarship)* [9270]
STC-Lone Star Chapter Traditional Education Scholarships *(Graduate, Undergraduate/Scholarship)* [9313]
Cecilia Steinfeldt Fellowships for Research in the Arts and Material Culture *(Professional development/Fellowship)* [9717]
TACS/Texas Tech University ISD Scholarships *(Undergraduate/Scholarship)* [9687]
Talbert Family Memorial Scholarships *(Undergraduate/Scholarship)* [3111]
TCDA Abbott IPCO Professional Scholarships *(Other/Scholarship)* [671]
TCDA Gandy Ink Professional Scholarships *(Professional development/Scholarship)* [672]
TCDA General Fund Scholarships *(Undergraduate/Scholarship)* [673]
TCDA Past Presidents Student Scholarships *(Undergraduate/Scholarship)* [674]
Texas Elks State Association Eagle Scout Scholarships *(Undergraduate/Scholarship)* [9697]
Texas Elks State Association Girl Scout Gold Award Scholarships *(Undergraduate/Scholarship)* [9698]
Texas Elks State Association Scholarships *(Undergraduate/Scholarship)* [9699]
Texas Music Educators Association Past-Presidents Memorial Scholarships *(Undergraduate/Scholarship)* [9707]
Texas Telephone Association Foundation Scholarships *(Undergraduate/Scholarship)* [9719]
Dr. Juan D. Villarreal/HDA Foundation Scholarships *(Undergraduate/Scholarship)* [4894]
Faye and Rendell Webb Scholarships *(Undergraduate/Scholarship)* [3112]
TCDA Cloys Webb Student Scholarships *(Undergraduate/Scholarship)* [675]
YWA Foundation Scholarships *(Graduate, Undergraduate/Scholarship)* [10766]

Utah

APTRA-Clete Roberts/Kathryn Dettman Memorial Journalism Scholarship *(Undergraduate/Scholarship)* [1818]
Edward S. Roth Manufacturing Engineering Scholarships *(Graduate, Undergraduate/Scholarship)* [9192]

Vermont

American Legion Department of Vermont Scholarships *(Undergraduate, High School/Scholarship)* [959]
NYU Langone Medical Center Science Student Scholarships *(Undergraduate, Graduate/Scholarship)* [109]

Virginia

H. Burton Bates Jr. Scholarships *(Graduate, Undergraduate/Scholarship)* [10402]
Bayly-Tiffany Scholarships *(Undergraduate/Scholarship)* [10301]
Bill Bernbach Diversity Scholarships *(Undergraduate/Scholarship)* [457]
Thomas M. Berry Jr. Scholarships *(Graduate, Undergraduate/Scholarship)* [10403]
Leo Bourassa Scholarships *(Undergraduate, Graduate/Scholarship)* [10398]
Leon Bradley Scholarship Program *(Undergraduate/Scholarship)* [575]
Betty Sams Christian Fellowships *(Doctorate/Fellowship)* [10396]
Cocke, Szpanka and Taylor Scholarships *(Undergraduate/Scholarship)* [10404]
Richard D. and Sheppard R. Cooke Memorial Scholarships *(Graduate/Scholarship)* [4695]
Palmer Farley Memorial Scholarships *(Graduate/Scholarship)* [4696]
V. Thomas Forehand, Jr. Scholarships *(Undergraduate/Scholarship)* [10302]
Jane S. Glenn Memorial Endowed Scholarships *(Undergraduate/Scholarship)* [8626]
Hampton Roads Sanitation District Environmental Scholarships *(Graduate/Scholarship)* [4699]
Dixon Hughes Goodman Scholarships *(Undergraduate, Graduate/Scholarship)* [10405]
Louis I. Jaffe Memorial Scholarships-ODU *(Graduate/Scholarship)* [4701]
Jefferson Graduate Fellowships *(Doctorate, Graduate/Fellowship)* [5564]
Kaprielian Memorial Scholarships *(Undergraduate/Scholarship)* [10303]
John Allen Love Scholarships *(Graduate, Undergraduate/Scholarship)* [10304]
Norfolk Southern Foundation Scholarships *(Undergraduate/Scholarship)* [1188]
NYU Langone Medical Center Science Student Scholarships *(Undergraduate, Graduate/Scholarship)* [109]
Operation JumpStart Scholarships *(Graduate/Scholarship)* [458]
Margaret E. Phillips Scholarships *(Undergraduate/Scholarship)* [10305]
Peter DeWitt Pruden and Phyliss Harrill Pruden Scholarships *(Undergraduate/Scholarship)* [10247]
Regions Riding Forward Scholarships Essay Contest *(Undergraduate/Scholarship)* [8536]
Hy Smith Endowment Fund *(Undergraduate/Scholarship)* [4704]
Florence L. Smith Medical Scholarships *(Graduate/Scholarship)* [4705]
VA AWWA Graduate Student Scholarships *(Graduate/Scholarship)* [1498]
Virginia Tech Doctoral Scholarship *(Doctorate/Scholarship)* [10406]
VSCPA Educational Foundation Graduate Scholarships *(Graduate/Scholarship)* [10407]
VSCPA Educational Foundation Minority Scholarships *(Graduate, Undergraduate/Scholarship)* [10408]
VSCPA Educational Foundation Undergraduate Scholarships *(Undergraduate/Scholarship)* [10409]
VSCPA PhD Accounting Scholarships *(Doctorate, Graduate/Scholarship)* [10410]
The L. Phil and Alice J. Wicker Scholarship *(Undergraduate/Scholarship)* [1763]
Ted G. Wilson Memorial Scholarships *(Undergraduate/Scholarship)* [8288]
Charles Fred Wonson Scholarships *(Undergraduate/Scholarship)* [10306]
Yount, Hyde & Barbour Scholarships *(Undergraduate/Scholarship)* [10411]

Washington

Bechtel Group Foundation Scholarships for Safety & Health *(Undergraduate/Scholarship)* [1409]
Beta Sigma Phi Visual Arts Scholarship *(Undergraduate/Scholarship)* [8869]
Boeing Company Scholarships *(Undergraduate/Scholarship)* [8870]
CFR Volunteer Internships *(Undergraduate, Graduate/Internship)* [3445]
College Success Foundation Chateau Ste. Michelle Scholarship Fund *(Undergraduate/Scholarship)* [3125]
College Success Foundation Leadership 1000 Scholarships *(Undergraduate/Scholarship)* [3126]
College Success Foundation Realize the Dream Scholarships *(Undergraduate/Scholarship)* [3127]
College Success Foundation Washington State Governors' Scholarship for Foster Youth *(Undergraduate/Scholarship)* [3128]
APTRA-Clete Roberts/Kathryn Dettman Memorial

Journalism Scholarship *(Undergraduate/Scholarship)* [1818]
Firland Foundation Graduate Pulmonary Nursing Fellowships *(Professional development/Fellowship)* [4034]
HACU/Denny's Hungry for Education Scholarships *(Undergraduate, Graduate/Scholarship)* [4883]
High School Academic Scholarship *(Undergraduate/Scholarship)* [8873]
Margaret Mallett Nursing Scholarship *(Undergraduate/Scholarship)* [8878]
Christopher Mesi Memorial Music Scholarships *(Undergraduate/Scholarship)* [2803]
Mill Creek Business Association Scholarships *(Undergraduate/Scholarship)* [6537]
Chapter 63 - Portland James E. Morrow Scholarships *(Graduate, Undergraduate/Scholarship)* [9189]
Eric Niemitalo Scholarships in Earth and Environmental Science *(Undergraduate/Scholarship)* [8879]
Cedric Northrop Fellowships *(Professional development/Fellowship)* [4035]
Rhonda J.B. O'Leary Memorial Scholarship *(Undergraduate, Graduate/Scholarship)* [3802]
Olympia Tumwater Foundation Traditional Scholarships *(Undergraduate/Scholarship)* [7608]
Olympia Tumwater Foundation Transitional (non-traditional) Scholarships *(Undergraduate/Scholarship)* [7609]
Chapter 63 - Portland Uncle Bud Smith Scholarships *(Undergraduate/Scholarship)* [9196]
STC-PSC Scholarships *(Undergraduate, Graduate/Scholarship)* [9315]
Janet Cullen Tanaka Scholarships *(Undergraduate/Scholarship)* [2096]
WALPA Lake Student Scholarships *(Undergraduate, Graduate/Scholarship)* [10466]
Washington City/County Management Association Scholarships *(Graduate/Scholarship)* [10438]
Washington CPA Foundation Scholarships *(Undergraduate/Scholarship)* [10452]
Washington State Nurses Association Foundation Scholarships (WSNF) *(Graduate, Undergraduate/Scholarship)* [10468]
George Waterman Memorial Scholarships *(Undergraduate/Scholarship)* [10453]
Why Get Your Blue On? Video Scholarships *(Graduate, Undergraduate/Award, Scholarship)* [10543]
WIGA Scholarships *(Postgraduate, Other, Undergraduate/Scholarship)* [10450]
Davis Wright Tremaine 1L Diversity Scholarships *(Undergraduate/Scholarship)* [3535]
WSGC Community College Transfer Scholarships *(Undergraduate/Scholarship)* [10455]

West Virginia

William (Billbo) Boston/Harold Knopp Scholarship *(Undergraduate/Scholarship)* [7815]
Freda Burge Scholarships *(Undergraduate/Scholarship)* [7817]
Cindy Curry Memorial Scholarships *(Undergraduate/Scholarship)* [7822]
Lawrence E. and Jean L. Davis Scholarships *(Undergraduate/Scholarship)* [7824]
David Edward Farson Scholarships *(Undergraduate/Scholarship)* [7827]
William E. "Bill" Gallagher Scholarships *(Undergraduate/Scholarship)* [7829]
H.G. Hardbarger Science and Mathematics Awards *(Undergraduate/Award)* [7835]
Holly Jackson-Wuller Memorial Scholarships *(Undergraduate/Scholarship)* [7842]
Dr. Charles Kelly Memorial Scholarships *(Undergraduate/Scholarship)* [7844]
Norfolk Southern Foundation Scholarships *(Undergraduate/Scholarship)* [1188]
NYU Langone Medical Center Science Student Scholarships *(Undergraduate, Graduate/Scholarship)* [109]
James H. Roberts Athletic Scholarships *(Undergraduate/Scholarship)* [7855]
James Robinson Memorial Scholarship - Ripley Rotary *(Undergraduate/Scholarship)* [7857]

Mary K. Smith Rector Scholarships *(Undergraduate/Scholarship)* [7866]
The L. Phil and Alice J. Wicker Scholarship *(Undergraduate/Scholarship)* [1763]

Wisconsin

Ahlswede, Norman & Marie Endowed Engineering Scholarship *(Undergraduate/Scholarship)* [10315]
William E. Barto Scholarships *(Undergraduate/Scholarship)* [3704]
Mary Ann Brichta Scholarships *(Undergraduate/Scholarship)* [10317]
Patricia Buchanan Memorial Scholarships *(Undergraduate/Scholarship)* [10318]
Robert Esser Student Achievement Scholarships *(Graduate, Undergraduate/Scholarship)* [5061]
Founding Fathers Leadership Scholarships *(Undergraduate/Scholarship)* [10617]
Carleton A. Friday Scholarship *(Undergraduate/Scholarship)* [6527]
Barry M. Goldwater Scholarships *(Undergraduate/Scholarship)* [10319]
Illinois Landscape Contractors Association Scholarships *(Undergraduate/Scholarship)* [5064]
Kemper K. Knapp Scholarships *(Undergraduate/Scholarship)* [10320]
George Koeppel Scholarships/All School *(Undergraduate/Scholarship)* [10321]
Abby Marlatt Scholarship *(Undergraduate/Scholarship)* [10322]
McBurney General Scholarships *(Undergraduate/Scholarship)* [10323]
Minority Teacher Loans *(Undergraduate, Graduate/Loan)* [9554]
John P. and Tashia F. Morgridge Scholarships *(Undergraduate/Scholarship)* [10324]
NACA Northern Plains Regional Student Leadership Scholarships *(Undergraduate/Scholarship)* [6730]
Hubert A. Nelson Scholarships *(Undergraduate/Scholarship)* [3718]
Nursing Student Loans *(Graduate/Loan)* [9555]
Pi Lambda Theta Scholarships *(Undergraduate/Scholarship)* [10325]
Powers-Knapp Scholarships *(Undergraduate/Scholarship)* [10326]
John A. and Jean Quinn Sullivan Scholarship Funds *(Undergraduate/Scholarship)* [3725]
University of Wisconsin-Madison/CALS Minority Scholarships *(Undergraduate/Scholarship)* [10327]
University of Wisconsin-Madison National Merit Scholarships *(Undergraduate/Scholarship)* [10329]
University of Wisconsin-Madison Single Parent Scholarships *(Undergraduate/Scholarship)* [10330]
UW-Madison Engineering Diversity Scholarships *(Undergraduate/Scholarship)* [10331]
UW-Madison Reserve Officers Training Corps Scholarships *(Undergraduate/Scholarship)* [10333]
UW-Madison School of Education Minority Scholarships *(Undergraduate/Scholarship)* [10334]
William F. Vilas Scholarships *(Undergraduate/Scholarship)* [10335]
Kenneth G. Weckel Scholarships *(Undergraduate/Scholarship)* [6528]
Wisconsin Broadcasters Association Foundation Student Scholarships *(Undergraduate/Scholarship)* [10621]
Wisconsin Lawton Minority Retention Grants *(Undergraduate/Grant)* [10336]

Wyoming

AISC/Rocky Mountain Steel Construction Association Scholarships *(Graduate/Scholarship)* [935]
APTRA-Clete Roberts/Kathryn Dettman Memorial Journalism Scholarship *(Undergraduate/Scholarship)* [1818]
Griffin Foundation Scholarships *(Undergraduate/Scholarship)* [4674]
Dorothy Mountain Memorial Scholarships *(Graduate/Scholarship)* [6135]

Harry Walts Memorial Graduate Scholarships *(Graduate/Scholarship)* [6136]

CANADA

AABP Amstutz Scholarships *(Undergraduate/Scholarship)* [466]
AABP Student Externship Program *(Undergraduate/Scholarship)* [469]
AAN Medical Student Summer Research Scholarships *(Graduate/Scholarship)* [412]
AANS Medical Student Summer Research Fellowships (MSSRF) *(Undergraduate/Fellowship)* [542]
AAS Korean Studies Scholarship Program *(Graduate/Scholarship)* [1858]
The AASSC Gurli Aagaard Woods Undergraduate Publication Awards *(Undergraduate/Award)* [1825]
The AASSC Marna Feldt Graduate Publication Awards *(Graduate/Award)* [1826]
AASSC Norwegian Travel Grants *(Professional development/Grant)* [1827]
Aboriginal Canadians Scholarship *(Undergraduate/Scholarship)* [7204]
Evelyn Joy Abramowicz Memorial Scholarships *(Undergraduate/Scholarship)* [5568]
ACI-NA Scholarships *(Graduate, Undergraduate/Scholarship)* [180]
Jack Ackroyd Scholarships *(Other/Scholarship)* [1878]
ADAC Foundation Scholarships *(Undergraduate/Scholarship)* [1767]
AECT Foundation Mentor Endowment Scholarships *(Doctorate, Graduate/Scholarship)* [1942]
AEF Educational Scholarship *(Undergraduate/Scholarship)* [234]
AFA Aboriginal Traditional Arts Individual Project Grants *(Professional development/Grant)* [236]
AFA Art Acquisition by Application Grants *(Professional development/Grant)* [237]
AFA Cultural Relations Project Grants *(Professional development/Grant)* [238]
AFA Dance Project Grants *(Professional development/Grant)* [239]
AFA Film and Video Arts Project Grants *(Professional development/Grant)* [240]
AFA Literary Arts Project Grants *(Professional development/Grant)* [241]
AFA Music Project Grants *(Professional development/Grant)* [242]
AFA Theatre & Performance Art Project Grants *(Professional development/Grant)* [243]
AFA Visual Arts and New Media Project Grants *(Professional development/Grant)* [244]
Affiliated Distributors Electrical Industry Scholarship Awards *(Undergraduate/Scholarship)* [3822]
AGE-WELL Graduate Student and Postdoctoral Awards in Technology and Aging *(Master's, Doctorate, Postdoctorate/Award)* [111]
AIA and the Global Automotive Aftermarket Symposium Scholarships *(Undergraduate/Scholarship)* [2131]
Alberta Association of Gerontology Student Awards - Edmonton Chapter *(Graduate, Undergraduate/Award)* [226]
Alberta Centennial Scholarships - Alberta *(Undergraduate/Scholarship)* [262]
Dulemba Aleksander and Stefania Scholarship *(Undergraduate/Scholarship)* [8571]
Alexander Graham Bell Canada Graduate Scholarship Program *(Doctorate, Master's/Scholarship)* [3401]
Hon. Lincoln Alexander Scholarships *(Undergraduate, Graduate/Scholarship)* [2277]
Stephanie Ali Memorial Scholarships *(Undergraduate/Scholarship)* [10279]
ALIS Fellowships for Full-time Studies in French *(Undergraduate/Fellowship)* [263]
ALIS International Education Awards - Ukraine *(Undergraduate/Scholarship)* [265]
Janet and Horace Allen Scholarships *(Undergraduate/Scholarship)* [266]
Alliance Pipeline Scholarships *(Other/Scholarship)* [2181]
Lorraine Allison Scholarship *(Graduate/Scholarship)* [1616]
Marjorie Almstrom Scholarships *(Undergraduate,*

CANADA

Master's/Scholarship) [10774]
ALS Canada Bridge Grants (Professional development/Grant) [365]
ALS Canada Doctoral Research Awards (Doctorate, Professional development/Fellowship) [366]
ALS Canada and Tim E. Noel Postdoctoral Fellowships (Postdoctorate, Professional development/Fellowship) [367]
Jaedyn Amann Memorial Scholarships (Undergraduate, Master's/Scholarship) [10775]
America Express Travel Scholarships (Undergraduate/Scholarship) [1436]
American Judges Association Law Student Essay Competition (Undergraduate/Prize) [952]
Bernard Amtmann Fellowships (Postgraduate, Other/Fellowship) [2258]
Dr. Andy Anderson Young Professional Awards (Professional development/Award) [8117]
Annette Urso Rickel Foundation Dissertation Award for Public Policy (Graduate/Scholarship) [1137]
Annual Research Doctoral and Postgraduate Fellowship Grant Program (Doctorate, Postdoctorate, Postgraduate, Advanced Professional/Fellowship, Grant) [2586]
ANS Research Grants (Professional development/Grant) [1030]
ANSER Graduate Student Awards for Research on Nonprofits and the Social Economy (Graduate/Award) [2030]
Aplastic Anemia and Myelodysplasia Association of Canada Scholarships (Graduate/Scholarship) [2694]
Applied Hospitality Degree Scholarships (Undergraduate/Scholarship) [2657]
Architects Association of PEI Scholarships (Undergraduate/Scholarship) [3309]
Arctic Physical Therapy Scholarship (Undergraduate/Scholarship) [1619]
Robin P. Armstrong Memorial Prize for Excellence in Native Studies Awards (Graduate/Award) [1880]
Robert Armstrong Memorial Scholarships (Undergraduate, Graduate/Scholarship) [10776]
Arts Graduate Scholarships (Graduate/Scholarship) [267]
ASA Graduate Scholarships (Graduate/Scholarship) [1243]
ASAC-CJAS PhD Research Grant Awards (Doctorate/Grant) [73]
Asia Pacific Foundation of Canada Junior Research Fellowships (Undergraduate, Master's/Fellowship) [4113]
Asia Pacific Foundation of Canada Media Fellowships (Professional development/Fellowship) [4114]
Asia Pacific Foundation of Canada Post-Graduate Research Fellowships (Master's, Doctorate/Fellowship) [4115]
Association of Desk and Derrick Clubs Education Trust Scholarships (Undergraduate/Scholarship) [1931]
ASTA Holland America Line Graduate Research Scholarships (Graduate/Scholarship) [1438]
Astra Zeneca Medical Scholarships (Advanced Professional/Scholarship) [7275]
AstraZeneca Scholarships (Doctorate/Scholarship) [2695]
Atkinson Fellowships in Public Policy (Professional development/Fellowship) [2111]
Atlantic Provinces Library Association Memorial Awards (Undergraduate/Scholarship) [2117]
Atlantic Salmon Federation Olin Fellowships (Graduate/Fellowship) [2120]
Joan Auld Scholarships (Undergraduate/Scholarship) [3310]
Avis Budget Group Scholarships (Graduate/Scholarship) [1440]
Azrieli Neurodevelopmental Research Program (Advanced Professional/Grant) [2350]
Airgas - Jerry Baker Scholarships (Undergraduate/Scholarship) [1509]
Victoria Baldwin Memorial Scholarships (Undergraduate, Master's/Award) [10777]
Lynn Ann Baldwin Scholarships (Master's/Scholarship) [1888]
Ball Horticultural Company Scholarships (Undergraduate/Scholarship) [798]

Bank of Canada Fellowship Award (Doctorate, Other/Fellowship, Grant) [2187]
Bank of Canada Governor's Awards (Doctorate, Other/Award, Grant) [2188]
Banting Postdoctoral Fellowships (Postdoctorate/Fellowship) [3402]
Helen Bassett Commemorative Student Award (Undergraduate, Graduate/Scholarship) [7221]
Baxter Corporation Canadian Research Awards in Anesthesia (Other/Award, Monetary) [2538]
BCPF Bursaries (Undergraduate/Scholarship) [9476]
Suzanne Beauregard Scholarships (Undergraduate/Scholarship) [4476]
Beaverbrook Media at McGill Student Paper Prize (Graduate/Prize) [2615]
Ed Becker Conference Travel Awards (Undergraduate, Graduate/Award) [3886]
Ann C. Beckingham Scholarships (Graduate, Other/Scholarship) [2645]
Dr. Ann C. Beckingham Scholarships (Doctorate/Scholarship) [2696]
Jenny Panitch Beckow Memorial Scholarships Canada (Undergraduate, Graduate/Scholarship) [5569]
Bell Aliant Medical Education Scholarships (Advanced Professional/Scholarship) [7276]
Harvey Bell Memorial Prize (Graduate/Award) [10271]
Beverlee Bell Scholarships in Human Rights and Democracy (Graduate/Scholarship) [3655]
A.G. Bell School Age Financial Aid Program (Undergraduate/Scholarship) [315]
Max Bell Senior Fellow Grants (Advanced Professional/Grant) [2219]
Viscount Bennett Fellowships (Graduate/Fellowship) [2581]
Henry Besner Memorial Scholarships (Undergraduate, Master's/Scholarship) [10778]
Harold Bettinger Scholarships (Undergraduate, Graduate/Scholarship) [800]
Leonard Bettinger Vocational Scholarships (Undergraduate, Vocational/Occupational/Scholarship) [801]
Dr. Noorali and Sabiya Bharwani Endowment (Undergraduate/Scholarship) [2253]
Hussein Jina Bharwani Memorial Endowment (Undergraduate/Scholarship) [2254]
BHCRI Bridge Funds (Advanced Professional, Professional development/Grant) [5012]
BHCRI Cancer Research Training Program Awards (Graduate, Postdoctorate, Advanced Professional, Professional development/Grant) [5013]
BHCRI Matching Funds (Advanced Professional, Professional development/Grant) [5014]
BHCRI Miscellaneous Funds (Advanced Professional, Professional development/Grant) [5015]
BHCRI Seed Funds (Advanced Professional, Professional development/Grant) [5016]
BHCRI Studentship Awards (Undergraduate, Graduate, Advanced Professional/Grant) [5017]
Biological Survey of Canada Scholarships (Postgraduate/Scholarship) [3887]
Lucie and Thornton Blackburn Scholarships (Graduate, Juris Doctorate/Scholarship) [2544]
Alex Blaski Memorial Scholarships (Undergraduate/Scholarship) [8572]
M. Hildred Blewett Fellowships (Postdoctorate/Fellowship) [1088]
Lawrence Bloomberg Entrance Awards (Postgraduate/Award) [10741]
BMO Capital Markets Lime Connect Equity through Education Scholarships (Undergraduate, Graduate/Scholarship) [6087]
BMO Financial Group Lime Connect Canada Scholarship Program for Students with Disabilities (Undergraduate, Graduate/Scholarship) [6088]
BMO Harris Scholarships (Advanced Professional/Scholarship) [7277]
Edith and Arnold N. Bodtker Grants (Undergraduate, Graduate/Grant, Internship) [3522]
Steve Bonk Scholarships (Postgraduate/Scholarship) [2766]
Lorne and Ruby Bonnell Scholarships (Undergraduate/Scholarship) [3311]
John H. Borden Scholarships (Postgraduate/Scholarship) [3888]

Maria and Czeslaw Borek Scholarships (Undergraduate/Scholarship) [8573]
Jim Bourque Scholarship (Undergraduate/Scholarship) [1617]
Herbie Bouwman Memorial Scholarships (Undergraduate, Master's/Scholarship) [10779]
CAG Margery Boyce Bursary Awards (Undergraduate/Award, Scholarship) [2553]
Eugene Boyko Memorial Scholarships (Undergraduate/Scholarship) [228]
Geoffrey Bradshaw Memorial Scholarships (Graduate/Scholarship) [10780]
Brain Canada-ALS Canada Career Transition Awards (Postdoctorate, Advanced Professional, Professional development/Grant) [2351]
Brain Canada-ALS Canada Discovery Grants (Advanced Professional, Professional development/Grant) [2352]
Brain Canada-ALS Canada Hudson Translational Team Grants (Advanced Professional, Professional development/Grant) [2353]
Brain Canada/CQDM "Focus on Brain" Partnership Program (Advanced Professional/Grant) [2354]
Brain Canada/NeuroDevNet Developmental Neurosciences Research Training Awards (Postdoctorate, Advanced Professional, Professional development/Grant) [2355]
Brain Canada/RBC Research Partnership in Mental Health Services for Children and Youth Funds (Advanced Professional/Grant) [2356]
James Bridenbaugh Memorial Scholarships (Undergraduate/Scholarship) [802]
Margaret Brine Graduate Scholarships (Graduate/Scholarship) [2634]
Louis J. Brody Q.C. Entrance Scholarships (Graduate/Scholarship) [10742]
Peter F. Bronfman Entrance Awards (Postgraduate/Award) [10743]
Peter F. Bronfman Scholarships of Merit (Postgraduate/Scholarship) [10744]
Brooks Scholarships (Graduate/Scholarship) [3894]
William A. and Ann M. Brothers Scholarships (Undergraduate/Scholarship) [1512]
CFSA Randal Brown & Associates Awards (Undergraduate/Award) [1911]
Robert K. Brown Scholarships (Undergraduate, Master's/Scholarship) [2278]
Pamfil and Maria Bujea Family Orthodox Christian Seminarian Scholarships (Undergraduate/Scholarship) [1225]
Sam Bull Memorial Scholarships (Undergraduate/Scholarship) [248]
Burger King Scholars Program (Undergraduate/Scholarship) [2411]
Burndy Canada Inc. Academic Achievement Awards (Undergraduate/Scholarship) [3823]
Business, Education and Technology Scholarships (Graduate, Undergraduate/Scholarship) [334]
Joan Butler Award in Perinatal Intensive Care Nursing (Advanced Professional/Award) [6852]
Leon C. Bynoe Memorial Scholarships (Undergraduate/Scholarship) [10280]
CAA National Capital Region Writing Contests (All/Award, Prize, Monetary) [2579]
CADE Bursary (Undergraduate/Scholarship) [2550]
CADE Scholarships (Undergraduate/Scholarship) [2551]
CAG Health and Health Care Study Group Awards (Graduate/Award) [1881]
CAHR Master's Level Scholarships (Master's/Scholarship) [2557]
CALL/ACBD Education Reserve Fund Grants (Professional development/Grant) [2561]
CALL/ACBD Research Grants (Graduate/Grant) [2562]
Cameco Corporation Scholarships in the Geological Sciences - Continuing Students (Undergraduate/Scholarship) [2524]
Cameco Corporation Scholarships in the Geological Sciences - Entering Students (Undergraduate/Scholarship) [2525]
Dalton Camp Awards (Undergraduate/Award, Monetary) [4305]
Thomas R. Camp Scholarships (Graduate/Scholarship) [1486]

CANADA

Theodore R. Campbell Scholarships (Undergraduate/Scholarship) [268]
Canada-Ukraine Parliamentary Program Internship Scholarships (CUPP) (Undergraduate/Scholarship, Internship) [10441]
Canadian Anesthesiologists' Society Research Awards (Other/Award) [2539]
Canadian Association of Cardiac Rehabilitation Graduate Scholarship Awards (Graduate/Scholarship) [2548]
Canadian Association of Geographers Historical Geography Study Group Awards (Master's, Graduate, Undergraduate/Award) [1882]
Canadian Association of Law Teachers Award for Academic Excellence (Other/Award) [2566]
Canadian Association for the Practical Study of Law in Education Fellowships (Graduate/Fellowship) [2573]
Canadian Association for Studies in Co-operation Scholarships Lemaire Co-operative Studies Awards (CASC) (Graduate, Undergraduate/Scholarship) [2611]
Canadian Blood Services Graduate Fellowship (Graduate/Fellowship) [2583]
Canadian Blood Services Postdoctoral Fellowship (Postdoctorate/Fellowship) [2584]
Canadian Cancer Society Travel Awards (Doctorate, Master's, Postdoctorate/Award) [2605]
Canadian Council of Technicians and Technologists Scholarships for Technology Students (Undergraduate/Scholarship) [3392]
The Canadian Derivatives Exchange Scholars Program (Graduate, Postgraduate/Scholarship) [2345]
Canadian Energy Law Foundation Graduate Scholarships in Law (Advanced Professional/Scholarship) [2620]
Canadian Evaluation Society Educational Fund Scholarships (Graduate/Scholarship) [4125]
Canadian Federation of Independent Grocers National Scholarships (Undergraduate/Scholarship) [4003]
Canadian Federation of University Women Etobicoke Bursary (Undergraduate/Scholarship) [10281]
Canadian Hard of Hearing Association Scholarship Programs (Undergraduate/Scholarship) [2651]
Canadian Home Economics Association Fellowships (Master's, Doctorate/Fellowship) [2629]
Canadian Hospitality Foundation College Entrance Scholarships (Undergraduate/Scholarship) [2658]
Canadian Hospitality Foundation University Entrance Scholarships (Undergraduate/Scholarship) [2659]
Canadian Hydrographic Association Student Awards (Undergraduate/Award, Monetary, Medal) [2662]
Canadian Identification Society Essay/Scholarship Awards (Advanced Professional, Professional development/Prize) [2664]
Canadian Iranian Foundation Scholarships (Undergraduate/Scholarship) [2677]
Canadian IT Law Association Student Writing Contest (Undergraduate/Prize) [2020]
Canadian Japanese-Mennonite Scholarships (Graduate/Scholarship) [6416]
Canadian Nurses Foundation Northern Award (Undergraduate/Scholarship) [2697]
Canadian Nurses Foundation Scholarships (Undergraduate, Master's, Doctorate/Scholarship) [2698]
Canadian Occupational Therapy Foundation Graduate Scholarships (Doctorate, Master's/Scholarship) [2717]
Canadian Occupational Therapy Foundation Invacare Master's Scholarships (Master's/Scholarship) [2718]
Canadian Pain Society Post-Doctoral Fellowship Awards (Postdoctorate/Fellowship) [2724]
Canadian Parking Association Scholarships (Undergraduate/Scholarship) [1921]
Canadian Picture Pioneers Scholarships (Undergraduate/Scholarship) [2734]
Canadian Polar Commission Scholarships (Doctorate, Graduate/Scholarship) [1933]
Canadian Poultry Research Council Postgraduate Scholarships (Postgraduate/Scholarship) [2736]
Canadian Sanitation Supply Association Scholarships (Undergraduate/Scholarship) [2738]

Canadian Seniors' Golf Association Scholarships (Undergraduate/Scholarship) [4477]
Canadian Society for the Study of Education Mentorship Awards (Other/Award) [9067]
Canadian Society for the Study of Education New Scholar Fellowships (CSSE) (Professional development/Fellowship) [9068]
Canadian Studies Postdoctoral Fellowships (Postdoctorate/Fellowship) [3398]
Canadian Technical Asphalt Association Scholarships (Undergraduate/Scholarship) [2762]
Canadian Water Resources Association Scholarships (Undergraduate/Scholarship) [1905]
CAPE Scholarships (Undergraduate, Postdoctorate/Scholarship) [2768]
Cardiac Health Foundation of Canada Scholarships (Graduate/Scholarship) [2790]
Thelma Cardwell Scholarships (Graduate/Scholarship) [2719]
Career Awards at the Scientific Interface (CASI) (Doctorate, Postdoctorate, Advanced Professional, Professional development/Grant) [2416]
John Carew Memorial Scholarships (Graduate/Scholarship) [803]
Carmangay Home and School Association Scholarships (Undergraduate/Scholarship) [269]
Herb Carnegie Scholarships (Undergraduate/Scholarship) [2279]
CARO-ELEKTA Research Fellowship Program (Professional development/Fellowship) [1900]
CAS/GE Healthcare Canada Inc. Research Awards (Other/Award) [2540]
CAS Trust Scholarship (Undergraduate/Scholarship) [2809]
CAS/Vitaid-LMA Residents' Research Grant Competition (Other/Award) [2541]
Fraser Milner Casgrain LLP Scholarships (Graduate, Juris Doctorate/Scholarship) [2280]
Fraser Milner Casgrain Scholarships (Other/Scholarship) [2182]
Catzman Awards for Professionalism and Civility (Advanced Professional, Professional development/Award) [80]
CBCF - Ontario Research Project Grants (Advanced Professional, Professional development/Grant) [2595]
CC Times Scholarships (Undergraduate/Scholarship) [2921]
CCFF Clinical Fellowships (Doctorate, Graduate/Fellowship) [4013]
CCFF Fellowships (Doctorate, Graduate/Fellowship) [4014]
CCFF Scholarships (Doctorate, Graduate/Scholarship) [4015]
CCLA Summer Legal Internships (Graduate/Internship) [1892]
CEMF Undergraduate Engineering Scholarships (Undergraduate/Scholarship) [2622]
CFN Interdisciplinary Fellowships Program (Graduate, Postdoctorate, Advanced Professional/Fellowship) [2638]
CFSA Aon Fire Protection Engineering Award (Undergraduate/Scholarship) [1912]
CFSA City of Markham, Buildings Standards Department Award (Undergraduate/Scholarship) [1913]
CFSA Fire Safety Awards (Postgraduate/Award, Monetary) [1914]
CFSA Leber Rubes Inc. Awards (Postgraduate/Award, Monetary) [1915]
CFSA LRI Engineering Award (Undergraduate/Scholarship) [1916]
CFSA Nadine International Inc. Awards (Undergraduate/Award) [1917]
CFSA Siemens Canada Award (Undergraduate/Scholarship) [1918]
CFSA Underwriters' Laboratories of Canada Awards (Undergraduate/Award) [1919]
CGNA Memorial Scholarship (Graduate, Other/Scholarship) [2646]
CGPF Endowments Conference Scholarships (Undergraduate/Scholarship) [2648]
Chapter 6 Fairfield County Scholarships (Undergraduate/Scholarship) [9177]
Chechahko Consumers Co-Op Ltd. Scholarships (Undergraduate, Master's/Scholarship) [10782]

Hadar Chemtob Memorial Scholarships (Undergraduate/Scholarship) [5574]
Bernard Chernos Essay Competition (Undergraduate/Prize) [1893]
Shirley Cheshire Memorial Scholarship Awards (Undergraduate/Scholarship) [6853]
Chevalier Award Scholarship (Undergraduate/Scholarship) [2618]
Childhood Cancer Survivor Scholarships (Undergraduate/Scholarship) [2903]
Chinese Professionals Association of Canada BMO Diversity Scholarships (Undergraduate/Scholarship) [2922]
Chinese Professionals Association of Canada Education Foundation Awards (High School/Award) [2923]
Chinese Professionals Association of Canada Journalism Scholarships (Undergraduate/Scholarship) [2924]
Chinese Professionals Association of Canada Professional Achievement Awards (Other/Award) [2925]
CHS - Bursary Program Scholarships (Undergraduate/Scholarship) [2653]
CHS - Mature Student Bursary Program Scholarships (Undergraduate/Scholarship) [2654]
CHS Scholarships (Undergraduate/Scholarship) [2655]
CIBC Medical Education Scholarships (Advanced Professional/Scholarship) [7278]
CIBC Scholarships (Undergraduate, Graduate/Scholarship) [2281]
CIFAR Global Scholars Program (Advanced Professional, Professional development/Scholarship) [2670]
CIHR Health Law, Ethics and Policy Fellowships (Graduate/Fellowship) [2942]
CIP Fellow's Travel Scholarships (Undergraduate/Scholarship) [2672]
CISDL Global Research Fellowship - Legal Research Fellows (Graduate/Fellowship) [2881]
CISDL Global Research Fellowships - Senior Research Fellows (Other/Fellowship) [2882]
City of Toronto Graduate Scholarships for Women in Mathematics (Master's, Doctorate/Scholarship) [10282]
City of Toronto Queen Elizabeth II Sesquicentennial Scholarships in Community Health Nursing for Graduates (Graduate/Scholarship) [10283]
City of Toronto Queen Elizabeth II Sesquicentennial Scholarships in Community Health Nursing for Undergraduates (Undergraduate/Scholarship) [10284]
City of Toronto Scholarships for Aboriginal Students (Graduate, Undergraduate/Scholarship) [10285]
City of Toronto Women's Studies Scholarships (Graduate, Undergraduate/Scholarship) [10286]
CLA/ACB Dafoe Scholarships (Graduate/Scholarship) [2679]
CLA-ACE Internship Program (Graduate, Juris Doctorate/Internship) [6013]
Greg Clerk Awards (Advanced Professional, Professional development/Award) [4118]
David H. Clift Scholarships (Graduate/Scholarship) [961]
CMOS-SCMO President's Prize (Professional development/Prize) [2682]
CN Scholarships for Women (Undergraduate/Scholarship) [2692]
CNIB Master's Scholarships (Master's/Scholarship) [2688]
CNST Scholarships (Doctorate, Graduate/Scholarship) [1934]
Marshall A. Cohen Entrance Awards (Postgraduate/Award) [10745]
Anna C. and Oliver C. Colburn Fellowships (Doctorate/Fellowship) [1606]
Robert N. Colwell Memorial Fellowships (Doctorate, Graduate/Fellowship) [1803]
Desmond Conacher Scholarships (Graduate/Scholarship) [9071]
Connor/Spafford Scholarships (Undergraduate/Scholarship) [4478]
Convectair Sustainable Development Scholarship Awards (Undergraduate/Scholarship) [3824]

CANADA

Roy Cooper Memorial Scholarships (Undergraduate/Scholarship) [5998]
COPA Scholarship Fund (Undergraduate/Scholarship) [2722]
Helen & Orval Couch Memorial Scholarships (Undergraduate, Master's/Scholarship) [10783]
Steve Cowan Memorial Scholarships (Undergraduate/Scholarship) [3471]
CPS Clinical Pain Management Fellowship Awards (Postgraduate/Fellowship) [2725]
CPS Excellence in Interprofessional Pain Education Awards (Other/Award) [2726]
CPS Interprofessional Nursing Project Awards (Other/Award) [2727]
CPS Knowledge Translation Research Awards (Other/Grant) [2728]
CPS Nursing Excellence in Pain Management Awards (Other/Award) [2729]
CPS Nursing Research and Education Awards (Other/Grant) [2730]
CPS Outstanding Pain Mentorship Awards (Other/Award) [2731]
CPS Trainee Research Awards (Doctorate/Grant, Award) [2732]
CRM-ISM Postdoctoral Fellowships (Postdoctorate/Fellowship) [9993]
Crohn's and Colitis Canada Grants in Aid of Research (Advanced Professional, Professional development/Grant) [3473]
Crohn's and Colitis Canada Innovations in IBD Research Grants (Advanced Professional, Professional development/Grant) [3474]
CSBS Student Prize Competition (Graduate/Prize) [2744]
CSCI Distinguished Scientist Lectures and Awards (Advanced Professional/Award) [9073]
CSEG Scholarship Trust Fund (Graduate, Undergraduate/Scholarship) [2748]
CSLA Leaders of Distinction Award (Professional development/Recognition) [2759]
CSLA Leadership Scholarships (Undergraduate/Scholarship) [2760]
CSMLS Student Scholarship Awards (Postgraduate/Scholarship) [2750]
CSOHNS Fellowships (Graduate/Fellowship) [2752]
CSSHE Masters Thesis/Project Awards (Master's/Award) [2756]
CSSHE Research Awards (Professional development/Award) [2757]
CTRF Scholarships for Graduate Study in Transportation (Graduate/Scholarship) [2764]
Culinary (1-Year Program) Scholarships (Undergraduate/Scholarship) [2660]
Roger Daley Postdoctoral Publication Awards (Postdoctorate/Monetary) [2683]
D&R Sobey Scholarships (Undergraduate/Scholarship) [9047]
Mark & Dorothy Danzker Scholarships (Postgraduate/Scholarship) [5592]
Amy and Tim Dauphinee Scholarships (Graduate/Scholarship) [2575]
Canadian Association for Studies in Co-operation Scholarships - Amy and Tim Dauphinee Scholarships (CASC) (Graduate/Scholarship) [2612]
Ruth and Victor David Scholarships (Undergraduate, Graduate/Scholarship) [5575]
Jim Davie Memorial Scholarships (Undergraduate, Master's/Scholarship) [10784]
Laurence Decore Awards for Student Leadership (Undergraduate/Scholarship) [271]
Earl Dedman Memorial Scholarships (Undergraduate/Scholarship) [804]
Delta Kappa Gamma Society International World Fellowships (Professional development/Fellowship) [3571]
Helen L. Dewar Scholarships (Undergraduate/Scholarship) [9729]
Diabetes Hope Foundation Scholarships (Undergraduate/Scholarship) [3614]
Dr. Allan A. Dixon Memorial Scholarships (Postgraduate/Scholarship) [2742]
William Donald Dixon Research Grants (Graduate, Undergraduate, Advanced Professional/Grant) [2665]
Julian Dobranowski Memorial Scholarships (Undergraduate/Scholarship) [8574]

Dr. Biljan Memorial Awards (Advanced Professional/Award, Grant) [2636]
Dominio of Canada Insurance Scholarships (Graduate/Scholarship) [8128]
Lloyd M. Dosdall Memorial Scholarships (Postgraduate/Scholarship) [3889]
Douglas-Coldwell Foundation Scholarships in Social Affairs (Graduate/Scholarship) [3656]
Tommy Douglas Memorial Scholarship (Undergraduate/Scholarship) [7205]
Mary Ellen Driscoll Scholarships (Undergraduate/Scholarship) [4479]
DSA Dante Prizes (Undergraduate/Prize, Monetary) [3524]
Lise M. Duchesneau Scholarship (Undergraduate/Scholarship) [1895]
Dr. Allan Duncan Memorial Scholarships (Undergraduate, Master's/Scholarship) [10785]
Bob Dyer/OEL Apprenticeship Scholarships (Undergraduate/Scholarship) [3825]
Joshua Dyke Family Scholarships (Undergraduate/Scholarship) [9730]
e8 Sustainable Energy Development Post-Doctoral Scholarship Programme (ESED) (Postdoctorate/Scholarship) [4460]
École Polytechnique Commemorative Awards (Master's, Doctorate, Graduate/Award, Fellowship) [2630]
EDC International Business Scholarships (Undergraduate/Scholarship) [2603]
The Edit My Paper Proofreading Scholarships (Undergraduate/Scholarship) [3785]
Edmonton Epilepsy Continuing Education Scholarships (Undergraduate/Scholarship) [3792]
EFC University and College Scholarships (Undergraduate/Scholarship) [3828]
Eli Lilly Graduate Scholarship (Graduate, Postgraduate/Scholarship) [1886]
Clay Elliott Scholarship Foundation Scholarships (Undergraduate/Scholarship) [3856]
endMS Doctoral Studentship Awards (Doctorate/Internship) [6614]
endMS Master's Studentship Awards (Master's/Internship) [6615]
endMS Postdoctoral Fellowships (Postdoctorate/Fellowship) [6616]
Entomological Society of Canada Postgraduate Awards (Postgraduate/Award) [3890]
Entomological Society of Saskatchewan Student Presentation Awards (Undergraduate/Award) [3895]
Entomological Society of Saskatchewan Travel Awards (Professional development/Award) [3896]
Extendicare Scholarships in Gerontology (Master's/Scholarship) [2699]
Fahs-Beck Fund for Research and Experimentation - Doctoral Dissertation Grants (Doctorate/Grant) [7347]
Fahs-Beck Fund for Research and Experimentation - Postdoctoral Grants (Postdoctorate/Grant) [7348]
Dr. Isaac Keillor Farrer, Advanced Medical Education Scholarships (Advanced Professional/Scholarship) [7279]
Fellowships in the PMAC-AGPC (Professional development/Fellowship) [8295]
FFB-C Postdoctoral Fellowships (Postdoctorate/Fellowship) [4262]
Field Aviation Co., Inc. Scholarships (Undergraduate/Scholarship) [159]
Fields Institute - Fields Research Immersion Fellowships (Postdoctorate/Fellowship) [4019]
Fieldwork Fellowships (Undergraduate/Award, Fellowship) [3927]
FINCAD Women in Finance Scholarships (Graduate/Scholarship) [4024]
Firefly Foundation/ASRP Spark Award (Postdoctorate, Advanced Professional/Grant) [371, 4032]
Martin Fischer Awards (Undergraduate/Award) [2649]
Flamenco Student Scholarships (Undergraduate, Professional development/Scholarship) [4070]
Follicular Lymphoma Research Grants (Advanced Professional/Grant) [6159]
Foresters Scholarships (Undergraduate/Scholarship) [5095]

Edward Foster Awards (Advanced Professional/Award) [2666]
Foundation for the Advancement of Aboriginal Youth Bursary Program (Undergraduate/Scholarship) [3389]
Foundation for the Advancement of Aboriginal Youth Scholarships (Undergraduate/Scholarship) [3390]
Terry Fox Memorial Scholarship (Undergraduate/Scholarship) [7206]
Friends of the Christofor Foundation Scholarships (Advanced Professional/Scholarship) [7280]
Henry Friesen Awards and Lectures (Doctorate/Award) [9074]
FTE Doctoral Fellowships (Doctorate, Graduate/Fellowship) [4154]
FTE North American Doctoral Fellowships (Doctorate, Graduate/Fellowship) [4155]
Future Leader in Radiocommunications Scholarships (Undergraduate/Scholarship) [3394]
FXRFC Medical Research Postdoctoral Fellowships (Postdoctorate/Fellowship) [4287]
GAAC Project Grants (Undergraduate, Professional development/Grant) [4445]
Gabriel Dumont College Graduate Student Bursary (Postgraduate, Master's, Doctorate/Scholarship) [3742]
Franciszek Gadzala Memorial Scholarships (Undergraduate/Scholarship) [8575]
Harry Gairey Scholarships (Undergraduate/Scholarship) [2282]
Dwight D. Gardner Scholarships (Undergraduate/Scholarship) [5186]
G.E. Lighting Canada Community Leadership Awards (Undergraduate/Award) [3830]
Geological Society of America Graduate Student Research Grants (Doctorate, Graduate/Grant) [4364]
Gilbreth Memorial Fellowships (Graduate/Scholarship, Fellowship) [5187]
Keith Gilmore Foundation - Diploma Scholarships (Other/Scholarship) [4423]
Keith Gilmore Foundation - Postgraduate Scholarships (Postgraduate/Scholarship) [4424]
Keith Gilmore Foundation - Undergraduate Scholarships (Undergraduate/Scholarship) [4425]
Senator James Gladstone Memorial Scholarships (Graduate, Undergraduate/Scholarship) [249]
Dr. Helen Preston Glass Fellowships (Doctorate/Fellowship) [2700]
Franciszek Glogowski Memorial Scholarships (Undergraduate/Scholarship) [8576]
Charles D. Gonthier Research Fellowships (Graduate, Advanced Professional/Fellowship) [2668]
Baxter Corporation - Jean Goodwill Scholarships (Graduate/Scholarship) [24]
Google Lime Scholarships for Students with Disabilities (Undergraduate, Graduate, Doctorate/Scholarship) [6089]
Lucille May Gopie Scholarships (Undergraduate, Graduate/Scholarship) [2283]
Wilhelmina Gordon Foundation Scholarships (Undergraduate/Scholarship) [6854]
Carl W. Gottschalk Research Scholar Grants (Professional development/Grant) [1381]
Graduate Research Awards for Disarmament, Arms Control and Non-Proliferation (Master's, Doctorate/Award) [8961]
Graduate Research-Travel Scholarships (Graduate/Scholarship) [3891]
Charles Hall Grandgent Awards (Graduate/Award, Monetary) [3525]
Grant Assistance Program for Autism Professionals - College Programs (Undergraduate/Grant) [7650]
Grant Assistance Program for Autism Professionals - Doctoral Programs (Doctorate/Grant) [7651]
Grant Assistance Program for Autism Professionals - Institutional Standards (Undergraduate, Graduate/Grant) [7652]
Grant Assistance Program for Autism Professionals - Masters Programs (Master's/Grant) [7653]
Grant Assistance Program for Autism Professionals - Professional Certification Programs (Undergraduate, Professional development/Grant) [7654]
Grant Assistance Program for Autism Professionals - Retroactive Assistance (Advanced Professional, Professional development/Grant) [7655]

Grant Assistance Program for Autism Professionals - Undergraduate Programs *(Undergraduate/Grant)* [7656]
Mona Gray Creative Arts Scholarships *(Graduate, Undergraduate/Scholarship)* [5593]
Graybar Canada Award of Excellence Scholarships *(Undergraduate/Scholarship)* [3832]
Leslie C. Green Veterans Scholarships *(Juris Doctorate, Advanced Professional/Scholarship)* [3458]
Reginald K. Groome Memorial Scholarships *(Undergraduate/Scholarship)* [8823]
Guelph Caribbean Canadian Association Undergraduate Scholarships *(Undergraduate/Scholarship)* [4679]
John Simon Guggenheim Memorial Fellowships - U.S. and Canadian Competition *(Advanced Professional/Fellowship)* [4684]
Guntley-Lorimer Science and Arts Scholarships *(Undergraduate/Scholarship)* [2284]
Hamilton Industrial Environmental Association Bursaries-Mohawk College *(Undergraduate/Scholarship)* [4691]
Al Hamilton Scholarships *(Undergraduate/Scholarship)* [2285]
Handweavers Guild of America and Dendel Scholarships *(Graduate, Undergraduate/Scholarship)* [4710]
Byron Hanke Fellowships *(Doctorate, Graduate, Undergraduate/Fellowship)* [4225]
Tom Hanson Photojournalism Awards *(All/Internship)* [4119]
Father J. Harold Conway Memorial Scholarships *(Postgraduate/Fellowship)* [7632]
B. Harper Bull Conservation Fellowships *(Graduate/Fellowship)* [9749]
Nicky & Ted Harrison Memorial Scholarships *(Undergraduate, Master's/Scholarship)* [10786]
Rona Hatt Master's Scholarships in Chemical Engineering *(Master's/Scholarship)* [2623]
Dr. E. Bruce Hendrick Scholarships *(All/Scholarship)* [9474]
Mary Jane Hendrie Memorial Scholarships *(Graduate, Undergraduate/Scholarship)* [10287]
Herb Stovel Scholarship Funds - Conference Bursaries *(Undergraduate, Graduate, Professional development/Scholarship)* [7199]
Herb Stovel Scholarship Funds - Project Bursaries *(Undergraduate, Graduate, Professional development/Scholarship)* [7200]
Robert N. Herbert Undergraduate Scholarships *(Undergraduate/Scholarship)* [9216]
Jim Hierlihy Memorial Scholarship *(Undergraduate/Scholarship)* [3911]
Judy Hill Memorial Scholarships *(Undergraduate/Scholarship)* [2701]
Geordie Hilton Academic Scholarships *(Undergraduate/Scholarship)* [4480]
Hispanic Serving Institution Scholarships (HSIS) *(Undergraduate/Scholarship)* [9870]
C.H.(Chuck) Hodgson Scholarships *(Undergraduate/Scholarship)* [10547]
Irving J. Hoffman Memorial Scholarships *(Undergraduate/Scholarship)* [10288]
Lois Hole Humanities and Social Sciences Scholarships *(Undergraduate/Scholarship)* [273]
Dr. Gilbert Hopson Medical Student Bursaries *(Undergraduate/Grant)* [7639]
Horizon Health Network Scholarships *(Advanced Professional/Scholarship)* [7281]
E.B. Horsman & Son Scholarships *(Undergraduate/Scholarship)* [3834]
Hosinec Family Scholarships *(Graduate, Undergraduate/Scholarship)* [10289]
Lloyd Houlden Memorial Research Fellowships *(Advanced Professional, Professional development/Fellowship)* [2559]
William B. Howell Scholarships *(Undergraduate/Scholarship)* [1515]
Goldwin Howland Scholarships *(Graduate/Scholarship)* [2720]
Christopher Hoy/ERT Scholarships *(Graduate/Scholarship)* [962]
John Hoyt Memorial Scholarships *(Undergraduate, Master's/Scholarship)* [10788]
Hubbell Canada LP "Electrical Industry Leadership" Scholarship Awards *(Undergraduate/Scholarship)* [3835]
Steven Huesing Scholarships *(Graduate, Undergraduate/Scholarship)* [3067]
Berton W. Huestis Memorial Scholarships *(Advanced Professional/Scholarship)* [7282]
Kathryn Huget Leadership Awards *(Master's, Doctorate/Award)* [2430]
Tertia M.C. Hughes Memorial Graduate Student Prize *(Graduate/Award, Prize)* [2684]
Humber College Institute of Technology and Advanced Learning Scholarships *(Undergraduate/Scholarship)* [5524]
John Peters Humphrey Student Fellowships *(Graduate/Fellowship)* [3459]
IBA Law Student Scholarship Foundation Scholarships *(Undergraduate/Scholarship)* [5130]
In-course Scholarships - Chinese Dance Workshop Scholarships *(Undergraduate/Scholarship)* [10290]
Indspire Health Careers Bursary and Scholarships *(Graduate, Undergraduate/Scholarship)* [5132]
Indspire Post-Secondary Education Scholarships *(Graduate, Undergraduate/Scholarship)* [5133]
Industrial R&D Fellowships *(Postdoctorate/Fellowship)* [3403]
Institute Community Support Program ICR Publication Prizes *(Undergraduate, Graduate, Postgraduate, Postdoctorate/Prize)* [5230]
Intensive Language Course Grants *(Doctorate/Grant)* [3609]
Inter American Press Association Scholarships *(Undergraduate/Scholarship)* [9061]
International Association of Foundation Drilling Scholarships for Civil Engineering Students *(Graduate/Scholarship)* [75]
International Association of Foundation Drilling Scholarships for Part-time Civil Engineering Graduate School Students *(Graduate/Scholarship)* [76]
International Council for Canadian Studies Graduate Student Scholarships *(Graduate/Scholarship)* [3399]
International GI Training Grant Award *(Professional development/Grant)* [685]
International Grenfell Association Bursary *(Undergraduate/Scholarship)* [5341]
International Grenfell Association Post-Secondary Bursaries *(Undergraduate/Scholarship)* [5342]
International Grenfell Association Secondary/High School Bursaries *(Undergraduate/Scholarship)* [5343]
International Law Research Program Fellowships *(Advanced Professional, Professional development/Fellowship)* [2884]
Investigators in the Pathogenesis of Infectious Disease Awards *(Doctorate, Postdoctorate, Professional development/Grant)* [2417]
Investors Group Scholarships for Not-For-Profit Leaders *(Other/Scholarship)* [2183]
IODE Canada Labrador Bursary *(Undergraduate/Scholarship)* [6855]
IRSST Doctoral Scholarship *(Doctorate/Fellowship)* [5152]
IRSST Doctoral Scholarships Abroad *(Doctorate/Fellowship)* [5153]
IRSST Doctoral Scholarships Supplement *(Doctorate/Fellowship)* [5154]
IRSST Masters Scholarships Supplement *(Master's/Fellowship)* [5156]
IRSST Masters Scholarships *(Master's/Scholarship)* [5155]
IRSST Postdoctoral Scholarships Abroad *(Postdoctorate/Fellowship)* [5158]
IRSST Postdoctoral Scholarships *(Postdoctorate/Fellowship)* [5157]
ISM Doctoral Fellowships *(Doctorate/Fellowship)* [5160]
ISM Scholarships for Graduate Studies *(Graduate/Scholarship)* [5161]
Dr. Karl C. Ivarson Scholarships *(Master's, Doctorate/Scholarship)* [113]
Jamaican Canadian Association Alberta Scholarship Program *(Undergraduate/Scholarship)* [5533]
Helen Janko Memorial Scholarships *(Undergraduate, Master's/Scholarship)* [10789]
Drzymala Janusz and Roma Scholarship *(Undergraduate/Scholarship)* [8577]
Airgas - Terry Jarvis Memorial Scholarships *(Undergraduate/Scholarship)* [1518]
Hon. Michaelle Jean Scholarships *(Undergraduate/Scholarship)* [2286]
Harry Jerome Legacy Scholarships *(Undergraduate, Graduate/Scholarship)* [2287]
Harry Johannes Scholarships *(Undergraduate, Graduate/Scholarship)* [10790]
Johnson & Johnson Scholarships *(Undergraduate/Scholarship)* [2702]
Douglas Johnson Memorial Scholarships *(Undergraduate, Master's/Scholarship)* [10791]
Kazimiera Juchniewicz Memorial Scholarships *(Undergraduate/Scholarship)* [8578]
Stefan and Weronika Kacperski Memorial Scholarships *(Undergraduate/Scholarship)* [8579]
Kalmen Kaplansky Scholarships in Economic and Social Rights *(Graduate/Scholarship)* [3657]
Kappa Kappa Gamma Foundation of Canada Graduate Scholarships *(Graduate, Doctorate/Scholarship)* [5777]
Lucile B. Kaufman Women's Scholarships *(Undergraduate/Scholarship)* [9184]
Dr. Terry Kavanagh Fellowships *(Graduate/Fellowship)* [2791]
E. Wayne Kay Co-op Scholarships *(Undergraduate/Scholarship)* [9185]
E. Wayne Kay Community College Scholarships *(Undergraduate/Scholarship)* [9186]
Gunild Keetman Scholarships *(Other, Undergraduate/Scholarship)* [7714]
Dr. Dorothy J. Kergin Fellowships *(Doctorate, Master's/Fellowship)* [2703]
Kerrwil's J.W. Kerr Continuing Education Scholarship Awards *(Undergraduate/Scholarship)* [3837]
Edgar Kerstan Memorial Scholarships *(Undergraduate/Scholarship)* [6420]
Keith Kevan Award *(Postgraduate/Award)* [3892]
KFOC Allied Health Doctoral Fellowship *(Doctorate/Fellowship)* [5825]
KFOC Allied Health Scholarships *(Graduate/Scholarship)* [5826]
KFOC Biomedical Fellowships *(Postdoctorate/Fellowship)* [5827]
KFOC Biomedical Scholarships *(Doctorate/Scholarship)* [5828]
Khaki University and Y.M.C.A. Memorial Scholarships *(Undergraduate/Scholarship)* [10291]
Helen and George Kilik Scholarships *(Undergraduate/Scholarship)* [274]
Killam Fellowships *(Undergraduate/Fellowship)* [4229]
Mackenzie King Open Scholarships *(Graduate/Scholarship)* [6366]
Annie Kirshenblatt Memorial Scholarships *(Graduate, Undergraduate/Scholarship)* [9751]
Flo Kitz Memorial Scholarships *(Undergraduate, Master's/Scholarship)* [10792]
Stefan and Janina Klimt Scholarships *(Undergraduate/Scholarship)* [8580]
George Kokocianski Memorial Scholarships *(Undergraduate/Scholarship)* [8581]
Anna and John Kolesay Memorial Scholarships *(Undergraduate/Scholarship)* [275]
Bernie Kom Memorial Awards *(Postgraduate/Award)* [10746]
Korean Studies Dissertation Workshop Funds *(Graduate/Fellowship)* [9056]
Krawczyk-Krane Family Scholarships *(Undergraduate/Scholarship)* [8582]
Robert Krembil Scholarships of Merit *(Doctorate/Scholarship)* [10747]
Leo J. Krysa Family Undergraduate Scholarships *(Undergraduate/Scholarship)* [2674]
Jan Kuropas Memorial Scholarships *(Undergraduate/Scholarship)* [8583]
Lafarge Community Leaders Scholarships *(Other/Scholarship)* [2184]
Alexander Fraser Laidlaw Fellowships *(Graduate/Fellowship, Scholarship)* [2576]
Canadian Association for Studies in Co-operation Scholarships - Alexander Fraser Laidlaw Fellowships *(Graduate/Fellowship)* [2613]
Allen T. Lambert Scholarships *(Postgraduate/Scholarship)* [10748]

CANADA

John and Lois Lamont Graduate Scholarship *(Graduate/Scholarship)* [2627]
James D. Lang Memorial Scholarships *(Graduate/Scholarship)* [2563]
Language Teacher Bursary Program Awards *(Other/Award)* [277]
Languages In Teacher Education Scholarships *(Undergraduate/Scholarship)* [278]
Larson Aquatic Research Support Scholarships (LARS) *(Graduate/Scholarship)* [1490]
Karen E. Latt Memorial Scholarships *(Graduate/Scholarship)* [5584]
Kenneth Laundy Entrance Scholarships *(Graduate/Scholarship)* [10749]
Law Foundation of British Columbia Graduate Fellowships *(Graduate/Fellowship)* [5941]
Law Foundation of Newfoundland and Labrador Law School Scholarships *(Advanced Professional/Scholarship)* [5943]
Robert G. Lawrence Prize *(Doctorate, Other, Graduate/Prize, Award)* [1902]
Queenie Leader Memorial Scholarships *(Undergraduate, Master's/Scholarship)* [10793]
The Leaders of Tomorrow Scholarships *(Undergraduate, Vocational/Occupational/Scholarship)* [3765]
Lemaire Co-operative Studies Awards *(Undergraduate, Graduate/Scholarship)* [2577]
Carol Anne Letheren Entrance Awards *(Postgraduate/Award, Scholarship)* [10750]
Lilly Scholarships in Religion for Journalists *(Other/Scholarship)* [8549]
Tecla Lin & Nelia Laroza Memorial Scholarships *(Undergraduate/Scholarship)* [2704]
LionsDeal Scholarships *(Undergraduate/Scholarship)* [6095]
Ian Lithgow Memorial Awards *(Master's/Award)* [10751]
Grant Livingston Memorial Scholarships *(Undergraduate, Master's/Scholarship)* [10794]
Long-term International Fellowships *(Professional development/Fellowship)* [3380]
Sir James Lougheed Awards of Distinction *(Doctorate, Graduate/Award)* [279]
Lowry Awards for Women of Excellence *(Undergraduate, Graduate, Advanced Professional/Award, Scholarship)* [3789]
Charles Luttman Scholarship *(Undergraduate/Scholarship)* [2536]
Dr. Sally Macdonald Scholarships *(Undergraduate, Master's/Scholarship)* [10795]
Dr. Arlene MacIntyre Medical Student Bursaries *(Undergraduate/Grant)* [7640]
CEMF Claudette MacKay-Lassonde Graduate Scholarships *(Doctorate, Postdoctorate/Scholarship)* [2624]
MAF Canada Scholarship Fund *(Undergraduate/Scholarship)* [6560]
Manhattan Street Capital Annual National Scholarships *(Undergraduate, Graduate, Doctorate/Scholarship)* [6227]
Markham-Colegrave International Scholarships *(Undergraduate/Scholarship)* [805]
Eleanor Jean Martin Award *(Master's/Scholarship)* [2705]
Dick Martin Scholarships *(Postgraduate/Scholarship)* [2609]
Beverley Mascoll Scholarships *(Undergraduate/Scholarship)* [2288]
Val Mason Scholarships *(Postgraduate/Scholarship)* [2746]
Elizabeth Massey Award *(Postgraduate/Award)* [2631]
Norman Matechuk Memorial Scholarships *(Undergraduate, Master's/Scholarship)* [10796]
Mature Student Scholarship *(Undergraduate/Scholarship)* [3912]
Al Maurer Awards *(Undergraduate, Graduate, Advanced Professional/Award, Scholarship)* [3790]
Tadeusz Maziarz Scholarships *(Undergraduate/Scholarship)* [8584]
John Mazurek Memorial-Morgex Insurance Scholarship *(Other/Scholarship)* [296]
Giuliano Mazzetti Scholarships *(Undergraduate/Scholarship)* [9188]
Robert R. McCain Memorial Scholarships *(Advanced Professional/Scholarship)* [7283]
Heather McCallum Scholarships *(Doctorate, Other/Scholarship)* [1903]
Hans McCorriston Motive Power Machinist Grant Programs *(Undergraduate/Scholarship)* [2132]
Joseph McCulley Educational Scholarships *(Graduate, Undergraduate/Scholarship)* [10292]
William H. McGannon Foundation Scholarships *(Graduate, Undergraduate/Scholarship)* [6364]
R. Tait Mckenzie Awards *(Professional development/Award)* [8118]
John J. McKetta Undergraduate Scholarships *(Undergraduate/Scholarship)* [905]
Louise McKinney Post-secondary Scholarships *(Undergraduate/Scholarship)* [280]
G. William McQuade Memorial Scholarships *(Advanced Professional/Scholarship)* [7284]
Douglas McRorie Memorial Scholarships *(Doctorate, Master's/Scholarship)* [114]
Dr. Ernest and Minnie Mehl Scholarships *(Undergraduate/Scholarship)* [281]
Mensa Canada General Scholarships *(Undergraduate/Scholarship)* [6421]
CAG Donald Menzies Bursary Awards *(Postgraduate/Scholarship, Award)* [2554]
Merck Frosst Canada Ltd. Postgraduate Pharmacy Fellowships *(Graduate/Fellowship)* [1957]
Al Mercury Scholarships *(Undergraduate/Scholarship)* [10293]
Metcalf Innovation Fellowships *(Advanced Professional, Professional development/Fellowship)* [4366]
Michener-Deacon Fellowship for Journalism Education *(Professional development/Fellowship)* [4121]
Bronislaw Michno Memorial Scholarships *(Undergraduate/Scholarship)* [8585]
Microsoft Research Graduate Women's Scholarships *(Graduate/Scholarship)* [6506]
Microsoft Research PhD Fellowships *(Doctorate/Fellowship)* [6507]
Military Nurses Association Scholarships *(Master's/Scholarship)* [2706]
Mineralogical Association of Canada Scholarships *(Doctorate, Graduate/Scholarship)* [2022]
Minerva Scholarships *(Undergraduate/Scholarship)* [2289]
Minnesota GLBT Educational Fund *(Undergraduate/Scholarship)* [8661]
MLA Continuing Education Awards (CE) *(Graduate/Grant)* [6390]
Francis H. Moffitt Memorial Scholarships *(Graduate, Undergraduate/Scholarship)* [1807]
Murray Montague Memorial Scholarships *(Undergraduate/Scholarship)* [4571]
Thomas More Scholarships *(Undergraduate/Scholarship)* [4487]
John H. Moss Scholarships *(Undergraduate/Scholarship)* [10294]
Movember Clinical Trials *(Advanced Professional/Grant)* [8304]
Movember Discovery Grants *(Advanced Professional, Professional development/Grant)* [8305]
Movember Rising Star in Prostate Cancer Research Awards *(Advanced Professional, Professional development/Grant)* [8306]
Movember Team Grants *(Advanced Professional, Professional development/Grant)* [8307]
Marvin Mundel Memorial Scholarships *(Undergraduate/Scholarship)* [5192]
Margaret Munro Award *(Undergraduate/Scholarship)* [2707]
Dr. Helen K. Mussallem Fellowships *(Master's/Scholarship)* [2708]
NAAMA Scholarships *(Undergraduate/Scholarship)* [6701]
Irwin Allen Nadal Entrance Awards *(Master's/Award)* [10752]
Miles Spencer Nadal Entrance Awards *(Master's/Award)* [10753]
National Board Technical Scholarships *(Undergraduate/Scholarship)* [6827]
National Greenhouse Manufacturers Association Scholarships *(Undergraduate/Scholarship)* [806]
National Society of Accountants Scholarship Program *(Undergraduate/Scholarship)* [7134]
Natural Sciences and Engineering Research Council Postgraduate Scholarships *(Doctorate/Scholarship)* [3404]
Marek Nawrot Memorial Scholarships *(Undergraduate/Scholarship)* [8586]
NB College of Physicians and Surgeons Medical Education Scholarships *(Advanced Professional/Scholarship)* [7285]
NCLEJ Law School Graduate Fellows and Volunteers *(Graduate/Fellowship)* [6848]
Nedien Hoganson Memorial Scholarships *(Undergraduate, Master's/Scholarship)* [10797]
Neuroscience Certification Bursary Awards *(Other/Award)* [1889]
Alan H. Neville Memorial Scholarships *(Undergraduate/Scholarship)* [335]
New Brunswick Nurses Association Scholarships *(Master's/Scholarship)* [2709]
Norman Nicholson Scholarships *(Undergraduate/Scholarship)* [2607]
Sharon Nield Memorial Scholarships *(Undergraduate/Scholarship)* [2710]
Erik Nielsen Memorial Scholarships *(Undergraduate, Master's/Scholarship)* [10798]
North American Conference on British Studies Dissertation Year Fellowships *(Doctorate, Postdoctorate/Fellowship)* [7443]
North American Conference on British Studies-Huntington Library Fellowships *(Doctorate, Postdoctorate/Fellowship)* [7444]
North American Society Fellowships *(Professional development/Fellowship)* [8119]
Northern Alberta Development Council Bursary Awards *(Undergraduate/Award)* [283]
Northern Alberta Development Council Bursary Partnership Program *(Undergraduate/Award)* [284]
Northern Resident Scholarships *(Doctorate, Graduate/Scholarship)* [1935]
Nova Scotia Salmon Association Scholarships *(Undergraduate/Scholarship)* [7556]
Mike and Flo Novovesky Scholarships *(Undergraduate/Scholarship)* [807]
Nuffield Canada Farming Scholarships *(Undergraduate/Scholarship)* [7558]
AEBC Rick Oakes Scholarships for the Arts *(Undergraduate/Scholarship)* [336]
OAS Academic Scholarships - Graduate *(Graduate/Scholarship)* [7722]
O'Brien Foundation Fellowships *(Postgraduate, Master's, Doctorate/Fellowship)* [7568]
Lawrence "Bud" Ohlman Memorial Scholarships *(Undergraduate/Scholarship)* [808]
OHTN Postdoctoral Fellowships *(Doctorate/Fellowship)* [7637]
Oil & Gas, Trades & Technology (OGTT) Bursary and Scholarship Awards (OGTT) *(Undergraduate/Scholarship)* [5134]
Omatsu FACL Scholarships *(Juris Doctorate, Advanced Professional/Scholarship)* [4001]
OMHF Postdoctoral Fellowships *(Postdoctorate/Fellowship)* [7648]
OMSBF Burlington Medical Student Bursaries *(Undergraduate/Grant)* [7641]
OMSBF District Four - Physician Care Bursaries *(Undergraduate/Grant)* [7642]
OMSBF Durham Medical Society Medical Student Bursaries *(Undergraduate/Grant)* [7643]
OMSBF Sun Life Financial Medical Student Bursaries *(Undergraduate/Grant)* [7644]
ONECA Four Directions Scholarship *(Undergraduate/Scholarship)* [7658]
OOBS Student Leadership Scholarships *(Undergraduate/Scholarship)* [7766]
Osram Sylvania Scholastic Achievement Awards *(Undergraduate/Scholarship)* [3838]
Ellis R. Ott Scholarships *(Graduate, Master's/Scholarship)* [1390]
Michael Oykhman Criminal Law and Evidence Scholarships *(Juris Doctorate, Advanced Professional/Scholarship)* [6455]
Parkinson Canada Basic Research Fellowships *(Advanced Professional/Fellowship)* [7876]
Parkinson Canada Clinical Movement Disorder Fellowships *(Advanced Professional, Professional development/Fellowship)* [7877]
Parkinson Canada Clinical Research Fellowships *(Professional development/Fellowship)* [7878]

Parkinson Canada Graduate Student Awards *(Graduate, Advanced Professional/Grant)* [7879]
Parkinson Canada New Investigator Award Grants *(Professional development/Grant)* [7880]
Parkinson Canada Pilot Project Grants *(Advanced Professional/Grant)* [7881]
Senator Norman Paterson Fellowships *(Doctorate/Scholarship)* [2711]
Q. O. (Quint) Patrick Scholarships *(Undergraduate/Scholarship)* [10548]
Arthur Paulin Automotive Aftermarket Scholarship Awards *(Postgraduate, Undergraduate/Scholarship)* [2133]
PEA Bursaries *(Undergraduate/Scholarship)* [8290]
PEA Scholarships *(Undergraduate/Scholarship)* [8291]
Robert L. Peaslee-Detroit Brazing and Soldiering Division Scholarships *(Undergraduate/Scholarship)* [1521]
PEO Educational Loan Funds *(Undergraduate, Master's, Doctorate/Loan)* [7954]
PEO Scholars Awards *(Doctorate/Award, Scholarship)* [7956]
Nalini Perera Little Lotus Bud Master's Scholarships *(Master's/Scholarship)* [2689]
Jim Perry Vocational Scholarships *(Undergraduate, Vocational/Occupational/Scholarship)* [809]
Persons Case Scholarships *(Undergraduate, Graduate/Scholarship)* [285]
Petroleum History Society Graduate Scholarships *(Graduate/Scholarship)* [8017]
PHE Canada National Award for Teaching Excellence in Physical Education *(Professional development/Recognition)* [8120]
PHE Canada Student Awards *(Undergraduate/Award)* [8121]
Shoshana Philipp (Kirshenblatt) R.N. Memorial Scholarships *(Graduate, Undergraduate/Scholarship)* [9752]
Philips Lighting Continuing Education Awards *(Undergraduate/Scholarship)* [3839]
Phillips Fund Grants for Native American Research *(Doctorate, Master's/Grant)* [1083]
Lowell Phillips Scholarships *(Undergraduate/Scholarship)* [3313]
Physiotherapy Foundation of Canada Research Grant *(Other/Grant)* [8129]
Eleonora Pidperyhora Scholarship *(Undergraduate/Scholarship)* [8587]
Ronald C. and Joyce Pierce - Mobile Section Named Scholarships *(Undergraduate/Scholarship)* [1522]
PIMS Postdoctoral Fellowships *(Doctorate/Fellowship)* [7791]
Dr. Adolph Piotrowski Memorial Art Scholarships *(Undergraduate/Scholarship)* [8588]
Pipe Line Contractors Association of Canada Student Bursary *(Undergraduate, Postgraduate/Scholarship)* [8142]
Platform Support Grants *(Advanced Professional/Grant)* [2357]
D.F. Plett Graduate Fellowships *(Graduate/Fellowship)* [8158]
Harriet and Leon Pomerance Fellowships *(Professional development/Fellowship)* [1610]
Postdoctoral Fellowships at the Fields Institute *(Postdoctorate/Fellowship)* [4020]
J.R. (Joe) Power National Scholarships *(Postgraduate/Scholarship)* [8383]
Prairie Baseball Academy Scholarships *(Undergraduate/Scholarship)* [286]
Gerald Pratley Award *(Doctorate, Graduate/Award)* [1884]
Diana M. Priestly Memorial Scholarships *(Undergraduate/Scholarship)* [2564]
Prince Edward Island Law Student Scholarships *(Undergraduate/Scholarship)* [5980]
Alexander Pringle Criminal Law Scholarships *(Advanced Professional/Scholarship)* [8280]
Prostate Cancer Canada Clinical Research Fellowships *(Advanced Professional/Fellowship)* [8308]
Prostate Cancer Canada Graduate Studentships *(Graduate, Doctorate/Grant)* [8309]
Prostate Cancer Canada Postdoctoral Research Fellowships *(Postdoctorate, Advanced Professional/Fellowship)* [8310]

Provincial and Regional 4-H Scholarships *(Undergraduate/Scholarship)* [9]
PSAC-AGR National Scholarships *(Postgraduate/Scholarship)* [8384]
PSAC - Coughlin National Scholarships *(Postgraduate/Scholarship)* [8385]
PSAC Regional Scholarships *(Postgraduate/Scholarship)* [8386]
Psychology Association of Saskatchewan Student Scholarships - Academic Achievement *(Master's, Doctorate/Scholarship)* [8320]
Psychology Association of Saskatchewan Student Scholarships - Research Based *(Master's, Doctorate/Scholarship)* [8321]
Doug Purvis Prize *(Other/Prize)* [2546]
A.O. Putnam Memorial Scholarships *(Undergraduate/Scholarship)* [5193]
Queen Elizabeth II Graduate Scholarship Program *(Doctorate, Graduate/Scholarship)* [287]
Diamond & James Quong Memorial Scholarships *(Undergraduate, Master's/Scholarship)* [10799]
RAB Design Lighting Award of Excellence *(Undergraduate/Scholarship)* [3840]
James K. Rathmell Jr. Memorial Scholarships *(Undergraduate, Graduate/Scholarship)* [810]
RBC Medical Education Scholarships *(Advanced Professional/Scholarship)* [7286]
Regional Development Corporation Scholarships *(Advanced Professional/Scholarship)* [7287]
Registered Apprenticeship Program/CTS Scholarships (RAP) *(Undergraduate/Scholarship)* [288]
J.H. Stewart Reid Memorial Fellowship Trust *(Doctorate/Fellowship, Award)* [8547]
W. Reymont Scholarships *(Undergraduate/Scholarship)* [8589]
Risk Management and Insurance Scholarships *(Undergraduate/Scholarship)* [8767]
Marion Roberts Memorial Scholarships *(Undergraduate/Scholarship)* [2134]
Gertrude J. Robinson Book Prize *(Professional development/Prize)* [2616]
R.O.E.A. Dumitru Golea Goldy-Gemu Scholarships *(Undergraduate/Scholarship)* [1227]
Roy Seymour Rogers and Geraldine Ruth Rogers Scholarships *(Undergraduate/Scholarship)* [9732]
Red Rogers Memorial Scholarships *(Undergraduate, Master's/Scholarship)* [10800]
Mandell and Lester Rosenblatt Undergraduate Scholarships *(Undergraduate/Scholarship)* [9217]
Robert Roy Awards *(Advanced Professional/Award, Recognition)* [1897]
Royal Bank Scholarships *(Undergraduate, Master's/Scholarship)* [2290]
RPNAS Baccalaureate Level Program Scholarships *(Undergraduate/Scholarship)* [8538]
RPNAS Doctorate Level Program Scholarship *(Doctorate/Scholarship)* [8539]
RPNAS Master's Level Program Scholarship *(Master's/Scholarship)* [8540]
RTDNF Scholarships *(Undergraduate, Graduate/Scholarship)* [8414]
Glen Ruby Memorial Scholarships *(Undergraduate/Scholarship)* [2754]
Rutherford Scholars *(Undergraduate/Scholarship)* [289]
Alexander Rutherford Scholarships for High School Achievement *(Undergraduate/Scholarship)* [290]
Chester & Maria Sadowski Memorial Scholarships *(Undergraduate/Scholarship)* [8590]
Saint Paul University Excellence Scholarships *(Undergraduate/Scholarship, Medal)* [8675]
Saint Paul University Financial Aid Bursaries *(Undergraduate, Graduate/Scholarship)* [8676]
AIST David H. Samson Canadian Scholarships *(Undergraduate/Scholarship)* [2006]
Sanofi Pasteur Scholarships *(Master's/Scholarship)* [2712]
SARP Education Assistance Grants *(Professional development/Grant)* [8762]
SARP Professional Development Grants *(Professional development/Grant)* [8763]
Saskatchewan Government Insurance Anniversary Scholarships *(Undergraduate/Scholarship)* [8770]
Saskatchewan Government Insurance Corporate Scholarships *(Undergraduate/Scholarship)* [8771]
François J. Saucier Prize in Applied Oceanography *(Professional development/Award, Prize)* [2685]
Savoy Foundation Postdoctoral and Clinical Research Fellowships *(Postdoctorate/Fellowship)* [4123]
Meta M. Sawyer Bursary Fund *(Undergraduate/Grant)* [7645]
Schlegel-UW RIA Scholarships *(Doctorate/Scholarship)* [2555]
Richard J. Schmeelk Fellowships *(Graduate/Fellowship)* [8790]
Schneider Electric Student Merit Awards *(Undergraduate/Scholarship)* [3841]
B.E. Schnurr Memorial Fund Research Grants *(Other/Grant)* [8130]
Scholarship Award of the Bell Aliant Pioneer Volunteers *(Undergraduate/Scholarship)* [2690]
Scholarships for the Next Generation of Scientists *(Postdoctorate/Scholarship)* [2777]
Tanna H. Schulich MBA Entrance Scholarships *(Graduate/Scholarship)* [10754]
Musia and Leon Schwartz Scholarships *(Undergraduate, Graduate/Scholarship)* [5586]
Scotiabank Medical Education Scholarships *(Advanced Professional/Scholarship)* [7288]
Scotiabank Scholarships *(Undergraduate/Scholarship)* [2291]
Seed Companies Scholarships *(Undergraduate, Graduate/Scholarship)* [811]
Senior Innovation Scholarships *(Undergraduate, Graduate/Scholarship)* [8146]
SFP Undergraduate Scholarships *(Undergraduate/Scholarship)* [8794]
Shastri Scholar Travel Subsidy Grants (SSTSG) *(Graduate, Professional development/Grant)* [8857]
Dr. Robert and Anna Shaw Scholarships *(Undergraduate/Scholarship)* [291]
Dr. Robert Norman Shaw Scholarships *(Undergraduate/Scholarship)* [292]
David S. Sheridan Canadian Research Awards *(Other/Award)* [2542]
Siemens Canada Academic Awards *(Undergraduate/Scholarship)* [3842]
Sigma Theta Tau International Scholarships *(Doctorate/Scholarship)* [2713]
Sloan Research Fellowships *(Doctorate/Fellowship)* [8988]
SME Directors Scholarships *(Undergraduate/Scholarship)* [9194]
SME Education Foundation Family Scholarships *(Undergraduate/Scholarship)* [9195]
Donald Smiley Prize *(Advanced Professional/Prize, Award, Recognition)* [1908]
Bolesław & Irena Sobczak Scholarships *(Undergraduate/Scholarship)* [8591]
Frank H. Sobey Awards for Excellence in Business Studies *(Undergraduate/Award)* [9048]
Sobeys & Empire Work Experience & Scholarship Program - Future Leaders Awards *(Other/Scholarship)* [9049]
Society of Graphic Designers of Canada Adobe Scholarships *(Undergraduate/Scholarship)* [9063]
Society of Graphic Designers of Canada Applied Arts Scholarships *(Undergraduate/Scholarship)* [9064]
Society of Graphic Designers of Canada Veer Scholarships *(Undergraduate/Scholarship)* [9065]
Dr. Paul and Gayle Sohi Medical Education Scholarships *(Advanced Professional/Scholarship)* [7289]
Carin Alma E. Somers Scholarship Trust *(Undergraduate/Scholarship)* [2118]
Sonepar Canada Scholarship Awards *(Undergraduate/Scholarship)* [3843]
Beatrice Drinnan Spence Scholarships *(Undergraduate, Vocational/Occupational/Scholarship)* [3766]
Jean and Manny Spinner Scholarships *(Undergraduate/Scholarship)* [5587]
SSHRC Doctoral Fellowship Program *(Doctorate/Fellowship, Scholarship)* [3396]
Standard Recognition of Excellence Awards *(Undergraduate/Scholarship)* [3844]
Lasek Stanisław and Aniela Scholarship *(Undergraduate/Scholarship)* [8592]
Taylor Statten Memorial Fellowships *(Graduate/Scholarship)* [10295]

CANADA

The Stanley H. Stearman Awards *(Undergraduate/Scholarship)* [7135]
Harry Steele Entrance Awards *(Postgraduate/Award)* [10755]
Evelyn Steele Memorial Scholarships *(Undergraduate, Master's/Scholarship)* [10802]
Stelpro Scholarships 360: Energizing Potential *(Undergraduate/Scholarship)* [3845]
H.H. Stern Grant Awards *(Advanced Professional, Professional development/Award, Grant)* [1898]
David Stockwood Memorial Prize *(Advanced Professional, Professional development/Prize)* [81]
Marlene Streit Golf Scholarships *(Undergraduate/Scholarship)* [4481]
Summerside-Natick International Friendship Hockey Scholarships *(Undergraduate/Scholarship)* [3314]
SuperKutz Scholarships *(Undergraduate/Scholarship)* [5892]
Syncrude/Athabasca University Aboriginal Scholarships *(Undergraduate/Scholarship)* [9627]
TAC Foundation-3M Canada Company Scholarships *(Graduate, Undergraduate/Scholarship)* [9768]
TAC Foundation-407 ETR Scholarships *(Undergraduate, Graduate/Scholarship)* [9769]
TAC Foundation-Amec Foster Wheeler Scholarships *(Undergraduate, Graduate/Scholarship)* [9770]
TAC Foundation-ATS Traffic Group of Companies Scholarships *(Undergraduate, Graduate/Scholarship)* [9771]
TAC Foundation-Canadian Council of Independent Laboratories Graduate Student Scholarships *(Graduate/Scholarship)* [9772]
TAC Foundation-CCMTA Road Safety Scholarships *(Undergraduate, Graduate/Scholarship)* [9773]
TAC Foundation-Cement Association of Canada Scholarships *(Graduate, Undergraduate/Scholarship)* [9774]
TAC Foundation-Dillon Consulting Scholarships *(Undergraduate, Graduate/Scholarship)* [9775]
TAC Foundation-Dr. Ralph Haas Graduate Student Scholarships *(Graduate/Scholarship)* [9776]
TAC Foundation-EllisDon Community College/CEGEP Scholarships *(Undergraduate/Scholarship)* [9777]
TAC Foundation-exp Scholarships *(Undergraduate, Graduate/Scholarship)* [9778]
TAC Foundation-Golder Associates Ltd. Scholarships *(Undergraduate, Graduate/Scholarship)* [9779]
TAC Foundation-HDR Corporation Graduate Student Scholarships *(Graduate/Scholarship)* [9780]
TAC Foundation-IBI Group Scholarships *(Undergraduate, Graduate/Scholarship)* [9781]
TAC Foundation-ISL Engineering Scholarships *(Undergraduate, Graduate/Scholarship)* [9782]
TAC Foundation-LEA Consulting Ltd. Scholarships *(Undergraduate, Graduate/Scholarship)* [9783]
TAC Foundation-MMM Group Limited Scholarships *(Undergraduate, Graduate/Scholarship)* [9784]
TAC Foundation-Municipalities Scholarships *(Undergraduate, Graduate/Scholarship)* [9785]
TAC Foundation-Parsons Scholarships *(Undergraduate, Graduate/Scholarship)* [9786]
TAC Foundation-Peto MacCallum Undergraduate & College Scholarships *(Undergraduate/Scholarship)* [9787]
TAC Foundation-Provinces and Territories Scholarships *(Undergraduate, Graduate/Scholarship)* [9788]
TAC Foundation-SNC Lavalin Scholarships *(Undergraduate, Graduate/Scholarship)* [9789]
TAC Foundation-Stantec Consulting Scholarships *(Graduate/Scholarship)* [9790]
TAC Foundation-Tetra Tech EBA Inc. Scholarships *(Undergraduate, Graduate/Scholarship)* [9791]
Katharine Whiteside Taylor Bursary *(Professional development/Scholarship)* [7807]
Betty & Charles Taylor Scholarships *(Advanced Professional/Scholarship)* [10803]
RABC William Taylor Scholarships *(Undergraduate/Scholarship)* [3846]
TD Bank Medical Education Scholarships *(Advanced Professional/Scholarship)* [7290]
TD Meloche-Monnex Scholarships *(Doctorate/Scholarship)* [2714]
Tell Us Your Story Scholarships *(Undergraduate/Scholarship)* [10495]
TEVA Canada Scholarship *(Undergraduate/Scholarship)* [2904]
The Cover Guy Annual Scholarships *(Undergraduate, Graduate/Scholarship)* [3463]
THFC Medical Research Grants *(Professional development/Grant)* [4834]
Thomas & Betts Scholarship Awards *(Undergraduate/Scholarship)* [3847]
Nadene M. Thomas Graduate Research Scholarships *(Graduate/Scholarship)* [297]
Dr. Andrew Thomson Prize in Applied Meteorology *(Professional development/Award, Prize)* [2686]
Ken Thomson Scholarships *(Undergraduate/Scholarship)* [1906]
TIAC / Parks Canada Sustainable Tourism Scholarships *(Undergraduate, Master's/Scholarship)* [9760]
John L. Tomasovic, Sr. Scholarships *(Undergraduate/Scholarship)* [812]
Dr. Henrik and Wanda Tonning Memorial Scholarships *(Advanced Professional/Scholarship)* [7291]
Evald Torokvei Foundation Scholarships *(Graduate/Scholarship)* [10296]
Toronto Rehab Scholarships in Rehabilitation-Related Research *(Graduate/Scholarship)* [9753]
Toyota Earth Day Scholarships *(Undergraduate/Scholarship)* [9764]
Transoft Solutions, Inc. Ahead of the Curve Scholarships (AOTC) *(Graduate, Undergraduate/Scholarship)* [5221]
Transportation Association of Canada Foundation Scholarships *(Graduate, Undergraduate/Scholarship)* [9792]
Marie Tremaine Fellowships *(Postgraduate, Other/Fellowship)* [2259]
Tristin Memorial Scholarships *(Undergraduate, Vocational/Occupational/Scholarship)* [5996]
Trudeau Fellowships - Regular *(Advanced Professional, Professional development/Fellowship)* [8135]
Trudeau Fellowships - Visiting *(Advanced Professional, Professional development/Fellowship)* [8136]
Trudeau Foundation Doctoral Scholarships *(Doctorate/Scholarship)* [8137]
Sam Tughan Scholarships *(Undergraduate/Scholarship)* [2739]
UMDF Clinical Research Fellowship Training Awards *(Professional development/Fellowship)* [9860]
United Parcel Service Scholarships for Female Students *(Undergraduate/Scholarship)* [5195]
United Parcel Service Scholarships for Minority Students *(Undergraduate/Scholarship)* [5196]
University of Toronto Nortel Institute Undergraduate Scholarships *(Undergraduate/Scholarship)* [10298]
University of Toronto SAC Undergraduate Grants *(Undergraduate/Grant)* [10299]
Claudette Upton Scholarships *(Undergraduate/Scholarship)* [3787]
USA/USA-Ukramerazha Scholarships *(Undergraduate/Scholarship)* [9982]
Vale Manitoba Operations Scholarships *(Undergraduate/Scholarship, Internship)* [9995]
Vale Master's in Engineering Scholarships *(Master's/Scholarship)* [2625]
Jacob and Rita Van Namen Marketing Scholarships *(Undergraduate/Scholarship)* [814]
John Vanderlee Award *(Undergraduate/Scholarship)* [2715]
Vanier Canada Graduate Scholarships *(Graduate/Scholarship)* [3405]
Dr. Csaba Oliver Vargha Medical Student Bursaries *(Undergraduate/Grant)* [7646]
Vectorworks Design Scholarships *(Undergraduate, Graduate/Scholarship, Prize)* [10367]
Jill Vickers Prize *(Other/Award)* [1909]
Philip F. Vineberg Travelling Fellowships in the Humanities *(Undergraduate/Scholarship)* [6368]
Visible Minorities Scholarship *(Undergraduate/Scholarship)* [7207]
Wagner-Torizuka Fellowships *(Professional development/Fellowship)* [9228]
Jane C. Waldbaum Archaeological Field School Scholarships *(Undergraduate/Scholarship)* [1611]
Myrtle & Earl Walker Scholarships *(Undergraduate/Scholarship)* [9199]
Martin Walmsley Fellowships for Technological Entrepreneurship *(Graduate/Fellowship)* [7627]
Flis Walter and Anna Memorial Scholarship *(Undergraduate/Scholarship)* [8593]
Robert E. Walter Memorial Scholarship *(Undergraduate/Scholarship)* [6168]
Dr. Frank and Audrey Wanamaker Medical Scholarships *(Advanced Professional/Scholarship)* [7292]
War Memorial Doctoral Scholarships *(Postgraduate/Scholarship)* [6856]
Colin Wasacase Scholarship *(Undergraduate/Scholarship)* [7659]
Glenn Watson Scholarships *(Undergraduate/Scholarship)* [9394]
WEDA Scholarship Program *(Professional development/Scholarship)* [10529]
John V. Wehausen Graduate Scholarships for Advanced Study in Ship Hydrodynamics and Wave Theory *(Graduate/Scholarship)* [9218]
William E. Weisel Scholarships *(Undergraduate/Scholarship)* [9201]
Dorothy Wellnitz Canadian Scholarships *(Undergraduate, Vocational/Occupational/Scholarship)* [1193]
WESCO Student Achievement Awards *(Undergraduate/Scholarship)* [3848]
W. Garfield Weston Awards for Northern Research *(Graduate, Postdoctorate/Fellowship)* [10421]
Weston Brain Institute Rapid Response Program *(Postdoctorate, Advanced Professional, Professional development/Grant)* [10423]
Portia White Scholarships *(Undergraduate/Scholarship)* [2292]
Whitehorse Shotokan Karate Club Scholarships *(Undergraduate, Master's/Scholarship)* [10804]
Ann Collins Whitmore Memorial Scholarship (ACWMS) *(Graduate/Scholarship)* [8131]
Wilkinson and Company LLP Scholarships *(Undergraduate/Scholarship)* [10559]
RS Williamson and Eliford Mott Memorial Scholarships *(Undergraduate/Scholarship)* [10549]
Dr. Alice E. Wilson Awards *(Graduate, Doctorate/Award, Fellowship)* [2632]
Ross A. Wilson Science Scholarships *(Undergraduate/Scholarship)* [9733]
Abel Wolman Fellowships *(Doctorate/Fellowship)* [1492]
Women in Coaching National Coaching Institute Scholarships *(Undergraduate/Scholarship)* [3069]
Geoffrey H. Wood Scholarships *(Undergraduate/Scholarship)* [2740]
Frank and Betty Woodhams Memorial Scholarships *(Undergraduate/Scholarship)* [6422]
World Book Graduate Scholarships in Library and Information Science *(Graduate/Scholarship)* [2680]
WRI Education Foundation Scholarships - Graduate *(Graduate/Scholarship)* [10611]
WRI Education Foundation Scholarships - High School Seniors *(Undergraduate/Scholarship)* [10612]
WRI Education Foundation Scholarships - Undergraduate *(Undergraduate/Scholarship)* [10613]
Pang Xiaoyan Scholarships *(Undergraduate/Scholarship)* [2926]
York Graduate Scholarships *(Graduate/Scholarship)* [10756]
Jessie Young Bursary Awards *(Other/Award)* [1890]
Jeff Young Memorial Scholarships *(Undergraduate, Master's/Scholarship)* [10805]
Youth Affairs Committee Rising Star Scholarships *(Undergraduate/Scholarship)* [5531]
Youth or the Environment Scholarships *(Other/Scholarship)* [2185]
The Yukon Foundation Medical Laboratory Scholarships *(Undergraduate, Master's/Award)* [10806]

Dr. Steven S. Zalcman Memorial Scholarships *(Graduate, Postgraduate/Scholarship)* [5589]

CANADA (BY PROVINCE)

Alberta

AIHS Graduate Studentships *(Master's, Doctorate, Professional development/Fellowship)* [251]

AIHS Media Fellowships - CBC Radio *(Undergraduate, Graduate/Fellowship)* [252]

AIHS Postgraduate Fellowships *(Postgraduate, Advanced Professional/Fellowship)* [253]

Alberta Association of Gerontology Student Awards *(Graduate/Award)* [225]

Alberta Award for the Study of Canadian Human Rights and Multiculturalism *(Doctorate, Graduate/Award)* [261]

Alberta Blue Cross Scholarships for Aboriginal Students *(Undergraduate/Scholarship)* [230]

Alberta Child Care Association Professional Development Grants *(Professional development/Grant)* [232]

Alberta Innovates Graduate Student Scholarships *(Graduate/Scholarship)* [256]

Alberta Innovates - Technology Futures Graduate Student Scholarships in ICT *(Doctorate, Graduate, Master's/Scholarship)* [257]

Alberta Innovates - Technology Futures Graduate Student Scholarships in Nanotechnology *(Doctorate, Graduate/Scholarship)* [258]

Alberta Innovates - Technology Futures Graduate Student Scholarships in Omics *(Doctorate, Graduate/Scholarship)* [259]

Alberta Teachers Association Doctoral Fellowships in Education *(Doctorate/Fellowship)* [294]

Alberta Teachers Association Educational Research Award *(Other/Scholarship)* [295]

Alberta Ukrainian Centennial Commemorative Scholarships *(Graduate/Scholarship)* [10440]

ALIS Graduate Student Scholarships *(Graduate/Scholarship)* [264]

Robert C. Carson Memorial Bursary *(Undergraduate/Scholarship)* [270]

CBCF - Prairies/NWT Grants in Basic Biomedical Research *(Advanced Professional, Professional development/Grant)* [2597]

CBCF - Prairies/NWT Grants in Clinical Research *(Advanced Professional, Professional development/Grant)* [2598]

CBCF - Prairies/NWT Grants in Health Services and Policy Research *(Advanced Professional, Professional development/Grant)* [2599]

CBCF - Prairies/NWT Postdoctoral Fellowships *(Postdoctorate, Professional development/Fellowship)* [2600]

CBCF - Prairies/NWT Research Grants in Psychosocial, Cultural and Environmental Determinants of Health *(Advanced Professional, Professional development/Grant)* [2601]

Earl and Countess of Wessex - World Championships in Athletics Scholarships *(Undergraduate/Scholarship)* [272]

AIHS Cy Frank Fellowships: Impact Assessment *(Doctorate, Professional development/Fellowship)* [254]

Grande Prairie 4-H District Scholarships *(Undergraduate/Scholarship)* [8]

Jason Lang Scholarships *(Undergraduate/Scholarship)* [276]

Siobhan Isabella Reid Memorial Scholarships *(Graduate, Undergraduate/Scholarship)* [5994]

Risk Management and Insurance Scholarships - University of Calgary *(Undergraduate/Scholarship)* [8768]

Servus Credit Union 4-H Scholarships *(Undergraduate/Scholarship)* [10]

Ukrainian Canadian Professional and Business Club Scholarships in Education *(Undergraduate/Scholarship)* [2675]

Viscount Bennett Scholarships *(Postgraduate, Advanced Professional/Scholarship)* [5969]

British Columbia

CBCF - BC/Yukon Region Breast Cancer Research Grants Competition *(Advanced Professional/Grant)* [2587]

CBCF - BC/Yukon Region Breast Cancer Survivor Dragon Boat Grants *(Professional development/Grant)* [2588]

CBCF - BC/Yukon Region Community Health Grants *(Professional development/Grant)* [2589]

CBCF - BC/Yukon Region Small Initiative Funds *(Professional development/Grant)* [2590]

GCABC Youth Scholarship Awards *(Undergraduate/Scholarship)* [4419]

Law Society of British Columbia Scholarships *(Graduate, Undergraduate/Scholarship)* [5978]

MSFHR Scholar Awards *(Advanced Professional, Professional development/Grant)* [8994]

MSFHR Trainee Awards *(Postdoctorate, Professional development/Grant)* [8995]

SPEATBC Scholarships *(Undergraduate, High School/Scholarship)* [9296]

Women's Health Research Foundation of Canada Scholarship Program *(Graduate/Scholarship)* [10658]

Manitoba

CBCF - Prairies/NWT Grants in Basic Biomedical Research *(Advanced Professional, Professional development/Grant)* [2597]

CBCF - Prairies/NWT Grants in Clinical Research *(Advanced Professional, Professional development/Grant)* [2598]

CBCF - Prairies/NWT Grants in Health Services and Policy Research *(Advanced Professional, Professional development/Grant)* [2599]

CBCF - Prairies/NWT Postdoctoral Fellowships *(Postdoctorate, Professional development/Fellowship)* [2600]

CBCF - Prairies/NWT Research Grants in Psychosocial, Cultural and Environmental Determinants of Health *(Advanced Professional, Professional development/Grant)* [2601]

New Brunswick

EFC Atlantic Region Scholarships *(Undergraduate/Scholarship)* [3827]

NBHRF/ASRP Doctoral Training Awards *(Doctorate/Grant)* [372, 7267]

NBHRF Bridge Grants *(Professional development/Grant)* [7268]

NBHRF Doctoral Studentships *(Doctorate/Grant)* [7269]

NBHRF Establishment Grants *(Professional development/Grant)* [7270]

NBHRF Health Research Strategic Initiative Grants *(Professional development/Grant)* [7271]

NBHRF Master's Studentships *(Master's/Grant)* [7272]

NBHRF Postdoctoral Fellowships *(Postdoctorate/Fellowship)* [7273]

Newfoundland and Labrador

Ocean Industries Student Research Awards *(Undergraduate, Graduate, Postdoctorate/Award)* [8557]

Northwest Territories

CBCF - Prairies/NWT Grants in Basic Biomedical Research *(Advanced Professional, Professional development/Grant)* [2597]

CBCF - Prairies/NWT Grants in Clinical Research *(Advanced Professional, Professional development/Grant)* [2598]

CBCF - Prairies/NWT Grants in Health Services and Policy Research *(Advanced Professional, Professional development/Grant)* [2599]

CBCF - Prairies/NWT Postdoctoral Fellowships *(Postdoctorate, Professional development/Fellowship)* [2600]

CBCF - Prairies/NWT Research Grants in Psychosocial, Cultural and Environmental Determinants of Health *(Advanced Professional, Professional development/Grant)* [2601]

NWT Law Foundation/Graeme Garson Scholarships *(Advanced Professional/Scholarship)* [7554]

Nova Scotia

EFC Atlantic Region Scholarships *(Undergraduate/Scholarship)* [3827]

Nunavut

CBCF - Prairies/NWT Grants in Basic Biomedical Research *(Advanced Professional, Professional development/Grant)* [2597]

CBCF - Prairies/NWT Grants in Clinical Research *(Advanced Professional, Professional development/Grant)* [2598]

CBCF - Prairies/NWT Grants in Health Services and Policy Research *(Advanced Professional, Professional development/Grant)* [2599]

CBCF - Prairies/NWT Postdoctoral Fellowships *(Postdoctorate, Professional development/Fellowship)* [2600]

CBCF - Prairies/NWT Research Grants in Psychosocial, Cultural and Environmental Determinants of Health *(Advanced Professional, Professional development/Grant)* [2601]

Ontario

Dr. Anderson Abbott Awards *(Undergraduate/Scholarship)* [10278]

AEBC Toronto Chapter Scholarships *(Undergraduate/Scholarship)* [333]

Mary Babcock Fellowships for Labour Studies Application *(Graduate/Fellowship)* [7629]

BCSF Scholarships *(Undergraduate/Scholarship)* [2294]

Doreen Brady Memorial Scholarships *(Postgraduate/Scholarship)* [7630]

Brown Dental Scholarships *(Undergraduate/Scholarship)* [5521]

Rose Cassin Memorial Scholarships *(Postgraduate/Scholarship)* [7631]

CBCF - Ontario Nurse and Allied Health Professional Fellowships *(Advanced Professional, Professional development/Fellowship)* [2592]

CBCF - Ontario Physician Fellowships *(Doctorate, Professional development/Fellowship)* [2593]

CBCF - Ontario Research Fellowships *(Doctorate, Postdoctorate, Professional development/Fellowship)* [2594]

Mary Anne Chambers Scholarships *(Undergraduate/Scholarship)* [5522]

CJF Canadian Journalism Fellowships *(Graduate, Other, Undergraduate/Fellowship)* [4117]

Educational Fellowships for Practicing Physicians *(Advanced Professional, Professional development/Fellowship)* [8123]

PSI Graham Farquharson Knowledge Translation Fellowships *(Advanced Professional, Professional development/Fellowship)* [8124]

Franklin Empire Scholarship Awards *(Undergraduate/Scholarship)* [3829]

Marcus Mosiah Garvey Scholarships *(Undergraduate/Scholarship)* [5523]

Gerrie Electric Memorial Scholarship Awards *(Undergraduate/Scholarship)* [3831]

Grant Assistance Program for Autism Professionals - Institutional Standards *(Undergraduate, Graduate/Grant)* [7652]

Hammond Power Solutions Inc. Outstanding Electrical Scholar Awards *(Undergraduate/Award)* [3833]

Norm Hollend Fellowships in Oncology *(Postdoctorate/Fellowship)* [6138]

I Have a Dream Scholarships *(Undergraduate/Scholarship)* [5525]

Ideal Supply Scholarship Awards *(Undergraduate/Scholarship)* [3836]

Joan Kamps Memorial Bursaries *(Undergraduate, Graduate, Postgraduate, Professional development/Scholarship)* [7633]

Margaret Lynch Religious Study Fellowships *(Graduate/Scholarship)* [7634]

John Alexander McLean Scholarships *(Undergraduate/Scholarship)* [9731]

R. Roy McMurtry Fellowships in Legal History *(Doctorate, Graduate/Fellowship)* [7760]

INTERNATIONAL

Dr. Ezra Nesbeth Scholarships *(Undergraduate/Scholarship)* [5526]
Norfolk Southern Foundation Scholarships *(Undergraduate/Scholarship)* [1188]
Ontario Women's Institute Scholarships *(Undergraduate/Scholarship)* [3997]
Gail Posluns Fellowships in Hematology *(Postdoctorate/Fellowship)* [6139]
PSI Healthcare Research by Community Physicians Grants *(Advanced Professional, Professional development/Grant)* [8125]
Resident Research Grants *(Postgraduate, Professional development/Grant)* [8126]
Cecilia Rowan Religious Study Fellowships *(Graduate/Fellowship)* [7635]
Ryerson Scholarships *(Undergraduate/Scholarship)* [5527]
Eva Smith Bursary *(Undergraduate/Scholarship)* [5528]
Brian Smith Memorial Scholarships *(Undergraduate/Scholarship)* [2348]
Barbara Thomas Bursary *(Undergraduate/Scholarship)* [5529]
Toronto Rehabilitation Institute Graduate Student Scholarships - Ontario Student Opportunities Trust Fund (OSOTF) *(Graduate/Scholarship)* [9754]
University of Toronto Accenture Scholarships *(Undergraduate/Scholarship)* [10297]
York Regional Police Scholarships *(Undergraduate/Scholarship)* [5530]
Youth Affairs Committee Rising Star Scholarships *(Undergraduate/Scholarship)* [5531]

Prince Edward Island

Orin Carver Scholarships *(Undergraduate/Scholarship)* [3312]
EFC Atlantic Region Scholarships *(Undergraduate/Scholarship)* [3827]

Quebec

Therese and David Bohbot Scholarships *(Undergraduate/Scholarship)* [5571]
Yvonne L. Bombardier Visual Arts Scholarships *(Master's, Doctorate/Scholarship)* [1665]
Harry Feldman Memorial Scholarships *(Undergraduate/Scholarship)* [5576]
Franklin Empire Scholarship Awards *(Undergraduate/Scholarship)* [3829]
Hammond Power Solutions Inc. Outstanding Electrical Scholar Awards *(Undergraduate/Award)* [3833]
Harry Hopmeyer Memorial Scholarships *(Undergraduate/Scholarship)* [5578]
Herbert H. Jasper Fellowships in Neurosciences *(Postdoctorate/Fellowship)* [2568]
Joseph Katz Memorial Scholarships *(Undergraduate/Scholarship)* [5580]
Micki and Norm Keesal Scholarships *(Undergraduate/Scholarship)* [5581]
Henriette and Marcel Korner Scholarships *(Undergraduate/Scholarship)* [5582]
Liela Klinger Kurztman Memorial Scholarships *(Undergraduate/Scholarship)* [5583]
Irene Brand Lieberman Memorial Scholarships *(Graduate, Postgraduate/Scholarship)* [5585]
Bernard Michael Tarshis Memorial Scholarships for Jewish Studies *(Undergraduate/Scholarship)* [5588]

Saskatchewan

Auto Body Technician Certificate Scholarships *(Undergraduate/Scholarship)* [8765]
Norm Bromberger Research Bursaries *(Undergraduate, Graduate/Scholarship)* [3469]
CBCF - Prairies/NWT Grants in Basic Biomedical Research *(Advanced Professional, Professional development/Grant)* [2597]
CBCF - Prairies/NWT Grants in Clinical Research *(Advanced Professional, Professional development/Grant)* [2598]
CBCF - Prairies/NWT Grants in Health Services and Policy Research *(Advanced Professional, Professional development/Grant)* [2599]
CBCF - Prairies/NWT Postdoctoral Fellowships *(Postdoctorate, Professional development/Fellowship)* [2600]
CBCF - Prairies/NWT Research Grants in Psychosocial, Cultural and Environmental Determinants of Health *(Advanced Professional, Professional development/Grant)* [2601]
Stan Hamilton Scholarships *(Undergraduate/Scholarship)* [8766]
Don Jaques Memorial Fellowships *(Graduate/Fellowship)* [8777]
Bernard Michel Scholarships *(Undergraduate/Scholarship)* [2526]
Poundmaker Memorial Scholarships *(Undergraduate/Scholarship)* [10272]
Saskatchewan Government Insurance Actuarial Science Scholarships *(Undergraduate/Scholarship)* [8769]
Saskatchewan Hockey Association Scholarships *(Undergraduate/Scholarship)* [8775]
Saskatchewan Pulse Growers Undergraduate Scholarships *(Undergraduate/Scholarship)* [8778]
Saskatchewan School Boards Association Education Scholarships *(Undergraduate/Scholarship)* [8781]
Saskatchewan School Boards Association Graduate Student Awards *(Graduate/Monetary)* [8782]
SGI Business Insurance Diploma Scholarships *(Undergraduate/Scholarship)* [8772]
SGI Research Grants *(Graduate/Grant)* [8773]
Dr. Alfred E. Slinkard Scholarships *(Graduate/Scholarship)* [8779]

Yukon Territory

Brian Campion Scholarship Scholarships *(Advanced Professional/Scholarship)* [10781]
CBCF - BC/Yukon Region Breast Cancer Research Grants Competition *(Advanced Professional/Grant)* [2587]
CBCF - BC/Yukon Region Breast Cancer Survivor Dragon Boat Grants *(Professional development/Grant)* [2588]
CBCF - BC/Yukon Region Community Health Grants *(Professional development/Grant)* [2589]
CBCF - BC/Yukon Region Small Initiative Funds *(Professional development/Grant)* [2590]
Yukon Law Foundation Scholarships *(Undergraduate/Scholarship)* [10808]

INTERNATIONAL

AAMC Foundation Engagement Program for International Curators Grants *(Advanced Professional, Professional development/Grant)* [1854]
American Welding Society International Scholarships *(Undergraduate, Graduate/Scholarship)* [1505]
Franklin Mosher Baldwin Memorial Fellowships *(Master's, Doctorate/Fellowship)* [5991]
The Bentley Cropping Systems Fellowship *(Graduate/Fellowship)* [2886]
David L. Boren Fellowships *(Graduate/Fellowship)* [5199]
David L. Boren Scholarships *(Undergraduate, College/Scholarship)* [5200]
Stephen Bronfman Scholarship Funds in Environmental Studies *(Graduate/Scholarship)* [5572]
CSSE ARTS Graduate Research Awards *(Graduate/Award)* [9069]
Amy and Tim Dauphinee Scholarships *(Graduate/Scholarship)* [2575]
Economic Club Business Study Abroad Scholarships *(Undergraduate/Scholarship)* [4589]
Barbara and Nicole Heacox Foreign Travel and Study Scholarship Fund *(Undergraduate/Scholarship)* [4522]
Alexander Fraser Laidlaw Fellowships *(Graduate/Fellowship, Scholarship)* [2576]
Harold Lancour Scholarship for Foreign Study *(Professional development/Scholarship)* [2240]
Lemaire Co-operative Studies Awards *(Undergraduate, Graduate/Scholarship)* [2577]
Multi-Country Research Fellowships *(Doctorate/Fellowship)* [3431]
James B. Pearson Fellowships *(Graduate/Scholarship)* [5659]
Satter Human Rights Fellowships *(Graduate, Master's, Juris Doctorate/Fellowship)* [4787]
UNESCO-L'Oreal for Women in Science International Fellowships *(Doctorate, Postdoctorate/Fellowship)* [6108]
Thomas J. Watson Fellowships *(Undergraduate/Fellowship)* [10493]
Weston Brain Institute International Fellowships in Neuroscience Program *(Graduate/Fellowship)* [10422]
Deborah Partridge Wolfe International Fellowships *(Graduate, Undergraduate/Fellowship)* [10820]
Marusia Yaworska Entrance Scholarships *(Graduate/Scholarship)* [10445]

INTERNATIONAL (BY REGION)

Africa

AIMS Long-term Research Grants *(Doctorate, Graduate/Grant)* [916]
AIMS Short-term Research Grants *(Doctorate/Grant)* [917]
ICNL Research Fellowships *(Advanced Professional, Professional development/Fellowship)* [5292]
Wadsworth African Fellowships *(Doctorate/Fellowship)* [10518]

Asia

ICNL Research Fellowships *(Advanced Professional, Professional development/Fellowship)* [5292]
International Society Annual Meeting Travel Grant *(Professional development/Grant)* [408]

Australasia

Our World Underwater Scholarship Society North American Rolex Scholarships *(Undergraduate, Professional development/Scholarship)* [7764]

Caribbean

AABP Student Externship Program *(Undergraduate/Scholarship)* [469]
Caribbean Hotel and Tourism Association Academic Scholarships *(Graduate, Undergraduate/Scholarship)* [2797]
IAF Fellowships *(Doctorate/Fellowship)* [5232]
ICNL Research Fellowships *(Advanced Professional, Professional development/Fellowship)* [5292]
TFI Latin America Media Arts Fund *(Professional development/Grant)* [9796]

East Asia

EAPSI Fellowships *(Doctorate, Graduate/Fellowship)* [7124]

Eurasia

ICNL Research Fellowships *(Advanced Professional, Professional development/Fellowship)* [5292]

Europe

Canadian Institute for Advanced Legal Studies French Language Scholarships *(Graduate, Advanced Professional/Scholarship)* [5149]
CES Pre-Dissertation Research Fellowships *(Graduate/Fellowship)* [3439]
Dalai Lama Trust Graduate Scholarships *(Graduate/Scholarship)* [3508]
Fieldwork Fellowships *(Undergraduate/Award, Fellowship)* [3927]
Google European Doctoral Fellowships *(Doctorate/Fellowship)* [4496]
HAESF Professional Internship Program *(Doctorate/Internship)* [5009]
ICNL Research Fellowships *(Advanced Profes-

sional, *Professional development/Fellowship*) [5292]
Individual Advanced Research Opportunities Program For Master's Students (*Graduate, Master's/Fellowship*) [5381]
International Society Annual Meeting Travel Grant (*Professional development/Grant*) [408]
IREX Individual Advanced Research Opportunities Program For Pre-doctoral Students (*Doctorate/Fellowship*) [5382]
IREX Individual Advanced Research Opportunities Program For Professionals (*Other/Fellowship*) [5383]
IREX Individual Advanced Research Opportunities Program for Postdoctoral Scholars (*Postdoctorate/Fellowship*) [5384]
Monte R. Mitchell Global Scholarships (*Undergraduate/Scholarship*) [168]
Our World Underwater Scholarship Society North American Rolex Scholarships (*Undergraduate, Professional development/Scholarship*) [7764]
Symantec Research Labs Graduate Fellowships (*Doctorate, Graduate/Fellowship*) [9625]
Terra Summer Residency Fellowships (*Master's, Doctorate/Fellowship*) [9684]

Latin America

IAF Fellowships (*Doctorate/Fellowship*) [5232]
ICNL Research Fellowships (*Advanced Professional, Professional development/Fellowship*) [5292]
International Society Annual Meeting Travel Grant (*Professional development/Grant*) [408]

Middle East

ICNL Research Fellowships (*Advanced Professional, Professional development/Fellowship*) [5292]

North America

American Association of Professional Apiculturists Research Scholarships (*Graduate, Undergraduate/Scholarship*) [568]
American Wine Society Educational Foundation Scholarships (*Graduate/Scholarship*) [1528]
Gloria Barron Wilderness Society Scholarship (*Graduate/Scholarship*) [10557]
Chronic Pain Medicine Research Grants (*Professional development/Grant*) [1403]
Dalai Lama Trust Graduate Scholarships (*Graduate/Scholarship*) [3508]
Enkhbaatar Demchig Field Research Fellowship Program (*Undergraduate/Fellowship*) [651]
A.C. Elias, Jr. Irish-American Research Travel Fellowships (*Other/Fellowship*) [1290]
Foundation for the Preservation of Honey Bees Graduate Scholarships (*Graduate/Scholarship*) [4281]
Independent Lubricant Manufacturers Association Scholarships (*Undergraduate/Scholarship*) [5093]
J. Merrill Knapp Research Fellowship (*Undergraduate/Fellowship*) [843]
Carl Koller Memorial Research Grants (*Professional development/Grant*) [1404]
Ilse Hanfmann, George Hanfmann and Machteld Mellink Fellowships (*Doctorate/Fellowship*) [1206]
Orthopaedic Trauma Association Research Grants (*Other/Grant*) [7753]
Our World Underwater Scholarship Society North American Rolex Scholarships (*Undergraduate, Professional development/Scholarship*) [7764]
Galvanize the Future: Edgar K. Schutz Scholarships (*Undergraduate, Graduate/Scholarship*) [838]
Wexner Graduate Fellowships/Davidson Scholars (*Graduate/Fellowship*) [10545]

Northwestern Mexico

Jones-Lovich Grants in Southwestern Herpetology (*Master's, Doctorate/Grant*) [4872]

Pacific Countries

EAPSI Fellowships (*Doctorate, Graduate/Fellowship*) [7124]

Scandinavia

American-Scandinavian Foundation Fellowships to Study in Scandinavia (*Graduate/Fellowship*) [1231]
American-Scandinavian Foundation Grants to Study in Scandinavia (*Graduate/Grant*) [1232]

South America

Dalai Lama Trust Graduate Scholarships (*Graduate/Scholarship*) [3508]
TFI Latin America Media Arts Fund (*Professional development/Grant*) [9796]

Southeast Asia

NIU-CSEAS Foreign Language and Area Studies (FLAS) Fellowships (*Undergraduate, Graduate/Fellowship*) [7518]

U.S. Territories

Birmingham-Southern College Eagle Scout Scholarships (*Undergraduate/Scholarship*) [6920]
BPW Foundation Career Advancement Scholarships (*Undergraduate/Scholarship*) [2422]
Epsilon Tau Pi's Soaring Eagle Scholarships (*Undergraduate/Scholarship*) [6924]
Gaebe Eagle Scout Awards (*Undergraduate/Scholarship*) [6925]
Zenon C.R. Hansen Leadership Scholarships (*Undergraduate/Scholarship*) [6926]
Klingenstein Fellowships in the Neurosciences (*Doctorate, Other/Fellowship*) [5838]
National MS Society New Jersey Metro Chapter Scholarship Program (*Undergraduate/Scholarship*) [7075]
OAS Scholarships for Professional Development - The ABC of Telecommunications (*Professional development/Scholarship*) [7726]
Alice Southworth Schulman, Class of 1954, Simmons Scholarships for Unitarian Universalist Women (*Undergraduate/Scholarship*) [9838]
University of Louisville Eagle Scout Scholarships (*Undergraduate/Scholarship*) [6932]

INTERNATIONAL (BY COUNTRY)

Afghanistan

Sue and Ken Dyer Foundation Travel Scholarships (*Undergraduate/Scholarship*) [4238]

Argentina

CEJIL Communications Internships (*Undergraduate, Graduate/Internship*) [2860]
CEJIL Legal Internships (*Graduate, Professional development/Internship*) [2861]
OAS Academic Scholarships - Graduate (*Graduate/Scholarship*) [7722]
The YFU Americas Scholarships (*Undergraduate/Scholarship*) [10770]

Australia

Abercrombie and Fitch Global Diversity and Leadership Scholar Awards (*Undergraduate/Scholarship*) [7158]
Australian-American Health Policy Fellowships (*Doctorate, Graduate/Fellowship*) [3159]
Dalai Lama Trust Graduate Scholarships (*Graduate/Scholarship*) [3508]
Morgan Stanley Pediatrics Fellowships (*Doctorate, Postdoctorate, Postgraduate, Graduate/Fellowship*) [618]

Austria

Barbara Potter Scholarships (*Professional development/Scholarship*) [1055]

Bangladesh

AIBS Junior Fellowships (*Doctorate/Fellowship*) [898]
AIBS Senior Fellowships (*Doctorate/Fellowship*) [899]

Barbados

OAS Academic Scholarships - Graduate (*Graduate/Scholarship*) [7722]

Bolivia

OAS Academic Scholarships - Graduate (*Graduate/Scholarship*) [7722]

Brazil

CEJIL Communications Internships (*Undergraduate, Graduate/Internship*) [2860]
CEJIL Legal Internships (*Graduate, Professional development/Internship*) [2861]
OAS Academic Scholarships - Graduate (*Graduate/Scholarship*) [7722]
The YFU Americas Scholarships (*Undergraduate/Scholarship*) [10770]

Chile

OAS Academic Scholarships - Graduate (*Graduate/Scholarship*) [7722]

China

Abercrombie and Fitch Global Diversity and Leadership Scholar Awards (*Undergraduate/Scholarship*) [7158]
China Google PhD Fellowships (*Doctorate/Fellowship*) [4494]

Colombia

OAS Academic Scholarships - Graduate (*Graduate/Scholarship*) [7722]

Costa Rica

CEJIL Communications Internships (*Undergraduate, Graduate/Internship*) [2860]
CEJIL Legal Internships (*Graduate, Professional development/Internship*) [2861]
OAS Academic Scholarships - Graduate (*Graduate/Scholarship*) [7722]
Rowe Family Fellowships (*Graduate/Fellowship*) [7742]

Cyprus

Olivia James Traveling Fellowships (*Professional development/Fellowship*) [1608]

Denmark

Edith and Arnold N. Bodtker Grants (*Undergraduate, Graduate/Grant, Internship*) [3522]

Dominican Republic

OAS Academic Scholarships - Graduate (*Graduate/Scholarship*) [7722]

Ecuador

OAS Academic Scholarships - Graduate (*Graduate/Scholarship*) [7722]
The YFU Americas Scholarships (*Undergraduate/Scholarship*) [10770]

INTERNATIONAL

Egypt

ARCE Funded Fellowships *(Doctorate, Postdoctorate/Fellowship)* [1195]
ARCE Research Associates Fellowships *(Doctorate, Postdoctorate, Professional development/Fellowship)* [1196]

El Salvador

OAS Academic Scholarships - Graduate *(Graduate/Scholarship)* [7722]

France

Kennedy T. Friend Scholarships *(Graduate, Undergraduate)* [325]
Newberry Library/Ecole Nationale des Chartes Exchange Fellowships *(Graduate/Fellowship)* [7420]
Pasteur Foundation Postdoctoral Fellowships *(Postdoctorate/Fellowship)* [7899]
Terra Foundation Postdoctoral Teaching Fellowships at the Institut National d'Histoire de l'Art, Paris *(Postdoctorate/Fellowship)* [9682]

Germany

Herzog August Bibliothek Wolfenbüttel Fellowships *(Postdoctorate/Fellowship)* [7409]
Leo Baeck Institute - DAAD Fellowships *(Doctorate/Fellowship)* [3602]
DAAD Learn German in Germany Grants *(Doctorate/Grant)* [3603]
DAAD Study Scholarship Awards *(Graduate/Scholarship)* [3604]
DAAD Undergraduate Scholarship Program *(Undergraduate/Scholarship)* [3605]
The Christoph Daniel Ebeling Fellowships *(Postdoctorate, Postgraduate/Fellowship)* [437]
European College of Liberal Arts Scholarships *(Undergraduate/Scholarship)* [9981]
Faculty Research Visit Grants *(Doctorate/Grant, Award)* [3606]
Hochschulsommerkurse *(Undergraduate/Grant, Award)* [3608]
Intensive Language Course Grants *(Doctorate/Grant)* [3609]
McCloy Fellowships in Agriculture *(Professional development/Fellowship)* [727]
McCloy Fellowships in Environmental Policy *(Professional development/Fellowship)* [728]
McCloy Fellowships in Journalism *(Professional development/Fellowship)* [729]
McCloy Fellowships in Urban Affairs *(Professional development/Fellowship)* [730]
Study Scholarships for Artists or Musicians *(Graduate/Scholarship)* [3610]

Ghana

ACLS African Humanities Fellowships *(Postdoctorate/Fellowship)* [734]
GCABC Youth Scholarship Awards *(Undergraduate/Scholarship)* [4419]
Next Generation Social Sciences in Africa: Doctoral Dissertation Completion Fellowships *(Doctorate/Fellowship)* [9057]
Next Generation Social Sciences in Africa: Doctoral Dissertation Proposal Fellowships *(Doctorate/Fellowship)* [9058]
Next Generation Social Sciences in Africa: Doctoral Dissertation Research Fellowship *(Doctorate/Fellowship)* [9059]

Greece

Olivia James Traveling Fellowships *(Professional development/Fellowship)* [1608]

Grenada

OAS Academic Scholarships - Graduate *(Graduate/Scholarship)* [7722]

Guam

Thomas R. Camp Scholarships *(Graduate/Scholarship)* [1486]
Larson Aquatic Research Support Scholarships (LARS) *(Graduate/Scholarship)* [1490]

India

Malayalee Engineers Association Scholarships *(Undergraduate/Fellowship)* [6225]

Iran

AIIrS Persian Language Study in Tehran Fellowships *(Graduate, Master's, Doctorate/Fellowship)* [913]
Short-term Senior Fellowships in Iranian Studies *(Professional development/Fellowship)* [914]

Ireland

A.C. Elias, Jr. Irish-American Research Travel Fellowships *(Other/Fellowship)* [1290]
George J. Mitchell Postgraduate Scholarships *(Postgraduate/Scholarship)* [6749]
George J. Mitchell Scholarships *(Postgraduate/Scholarship)* [10349]

Israel

Awards for Judaic Studies and/or Studies in Israel *(Undergraduate, Postgraduate/Scholarship)* [5591]
Jenny Panitch Beckow Memorial Scholarships Israel *(Graduate/Scholarship)* [5570]
Bernice and Gordon Brown Scholarships *(Undergraduate/Scholarship)* [5573]
Harry Feldman Memorial Scholarships *(Undergraduate/Scholarship)* [5576]
Jack Gitlitz CA Memorial Scholarships for Study in Israel *(Undergraduate/Scholarship)* [5577]
Jane R. Glaser Scholarships *(Undergraduate/Scholarship)* [1476]
Mitchell Karper Memorial Scholarships *(Undergraduate/Scholarship)* [5579]
Canadian Zionist Federation - Dr. Leon Aryeh Kronitz Scholarships *(Undergraduate, Graduate/Scholarship)* [2640]
Hushy Lipton Memorial Scholarship Funds *(Undergraduate, Graduate, Postgraduate/Scholarship)* [2641]
Morris M. Pulver Scholarship Funds *(Undergraduate, Graduate, Postgraduate/Scholarship)* [2642]
Rothberg International School Graduate Merit Scholarships *(Graduate, Master's/Scholarship)* [2643]
Joel A. Weinstein Memorial Scholarships *(Postgraduate, Undergraduate/Scholarship)* [5594]

Italy

Aaron Copland Bogliasco Fellowships in Music *(Professional development/Fellowship)* [2325]
Leo Biaggi de Blasys Bogliasco Fellowships *(Professional development/Fellowship)* [2326]
John Burroughs Bogliasco Fellowships *(Professional development/Fellowship)* [2328]
Olivia James Traveling Fellowships *(Professional development/Fellowship)* [1608]
Jerome Robbins Bogliasco Fellowships in Dance *(Professional development/Fellowship)* [2329]
Kress/AAR Fellowships *(Professional development/Fellowship)* [1855]
New Museum Bogliasco Fellowship in Visual Art *(Professional development/Fellowship)* [2330]
Roger Sessions Memorial Bogliasco Fellowships in Music *(Professional development/Fellowship)* [2331]
Helen M. Woodruff Fellowships *(Professional development/Fellowship)* [1612]

Jamaica

OAS Academic Scholarships - Graduate *(Graduate/Scholarship)* [7722]

Japan

Abe Fellowship Program *(Professional development/Fellowship)* [9051]
Crown Prince Akihito Scholarship Foundation *(Graduate/Scholarship)* [5535]
International Affairs Fellowships in Japan (IAF-J) *(Professional development/Fellowship)* [3447]
Japan Foundation, New York Doctoral Fellowship Program *(Doctorate/Fellowship)* [5537]
Japan Foundation, New York Long-Term Research Fellowship Program *(Professional development/Fellowship)* [5538]
Japan Foundation, New York Short-Term Fellowship Program *(Professional development/Fellowship)* [5539]
Japan Society for the Promotion of Science Fellowship Program *(Doctorate/Fellowship)* [9055]
KCC-JEE Graduate Fellowships *(Graduate/Fellowship)* [5855]

Jordan

ACOR-CAORC Pre-Doctorate Fellowships *(Graduate, Doctorate/Fellowship)* [654]
Pierre and Patricia Bikai Fellowships *(Graduate/Fellowship)* [655]
Bert and Sally de Vries Fellowships *(Undergraduate, Graduate/Fellowship)* [656]
Jennifer C. Groot Memorial Fellowships *(Undergraduate, Graduate/Fellowship)* [657]
Harrell Family Fellowships *(Undergraduate, Graduate/Fellowship)* [658]
Burton MacDonald and Rosemarie Sampson Fellowships *(Undergraduate, Graduate/Fellowship)* [659]
Kenneth W. Russell Memorial Fellowships *(Undergraduate, Graduate/Fellowship)* [661]
James A. Sauer Memorial Fellowships *(Graduate/Fellowship)* [662]

Mexico

Thomas R. Camp Scholarships *(Graduate/Scholarship)* [1486]
Dwight D. Gardner Scholarships *(Undergraduate/Scholarship)* [5186]
Geological Society of America Graduate Student Research Grants *(Doctorate, Graduate/Grant)* [4364]
Gilbreth Memorial Fellowships *(Graduate/Scholarship, Fellowship)* [5187]
Larson Aquatic Research Support Scholarships (LARS) *(Graduate/Scholarship)* [1490]
John J. McKetta Undergraduate Scholarships *(Undergraduate/Scholarship)* [905]
Marvin Mundel Memorial Scholarships *(Undergraduate/Scholarship)* [5192]
OAS Academic Scholarships - Graduate *(Graduate/Scholarship)* [7722]
A.O. Putnam Memorial Scholarships *(Undergraduate/Scholarship)* [5193]
Ronald L. Schmied Scholarships *(Other, Undergraduate/Scholarship)* [4686]
TFI Latin America Media Arts Fund *(Professional development/Grant)* [9796]
UC MEXUS-CONACYT Postdoctoral Research Fellowships *(Postdoctorate/Fellowship)* [10118]
United Parcel Service Scholarships for Female Students *(Undergraduate/Scholarship)* [5195]
United Parcel Service Scholarships for Minority Students *(Undergraduate/Scholarship)* [5196]
Abel Wolman Fellowships *(Doctorate/Fellowship)* [1492]

Mongolia

ACMS Library Fellowships *(Graduate, Other/Fellowship)* [649]
ACMS U.S.-Mongolia Field Research Fellowship Program *(Graduate, Undergraduate/Fellowship)* [650]
Enkhbaatar Demchig Field Research Fellowship Program *(Undergraduate/Fellowship)* [651]

Nigeria

ACLS African Humanities Fellowships *(Postdoctorate/Fellowship)* [734]
Next Generation Social Sciences in Africa: Doctoral Dissertation Completion Fellowships *(Doctorate/Fellowship)* [9057]
Next Generation Social Sciences in Africa: Doctoral Dissertation Proposal Fellowships *(Doctorate/Fellowship)* [9058]
Next Generation Social Sciences in Africa: Doctoral Dissertation Research Fellowship *(Doctorate/Fellowship)* [9059]
NWAG Nigeria Scholarships *(Undergraduate/Scholarship)* [7432]

Norway

Sons of Norway Foundation Scholarships to Oslo International Summer School *(Undergraduate/Scholarship)* [9346]

Pakistan

Dr. Feroz Ahmed Memorial Educational Post-Graduate Scholarships *(Doctorate, Postgraduate/Scholarship)* [8965]
AIPS Long Term Fellowships *(Doctorate, Postdoctorate/Fellowship)* [919]
AIPS Post-Doctoral Fellowships *(Postdoctorate/Fellowship)* [920]
AIPS Pre-Doctoral Fellowships *(Doctorate, Graduate/Fellowship)* [921]
AIPS Short Term Fellowships *(Doctorate, Postdoctorate/Fellowship)* [922]

Panama

OAS Academic Scholarships - Graduate *(Graduate/Scholarship)* [7722]
A. Stanley Rand Fellowships Program *(Undergraduate, Doctorate, Postdoctorate/Fellowship)* [9037]
Earl S. Tupper 3-year Postdoctoral Fellowships in Tropical Biology *(Postdoctorate/Fellowship)* [9039]

Peru

William L. Brown Fellowships *(Graduate/Fellowship)* [7735]
David and Deborah Clark Fellowships *(Graduate/Fellowship)* [7736]
Rexford Daubenmire Fellowships *(Graduate/Fellowship)* [7737]
Dole Food Fellowships *(Graduate/Fellowship)* [7738]
Emily P. Foster Fellowships *(Graduate/Fellowship)* [7739]
OAS Academic Scholarships - Graduate *(Graduate/Scholarship)* [7722]
Peace Frogs Fellowships *(Graduate/Fellowship)* [7741]
Lillian and Murray Slatkin Fellowships *(Graduate/Fellowship)* [7743]
F. Christian and Betty Thompson Fellowships *(Graduate/Fellowship)* [7745]

Portugal

Archaeology of Portugal Fellowships *(Professional development/Fellowship)* [1605]

Puerto Rico

Horatio Alger National Scholarships *(Undergraduate/Scholarship)* [4948]
Army Health Professions Scholarships Program *(Professional development/Scholarship)* [9878]
Buick Achievers Scholarship Program *(Undergraduate/Scholarship)* [4359]
Thomas R. Camp Scholarships *(Graduate/Scholarship)* [1486]
CHCI Scholarships *(Undergraduate, Graduate/Scholarship)* [3354]
HACU/JCPenny Leadership Excellence Scholarships *(Undergraduate, Graduate/Scholarship)* [4886]
HACU/KIA Motors America, Inc. Scholarships *(Undergraduate, Graduate/Scholarship)* [4887]
Hispanic Association of Colleges and Universities Scholarships *(Undergraduate/Scholarship)* [4890]
Larson Aquatic Research Support Scholarships (LARS) *(Graduate/Scholarship)* [1490]
Peermusic Latin Scholarship *(Undergraduate/Scholarship)* [2320]
SHPE Dissertation Scholarship *(Doctorate/Scholarship)* [9130]
SHPE Professional Scholarship *(Master's, Doctorate/Scholarship)* [9131]

South Africa

ACLS African Humanities Fellowships *(Postdoctorate/Fellowship)* [734]
Next Generation Social Sciences in Africa: Doctoral Dissertation Completion Fellowships *(Doctorate/Fellowship)* [9057]
Next Generation Social Sciences in Africa: Doctoral Dissertation Proposal Fellowships *(Doctorate/Fellowship)* [9058]
Next Generation Social Sciences in Africa: Doctoral Dissertation Research Fellowship *(Doctorate/Fellowship)* [9059]

South Korea

Abercrombie and Fitch Global Diversity and Leadership Scholar Awards *(Undergraduate/Scholarship)* [7158]

Sri Lanka

AISLS Fellowships Program *(Doctorate/Fellowship)* [930]

Sweden

Lilly Lorenzen Scholarships *(Undergraduate/Scholarship)* [1470]
Malmberg Scholarships *(Undergraduate/Scholarship)* [1471]

Switzerland

Medicus Student Exchange Scholarships *(Graduate, Undergraduate/Scholarship)* [9619]

Tanzania

ACLS African Humanities Fellowships *(Postdoctorate/Fellowship)* [734]
Godparents for Tanzania Scholarship *(Undergraduate/Scholarship)* [4464]
Next Generation Social Sciences in Africa: Doctoral Dissertation Completion Fellowships *(Doctorate/Fellowship)* [9057]
Next Generation Social Sciences in Africa: Doctoral Dissertation Proposal Fellowships *(Doctorate/Fellowship)* [9058]
Next Generation Social Sciences in Africa: Doctoral Dissertation Research Fellowship *(Doctorate/Fellowship)* [9059]

Trinidad and Tobago

OAS Academic Scholarships - Graduate *(Graduate/Scholarship)* [7722]

Turkey

ARIT Fellowships in the Humanities and Social Sciences in Turkey *(Postdoctorate, Graduate/Fellowship)* [1201]
ARIT National Endowment for the Humanities Advanced Fellowships for Research in Turkey *(Postdoctorate/Fellowship)* [1202]
ARIT Summer Fellowships for Intensive Advanced Turkish Language Study *(Graduate, Undergraduate/Fellowship)* [1203]
Institute of Turkish Studies Post-Doctoral Summer Travel-Research Grants *(Postdoctorate/Grant)* [5224]
Institute of Turkish Studies Sabbatical Research Grants *(Other/Grant)* [5225]
Institute of Turkish Studies Summer Language Study Grants in Turkey *(Graduate/Grant)* [5226]

Olivia James Traveling Fellowships *(Professional development/Fellowship)* [1608]

Uganda

ACLS African Humanities Fellowships *(Postdoctorate/Fellowship)* [734]
Next Generation Social Sciences in Africa: Doctoral Dissertation Completion Fellowships *(Doctorate/Fellowship)* [9057]
Next Generation Social Sciences in Africa: Doctoral Dissertation Proposal Fellowships *(Doctorate/Fellowship)* [9058]
Next Generation Social Sciences in Africa: Doctoral Dissertation Research Fellowship *(Doctorate/Fellowship)* [9059]

Ukraine

Alberta Ukrainian Centennial Commemorative Scholarships *(Graduate/Scholarship)* [10440]
ALIS International Education Awards - Ukraine *(Undergraduate/Scholarship)* [265]
Mychajlo Dmytrenko Fine Arts Foundation Scholarships *(Undergraduate/Scholarship)* [9980]

United Arab Emirates

Abercrombie and Fitch Global Diversity and Leadership Scholar Awards *(Undergraduate/Scholarship)* [7158]

United Kingdom

Abercrombie and Fitch Global Diversity and Leadership Scholar Awards *(Undergraduate/Scholarship)* [7158]
Baker and McKenzie Graduate Legal Studies Scholarships *(Graduate, Professional development/Scholarship)* [2176]
Hilda E. Bretzlaff Foundation Scholarships *(Undergraduate/Scholarship, Grant)* [2363]
The Churchill Scholarships *(Postgraduate/Scholarship)* [2940]
Gates Cambridge Scholarships *(Graduate, Master's, Doctorate, Postgraduate, Postdoctorate/Scholarship)* [6746]
Janelia Farm Graduate Program *(Graduate/Award)* [4978]
Mackenzie King Travelling Scholarships *(Graduate/Scholarship)* [6367]
London Goodenough Association of Canada Scholarships *(Graduate/Scholarship)* [6105]
Right Honourable Paul Martin Sr. Scholarships *(Graduate/Scholarship)* [5150]
George J. Mitchell Postgraduate Scholarships *(Postgraduate/Scholarship)* [6749]
George J. Mitchell Scholarships *(Postgraduate/Scholarship)* [10349]
MSGC Undergraduate-Under-Represented Minority Fellowship Program *(Undergraduate/Fellowship)* [6485]
Saint Andrews Scholarships *(Undergraduate/Scholarship)* [8670]
Joseph S. Steinberg Emerging Jewish Filmmaker Fellowships *(Undergraduate, Graduate/Fellowship)* [2856]
Terra Foundation Postdoctoral Teaching Fellowships at the Courtauld Institute of Art, London *(Postdoctorate/Fellowship)* [9681]
U.S.-U.K. Young Investigator Exchange Fellowship *(Postdoctorate/Fellowship)* [376]
USA/USA-Ukramerazha Scholarships *(Undergraduate/Scholarship)* [9982]

Uruguay

OAS Academic Scholarships - Graduate *(Graduate/Scholarship)* [7722]
The YFU Americas Scholarships *(Undergraduate/Scholarship)* [10770]

Venezuela

The YFU Americas Scholarships *(Undergraduate/Scholarship)* [10770]

Special Recipient Index

This index arranges awards according to qualifying factors related to membership or affiliation. Awards are listed under all appropriate headings. Each citation is followed by the study level and award type, which appear in parentheses. Numbers following the parenthetical information indicate the book entry number for particular awards, not page numbers.

African American

AAMFT Minority Fellowships *(Doctorate, Graduate/Fellowship)* [538]
Acoustical Society of America Minority Fellowships *(Graduate/Fellowship)* [52]
Actuarial Diversity Scholarship *(Undergraduate/Scholarship)* [60]
Affirmative Action Student Scholarship Mini-Grant Travel Awards *(Undergraduate, Master's, Doctorate/Grant)* [30]
AFPE Pre-Doctoral Fellowships in Pharmaceutical Sciences for Underrepresented Minorities *(Doctorate, Graduate/Fellowship)* [828]
African American Network - Carolinas Scholarship Fund *(Undergraduate/Scholarship)* [4174]
AIChE Minority Scholarship Awards for College Students *(Undergraduate/Scholarship)* [903]
AIChE Minority Scholarship Awards for Incoming College Freshmen *(Undergraduate/Scholarship)* [904]
Air Products and Chemicals, Inc. Scholarships *(Undergraduate/Scholarship)* [1975]
Emma and Meloid Algood Tuition Scholarships *(Graduate, Undergraduate/Scholarship)* [6718]
AMA Foundation Minority Scholars Awards *(Graduate/Scholarship)* [989]
American Association for Cancer Research Minority Scholar Awards *(Graduate/Award)* [472]
AMS/Industry Minority Scholarships *(Undergraduate/Scholarship)* [1000]
ANA Multicultural Excellence Scholarship Fund (MAIP) *(Graduate, Undergraduate/Internship)* [456]
APS Scholarships for Minority Undergraduate Physics Majors *(Undergraduate/Scholarship)* [7138]
APSA Minority Fellows Program *(Doctorate/Fellowship)* [1113]
APTA Minority Scholarships - Faculty Development Scholarships *(Postdoctorate/Scholarship)* [1096]
APTA Minority Scholarships - Physical Therapist Assistant Students *(Undergraduate/Scholarship)* [1097]
APTA Minority Scholarships - Physical Therapist Students *(Undergraduate/Scholarship)* [1098]
ASA Minority Fellowship Program (ASA MFP) *(Graduate, Doctorate, Professional development/Fellowship)* [1445]
ASGP Graduate Research Fellowships *(Graduate/Fellowship)* [223]
AWG Minority Scholarships *(Undergraduate/Scholarship)* [2093]
Michael Baker Corp. Scholarship for Diversity in Engineering *(Undergraduate/Scholarship)* [1976]
Ballard Family Foundation Scholarships *(Undergraduate/Scholarship)* [8688]
Dr. Johnella Banks Memorial Scholarships *(Undergraduate/Scholarship)* [2298]
Dr. Joyce Beckett Scholarships *(Graduate, Undergraduate/Scholarship)* [6719]
Bill Bernbach Diversity Scholarships *(Undergraduate/Scholarship)* [457]
Black Men Building Resources Scholarships *(Undergraduate/Scholarship)* [4576]
F.A. and Charlotte Blount Scholarships *(Undergraduate/Scholarship)* [10571]
Ellis J. Bonner Scholarships *(Graduate/Scholarship)* [6754]
Leon Bradley Scholarship Program *(Undergraduate/Scholarship)* [575]
Selena Danette Brown Book Scholarships *(Graduate, Undergraduate/Scholarship)* [6720]
Ron Brown Scholars Program *(Undergraduate/Scholarship)* [2387]
Robert A. Catlin/David W. Long Memorial Fellowships *(Graduate/Fellowship)* [1104]
CBC Spouses Education Scholarship Fund *(Graduate, Undergraduate/Scholarship)* [3345]
CBCF Congressional Fellows Program *(Other/Fellowship)* [3348]
CIGNA Healthcare Graduate Scholarships *(Graduate/Scholarship)* [6957]
CIGNA Healthcare Undergraduate Scholarships *(Undergraduate/Scholarship)* [6958]
CSF McCall Educational Scholarships *(Undergraduate/Scholarship)* [2971]
Ruth DeMoss Scholarships *(Undergraduate/Scholarship)* [8701]
Development Fund for Black Students in Science and Technology Scholarships *(Undergraduate/Scholarship)* [3612]
Joseph M. Dorgan Scholarship *(Undergraduate/Scholarship)* [3666]
Dunbar Heritage Scholarships *(Undergraduate/Scholarship)* [9427]
Evans and Petree Law Firm Scholarship *(Undergraduate/Scholarship)* [10159]
FICPA Educational Foundation 1040K Race Scholarships *(Undergraduate/Scholarship)* [4098]
Florida Education Fund McKnight Doctoral Fellowships *(Graduate/Fellowship)* [4085]
Andrew Foster Scholarships *(Undergraduate/Scholarship)* [6815]
John Hope Franklin Dissertation Fellowships *(Doctorate/Fellowship)* [1080]
Fraser Stryker Diversity Scholarships *(Undergraduate/Scholarship)* [4293]
FTE Dissertation Fellowships *(Graduate, Doctorate/Fellowship)* [4153]
FTE Doctoral Fellowships *(Doctorate, Graduate/Fellowship)* [4154]
Sam Gallant Memorial Scholarships *(Graduate, Undergraduate/Scholarship)* [1643]
The Gates Millennium Scholars *(Undergraduate/Scholarship)* [4903]
Florence S. Gaynor Scholarships *(Graduate/Scholarship)* [6755]
GFOA Minorities in Government Finance Scholarship *(Graduate, Undergraduate/Scholarship)* [4502]
HSF/Marathon Oil College Scholarship Program *(Undergraduate/Scholarship)* [4905]
The Hyatt Hotels Fund For Minority Lodging Management Students *(Undergraduate/Scholarship)* [860]
International Association of Black Actuaries Scholarships *(Undergraduate/Scholarship)* [5248]
Jack and Jill of America National Scholarships Program *(Undergraduate/Scholarship)* [5490]
Ruth E. Jenkins Scholarships *(Undergraduate/Scholarship)* [8709]
E.J. Josey Scholarships *(Graduate/Scholarship, Award)* [2296]
Martin Luther King Law Scholarship *(Undergraduate/Scholarship)* [3680]
KPMG Foundation Minority Accounting Doctoral Scholarships *(Doctorate/Scholarship)* [5885]
The Lagrant Foundation - Graduate Students Scholarships *(Graduate/Scholarship)* [5900]
The Lagrant Foundation - Undergraduate Students Scholarships *(Undergraduate/Scholarship)* [5901]
Herbert Lehman Education Scholarships *(Undergraduate/Scholarship)* [6646]
LITA/LSSI Minority Scholarships *(Graduate/Scholarship)* [6072]
LITA/OCLC Minority Scholarships *(Graduate/Scholarship)* [6073]
CH2M - Willie T. Loud Scholarships *(Undergraduate, Graduate/Scholarship)* [6959]
Dr. Julianne Malveaux Scholarships *(Undergraduate/Scholarship)* [6762]
Many Voices Fellowships *(Other/Fellowship)* [8153]
Howard Mayer Brown Fellowship *(Graduate/Fellowship)* [1021]
Medical Library Association Scholarships for Minority Students *(Graduate/Scholarship)* [6389]
Minority Teachers of Illinois Scholarships (MTI) *(Undergraduate/Scholarship)* [5078]
MLA/NLM Spectrum Scholarship Program *(Undergraduate/Scholarship)* [6391]
Dr. Blanca Moore-Velez Woman of Substance Scholarships *(Undergraduate/Scholarship)* [6763]
Archie Motley Memorial Scholarships for Minority Students *(Graduate/Scholarship)* [6517]
NABA National Scholarship Program *(Graduate, Undergraduate/Scholarship)* [6716]
NACA Multicultural Professional Development Grant *(Undergraduate, Graduate, Professional development/Grant)* [6729]
NANBPWC National Scholarships *(Undergraduate/Scholarship)* [6764]
National Black Deaf Advocate Scholarships *(Graduate, Undergraduate/Scholarship)* [6816]
National Dental Hygienists' Association Scholarships *(Undergraduate/Scholarship)* [6916]
National Medical Fellowships Need-Based Scholarships *(Undergraduate/Scholarship)* [7061]
OAH-IEHS Huggins-Quarles Dissertation Awards *(Doctorate, Graduate/Grant)* [7718]
Operation JumpStart Scholarships *(Graduate/Scholarship)* [458]
Pearman Family Scholarships *(Undergraduate/Scholarship)* [8720]
PlasticPlace Young Entrepreneurs Scholarships *(Undergraduate/Scholarship)* [8148]
Judith McManus Price Scholarships *(Undergraduate, Graduate/Scholarship)* [1106]
PRSA Diversity Multicultural Scholarships *(Undergraduate/Scholarship)* [8378]
Haynes Rice Scholarships *(Graduate/Scholarship)* [6756]
Ronald McDonald House Charities African American Future Achievers Scholarships *(Undergraduate/Scholarship)* [8639]

ASIAN AMERICAN

Carl A. Scott Book Scholarships (Undergraduate/Scholarship) [3456]
Alfred P. Sloan Foundation Graduate Scholarships - Sloan Minority Ph.D. Program (Doctorate/Scholarship) [6684]
Robert Toigo Foundation Fellowships (Master's/Fellowship) [9747]
Marie Trahan/Susman Godfrey Scholarships (Undergraduate/Scholarship) [9820]
Jacki Tuckfield Memorial Graduate Business Scholarship Fund (Doctorate, Graduate, Master's/Scholarship) [6453]
The UCSD Black Alumni Scholarship for Arts and Humanities (Undergraduate/Scholarship) [8736]
The UCSD Black Alumni Scholarships for Engineering, Mathematics and Science (Undergraduate/Scholarship) [8737]
UNCF/Merck Graduate Science Research Dissertation Fellowships (Graduate/Fellowship) [6426, 9862]
UNCF/Merck Postdoctoral Science Research Fellowships (Postdoctorate/Fellowship) [6427, 9863]
Valuing Diversity PhD Scholarships (Doctorate/Scholarship) [983]
Francis X. Weninger Scholarships (Undergraduate/Scholarship) [10726]
White Collar Defense Diversity Scholarships (Undergraduate, Advanced Professional/Scholarship) [8239]
Ann Cook Whitman Washington, DC Scholarships (Undergraduate/Scholarship) [4417]
Leon Williams Scholarships (Undergraduate/Scholarship) [8741]
Cenie Jomo Williams Tuition Scholarships (Graduate, Undergraduate/Scholarship) [6721]
Hugh and Helen Wood Nepales Scholarships (Undergraduate/Scholarship) [2233]
Woodrow Wilson-Rockefeller Brothers Fund Fellowships for Aspiring Teachers of Color (Undergraduate/Fellowship) [10682]
L and T Woolfolk Memorial Scholarships (Undergraduate/Scholarship) [3026]
Xerox Technical Minority Scholarships (Graduate, Undergraduate/Scholarship) [10737]
Youth Empowerment Summit Scholarships (Undergraduate/Scholarship) [6817]

Asian American

AAMFT Minority Fellowships (Doctorate, Graduate/Fellowship) [538]
Kyutaro and Yasuo Abiko Memorial Scholarships (Undergraduate/Scholarship) [5547]
Affirmative Action Student Scholarship Mini-Grant Travel Awards (Undergraduate, Master's, Doctorate/Grant) [30]
Air Products and Chemicals, Inc. Scholarships (Undergraduate/Scholarship) [1975]
ANA Multicultural Excellence Scholarship Fund (MAIP) (Graduate, Undergraduate/Internship) [456]
Anheuser-Busch NAPABA Law Foundation Presidential Scholarships (Undergraduate/Scholarship) [6703]
APABA-SV Scholarships (Advanced Professional/Scholarship) [1786]
APALA Scholarship Award (Doctorate, Master's/Scholarship) [1788]
APIASF Scholarships (Undergraduate/Scholarship) [1792]
APSA Minority Fellows Program (Doctorate/Fellowship) [1113]
APTA Minority Scholarships - Faculty Development Scholarships (Postdoctorate/Scholarship) [1096]
APTA Minority Scholarships - Physical Therapist Assistant Students (Undergraduate/Scholarship) [1097]
APTA Minority Scholarships - Physical Therapist Students (Undergraduate/Scholarship) [1098]
ASA Minority Fellowship Program (ASA MFP) (Graduate, Doctorate, Professional development/Fellowship) [1445]
Michael Baker Corp. Scholarship for Diversity in Engineering (Undergraduate/Scholarship) [1976]
Leon Bradley Scholarship Program (Undergraduate/Scholarship) [575]

Calvin Alumni Association-New Jersey Scholarships (Undergraduate/Scholarship) [2498]
Calvin Alumni Association-Washington, Lynden Scholarships (Undergraduate/Scholarship) [2505]
Alice Yuriko Endo Memorial Scholarships (Undergraduate/Scholarship) [5549]
Fraser Stryker Diversity Scholarships (Undergraduate/Scholarship) [4293]
The Gates Millennium Scholars (Undergraduate/Scholarship) [4903]
GFOA Minorities in Government Finance Scholarship (Graduate, Undergraduate/Scholarship) [4502]
HANA Scholarships (Undergraduate, Graduate, Doctorate/Scholarship) [9852]
Thomas T. Hayashi Memorial Scholarships (Graduate/Scholarship) [5550]
HSF/Marathon Oil College Scholarship Program (Undergraduate/Scholarship) [4905]
The Hyatt Hotels Fund For Minority Lodging Management Students (Undergraduate/Scholarship) [860]
Magoichi and Shizuko Kato Memorial Scholarships (Graduate, Master's, Doctorate/Scholarship) [5552]
Sam and Florice Kuwahara Memorial Scholarship (Undergraduate/Scholarship) [5553]
The Lagrant Foundation - Graduate Students Scholarships (Graduate/Scholarship) [5900]
The Lagrant Foundation - Undergraduate Students Scholarships (Undergraduate/Scholarship) [5901]
Las Vegas Chinatown Scholarships (Undergraduate/Scholarship) [8352]
LITA/LSSI Minority Scholarships (Graduate/Scholarship) [6072]
LITA/OCLC Minority Scholarships (Graduate/Scholarship) [6073]
Howard Mayer Brown Fellowship (Graduate/Fellowship) [1021]
Medical Library Association Scholarships for Minority Students (Graduate/Scholarship) [6389]
Minority Teachers of Illinois Scholarships (MTI) (Undergraduate/Scholarship) [5078]
MLA/NLM Spectrum Scholarship Program (Undergraduate/Scholarship) [6391]
Archie Motley Memorial Scholarships for Minority Students (Graduate/Scholarship) [6517]
NACA Multicultural Professional Development Grant (Undergraduate, Graduate, Professional development/Grant) [6729]
Operation JumpStart Scholarships (Graduate/Scholarship) [458]
PlasticPlace Young Entrepreneurs Scholarships (Undergraduate/Scholarship) [8148]
PRSA Diversity Multicultural Scholarships (Undergraduate/Scholarship) [8378]
Rosa Quezada Memorial Education Scholarships (Undergraduate/Scholarship) [3361]
Ronald McDonald House Charities Scholarships in Asia (Undergraduate/Scholarship) [8642]
SCCLA Fellowships (Graduate/Fellowship) [9398]
SCCLA Scholarships (Graduate/Scholarship) [9399]
Carl A. Scott Book Scholarships (Undergraduate/Scholarship) [3456]
Dr. Kiyoshi Sonoda Memorial Scholarships (Graduate, Master's, Doctorate/Scholarship) [5559]
Taiwanese American Community Scholarships (Undergraduate/Scholarship) [9634]
Robert Toigo Foundation Fellowships (Master's/Fellowship) [9747]
Woodrow Wilson-Rockefeller Brothers Fund Fellowships for Aspiring Teachers of Color (Undergraduate/Fellowship) [10682]
Xerox Technical Minority Scholarships (Graduate, Undergraduate/Scholarship) [10737]
Minoru Yasui Memorial Scholarships (Graduate, Master's, Doctorate/Scholarship) [5560]

Association membership

4th Infantry Division Association Memorial Scholarships (All/Scholarship) [6670]
AAA Postdoctoral Fellowship Program (Postdoctorate/Fellowship) [460]
AAAA Scholarship Program (Undergraduate, Graduate/Scholarship) [1710]

AAACN Education Scholarships (Undergraduate/Scholarship) [386]
AAACN Research Grants (Undergraduate/Grant) [387]
AAACN Scholarships (Undergraduate/Scholarship) [388]
AABP Bovine Veterinary Student Recognition Awards (Undergraduate/Scholarship) [467]
AABP Education Grants (Undergraduate/Grant) [468]
AACD Dentist Fellowships (Professional development/Fellowship) [405]
AACD Laboratory Fellowships (Professional development/Fellowship) [406]
AACN Continuing Professional Development Scholarships (Advanced Professional, Other/Scholarship) [490]
AACPDM Student Scholarships (Professional development/Scholarship) [399]
AACPDM Transformative Practice Grants (Professional development/Grant) [400]
AACR Scholar-in-Training Awards: Other Conferences and Meetings (Graduate, Postdoctorate, Professional development/Grant) [471]
AACT Junior Investigator Research Grants (Professional development/Grant) [402]
AACT Toxicology Trainee Research Grants (Professional development/Grant) [403]
AAEP Foundation Past Presidents' Research Fellowships (Graduate, Professional development/Scholarship) [496]
AAG Dissertation Research Grants (Doctorate/Grant) [1829]
AAI Careers in Immunology Fellowship Program (Graduate, Doctorate, Postdoctorate/Fellowship) [506]
AAI Public Policy Fellows Program (PPFP) (Doctorate, Postdoctorate/Fellowship) [507]
AAIDD Fellowship (Advanced Professional, Professional development/Fellowship) [511]
AAJ Trial Advocacy Scholarships (Undergraduate/Scholarship) [515]
AALL Leadership Academy Grants (Professional development/Grant) [519]
AALL Minority Leadership Development Award (Graduate/Award) [520]
AALL Research Funds (Professional development/Grant) [521]
AALL Scholarships for Continuing Education Classes (Postgraduate/Scholarship) [522]
AALL Technical Services SIS Active Member Grant (Professional development/Grant) [523]
AALL Technical Services SIS Experienced Member General Grant (Professional development/Grant) [524]
AALL Technical Services SIS Leadership Academy Grant (Professional development/Grant) [525]
AALL Technical Services SIS Management Institute Grant (Professional development/Grant) [526]
AALL Technical Services SIS New Member General Grant (Professional development/Grant) [527]
AAMA Houston Chapter Health Training Scholarships (Other/Scholarship) [1601]
AAMC Foundation Engagement Program for International Curators Grants (Advanced Professional, Professional development/Grant) [1854]
AAN Clinical Research Training Fellowships (Other/Fellowship) [410]
AAN Medical Student Summer Research Scholarships (Graduate/Scholarship) [412]
AAOHN Professional Development Scholarships - Continuing Education (Other/Scholarship) [551]
AAS-American Historical Print Collectors Society Fellowships (Doctorate/Fellowship) [428]
AAS-American Society for Eighteenth Century Studies Fellowships (Postdoctorate/Fellowship) [429]
AAS Fellowships for Creative and Performing Artists and Writers (Professional development/Fellowship, Award) [430]
AAS National Endowment for the Humanities Long-Term Fellowships (Postdoctorate/Fellowship) [431]
AASLD Advanced/Transplant Hepatology Fellowships (Professional development/Fellowship) [581]
AASLD Autoimmune Liver Diseases Pilot Research

Special Recipient Index

Awards *(Graduate, Doctorate, Postdoctorate, Professional development/Award, Grant)* [582]
AASLD Career Development Awards in Liver Transplantation *(Professional development/Grant)* [583]
AASLD Clinical and Translational Research Awards *(Professional development/Grant)* [584]
AASSC Norwegian Travel Grants *(Professional development/Grant)* [1827]
AATS/STS Cardiothoracic Ethics Forum Scholarships *(Professional development/Scholarship)* [597]
AAUW Career Development Grants *(Graduate, Advanced Professional, Professional development/Grant)* [20]
AAZK/AZA Advances in Animal Keeping Course Grants *(Professional development/Grant)* [608]
AAZK Conservation, Preservation and Restoration Grants *(Professional development/Grant)* [609]
AAZK Professional Development Grants *(Professional development/Grant)* [610]
AAZK Research Grants *(Professional development/Grant)* [611]
ABA Scholarships *(Undergraduate/Scholarship)* [626]
ABC-Clio Research Grants *(Graduate/Grant)* [9208]
Alejandro "Alex" Abecia Reaching High Scholarships *(Undergraduate/Scholarship)* [3084]
Abercrombie and Fitch Global Diversity and Leadership Scholar Awards *(Undergraduate/Scholarship)* [7158]
Ruth Abernathy Presidential Scholarships *(Graduate, Undergraduate/Scholarship)* [9128]
Kyutaro and Yasuo Abiko Memorial Scholarships *(Undergraduate/Scholarship)* [5547]
Aboriginal Canadians Scholarship *(Undergraduate/Scholarship)* [7204]
Academy of Neonatal Nursing Conference Scholarships *(Professional development/Scholarship)* [44]
ACJA-LAE Student Paper Competitions *(Undergraduate, Graduate/Scholarship)* [752]
Jack Ackroyd Scholarships *(Other/Scholarship)* [1878]
ACMS Intensive Mongolian Language Fellowship Program *(Undergraduate/Fellowship)* [648]
ACMS Library Fellowships *(Graduate, Other/Fellowship)* [649]
ACMS U.S.-Mongolia Field Research Fellowship Program *(Graduate, Undergraduate/Fellowship)* [650]
ACNM Foundation, Inc. Fellowships for Graduate Education *(Doctorate, Postdoctorate/Fellowship, Grant)* [692]
ACPA Foundation Annual Fund *(Professional development/Grant)* [695]
ACS/ASA Health Policy and Management Scholarships *(Professional development/Scholarship)* [1468]
ACSUS Distinguished Dissertation Awards *(Doctorate/Award)* [1875]
RPMDA/Ed Adams Memorial Scholarships *(Other/Scholarship)* [8567]
ADHA IOH Sigma Phi Alpha Graduate Scholarships *(Graduate/Scholarship)* [775]
AE Flight Training Scholarships *(Other/Scholarship)* [7436]
AE Jet Type Rating Scholarships *(Other/Scholarship)* [7437]
AE Technical Training Scholarships *(Other/Scholarship)* [7438]
AECT Foundation Mentor Endowment Scholarships *(Doctorate, Graduate/Scholarship)* [1942]
AED Student Early Career Investigator Travel Fellowships *(Undergraduate, Graduate, Postdoctorate, Postgraduate/Fellowship)* [32]
AED Student Research Grants *(Undergraduate, Graduate, Postgraduate/Grant)* [33]
AEF Educational Scholarship *(Undergraduate/Scholarship)* [234]
Afdhal/McHutchison LIFER Awards *(Postdoctorate, Professional development/Grant)* [587]
AFSA Chapter 155 Division 1 Scholarships - Category 1 *(Undergraduate/Scholarship)* [130]
AFSA Chapter 155 Division 1 Scholarships - Category 2 *(Undergraduate/Scholarship)* [131]
AFSA Chapter 155 Division 1 Scholarships - Cat-

egory 3 *(Undergraduate/Scholarship)* [132]
AFT-Oregon Union Plus Credit Card Scholarship *(Undergraduate/Scholarship)* [792]
AfterCollege-AACN Scholarships *(Undergraduate, Master's, Doctorate/Scholarship)* [96]
AfterCollege Occupational Therapy Scholarships *(Master's, Doctorate/Scholarship)* [99]
AGC Foundation Outstanding Educator Awards *(Other/Award)* [1812]
AGC New York State Chapter Scholarship Program *(Undergraduate/Scholarship)* [1814]
AH&LEF American Express Scholarship *(Undergraduate/Scholarship)* [858]
Ahepa Buckeye Scholarship Awards *(Undergraduate/Scholarship)* [119]
AHNS/AAO-HNS Young Investigator Award *(Other/Grant)* [845]
AIA and the Global Automotive Aftermarket Symposium Scholarships *(Undergraduate/Scholarship)* [2131]
AIA Graduate Student Travel Awards *(Graduate/Grant)* [1603]
AIBS Junior Fellowships *(Doctorate/Fellowship)* [898]
AIBS Senior Fellowships *(Doctorate/Fellowship)* [899]
AIChE Minority Scholarship Awards for College Students *(Undergraduate/Scholarship)* [903]
AIMS Long-term Research Grants *(Doctorate, Graduate/Grant)* [916]
AIMS Short-term Research Grants *(Doctorate/Grant)* [917]
Air Force Association/Grantham Scholarships *(Undergraduate/Scholarship)* [121]
Air Force Sergeants Association Scholarship Program *(Undergraduate/Scholarship)* [128]
Air Traffic Control Association Full-time Employee Student Scholarships *(Other/Scholarship)* [135]
Air Traffic Control Association Non-employee Student Scholarships *(Undergraduate/Scholarship)* [136]
AISES Intel Scholarships *(Graduate, Undergraduate/Scholarship)* [887]
AISES Summer Internships *(Undergraduate, Graduate/Internship)* [888]
AISLS Grants for Language Instruction *(Doctorate/Grant)* [931]
AIST Baltimore Member Chapter Scholarships *(Undergraduate/Scholarship)* [1989]
AIST Midwest Member Chapter - Engineering Scholarships *(Undergraduate/Scholarship)* [1990]
AIST Midwest Member Chapter - Non-Engineering Scholarships *(Undergraduate/Scholarship)* [1991]
AIST Midwest Member Chapter - Western States Scholarships *(Undergraduate/Scholarship)* [1992]
AIST Northwest Member Chapter Scholarships *(Undergraduate/Scholarship)* [1993]
AIST Ohio Valley Chapter Scholarships *(Undergraduate/Scholarship)* [1994]
AIST San Francisco Member Chapter Scholarships *(Undergraduate/Scholarship)* [1995]
AJL Conference Stipends *(Graduate/Grant)* [2010]
Alabama ARN Scholarship *(Professional development/Scholarship)* [2054]
Alabama Horse Council Scholarships *(Undergraduate/Scholarship)* [203]
Alamo Area Paralegal Association Educational Scholarships *(Undergraduate, Professional development/Scholarship)* [209]
Alberta Holstein Association Scholarships *(Undergraduate/Scholarship)* [246]
Alberta Teachers Association Doctoral Fellowships in Education *(Doctorate/Fellowship)* [294]
Alberta Teachers Association Educational Research Award *(Other/Scholarship)* [295]
Neil Alexander Scholarships *(Undergraduate/Scholarship)* [6688]
ALL-SIS Conference of Newer Law Librarians Grants *(Professional development/Grant)* [528]
Dorothea E. Allen Scholarship *(Undergraduate/Scholarship)* [4427]
ALOA Scholarship Foundation *(Undergraduate/Scholarship)* [1816]
Alpha Tau Omega Graduate Scholarships *(Graduate/Scholarship)* [359]
Robert E. Altenhofen Memorial Scholarships

(Graduate, Undergraduate/Scholarship) [1802]
American Academy of Periodontology Educator Scholarships *(Postdoctorate/Scholarship)* [420]
American Art Therapy Association Anniversary Scholarships *(Graduate/Scholarship)* [448]
American Association of Cereal Chemists Graduate Fellowships *(Graduate/Fellowship)* [12]
American Association for Hand Surgery Annual Research Awards *(Other/Award)* [500]
American Association of Professional Apiculturists Research Scholarships *(Graduate, Undergraduate/Scholarship)* [568]
American Association of University Women American Fellowships *(Doctorate, Postdoctorate/Fellowship)* [599]
American Association of University Women Career Development Grants *(Postgraduate/Grant)* [600]
American Association for Women in Community Colleges Scholarship LEADERS Institute *(Other/Scholarship)* [606]
American Conifer Society Scholarships *(Undergraduate/Scholarship)* [714]
American Criminal Justice Association - Lambda Alpha Epsilon Student Scholarships - Graduate Level *(Undergraduate, Master's, Doctorate/Scholarship)* [753]
American Darts Organization Memorial Scholarship *(Undergraduate/Scholarship)* [767]
American Dental Hygienists' Association Institute for Oral Health Research Grants *(Master's/Fellowship)* [776]
American Division Veterans Association Scholarships *(Undergraduate/Scholarship)* [383]
American Institute of Physics Congressional Science Fellowships *(Doctorate/Fellowship)* [924]
American Institute of Physics State Department Science Fellowships *(Doctorate/Fellowship)* [925]
American Legion Boys/Girls State Scholarships *(Undergraduate/Scholarship)* [6017]
American Legion Department of Vermont Scholarships *(Undergraduate, High School/Scholarship)* [959]
American Legion Eagle Scout of the Year Scholarships *(Undergraduate/Scholarship)* [6918]
American Lung Association Scholar Program *(Professional development/Grant)* [979]
American Nephrology Nurses' Association Evidence-Based Research Grants *(Other/Grant)* [1025]
American Nephrology Nurses' Association Research Grants *(Doctorate, Graduate/Grant)* [1026]
American Pediatric Surgical Nurses Association Educational Grants *(Other/Grant)* [1076]
American Planning Association ENRE Student Fellowship Program *(Graduate/Fellowship)* [1103]
American Psychology-Law Society Dissertation Awards *(Graduate/Award)* [1155]
American Psychology-Law Society Early Career Professional Grants-In-Aid *(Other/Grant)* [1156]
American Psychology-Law Society Student Grants-In-Aid *(Graduate/Grant)* [1157]
American Society of Electroneurodiagnostic Technologists Student Education Grants (ASET) *(Undergraduate/Grant)* [1300]
American Society of Mammalogists - Fellowships in Mammalogy *(Graduate/Fellowship)* [1356]
American Society of Mammalogists Grants-in-Aid of Research *(Graduate, Undergraduate/Grant)* [1357]
American Society for Microbiology International Fellowships for Africa *(Postdoctorate/Fellowship)* [1365]
American Society for Microbiology International Fellowships for Asia *(Postdoctorate/Fellowship)* [1366]
American Society for Microbiology International Fellowships for Latin America and the Caribbean *(Postdoctorate/Fellowship)* [1367]
American Society for Microbiology Undergraduate Research Fellowships *(Undergraduate/Fellowship)* [1368]
American Society of Naval Engineers Scholarships (ASNE) *(Graduate, Undergraduate/Scholarship)* [1379]
American Sokol Merit Awards *(Undergraduate/Scholarship, Recognition)* [1448]

ASSOCIATION MEMBERSHIP

American Speech Language Hearing Foundation Endowed Scholarships *(Graduate, Master's, Doctorate/Scholarship)* [1451]
American Water Ski Educational Foundation Scholarships *(Undergraduate/Scholarship)* [10351]
American Welding Society District Scholarships *(Undergraduate/Scholarship)* [1503]
American Welding Society International Scholarships *(Undergraduate, Graduate/Scholarship)* [1505]
Anna Ames Clinical Excellence Student Grants *(Undergraduate/Grant)* [2481]
AMS Teacher Education Scholarships *(Undergraduate/Scholarship)* [1007]
AMSA Graduate Student Research Poster Competition Award *(Undergraduate, Doctorate, Master's/Award)* [987]
AMSN Career Mobility Scholarship Awards *(Undergraduate, Doctorate/Scholarship)* [37]
AMSSM-ACSM Clinical Research Grants *(Professional development/Grant)* [993]
AMTA Past Presidents' Conference Scholar Awards *(Professional development/Award)* [1010]
AMTA Student Conference Scholar Awards *(Undergraduate, Graduate/Award)* [1011]
AMTF Graduate Scholarships *(Graduate/Scholarship)* [1259]
Bernard Amtmann Fellowships *(Postgraduate, Other/Fellowship)* [2258]
ANCA Scholarships *(Undergraduate/Scholarship)* [1712]
Mary Louise Andersen Scholarship *(Undergraduate/Scholarship)* [1574]
The Anderson Group Summer Institute Scholarships *(Other/Scholarship)* [1553]
A.T. Anderson Memorial Scholarships *(Graduate, Undergraduate/Scholarship)* [889]
Earl I. Anderson Scholarships *(Undergraduate/Scholarship)* [1722]
Dr. Andy Anderson Young Professional Awards *(Professional development/Award)* [8117]
Grace Andow Memorial Scholarships *(Undergraduate, Graduate/Scholarship)* [5548]
Cindy Andrews Educational Scholarships *(Undergraduate/Scholarship)* [8447]
Richard E. Andrews Memorial Scholarships *(Undergraduate/Scholarship)* [627]
ANF/ANN-FNRE Nursing Research Grants *(Professional development/Grant)* [1042]
ANF/ENRS Nursing Research Grants *(Professional development/Grant)* [1043]
Angus Foundation General Undergraduate Student Scholarships *(Undergraduate/Scholarship)* [1557]
Angus Foundation Graduate Student Degree Scholarship Program *(Graduate/Scholarship)* [1558]
Angus Foundation Scholarships *(Undergraduate/Scholarship)* [7032]
ANNA Nephrology Nurse Researcher Awards *(Doctorate, Graduate/Award)* [1027]
Anne Friedberg Innovative Scholarship Awards *(Other/Scholarship)* [9104]
AOFAS Research Grants Program *(Graduate/Grant)* [1060]
AOSA Research Grants *(Undergraduate/Grant)* [1053]
AOSA Research Partnership Grants *(Professional development/Grant)* [1054]
APAGS-CLGBTC Grant Program *(Graduate/Grant)* [1131]
APALA Scholarship Award *(Doctorate, Master's/Scholarship)* [1788]
APC High School Scholarship Awards *(Undergraduate/Scholarship)* [78]
APhA Auxilliary Scholarship *(Undergraduate/Scholarship)* [1575]
APHF Academic Scholarships *(Undergraduate/Scholarship)* [1069]
APS Society Convention Research Awards *(Undergraduate, Graduate/Award)* [8318]
APS Student Research Award *(Undergraduate, Graduate/Award)* [2045]
APSA Presidency Research Group Fellowships *(Graduate, Postgraduate/Fellowship)* [1118]
APSA Small Research Grant Program *(Doctorate/Grant)* [1114]

APT US&C Scholarships *(Advanced Professional/Scholarship)* [2050]
APTA Minority Scholarships - Physical Therapist Students *(Undergraduate/Scholarship)* [1098]
ARA Scholarship Awards *(Undergraduate/Scholarship)* [2136]
ARAFCS Doctoral Scholarships *(Doctorate/Scholarship)* [1646]
ARAFCS Masters Scholarships *(Graduate/Scholarship)* [1647]
Archaeology of Portugal Fellowships *(Professional development/Fellowship)* [1605]
George F. Archambault Scholarship *(Undergraduate/Scholarship)* [1576]
NHCGNE Patricia G. Archbold Predoctoral Scholar Award *(Doctorate/Scholarship)* [6982]
AREMA Committee 24 - Education and Training Scholarships *(Undergraduate/Scholarship)* [1178]
AREMA Michigan Tech Alumni Scholarships *(Graduate, Undergraduate/Scholarship)* [1181]
A.R.F.O.R.A. Undergraduate Scholarships for Women *(Undergraduate/Scholarship)* [1224]
Norma Arnold Clerical Scholarships *(Undergraduate/Scholarship)* [6221]
Jane B. Aron Doctoral Fellowships *(Doctorate/Fellowship)* [6787]
ARS of Eastern USA Lazarian Graduate Scholarship *(Master's, Doctorate/Scholarship)* [1680]
The Artist in Landscape Design Scholarship by Fullmer's Landscaping *(Undergraduate/Scholarship)* [7581]
ASA Student Forum Travel Awards *(Undergraduate, Graduate/Grant)* [1446]
ASBA College Scholarship Grant Program *(Postgraduate/Scholarship)* [1239]
ASBC Foundation Graduate Scholarships *(Graduate/Scholarship)* [1247]
ASBC Foundation Undergraduate Scholarships *(Undergraduate/Scholarship)* [1248]
ASCO/CCF Young Investigator Awards *(Professional development, Advanced Professional/Grant)* [3369]
ASCP Phlebotomy Scholarships *(Undergraduate/Scholarship)* [1262]
ASECS Innovative Course Design Competition *(Undergraduate/Award)* [1284]
ASECS Women's Caucus Editing and Translation Fellowships *(Doctorate/Fellowship)* [1285]
ASET Scholarships *(Other/Scholarship)* [1301]
ASHFoundation New Century Scholars Doctoral Scholarships *(Doctorate/Scholarship)* [1455]
ASHFoundation Scholarships for NSSLHA Members *(Graduate/Scholarship)* [1458]
ASIS Foundation Chapter Matching Scholarships *(Undergraduate/Scholarship)* [1794]
ASLA Council of Fellow Scholarships *(Undergraduate/Scholarship)* [1346]
ASLMS Research Grants *(Postdoctorate/Grant)* [1349]
ASM Congressional Science Fellowships *(Postdoctorate/Fellowship)* [1370]
ASNT Fellowship Award *(Graduate/Fellowship, Award)* [1384]
Myron "Ted" Asplin Foundation Scholarships *(Undergraduate/Scholarship)* [5097]
Association for the Advancement of Baltic Studies Dissertation Grants for Graduate Students *(Doctorate/Grant)* [1823]
Association of Desk and Derrick Clubs Education Trust Scholarships *(Undergraduate/Scholarship)* [1931]
Association of Donor Recruitment Professionals Hughes Scholarships *(Other/Scholarship)* [1937]
Association of Donor Recruitment Professionals Presidential Scholarships *(Other/Scholarship)* [1938]
Association of Flight Attendants Scholarship Fund *(Undergraduate/Scholarship)* [1963]
Association of Government Accountants Undergraduate/Graduate Scholarships for Community Service Accomplishments *(Graduate, Undergraduate/Scholarship)* [1971]
Association of Government Accountants Undergraduate/Graduate Scholarships for Full-time study *(Graduate, Undergraduate/Scholarship)* [1972]

Special Recipient Index

Association of Government Accountants Undergraduate/Graduate Scholarships for Part-time study *(Graduate, Undergraduate/Scholarship)* [1973]
Association for Psychological Science Student Grants (APS) *(Graduate, Undergraduate/Grant)* [2046]
ASTR Research Fellowships *(Other/Fellowship)* [1433]
ASTRO Junior Faculty Career Research Training Awards *(Advanced Professional, Professional development/Grant)* [1392]
ASTRO Residents/Fellows in Radiation Oncology Research Seed Grants *(Advanced Professional, Professional development/Grant)* [1394]
ASTRO/ROI Comparative Effectiveness Research Awards *(Professional development/Grant)* [1395]
ATS Abstract Scholarships *(Undergraduate, Graduate, Doctorate/Scholarship)* [1473]
AUA Foundation Urology Research Bridge Awards *(Postgraduate/Award)* [10346]
AVMA Fellowship Program *(Professional development/Fellowship)* [1478]
Award for Outstanding Doctoral Dissertation in Laser Science *(Doctorate/Award)* [1086]
AWMA Niagara Frontier Section College Scholarships *(Graduate, Undergraduate/Scholarship)* [149]
Mary Babcock Fellowships for Labour Studies Application *(Graduate/Fellowship)* [7629]
Bachelor of Science in Nursing Academic Scholarships *(Graduate/Scholarship)* [6656]
Paula Backscheider Archival Fellowships *(Other/Fellowship)* [1286]
BACUS Scholarships *(Graduate, Undergraduate/Scholarship)* [9467]
Morton Bahr Scholarships *(Undergraduate/Scholarship)* [3165]
Bailey/Hollister Scholarships *(Graduate, Professional development/Scholarship)* [7935]
Lincoln C. Bailey Memorial Scholarship Fund *(Undergraduate/Scholarship)* [5390]
Sandra Sebrell Bailey Scholarships *(Undergraduate/Scholarship)* [3579]
Baker and McKenzie Graduate Legal Studies Scholarships *(Graduate, Professional development/Scholarship)* [2176]
Lynn Ann Baldwin Scholarships *(Master's/Scholarship)* [1888]
Balestreri/Cutino Scholarships *(Undergraduate/Scholarship)* [757]
Brenda S. Bank Educational Workshop Scholarships *(Undergraduate/Scholarship)* [9123]
Leslie Baranowski Scholarships for Professional Excellence *(Professional development/Scholarship)* [5144]
Thomas J. Bardos Science Education Awards for Undergraduate Students *(Undergraduate/Award)* [473]
TCDA Carroll Barnes Student Scholarships *(Undergraduate/Scholarship)* [668]
Marguerite Ross Barnett Research Grant *(Graduate, Postdoctorate/Grant)* [1119]
Walt Bartram Memorial Education Award, Region 12 and Chapter 119 *(Undergraduate/Scholarship)* [9167]
Baxter Corporation Canadian Research Awards in Anesthesia *(Other/Award, Monetary)* [2538]
Suzanne Beauregard Scholarships *(Undergraduate/Scholarship)* [4476]
Beaverbrook Media at McGill Student Paper Prize *(Graduate/Prize)* [2615]
Bechtel Engineering and Science Scholarships *(Undergraduate/Scholarship)* [6278]
Ed Becker Conference Travel Awards *(Undergraduate, Graduate/Award)* [3886]
Ann C. Beckingham Scholarships *(Graduate, Other/Scholarship)* [2645]
Clifford L. Bedford Scholarship Award *(Undergraduate/Scholarship)* [5177]
Hannah Beiter Graduate Student Research Grants *(Doctorate, Graduate/Grant)* [2909]
AG Bell College Scholarship Awards *(Undergraduate, Graduate/Scholarship)* [314]
Betty Bell Scholarship Fund *(Undergraduate/Scholarship)* [4922]

Special Recipient Index — Association Membership

Samuel Flagg Bemis Dissertation Research Grants *(Doctorate, Graduate/Grant)* [9133]
Reckitt Benckiser Student Scholarships *(Graduate/Scholarship)* [6771]
Viscount Bennett Fellowships *(Graduate/Fellowship)* [2581]
Elizabeth Benson Scholarship Awards *(Undergraduate/Scholarship)* [8542]
Rosalie Bentzinger Scholarships *(Doctorate/Scholarship)* [9849]
Fred Berg Awards *(Undergraduate/Award)* [3796]
Bergman Scholarships *(Undergraduate/Scholarship)* [7487]
ARRS/Leonard Berlin Scholarships in Medical Professionalism *(Other/Scholarship)* [1222]
Stuart L. Bernath Dissertation Grants *(Doctorate, Graduate/Grant)* [9134]
Jean Clark Berry Scholarships *(Graduate, Undergraduate/Scholarship)* [5693]
Beta Sigma Phi Visual Arts Scholarship *(Undergraduate/Scholarship)* [8869]
BHCRI Bridge Funds *(Advanced Professional, Professional development/Grant)* [5012]
BHCRI Matching Funds *(Advanced Professional, Professional development/Grant)* [5014]
BHCRI Miscellaneous Funds *(Advanced Professional, Professional development/Grant)* [5015]
BHCRI Seed Funds *(Advanced Professional, Professional development/Grant)* [5016]
Birmingham District Alabama Dietetic Association Scholarships *(Graduate, Undergraduate/Scholarship)* [196]
Graduate Student Honoraria - Elmer C. Birney Awards *(Master's, Doctorate/Award)* [1358]
Eileen Blackey Doctoral Fellowships *(Doctorate/Fellowship)* [6788]
William T. Blackwell Scholarship Fund *(Undergraduate/Scholarship)* [7019]
Mitzi and William Blahd, MD Pilot Research Grants *(Doctorate/Grant)* [9220]
Beatrice K. Blair Scholarships *(Undergraduate/Scholarship)* [2305]
Ellin Bloch and Pierre Ritchie Diversity Dissertation Grant *(Graduate/Grant)* [1132]
BMES Graduate and Undergraduate Student Awards *(Graduate, Undergraduate/Award)* [2271]
Board of Certification for Emergency Nursing (BCEN) Undergraduate Scholarships *(Undergraduate/Scholarship)* [3860]
Sandra Bobbitt Continuing Education Scholarship *(Undergraduate/Scholarship)* [2032]
Edith and Arnold N. Bodtker Grants *(Undergraduate, Graduate/Grant, Internship)* [3522]
Boeing Company Scholarships *(Undergraduate/Scholarship)* [8870]
BOMA/NY Scholarships *(Undergraduate/Scholarship)* [2404]
Ellis J. Bonner Scholarships *(Graduate/Scholarship)* [6754]
Stephen Botein Fellowships *(Doctorate/Fellowship)* [433]
Bound to Stay Bound Books Scholarships *(Graduate/Scholarship)* [2017]
CAG Margery Boyce Bursary Awards *(Undergraduate/Award, Scholarship)* [2553]
W. Scott Boyd Group Grants *(Advanced Professional/Grant)* [5282]
Boyle Family Scholarship *(Undergraduate/Scholarship)* [1577]
Paul W. Bradley Scholarships *(Undergraduate/Scholarship)* [7377]
Doreen Brady Memorial Scholarships *(Postgraduate/Scholarship)* [7630]
TACS/A. Bragas and Associates Student Scholarships *(Undergraduate/Scholarship)* [9686]
Byard Braley Scholarship *(Undergraduate/Scholarship)* [5462]
Theodore E.D. Braun Research Travel Fellowships *(Other/Fellowship)* [1287]
Dvora Brodie Scholarships *(Graduate, Postgraduate, Undergraduate/Scholarship)* [4829]
John G. Brokaw Scholarships *(Undergraduate/Scholarship)* [7227]
Selena Danette Brown Book Scholarships *(Graduate, Undergraduate/Scholarship)* [6720]
VPPPA Stephen Brown Scholarships *(Graduate, Undergraduate/Scholarship)* [10417]
Regina Brown Undergraduate Student Fellowships *(Undergraduate/Fellowship)* [6879]
Scott Brownlee Memorial Scholarships *(Undergraduate, Graduate/Scholarship)* [6582]
Robert W. Brunsman Memorial Scholarship *(Professional development/Scholarship)* [5360]
BSA Educational Scholarships *(Undergraduate/Scholarship)* [2426]
Pamfil and Maria Bujea Family Orthodox Christian Seminarian Scholarships *(Undergraduate/Scholarship)* [1225]
ACLS Frederick Burkhardt Residential Fellowships *(Other/Fellowship)* [434]
Dr. F. Ross Byrd Scholarships *(Graduate, Vocational/Occupational, Postgraduate/Scholarship)* [10463]
CAA National Capital Region Writing Contests *(All/Award, Prize, Monetary)* [2579]
CAAO Scholarship *(Professional development/Scholarship)* [3356]
CAG Health and Health Care Study Group Awards *(Graduate/Award)* [1881]
Calgary USAEE/IAEE North American Conference Registration Fee Scholarships *(Undergraduate/Scholarship)* [9883]
CALL/ACBD Education Reserve Fund Grants *(Professional development/Grant)* [2561]
CALL/ACBD Research Grants *(Graduate/Grant)* [2562]
Calvin Alumni Association-Michigan Lakeshore Scholarships *(Undergraduate/Scholarship)* [2496]
Calvin Alumni Association-Michigan, Lansing Scholarships *(Undergraduate/Scholarship)* [2497]
Calvin Alumni Association-Southeast Michigan Scholarships *(Undergraduate/Scholarship)* [2500]
Calvin Alumni Association-Southwest Michigan, Kalamazoo Scholarships *(Undergraduate/Scholarship)* [2503]
Calvin Alumni Association-Washington, D.C. Scholarships *(Undergraduate/Scholarship)* [2504]
Stuart Cameron and Margaret McLeod Memorial Scholarships (SCMS) *(Graduate, Undergraduate/Scholarship)* [5205]
Wesley C. Cameron Scholarships *(Undergraduate/Scholarship)* [7228]
Canadian Anesthesiologists' Society Research Awards *(Other/Award)* [2539]
Canadian Association of Cardiac Rehabilitation Graduate Scholarship Awards *(Graduate/Scholarship)* [2548]
Canadian Council of Technicians and Technologists Scholarships for Technology Students *(Undergraduate/Scholarship)* [3392]
Canadian Identification Society Essay/Scholarship Awards *(Advanced Professional, Professional development/Prize)* [2664]
Canadian Occupational Therapy Foundation Graduate Scholarships *(Doctorate, Master's/Scholarship)* [2717]
Canadian Occupational Therapy Foundation Invacare Master's Scholarships *(Master's/Scholarship)* [2718]
Canadian Parking Association Scholarships *(Undergraduate/Scholarship)* [1921]
Canadian Water Resources Association Scholarships *(Undergraduate/Scholarship)* [1905]
Therese A. Cannon Educational Scholarships *(Other/Scholarship)* [5372]
CANS/SNRS Dissertation Research Grants *(Doctorate/Grant)* [9405]
CAODC Occupational Health and Safety Scholarships *(Professional development/Scholarship)* [2570]
CAODC Scholarship Program *(Undergraduate/Scholarship)* [2571]
Cardiac Health Foundation of Canada Scholarships *(Graduate/Scholarship)* [2790]
Thelma Cardwell Scholarships *(Graduate/Scholarship)* [2719]
Career Development Scholarships *(Postdoctorate, Postgraduate/Scholarship)* [4129]
John L. Carey Scholarship Awards *(Graduate/Scholarship)* [901]
AABA Read Carlock Memorial Scholarship Fund *(Other/Scholarship)* [1625]
CARO-ELEKTA Research Fellowship Program *(Professional development/Fellowship)* [1900]
Carolinas-Virginias Retail Hardware Scholarships *(Undergraduate/Scholarship)* [4184]
CAS/GE Healthcare Canada Inc. Research Awards *(Other/Award)* [2540]
CAS/Vitaid-LMA Residents' Research Grant Competition *(Other/Award)* [2541]
TCDA Jim and Glenda Casey Professional Scholarships *(Other/Scholarship)* [669]
Rose Cassin Memorial Scholarships *(Postgraduate/Scholarship)* [7631]
Catholic Aid Association's Post-High School Tuition Scholarships *(Undergraduate/Scholarship)* [2818]
CC Times Scholarships *(Undergraduate/Scholarship)* [2921]
CCF Career Development Award *(Professional development/Grant)* [3371]
CCF Improving Cancer Care Grants *(Professional development, Doctorate/Grant)* [3372]
CCF Merit Award *(Professional development, Doctorate/Award)* [3373]
CCWH/Berkshire Conference of Women Historians Graduate Student Fellowships *(Doctorate/Fellowship)* [3418]
Cedarcrest Farms Scholarships *(Graduate, Undergraduate/Scholarship)* [944]
Cengage Travel Award for Teachers of Reading at a Community College *(Professional development/Monetary)* [3123]
Certified Municipal Clerk Scholarships (CMC) *(Other/Scholarship)* [5350]
CGNA Memorial Scholarship *(Graduate, Other/Scholarship)* [2646]
Chaîne des Rôtisseurs Scholarships *(Undergraduate/Scholarship)* [758]
Jeanne S. Chall Research Fellowship *(Doctorate, Graduate/Fellowship)* [5355]
Logan S. Chambers Individual Scholarships *(Other/Scholarship)* [5283]
Chambliss Astronomy Achievement Student Awards *(Undergraduate, Graduate/Award)* [614]
Nancy J. Chapman Scholarships *(Other/Scholarship)* [1939]
Chapter 31 - Peoria Endowed Scholarships *(Undergraduate/Scholarship)* [9173]
Chapter 93 - Albuquerque Scholarships *(Undergraduate/Scholarship)* [9179]
Chapter 198 - Downriver Detroit Scholarships *(Graduate, Undergraduate/Scholarship)* [9171]
Charles H. Bussmann Graduate Scholarship *(Graduate, Undergraduate/Scholarship)* [6271]
Emilie Du Chatelet Awards *(Doctorate/Award)* [1288]
CCWH Nupur Chaudhuri First Article Prizes *(Professional development/Prize)* [3419]
Sgt. Cherven Scholarship *(Undergraduate/Scholarship)* [6312]
Chevalier Award Scholarship *(Undergraduate/Scholarship)* [2618]
Childbirth Educator Program Scholarships *(All/Scholarship)* [5909]
Children of Evangeline Section Scholarships *(Graduate, Undergraduate/Scholarship)* [9249]
Chinese Professionals Association of Canada BMO Diversity Scholarships *(Undergraduate/Scholarship)* [2922]
Chinese Professionals Association of Canada Journalism Scholarships *(Undergraduate/Scholarship)* [2924]
Christian Pharmacists Fellowship International *(Advanced Professional/Fellowship)* [2934]
Irene R. Christman Scholarship *(Undergraduate/Scholarship)* [7939]
Chronic Pain Medicine Research Grants *(Professional development/Grant)* [1403]
CIP Fellow's Travel Scholarships *(Undergraduate/Scholarship)* [2672]
Civil Air Patrol Flight Scholarships *(Undergraduate/Scholarship)* [3039]
Civitan Shropshire Scholarships *(Undergraduate, Vocational/Occupational/Scholarship)* [3041]
CLA/CP Scholarship *(Other/Scholarship)* [8672]
Claes Nobel Academic Scholarships for Members *(High School/Scholarship)* [7159]

ASSOCIATION MEMBERSHIP — Special Recipient Index

Clan Ross Foundation Scholarships (Undergraduate/Scholarship) [3043]
IADR John Clarkson Fellowship (Postdoctorate/Fellowship) [5250]
James L. Clifford Prize (Other/Prize, Monetary) [1289]
CMAA Student Conference Travel Grants (Undergraduate/Grant) [3061]
CMOS-SCMO President's Prize (Professional development/Prize) [2682]
The Helena B. Cobb Annual Scholarships (Undergraduate, Vocational/Occupational/Scholarship) [10665]
The Helena B. Cobb Four-Year Higher Education Grants (Undergraduate, Vocational/Occupational/Scholarship) [10666]
J.C. and Rheba Cobb Memorial Scholarships (Undergraduate/Scholarship) [6867]
Evelyn L. Cockrell Memorial Scholarship Award (Undergraduate/Scholarship) [9701]
American Academy of Periodontology Dr. D. Walter Cohen Teaching Fellowships (Postdoctorate/Fellowship) [421]
Anna C. and Oliver C. Colburn Fellowships (Doctorate/Fellowship) [1606]
Arthur H. Cole Grants in Aid (Doctorate/Grant, Award) [3779]
Colgate-Palmolive/HDA Foundation Scholarships (Master's, Postgraduate/Scholarship) [4892]
Captain Winifred Quick Collins Scholarships (Undergraduate/Scholarship) [7229]
Communal Studies Association Research Fellowships (Graduate/Fellowship) [3163]
Comparative Effectiveness Research Professorship (CERP) (Professional development, Doctorate/Grant) [3374]
Alan Compton and Bob Stanley Professional Scholarships (Professional development/Scholarship) [2192]
Conduct and Utilization of Research in Nursing (CURN) Awards (Professional development/Award) [6476]
Al Conklin and Bill de Decker Business Aviation Management Scholarships (Undergraduate/Scholarship) [6830]
Continuing Education Awards (Undergraduate/Scholarship, Award) [6778]
Jorge Espejel Contreras IALEIA Scholarship Award (Undergraduate/Scholarship) [5266]
COPA Scholarship Fund (Undergraduate/Scholarship) [2722]
Correctional Education Association Scholarships (Graduate, Undergraduate/Scholarship) [3427]
NSS Sara Corrie Memorial Grants (Professional development/Grant) [7181]
Richard P. Covert, Ph.D./FHIMSS Scholarships for Management Systems (Graduate, Postgraduate, Undergraduate/Scholarship) [4830]
CPS Excellence in Interprofessional Pain Education Awards (Other/Award) [2726]
CPS Interprofessional Nursing Project Awards (Other/Award) [2727]
CPS Knowledge Translation Research Awards (Other/Grant) [2728]
CPS Nursing Excellence in Pain Management Awards (Other/Award) [2729]
CPS Nursing Research and Education Awards (Other/Grant) [2730]
CPS Outstanding Pain Mentorship Awards (Other/Award) [2731]
CPS Trainee Research Awards (Doctorate/Grant, Award) [2732]
CRMA Scholarships (Graduate, Undergraduate/Scholarship) [2899]
CSA Fraternal Life Scholarships (Undergraduate/Scholarship) [3483]
CSCI Distinguished Scientist Lectures and Awards (Advanced Professional/Award) [9073]
CSLA Leaders of Distinction Award (Professional development/Recognition) [2759]
CSLA Leadership Scholarships (Undergraduate/Scholarship) [2760]
CSMLS Student Scholarship Awards (Postgraduate/Scholarship) [2750]
CSSE ARTS Graduate Research Awards (Graduate/Award) [9069]

CTP Scholarship Program (Other/Scholarship) [7113]
Linda Cullen Memorial Scholarships (Undergraduate/Scholarship) [759]
The Cure Starts Now Foundation Grants (Graduate, Doctorate/Grant) [3492]
Nancy Curry Scholarships (Vocational/Occupational/Scholarship) [8804]
Jennifer Curtis Byler Scholarships (Undergraduate/Scholarship) [7188]
DA Davidson Presidential Scholarships (Undergraduate/Scholarship) [10436]
DAAD Study Scholarship Awards (Graduate/Scholarship) [3604]
DAI Fellowships for Study in Berlin (Doctorate/Fellowship) [1607]
John L. Dales Standard Scholarship (Undergraduate/Scholarship) [8827]
Malcolm U. Dantzler Scholarships (Other/Scholarship) [9363]
DAPA Student Member Scholarships (Undergraduate/Scholarship) [3512]
Mary Mouzon Darby Undergraduate Scholarships (Undergraduate/Scholarship) [4985]
Antenore C. "Butch" Davanzo Scholarships (Graduate, Undergraduate/Scholarship) [6502]
The Dave Family "Humor Studies" Scholarships (Undergraduate, Graduate/Scholarship) [1848]
Davis Memorial Foundation Scholarships (Graduate, Undergraduate/Scholarship) [3533]
Edilia and François Auguste de Montêquin Fellowships (Doctorate/Fellowship) [9083]
Walter M. Decker Point Scholarships (Graduate, Undergraduate/Scholarship) [8173]
Anthony R. Dees Educational Workshop Scholarships (Undergraduate/Scholarship) [9124]
Edward Delaney Scholarships (Professional development/Scholarship) [1982]
Delta Gamma Undergraduate Merit-Based Scholarships (Undergraduate/Scholarship) [3569]
DEMCO New Leaders Travel Grants (Professional development/Grant) [8372]
Albert W. Dent Graduate Student Scholarships (Undergraduate/Scholarship) [687]
Descendant Scholarships (Undergraduate/Scholarship) [3500]
Diabetes Scholars Foundation College Scholarships (Undergraduate/Scholarship) [3616]
Edwina Eustis Dick Scholarship for Music Therapy Interns (Graduate/Scholarship) [1012]
Diversity Executive Leadership Program Scholarships (Other/Scholarship) [1778]
Robert A. and Barbara Divine Graduate Student Travel Grants (Graduate/Grant) [9136]
Dr. Allan A. Dixon Memorial Scholarships (Postgraduate/Scholarship) [2742]
William Donald Dixon Research Grants (Graduate, Undergraduate, Advanced Professional/Grant) [2665]
Peggy Dixon Two-Year Scholarships (Undergraduate/Scholarship) [9254]
Charles Dobbins FTA Scholarships (Undergraduate, Vocational/Occupational/Scholarship) [4316]
Dr. Biljan Memorial Awards (Advanced Professional/Award, Grant) [2636]
Tommy Douglas Memorial Scholarship (Undergraduate/Scholarship) [7205]
Chapter 116 - Kalamazoo - Roscoe Douglas Scholarships (Undergraduate/Scholarship) [9180]
The "Drawn to Art" Fellowships (Doctorate/Fellowship) [436]
Charles Drew Scholarships (Other/Scholarship) [1940]
Richard Drukker Memorial Scholarships (Undergraduate/Scholarship) [7326]
Lise M. Duchesneau Scholarship (Undergraduate/Scholarship) [1895]
Julia M. Duckwall Scholarships (Professional development/Scholarship) [1983]
H.J. "Duke" Ellington Memorial Scholarship Award (Undergraduate/Scholarship) [7513]
Marvin and Joanell Dyrstad Scholarship (Undergraduate/Scholarship) [1578]
Josephine P. White Eagle Scholarships (Undergraduate, Graduate/Scholarship) [4911]
Amelia Earhart Memorial Academic Scholarships (Undergraduate/Scholarship) [7439]
The Christoph Daniel Ebeling Fellowships (Postdoctorate, Postgraduate/Fellowship) [437]
ECA Applied Urban Communication Research Grants (Professional development/Grant) [3768]
ECA Centennial Scholarships (Master's, Doctorate/Scholarship) [3769]
James Echols Scholarship Award (Undergraduate/Scholarship) [2434]
Education Advancement Scholarships (Graduate, Master's, Doctorate/Scholarship) [548]
Educational Audiology Association Doctoral Scholarships (Doctorate/Scholarship) [3797]
Esther Edwards Graduate Scholarships (Doctorate, Professional development/Scholarship) [9851]
Carli Edwards Memorial Scholarships (Undergraduate/Scholarship) [8871]
EHA Exploratory Travel and Data Grants (Doctorate/Grant) [3780]
EHA Graduate Dissertation Fellowships (Doctorate/Fellowship) [3781]
Harold E. Eisenberg Foundation Scholarships (Other/Scholarship) [5304]
Farouk El-Baz Student Research Grants (Graduate, Undergraduate/Grant) [4363]
Eli Lilly and Company/Black Data Processing Associates Scholarships (Undergraduate/Scholarship) [2206]
Eli Lilly Graduate Scholarship (Graduate, Postgraduate/Scholarship) [1886]
A.C. Elias, Jr. Irish-American Research Travel Fellowships (Other/Fellowship) [1290]
ENA Foundation Annual Conference Scholarships (Advanced Professional, Professional development/Scholarship) [3861]
ENA Foundation Seed Research Grants (Master's, Advanced Professional/Grant) [3862]
ENA Foundation State Challenge Undergraduate Scholarship (Undergraduate/Scholarship) [3858]
Alice Yuriko Endo Memorial Scholarships (Undergraduate/Scholarship) [5549]
Endocrine Society Summer Research Fellowships (Graduate, Undergraduate/Fellowship) [3864]
Endodontic Research Grants (Graduate/Grant) [493]
Endourological Society Fellowships (Professional development/Fellowship) [3867]
Jane Engelberg Memorial Fellowship (Professional development/Fellowship) [7156]
Harold E. Ennes Scholarships (Graduate, Other/Award, Scholarship) [9092]
Entomological Society of Saskatchewan Travel Awards (Professional development/Award) [3896]
Epsilon Mu Scholarships (Graduate, Undergraduate/Scholarship) [5714]
ERDAS Internship (Graduate/Internship, Award) [1804]
Jack Ervin EDI Scholarships (Other/Scholarship) [7460]
NSPF Ray B. Essick Scholarship Awards (Other/Scholarship) [7192]
FACT "Second Chance" Scholarship Program (Undergraduate/Scholarship) [3999]
FAER Mentored Research Training Grants (Professional development/Grant) [4163]
FAER Research in Education Grants (Advanced Professional/Grant) [4164]
Claire M. Fagin Fellow Award (Doctorate/Fellowship) [6983]
AIST Benjamin F. Fairless Scholarships (Undergraduate/Scholarship) [1996]
Families of Freedom Scholarship Fund - America Scholarships (Undergraduate, Vocational/Occupational/Scholarship) [3956]
William M. Fanning Maintenance Scholarships (Undergraduate/Scholarship) [6831]
John S.W. Fargher, Jr. Scholarships (Graduate/Scholarship) [5185]
Lillian and Alex Feir Graduate Student Travel Awards (Master's, Doctorate/Award) [3880]
Fellowships in the PMAC-AGPC (Professional development/Fellowship) [8295]
Fieldwork Fellowships (Undergraduate/Award, Fellowship) [3927]
William A. Fischer Memorial Scholarships (Graduate/Scholarship) [1805]

Special Recipient Index

ASSOCIATION MEMBERSHIP

Dr. Joseph Fitzsimmons Scholarships *(Doctorate/Scholarship)* [9959]
Flamenco Student Scholarships *(Undergraduate, Professional development/Scholarship)* [4070]
Charlie Fleming Education Fund Scholarships *(Undergraduate/Scholarship)* [7195]
FLEOA Foundation Scholarship Program *(Undergraduate/Scholarship)* [3991]
Grant H. Flint International Scholarships - Category I *(Undergraduate/Scholarship)* [9337]
Grant H. Flint International Scholarships - Category II *(Undergraduate/Scholarship)* [9338]
Florida Public Health Association Public Health Graduate Scholarships *(Graduate/Scholarship)* [4108]
FMA-FEEA Scholarship Program *(Undergraduate/Scholarship)* [3993]
Gail Goodell Folsom Memorial Scholarships *(Undergraduate/Scholarship)* [6650]
Frank Fong Scholarships *(Undergraduate/Scholarship)* [9076]
A. Ward Ford Memorial Research Grants *(Postdoctorate, Professional development/Grant)* [1351]
Nancy B. Forest and L. Michael Honaker Master's Grant for Research in Psychology *(Graduate/Grant)* [1133]
Foresters Scholarships *(Undergraduate/Scholarship)* [5095]
Edward Foster Awards *(Advanced Professional/Award)* [2666]
Emily P. Foster Fellowships *(Graduate/Fellowship)* [7739]
Founding Fathers Leadership Scholarships *(Undergraduate/Scholarship)* [10617]
Founding Mothers' Student Scholarships - Graduate *(Graduate/Scholarship)* [2015]
Terry Fox Memorial Scholarship *(Undergraduate/Scholarship)* [7206]
Gloria Francke Scholarship *(Undergraduate/Scholarship)* [1579]
Kevin Freeman Travel Grants *(Graduate, Other/Grant)* [6627]
Don Freeman Work-in-Progress Grants *(Advanced Professional/Grant)* [9096]
Friends of Mary Automotive Scholarships *(Undergraduate/Scholarship)* [8872]
FSF Student Travel Grant *(Undergraduate, Graduate/Grant)* [4135]
Arthur Flagler Fultz Research Awards *(Professional development/Grant)* [1013]
Future Leaders of Manufacturing Scholarships *(Graduate, Undergraduate/Scholarship)* [9181]
Future STEM Teacher Scholarship *(Undergraduate/Scholarship)* [9657]
GAAC Project Grants *(Undergraduate, Professional development/Grant)* [4445]
Mearl K. Gable II Memorial Grants *(Other/Grant)* [4709]
Gamewarden Scholarship program *(High School, Undergraduate, Vocational/Occupational/Scholarship)* [4320]
Gamma Sigma Alpha Graduate Scholarships *(Graduate/Scholarship)* [4322]
John A. Gans Scholarship *(Undergraduate/Scholarship)* [1580]
William R. Gard Memorial Scholarships *(Undergraduate/Scholarship)* [6654]
Jewell Gardiner Scholarships *(Undergraduate/Scholarship)* [2473]
Gardner Foundation Infusion Nurses Society Education Scholarships *(Professional development/Scholarship)* [5145]
Dwight D. Gardner Scholarships *(Undergraduate/Scholarship)* [5186]
A.R.F.O.R.A. Martha Gavrila Scholarships for Women *(Postgraduate/Scholarship)* [1226]
GAWP Graduate Scholarships *(Graduate/Scholarship)* [4377]
Florence S. Gaynor Scholarships *(Graduate/Scholarship)* [6755]
GCSAA Scholars Competition *(Undergraduate/Scholarship)* [4483]
GCSAA Student Essay Contest *(Graduate, Undergraduate/Prize)* [4484]
GED Jump Start Scholarships *(Professional development/Scholarship)* [8805]

Lawrence Gelfand - Armin Rappaport - Walter LaFeber Dissertation Fellowships *(Doctorate, Graduate/Fellowship)* [9137]
Elaine Gelman Scholarship Awards *(Undergraduate/Scholarship)* [6772]
Generation III Scholarships *(Undergraduate/Scholarship)* [3783]
Geological Society of America Graduate Student Research Grants *(Doctorate, Graduate/Grant)* [4364]
Doris Y. and John J. Gerber Scholarships *(Undergraduate/Scholarship)* [10464]
Walter Gerboth Awards *(Other/Award)* [6628]
Anthony Gerharz Scholarships *(Undergraduate, Graduate/Scholarship)* [6583]
IDSA Gianninoto Graduate Scholarships *(Graduate, Undergraduate/Scholarship)* [5136]
Robert D. Gibson Scholarship *(Undergraduate/Scholarship)* [1581]
Gilbreth Memorial Fellowships *(Graduate/Scholarship, Fellowship)* [5187]
AIST Midwest Member Chapter - Jack Gill Scholarships *(Undergraduate/Scholarship)* [1997]
Leo Gilmartin Scholarships *(Undergraduate/Scholarship)* [8167]
Lawrence Ginocchio Aviation Scholarships *(Undergraduate/Scholarship)* [6833]
J. Robert Gladden Orthopaedic Society International Traveling Fellowship *(Undergraduate/Fellowship)* [4443]
John Glaser Scholarships *(Undergraduate/Scholarship)* [3121]
GLATA Living Memorial Doctorate Scholarships *(Doctorate, Graduate/Fellowship)* [4653]
GLATA Living Memorial Graduate Scholarships *(Graduate/Fellowship, Scholarship)* [4654]
Globe-Trotters Member Chapter Scholarships *(Undergraduate, Postgraduate/Scholarship)* [1998]
Alfred B. Glossbrenner Scholarships *(Undergraduate/Scholarship)* [1999]
Shirley J. Gold Scholarship *(Undergraduate/Scholarship)* [793]
Golden Key Graduate Scholar Awards *(Graduate, Master's, Doctorate/Scholarship)* [6747]
Golden Key Study Abroad Scholarships *(Undergraduate/Scholarship)* [4472]
Sarah "Sally" Ives Gore Gamma Kappa Sapphire Scholarships *(Graduate, Undergraduate/Scholarship)* [5728]
TCDA Bill Gorham Student Scholarships *(Undergraduate/Scholarship)* [670]
Consuelo W. Gosnell Memorial Scholarships *(Graduate/Fellowship)* [6789]
Louis Gottschalk Prize *(Other/Prize)* [1291]
Carl W. Gottschalk Research Scholar Grants *(Professional development/Grant)* [1381]
Graduate Realtor Institute Scholarships *(Graduate/Scholarship)* [5817]
Graduate Student Travel Grants *(Doctorate, Master's/Grant)* [462]
Graduate Student Travel Grants *(Graduate, Other/Grant)* [9111]
Grande Prairie 4-H District Scholarships *(Undergraduate/Scholarship)* [8]
AMA/Charles H. Grant Scholarships *(Undergraduate/Scholarship)* [39]
IADR John Gray Fellowship *(Other/Fellowship)* [5251]
Great Lakes Section Diversity Scholarship *(Graduate, Undergraduate/Scholarship)* [5178]
Bishop Charles P. Greco Graduate Fellowships *(Graduate, Master's/Fellowship)* [5853]
Robert D. Greenberg Scholarships *(Graduate, Other/Scholarship)* [9093]
Reginald K. Groome Memorial Scholarships *(Undergraduate/Scholarship)* [8823]
Charles Grossman Graduate Scholarships *(Graduate/Scholarship)* [5306]
Ronald P. Guerrette Future Farmers of America Scholarship Fund *(Undergraduate/Scholarship)* [6196]
Eleanor Guetzloe Undergraduate Scholarship *(Undergraduate/Scholarship)* [3433]
Gulf Coast Past President's Scholarships *(Undergraduate/Scholarship)* [1413]

Larry Gulley Scholarships *(Undergraduate/Scholarship)* [9125]
Wesley R. Habley NACADA Summer Institute Scholarships *(Other/Scholarship)* [6672]
Lee Hakel Graduate Student Scholarship *(Doctorate/Scholarship)* [9152]
Joyce C. Hall College Scholarships *(Undergraduate/Scholarship)* [7960]
Chappie Hall Scholarship Program *(Undergraduate/Scholarship)* [2]
HANA Scholarships *(Undergraduate, Graduate, Doctorate/Scholarship)* [9852]
Father J. Harold Conway Memorial Scholarships *(Postgraduate/Fellowship)* [7632]
Carroll Hart Scholarship *(Graduate/Scholarship)* [9126]
Gabe A. Hartl Scholarships *(Undergraduate/Scholarship)* [137]
Thomas T. Hayashi Memorial Scholarships *(Graduate/Scholarship)* [5550]
HBO Point Scholarships *(Graduate, Undergraduate/Scholarship)* [8177]
Health Policy Scholarship for General Surgeons *(Professional development/Scholarship)* [697]
Healthcare Information Management Systems Scholarships *(Graduate, Postgraduate, Undergraduate/Scholarship)* [4831]
Joseph T. Helling Scholarship Fund *(Undergraduate/Scholarship)* [5106]
Hench Post-Dissertation Fellowship *(Postdoctorate/Fellowship)* [438]
Gerald V. Henderson Memorial Scholarships *(Undergraduate, Graduate/Scholarship)* [9210]
Henley-Putnam University Scholarships *(Other/Scholarship)* [5267]
John P. Hennessey Scholarships *(Graduate, Undergraduate/Scholarship)* [6503]
Gene Henson Scholarships *(Undergraduate/Scholarship)* [2113]
Peter Hess Scholarships *(Undergraduate/Scholarship)* [4338]
Jim Hierlihy Memorial Scholarship *(Undergraduate/Scholarship)* [3911]
Jim and Nancy Hinkle Travel Grants *(Graduate/Grant)* [4856]
Hispanic Association of Colleges and Universities Scholarships *(Undergraduate/Scholarship)* [4890]
HLS/MLA Professional Development Grants *(Other/Grant)* [6386]
C.H.(Chuck) Hodgson Scholarships *(Undergraduate/Scholarship)* [10547]
Henry Hoffman Memorial Scholarship Fund *(Undergraduate/Scholarship)* [6740]
Miriam Hoffman Scholarships *(Undergraduate, Graduate/Scholarship)* [9853]
Michael J. Hogan Language Fellowships *(Graduate/Fellowship)* [9138]
Alan Holoch Memorial Grants *(Professional development/Grant)* [531]
Governor James E. Holshouser Professional Development Scholarships *(Other/Scholarship)* [7461]
W. Stull Holt Dissertation Fellowships *(Doctorate, Graduate/Scholarship)* [9139]
Sam J. Hord Memorial Scholarships *(Undergraduate/Scholarship)* [9381]
Edward L. Horne, Jr. Scholarships *(Advanced Professional/Scholarship)* [7732]
Graduate Student Honoraria - A. Brazier Howell Awards *(Master's, Doctorate/Award)* [1359]
Goldwin Howland Scholarships *(Graduate/Scholarship)* [2720]
Chun-tu Hsueh Fellowship for International Scholars *(Graduate, Postdoctorate/Grant)* [1120]
Humanism in Medicine Scholarships *(Undergraduate/Scholarship)* [9600]
Anna C. Hume Scholarships *(Undergraduate/Scholarship)* [4428]
Carrie Hunter-Tate Award *(Undergraduate, Graduate/Scholarship)* [6794]
IAAI Scholarship Foundation Accounting Scholarships *(Undergraduate/Scholarship)* [5091]
IAESTE United States Internships *(Undergraduate/Internship)* [3489]
IALD Education Trust Scholarship Program *(Graduate, Undergraduate/Scholarship)* [5271]
IARS Mentored Research Awards (IMRA) *(Profes-*

sional development/Grant) [5242]
IASP Visiting Professor Grants (Professional development/Grant) [5275]
IBEA Graduate Scholarships (Graduate/Scholarship) [5056]
ICDA Graduate Scholarships (Graduate/Scholarship) [5464]
ICDA Research Grants (Graduate/Grant) [5465]
Ice Skating Institute of America Education Foundation Scholarships (Undergraduate/Scholarship) [5031]
IDA Fellowship Awards (Other/Fellowship) [5320]
IDTA Freestyle Scholarships (Undergraduate/Scholarship) [5317]
IFDA Student Member Scholarships (Undergraduate/Scholarship) [5338]
Ella R. Ifill Fund (Undergraduate/Scholarship) [6199]
IIE Council of Fellows Undergraduate Scholarships (Undergraduate/Scholarship) [5188]
IISE Presidents Scholarships (Undergraduate/Scholarship) [5189]
Illinois Association of Chamber of Commerce Executives Scholarships (Professional development/Scholarship) [5054]
IMA Memorial Education Fund Scholarships (MEF) (Graduate, Undergraduate/Scholarship) [5206]
Independent Professional Seed Association Student Recognition Awards (Undergraduate/Scholarship) [5098]
Indiana FFA Association State Fair Scholarship (Undergraduate/Scholarship) [5110]
Individual Professional Development Scholarship (Professional development/Scholarship) [4161]
Terrance N. Ingraham Pediatric Optometry Residency Support (Graduate/Fellowship) [416]
INIA Scholarship Program (Undergraduate/Scholarship) [5363]
Institute of Food Technologists Graduate Scholarships (Graduate/Scholarship) [5171]
International Association for Food Protection - Student Travel Scholarship Program (Undergraduate, Graduate/Scholarship) [5258]
International Association of Wildland Fire Graduate-Level Scholarships (Doctorate, Graduate/Scholarship) [5278]
International Development and Education Award in Palliative Care (Professional development/Award) [3376]
International Development and Education Awards (Professional development, Doctorate/Grant) [3377]
International Door Association Scholarship Foundation Program (Undergraduate, Vocational/Occupational/Scholarship) [5322]
International Executive Housekeepers Association Education Foundation Scholarship Awards (Undergraduate/Scholarship) [5324]
International Executive Housekeepers Association Spartan Scholarship Awards (Undergraduate/Scholarship) [5325]
International Innovation Grants (Professional development/Grant) [3378]
IOIA Organic Community Initiative Scholarships (Other/Scholarship) [5369]
ISDS Graduate Student Scholarships (Doctorate, Graduate/Scholarship) [5416]
ISID Small Grant (Postdoctorate, Professional development/Grant) [5425]
ISRS Graduate Fellowships (Doctorate, Graduate/Fellowship) [5429]
ITAA Graduate Student Best Paper Award (Graduate/Monetary) [5442]
ITEEA Greer/FTE Grants (Other/Grant) [5437]
ITNS Research Grants (Other/Grant) [5449]
Dr. Karl C. Ivarson Scholarships (Master's, Doctorate/Scholarship) [113]
Graduate Student Honoraria - Anna M. Jackson Awards (Master's, Doctorate/Award) [1360]
Freddy L. Jacobs Scholarships (Undergraduate/Scholarship) [5284]
Jagiellonian University Summer Program Scholarship (Professional development/Scholarship) [8204]
Jamaican Canadian Association Alberta Scholarship Program (Undergraduate/Scholarship) [5533]

Olivia James Traveling Fellowships (Professional development/Fellowship) [1608]
Sister Rita Jeanne Scholarships (Undergraduate/Monetary, Scholarship) [5626]
Gaynold Jensen Education Stipends (Postdoctorate, Other/Scholarship) [3622]
Nancy Lorraine Jensen Memorial Scholarships (Undergraduate/Scholarship) [9345]
Stanley "Doc" Jensen Scholarships (Undergraduate/Scholarship) [760]
Reverend H. John and Asako Yamashita Memorial Scholarships (Graduate/Scholarship) [5551]
John F. Kennedy Scholarship Award (Undergraduate/Scholarship) [2435]
Joseph C. Johnson Memorial Grants (Undergraduate/Grant, Scholarship) [1252]
Gregory D. Johnson Memorial Scholarships (Doctorate, Graduate, Master's/Scholarship) [7036]
Professor Emeritus Dr. Bill Johnson Memorial Scholarships (Undergraduate/Scholarship) [8874]
OOIDA Mary Johnston Scholarships (Undergraduate/Scholarship) [7785]
Jones-Lovich Grants in Southwestern Herpetology (Master's, Doctorate/Grant) [4872]
Joseph H. Fichter Research Grants (Other/Grant) [2071]
Journey Toward Ordained Ministry Scholarships (Undergraduate, Graduate/Scholarship) [9854]
Mike Kabo Global Scholarships (Other/Scholarship) [4456]
Sam Kalman Scholarship (Undergraduate/Scholarship) [1582]
Shripat Kamble Urban Entomology Graduate Student Awards for Innovative Research (Doctorate/Recognition, Grant) [3881]
Joan Kamps Memorial Bursaries (Undergraduate, Graduate, Postgraduate, Professional development/Scholarship) [7633]
Kaplan Scholarships (Graduate/Scholarship) [4898]
Kappa Delta Phi Scholarship Program (Postgraduate/Scholarship) [1046]
The ISASI Rudolf Kapustin Memorial Scholarships (Undergraduate/Scholarship) [5394]
Philip R. Karr, III Scholarship Fund (Graduate/Scholarship) [4378]
Magoichi and Shizuko Kato Memorial Scholarships (Graduate, Master's, Doctorate/Scholarship) [5552]
Gunild Keetman Scholarships (Other, Undergraduate/Scholarship) [7714]
Rita Mae Kelly Fund (Graduate, Doctorate/Fellowship) [1121]
Kathleen Kelly Undergraduate Scholarship Award (Undergraduate/Scholarship) [8374]
Robert E. Kelsey Annual Scholarship (Undergraduate/Scholarship) [7933]
Willmoore H. Kendall Scholarships (Professional development/Scholarship) [3062]
Keith Kevan Award (Postgraduate/Award) [3892]
KHIMA Graduate Scholarships (Graduate/Scholarship) [5661]
Julia Kiene Fellowships in Electrical Energy (Graduate/Fellowship) [10660]
The Margie Klein "Paper Plate" Scholarships (Undergraduate/Scholarship) [1850]
AALL/Wolters Kluwer Law & Business Grants (Professional development/Grant) [532]
Robert E. Knight Professional Scholarships (Graduate/Scholarship) [9692]
Elva Knight Research Grants (Professional development/Grant) [5356]
Glenn Knudsvig Memorial Scholarships (Graduate, Undergraduate/Scholarship) [679]
Ina Knutsen Scholarships (Undergraduate/Scholarship) [8875]
Gwin J. and Ruth Kolb Research Travel Fellowships (Doctorate, Other/Fellowship) [1294]
Carl Koller Memorial Research Grants (Professional development/Grant) [1404]
AIST Willy Korf Memorial Fund (Undergraduate/Scholarship) [2000]
Marcia J. Koslov Scholarship (Professional development/Grant) [533]
Eugene and Elinor Kotur Scholarship Trust Fund (Undergraduate, Graduate/Scholarship) [10443]

Michael Kraus Research Grants (Doctorate/Grant) [854]
Kress/AAR Fellowships (Professional development/Fellowship) [1855]
David A. Kronick Travelling Fellowships (Doctorate, Graduate/Fellowship) [6387]
Melvin Kruger Endowed Scholarships (Graduate, Undergraduate/Scholarship) [8644]
Eldon E. and JoAnn C. Kuhns Family Scholarships (Undergraduate, Graduate/Scholarship) [6584]
Sam and Florice Kuwahara Memorial Scholarship (Undergraduate/Scholarship) [5553]
Henry and Chiyo Kuwahara Memorial Scholarships (Undergraduate, Graduate/Scholarship) [5554]
Anne Emery Kyllo Professional Scholarships (Professional development/Scholarship) [1014]
Ron LaFreniere Business Administration Scholarship (Undergraduate/Scholarship) [8877]
Frank S. Land Scholarships (Undergraduate/Scholarship) [3598]
James D. Lang Memorial Scholarships (Graduate/Scholarship) [2563]
Lansdale Public Policy Fellowship (Advanced Professional, Professional development/Fellowship) [1245]
Laser Technology, Engineering and Applications Scholarships (Graduate, Undergraduate/Scholarship) [9469]
Daniel Lasky Scholarship Fund (Undergraduate/Scholarship) [7081]
Jay and Deborah Last Fellowships (Doctorate/Fellowship) [440]
Candia Baker Laughlin Certification Scholarships (Undergraduate/Scholarship) [389]
Willie D. Lawson, Jr. Memorial Scholarships (Doctorate, Graduate, Other/Scholarship) [6819]
Lee Womack Scholarship Fund (Undergraduate/Scholarship) [6570]
The Leesfield/AAJ Law Student Scholarships (Undergraduate/Scholarship) [517]
The Legacy Fellowships (Doctorate/Fellowship) [441]
Lemelson Student Fellowships (Graduate/Award) [9282]
Myra Levick Scholarships (Graduate/Scholarship) [449]
Herbert Levy Memorial Scholarship (Undergraduate/Scholarship) [9255]
Ta Liang Memorial Awards (Graduate/Grant, Award) [1806]
AIST Ronald E. Lincoln Memorial Scholarships (Undergraduate/Scholarship) [2001]
Litherland/FTEE Scholarships (Undergraduate/Scholarship) [5438]
Littleton-Griswold Research Grants (Doctorate/Grant) [855]
Long-term International Fellowships (Professional development/Fellowship) [3380]
D.J. Lovell Scholarships (Graduate, Undergraduate/Scholarship) [9470]
LPHA Scholarships (Graduate, Undergraduate/Scholarship) [6122]
Juan and Esperanza Luna Scholarship (Undergraduate/Scholarship) [1583]
Luso-American Fraternal Federation B-2 Scholarships (Postgraduate/Scholarship) [6149]
Luso-American Fraternal Federation B-3 Scholarships (Professional development/Scholarship) [6150]
Luso-American Fraternal Federation B-4 Scholarships (Professional development/Scholarship) [6151]
Charles Luttman Scholarship (Undergraduate/Scholarship) [2536]
Margaret Lynch Religious Study Fellowships (Graduate/Scholarship) [7634]
The C. Lyons Fellowship Program (Advanced Professional/Fellowship) [7047]
Verne LaMarr Lyons Memorial Scholarships (Graduate, Master's/Fellowship) [6790]
MAC Emeritus Scholarships for First-Time Meeting Attendees (Professional development/Scholarship) [6516]
Carol E. Macpherson Memorial Scholarship (Graduate, Undergraduate/Scholarship) [10203]

Andrew Macrina Scholarships *(Undergraduate/Scholarship)* [761]
MAES Founders Scholarships *(Graduate, Undergraduate/Scholarship)* [6178]
MAES General Scholarships *(Graduate, Undergraduate/Scholarship)* [6179]
MAES Graduate Scholarships *(Graduate/Scholarship)* [6180]
MAES Padrino/Madrina Scholarships *(Graduate, Undergraduate/Scholarship)* [6181]
MAES Pipeline Scholarships *(Graduate, Undergraduate/Scholarship)* [6182]
MAES Presidential Scholarships *(Graduate, Undergraduate/Scholarship)* [6183]
Dr. Edward May Magruder Medical Scholarships *(Undergraduate/Scholarship)* [677]
Maine Graphic Arts Association Scholarships *(Undergraduate/Scholarship)* [6215]
Maley/FTE Scholarships *(Graduate/Scholarship)* [5439]
Maley/FTEE Teacher Scholarships *(Professional development/Scholarship)* [5440]
Margaret Mallett Nursing Scholarship *(Undergraduate/Scholarship)* [8878]
NBCFAE Mamie W. Mallory National Scholarship Program *(Undergraduate/Scholarship)* [6813]
Sue A. Malone Scholarships *(Doctorate, Graduate, Professional development/Scholarship)* [5662]
David C. Maloney Scholarships *(Undergraduate/Scholarship)* [7079]
Lyle Mamer Fellowships *(Graduate/Fellowship, Award)* [10661]
March of Dimes Graduate Nursing Scholarships *(Graduate/Scholarship)* [6234]
Harold and Inge Marcus Scholarships *(Undergraduate/Scholarship)* [5191]
Marine Technology Society ROV Scholarships (MTS ROV) *(Undergraduate, Graduate/Scholarship)* [6272]
Marliave Scholarship Fund *(Undergraduate/Scholarship, Grant)* [1948]
Ray and Gertrude Marshall Scholarships *(Undergraduate/Scholarship)* [762]
Martha Weston Grant *(Advanced Professional/Grant)* [9097]
The Maschhoffs Pork Production Scholarships *(Undergraduate/Scholarship)* [7037]
Val Mason Scholarships *(Postgraduate/Scholarship)* [2746]
Master Municipal Clerks Academy Scholarships *(Other/Scholarship)* [5351]
Master's Degree with a Major in Nursing Academic Scholarships *(Graduate/Scholarship)* [6657]
Noel D. Matkin Awards *(Undergraduate/Award)* [3798]
Rene Matos Memorial Scholarships *(Undergraduate, Vocational/Occupational/Scholarship)* [6996]
Antonio Mattos Memorial Scholarships *(Undergraduate/Scholarship)* [6152]
Mature Student Scholarship *(Undergraduate/Scholarship)* [3912]
Clara Mayo Grants Program *(Graduate/Grant)* [9290]
John Mazurek Memorial-Morgex Insurance Scholarship *(Other/Scholarship)* [296]
MCBA Scholarship *(Undergraduate/Scholarship)* [6465]
McCloy Fellowships in Agriculture *(Professional development/Fellowship)* [727]
Hans McCorriston Motive Power Machinist Grant Programs *(Undergraduate/Scholarship)* [2132]
Foster G. McGaw Graduate Student Scholarships *(Graduate/Scholarship)* [688]
Richard McGrath Memorial Fund Awards *(Undergraduate/Award)* [755]
McJulien Minority Graduate Scholarships *(Graduate/Scholarship)* [1944]
AIST Midwest Member Chapter - Betty McKern Scholarships *(Undergraduate/Scholarship)* [2002]
John J. McKetta Undergraduate Scholarships *(Undergraduate/Scholarship)* [905]
Arthur Patch McKinlay Scholarships *(Graduate, Undergraduate/Scholarship)* [680]
McKinney Sisters Undergraduate Scholarships *(Undergraduate/Scholarship)* [3556]

Ruth McMillan Student Grants *(Undergraduate/Grant)* [2482]
National Association of Pediatric Nurse Practitioners McNeil Rural and Underserved Scholarships *(Graduate/Scholarship)* [6774]
MCRTA Book Scholarships *(Undergraduate/Scholarship)* [6449]
MDA Development Grants *(Doctorate/Grant)* [6622]
MDA Research Grants *(Advanced Professional/Grant)* [6623]
David Meador Foundation - Club Management Student Scholarships *(Undergraduate/Scholarship)* [7295]
The Medalist Club Post Graduate Scholarships *(Postgraduate/Scholarship)* [6376]
Medford Rogue Rotary Scholarship *(Undergraduate/Scholarship)* [6380]
Medical Student Rotation for Underrepresented Populations *(Graduate/Grant)* [3381]
Medina County Retired Teachers Association Scholarship *(Undergraduate/Scholarship)* [6400]
Susan R. Meisinger Fellowship for Graduate Study in HR *(Graduate, Master's, Advanced Professional/Fellowship)* [9146]
Frederic G. Melcher Scholarships *(Graduate/Scholarship)* [2018]
Mellon-CES Dissertation Completion Fellowships *(Graduate/Fellowship)* [3440]
Terry Mellor Continuing Education Grant *(Undergraduate/Grant)* [9480]
MELNA Scholarship *(Undergraduate, Graduate/Scholarship)* [6217]
CAG Donald Menzies Bursary Awards *(Postgraduate/Scholarship, Award)* [2554]
MESA Student Travel Fund *(Undergraduate/Grant)* [6511]
Scott Mesh Honorary Grant for Research in Psychology *(Graduate/Grant)* [1134]
Edmond A. Metzger Scholarships *(Undergraduate/Scholarship)* [1747]
Theodore Meyer Scholarships *(Undergraduate, Graduate/Scholarship)* [1015]
MICA Scholarships *(Undergraduate/Scholarship)* [6532]
Michigan Education Association Scholarships *(Undergraduate/Scholarship)* [6470]
Beth Middleton Memorial Scholarships *(Undergraduate/Scholarship)* [3961]
Midlothian Rotary Club "Service Above Self" Scholarship *(Undergraduate/Scholarship)* [6513]
Milan Getting Scholarships *(Undergraduate/Scholarship)* [9335]
Cheryl Allyn Miller Award *(Doctorate, Graduate/Monetary)* [9332]
Warren E. Miller Fellowship in Electoral Politics *(Advanced Professional, Graduate, Postdoctorate/Fellowship)* [1122]
Mineral & Metallurgical Processing Division Scholarships and Richard Klimpel Memorial Scholarships *(Undergraduate, Graduate/Scholarship)* [9211]
Mary Minglen Scholarship Program *(Postgraduate/Scholarship)* [1047]
Minnesota Health Information Management Association Scholarships *(Undergraduate/Scholarship)* [6547]
Minnesota State Archery Association Scholarships Program *(Undergraduate/Scholarship)* [6551]
MLA Continuing Education Awards (CE) *(Graduate/Grant)* [6390]
MLA Financial Assistance *(Graduate, Advanced Professional/Grant)* [6567]
MLA Research, Development, and Demonstration Project Grants *(Graduate/Grant)* [6392]
MODNA Nursing Education Scholarships *(Doctorate, Graduate/Fellowship)* [6509]
Antoinette M. Molinari Memorial Scholarships *(Doctorate/Scholarship)* [417]
Farmers Union Industries Foundation Stanley Moore Scholarships *(Undergraduate/Scholarship)* [7488]
NFU Foundation Stanley Moore Scholarships *(Undergraduate/Scholarship)* [7489]
Chapter 63 - Portland James E. Morrow Scholarships *(Graduate, Undergraduate/Scholarship)* [9189]
Mortar Board National Foundation Fellowships *(Postdoctorate/Fellowship)* [6600]

Wilma Motley Memorial California Merit Scholarships *(Undergraduate/Scholarship)* [777]
MPI CRV Scholarships *(Other/Scholarship)* [6402]
MPI-WI Founders Grant Program *(Professional development/Grant)* [6405]
MSCPA Scholarship - Montana Tech *(Undergraduate, Graduate/Scholarship)* [6585]
MSCPA Scholarship - MSU Bozeman *(Undergraduate, Graduate/Scholarship)* [6586]
MSCPA Scholarship - University of Montana *(Undergraduate, Graduate/Scholarship)* [6587]
MSEA/SEIU Part-time Student Members Scholarships *(Undergraduate/Scholarship)* [6223]
The MTS Student Scholarship for Graduate Students *(Graduate/Scholarship)* [6273]
The MTS Student Scholarship for Graduating High School Seniors *(Undergraduate/Scholarship)* [6274]
The MTS Student Scholarship for Two-Year, Technical, Engineering and Community College Students *(Undergraduate/Scholarship)* [6275]
Mueller Undergraduate Scholarships *(Undergraduate/Scholarship)* [10618]
Multicultural Work-in-Progress Grant *(Advanced Professional/Grant)* [9098]
Marvin Mundel Memorial Scholarships *(Undergraduate/Scholarship)* [5192]
Clarence & Josephine Myers Undergraduate Scholarships *(Graduate, Undergraduate/Scholarship)* [9190]
NAAE Upper Division Scholarships *(Undergraduate/Scholarship)* [6712]
NABA National Scholarship Program *(Graduate, Undergraduate/Scholarship)* [6716]
NACADA Scholarships *(Graduate/Scholarship)* [6673]
NAFA Scholarship Programs *(Undergraduate/Scholarship)* [6690]
IADR Toshio Nakao Fellowship *(Other/Fellowship)* [5252]
NARFE-FEEA Scholarship Awards Program *(Undergraduate/Scholarship)* [6686]
NASE Future Entrepreneur *(Undergraduate/Scholarship)* [6784]
Kermit B. Nash Academic Scholarships *(Undergraduate/Scholarship)* [8891]
National AAHAM Scholarships *(Undergraduate/Scholarship)* [504]
National Association for the Self-Employed Scholarships *(Professional development/Scholarship)* [6785]
National Ataxia Foundation Research Grants *(Other/Grant)* [6807]
National Beta Club Scholarships *(Undergraduate/Scholarship)* [6809]
National Black Deaf Advocate Scholarships *(Graduate, Undergraduate/Scholarship)* [6816]
National Black Nurses Association Scholarships *(Undergraduate/Scholarship)* [6823]
National Council on Public History Graduate Student Travel Awards *(Doctorate, Graduate/Grant)* [6882]
National Council on Public History Student Project Awards *(Undergraduate/Grant)* [6883]
National Court Reporters Association Student Intern Scholarship *(Undergraduate/Scholarship)* [6897]
National Dairy Herd Information Association Scholarship Program *(Undergraduate/Scholarship)* [6903]
National Dental Hygienists' Association Scholarships *(Undergraduate/Scholarship)* [6916]
National Guard Association of Rhode Island Scholarship *(Undergraduate/Scholarship)* [6978]
National Huguenot Society College and Postgraduate Student Scholarships *(Undergraduate, Postgraduate/Scholarship)* [7006]
National Judges Association Scholarships *(Other/Scholarship)* [7030]
National Junior Swine Association Outstanding Member Scholarships *(Graduate/Scholarship)* [7038]
National Merit Harris Corporation Scholarship Program *(Undergraduate/Scholarship)* [4729]
National Recreation and Park Association Diversity Scholarships *(Undergraduate/Scholarship)* [7118]
National Slovak Society Senior Scholarships *(Un-*

dergraduate, Vocational/Occupational/Scholarship) [7132]
National Swimming Pool Foundation Scholarship Awards (Other/Scholarship) [7193]
National Technical Honor Society Scholarships (Professional development/Scholarship) [2424]
National Technical Honor Society Scholarships (Undergraduate/Scholarship) [3962]
National Women's Studies Association Lesbian Caucus Award (Master's, Doctorate/Award, Grant) [7218]
NBMBAA Graduate Scholarships Program (Graduate/Scholarship) [6821]
NCECA Graduate Student Fellowships (Graduate/Fellowship) [6880]
NCPA Foundation Presidential Scholarships (Undergraduate/Scholarship) [6869]
NCRF New Professional Reporter Grant (Other/Grant) [6898]
NCTE Research Foundation Grants (Other/Grant) [6885]
NCTM Emerging Teacher-Leaders in Elementary School Mathematics Grants for Grades K-5 Teachers (Other/Grant) [6889]
NCTM School In-Service Training Grants for Grades 6-8 Teachers (Undergraduate/Grant) [6891]
NCTM School In-Service Training Grants for Grades 9-12 Teachers (Undergraduate/Grant) [6892]
NCTM School In-Service Training Grants for Grades K-5 Teachers (Undergraduate/Grant) [6893]
NDIA Picatinny Chapter Scholarships (Undergraduate/Scholarship) [6909]
NDTA Academic Scholarship Program A (Undergraduate/Scholarship) [6913]
NDTA Academic Scholarship Program B (Undergraduate/Scholarship) [6914]
Nebraska Farm Bureau Greater Horizon Scholarships (Undergraduate/Scholarship) [7240]
Nebraska Paralegal Association Student Scholarships (Undergraduate/Scholarship) [7247]
NEHA/AAS Scholarship (Graduate, Undergraduate/Scholarship) [6943]
NELA Conference Scholarships (All/Scholarship) [7297]
Bill Nelson Scholarship Endowment (BNSE) (Undergraduate, Graduate/Scholarship) [7768]
AIST Midwest Member Chapter - Don Nelson Scholarships (Undergraduate/Scholarship) [2003]
NEMLA Summer Fellowships (Graduate, Other/Fellowship) [7511]
NEMRA Educational Scholarship Foundation (Undergraduate, Vocational/Occupational/Scholarship) [6941]
New Hampshire Snowmobile Association Book Scholarships (Undergraduate/Scholarship) [7313]
New York State Association of Agricultural Fairs Scholarships (Undergraduate/Scholarship) [7361]
NFPA/PACE Scholarships (Other/Scholarship) [6951]
NFPA Youth Scholarships (Undergraduate, Vocational/Occupational/Scholarship) [6961]
NGAT Educational Scholarships (Graduate, Undergraduate/Scholarship) [6980]
NHAEOP Member Scholarships (Undergraduate/Scholarship) [7299]
NHS National Scholarships (Undergraduate/Scholarship) [7000]
NHS Regional Scholarships (Undergraduate/Scholarship) [7001]
NIABA/NIAF Scholarships (Graduate/Scholarship) [7025]
NIBA Presidential Scholarships (Undergraduate/Scholarship) [7010]
Norman Nicholson Scholarships (Undergraduate/Scholarship) [2607]
AIST Midwest Member Chapter - Mel Nickel Scholarships (Undergraduate/Scholarship) [2004]
Eric Niemitalo Scholarships in Earth and Environmental Science (Undergraduate/Scholarship) [8879]
Louise A. Nixon Scholarships (Graduate/Scholarship) [7245]
NJSA Visionary Leader Scholarships (Graduate/Scholarship) [7039]
NLBRA National Royalty Scholarships (Undergraduate/Scholarship) [7054]

NLBRA Rainwater Scholarships (Undergraduate/Scholarship) [7055]
NLBRA World All Around Scholarships (Undergraduate/Scholarship) [7056]
NLBRA World Event Scholarships (Undergraduate/Scholarship) [7057]
NLBRA/Wrangler Academic Scholarships (Undergraduate/Scholarship) [7058]
NLBRA Youth Board Officer Scholarships (Undergraduate/Scholarship) [7059]
NMIA Scholarship Program (Undergraduate, Graduate/Scholarship) [7071]
NMSC Corporate-Sponsored Achievement Scholarship Awards (Undergraduate/Scholarship) [7065]
Non Commissioned Officers Association Scholarships (Undergraduate/Scholarship) [7441]
Nor' Easters Scholarships - Four-year Program (Undergraduate/Scholarship) [4915]
Nor' Easters Scholarships - Two-year Program (Undergraduate/Scholarship) [4916]
Nordic Ski Association of Anchorage Scholarships (Undergraduate/Scholarship) [221]
North Alabama Dietetic Association Scholarships (Graduate, Undergraduate/Scholarship) [197]
North American Society Fellowships (Professional development/Fellowship) [8119]
North Central, Region 9 Scholarships (Undergraduate/Scholarship) [9191]
North Dakota Farmers Union Scholarships (Undergraduate/Scholarship) [7491]
North Florida Chapter Safety Education Scholarships (Graduate, Undergraduate/Scholarship) [1423]
North Texas Relocation Professionals Scholarships (Undergraduate/Scholarship) [7505]
NorthCoast Medical Scholarship Program (Postgraduate/Scholarship) [1048]
Northeast Alabama District Dietetic Association Scholarships (Graduate, Undergraduate/Scholarship) [198]
Northeastern Illinois Chapter Scholarships (Graduate, Undergraduate/Scholarship) [1424]
Northern California Chapter of HIMSS Scholarships (Graduate, Postgraduate, Undergraduate/Scholarship) [4832]
NPM Academic Scholarships (Graduate, Undergraduate/Scholarship) [6768]
NPM Program Scholarships (Undergraduate/Scholarship) [6769]
NSHSS Academic Paper Awards (High School/Scholarship) [7160]
NSHSS National Scholar Awards (High School/Scholarship) [7161]
NSPS Scholarships (Undergraduate/Scholarship) [7175]
NSS Conservation Grants (Advanced Professional/Grant) [7182]
NSSA/NSCA Collegiate Scholarships (Undergraduate/Scholarship) [7186]
NTHS/HOSA Scholarships (Undergraduate/Scholarship) [7197]
Nuts, Bolts and Thingamajigs Scholarships (Undergraduate, Vocational/Occupational/Scholarship) [7562]
NWSA Graduate Scholarships (Graduate/Scholarship) [7219]
NYLA-Dewey Scholarship (Master's, Undergraduate/Scholarship) [7357]
Dennis J. O'Brien USAEE/IAEE Best Student Paper Award (Undergraduate/Award) [9884]
Jeff Oliphant Memorial Post-Graduate Scholarships (Postgraduate/Scholarship) [10619]
Roy C. and Dorothy Jean Olson Memorial Scholarships (Undergraduate/Scholarship) [5361]
Omicron Delta Kappa Foundation Scholarships (Graduate/Scholarship) [7611]
Oncology Trainee Travel Awards (Professional development/Grant) [3383]
Frank Oppenheimer Scholarship Program (Postgraduate/Scholarship) [1049]
Optical Design and Engineering Scholarships (Graduate, Undergraduate/Scholarship) [9471]
Organization of Black Aerospace Professionals General Scholarships (All/Scholarship) [7733]
Orthopaedic Trauma Association Research Grants (Other/Grant) [7753]

Mary Reiko Osaka Memorial Scholarships (Undergraduate, Graduate/Scholarship) [5555]
OSCA Graduate Student Scholarship Program (Graduate/Scholarship) [7590]
Donald F. and Mildred Topp Othmer National Scholarship Awards (Undergraduate/Scholarship) [906]
Elvina Jane Owen Awards (Graduate, Undergraduate/Scholarship) [9855]
Casilda Pagan Educational/Vocational Scholarships (Graduate, Undergraduate, Postgraduate/Scholarship) [4964]
Paleontological Society Student Research Grants (Graduate, Undergraduate/Grant) [17]
Robert R. Palmer Research Travel Fellowships (Other/Fellowship) [1296]
Pan Pacific Law Enforcement Scholarships (Undergraduate/Scholarship) [8745]
Joseph M. Parish Memorial Grants (Undergraduate/Scholarship, Grant) [1253]
Parking Industry Institute Scholarship Program (Undergraduate/Scholarship) [7094]
Ted Parnell Scholarship (Undergraduate/Scholarship) [10772]
The Paros-Digiquartz Scholarships (Graduate, Undergraduate/Scholarship) [6276]
Carl Parsell Scholarship Fund (Undergraduate/Scholarship) [6459]
Q. O. (Quint) Patrick Scholarships (Undergraduate/Scholarship) [10548]
Walter S. Patterson Scholarships (Graduate/Scholarship) [2370]
Arthur Paulin Automotive Aftermarket Scholarship Awards (Postgraduate, Undergraduate/Scholarship) [2133]
Ray, NORP and Katie, WOKTE Pautz Scholarships (Undergraduate/Scholarship) [1750]
PCCE Scholarship (Undergraduate/Scholarship) [6952]
PDF-PSG Mentored Clinical Research Awards (Professional development/Award) [7886]
PEA Bursaries (Undergraduate/Scholarship) [8290]
PEA Scholarships (Undergraduate/Scholarship) [8291]
Pediatric Endocrinology Nursing Society Academic Education Scholarships (Undergraduate/Scholarship) [7926]
Pediatric Endocrinology Nursing Society Convention Reimbursement Awards (Undergraduate/Award) [7927]
Joaquim Pereira Memorial Scholarships (Undergraduate/Scholarship) [6153]
Kate B. and Hall J. Peterson Fellowships (Doctorate/Fellowship) [443]
Silvio and Eugenia Petrini Grants (Other/Grant) [4711]
Petroleum Packaging Council Scholarships (Undergraduate/Scholarship) [8019]
PGSF Scholarships (Undergraduate/Scholarship) [8284]
William Philpott Scholarships (Undergraduate/Scholarship) [2269]
Ed Phinney Commemorative Scholarships (Graduate, Undergraduate/Scholarship) [681]
Peter L. Picknelly Honorary Scholarships (Undergraduate/Scholarship) [640]
David Pilon Scholarships for Training in Professional Psychology (Graduate/Scholarship) [1135]
Pipe Line Contractors Association of Canada Student Bursary (Undergraduate, Postgraduate/Scholarship) [8142]
Stephen D. Pisinski Memorial Scholarships (Undergraduate/Scholarship) [8376]
Christopher Mark Pitkin Memorial Scholarships (Undergraduate/Scholarship) [6994]
Pitsenbarger Awards (Undergraduate/Grant, Award) [125]
Betsy Plank/PRSSA Scholarships (Undergraduate/Scholarship) [8377]
Katherine Barton Platt Excavation Fellowships (Other, Undergraduate/Fellowship) [1237]
PLUS Foundation Financial Aid Scholarships (Undergraduate/Scholarship) [8168]
PNAA Nursing Scholarship Award (Master's, Doctorate/Scholarship) [8113]
Daniel H. Pokorny Memorial Scholarship Awards (Undergraduate/Scholarship) [8543]

Police Explorer Scholarships Program *(Undergraduate/Scholarship)* [4106]
Polish American Club of North Jersey Scholarships *(Graduate, Undergraduate/Scholarship)* [5881]
Polish National Alliance of Brooklyn, USA Scholarships *(Undergraduate/Scholarship)* [5882]
Harriet and Leon Pomerance Fellowships *(Professional development/Fellowship)* [1610]
Portable Sanitation Association International Scholarship Fund *(Undergraduate/Scholarship)* [8207]
Porter Physiology Development Fellowship Awards *(Doctorate/Fellowship)* [1100]
AFT Robert Porter Scholarship Program *(Undergraduate/Scholarship)* [795]
Barbara Potter Scholarships *(Professional development/Scholarship)* [1055]
J.R. (Joe) Power National Scholarships *(Postgraduate/Scholarship)* [8383]
Presbyterian Association of Musicians Scholarships *(All/Scholarship)* [8217]
Diana M. Priestly Memorial Scholarships *(Undergraduate/Scholarship)* [2564]
Print and Graphics Scholarship Foundation Awards (PGSF-GATF) *(Graduate, Undergraduate/Scholarship, Fellowship)* [8282]
Procter & Gamble Professional Oral Health/HDA Foundation Scholarships *(Undergraduate/Scholarship)* [4893]
Professional Development and Education Fund (PDEF) Professional Development Scholarships *(Professional development/Scholarship)* [9223]
Provincial and Regional 4-H Scholarships *(Undergraduate/Scholarship)* [9]
Barbara F. Prowant Nursing Research Grants *(Graduate/Grant)* [1028]
Prudential 1L Summer Internships *(Postgraduate/Internship)* [6706]
Neil Pruitt, Sr. Memorial Scholarships *(Undergraduate/Scholarship)* [6870]
Joseph E. Pryor Graduate Fellowships *(Graduate/Fellowship, Scholarship)* [343]
PSAC-AGR National Scholarships *(Postgraduate/Scholarship)* [8384]
PSAC - Coughlin National Scholarships *(Postgraduate/Scholarship)* [8385]
PSAC Regional Scholarships *(Postgraduate/Scholarship)* [8386]
Paul Pumpian Scholarship *(Undergraduate/Scholarship)* [1584]
A.O. Putnam Memorial Scholarships *(Undergraduate/Scholarship)* [5193]
AIST Judith A. Quinn Detroit Member Chapter Scholarship *(Undergraduate/Scholarship)* [2005]
Railroad and Mine Workers Memorial Scholarships *(Graduate/Scholarship)* [5556]
Tom D. Ralls Memorial Scholarship *(Professional development/Scholarship)* [4285]
The NASSCO Jeffrey D. Ralston Memorial Scholarship *(Undergraduate/Scholarship)* [6668]
Lenny Ravich "Shalom" Scholarships *(Advanced Professional/Scholarship)* [1851]
Rawley Silver Awards for Excellence *(Graduate/Scholarship)* [450]
The Reese Fellowships *(Doctorate/Fellowship)* [444]
Research Resident/Fellow Grants *(Professional development/Grant)* [8417]
Resident Travel Award for Underrepresented Populations *(Professional development/Award)* [3386]
Thomson Reuters/MLA Doctoral Fellowships *(Doctorate, Graduate/Fellowship)* [6393]
Reynoldsburg-Pickerington Rotary Club High School Scholarship *(Undergraduate/Scholarship)* [8595]
Haynes Rice Scholarships *(Graduate/Scholarship)* [6756]
Henry and Sylvia Richardson Research Grant *(Postdoctorate/Grant)* [3883]
J. Milton Richardson Theological Fellowships *(Graduate/Fellowship)* [363]
ANN Ingrid Josefin Ridky Academic Scholarships *(Undergraduate, Graduate/Scholarship)* [45]
Donald Riebhoff Memorial Scholarships *(Undergraduate/Scholarship)* [1753]
John T. Riordan Professional Education Scholarships *(Other/Scholarship)* [5307]
Riverside Sheriffs Association Member Scholarship Program *(Graduate, Undergraduate/Scholarship)* [8622]
Robert J. McNamara Student Paper Awards *(Graduate/Award)* [2072]
Marion Roberts Memorial Scholarships *(Undergraduate/Scholarship)* [2134]
Samuel Robinson Awards *(Undergraduate/Award)* [8219]
Gertrude J. Robinson Book Prize *(Professional development/Prize)* [2616]
Helen M. Robinson Grants *(Doctorate/Award, Monetary, Grant)* [5357]
NKA Dr. Violet B. Robinson Memorial Graduate Scholarship *(Advanced Professional/Scholarship)* [7043]
Claude Robinson Scholarships *(Undergraduate/Scholarship)* [7040]
Paul S. Robinson Scholarships *(Undergraduate/Scholarship)* [9115]
Rochelle Scholarship *(College/Scholarship)* [6124]
Paul W. Rodgers Scholarship *(Undergraduate, Master's, Doctorate/Scholarship)* [5261]
R.O.E.A. Dumitru Golea Goldy-Gemu Scholarships *(Undergraduate/Scholarship)* [1227]
Joseph Wood Rogers Memorial Scholarships *(Undergraduate/Scholarship)* [8880]
Betty Rose Scholarships *(Undergraduate/Scholarship)* [1276]
Mandell and Lester Rosenblatt Undergraduate Scholarships *(Undergraduate/Scholarship)* [9217]
Barbara Rosenblum Cancer Dissertation Scholarships *(Doctorate/Scholarship, Scholarship)* [9333]
IADR Norton Ross Fellowship *(Postgraduate/Fellowship)* [5253]
Colonel Jerry W. Ross Scholarship *(Undergraduate/Scholarship)* [1585]
Ross Trust Future School Counselors Essay Competition *(Master's, Doctorate/Award, Prize)* [750]
Marion and Donald Routh Student Research Grants *(Undergraduate/Grant)* [1572]
Cecilia Rowan Religious Study Fellowships *(Graduate/Fellowship)* [7635]
Robert Roy Awards *(Advanced Professional/Award, Recognition)* [1897]
RPNAS Baccalaureate Level Program Scholarships *(Undergraduate/Scholarship)* [8538]
RPNAS Doctorate Level Program Scholarships *(Doctorate/Scholarship)* [8539]
RPNAS Master's Level Program Scholarship *(Master's/Scholarship)* [8540]
RSNA/AUR/APDR/SCARD Radiology Education Research Development Grant *(Professional development/Grant)* [8418]
RSNA Education Scholar Grant *(Professional development/Grant)* [8419]
RSNA Research Scholar Grants *(Professional development/Grant)* [8420]
RSNA Research Seed Grants *(Professional development/Grant)* [8421]
Hermann G. Rusch Scholarships *(Other/Scholarship, Grant)* [763]
Russell Athletics Scholarship *(Undergraduate/Scholarship)* [2109]
The Anthony C. Russo Scholarships *(Graduate/Scholarship)* [7115]
IOIA Andrew Rutherford Scholarships *(Other/Scholarship)* [5370]
Safer Athletic Field Environments Scholarships (SAFE) *(Graduate, Undergraduate/Scholarship)* [9481]
SAH Study Tour Fellowships *(Graduate/Fellowship)* [9085]
Sons and Daughters Don Sahli-Kathy Woodall Scholarships *(Graduate, Undergraduate/Scholarship)* [9678]
St. Louis Paralegal Association Student Scholarships *(Undergraduate/Scholarship)* [8673]
Salvatori Fellowships *(Graduate/Fellowship)* [5234]
AIST David H. Samson Canadian Scholarships *(Undergraduate/Scholarship)* [2006]
Frank Sarli Memorial Scholarship *(Undergraduate/Scholarship)* [6899]
SARP Education Assistance Grants *(Professional development/Grant)* [8762]
SARP Professional Development Grants *(Professional development/Grant)* [8763]
Saskatchewan Hockey Association Scholarships *(Undergraduate/Scholarship)* [8775]
Saskatchewan Trucking Association Scholarships *(Undergraduate/Scholarship)* [8784]
Sho Sato Memorial Scholarships *(Undergraduate, Graduate/Scholarship)* [5557]
François J. Saucier Prize in Applied Oceanography *(Professional development/Award, Prize)* [2685]
SC and R Foundation Scholarships *(Undergraduate/Scholarship)* [9460]
SCBWI Work-in-Progress Awards *(Advanced Professional/Grant, Award)* [9101]
Schallek Awards *(Graduate/Award)* [6397]
Schallek Fellowships *(Graduate/Fellowship)* [6398]
Schlegel-UW RIA Scholarships *(Doctorate/Scholarship)* [2555]
Harold W. Schloss Memorial Scholarship Fund *(Undergraduate/Scholarship)* [2810]
Bernadotte E. Schmitt Grants *(Doctorate/Grant)* [856]
Stanley M. Schoenfeld Memorial Scholarship *(Postgraduate/Scholarship)* [7363]
School Library Paraprofessional Scholarships - Southern Region *(Advanced Professional/Scholarship)* [2474]
School Nutrition Association of Kansas Education Scholarship *(Undergraduate/Scholarship)* [8810]
Kurt H. and Donna M. Schuler Cash Grants *(Undergraduate/Scholarship, Grant)* [1254]
Alice Southworth Schulman, Class of 1954, Simmons Scholarships for Unitarian Universalist Women *(Undergraduate/Scholarship)* [9838]
Richard E. Schultes Research Awards *(Graduate/Grant, Award)* [9113]
Karen Schuvie Scholarships *(Undergraduate/Scholarship, Loan)* [5663]
AIST William E. Schwabe Memorial Scholarships *(Undergraduate/Scholarship)* [2007]
Schwan's Food Service Scholarships *(Vocational/Occupational/Scholarship)* [8806]
IADR David B. Scott Fellowship *(Professional development/Fellowship, Award)* [5254]
Glenn T. Seaborg Congressional Science and Engineering Fellowships *(Professional development/Fellowship)* [1040]
Seaman Family Scholarships *(Undergraduate/Scholarship)* [3108]
Seldovia Native Association Achievement Scholarships *(Undergraduate, Graduate/Scholarship)* [8829]
Seldovia Native Association General Scholarships *(Undergraduate, Graduate/Scholarship)* [8830]
SEMA Memorial Scholarships *(Graduate, Undergraduate/Scholarship)* [9464]
William "Buddy" Sentner Scholarship Awards *(Undergraduate/Scholarship)* [566]
Servus Credit Union 4-H Scholarships *(Undergraduate/Scholarship)* [10]
Hubert K. and JoAnn Seymour Scholarships *(Undergraduate/Scholarship)* [7492]
Al Shackleford and Dan Martin Professional Scholarships *(Professional development/Scholarship)* [2193]
Barbara A. Shacochis Scholarships *(Undergraduate/Scholarship)* [8003]
SHAFR Dissertation Completion Fellowships *(Doctorate/Fellowship)* [9140]
William H. Shannon Fellowships *(Graduate, Undergraduate/Fellowship)* [5445]
Benjamin G. Shatz Scholarships *(Undergraduate/Scholarship)* [8004]
Anne Shaw Fellowships *(Graduate/Fellowship)* [9727]
Sheet Metal And Air Conditioning Contractors' National Association College of Fellows Scholarships *(Undergraduate/Scholarship)* [8859]
Robert P. Sheppard Leadership Awards *(High School/Scholarship)* [7162]
David S. Sheridan Canadian Research Awards *(Other/Award)* [2542]
Shields-Gillespie Scholarships *(Other/Scholarship)* [1056]
Chiyoko and Thomas Shimazaki Scholarships *(Graduate/Scholarship)* [5558]
Jason Shipley Memorial Scholarships *(Undergraduate/Scholarship)* [7041]

Shoreline Community College Full-Time Continuing Students Scholarships *(Undergraduate/Scholarship)* [8881]
Shoreline Community College Part-Time Students Scholarships *(Undergraduate/Scholarship)* [8882]
Shoreline - Lake Forest Park High School Scholarship *(Undergraduate/Scholarship)* [8883]
SHPE Dissertation Scholarship *(Doctorate/Scholarship)* [9130]
SHPE Professional Scholarship *(Master's, Doctorate/Scholarship)* [9131]
SHRM Certification Scholarships - Individual *(Professional development/Scholarship)* [9147]
SHRM Foundation Academic Scholarships *(Graduate, Undergraduate/Scholarship)* [9148]
SICB Fellowships of Graduate Student Travel (FGST) *(Graduate/Fellowship)* [9157]
SICB Grants-in-Aid of Research Program (GIAR) *(Graduate/Grant)* [9158]
Norman Siegel Research Scholar Grants *(Doctorate/Grant)* [1382]
Jeff Siegel Scholarships *(Undergraduate/Scholarship)* [7359]
Siemens-ASCP Scholarship *(Undergraduate/Scholarship)* [1263]
Siemens Clinical Advancement Scholarship *(Undergraduate, Master's/Scholarship)* [1400]
APSAIL's Ralph Silverman Memorial Scholarships *(Undergraduate/Scholarship)* [2126]
Willard B. Simmons Sr. Memorial Scholarships *(Undergraduate/Scholarship)* [6871]
Helen J. Sioussat/Fay Wells Scholarships *(Graduate/Scholarship)* [2371]
Lillian and Murray Slatkin Fellowships *(Graduate/Fellowship)* [7743]
SME Coal and Energy Division Scholarships *(Undergraduate/Scholarship)* [9212]
SME Education Foundation Family Scholarships *(Undergraduate/Scholarship)* [9195]
SME Environmental Division Scholarships *(Undergraduate, Graduate/Scholarship)* [9213]
SMFM/AAOGF Scholarship Awards *(Graduate/Scholarship)* [9206]
Donald Smiley Prize *(Advanced Professional/Prize, Award, Recognition)* [1908]
Henry DeWitt Smith Graduate Scholarships *(Graduate/Scholarship)* [9214]
Gladys Ann Smith Greater Los Angeles Women's Council Scholarships *(Undergraduate/Scholarship)* [7230]
Brian and Cathy Smith Memorial Fund *(Graduate/Scholarship)* [1016]
Chapter 63 - Portland Uncle Bud Smith Scholarships *(Undergraduate/Scholarship)* [9196]
SNF Professional Growth Scholarships *(Graduate, Undergraduate/Scholarship)* [8807]
SNMMI-TS Advanced Practitioner Program Scholarship *(Professional development/Scholarship)* [9224]
SNMMI-TS Bachelor's Degree Completion Scholarships *(Undergraduate/Scholarship)* [9225]
SNNMI Predoctoral Molecular Imaging Scholar Program *(Doctorate/Scholarship)* [9226]
Snowmobile Association of Massachusetts Scholarships *(Undergraduate/Scholarship)* [9045]
SNRS Dissertation Research Grants *(Doctorate/Grant)* [9406]
SNRS Research Grants *(Professional development/Grant)* [9407]
SNRS/STTI Research Grants *(Professional development/Grant)* [9408]
SOAP/Kybele International Outreach Grant *(Advanced Professional, Professional development/Grant)* [9231]
SOBP Travel Fellowship Award-Early Career Investigator(International) *(Postdoctorate/Award)* [9090]
Society of Allied Weight Engineers Scholarships *(Undergraduate/Scholarship)* [9077]
Society for the Arts in Healthcare Student Scholarships *(Doctorate, Graduate, Undergraduate/Scholarship)* [9088]
Society of Graphic Designers of Canada Adobe Scholarships *(Undergraduate/Scholarship)* [9063]
Society of Graphic Designers of Canada Applied Arts Scholarships *(Undergraduate/Scholarship)* [9064]

Society of Graphic Designers of Canada Veer Scholarships *(Undergraduate/Scholarship)* [9065]
Society of Louisiana Certified Public Accountants Scholarships *(Undergraduate, Graduate/Scholarship)* [9165]
Society of Marine Port Engineers Scholarship Loans *(Undergraduate/Scholarship loan)* [9204]
Society of Pediatric Nurses Educational Scholarships *(Graduate, Other/Scholarship)* [9241]
Society for Pediatric Radiology Research Fellows *(Graduate, Other/Fellowship)* [9243]
Society for Pediatric Radiology Seed Grants *(Graduate, Other/Grant)* [9244]
Society for the Scientific Study of Sexuality Student Research Grants *(Undergraduate/Grant)* [9302]
SOHN Allied Health to BSN Degree Scholarship *(Undergraduate/Scholarship)* [9233]
SOHN Graduate Degree Scholarship *(Undergraduate/Scholarship)* [9234]
SOHN RN to BSN Degree Scholarship *(Undergraduate/Scholarship)* [9235]
Carrie Fox Solin Blow Molding Division Memorial Scholarships *(Undergraduate/Scholarship)* [9268]
SOMA Student Research Fellowships *(Undergraduate/Fellowship)* [9601]
Dr. Kiyoshi Sonoda Memorial Scholarships *(Graduate, Master's, Doctorate/Scholarship)* [5559]
Sons of Norway Foundation Scholarships to Oslo International Summer School *(Undergraduate/Scholarship)* [9346]
SOPHE/CDC Student Fellowships in Injury Prevention *(Graduate/Fellowship)* [9294]
SORP Student Conference Scholarship *(Graduate, Undergraduate/Scholarship)* [9237]
South Carolina Public Health Association Scholarships *(Undergraduate/Scholarship)* [9364]
South Carolina Scholastic Press Association Scholarships *(Undergraduate/Scholarship)* [9370]
South Carolina Scholastic Press Association Yearbook Scholarships *(Undergraduate/Scholarship)* [9371]
South Central Modern Language Association Fellowships *(Doctorate, Postdoctorate/Fellowship)* [7424]
South Central Power Scholarships *(Undergraduate/Scholarship)* [9373]
South Jersey Golf Association Scholarships *(Undergraduate/Scholarship)* [9379]
Southeast Alabama Dietetic Association Scholarships *(Graduate, Undergraduate/Scholarship)* [200]
Southwest Movers Association Scholarships *(Undergraduate/Scholarship)* [9454]
Master Sergeant William Sowers Memorial Scholarships *(Undergraduate/Scholarship)* [133]
Michael P. Spadafora Medical Toxicology Travel Awards *(Professional development/Grant)* [690]
SPE Student Awards for Innovations in Imaging *(Undergraduate, Graduate/Scholarship)* [9252]
Special Fund for the Study of Women and Politics *(Graduate, Postdoctorate/Grant)* [1123]
Spice Box Grants *(Advanced Professional/Grant)* [764]
SPIE Student Author Travel Grants *(Graduate, Undergraduate/Grant)* [9472]
SPOOM Research Grants *(Graduate/Grant)* [9277]
Spouse Tuition Aid Loan Program (STAP) *(Undergraduate, Graduate/Loan)* [7236]
SPS Future Teacher Scholarships *(Undergraduate/Scholarship)* [9256]
SPS Leadership Scholarships *(Undergraduate/Scholarship)* [9257]
SPSSI Grants-In-Aid Program *(Graduate, Postdoctorate/Grant)* [9287]
The SSPI Mid-Atlantic Chapter Scholarships *(Graduate, Undergraduate/Scholarship)* [9300]
Steven A. Stahl Research Grants *(Graduate/Grant)* [5358]
A.R.O.Y. Stanitz Scholarships *(Undergraduate/Scholarship)* [1228]
Peggy P. Starks Scholarship *(Postgraduate/Scholarship)* [9702]
The Stanley H. Stearman Awards *(Undergraduate/Scholarship)* [7135]
Robert P. Stearns/SCS Engineers Scholarships *(Graduate/Scholarship)* [9339]

Marianne M. Stenvig Scholarships *(Master's, Doctorate/Scholarship)* [9375]
Elizabeth Coulter Stephenson Scholarships *(Undergraduate/Scholarship, Grant)* [3595]
H.H. Stern Grant Awards *(Advanced Professional, Professional development/Award, Grant)* [1898]
Raymond H. Stetson Scholarships in Phonetics and Speech Science *(Graduate/Scholarship)* [54]
Christine K. Stevens Development Scholarships *(Undergraduate, Graduate/Scholarship)* [1017]
Dan Stewart Scholarships *(Other/Scholarship)* [7462]
Ralph W. Stone Graduate Fellowships *(Graduate/Fellowship, Grant)* [7184]
Martin L. Stout Scholarships *(Undergraduate, Graduate/Scholarship)* [1949]
Study Scholarships for Artists or Musicians *(Graduate/Scholarship)* [3610]
AIST Southeast Member Chapter Gene Suave Scholarships *(Undergraduate/Scholarship)* [2008]
Subic Bay-Cubi Point Scholarships *(Undergraduate/Scholarship)* [7231]
Caroline tum Suden/Frances Hellebrandt Professional Opportunity Awards *(Postdoctorate, Other/Award)* [1101]
VPPPA William Sullivan Scholarships *(Graduate, Undergraduate/Scholarship)* [10418]
William A. Sullivan Scholarships *(Undergraduate/Scholarship)* [7232]
Superior District Legislative Mentoring Student Grants RT to DC *(Undergraduate/Grant)* [2484]
Superior District Legislative Mentoring Student Grants *(Undergraduate/Grant)* [2483]
SUS Foundation Junior Faculty Grants *(Other/Grant)* [9320]
SUT Houston Undergraduate Scholarships *(Undergraduate/Scholarship)* [9318]
Margaret Svec Scholarships *(Undergraduate/Scholarship)* [8884]
Tailhook Educational Foundation Scholarship Program *(Undergraduate/Scholarship)* [9632]
Alexander M. Tanger Scholarships *(Graduate/Scholarship)* [2372]
William J. Tangye Scholarships *(Undergraduate/Scholarship)* [5302]
Alex Tanous Scholarship Award *(Undergraduate/Scholarship)* [9642]
Ryan "Munchie" Taylor Memorial Scholarships *(Undergraduate/Scholarship)* [6154]
TCA Outstanding Graduate Student Awards *(Graduate/Award)* [9695]
TCA Scholarship *(Undergraduate/Scholarship)* [9800]
TCATA College Scholarship Program *(Undergraduate/Scholarship)* [9721]
TCDA Abbott IPCO Professional Scholarships *(Other/Scholarship)* [671]
TCDA Gandy Ink Professional Scholarships *(Professional development/Scholarship)* [672]
TCDA General Fund Scholarships *(Undergraduate/Scholarship)* [673]
TCDA Past Presidents Student Scholarships *(Undergraduate/Scholarship)* [674]
Teacher Librarian Scholarships *(Master's/Scholarship)* [2475]
Marvin H. and Kathleen G. Teget Leadership Scholarships *(Undergraduate/Scholarship)* [9602]
Telford Scholarships *(Undergraduate/Scholarship)* [40]
Mary L. Tenopyr Graduate Student Scholarships *(Doctorate/Scholarship)* [9154]
Texas Computer Education Association Professional Educator Grants *(Other/Grant)* [9693]
Theatre Guild Scholarship *(Undergraduate/Scholarship)* [9725]
Nadene M. Thomas Graduate Research Scholarships *(Graduate/Scholarship)* [297]
Charles C. Thomas Scholarship *(Undergraduate/Scholarship)* [1586]
F. Christian and Betty Thompson Fellowships *(Graduate/Fellowship)* [7745]
Dr. Andrew Thomson Prize in Applied Meteorology *(Professional development/Award, Prize)* [2686]
The Joyce Tracy Fellowships *(Doctorate/Fellowship)* [446]

TRALA Industry Scholarship Awards *(Undergraduate/Scholarship)* [9798]
Translational Research Professorship *(Professional development/Internship)* [3387]
Edward Traurig Scholarships *(Undergraduate/Scholarship)* [10484]
Marie Tremaine Fellowships *(Postgraduate, Other/Fellowship)* [2259]
Tri Delta Northern Virginia Alumnae Chapter Scholarships *(Undergraduate/Scholarship)* [3564]
Tribute Fund Community Grant *(Professional development/Grant)* [9102]
Truckload Carriers Association Scholarships *(Undergraduate/Scholarship)* [9801]
Two Year/Community Broadcast Education Association Scholarship Awards *(Graduate/Scholarship)* [2373]
TxHIMA HIA-HIT Scholarship *(Undergraduate/Scholarship)* [9703]
Florence Tyson Grants to Study Music Psychotherapy *(Professional development/Grant)* [1018]
UAF Alumni Association Scholarships *(Undergraduate/Scholarship)* [10100]
UFCW Local Union Scholarships *(Undergraduate/Scholarship)* [9847]
Sandy Ulm Scholarships *(Undergraduate/Scholarship)* [4081]
Union Plus Scholarship Program *(Undergraduate/Scholarship)* [5451]
United Methodist General Scholarships *(Undergraduate, Graduate/Scholarship)* [9856]
United Parcel Service Scholarships for Female Students *(Undergraduate/Scholarship)* [5195]
U.S. Aircraft Insurance Group Professional Development Program (USAIG PDP) Scholarships *(Undergraduate/Scholarship)* [6839]
U.S. Bates Scholarship Program *(Undergraduate/Scholarship)* [5452]
UnitedAg Scholarship Program *(Undergraduate/Scholarship)* [9988]
University of Texas at Austin Special Research Grants *(Professional development/Grant)* [10276]
Claudette Upton Scholarships *(Undergraduate/Scholarship)* [3787]
USAWOASF/Grantham University On-Line Scholarships *(Graduate, Undergraduate/Scholarship)* [9880]
USAWOASF Regular Scholarships *(Undergraduate/Scholarship)* [9881]
John D. Utterback Scholarship Program *(Undergraduate/Scholarship)* [322]
VA AWWA Graduate Student Scholarships *(Graduate/Scholarship)* [1498]
Winifred Van Hagen/Rosalind Cassidy Scholarship Award *(Undergraduate/Scholarship)* [2436]
Gary Vanden Berg Internship Grant *(Undergraduate/Grant)* [9482]
Varian Radiation Therapy Advancement Scholarship *(Undergraduate, Master's, Doctorate/Scholarship)* [1401]
Vascular Surgery Trainee Advocacy Travel Scholarship *(Advanced Professional, Professional development/Scholarship, Grant)* [9326]
Dr. Juan D. Villarreal/HDA Foundation Scholarships *(Undergraduate/Scholarship)* [4894]
Paul A. Volcker Endowment for Public Service Research and Education *(Doctorate/Grant)* [1116]
Abe Voron Scholarships *(Graduate/Scholarship)* [2374]
VPPPA June Brothers Scholarships *(Graduate, Undergraduate/Scholarship)* [10419]
Chapter 4 - Lawrence A. Wacker Memorial Scholarships *(Undergraduate/Scholarship)* [9198]
Jack H. Wagner Scholarships *(Graduate, Undergraduate/Scholarship)* [6504]
Vincent T. Wasilewski Scholarships *(Graduate/Scholarship)* [2375]
Waterbury Bar Association Scholarships *(Undergraduate/Scholarship)* [10485]
Stand Watie Scholarships *(Undergraduate/Scholarship)* [9343]
ASM Robert D. Watkins Graduate Research Fellowships *(Postdoctorate/Fellowship)* [1373]
WBA Bar President's Scholarships *(Undergraduate/Scholarship)* [10486]

Richard M. Weaver Fellowships *(Graduate/Fellowship)* [5235]
TCDA Cloys Webb Student Scholarships *(Undergraduate/Scholarship)* [675]
WEDA Scholarship Program *(Professional development/Scholarship)* [10529]
WEF Canham Graduate Studies Scholarships *(Graduate/Scholarship)* [10480]
John V. Wehausen Graduate Scholarships for Advanced Study in Ship Hydrodynamics and Wave Theory *(Graduate/Scholarship)* [9218]
Edith Weingarten Scholarship Program *(Postgraduate/Scholarship)* [1050]
Susan C. Weiss Clinical Advancement Scholarships *(Other/Scholarship)* [9229]
Western Society of Weed Science Outstanding Student Scholarship Program *(Graduate, Undergraduate/Scholarship)* [10541]
Robert B. Westover Scholarships *(Undergraduate/Scholarship)* [4347]
Stan Wheeler Mentorship Awards *(Other/Award)* [5976]
WHIMA Established Professional Scholarship *(Graduate/Scholarship)* [10623]
Larry B. Wickham Memorial Scholarship for Graduate Studies *(Graduate/Scholarship)* [6608]
WIGA Scholarships *(Postgraduate, Other, Undergraduate/Scholarship)* [10450]
Wild Felid Legacy Scholarships *(Graduate/Scholarship)* [10555]
Willard & Spackman Scholarship Program *(Postgraduate/Scholarship)* [1051]
Rodney Williams Legacy Scholarships *(Undergraduate/Scholarship)* [10150]
BM1 James Elliott Williams Memorial Scholarship Fund *(Undergraduate/Scholarship)* [7922]
Alice Hinchcliffe Williams, RDH, MS Graduate Scholarships *(Graduate/Scholarship)* [10394]
E. E. Williams Research Grants *(Master's, Doctorate/Grant)* [4873]
Aubrey L. Williams Research Travel Fellowships *(Doctorate/Fellowship)* [1298]
CSM Virgil R. Williams Scholarships *(Undergraduate/Scholarship)* [3871]
Cenie Jomo Williams Tuition Scholarships *(Graduate, Undergraduate/Scholarship)* [6721]
RS Williamson and Eliford Mott Memorial Scholarships *(Undergraduate/Scholarship)* [10549]
Beverly Willis Architecture Foundation Travel Fellowship *(Doctorate/Fellowship)* [9086]
John Charles Wilson and Robert Doran Sr. Scholarships *(Undergraduate/Scholarship)* [5246]
Winston Build Your Future Scholarship *(Graduate, Undergraduate, Vocational/Occupational/Scholarship)* [8808]
WOCN Advanced Education Scholarships *(Graduate/Scholarship)* [10716]
Paul R. Wolf Memorial Scholarships *(Graduate/Scholarship)* [1809]
Women in Cancer Research Scholar Awards *(Graduate, Postdoctorate/Award)* [475]
Women's Jewelry Association Member Grants *(Professional development/Grant)* [10663]
Women's Leadership Training Grant *(Advanced Professional, Professional development/Grant)* [9327]
Dr. Harold S. Wood Awards for Excellence *(Undergraduate/Award)* [4349]
Wood Fruitticher Grocery Company, Inc. Scholarships *(Graduate, Undergraduate/Scholarship)* [201]
Irene Woodall Graduate Scholarships *(Master's/Scholarship)* [778]
Patty Wooten Scholarships *(Professional development/Scholarship, Award, Recognition)* [1852]
Pang Xiaoyan Scholarships *(Undergraduate/Scholarship)* [2926]
Minoru Yasui Memorial Scholarships *(Graduate, Master's, Doctorate/Scholarship)* [5560]
Gary Yoshimura Scholarships *(Graduate/Scholarship)* [8379]
Alma H. Young Emerging Scholar Awards *(Doctorate/Award, Monetary)* [10344]
Z/I Imaging Scholarships *(Graduate/Scholarship)* [1810]
Lisa Zaken Awards For Excellence *(Graduate, Undergraduate/Award, Monetary)* [5197]

Disabled

AAHD Scholarships *(Graduate, Undergraduate/Scholarship)* [502]
Anthony Abbene Scholarships *(Undergraduate/Scholarship)* [5025]
Evelyn Joy Abramowicz Memorial Scholarships *(Undergraduate/Scholarship)* [5568]
AEBC Toronto Chapter Scholarships *(Undergraduate/Scholarship)* [333]
Alabama Scholarships for Dependents of Blind Parents *(Undergraduate/Scholarship)* [192]
Justin Scot Alston Memorial Scholarships *(Undergraduate/Scholarship)* [5026]
American Council of the Blind Scholarships *(Graduate, Undergraduate/Scholarship)* [720]
American Speech Language Hearing Foundation Endowed Scholarships *(Graduate, Master's, Doctorate/Scholarship)* [1451]
Gladys C. Anderson Memorial Scholarships *(Graduate, Undergraduate/Scholarship)* [818]
Ethel Louise Armstrong Foundation Scholarships *(Graduate/Scholarship)* [8750]
ASGP Graduate Research Fellowships *(Graduate/Fellowship)* [223]
Robby Baker Memorial Scholarships *(Undergraduate/Scholarship)* [299]
Elsa Barton Educational Scholarship Fund *(Undergraduate, Vocational/Occupational/Scholarship)* [1127]
BCPF Bursaries *(Undergraduate/Scholarship)* [9476]
BEF Scholarships of the Arts *(Graduate, Undergraduate/Scholarship)* [2337]
A.G. Bell School Age Financial Aid Program *(Undergraduate/Scholarship)* [315]
Law Offices of David A. Black Annual Hearing Impaired Scholarships *(All/Scholarship)* [5957]
BMO Capital Markets Lime Connect Equity through Education Scholarships *(Undergraduate, Graduate/Scholarship)* [6087]
BMO Financial Group Lime Connect Canada Scholarship Program for Students with Disablilities *(Undergraduate, Graduate/Scholarship)* [6088]
Diana Brown Endowed Scholarships *(Undergraduate/Scholarship)* [6018]
Business, Education and Technology Scholarships *(Graduate, Undergraduate/Scholarship)* [334]
California Council of the Blind Scholarships *(Undergraduate, Graduate/Scholarship)* [8751]
Canadian Hard of Hearing Association Scholarship Programs *(Undergraduate/Scholarship)* [2651]
Karen D. Carsel Memorial Scholarships *(Graduate/Scholarship)* [819]
ChairScholars National Scholarship Program *(Undergraduate/Scholarship)* [2889]
CHEA Undergraduate Scholarship Program for Students with Disabilities *(Undergraduate/Scholarship)* [2464]
Kevin Child Scholarships *(Undergraduate/Scholarship)* [6987]
John and Ruth Childe Scholarships *(Undergraduate/Scholarship)* [9422]
CNIB Master's Scholarships *(Master's/Scholarship)* [2688]
Roy Cooper Memorial Scholarships *(Undergraduate/Scholarship)* [5998]
Pfizer Soozie Courter Hemophilia Scholarship Program *(Undergraduate/Scholarship)* [6988]
Cystic Fibrosis Scholarship Foundation *(Undergraduate/Scholarship)* [3494]
C. Rodney Demarest Memorial Scholarships *(Undergraduate/Scholarship)* [4747]
Rudolph Dillman Memorial Scholarships *(Graduate, Undergraduate/Scholarship)* [820]
Disability Care Center Disabled Student Scholarships *(Undergraduate/Scholarship)* [3629]
Disabled War Veterans Scholarships *(Undergraduate/Scholarship)* [90]
Diversity Executive Leadership Program Scholarships *(Other/Scholarship)* [1778]
"Education is Power" Scholarships *(Undergraduate/Scholarship)* [6989]
Boomer Esiason Foundation General Academic

Scholarships (Undergraduate, Graduate/Scholarship) [2338]
ExeptionalNurse.com Scholarships (Undergraduate, Graduate/Scholarship) [3940]
Exercise For Life Athletic Scholarships Program (Undergraduate/Scholarship) [2339]
Families of Freedom Scholarship Fund - America Scholarships (Undergraduate, Vocational/Occupational/Scholarship) [3956]
Anne M. Fassett Scholarships (Undergraduate, Graduate/Scholarship) [9428]
Feldman Law Firm Disabled Veterans Scholarships (All/Scholarship) [4009]
Andrew Foster Scholarships (Undergraduate/Scholarship) [6815]
R.L. Gillette Scholarships (Undergraduate/Scholarship) [821]
Millie Gonzalez Memorial Scholarships (Undergraduate/Scholarship) [4859]
Google Lime Scholarships for Students with Disabilities (Undergraduate, Graduate, Doctorate/Scholarship) [6089]
GuildScholar Awards (Undergraduate/Scholarship) [5596]
Delta Gamma Foundation Florence Margaret Harvey Memorial Scholarships (Graduate, Undergraduate/Scholarship) [822]
Professor Ulla Hedner Scholarships (Undergraduate/Scholarship) [6991]
Dr. E. Bruce Hendrick Scholarships (All/Scholarship) [9474]
Jim Hierlihy Memorial Scholarship (Undergraduate/Scholarship) [3911]
Irving J. Hoffman Memorial Scholarships (Undergraduate/Scholarship) [10288]
Mike Hylton and Ron Niederman Memorial Scholarships (Undergraduate/Scholarship) [4861]
Individual K-Grants (All/Grant) [5823]
Innovative Grants-Pilot and Research Tool Grants (Postdoctorate/Grant) [5641]
JDRF Postdoctoral Fellowships (Postdoctorate/Fellowship) [5644]
Kenneth Jernigan Scholarships (Undergraduate/Scholarship) [6947]
Kawano Family Scholarships (Undergraduate/Scholarship) [8711]
Kelly Law Team Annual Down Syndrome Scholarships (All/Scholarship) [5811]
P. Johnson and C. Kolb Memorial Scholarships (Undergraduate, Graduate, Master's, Doctorate/Scholarship) [8752]
The Leaders of Tomorrow Scholarships (Undergraduate, Vocational/Occupational/Scholarship) [3765]
Lighthouse International Scholarships - College-bound Awards (High School, Undergraduate/Scholarship) [6083]
Lighthouse International Scholarships - Graduate Awards (Graduate/Scholarship) [6084]
Lighthouse International Scholarships - Undergraduate Awards (Undergraduate/Scholarship) [6085]
Lutheran Student Scholastic and Service Scholarships - College and University Students (Undergraduate/Scholarship) [2248]
Katie MacDonald Memorial Scholarships (Graduate, Undergraduate/Scholarship) [9865]
Lawrence Madeiros Scholarships (Undergraduate/Scholarship) [6992]
Mary Main Memorial Scholarships (Undergraduate/Scholarship) [4762]
Kaia Lynn Markwalter Endowed Scholarships (Undergraduate/Scholarship) [6044]
Eric Martinez Memorial Scholarships (Graduate, Undergraduate/Scholarship) [9866]
Mature Student Scholarship (Undergraduate/Scholarship) [3912]
McBurney General Scholarships (Undergraduate/Scholarship) [10323]
Doreen McMullan McCarthy Memorial Academic Scholarship for Women with Bleeding Disorders (Undergraduate/Scholarship) [6993]
Elizabeth Nash Foundation Scholarships (Undergraduate, Graduate/Scholarship) [6663]
National Black Deaf Advocate Scholarships (Graduate, Undergraduate/Scholarship) [6816]
National MS Society New Jersey Metro Chapter Scholarship Program (Undergraduate/Scholarship) [7075]
NBCUniversal Tony Coelho Media Scholarships (Undergraduate, Graduate/Scholarship) [555]
Alan H. Neville Memorial Scholarships (Undergraduate/Scholarship) [335]
George H. Nofer Scholarships for Law and Public Policy (Graduate/Scholarship) [316]
AEBC Rick Oakes Scholarships for the Arts (Undergraduate/Scholarship) [336]
Charles and Melva T. Owen Memorial Scholarships (Undergraduate/Scholarship) [6948]
E.U. and Gene Parker Scholarships (Undergraduate/Scholarship) [6949]
Nalini Perera Little Lotus Bud Master's Scholarships (Master's/Scholarship) [2689]
Lowell Phillips Scholarships (Undergraduate/Scholarship) [3313]
Christopher Mark Pitkin Memorial Scholarships (Undergraduate/Scholarship) [6994]
Rehabmart.com Scholarships (Undergraduate/Scholarship) [8545]
Betty Rendel Scholarships (Undergraduate/Scholarship) [6955]
Rimington Trophy Scholarships (Undergraduate, Graduate/Scholarship) [2340]
Rosemary Quigley Memorial Scholarships (Undergraduate, Graduate/Scholarship) [2341]
Travis Roy Foundation Individual Grants (All/Grant) [8652]
Paul and Ellen Ruckes Scholarships (Graduate, Undergraduate/Scholarship) [823]
Sacks For CF Scholarships (Professional development/Scholarship) [2342]
Kevin Saunders Wheelchair Success Scholarships (Undergraduate/Scholarship) [3107]
Bill Sawyer Memorial Scholarships (Undergraduate/Scholarship) [6052]
Dale M. Schoettler Scholarships (Undergraduate, Graduate/Scholarship) [8753]
Scholarship Award of the Bell Aliant Pioneer Volunteers (Undergraduate/Scholarship) [2690]
Sentinels of Freedom Scholarships (Advanced Professional/Scholarship) [8843]
Sertoma Communicative Disorders Scholarship (Undergraduate/Scholarship) [8849]
Sertoma Hard of Hearing and Deaf Scholarships (Undergraduate/Scholarship) [8850]
Esther M. Smith Scholarships (Undergraduate/Scholarship) [3188]
Beatrice Drinnan Spence Scholarships (Undergraduate, Vocational/Occupational/Scholarship) [3766]
Dr. Gunnar B. Stickler Scholarships (Undergraduate, Vocational/Occupational/Scholarship) [9578]
Bonnie Strangio Education Scholarships (Graduate, Undergraduate/Scholarship) [2343]
Mario J. Tocco Hydrocephalus Foundation Scholarships (Undergraduate/Scholarship) [5028]
Toronto Rehab Scholarships in Rehabilitation-Related Research (Graduate/Scholarship) [9753]
Ferdinand Torres Scholarships (Graduate, Undergraduate/Scholarship) [824]
Tristin Memorial Scholarships (Undergraduate, Vocational/Occupational/Scholarship) [5996]
Redlands Evening Lions Club - Barbara Westen Memorial Scholarships (Undergraduate/Scholarship) [8529]
Timothy Wiese Memorial Scholarships (Undergraduate, Graduate/Scholarship) [8754]
Youth Empowerment Summit Scholarships (Undergraduate/Scholarship) [6817]

Employer affiliation

ABA Members Scholarships for ABA Bus and Tour Operators Only (Undergraduate/Scholarship) [637]
ABA Members Scholarships for All ABA Member Companies (Undergraduate, Graduate/Scholarship) [638]
AOF/Johnson & Johnson Vision Care - Innovation in Education Grants (Advanced Professional, Professional development/Grant) [414]
APDA Research Grants (Other/Grant) [1073]
APSA U.S. Federal Executives Fellowships (Advanced Professional, Professional development/Fellowship) [1115]
Don Aron Scholarships (Undergraduate/Scholarship) [6875]
ASA/NSF/BLS Fellowships (Graduate/Fellowship) [1463]
Tom Babcox Memorial Scholarships (Professional development/Scholarship) [2124]
Bank of Canada Fellowship Award (Doctorate, Other/Fellowship, Grant) [2187]
Bank of Canada Governor's Awards (Doctorate, Other/Award, Grant) [2188]
Donald H. Bernstein/John B. Talbert, Jr. Scholarships (Undergraduate/Scholarship) [4179]
BSA Educational Scholarships (Undergraduate/Scholarship) [2426]
Burger King Employee Scholars Program (Undergraduate/Scholarship) [2410]
Burndy Canada Inc. Academic Achievement Awards (Undergraduate/Scholarship) [3823]
CAODC Occupational Health and Safety Scholarships (Professional development/Scholarship) [2570]
Carolinas-Virginias Retail Hardware Scholarships (Undergraduate/Scholarship) [4184]
Cengage Learning Scholarships Program (Undergraduate/Scholarship) [2839]
Christmas Tree Chapter Scholarship Awards (Undergraduate/Scholarship) [7692]
COPA Scholarship Fund (Undergraduate/Scholarship) [2722]
Copper and Brass Servicenter Association Inc. Scholarship Program (Undergraduate/Scholarship) [3421]
Crowder Scholarships (Undergraduate/Scholarship) [4192]
Colonel Richard M. Dawson Highway Patrol Scholarship Fund (Undergraduate/Scholarship) [3222]
DBI Scholarships Fund (Undergraduate/Scholarship) [3223]
Donald J. DeYoung Scholarships (Undergraduate/Scholarship) [4588]
Downeast Energy Scholarships (Undergraduate/Scholarship) [3659]
Bob Dyer/OEL Apprenticeship Scholarships (Undergraduate/Scholarship) [3825]
Eaton Awards of Academic Achievement (Undergraduate/Scholarship) [3826]
Bill Egan Scholarship Program (Undergraduate/Scholarship) [7694]
Dr. Robert Elliott Memorial Scholarships (Undergraduate/Scholarship) [6351]
Pauline Elliott Scholarships (Undergraduate/Scholarship) [6352]
Robert C. Erb Sr. Scholarships (Undergraduate/Scholarship) [6353]
Fahs-Beck Fund for Research and Experimentation - Postdoctoral Grants (Postdoctorate/Grant) [7348]
Jack B. Fisher Scholarship Fund (Undergraduate/Scholarship) [9501]
Laura M. Fleming Scholarships (Undergraduate, Vocational/Occupational/Scholarship) [4194]
Captain Ernest Fox Perpetual Scholarships (Undergraduate/Scholarship) [3080]
Phil Friel Scholarships (Undergraduate/Scholarship) [6354]
Peter M. Gargano Scholarship Fund (Undergraduate/Scholarship) [3709]
Leo Gilmartin Scholarships (Undergraduate/Scholarship) [8167]
Alex Gissler Memorial Scholarships (Undergraduate/Scholarship) [6355]
Grant Assistance Program for Autism Professionals - College Programs (Undergraduate/Grant) [7650]
Grant Assistance Program for Autism Professionals - Doctoral Programs (Doctorate/Grant) [7651]
Grant Assistance Program for Autism Professionals - Institutional Standards (Undergraduate, Graduate/Grant) [7652]
Grant Assistance Program for Autism Professionals - Masters Programs (Master's/Grant) [7653]
Grant Assistance Program for Autism Professionals - Professional Certification Programs (Undergraduate, Professional development/Grant) [7654]

Grant Assistance Program for Autism Professionals - Retroactive Assistance *(Advanced Professional, Professional development/Grant)* [7655]
Grant Assistance Program for Autism Professionals - Undergraduate Programs *(Undergraduate/Grant)* [7656]
Henry Hoffman Memorial Scholarship Fund *(Undergraduate/Scholarship)* [6740]
Institute of Turkish Studies Sabbatical Research Grants *(Other/Grant)* [5225]
International Affairs Fellowships in Nuclear Security (IAF-NS) *(Professional development/Fellowship)* [3448]
Kerrwil's J.W. Kerr Continuing Education Scholarship Awards *(Undergraduate/Scholarship)* [3837]
Melvin Kruger Endowed Scholarship Program *(Undergraduate, Vocational/Occupational/Scholarship)* [7122]
Stan Lencki Scholarships *(Undergraduate/Scholarship)* [6356]
Lilly Scholarships in Religion for Journalists *(Other/Scholarship)* [8549]
Loan Forgiveness Scholarships *(Graduate, Undergraduate/Loan, Scholarship)* [9463]
Rick Mahoney Scholarships *(Undergraduate/Scholarship)* [6357]
Al Maurer Awards *(Undergraduate, Graduate, Advanced Professional/Award, Scholarship)* [3790]
NACADA Scholarships *(Graduate/Scholarship)* [6673]
National Sheriffs' Association Scholarship Program *(Graduate, Undergraduate/Scholarship)* [7130]
NDSGC Summer Faculty Fellowships *(Professional development/Scholarship, Fellowship)* [7496]
Bill Nelson Scholarship Endowment (BNSE) *(Undergraduate, Graduate/Scholarship)* [7768]
NHPGA Apprentice Scholarships *(Undergraduate/Scholarship)* [6358]
Louise A. Nixon Scholarships *(Graduate/Scholarship)* [7245]
Ohio Association of Broadcaster's Kids Scholarships *(Undergraduate/Scholarship)* [7572]
OPERF Educator and Student Awards *(Professional development/Grant)* [7756]
Packard Fellowships for Science and Engineering *(Professional development/Fellowship)* [7793]
Paper Stock Industries Chapter ISRI RRF Scholarship *(Undergraduate/Scholarship)* [7801]
PARMA Scholarships *(Undergraduate/Scholarship)* [8325]
Pembroke Center Faculty Fellowships *(Professional development/Fellowship)* [2389]
Walter T. Philippy Scholarships *(Undergraduate/Scholarship)* [6359]
Philips Lighting Continuing Education Awards *(Undergraduate/Scholarship)* [3839]
Pipe Line Contractors Association of Canada Student Bursary *(Undergraduate, Postgraduate/Scholarship)* [8142]
PLUS Foundation Financial Aid Scholarships *(Undergraduate/Scholarship)* [8168]
David J. Pollini Scholarships *(Undergraduate/Scholarship)* [6360]
Pope Scholarship Awards *(Undergraduate/Scholarship)* [6361]
Raytheon Scholarship Program *(Undergraduate/Scholarship)* [8440]
Rehabmart.com Scholarships *(Undergraduate/Scholarship)* [8545]
Retail Chapter Scholarship Awards *(Undergraduate/Scholarship)* [7701]
Anthony Rizzo Scholarship Award *(Professional development/Scholarship)* [7514]
Rotary Public Safety Scholarships *(Undergraduate/Scholarship)* [4212]
Saskatchewan Government Insurance Corporate Scholarships *(Undergraduate/Scholarship)* [8771]
Saskatchewan Trucking Association Scholarships *(Undergraduate/Scholarship)* [8784]
Jim Sheerin Scholarships *(Undergraduate/Scholarship)* [6362]
Smith Family Awards Program for Excellence in Biomedical Research *(Advanced Professional, Professional development/Grant)* [4823]
Ronald T. Smith Family Scholarships *(Undergraduate, Graduate/Scholarship)* [4621]
Sobeys & Empire Work Experience & Scholarship Program - Future Leaders Awards *(Other/Scholarship)* [9049]
Matt Stager Memorial Scholarship Fund *(Undergraduate/Scholarship)* [10482]
Charles H. Stone Scholarships *(Undergraduate/Scholarship)* [2081]
Texas Mutual Scholarship Program *(Undergraduate, Vocational/Occupational/Scholarship)* [9709]
TRALA Industry Scholarship Awards *(Undergraduate/Scholarship)* [9798]
Turner Family Scholarships *(Undergraduate, Vocational/Occupational/Scholarship)* [4217]
U.V.A. Faculty Fellowships *(Professional development/Fellowship)* [10313]
Vector Marketing Canadian Scholarship Awards *(Undergraduate/Scholarship)* [10365]
Laramie Walden Memorial Fund *(Undergraduate/Scholarship)* [4219]
Walmart Associate Scholarships *(Undergraduate/Scholarship)* [10425]
WEDA Scholarship Program *(Professional development/Scholarship)* [10529]
Fred C. Wikoff, Jr. Scholarships *(Undergraduate, Vocational/Occupational/Scholarship)* [4220]
Willamette Chapter Scholarship Awards *(Undergraduate/Scholarship)* [7702]

Ethnic group membership

AAMA Houston Chapter Health Training Scholarships *(Other/Scholarship)* [1601]
Accenture American Indian Scholarship Program *(Graduate, Undergraduate/Scholarship)* [880]
Adler Pollock & Sheehan Diversity Scholarships *(Undergraduate/Scholarship)* [71]
AGBU Heritage Scholar Grant *(Undergraduate/Scholarship, Grant)* [1673]
AIGC Fellowships - Graduate *(Graduate/Fellowship)* [881]
Alberta Blue Cross Scholarships for Aboriginal Students *(Undergraduate/Scholarship)* [230]
Alberta Ukrainian Centennial Commemorative Scholarships *(Graduate/Scholarship)* [10440]
Dulemba Aleksander and Stefania Scholarship *(Undergraduate/Scholarship)* [8571]
Hon. Lincoln Alexander Scholarships *(Undergraduate, Graduate/Scholarship)* [2277]
AMLN Scholarships for Arab American Students *(Graduate, Undergraduate/Scholarship)* [1003]
APTA Minority Scholarships - Faculty Development Scholarships *(Postdoctorate/Scholarship)* [1096]
APTA Minority Scholarships - Physical Therapist Assistant Students *(Undergraduate/Scholarship)* [1097]
APTA Minority Scholarships - Physical Therapist Students *(Undergraduate/Scholarship)* [1098]
Armenian American Citizen's League Scholarships *(Undergraduate/Scholarship)* [1682]
Armenian American Medical Association Scholarships *(Undergraduate/Scholarship)* [1683]
Armenian American Pharmacists' Association Scholarships *(Graduate/Scholarship)* [1684]
Armenian Bar Association Graduate Scholarships in Law *(Graduate/Scholarship)* [1669]
Armenian General Athletic Union Scholarships *(Undergraduate/Scholarship)* [1685]
Armenian Professional Society Graduate Student Scholarships *(Graduate/Scholarship)* [1675]
Armenian Relief Society Scholarships *(Graduate, Undergraduate/Scholarship)* [1686]
ARS Undergraduate Scholarships *(Undergraduate/Scholarship)* [1677]
Arts Council of Greater Grand Rapids Minority Scholarships *(Undergraduate/Scholarship)* [4574]
ASC Graduate Fellowships for Ethnic Minorities *(Doctorate/Fellowship)* [1280]
Asian and Pacific Islander Queers Sisters Scholarships *(Undergraduate/Scholarship)* [8242]
ASLA Council of Fellow Scholarships *(Undergraduate/Scholarship)* [1346]
Michael M. Assarian Scholarships *(Undergraduate/Scholarship)* [1687]
Association of American Indian Physicians Scholarships *(Graduate, Undergraduate/Scholarship)* [1838]
John M. Azarian Memorial Armenian Youth Scholarship Fund *(Undergraduate/Scholarship)* [1688]
Baker Donelson Diversity Scholarships *(Undergraduate/Scholarship)* [2170]
Baker and Hostetler Diversity Fellowships *(Undergraduate/Fellowship)* [2172]
Baker and McKenzie Diversity Fellowships *(Postgraduate, Professional development/Fellowship)* [2175]
Guthikonda BasavapunnaRao and Umadevi Scholarships *(Graduate/Scholarship)* [9667]
Helen Bassett Commemorative Student Award *(Undergraduate, Graduate/Scholarship)* [7221]
Dennis J. Beck Memorial Scholarships *(Undergraduate/Scholarship)* [5498]
Harvey Bell Memorial Prize *(Graduate/Award)* [10271]
BIE-Loan for Service for Graduates *(Graduate/Loan)* [882]
Alex Blaski Memorial Scholarships *(Undergraduate/Scholarship)* [8572]
Hagop Bogigian Scholarship Fund *(Undergraduate/Scholarship)* [1689]
Bohemian Lawyers Association of Chicago Scholarships *(Graduate/Scholarship)* [2333]
Maria and Czeslaw Borek Scholarships *(Undergraduate/Scholarship)* [8573]
Corris Boyd Scholarships *(Master's/Scholarship)* [2085]
Cathy L. Brock Memorial Scholarships *(Graduate/Scholarship)* [5167]
Brown Dental Scholarships *(Undergraduate/Scholarship)* [5521]
Buckfire & Buckfire, P.C. Law School Diversity Scholarships *(Graduate/Scholarship)* [2399]
Buckfire & Buckfire, P.C. Medical Diversity Scholarships *(Advanced Professional/Scholarship)* [2400]
Armen H. Bululian Scholarships *(Undergraduate/Scholarship)* [1690]
Leon C. Bynoe Memorial Scholarships *(Undergraduate/Scholarship)* [10280]
California Bar Foundation 3L Diversity Scholarships *(Undergraduate/Scholarship)* [2443]
Canada-Ukraine Parliamentary Program Internship Scholarships (CUPP) *(Undergraduate/Scholarship, Internship)* [10441]
CANFIT Nutrition, Physical Education and Culinary Arts Scholarships *(Graduate, Undergraduate/Scholarship)* [3167]
Carlos M. Castaneda Journalism Scholarships *(Graduate/Scholarship)* [2807]
Mary Anne Chambers Scholarships *(Undergraduate/Scholarship)* [5522]
Cintas Foundation Fellowships in Architecture *(Professional development/Fellowship)* [3031]
Cintas Foundation Fellowships in Visual Arts *(Professional development/Fellowship)* [3032]
Citi Foundation Scholarship Program *(Undergraduate/Scholarship)* [866]
City of Toronto Scholarships for Aboriginal Students *(Graduate, Undergraduate/Scholarship)* [10285]
Coca-Cola First Generation Scholarships *(Undergraduate/Scholarship)* [867]
Colombian Education Fund Scholarships *(Undergraduate/Scholarship)* [3130]
Constantinople Armenian Relief Society Scholarships (CARS) *(Undergraduate/Scholarship)* [1691]
CPA Foundation Minority Scholarships *(Graduate/Scholarship)* [2471]
AWG Maria Luisa Crawford Field Camp Scholarships *(Undergraduate/Scholarship)* [2095]
Dalai Lama Trust Graduate Scholarships *(Graduate/Scholarship)* [3508]
Karekin DerAvedision Memorial Endowment Fund *(Undergraduate/Scholarship)* [1692]
Achille and Irene Despres, William and Andre Scholarships *(Undergraduate/Scholarship)* [4587]
Julian Dobranowski Memorial Scholarships *(Undergraduate/Scholarship)* [8574]
Dr. Michael Dorizas Memorial Scholarships *(Undergraduate/Scholarship)* [4846]
Robert E. Dougherty Scholarships *(Undergraduate, Postgraduate/Scholarship)* [3339]
Margaret Dowell-Gravatt, M.D. Scholarships *(Undergraduate/Scholarship)* [2226]

James Echols Scholarship Award *(Undergraduate/Scholarship)* [2434]
George and Isabelle Elanjian Scholarships *(Undergraduate/Scholarship)* [10198]
Emmanuel Bible College Scholarships *(Undergraduate/Scholarship)* [1693]
Bruce T. and Jackie Mahi Erickson Grant *(Graduate, Undergraduate/Grant)* [7907]
Clay Ford Florida Board of Accountancy Minority Scholarships *(Undergraduate/Scholarship)* [4083]
Forté Fellowships *(Master's/Fellowship)* [4151]
Brandon Fradd Fellowship *(Professional development/Fellowship)* [3033]
Franchise Law Diversity Scholarship Awards *(Undergraduate/Scholarship)* [5336]
FTE North American Doctoral Fellowships *(Doctorate, Graduate/Fellowship)* [4155]
GAPA Scholarships *(Undergraduate/Scholarship)* [4327]
Garikian Scholarship Fund *(Undergraduate/Scholarship)* [1694]
Marcus Mosiah Garvey Scholarships *(Undergraduate/Scholarship)* [5523]
GCABC Youth Scholarship Awards *(Undergraduate/Scholarship)* [4419]
General Mills Foundation Scholarships *(Undergraduate/Scholarship)* [869]
German Historical Institute Doctoral and Postdoctoral Fellowships *(Doctorate, Postgraduate/Fellowship)* [4395]
Franciszek Glogowski Memorial Scholarships *(Undergraduate/Scholarship)* [8576]
Glenn Godfrey Memorial Scholarships *(Undergraduate, Graduate/Scholarship)* [5864]
Goldman Sachs/Matsuo Takabuki Commemorative Scholarships *(Graduate/Scholarship)* [7908]
Charles F. Gould Endowment Scholarships *(Undergraduate/Scholarship)* [10020]
Greenlining Institute Fellowships *(Graduate/Fellowship)* [4670]
Guelph Caribbean Canadian Association Undergraduate Scholarships *(Undergraduate/Scholarship)* [4679]
Hai Guin Scholarships Association *(Undergraduate/Scholarship)* [1695]
Calouste Gulbenkian Foundation Scholarships *(Undergraduate/Scholarship)* [1696]
Stan Hamilton Scholarships *(Undergraduate/Scholarship)* [8766]
Isaac and Mary Harbottle Scholarships *(Graduate, Undergraduate/Scholarship)* [7909]
Hellenic University Club of Philadelphia Founders Scholarships *(Undergraduate/Scholarship)* [4847]
Nicholas S. Hetos, DDS, Memorial Graduate Scholarships *(Graduate, Doctorate/Scholarship)* [4848]
Lucy Hsu Ho Scholarships *(Undergraduate/Scholarship)* [2229]
Zelle Hofmann Diversity in Law Scholarships *(Undergraduate/Scholarship)* [10812]
Kaspar Hovannisian Memorial Scholarships *(Graduate/Scholarship)* [1697]
Hirair and Anna Hovnanian Foundation Presidential Scholarships *(Undergraduate/Scholarship)* [1698]
Hirair and Anna Hovnanian Foundation Scholarships *(Undergraduate/Scholarship)* [1699]
I Have a Dream Scholarships *(Undergraduate/Scholarship)* [5525]
IABA Scholarships *(Graduate/Scholarship)* [5476]
Indspire Post-Secondary Education Scholarships *(Graduate, Undergraduate/Scholarship)* [5133]
ISF Undergraduate Scholarships *(Undergraduate/Scholarship)* [5479]
Jamaican Canadian Association Alberta Scholarship Program *(Undergraduate/Scholarship)* [5533]
Drzymala Janusz and Roma Scholarship *(Undergraduate/Scholarship)* [8577]
Dr. Ali Jarrahi Merit Scholarships *(Undergraduate/Scholarship)* [5480]
Rev. and Mrs. A.K. Jizmejian Educational Fund *(Undergraduate/Scholarship)* [1700]
Journey Toward Ordained Ministry Scholarships *(Undergraduate, Graduate/Scholarship)* [9854]
Kazimiera Juchniewicz Memorial Scholarships *(Undergraduate/Scholarship)* [8578]
Clem Judd Jr. Memorial Scholarships *(Undergraduate/Scholarship)* [4799]
Stefan and Weronika Kacperski Memorial Scholarships *(Undergraduate/Scholarship)* [8579]
Daniel Kahikina and Millie Akaka Scholarships *(Graduate, Undergraduate/Scholarship)* [7910]
Gladys Kamakakūokalani 'Ainoa Brandt Scholarships *(Graduate, Undergraduate/Scholarship)* [7911]
Kamehameha Schools Class of 1968 "Ka Poli O Kaiona" Scholarships *(Graduate, Undergraduate/Scholarship)* [7912]
Kamehameha Schools Class of 1972 Scholarships *(Graduate, Undergraduate/Scholarship)* [7913]
Kaprielian Memorial Scholarships *(Undergraduate/Scholarship)* [10303]
KASF Chair Scholarships *(Graduate, Undergraduate/Scholarship)* [5873]
KASF Designated Scholarships *(Graduate, Undergraduate/Scholarship)* [5874]
KEF Academic Scholarships *(Undergraduate, Graduate/Scholarship)* [5865]
KEF College/University Basic Scholarships *(Undergraduate/Scholarship)* [5866]
KEF Vocational Education Scholarship *(Undergraduate/Scholarship)* [5867]
Dr. Elemér and Éva Kiss Scholarship Fund *(Undergraduate/Scholarship)* [5006]
Stefan and Janina Klimt Scholarships *(Undergraduate/Scholarship)* [8580]
Knights of Vartan, Fresno Lodge No. 9 Scholarships *(Undergraduate/Scholarship)* [1701]
George Kokociński Memorial Scholarships *(Undergraduate/Scholarship)* [8581]
Eugene and Elinor Kotur Scholarship Trust Fund *(Undergraduate, Graduate/Scholarship)* [10443]
Krawczyk-Krane Family Scholarships *(Undergraduate/Scholarship)* [8582]
Krist-Reavley Minority Scholarships *(Undergraduate/Scholarship)* [7987]
Jan Kuropas Memorial Scholarships *(Undergraduate/Scholarship)* [8583]
Lazarian Graduate Scholarships *(Graduate/Scholarship)* [1678]
Danny T. Le Memorial Scholarships *(Undergraduate/Scholarship)* [10385]
LeClairRyan Diversity Scholarships *(Undergraduate/Scholarship)* [6000]
LLN Student Scholarships *(Undergraduate/Scholarship)* [5939]
Louisville Institute First Book Grants for Minority Scholars *(Doctorate/Grant)* [6129]
Dan and Rachel Mahi Educational Scholarships *(Graduate, Undergraduate/Scholarship)* [7914]
Mangasar M. Mangasarian Scholarship Fund *(Graduate/Scholarship)* [1702]
Mas Family Scholarships *(Graduate, Undergraduate/Scholarship)* [6304]
Larry Matfay Cultural Heritage Scholarships *(Undergraduate, Graduate/Scholarship)* [5868]
Howard Mayer Brown Fellowship *(Graduate/Fellowship)* [1021]
Tadeusz Maziarz Scholarships *(Undergraduate/Scholarship)* [8584]
Menominee Tribal Scholarships *(Undergraduate, Graduate/Scholarship)* [6418]
Michigan Auto Law Student Diversity Scholarships *(Undergraduate/Scholarship)* [6463]
Bronislaw Michno Memorial Scholarships *(Undergraduate/Scholarship)* [8585]
George Hi'ilani Mills Perpetual Fellowships *(Graduate/Fellowship)* [7915]
Ralph Modjeski Scholarships *(Graduate, Undergraduate/Scholarship)* [8198]
Momeni Foundation Scholastic Achievement Scholarships *(Undergraduate/Scholarship)* [7021]
Morgan Stanley Tribal Scholars Program *(Undergraduate/Scholarship)* [870]
James B. Morris Scholarships *(Undergraduate/Scholarship)* [6598]
Dwight Mosley Scholarships *(Undergraduate/Scholarship)* [9976]
John R. Mott Scholarships *(Undergraduate/Scholarship)* [6604]
NAAMA Scholarships *(Undergraduate/Scholarship)* [6701]
NABA National Scholarship Program *(Graduate, Undergraduate/Scholarship)* [6716]
NACA Multicultural Professional Development Grant *(Undergraduate, Graduate, Professional development/Grant)* [6729]
Chereddi NarayanaRao and Radhamanohari Scholarships *(Graduate/Scholarship)* [9668]
National Association for Armenian Studies and Research Scholarships *(Graduate, Postgraduate/Scholarship)* [1703]
National GEM Consortium - MS Engineering Fellowships *(Graduate/Fellowship)* [6967]
National GEM Consortium - PhD Engineering Fellowships *(Doctorate, Graduate/Fellowship)* [6968]
National GEM Consortium - PhD Science Fellowships *(Doctorate, Graduate/Fellowship)* [6969]
National Iranian American Council Fellowships *(Graduate, Undergraduate/Fellowship)* [7022]
National Medical Fellowships Need-Based Scholarships *(Undergraduate/Scholarship)* [7061]
National Recreation and Park Association Diversity Scholarships *(Undergraduate/Scholarship)* [7118]
Native Hawaiian Chamber of Commerce Scholarships *(Graduate, Undergraduate/Scholarship)* [7916]
Native Hawaiian Visual Arts Scholarships *(Graduate, Undergraduate/Scholarship)* [7917]
Marek Nawrot Memorial Scholarships *(Undergraduate/Scholarship)* [8586]
NCACPA Outstanding Minority Accounting Student Scholarships *(Undergraduate/Scholarship)* [7451]
Dr. Ezra Nesbeth Scholarships *(Undergraduate/Scholarship)* [5526]
Amelia and Emanuel Nessell Scholarships *(Undergraduate/Scholarship)* [3719]
Le Hoang Nguyen College Scholarships (LHN) *(Undergraduate/Scholarship)* [10386]
The Thuy Nguyen Scholarships *(High School/Scholarship)* [10387]
NIAC Iranian-American Scholarship Fund *(Undergraduate, Graduate/Scholarship)* [7023]
NIAF Scholarships - General Category I *(Undergraduate, Graduate, Postgraduate/Scholarship)* [7027]
Nissan North America, Inc. Scholarships *(Undergraduate/Scholarship)* [871]
NUF Fellowships *(Graduate, Postgraduate, Other/Fellowship)* [7209]
NWAG Georgia, USA Scholarships *(Undergraduate/Scholarship)* [7431]
NWAG Nigeria Scholarships *(Undergraduate/Scholarship)* [7432]
Omatsu FACL Scholarships *(Juris Doctorate, Advanced Professional/Scholarship)* [4001]
ONECA Four Directions Scholarship *(Undergraduate/Scholarship)* [7658]
M. Dick Osumi Civil Rights and Public Interest Scholarship *(Graduate, Undergraduate/Scholarship)* [5543]
Outlaw Student's Minority Scholarships *(Undergraduate/Scholarship)* [9596]
Dr. Nicholas Padis Memorial Graduate Scholarships *(Graduate/Scholarship)* [4849]
The PanHellenic Scholarships *(Undergraduate/Scholarship)* [7797]
Pepperdine University School of Law Armenian Student Scholarships *(Undergraduate/Scholarship)* [7996]
Eleonora Pidperyhora Scholarship *(Undergraduate/Scholarship)* [8587]
Dr. Adolph Piotrowski Memorial Art Scholarships *(Undergraduate/Scholarship)* [8588]
Porter Physiology Development Fellowship Awards *(Doctorate/Fellowship)* [1100]
Poundmaker Memorial Scholarships *(Undergraduate/Scholarship)* [10272]
Powers-Knapp Scholarships *(Undergraduate/Scholarship)* [10326]
Josef Princ Memorial Scholarships *(Undergraduate/Scholarship)* [8360]
Prince Henry Society Scholarships *(Undergraduate/Scholarship)* [8278]
Guthikonda Ramabrahmam and Balamani *(Graduate/Scholarship)* [9669]
Geeta Rastogi Memorial Scholarships *(Undergraduate/Scholarship)* [10338]
W. Reymont Scholarships *(Undergraduate/Scholarship)* [8589]

Special Recipient Index

FRATERNAL ORGANIZATION MEMBERSHIP

William S. Richardson Commemorative Scholarships *(Graduate/Scholarship)* [7918]
Ameen Rihani Scholarship Program *(Undergraduate/Scholarship)* [1599]
Risk Management and Insurance Scholarships *(Undergraduate/Scholarship)* [8767]
Elliott C. Roberts Scholarships *(Graduate/Scholarship)* [5168]
R.O.E.A. Dumitru Golea Goldy-Gemu Scholarships *(Undergraduate/Scholarship)* [1227]
Ryerson Scholarships *(Undergraduate/Scholarship)* [5527]
Chester & Maria Sadowski Memorial Scholarships *(Undergraduate/Scholarship)* [8590]
St. James Armenian Church Memorial Scholarships *(Undergraduate/Scholarship)* [1704]
SAJA Journalism Scholarships *(Undergraduate, Graduate/Scholarship)* [9356]
SALEF Health Career Scholarships *(Undergraduate, Graduate/Scholarship)* [8680]
Serbian Bar Association of America Scholarships *(Graduate/Scholarship)* [8847]
Gadde Sitaramamma and Tirupataiah Scholarships *(Graduate/Scholarship)* [9670]
Allogan Slagle Memorial Scholarships *(Undergraduate, Graduate/Scholarship)* [1835]
Eva Smith Bursary *(Undergraduate/Scholarship)* [5528]
Boleslaw & Irena Sobczak Scholarships *(Undergraduate/Scholarship)* [8591]
Sovereign Nations Scholarships *(Undergraduate/Scholarship)* [872]
Iwalani Carpenter Sowa Scholarships *(Graduate/Scholarship)* [7919]
SREB-State Doctoral Scholars Program - Dissertation Awards *(Doctorate/Scholarship, Award)* [9410]
SREB-State Doctoral Scholars Program - Doctoral Awards *(Doctorate, Graduate/Scholarship)* [9411]
Lasek Stanisław and Aniela Scholarship *(Undergraduate/Scholarship)* [8592]
Vallabhaneni Sukundamma and Lakshmaiah Scholarships *(Graduate/Scholarship)* [9671]
Syncrude/Athabasca University Aboriginal Scholarships *(Undergraduate/Scholarship)* [9627]
Hazaros Tabakoglu Scholarship Fund *(Undergraduate/Scholarship)* [1705]
TANA Foundation Graduate Scholarships *(Graduate/Scholarship)* [9672]
Dr. Peter A. Theodos Memorial Graduate Scholarships *(Undergraduate, Graduate/Scholarship)* [4850]
Barbara Thomas Bursary *(Undergraduate/Scholarship)* [5529]
Aram Torossian Memorial Scholarships *(Undergraduate/Scholarship)* [1706]
Vera Tran Memorial Scholarships *(Undergraduate/Scholarship)* [10388]
Transamerica Retirement Solutions Leaders in Health Care Scholarships *(Graduate/Scholarship)* [5169]
Richard R. Tufenkian Memorial Scholarships *(Undergraduate/Scholarship)* [1671]
Morris K. Udall Scholarships *(Undergraduate/Scholarship)* [9825]
Union of Marash Armenian Scholarships *(Undergraduate, Graduate/Scholarship)* [1707]
University of Wisconsin-Madison Chancellor's Scholarships *(Undergraduate/Scholarship)* [10328]
Adolph Van Pelt Special Fund for Indians Scholarships *(Undergraduate/Scholarship)* [1836]
Kodali Veeraiah and Sarojini Scholarships *(Graduate/Scholarship)* [9673]
Dimitri J. Ververelli Memorial Scholarship for Architecture and/or Engineering *(Undergraduate/Scholarship)* [4851]
VSCPA Educational Foundation Minority Scholarships *(Graduate, Undergraduate/Scholarship)* [10408]
Flis Walter and Anna Memorial Scholarship *(Undergraduate/Scholarship)* [8593]
Colin Wasacase Scholarship *(Undergraduate/Scholarship)* [7659]
Wells Fargo American Indian Scholarships - Graduate *(Graduate/Scholarship)* [883]

Wellstone Fellowships for Social Justice *(Graduate/Fellowship)* [3959]
Wisconsin Lawton Minority Retention Grants *(Undergraduate/Grant)* [10336]
Denis Wong and Associates Scholarships *(Graduate, Undergraduate/Scholarship)* [7920]
York Regional Police Scholarships *(Undergraduate/Scholarship)* [5530]
Youth Affairs Committee Rising Star Scholarships *(Undergraduate/Scholarship)* [5531]
Harry and Angel Zerigian Scholarships *(Undergraduate/Scholarship)* [1708]

Fraternal organization membership

Nancy Ashley Adams/Ashley Adams Koetje Scholarships *(Undergraduate/Scholarship)* [3547]
Gladys Ross Carlson Adelphe Scholarship Fund *(Undergraduate, Graduate/Award)* [5688]
ADHA IOH Sigma Phi Alpha Graduate Scholarships *(Graduate/Scholarship)* [775]
ALD Graduate Fellowships *(Graduate/Fellowship)* [6696]
Margaret M. Alkek Scholarships *(Undergraduate/Scholarship)* [3548]
Alpha Chi Omega Love and Loyalty Grants *(Professional development/Grant)* [346]
Alpha Chi Sigma Scholarship Awards *(Graduate, Undergraduate/Scholarship)* [348]
Alpha Delta Gamma Educational Foundation Scholarships *(Undergraduate, Graduate/Scholarship)* [350]
Alpha Kappa Alpha - Educational Advancement Foundation Financial Need-Based Scholarships *(Graduate, Undergraduate/Scholarship)* [352]
Alpha Kappa Alpha - Educational Advancement Foundation Merit Scholarships *(Graduate, Undergraduate/Scholarship)* [353]
Anchor Plastics Scholarships *(Graduate, Undergraduate/Scholarship)* [8072]
Margaret J. Andrew Memorial Scholarships *(Undergraduate, Graduate/Scholarship)* [8909]
Hettie Margaret Anthony Fellowship *(Doctorate/Fellowship)* [5779]
Hettie M. Anthony Fellowships *(Doctorate/Fellowship)* [5787]
Austin Alumnae Association Beta Xi Scholarship *(Undergraduate/Scholarship)* [5690]
Francis Warren Baker Memorial Scholarships *(Undergraduate/Scholarship)* [8910]
Beta Lambda Project 2000 Scholarship *(Undergraduate/Scholarship)* [5694]
Beta Mu Project 2000 Scholarships *(Undergraduate/Scholarship)* [5695]
Beta Omega Scholarships *(Undergraduate/Scholarship)* [8911]
Beta Pi Project 2000 Scholarship in Memory of Kristy LeMond *(Undergraduate/Scholarship)* [5696]
Beta Province Project 2000 Scholarships *(Undergraduate/Scholarship)* [5697]
Beta Sigma Scholarships *(Undergraduate/Scholarship)* [8912]
Beta Tau Scholarship Fund *(Undergraduate/Scholarship)* [5698]
Beta Theta Memorial Scholarships *(Graduate, Undergraduate/Scholarship)* [5699]
Beta Xi Project 2000 Scholarships *(Undergraduate/Scholarship)* [5700]
Beta Zeta Project 2000 Scholarships *(Undergraduate/Scholarship)* [5701]
Mildred Cater Bradham Social Work Fellowships *(Graduate, Professional development/Fellowship)* [10814]
William J. Brennan Graduate Assistant Fellowships *(Graduate/Fellowship)* [7678]
Houston Alumnae Association, Doris Krikham Brokaw Memorial Adelphe Scholarship *(Undergraduate, Graduate/Scholarship)* [5703]
Seth R. and Corrine H. Brooks Memorial Scholarships *(Undergraduate/Scholarship)* [2246]
Marjorie M. Brown Dissertation Fellowship *(Doctorate/Fellowship)* [5780]
Marjorie M. Brown Fellowship Program *(Postdoctorate/Fellowship)* [5788]

Walta Wilkinson Carmichael Scholarships *(Undergraduate/Scholarship)* [8913]
Christine Kerr Cawthorne Scholarships *(Undergraduate/Scholarship)* [8914]
S. Penny Chappell Scholarships *(Undergraduate/Scholarship)* [8085]
Charline Chilson Scholarships *(Undergraduate/Scholarship)* [3580]
Clan Ross Foundation Scholarships *(Undergraduate/Scholarship)* [3043]
Thomas Arkle Clark Scholar-Leader of the Year Endowed Scholarships *(Graduate, Undergraduate/Scholarship)* [8061]
Geraldine Clewell Fellowships - Doctoral Student *(Graduate/Fellowship)* [8086]
Geraldine Clewell Fellowships - Masteral *(Graduate/Fellowship)* [8087]
Geraldine Clewell Scholarships - Undergraduate *(Undergraduate/Scholarship)* [8088]
Closs/Parnitzke/Clarke Scholarships *(Undergraduate/Scholarship)* [8089]
Maridell Braham Condon Scholarships *(Undergraduate/Scholarship)* [8915]
Beta Nu/Caryl Cordis D'hondt Scholarships *(Undergraduate/Scholarship)* [8916]
Theta/Caryl Cordis D'hondt Scholarships *(Undergraduate/Scholarship)* [8917]
Cornaro Scholarships for Graduate Studies *(Graduate/Scholarship)* [5686]
CSA Fraternal Life Scholarships *(Undergraduate/Scholarship)* [3483]
Dallas Alumnae Association Gamma Phi Chapter Scholarships *(Undergraduate/Scholarship)* [5705]
Lucile Caswell Davids Memorial Adelphe Scholarships *(Undergraduate, Graduate/Scholarship)* [5706]
Arlene Davis Scholarships *(Undergraduate/Scholarship)* [3581]
Delta Chi Alumnae Memorial Scholarships *(Undergraduate/Scholarship)* [8918]
Delta Epsilon Sigma Graduate Fellowships *(Graduate/Fellowship)* [3566]
Delta Epsilon Sigma Undergraduate Scholarships *(Undergraduate/Scholarship)* [3567]
Delta Kappa Project 2000 Scholarships *(Undergraduate/Scholarship)* [5707]
Delta Nu Alpha Foundation Scholarships *(Undergraduate/Scholarship)* [3573]
Delta Nu Project 2000 Scholarships *(Undergraduate/Scholarship)* [5708]
Delta Phi Epsilon Educational Foundation Scholarships *(Undergraduate, Graduate/Scholarship)* [3575]
Delta Project 2000 Scholarships *(Undergraduate/Scholarship)* [5709]
Delta Tau Project 2000 Scholarships *(Undergraduate/Scholarship)* [5710]
Delta Upsilon Project 2000 Nowell Memorial Scholarships *(Undergraduate/Scholarship)* [5711]
Delta Zeta Undergraduate Scholarships *(Undergraduate/Scholarship)* [3582]
Denton Scholarships *(Graduate/Scholarship)* [8897]
Jean Dearth Dickerscheid Fellowships *(Graduate/Fellowship)* [8090]
Scott Dominguez - Craters of the Moon Chapter Scholarships *(Graduate, Undergraduate/Scholarship)* [1412]
Wilma Sackett Dressel Scholarships *(Undergraduate/Scholarship)* [8919]
Margaret Drew Alpha Fellowships *(Graduate/Fellowship)* [8091]
Durning Sisters Scholarships *(Graduate/Scholarship)* [3549]
Enterprise Rent-A-Car Scholarships *(Graduate, Undergraduate/Scholarship)* [8073]
Epsilon Delta Project 2000 Scholarships *(Undergraduate/Scholarship)* [5713]
Epsilon Epsilon Scholarships *(Undergraduate/Scholarship)* [8920]
Epsilon Tau Scholarships *(Undergraduate/Scholarship)* [8921]
Harriet Erich Graduate Fellowships *(Graduate/Fellowship, Scholarship)* [3550]
Falcon Achievement Scholarships *(Undergraduate/Scholarship)* [8200]
Federated Insurance Scholarships *(Graduate, Un-*

FRATERNAL ORGANIZATION MEMBERSHIP — Special Recipient Index

dergraduate/Scholarship) [8074]
Marjorie Gosselin Fitzgerald, Upsilon, Permanently Restricted Scholarship Fund *(Undergraduate/Scholarship)* [5717]
Foresters Scholarships *(Undergraduate/Scholarship)* [5095]
Stephen J. Fortgang/University of Northern Iowa Chapter Scholarship *(Undergraduate/Scholarship)* [5670]
Genevieve Forthun Scholarships *(Undergraduate/Scholarship)* [8092]
Mary Metzger Fouse Memorial Scholarship Fund *(Undergraduate/Scholarship)* [5718]
Mary Weiking Franken Scholarships *(Undergraduate/Scholarship)* [8093]
Marian Johnson Frutiger Scholarships *(Undergraduate/Scholarship)* [8922]
Louise Bales Gallagher Scholarships *(Undergraduate/Scholarship)* [3551]
Gamma Chi Project 2000 Scholarships *(Undergraduate/Scholarship)* [5720]
Gamma Iota Scholarships - Gamma Tau *(Undergraduate/Scholarship)* [8923]
Gamma Iota Scholarships - Kappa Eta *(Undergraduate/Scholarship)* [8924]
Gamma Iota Scholarships - Zeta Kappa *(Undergraduate/Scholarship)* [8925]
Gamma Iota Scholarships - Zeta Nu *(Undergraduate/Scholarship)* [8926]
Gamma Mu Project 2000 Scholarships *(Undergraduate/Scholarship)* [5721]
Gamma Pi Project 2000 Scholarships *(Undergraduate/Scholarship)* [5722]
Gamma Sigma Alpha Graduate Scholarships *(Graduate/Scholarship)* [4322]
Gamma Theta Project 2000 Scholarships *(Undergraduate/Scholarship)* [5723]
Gamma Zeta Project 2000 Scholarships *(Undergraduate/Scholarship)* [5724]
Eugene Garfield Doctoral Dissertation Fellowship *(Doctorate/Fellowship)* [2239]
General Falcon Scholarships *(Undergraduate/Scholarship)* [8201]
Elizabeth Tucker Gessley Scholarship *(Undergraduate/Scholarship)* [5727]
Gleaner Life Insurance Society Scholarships *(Undergraduate/Scholarship)* [4447]
Richard C. Gorecki Scholarships *(Undergraduate/Scholarship)* [8202]
Lucille Cheever Graubart/Lambda Scholarships *(Undergraduate/Scholarship)* [8927]
Anna Munger Greenwood Memorial Adelphe Scholarship *(Undergraduate/Scholarship)* [5729]
Elizabeth M. Gruber Scholarships *(Graduate/Scholarship)* [3583]
Mary Ewing Guthrey/Mary Keller Moyer Memorial Scholarship *(Undergraduate, Graduate/Scholarship)* [5730]
Suzanne Lovell Hadsell Memorial Scholarship *(Undergraduate, Graduate/Scholarship)* [5731]
Anna E. Hall Memorial Scholarships *(Undergraduate, Graduate/Scholarship)* [8055]
Caitlin Hammaren Memorial Scholarship *(Undergraduate/Scholarship)* [5732]
Tommie J. Hamner Scholarships *(Undergraduate/Scholarship)* [8094]
Dolores Ruth Heady Hardy Memorial Scholarship *(Undergraduate/Scholarship)* [5733]
William H. Harris Memorial Scholarships *(Graduate, Undergraduate/Scholarship)* [8075]
Peg Hart Harrison Memorial Scholarships *(Undergraduate, Graduate/Scholarship)* [3552]
Edith Head Scholarships *(Undergraduate/Scholarship)* [3584]
Lavonne Heghinian Scholarships *(Undergraduate/Scholarship)* [3585]
Jessica M. Herron, Epsilon Nu, Memorial Scholarship *(Undergraduate/Scholarship)* [5734]
Herschede Engineering Scholarships *(Graduate/Scholarship)* [8898]
Houston/Nancy Holliman Scholarships *(Undergraduate/Scholarship)* [3586]
Sandra Jo Hornick Scholarships *(Undergraduate/Scholarship)* [5671]
Houston Alumnae Association, Eunice "Scotty" Scott Siverson Memorial Adelphe Scholarship *(Undergraduate, Graduate/Scholarship)* [5735]
Sarah Jane Houston Scholarships *(Undergraduate/Scholarship)* [3587]
Huenefeld/Denton Scholarships *(Undergraduate/Scholarship)* [3588]
Betty Jo Creighton Hunkele Adelphe Scholarship *(Undergraduate/Scholarship)* [5736]
Iris Scholarship *(Undergraduate/Scholarship)* [5737]
Hazel D. Isbell Fellowships *(Graduate/Fellowship, Scholarship)* [5553]
Jackman Scholarships *(Undergraduate/Scholarship)* [8095]
Jacque Placette Chapman Master's Fellowships *(Graduate, Master's/Fellowship)* [7679]
Elise Reed Jenkins Memorial Scholarships - Gamma Lambda *(Undergraduate/Scholarship)* [8928]
Elise Reed Jenkins Memorial Scholarships - Gamma Psi *(Undergraduate/Scholarship)* [8929]
Martha Combs Jenkins Scholarships *(Undergraduate/Scholarship)* [8096]
Wilma Winberg Johnson Adelphe Scholarship for Chapter Consultants *(Undergraduate/Scholarship)* [5738]
Kappa Kappa Gamma Foundation Project 2000 Scholarships *(Undergraduate/Scholarship)* [5739]
Kappa Kappa Gamma Graduate Scholarships *(Graduate/Scholarship)* [5740]
Kappa Kappa Gamma Undergraduate Scholarships *(Undergraduate/Scholarship)* [5741]
Kappa Omicron Nu Leadership Undergraduate Scholarships *(Undergraduate/Scholarship)* [5781]
Kappa Omicron Nu National Alumni Fellowships *(Graduate/Fellowship)* [5782]
Kappa Project 2000 Scholarships *(Undergraduate/Scholarship)* [5742]
Kappa Sigma Scholarship/Leadership Awards *(Undergraduate/Scholarship)* [5792]
Kappa Zeta Scholarships *(Undergraduate/Scholarship)* [8930]
KDP International Scholarship Program - President Scholarship *(Undergraduate, Graduate, Doctorate/Scholarship)* [5674]
Debbie Khalil Memorial Scholarships *(Graduate, Undergraduate/Scholarship)* [8076]
Treva C. Kintner Scholarships *(Undergraduate/Scholarship)* [8097]
Dr. Eva Kleinpeter Scholarship *(Undergraduate/Scholarship)* [5676]
KON/GEICO LeaderShape Undergraduate Scholarship *(Undergraduate/Scholarship)* [5789]
KON National Alumni Chapter Grant *(Professional development/Grant)* [5783]
KON New Initiatives Grant *(Professional development/Grant)* [5784]
Emily Day Koppell Memorial Adelphe Scholarship *(Undergraduate, Graduate/Scholarship)* [5743]
KTA Chapter Adviser Research Grant Award *(Professional development/Grant)* [5794]
Elaine Johnson Lampert Journalism Memorial Adelphe Scholarship *(Graduate/Award)* [5745]
Katherine Roberts LaPorte Memorial Adelphe Scholarship *(Undergraduate/Scholarship)* [5746]
Betsy B. and Garold A. Leach Scholarships for Museum Studies *(Undergraduate/Scholarship)* [3589]
V.A. Leonard Scholarships *(Graduate, Undergraduate/Scholarship)* [356]
Elsa Ludeke Graduate Scholarships *(Graduate/Scholarship)* [3590]
Eileen C. Maddex Fellowships *(Graduate/Fellowship)* [5785]
Madson Graduate Scholarships *(Graduate/Scholarship)* [8899]
Marisol Scholarship *(Undergraduate/Scholarship)* [5750]
Sarah Shinn Marshall Scholarships *(Undergraduate/Scholarship)* [3554]
Martin Sisters Scholarships *(Undergraduate/Scholarship)* [3555]
Margaret Edwards Mason Adelphe Scholarship *(Undergraduate, Graduate/Scholarship)* [5751]
Nancy B. Woolridge McGee Graduate Fellowships *(Graduate/Fellowship)* [10819]
Mary Bowles McInnis Adelphe Scholarship *(Undergraduate/Scholarship)* [5752]
John L. and Eleanore I. Mckinley Scholarships *(Undergraduate/Scholarship)* [3591]
Joan Reagin McNeill Scholarships - Alpha Theta *(Undergraduate/Scholarship)* [8931]
Joan Reagin McNeill Scholarships - Theta Phi *(Undergraduate/Scholarship)* [8932]
Mihaly Russin Scholarship Awards *(Graduate/Scholarship)* [8656]
Military Service Scholarships *(Graduate, Undergraduate/Scholarship)* [8900]
Thomas S. Morgan Memorial Scholarship *(Graduate, Master's/Scholarship)* [8044]
Mu Alpha Theta Summer Grants *(Undergraduate, Graduate/Grant)* [6610]
Carol Nelson Scholarship *(Undergraduate/Scholarship)* [5753]
Evelyn S. Nish Scholarships *(Undergraduate/Scholarship)* [8933]
Northwestern Mutual Financial Network Scholarships *(Graduate, Undergraduate/Scholarship)* [8077]
WillEtta Long Oates, Gamma Nu, Memorial Scholarship *(Undergraduate, Graduate/Scholarship)* [5754]
Omicron Nu Research Fellowships *(Postdoctorate/Fellowship)* [5790]
Order of Omega Doctoral Fellowships *(Doctorate, Graduate/Fellowship)* [7680]
Cissy McDaniel Parker Scholarships *(Undergraduate/Scholarship)* [3557]
William E. Parrish Scholarships *(Graduate, Master's/Scholarship)* [8045]
Gail Patrick Charitable Trust Scholarships *(Undergraduate/Scholarship)* [3593]
Peale Scholarship Grant *(Professional development/Scholarship)* [8058]
Martha Mitchell Pearson Memorial Scholarship *(Undergraduate, Graduate/Scholarship)* [5755]
Phi Alpha Theta Doctoral Scholarships *(Doctorate/Scholarship)* [8046]
Phi Alpha Theta Faculty Advisor Research Grant *(Other/Grant)* [8047]
Phi Delta Gamma Academic Achievement Awards *(Undergraduate/Scholarship)* [8059]
Phi Eta Sigma Distinguished Member Scholarships - Graduate or Professional *(Graduate, Other/Scholarship)* [8062]
Phi Eta Sigma Distinguished Member Scholarships - Undergraduate *(Undergraduate/Scholarship)* [8063]
Phi Eta Sigma Undergraduate Scholarship Awards *(Undergraduate/Scholarship)* [8064]
Phi Kappa Phi Fellowships *(Graduate, Undergraduate/Fellowship)* [8066]
Phi Kappa Sigma Foundation Scholarship *(Undergraduate/Scholarship)* [8068]
Phi Kappa Sigma Need-Based Scholarships *(Undergraduate/Scholarship)* [8069]
Phi Kappa Sigma Participation-Based Scholarships *(Undergraduate/Scholarship)* [8070]
Phi Sigma Epsilon Past National President Scholarships *(Graduate, Undergraduate/Scholarship)* [8078]
Phi Theta Kappa Scholarships *(Undergraduate/Scholarship)* [5124]
Phi Upsilon Omicron Candle Fellowships *(Graduate/Fellowship)* [8098]
Phi Upsilon Omicron Challenge Scholarships *(Undergraduate/Scholarship)* [8099]
Phi Upsilon Omicron Diamond Anniversary Fellowships *(Graduate/Fellowship)* [8100]
Phi Upsilon Omicron Founders Fellowships *(Graduate/Fellowship)* [8101]
Phi Upsilon Omicron Golden Anniversary Scholarships *(Undergraduate/Scholarship)* [8102]
Phi Upsilon Omicron Past Presidents Scholarships *(Undergraduate/Scholarship)* [8103]
Phi Upsilon Omicron Presidents Research Fellowships *(Graduate/Fellowship)* [8104]
Pi Gamma Mu Scholarships *(Graduate/Scholarship)* [8133]
Pi Project 2000 Tali James Memorial Scholarships *(Undergraduate/Scholarship)* [5756]
John Pine Memorial Scholarships *(Doctorate, Graduate/Scholarship)* [8048]
Joseph E. Pryor Graduate Fellowships *(Graduate/*

Fellowship, Scholarship) [343]
Cheryl White Pryor Memorial Scholarships (Undergraduate/Scholarship) [3558]
Phillis Brinton Pryor Panhellenic Scholarship (Undergraduate/Scholarship) [5757]
Marie Mathew Rask-Gamma Omicron Educational Endowment (Undergraduate/Scholarship) [5758]
Rho Chi, AFPE First Year Graduate Fellowships (Doctorate, Graduate/Fellowship) [8597]
Rho Chi Society Clinical Research Scholarships (Postdoctorate/Scholarship) [8598]
Lois McDonald Rinehart Adelphe Scholarship (Undergraduate, Graduate/Scholarship) [5759]
Nell Bryant Robinson Scholarships (Undergraduate/Scholarship) [8105]
Sandra Journey Rolf Scholarship Fund (Undergraduate, Graduate/Scholarship) [5760]
Dorothy Worden Ronken Scholarships (Graduate/Scholarship) [3594]
Susanna Stover Root Memorial Scholarship (Undergraduate/Scholarship) [5761]
Lucile Rust Scholarships (Undergraduate/Scholarship) [8106]
Saints Cyril and Methodius Scholarships (Undergraduate/Scholarship) [8657]
Margaret Jerome Sampson Scholarships (Undergraduate/Scholarship) [8107]
Mary Turnbull Schacht Memorial Scholarships (Undergraduate/Scholarship) [8934]
Lillian P. Schoephoerster Scholarships (Undergraduate/Scholarship) [8108]
A.J. and Lynda Hare Scribante Scholarship Fund (Undergraduate/Scholarship) [5762]
Frank B. Sessa Scholarship (Professional development/Scholarship) [2241]
Josephine Kerbey Shaw Memorial Undergraduate Scholarship (Undergraduate/Scholarship) [5763]
Regina B. Shearn Scholarships (Graduate, Undergraduate/Scholarship) [357]
Susan Goldsmith Shelley Scholarship (Undergraduate/Scholarship) [5764]
Lynn Brower Shonk Memorial Scholarship (Undergraduate/Scholarship) [5765]
Sigma Kappa Foundation Alumnae Continuing Education Scholarships (Undergraduate/Scholarship) [8935]
Sigma Kappa Foundation Alzheimer's/Gerontology Scholarships (Graduate/Scholarship) [8936]
Sigma Kappa Foundation Founders' Scholarships (Undergraduate/Scholarship) [8937]
Sigma Kappa Foundation Gerontology Scholarships (Undergraduate/Scholarship) [8938]
Sigma Kappa Foundation Michigan Scholarships (Undergraduate/Scholarship) [8939]
Ann Kelsay Small Scholarship (Undergraduate/Scholarship) [5766]
Helen D. Snow Memorial Scholarship (Undergraduate/Scholarship) [8056]
SNRS/STTI Research Grants (Professional development/Grant) [9408]
Sons of Union Veterans of the Civil War Scholarships (Undergraduate/Scholarship) [9348]
Elin J. Stene/Xi Scholarships (Undergraduate/Scholarship) [8940]
Dell Chenoweth Stifel Scholarship (Graduate/Scholarship) [5767]
Sutherland/Purdy Scholarships (Undergraduate/Scholarship) [8109]
Lorraine E. Swain Scholarships (Undergraduate/Scholarship) [8941]
Barber Owen Thomas Scholarships (Undergraduate/Scholarship) [8942]
Matilda B. Thompson Scholarship (Undergraduate/Scholarship) [4929]
Thornberg/Havens Scholarships (Undergraduate/Scholarship) [3596]
Richard Cecil Todd and Clauda Pennock Todd Tripod Scholarships (Graduate, Undergraduate/Scholarship) [8082]
Tri Delta Alpha Eta Scholarships (Undergraduate/Scholarship) [3559]
Tri Delta Alpha Rho Leadership Scholarships (Undergraduate/Scholarship) [3560]
Tri Delta Atlanta Alumnae Achievement Scholarships (Undergraduate/Scholarship) [3561]
Tri Delta Beta Gamma Memorial Scholarships (Undergraduate/Scholarship) [3562]
Tri Delta Houston Alumnae Chapter Graduate Fellowships (Graduate/Fellowship, Scholarship) [3563]
Jo Anne J. Trow Scholarships (Undergraduate/Scholarship) [6697]
Graydon A. Tunstall Undergraduate Student Scholarships (Undergraduate/Scholarship) [8049]
UPE Scholarship Awards (Graduate, Undergraduate/Scholarship) [10342]
Vector Marketing Scholarships (Graduate, Undergraduate/Scholarship) [8079]
Irma E. Voigt Memorial Scholarships (Undergraduate/Scholarship) [8943]
Jane and Gregg Waddill Memorial Adelphe Scholarship (Undergraduate/Scholarship) [5768]
Helen Zick Walker Adelphe Scholarship (Undergraduate/Scholarship) [5769]
Lynn McNabb Walton Adelphe Scholarhship (Undergraduate/Scholarship) [5770]
Jean Hess Wells Memorial Adelphe Graduate Scholarship (Graduate/Scholarship) [5771]
Jean Hess Wells Memorial Adelphe (Undergraduate/Scholarship) [5772]
Whan Memorial Scholarships (Graduate, Undergraduate/Scholarship) [8080]
Alice Hersey Wick Scholarships (Undergraduate/Scholarship) [8944]
Andrea Will Memorial Scholarships (Undergraduate/Scholarship) [8945]
Nona Hobbs Wolfe Memorial Scholarship (Undergraduate/Scholarship) [5774]
Rolla F. Wood Graduate Scholarships (Graduate/Scholarship) [8083]
Donnell B. Young Scholarships (Undergraduate/Scholarship) [308]
Youth Partners Accessing Capital (PAC) (Undergraduate/Scholarship) [354]
Zeta Sigma Project 2000 Scholarships (Undergraduate/Scholarship) [5775]
A.F. Zimmerman Scholarships (Graduate, Master's/Scholarship) [8050]

Hispanic American

AAMFT Minority Fellowships (Doctorate, Graduate/Fellowship) [538]
Acoustical Society of America Minority Fellowships (Graduate/Fellowship) [52]
Actuarial Diversity Scholarship (Undergraduate/Scholarship) [60]
Affirmative Action Student Scholarship Mini-Grant Travel Awards (Undergraduate, Master's, Doctorate/Grant) [30]
AFPE Pre-Doctoral Fellowships in Pharmaceutical Sciences for Underrepresented Minorities (Doctorate, Graduate/Fellowship) [828]
AHETEMS General Scholarships (Undergraduate, Graduate/Scholarship) [8888]
AHETEMS Professional Scholarships (Graduate/Scholarship) [8889]
AIChE Minority Scholarship Awards for College Students (Undergraduate/Scholarship) [903]
AIChE Minority Scholarship Awards for Incoming College Freshmen (Undergraduate/Scholarship) [904]
Air Products and Chemicals, Inc. Scholarships (Undergraduate/Scholarship) [1975]
ALPFA Scholarship Programs (Graduate, Undergraduate/Scholarship) [2013]
AMA Foundation Minority Scholars Awards (Graduate/Scholarship) [989]
American Association for Cancer Research Minority Scholar Awards (Graduate/Award) [472]
American GI Forum of San Jose Scholarships (Undergraduate/Scholarship) [8756]
American Society for Microbiology International Fellowships for Latin America and the Caribbean (Postdoctorate/Fellowship) [1367]
AMS/Industry Minority Scholarships (Undergraduate/Scholarship) [1000]
ANA Multicultural Excellence Scholarship Fund (MAIP) (Graduate, Undergraduate/Internship) [456]
APS Scholarships for Minority Undergraduate Physics Majors (Undergraduate/Scholarship) [7138]
APSA Fund for Latino Scholarship (Undergraduate, Graduate/Scholarship) [1111]
APSA Minority Fellows Program (Doctorate/Fellowship) [1113]
APTA Minority Scholarships - Faculty Development Scholarships (Postdoctorate/Scholarship) [1096]
APTA Minority Scholarships - Physical Therapist Assistant Students (Undergraduate/Scholarship) [1097]
APTA Minority Scholarships - Physical Therapist Students (Undergraduate/Scholarship) [1098]
Frank G. Araujo Memorial Scholarships (Undergraduate/Scholarship) [8449]
ASA Minority Fellowship Program (ASA MFP) (Graduate, Doctorate, Professional development/Fellowship) [1445]
ASGP Graduate Research Fellowships (Graduate/Fellowship) [223]
AWG Minority Scholarships (Undergraduate/Scholarship) [2093]
Michael Baker Corp. Scholarship for Diversity in Engineering (Undergraduate/Scholarship) [1976]
Becas Univision Scholarship Program (Undergraduate, Graduate/Scholarship) [4902]
Bill Bernbach Diversity Scholarships (Undergraduate/Scholarship) [457]
Thomas M. Blake Memorial Scholarships (Undergraduate/Scholarship) [3360]
F.A. and Charlotte Blount Scholarships (Undergraduate/Scholarship) [10571]
Maria Gonzales Borrero Scholarships (Undergraduate/Scholarship) [4740]
Leon Bradley Scholarship Program (Undergraduate/Scholarship) [575]
BSF General Scholarship Awards (Undergraduate, Vocational/Occupational/Scholarship) [2197]
Carlos M. Castaneda Journalism Scholarships (Graduate/Scholarship) [2807]
CHCI Graduate Fellowships (Graduate/Fellowship) [3352]
CHCI Public Policy Fellowships (Professional development/Fellowship) [3353]
CHCI Scholarships (Undergraduate, Graduate/Scholarship) [3354]
Citi/TELACU Scholars Mentoring Program (Undergraduate/Scholarship) [9659]
Columbus Citizens Foundation College Scholarships (Undergraduate/Scholarship) [3151]
Columbus Citizens Foundation High School Scholarships (Undergraduate/Scholarship) [3152]
Connecticut Association of Latinos in Higher Education Scholarships (Undergraduate/Scholarship) [4744]
Lydia Cruz and Sandra Maria Ramos Scholarships (Undergraduate/Scholarship) [3577]
Davis Family Scholarships (Undergraduate/Scholarship) [8700]
Ruth DeMoss Scholarships (Undergraduate/Scholarship) [8701]
FAIC Latin American and Caribbean Scholars Program (Other/Scholarship) [908]
Fleming/Blaszcak Scholarships (Undergraduate, Graduate/Scholarship) [9262]
Florida Education Fund McKnight Doctoral Fellowships (Graduate/Fellowship) [4085]
Foundation of American Institute for Conservation Lecture Grants (Other/Grant) [909]
John Hope Franklin Dissertation Fellowships (Doctorate/Fellowship) [1080]
Fraser Stryker Diversity Scholarships (Undergraduate/Scholarship) [4293]
The Gates Millennium Scholars (Undergraduate/Scholarship) [4903]
GFOA Minorities in Government Finance Scholarship (Graduate, Undergraduate/Scholarship) [4502]
Glendale Latino Association Scholarships (Undergraduate/Scholarship) [4449]
Google Hispanic College Fund Scholarships (Graduate, Undergraduate/Scholarship) [4497]
HACU/NASCAR Scholarships (Graduate, Undergraduate/Scholarship) [4888]
HANA Scholarships (Undergraduate, Graduate, Doctorate/Scholarship) [9852]
HFMH Bilingual Scholarships for Mental Health

Workforce Diversity *(Graduate/Scholarship)* [4913]
Hispanic Association of Colleges and Universities Scholarships *(Undergraduate/Scholarship)* [4890]
Hispanic Metropolitan Chamber Scholarships *(Graduate, Undergraduate/Scholarship)* [4900]
Hispanic Scholarship Fund General College Scholarship Program (HSF) *(Undergraduate/Scholarship)* [4904]
HSF/Marathon Oil College Scholarship Program *(Undergraduate/Scholarship)* [4905]
HSF/Wells Fargo Scholarship Program *(Undergraduate/Scholarship)* [4906]
The Hyatt Hotels Fund For Minority Lodging Management Students *(Undergraduate/Scholarship)* [860]
Inter American Press Association Scholarships *(Undergraduate/Scholarship)* [9061]
Italian Language Scholarships *(Undergraduate/Scholarship)* [7682]
Kaplan Scholarships *(Graduate/Scholarship)* [4898]
KPMG Foundation Minority Accounting Doctoral Scholarships *(Doctorate/Scholarship)* [5885]
La Voz Latina Scholarships *(Undergraduate/Scholarship)* [3290]
LAEF Scholarships *(Undergraduate/Scholarship)* [5937]
LAFS - Cal State University San Marcos General Scholarships *(Undergraduate/Scholarship)* [2212]
The Lagrant Foundation - Graduate Students Scholarships *(Graduate/Scholarship)* [5900]
The Lagrant Foundation - Undergraduate Students Scholarships *(Undergraduate/Scholarship)* [5901]
Latinos for Dental Careers Scholarships *(Undergraduate/Scholarship)* [2830]
LITA/LSSI Minority Scholarships *(Graduate/Scholarship)* [6072]
LITA/OCLC Minority Scholarships *(Graduate/Scholarship)* [6073]
LLN Student Scholarships *(Undergraduate/Scholarship)* [5939]
LULAC GM Scholarships *(Graduate, High School, Undergraduate, Vocational/Occupational/Award)* [5988]
LULAC National Scholarship Fund (LNSF) *(Graduate, Undergraduate/Scholarship)* [5989]
MABF Scholarships *(Postgraduate/Scholarship)* [6442]
Howard Mayer Brown Fellowship *(Graduate/Fellowship)* [1021]
Medical Library Association Scholarships for Minority Students *(Graduate/Scholarship)* [6389]
Rixio Medina and Associates Hispanics in Safety Scholarships *(Graduate, Undergraduate/Scholarship)* [1422]
Mexican American Legal Defense and Educational Fund Law School Scholarships *(Undergraduate/Scholarship)* [6447]
MillerCoors Engineering and Sciences Scholarships *(Undergraduate/Scholarship)* [68]
MillerCoors National Scholarships *(Undergraduate/Scholarship)* [69]
Minority Teachers of Illinois Scholarships (MTI) *(Undergraduate/Scholarship)* [5078]
MLA/NLM Spectrum Scholarship Program *(Undergraduate/Scholarship)* [6391]
Archie Motley Memorial Scholarships for Minority Students *(Graduate/Scholarship)* [6517]
NACA Multicultural Professional Development Grant *(Undergraduate, Graduate, Professional development/Grant)* [6729]
National Medical Fellowships Need-Based Scholarships *(Undergraduate/Scholarship)* [7061]
National Organization of Italian-American Women Scholarships *(Undergraduate, Graduate/Scholarship)* [7083]
NHFA Scholarships *(Graduate/Scholarship)* [6998]
NSHMBA Scholarships *(Graduate/Scholarship)* [7164]
Frank del Olmo Memorial Scholarships *(Undergraduate/Scholarship)* [2826]
Operation JumpStart Scholarships *(Graduate/Scholarship)* [458]
Order Sons of Italy Foundation General Scholarships *(Graduate, Undergraduate/Scholarship)* [7683]
Casilda Pagan Educational/Vocational Scholarships *(Graduate, Undergraduate, Postgraduate/Scholarship)* [4964]
Rudy Perez Songwriting Scholarships *(Undergraduate/Scholarship)* [1275]
PlasticPlace Young Entrepreneurs Scholarships *(Undergraduate/Scholarship)* [8148]
Portuguese American Police Association Scholarships *(Undergraduate/Scholarship)* [8211]
Judith McManus Price Scholarships *(Undergraduate, Graduate/Scholarship)* [1106]
Miguel Pro Scholarships *(Undergraduate/Scholarship)* [10724]
PRSA Diversity Multicultural Scholarships *(Undergraduate/Scholarship)* [8378]
Rosa Quezada Memorial Education Scholarships *(Undergraduate/Scholarship)* [3361]
Ronald McDonald House Charities/HACER Scholarships *(Undergraduate/Scholarship)* [8640]
Leo S. Rowe Pan American Fund *(Graduate, Undergraduate/Loan)* [7730]
Lucille and Edward R. Roybal Foundation Public Health Scholarships *(Graduate, Undergraduate/Scholarship)* [8654]
SALEF Health Career Scholarships *(Undergraduate, Graduate/Scholarship)* [8680]
Henry Salvatori Scholarships *(Undergraduate/Scholarship)* [7684]
Leo and Trinidad Sanchez Scholarships *(Undergraduate/Scholarship)* [8956]
Carl A. Scott Book Scholarships *(Undergraduate/Scholarship)* [3456]
Alfred P. Sloan Foundation Graduate Scholarships - Sloan Minority Ph.D. Program *(Doctorate/Scholarship)* [6684]
John Soto Scholarships *(Undergraduate/Scholarship)* [3362]
Robert Toigo Foundation Fellowships *(Master's/Fellowship)* [9747]
Toyota/TELACU Scholarships *(Undergraduate/Scholarship)* [9661]
United Health Foundation National Association of Hispanic Nurses Scholarships *(Graduate, Undergraduate/Scholarship)* [6758]
Marta Vallin Memorial Scholarships *(Undergraduate/Scholarship)* [3363]
Valuing Diversity PhD Scholarships *(Doctorate/Scholarship)* [983]
White Collar Defense Diversity Scholarships *(Undergraduate, Advanced Professional/Scholarship)* [8239]
Woodrow Wilson-Rockefeller Brothers Fund Fellowships for Aspiring Teachers of Color *(Undergraduate/Fellowship)* [10682]
Xerox Technical Minority Scholarships *(Graduate, Undergraduate/Scholarship)* [10737]

Military

AAAA Scholarship Program *(Undergraduate, Graduate/Scholarship)* [1710]
ACHE/American Legion Auxiliary Scholarships *(Undergraduate/Scholarship)* [184]
Afghanistan and Iraq War Veterans Scholarship *(Undergraduate/Scholarship)* [88]
The Agnes Sopcak Memorial Scholarship *(Undergraduate/Scholarship)* [10649]
Alabama Gi Dependents' Educational Benefit Program *(Undergraduate/Scholarship)* [190]
Alabama National Guard Educational Assistance Program *(Undergraduate/Scholarship)* [191]
The American Legion Legacy Scholarships *(Undergraduate/Scholarship)* [954]
Admiral Mike Boorda Loans Program *(Undergraduate/Loan)* [7234]
Lt. General Douglas D. Buchholz Memorial Scholarship *(Undergraduate/Scholarship)* [89]
Buick Achievers Scholarship Program *(Undergraduate/Scholarship)* [4359]
Captain Jodi Callahan Memorial Scholarships *(Graduate, Master's/Scholarship)* [122]
Commander Ronald J. Cantin Scholarships *(Undergraduate/Scholarship)* [3075]
CFR Military Fellowships *(Professional development/Fellowship)* [3442]
Commander Daniel J. Christovich Scholarship Fund *(Undergraduate/Scholarship)* [3076]
Clay Maitland CGF Scholarship *(Undergraduate/Scholarship)* [3077]
Coast Guard Foundation Enlisted Education Grants *(Advanced Professional/Grant)* [3078]
LaRue A. Ditmore Music Scholarships *(Undergraduate/Scholarship)* [10650]
Dolphin Scholarships *(Undergraduate/Scholarship)* [3651]
Sergeant Major Douglas R. Drum Memorial Scholarship Fund *(Undergraduate/Scholarship)* [1005]
The Fallen Heroes Scholarships *(Undergraduate/Scholarship)* [3079]
FEEA-NTEU Scholarships *(Graduate, Postgraduate, Undergraduate/Scholarship)* [3989]
Freedom Alliance Scholarships *(Undergraduate/Scholarship)* [4299]
Lily H. Gridley Memorial Scholarships *(Undergraduate/Scholarship)* [10651]
Hardy, Wolf & Downing Scholarships *(Undergraduate, Graduate/Scholarship)* [4719]
Hope for the Warriors Spouse/Caregiver Scholarships *(Undergraduate, Graduate/Scholarship)* [4933]
Imagine America Military Awards Program *(Undergraduate/Scholarship, Grant)* [5084]
Khaki University and Y.M.C.A. Memorial Scholarships *(Undergraduate/Scholarship)* [10291]
Casey Laine Armed Forces Scholarships *(Undergraduate/Scholarship)* [3101]
First Lieutenant Scott McClean Love Memorial Scholarship - Children of Soldiers *(Undergraduate, Vocational/Occupational/Scholarship)* [1714]
First Lieutenant Scott McClean Love Memorial Scholarship - Spouses of Soldiers *(Undergraduate, Vocational/Occupational/Scholarship)* [1715]
Maine Vietnam Veterans Scholarships *(Advanced Professional/Scholarship)* [6204]
Marine Corps League National Scholarships *(Undergraduate/Scholarship)* [6269]
Corporal Joseph Martinez U.S. Army/Durango High School AFJROTC *(Undergraduate/Scholarship)* [8354]
MCEA Financial Assistance Award *(Undergraduate/Scholarship)* [6267]
MOAA American Patriot Scholarships *(Undergraduate/Scholarship)* [6534]
Naval Helicopter Association Scholarships *(Undergraduate, Graduate/Scholarship)* [7223]
North American Van Lines Military Scholarship Competition *(Undergraduate/Scholarship)* [7449]
North Carolina Heroes Financial Hardship Grant *(All/Grant)* [7466]
Captain Jennifer Shafer Odom Memorial Scholarships - Children of Soldiers *(Undergraduate, Vocational/Occupational/Scholarship)* [1716]
Captain Jennifer Shafer Odom Memorial Scholarships - Spouses of Soldiers *(Undergraduate/Scholarship)* [1717]
Pitsenbarger Awards *(Undergraduate/Grant, Award)* [125]
General John Paul Ratay Educational Grants *(Undergraduate/Grant)* [6535]
Samsung American Legion Scholarships *(Undergraduate/Scholarship)* [957]
Seabee Memorial Scholarship Association Scholarships *(Undergraduate/Scholarship)* [9043]
Lewis L. Seaman Junior Enlisted Awards for Outstanding Operational Support *(Professional development/Recognition)* [1541]
Sentinels of Freedom Scholarships *(Advanced Professional/Scholarship)* [8843]
Colonel Nate Smith Memorial Scholarships *(Graduate, Undergraduate/Scholarship)* [6374]
Arnold Sobel Scholarships *(Undergraduate/Scholarship)* [3081]
ThanksUSA Scholarships *(Undergraduate, Vocational/Occupational/Scholarship)* [9723]
Tillman Scholars Program *(Undergraduate, Graduate/Scholarship)* [7901]
USS Coral Sea Remembrance Scholarships *(Undergraduate/Scholarship)* [10358]
The Vander Putten Family Scholarships *(Advanced Professional/Scholarship)* [3082]
Wells Fargo Veterans Scholarships Program *(Undergraduate/Scholarship)* [10512]

Ethyl and Armin Wiebke Memorial Scholarships *(Undergraduate/Scholarship)* [10652]
Michael Wilson Scholarships *(Undergraduate/Scholarship)* [126]
Women's Overseas and Service League Scholarships for Women *(Undergraduate/Scholarship)* [10670]

Minority

AALL Minority Leadership Development Award *(Graduate/Award)* [520]
AAPM Diversity Recruitment through Education and Mentoring Program (MUSE) *(Undergraduate/Fellowship)* [557]
Dr. Anderson Abbott Awards *(Undergraduate/Scholarship)* [10278]
Aboriginal Canadians Scholarship *(Undergraduate/Scholarship)* [7204]
ACNM Foundation Midwives of Color-Watson Midwifery Student Scholarship *(Undergraduate/Scholarship)* [693]
Acoustical Society of America Minority Fellowships *(Graduate/Fellowship)* [52]
Actuarial Diversity Scholarship *(Undergraduate/Scholarship)* [60]
EFWA Moss Adams Foundation Scholarships *(Undergraduate/Scholarship)* [3800]
Adler Pollock & Sheehan Diversity Scholarships *(Undergraduate/Scholarship)* [71]
AERA Minority Fellowship Program in Education Research *(Doctorate/Fellowship)* [784]
AFA Aboriginal Traditional Arts Individual Project Grants *(Professional development/Grant)* [236]
AFPE Pre-Doctoral Fellowships in Pharmaceutical Sciences for Underrepresented Minorities *(Doctorate, Graduate/Fellowship)* [828]
AfterCollege STEM Inclusion Scholarships *(Undergraduate, Graduate/Scholarship)* [102]
AIChE Minority Scholarship Awards for Incoming College Freshmen *(Undergraduate/Scholarship)* [904]
Hon. Lincoln Alexander Scholarships *(Undergraduate, Graduate/Scholarship)* [2277]
Alliance of Black Culinarians Scholarships *(Undergraduate/Scholarship)* [8330]
AMA Foundation Minority Scholars Awards *(Graduate/Scholarship)* [989]
American Association of Blacks in Energy Scholarships *(Undergraduate/Scholarship)* [464]
American Association for Cancer Research Minority Scholar Awards *(Graduate/Award)* [472]
American Association of University Women Master's and First Professional Awards *(Other/Award)* [602]
American Association of University Women Selected Professions Fellowships *(Other/Fellowship)* [603]
American Dental Association Minority Dental Student Scholarships *(Undergraduate/Scholarship)* [773]
American Philological Association Minority Student Summer Fellowships *(Undergraduate/Fellowship)* [9106]
American Speech Language Hearing Foundation Endowed Scholarships *(Graduate, Master's, Doctorate/Scholarship)* [1451]
American Speech Language Hearing Foundation Scholarships for Minority Students *(Graduate, Master's, Doctorate/Scholarship)* [1454]
William G. Anderson, DO, Minority Scholarships *(Undergraduate/Scholarship)* [1063]
Judge Isaac Anderson, Jr. Scholarships *(Undergraduate/Scholarship)* [9418]
Warren M. Anderson Scholarships *(Undergraduate/Scholarship)* [5115]
APSA Minority Fellows Program *(Doctorate/Fellowship)* [1113]
APTA Minority Scholarships - Faculty Development Scholarships *(Postdoctorate/Scholarship)* [1096]
APTA Minority Scholarships - Physical Therapist Assistant Students *(Undergraduate/Scholarship)* [1097]
Arent Fox Diversity Scholarships *(Graduate, Juris Doctorate/Scholarship)* [1621]
Judge Sidney M. Aronovitz Memorial Scholarships *(Undergraduate/Scholarship)* [6451]
Arts Council of Greater Grand Rapids Minority Scholarships *(Undergraduate/Scholarship)* [4574]
ASA Minority Fellowship Program (ASA MFP) *(Graduate, Doctorate, Professional development/Fellowship)* [1445]
ASC Graduate Fellowships for Ethnic Minorities *(Doctorate/Fellowship)* [1280]
ASEH Minority Travel Grants *(Graduate, Other/Grant)* [1309]
ASGP Graduate Research Fellowships *(Graduate/Fellowship)* [223]
ASLA Council of Fellow Scholarships *(Undergraduate/Scholarship)* [1346]
ASM Undergraduate Research Capstone Program *(Undergraduate/Fellowship)* [1372]
ASTRO Minority Summer Fellowship Awards *(Postgraduate, Professional development/Fellowship)* [1393]
Michael Baker Corp. Scholarship for Diversity in Engineering *(Undergraduate/Scholarship)* [1976]
Baker and McKenzie Diversity Fellowships *(Postgraduate, Professional development/Fellowship)* [2175]
Donald W. Banner Diversity Scholarships for Law Students *(Graduate/Scholarship)* [2190]
Bay Area Minority Law Student Scholarships *(Graduate, Undergraduate/Scholarship)* [2195]
BCSF Scholarships *(Undergraduate/Scholarship)* [2294]
Dennis J. Beck Memorial Scholarships *(Undergraduate/Scholarship)* [5498]
Lucie and Thornton Blackburn Scholarships *(Graduate, Juris Doctorate/Scholarship)* [2544]
Ellen Blodgett Memorial Scholarships *(Undergraduate/Scholarship)* [7375]
Jim Bourque Scholarship *(Undergraduate/Scholarship)* [1617]
Corris Boyd Scholarships *(Master's/Scholarship)* [2085]
Leon Bradley Scholarship Program *(Undergraduate/Scholarship)* [575]
Farella Braun + Martel LLP 1L Diversity Scholarship Program *(Undergraduate/Scholarship)* [3968]
Mary Ann Brichta Scholarships *(Undergraduate/Scholarship)* [10317]
Cathy L. Brock Memorial Scholarships *(Graduate/Scholarship)* [5167]
George M. Brooker, CPM Diversity Collegiate Scholarship *(Graduate, Undergraduate/Scholarship)* [5215]
Robert K. Brown Scholarships *(Undergraduate, Master's/Scholarship)* [2278]
Patricia Buchanan Memorial Scholarships *(Undergraduate/Scholarship)* [10318]
Buckfire & Buckfire, P.C. Law School Diversity Scholarships *(Graduate/Scholarship)* [2399]
Buckfire & Buckfire, P.C. Medical Diversity Scholarships *(Advanced Professional/Scholarship)* [2400]
Buick Achievers Scholarship Program *(Undergraduate/Scholarship)* [4359]
Burroughs Wellcome Travel Fellowships *(Undergraduate, Graduate, Professional development, Grant)* [9305]
Dave Caldwell Scholarships *(Graduate/Scholarship)* [1485]
California Bar Foundation 3L Diversity Scholarships *(Undergraduate/Scholarship)* [2443]
Herb Carnegie Scholarships *(Undergraduate/Scholarship)* [2279]
Deloris Carter Hampton Scholarships *(Undergraduate/Scholarship)* [8247]
Fraser Milner Casgrain LLP Scholarships *(Graduate, Juris Doctorate/Scholarship)* [2280]
CIBC Scholarships *(Undergraduate, Graduate/Scholarship)* [2281]
Justice Robert L. Clifford Fellowships *(Undergraduate/Fellowship)* [6593]
Holly Cornell Scholarship *(Master's/Scholarship)* [1488]
Council on Social Work Education Minority Fellowship Program for Doctoral Students *(Postdoctorate/Fellowship)* [3454]
CPA Foundation Minority Scholarships *(Graduate/Scholarship)* [2471]
Albert W. Dent Graduate Student Scholarships *(Undergraduate/Scholarship)* [687]
Albert and Jane Dewey Scholarships *(Undergraduate/Scholarship)* [4748]
Diversity Executive Leadership Program Scholarships *(Other/Scholarship)* [1778]
Dow Chemical Company Fellowships *(Graduate/Fellowship)* [7085]
James Echols Scholarship Award *(Undergraduate/Scholarship)* [2434]
E.I. DuPont Graduate Fellowship *(Graduate/Fellowship)* [7086]
Eli Lilly and Company/Black Data Processing Associates Scholarships *(Undergraduate/Scholarship)* [2206]
ESA Foundation Scholarship Program *(Undergraduate/Scholarship)* [3878]
Ethnic Minority and Women's Enhancement Postgraduate Scholarships *(Graduate/Scholarship)* [6862]
FASEB MARC Travel Awards *(Undergraduate, Graduate, Postdoctorate/Award)* [9306]
Dr. James A. Ferguson Emerging Infectious Diseases Fellowships *(Graduate/Fellowship)* [5815]
Fermilab Summer Internships in Science and Technology *(Undergraduate/Internship)* [9901]
Fred Finch Scholarships *(Undergraduate/Scholarship)* [9816]
Fine Arts Association Minority Scholarships *(Undergraduate/Scholarship)* [4026]
Finnegan Diversity Scholarships *(Juris Doctorate/Scholarship)* [4030]
Clay Ford Florida Board of Accountancy Minority Scholarships *(Undergraduate/Scholarship)* [4083]
Forté Fellowships *(Master's/Fellowship)* [4151]
Franchise Law Diversity Scholarship Awards *(Undergraduate/Scholarship)* [5336]
Fredrikson and Byron Foundation Minority Scholarships *(Undergraduate/Scholarship)* [4297]
Harry Gairey Scholarships *(Undergraduate/Scholarship)* [2282]
Lucille May Gopie Scholarships *(Undergraduate, Graduate/Scholarship)* [2283]
Priscilla Green Scholarships *(Undergraduate/Scholarship)* [3465]
Greenlining Institute Fellowships *(Graduate/Fellowship)* [4670]
Guntley-Lorimer Science and Arts Scholarships *(Undergraduate/Scholarship)* [2284]
Hackett Family Scholarships *(Undergraduate/Scholarship)* [4597]
Al Hamilton Scholarships *(Undergraduate/Scholarship)* [2285]
Dick and Pat Hazel Minority Scholarships *(Undergraduate/Scholarship)* [3180]
HFMH Bilingual Scholarships for Mental Health Workforce Diversity *(Graduate/Scholarship)* [4913]
Zelle Hofmann Diversity in Law Scholarships *(Undergraduate/Scholarship)* [10812]
HRSA Scholarships for Disadvantaged Students *(Undergraduate/Scholarship)* [9923]
Innovative Grants-Pilot and Research Tool Grants *(Postdoctorate/Grant)* [5641]
Jackie Robinson Scholarships *(Undergraduate/Scholarship)* [5495]
JDRF Postdoctoral Fellowships *(Postdoctorate/Fellowship)* [5644]
Hon. Michaelle Jean Scholarships *(Undergraduate/Scholarship)* [2286]
Harry Jerome Legacy Scholarships *(Undergraduate, Graduate/Scholarship)* [2287]
JLTLA Judge's Scholarships *(Undergraduate/Scholarship)* [9817]
JLTLA Minority Law Student Scholarships *(Undergraduate/Scholarship)* [9818]
Sylvia Taylor Johnson Fellowships in Educational Measurement *(Doctorate/Fellowship)* [3808]
Johnson and Johnson/AACN Minority Nurse Faculty Scholars *(Graduate/Scholarship)* [480]
MCCA Lloyd M. Johnson, Jr. Scholarships *(Graduate/Scholarship)* [6553]
Barbara Jordan Scholarships *(Undergraduate/Scholarship)* [9819]
Kegler Brown Diversity Scholarship *(Graduate/Scholarship)* [5804]
League of Latin American Citizens General Electric Scholarships *(Undergraduate/Scholarship)* [5987]

NATIVE AMERICAN

Louisville Institute First Book Grants for Minority Scholars *(Doctorate/Grant)* [6129]
Beverley Mascoll Scholarships *(Undergraduate/Scholarship)* [2288]
Howard Mayer Brown Fellowship *(Graduate/Fellowship)* [1021]
McClatchy Minority Scholarship and Fellowship *(Undergraduate/Scholarship)* [9369]
McJulien Minority Graduate Scholarships *(Graduate/Scholarship)* [1944]
John McLendon Memorial Minority Postgraduate Scholarships *(Postdoctorate/Scholarship)* [6738]
Medical Library Association Scholarships for Minority Students *(Graduate/Scholarship)* [6389]
Michigan Auto Law Student Diversity Scholarships *(Undergraduate/Scholarship)* [6463]
Milbank Diversity Scholars Program *(Undergraduate/Scholarship)* [6530]
Dolphus E. Milligan Graduate Fellowships *(Graduate/Fellowship)* [7087]
Minerva Scholarships *(Undergraduate/Scholarship)* [2289]
Minority-Serving Institution Faculty Scholar Awards *(Doctorate/Award)* [474]
Minority Teacher Loans *(Undergraduate, Graduate/Loan)* [9554]
John P. and Tashia F. Morgridge Scholarships *(Undergraduate/Scholarship)* [10324]
James B. Morris Scholarships *(Undergraduate/Scholarship)* [6598]
MSGC Undergraduate-Under-Represented Minority Fellowship Program *(Undergraduate/Fellowship)* [6485]
NACA Multicultural Professional Development Grant *(Undergraduate, Graduate, Professional development/Grant)* [6729]
NASP-ERT Minority Scholarships for Graduate Training in School Psychology *(Graduate/Scholarship)* [6780]
National GEM Consortium - MS Engineering Fellowships *(Graduate/Fellowship)* [6967]
National GEM Consortium - PhD Engineering Fellowships *(Doctorate, Graduate/Fellowship)* [6968]
National GEM Consortium - PhD Science Fellowships *(Doctorate, Graduate/Fellowship)* [6969]
National Recreation and Park Association Diversity Scholarships *(Undergraduate/Scholarship)* [7118]
NBMBAA Graduate Scholarships Program *(Graduate/Scholarship)* [6821]
NCACPA Outstanding Minority Accounting Student Scholarships *(Undergraduate/Scholarship)* [7451]
NJPA Foundation Scholarship for Research on Diversity Issues *(Graduate/Scholarship)* [7329]
NOBCChE Procter and Gamble Fellowships *(Graduate/Fellowship)* [7088]
NUF Fellowships *(Graduate, Postgraduate, Other/Fellowship)* [7209]
Ohio Newspaper Association Minority Scholarships *(Undergraduate/Scholarship)* [7577]
Ohio Space Grant Consortium Special Minority Fellowships *(Doctorate, Graduate, Master's/Fellowship)* [7595]
Royce Osborn Minority Scholarship *(Undergraduate/Scholarship)* [1398]
Outlaw Student's Minority Scholarships *(Undergraduate/Fellowship)* [9596]
Perkins Coie 1L Diversity Fellowships *(Postgraduate/Fellowship)* [8011]
Pi Lambda Theta Scholarships *(Undergraduate/Scholarship)* [10325]
PlasticPlace Young Entrepreneurs Scholarships *(Undergraduate/Scholarship)* [8148]
Donald and Susie Polden Dean's Scholarships *(Undergraduate/Scholarship)* [10171]
Justice Stewart G. Pollock Fellowships *(Undergraduate/Fellowship)* [6594]
Porter Physiology Development Fellowship Awards *(Doctorate/Fellowship)* [1100]
George V. Powell Diversity Scholarships *(Graduate/Scholarship)* [5920]
Powers-Knapp Scholarships *(Undergraduate/Scholarship)* [10326]
Judith McManus Price Scholarships *(Undergraduate, Graduate/Scholarship)* [1106]
Pride Foundation Social Work Scholarships *(Undergraduate/Scholarship)* [8260]
Lendon N. Pridgen, GlaxoSmithKline - NOBCChE Fellowships *(Graduate/Fellowship)* [7089]
Public Interest Fellowships for Law Students of Color *(Undergraduate/Fellowship)* [4491]
Elliott C. Roberts Scholarships *(Graduate/Scholarship)* [5168]
Edward S. Roth Manufacturing Engineering Scholarships *(Graduate, Undergraduate/Scholarship)* [9192]
Royal Bank Scholarships *(Undergraduate, Master's/Scholarship)* [2290]
Scotiabank Scholarships *(Undergraduate/Scholarship)* [2291]
Shell Incentive Scholarship Fund *(Undergraduate/Scholarship)* [8861]
Ralph W. Shrader Diversity Scholarship *(Graduate/Scholarship)* [91]
Alfred P. Sloan Foundation Graduate Scholarships - Sloan Minority Ph.D. Program *(Doctorate/Scholarship)* [6684]
Eastman Kodak Dr. Theophilus Sorrell Fellowships *(Graduate/Fellowship)* [7090]
SRC Master's Scholarships Program (MSP) *(Graduate, Master's/Scholarship)* [8835]
SREB-State Doctoral Scholars Program - Dissertation Awards *(Doctorate/Scholarship, Award)* [9410]
SREB-State Doctoral Scholars Program - Doctoral Awards *(Doctorate, Graduate/Scholarship)* [9411]
George A. Strait Minority Scholarship *(Graduate/Scholarship)* [536]
Surety and Fidelity Industry Intern and Scholarship Program for Minority Students *(Undergraduate/Scholarship)* [9614]
TechChecks Business Leadership Scholarships *(Undergraduate/Scholarship)* [9650]
Thurgood Marshall Fellowships Program *(Undergraduate/Fellowship)* [7345]
Marie Trahan/Susman Godfrey Scholarships *(Undergraduate/Scholarship)* [9820]
Transamerica Retirement Solutions Leaders in Health Care Scholarships *(Graduate/Scholarship)* [5169]
Ira G. Turpin Scholars Fund *(Undergraduate/Scholarship)* [9541]
UAF College of Liberal Arts - Anchorage Daily News Journalism Awards *(Undergraduate/Scholarship)* [10094]
United Parcel Service Scholarships for Minority Students *(Undergraduate/Scholarship)* [5196]
University of Wisconsin-Madison/CALS Minority Scholarships *(Undergraduate/Scholarship)* [10327]
University of Wisconsin-Madison Chancellor's Scholarships *(Undergraduate/Scholarship)* [10328]
UW-Madison Engineering Diversity Scholarships *(Undergraduate/Scholarship)* [10331]
UW-Madison School of Education Minority Scholarships *(Undergraduate/Scholarship)* [10334]
Visible Minorities Scholarship *(Undergraduate/Scholarship)* [7207]
VSCPA Educational Foundation Minority Scholarships *(Graduate, Undergraduate/Scholarship)* [10408]
Warner Norcross & Judd Minority Scholarships *(Undergraduate/Scholarship)* [10427]
ASM Robert D. Watkins Graduate Research Fellowships *(Postdoctorate/Fellowship)* [1373]
Wellstone Fellowships for Social Justice *(Graduate/Fellowship)* [3959]
Paul D. White Scholarship *(Undergraduate/Scholarship)* [2173]
Portia White Scholarships *(Undergraduate/Scholarship)* [2292]
Sidney B. Williams, Jr. Scholarships *(Undergraduate/Scholarship)* [942]
Wisconsin Lawton Minority Retention Grants *(Undergraduate/Grant)* [10336]

Native American

Accenture American Indian Scholarship Program *(Graduate, Undergraduate/Scholarship)* [880]
Acoustical Society of America Minority Fellowships *(Graduate/Fellowship)* [52]
Actuarial Diversity Scholarship *(Undergraduate/Scholarship)* [60]
Affirmative Action Student Scholarship Mini-Grant Travel Awards *(Undergraduate, Master's, Doctorate/Grant)* [30]
AIChE Minority Scholarship Awards for College Students *(Undergraduate/Scholarship)* [903]
AIChE Minority Scholarship Awards for Incoming College Freshmen *(Undergraduate/Scholarship)* [904]
AIGC Fellowships - Graduate *(Graduate/Fellowship)* [881]
Air Products and Chemicals, Inc. Scholarships *(Undergraduate/Scholarship)* [1975]
AISES Intel Scholarships *(Graduate, Undergraduate/Scholarship)* [887]
Alaska Native Medical Center Auxiliary Scholarships *(Undergraduate/Scholarship)* [10005]
AMA Foundation Minority Scholars Awards *(Graduate/Scholarship)* [989]
American Indian Fellowship in Business Scholarships *(Graduate, Master's, Undergraduate/Scholarship)* [6844]
AMS/Industry Minority Scholarships *(Undergraduate/Scholarship)* [1000]
ANA Multicultural Excellence Scholarship Fund (MAIP) *(Graduate, Undergraduate/Internship)* [456]
A.T. Anderson Memorial Scholarships *(Graduate, Undergraduate/Scholarship)* [889]
APS Scholarships for Minority Undergraduate Physics Majors *(Undergraduate/Scholarship)* [7138]
APSA Minority Fellows Program *(Doctorate/Fellowship)* [1113]
APTA Minority Scholarships - Faculty Development Scholarships *(Postdoctorate/Scholarship)* [1096]
APTA Minority Scholarships - Physical Therapist Assistant Students *(Undergraduate/Scholarship)* [1097]
APTA Minority Scholarships - Physical Therapist Students *(Undergraduate/Scholarship)* [1098]
ASA Minority Fellowship Program (ASA MFP) *(Graduate, Doctorate, Professional development/Fellowship)* [1445]
Elizabeth and Sherman Asche Memorial Scholarships *(Graduate, Undergraduate/Scholarship)* [1832]
ASGP Graduate Research Fellowships *(Graduate/Fellowship)* [223]
AWG Minority Scholarships *(Undergraduate/Scholarship)* [2093]
Michael Baker Corp. Scholarship for Diversity in Engineering *(Undergraduate/Scholarship)* [1976]
Notah Begay III Scholarship Program *(Undergraduate/Scholarship)* [300]
Bill Bernbach Diversity Scholarships *(Undergraduate/Scholarship)* [457]
BIE-Loan for Service for Graduates *(Graduate/Loan)* [882]
Leon Bradley Scholarship Program *(Undergraduate/Scholarship)* [575]
Buder Scholarships for American Indian Law Students *(Juris Doctorate/Scholarship)* [10474]
Sam Bull Memorial Scholarships *(Undergraduate/Scholarship)* [248]
Calista Education and Culture Scholarships *(Graduate, Undergraduate, Vocational/Occupational/Scholarship)* [2490]
CERT College Scholarships *(Graduate, Undergraduate/Scholarship)* [3435]
Cherokee Nation Graduate Scholarships *(Graduate/Scholarship)* [2893]
Cherokee Nation Pell Scholarships *(Undergraduate/Scholarship)* [2894]
Cherokee Nation Scholarships *(Undergraduate/Scholarship)* [2895]
Vine Deloria Jr. Memorial Scholarships *(Graduate, Professional development/Scholarship)* [868]
Ruth DeMoss Scholarships *(Undergraduate/Scholarship)* [8701]
Josephine P. White Eagle Scholarships *(Undergraduate, Graduate/Scholarship)* [4911]
John Hope Franklin Dissertation Fellowships *(Doctorate/Fellowship)* [1080]
Fraser Stryker Diversity Scholarships *(Undergraduate/Scholarship)* [4293]

The Gates Millennium Scholars (Undergraduate/Scholarship) [4903]
GFOA Minorities in Government Finance Scholarship (Graduate, Undergraduate/Scholarship) [4502]
William Harrison Gill Education Fund (Undergraduate/Scholarship) [2228]
Senator James Gladstone Memorial Scholarships (Graduate, Undergraduate/Scholarship) [249]
HANA Scholarships (Undergraduate, Graduate, Doctorate/Scholarship) [9852]
Muriel Hannah Scholarships in Art (Undergraduate, Graduate/Scholarship) [10062]
HSF/Marathon Oil College Scholarship Program (Undergraduate/Scholarship) [4905]
Indian Health Service Professionals Program (Undergraduate/Scholarship) [875]
International Order of the King's Daughters and Sons North American Indian Scholarship Program (Undergraduate/Scholarship) [876]
Kilbuck Family Native American Scholarships (Undergraduate/Scholarship) [2230]
KPMG Foundation Minority Accounting Doctoral Scholarships (Doctorate/Scholarship) [5885]
The Lagrant Foundation - Graduate Students Scholarships (Graduate/Scholarship) [5900]
The Lagrant Foundation - Undergraduate Students Scholarships (Undergraduate/Scholarship) [5901]
LITA/LSSI Minority Scholarships (Graduate/Scholarship) [6072]
LITA/OCLC Minority Scholarships (Graduate/Scholarship) [6073]
AILA Virginia Mathews Memorial Scholarships (Graduate/Scholarship) [885]
Howard Mayer Brown Fellowship (Graduate/Fellowship) [1021]
Medical Library Association Scholarships for Minority Students (Graduate/Scholarship) [6389]
Minority Teachers of Illinois Scholarships (MTI) (Undergraduate/Scholarship) [5078]
MLA/NLM Spectrum Scholarship Program (Undergraduate/Scholarship) [6391]
Archie Motley Memorial Scholarships for Minority Students (Graduate/Scholarship) [6517]
NACA Multicultural Professional Development Grant (Undergraduate, Graduate, Professional development/Grant) [6729]
National Medical Fellowships Need-Based Scholarships (Undergraduate/Scholarship) [7061]
Native American Community Scholars Awards (Graduate/Fellowship) [9013]
Native American Education Grants (Graduate, Undergraduate/Grant) [877]
Native American Visiting Student Awards (Graduate/Fellowship) [9014]
NDSGC American Indian Scholarships (Undergraduate/Scholarship) [7494]
NMNH American Indian Program Fellowships (Graduate/Fellowship) [9034]
Operation JumpStart Scholarships (Graduate/Scholarship) [458]
PlasticPlace Young Entrepreneurs Scholarships (Undergraduate/Scholarship) [8148]
Judith McManus Price Scholarships (Undergraduate, Graduate/Scholarship) [1106]
PRSA Diversity Multicultural Scholarships (Undergraduate/Scholarship) [8378]
SAA Native American Scholarships (Undergraduate, Graduate, Professional development/Scholarship) [9079]
David W. Schacht Native American Student Scholarships (Undergraduate/Scholarship) [2231]
Carl A. Scott Book Scholarships (Undergraduate/Scholarship) [3456]
Seldovia Native Association Achievement Scholarships (Undergraduate, Graduate/Scholarship) [8829]
Seldovia Native Association General Scholarships (Undergraduate, Graduate/Scholarship) [8830]
Sidley Prelaw Scholars Initiative (Undergraduate/Scholarship) [8895]
Allogan Slagle Memorial Scholarships (Undergraduate, Graduate/Scholarship) [1835]
Alfred P. Sloan Foundation Graduate Scholarships - Sloan Indigenous Graduate Partnership (Master's, Doctorate/Scholarship) [6683]

Alfred P. Sloan Foundation Graduate Scholarships - Sloan Minority Ph.D. Program (Doctorate/Scholarship) [6684]
Helen J. and Harold Gilman Smith Scholarships (Graduate, Undergraduate/Scholarship) [2232]
Robert Toigo Foundation Fellowships (Master's/Fellowship) [9747]
Morris K. Udall Scholarships (Undergraduate/Scholarship) [9825]
United South and Eastern Tribes Scholarship Fund (Undergraduate/Scholarship) [9868]
U.S. BIA Indian Higher Education Grants (Undergraduate/Grant) [878]
Valuing Diversity PhD Scholarships (Doctorate/Scholarship) [983]
Adolph Van Pelt Special Fund for Indians Scholarships (Undergraduate/Scholarship) [1836]
John D. Voelker Foundation Native American Scholarships (Undergraduate/Scholarship) [10415]
Wells Fargo American Indian Scholarships - Graduate (Graduate/Scholarship) [883]
Western Michigan Society of Health-System Pharmacists Scholarships (Undergraduate/Scholarship) [10533]
WIEA Scholarships (Doctorate, Graduate, Undergraduate/Scholarship) [10625]
WIGA Scholarships (Postgraduate, Other, Undergraduate/Scholarship) [10450]
Woksape Oyate: "Wisdom of the People" Distinguished Scholars Awards (Undergraduate/Scholarship) [873]
Woodrow Wilson-Rockefeller Brothers Fund Fellowships for Aspiring Teachers of Color (Undergraduate/Fellowship) [10682]
Xerox Technical Minority Scholarships (Graduate, Undergraduate/Scholarship) [10737]

Other

AAFSW College Merit Scholarship (College, Undergraduate/Scholarship) [1820]
Adelson Family Scholarships (Undergraduate/Scholarship) [8328]
AfterCollege Business Student Scholarships (Undergraduate, Graduate, Doctorate/Scholarship) [97]
AfterCollege Engineering Student Scholarships (Undergraduate, Graduate, Doctorate, Master's/Scholarship) [98]
AfterCollege Physical Therapist Student Scholarships (Undergraduate, Master's, Doctorate/Scholarship) [100]
AfterCollege Science Student Scholarships (Undergraduate, Graduate, Doctorate/Scholarship) [101]
AfterCollege Succurro Scholarships (Undergraduate, Graduate, Doctorate/Scholarship) [103]
American Acne and Rosacea Society Mentorship Grant (Professional development/Grant) [426]
American Association of State Troopers Scholarship Foundation First Scholarships (Undergraduate/Scholarship) [577]
American Association of State Troopers Scholarship Foundation Second Scholarships (Undergraduate/Scholarship) [578]
American Federation of Police and Concerned Citizen Scholarships (Undergraduate/Scholarship) [790]
Anaheim Police Survivors and Scholarship Fund (Undergraduate/Scholarship) [1549]
Anchor Scholarship Foundation Scholarships (Undergraduate/Scholarship) [9616]
APS Scholarships for Minority Undergraduate Physics Majors (Undergraduate/Scholarship) [7138]
Army Health Professions Scholarships Program (Professional development/Scholarship) [9878]
Asian and Pacific Islander Queers Sisters Scholarships (Undergraduate/Scholarship) [8242]
Association of the United States Navy Scholarships (Undergraduate/Scholarship) [2083]
Birmingham-Southern College Eagle Scout Scholarships (Undergraduate/Scholarship) [6920]
Camp Network Counselor Appreciation Scholarships (Undergraduate/Scholarship) [2528]
Local 827 Peter J. Casey Scholarships (Undergraduate/Scholarship) [5288]
CBCF - BC/Yukon Region Breast Cancer Survivor

Dragon Boat Grants (Professional development/Grant) [2588]
City of Sanibel Employee Dependent Scholarships (Undergraduate/Scholarship) [9423]
Convectair Sustainable Development Scholarship Awards (Undergraduate/Scholarship) [3824]
George Dale Scholarship Fund (Undergraduate/Scholarship) [1776]
Davis-Putter Scholarships Fund (Undergraduate, Graduate/Scholarship) [8659]
Brian M. Day Scholarships (Undergraduate/Scholarship) [8252]
Mike and Gail Donley Spouse Scholarships (Undergraduate, Graduate, Postgraduate/Scholarship) [123]
Drake University Law School Law Opportunity Scholarships - Disadvantage (Undergraduate/Scholarship) [3667]
Drake University Law School Law Opportunity Scholarships - Diversity (Undergraduate/Scholarship) [3668]
Edward Leon Duhamel Scholarship Fund (Undergraduate/Scholarship) [8605]
Federal Court Bench and Bar Scholarships (Undergraduate/Scholarship) [10160]
Lt. Colonel Romeo and Josephine Bass Ferretti Scholarships (Undergraduate/Scholarship) [124]
Foundation of the Federal Bar Association Public Service Scholarship Award (Undergraduate/Scholarship) [4260]
Greater Seattle Business Association Scholarships (GSBA Scholarships) (Undergraduate/Scholarship) [4658]
Hellenic Times Scholarships (Undergraduate, Graduate/Scholarship) [4843]
Zelle Hofmann Diversity in Law Scholarships (Undergraduate/Scholarship) [10812]
C.D. Howard Scholarships (Undergraduate/Scholarship) [5298]
ICMA Local Government Management Fellowships (Master's/Fellowship) [5296]
Illinois Division Scholarships (Undergraduate/Scholarship) [6519]
International Code Council Foundation General Scholarship Fund (Undergraduate/Scholarship) [5299]
ISTTE Scholarships (Graduate, Undergraduate/Scholarship) [5435]
V.J. Johnson Memorial Scholarships (Undergraduate/Scholarship) [579]
Joint Japan/World Bank Graduate Scholarship Program for Developing Country National (JJ/WB-GSP) (Graduate/Scholarship) [10696]
Kansas City Division Scholarships (Undergraduate/Scholarship) [6521]
KASF General Scholarships (Undergraduate, Graduate, Professional development/Scholarship) [5875]
The Lanford Family Highway Worker Memorial Scholarship Program (Undergraduate/Scholarship) [1219]
Steven A. Leahy Law Office Marine Service/Law School Scholarships (Postgraduate/Scholarship) [5955]
Maine Community College Scholarships (Undergraduate/Scholarship) [6222]
Med Technology and Clinical Lab Science Scholarships (Undergraduate/Scholarship) [104]
Fred & Lena Meijer Scholarships (Undergraduate/Scholarship) [4610]
Carl J. Mejel Scholarship (Undergraduate/Scholarship) [794]
Benchwarmers of Redlands-Jess Mercado Football Scholarships (Undergraduate/Scholarship) [8497]
National Board Technical Scholarships (Undergraduate/Scholarship) [6827]
J.W. "Bill" Neese Scholarships (Undergraduate/Scholarship) [5300]
Mike Niemeyer Memorial Football Scholarships (Undergraduate/Scholarship) [8506]
NSA Electrical Engineering Student Scholarships (Undergraduate, Graduate, Doctorate/Scholarship) [107]
NSA Mathematics and Computer Science Student Scholarships (Undergraduate, Graduate, Doctorate/Scholarship) [108]

Charlie O'Meilia Scholarships *(Undergraduate/Scholarship)* [5301]
Ozarks Division Scholarships *(Undergraduate/Scholarship)* [6524]
Robert B. and Dorothy Pence Scholarships *(Undergraduate/Scholarship)* [9443]
Point Foundation Scholarships *(Undergraduate/Scholarship)* [8662]
Pride Foundation Social Work Scholarships *(Undergraduate/Scholarship)* [8260]
Psychology Association of Saskatchewan Student Scholarships - Academic Achievement *(Master's, Doctorate/Scholarship)* [8320]
Psychology Association of Saskatchewan Student Scholarships - Research Based *(Master's, Doctorate/Scholarship)* [8321]
Michael J. Quill Scholarships *(Undergraduate/Scholarship)* [9766]
RBPA Scholarships *(All/Scholarship)* [8425]
Redlands High School Boy's Varsity Volleyball Scholarships *(Undergraduate/Scholarship)* [8512]
Redlands High School Mock Trial Scholarships *(Undergraduate/Scholarship)* [8514]
Retired League Postmasters Scholarship Program *(Undergraduate/Scholarship)* [8569]
Robert S. McNamara Fellowships Program (RSMFP) *(Doctorate/Fellowship)* [10698]
Harold W. Rosenthal Fellowships in International Relations *(Professional development/Fellowship, Internship)* [2043]
Saskatchewan Government Insurance Anniversary Scholarships *(Undergraduate/Scholarship)* [8770]
Albert F. Shanker Scholarship *(Undergraduate/Scholarship)* [796]
Simonton Windows Scholarships *(Undergraduate/Scholarship)* [7864]
Ronald T. Smith Family Scholarships *(Undergraduate, Graduate/Scholarship)* [4621]
Southwest Florida Deputy Sheriffs Association Fund Scholarships *(Undergraduate/Scholarship)* [9450]
SPE Vinyl Plastics Division Educational Grants *(Undergraduate/Grant)* [9275]
Thomas P. Thornton Scholarships *(Undergraduate/Scholarship)* [5089]
UW-Madison GLBT Alumni Council Scholarships *(Undergraduate, Graduate/Scholarship)* [10332]
Veterans of Foreign Wars Scout of the Year *(Undergraduate/Scholarship)* [6935]
WAEPA Scholarship Program *(Undergraduate/Scholarship)* [10711]

Religious affiliation

Stephanie Ali Memorial Scholarships *(Undergraduate/Scholarship)* [10279]
Rick Arkans Eagle Scout Scholarships *(Undergraduate/Scholarship)* [6919]
Associated Women for Pepperdine Scholarships *(Undergraduate/Scholarship)* [7962]
Martha and Robert Atherton Ministerial Scholarships *(Master's/Scholarship)* [9831]
Lewis B. Barber Memorial Scholarships *(Undergraduate/Scholarship)* [9419]
James R. and Geraldine F. Bertelsen Scholarships *(Undergraduate/Scholarship)* [8691]
The Bishop James C. Baker Award *(Doctorate/Scholarship)* [9850]
Mary E. Bivins Foundation Religious Scholarship Program *(Graduate, Undergraduate/Scholarship)* [2275]
Olympia Brown and Max Kapp Awards *(Master's/Scholarship)* [9832]
Bernard B. and Mary L. Brusin Scholarships *(Undergraduate/Scholarship)* [3705]
Catholic Biblical Association of America Scholarships *(Undergraduate/Scholarship)* [2812]
Chautauqua Scholarships Program *(Undergraduate/Scholarship)* [5367]
Children of Unitarian Universalist Ministers College Scholarships *(Undergraduate/Scholarship)* [9833]
CMSF Scholarships *(Undergraduate, Graduate/Scholarship)* [2932]
The Helena B. Cobb Annual Scholarships *(Undergraduate, Vocational/Occupational/Scholarship)* [10665]
The Helena B. Cobb Four-Year Higher Education Grants *(Undergraduate, Vocational/Occupational/Scholarship)* [10666]
CSF Graduate Fellowships *(Graduate/Fellowship)* [2936]
Mary Mouzon Darby Undergraduate Scholarships *(Undergraduate/Scholarship)* [4985]
Christopher Demetris Memorial Scholarships *(Undergraduate/Scholarship)* [4845]
Emmett J. Doerr Memorial Distinguished Scout Scholarships *(Undergraduate/Scholarship)* [6921]
Dollar-A-Day Academic Scholarships *(Graduate, Undergraduate/Scholarship)* [3649]
Pauly D'Orlando Memorial Art Scholarships *(Graduate, Undergraduate/Scholarship)* [9834]
Eastern Orthodox Scouting Scholarships *(Undergraduate/Scholarship)* [6923]
David Eaton Scholarships *(Master's/Scholarship)* [9835]
Emmanuel Bible College Scholarships *(Undergraduate/Scholarship)* [1693]
FEF Scholarships *(Undergraduate/Scholarship)* [3952]
Doris W. Frey Memorial Scholarships *(Undergraduate, Graduate/Scholarship)* [9430]
Greek Orthodox Archdiocese of America Paleologos Graduate Scholarships *(Graduate/Scholarship)* [4666]
Harvey Fellows Program *(Graduate/Fellowship)* [6632]
Islamic Scholarship Fund Scholarships (ISF) *(Postgraduate, Undergraduate/Scholarship)* [5484]
Jewish Federation Academic Scholarships *(Graduate, Undergraduate/Scholarship)* [5598]
Rev. and Mrs. A.K. Jizmejian Educational Fund *(Undergraduate/Scholarship)* [1700]
Lutheran Student Scholastic and Service Scholarships - College and University Students *(Undergraduate/Scholarship)* [2248]
MACC Scholarships *(Other/Scholarship)* [6444]
NPM Academic Scholarships *(Graduate, Undergraduate/Scholarship)* [6768]
Margaret E. Phillips Scholarships *(Undergraduate/Scholarship)* [10305]
David Pohl Scholarships *(Master's/Scholarship)* [9836]
Roy H. Pollack Scholarships *(Graduate, Master's/Scholarship)* [9837]
St. James Armenian Church Memorial Scholarships *(Undergraduate/Scholarship)* [1704]
Joseph Sumner Smith Scholarships *(Undergraduate/Scholarship)* [9839]
Richard S. Smith Scholarships *(Undergraduate/Scholarship)* [9858]
Marion Barr Stanfield Art Scholarships *(Graduate, Undergraduate/Scholarship)* [9840]
Otto M. Stanfield Law Scholarships *(Graduate/Scholarship)* [9841]
Anne Sturrock Nursing Scholarships *(Undergraduate, Graduate/Scholarship)* [9451]
Rev. Chuck and Nancy Thomas Scholarships *(Professional development/Scholarship)* [9842]
Thomas and Glenna Trimble Endowed Scholarships *(Undergraduate/Scholarship)* [8007]
Chester M. Vernon Memorial Eagle Scout Scholarships *(Undergraduate/Scholarship)* [6934]
Von Ogden Vogt Scholarships *(Master's/Scholarship)* [9843]
Frank L. Weil Memorial Eagle Scout Scholarships *(Undergraduate/Scholarship)* [6936]
Wexner Graduate Fellowships/Davidson Scholars *(Graduate/Fellowship)* [10545]
The Brian J. White Endowed Law Scholarships *(Undergraduate/Scholarship)* [8008]
Young Christian Leaders Scholarships *(Undergraduate/Scholarship)* [10760]

Union affiliation

Duluth Building and Construction Trades Council Scholarships *(Undergraduate/Scholarship)* [3707]
HBI-BGI Scholar-in-Residence Program *(Undergraduate/Scholarship)* [2359]
Raymond A. Kent-Navy V-12/ROTC Scholarships *(Undergraduate/Scholarship)* [10145]
North Dakota Farmers Union Co-op House Scholarships *(Undergraduate/Scholarship)* [7490]
Sons of Union Veterans of the Civil War Scholarships *(Undergraduate/Scholarship)* [9348]
Utility Workers Union of America Scholarship Program *(Undergraduate/Scholarship)* [10360]

Veteran

Afghanistan and Iraq War Veterans Scholarship *(Undergraduate/Scholarship)* [88]
AMVETS National Scholarships - Entering College Freshmen *(Undergraduate/Scholarship)* [1545]
AMVETS National Scholarships - For Veterans *(Undergraduate/Scholarship)* [1546]
AMVETS National Scholarships - JROTC *(Undergraduate/Scholarship)* [1547]
Buick Achievers Scholarship Program *(Undergraduate/Scholarship)* [4359]
Disabled War Veterans Scholarships *(Undergraduate/Scholarship)* [90]
Feldman Law Firm Disabled Veterans Scholarships *(All/Scholarship)* [4009]
Forsyth County Nursing Scholarships *(Undergraduate/Scholarship)* [10581]
Leslie C. Green Veterans Scholarships *(Juris Doctorate, Advanced Professional/Scholarship)* [3458]
Imagine America Military Awards Program *(Undergraduate/Scholarship, Grant)* [5084]
Maine Vietnam Veterans Scholarships *(Advanced Professional/Scholarship)* [6204]
H. H. McKnight Memorial Scholarships *(Undergraduate/Scholarship)* [10168]
North American Van Lines Military Scholarship Competition *(Undergraduate/Scholarship)* [7449]
Scholarships for Veterans with Post-Traumatic Stress Disorder *(All/Scholarship)* [8624]
Sons of Union Veterans of the Civil War Scholarships *(Undergraduate/Scholarship)* [9348]
Wells Fargo Veterans Scholarships Program *(Undergraduate/Scholarship)* [10512]
Women's Army Corps Veterans Association Scholarships *(Undergraduate/Scholarship)* [10654]

Sponsor and Scholarship Index

This index lists, in a single alphabetic sequence, all of the administering and sponsoring organizations and awards covered in the "Sponsors and Their Scholarships" section. Also included are co-sponsoring organizations and organization acronyms. The numbers that follow citations indicate the book entry numbers for particular organizations and awards, not page numbers. Book entry numbers for administering organizations appear in boldface type.

1Dental Dentistry Scholarships [6]
1Dental.com **[5]**
4-H Alberta **[7]**
4th Infantry Division Association Memorial Scholarships [6670]
The "21" Endowed Scholarships [6015]
101st Airborne Division Association **[1]**
180 Medical College Scholarship Program [4]
180 Medical, Inc. **[3]**
AAA Postdoctoral Fellowship Program [460]
AAAA Scholarship Program [1710]
AAACN Conference Scholarships for Nursing Students [385]
AAACN Education Scholarships [386]
AAACN Research Grants [387]
AAACN Scholarships [388]
AAAS Mass Media Science and Engineering Fellowship [453]
AAAS Science and Technology Policy Fellowships [454]
AABP Amstutz Scholarships [466]
AABP Bovine Veterinary Student Recognition Awards [467]
AABP Education Grants [468]
AABP Student Externship Program [469]
AACC International **[11]**
AACD Dentist Fellowships [405]
AACD Laboratory Fellowships [406]
AACE International **[13]**
AACE International Competitive Scholarships [14]
AACN Continuing Professional Development Scholarships [490]
AACOM Scholar in Residence Program [482]
AACPDM Student Scholarships [399]
AACPDM Transformative Practice Grants [400]
AACR Scholar-in-Training Awards: Other Conferences and Meetings [471]
AACT Junior Investigator Research Grants [402]
AACT Toxicology Trainee Research Grants [403]
AACTE Outstanding Book Awards [484]
AACTE Outstanding Dissertation Awards [485]
AAEP/ALSIC Scholarships [495]
AAEP Foundation Past Presidents' Research Fellowships [496]
AAFPE LEX Scholarships [553]
AAFSW College Merit Scholarship [1820]
AAG Dissertation Research Grants [1829]
AAHD Scholarships [502]
AAI Careers in Immunology Fellowship Program [506]
AAI Public Policy Fellows Program (PPFP) [507]
AAIB Scholarships [509]
AAIDD Fellowship [511]
AAJ Trial Advocacy Scholarships [515]
AAJUW Scholarships [513]
AALL Leadership Academy Grants [519]
AALL Minority Leadership Development Award [520]
AALL Research Funds [521]
AALL Scholarships for Continuing Education Classes [522]
AALL Technical Services SIS Active Member Grant [523]
AALL Technical Services SIS Experienced Member General Grant [524]

AALL Technical Services SIS Leadership Academy Grant [525]
AALL Technical Services SIS Management Institute Grant [526]
AALL Technical Services SIS New Member General Grant [527]
AAMA Houston Chapter Health Training Scholarships [1601]
AAMC Foundation Engagement Program for International Curators Grants [1854]
AAMFT Minority Fellowships [538]
AAN Clinical Research Training Fellowships [410]
AAN International Scholarship Award [411]
AAN Medical Student Summer Research Scholarships [412]
A&WMA Scholarships [139]
AANS Medical Student Summer Research Fellowships (MSSRF) [542]
AAOHN Professional Development Scholarships - Academic Study [550]
AAOHN Professional Development Scholarships - Continuing Education [551]
AAPM Diversity Recruitment through Education and Mentoring Program (MUSE) [557]
AAPM Fellowships for Graduate Study in Medical Physics [558]
AAPM Summer Undergraduate Fellowships [559]
Aaron Copland Bogliasco Fellowships in Music [2325]
Leroy F. Aarons Scholarships [7049]
AAS-American Historical Print Collectors Society Fellowships [428]
AAS-American Society for Eighteenth Century Studies Fellowships [429]
AAS CIAC Small Grants [1857]
AAS Fellowships for Creative and Performing Artists and Writers [430]
AAS Korean Studies Scholarship Program [1858]
AAS National Endowment for the Humanities Long-Term Fellowships [431]
AAS-Northeast Modern Language Association Fellowships [432]
AASA Educational Administration Scholarship Awards [572]
AASLD Advanced/Transplant Hepatology Fellowships [581]
AASLD Autoimmune Liver Diseases Pilot Research Awards [582]
AASLD Career Development Awards in Liver Transplantation [583]
AASLD Clinical and Translational Research Awards [584]
AASLD NP/PA Clinical Hepatology Fellowships [585]
AASLD Pinnacle Research Awards in Liver Disease [586]
AASP - The Palynological Society (AASP) **[15]**
The AASSC Gurli Aagaard Woods Undergraduate Publication Awards [1825]
The AASSC Marna Feldt Graduate Publication Awards [1826]
AASSC Norwegian Travel Grants [1827]
AAST/ETHICON Research Grants in Local Wound Haemostatics and Hemorrhage Control Scholarships [589]

AAST/KCI Research Grant [590]
AAST Medical Student, Resident and In-Training Fellow Scholarships [591]
AATS Cardiothoracic Surgery Resident Poster Competition [593]
AATS Medical Students Summer Intern Scholarships [594]
AATS Perioperative/Team-Based Care Poster Competition [595]
AATS Resident Critical Care Scholarships [596]
AATS/STS Cardiothoracic Ethics Forum Scholarships [597]
AAUW American Fellowships [19]
AAUW Career Development Grants [20]
AAUW International Fellowships [21]
AAUW Legal Advocacy Fund (AAUW/LAF) **[18]**
AAUW Selected Professions Fellowships [22]
AAZK/AZA Advances in Animal Keeping Course Grants [608]
AAZK Conservation, Preservation and Restoration Grants [609]
AAZK Professional Development Grants [610]
AAZK Research Grants [611]
ABA Diversity Scholarships [636]
ABA Members Scholarships for ABA Bus and Tour Operators Only [637]
ABA Members Scholarships for All ABA Member Companies [638]
ABA Scholarships [626]
Anthony Abbene Scholarships [5025]
Dr. Anderson Abbott Awards [10278]
Clifford V. Abbott Memorial Scholarships [9561]
ABC-Clio Research Grants [9208]
Jordan Abdo Memorial Scholarship [9417]
Abe Fellowship Program [9051]
Abe Fellowships for Journalists [9052]
Alejandro "Alex" Abecia Reaching High Scholarships [3084]
Abercrombie and Fitch Global Diversity and Leadership Scholar Awards [7158]
Ruth Abernathy Presidential Scholarships [9128]
ABF Doctoral/Post-Doctoral Fellowships [622]
ABF Law and Social Science Dissertation Fellowship and Mentoring Program [623]
ABF Montgomery Summer Research Diversity Fellowships in Law and Social Science [624]
ABFSE National Scholarship Program [629]
Kyutaro and Yasuo Abiko Memorial Scholarships [5547]
Aboriginal Canadians Scholarship [7204]
Aboriginal Nurses Association of Canada (ANAC) **[23]**
Emily and Roland Abraham Educational Funds [3316]
Abraham Lincoln Brigade Archives **[25]**
Evelyn Joy Abramowicz Memorial Scholarships [5568]
Evelyn Abrams Memorial Scholarships [8327]
Frederick B. Abramson Memorial Foundation **[27]**
Frederick B. Abramson Memorial Foundation Scholarships [28]
ABTA Discovery Grant Program [631]
ABTA Medical Student Summer Fellowship Program [632]

ABTA Translational Grant Program [633]
Academy of Criminal Justice Sciences (ACJS) **[29]**
Academy for Eating Disorders (AED) **[31]**
Academy of Laser Dentistry (ALD) **[34]**
Academy of Medical-Surgical Nurses (AMSN) **[36]**
Academy of Model Aeronautics (AMA) **[38]**
Academy of Motion Picture Arts and Sciences (AMPAS) **[41]**
Academy of Motion Picture Arts and Sciences Student Academy Awards [42]
The Academy of Neonatal Nursing **[43]**
Academy of Neonatal Nursing Conference Scholarships [44]
Academy of Television Arts and Sciences Foundation **[46]**
Accenture American Indian Scholarship Program [880]
Accounting and Financial Women's Alliance (AFWA) **[48]**
ACHE/American Legion Auxiliary Scholarships [184]
ACHE Junior and Community College Athletic Scholarships [185]
ACHE Junior and Community College Performing Arts Scholarships [186]
ACHE Police Officers and Firefighters Survivors' Educational Assistance Programs [187]
ACHE Senior Adult Scholarships [188]
ACHE Two-Year College Academic Scholarships [189]
The Achieve Physical Therapy and Fitness Scholarship [9580]
ACI BASF Construction Chemicals Student Fellowships [701]
ACI Cagley ACI Student Fellowships [702]
ACI Foundation Scholarships [703]
ACI-NA Scholarships [180]
ACI President's Fellowships [704]
ACI W.R. Grace Scholarships [705]
ACJA-LAE Student Paper Competitions [752]
Wayne D. Ackerman Family Scholarship Fund [9491]
Jack Ackroyd Scholarships [1878]
ACLS African Humanities Fellowships [734]
ACLS Collaborative Research Fellowships [735]
ACLS Fellowships [736]
ACMPE Scholarship Fund Program [6384]
ACMS Intensive Mongolian Language Fellowship Program [648]
ACMS Library Fellowships [649]
ACMS U.S.-Mongolia Field Research Fellowship Program [650]
ACNL Research Scholarships [1869]
ACNM Foundation, Inc. Fellowships for Graduate Education [692]
ACNM Foundation Midwives of Color-Watson Midwifery Student Scholarship [693]
ACOR-CAORC Post-Graduate Fellowships [653]
ACOR-CAORC Pre-Doctorate Fellowships [654]
Acoustical Society of America (ASA) **[51]**
Acoustical Society of America Minority Fellowships [52]
ACPA Foundation Annual Fund [695]
Andreas Acrivos Dissertation Award in Fluid Dynamics [1085]
ACS/ASA Health Policy and Management Scholarships [1468]
ACS Doctoral Degree Scholarships in Cancer Nursing [642]
ACS Graduate Scholarships in Cancer Nursing Practice [643]
ACS Law Fellowships [716]
ACS Rubber Division Undergraduate Scholarships [666]
ACSO Scholarships [1633]
ACSUS Distinguished Dissertation Awards [1875]
Action Institute for the Study of Religion and Liberty **[55]**
Actuarial Diversity Scholarship [60]
The Actuarial Foundation **[59]**
ACUI Research and Education Grant [1925]
ACVO Best Resident Manuscript Awards [699]
ADAA Career Development Travel Awards [1569]
ADAC Foundation Scholarships [1767]
Nancy Ashley Adams/Ashley Adams Koetje Scholarships [3547]
EFWA Moss Adams Foundation Scholarships [3800]

Ruth D. Adams Fund [4037]
Mamie Adams Memorial Awards [6016]
The Clarke B. Adams Memorial Foundation Lapeer County Community Foundation Fund [5928]
Lt. Holly Adams Memorial Scholarships [3209]
RPMDA/Ed Adams Memorial Scholarships [8567]
Ruth Adams Memorial Scholarships [8442]
Henry S. and Carolyn Adams Scholarship Fund [4172]
Frederick G. Adams Scholarships [4735]
Henry Adams Scholarships [1326]
Adelante Fund **[65]**
Adelante Fund Hope Scholarships, CPS Energy Dependents [66]
Adelante Fund Hope Scholarships, San Antonio, TX Students [67]
Carl Joseph Adelhardt Memorial Scholarships [4329]
Gladys Ross Carlson Adelphe Scholarship Fund [5688]
Adelson Family Scholarships [8328]
Adelson Scholarships [8329]
ADHA IOH Sigma Phi Alpha Graduate Scholarships [775]
Howard E. and Wilma J. Adkins Memorial Scholarships [1502]
Adler Pollock & Sheehan Diversity Scholarships [71]
Adler Pollock & Sheehan, P.C. **[70]**
ADMA International Scholarship [2144]
Administrative Sciences Association of Canada (ASAC) **[72]**
Adolescent/Young Adult Lymphoma Cooperative Groups Correlative Studies Grants [6156]
Herb Adrian Memorial Scholarship Fund [4173]
ADSC: The International Association of Foundation Drilling **[74]**
Adult Students in Scholastic Transition Scholarships (ASIST) [3935]
Advance Degree and Clinical Research Training Grants in Alpha-1 Antitrypsin Deficiency [1208]
Advance Prevention Lawsuit Legal Scholarships [5982]
Advertising Production Club of New York (APC) **[77]**
"Advice to Your High School Self" Scholarships [2534]
Advocates' Society (AS) **[79]**
AE Flight Training Scholarships [7436]
AE Jet Type Rating Scholarships [7437]
AE Technical Training Scholarships [7438]
AEBC Toronto Chapter Scholarships [333]
AECT Foundation Mentor Endowment Scholarships [1942]
AECT Legacy Scholarship [1943]
AED Student Early Career Investigator Travel Fellowships [32]
AED Student Research Grants [33]
AEF Educational Scholarship [234]
AERA-AIR Fellows Program [782]
AERA-ETS Fellowship Program in Measurement and Education Research [783]
AERA Minority Fellowship Program in Education Research [784]
Aerospace Corporation Science and Engineering Student Scholarships [95]
Aerospace States Association (ASA) **[82]**
AES Educational Foundation Grants [2122]
AESF Foundation Scholarships [6796]
AFA Aboriginal Traditional Arts Individual Project Grants [236]
AFA Art Acquisition by Application Grants [237]
AFA Cultural Relations Project Grants [238]
AFA Dance Project Grants [239]
AFA Film and Video Arts Project Grants [240]
AFA Literary Arts Project Grants [241]
AFA Music Project Grants [242]
AFA Theatre & Performance Art Project Grants [243]
AFA Visual Arts and New Media Project Grants [244]
AFCEA Cyber Studies and Intelligence Scholarships [85]
AFCEA International **[84]**
AFCEA Scholarship for Working Professionals [86]
AFCEA Science, Technology, Engineering and Math Teachers Scholarships [87]
Afdhal/McHutchison LIFER Awards [587]

Affiliated Distributors Electrical Industry Scholarship Awards [3822]
AFFIRM University Scholarships [1961]
Affirmative Action Student Scholarship Mini-Grant Travel Awards [30]
Afghanistan and Iraq War Veterans Scholarship [88]
AFPE Gateway Research Scholarships [826]
AFPE Pre-Doctoral Fellowships in Pharmaceutical Sciences [827]
AFPE Pre-Doctoral Fellowships in Pharmaceutical Sciences for Underrepresented Minorities [828]
AFPPA Student Scholarships [1959]
African American Network - Carolinas Scholarship Fund [4174]
African American Success Foundation (AASF) **[92]**
AFSA Chapter 155 Division 1 Scholarships - Category 1 [130]
AFSA Chapter 155 Division 1 Scholarships - Category 2 [131]
AFSA Chapter 155 Division 1 Scholarships - Category 3 [132]
AFSP - Distinguished Investigator Grants [830]
AFSP Postdoctoral Research Fellowships [831]
AFSP Standard Research Grants [832]
AFSP Young Investigator Grants [833]
AFT-Oregon Union Plus Credit Card Scholarship [792]
AfterCollege/AACN Nursing Scholarships [479]
AfterCollege-AACN Scholarships [96]
AfterCollege **[94]**
AfterCollege Business Student Scholarships [97]
AfterCollege Engineering Student Scholarships [98]
AfterCollege Occupational Therapy Scholarships [99]
AfterCollege Physical Therapist Student Scholarships [100]
AfterCollege Science Student Scholarships [101]
AfterCollege STEM Inclusion Scholarships [102]
AfterCollege Succurro Scholarships [103]
AFWA Masters Degree Scholarships [49]
AFWA Undergraduate Scholarships [50]
AGBU Heritage Scholar Grant [1673]
AGC Foundation Outstanding Educator Awards [1812]
AGC New York State Chapter Scholarship Program [1814]
AGE-WELL Graduate Student and Postdoctoral Awards in Technology and Aging [111]
Aging Gracefully across Environments using Technology to Support Wellness, Engagement and Long Life (AGE-WELL) **[110]**
The Agnes Sopcak Memorial Scholarship [10649]
Agricultural Institute of Canada (AIC) **[112]**
Agriculture Future of America (AFA) **[115]**
Agriculture Future of America Community Scholarships [116]
Agriculture Future of America Scholarships [117]
AGWT Baroid Scholarships [840]
AH&LEF American Express Scholarship [858]
AHCJ Reporting Fellowships on Health Care Performance [3158]
Patty Ahearn Victoria Elementary Scholarships [8443]
Ahepa Buckeye Scholarship Awards [119]
Ahepa Buckeye Scholarship Foundation **[118]**
AHEPA Family District No. 1 Scholarships [849]
AHETEMS/ExxonMobil Scholarships [8887]
AHETEMS General Scholarships [8888]
AHETEMS Professional Scholarships [8889]
Ahlswede, Norman & Marie Endowed Engineering Scholarship [10315]
Dr. Feroz Ahmed Memorial Educational Post-Graduate Scholarships [8965]
AHNS/AAO-HNS Young Investigator Award [845]
AHNS Pilot Research Grants [846]
Ahrens Charitable Trust Scholarship [4558]
AIA Alaska Scholarships [893]
AIA and the Global Automotive Aftermarket Symposium Scholarships [2131]
AIA Graduate Student Travel Awards [1603]
AIA Northeast Illinois Student Scholarships [895]
AIAA Foundation Scholarship Program [891]
AIBS Junior Fellowships [898]
AIBS Senior Fellowships [899]
AIChE Minority Scholarship Awards for College Students [903]

AIChE Minority Scholarship Awards for Incoming College Freshmen [904]
AIEA Presidential Fellows Program [1985]
AIGC Fellowships - Graduate [881]
AIHS Graduate Studentships [251]
AIHS Media Fellowships - CBC Radio [252]
AIHS Postgraduate Fellowships [253]
AIIrS Persian Language Study in Tehran Fellowships [913]
AIMS Long-term Research Grants [916]
AIMS Short-term Research Grants [917]
AIPN Student Scholarships [1987]
AIPS Long Term Fellowships [919]
AIPS Post-Doctoral Fellowships [920]
AIPS Pre-Doctoral Fellowships [921]
AIPS Short Term Fellowships [922]
AIR Dissertation Grants [1980]
Air Force Association (AFA) **[120]**
Air Force Association/Grantham Scholarships [121]
Air Force Sergeants Association (AFSA) **[127]**
Air Force Sergeants Association Chapter 155 **[129]**
Air Force Sergeants Association Scholarship Program [128]
Air Products and Chemicals, Inc. Scholarships [1975]
AIR Research Grants [1981]
Air Traffic Control Association (ATCA) **[134]**
Air Traffic Control Association Full-time Employee Student Scholarships [135]
Air Traffic Control Association Non-employee Student Scholarships [136]
Air & Waste Management Association (A&WMA) **[138]**
Air and Waste Management Association - Golden West Section (A&WMA-GWS) **[144]**
Air and Waste Management Association - Louisiana Section **[146]**
Air and Waste Management Association - Niagara Frontier Section (AWMA-NFS) **[148]**
Air and Waste Management Association - Northern and Central New Jersey Chapter (A&WMA NCNJ) **[151]**
Aircraft Electronics Association (AEA) **[153]**
Aircraft Owners and Pilots Association Scholarships [154]
Airport Minority Advisory Council Educational and Scholarship Program (AMACESP) **[177]**
Airports Council International - North America (ACI-NA) **[179]**
AISC/Great Lakes Fabricators and Erectors Association Fellowships [933]
AISC/Ohio Structural Steel Association Scholarships [934]
AISC/Rocky Mountain Steel Construction Association Scholarships [935]
AISC/Southern Association of Steel Fabricators Scholarships [936]
AISES Intel Scholarships [887]
AISES Summer Internships [888]
AISLS Dissertation Planning Grants [929]
AISLS Fellowships Program [930]
AISLS Grants for Language Instruction [931]
Justice John F. Aiso Scholarships [5541]
AIST Baltimore Member Chapter Scholarships [1989]
AIST Midwest Member Chapter - Engineering Scholarships [1990]
AIST Midwest Member Chapter - Non-Engineering Scholarships [1991]
AIST Midwest Member Chapter - Western States Scholarships [1992]
AIST Northwest Member Chapter Scholarships [1993]
AIST Ohio Valley Chapter Scholarships [1994]
AIST San Francisco Member Chapter Scholarships [1995]
AJL Conference Stipends [2010]
AJL Scholarship Fund [2011]
Ak-Sar-Ben Scholarships [4935]
Crown Prince Akihito Scholarship Foundation [5535]
Akron Bar Association Foundation **[181]**
Akron Bar Association Foundation Scholarships [182]
ALA Allergic Respiratory Diseases Research Award [969]
Alabama ARN Scholarship [2054]

Alabama Commission on Higher Education **[183]**
Alabama Dietetic Association (ALDA) **[195]**
Alabama Gi Dependents' Educational Benefit Program [190]
Alabama Horse Council (AHC) **[202]**
Alabama Horse Council Scholarships [203]
Alabama Law Foundation **[204]**
Alabama National Guard Educational Assistance Program [191]
Alabama Power Scholarships [7529]
Alabama Scholarships for Dependents of Blind Parents [192]
Alabama Student Assistance Programs [193]
Alabama Student Grant Programs [194]
Alamo Area Paralegal Association (AAPA) **[208]**
Alamo Area Paralegal Association Educational Scholarships [209]
Alamo IFT Scholarship [5175]
Alamogordo Music Theatre (AMT) **[210]**
Jonathan Alan Scholarship Fund [10497]
Alaska Aerospace Development Corporation Scholarships [10004]
Alaska Airmen Association **[214]**
Alaska Broadcasters Association (ABA) **[218]**
Alaska Community Foundation **[220]**
Alaska Native Medical Center Auxiliary Scholarships [10005]
Alaska Press Club Scholarships [10006]
Alaska Space Grant Program (ASGP) **[222]**
Albert Einstein Distinguished Educator Fellowships (AEF) [9794]
Bette Lou Albert, New Mexico, Memorial Scholarship Fund [5689]
Alberta Association on Gerontology (AAG) **[224]**
Alberta Association of Gerontology Student Awards [225]
Alberta Association of Gerontology Student Awards - Edmonton Chapter [226]
Alberta Award for the Study of Canadian Human Rights and Multiculturalism [261]
Alberta Barley Commission **[227]**
Alberta Blue Cross **[229]**
Alberta Blue Cross Scholarships for Aboriginal Students [230]
Alberta Centennial Scholarships - Alberta [262]
Alberta Child Care Association (ACCA) **[231]**
Alberta Child Care Association Professional Development Grants [232]
Alberta Equestrian Federation (AEF) **[233]**
Alberta Foundation for the Arts **[235]**
Alberta Holstein Association **[245]**
Alberta Holstein Association Scholarships [246]
Alberta Indian Investment Corporation (AIIC) **[247]**
Alberta Innovates Graduate Student Scholarships [256]
Alberta Innovates - Health Solutions **[250]**
Alberta Innovates - Technology Futures (AITF) **[255]**
Alberta Innovates - Technology Futures Graduate Student Scholarships in ICT [257]
Alberta Innovates - Technology Futures Graduate Student Scholarships in Nanotechnology [258]
Alberta Innovates - Technology Futures Graduate Student Scholarships in Omics [259]
Alberta Learning Information Service - Alberta Scholarship Program **[260]**
Alberta Teachers' Association (ATA) **[293]**
Alberta Teachers Association Doctoral Fellowships in Education [294]
Alberta Teachers Association Educational Research Award [295]
Alberta Ukrainian Centennial Commemorative Scholarships [10440]
Bruce and Betty Alberts Endowed Scholarships in Physiology [6243]
Albinas Elskus Scholarship [9488]
Albuquerque Community Foundation (ACF) **[298]**
ALCOA Foundation Corporate Scholarships [4645]
ALD Graduate Fellowships [6696]
Alden Kindred of America (AKA) **[307]**
Owen F. Aldis Scholarship Fund [5420]
Dulemba Aleksander and Stefania Scholarship [8571]
Aleut Foundation **[309]**
Alex Scholarship Funds [6280]
Anne L. Alexander and Blaise Robert Alexander Memorial Scholarships [4038]
Alexander Graham Bell Association for the Deaf and Hard of Hearing (AG Bell) **[313]**
Alexander Graham Bell Canada Graduate Scholarship Program [3401]
William Tasse Alexander Scholarship Fund [4175]
Hon. Lincoln Alexander Scholarships [2277]
Neil Alexander Scholarships [6688]
Alex's Lemonade Stand Foundation (ALSF) **[317]**
Alex's Lemonade Stand Foundation Epidemiology Grants [318]
Alex's Lemonade Stand Foundation Innovation Grants [319]
Alex's Lemonade Stand Foundation Young Investigator Grants [320]
ALF Postdoctoral Research Fellowship Award [966]
Floyd S. Alford Jr. Scholarships [10212]
Horatio Alger Delaware Scholarships [4936]
Horatio Alger District of Columbia, Maryland and Virginia Scholarships [4937]
Horatio Alger Florida Scholarships [4938]
Horatio Alger Georgia Scholarships [4939]
Horatio Alger Illinois Scholarships [4940]
Horatio Alger Indiana Scholarships [4941]
Horatio Alger Kentucky Scholarships [4942]
Horatio Alger Lola and Duane Hagadone Idaho Scholarships [4943]
Horatio Alger Louisiana Scholarships [4944]
Horatio Alger Minnesota Scholarships [4945]
Horatio Alger Missouri Scholarships [4946]
Horatio Alger Montana Scholarships [4947]
Horatio Alger National Scholarships [4948]
Horatio Alger North Dakota Scholarships [4949]
Horatio Alger Pennsylvania Scholarships [4950]
Horatio Alger South Dakota Scholarships [4951]
Horatio Alger Texas - Fort Worth Scholarships [4952]
Horatio Alger Texas Scholarships [4953]
Horatio Alger Utah Scholarships [4954]
Horatio Alger Washington Scholarships [4955]
Horatio Alger Wyoming Scholarships [4956]
Emma and Meloid Algood Tuition Scholarships [6718]
Stephanie Ali Memorial Scholarships [10279]
ALIS Fellowships for Full-time Studies in French [263]
ALIS Graduate Student Scholarships [264]
ALIS International Education Awards - Ukraine [265]
Margaret M. Alkek Scholarships [3548]
All-American Vector Marketing Scholarship Program [10364]
ALL-SIS Conference of Newer Law Librarians Grants [528]
All Star Association **[321]**
Allegheny County Bar Foundation (ACBF) **[323]**
Allegheny County Medical Society Medical Student Scholarships (ACMS) [4274]
Robinson G. Allen Athletic Memorial Scholarships [8444]
Frances C. Allen Fellowships [7408]
William A. Allen Memorial Metal Shop/Auto Body Scholarships [8445]
Dorothea E. Allen Scholarship [4427]
Allen - Marty Allen Scholarships [3085]
Janet and Horace Allen Scholarships [266]
Alliance of Black Culinarians Scholarships [8330]
Alliance Defending Freedom (ADF) **[330]**
Alliance Defending Freedom - Blackstone Legal Fellowships [331]
Alliance for Equality of Blind Canadians (AEBC) **[332]**
Alliance Francaise of Hartford Harpin/Rohinsky Scholarships [4736]
Alliance Medical Education Scholarship Fund (AMES) [4275]
Alliance Pipeline Scholarships [2181]
Alliance of Technology and Women (ATW) **[337]**
Allied Health Care Professional Scholarships [5070]
Lorraine Allison Scholarship [1616]
Allman Medical Scholarship [6555]
Gordon Allport Intergroup Relations Prize [9289]
Marjorie Almstrom Scholarships [10774]
ALOA Scholarship Foundation [1816]
Tillie B. Alperin Scholarship [10156]
ALPFA Scholarship Programs [2013]
Alpha Chi (AX) **[339]**

ALPHA

Alpha Chi Omega **[345]**
Alpha Chi Omega Love and Loyalty Grants [346]
Alpha Chi Sigma Fraternity, Inc. **[347]**
Alpha Chi Sigma Scholarship Awards [348]
Alpha Delta Gamma (ADG) **[349]**
Alpha Delta Gamma Educational Foundation Scholarships [350]
Alpha Kappa Alpha Educational Advancement Foundation (AKA-EAF) **[351]**
Alpha Kappa Alpha - Educational Advancement Foundation Financial Need-Based Scholarships [352]
Alpha Kappa Alpha - Educational Advancement Foundation Merit Scholarships [353]
Alpha Mu Tau Undergraduate Scholarships [1258]
Alpha Phi Sigma **[355]**
Alpha Tau Omega (ATO) **[358]**
Alpha Tau Omega Graduate Scholarships [359]
Alpha Tau Omega Undergraduate Scholarships [360]
ALS Canada **[364]**
ALS Canada Bridge Grants [365]
ALS Canada Doctoral Research Awards [366]
ALS Canada and Tim E. Noel Postdoctoral Fellowships [367]
Justin Scot Alston Memorial Scholarships [5026]
Phillip Alston Scholarships [10213]
Martin K. Alsup Scholarships [7811]
Robert E. Altenhofen Memorial Scholarships [1802]
Alter-Cine Foundation **[368]**
Altrusa International of Grand Rapids Scholarships [4573]
Alzheimer Society of Canada (ASC) **[370]**
Alzheimer's Association **[373]**
AMA Foundation Minority Scholars Awards [989]
AMA Foundation Physicians of Tomorrow Scholarships [990]
AMACESP Student Scholarships [178]
Jaedyn Amann Memorial Scholarships [10775]
Amato Sanita Attorney at Law **[378]**
The Ambrose-Ramsey Trust [7812]
Ambucs Resource Center **[380]**
AMBUCS Scholarships for Therapists Program [381]
Amelia Earhart Fellowship Program [10824]
Lou Amen Legacy Scholarships [2446]
America Express Travel Scholarships [1436]
America Responds Memorial Scholarships [1406]
Americal Division Veterans Association (ADVA) **[382]**
American Academy of Ambulatory Care Nursing (AAACN) **[384]**
American Academy of Attorney-CPAs (AAA-CPA) **[390]**
American Academy of Audiology (AAA) **[392]**
American Academy for Cerebral Palsy and Developmental Medicine (AACPDM) **[398]**
American Academy of Clinical Toxicology (AACT) **[401]**
American Academy of Cosmetic Dentistry (AACD) **[404]**
American Academy of Dermatology (AAD) **[407]**
American Academy of Neurology (AAN) **[409]**
American Academy of Optometry (AAO) **[413]**
American Academy of Periodontology (AAP) **[419]**
American Academy of Periodontology Educator Scholarships [420]
American Academy in Rome **[423]**
American Acne and Rosacea Society (AARS) **[425]**
American Acne and Rosacea Society Mentorship Grant [426]
American Antiquarian Society (AAS) **[427]**
American Art Therapy Association (AATA) **[447]**
American Art Therapy Association Anniversary Scholarships [448]
American Association for the Advancement of Science (AAAS) **[452]**
American Association of Advertising Agencies (AAAA) **[455]**
American Association of Anatomists (AAA) **[459]**
American Association for Applied Linguistics (AAAL) **[461]**
American Association of Blacks in Energy (AABE) **[463]**
American Association of Blacks in Energy Scholarships [464]

American Association of Bovine Practitioners (AABP) **[465]**
American Association for Cancer Research (AACR) **[470]**
American Association for Cancer Research Minority Scholar Awards [472]
American Association of Candy Technologists (AACT) **[476]**
American Association of Cereal Chemists Graduate Fellowships [12]
American Association of Colleges of Nursing (AACN) **[478]**
American Association of Colleges of Osteopathic Medicine (AACOM) **[481]**
American Association of Colleges for Teacher Education (AACTE) **[483]**
American Association of Critical-Care Nurses (AACN) **[489]**
American Association of Endodontists (AAE) **[491]**
American Association of Equine Practitioners (AAEP) **[494]**
American Association of Family and Consumer Sciences (AAFCS) **[497]**
American Association of Family and Consumer Sciences Undergraduate Scholarships [498]
American Association for Hand Surgery (AAHS) **[499]**
American Association for Hand Surgery Annual Research Awards [500]
American Association on Health and Disability (AAHD) **[501]**
American Association of Healthcare Administrative Management (AAHAM) **[503]**
American Association of Immunologists (AAI) **[505]**
American Association for the Improvement of Boxing (AAIB) **[508]**
American Association on Intellectual and Developmental Disabilities (AAIDD) **[510]**
American Association of Japanese University Women (AAJUW) **[512]**
American Association for Justice (AAJ) **[514]**
American Association of Law Libraries (AALL) **[518]**
American Association for Marriage and Family Therapy (AAMFT) **[537]**
American Association of Medical Assistants (AAMA) **[539]**
American Association of Neurological Surgeons (AANS) **[541]**
American Association of Neuroscience Nurses (AANN) **[544]**
American Association of Nurse Practitioners (AANP) **[547]**
American Association of Occupational Health Nurses (AAOHN) **[549]**
American Association for Paralegal Education (AAFPE) **[552]**
American Association of People with Disabilities (AAPD) **[554]**
American Association of Physicists in Medicine (AAPM) **[556]**
American Association of Physics Teachers (AAPT) **[561]**
American Association of Plastic Surgeons (AAPS) **[563]**
American Association of Plastic Surgeons Academic Scholars Program [564]
American Association of Police Polygraphists (AAPP) **[565]**
American Association of Professional Apiculturists (AAPA) **[567]**
American Association of Professional Apiculturists Research Scholarships [568]
American Association of Railroad Superintendents (AARS) **[569]**
American Association of School Administrators (AASA) **[571]**
American Association of School Personnel Administrators (AASPA) **[574]**
American Association of State Troopers (AAST) **[576]**
American Association of State Troopers Scholarship Foundation First Scholarships [577]
American Association of State Troopers Scholarship Foundation Second Scholarships [578]
American Association of Stratigraphic Palynologists

Student Scholarships [16]
American Association for the Study of Liver Diseases (AASLD) **[580]**
American Association for the Surgery of Trauma (AAST) **[588]**
American Association for Thoracic Surgery (AATS) **[592]**
American Association of University Women (AAUW) **[598]**
American Association of University Women American Fellowships [599]
American Association of University Women Career Development Grants [600]
American Association of University Women International Fellowships [601]
American Association of University Women Master's and First Professional Awards [602]
American Association of University Women Selected Professions Fellowships [603]
American Association for Women in Community Colleges (AAWCC) **[604]**
American Association for Women in Community Colleges Regional Scholarships [605]
American Association for Women in Community Colleges Scholarship LEADERS Institute [606]
American Association of Zoo Keepers (AAZK) **[607]**
American Astronomical Society (AAS) **[612]**
American Australian Association (AAA) **[617]**
American Bar Association Commission on Homelessness and Poverty **[619]**
American Bar Foundation (ABF) **[621]**
American Birding Association (ABA) **[625]**
American Board of Funeral Service Education (ABFSE) **[628]**
American Brain Tumor Association (ABTA) **[630]**
American Bus Association (ABA) **[635]**
American Bus Association Academic Merit Scholarships [639]
American Business Women's Association Sarasota Sunrise Chapter Scholarships [3317]
American Cancer Society (ACS) **[641]**
American Cancer Society - Postdoctoral Fellowships [644]
American Cancer Society - Research Scholar Grants [645]
American Center for Mongolian Studies (ACMS) **[647]**
American Center for Oriental Research **[652]**
American Ceramic Society (ACerS) **[663]**
American Chemical Society - Rubber Division **[665]**
American Choral Directors Association - Texas Chapter **[667]**
American Clan Gregor Society (ACGS) **[676]**
American Classical League (ACL) **[678]**
American College of Chiropractic Orthopedists (ACCO) **[682]**
American College of Gastroenterology (ACG) **[684]**
American College of Healthcare Executives (ACHE) **[686]**
American College of Medical Toxicology (ACMT) **[689]**
American College of Nurse-Midwives Foundation (ACNM) **[691]**
American College Personnel Association (ACPA) **[694]**
American College of Surgeons (ACS) **[696]**
American College of Veterinary Ophthalmologists (ACVO) **[698]**
American Concrete Institute (ACI) **[700]**
American Conifer Society (ACS) **[713]**
American Conifer Society Scholarships [714]
American Constitution Society for Law and Policy (ACS) **[715]**
American Copy Editors Society Education Fund (ACES) **[717]**
American Council of the Blind Scholarships [720]
American Council of Blind Students (ACBS) **[719]**
American Council of Engineering Companies of Illinois (ACEC-IL) **[721]**
American Council of Engineering Companies of Illinois Scholarships [722]
American Council on Germany (ACG) **[723]**
American Council of Independent Laboratories (ACIL) **[731]**
American Council of Independent Laboratories Scholarships [732]

American Council of Learned Societies (ACLS) [733]
American Councils for International Education [745]
American Councils for International Education Critical Language Scholarships [746]
American Counsel Association (ACA) [747]
American Counsel Association Scholarships [748]
American Counseling Association (ACA) [749]
American Criminal Justice Association - Lambda Alpha Epsilon (ACJA-LAE) [751]
American Criminal Justice Association - Lambda Alpha Epsilon Student Scholarships - Graduate Level [753]
American Criminal Justice Association - Lambda Alpha Epsilon Student Scholarships - Upper and Lower Division Levels [754]
American Culinary Federation (ACF) [756]
American Darts Organization (ADO) [766]
American Darts Organization Memorial Scholarship [767]
American Dental Association (ADA) [768]
American Dental Association Allied Dental Student Scholarships [769]
American Dental Association Dental Assisting Scholarship Program [770]
American Dental Association Dental Hygiene Scholarship Program [771]
American Dental Association Dental Laboratory Technology Scholarship Program [772]
American Dental Association Minority Dental Student Scholarships [773]
American Dental Hygienists' Association Institute for Oral Health (ADHA IOH) [774]
American Dental Hygienists' Association Institute for Oral Health Research Grants [776]
American Diabetes Association (ADA) [779]
American Diabetes Association and Boehringer Ingelheim Research Award: Chronic Kidney Disease and Renal Insufficiency in the Setting of Diabetes [780]
American Division Veterans Association Scholarships [383]
American Educational Research Association (AERA) [781]
American Enterprise Institute [785]
American Enterprise Institute National Research Initiative Fellowships (NRI) [786]
American Express Professional Development Scholarships [859]
American Federation for Aging Research (AFAR) [787]
American Federation of Police and Concerned Citizen Scholarships [790]
American Federation of Police and Concerned Citizens (AFP&CC) [789]
American Federation of Teachers - Oregon (AFT) [791]
American Floral Endowment (AFE) [797]
American Foreign Service Association (AFSA) [815]
American Foreign Service Association Scholarship Fund [816]
American Foundation for the Blind (AFB) [817]
American Foundation for Pharmaceutical Education (AFPE) [825]
American Foundation for Suicide Prevention (AFSP) [829]
American Foundation for Suicide and Prevention Pilot Grants [834]
American Foundry Society [835]
American Galvanizers Association (AGA) [837]
American GI Forum of San Jose Scholarships [8756]
American Ground Water Trust (AGWT) [839]
American Guild of Organists, Canton Chapter Charitable Fund [9492]
American Handel Society (AHS) [842]
American Head and Neck Society (AHNS) [844]
American Hellenic Educational Progressive Association - District No. 1 [848]
American Historical Association (AHA) [850]
American Historical Association Fellowships in Aerospace History [851]
American Hotel & Lodging Educational Foundation (AH&LEF) [857]
American Indian College Fund [865]

American Indian Education Fund (AIEF) [874]
American Indian Endowed Scholarships [10470]
American Indian Fellowship in Business Scholarships [6844]
American Indian Graduate Center (AIGC) [879]
American Indian Library Association (AILA) [884]
American Indian Science and Engineering Society (AISES) [886]
American Institute of Aeronautics and Astronautics (AIAA) [890]
American Institute of Architects - Alaska [892]
American Institute of Architects - Northeast Illinois (AIA NEI) [894]
American Institute of Bangladesh Studies (AIBS) [897]
American Institute of Certified Public Accountants (AICPA) [900]
American Institute of Chemical Engineers (AIChE) [902]
American Institute for Conservation of Historic & Artistic Works [907]
American Institute for Economic Research (AIER) [910]
American Institute for Economic Research Student Summer Fellowships [911]
American Institute of Iranian Studies (AIIrS) [912]
American Institute for Maghrib Studies (AIMS) [915]
American Institute of Pakistan Studies (AIPS) [918]
American Institute of Physics (AIP) [923]
American Institute of Physics Congressional Science Fellowships [924]
American Institute of Physics State Department Science Fellowships [925]
American Institute of Polish Culture (AIPC) [926]
American Institute for Sri Lankan Studies (AISLS) [928]
American Institute of Steel Construction (AISC) [932]
American Institute of Wine and Food (AIWF) [938]
American Intellectual Property Law Education Foundation (AIPLEF) [940]
American Jersey Cattle Association (AJCA) [943]
American Jewish Archives (AJA) [946]
American Jewish Historical Society (AJHS) [948]
American Judges Association (AJA) [951]
American Judges Association Law Student Essay Competition [952]
American Legion (AL) [953]
American Legion Boys/Girls State Scholarships [6017]
American Legion Department of Vermont [958]
American Legion Department of Vermont Scholarships [959]
American Legion Eagle Scout of the Year Scholarships [6918]
The American Legion Legacy Scholarships [954]
American Library Association (ALA) [960]
American Livebearer Association (ALA) [963]
American Liver Foundation (ALF) [965]
American Liver Foundation Liver Scholar Awards [967]
American Lung Association Biomedical Research Grants [970]
American Lung Association Clinical Patient Care Research Grants [971]
American Lung Association Dalsemer Research Grants [972]
American Lung Association DeSousa Awards [973]
American Lung Association in the District of Columbia (ALA) [968]
American Lung Association Lung Cancer Discovery Awards [974]
American Lung Association in New Jersey [978]
American Lung Association Scholar Program [979]
American Lung Association Senior Research Training Fellowships [975]
American Lung Association Social-Behavioral Research Grants [976]
American Marketing Association Foundation (AMAF) [980]
American Mathematical Society (AMS) [984]
American Meat Science Association (AMSA) [986]
American Medical Association (AMA) [988]
American Medical Society for Sports Medicine (AMSSM) [992]

American Men's Studies Association (AMSA) [994]
American Meteorological Society (AMS) [996]
American MidEast Leadership Network (AMLN) [1002]
American Military Retirees Association (AMRA) [1004]
American Montessori Society (AMS) [1006]
American Music Therapy Association (AMTA) [1009]
American Musicological Society (AMS) [1019]
American National Red Cross [1022]
American Nephrology Nurses' Association (ANNA) [1024]
American Nephrology Nurses' Association Evidence-Based Research Grants [1025]
American Nephrology Nurses' Association Research Grants [1026]
American Neurotology Society (ANS) [1029]
American Nuclear Society (ANS) [1031]
American Nuclear Society Incoming Freshman Scholarships [1032]
American Nuclear Society Nevada Section Scholarships [8331]
American Nuclear Society Undergraduates Scholarships [1033]
American Nurses Foundation (ANF) [1041]
American Occupational Therapy Foundation (AOTF) [1045]
American Orff-Schulwerk Association (AOSA) [1052]
American Oriental Society (AOS) [1057]
American Orthopedic Foot and Ankle Society (AOFAS) [1059]
American Osteopathic Foundation (AOF) [1062]
American Otological Society (AOS) [1066]
American Paint Horse Foundation (APHA) [1068]
American Parkinson Disease Association (APDA) [1070]
American Pediatric Surgical Nurses Association (APSNA) [1075]
American Pediatric Surgical Nurses Association Educational Grants [1076]
American Philological Association Minority Student Summer Fellowships [9106]
American Philosophical Society (APS) [1077]
American Philosophical Society Library Resident Research Fellowships [1078]
American Physical Society (APS) [1084]
American Physical Therapy Association (APTA) [1095]
American Physiological Society (APS) [1099]
American Planning Association (APA) [1102]
American Planning Association ENRE Student Fellowship Program [1103]
American Political Science Association (APSP) [1107]
American Political Science Association - Centennial Center for Political Science and Public Affairs [1117]
American Polygraph Association (APA) [1124]
American Psychiatric Association Alliance (APAA) [1126]
American Psychoanalytic Association (APSAA) [1128]
American Psychoanalytic Association Fellowships [1129]
American Psychological Association of Graduate Students (APAGS) [1130]
American Psychological Foundation (APF) [1136]
American Psychology-Law Society (AP-LS) [1154]
American Psychology-Law Society Dissertation Awards [1155]
American Psychology-Law Society Early Career Professional Grants-In-Aid [1156]
American Psychology-Law Society Student Grants-In-Aid [1157]
American Public Power Association (APPA) [1159]
American Public Transportation Foundation (APFT) [1161]
American Quarter Horse Foundation Scholarships [1171]
American Quarter Horse Youth Association (AQHYA) [1170]
American Quilt Study Group (AQSG) [1172]
American Radio Relay League Louisiana Memorial Scholarships [1721]

AMERICAN

American Railway Engineering and Maintenance-of-Way Association (AREMA) [1174]
American Railway Engineering and Maintenance-of-Way Association Scholarships [1175]
American Rental Association Foundation [1190]
American Rental Association Foundation Scholarships [1191]
American Research Center in Egypt (ARCE) [1194]
American Research in the Humanities in China Fellowships [737]
American Research Institute in Turkey (ARIT) [1200]
American Respiratory Care Foundation [1207]
American Road & Transportation Builders Association (ARTBA) [1218]
American Roentgen Ray Society (ARRS) [1220]
American Roentgen Ray Society Scholarships [1221]
American Romanian Orthodox Youth (AROY) [1223]
The American-Scandinavian Foundation (ASF) [1229]
American-Scandinavian Foundation Fellowships and Grants to Study in America [1230]
American-Scandinavian Foundation Fellowships to Study in Scandinavia [1231]
American-Scandinavian Foundation Grants to Study in Scandinavia [1232]
American-Scandinavian Foundation Translation Prize [1233]
American Schools of Oriental Research (ASOR) [1236]
American Senior Benefits Association (ASBA) [1238]
American Sheep Industry Association (ASI) [1240]
American Shotcrete Association (ASA) [1242]
American Society of Anesthesiologists (ASA) [1244]
American Society of Brewing Chemists (ASBC) [1246]
American Society of Business Publication Editors (ASBPE) [1249]
American Society of Certified Engineering Technicians (ASCET) [1251]
American Society of Cinematographers (ASC) [1255]
American Society for Clinical Laboratory Science (ASCLS) [1257]
American Society for Clinical Pathology (ASCP) [1261]
American Society of Colon and Rectal Surgeons (ASCRS) [1264]
American Society of Colon and Rectal Surgeons International Fellowships [1265]
American Society of Colon and Rectal Surgeons Travel Scholarships [1266]
American Society of Composers, Authors and Publishers Foundation (ASCAP) [1267]
American Society of Crime Laboratory Directors (ASCLD) [1277]
American Society of Crime Laboratory Directors Scholarships [1278]
American Society of Criminology (ASC) [1279]
American Society for Eighteenth-Century Studies (ASECS) [1282]
American Society of Electroneurodiagnostic Technologists (ASET) [1299]
American Society of Electroneurodiagnostic Technologists Student Education Grants (ASET) [1300]
American Society for Engineering Education (ASEE) [1302]
American Society for Enology and Viticulture (ASEV) [1306]
American Society for Enology and Viticulture Scholarships [1307]
American Society for Environmental History (ASEH) [1308]
American Society of Genealogists (ASG) [1320]
American Society of Health-System Pharmacists (ASHP) [1322]
American Society of Heating, Refrigerating and Air-Conditioning Engineers (ASHRAE) [1325]
American Society of Heating, Refrigerating, and Air-Conditioning Memorial Scholarships [1327]
American Society for Horticultural Science [1335]

American Society for Horticultural Science Student Travel Grants [1336]
American Society of Interior Designers (ASID) [1340]
American Society of International Law (ASIL) [1343]
American Society of Landscape Architects (ASLA) [1345]
American Society for Laser Medicine and Surgery (ASLMS) [1348]
American Society for Legal History (ASLH) [1353]
American Society of Mammalogists (ASM) [1355]
American Society of Mammalogists - Fellowships in Mammalogy [1356]
American Society of Mammalogists Grants-in-Aid of Research [1357]
American Society for Mass Spectrometry (ASMS) [1362]
American Society for Microbiology (ASM) [1364]
American Society for Microbiology International Fellowships for Africa [1365]
American Society for Microbiology International Fellowships for Asia [1366]
American Society for Microbiology International Fellowships for Latin America and the Caribbean [1367]
American Society for Microbiology Undergraduate Research Fellowships [1368]
American Society of Military Comptrollers (ASMC) [1374]
American Society of Military Comptrollers National Scholarship Program [1375]
American Society of Mining and Reclamation (ASMR) [1376]
American Society of Mining and Reclamation Memorial Scholarships [1377]
American Society of Naval Engineers (ASNE) [1378]
American Society of Naval Engineers Scholarships (ASNE) [1379]
American Society of Nephrology (ASN) [1380]
American Society for Nondestructive Testing (ASNT) [1383]
American Society of Podiatric Medical Assistants (ASPMA) [1386]
American Society for Quality (ASQ) [1388]
American Society for Radiation Oncology (ASTRO) [1391]
American Society of Radiologic Technologists Education and Research Foundation (ASRT) [1396]
American Society of Regional Anesthesia and Pain Medicine (ASRA) [1402]
American Society of Safety Engineers (ASSE) [1405]
American Society of Safety Engineers Construction Safety Scholarships [1407]
American Society for Theatre Research (ASTR) [1432]
American Society of Travel Agents (ASTA) [1435]
American Sociological Association (ASA) [1444]
American Sokol Merit Awards [1448]
American Sokol Organization (ASO) [1447]
American Speech Language Hearing Foundation (ASHF) [1449]
American Speech Language Hearing Foundation Clinical Research Grants [1450]
American Speech Language Hearing Foundation Endowed Scholarships [1451]
American Speech Language Hearing Foundation General Scholarships [1452]
American Speech Language Hearing Foundation Scholarships for International Students [1453]
American Speech Language Hearing Foundation Scholarships for Minority Students [1454]
American Statistical Association (ASA) [1462]
American Surgical Association (ASA) [1467]
American Swedish Institute (ASI) [1469]
American Thoracic Society (ATS) [1472]
American University School of Public Affairs [1475]
American Veterinary Medical Association (AVMA) [1477]
American Water Resources Association - Colorado Section [1479]
American Water Ski Educational Foundation Scholarships [10351]
American Water Works Association (AWWA) [1481]

American Water Works Association - Florida Section (FSAWWA) [1493]
American Water Works Association - Illinois Section [1495]
American Water Works Association - Virginia Section (VA AWWA) [1497]
American Watercolor Society (AWS) [1499]
American Watercolor Society Scholarship Program for Art Teachers [1500]
American Welding Society (AWS) [1501]
American Welding Society District Scholarships [1503]
American Welding Society Graduate Research Fellowships [1504]
American Welding Society International Scholarships [1505]
American Welding Society National Scholarships [1506]
American Welding Society Past Presidents Scholarships [1507]
American Wine Society Educational Foundation (AWSEF) [1527]
American Wine Society Educational Foundation Scholarships [1528]
American Woman's Society of Certified Public Accountants (AWSCPA) [1529]
Americans for Informed Democracy (AID) [1531]
Americans for Informed Democracy Global Scholar Program [1532]
AmeriGlide [1533]
AmeriGlide Achiever Scholarships [1534]
Anna Ames Clinical Excellence Student Grants [2481]
amfAR, The Foundation for AIDS Research [1535]
Arsham Amirikian Engineering Scholarships [1508]
AMLN Scholarships for Arab American Students [1003]
AMS Centennial Fellowships [985]
AMS Freshman Undergraduate Scholarships [997]
AMS Graduate Fellowships in the History of Science [998]
AMS/Industry/Government Graduate Fellowships [999]
AMS/Industry Minority Scholarships [1000]
AMS Teacher Education Scholarships [1007]
AMS Undergraduate Named Scholarships [1001]
AMSA Graduate Student Research Poster Competition Award [987]
AMSN Career Mobility Scholarship Awards [37]
AMSSM-ACSM Clinical Research Grants [993]
AMSUS Dentist Awards [1538]
AMSUS Nursing Awards [1539]
AMSUS Physician Awards [1540]
AMSUS - The Society of Federal Health Professionals [1537]
AMTA Past Presidents' Conference Scholar Awards [1010]
AMTA Student Conference Scholar Awards [1011]
AMTF Graduate Scholarships [1259]
Bernard Amtmann Fellowships [2258]
Amusement & Music Operators Association (AMOA) [1542]
AMVETS [1544]
AMVETS National Scholarships - Entering College Freshmen [1545]
AMVETS National Scholarships - For Veterans [1546]
AMVETS National Scholarships - JROTC [1547]
ANA Multicultural Excellence Scholarship Fund (MAIP) [456]
Anaheim Police Association (APA) [1548]
Anaheim Police Survivors and Scholarship Fund [1549]
ANCA Scholarships [1712]
Anchor Environmental [1550]
Anchor Plastics Scholarships [8072]
Anchor QEA Environmental Scholarships [1551]
Anchor Scholarship Foundation Scholarships [9616]
Andersen Nontraditional Scholarships for Women's Education and Retraining (ANSWER) [4176]
Mary Louise Andersen Scholarship [1574]
William G. Anderson, DO, Minority Scholarships [1063]
The Anderson Group Summer Institute [1552]
The Anderson Group Summer Institute Scholarships [1553]

Henry H. Anderson, Jr. Sail Training Scholarship [9640]
Judge Isaac Anderson, Jr. Scholarships [9418]
A.T. Anderson Memorial Scholarships [889]
Charles Lee Anderson Memorial Scholarships [3275]
Gladys C. Anderson Memorial Scholarships [818]
Roy Anderson Memorial Scholarships [3140]
Earl I. Anderson Scholarships [1722]
Kathy D. and Stephen J. Anderson Scholarships [3210]
Ora E. Anderson Scholarships [4167]
Redlands Rotary Club - Donald C. Anderson Scholarships [8446]
Michael P. Anderson Scholarships in Space Science [7137]
Warren M. Anderson Scholarships [5115]
Dr. Andy Anderson Young Professional Awards [8117]
Grace Andow Memorial Scholarships [5548]
Margaret J. Andrew Memorial Scholarships [8909]
Cindy Andrews Educational Scholarships [8447]
William H. Andrews/HAWS Scholarships [10569]
Richard E. Andrews Memorial Scholarships [627]
Marvin A. Andrews Scholarships/Internships [1630]
Androscoggin County Chamber of Commerce **[1554]**
Androscoggin County Chamber of Commerce Adult Scholarships [1555]
ANF/ANN-FNRE Nursing Research Grants [1042]
ANF/ENRS Nursing Research Grants [1043]
ANF/STTI Nursing Research Grants [1044]
Angus Foundation **[1556]**
Angus Foundation General Undergraduate Student Scholarships [1557]
Angus Foundation Graduate Student Degree Scholarship Program [1558]
Angus Foundation Scholarships [7032]
Angus/Talon Youth Educational Learning Program Endowment Fund [1559]
Anheuser-Busch NAPABA Law Foundation Presidential Scholarships [6703]
Animal Compassion Undergraduate Scholarships [8015]
ANNA Nephrology Nurse Researcher Awards [1027]
Annapolis Rotary Club **[1560]**
Anne Frank Center U.S.A. (AFC USA) **[1562]**
Anne Friedberg Innovative Scholarship Awards [9104]
Leonore Annenberg Teaching Fellowships [10677]
Annette Urso Rickel Foundation Dissertation Award for Public Policy [1137]
Annual Research Doctoral and Postgraduate Fellowship Grant Program [2586]
Annuity.org **[1564]**
Annuity.org Scholarships [1565]
ANS Research Grants [1030]
ANSER Graduate Student Awards for Research on Nonprofits and the Social Economy [2030]
Hettie Margaret Anthony Fellowship [5779]
Hettie M. Anthony Fellowships [5787]
Antimicrobial Stewardship Fellowship Award [7929]
Antioch University New England - Center for Tropical Ecology and Conservation (CTEC) **[1566]**
Anxiety and Depression Association of America (ADAA) **[1568]**
AOF/Johnson & Johnson Vision Care - Innovation in Education Grants [414]
AOFAS Research Grants Program [1060]
AORN Academic Scholarships [2035]
AORN Administrator Skills Course [2036]
AORN Foundation Scholarship Program [2037]
AOS Research Training Fellowships [1067]
AOSA Research Grants [1053]
AOSA Research Partnership Grants [1054]
APA Division 54: Society of Pediatric Psychology (SPP) **[1570]**
APA Society Convention Research Awards [8317]
APABA-SV Scholarships [1786]
APAGS-CLGBTC Grant Program [1131]
APALA Scholarship Award [1788]
APC High School Scholarship Awards [78]
APDA Medical Students Summer Fellowships [1071]
APDA Postdoctoral Research Fellowships [1072]
APDA Research Grants [1073]

APF/COGDOP Graduate Research Scholarships [1138]
APF High School Psychology Teacher Network Grants [1139]
APF Professional Development Awards for High School Psychology Teachers [1140]
APF Visionary Grants [1141]
APhA Auxilliary Scholarship [1575]
APhA Foundation **[1573]**
APHF Academic Scholarships [1069]
APHL Emerging Infectious Diseases Fellowships [2048]
APIASF Scholarships [1792]
Aplastic Anemia and MDS International Foundation (AA&MDSIF) **[1587]**
Aplastic Anemia and Myelodysplasia Association of Canada Scholarships [2694]
Appalachian School of Law (ASL) **[1589]**
Appalachian School of Law Merit Scholarship Program [1590]
Appel Law Firm, LLP **[1591]**
Applied Hospitality Degree Scholarships [2657]
Applied Motion Products, Inc. **[1593]**
Appraisal Institute Education Trust **[1595]**
Appraisal Institute Education Trust Undergraduate Scholarships [1596]
APS/ASU Scholarships [8139]
APS/Maricopa County Community Colleges Scholarships [8140]
APS Scholarships for Minority Undergraduate Physics Majors [7138]
APS Society Convention Research Awards [8318]
APS Student Research Award [2045]
APSA Congressional Fellowship for Communications Scholars and Journalists [1108]
APSA Congressional Fellowships [4398]
APSA Congressional Fellowships for Journalists [1109]
APSA Congressional Fellowships for Political Scientists [1110]
APSA Fund for Latino Scholarship [1111]
APSA/Health and Aging Policy Fellowships [1112]
APSA Minority Fellows Program [1113]
APSA Presidency Research Group Fellowships [1118]
APSA Small Research Grant Program [1114]
APSA U.S. Federal Executives Fellowships [1115]
APT US&C Scholarships [2050]
APTA Minority Scholarships - Faculty Development Scholarships [1096]
APTA Minority Scholarships - Physical Therapist Assistant Students [1097]
APTA Minority Scholarships - Physical Therapist Students [1098]
Aquatics Booster Club Scholarships [8448]
ARA Scholarship Awards [2136]
Arab American Institute (AAI) **[1597]**
Arab American Medical Association Houston Chapter (AAMA) **[1600]**
ARAFCS Doctoral Scholarships [1646]
ARAFCS Masters Scholarships [1647]
Frank G. Araujo Memorial Scholarships [8449]
ARCADIS Scholarships [1482]
ARCE Funded Fellowships [1195]
ARCE Research Associates Fellowships [1196]
Archaeological Institute of America (AIA) **[1602]**
Archaeological Institute of America Fellowships for Study in the U.S. [1604]
Archaeology of Portugal Fellowships [1605]
George F. Archambault Scholarship [1576]
NHCGNE Patricia G. Archbold Predoctoral Scholar Award [6982]
Architects Association of PEI Scholarships [3309]
Architectural Precast Association (APA) **[1613]**
Arctic Institute of North America (AINA) **[1615]**
Arctic Physical Therapy Fairbanks [1618]
Arctic Physical Therapy Scholarship [1619]
Mike Ardaw Scholarships [10007]
AREMA Committee 12 - Rail Transit Scholarships [1176]
AREMA Committee 18 - Light Density and Short Line Railways Scholarships [1177]
AREMA Committee 24 - Education and Training Scholarships [1178]
AREMA Committee 27 - Maintenance-of-Way Work Equipment Scholarships [1179]

AREMA Committee 33 - Electric Energy Utilization Scholarships [1180]
AREMA Michigan Tech Alumni Scholarships [1181]
AREMA Presidential Spouse Scholarships [1182]
Arent Fox Diversity Scholarships [1621]
Arent Fox L.L.P. **[1620]**
A.R.F.O.R.A. Undergraduate Scholarships for Women [1224]
ARIT Fellowships in the Humanities and Social Sciences in Turkey [1201]
ARIT National Endowment for the Humanities Advanced Fellowships for Research in Turkey [1202]
ARIT Summer Fellowships for Intensive Advanced Turkish Language Study [1203]
Arizona Airports Association (AZAA) **[1622]**
Arizona Artist Blacksmith Association (AABA) **[1624]**
Arizona Christian School Tuition Organization (ACSTO) **[1626]**
Arizona City/County Management Association (ACMA) **[1629]**
Arizona Cowpuncher's Scholarship Organization (ACSO) **[1632]**
Arizona Hydrological Society (AHS) **[1634]**
Arizona Hydrological Society Scholarships [1635]
Arizona Nursery Association (ANA) **[1636]**
Arizona Nursery Association Scholarships [1637]
Arizona Nurses Association (AzNA) **[1638]**
Arizona Nurses Foundation Scholarships [1639]
Arizona Society of Certified Public Accountants (ASCPA) **[1640]**
Rick Arkans Eagle Scout Scholarships [6919]
Arkansas Association of Family and Consumer Sciences (ARAFCS) **[1645]**
Arkansas Environmental Federation (AEF) **[1648]**
Arkansas Green Industry Association (AGIA) **[1650]**
Arkansas Green Industry Association Professional Grants [1651]
Arkansas Green Industry Association Student Scholarships [1652]
Arkansas Library Association (ArLA) **[1653]**
Arkansas Nurses Association (ARNA) **[1655]**
Arkansas Public Health Association (APHA) **[1658]**
Arkansas Public Health Association Scholarships [1659]
Arkansas Single Parent Scholarship Fund (ASPSF) **[1660]**
Arkansas Single Parent Scholarships [1661]
Arkansas State University (ASU) **[1662]**
Arkansas State University Mountain Home Scholarships [1663]
ArLA Scholarships [1654]
Arlyn Scales Awards for Science and Technology [3035]
Fondation J. Armand Bombardier **[1664]**
Armed Forces Communications and Electronics Association San Diego Chapter **[1666]**
Connie "Chelo" Armendariz Memorial Scholarships [8450]
Armenian American Citizen's League Scholarships [1682]
Armenian American Medical Association Scholarships [1683]
Armenian American Pharmacists' Association Scholarships [1684]
Armenian Bar Association **[1668]**
Armenian Bar Association Graduate Scholarships in Law [1669]
Armenian Educational Foundation (AEF) **[1670]**
Armenian General Athletic Union Scholarships [1685]
Armenian General Benevolent Union (AGBU) **[1672]**
Armenian Professional Society (APS) **[1674]**
Armenian Professional Society Graduate Student Scholarships [1675]
Armenian Relief Society - Eastern United States **[1676]**
Armenian Relief Society of Eastern U.S.A. (ARSER) **[1679]**
Armenian Relief Society Scholarships [1686]
Armenian Students' Association of America Inc. (ASA) **[1681]**
Ethel Louise Armstrong Foundation Scholarships [8750]
Robin P. Armstrong Memorial Prize for Excellence in

Native Studies Awards [1880]
Robert Armstrong Memorial Scholarships [10776]
Louis Armstrong Scholarships [1268]
Army Aviation Association of America (AAAA) **[1709]**
Army Health Professions Scholarships Program [9878]
Army Nurse Corps Association (ANCA) **[1711]**
Army Scholarship Foundation **[1713]**
Richard E. Arnason Court Scholarships [3409]
Norma Arnold Clerical Scholarships [6221]
Paul Arnold Memorial Scholarships [8241]
Tara Lynn Arnold Scholarships [9562]
Aaron Arnoldsen Memorial Golf Tournament **[1718]**
Aaron Edward Arnoldsen Memorial Scholarships [1719]
ARNOVA Emerging Scholar Awards [2056]
Jane B. Aron Doctoral Fellowships [6787]
Don Aron Scholarships [6875]
Judge Sidney M. Aronovitz Memorial Scholarships [6451]
Kush Arora Federal Criminal Justice Reform Scholarships [8227]
Luis Arreola Memorial Scholarships [8686]
ARRL Foundation (ARRLF) **[1720]**
ARRL Foundation General Fund Scholarships [1723]
ARRL Foundation PHD Scholarships [1724]
ARRLF Mississippi Scholarships [1725]
ARS of Eastern USA Lazarian Graduate Scholarship [1680]
ARS Undergraduate Scholarships [1677]
Art Dealers Association of Canada (ADAC) **[1766]**
Arthritis Foundation (AF) **[1768]**
Arthritis Foundation - Arizona **[1773]**
Arthritis Foundation Doctoral Dissertation Awards for Arthritis Health Professionals [1769]
Arthritis Foundation Innovative Research Grants [1770]
Arthritis Foundation Investigator Awards [1771]
Arthritis Foundation Postdoctoral Fellowships [1772]
Artist-in-Residence Workspace Grant [2843]
The Artist in Landscape Design Scholarship by Fullmer's Landscaping [7581]
Arts Council of Greater Grand Rapids Minority Scholarships [4574]
Arts Council of Princeton (ACP) **[1775]**
Arts Graduate Scholarships [267]
David Arver Memorial Scholarships [155]
Dutch and Ginger Arver Scholarships [156]
Chester Arzell and Helen Miller Montgomery Scholarships [10570]
ASA Graduate Scholarships [1243]
ASA Minority Fellowship Program (ASA MFP) [1445]
ASA/NSF/BLS Fellowships [1463]
ASA Student Forum Travel Awards [1446]
ASAC-CJAS PhD Research Grant Awards [73]
ASAE: The Center for Association Leadership **[1777]**
ASBA College Scholarship Grant Program [1239]
ASBC Foundation Graduate Scholarships [1247]
ASBC Foundation Undergraduate Scholarships [1248]
Benjamin Asbell Memorial Scholarships [2507]
ASBPE Young Leaders Scholarships [1250]
ASC Graduate Fellowships for Ethnic Minorities [1280]
Ascend **[1779]**
Elizabeth and Sherman Asche Memorial Scholarships [1832]
ASCO/CCF Young Investigator Awards [3369]
ASCP Phlebotomy Scholarships [1262]
ASCPA High School Scholarships [1641]
ASECS Graduate Student Research Paper Awards [1283]
ASECS Innovative Course Design Competition [1284]
ASECS Women's Caucus Editing and Translation Fellowships [1285]
ASEE/NSF Small Business Postdoctoral Research Diversity Fellowships [1303]
ASEH Minority Travel Grants [1309]
Officer Brian A. Aselton Memorial Scholarships [4737]
ASET Scholarships [1301]

ASF/Annika Teig/Skidmore, Owings and Merrill Fellowships [1234]
ASG Scholar Awards [1321]
ASGP Graduate Research Fellowships [223]
ASHARE Undergraduate Engineering Scholarships [1328]
Ashburn Institute (AI) **[1781]**
ASHFoundation New Century Scholars Doctoral Scholarships [1455]
ASHFoundation New Century Scholars Research Grants [1456]
ASHFoundation New Investigators Research Grants [1457]
ASHFoundation Scholarships for NSSLHA Members [1458]
ASHFoundation Speech Science Research Grants [1459]
ASHFoundation Student Research Grants in Audiology [1460]
ASHFoundation Student Research Grants in Early Childhood Language Development [1461]
ASHP Student Research Awards [1323]
ASHS Industry Division Student Travel Grants [1337]
ASHS Scholars Awards [1338]
ASI Sheep Heritage Foundation Memorial Scholarship [1241]
Asia-Pacific Biomedical Research Foundation Merit Awards [9304]
Asia Pacific Foundation of Canada Junior Research Fellowships [4113]
Asia Pacific Foundation of Canada Media Fellowships [4114]
Asia Pacific Foundation of Canada Post-Graduate Research Fellowships [4115]
Asian Development Bank - Japan Scholarships [3759]
Asian Pacific American Advocates **[1783]**
Asian Pacific American Bar Association of Silicon Valley (APABA-SV) **[1785]**
Asian Pacific American Librarians Association (APALA) **[1787]**
Asian/Pacific Bar Association of Sacramento (ABAS) **[1789]**
Asian/Pacific Bar Association of Sacramento Law Foundation Scholarship [1790]
Asian and Pacific Islander American Scholarship Fund (APIASF) **[1791]**
Asian and Pacific Islander Queers Sisters Scholarships [8242]
ASID Foundation Legacy Scholarships for Graduate Students [1341]
ASIS Foundation Chapter Matching Scholarships [1794]
ASIS International **[1793]**
ASLA Council of Fellow Scholarships [1346]
ASLA Council of Fellows Scholarships [5913]
ASLMS Research Grants [1349]
ASLMS Student Research Grants [1350]
ASM/CDC Program in Infectious Disease and Public Health Microbiology [1369]
ASM Congressional Science Fellowships [1370]
ASM Science Teaching Fellowships - Student [1371]
ASM Undergraduate Research Capstone Program [1372]
ASME International **[1795]**
ASMS Research Awards [1363]
ASNT Fellowship Award [1384]
ASPIRE Rheumatology and Dermatology Research Awards [8023]
Myron "Ted" Asplin Foundation Scholarships [5097]
ASPPH/CDC Public Health Fellowship Program [2060]
ASPPH/EPA Environmental Health Fellowship Program [2061]
ASPPH/NHTSA Public Health Fellowship Program [2062]
ASPPH Public Health Policy Fellowship Program [2063]
ASPPH Public Health Preparedness Fellowship Program [2064]
ASPRS, The Imaging and Geospatial Information Society **[1801]**
Len Assante Scholarship Fund [6976]
Michael M. Assarian Scholarships [1687]
ASSE Diversity Committee Scholarships [1408]

Darrell and Palchie Asselin Scholarships [3703]
Associated General Contractors of America (AGC) **[1811]**
Associated General Contractors of Connecticut Scholarships [3365]
Associated General Contractors of New York State **[1813]**
Associated Locksmiths of America (ALOA) **[1815]**
Associated Press Television and Radio Association (APTRA) **[1817]**
Associated Women for Pepperdine Scholarships [7962]
Associates of the American Foreign Service Worldwide (AAFSW) **[1819]**
Associates in Behavioral Health Scholarships [8243]
Association for the Advancement of Baltic Studies (AABS) **[1822]**
Association for the Advancement of Baltic Studies Dissertation Grants for Graduate Students [1823]
Association for the Advancement of Scandinavian Studies in Canada **[1824]**
Association of American Geographers (AAG) **[1828]**
Association on American Indian Affairs (AAIA) **[1831]**
Association of American Indian Physicians (AAIP) **[1837]**
Association of American Indian Physicians Scholarships [1838]
Association of American Medical Colleges (AAMC) **[1839]**
Association of Applied Paleontological Sciences (AAPS) **[1841]**
Association for Applied and Therapeutic Humor (AATH) **[1847]**
Association of Art Museum Curators (AAMC) **[1853]**
Association for Asian Studies (AAS) **[1856]**
Association for Behavior Analysis International (ABAI) **[1859]**
Association of Black Women Lawyers of New Jersey **[1862]**
Association of Black Women Physicians (ABWP) **[1864]**
Association of Business Information & Media Companies (ABM) **[1866]**
Association of California Nurse Leaders Kern County Chapter **[1868]**
Association of California Water Agencies (ACWA) **[1870]**
Association of California Water Agencies Scholarships [1871]
Association for Canadian Studies in the United States (ACSUS) **[1874]**
Association Canadienne des Chefs de Police **[1877]**
Association Canadienne Des Géographes (ACG) **[1879]**
Association Canadienne d'Études Cinématographiques (ACEC) **[1883]**
Association Canadienne du Diabete **[1885]**
Association Canadienne des Infirmières et Infirmiers en Sciences Neurologiques (ACIISN) **[1887]**
Association Canadienne des Libertes Civiles **[1891]**
Association Canadienne des Parajuristes **[1894]**
Association Canadienne des Professeurs de Langues Secondes (ACPLS) **[1896]**
Association Canadienne de Radio-Oncologie (ACRO) **[1899]**
Association Canadienne de la Recherche Théâtrale **[1901]**
Association Canadienne des Ressources Hydriques (ACRH) **[1904]**
Association Canadienne de Science Politique **[1907]**
Association Canadienne de Securite Incendie **[1910]**
Association Canadienne du Stationnement (ACS) **[1920]**
Association of Certified Fraud Examiners (ACFE) **[1922]**
Association of College Unions International (ACUI) **[1924]**
Association for Compensatory Educators of Texas (ACET) **[1927]**
Association for Compensatory Educators of Texas

Paraprofessionals Scholarships [1928]
Association for Compensatory Educators of Texas Scholarships [1929]
Association of Desk and Derrick Clubs (ADDC) **[1930]**
Association of Desk and Derrick Clubs Education Trust Scholarships [1931]
Association universitaire canadienne d'études nordique **[1932]**
Association of Donor Recruitment Professionals (ADRP) **[1936]**
Association of Donor Recruitment Professionals Hughes Scholarships [1937]
Association of Donor Recruitment Professionals Presidential Scholarships [1938]
Association for Educational Communications and Technology (AECT) **[1941]**
Association of Energy Engineers (AEE) **[1945]**
Association of Energy Engineers Foundation Scholarship Program [1946]
Association of Environmental & Engineering Geologists **[1947]**
Association of Environmental Engineering and Science Professors Foundation (AEESP) **[1950]**
Association des Facultes de Pharmacie du Canada (AFPC) **[1956]**
Association of Family Practice Physician Assistants (AFPPA) **[1958]**
Association for Federal Information Resources Management (AFFIRM) **[1960]**
Association of Flight Attendants - CWA (AFA-CWA) **[1962]**
Association of Flight Attendants Scholarship Fund [1963]
Association of Food and Drug Officials (AFDO) **[1964]**
Association of Former Intelligence Officers (AFIO) **[1967]**
Association of Government Accountants (AGA) **[1970]**
Association of Government Accountants Undergraduate/Graduate Scholarships for Community Service Accomplishments [1971]
Association of Government Accountants Undergraduate/Graduate Scholarships for Full-time study [1972]
Association of Government Accountants Undergraduate/Graduate Scholarships for Part-time study [1973]
Association of Independent Colleges and Universities of Pennsylvania (AICUP) **[1974]**
Association for Institutional Research (AIR) **[1979]**
Association of International Education Administrators (AIEA) **[1984]**
Association of International Petroleum Negotiators (AIPN) **[1986]**
Association for Iron and Steel Technology (AIST) **[1988]**
Association of Jewish Libraries (AJL) **[2009]**
Association of Latino Professionals in Finance and Accounting (ALPFA) **[2012]**
Association of Leadership Educators, Inc. (ALE) **[2014]**
Association for Library Service to Children (ALSC) **[2016]**
Association canadienne du droit des technologies de l'information **[2019]**
Association Minéralogique du Canada **[2021]**
Association of Moving Image Archivists (AMIA) **[2023]**
Association for Nonprofit and Social Economy Research **[2029]**
Association of Occupational Health Professionals in Healthcare (AOHP) **[2031]**
Association of PeriOperative Registered Nurses (AORN) **[2034]**
Association of Postgraduate Physician Assistant Programs (APPAP) **[2038]**
Association for Preservation Technology International (APT) **[2040]**
Association for Preservation Technology International Student Scholarships [2041]
Association of Professional Schools of International Affairs (APSIA) **[2042]**
Association for Psychological Science (APS) **[2044]**

Association for Psychological Science Student Grants (APS) [2046]
Association for Public Health Laboratories (APHL) **[2047]**
Association of Public Treasurers of the United States and Canada (APT US & C) **[2049]**
Association of Rehabilitation Nurses (ARN) **[2051]**
Association of Rehabilitation Nurses - Alabama Chapter **[2053]**
Association for Research on Nonprofit Organizations and Voluntary Action (ARNOVA) **[2055]**
Association of School Business Officials of Maryland and the District of Columbia (ASBO-MD&DC) **[2057]**
Association of Schools and Programs of Public Health (ASPPH) **[2059]**
Association of Science-Technology Centers (ASTC) **[2066]**
Association of Seventh-Day Adventist Librarians (ASDAL) **[2068]**
Association for the Sociology of Religion (ASR) **[2070]**
Association of State Dam Safety Officials (ASDSO) **[2073]**
Association of State Dam Safety Officials Undergraduate Scholarships [2074]
Association of Surgical Technologists (AST) **[2075]**
Association of Texas Professional Educators Foundation **[2077]**
Association of Textile, Apparel and Materials Professionals (AATCC) **[2080]**
Association of the United States Navy (AUSN) **[2082]**
Association of the United States Navy Scholarships [2083]
Association of University Programs in Health Administration (AUPHA) **[2084]**
Association for Women in Architecture + Design (AWA+D) **[2088]**
Association for Women in Architecture Scholarships [2089]
Association for Women in Computing - Houston Chapter **[2090]**
Association for Women Geoscientists (AWG) **[2092]**
Association for Women in Mathematics (AWM) **[2097]**
Association for Women in Sports Media (AWSM) **[2100]**
Association for Women in Sports Media Internship/Scholarship Program [2101]
Association of Zoo Veterinary Technicians (AZVT) **[2102]**
ASTA Alaska Airlines Scholarships [1437]
ASTA Holland America Line Graduate Research Scholarships [1438]
ASTA Rigby, Healy, Simmons Scholarships [1439]
ASTR Research Fellowships [1433]
Astra Zeneca Medical Scholarships [7275]
AstraZeneca Scholarships [2695]
ASTRO Junior Faculty Career Research Training Awards [1392]
ASTRO Minority Summer Fellowship Awards [1393]
ASTRO Residents/Fellows in Radiation Oncology Research Seed Grants [1394]
ASTRO/ROI Comparative Effectiveness Research Awards [1395]
Astronaut Scholarship Foundation (ASF) **[2104]**
Astronaut Scholarship Foundation Scholarships [2105]
AT&T Business Internship Awards [10214]
Athenaeum of Philadelphia (PAT) **[2106]**
Martha and Robert Atherton Ministerial Scholarships [9831]
Athletic Equipment Managers Association (AEMA) **[2108]**
Atkinson Charitable Foundation **[2110]**
Atkinson Fellowships in Public Policy [2111]
ISA Aerospace Industries Division - William H. Atkinson Scholarships [5396]
Atlanta Association of Legal Administrators (AALA) **[2112]**
Atlantic County Bar Association **[2114]**
Atlantic Provinces Library Association (APLA) **[2116]**

Atlantic Provinces Library Association Memorial Awards [2117]
Atlantic Salmon Federation (ASF) **[2119]**
Atlantic Salmon Federation Olin Fellowships [2120]
Atlas Shrugged Essay Contest [2163]
ATS Abstract Scholarships [1473]
Attorney-CPA Foundation Scholarships [391]
Elaine Atwood Scholarship [10049]
AUA Foundation Urology Research Bridge Awards [10346]
Aubespin Scholarships [718]
Audio Engineering Society (AES) **[2121]**
A. B. and Hazel Augenstein Scholarship Funds [6281]
Herzog August Bibliothek Wolfenbüttel Fellowships [7409]
Joan Auld Scholarships [3310]
Frank H. Ault Scholarships [8687]
H. Thomas Austern Memorial Writing Competition [4127]
Austin Alumnae Association Beta Xi Scholarship [5690]
Australian-American Health Policy Fellowships [3159]
Auto Accident Law Firm Survivor Scholarships [1592]
Auto Body Technician Certificate Scholarships [8765]
Auto Care Association **[2123]**
Auto-Pets **[2128]**
Auto-Pets "Out-of-the-Box Thinking" Scholarships [2129]
Automotive Industries Association of Canada (AIAC) **[2130]**
Automotive Recyclers Association (ARA) **[2135]**
Automotive Technician Scholarship Program [6344]
Automotive Women's Alliance Foundation (AWAF) **[2137]**
Automotive Women's Alliance Foundation Scholarships [2138]
Auxiliary Undergraduate Scholarships [1796]
AVAC: Global Advocacy for HIV Prevention **[2139]**
AvaCare Medical **[2141]**
AvaCare Medical Scholarships [2142]
Dr. Noyes L. Avery, Jr. and Ann E. Avery Scholarships [4575]
Aviation Distributors and Manufacturers Association (ADMA) **[2143]**
Avis Budget Group Scholarships [1440]
AVMA Fellowship Program [1478]
AVS Applied Surface Science Division Awards [2146]
AVS Biomaterial Interfaces Division - Early Career Researchers Awards [2147]
AVS Electronic Materials and Photonic Division Postdoctoral Award [2148]
AVS Manufacturing Science and Technology Group Awards [2149]
AVS MEMS and NEMS Technical Group Best Paper Awards [2150]
AVS Nanometer-Scale Science and Technology Division Graduate Award [2151]
AVS Science and Technology Society (AVS) **[2145]**
AVS Spectroscopic Ellipsometry Focus Topic Graduate Student Awards [2152]
AVS Thin Film Division James Harper Awards [2153]
Award for Outstanding Doctoral Dissertation in Laser Science [1086]
Award for Outstanding Doctoral Thesis Research in Biological Physics [1087]
Awards for Judaic Studies and/or Studies in Israel [5591]
AWG Minority Scholarships [2093]
AWM Mathematics Travel Grants [2098]
AWMA Louisiana Section Scholarships [147]
AWMA Niagara Frontier Section College Scholarships [149]
AWSCPA National Scholarships [1530]
AWWA American Water Scholarships [1483]
AWWA Illinois Section Safe Water Scholarship Awards [1496]
AXA Achievement Scholarships [2161]
AXA Equitable **[2160]**
Susan Ayers Memorial Scholarships [8332]
Ayn Rand Institute (ARI) **[2162]**

Ayn Rand Institute Anthem Essay Contest [2164]
Ayn Rand Institute Fountainhead Essay Contest [2165]
William Stone Ayres Scholarship [3661]
John M. Azarian Memorial Armenian Youth Scholarship Fund [1688]
Azrieli Neurodevelopmental Research Program [2350]
B-Brave McMahon/Stratton Scholarship Fund [4039]
Mary Babcock Fellowships for Labour Studies Application [7629]
Tom Babcox Memorial Scholarships [2124]
Bach Organ Scholarship [8602]
Bachelor of Science in Nursing Academic Scholarships [6656]
Paula Backscheider Archival Fellowships [1286]
BACUS Scholarships [9467]
Leo Baeck Institute - DAAD Fellowships [3602]
BAFTX Early Starters Awards [2365]
BAFTX Graduate Awards [2366]
BAFTX Junior Achievers Awards [2367]
BAFTX Undergraduate Awards [2368]
Baha'i Faith Scholarships for Racial Harmony [8451]
Morton Bahr Scholarships [3165]
Marian Breland Bailey Award [1860]
The Bailey Family Foundation **[2166]**
The Bailey Family Foundation College Scholarship Program [2167]
The Bailey Family Foundation High School Scholarships Program [2168]
Bailey/Hollister Scholarships [7935]
Lincoln C. Bailey Memorial Scholarship Fund [5390]
Esther Tuttle Bailey Memorial Scholarships [5691]
Bambi Bailey Scholarships [3197]
Barbara Bailey Scholarships [8244]
Sandra Sebrell Bailey Scholarships [3579]
Mark B. Bain Graduate Fellowship [4980]
Marian Wood Baird Scholarships [9973]
Michael Baker Corp. Scholarship for Diversity in Engineering [1976]
Baker, Donelson, Bearman, Caldwell and Berkowitz, P.C. **[2169]**
Baker Donelson Diversity Scholarships [2170]
Baker and Hostetler Diversity Fellowships [2172]
Baker and Hostetler LLP **[2171]**
Baker and McKenzie Diversity Fellowships [2175]
Baker and McKenzie Graduate Legal Studies Scholarships [2176]
Baker and McKenzie L.L.P. **[2174]**
Dr. Jon Baker Memorial Scholarship [10050]
Francis Warren Baker Memorial Scholarships [8910]
Richard L. Baker Memorial Scholarships [9563]
Robby Baker Memorial Scholarships [299]
Airgas - Jerry Baker Scholarships [1509]
ACI Baker Student Fellowships [706]
ACI Elmer Baker Student Fellowships [707]
George C. Balch Scholarships [9958]
Bernt Balchen, Jr. and Olav Jorgen Hegge Hardingfele Scholarships [4717]
Birgit Baldwin Fellowships [6395]
Norman S. Baldwin Fishery Science Scholarship [5260]
Franklin Mosher Baldwin Memorial Fellowships [5991]
Victoria Baldwin Memorial Scholarships [10777]
Lynn Ann Baldwin Scholarships [1888]
Donald A. Baldwin Sr. Business Aviation Management Scholarships [6829]
Balestreri/Cutino Scholarships [757]
Ball Horticultural Company Scholarships [798]
Vic and Margaret Ball Student Intern Scholarships [799]
Ballantyne Resident Research Grants [847]
Ballard Family Foundation Scholarships [8688]
Leighton M. Ballew Directing Scholarships [9387]
G. Thomas Balsbaugh Memorial Scholarship Fund [4231]
Baltimore City Community College (BCCC) **[2177]**
B&W Y-12 Scholarship Fund [3752]
Banff Centre - Leadership Development **[2180]**
Bank of America Junior Achievement Scholarship Fund [4177]
Bank of Canada **[2186]**
Bank of Canada Fellowship Award [2187]
Bank of Canada Governor's Awards [2188]

Brenda S. Bank Educational Workshop Scholarships [9123]
Dr. Johnella Banks Memorial Scholarships [2298]
Harvey Washington Banks Scholarships in Astronomy [7139]
Sharon D. Banks Undergraduate Memorial Scholarships [10674]
Banner Bank Business Scholarships [6057]
Donald W. Banner Diversity Scholarships for Law Students [2190]
Mark T. Banner Scholarships for Law Students [6093]
Banner & Witcoff, Ltd. **[2189]**
James M. Banovetz Illinois Local Government Fellowships [5059]
Banting Postdoctoral Fellowships [3402]
Michael Bany Memorial Scholarships [2944]
Baptist Communicators Association (BCA) **[2191]**
Bar Association of San Francisco (BASF) **[2194]**
Bernice Barabash Sports Scholarships [5497]
Barakat Trust and Barakat Foundation Scholarships [1598]
Cynthia and Alan Baran Fine Arts and Music Scholarships [3211]
Leslie Baranowski Scholarships for Professional Excellence [5144]
Barbara Jordan Memorial Scholarships [2078]
Joe Barbarow Memorial Scholarships [7813]
Lewis B. Barber Memorial Scholarships [9419]
Jack R. Barckhoff Welding Management Scholarships [1510]
Thomas J. Bardos Science Education Awards for Undergraduate Students [473]
Edgar Barge Memorial Scholarships [4559]
UAA Michael Baring-Gould Memorial Scholarship [10051]
TCDA Carroll Barnes Student Scholarships [668]
Marguerite Ross Barnett Research Grant [1119]
Gina L. Barnhart Memorial Scholarship Fund [4040]
Barrientos Scholarship Foundation (BSF) **[2196]**
Zachary Barriger Memorial Scholarships [3086]
Robbie Barron Memorial Scholarships [4232]
Gloria Barron Wilderness Society Scholarship [10557]
Barta-Lehman Musical Scholarships [8689]
Eivind H. Barth, Jr. Memorial Scholarships [2508]
Barth Syndrome Foundation (BSF) **[2198]**
Walter and Marilyn Bartlett Scholarships [2945]
William E. Barto Scholarships [3704]
Elsa Barton Educational Scholarship Fund [1127]
Walt Bartram Memorial Education Award, Region 12 and Chapter 119 [9167]
Guthikonda BasavapunnaRao and Umadevi Scholarships [9667]
Bascom Hill Society Scholarships [10316]
Basic Research Fellowship Program [634]
Helen Bassett Commemorative Student Award [7221]
Charles A. Bassett Endowed Memorial Scholarship Fund [4510]
Bat Conservation International (BCI) **[2200]**
Bat Conservation International Student Research Scholarships [2201]
H. Burton Bates Jr. Scholarships [10402]
Jim Batten Community Newspaper Internships [10215]
Lewis and Gurry Batten/Sand Plains Educational Trust Scholarships [7814]
Raymond B. Bauer Research Award [6479]
Marian Sims Baughn Scholarships [5692]
Hazel Reed Baumeister Scholarship Program [8947]
Baxter Corporation Canadian Research Awards in Anesthesia [2538]
Bob Baxter Scholarships [7106]
Bay Area Minority Law Student Scholarships [2195]
Lawrence Bayer Business Administration Scholarships [10008]
Timothy Baylink Good Fellowship Awards [8452]
John Bayliss Broadcast Foundation Internship Programs [2203]
John Bayliss Broadcast Foundation **[2202]**
John Bayliss Broadcast Foundation Radio Scholarships [2204]
Bayly-Tiffany Scholarships [10301]
BCCC Foundation General Scholarship Fund [2178]
BCCC Workforce Creation Scholarships [2179]

BCPF Bursaries [9476]
BCSF Scholarships [2294]
BDC Visiting Fellowships [2382]
BDPA Education Technology Foundation (BETF) **[2205]**
Willa Beach-Porter Music Scholarships [2873]
Beatitudes Fellowships [2208]
The Beatitudes Society **[2207]**
Catherine H. Beattie Fellowships [2867]
Jane Beattie Memorial Scholarships [9160]
Suzanne Beauregard Scholarships [4476]
Beaver Medical Clinic-Glen Adams Scholarship Awards [8453]
Beaver Medical Clinic-H.E.A.R.T. Scholarship Awards [8454]
Beaver Medical Clinic-Premed Scholarship Awards [8455]
Don C. Beaver Memorial Scholarships [2447]
Beaverbrook Media at McGill Student Paper Prize [2615]
BECA Foundation **[2209]**
BECA Foundation General Scholarships Fund [2210]
Beca #Traductor Scholarships [9458]
Becas Univision Scholarship Program [4902]
Bechtel Engineering and Science Scholarships [6278]
Bechtel Group Foundation Scholarships for Safety & Health [1409]
O.J. Beck, Jr. Memorial Scholarships [3087]
Dennis J. Beck Memorial Scholarships [5498]
Beck-Pfann Memorial Scholarships [7964]
Garvin L. Beck Scholarships [8456]
Ed Becker Conference Travel Awards [3886]
Dr. Joyce Beckett Scholarships [6719]
Ann C. Beckingham Scholarships [2645]
Dr. Ann C. Beckingham Scholarships [2696]
Jenny Panitch Beckow Memorial Scholarships Canada [5569]
Jenny Panitch Beckow Memorial Scholarships Israel [5570]
Clifford L. Bedford Scholarship Award [5177]
BedwettingStore.com Design a Mascot Scholarships [5635]
Raymond and Donald Beeler Memorial Scholarships [8457]
BEF Scholarships of the Arts [2337]
Notah Begay III Scholarship Program [300]
Charles E. Behlke Engineering Memorial Scholarships [10009]
Beinecke Rare Book and Manuscript Library **[2213]**
Beinecke Rare Book and Manuscript Library Visiting Postdoctoral Scholar Fellowships [2214]
N.S. Beinstock Fellowships [8402]
Hannah Beiter Graduate Student Research Grants [2909]
Bel Canto Vocal Scholarship Foundation **[2216]**
Bel Canto Vocal Scholarship Foundation Vocal Competition [2217]
Belfer-Aptman Dissertation Research Awards [6409]
Bell Aliant Medical Education Scholarships [7276]
AG Bell College Scholarship Awards [314]
Max Bell Foundation **[2218]**
Alfred D. Bell, Jr. Travel Grants [4137]
John Bell and Lawrence Thornton Scholarship Fund [4738]
Harvey Bell Memorial Prize [10271]
Ray and Mary Bell Memorial Scholarships [8690]
Betty Bell Scholarship Fund [4922]
Beverlee Bell Scholarships in Human Rights and Democracy [3655]
A.G. Bell School Age Financial Aid Program [315]
Max Bell Senior Fellow Grants [2219]
Bradley Stuart Beller Special Merit Award [3370]
Bellevue PFLAG Scholarships [8245]
Belmont University Commercial Music Showcase Scholarships [3212]
David Beltran Memorial Scholarships [8458]
Mark A. Beltz Scholarship [10052]
Samuel Flagg Bemis Dissertation Research Grants [9133]
Ben Meadows Company Inc. **[2220]**
Reckitt Benckiser Student Scholarships [6771]
Richard W. Bendicksen Memorial Scholarships [1726]

Bill Bendiner and Doug Morgenson Scholarships [8246]
H. Y. Benedict Fellowships [340]
George Benes, MD & Michael Mallee, EdD Point Scholarships [8170]
Arthur Lockwood Beneventi Law Scholarships [7149]
Dave Benferado Scholarships [140]
Benign Essential Blepharospasm Research Foundation (BEBRF) **[2223]**
Benign Essential Blepharospasm Research Foundation Research Grants [2224]
HDR/Henry "Bud" Benjes Scholarships [1484]
Viscount Bennett Fellowships [2581]
Jean Bennett Memorial Student Travel Grants [7671]
Casey Bennett Scholarships [4007]
Reverend E.F. Bennett Scholarships [3088]
William Bennett W7PHO Memorial Scholarships [1727]
Price Benowitz Social Justice Scholarships [8228]
Pete and Ellen Bensley Memorial Scholarship Fund [4178]
Elizabeth Benson Scholarship Awards [8542]
The Bentley Cropping Systems Fellowship [2886]
Benton County Foundation (BCF) **[2225]**
Benton-Meier Neuropsychology Graduate Scholarships [1142]
George Oliver Benton Memorial Scholarships [3213]
Linn-Benton County Scholarships [7709]
Rosalie Bentzinger Scholarships [9849]
Lester G. Benz Memorial Scholarships for College Journalism Study [8396]
Fred Berg Awards [3796]
Charlotte V. Bergen Scholarships [1269]
Bergman Scholarships [7487]
Bergmann Family Scholarship Funds [6282]
The Joseph Berkman, and Michael and Sarah Chipkin Holocaust/Genocide Studies Award [9581]
Berkowitz Fellowships [9743]
Berks County Community Foundation (BCCF) **[2234]**
ARRS/Leonard Berlin Scholarships in Medical Professionalism [1222]
Louise Berman Fellows Award [5667]
Richard L. Bernardi Memorial Scholarships [3276]
Stuart L. Bernath Dissertation Grants [9134]
Myrna F. Bernath Fellowships [9135]
Bill Bernbach Diversity Scholarships [457]
Hon. Peggy Bernheim Memorial Scholarships [2377]
Robert L. Bernstein Fellowships in International Human Rights [4994]
Donald H. Bernstein/John B. Talbert, Jr. Scholarships [4179]
Thomas M. Berry Jr. Scholarships [10403]
Jean Clark Berry Scholarships [5693]
James R. and Geraldine F. Bertelsen Scholarships [8691]
Henry Besner Memorial Scholarships [10778]
Best Price Nutrition **[2236]**
Best Price Nutrition and Health Scholarships [2237]
Beta Lambda Project 2000 Scholarship [5694]
Beta Mu Project 2000 Scholarships [5695]
Beta Omega Scholarships [8911]
Beta Phi Mu **[2238]**
Beta Pi Project 2000 Scholarship in Memory of Kristy LeMond [5696]
Beta Pi Sigma Sorority **[2243]**
Beta Pi Sigma Sorority Scholarships (BPSSS) [2244]
Beta Province Project 2000 Scholarships [5697]
Beta Sigma Phi Visual Arts Scholarship [8869]
Beta Sigma Scholarships [8912]
Beta Tau Scholarship Fund [5698]
Beta Theta Memorial Scholarships [5699]
Beta Theta Pi **[2245]**
Beta Xi Project 2000 Scholarships [5700]
Beta Zeta Project 2000 Scholarships [5701]
Bethesda Lutheran Communities **[2247]**
Bethune-Cookman University (B-CU) **[2249]**
Bethune-Cookman University Excelsior Scholarship Level 1 [2250]
Bethune-Cookman University Presidential Scholarships [2251]
Harold Bettinger Scholarships [800]
Leonard Bettinger Vocational Scholarships [801]

William and Dorothy Bevan Scholarship [1143]
Albert J. Beveridge Grants for Research in the Western Hemisphere [852]
Beverly Estate Scholarship [3662]
Dr. Noorali and Sabiya Bharwani Endowment [2253]
Hussein Jina Bharwani Memorial Endowment [2254]
Noorali Bharwani Professional Corp. **[2252]**
BHCRI Bridge Funds [5012]
BHCRI Cancer Research Training Program Awards [5013]
BHCRI Matching Funds [5014]
BHCRI Miscellaneous Funds [5015]
BHCRI Seed Funds [5016]
BHCRI Studentship Awards [5017]
Leo Biaggi de Blasys Bogliasco Fellowships [2326]
Bibliographical Society of America (BSA) **[2255]**
Bibliographical Society of Canada (BSC) **[2257]**
BIE-Loan for Service for Graduates [882]
Big Sandy Community and Technical College (BSCTC) **[2260]**
James L. Biggane Fellowships in Finance [7367]
Bill and Nell Biggs Scholarships [10088]
Pierre and Patricia Bikai Fellowships [655]
James Bilder Scholarships [9420]
Jan Bingle Scholarships [3055]
Helen & Bob Bintz Scholarship Funds [6283]
BioCommunications Association (BCA) **[2263]**
Biogen Idec Hemophilia Scholarship Program [2310]
Biological Survey of Canada Scholarships [3887]
Biomagnetic Therapy Association (BTA) **[2268]**
Biomedical Engineering Society (BMES) **[2270]**
BioRx/Hemophilia of North Carolina Educational Scholarships [6985]
Birmingham District Alabama Dietetic Association Scholarships [196]
Birmingham Public School (BPS) **[2272]**
Birmingham-Southern College Eagle Scout Scholarships [6920]
Birmingham Student Scholarships [2273]
Graduate Student Honoraria - Elmer C. Birney Awards [1358]
Bisexual Foundation Scholarships [9284]
The Bishop James C. Baker Award [9850]
Lebbeus F. Bissell Scholarships [4739]
Mary E. Bivins Foundation **[2274]**
Mary E. Bivins Foundation Religious Scholarship Program [2275]
Dr. Richard E. Bjork Memorial Graduate Study Award [9582]
Ted Bjornn University of Idaho Graduate Student Scholarships [5033]
Ted Bjornn University of Idaho Undergraduate Student Scholarships [5034]
Law Offices of David A. Black Annual Hearing Impaired Scholarships [5957]
Black Business and Professional Association (BBPA) **[2276]**
Black Canadian Scholarship Fund **[2293]**
Black Caucus of the American Library Association (BCALA) **[2295]**
Thomas F. Black, Jr. Memorial Scholarships [8600]
Black Men Building Resources Scholarships [4576]
Black Nurses Association of Greater Washington **[2297]**
Black Rock Arts Foundation (BRAF) **[2300]**
William Verbon Black Scholarships [205]
Black Theatre Network (BTN) **[2302]**
Lucie and Thornton Blackburn Scholarships [2544]
Reid Blackburn Scholarships [7107]
Eileen Blackey Doctoral Fellowships [6788]
William T. Blackwell Scholarship Fund [7019]
Mitzi and William Blahd, MD Pilot Research Grants [9220]
Blair Chiropractic Society **[2304]**
Beatrice K. Blair Scholarships [2305]
Thomas M. Blake Memorial Scholarships [3360]
Blakemore Foundation **[2306]**
Blakemore Freeman Fellowships [2307]
Blakemore Refresher Grants [2308]
Margaret Blanchard Dissertation Support Fund [10216]
Alex Blaski Memorial Scholarships [8572]
Bleeding Disorders Alliance Illinois (BDAI) **[2309]**
Joan Blend Scholarship Fund [9493]
M. Hildred Blewett Fellowships [1088]
Blinded Veterans Association (BVA) **[2311]**

Everitt P. Blizard Scholarships [1034]
Ellin Bloch and Pierre Ritchie Diversity Dissertation Grant [1132]
Jeanne Humphrey Block Dissertation Award [4784]
Ellen Blodgett Memorial Scholarships [7375]
Blood Assurance Foundation **[2313]**
Lawrence Bloomberg Entrance Awards [10741]
F.A. and Charlotte Blount Scholarships [10571]
Blues Heaven Foundation (BHF) **[2315]**
BMES Graduate and Undergraduate Student Awards [2271]
BMI Foundation **[2317]**
BMO Capital Markets Lime Connect Equity through Education Scholarships [6087]
BMO Financial Group Lime Connect Canada Scholarship Program for Students with Disablilities [6088]
BMO Harris Scholarships [7277]
Board of Certification for Emergency Nursing (BCEN) Undergraduate Scholarships [3860]
Board of Young Adult Advisors Scholarships [9827]
David and Camille Boatwright Endowed Scholarships [7965]
Sandra Bobbitt Continuing Education Scholarship [2032]
Edith and Arnold N. Bodtker Grants [3522]
Boeing Company Scholarships [8870]
B.O.G. Pest Control **[2322]**
B.O.G. Pest Control Scholarship Funds [2323]
Gerald J. and Helen Bogen Fund [4660]
Hagop Bogigian Scholarship Fund [1689]
Bogliasco Fellowships [2327]
Bogliasco Foundation - Liguria Study Center for the Arts and Humanities **[2324]**
Therese and David Bohbot Scholarships [5571]
Bohemian Lawyers Association of Chicago **[2332]**
Bohemian Lawyers Association of Chicago Scholarships [2333]
Bolick Foreign Student Scholarships [10010]
Brian Bolton Graduate/Mature Student Essay Awards [4301]
Friends of Megan Bolton Memorial Fund [4233]
Dorothy M. Bolyard Memorial Scholarships [8692]
BOMA/NY Scholarships [2404]
Yvonne L. Bombardier Visual Arts Scholarships [1665]
Carol Bond Community College Scholarships [7479]
Carol Bond University Scholarships [7480]
Steve Bonk Scholarships [2766]
Lorne and Ruby Bonnell Scholarships [3311]
Barbara Bonnema Memorial Scholarships [8459]
Ellis J. Bonner Scholarships [6754]
Sam L. Booke, Sr. Scholarships [10572]
Boomer Benefits **[2334]**
Boomer Benefits Scholarships [2335]
Boomer Esiason Foundation (BEF) **[2336]**
Admiral Mike Boorda Loans Program [7234]
T. Frank Booth Memorial Scholarship Fund [4180]
John H. Borden Scholarships [3888]
Maria and Czeslaw Borek Scholarships [8573]
David L. Boren Fellowships [5199]
David L. Boren Scholarships [5200]
David L. Boren Undergraduate Scholarships [1968]
Dr. Anita Borg Memorial Scholarships - USA [4493]
Maria Gonzales Borrero Scholarships [4740]
Geraldine Geistert Boss Scholarships [4577]
Tom Bost Scholarships [10217]
Boston City Federation "Return to School" Scholarships [4351]
William (Billbo) Boston/Harold Knopp Scholarship [7815]
Boston Intercollegiate Alumnae Association Adelphe Scholarship [5702]
Stephen Botein Fellowships [433]
Dr. George T. Bottomley Scholarships [6350]
Richard J. Bouchard AECOM Scholarships [1162]
Bound to Stay Bound Books Scholarships [2017]
Leo Bourassa Scholarships [10398]
Jim Bourque Scholarship [1617]
Bourse de Montreal Inc. **[2344]**
Rev. Andrew L. Bouwhuis Memorial Scholarship Program [2814]
Herbie Bouwman Memorial Scholarships [10779]
MAC Louisa Bowen Memorial Scholarships for Graduate Students in Archival Administration [6515]

William R. Bowen Scholarships [3171]
Kathi Bowles Scholarships for Women in Technology [2091]
Billy Bowling Memorial Scholarship [7530]
Boy Scouts of America Troop 3 Scholarships - Art Till/Nathan E. Smith Memorial Scholarships [8460]
CAG Margery Boyce Bursary Awards [2553]
Dr. Betty J. Boyd-Beu and Edwin G. Beu, Jr. Scholarships [10011]
W. Scott Boyd Group Grants [5282]
Corris Boyd Scholarships [2085]
Dody Boyd Scholarships [3214]
Verna Curry Boyer Scholarships [9564]
Eugene Boyko Memorial Scholarships [228]
Boyle Family Scholarship [1577]
Boys and Girls Club of Ottawa **[2346]**
BPW Foundation Career Advancement Scholarships [2422]
Mildred Cater Bradham Social Work Fellowships [10814]
Carol June Bradley Awards [6625]
Charles Bradley Memorial Scholarships [4723]
William L. Bradley Memorial Scholarships [7376]
Leon Bradley Scholarship Program [575]
Paul W. Bradley Scholarships [7377]
Geoffrey Bradshaw Memorial Scholarships [10780]
Doreen Brady Memorial Scholarships [7630]
Edward J. Brady Memorial Scholarships [1511]
W. Philip Braender and Nancy Coleman Braender Scholarships [4741]
BRAF Grants [2301]
TACS/A. Bragas and Associates Student Scholarships [9686]
Susan Brager Occupational Education Scholarships [8333]
AFCEA San Diego Buck Bragunier Leadership Scholarship [1667]
Brain Canada-ALS Canada Career Transition Awards [2351]
Brain Canada-ALS Canada Discovery Grants [2352]
Brain Canada-ALS Canada Hudson Translational Team Grants [2353]
Brain Canada/CQDM "Focus on Brain" Partnership Program [2354]
Brain Canada Foundation **[2349]**
Brain Canada/NeuroDevNet Developmental Neurosciences Research Training Awards [2355]
Brain Canada/RBC Research Partnership in Mental Health Services for Children and Youth Funds [2356]
Pat Brakke Political Science Scholarship [10053]
Byard Braley Scholarship [5462]
George and Mary Brammer Scholarship [3663]
The Helen and Edward Brancati Teacher Development Scholarships [2783]
Brandeis University - Hadassah-Brandeis Institute (HBI) **[2358]**
Brandner Law Firm **[2360]**
Linda Brandt Research Awards [2039]
Erika A. and George E. Brattain Sr. Scholarship Fund [10498]
Farella Braun + Martel LLP 1L Diversity Scholarship Program [3968]
Theodore E.D. Braun Research Travel Fellowships [1287]
Breakthrough to Nursing Scholarships [4268]
Ann Marie Bredefeld Scholarships [7966]
Kenneth H. Breeden Scholarships [5924]
Marion Luna Brem/Pat McNeil Health and Education Scholarships [3089]
William J. Brennan Graduate Assistant Fellowships [7678]
Brent R. Churchill Memorial Scholarships [6191]
Breslauer Family Scholarships [8693]
Hilda E. Bretzlaff Foundation (HEBF) **[2362]**
Hilda E. Bretzlaff Foundation Scholarships [2363]
Rick Brewer Scholarships [10218]
Mary Ann Brichta Scholarships [10317]
James Bridenbaugh Memorial Scholarships [802]
Lloyd Bridges Scholarships [2835]
Tommy Bright Scholarship Fund [4923]
Parsons Brinckerhoff-Jim Lammie Scholarships [1163]
Margaret Brine Graduate Scholarships [2634]
Wade O. Brinker Resident Research Award [10378]

British American Foundation of Texas (BAFTX) **[2364]**
Broadcast Education Association (BEA) **[2369]**
Broadcast Education and Development Program [3134]
Cathy L. Brock Memorial Scholarships [5167]
Margaret Martin Brock Scholarships in Law [7967]
Kae and Kay Brockermeyer Endowed Scholarships [7968]
Louise A. Broderick San Diego County Scholarships [8694]
Dvora Brodie Scholarships [4829]
Louis J. Brody Q.C. Entrance Scholarships [10742]
Ross P. Broesamle Educational Scholarship Fund [5929]
Houston Alumnae Association, Doris Krikham Brokaw Memorial Adelphe Scholarship [5703]
John G. Brokaw Scholarships [7227]
Norm Bromberger Research Bursaries [3469]
Peter F. Bronfman Entrance Awards [10743]
Stephen Bronfman Scholarship Funds in Environmental Studies [5572]
Peter F. Bronfman Scholarships of Merit [10744]
Bronx County Bar Association **[2376]**
The Brookdale Foundation **[2379]**
Brookdale Leadership in Aging Fellowships [2380]
Shirley J. Brooke Endowed Scholarships [7969]
George M. Brooker, CPM Diversity Collegiate Scholarship [5215]
Brookings Doha Center (BDC) **[2381]**
Seth R. and Corrine H. Brooks Memorial Scholarships [2246]
Brooks Scholarships [3894]
Carl E. Brooks Scholarships [9421]
Dorothy B. Brothers Executive Scholarship Program [10656]
William A. and Ann M. Brothers Scholarships [1512]
Henry Broughton, K2AE Memorial Scholarships [1728]
CFSA Randal Brown & Associates Awards [1911]
Selena Danette Brown Book Scholarships [6720]
Brown Dental Scholarships [5521]
Marjorie M. Brown Dissertation Fellowship [5780]
Diana Brown Endowed Scholarships [6018]
Marjorie M. Brown Fellowship Program [5788]
William L. Brown Fellowships [7735]
John Carter Brown Library **[2383]**
John Carter Brown Library Long-Term Fellowships [2384]
John Carter Brown Library Short-Term Fellowships [2385]
Olympia Brown and Max Kapp Awards [9832]
Catherine Amelia Thew Brown Memorial Scholarship Funds [6284]
Milton and Edith Brown Memorial Scholarships [2946]
Quincy Brown Memorial Scholarships [8461]
Ruby A. Brown Memorial Scholarships [3753]
Jesse Brown Memorial Youth Scholarship Program [3632]
JoAhn Brown-Nash Memorial Scholarships [3215]
Ron Brown Scholar Program **[2386]**
Ron Brown Scholars Program [2387]
Bernice and Gordon Brown Scholarships [5573]
D.C. and Virginia Brown Scholarships [3090]
Harry and Lucille Brown Scholarships [4578]
Jack H. Brown Scholarships [2448]
Mary L. Brown Scholarships [5467]
Mary Lou Brown Scholarships [1729]
Charles S. Brown Scholarships in Physics [7140]
Robert K. Brown Scholarships [2278]
VPPPA Stephen Brown Scholarships [10417]
Warren K. Brown Scholarships [1410]
Richard A. Brown Student Scholarships [9691]
Regina Brown Undergraduate Student Fellowships [6879]
Brown University - Pembroke Center for Teaching and Research on Women **[2388]**
Peggy Browning Fund - Chicago School-Year Fellowships [2394]
Peggy Browning Fund **[2393]**
Scott Brownlee Memorial Scholarships [6582]
Hollis Brownstein Research Grants [6011]
Chester H. Bruce Memorial Scholarships [7816]
Sheriff W. Bruce Umpleby Law Enforcement Scholarship Fund [9494]

Robert W. Brunsman Memorial Scholarship [5360]
Katie Brush Memorial Scholarships [3056]
Bernard B. and Mary L. Brusin Scholarships [3705]
William and Clara Bryan Scholarships [3216]
Bryant Essay Scholarships [2396]
Edward C. Bryant Scholarship for an Outstanding Graduate Student in Survey Statistics [1464]
Bryant Surety Bonds, Inc. **[2395]**
Bryant Visual Content Scholarships [2397]
BSA Educational Scholarships [2426]
BSF General Scholarship Awards [2197]
BSF Science and Medicine Research Grants [2199]
Patricia Buchanan Memorial Scholarships [10318]
Lt. General Douglas D. Buchholz Memorial Scholarship [89]
John and Elisabeth Buck Endowed Scholarships [6244]
Peter Buck Fellowships Program - Graduate [9030]
Peter Buck Fellowships Program - Postdoctoral [9031]
Buckfire & Buckfire, P.C. **[2398]**
Buckfire & Buckfire, P.C. Law School Diversity Scholarships [2399]
Buckfire & Buckfire, P.C. Medical Diversity Scholarships [2400]
Buder Scholarships for American Indian Law Students [10474]
Walter and Louise Buell Graduate Scholarships [4142]
Susan Thompson Buffett Foundation Scholarships [2402]
Susan Thompson Buffett Foundation **[2401]**
Gary L. Buffington Memorial Scholarships [5138]
Tien Bui Memorial Scholarships [10573]
Buick Achievers Scholarship Program [4359]
Building Owners and Managers Association of Greater New York (BOMANY) **[2403]**
Pamfil and Maria Bujea Family Orthodox Christian Seminarian Scholarships [1225]
Sam Bull Memorial Scholarships [248]
Bulletin of the Atomic Scientists **[2405]**
William S. Bullinger Scholarships [3983]
Armen H. Bululian Scholarships [1690]
Bunker Family Association (BFA) **[2407]**
Bunnell Scholarships [10012]
Mike Buoncristiano Memorial Scholarship Fund [6287]
William T. Burbage Family Memorial Scholarships [3172]
C. Lalor Burdick Scholarships [6245]
George M. Burditt Scholarships [1965]
Freda Burge Scholarships [7817]
Max M. Burger Endowed Scholarships in Embryology [6246]
Graduate Fellowship Program - Robert M. Burger Fellowships [8832]
Burger King Employee Scholars Program [2410]
Burger King McLamore Foundation **[2409]**
Burger King Scholars Program [2411]
Dorothy and Dick Burgess Scholarships [5499]
Richard J. Burk, Jr. Fellowships [4808]
Loyal D. Burkett Memorial Scholarships [10013]
ACLS Frederick Burkhardt Residential Fellowships [434]
Frederick Burkhardt Residential Fellowships for Recently Tenured Scholars [738]
Ralph Burkhardt Scholarship Fund [10499]
Burndy Canada Inc. Academic Achievement Awards [3823]
Cecil E. Burney Scholarships [3091]
John Burroughs Bogliasco Fellowships [2328]
Burroughs Wellcome Fund **[2412]**
Burroughs Wellcome Fund Collaborative Research Travel Grants (CRTG) [2413]
Burroughs Wellcome Travel Fellowships [9305]
Wes Burton Memorial Scholarships [10574]
Bush Artist Fellowships [2419]
Bush Fellowship Program [2420]
Bush Foundation **[2418]**
Business, Education and Technology Scholarships [334]
Business and Professional Women's Foundation (BPWF) **[2421]**
Business Professionals of America (BPA) **[2423]**
Business Solution Association (BSA) **[2425]**
Lindsay Buster Memorial Scholarships [3277]

Joan Butler Award in Perinatal Intensive Care Nursing [6852]
Walter Byers Postgraduate Scholarships [6861]
Leon C. Bynoe Memorial Scholarships [10280]
byourself Scholarship Fund [3318]
Robert C. Byrd Honors Scholarships [5071]
Dr. F. Ross Byrd Scholarships [10463]
George J. Bysiewicz Scholarship Fund [3198]
C200 Scholar Awards [3156]
CAA National Capital Region Writing Contests [2579]
CAAO Scholarship [3356]
Johnston Cabaniss Scholarships [206]
Cactus and Succulent Society of America (CSSA) **[2427]**
CADE Bursary [2550]
CADE Scholarships [2551]
Cadmus Communications Corporation Graphics Scholarship Endowment Fund [4181]
Edwin Anthony and Adelaide Boudreaux Cadogan Scholarships [8747]
CAG Health and Health Care Study Group Awards [1881]
CAHR Master's Level Scholarships [2557]
Cal State San Marcos Alumna Scholarships [2486]
Cesar A. Calas/FES Miami Chapter Scholarships [4087]
Tese Caldarelli Memorial Scholarships [6723]
Joseph R. Calder, Jr., MD Scholarship Fund [4041]
Dave Caldwell Scholarships [1485]
Caledonia Alumni Association Scholarship Funds [6285]
The Calgary Foundation **[2429]**
Calgary USAEE/IAEE North American Conference Registration Fee Scholarships [9883]
Calhoun Community College **[2431]**
Calhoun County Auburn University Scholarships [3260]
Calhoun Valedictorian, Salutatorian/Top 5 Scholarships [2432]
California Association of Family and Consumer Sciences - San Diego Chapter Scholarships (CAFCS) [8695]
California Association for Health, Physical Education, Recreation, and Dance (CAHPERD) **[2433]**
California Association of Pest Control Advisers (CAPCA) **[2437]**
California Association of Private Postsecondary Schools (CAPPS) **[2439]**
California Bar Foundation 1L Diversity Scholarships [2442]
California Bar Foundation 3L Diversity Scholarships [2443]
California Bar Foundation **[2441]**
California Council of the Blind Scholarships [8751]
California Grocers Association (CGA) **[2445]**
California Groundwater Association (CGA) **[2461]**
California Groundwater Association Scholarships [2462]
California-Hawaii Elks Association (CHEA) **[2463]**
California Landscape Contractors Association (CLCA) **[2466]**
California Police Youth Charities (CPYC) **[2468]**
California Psychological Association (CPA) **[2470]**
California School Library Association (CSLA) **[2472]**
California Scottish Rite Foundation **[2476]**
California Scottish Rite Foundation Scholarships [2477]
California Sea Grant **[2478]**
California Sea Grant State Fellowship [2479]
California Society of Radiologic Technologists (CSRT) **[2480]**
California State University San Marcos Alumni Association (CSUSM) **[2485]**
California Waterfowl Association (CWA) **[2487]**
Calihan Academic Fellowships [56]
Calihan Travel Grants [57]
Calista Corp. **[2489]**
Calista Education and Culture Scholarships [2490]
CALL/ACBD Education Reserve Fund Grants [2561]
CALL/ACBD Research Grants [2562]
Harry D. Callahan Educational Trust [9495]
Captain Jodi Callahan Memorial Scholarships [122]
W.L. Calvert Memorial Scholarships [4966]
Calvin Alumni Association **[2491]**

Calvin Alumni Association British Columbia Scholarships [2492]
Calvin Alumni Association California- Bay Area Scholarships [2493]
Calvin Alumni Association Florida-Gulf Coast Scholarships [2494]
Calvin Alumni Association-Illinois Scholarships [2495]
Calvin Alumni Association-Michigan Lakeshore Scholarships [2496]
Calvin Alumni Association-Michigan, Lansing Scholarships [2497]
Calvin Alumni Association-New Jersey Scholarships [2498]
Calvin Alumni Association-South Florida Scholarships [2499]
Calvin Alumni Association-Southeast Michigan Scholarships [2500]
Calvin Alumni Association-Southeastern Wisconsin Scholarships [2501]
Calvin Alumni Association Southern California Chapter Scholarships [2502]
Calvin Alumni Association-Southwest Michigan, Kalamazoo Scholarships [2503]
Calvin Alumni Association-Washington, D.C. Scholarships [2504]
Calvin Alumni Association-Washington, Lynden Scholarships [2505]
Camden County Bar Association (CCBA) **[2506]**
Camden County College **[2521]**
Camden County College Foundation Scholarships [2522]
Cameco Corp. **[2523]**
Cameco Corporation Scholarships in the Geological Sciences - Continuing Students [2524]
Cameco Corporation Scholarships in the Geological Sciences - Entering Students [2525]
Stuart Cameron and Margaret McLeod Memorial Scholarships (SCMS) [5205]
Wesley C. Cameron Scholarships [7228]
Camille and Henry Dreyfus Foundation - Senior Scientist Mentor Program [3695]
Dalton Camp Awards [4305]
Camp Network **[2527]**
Camp Network Counselor Appreciation Scholarships [2528]
Thomas R. Camp Scholarships [1486]
Lucille Campbell Scholarship Fund [10500]
Robert G. Campbell Scholarships [8462]
Theodore R. Campbell Scholarships [268]
Brian Campion Scholarship Scholarships [10781]
Campus Compact **[2529]**
Campus Discovery **[2531]**
Campus Discovery Scholarships [2532]
CampusDiscovery.com **[2533]**
Canada-Ukraine Parliamentary Program Internship Scholarships (CUPP) [10441]
Canadian Aeronautics and Space Institute (CASI) **[2535]**
Canadian Anesthesiologists' Society (CAS) **[2537]**
Canadian Anesthesiologists' Society Research Awards [2539]
Canadian Association of Black Lawyers (CABL) **[2543]**
Canadian Association for Business Economics (CABE) **[2545]**
Canadian Association of Cardiac Rehabilitation (CACR) **[2547]**
Canadian Association of Cardiac Rehabilitation Graduate Scholarship Awards [2548]
Canadian Association of Drilling Engineers (CADE) **[2549]**
Canadian Association of Geographers Historical Geography Study Group Awards [1882]
Canadian Association on Gerontology **[2552]**
Canadian Association for HIV Research (CAHR) **[2556]**
Canadian Association of Insolvency and Restructuring Professionals (CAIRP) **[2558]**
Canadian Association of Law Libraries (CALL) **[2560]**
Canadian Association of Law Teachers (CALT) **[2565]**
Canadian Association of Law Teachers Award for Academic Excellence [2566]
Canadian Association for Neuroscience **[2567]**

Canadian Association of Oilwell Drilling Contractors (CAODC) **[2569]**
Canadian Association for the Practical Study of Law in Education (CAPSLE) **[2572]**
Canadian Association for the Practical Study of Law in Education Fellowships [2573]
Canadian Association for Studies in Co-operation (CASC) **[2574]**
Canadian Association for Studies in Co-operation Scholarships Lemaire Co-operative Studies Awards (CASC) [2611]
Canadian Authors Association-Ottawa Branch **[2578]**
The Canadian Bar Association (CBA) **[2580]**
Canadian Blood Services **[2582]**
Canadian Blood Services Graduate Fellowship [2583]
Canadian Blood Services Postdoctoral Fellowship [2584]
Canadian Breast Cancer Foundation - BC/Yukon **[2585]**
Canadian Breast Cancer Foundation - Ontario **[2591]**
Canadian Breast Cancer Foundation - Prairies/NWT Region **[2596]**
Canadian Bureau for International Education (CBIE) **[2602]**
Canadian Cancer Society Research Institute (CCSRI) **[2604]**
Canadian Cancer Society Travel Awards [2605]
Canadian Cartographic Association (CCA) **[2606]**
Canadian Centre for Occupational Health and Safety (CCOHS) **[2608]**
Canadian Co-operative Association (CCA) **[2610]**
Canadian Communication Association (CCA) **[2614]**
Canadian Consumer Specialty Products Association (CCSPA) **[2617]**
Canadian Council of Technicians and Technologists Scholarships for Technology Students [3392]
The Canadian Derivatives Exchange Scholars Program [2345]
Canadian Energy Law Foundation **[2619]**
Canadian Energy Law Foundation Graduate Scholarships in Law [2620]
Canadian Engineering Memorial Foundation **[2621]**
Canadian Evaluation Society Educational Fund Scholarships [4125]
Canadian Federation of Independent Grocers National Scholarships [4003]
Canadian Federation for Sexual Health (CFSH) **[2626]**
Canadian Federation of University Women (CFUW) **[2628]**
Canadian Federation of University Women, Edmonton Branch **[2633]**
Canadian Federation of University Women Etobicoke Bursary [10281]
Canadian Fertility and Andrology Society (CFAS) **[2635]**
Canadian Frailty Network **[2637]**
Canadian Friends of the Hebrew University of Jerusalem (CFHU) **[2639]**
Canadian Gerontological Nursing Association (CGNA) **[2644]**
Canadian Group Psychotherapy Association **[2647]**
Canadian Hard of Hearing Association (CHHA) **[2650]**
Canadian Hard of Hearing Association Scholarship Programs [2651]
Canadian Hemophilia Society (CHS) **[2652]**
Canadian Home Economics Association Fellowships [2629]
Canadian Hospitality Foundation (CHF) **[2656]**
Canadian Hospitality Foundation College Entrance Scholarships [2658]
Canadian Hospitality Foundation University Entrance Scholarships [2659]
Canadian Hydrographic Association (CHA) **[2661]**
Canadian Hydrographic Association Student Awards [2662]
Canadian Identification Society (CIS) **[2663]**
Canadian Identification Society Essay/Scholarship Awards [2664]
Canadian Institute for the Administration of Justice (CIAJ) **[2667]**

CANADIAN

Canadian Institute for Advanced Legal Studies French Language Scholarships [5149]
Canadian Institute for Advanced Research (CIFAR) **[2669]**
Canadian Institute of Planners (CIP) **[2671]**
Canadian Institute of Ukrainian Studies (CIUS) **[2673]**
Canadian Iranian Foundation (CIF) **[2676]**
Canadian Iranian Foundation Scholarships [2677]
Canadian IT Law Association Student Writing Contest [2020]
Canadian Japanese-Mennonite Scholarships [6416]
Canadian Library Association (CLA) **[2678]**
Canadian Meteorological and Oceanographic Society (CMOS) **[2681]**
Canadian National Institute for the Blind (CNIB) **[2687]**
Canadian National Railway Co. **[2691]**
Canadian Nurses Foundation (CNF) **[2693]**
Canadian Nurses Foundation Northern Award [2697]
Canadian Nurses Foundation Scholarships [2698]
Canadian Occupational Therapy Foundation (COTF) **[2716]**
Canadian Occupational Therapy Foundation Graduate Scholarships [2717]
Canadian Occupational Therapy Foundation Invacare Master's Scholarships [2718]
Canadian Office Products Association (COPA) **[2721]**
Canadian Pain Society (CPS) **[2723]**
Canadian Pain Society Post-Doctoral Fellowship Awards [2724]
Canadian Parking Association Scholarships [1921]
Canadian Picture Pioneers (CPP) **[2733]**
Canadian Picture Pioneers Scholarships [2734]
Canadian Polar Commission Scholarships [1933]
Canadian Poultry Research Council **[2735]**
Canadian Poultry Research Council Postgraduate Scholarships [2736]
Canadian Sanitation Supply Association (CSSA) **[2737]**
Canadian Sanitation Supply Association Scholarships [2738]
Canadian Seniors' Golf Association Scholarships [4477]
Canadian Simmental Association (CSA) **[2741]**
Canadian Society of Biblical Studies (CSBS) **[2743]**
Canadian Society of Club Managers (CSCM) **[2745]**
Canadian Society of Exploration Geophysicists (CSEG) **[2747]**
Canadian Society for Medical Laboratory Science (CSMLS) **[2749]**
Canadian Society for Otolaryngology - Head and Neck Surgery (CSOHNS) **[2751]**
Canadian Society of Petroleum Geologists (CSPG) **[2753]**
Canadian Society for the Study of Education Mentorship Awards [9067]
Canadian Society for the Study of Education New Scholar Fellowships (CSSE) [9068]
Canadian Society for the Study of Higher Education (CSSHE) **[2755]**
Canadian Student Leadership Association (CSLA) **[2758]**
Canadian Studies Postdoctoral Fellowships [3398]
Canadian Technical Asphalt Association (CTAA) **[2761]**
Canadian Technical Asphalt Association Scholarships [2762]
Canadian Transportation Research Forum (CTRF) **[2763]**
Canadian Water Resources Association Scholarships [1905]
Canadian Water and Wastewater Association (CWWA) **[2765]**
Canadians for Access to Professional Education **[2767]**
Cancer for College (CFC) **[2769]**
Cancer for College Scholarships [2770]
Cancer Research Institute (CRI) **[2771]**
Cancer Research Society (CRS) **[2776]**
Cancer Survivors' Fund **[2778]**
Cancer Survivors' Fund Scholarships [2779]
C&F Abogados **[2780]**

CANFIT Nutrition, Physical Education and Culinary Arts Scholarships [3167]
Annie J. Cannon Award in Astronomy [613]
Therese A. Cannon Educational Scholarships [5372]
Agustin C. Cano Memorial Scholarships [8334]
CANS/SNRS Dissertation Research Grants [9405]
Commander Ronald J. Cantin Scholarships [3075]
CAODC Occupational Health and Safety Scholarships [2570]
CAODC Scholarship Program [2571]
John Caoile Memorial Scholarships [8335]
CAPAL Public Service Scholarships [3341]
Cape Coral Community Foundation (CCCF) **[2782]**
Cape Fear Community College Foundation **[2785]**
Cape Fear Community College Merit Scholarships [2786]
CAPE Scholarships [2768]
Capital City AIDS Fund (CCAF) **[2787]**
Rhea Sourifman Caplin Memorial Scholarships [4742]
Kasie Ford Capling Memorial Scholarship Endowment Fund [4182]
Lester J. Cappon Fellowships in Documentary Editing [7410]
Cardiac Health Foundation of Canada **[2789]**
Cardiac Health Foundation of Canada Scholarships [2790]
Daniel Cardillo Charitable Fund [6192]
Thelma Cardwell Scholarships [2719]
Career Awards for Medical Scientists (CAMS) [2414]
Career Awards for Science and Mathematics Teachers [2415]
Career Awards at the Scientific Interface (CASI) [2416]
Career Development Scholarships [4129]
Career Mobility Scholarships [4269]
Career Transition For Dancers (CTFD) **[2792]**
CareerFitter Scholarships [2795]
CareerFitter.com **[2794]**
CareFusion Fellowships for Neonatal and Pediatric Therapists [1209]
Beth Carew Memorial Scholarships [6986]
John Carew Memorial Scholarships [803]
John L. Carey Scholarship Awards [901]
Caribbean Actuarial Scholarship [61]
Caribbean Hotel and Tourism Association Academic Scholarships [2797]
Caribbean Hotel and Tourism Association (CHTA) **[2796]**
William F. Carl Scholarships [7470]
AABA Read Carlock Memorial Scholarship Fund [1625]
Glen and Babs Carlson Endowed Scholarships [6019]
Lyle Carlson Wildlife Management Scholarships [10014]
Dan Carman Attorney at Law Criminal Defense Scholarships [3520]
Carmangay Home and School Association Scholarships [269]
Walta Wilkinson Carmichael Scholarships [8913]
Carnegie Institution for Science **[2798]**
Carnegie Observatories Graduate Research Fellowships [2799]
Herb Carnegie Scholarships [2279]
Julian E. Carnes Scholarship Fund [4183]
CARO-ELEKTA Research Fellowship Program [1900]
Carolinas-Virginias Retail Hardware Scholarships [4184]
Carollo Engineers Scholarships [1487]
Jeffrey Carollo Music Scholarships [7323]
Pete Carpenter Fellowship [2318]
Carpenters' Company of the City and County of Philadelphia **[2800]**
Carpenters' Company Scholarships [2801]
Walter and Elsie Carr Endowed Scholarships [6020]
Willis H. Carrier Scholarships [1329]
Eugene Carroll Scholarships [2947]
Karen D. Carsel Memorial Scholarships [819]
Robert C. Carson Memorial Bursary [270]
Rachel Carson Prize [1310]
Gene Carte Student Paper Competition Awards [1281]
Deloris Carter Hampton Scholarships [8247]
Leigh Carter Scholarships [3217]

Letitia B. Carter Scholarships [8563]
Orin Carver Scholarships [3312]
CAS/GE Healthcare Canada Inc. Research Awards [2540]
CAS Trust Scholarship [2809]
CAS/Vitaid-LMA Residents' Research Grant Competition [2541]
CASBS Fellowships [2841]
Cascade Blues Association (CBA) **[2802]**
Cascara Vacation Rentals **[2804]**
Cascara Vacation Rentals Hospitality Matters Scholarships [2805]
Casey Family Services Alumni Scholarships [4157]
TCDA Jim and Glenda Casey Professional Scholarships [669]
Elton Casey Scholarships [10219]
Local 827 Peter J. Casey Scholarships [5288]
Fraser Milner Casgrain LLP Scholarships [2280]
Fraser Milner Casgrain Scholarships [2182]
George H. and Anna Casper Fund [9496]
Orrie and Dorothy Cassada Scholarships [4579]
Rose Cassin Memorial Scholarships [7631]
Fundación Educativa Carlos M. Castañeda (FECMC) **[2806]**
Carlos M. Castaneda Journalism Scholarships [2807]
The Kerri Castellini Women's Leadership Scholarships [8229]
Casualty Actuarial Society (CAS) **[2808]**
Catholic Aid Association's Post-High School Tuition Scholarships [2818]
Catholic Biblical Association of America (CBA) **[2811]**
Catholic Biblical Association of America Scholarships [2812]
Catholic Library Association (CLA) **[2813]**
Catholic Relief Services (CRS) **[2815]**
Catholic Relief Services Summer Internships [2816]
Catholic United Financial **[2817]**
Robert A. Catlin/David W. Long Memorial Fellowships [1104]
Catzman Awards for Professionalism and Civility [80]
Cave Conservancy Foundation **[2819]**
Cave Conservancy Foundation Graduate and Undergraduate Fellowships [2823]
Cave Conservancy of the Virginias (CCV) **[2822]**
Christine Kerr Cawthorne Scholarships [8914]
Llewellyn L. Cayvan String Instrument Scholarships [4580]
CBC Spouses Education Scholarship Fund [3345]
CBC Spouses Heineken USA Performing Arts Scholarships [3346]
CBC Spouses Visual Arts Scholarships [3347]
CBCF - BC/Yukon Region Breast Cancer Research Grants Competition [2587]
CBCF - BC/Yukon Region Breast Cancer Survivor Dragon Boat Grants [2588]
CBCF - BC/Yukon Region Community Health Grants [2589]
CBCF - BC/Yukon Region Small Initiative Funds [2590]
CBCF Congressional Fellows Program [3348]
CBCF - Ontario Nurse and Allied Health Professional Fellowships [2592]
CBCF - Ontario Physician Fellowships [2593]
CBCF - Ontario Research Fellowships [2594]
CBCF - Ontario Research Project Grants [2595]
CBCF - Prairies/NWT Grants in Basic Biomedical Research [2597]
CBCF - Prairies/NWT Grants in Clinical Research [2598]
CBCF - Prairies/NWT Grants in Health Services and Policy Research [2599]
CBCF - Prairies/NWT Postdoctoral Fellowships [2600]
CBCF - Prairies/NWT Research Grants in Psychosocial, Cultural and Environmental Determinants of Health [2601]
CC Times Scholarships [2921]
CCF Academic Fellowships in Karst Studies - Graduate [2820]
CCF Academic Fellowships in Karst Studies - Undegraduate [2821]
CCF Career Development Award [3371]
CCF Improving Cancer Care Grants [3372]

CCF Merit Award [3373]
CCFA Career Development Awards [3476]
CCFA Research Fellowship Awards [3477]
CCFA Student Research Fellowship Awards [3478]
CCFF Clinical Fellowships [4013]
CCFF Fellowships [4014]
CCFF Scholarships [4015]
C.C.H.R.M.A. Scholarships [3092]
CCLA Summer Legal Internships [1892]
CCNMA: Latino Journalists of California **[2824]**
CCSD School Counselors' Scholarships [8336]
CCU Alumni Endowed Scholarships [3136]
CCWH/Berkshire Conference of Women Historians Graduate Student Fellowships [3418]
CDA Foundation **[2827]**
CDA Foundation Allied Dental Student Scholarships [2828]
CDA Foundation Dental Student Scholarships [2829]
CDC Foundation **[2832]**
CDC Presidential Management Fellows Program [9917]
CDC Preventive Medicine Residency and Fellowships [9918]
CDC Public Health Informatics Fellowships [9919]
L.B. Cebik, W4RNL, and Jean Cebik, N4TZP, Memorial Scholarships [1730]
Betty J. Cecere Memorial Scholarship Endowment Fund [10501]
CEDAM International **[2834]**
Cedarcrest Farms Scholarships [944]
CEJIL Communications Internships [2860]
CEJIL Legal Internships [2861]
Celler Legal, P.A. **[2836]**
Celler Legal P.A. Employment Skills Scholarship Program [2837]
CEMF Undergraduate Engineering Scholarships [2622]
Cengage Learning Inc. **[2838]**
Cengage Learning Scholarships Program [2839]
Cengage Travel Award for Teachers of Reading at a Community College [3123]
DAR Centennial Scholarship [7150]
Center for Advanced Study in the Behavioral Sciences (CASBS) **[2840]**
Center for Book Arts (CBA) **[2842]**
Center for Craft, Creativity and Design (CCCD) **[2844]**
Center for the Education of Women Scholarships [10195]
Center for the Education of Women Student Research Grants [10196]
Center for Engineering in Medicine Predoctoral Fellows Program [6316]
Center for Global Initiatives **[2846]**
Center for International Environmental Law (CIEL) **[2848]**
Center for Jewish History (CJH) **[2850]**
The Center for Justice & Accountability **[2857]**
Center for Justice and International Law **[2859]**
Center for Lesbian and Gay Studies Fellowships [2863]
Center for LGBTQ Studies (CLAGS) **[2862]**
Center for Plant Conservation (CPC) **[2866]**
Centerville-Abington Dollars for Scholars [10502]
Central Arizona DX Association Scholarships [1731]
Central Florida Jazz Society (CFJS) **[2868]**
Central Florida Jazz Society Scholarships [2869]
Central Ohio Diabetes Association (CODA) **[2870]**
Central Texas Bluegrass Association (CTBA) **[2872]**
CentraState Associated Auxiliaries Scholarships [2875]
CentraState Band Aid Open Committee Scholarships [2876]
CentraState Healthcare Foundation **[2874]**
CentraState Healthcare Foundation Health Professions Scholarships [2877]
Centre for International Sustainable Development Law (CISDL) **[2879]**
Centre pour l'Innovation dans la Gouvernance Internationale **[2883]**
Centre de Recherches pour le Développement International (CRDI) **[2885]**
CERT College Scholarships [3435]
Certified Municipal Clerk Scholarships (CMC) [5350]
Certified Neuroscience Registered Nurse Recertification Grant Program [545]
Cerutti Group Scholarships [4646]
Arthur and Gladys Cervenka Scholarships [9168]
CES Conference Travel Grants [3437]
CES First Article Prize [3438]
CES Pre-Dissertation Research Fellowships [3439]
CF Abogados Legal Scholarships [2781]
CfA Postdoctoral Fellowships [4780]
CFN Interdisciplinary Fellowships Program [2638]
CFNIL Community Foundation Scholarships [3278]
CFNIL Senior Memorial Scholarships [3279]
CFR Military Fellowships [3442]
CFR National Intelligence Fellowships [3443]
CFR Stanton Nuclear Security Fellowships [3444]
CFR Volunteer Internships [3445]
CFSA Aon Fire Protection Engineering Award [1912]
CFSA City of Markham, Buildings Standards Department Award [1913]
CFSA Fire Safety Awards [1914]
CFSA Leber Rubes Inc. Awards [1915]
CFSA LRI Engineering Award [1916]
CFSA Nadine International Inc. Awards [1917]
CFSA Siemens Canada Award [1918]
CFSA Underwriters' Laboratories of Canada Awards [1919]
CFT/ACPSOP Scholarships [2948]
CGNA Memorial Scholarship [2646]
CGPF Endowments Conference Scholarships [2648]
CH2M Hill/AEESP Outstanding Doctoral Dissertation Award [1951]
Rick Chace Foundation Scholarships [2024]
Chaîne des Rôtisseurs Scholarships [758]
ChairScholars Florida Scholarship Program [2888]
ChairScholars Foundation **[2887]**
ChairScholars National Scholarship Program [2889]
Jeanne S. Chall Research Fellowship [5355]
Challenge Met Scholarships [1732]
Mariam K. Chamberlain Fellowships in Women and Public Policy [5228]
Logan S. Chambers Individual Scholarships [5283]
Mary Anne Chambers Scholarships [5522]
Chambersburg/Fannett-Metal School District Scholarship Fund [4234]
Chambliss Astronomy Achievement Student Awards [614]
Bryan A. Champion Memorial Scholarship [7582]
Emi Chance for Aspiring Artists Scholarship [10054]
Jason Chaney Memorial Scholarship Fund [10503]
Channabasappa Memorial Scholarships [5319]
Harry H. and Floy B. Chapin Scholarships [3280]
Nancy J. Chapman Scholarships [1939]
S. Penny Chappell Scholarships [8085]
Chapter 1 - Detroit Founding Chapter Undergraduate Scholarships [9169]
Chapter 6 Fairfield County Scholarships [9177]
Chapter 17 - St. Louis Scholarships [9170]
Chapter 23 - Quad Cities Iowa/Illinois Scholarships [9172]
Chapter 31 - Peoria Endowed Scholarships [9173]
Chapter 52 - Wichita Scholarships [9175]
Chapter 56 - Fort Wayne Scholarships [9176]
Chapter 67 - Phoenix Scholarships [9178]
Chapter 93 - Albuquerque Scholarships [9179]
Chapter 198 - Downriver Detroit Scholarships [9171]
Chapter 311 - Tri City Scholarships [9174]
Charles A. Lindbergh Fellowships [9021]
Charles H. Bussmann Graduate Scholarship [6271]
Charlotte Housing Authority Scholarship Fund (CHASF) [4185]
Charlotte-Mecklenburg Schools Scholarship Incentive Program [4186]
Emilie Du Chatelet Awards [1288]
CCWH Nupur Chaudhuri First Article Prizes [3419]
Chautauqua Scholarships Program [5367]
Cesar E. Chavez Scholarships [8463]
CHCI Graduate Fellowships [3352]
CHCI Public Policy Fellowships [3353]
CHCI Scholarships [3354]
CHEA Undergraduate Scholarship Program for Students with Disabilities [2464]
CHEA Vocational Grants [2465]
Cheatham County Community Foundation Scholarships [3218]
Chechahko Consumers Co-Op Ltd. Scholarships [10782]
Cheerful Giver Scholarships [8696]
Chemical Heritage Foundation (CHF) **[2890]**
Chemical Heritage Foundation Travel Grants (CHF) [2891]
Hadar Chemtob Memorial Scholarships [5574]
Bernard Chernos Essay Competition [1893]
Cherokee Nation **[2892]**
Cherokee Nation Graduate Scholarships [2893]
Cherokee Nation Pell Scholarships [2894]
Cherokee Nation Scholarships [2895]
Sgt. Cherven Scholarship [6312]
Shirley Cheshire Memorial Scholarship Awards [6853]
Chevalier Award Scholarship [2618]
Cheyenne High School Desert Shields Scholarship [8337]
Melba Dawn Chiarenza Scholarship Fund [10504]
Chicago Bar Foundation (CBF) **[2896]**
Chicago FM Club Scholarships [1733]
Chicago Railroad Mechanical Association (CRMA) **[2898]**
Chicana/Latina Foundation (CLF) **[2900]**
Chicana Latina Scholarship Fund [2901]
Kevin Child Scholarships [6987]
Childbirth Educator Program Scholarships [5909]
John and Ruth Childe Scholarships [9422]
Childhood Cancer Canada Foundation **[2902]**
Childhood Cancer Survivor Scholarships [2903]
Children of Evangeline Section Scholarships [9249]
Children of Unitarian Universalist Ministers College Scholarships [9833]
Children's Hospital of Philadelphia **[2905]**
Children's Literature Association (ChLA) **[2908]**
Children's Scholarship Fund of Charlotte [4187]
The Children's Tumor Foundation (CTF) **[2910]**
A Child's Hope International **[2912]**
Jane Coffin Childs Memorial Fund - Medical Research Fellowships [2915]
Jane Coffin Childs Memorial Fund for Medical Research [2914]
Charline Chilson Scholarships [3580]
China Google PhD Fellowships [4494]
Chinese American Medical Society (CAMS) **[2916]**
Chinese American Medical Society Summer Research Fellowships Program [2917]
Chinese Professionals Association of Canada (CPAC) **[2920]**
Chinese Professionals Association of Canada BMO Diversity Scholarships [2922]
Chinese Professionals Association of Canada Education Foundation Awards [2923]
Chinese Professionals Association of Canada Journalism Scholarships [2924]
Chinese Professionals Association of Canada Professional Achievement Awards [2925]
Helen Krich Chinoy Dissertation Research Fellowships [1434]
CHOIR MD Post-Residency Fellowship in Health Services Research [10376]
Choose Your Future Scholarships [3219]
Chopin Foundation of the United States **[2927]**
Chopin Foundation of the United States Scholarships [2928]
Chopivsky Fellowships [10442]
CHOPR Postdoctoral Fellowships [10267]
Choristers Guild (CG) **[2929]**
Chrétien International Research Grants [615]
CHRGJ Emerging Human Rights Scholarship Conference [7398]
CHRGJ International Human Rights Fellowships [7399]
CHRGJ Students Human Rights Scholars Program [7400]
Betty Sams Christian Fellowships [10396]
Frances N. Christian Memorial Endowment Nursing Scholarship [9583]
Almeric Christian Memorial Scholarships [10392]
Christian Missionary Scholarship Foundation (CMSF) **[2931]**
Christian Pharmacists Fellowship International [2934]
Christian Pharmacists Fellowship International (CPFI) **[2933]**
Christian Scholarship Foundation (CSF) **[2935]**
Irene R. Christman Scholarship [7939]
Christmas Tree Chapter Scholarship Awards [7692]

Commander Daniel J. Christovich Scholarship Fund [3076]
Chronic Lymphocytic Leukemia Collaborative Grants [6157]
Chronic Pain Medicine Research Grants [1403]
Chrysalis Scholarships [2094]
Chrysler Technical Scholarship Fund [3545]
CHS - Bursary Program Scholarships [2653]
CHS - Mature Student Bursary Program Scholarships [2654]
CHS Scholarships [2655]
Church Hill Classics Ltd. **[2937]**
Winston Churchill Foundation of the United States (WCFUS) **[2939]**
The Churchill Scholarships [2940]
CIA Undergraduate Scholarships [1969]
CIBC Medical Education Scholarships [7278]
CIBC Scholarships [2281]
CIFAR Global Scholars Program [2670]
CIGNA Healthcare Graduate Scholarships [6957]
CIGNA Healthcare Undergraduate Scholarships [6958]
CIHR Health Law, Ethics and Policy Fellowships [2942]
CIHR Training Program in Health Law and Policy **[2941]**
Cincinnati High School Scholarships [2949]
Cincinnati Scholarship Foundation (CSF) **[2943]**
Cinestory Fellowship [3029]
Cinestory Foundation **[3028]**
Cintas Foundation **[3030]**
Cintas Foundation Fellowships in Architecture [3031]
Cintas Foundation Fellowships in Visual Arts [3032]
CIP Fellow's Travel Scholarships [2672]
Circuits & Systems Inc. **[3034]**
Antonio Cirino Memorial Art Education Fellowships [8603]
CISDL Global Research Fellowship - Associate Fellows [2880]
CISDL Global Research Fellowship - Legal Research Fellows [2881]
CISDL Global Research Fellowships - Senior Research Fellows [2882]
Citi Foundation Scholarship Program [866]
Citi/TELACU Scholars Mentoring Program [9659]
City Bar Diversity Fellowships Program [7343]
City of Sanibel Employee Dependent Scholarships [9423]
City of Toronto Graduate Scholarships for Women in Mathematics [10282]
City of Toronto Queen Elizabeth II Sesquicentennial Scholarships in Community Health Nursing for Graduates [10283]
City of Toronto Queen Elizabeth II Sesquicentennial Scholarships in Community Health Nursing for Undergraduates [10284]
City of Toronto Scholarships for Aboriginal Students [10285]
City of Toronto Women's Studies Scholarships [10286]
Civic Music Association of Milwaukee **[3036]**
Civil Air Patrol (CAP) **[3038]**
Civil Air Patrol Flight Scholarships [3039]
Civitan International (CI) **[3040]**
Civitan Shropshire Scholarships [3041]
CJA Legal Internships [2858]
CJF Canadian Journalism Fellowships [4117]
CJH Graduate Research Fellowships [2851]
CJH Visiting Scholars Program [2852]
CLA/ACB Dafoe Scholarships [2679]
CLA-ACE Internship Program [6013]
CLA/CP Scholarship [8672]
Clackamas Chapter Scholarship Awards [7693]
Clackamas County Farm Bureau Scholarships [7705]
Claes Nobel Academic Scholarships for Members [7159]
Clan Ross America **[3042]**
Clan Ross Foundation Scholarships [3043]
Cecil Earl Clapp, Sr. Memorial Scholarship [7531]
Claremont McKenna College - Henry Kravis Leadership Institute **[3044]**
David and Deborah Clark Fellowships [7736]
Michele Clark Fellowships [8403]
Vickie Clark-Flaherty Scholarships [7471]

Willis W. and Ethel M. Clark Foundation Fellowships [3049]
Willis W. and Ethel M. Clark Foundation **[3048]**
Clark High School Academy of Finance Scholarships [8338]
Howard A. Clark Horticulture Scholarships [3220]
Robert A. Clark Memorial Educational Scholarships [7166]
Thomas Arkle Clark Scholar-Leader of the Year Endowed Scholarships [8061]
Athalie Clarke Endowed Scholarships [7970]
Lucy and Charles W.E. Clarke Scholarships [1797]
IADR John Clarkson Fellowship [5250]
Classic Wines of California Scholarships [2449]
Clay Maitland CGF Scholarship [3077]
Clay Postdoctoral Fellowships [4781]
Aim High Jerry Clay Scholarships [4581]
CLCA Landscape Educational Advancement Foundation Educational Grant Program [2467]
Brian Dane Cleary Memorial Scholarships [7971]
Lula Faye Clegg Memorial Scholarship Fund [4188]
Bruce Clement Post-Secondary Education Scholarships [7311]
Tyler Clementi Point Scholarship [8171]
Greg Clerk Awards [4118]
Cleveland Executive Fellowships (CEF) [3051]
Cleveland Leadership Center **[3050]**
Geraldine Clewell Fellowships - Doctoral Student [8086]
Geraldine Clewell Fellowships - Masteral [8087]
Geraldine Clewell Scholarships - Undergraduate [8088]
Justice Robert L. Clifford Fellowships [6593]
James L. Clifford Prize [1289]
David H. Clift Scholarships [961]
Bryan Cline Memorial Soccer Scholarship Program [301]
Clinic for the Rehabilitation of Wildlife (CROW) **[3052]**
Clinical Nurse Specialist Foundation **[3054]**
Clinical Project Funding for Advanced Practice Oncology Nurses [7616]
Clinical Research Fellowship for Medical Students [3699]
Clinician Scientist Development Awards [7883]
Edward Rollin Clinton Memorial for Music [10055]
George H. Clinton Scholarship Fund [7818]
Paul W. Clopper Scholarship Grant for Junior Dental Students [5068]
Closs/Parnitzke/Clarke Scholarships [8089]
The Club Foundation Faculty Research Grants [3060]
Club Managers Association of America (CMAA) **[3059]**
The Club at Morningside Scholarships [8697]
Clubs of America **[3064]**
The Clubs of America Scholarships Award for Career Success [3065]
CMA Private Lesson Program: Instrumental Scholarships for Elementary and Middle School Students [3037]
CMAA Student Conference Travel Grants [3061]
CMC-KLI Leadership Research Fellowship [3045]
CMC-KLI Social Sector Internship Program [3046]
CMC-KLI Social Sector Research Fellowship [3047]
CME Beef Industry Scholarships [6841]
CMH Dissertation Fellowships [9876]
CMOS-SCMO President's Prize [2682]
CMSF Scholarships [2932]
CN Scholarships for Women [2692]
CNA Foundation Scholarships [1411]
CNIB Master's Scholarships [2688]
CNS-UCSB Graduate Fellowships for Science and Engineering [10127]
CNST Scholarships [1934]
COACH: Canada's Health Informatics Association **[3066]**
Coaching Association of Canada (CAC) **[3068]**
Coalition of Higher Education Assistance Organizations (COHEAO) **[3070]**
Coalition for Networked Information (CNI) **[3072]**
Coast Guard Foundation **[3074]**
Coast Guard Foundation Enlisted Education Grants [3078]
Coastal Bend Community Foundation (CBCF) **[3083]**

The Helena B. Cobb Annual Scholarships [10665]
The Helena B. Cobb Four-Year Higher Education Grants [10666]
J.C. and Rheba Cobb Memorial Scholarships [6867]
Gordon W. and Agnes P. Cobb Scholarships [3754]
John Coburn and Harold Winters Student Award in Plasma Science and Technology [2154]
Coca-Cola First Generation Scholarships [867]
Coca-Cola Scholars Foundation **[3114]**
Coca-Cola Scholars Program Scholarships [3115]
Geri Coccodrilli Culinary Scholarship Fund [4511]
Cocke, Szpanka and Taylor Scholarships [10404]
The April Cockerham DREAM Act Scholarships [8230]
Evelyn L. Cockrell Memorial Scholarship Award [9701]
Frank M. Coda Scholarships [1330]
CODY Foundation Fund [4235]
Coeur d'Alene Alumni Scholarships [6021]
Steven L. Coffey Memorial Scholarships [3755]
Thomas D. Coffield Scholarships [4582]
Claude T. Coffman Memorial Scholarships [10157]
Donald O. Coffman Scholarships [8248]
Ruth M. Cogan Scholarship Fund [9497]
COHEAO Scholarships [3071]
Marshall A. Cohen Entrance Awards [10745]
American Academy of Periodontology Dr. D. Walter Cohen Teaching Fellowships [421]
Ardis Cohoon Scholarships [10220]
Anna C. and Oliver C. Colburn Fellowships [1606]
Warren E. "Whitey" Cole American Society of Highway Engineers Scholarships [4042]
Cole Family Scholarships [8249]
Cole Foundation Undergraduate Scholarship Program [4189]
Arthur H. Cole Grants in Aid [3779]
Paul Cole Scholarships [9221]
Sally Cole Visual Arts Scholarship Fund [4190]
Dennis Coleman Choral Conducting Scholarships [8250]
Dennis Coleman Memorial Scholarships [8251]
The Coleopterists Society (CS) **[3116]**
Coleopterists Society - Youth Incentive Award [3117]
Colgate-Palmolive/HDA Foundation Scholarships [4892]
College Art Association (CAA) **[3118]**
College Art Association Wyeth Publication Grants [3119]
The College Club of Hartford Scholarships [4743]
College of Engineering and Physical Sciences Industry Scholarships [10208]
College of Healthcare Information Management Executives (CHIME) **[3120]**
College Reading and Learning Association (CRLA) **[3122]**
College Success Foundation (CSF) **[3124]**
College Success Foundation Chateau Ste. Michelle Scholarship Fund [3125]
College Success Foundation Leadership 1000 Scholarships [3126]
College Success Foundation Realize the Dream Scholarships [3127]
College Success Foundation Washington State Governors' Scholarship for Foster Youth [3128]
Irene Culver Collins and Louis Franklin Collins Scholarships [3173]
Captain Winifred Quick Collins Scholarships [7229]
Elmer and Rosa Lee Collins Scholarships [10575]
Lloyd E. and Rachel S. Collins Scholarships [10576]
Paul Collins Scholarships [4583]
Colombian Education Fund **[3129]**
Colombian Education Fund Scholarships [3130]
Colorado Association of Stormwater and Floodplain Managers (CASFM) **[3131]**
Colorado Broadcasters Association (CBA) **[3133]**
Colorado Christian University Alumni Association **[3135]**
Colorado Hotel and Lodging Association (CH&LA) **[3137]**
Colorado Nurses Foundation (CNF) **[3139]**
Colorado Nurses Foundation Nightingale Scholarships [3141]
Colorado Society of Certified Public Accountants (COCPA) **[3146]**
ColorMasters Scholarships [4333]
Columbus Citizens Foundation **[3150]**

Columbus Citizens Foundation College Scholarships [3151]
Columbus Citizens Foundation High School Scholarships [3152]
Colvin Law Offices **[3153]**
John R. Colvin Legal Scholarships [3154]
Robert N. Colwell Memorial Fellowships [1803]
Committee of 200 (C200) **[3155]**
The Commonwealth Fund **[3157]**
Commonwealth "Good Citizen" Scholarships [1977]
Communal Studies Association (CSA) **[3162]**
Communal Studies Association Research Fellowships [3163]
Communications Workers of America Canada (CWA) **[3164]**
Communities Adolescent Nutrition and Fitness Program (CANFIT) **[3166]**
Community Bank - Lee Guggisberg Foundation Memorial Scholarships [8464]
Community-based Natural Resource Management Assistantships [3169]
Community Forestry and Environmental Research Partnerships (CEFRP) **[3168]**
Community Foundation of the Eastern Shore (CFES) **[3170]**
Community Foundation of the Fox River Valley **[3191]**
Community Foundation of the Fox River Valley Scholarships [3192]
Community Foundation for Greater Atlanta **[3193]**
Community Foundation for Greater New Haven **[3196]**
Community Foundation of Greene County (CFGC) **[3203]**
Community Foundation of Middle Tennessee (CFMT) **[3208]**
Community Foundation of Northeast Alabama (CFNEA) **[3259]**
Community Foundation of Northern Illinois **[3274]**
Community Foundation of Prince Edward Island (CFPEI) **[3308]**
Community Foundation of Sarasota County **[3315]**
Community Foundation for Southeast Michigan (CFSEM) **[3324]**
The Community Foundation Student Education Loan Funds for Gay and Lesbians [3221]
Community Foundation of Western Massachusetts **[3334]**
Community Foundation of Western Massachusetts Community Scholarship Program [3335]
Community Legal Services of Philadelphia (CLS) **[3336]**
Community Legal Services of Philadelphia Fellowships [3337]
Comparative Effectiveness Research Professorship (CERP) **[3374]**
Comparative Perspectives on Chinese Culture and Society Grants [739]
Composite Panel Association (CPA) **[3338]**
Alan Compton and Bob Stanley Professional Scholarships [2192]
Tom and Judith Comstock Scholarships [1734]
Desmond Conacher Scholarships [9071]
Condon Prize for Best Student Essay in Psychological Anthropology [9281]
Maridell Braham Condon Scholarships [8915]
Conduct and Utilization of Research in Nursing (CURN) Awards [6476]
Conference on Asian Pacific American Leadership (CAPAL) **[3340]**
Conference of State Bank Supervisors (CSBS) **[3342]**
Conference of State Bank Supervisors Graduate School Scholarships [3343]
Conference and Workshop Grants [10514]
Congressional Black Caucus Foundation (CBCF) **[3344]**
Congressional Fellows on Women and Public Policy [10672]
Congressional Hispanic Caucus Institute **[3351]**
Congressional Research Awards [3626]
Al Conklin and Bill de Decker Business Aviation Management Scholarships [6830]
T.L. Conlan Scholarships [2950]
Connecticut Association of Assessing Officers (CAAO) **[3355]**

Connecticut Association of Land Surveyors (CALS) **[3357]**
Connecticut Association of Land Surveyors Memorial Scholarships [3358]
Connecticut Association of Latinos in Higher Education (CALAHE) **[3359]**
Connecticut Association of Latinos in Higher Education Scholarships [4744]
Connecticut Construction Industries Association (CCIA) **[3364]**
Connecticut Mortgage Bankers Social Affairs Committee Scholarships [4745]
Connecticut Space Grant College Consortium **[3366]**
Connecticut Space Grant College Consortium Undergraduate Research Fellowships [3367]
Cecelia Connelly Memorial Scholarships in Underwater Archaeology [10638]
Dwight O. Conner and Ellen Conner Lepp/Danhart Scholarships [7819]
Karen Connick Memorial Scholarships [4560]
Louis M. Connor Jr. Scholarships [10221]
Connor/Spafford Scholarships [4478]
Conquer Cancer Foundation **[3368]**
Conseil Canadien pour le Commerce Autochtone **[3388]**
Conseil Canadien des Techniciens et Technologues (CCTT) **[3391]**
Conseil Consultatif Canadiene de la Radio **[3393]**
Conseil de recherches en sciences humaines **[3395]**
Conseil International d'Études Canadiennes (CIEC) **[3397]**
Conseil de Recherches en Sciences Naturelles et en Génie du Canada **[3400]**
Conservation Department Program Fellowships [9028]
Constangy, Brooks and Smith Diversity Scholars Awards [3407]
Constangy, Brooks, Smith & Prophete L.L.P. **[3406]**
Constant Memorial Scholarship [8604]
Constantinople Armenian Relief Society Scholarships (CARS) [1691]
Consumer Law Public Service Fellowships [8433]
Contemporary Club Scholarships [8465]
Continuing Education Awards [6778]
Contra Costa County Bar Association (CCCBA) **[3408]**
Jorge Espejel Contreras IALEIA Scholarship Award [5266]
Convectair Sustainable Development Scholarship Awards [3824]
Convergence Assistantship Grants [4708]
Rosemary Cook Education Scholarships [4584]
Irving W. Cook WA0CGS Scholarships [1735]
Jack Kent Cooke Dissertation Fellowship Award [5492]
Jack Kent Cooke Foundation College Scholarships [3411]
Jack Kent Cooke Foundation Graduate Scholarships [3412]
Jack Kent Cooke Foundation (JKCF) **[3410]**
Jack Kent Cooke Foundation Undergraduate Transfer Scholarships [3413]
Jack Kent Cooke Foundation Young Scholars [3414]
Jack Kent Cooke Graduate Arts Awards [5493]
Richard D. and Sheppard R. Cooke Memorial Scholarships [4695]
Cooley Diversity Fellowship [3416]
Cooley L.L.P. **[3415]**
Roy Cooper Memorial Scholarships [5998]
Madison and Edith Cooper Scholarships [8698]
Coordinating Council for Women in History (CCWH) **[3417]**
COPA Scholarship Fund [2722]
Cope Middle School PTSA Scholarships [8466]
Rob Copeland Memorial Scholarships [6022]
Copper and Brass Servicenter Association (CBSA) **[3420]**
Copper and Brass Servicenter Association Inc. Scholarship Program [3421]
Beta Nu/Caryl Cordis D'hondt Scholarships [8916]
Theta/Caryl Cordis D'hondt Scholarships [8917]
Charles Clarke Cordle Memorial Scholarships [1736]
Valdemar A. Cordova Scholarships [6110]

Bill Cormack Scholarships [9706]
Cornaro Scholarships for Graduate Studies [5686]
D.C. Cornelius Memorial Scholarships [10577]
Holly Cornell Scholarship [1488]
Corning Outstanding Student Paper Competition [7672]
Coro **[3422]**
Coro Fellows Program in Public Affairs [3423]
The Corp - More Uncommon Grounds Scholarships [9604]
The Corp - Students of Georgetown Inc. Coke Scholarships [9605]
The Corp - Students of Georgetown Inc. Textbook Scholarships [9606]
Corporate Counsel Women of Color (CCWC) **[3424]**
Correctional Education Association (CEA) **[3426]**
Correctional Education Association Scholarships [3427]
NSS Sara Corrie Memorial Grants [7181]
Tom Cory Memorial Scholarships [1614]
COTA Scholarships for Occupational Therapy Assistants [7762]
Cottrell Scholar Awards (CSA) [8555]
Dr. George C. Cotzias Memorial Fellowship [1074]
Dave Couch Memorial Scholarships [7820]
Helen & Orval Couch Memorial Scholarships [10783]
SRC NRI Hans J. Coufal Fellowships [8838]
Jennifer Coulter Memorial Scholarships [7821]
Council for the Advancement of Science Writing (CASW) **[3428]**
Council of American Overseas Research Centers (CAORC) **[3430]**
Council for Children with Behavior Disorders **[3432]**
Council of Energy Resource Tribes (CERT) **[3434]**
Council for European Studies (CES) **[3436]**
Council on Foreign Relations (CFR) **[3441]**
Council on Library and Information Resources (CLIR) **[3449]**
Council on Social Work Education (CSWE) **[3453]**
Council on Social Work Education Minority Fellowship Program for Doctoral Students [3454]
Council on Social Work Education Scholars Program [3455]
Counseil Canadien de droit International **[3457]**
Courage to Grow **[3460]**
Courage to Grow Scholarships [3461]
Pfizer Soozie Courter Hemophilia Scholarship Program [6988]
COUSE-Gram Scholarships [9424]
The Cover Guy **[3462]**
Richard P. Covert, Ph.D./FHIMSS Scholarships for Management Systems [4830]
The Joe E. Covington Awards for Research on Bar Admissions Testing [6873]
Steve Cowan Memorial Scholarships [3471]
Hon. Joseph W. Cowgill Memorial Scholarships [2509]
Reuben R. Cowles Youth Awards [945]
Justin Forrest Cox "Beat the Odds" Memorial Scholarships [3093]
Gertrude M. Cox Scholarships [1465]
CPA Foundation Minority Scholarships [2471]
CPS Clinical Pain Management Fellowship Awards [2725]
CPS Excellence in Interprofessional Pain Education Awards [2726]
CPS Interprofessional Nursing Project Awards [2727]
CPS Knowledge Translation Research Awards [2728]
CPS Nursing Excellence in Pain Management Awards [2729]
CPS Nursing Research and Education Awards [2730]
CPS Outstanding Pain Mentorship Awards [2731]
CPS Trainee Research Awards [2732]
Craft Research Fund Grants [2845]
Crafton Elementary School PTA Scholarships [8467]
Crafton Hills College Foundation Scholarships [8468]
Margaret T. Craig Community Service Scholarships [3281]
J. Craig and Page T. Smith Scholarships [8999]
Crain Educational Grant Program [8948]

Robert E. Cramer Product Design and Development Scholarship [9259]
Rick Crane Group Real Estate Scholarship Fund [6023]
Gerald M. Crane Music Award Scholarships [4585]
Mike Crapo Math and Science Scholarship Fund [5040]
George W. Crawford Black Bar Association **[3464]**
Meredith P. Crawford Fellowships in I/O Psychology [4990]
AWG Maria Luisa Crawford Field Camp Scholarships [2095]
Mable B. Crawford Memorial Scholarships [10015]
Crawford Scholarships [8699]
Creative Glass Center of America (CGCA) **[3466]**
Creative Glass Center of America Fellowships [3467]
Credit Union Central of Saskatchewan **[3468]**
CRI Clinic and Laboratory Integration Program Grants (CLIP) [2772]
CRI Irvington Postdoctoral Fellowship Program [2773]
CRI Irvington Postdoctoral Fellowships [2774]
Crisis Intervention and Suicide Prevention Centre of British Columbia **[3470]**
Critical Language Scholarships for Intensive Summer Institutes [1204]
CRM-ISM Postdoctoral Fellowships [9993]
CRMA Scholarships [2899]
Judy Crocker Memorial Scholarship Fund [4191]
Crohn's and Colitis Canada **[3472]**
Crohn's and Colitis Canada Grants in Aid of Research [3473]
Crohn's and Colitis Canada Innovations in IBD Research Grants [3474]
Crohn's and Colitis Foundation of America (CCFA) **[3475]**
Crohn's and Colitis Foundation of America Senior Research Awards [3479]
Cromwell Fellowships [1354]
Redlands Rotary Club - Ernest L. Cronemeyer Memorial Scholarships [8469]
Kathryn M. Cronin Scholarships [10222]
CrossLites **[3480]**
CrossLites Scholarships [3481]
R.G. and Ruth Crossno Memorial Scholarships [3756]
CROW Fellowships [3053]
Crowder Scholarships [4192]
Howard A. Crum Student Scholarships [10179]
Rebecca Lee Crumpler, M.D. Scholarships [1865]
Lydia Cruz and Sandra Maria Ramos Scholarships [3577]
CSA Fraternal Life **[3482]**
CSA Fraternal Life Scholarships [3483]
CSBS Student Prize Competition [2744]
CSCI Distinguished Scientist Lectures and Awards [9073]
CSCPA College Scholarships [3147]
CSCPA High School Scholarships [3148]
CSCPA Sophomore Scholarships [3149]
CSEG Scholarship Trust Fund [2748]
CSF Ach Family Scholarships [2951]
CSF Barr Foundation Scholarships [2952]
CSF Barrett Family Scholarships [2953]
CSF Borden Inc. Scholarships [2954]
CSF Castellini Foundation Scholarships [2955]
CSF Cincinnati Bell Scholarships [2956]
CSF Cincinnati Financial Corporation Scholarships [2957]
CSF Crosset Family Scholarships [2958]
CSF Dater Foundation Scholarships [2959]
CSF Duke Energy Scholarships [2960]
CSF Farmer Family Foundation Scholarships [2961]
CSF Fifth Third Bank Combined Scholarships [2962]
CSF Fletemeyer Family Scholarships [2963]
CSF Gardner Foundation Scholarships [2964]
CSF Goldman, Sachs and Company Scholarships [2965]
CSF Graduate Fellowships [2936]
CSF H.C. Schott Foundation Scholarships [2966]
CSF Heidelberg Distributing Co. Scholarships [2967]
CSF Heinz Pet Products Scholarships [2968]
CSF Juilfs Foundation Scholarships [2969]
CSF Kroger Cincinnati/Dayton Scholarships [2970]

CSF McCall Educational Scholarships [2971]
CSF Midland Company Scholarships [2972]
CSF Nethercott Family Scholarships [2973]
CSF Ohio National Foundation Scholarships [2974]
CSF Pepper Family Scholarships [2975]
CSF Pichler Family Scholarships [2976]
CSF PNC Bank Scholarships [2977]
CSF Procter and Gamble Scholarships [2978]
CSF Scripps Headliners Scholarships [2979]
CSF Semple Foundation Scholarships [2980]
CSF Union Central 135th Anniversary Scholarships [2981]
CSF U.S. Bank N.A. Scholarships [2982]
CSF Western-Southern Foundation Scholarships [2983]
CSF Woodward Trustees Scholarships [2984]
CSF Wynne Family Memorial Scholarships [2985]
CSLA Leaders of Distinction Award [2759]
CSLA Leadership Scholarships [2760]
CSMLS Student Scholarship Awards [2750]
CSOHNS Fellowships [2752]
CSSA Research Grants [2428]
CSSE ARTS Graduate Research Awards [9069]
CSSHE Masters Thesis/Project Awards [2756]
CSSHE Research Awards [2757]
CSX Scholarships [1183]
CTEC Internships [1567]
CTF Young Investigator Awards (CTF-YIA) [2911]
CTFS-ForestGEO Research Grants Program [9041]
CTFS Research Grants Program [9036]
CTP Scholarship Program [7113]
CTRF Scholarships for Graduate Study in Transportation [2764]
Cuban American Bar Association (CABA) **[3484]**
Cuban American Bar Association Scholarships [3485]
John P. Culhane Professional Pilot Scholarships [215]
Culinary (1-Year Program) Scholarships [2660]
The Culinary Trust (TCT) **[3486]**
Linda Cullen Memorial Scholarships [759]
Murtha Cullina LLP Scholarships Fund [3199]
Cultural Vistas **[3488]**
Esther Cummings Memorial Scholarships [7378]
Brian Cummins Memorial Scholarships [4746]
John S. and Marjoria R. Cunningham Camp Scholarships [6193]
Laura Moore Cunningham Foundation General Scholarships [6024]
John J. Cunningham Memorial Scholarships [1184]
The Cure Starts Now Foundation **[3491]**
The Cure Starts Now Foundation Grants [3492]
Tsutako Curo Scholarships [8339]
Curry Awards for Girls and Young Women [8949]
Cindy Curry Memorial Scholarships [7822]
Nancy Curry Scholarships [8804]
John J. Curtin, Jr. Fellowships [620]
Michael D. Curtin Renaissance Student Memorial Scholarships [3757]
Curtis/Breeden Scholarships [2986]
Jennifer Curtis Byler Scholarships [7188]
Don and Barbara Curtis Excellence Fund for Extracurricular Student Activities [10223]
Dewey Lee Curtis Scholarships [3541]
Cystic Fibrosis Foundation **[3493]**
Cystic Fibrosis Scholarship Foundation [3494]
DA Davidson Presidential Scholarships [10436]
DAAD Learn German in Germany Grants [3603]
DAAD Study Scholarship Awards [3604]
DAAD Undergraduate Scholarship Program [3605]
DACOR **[3495]**
DACOR Graduate Fellowships for Study of International Affairs [3496]
Daedalian Foundation (DF) **[3498]**
Daedalian Foundation Matching Scholarships Program [3499]
Daggy Youth/Student Scholarships [5444]
Jason Dahnert Memorial Scholarships [4143]
DAI Fellowships for Study in Berlin [1607]
Detroit Section/Robert G. Dailey Scholarship [9260]
Daily Lineups **[3503]**
Daily Lineups Scholarship Awards [3504]
Dairy Farmers of America Inc. (DFA) **[3505]**
Dairy Farmers of America Scholarships [3506]
Dake Community Manufacturing Scholarships [4512]

Dalai Lama Trust **[3507]**
Dalai Lama Trust Graduate Scholarships [3508]
Daland Fellowships in Clinical Investigation [1079]
Dalcroze Society of America (DSA) **[3509]**
Dalcroze Society of America Memorial Scholarships [3510]
Chester Dale Fellowships [6429]
George Dale Scholarship Fund [1776]
John L. Dales Standard Scholarship [8827]
Roger Daley Postdoctoral Publication Awards [2683]
Dallas Alumnae Association Adelphe Scholarships [5704]
Dallas Alumnae Association Gamma Phi Chapter Scholarships [5705]
Dallas Area Paralegal Association **[3511]**
Serena D. Dalton Scholarships [10578]
Marvin E. Daly Memorial Scholarship [7532]
Damon Runyon Cancer Research Foundation **[3513]**
Damon Runyon Cancer Research Foundation Fellowships [3514]
Damon Runyon Physician-Scientist Training Awards [3515]
Damon Runyon-Rachleff Innovation Awards [3516]
Damon Runyon-Sohn Pediatric Cancer Fellowship Awards [3517]
Dan Carman Attorney at Law, PLLC **[3519]**
June Danby and Pat Pearse Education Scholarships [5500]
D&A Florida Scholarships [9425]
D&R Sobey Scholarships [9047]
Arthur H. Daniels Scholarships [8470]
Danish America Heritage Society (DAHS) **[3521]**
Dante Society of America (DSA) **[3523]**
Malcolm U. Dantzler Scholarships [9363]
Mark & Dorothy Danzker Scholarships [5592]
DAPA Student Member Scholarships [3512]
Mary Mouzon Darby Undergraduate Scholarships [4985]
Darden Restaurants Point Scholarships [8172]
The Hugh and Hazel Darling Dean Scholarships [7972]
Darling Foundation Endowed School of Law Scholarships [7973]
Darooge Family Scholarships [4586]
Doctors Ira and Udaya Dash Nursing Scholarships [9426]
Rexford Daubenmire Fellowships [7737]
Amy and Tim Dauphinee Scholarships [2575]
Canadian Association for Studies in Co-operation Scholarships - Amy and Tim Dauphinee Scholarships (CASC) [2612]
Frank L. Dautriel Memorial Scholarships for Graduates [6116]
Frank L. Dautriel Memorial Scholarships for Undergraduates [6117]
Antenore C. "Butch" Davanzo Scholarships [6502]
The Dave Family "Humor Studies" Scholarships [1848]
David Library of the American Revolution **[3526]**
David Library Fellowships [3527]
David Mann Law Office **[3528]**
David Meador Foundation - Hospitality-Food Service Scholarships [7294]
Ruth and Victor David Scholarships [5575]
Lucile Caswell Davids Memorial Adelphe Scholarships [5706]
Jim Davie Memorial Scholarships [10784]
Clifford W. and Doris E. Davis Educational Scholarship Fund [3319]
Davis Family Scholarships [8700]
Davis Foundation Postdoctoral Fellowships [4814]
The William H. Davis, Jr. Scholarship Fund [3204]
Davis Levin Livingston **[3530]**
Davis Memorial Foundation **[3532]**
Davis Memorial Foundation Scholarships [3533]
Dwight F. Davis Memorial Scholarships [9974]
Estelle Davis Memorial Scholarships [2987]
Johnny Davis Memorial Scholarships [157]
Davis-Putter Scholarships Fund [8659]
Larry Dean Davis Scholarship Program [7924]
Arlene Davis Scholarships [3581]
Fran Morgenstern Davis Scholarships [1270]
James Davis Scholarships [10224]
James H. Davis Scholarships [4100]

Kenneth D. and Katherine D. Davis Scholarships [7823]
Lawrence E. and Jean L. Davis Scholarships [7824]
Raymond Davis Scholarships [9150]
Davis Wright Tremaine L.L.P. (DWT) **[3534]**
Colonel Richard M. Dawson Highway Patrol Scholarship Fund [3222]
Brian M. Day Scholarships [8252]
Dayton Amateur Radio Association Scholarships [1737]
DBA Student Scholarships [3653]
DBI Scholarships Fund [3223]
DCH Freehold Toyota Scholarships [2878]
Edilia and François Auguste de Montêquin Fellowships [9083]
Bert and Sally de Vries Fellowships [656]
Kenneth J. De Witt NASA/OSGC Scholarship at The University of Toledo [7592]
Alphonso Deal Scholarship Awards [6825]
B.J. Dean Scholarships [3224]
Derek Lee Dean Soccer Scholarships [3094]
Steve Dearduff Scholarships [3194]
Death Valley '49ers, Inc. **[3536]**
Death Valley '49ers Scholarships [3537]
Don Debolt Franchising Scholarship Program [5335]
Matthew Debono Memorial Scholarship Funds [1588]
Debt.com **[3538]**
Debt.com Scholarships [3539]
Julia B. DeCapua Fund [4661]
Walter M. Decker Point Scholarships [8173]
Decommissioning, Decontamination and Reutilization Scholarships [1035]
The Decorative Arts Trust **[3540]**
Laurence Decore Awards for Student Leadership [271]
Earl Dedman Memorial Scholarships [804]
DEED Student Research Grant/Internships [1160]
Anthony R. Dees Educational Workshop Scholarships [9124]
DefensiveDriving.com **[3542]**
DefensiveDriving.com Scholarships [3543]
Edward Delaney Scholarships [1982]
Jane Delano Student Nurse Scholarships [1023]
Jan DiMartino Delany Memorial Scholarships [4236]
Delaware Community Foundation (DCF) **[3544]**
Antonia Dellas Memorial Scholarships [5501]
Martha Delman and Milton Arthur Krug Endowed Scholarships [7974]
Vine Deloria Jr. Memorial Scholarships [868]
Delta Chi Alumnae Memorial Scholarships [8918]
Delta Delta Delta **[3546]**
Delta Epsilon Sigma (DES) **[3565]**
Delta Epsilon Sigma Graduate Fellowships [3566]
Delta Epsilon Sigma Undergraduate Scholarships [3567]
Delta Faucet Scholarships [8160]
Delta Gamma **[3568]**
Delta Gamma Undergraduate Merit-Based Scholarships [3569]
Delta Iota Alumni Scholarships [8967]
The Delta Kappa Gamma Society International **[3570]**
Delta Kappa Gamma Society International World Fellowships [3571]
Delta Kappa Project 2000 Scholarships [5707]
Delta Nu Alpha Foundation Scholarships [3573]
Delta Nu Alpha Transportation Fraternity (DNA) **[3572]**
Delta Nu Project 2000 Scholarships [5708]
Delta Phi Epsilon Educational Foundation Scholarships [3575]
Delta Phi Epsilon Sorority (DPHIE) **[3574]**
Delta Project 2000 Scholarships [5709]
Delta Tau Lambda Sorority, Inc. (DTL) **[3576]**
Delta Tau Project 2000 Scholarships [5710]
Delta Upsilon Project 2000 Nowell Memorial Scholarships [5711]
Delta Zeta Sorority **[3578]**
Delta Zeta Undergraduate Scholarships [3582]
C. Rodney Demarest Memorial Scholarships [4747]
Law Offices of Michael A. DeMayo Scholarships [5963]
Enkhbaatar Demchig Field Research Fellowship Program [651]
DEMCO New Leaders Travel Grants [8372]

Christopher Demetris Memorial Scholarships [4845]
DeMolay International **[3597]**
Inez Demonet Scholarship [10373]
Ruth DeMoss Scholarships [8701]
Albert W. Dent Graduate Student Scholarships [687]
Michael Denton Scholarship [7533]
Denton Scholarships [8897]
John Denver Music Scholarships [1271]
Denver Scholarship Foundation (DSF) **[3599]**
Denver Scholarship Foundation Scholarships [3600]
Dick Depaolis Memorial Scholarships [3325]
Depression and ADHD Fellowships [5840]
DEPS Graduate Scholarship Program [3624]
Karekin DerAvedision Memorial Endowment Fund [1692]
Derivative Duo Scholarships [8253]
Herman H. Derksen Scholarships [8702]
Pat Dermargosian Memorial Scholarships [8471]
Descendant Scholarships [3500]
Libby Deschenes Prize for Applied Research [10537]
Design and Multimedia Internships - New York [4430]
Achille and Irene Despres, William and Andre Scholarships [4587]
Detroit Economic Club Scholarship [3326]
APTRA-Clete Roberts/Kathryn Dettman Memorial Journalism Scholarship [1818]
Deutscher Akademischer Austausch Dienst (DAAD) **[3601]**
Development Fund for Black Students in Science and Technology (DFBSST) **[3611]**
Development Fund for Black Students in Science and Technology Scholarships [3612]
Helen L. Dewar Scholarships [9729]
Albert and Jane Dewey Scholarships [4748]
Donald J. DeYoung Scholarships [4588]
Dezao Legal Awards [5959]
Jenny d'Héricourt Fellowships [435]
Edward D. Di Loreto-Odell S. McConnell Scholarships [7975]
Diabetes Hope Foundation **[3613]**
Diabetes Hope Foundation Scholarships [3614]
Diabetes Scholars Foundation (DSF) **[3615]**
Diabetes Scholars Foundation College Scholarships [3616]
Julio C. Diaz Academic Scholarship [9498]
Edwina Eustis Dick Scholarship for Music Therapy Interns [1012]
Jean Dearth Dickerscheid Fellowships [8090]
Dickey Rural Networks (DRN) **[3617]**
Dickey Rural Networks College Scholarship Program [3618]
Bill Dickey Scholarship Association **[3619]**
Bill Dickey Scholarship Association Scholarships [3620]
Dietetics in Health Care Communities (DHCC) **[3621]**
Diffuse Large B-Cell Lymphoma Explorations Grants [6158]
Robert Martz DiGiacomo Memorial Scholarship Fund [9499]
Rudolph Dillman Memorial Scholarships [820]
Carol DiMaiti Scholarship Awards [6308]
Gretchen Dimico Memorial Scholarships [6025]
The E.R. and Lilian B. Dimmette Scholarship Fund [4193]
Raymond DiPaglia Endowment Scholarship [3664]
The Angie Dipietro Women in Business Scholarships [8231]
Directed Energy Professional Society (DEPS) **[3623]**
Dirksen Congressional Center **[3625]**
The Disability Care Center **[3628]**
Disability Care Center Disabled Student Scholarships [3629]
Disability Care Center Special Education Scholarships [3630]
Disabled American Veterans (DAV) **[3631]**
Disabled War Veterans Scholarships [90]
Discover Bar Exam Loans [3634]
Discover Financial Services (DFS) **[3633]**
Discover Graduate Loans [3635]
Discover Health Professions Loans [3636]
Discover Law Loans [3637]
Discover MBA Loans [3638]

Discover Residency Loans [3639]
Dissertation Award in Hadronic Physics [1089]
Dissertation Fellowships in East European Studies [740]
Dissertation Proposal Development Fellowships [9053]
The Distinguished Flying Cross Society (DFCS) **[3640]**
Distinguished Flying Cross Society Scholarships [3641]
Distinguished Young Women **[3642]**
Distinguished Young Women Scholarships [3643]
LaRue A. Ditmore Music Scholarships [10650]
Diversity Executive Leadership Program Scholarships [1778]
Diversity Fellowship Program (DFP) [6589]
Robert A. and Barbara Divine Graduate Student Travel Grants [9136]
Dixon Hughes Goodman L.L.P. **[3644]**
Dixon Hughes Goodman LLP Annual Scholarship [3645]
Dr. Allan A. Dixon Memorial Scholarships [2742]
William Donald Dixon Research Grants [2665]
Daniel B. Dixon Scholarships [324]
Peggy Dixon Two-Year Scholarships [9254]
Mychajlo Dmytrenko Fine Arts Foundation Scholarships [9980]
Grace O. Doane Scholarship [3665]
Charles Dobbins FTA Scholarships [4316]
Julian Dobranowski Memorial Scholarships [8574]
Dr. Biljan Memorial Awards [2636]
Dr. Mac Scholarships [3225]
Doctoral Dissertation Grants [5386]
Document Management and Graphic Communications Industry Scholarships [3852]
Documentary Film Grants [369]
Doddridge County Promise Scholarships [7825]
F. Atlee Dodge Maintenance Scholarships [216]
Jim Dodson Law Scholarships [5600]
Robert Winchester Dodson Scholarships [10225]
DOE Computational Science Graduate Fellowships (DOE CSGF) [5887]
Emmett J. Doerr Memorial Distinguished Scout Scholarships [6921]
Dofflemyer Scholarships [6922]
Dog Fence DIY **[3646]**
Dole Food Fellowships [7738]
Dollar-A-Day Academic Scholarships [3649]
Dollar-A-Day Scholarship Fund **[3648]**
Dolphin Scholarship Foundation **[3650]**
Dolphin Scholarships [3651]
Scott Dominguez - Craters of the Moon Chapter Scholarships [1412]
Dominican Bar Association (DBA) **[3652]**
Dominio of Canada Insurance Scholarships [8128]
Marion Jones Donaldson Scholarship Fund [4043]
Hon. Ralph W.E. Donges Memorial Scholarships [2510]
Doniphan Community Foundation Scholarships [4561]
Mike and Gail Donley Spouse Scholarships [123]
Harry A. Donn Scholarships [4749]
Mickey Donnelly Memorial Scholarships [8340]
Jim Doogan Memorial Scholarships [10096]
Dorchester Woman's Club Music Scholarship - Voice [4352]
Joseph M. Dorgan Scholarship [3666]
Dr. Michael Dorizas Memorial Scholarships [4846]
Pauly D'Orlando Memorial Art Scholarships [9834]
Lloyd M. Dosdall Memorial Scholarships [3889]
Father Connie Dougherty Scholarships [3320]
Robert E. Dougherty Scholarships [3339]
Douglas-Coldwell Foundation (DCF) **[3654]**
Douglas-Coldwell Foundation Scholarships in Social Affairs [3656]
Tommy Douglas Memorial Scholarship [7205]
Chapter 116 - Kalamazoo - Roscoe Douglas Scholarships [9180]
Douglass Foundation Fellowship in American Art [9001]
Douglass Foundation Fellowships in American Art [6430]
Harold K. Douthit Regional Scholarships [7576]
Dow Chemical Company Fellowships [7085]
Margaret Dowell-Gravatt, M.D. Scholarships [2226]
Downeast Energy and Building Supply **[3658]**

Downeast Energy Scholarships [3659]
Downeast Feline Scholarships [6194]
Jay and Rheba Downes Memorial Scholarships [3095]
W.B.H. Dowse Fellowships [6326]
Rodger Doxsey Travel Prizes [616]
Helen Cashatt Drais Memorial Adelphe Scholarships [5712]
Drake University Law School **[3660]**
Drake University Law School Law Opportunity Scholarships - Disadvantage [3667]
Drake University Law School Law Opportunity Scholarships - Diversity [3668]
Drake University Law School Public Service Scholarships [3669]
Drama Therapy Fund **[3692]**
Lou Drane Music Scholarships [4237]
The "Drawn to Art" Fellowships [436]
C. Cleveland Drennon, Jr. Memorial Scholarships [10158]
Wilma Sackett Dressel Scholarships [8919]
Margaret Drew Alpha Fellowships [8091]
Charles Drew Scholarships [1940]
Camille and Henry Dreyfus Foundation, Inc. **[3694]**
Louis Dreyfus Warner-Chappell City College Scholarships [1272]
Thomas J. Drinan Memorial Fellowships [8434]
Drinkwater Family Scholarships [8703]
Mary Ellen Driscoll Scholarships [4479]
Drug Development Research Professorship [3375]
Richard Drukker Memorial Scholarships [7326]
Sergeant Major Douglas R. Drum Memorial Scholarship Fund [1005]
Harold D. Drummond Scholarships [5668]
Dry Defender Protect Your Bed Scholarships [5636]
DSA Dante Prizes [3524]
DSACF Modern Woodmen of America Scholarships [3706]
Henry Belin du Pont Dissertation Fellowships [4688]
Henry Belin du Pont Research Grants [4689]
Martin Duberman Fellowships [2864]
Dublin San Ramon Services District **[3696]**
DuBois Brothers Scholarships [2511]
Charles Dubose Scholarships [4750]
Lise M. Duchesneau Scholarship [1895]
John W. Duckett Jr., AFUD Pediatric Research Scholarships [9246]
The Steve Duckett Local Conservation Scholarships [8232]
Julia M. Duckwall Scholarships [1983]
Mark Duda Scholarship Fund [6288]
Deborah Gandee Dudding Memorial Scholarships [7826]
Edward Leon Duhamel Scholarship Fund [8605]
Doris Duke Charitable Foundation (DDCF) **[3698]**
Doris Duke Conservation Fellows Program [10678]
H.J. "Duke" Ellington Memorial Scholarship Award [7513]
Duke University and University of North Carolina Rotary Peace Center **[3700]**
Duluth Building and Construction Trades Council Scholarships [3707]
Duluth Central High School Alumni Scholarships [3708]
Duluth Superior Area Community Foundation **[3702]**
Dumbarton Oaks Fellowships [3728]
Dumbarton Oaks Junior Fellowships [3729]
Dumbarton Oaks Research Library and Collection **[3727]**
Dumbarton Oaks Research Library and Collection Bliss Symposium Awards [3730]
Dumbarton Oaks Research Library and Collection Graduate Research Workshops [3731]
Dumbarton Oaks Research Library and Collection One-Month Research Stipends [3732]
Dumbarton Oaks Research Library and Collection Post-Baccalaureate Media Fellowships [3733]
Dumbarton Oaks Research Library and Collection Project Grants [3734]
Dumbarton Oaks Research Library and Collection Short-Term Predoctoral Residencies Grants [3735]
Dumbarton Oaks Research Library and Collection Summer Fellowships [3736]
Dumbarton Oaks Research Library and Collection Summer Internships for Harvard Students [3737]

Dumbarton Oaks Research Library and Collection Post-Doctoral Teaching Fellowships [3738]
Gabriel Dumont Institute of Native Studies and Applied Research (GDI) **[3741]**
Dunbar Heritage Scholarships [9427]
Duncan Aviation Scholarships [158]
Dr. Allan Duncan Memorial Scholarships [10785]
Wade and Marcelene Duncan Scholarships [10579]
Ed Dunkelblau Scholarships [1849]
Travis Dunning Memorial Scholarships [8341]
William R. Durham/Theater Scholarships [3282]
Durning Sisters Scholarships [3549]
Joe Durso, Jr. Memorial Scholarships [6576]
Dutchess County Bar Association (DCBA) **[3743]**
Sue and Ken Dyer Foundation Travel Scholarships [4238]
Bob Dyer/OEL Apprenticeship Scholarships [3825]
Joshua Dyke Family Scholarships [9730]
Marvin and Joanell Dyrstad Scholarship [1578]
Dystonia Medical Research Foundation (DMRF) **[3745]**
Dystonia Medical Research Foundation Clinical Fellowships [3746]
e8 Sustainable Energy Development Post-Doctoral Scholarship Programme (ESED) [4460]
EAA Tuition Scholarships [3873]
EAA Workshop Scholarships [3874]
Josephine P. White Eagle Scholarships [4911]
Eagles Fly for Leukemia Scholarships [2906]
EAIA Research Grants [3748]
Howard G. and Gladys A. Eakes Memorial Scholarships [4562]
EAPSI Fellowships [7124]
Amelia Earhart Memorial Academic Scholarships [7439]
Earl and Countess of Wessex - World Championships in Athletics Scholarships [272]
Earl Warren Civil Rights Training Scholarships [6645]
Early American Industries Association (EAIA) **[3747]**
Early-Career Patient-Oriented Diabetes Research Awards [5640]
Early Career Postdoctoral Fellowships in East European Studies [741]
Early Childhood Educators Scholarship Program [6342]
Robert E. Early Memorial Scholarship [3670]
Earthquake Engineering Research Institute (EERI) **[3749]**
Bob East Scholarships [7108]
East Tennessee Foundation (ETF) **[3751]**
East-West Center (EWC) **[3758]**
East-West Center Graduate Degree Fellowships [3760]
Patricia Hughes Eastaugh Teaching Scholarship [10016]
Easter Seals Ontario **[3764]**
Eastern Communication Association (ECA) **[3767]**
Eastern Orthodox Scouting Scholarships [6923]
Eastern Shore Building Industry Association Scholarships [3174]
Eastman Community Music School (ECMS) **[3770]**
Eaton Awards of Academic Achievement [3826]
David Eaton Scholarships [9835]
The Christoph Daniel Ebeling Fellowships [437]
Ellen Eberhardt Memorial Scholarships [9565]
ECA Applied Urban Communication Research Grants [3768]
ECA Centennial Scholarships [3769]
Echoing Green **[3772]**
Echoing Green Black Male Achievement Fellowships [3773]
Echoing Green Climate Fellowships [3774]
Echoing Green Global Fellowships [3775]
James Echols Scholarship Award [2434]
W. Wesley Eckenfelder Gradute Research Award [1952]
ECMS Scholarships [3771]
École Polytechnique Commemorative Awards [2630]
Ecological Society of America (ESA) **[3776]**
Economic Club Business Study Abroad Scholarships [4589]
Economic Club of Grand Rapids Scholarships [4590]
Economic History Association (EHA) **[3778]**

Ed Bradley Scholarships [8404]
EDC International Business Scholarships [2603]
Margaret Eddy Scholarships [7379]
Edgecliff Alumni Awards [10718]
Edgecliff McAuley Art Scholarships [10719]
Edgecliff McAuley Music Scholarships [10720]
EDiS Company **[3782]**
The Edit My Paper Proofreading Scholarships [3785]
EditMyPaper.ca **[3784]**
Editors' Association of Canada (EAC) **[3786]**
S. Randolph Edmonds Young Scholars Competition [2303]
Melanie and Todd Edmonson Memorial Scholarships [3261]
Edmonton Community Foundation **[3788]**
Edmonton Epilepsy Association (EEA) **[3791]**
Edmonton Epilepsy Continuing Education Scholarships [3792]
Edon Farmers Cooperative Association Inc. **[3793]**
Edon Farmers Cooperative Scholarships [3794]
Education Advancement Scholarships [548]
Education Factor Scholarships [6378]
"Education is Power" Scholarships [6989]
Educational Audiology Association (EAA) **[3795]**
Educational Audiology Association Doctoral Scholarships [3797]
Educational and Cultural Affairs Alumni Small Grants Program (ECA) [5380]
Educational Fellowships for Practicing Physicians [8123]
The Educational Foundation of KyCPA Scholarships [5821]
The Educational Foundation for Women in Accounting (EFWA) **[3799]**
Educational Research Center of America (ERCA) **[3803]**
Educational Testing Service (ETS) **[3805]**
EDvestinU(r) National Monthly Scholarships [7309]
Edward R. Murrow Press Fellowships [3446]
The Edwards Annual College Scholarships [3810]
Esther Edwards Graduate Scholarships [9851]
The Edwards Law Firm **[3809]**
Carli Edwards Memorial Scholarships [8871]
Palo Verde High School - Barbara Edwards Memorial Scholarships [8342]
Jimmy Edwards Scholarships [3226]
EERI/FEMA Graduate Fellowship in Earthquake Hazard Reduction [3750]
EFC Atlantic Region Scholarships [3827]
EFC University and College Scholarships [3828]
John and Alice Egan Multi-Year Mentioning Scholarships [3501]
Bill Egan Scholarship Program [7694]
UAA Governor William A. Egan Scholarship [10056]
EHA Exploratory Travel and Data Grants [3780]
EHA Graduate Dissertation Fellowships [3781]
E.I. DuPont Graduate Fellowship [7086]
The Eichholz Law Firm **[3811]**
John R. Eidson Jr., Scholarships [3096]
Mike Eidson Scholarships [516]
Eight and Forty Lung and Respiratory Disease Nursing Scholarships [955]
Hillel Einhorn New Investigator Award [9161]
Eisbrouch Marsh, LLC **[3813]**
Eisbrouch & Marsh Scholarship Awards [3814]
Harold E. Eisenberg Foundation Scholarships [5304]
Jeri Eiserman, RRT Professional Education Research Fellowships [1210]
EJI Justice Fellowship [3916]
Farouk El-Baz Student Research Grants [4363]
El Dorado County Mineral and Gem Society **[3815]**
El Dorado County Mineral and Gem Society Scholarships [3816]
El Pomar Scholarships [3818]
El Pomar Foundation **[3817]**
George and Isabelle Elanjian Scholarships [10198]
W. Eldridge and Emily Lowe Scholarships [8968]
eLearning.net **[3819]**
Electro-Federation Canada (EFC) **[3821]**
Electrochemical Society (ECS) **[3849]**
Electronic Document Systems Foundation (EDSF) **[3851]**
Herman E. Elgar Memorial Scholarship [3671]
Eli Lilly and Company/Black Data Processing Asso-

ciates Scholarships [2206]
Eli Lilly Graduate Scholarship [1886]
A.C. Elias, Jr. Irish-American Research Travel Fellowships [1290]
Elie Wiesel Prize in Ethics [10553]
Virginia Elizabeth and Alma Vane Taylor Nursing Scholarship [10580]
Elks National Foundation (ENF) **[3853]**
Dr. Robert Elliott Memorial Scholarships [6351]
Clay Elliott Scholarship Foundation **[3855]**
Clay Elliott Scholarship Foundation Scholarships [3856]
Optimist Club of Redlands - Virginia Elliott Scholarships [8472]
Pauline Elliott Scholarships [6352]
Robert A. Ellis Scholarships in Physics [7141]
William P. Elrod Memorial Scholarships [9656]
Emerald Empire Chapter Scholarship Awards [7695]
Emergency Medicine Physician Scholarships for Health Information Management Program [9500]
Emergency Nurses Association (ENA) **[3857]**
Thomas J. Emery Memorial Scholarships [2988]
EMLF Law Student Scholarships [3869]
Emmanuel Bible College Scholarships [1693]
EMS Scholarship Awards [8150]
ENA Foundation **[3859]**
ENA Foundation Annual Conference Scholarships [3861]
ENA Foundation Seed Research Grants [3862]
ENA Foundation State Challenge Undergraduate Scholarship [3858]
Thomas O. Enders Graduate Fellowships [1876]
endMS Doctoral Studentship Awards [6614]
endMS Master's Studentship Awards [6615]
endMS Postdoctoral Fellowships [6616]
Alice Yuriko Endo Memorial Scholarships [5549]
Endocrine Society **[3863]**
Endocrine Society Summer Research Fellowships [3864]
Endodontic Educator Fellowship Award [492]
Endodontic Research Grants [493]
Endourological Society **[3866]**
Endourological Society Fellowships [3867]
Endowment Fund for Education Grants [2264]
Endowment Fund for Education, Loans [2265]
Endowment Fund for Education, Loans/Grants for Educational Materials [2266]
Endowment Fund for Education, Loans/Grants for Equipment [2267]
Energy and Mineral Law Foundation (EMLF) **[3868]**
ENF Most Valuable Student Scholarships [3854]
Engaged Anthropology Grants [10515]
Jane Engelberg Memorial Fellowship [7156]
Enhanced Insurance Scholarships Program [10340]
Enlisted Association of National Guard of the United States (EANGUS) **[3870]**
Harold E. Ennes Scholarships [9092]
Ennis Arts Association (EAA) **[3872]**
Irene Winifred Eno Grants [1342]
Ensurify **[3875]**
Ensurify Safe Driving Scholarships [3876]
Enterprise Rent-A-Car Scholarships [8073]
Entertainment Media Internships - Los Angeles [4431]
Entertainment Software Association (ESA) **[3877]**
Entomological Foundation **[3879]**
Entomological Society of Canada (ESC) **[3885]**
Entomological Society of Canada Postgraduate Awards [3890]
Entomological Society of Saskatchewan **[3893]**
Entomological Society of Saskatchewan Student Presentation Awards [3895]
Entomological Society of Saskatchewan Travel Awards [3896]
Lindsay M. Entz Memorial Scholarships [4044]
Environmental Law Institute (ELI) **[3897]**
Environmental Research and Education Foundation (EREF) **[3899]**
Environmental Research and Education Foundation Scholarships [3900]
EPA Science to Achieve Results Fellowships (STAR) [9932]
Epilepsy Foundation **[3901]**
Epilepsy Foundation Behavioral Sciences Post-Doctoral Fellowships [3902]

Epilepsy Foundation Behavioral Sciences Student Fellowships [3903]
Epilepsy Foundation Health Sciences Student Fellowships [3904]
Epilepsy Foundation Post-doctoral Research and Training Fellowships [3905]
Epilepsy Foundation Pre-doctoral Research Training Fellowships [3906]
Epilepsy Foundation Research Grants [3907]
Epilepsy Foundation Research and Training Fellowships for Clinicians [3908]
Epilepsy Newfoundland and Labrador (ENL) **[3910]**
Epsilon Delta Project 2000 Scholarships [5713]
Epsilon Epsilon Scholarships [8920]
Epsilon Mu Scholarships [5714]
Epsilon Sigma Alpha (ESA) **[3913]**
Epsilon Tau Pi's Soaring Eagle Scholarships [6924]
Epsilon Tau Scholarships [8921]
Dena Epstein Awards for Archival and Library Research in American Music [6626]
Alan R. Epstein "Reach for the Stars" Scholarships [6452]
Lee Epstein Scholarship Fund [6289]
Equal Justice Initiative (EJI) **[3915]**
Equal Justice Works **[3917]**
Equal Justice Works Fellowship Program [3918]
Equity Foundation **[3919]**
Robert C. Erb Sr. Scholarships [6353]
ERCA Community Contribution Scholarships [3804]
ERDAS Internship [1804]
Harriet Erich Graduate Fellowships [3550]
Erickson Education Scholarships [4513]
Bruce T. and Jackie Mahi Erickson Grant [7907]
Erickson Merkel Foundation **[3924]**
Erickson-Zoellers Point Scholarships [8174]
Ernest Hemingway Research Grants [4855]
The Eleanor A. Ernest Scholarships [5502]
Melissa Eleanor Ernest Scholarships [5503]
Robert P. Ernest Scholarships [5504]
Kevin Ernst Memorial Scholarship Fund [4514]
Ernst and Young Scholarships [1780]
Judge Samuel J. Ervin, III Fellowships [6004]
Jack Ervin EDI Scholarships [7460]
Extrusion Division/Lew Erwin Memorial Scholarship [9261]
ESA Foundation Life Grants [3914]
ESA Foundation Scholarship Program [3878]
Boomer Esiason Foundation General Academic Scholarships [2338]
Charles A. Esser Memorial Scholarships [1631]
Robert Esser Student Achievement Scholarships [5061]
NSPF Ray B. Essick Scholarship Awards [7192]
R. Wayne Estes Endowed Scholarships [7976]
Larry L. Etherton Scholarships [1185]
Ethnic Minority and Women's Enhancement Postgraduate Scholarships [6862]
Etruscan Foundation (EF) **[3926]**
ETS Postdoctoral Fellowships [3806]
Alex J. Ettl Grants [7127]
Eurasia Foundation **[3928]**
European College of Liberal Arts Scholarships [9981]
Eustace-Kwan Family Foundation Scholarships [8950]
Chick Evans Caddie Scholarships [10531]
Lee S. Evans/National Housing Endowment Scholarships [7003]
Evans and Petree Law Firm Scholarship [10159]
J. Everett and Louise Light Scholarships [5669]
Clifton W. Everett, Sr. Community Lawyer Fellowships [6005]
Everglades Foundation **[3930]**
Everglades Foundation Fellowship [3931]
Everglades Foundation Internship [3932]
Everglades Foundation Scholarships [3933]
Lyle and Rlene Everingham Family Scholarships [2989]
Lyle Everingham Scholarships [2990]
Excel Staffing Companies Scholarships for Excellence in Continuing Education [302]
Excellence in Geographic Information Systems Scholarships [10017]
Executive Women International (EWI) **[3934]**
Executive Women International Scholarship Program (EWISP) [3936]

Executive Women's Golf Association (EWGA) **[3937]**
ExeptionalNurse.com **[3939]**
ExeptionalNurse.com Scholarships [3940]
Exercise For Life Athletic Scholarships Program [2339]
The Expert Institute **[3941]**
The Expert Institute Legal Blog Post Writing Contest [3942]
Experts Exchange **[3943]**
Experts Exchange Scholarships Contest [3944]
The Explorers Club **[3945]**
Express Medical Supply **[3947]**
Express Medical Supply Scholarships [3948]
Extendicare Scholarships in Gerontology [2699]
William C. Ezell Fellowships [415]
Facebook Fellowships Program [3950]
Facebook Inc. **[3949]**
FACS Graduate Fellowships [6798]
FACT "Second Chance" Scholarship Program [3999]
Faculty Research Visit Grants [3606]
Fadel Educational Foundation, Inc. (FEF) **[3951]**
Faegre Baker Daniels Diversity & Inclusion Fellowships [3954]
Faegre Baker Daniels L.L.P. **[3953]**
FAER Mentored Research Training Grants [4163]
FAER Research in Education Grants [4164]
FAER Research Fellowship Grants [4165]
Claire M. Fagin Fellow Award [6983]
Fahs-Beck Fund for Research and Experimentation - Doctoral Dissertation Grants [7347]
Fahs-Beck Fund for Research and Experimentation - Postdoctoral Grants [7348]
FAIC Latin American and Caribbean Scholars Program [908]
Wayne G. Failor Scholarships [7947]
Fairbanks Chapter Legacy Scholarships [10097]
Sherman Fairchild Post Graduate Fellowships in Conservation [6591]
D.J. Fairgrave Education Trust [3672]
AIST Benjamin F. Fairless Scholarships [1996]
Faith Initiatives Internships - New York [4432]
Falcon Achievement Scholarships [8200]
Magnetic Interfaces and Nanostructures Division - The Leo M. Falicov Student Award [2155]
Fall Fellowships in Korean Studies [5870]
The Fallen Heroes Scholarships [3079]
James Mackenzie Fallows Scholarships Honoring Gertrude Baccus [8473]
James Mackenzie Fallows Scholarships Honoring William Cunningham [8474]
Families of Freedom Scholarship Fund **[3955]**
Families of Freedom Scholarship Fund - America Scholarships [3956]
Families USA **[3957]**
Family, Career and Community Leaders of America (FCCLA) **[3960]**
Family and Children's Services of Lebanon County Fund [4239]
FAMU Presidential Scholarship - Florida Community College Scholarships [4076]
Fanconi Anemia Research Fund (FARF) **[3963]**
Fanconi Anemia Research Grants [3964]
William M. Fanning Maintenance Scholarships [6831]
The Fantasy Sports Daily **[3965]**
The Fantasy Sports Daily Scholarship Program - General Scholarship for Advanced Education [3966]
Farella Braun Martel L.L.P. **[3967]**
John S.W. Fargher, Jr. Scholarships [5185]
Judge McIntyre Faries Scholarships [7977]
Palmer Farley Memorial Scholarships [4696]
Farm Equipment Manufacturers Association (FEMA) **[3969]**
Walter Moran Farmer Scholarships [10475]
Farmington UNICO Scholarships [4751]
PSI Graham Farquharson Knowledge Translation Fellowships [8124]
W.D. Farr Scholarships [6842]
Dr. Isaac Keillor Farrer, Advanced Medical Education Scholarships [7279]
David Edward Farson Scholarships [7827]
Bertha M. Fase Memorial Scholarship Fund [4515]
FASEB MARC Travel Awards [9306]
Anne M. Fassett Scholarships [9428]

FAUST

Miklos Faust International Travel Awards [1339]
James R. Favor Risk Management Scholarship Fund [5715]
FCA Grants to Artists [4227]
FCBA Foundation **[3971]**
FCBA Foundation College Scholarship Program [3972]
FCBA Foundation Internship Stipends for Law Students [3973]
FCBA Foundation Law School Scholarships [3974]
FCIL Schaffer Grants for Foreign Law Librarians [529]
Fecon Scholarships [4088]
Federal Alliance For Safe Homes (FLASH) **[3975]**
Federal Circuit Bar Association (FCBA) **[3982]**
Federal Court Bench and Bar Scholarships [10160]
Federal Employee Education and Assistance Fund (FEEA) **[3988]**
Federal Law Enforcement Officers Association (FLEOA) **[3990]**
Federal Managers Association (FMA) **[3992]**
The Federalist Society **[3994]**
Federalsburg Rotary Club Scholarships [3175]
Federated Insurance Scholarships [8074]
Federated Women's Institutes of Ontario **[3996]**
Federation of American Consumers and Travelers (FACT) **[3998]**
Federation of Asian Canadian Lawyers **[4000]**
Fédération Canadienne des Épiciers Indépendants **[4002]**
Federation of Diocesan Liturgical Commissions (FDLC) **[4004]**
Adrienne Zoe Fedok Art and Music Scholarships [4240]
FEEA-NTEU Scholarships [3989]
Nolan W. Feeser Scholarship Fund [4045]
FEF Scholarships [3952]
Lola Fehr: Nightingale Scholarships [3142]
Virginia Valk Fehsenfeld Scholarships [4591]
FEI Co. **[4006]**
Ruth B. Fein Prize [949]
Symee Ruth Feinberg Memorial Scholarships [4752]
Lillian and Alex Feir Graduate Student Travel Awards [3880]
Fejos Postdoctoral Fellowships in Ethnographic Film [10516]
Feldman Law Firm Disabled Veterans Scholarships [4009]
The Feldman Law Firm, PLLC **[4008]**
Harry Feldman Memorial Scholarships [5576]
Feldman & Royle, Attorneys at Law **[4010]**
Feldman & Royle, Attorneys at Law Autism Scholarships [4011]
Milton Feldstein Memorial Scholarships [141]
Fellowship on Women & Public Policy [10102]
Fellowships in the PMAC-AGPC [8295]
The Judy Felt Memorial Volunteerism Scholarship [1821]
Reese Felts Scholarships [10226]
Diane Ross Fennekohl Endowment Fund for Education [5716]
John E. Fenton, Jr. Public Service Awards [8435]
Dr. James A. Ferguson Emerging Infectious Diseases Fellowships [5815]
Fermilab Internships for Physics Majors [9899]
Fermilab Science Undergraduate Laboratory Internship [9900]
Fermilab Summer Internships in Science and Technology [9901]
Lt. Colonel Romeo and Josephine Bass Ferretti Scholarships [124]
FFA Scholarship [7583]
FFB-C Postdoctoral Fellowships [4262]
FHSMAI Scholarship Program [4264]
Mary Lou Fiala Fellowships [5305]
Fibrose Kystique Canada **[4012]**
FICE Scholarships [4089]
FICPA Educational Foundation 1040K Race Scholarships [4098]
Field Aviation Co., Inc. Scholarships [159]
Field Museum Graduate Student Fellowships [4017]
Field Museum of Natural History **[4016]**
Carole Fielding Student Grant [10131]
Fields Institute **[4018]**
Fields Institute - Fields Research Immersion Fellowships [4019]

Beth K. Fields Scholarships [10144]
Fieldwork Fellowships [3927]
Filipino Bar Association of Northern California (FBANC) **[4021]**
Filipino Bar Association of Northern California Scholarships (FBANC) [4022]
Christine Filipovich Scholarships [3057]
FinancialCAD Corp. **[4023]**
Alan R. and Barbara D. Finberg Fellowships [4998]
FINCAD Women in Finance Scholarships [4024]
E. Lanier Finch Scholarships [4375]
Fred Finch Scholarships [9816]
Herb and Anne Fincher Memorial Scholarships [3176]
William Robert Findley Graduate Chemistry Scholarship [7151]
Fine Arts Association (FAA) **[4025]**
Fine Arts Association Minority Scholarships [4026]
Fine Arts Association United Way Scholarships [4027]
Sakura Finetek Student Scholarships [7167]
Gordy Fink Memorial Scholarships [8343]
Helen R. Finley-Loescher and Stephen Loescher Scholarships [3283]
Finnegan Diversity Scholarships [4030]
Finnegan, Henderson, Farabow, Garrett and Dunner L.L.P. **[4029]**
Firefly Foundation **[4031]**
Firefly Foundation/ASRP Spark Award, [371], [4032]
Firland Foundation **[4033]**
Firland Foundation Graduate Pulmonary Nursing Fellowships [4034]
First Community Foundation of Pennsylvania, Williamsport-Lycoming **[4036]**
FIRST Operator Certification Awards [4074]
Eugenia Vellner Fischer Award for the Performing Arts [6556]
Martin Fischer Awards [2649]
William A. Fischer Memorial Scholarships [1805]
Fish & Richardson 1L Diversity Fellowships [4066]
Fish & Richardson P.C. **[4065]**
The Fisher-Clark Memorial Endowed Scholarships [6026]
Joseph L. Fisher Doctoral Dissertation Fellowships [8561]
Allison E. Fisher Memorial Fund **[4067]**
Charles N. Fisher Memorial Scholarships [1738]
Arthur and Juna Fisher Memorial Track Scholarships [8475]
Jack B. Fisher Scholarship Fund [9501]
Allison E. Fisher Scholarships [4068]
Ameel J. Fisher Scholarships [10227]
Sergeant Paul Fisher Scholarships [6907]
Marjorie Gosselin Fitzgerald, Upsilon, Permanently Restricted Scholarship Fund [5717]
Dr. Joseph Fitzsimmons Scholarships [9959]
Gloria Flaherty Scholarships [4466]
Scott A. Flahive Memorial Scholarship Fund [4516]
Flamenco de la Isla Society **[4069]**
Flamenco Student Scholarships [4070]
FLASH Social Science Scholarships [3976]
Reuben H. Fleet Memorial Scholarships [8704]
Albert Flegenheimer Memorial Scholarships [6494]
Fleming/Blaszcak Scholarships [9262]
Charlie Fleming Education Fund Scholarships [7195]
Sue Fleming Memorial Scholarships [2440]
Laura M. Fleming Scholarships [4194]
FLEOA Foundation Scholarship Program [3991]
Flexible Packaging Association (FPA) **[4071]**
Flexographic Technical Association (FTA) **[4073]**
Flight Attendants/Flight Technician Scholarships [6832]
Grant H. Flint International Scholarships - Category I [9337]
Grant H. Flint International Scholarships - Category II [9338]
Dave Florence Scholarship Fund [6290]
Florence Young Memorial Scholarships [1833]
Brendan Flores Alumni Leadership Circle Scholarship - Clark High School [8344]
Florida A&M University - Environmental Sciences Institute (ESI) **[4075]**
Florida Association of Directors of Nursing Administration (FADONA) **[4078]**

Florida Association for Media in Education (FAME) **[4080]**
Florida Automotive Industry Scholarships [2125]
Florida Department of Business and Professional Regulation (DBPR) **[4082]**
Florida Education Fund (FEF) **[4084]**
Florida Education Fund McKnight Doctoral Fellowships [4085]
Florida Engineering Society (FES) **[4086]**
Florida Engineering Society University Scholarships [4090]
Florida Fertilizer & Agrichemical Association (FFAA) **[4095]**
Florida Fertilizer and Agrichemical Association Scholarships [4096]
Florida Institute of Certified Public Accountants (FICPA) **[4097]**
Florida Nursery, Growers and Landscape Association (FNGLA) **[4099]**
Florida Nurses Association (FNA) **[4101]**
Florida Nurses Foundation Scholarships [4102]
Florida Outdoor Writers Association (FOWA) **[4103]**
Florida Outdoor Writers Association Scholarships [4104]
Florida Police Chiefs Association (FPCA) **[4105]**
Florida Public Health Association (FPHA) **[4107]**
Florida Public Health Association Public Health Graduate Scholarships [4108]
Florida Public Health Association Public Health Undergraduate Scholarships [4109]
Florida Public Transportation Association Scholarships (FPTA) [1164]
Florida Retired Educators Association (FREA) **[4110]**
Floto-Peel Family Scholarship Fund [4517]
Barney Flynn Memorial Scholarships [3097]
John Flynn Memorial Scholarships [3284]
Paul B. and Aline Flynn Scholarships [9429]
FMA-FEEA Scholarship Program [3993]
Lydia Fohn-Hansen/Lola Hill Memorial Scholarships [10018]
Alice J. Foit Scholarships [9502]
Follicular Lymphoma Research Grants [6159]
Gail Goodell Folsom Memorial Scholarships [6650]
Fondation Asie Pacifique du Canada **[4112]**
Fondation pour le journalisme canadien **[4116]**
Fondation des Prix Michener **[4120]**
Fondation Savoy **[4122]**
Fonds de la Société canadienne d' évaluation pour l'éducation **[4124]**
Frank Fong Scholarships [9076]
Food and Drug Law Institute (FDLI) **[4126]**
Food Processing Suppliers Association (FPSA) **[4128]**
Foot Locker Foundation, Inc. **[4130]**
Foot Locker Scholar Athletes [4131]
For the Love of Chocolate Foundation Scholarships [4133]
For the Love of Chocolate Scholarship Foundation **[4132]**
Clay Ford Florida Board of Accountancy Minority Scholarships [4083]
Ford Foundation Dissertation Fellowships [6675]
Ford Foundation Diversity Fellowships [6676]
Ford Foundation Postdoctoral Fellowships [6677]
Ford Foundation Predoctoral Fellowships [6678]
A. Ward Ford Memorial Research Grants [1351]
Michael D. Ford Memorial Scholarship [10057]
Ford Motor Company Scholarship [10113]
Anne Ford Scholarships [6850]
V. Thomas Forehand, Jr. Scholarships [10302]
Forensic Sciences Foundation (FSF) **[4134]**
Forest History Society (FHS) **[4136]**
Nancy B. Forest and L. Michael Honaker Master's Grant for Research in Psychology [1133]
Foresters Scholarships [5095]
The FormsBirds Scholarships [4140]
Formsbirds.com **[4139]**
Leland Stanford Forrest Scholarship [3673]
Forsyth County Nursing Scholarships [10581]
Forsyth County United Way Scholarships [5925]
Fort Atkinson Community Foundation **[4141]**
Forté Fellowships [4151]
Forté Foundation **[4150]**
Stephen J. Fortgang/University of Northern Iowa Chapter Scholarship [5670]

Genevieve Forthun Scholarships [8092]
Forum for Theological Exploration (FTE) **[4152]**
Edward Foster Awards [2666]
Foster Care to Success (FC2S) **[4156]**
Emily P. Foster Fellowships [7739]
Dr. Nancy Foster Scholarship Program, [7077], **[4158]**
Andrew Foster Scholarships [6815]
Dr. Nancy Foster Scholarships [4159]
Fostering Hope Scholarships Fund [7828]
Foundation for the Advancement of Aboriginal Youth Bursary Program [3389]
Foundation for the Advancement of Aboriginal Youth Scholarships [3390]
Foundation of the American Institute for Conservation of Historic & Artistic Works **[4160]**
Foundation of American Institute for Conservation Lecture Grants [909]
Foundation for Anesthesia Education and Research (FAER) **[4162]**
Foundation for Appalachian Ohio **[4166]**
Foundation for the Carolinas (FFTC) **[4171]**
Foundation for the Carolinas Rotary Scholarship Fund [4195]
Foundation for Community Association Research **[4224]**
Foundation for Contemporary Arts (FCA) **[4226]**
Foundation for Educational Exchange between Canada and the United States of America **[4228]**
Foundation for Enhancing Communities **[4230]**
Foundation of the Federal Bar Association (FFBA) **[4259]**
Foundation of the Federal Bar Association Public Service Scholarship Award [4260]
Foundation Fighting Blindness (FFB) **[4261]**
Foundation of the Hospitality Sales and Marketing Association International **[4263]**
Foundation of the International Association of Defense Counsel (IADC) **[4265]**
Foundation of the National Student Nurses Association (FNSNA) **[4267]**
The Foundation of the National Student Nurses' Association Scholarships [7190]
Foundation for Neonatal Research and Education (FNRE) **[4271]**
Foundation for Neonatal Research and Education Scholarships [4272]
Foundation of the Pennsylvania Medical Society **[4273]**
Foundation for the Preservation of Honey Bees Graduate Scholarships [4281]
Foundation for the Preservation of Honey Bees, Inc. **[4280]**
Foundation Relations Internships - Los Angeles [4433]
Foundation for Seacoast Health **[4282]**
Foundation for Seacoast Health Scholarships [4283]
Foundation for Surgical Technology Scholarships [2076]
Founding Fathers Leadership Scholarships [10617]
Founding Mothers' Student Scholarships - Graduate [2015]
Mary Metzger Fouse Memorial Scholarship Fund [5718]
Howard Fox Memorial Law Scholarships [2235]
Don Fox Memorial Scholarship [211]
Terry Fox Memorial Scholarship [7206]
Captain Ernest Fox Perpetual Scholarships [3080]
FPA Summer Internships Program [4072]
FPDA Motion and Control Network **[4284]**
Brandon Fradd Fellowship [3033]
Fragile X Research Foundation of Canada (FXRFC) **[4286]**
William A. Fraker Student Heritage Awards [1256]
Frame My Future Scholarships Contest [2938]
Franchise Law Diversity Scholarship Awards [5336]
Joe Francis Haircare Scholarship Foundation **[4288]**
Joe Francis Haircare Scholarships [4289]
Parker B. Francis Respiratory Research Grants [1211]
Gloria Francke Scholarship [1579]
Joe Francomano Scholarships [5630]
AIHS Cy Frank Fellowships: Impact Assessment [254]
Mayme and Herb Frank Scholarship Program [1782]

Johnny & Sarah Frank Scholarships [10019]
Michael W. and Jean D. Franke Family Foundation Scholarships [1186]
Loren Frankel Memorial Scholarships [995]
Mary Weiking Franken Scholarships [8093]
The Ginny Frankenthaler Memorial Scholarships [9385]
John Hope Franklin Dissertation Fellowships [1080]
Franklin District Medical Society **[4290]**
James Franklin and Dorothy J. Warnell Scholarship Fund [3321]
Franklin Elementary School PTA Scholarships [8476]
Franklin Empire Scholarship Awards [3829]
John Hope Franklin Prize [5971]
Franklin Research Grants [1081]
Benjamin Franklin Trust Fund [4046]
Violet and Cyril Franks Scholarship [1144]
John L. and Victory E. Frantz Scholarship [4518]
Joseph Frasca Excellence in Aviation Scholarships [10104]
Fraser Family Scholarships [8345]
Fraser Stryker **[4292]**
Fraser Stryker Diversity Scholarships [4293]
FRAXA Postdoctoral Fellowships [4295]
FRAXA Research Foundation **[4294]**
FREA Scholarship [4111]
Fred and Avery Test Scholarships [10180]
Jan and Glenn Fredericks Scholarship [10058]
Fredrikson and Byron Foundation Minority Scholarships [4297]
Fredrikson and Byron P.A. **[4296]**
Emanuel R. Freedman Scholarships [7772]
Freedom Alliance **[4298]**
Freedom Alliance Scholarships [4299]
Freedom From Religion Foundation (FFRF) **[4300]**
Kevin Freeman Travel Grants [6627]
Don Freeman Work-in-Progress Grants [9096]
Malcolm and Mildred Freidberg Fellowships [6327]
The French Culinary Institute Classic Pastry Arts Scholarships [3487]
Ardell French Memorial Scholarship [10059]
Richard A. Freund International Scholarships [1389]
Ludo Frevel Crystallography Scholarships [5294]
Doris W. Frey Memorial Scholarships [9430]
Carleton A. Friday Scholarship [6527]
Dale E. Fridell Memorial Scholarships [9593]
Fried, Frank, Harris, Shriver and Jacobson Fellowships [4303]
Fried, Frank, Harris, Shriver and Jacobson L.L.P. **[4302]**
MHS Marc Friedlaender Fellowships [6328]
William A. Friedlander Scholarships [2991]
A.E. Robert Friedman Scholarships [7795]
Phil Friel Scholarships [6354]
Joel R. Friend Scholarships [2227]
Kennedy T. Friend Scholarships [325]
Friends of Canadian Broadcasting (FCB) **[4304]**
Friends of the Christofor Foundation Scholarships [7280]
Friends of Coal Scholarships [10523]
Friends of Mary Automotive Scholarships [8872]
Friends of Project 10 Inc. **[4306]**
Friends of Project 10 Models of Excellence Scholarships [4307]
Henry Friesen Awards and Lectures [9074]
Froberg-Suess JD/MBA Scholarships [7978]
Dean A. Froehlich Endowed Scholarships [6027]
Melbourne and Alice E. Frontjes Scholarships [4592]
Patricia and Phillip Frost Fellowships [9002]
"Frugal Student" Scholarships [7950]
Fruits and Vegetable Industries Scholarships [6487]
Marian Johnson Frutiger Scholarships [8922]
William and Francis Fry Honorary Fellowships for Contributions to Therapeutic Ultrasound [5431]
Mary Alice Fry Memorial Scholarships [5719]
FSF Student Travel Grant [4135]
FTE Dissertation Fellowships [4153]
FTE Doctoral Fellowships [4154]
FTE North American Doctoral Fellowships [4155]
Gerard Swartz Fudge Memorial Scholarships [5027]
Keiko Fukuda Scholarships [9960]
Kathryn Fuller Science for Nature Post-Doctoral Fellowships [10707]
Don and Eileen Fulton Nursing Scholarships [9566]

Arthur Flagler Fultz Research Awards [1013]
Daniel G. and Helen I. Fultz Scholarship Fund [4047]
Fund for American Studies (TFAS) **[4308]**
Arkansas Nursing Foundation - Dorothea Fund Scholarships [1656]
Funeral Service Foundation (FSF) **[4311]**
Fur Takers of America (FTA) **[4315]**
Donald M. Furbush Professional Development Grants [5216]
Dr. Horace Furumoto Innovations Professional Development - Young Investigator Awards [1352]
Future CPA Scholarships [1642]
Future Leader Initial NCTM Annual Meeting Attendance Awards [6888]
Future Leader in Radiocommunications Scholarships [3394]
Future Leaders of Manufacturing Scholarships [9181]
Future STEM Teacher Scholarship [9657]
FXRFC Medical Research Postdoctoral Fellowships [4287]
GAAC Project Grants [4445]
Mearl K. Gable II Memorial Grants [4709]
Gabriel Dumont College Graduate Student Bursary [3742]
Gaddy Student Scholarships [10582]
Franciszek Gadzala Memorial Scholarships [8575]
Gaebe Eagle Scout Awards [6925]
Harry Gairey Scholarships [2282]
Farley Moody Galbraith Scholarship Fund [3262]
Thomas W. Gallagher Scholarships Fund [9503]
Louise Bales Gallagher Scholarships [3551]
William E. "Bill" Gallagher Scholarships [7829]
Whitney Laine Gallahar Memorial Scholarship Fund [3263]
Sam Gallant Memorial Scholarships [1643]
Gallery Collection **[4317]**
The Gallery Collection's Create-A-Greeting Card Scholarships [4318]
Carolyn Gallmeyer Scholarships [4593]
Mathilda and Carolyn Gallmeyer Scholarships [4594]
Gallo Blue Chip Scholarships [4724]
Priscilla Gamble Scholarships [2992]
Gamewarden Scholarship program [4320]
Gamewardens Association, Vietnam to Present **[4319]**
Gamma Chi Project 2000 Scholarships [5720]
Gamma Iota Scholarships - Gamma Tau [8923]
Gamma Iota Scholarships - Kappa Eta [8924]
Gamma Iota Scholarships - Zeta Kappa [8925]
Gamma Iota Scholarships - Zeta Nu [8926]
Gamma Mu Project 2000 Scholarships [5721]
Gamma Pi Project 2000 Scholarships [5722]
Gamma Sigma Alpha (GSA) **[4321]**
Gamma Sigma Alpha Graduate Scholarships [4322]
Gamma Theta Project 2000 Scholarships [5723]
Gamma Zeta Project 2000 Scholarships [5724]
Guy P. Gannett Scholarships [6195]
John A. Gans Scholarship [1580]
Gantenbein Medical Fund Fellowship [3497]
Veronica Gantt Memorial Scholarships [8346]
GAPA Scholarships [4327]
Joel Garcia Memorial Scholarship [2825]
Michael and Gina Garcia Rail Engineering Scholarships [1187]
William R. Gard Memorial Scholarships [6654]
Garden Club of America (GCA) **[4323]**
Garden Club of America Awards in Tropical Botany (GCA) [4324]
Garden Club Council of Winston-Salem and Forsyth County Council Scholarships [10583]
Jewell Gardiner Scholarships [2473]
IGS John Gardner Fellowship [10108]
Gardner Foundation Infusion Nurses Society Education Scholarships [5145]
Robert Gardner Memorial Fellowships [4809]
Dwight D. Gardner Scholarships [5186]
Victoria M. Gardner Scholarships [10228]
Eugene Garfield Doctoral Dissertation Fellowship [2239]
Peter M. Gargano Scholarship Fund [3709]
Garikian Scholarship Fund [1694]
Garmin Scholarships [160]
Gerald Garner Memorial Scholarships [7979]

Gail Garner R.I.S.E. Memorial Scholarships [8477]
NWT Law Foundation/Graeme Garson Scholarships [7554]
Marcus Mosiah Garvey Scholarships [5523]
Kays Gary Scholarships [10229]
Ethel Mae Gaston Memorial Scholarships [7380]
Edwin W. Gaston Scholarships [341]
Gates Cambridge Scholarships [6746]
The Gates Millennium Scholars [4903]
Marian P. and David M. Gates Scholarship for Non-Residents [10181]
Kappa Kappa Gamma Foundation - Mary Maxwell Gates Scholarships [5725]
Stephen Gates Scholarships [10230]
Frank Caleb & Margaret Thompson Gates Student Scholarships [10182]
David A. and Pamela A. Gault Charitable Fund [9504]
Gauthier Family Scholarship Fund [4519]
A.R.F.O.R.A. Martha Gavrila Scholarships for Women [1226]
GAWP Graduate Scholarships [4377]
Gay Asian Pacific Alliance Foundation (GAPA) **[4326]**
Gay and Lesbian Business Association of Santa Barbara (GLBA) **[4328]**
Lowell Gaylor Memorial Scholarships [161]
Florence S. Gaynor Scholarships [6755]
GCABC Youth Scholarship Awards [4419]
GCSAA Scholars Competition [4483]
GCSAA Student Essay Contest [4484]
G.E. Aviation Scholarships [2993]
G.E. Lighting Canada Community Leadership Awards [3830]
GED Jump Start Scholarships [8805]
GEF Scholarship Program [4647]
Gehring Memorial Foundation Scholarships [5100]
Milacron Geier Scholarships [2994]
Victoria S. and Bradley L. Geist Scholarships [4795]
Lawrence Gelfand - Armin Rappaport - Walter LaFeber Dissertation Fellowships [9137]
Irma Gelhausen Scholarship Fund [5930]
Joseph H. Gellert/Dutchess County Bar Association Scholarships [3744]
Elaine Gelman Scholarship Awards [6772]
Gemological Institute of America (GIA) **[4332]**
The Gene and John Athletic Scholarships [9589]
General Aviation Manufacturers Association (GAMA) **[4348]**
General Falcon Scholarships [8201]
General Federation of Women's Clubs of Massachusetts **[4350]**
General Mills Foundation Scholarships [869]
General Motors Foundation **[4358]**
General Scholarships for Higher Learning [4960]
Generation III Scholarships [3783]
Genesee Finger Lakes Chapter of Air and Waste Management Association (GFL AWMA) **[4360]**
Geological Society of America (GSA) **[4362]**
Geological Society of America Graduate Student Research Grants [4364]
George Cedric Metcalf Charitable Foundation **[4365]**
George Foreman Tribute to Lyndon B. Johnson Scholarships [8405]
George W. and Ethel B. Hoefler Fund [3322]
Georgetown Working League **[4367]**
Georgetown Working League Scholarships [4368]
Georgia Association of Broadcasters (GAB) **[4374]**
Georgia Association of Water Professionals (GAWP) **[4376]**
Georgia Engineering Foundation **[4379]**
Georgia Engineering Foundation Scholarships [4380]
Georgia Gerontology Society **[4381]**
Georgia Library Association (GLA) **[4383]**
Georgia Press Educational Foundation (GPEF) **[4386]**
Gerber Foundation **[4391]**
Gerber Foundation Merit Scholarships [4392]
Doris Y. and John J. Gerber Scholarships [10464]
Daniel Gerber, Sr. Medallion Scholarships [4393]
Walter Gerboth Awards [6628]
Anthony Gerharz Scholarships [6583]
German Historical Institute (GHI) **[4394]**

German Historical Institute Doctoral and Postdoctoral Fellowships [4395]
German Historical Institute Fellowships at the Horner Library [4396]
German Marshall Fund of the United States (GMF) **[4397]**
German Society of Pennsylvania (GSP) **[4403]**
German Society Scholarships [4404]
German Studies Research Grants [3607]
Bunny Kline Gerner and Robin Gerner Doty Memorial Adelphe Scholarships [5726]
Gerrie Electric Memorial Scholarship Awards [3831]
Eloise Gerry Fellowships [8904]
Elizabeth Tucker Gessley Scholarship [5727]
Getty Conservation Guest Scholar Grants [4406]
Getty Foundation **[4405]**
Getty Foundation Library Research Grants [4407]
Getty GRI-NEH Postdoctoral Fellowships [4408]
Getty Postdoctoral Fellowships [4409]
Getty Postdoctoral Fellowships in Conservation Science [4410]
Getty Predoctoral Fellowships [4411]
Getty Research Exchange Fellowship Program for Cultural Heritage Preservation [1205]
Getty Scholar Grants [4412]
Gettysburg College - Eisenhower Institute **[4413]**
GFLC AWMA Scholarships [4361]
GFOA Minorities in Government Finance Scholarship [4502]
GFWC Women's Club of South County Scholarships [8606]
GFWCMA Communication Disorder/Speech Therapy Scholarships [4353]
Ghana-Canada Association of British Columbia (GCABC) **[4418]**
GIA Scholarship- Distance Education eLearning [4334]
GIA Scholarships - On Campus [4335]
IDSA Gianninoto Graduate Scholarships [5136]
Emily V. Gibbes Scholarships [7381]
John J. Gibbons Fellowships in Public Interest and Constitutional Law [4421]
Gibbons P.C. **[4420]**
Laverne L. Gibson Memorial Scholarships [7830]
Robert D. Gibson Scholarship [1581]
Joy Gibson Scholarships [10231]
Tom Gifford Scholarships [4520]
Shane Gilbert Memorial Scholarships [7831]
Margaret S. Gilbert Scholarship Fund [9505]
Gilbreth Memorial Fellowships [5187]
Terry M. Giles Honor Scholar Program [7980]
Composites Division/Harold Giles Scholarship [9263]
William Harrison Gill Education Fund [2228]
AIST Midwest Member Chapter - Jack Gill Scholarships [1997]
R.L. Gillette Scholarships [821]
Gilliam Fellowships for Advanced Study [4974]
Benjamin A. Gilman International Scholarship [10060]
Leo Gilmartin Scholarships [8167]
Keith Gilmore Foundation - Diploma Scholarships [4423]
Keith Gilmore Foundation **[4422]**
Keith Gilmore Foundation - Postgraduate Scholarships [4424]
Keith Gilmore Foundation - Undergraduate Scholarships [4425]
Susan Kay Munson Gilmore Memorial Scholarships [3285]
Allan Gilmour & Eric Jirgens Point Scholarships [8175]
Jack R. Gilstrap Scholarships [1165]
Lawrence Ginocchio Aviation Scholarships [6833]
Girls Incorporated of the Greater Capital Region **[4426]**
Alex Gissler Memorial Scholarships [6355]
Jack Gitlitz CA Memorial Scholarships for Study in Israel [5577]
GJEC Dissertation Completion Fellowships [6490]
GLA Beard Scholarships [4384]
GLA Hubbard Scholarships [4385]
GLAAD **[4429]**
GLAAD Communications/PR Internships - New York [4434]
GLAAD News Internships - New York [4435]

GLAAD Spanish-Language and Latino Media Internships - Los Angeles [4436]
GLAAD Youth Issues Internships - New York [4437]
J. Robert Gladden Orthopaedic Society International Traveling Fellowship [4443]
J. Robert Gladden Orthopaedic Society (JRGOS) **[4442]**
Senator James Gladstone Memorial Scholarships [249]
Jane R. Glaser Scholarships [1476]
John Glaser Scholarships [3121]
Glass Art Association of Canada (GAAC) **[4444]**
Dr. Helen Preston Glass Fellowships [2700]
Jane Glassco Northern Fellowships [4500]
GLATA Living Memorial Doctorate Scholarships [4653]
GLATA Living Memorial Graduate Scholarships [4654]
Herman and Bess Glazer Scholarship Fund [4662]
Glazing Industry Scholarships [8347]
Gleaner Life Insurance Society (GLIS) **[4446]**
Gleaner Life Insurance Society Scholarships [4447]
Glendale Latino Association (GLA) **[4448]**
Glendale Latino Association Scholarships [4449]
Glenn/AFAR Scholarships for Research in the Biology of Aging [788]
Jane S. Glenn Memorial Endowed Scholarships [8626]
Glenn Miller Birthplace Society (GMBS) **[4450]**
Glenn Miller Scholarships [4451]
Glens Falls Foundation **[4452]**
Global Business Travel Association (GBTA) **[4455]**
Global Scholarship Alliance (GSA) **[4457]**
Global Sustainable Electricity Partnership **[4459]**
Global Volcanism Program for Visiting Scientist/Postdoctoral Fellowships [9032]
Globe-Trotters Member Chapter Scholarships [1998]
Franciszek Glogowski Memorial Scholarships [8576]
Alfred B. Glossbrenner Scholarships [1999]
Bud Glover Memorial Scholarships [162]
Irene Carlson Gnaedinger Memorial Scholarships [6028]
Dr. Robert H. Goddard Memorial Scholarships [7179]
Goddard Systems **[4461]**
Glenn Godfrey Memorial Scholarships [5864]
Godparents for Tanzania **[4463]**
Godparents for Tanzania Scholarship [4464]
Rosen Goertz Point Scholarship [8176]
Goethe Society of North America (GSNA) **[4465]**
Shirley J. Gold Scholarship [793]
William Goldberg Diamond Corp. Scholarships [4336]
Daniel B. Goldberg Scholarship [4503]
Golden Belt Community Foundation **[4467]**
Golden Eagle Coins L.L.C. **[4469]**
Golden Eagle Coins Scholarships [4470]
Golden Key Graduate Scholar Awards [6747]
Golden Key International Honour Society (GKIHS) **[4471]**
Golden Key Study Abroad Scholarships [4472]
William R. Goldfarb Memorial Scholarships [1739]
Goldia.com **[4473]**
Goldia.com Jewelry Scholarships [4474]
Rhode Island Commission on Women/Freda H. Goldman Education Awards [8607]
Dr. Guido Goldman Fellowships [724]
Goldman Sachs/Matsuo Takabuki Commemorative Scholarships [7908]
Alois and Marie Goldmann Scholarship Fund [5041]
Barry M. Goldwater Scholarships [10319]
Golf Canada **[4475]**
Golf Course Superintendents Association of America (GCSAA) **[4482]**
Joshua Gomes Memorial Scholarship Fund [6990]
Charles D. Gonthier Research Fellowships [2668]
Gonzaga University School of Law **[4486]**
Millie Gonzalez Memorial Scholarships [4859]
Goodman Acker, P.C. **[4488]**
Goodman Acker Scholarships [4489]
Victor and Ruth N. Goodman Memorial Scholarships [4697]
Baxter Corporation - Jean Goodwill Scholarships [24]
Goodwin Procter L.L.P. **[4490]**

James L. and Genevieve H. Goodwin Scholarships [4753]
Google-American Indian Science and Engineering Society Scholarships [4495]
Google European Doctoral Fellowships [4496]
Google Hispanic College Fund Scholarships [4497]
Google Inc. **[4492]**
Google Lime Scholarships for Students with Disabilities [6089]
Google US/Canada PhD Fellowships [4498]
Richard Goolsby Scholarship Fund [4196]
Lucille May Gopie Scholarships [2283]
The Gordon Foundation **[4499]**
Wilhelmina Gordon Foundation Scholarships [6854]
Barnett D. Gordon Scholarships [5101]
FAMU Presidential Scholarship - George W. Gore Assistantship Scholarship [4077]
Sarah "Sally" Ives Gore Gamma Kappa Sapphire Scholarships [5728]
Pauline LaFon Gore Scholarships [3227]
Richard C. Gorecki Scholarships [8202]
TCDA Bill Gorham Student Scholarships [670]
Nettie and Jesse Gorov Scholarships [3286]
Consuelo W. Gosnell Memorial Scholarships [6789]
American Association of University Women Sue Gottcent Memorial Scholarship Fund [9431]
Louis Gottschalk Prize [1291]
Carl W. Gottschalk Research Scholar Grants [1381]
Norma Gotwalt Scholarship Fund [4241]
Charles F. Gould Endowment Scholarships [10020]
Government Documents Special Interest Section - Veronica Maclay Student Grants [530]
Government Finance Officers Association of United States and Canada (GFOA) **[4501]**
Wilford Hayes Gowen Scholarship Fund [10161]
Goya Scholarships [8852]
William L. Graddy Law School Scholarships [9432]
Graduate Fellowship Program - Research Fellowships (GFP) [8833]
Graduate Fellowships in Alternatives in Scientific Research [5333]
Graduate Realtor Institute Scholarships [5817]
Graduate Research Awards for Disarmament, Arms Control and Non-Proliferation [8961]
Graduate Research-Travel Scholarships [3891]
Graduate Student Travel Grants, [462], [9111]
A. Allen Graffham Research Grants [1842]
Graham and Dunn 1L Diversity Fellowships [4506]
Graham and Dunn P.C. **[4505]**
Rachel Graham Memorial Scholarships [8478]
Jim Graham Scholarships [7482]
Grand Canyon Historical Society (GCHS) **[4507]**
Grand Canyon Historical Society Scholarships [4508]
Grand Haven Area Community Foundation **[4509]**
Grand Haven Offshore Challenge Scholarship Fund [4521]
Grand Island Community Foundation **[4557]**
Grand Lodge of Saskatchewan **[4570]**
Grand Rapids Community Foundation (GRCF) **[4572]**
Grand Rapids Scholarship Association [4595]
Grand Rapids University Prep Founder's Scholarships [4596]
Grande Prairie 4-H District Scholarships [8]
Charles Hall Grandgent Awards [3525]
Grandmothers for Peace International (GPI) **[4638]**
Granger Business Association (GBA) **[4640]**
Granger Business Association College Scholarships [4641]
Grant Assistance Program for Autism Professionals - College Programs [7650]
Grant Assistance Program for Autism Professionals - Doctoral Programs [7651]
Grant Assistance Program for Autism Professionals - Institutional Standards [7652]
Grant Assistance Program for Autism Professionals - Masters Programs [7653]
Grant Assistance Program for Autism Professionals - Professional Certification Programs [7654]
Grant Assistance Program for Autism Professionals - Retroactive Assistance [7655]
Grant Assistance Program for Autism Professionals - Undergraduate Programs [7656]
Russ Grant Memorial Scholarship for Tennis [7832]
AMA/Charles H. Grant Scholarships [39]

Grass Fellowships at the Marine Biological Laboratory [4643]
Grass Foundation **[4642]**
Lucille Cheever Graubart/Lambda Scholarships [8927]
Paul and Helen L. Grauer Scholarships [1740]
Thomas B. Grave and Elizabeth F. Grave Scholarships [6247]
Caswell Grave Scholarships [6248]
Camille F. Gravel, Jr. Scholarships [6114]
Gravure Education Foundation (GEF) **[4644]**
Gravure Publishing Council Scholarships [4648]
Mona Gray Creative Arts Scholarships [5593]
Ken Gray Endowment Scholarship [10061]
IADR John Gray Fellowship [5251]
Alexander G. Gray, Jr. Scholarships [6340]
Zelma Gray Medical School Scholarships [4168]
Arkansas Nursing Foundation - Mary Gray Scholarships [1657]
Graybar Canada Award of Excellence Scholarships [3832]
Grays Harbor Community Foundation **[4650]**
Grays Harbor Community Foundation Scholarships [4651]
Great Falls Broadcasters Association Scholarships [6577]
Great Lakes Athletic Trainers Association (GLATA) **[4652]**
Great Lakes Commission (GLC) **[4655]**
Great Lakes Commission Sea Grant Fellowships [4656]
Great Lakes Section Diversity Scholarship [5178]
GREAT MINDS Collegiate Scholarship Program [338]
Greater Cincinnati Scholarships Association [2995]
Greater Research Opportunities (GRO) Undergraduate Fellowships [9933]
Greater Seattle Business Association (GSBA) **[4657]**
Greater Seattle Business Association Scholarships (GSBA Scholarships) [4658]
Greater Valley Chamber of Commerce **[4659]**
Greater Washington Society of Certified Public Accountants (GWSCPA) **[4663]**
Frank L. Greathouse Government Accounting Scholarship [4504]
Bishop Charles P. Greco Graduate Fellowships [5853]
Philip F. Greco Memorial Scholarships [6170]
Greek Orthodox Archdiocese of America **[4665]**
Greek Orthodox Archdiocese of America Paleologos Graduate Scholarships [4666]
Green Hill Yacht and Country Club Scholarships [3177]
Green Knight Economic Development Corporation (GKEDC) **[4667]**
Green Knight Economic Development Corporation Scholarships [4668]
Crystal Green Memorial Scholarship [2314]
James H. and Shirley L. Green Scholarship Fund [9506]
Howard L. Green Scholarships [7317]
Priscilla Green Scholarships [3465]
William G. and Mayme J. Green Scholarships [4754]
K2TEO Martin J. Green, Sr. Memorial Scholarships [1741]
Leslie C. Green Veterans Scholarships [3458]
Helen R. Greenamyer Memorial Scholarships [9567]
Robert D. Greenberg Scholarships [9093]
Michael Greenberg Student Writing Competition [7052]
Richard L. Greene Dissertation Award [1090]
Curt Greene Memorial Scholarships [4725]
Elizabeth Greenhalgh Memorial Scholarships in Journalism, Graphic Arts, or Photography [10639]
Greenlining Institute **[4669]**
Greenlining Institute Fellowships [4670]
Guy P. Greenwald Jr. Endowed Scholarships [7981]
Greenwich Scholarship Association (GSA) **[4671]**
Greenwich Scholarship Association Scholarships (GSA) [4672]
Anna Munger Greenwood Memorial Adelphe Scholarship [5729]
Francis Harris Gresham Scholarships [9433]
Lily H. Gridley Memorial Scholarships [10651]

Griffin Foundation **[4673]**
Griffin Foundation Scholarships [4674]
Velma Shotwell Griffin Memorial Scholarship Fund [9507]
Homajean Grisham Memorial Scholarship [7534]
Enid Hall Griswold Memorial Scholarships [7152]
Andrew Gronholdt Arts Scholarship Awards [310]
Reginald K. Groome Memorial Scholarships [8823]
Jennifer C. Groot Memorial Fellowships [657]
Caroline L. Gross Fellowships [7304]
Katherine M. Grosscup Scholarships [4325]
Charles Grossman Graduate Scholarships [5306]
F.C. Grote Fund Scholarships [326]
Kathern F. Gruber Scholarship Program [2312]
Elizabeth M. Gruber Scholarships [3583]
Jack M. and Mary Lou Gruber Scholarships [6029]
Gruwell Scholarships [3178]
GSA Scholarships for International Nurses [4458]
Guajardo & Marks Law School Scholarships [4676]
Guajardo & Marks LLP **[4675]**
Guelph Caribbean Canadian Association **[4677]**
Guelph Caribbean Canadian Association Graduate Scholarships [4678]
Guelph Caribbean Canadian Association Undergraduate Scholarships [4679]
Melissa Ann Guerra Scholarships [3098]
Ronald P. Guerrette Future Farmers of America Scholarship Fund [6196]
Eleanor Guetzloe Undergraduate Scholarship [3433]
Harry Frank Guggenheim Dissertation Fellowships [4681]
Guggenheim Fellowships [9022]
Harry Frank Guggenheim Foundation (HFG) **[4680]**
Harry Frank Guggenheim Foundation Research Grants [4682]
John Simon Guggenheim Memorial Fellowships - U.S. and Canadian Competition [4684]
John Simon Guggenheim Memorial Foundation **[4683]**
Bobette Bibo Gugliotta Memorial Scholarships for Creative Writing [8951]
Jimmy Guild Memorial Scholarships [6030]
GuildScholar Awards [5596]
Catharine Wilder Guiles Scholarships [6197]
Hai Guin Scholarships Association [1695]
Guin-Stanford Scholarships [3264]
Calouste Gulbenkian Foundation Scholarships [1696]
Gulf and Caribbean Fisheries Institute (GCFI) **[4685]**
Gulf Coast Past President's Scholarships [1413]
Larry Gulley Scholarships [9125]
Harold Gulliksen Psychometric Research Fellowships [3807]
Warren and Rosalie Gummow Endowed Scholarships [7982]
Scott A. Gunder, MD, DCMS Presidential Scholarships [4276]
SME Education Foundation Connie & Robert T. Gunter Scholarships [9182]
Guntley-Lorimer Science and Arts Scholarships [2284]
George Gurney Fellowships [9003]
Patricia S. Gustafson '56 Memorial Scholarships [3710]
George Gustafson HSE Memorial Scholarships [1414]
Mary Ewing Guthrey/Mary Keller Moyer Memorial Scholarship [5730]
Guzkowski Family Scholarships [8479]
Sara Gwisdalla Memorial Scholarships [7833]
GWS Scholarships [145]
GWSCPA Scholarships [4664]
Ed Haas Memorial Scholarships [9568]
Wesley R. Habley NACADA Summer Institute Scholarships [6672]
Hackett Family Scholarships [4597]
Louise Wallace Hackney Fellowships for the Study of Chinese Art [1058]
HACU/Denny's Hungry for Education Scholarships [4883]
HACU/Empacadora Fruticola Santa Ines S.A. de C.V. Scholarships [4884]
HACU/Gilberto Salazar Escoboza Scholarships [4885]

HACU/JCPenny Leadership Excellence Scholarships [4886]
HACU/KIA Motors America, Inc. Scholarships [4887]
HACU/NASCAR Scholarships [4888]
HACU/Videxport S.A. de C.V. Scholarships [4889]
Perry F. Hadlock Memorial Scholarships [1742]
Suzanne Lovell Hadsell Memorial Scholarship [5731]
HAESF Graduate Scholarships [5008]
HAESF Professional Internship Program [5009]
HAESF Senior Leaders and Scholars Fellowships [5010]
Joseph E. Hagan Memorial Scholarships [4312]
Hagley Museum and Library [4687]
Leslie Jane Hahn Memorial Scholarships [8705]
Jerome Hake Engineering Scholarships [4144]
Lee Hakel Graduate Student Scholarship [9152]
Gene Halker Memorial Scholarships [4145]
Hall of Achievement Scholarships [2450]
Stephen K. Hall ACWA Water Law and Policy Scholarships [1872]
Joyce C. Hall College Scholarships [7960]
Hall County Medical Society Scholarships [4563]
Anna E. Hall Memorial Scholarships [8055]
Chappie Hall Scholarship Program [2]
Guy D. and Mary Edith Halladay Graduate Scholarships [4598]
Guy D. and Mary Edith Halladay Music Scholarships [4599]
David J. Hallissey Memorial Internships [1441]
Harold B. Halter Memorial Scholarship [3970]
Patty Hamilton Early Childhood Development Scholarships [10021]
Hamilton Industrial Environmental Association (HIEA) [4690]
Hamilton Industrial Environmental Association Bursaries-Mohawk College [4691]
Alice Hamilton Prize [1311]
TIAA-CREF Ruth Simms Hamilton Research Fellowships [9737]
Al Hamilton Scholarships [2285]
Stan Hamilton Scholarships [8766]
Dwight A. Hamilton Scottish Rite Foundation of Colorado Graduate Scholarships [8821]
George and Mary Josephine Hamman Foundation [4692]
George and Mary Josephine Hamman Foundation Scholarships [4693]
Caitlin Hammaren Memorial Scholarship [5732]
Richard A. Hammill Scholarship Fund [981]
Jay Hammond Memorial Scholarships [10098]
Hammond Power Solutions Inc. Outstanding Electrical Scholar Awards [3833]
Tommie J. Hamner Scholarships [8094]
Harry Hampton Fund Scholarship [4733]
Hampton Roads Association of Social Workers Scholarships [4698]
Hampton Roads Community Foundation [4694]
Hampton Roads Sanitation District Environmental Scholarships [4699]
HANA Scholarships [9852]
Morris Hanauer Scholarships [4337]
Hancock Family Snow Hill High School Scholarships [3179]
Robert Hancock Memorial Scholarship Awards [6498]
Pauline Hand Memorial Scholarships [9569]
Handweavers Guild of America (HGA) [4707]
Handweavers Guild of America and Dendel Scholarships [4710]
Vincent S. Haneman-Joseph B. Perskie Memorial Foundation Scholarships [2115]
Byron Hanke Fellowships [4225]
Clayburn and Garnet R. Hanna Scholarships [7834]
Muriel Hannah Scholarships in Art [10062]
Zenon C.R. Hansen Leadership Scholarships [6926]
Martha and Oliver Hansen Memorial Scholarships [5505]
Tom Hanson Photojournalism Awards [4119]
Clement T. Hanson Scholarships [6569]
Duane Hanson Scholarships [1331]
The Haraldson Foundation [4712]
Haraldson Foundation Scholarships [4713]
Harbor Breeze Corp. [4714]
Isaac and Mary Harbottle Scholarships [7909]

Hardanger Fiddle Association of America (HFAA) [4716]
H.G. Hardbarger Science and Mathematics Awards [7835]
Bob and Dawn Hardy Automotive Scholarships [5506]
Dolores Ruth Heady Hardy Memorial Scholarship [5733]
Hardy Wolf & Downing Injury Lawyers [4718]
Hardy, Wolf & Downing Scholarships [4719]
Harkness Fellowships in Health Care Policy and Practice [3160]
Bryce Harlow Fellowship Program [4721]
Bryce Harlow Foundation [4720]
Matt Harmon Memorial Scholarships [9434]
North Las Vegas Firefighters William J. Harnedy Memorial Scholarships [8348]
Harness Horse Youth Foundation (HHYF) [4722]
Harness Tracks of America (HTA) [4726]
Harness Tracks of America Scholarship Fund [4727]
Father J. Harold Conway Memorial Scholarships [7632]
B. Harper Bull Conservation Fellowships [9749]
Walter and Lucille Harper Scholarships [5806]
Harrell Family Fellowships [658]
Harris Corp. [4728]
H.H. Harris Foundation Scholarships [836]
Marcia S. Harris Legacy Fund Scholarships [8564]
Leon Harris/Les Nichols Memorial Scholarships to Spartan College of Aeronautics & Technology [163]
William H. Harris Memorial Scholarships [8075]
Harris Personal Injury Lawyers, Inc. [4730]
Frank and Charlene Harris Scholarships [3228]
Eileen Harrison Education Scholarships [4146]
Nicky & Ted Harrison Memorial Scholarships [10786]
Peg Hart Harrison Memorial Scholarships [3552]
Morton and Beatrice Harrison Scholarship Fund [4048]
Lullelia W. Harrison Scholarships in Counseling [10815]
Harrisville Lions Club Scholarships [7836]
Harry Hampton Memorial Wildlife, Inc. [4732]
Harry S. Truman Scholarships [9803]
Claude B. Hart Memorial Scholarships [10584]
Carroll Hart Scholarship [9126]
Ida L. Hartenberg Charitable Scholarships [4755]
Hartford Foundation for Public Giving [4734]
Hartford Grammar School Scholarships [4756]
Hartford Public Library [4775]
Hartford Whalers Booster Club (HWBC) [4777]
Hartford Whalers Booster Club Scholarships [4778]
Gabe A. Hartl Scholarships [137]
Harry Hartleben Scholarships [7837]
Gail L. Hartshorn Memorial Fund [7838]
William T. Hartzell Memorial Scholarships [8480]
Harvard-Smithsonian Center for Astrophysics (CFA) [4779]
Harvard University Faculty of Arts & Sciences - Institute for Quantitative Social Science - Henry A. Murray Research Archive [4783]
Harvard University Law School [4785]
Harvard University - Law School - Program on Negotiation (PON) [4788]
Harvey Fellows Program [6632]
Delta Gamma Foundation Florence Margaret Harvey Memorial Scholarships [822]
Hasbrook & Hasbrook [4792]
Donald F. Hastings Scholarships [1513]
Donald and Shirley Hastings Scholarships [1514]
Rona Hatt Master's Scholarships in Chemical Engineering [2623]
Gretchen Hauff Memorial Scholarships [8349]
Gregory Linn Haught Citizenship Awards [7839]
Dorcas Edmonson Haught Scholarships [7840]
Charles Hauser Scholarships [10232]
AISC Education Foundation - Fred R. Havens Fund [937]
Hawaii Community Foundation [4794]
Hawaii Lodging and Tourism Association (HLTA) [4797]
Hawaii Pacific Gerontological Society (HPGS) [4800]
Lex and Scott Hawkins Endowed Scholarship [3674]
Don C. Hawkins Memorial Scholarships [164]

Thomas T. Hayashi Memorial Scholarships [5550]
R. Garn Haycock Memorial Scholarships [8481]
Edward and Cora Hayes Scholarship [3675]
Samuel P. Hays Research Fellowships [1312]
Dick and Pat Hazel Minority Scholarships [3180]
Hazen and Sawyer Scholarships [1489]
HBI-BGI Scholar-in-Residence Program [2359]
HBO Point Scholarships [8177]
HCF Community Scholarships Fund [4796]
HDSA Research Grants [5019]
Edith Head Scholarships [3584]
M.G. "Doc" Headley Scholarships [9570]
Health in Aging Foundation [4803]
Health Effects Institute (HEI) [4805]
Health Physics Society (HPS) [4807]
Health Policy Scholarship for General Surgeons [697]
Health Professional Nursing Student Loans [6565]
Health Resources in Action [4813]
Health Services Research Dissertation Awards [9914]
Healthcare Financial Management Association - Connecticut Chapter [4826]
Healthcare Information Management Systems Scholarships [4831]
Healthcare Information and Management Systems Society (HIMSS) [4828]
Annamae Heaps Law Scholarship [3676]
Hearing Foundation of Canada (TFHC) [4833]
William Randolph Hearst Endowed Scholarships [7382]
Dr. James H. Heckman Memorial Scholarship Fund [9508]
HECUA Scholarship for Community Engagement [4878]
HECUA Scholarship for Social Justice [4879]
Lenore and George Hedla Accounting Scholarship [10063]
Professor Ulla Hedner Scholarships [6991]
Richard Heekin Scholarships [2996]
Howell Heflin Memorial Scholarship [7535]
Lavonne Heghinian Scholarships [3585]
Barbara and Nicole Heacox Foreign Travel and Study Scholarship Fund [4522]
Dale O. Heimberger CRNA Memorial Scholarship Fund [9509]
Joel T. Heinen Undergraduate Support Scholarships [10183]
Heisler Law Office [4835]
Steven H. Heisler Law Scholarships [4836]
Helen Steiner Rice Scholarships [2997]
Helicopter Foundation International (HFI) [4837]
Helicopter Foundation International Commercial Helicopter Rating Scholarships [4838]
Helicopter Foundation International Maintenance Technician Certificate Scholarships [4839]
Hellenic Times Scholarship Fund [4842]
Hellenic Times Scholarships [4843]
Hellenic University Club of Philadelphia (HUC) [4844]
Hellenic University Club of Philadelphia Founders Scholarships [4847]
Joan Heller-Diane Bernard Fellowships [2865]
Joseph T. Helling Scholarship Fund [5106]
Helm Family Scholarships [8706]
John M. Helmick Law Scholarship [3677]
Helsell Fetterman L.L.P. [4852]
ASIL Arthur C. Helton Fellowship Program [1344]
Arthur Helton Fellowships [7401]
Clinton J. Helton Manufacturing Scholarships [9183]
Hemingway Foundation and Society [4854]
Hemlow Prize in Burney Studies [1292]
Jeanne H. Hemmingway Scholarships [3711]
Hemophilia Federation of America (HFA) [4858]
Hemophilia Federation of America Educational Scholarships [4860]
Hench Post-Dissertation Fellowship [438]
John Henderson Endowment Scholarships [10022]
Douglas B. Henderson Leadership Scholarships [3984]
The Henderson Memorial Endowed Scholarships [6031]
Gerald V. Henderson Memorial Scholarships [9210]
Doris Hendren Memorial Scholarships [8707]
Dr. E. Bruce Hendrick Scholarships [9474]

Marjorie M. Hendricks Environmental Education Scholarship Fund [4523]
Mary Jane Hendrie Memorial Scholarships [10287]
Henigson Human Rights Fellowships [4786]
SNMMI Robert E. Henkin, MD, Government Relations Fellowship [9222]
Henley-Putnam University Scholarships [5267]
John P. Hennessey Scholarships [6503]
Allan F. Henry/Paul A. Greebler Scholarships [1036]
Gene Henson Scholarships [2113]
Herb Society of America (HSA) **[4862]**
Herb Stovel Scholarship Funds - Conference Bursaries [7199]
Herb Stovel Scholarship Funds - Project Bursaries [7200]
Herbert Hoover Uncommon Student Awards [4931]
Richard A. Herbert Memorial Scholarships [1480]
Robert N. Herbert Undergraduate Scholarships [9216]
Hereditary Disease Foundation (HDF) **[4868]**
Hereditary Disease Foundation Basic Research Grants [4869]
Herbert Herff Presidential Law Scholarships [10162]
Michael Herman Scholarships [4524]
Manuel Hernandez, Jr. Foundation Scholarships [3099]
Catarino and Evangelina Hernández Research Fellowships in Latino History [9713]
Herpetologists' League (HL) **[4870]**
The Herpetologists' League Graduate Research Award [4871]
Purdue University Ray W. Herrick Laboratories Research Fellowship [8388]
Jessica M. Herron, Epsilon Nu, Memorial Scholarship [5734]
Ella Beren Hersch Scholarships [7841]
Herschede Engineering Scholarships [8898]
Isabel M. Herson Scholarships in Education [10816]
The Hertz Foundation **[4874]**
Hertz Foundation Graduate Fellowship Award [4875]
Hertz Foundation Graduate Fellowships [6748]
Hertz Foundation Thesis Prize [4876]
Wayne E. Hesch Memorial Scholarship [1543]
Darrel Hess Community College Geography Scholarships [1830]
Beth B. Hess Memorial Scholarships [9331]
Peter Hess Scholarships [4338]
Melvyn F. Hester Scholarships [7383]
Nicholas S. Hetos, DDS, Memorial Graduate Scholarships [4848]
Caroline M. Hewins Scholarships [4776]
HFMA Connecticut Chapter Scholarships [4827]
HFMH Bilingual Scholarships for Mental Health Workforce Diversity [4913]
HGS Foundation Undergraduate Scholarships [4967]
HHMI International Student Research Fellowships [4975]
HHMI Medical Research Fellowships [4976]
HIAA Graduate Student Travel Grants [4908]
Dwight Hibbard Scholarships [2998]
Mark and Michelle Hiepler Endowed Scholarships [7983]
Hierholzer-Fojtik Scholarship Fund [4525]
Jim Hierlihy Memorial Scholarship [3911]
Regina Higdon Scholarships [3229]
Howard B. Higgins South Carolina Dental Scholarships [4197]
High School Academic Scholarship [8873]
John Higham Travel Grants, [5087], [7716]
Higher Education Consortium for Urban Affairs (HECUA) **[4877]**
Robert S. Hilbert Memorial Student Travel Grants [7673]
Wayne Hildebrant Police Scholarship Fund [5931]
Hill Country Master Gardeners **[4880]**
Hill Country Master Gardeners Horticulture Scholarships [4881]
Judy Hill Memorial Scholarships [2701]
Clair A. Hill Scholarships [1873]
Gus and Henrietta Hill Scholarships [3712]
Judge Delmas C. Hill Scholarships [10429]
Geordie Hilton Academic Scholarships [4480]
Conrad N. Hilton Scholarships [4414]
D. Glenn Hilts Scholarships [2069]
Lucy Hilty Research Grants [1173]

Brooke Hindle Postdoctoral Fellowships [9142]
Jim and Nancy Hinkle Travel Grants [4856]
Hinman-Jensen Endowed Scholarships [6032]
HIPLA Judicial Fellowships [4969]
HIPLA Scholarships for University of Houston Law Center Students [4970]
Hispanic Association of Colleges and Universities (HACU) **[4882]**
Hispanic Association of Colleges and Universities Scholarships [4890]
Hispanic Dental Association (HDA) **[4891]**
Hispanic Faculty Staff Association (HFSA) **[4895]**
Hispanic Lawyers Association of Illinois (HLAI) **[4897]**
Hispanic Metropolitan Chamber (HMC) **[4899]**
Hispanic Metropolitan Chamber Scholarships [4900]
Hispanic Scholarship Fund (HSF) **[4901]**
Hispanic Scholarship Fund General College Scholarship Program (HSF) [4904]
Hispanic Serving Institution Scholarships (HSIS) [9870]
Historians of Islamic Art Association (HIAA) **[4907]**
Historically Black College or University Scholarships (HBCUS) [9871]
HIV Prevention Research Advocacy Fellowships [2140]
Albert H. Hix, W8AH Memorial Scholarships [1743]
HLS/MLA Professional Development Grants [6386]
Ho-Chunk Nation **[4910]**
Lucy Hsu Ho Scholarships [2229]
Lou Hochberg Awards - University/College Essay Awards [7747]
Lou Hochberg Awards - University Thesis/Dissertation Awards [7748]
Hochschulsommerkurse [3608]
C.H.(Chuck) Hodgson Scholarships [10547]
James E. Hoff, S.J. Scholars [10721]
Florette B. Hoffheimer Scholarships [2999]
Dorothy M. and Earl S. Hoffman Award [2156]
Hoffman Family Scholarship Fund [4526]
Henry Hoffman Memorial Scholarship Fund [6740]
Irving J. Hoffman Memorial Scholarships [10288]
Robert and Elaine Hoffman Memorial Scholarships [10163]
Electronics Division Lewis C. Hoffman Scholarships [664]
Miriam Hoffman Scholarships [9853]
Zelle Hofmann Diversity in Law Scholarships [10812]
Michael J. Hogan Language Fellowships [9138]
The Thelma S. Hoge Memorial Scholarship Fund [3205]
Raymond T. Hoge Scholarship Fund [9510]
Hogg Foundation for Mental Health **[4912]**
Michael J. Hoggard Memorial Scholarships [8350]
R.W. "Bob" Holden Memorial Scholarships [4798]
Lois Hole Humanities and Social Sciences Scholarships [2143]
Norm Hollend Fellowships in Oncology [6138]
Polly Holliday Scholarships [9388]
Houston/Nancy Holliman Scholarships [3586]
Hollis NorEasters Snowmobile Club **[4914]**
Cleve Holloway Memorial Scholarship Fund [3265]
Joseph A. Holmes Safety Association (JAHSA) **[4917]**
Joseph A. Holmes Safety Association Scholarships [4918]
Wilbert L. and Zora F. Holmes Scholarship Endowment Fund [4198]
Robert Holmes Scholarship [3327]
Holocaust and Human Rights Center of Maine (HHRC) **[4919]**
Alan Holoch Memorial Grants [531]
Governor James E. Holshouser Professional Development Scholarships [7461]
W. Stull Holt Dissertation Fellowships [9139]
Arthur and Janet Holzheimer Fellowship in the History of Cartography [7411]
Holzheimer Memorial Student Scholarship for Economic Development Planning [1105]
Home Builders Association of Kentucky (HBAK) **[4921]**
HomeCity Real Estate **[4924]**
HomeCity Real Estate Scholarships [4925]
Homeless Children's Education Fund **[4926]**
Honeywell Avionics Scholarships [165]

Honor Society of Phi Kappa Phi - North Dakota State University Chapter 10 **[4928]**
Charles H. Hood Foundation Child Health Research Awards Program [4815]
Kathryn Hookanson Law Fellowship [10164]
Hoover Presidential Foundation **[4930]**
Lillie Hope-McGarvey Health Scholarship Awards [311]
Hope Through Learning Awards [4927]
Hope for the Warriors **[4932]**
Hope for the Warriors Spouse/Caregiver Scholarships [4933]
Johns Hopkins Department of Emergency Medicine Administration Fellowships [5607]
Frank and Gladys Hopkins Endowed Scholarships [6033]
Minnie Hopkins Memorial Scholarship Fund of Lathrop/Compton School [9511]
Harry Hopmeyer Memorial Scholarships [5578]
Dr. Gilbert Hopson Medical Student Bursaries [7639]
Horatio Alger Ak-Sar-Ben Scholarships [4957]
Horatio Alger Association of Distinguished Americans (HAADA) **[4934]**
Horatio Alger Idaho University Scholarships [4958]
Sam J. Hord Memorial Scholarships [9381]
Seth Horen, K1LOM Memorial Scholarships [1744]
Horizon Health Network Scholarships [7281]
Brenda Renee Horn Memorial Scholarship [4313]
Edward L. Horne, Jr. Scholarships [7732]
Sandra Jo Hornick Scholarships [5671]
Judge and Mrs. Robert D. Horowitz Legal Scholarship Fund [9512]
E.B. Horsman & Son Scholarships [3834]
Detroit Tigers Willie Horton Scholarship [3328]
Hosinec Family Scholarships [10289]
J. Jay Hostetler Scholarships [5672]
HotelsCheap.org **[4959]**
John C. "Jack" Hough Memorial Law Scholarship [10165]
Max and Julia Houghton Duluth Central Scholarships [3713]
Houghton Mifflin Harcourt Co. **[4961]**
Lloyd Houlden Memorial Research Fellowships [2559]
Roberta L. Houpt Scholarship Fund [4242]
House of Puerto Rico San Diego **[4963]**
Alston S. Householder Fellowships [9907]
Houston Alumnae Association, Eunice "Scotty" Scott Siverson Memorial Adelphe Scholarship [5735]
Houston Geological Society (HGS) **[4965]**
Houston Intellectual Property Law Association (HIPLA) **[4968]**
Paul Green Houston Scholarships [10233]
Sarah Jane Houston Scholarships [3587]
Houtan Scholarship Foundation **[4971]**
Houtan Scholarships [4972]
Kaspar Hovannisian Memorial Scholarships [1697]
Hirair and Anna Hovnanian Foundation Presidential Scholarships [1698]
Hirair and Anna Hovnanian Foundation Scholarships [1699]
Howard Hughes Medical Institute (HHMI) **[4973]**
Howard Hughes Medical Institute (HHMI) - Janelia Farm Research Campus **[4977]**
Barbara J. and M. William Howard Jr. Scholarships [7384]
C.D. Howard Scholarships [5298]
Roger and Joyce Howe Scholarships [3000]
Graduate Student Honoraria - A. Brazier Howell Awards [1359]
William C. Howell Scholarship [1145]
William B. Howell Scholarships [1515]
Goldwin Howland Scholarships [2720]
Christopher Hoy/ERT Scholarships [962]
Donald Hoy Memorial Scholarships [10787]
Carol Hoy Scholarship Fund [4243]
John Hoyt Memorial Scholarships [10788]
HPGS/ALOH Graduate Scholarships [4801]
HPGS Undergraduate Scholarships [4802]
HRET Health Career Scholarships [7319]
HRH Prince Alwaleed Bin Talal ISNA Fellowships [5486]
HRSA Scholarships for Disadvantaged Students [9923]

HSF/Marathon Oil College Scholarship Program [4905]
HSF/Wells Fargo Scholarship Program [4906]
Chun-tu Hsueh Fellowship for International Scholars [1120]
Albert W. and Mildred Hubbard Scholarships [8708]
Hubbell Canada LP "Electrical Industry Leadership" Scholarship Awards [3835]
Huber Engineered Woods Product Evaluation Scholarships [3977]
Amber Huber Memorial Scholarships [3287]
Hudson River Foundation (HRF) **[4979]**
Huenefeld/Denton Scholarships [3588]
A. Joseph Huerta "Puedo" Scholarships [3100]
Steven Huesing Scholarships [3067]
Berton W. Huestis Memorial Scholarships [7282]
Kathryn Huget Leadership Awards [2430]
Dixon Hughes Goodman Scholarships [10405]
Dale Hughes, Jr. Memorial Scholarships [9571]
Roger K. Hughes Legacy Scholarships [2451]
Hughes Memorial Foundation **[4982]**
Hughes Memorial Foundation Scholarships [4983]
Tertia M.C. Hughes Memorial Graduate Student Prize [2684]
Paul A. Hughes Memorial Scholarships [2452]
Mary M. Hughes Research Fellowships in Texas History [9714]
Huguenot Society of South Carolina **[4984]**
Huguenot Society of South Carolina Graduate Scholarships [4986]
Human Race Theatre Company **[4987]**
Human Resources Research Organization (HumRRO) **[4989]**
Human Rights Campaign (HRC) **[4991]**
Human Rights in China (HRIC) **[4993]**
Human Rights Resource Center (HRRC) **[4995]**
Human Rights Watch (HRW) **[4997]**
The Humane Society of the United States (HSUS) **[5001]**
Humane Studies Fellowships [5183]
Humanism in Medicine Scholarships [9600]
Humber College Institute of Technology and Advanced Learning Scholarships [5524]
Humboldt State University - Schatz Energy Research Center (SERC) **[5003]**
Anna C. Hume Scholarship [4428]
Kevin Hummer Point Scholarships [8178]
John Peters Humphrey Student Fellowships [3459]
Cecil C. Humphreys Law Fellowships [10166]
Hungarian American Coalition (HAC) **[5005]**
Hungarian-American Enterprise Scholarship Fund (HAESF) **[5007]**
Betty Jo Creighton Hunkele Adelphe Scholarship [5736]
Dr. Richard M. Hunt Fellowships [725]
Hunt Postdoctoral Fellowships [10517]
Frederick V. Hunt Postdoctoral Research Fellowships in Acoustics [53]
Beatrice Hunter Cancer Research Institute (BHCRI) **[5011]**
Michael A. Hunter Memorial Scholarships [2907]
Carrie Hunter-Tate Award [6794]
Donald and Florence Hunting Scholarships [4600]
Curtis E. Huntington Memorial Scholarship [62]
Huntington's Disease Society of America (HDSA) **[5018]**
Huntington's Disease Society of America Research Fellowships [5020]
Sang Ok Hur Scholarships [7385]
James F. Hurley III Bicentennial Merit Scholarships [10234]
Walter Doc Hurley Scholarship [4757]
Zora Neale Hurston Scholarships [10817]
Norman E. and Mary-Belle Huston Scholarships [5397]
Dr. James L. Hutchinson and Evelyn Ribbs Hutchinson Medical School Scholarship Fund [8952]
The Hyatt Hotels Fund For Minority Lodging Management Students [860]
Hydro Research Foundation (HRF) **[5022]**
Hydro Research Foundation Fellowships [5023]
Hydrocephalus Association (HA) **[5024]**
Mike Hylton and Ron Niederman Memorial Scholarships [4861]
Libbie H. Hyman Memorial Scholarships [9156]

The Steve Hymans Extended Stay Scholarship Program [861]
Hypertherm International HyTech Leadership Scholarships [1516]
I Have a Dream Scholarships [5525]
IAAI Scholarship Foundation Accounting Scholarships [5091]
IAAP Wings Chapter Scholarships [5244]
IABA Scholarships [5476]
IAEM Scholarship Program [5256]
IAESTE United States Internships [3489]
IAF Fellowships [5232]
IAHCSMM-Purdue University Scholarship Awards [5263]
IALD Education Trust Scholarship Program [5271]
IALL Regular Bursaries [5269]
IARS Mentored Research Awards (IMRA) [5242]
IARSLCE Graduate Student Scholarships [5273]
IASC Associate Fellowships [10308]
IASC Doctoral Fellowships - Dissertation [10309]
IASC Doctoral Fellowships - Pre-Dissertation [10310]
IASC Postdoctoral Fellowships [10311]
IASC Visiting Fellowships [10312]
IASP Visiting Professor Grants [5275]
IAWP International Scholarship Award [5280]
IBA Law Student Scholarship Foundation Scholarships [5130]
IBEA Graduate Scholarships [5056]
IBEA Undergraduate Scholarships [5057]
Iberdrola USA Scholarships [6198]
ICAFS Idaho Graduate Student Scholarships [5035]
ICAFS Idaho High School Student Scholarships [5036]
ICAFS Idaho Undergraduate Student Scholarships [5037]
ICDA Graduate Scholarships [5464]
ICDA Research Grants [5465]
Ice Skating Institute (ISI) **[5030]**
Ice Skating Institute of America Education Foundation Scholarships [5031]
ICJS Short-Term Fellowships [8997]
ICMA Local Government Management Fellowships [5296]
ICNL Research Fellowships [5292]
IDA Fellowship Awards [5320]
Idaho Chapter of the American Fisheries Society (ICAFS) **[5032]**
Idaho Community Foundation (ICF) **[5039]**
Idaho Nursery and Landscape Association (INLA) **[5047]**
Idaho Nursery and Landscape Association Scholarships [5048]
Idaho Nursing and Health Professions Scholarships [5042]
Idaho Opportunity Scholarships [9547]
Idaho Society of CPA's Scholarships [5043]
Idaho State Board of Education **[5049]**
Idaho State Broadcasters Association (ISBA) **[5051]**
Ideal Supply Scholarship Awards [3836]
David Iden Memorial Safety Scholarships [1415]
IDTA Freestyle Scholarships [5317]
IFDA Student Member Scholarships [5338]
Ella R. Ifill Fund [6199]
IFMA Foundation Scholarships [5327]
IFSEA Worthy Goal Scholarships [5329]
IIE Council of Fellows Undergraduate Scholarships [5188]
IILJ Scholarships [5202]
IILJ Visiting Fellowships and Research [5203]
IISE Presidents Scholarships [5189]
Illinois Association of Chamber of Commerce Executives (IACCE) **[5053]**
Illinois Association of Chamber of Commerce Executives Scholarships [5054]
Illinois Business Education Association (IBEA) **[5055]**
Illinois City County Management Association (ILCMA) **[5058]**
Illinois Division Scholarships [6519]
Illinois Future Teacher Corps Scholarships [5072]
Illinois Lake Management Association (ILMA) **[5060]**
Illinois Lake Management Association Undergraduate/Graduate Scholarships [5062]

Illinois Landscape Contractors Association (ILCA) **[5063]**
Illinois Landscape Contractors Association Scholarships [5064]
Illinois Society of Professional Engineers (ISPE) **[5065]**
Illinois Special Education Teacher Tuition Waiver Scholarships (SETTW) [5073]
Illinois State Dental Society (ISDS) **[5067]**
Illinois Student Assistance Commission (ISAC) **[5069]**
Illinois Student Assistance Commission Medical Student Scholarships [5074]
Illinois Student Assistance Commission Merit Recognition Scholarships (MRS) [5075]
Illinois Student Assistance Commission Nurse Educator Scholarships (NESP) [5076]
Illinois Student Assistance Commission Nursing Education Scholarships [5077]
Illuminator Educational Foundation Scholarships [2453]
ILSA Internships [5353]
IMA Memorial Education Fund Scholarships (MEF) [5206]
Image **[5079]**
Imagine America College Scholarships for High School Students [5083]
Imagine America Foundation (IAF) **[5082]**
Imagine America Military Awards Program [5084]
Imagine America Scholarships for Adult Students [5085]
Elmer S. Imes Scholarships in Physics [7142]
John L. Imhoff Scholarships [5190]
David G. Imig Awards for Distinguished Achievement in Teacher Education [486]
Immigration and Ethnic History Society (IEHS) **[5086]**
IMS AWWA Graduate Science and Engineering Scholarships [5239]
In-course Scholarships - Chinese Dance Workshop Scholarships [10290]
Incorporated Society of Irish American Lawyers (ISIAL) **[5088]**
Independent Accountants Association of Illinois (IAAI) **[5090]**
Independent Lubricant Manufacturers Association (ILMA) **[5092]**
Independent Lubricant Manufacturers Association Scholarships [5093]
Independent Order of Foresters **[5094]**
Independent Professional Seed Association (IPSA) **[5096]**
Independent Professional Seed Association Student Recognition Awards [5098]
Independent University Alumni Association at Lowell **[5099]**
Independent University Alumni Association Scholarships [5102]
Indian Health Service Professionals Program [875]
Indiana Alumni Scholarships [10722]
Indiana Bar Foundation (IBF) **[5105]**
Indiana Broadcasters Association (IBA) **[5107]**
Indiana Broadcasters Association College Scholarship Program [5108]
Indiana FFA Association **[5109]**
Indiana FFA Association State Fair Scholarship [5110]
Indiana Library Federation (ILF) **[5111]**
Indiana State University Academic Excellence Scholarships [5116]
Indiana State University Academic Promise Scholarships [5126]
Indiana State University (ISU) **[5114]**
Indiana State University Alumni Association (ISUAA) **[5125]**
Indiana State University Creative and Performing Arts Awards [5127]
Indiana State University Incentive Scholarships [5117]
Indiana State University President's Scholarships [5118]
Indiana State University Rural Health Scholarships [5119]
Indiana State University Transfer Student Scholarships [5120]
Indigenous Bar Association (IBA) **[5129]**

Individual Advanced Research Opportunities Program For Master's Students [5381]
Individual K-Grants [5823]
Individual Professional Development Scholarship [4161]
Indonesian Directorate General of Higher Education Scholarships [3761]
Indspire **[5131]**
Indspire Health Careers Bursary and Scholarships [5132]
Indspire Post-Secondary Education Scholarships [5133]
Industrial Designers Society of America (IDSA) **[5135]**
Industrial R&D Fellowships [3403]
Industrial Supply Association (ISA) **[5137]**
INF Scholarships [5472]
Influenster **[5139]**
Influenster Code Like a Girl Scholarships [5140]
Informatics Post Doctoral Fellowships [8027]
Informatics Pre Doctoral Fellowships [8028]
Informatics Sabbatical Fellowships [8029]
Information Age Publishing Graduate Student Book Scholarships [5142]
Information Age Publishing Inc. (IAP) **[5141]**
Infusion Nurses Society (INS) **[5143]**
Terrance N. Ingraham Pediatric Optometry Residency Support [416]
Jennifer Ingrum Scholarships [3230]
INIA Scholarship Program [5363]
Injury Scholarships [4731]
Inland Northwest Business Alliance Scholarships (INBA) [8254]
Innovations in Software Scholarships [10758]
Innovative Grants-Pilot and Research Tool Grants [5641]
Insite Solutions **[5146]**
Inspire our Future Scholarships [9648]
Institut canadien d' études juridiques supérieures **[5148]**
Institut de Recherche Robert-Sauve en Sante et en Securite du Travail (IRSST) **[5151]**
Institut des Sciences Mathematiques (ISM) **[5159]**
Institute of Actuaries of Australia (IAAust) **[5162]**
Institute for Anarchist Studies **[5164]**
Institute for Anarchist Studies Grants for Radical Writers and Translators [5165]
Institute Community Support Program ICR Publication Prizes [5230]
Institute for Diversity in Health Management **[5166]**
Institute of Food Technologists (IFT) **[5170]**
Institute of Food Technologists - Alamo Section **[5174]**
Institute of Food Technologists Graduate Scholarships [5171]
Institute of Food Technologists - Great Lakes Section **[5176]**
Institute of Food Technologists Junior/Senior Scholarships [5172]
Institute of Food Technologists Sophomore Scholarships [5173]
Institute for Health Metrics and Evaluation (IHME) **[5179]**
Institute for Health Metrics and Evaluation Post Bachelor Fellowships [5180]
Institute for Health Metrics and Evaluation Post Graduate Fellowships [5181]
Institute for Humane Studies (IHS) **[5182]**
Institute of Industrial and Systems Engineers **[5184]**
Institute of International Education (IIE) **[5198]**
Institute for the International Education of Students Faculty Fellowships [7412]
Institute for International Law and Justice (IILJ) **[5201]**
Institute of Management Accountants FAR Doctoral Student Grants Program [5207]
Institute of Management Accountants, Inc. (IMA) **[5204]**
Institute-NEH Postdoctoral Fellowships [7613]
Institute for Public Policy Research (IPPR) **[5208]**
Institute for Public Relations (IPR) **[5211]**
Institute of Real Estate Management (IREM) **[5214]**
Institute of Transportation Engineers (ITE) **[5218]**
Institute of Transportation Engineers - Texas District Fellowships [5219]

Institute of Transportation Engineers - Western District Fellowships [5220]
Institute of Turkish Studies (ITS) **[5222]**
Institute of Turkish Studies Dissertation Writing Grants [5223]
Institute of Turkish Studies Post-Doctoral Summer Travel-Research Grants [5224]
Institute of Turkish Studies Sabbatical Research Grants [5225]
Institute of Turkish Studies Summer Language Study Grants in Turkey [5226]
Institute for Women's Policy Research (IWPR) **[5227]**
Instituts de recherche en sainté du Canada **[5229]**
Instructional Design & Learning Technologies Scholarships [3820]
Integra Foundation NNF Research Grant Awards [546]
Intensive Language Course Grants [3609]
Inter-American Foundation (IAF) **[5231]**
Inter American Press Association Scholarships [9061]
Intercollegiate Studies Institute (ISI) **[5233]**
Intermediaries & Reinsurance Underwriters Association, Inc. (IRU Inc.) **[5236]**
Intermediaries and Reinsurance Underwriters Association Summer Intern Scholarships Program [5237]
Intermountain Section American Water Works Association **[5238]**
International Affairs Fellowships in Japan (IAF-J) [3447]
International Affairs Fellowships in Nuclear Security (IAF-NS) [3448]
International Anesthesia Research Society (IARS) **[5241]**
International Association of Administrative Professionals Wings Chapter **[5243]**
International Association of Arson Investigators (IAAI) **[5245]**
International Association of Black Actuaries (IABA) **[5247]**
International Association of Black Actuaries Scholarships [5248]
International Association for Dental Research (IADR) **[5249]**
International Association of Emergency Managers (IAEM) **[5255]**
International Association for Food Protection (IAFP) **[5257]**
International Association for Food Protection - Student Travel Scholarship Program [5258]
International Association of Foundation Drilling Scholarships for Civil Engineering Students [75]
International Association of Foundation Drilling Scholarships for Part-time Civil Engineering Graduate School Students [76]
International Association for Great Lakes Research (IAGLR) **[5259]**
International Association of Healthcare Central Service Materiel Management (IAHCSMM) **[5262]**
International Association of Law Enforcement Intelligence Analysts (IALEIA) **[5265]**
International Association of Law Libraries (IALL) **[5268]**
International Association of Lighting Designers (IALD) **[5270]**
International Association for Research on Service-Learning and Community Engagement (IARSLCE) **[5272]**
International Association for the Study of Pain (IASP) **[5274]**
International Association of Wildland Fire (IAWF) **[5277]**
International Association of Wildland Fire Graduate-Level Scholarships [5278]
International Association of Women Police (IAWP) **[5279]**
International Association of Workforce Professionals (IAWP) **[5281]**
International Bowling Media Association (IBMA) **[5285]**
International Brotherhood of Electrical Workers - Local Union 827 **[5287]**
International Catacomb Society (ICS) **[5289]**

International Center for Not-for-Profit Law (ICNL) **[5291]**
International Centre for Diffraction Data (ICDD) **[5293]**
International City/County Management Association (ICMA) **[5295]**
International Code Council (ICC) **[5297]**
International Code Council Foundation General Scholarship Fund [5299]
International Code Council Scholarships [3978]
International Council for Canadian Studies Graduate Student Scholarships [3399]
International Council of Shopping Centers Foundation **[5303]**
International Council on Systems Engineering (INCOSE) **[5309]**
International Dairy-Deli-Bakery Association (IDDBA) **[5313]**
International Dairy-Deli-Bakery Association Undergraduate/Graduate Scholarships [5314]
International Dance Teachers' Association (IDTA) **[5316]**
International Desalination Association (IDA) **[5318]**
International Development and Education Award in Palliative Care [3376]
International Development and Education Awards [3377]
International Dissertation Research Fellowship (IDRF) [9054]
International Doctoral Scholarships for Studies Specializing in Jewish Fields [6411]
International Door Association (IDA) **[5321]**
International Door Association Scholarship Foundation Program [5322]
International Executive Housekeepers Association (IEHA) **[5323]**
International Executive Housekeepers Association Education Foundation Scholarship Awards [5324]
International Executive Housekeepers Association Spartan Scholarship Awards [5325]
International Facility Management Association Foundation **[5326]**
International Fellowships in Jewish Studies and Jewish Culture [6412]
International Food Service Executives Association (IFSEA) **[5328]**
International Foodservice Editorial Council (IFEC) **[5330]**
International Foodservice Editorial Council Scholarships [5331]
International Foundation for Ethical Research (IFER) **[5332]**
International Franchise Association (IFA) **[5334]**
International Furnishings and Design Association (IFDA) **[5337]**
International Furnishings and Design Association Part-time Student Scholarships [5339]
International GI Training Grant Award [685]
International Grenfell Association (IGA) **[5340]**
International Grenfell Association Bursary [5341]
International Grenfell Association Post-Secondary Bursaries [5342]
International Grenfell Association Secondary/High School Bursaries [5343]
International Horn Society (IHS) **[5344]**
International Information Systems Security Certification Consortium (ISC2) **[5347]**
International Innovation Grants [3378]
International Institute for Municipal Clerks (IIMC) **[5349]**
International Law Research Program Fellowships [2884]
International Law Students Association (ILSA) **[5352]**
International Literacy Association (ILA) **[5354]**
International Management Council Scholarships (IMC) [3288]
International Military Community Executives Association (IMCEA) **[5359]**
International Narcotics Interdiction Association (INIA) **[5362]**
International Nurses Society on Addictions (IntNSA) **[5364]**
International Operators Scholarship [6834]
International Order of the King's Daughters and Sons (IOKDS) **[5366]**

INTERNATIONAL

International Order of the King's Daughters and Sons North American Indian Scholarship Program [876]
International Organic Inspectors Association (IOIA) **[5368]**
International Practice Management Association (IPMA) **[5371]**
International Precious Metals Institute (IPMI) **[5373]**
International Public Management Association for Human Resources (IPMA-HR) **[5375]**
International Radio and Television Society Foundation (IRTS) **[5377]**
International Radio and Television Society Foundation Summer Fellowships Program [5378]
International Research and Exchanges Board (IREX) **[5379]**
The International Research Foundation for English Language Education (TIRF) **[5385]**
International Rett Syndrome Foundation (IRSF) **[5387]**
International Safety Equipment Association (ISEA) **[5389]**
International Sanitary Supply Association (ISSA) **[5391]**
International Sanitary Supply Association Foundation Scholarships [5392]
International Scholars Program for Young Vascular Surgeons [9325]
International Scholarship Programs for Community Service [6413]
International Society of Air Safety Investigators (ISASI) **[5393]**
International Society Annual Meeting Travel Grant [408]
International Society of Automation (ISA) **[5395]**
International Society for Disease Surveillance (ISDS) **[5415]**
International Society of Explosives Engineers (ISEE) **[5417]**
International Society for Human Ethology (ISHE) **[5419]**
International Society for Humor Studies (ISHS) **[5421]**
International Society for Humor Studies Graduate Student Awards (GSA) [5422]
International Society for Humor Studies Scholarly Contribution Awards (SCA) [5423]
International Society for Infectious Diseases (ISID) **[5424]**
International Society of Offshore and Polar Engineers (ISOPE) **[5426]**
International Society for Reef Studies (ISRS) **[5428]**
International Society for Therapeutic Ultrasound (ISTU) **[5430]**
International Society of Travel and Tourism Educators (ISTTE) **[5434]**
International Technology and Engineering Educators Association (ITEEA) **[5436]**
International Textile and Apparel Association (ITAA) **[5441]**
International Thomas Merton Society (ITMS) **[5443]**
International Trademark Association (INTA) **[5446]**
International Trademark Association-Ladas Memorial Awards [5447]
International Trainee Scholarships (ITS) [1474]
International Transplant Nurses Society (ITNS) **[5448]**
International Union of Bricklayers and Allied Craftworkers (BAC) **[5450]**
International Union of Operating Engineers - Local 564 **[5453]**
International Women's Fishing Association (IWFA) **[5455]**
International Women's Fishing Association Scholarship Trust [5456]
International Women's Media Foundation (IWMF) **[5457]**
Internet Society **[5459]**
Internet Society Fellowships to the IETF [5460]
Interracial Scholarship Fund of Greater Hartford [4758]
Investigators in the Pathogenesis of Infectious Disease Awards [2417]
Investors Group Scholarships for Not-For-Profit Leaders [2183]

IODE Canada Labrador Bursary [6855]
IOIA Organic Community Initiative Scholarships [5369]
Iowa Association of Electric Cooperatives - Electric Cooperative Pioneer Trust Fund Scholarship [3678]
Iowa Association for Justice (IAJ) **[5461]**
Iowa Choral Directors Association (ICDA) **[5463]**
Iowa Court Reporters Association (ICRA) **[5466]**
Iowa Division Scholarships [6520]
Iowa Journalism Institute Scholarships [5473]
Iowa Library Association (ILA) **[5468]**
Iowa Library Association Foundation Scholarships [5469]
Iowa Newspaper Association (INA) **[5471]**
Susan K. Ipacs Nursing Legacy Scholarships [4169]
IPMA-HR Graduate Study Fellowships [5376]
IPPR Events Internships [5209]
IPR Pathfinder Award [5212]
Iranian American Bar Association (IABA) **[5475]**
Iranian Scholarship Foundation (ISF) **[5477]**
IREX Individual Advanced Research Opportunities Program For Pre-doctoral Students [5382]
IREX Individual Advanced Research Opportunities Program For Professionals [5383]
IREX Individual Advanced Research Opportunities Program for Postdoctoral Scholars [5384]
Iris Scholarship [5737]
James P. Irish Scholarship [3679]
Greg Irons Award Fund [3714]
Harriet Irsay Scholarships [927]
IRSF Mentored Training Fellowships [5388]
IRSST Doctoral Scholarship [5152]
IRSST Doctoral Scholarships Abroad [5153]
IRSST Doctoral Scholarships Supplement [5154]
IRSST Masters Scholarships [5155]
IRSST Masters Scholarships Supplement [5156]
IRSST Postdoctoral Scholarships Abroad [5158]
IRSST Postdoctoral Scholarships [5157]
ISA Educational Foundation Scholarships [5398]
ISA Executive Board Scholarships [5399]
ISA Section and District Scholarships - Houston [5400]
ISA Section and District Scholarships - Lehigh Valley [5401]
ISA Section and District Scholarships - Richmond Hopewell [5402]
ISA Section and District Scholarships - Southwestern Wyoming [5403]
ISA Section and District Scholarships - Texas, Louisiana and Mississippi [5404]
ISA Section and District Scholarships - Wilmington [5405]
ISA Technical Division Scholarships - Analysis Division [5406]
ISA Technical Division Scholarships - Chemical and Petroleum Industries Division [5407]
ISA Technical Division Scholarships - Food and Pharmaceutical Industries Division [5408]
ISA Technical Division Scholarships - Power Industry Division [5409]
ISA Technical Division Scholarships - Process Measurement and Control Division [5410]
ISA Technical Division Scholarships - Pulp and Paper Industry Division [5411]
ISA Technical Division Scholarships - Test Measurement Division [5412]
ISA Technical Division Scholarships - Water and Wastewater Industries Division [5413]
ISBA General Scholarships [5052]
Hazel D. Isbell Fellowships [3553]
(ISC)2 Foundation Information Security Scholarships [5348]
ISCALC International Scholarship Fund [4049]
ISDS Graduate Student Scholarships [5416]
ISF Excellence in Community Service Scholarships [5478]
ISF Undergraduate Scholarships [5479]
ISID Small Grant [5425]
Islamic Research Foundation International (IRFI) **[5481]**
Islamic Scholarship Fund (ISF) **[5483]**
Islamic Scholarship Fund Scholarships (ISF) [5484]
Islamic Society of North America (ISNA) **[5485]**
Island Institute Scholarship Fund [6200]
ISM Doctoral Fellowships [5160]

ISM Scholarships for Graduate Studies [5161]
Broughton Isom Memorial Scholarship [7536]
ISOPE Offshore Mechanics Scholarships for Outstanding Students [5427]
ISPE Foundation Scholarships [5066]
ISRS Graduate Fellowships [5429]
ISTTE Scholarships [5435]
ISTU Student Prize [5432]
ISU Child of Alumni Book Voucher Awards [5128]
ISU Gongaware Scholarships [5121]
ISU Networks Scholarships College of Business [5122]
ITAA Graduate Student Best Paper Award [5442]
Italian Language Scholarships [7682]
ITEEA Greer/FTE Grants [5437]
ITNS Research Grants [5449]
ITW Welding Companies Scholarships [1517]
Ivanhoe Foundation **[5487]**
Ivanhoe Foundation Fellowships [5488]
Dr. Karl C. Ivarson Scholarships [113]
Bob and Mary Ives Scholarships [5414]
Jack Family Scholarships [4601]
Jack and Jill of America Foundation, Inc. (JJAF) **[5489]**
Jack and Jill of America National Scholarships Program [5490]
Jack Kent Cooke Inc. **[5491]**
Virginia C. Jack and Ralph L. Jack Scholarships [9513]
Jackie Robinson Foundation (JRF) **[5494]**
Jackie Robinson Scholarships [5495]
Jackman Scholarships [8095]
Graduate Student Honoraria - Anna M. Jackson Awards [1360]
The Jackson Club Scholarships [3715]
Jackson Community Foundation (JCF) **[5496]**
Jackson High School Alumni Scholarship Fund [9514]
Edward Jackson International Scholarships [10235]
Holly Jackson-Wuller Memorial Scholarships [7842]
Ruth K. Jacobs Memorial Scholarships [2930]
Donald Wills Jacobs Scholarships [10023]
Freddy L. Jacobs Scholarships [5284]
Eric L. Jacobson Memorial Scholarships [8482]
Dwight P. Jacobus Scholarships [2058]
Jacque Placette Chapman Master's Fellowships [7679]
Louis I. Jaffe Memorial Scholarships-NSU Alumni [4700]
Louis I. Jaffe Memorial Scholarships-ODU [4701]
Jagiellonian University Summer Program Scholarship [8204]
Jain Foundation **[5517]**
Jain Foundation Merit-Based Scholarships [5518]
Jain Foundation Social-Media Scholarships [5519]
Gregori Jakovina Endowment Scholarships [3920]
Cory Jam Memorial Award Fund [3716]
Jamaican Canadian Association **[5520]**
Jamaican Canadian Association Alberta (JCAA) **[5532]**
Jamaican Canadian Association Alberta Scholarship Program [5533]
Jamail/Long Challenge Grant Scholarships [4896]
Peter and Malina James and Dr. Louis P. James Legacy Scholarships [1146]
Olivia James Traveling Fellowships [1608]
J. Franklin Jameson Fellowships in American History [853]
Jan Jancin Competition Awards [941]
Janelia Farm Graduate Program [4978]
Helen Janko Memorial Scholarships [10789]
Janssen Therapeutics Point Scholarships [8179]
Drzymala Janusz and Roma Scholarship [8577]
Japan-American Society of Hawaii (JASH) **[5534]**
Japan Foundation, New York (JFNY) **[5536]**
Japan Foundation, New York Doctoral Fellowship Program [5537]
Japan Foundation, New York Long-Term Research Fellowship Program [5538]
Japan Foundation, New York Short-Term Fellowship Program [5539]
Japan Indonesia Presidential Scholarship Program [10695]
Japan Society for the Promotion of Science Fellowship Program [9055]
Japanese American Bar Association (JABA) **[5540]**

Japanese American Citizens League (JACL) [5546]
Don Jaques Memorial Fellowships [8777]
Dr. Ali Jarrahi Merit Scholarships [5480]
Carl and Lucille Jarrett Scholarship Fund [4050]
Airgas - Terry Jarvis Memorial Scholarships [1518]
Herbert H. Jasper Fellowships in Neurosciences [2568]
Jacob K. Javits Fellowships Program [9894]
JCC Association [5561]
JCC Association Graduate Education Scholarships [5562]
JCCF Equal Voice Journalism Scholarship [10152]
JDRF Advanced Postdoctoral Fellowships [5642]
JDRF Career Development Awards [5643]
JDRF Postdoctoral Fellowships [5644]
JEA Future Teacher Scholarships [5625]
Hon. Michaelle Jean Scholarships [2286]
Sister Rita Jeanne Scholarships [5626]
Jefferson Graduate Fellowships [5564]
Jefferson Scholars Foundation [5563]
Jefferson Science Associates L.L.C. (JSA) [5565]
Jeffress Trust Awards Program in Interdisciplinary Research [4816]
John Jeffries Meteorology Scholarships [3979]
Erin L. Jenkins Memorial Scholarship Fund [4244]
Elise Reed Jenkins Memorial Scholarships - Gamma Lambda [8928]
Elise Reed Jenkins Memorial Scholarships - Gamma Psi [8929]
John H. Jenkins Research Fellowships in Texas History [9715]
Martha Combs Jenkins Scholarships [8096]
Ruth E. Jenkins Scholarships [8709]
Gaynold Jensen Education Stipends [3622]
Walter J. Jensen Fellowships [8052]
Nancy Lorraine Jensen Memorial Scholarships [9345]
Stanley "Doc" Jensen Scholarships [760]
Jerman-Cahoon Student Scholarship [1397]
Kenneth Jernigan Scholarships [6947]
Jerome Fellowships [8152]
Harry Jerome Legacy Scholarships [2287]
Jerome Robbins Bogliasco Fellowships in Dance [2329]
The Jewish Community Foundation of Montreal [5567]
Jewish Federation Academic Scholarships [5598]
Jewish Foundation of Manitoba [5590]
Jewish Guild for the Blind (JGB) [5595]
Jewish Vocational Service (JVS) [5597]
Jim Dodson Law [5599]
Brian Jimenez Memorial Scholarships [8483]
Rev. and Mrs. A.K. Jizmejian Educational Fund [1700]
JLTLA Judge's Scholarships [9817]
JLTLA Minority Law Student Scholarships [9818]
JMA Architecture Studios Scholarships [8351]
Oliver Joel and Ellen Pell Denny Healthcare Scholarship Fund [10585]
Harry Johannes Scholarships [10790]
Reverend H. John and Asako Yamashita Memorial Scholarships [5551]
John F. Kennedy Presidential Library and Museum [5601]
John F. Kennedy Scholarship Award [2435]
Johnny Bench Scholarships [3001]
Johns Hopkins Medicine - Department of Emergency Medicine [5606]
Johns Hopkins Medicine Disaster Fellowships [5608]
Johns Hopkins Medicine Emergency Medical Services Fellowship [5609]
Johns Hopkins Medicine International Emergency and Public Health Fellowships [5610]
Johns Hopkins Medicine Medical Education Fellowships [5611]
Johns Hopkins Medicine Observation Medicine Fellowships [5612]
Johns Hopkins Medicine Research Fellowships [5613]
Johns Hopkins Medicine Ultrasound Fellowships [5614]
Johns Hopkins University/Applied Physics Laboratory Alexander Kossiakoff Scholarships [5310]
Wilma Winberg Johnson Adelphe Scholarship for Chapter Consultants [5738]

Alvin H. Johnson AMS 50 Dissertation Fellowships [1020]
Sylvia Taylor Johnson Fellowships in Educational Measurement [3808]
Robert Wood Johnson Foundation Health Policy Fellows Program [8629]
Johnson and Johnson/AACN Minority Nurse Faculty Scholars [480]
Johnson & Johnson Scholarships [2702]
MCCA Lloyd M. Johnson, Jr. Scholarships [6553]
Margaret G. Johnson and Marge J. Stout Scholarships [6034]
Bernadine Johnson-Marshall and Martha Bell Williams Scholarships [1863]
Joseph C. Johnson Memorial Grants [1252]
Douglas Johnson Memorial Scholarships [10791]
Gregory D. Johnson Memorial Scholarships [7036]
Professor Emeritus Dr. Bill Johnson Memorial Scholarships [8874]
V.J. Johnson Memorial Scholarships [579]
James V. Johnson Scholarship Fund [4199]
Camilla C. Johnson Scholarships [4602]
Chip Johnson Scholarships [9435]
Ella Wilson Johnson Scholarships [3002]
Stella B. Johnson Scholarships [10586]
The Johnson & Wales Scholarships [5631]
Nancy Johnston Memorial Scholarships [9675]
OOIDA Mary Johnston Scholarships [7785]
Joint Japan/World Bank Graduate Scholarship Program for Developing Country National (JJ/WB-GSP) [10696]
Joint Japan/World Bank Graduate Scholarship Program for Japanese National (JJ/WBGSP) [10697]
Redlands Council PTA - Dorothy Jolley Memorial Scholarships [8484]
Mary Jon and J. P. Bryan Leadership in Education Awards [9716]
Louis August Jonas Foundation (LAJF) [5615]
George E. Jonas Scholarships [5616]
Napoleon A. Jones, III Memorial Scholarships [8710]
Greater Baton Rouge Chapter - Don Jones Excellence in Safety Scholarships [1416]
The Howard and Georgeanna Jones Foundation for Reproductive Medicine [5617]
Jones-Lovich Grants in Southwestern Herpetology [4872]
Annabel Lambeth Jones Scholarships [4200]
Barbara Jordan Scholarships [9819]
David J. Joseph Company Scholarships [3003]
Joseph H. Fichter Research Grants [2071]
E.J. Josey Scholarships [2296]
Alice Newell Joslyn Medical Fund [2211]
Journalism Association of Community Colleges (JACC) [5621]
Journalism Education Association (JEA) [5624]
Journey Toward Ordained Ministry Scholarships [9854]
Journyx Inc. [5627]
Journyx Scholarships [5628]
Leslie W. Joyce and Paul W. Thayer Graduate Fellowship in I-O Psychology [9153]
JSA/Jefferson Lab Graduate Fellowships [5566]
JSR Foundation Endowed School of Law Scholarships [7984]
Kazimiera Juchniewicz Memorial Scholarships [8578]
Clem Judd Jr. Memorial Scholarships [4799]
George E. Judd Scholarships [9436]
Woodrow Judkins Endowed Scholarships [7985]
Martha Julian Memorial Scholarship [212]
Junior Achievement (JA) [5629]
Junior Achievement of East Central Ohio, Inc. Scholarship Fund [9515]
Junior Firefighter Scholarships [7211]
James W. Junior and Jane T. Brown Scholarships [4527]
Junior Service League of LaGrange, Inc. [5632]
George W. Juno Memorial Scholarships [4339]
Just Health Shops [5634]
JustNebulizers.com Respiratory Care Scholarships [5637]
JustWalkers.com Mobility Scholarships [5638]
Juvenile Diabetes Research Foundation International (JDRF) [5639]
JW Surety Bonds [5645]

JW Surety Bonds Scholarships [5646]
K & W Cafeterias Scholarships [7472]
Mike Kabo Global Scholarships [4456]
Stefan and Weronika Kacperski Memorial Scholarships [8579]
Annette Kade Fellowships [6431]
Edward G. Kaelber Scholarships [6201]
Daniel Kahikina and Millie Akaka Scholarships [7910]
Kaiser Family Foundation (KFF) [5647]
Kaiser Media Fellowships in Health Reporting [5648]
David A. Kaiser Memorial Scholarship Fund [9516]
Kaiser Permanente - Division of Research [5649]
Kaiser Permanente Northern California Delivery Science Fellowships Program [5650]
Judge Edward Y. Kakita Memorial Scholarships [5542]
Sam Kalman Scholarship [1582]
Gladys Kamakaküokalani 'Ainoa Brandt Scholarships [7911]
Shripat Kamble Urban Entomology Graduate Student Awards for Innovative Research [3881]
Kamehameha Schools Class of 1968 "Ka Poli O Kaiona" Scholarships [7912]
Kamehameha Schools Class of 1972 Scholarships [7913]
Benjamin Kaminer Endowed Scholarships in Physiology [6249]
Joan Kamps Memorial Bursaries [7633]
WLALA Fran Kandel Public Interest Grants [10646]
Martin S. Kane Memorial Community Service Award Scholarships [3181]
Kansas Association of Broadcasters (KAB) [5651]
Kansas Association of Broadcasters Scholarships [5652]
Kansas Board of Regents (KBOR) [5653]
Kansas City Division Scholarships [6521]
Kansas Dental Education Opportunities Program [5654]
Kansas Distinguished Scholarship Program [5655]
Kansas Health Information Management Association (KHIMA) [5660]
Kansas Nurse Educator Service Scholarships [5656]
Kansas Optometry Service Scholarships [5657]
Kansas Osteopathic Medical Service Scholarships [5658]
Walter Kapala Scholarships [4759]
Joseph Kaplan Fund [5103]
Kaplan Lawyers PC [5664]
Kaplan Lawyers PC Legal Scholarships [5665]
Don Kaplan Legacy Scholarships [2454]
Kaplan Scholarships [4898]
Steve Kaplan TV and Film Studies Scholarships [1273]
Kalmen Kaplansky Scholarships in Economic and Social Rights [3657]
Kappa Delta Phi Scholarship Program [1046]
Kappa Delta Pi (KDP) [5666]
Kappa Gamma Pi [5685]
Kappa Kappa Gamma [5687]
Kappa Kappa Gamma Foundation of Canada [5776]
Kappa Kappa Gamma Foundation of Canada Graduate Scholarships [5777]
Kappa Kappa Gamma Foundation Project 2000 Scholarships [5739]
Kappa Kappa Gamma Graduate Scholarships [5740]
Kappa Kappa Gamma Undergraduate Scholarships [5741]
Kappa Omicron Nu (KON) [5778]
Kappa Omicron Nu Honor Society [5786]
Kappa Omicron Nu Leadership Undergraduate Scholarships [5781]
Kappa Omicron Nu National Alumni Fellowships [5782]
Kappa Project 2000 Scholarships [5742]
Kappa Sigma Fraternity [5791]
Kappa Sigma Scholarship/Leadership Awards [5792]
Kappa Tau Alpha (KTA) [5793]
Kappa Zeta Scholarships [8930]
Kaprielian Memorial Scholarships [10303]
The ISASI Rudolf Kapustin Memorial Scholarships [5394]
Josephine de Karman Fellowship Trust [5795]

Josephine de Karman Fellowships [5796]
Mitchell Karper Memorial Scholarships [5579]
Philip R. Karr, III Scholarship Fund [4378]
K.A.S.A Memorial Scholarships [7843]
KASF Chair Scholarships [5873]
KASF Designated Scholarships [5874]
KASF General Scholarships [5875]
Ken Kashiwahara Scholarships [8399]
Magoichi and Shizuko Kato Memorial Scholarships [5552]
Joseph Katz Memorial Scholarships [5580]
Ka'u Chamber of Commerce **[5797]**
Ka'u Chamber of Commerce College Scholarships [5798]
Ken and Romaine Kauffman Scholarship Fund [4245]
Lucile B. Kaufman Women's Scholarships [9184]
N.G. Kaul Memorial Scholarships [7403]
Dr. Terry Kavanagh Fellowships [2791]
William and Beatrice Kavanaugh Scholarships [5507]
Kawano Family Scholarships [8711]
E. Wayne Kay Co-op Scholarships [9185]
E. Wayne Kay Community College Scholarships [9186]
E. Wayne Kay High School Scholarships [9187]
KCC Foundation Gold Key Scholarships [5807]
KCC Foundation Scholarships [5808]
KCC-JEE Graduate Fellowships [5855]
KCC Trustee Scholarships [5809]
KDP Huntington Bank Scholarship [5673]
KDP International Scholarship Program - President Scholarship [5674]
KDP MBNA Scholarships [5675]
Keats-Shelley Association of America (KSAA) **[5799]**
Doc Keen Memorial Scholarships [9437]
Donald Keene Center of Japanese Culture **[5801]**
Keepers Preservation Education Fund [6202]
Micki and Norm Keesal Scholarships [5581]
Gunild Keetman Scholarships [7714]
Glenn Keever Scholarships [10236]
KEF Academic Scholarships [5865]
KEF College/University Basic Scholarships [5866]
KEF Vocational Education Scholarship [5867]
Kegler Brown Diversity Scholarship [5804]
Kegler, Brown, Hill, and Ritter Company, L.P.A **[5803]**
Maude Keisling/Cumberland County Extension Homemakers Scholarships [3231]
Annette and Ernest Keith Scholarships [8485]
Anna-Maria and Stephen M. Kellen Fellowships [726]
John W. Kelley Memorial Scholarships [9572]
Kellogg Community College Foundation **[5805]**
Rita Mae Kelly Fund [1121]
Kelly Law Team **[5810]**
Kelly Law Team Annual Down Syndrome Scholarships [5811]
Dr. Charles Kelly Memorial Scholarships [7844]
Kathleen Kelly Undergraduate Scholarship Award [8374]
Robert E. Kelsey Annual Scholarship [7933]
Willmoore H. Kendall Scholarships [3062]
The Deana Kendrick Foundation (TDKF) **[5812]**
Kendrick Foundation, Inc. Scholarships [5813]
Alexander Kendrick Memorial Scholarships [7773]
Kennedy Krieger Institute (KKI) **[5814]**
Southwest Ohio Environmental Horticulture Association (SOEHA) Lloyd W. Kennedy Scholarship [7584]
Oscar Kenshur Book Prize [1293]
Raymond A. Kent-Navy V-12/ROTC Scholarships [10145]
Kentucky Alumni Club Scholarships - Frankfort/Capital Region Alumni Club [10146]
Kentucky Alumni Club Scholarships - Lexington/Central Kentucky Alumni Club [10147]
Kentucky Alumni Club Scholarships - Somerset/Lake Cumberland Area Alumni Club [10148]
Kentucky Association of Realtors (KAR) **[5816]**
Kentucky Educational Excellence Scholarships [2261]
Kentucky Paralegal Association (KPA) **[5818]**
Kentucky Paralegal Association Student Scholarships [5819]

Kentucky Society of Certified Public Accountants (KyCPA) **[5820]**
Dr. Dorothy J. Kergin Fellowships [2703]
Kerrwil's J.W. Kerr Continuing Education Scholarship Awards [3837]
Kerrigan Scholarships [7986]
Edgar Kerstan Memorial Scholarships [6420]
Judge Oliver Kessel Memorial Scholarships - Ripley Rotary [7845]
Ashley E. Ketcher Memorial Scholarships [3289]
Ketchum Excellence in Public Relations Research Award [5213]
Keith Kevan Award [3892]
Kevin Kitchnefsky Foundation **[5822]**
KFOC Allied Health Doctoral Fellowship [5825]
KFOC Allied Health Scholarships [5826]
KFOC Biomedical Fellowships [5827]
KFOC Biomedical Scholarships [5828]
Khaki University and Y.M.C.A. Memorial Scholarships [10291]
Debbie Khalil Memorial Scholarships [8076]
Graduate Fellowship Program - Mahboob Khan/Advanced Micro Devices Fellowships [8834]
KHEAA Teacher Scholarship [2262]
KHIMA Graduate Scholarships [5661]
Michael Kidger Memorial Scholarships in Optical Design [9468]
Kidney Foundation of Canada (KFOC) **[5824]**
The Michael Kiely Strong Roots Scholarships [8233]
Julia Kiene Fellowships in Electrical Energy [10660]
Mary and Millard Kiker Scholarships [4201]
Kilbuck Family Native American Scholarships [2230]
Bernard Kilgore Memorial Scholarships [7327]
Helen and George Kilik Scholarships [274]
Killam Fellowships [4229]
Killingworth Foundation **[5829]**
Killingworth Foundation Scholarships [5830]
Kimberly Elementary School PTA Scholarships [8486]
Douglas Gray Kimel Scholarships [10587]
Sidney Kimmel Foundation for Cancer Research **[5831]**
Kimmel Scholars Award [5832]
James N. Kincanon Scholarships [8627]
Arthur M. and Berdena King Eagle Scout Scholarships [6927]
Kit C. King Graduate Scholarships [7109]
King Ice **[5833]**
King Ice Scholarships [5834]
Larry King/Jeffrey Fashion Cares Point Scholarship [8180]
Martin Luther King Jr. Scholarship Association **[5835]**
Martin Luther King Jr. Scholarships [5836]
Martin Luther King Law Scholarship [3680]
Mackenzie King Open Scholarships [6366]
Steven G. King Play Environments Scholarships [5914]
Forest A. King Scholarship [3681]
Jessica King Scholarships [3490]
Don King Student Fellowships [5021]
Mackenzie King Travelling Scholarships [6367]
Charles A. King Trust Postdoctoral Research Fellowships [4817]
Kingsbury Elementary School PTA Scholarships [8487]
Southwest Chapter Roy Kinslow Scholarships [1417]
Treva C. Kintner Scholarships [8097]
Kiplinger Fellowship [7599]
Isabel Mayer Kirkpatrick Scholarships [9438]
Ruth L. Kirschstein NRSA Individual Pre-Doctoral Fellowships [9926]
Annie Kirshenblatt Memorial Scholarships [9751]
Kislak Fellowships in American Studies [5844]
Kislak Short Term Fellowships Opportunities in American Studies [5845]
Dr. Elemér and Éva Kiss Scholarship Fund [5006]
Tamo Kitaura Scholarships [9961]
AACT John Kitt Memorial Scholarships [477]
Flo Kitz Memorial Scholarships [10792]
Kiwanis Club of Escondido Scholarships [8712]
Kiwanis Club of Redlands Foundation Academic Excellence Scholarships [8488]
Klarman Family Foundation Grants Program in Eating Disorders Research [4818]

Louis T. Klauder Scholarships [1166]
Jane M. Klausman Women in Business Scholarships [10826]
Robert A. Kleckner Scholarships [9439]
The Margie Klein "Paper Plate" Scholarships [1850]
Gerda and Kurt Klein Scholarships [4962]
Chris L. Kleinke Scholarship [10064]
Dr. Eva Kleinpeter Scholarship [5676]
Stefan and Janina Klimt Scholarships [8580]
Klingenfeld Fellowships in the Neurosciences [5838]
Esther A. and Joseph Klingenstein Fund, Inc **[5837]**
Klingenstein Third Generation Foundation (KTGF) **[5839]**
Klingon Language Institute (KLI) **[5841]**
Raymond and Augusta Klink Scholarships [3004]
Arthur Klorfein Scholarship and Fellowship Fund [6250]
John W. Kluge Center at the Library of Congress **[5843]**
Kluge Fellowships [5846]
American Marketing Association-Connecticut Chapter, Anna C. Klune Memorial Scholarships [4760]
Joseph H. Klupenger Scholarship Awards [7696]
AALL/Wolters Kluwer Law & Business Grants [532]
J. Merrill Knapp Research Fellowship [843]
Kemper K. Knapp Scholarships [10320]
Robert C. and Judith L. Knapp Scholarships [4147]
Iver and Cora Knapstad Scholarships [10024]
John A. Knauss Marine Policy Fellowship [9890]
John S. Knight Fellowships [5849]
John S. Knight Journalism Fellowships at Stanford **[5848]**
Robert E. Knight Professional Scholarships [9692]
Elva Knight Research Grants [5356]
Knight-Wallace Fellows at Michigan **[5850]**
Knight-Wallace Fellowship [5851]
Knights of Columbus **[5852]**
Knights of Vartan, Fresno Lodge No. 9 Scholarships [1701]
Jane Shaw Knox Graduate Scholarships [4148]
Knox-Hume Scholarships [3232]
Kris Knudson Memorial Scholarship [10065]
Glenn Knudsvig Memorial Scholarships [679]
Ina Knutsen Scholarships [8875]
Kobe College Corporation-Japan Education Exchange (KCC-JEE) **[5854]**
Koch Scholars Program [10430]
Kodak Fellowships in Film Preservation [2025]
Seth Koehler Central High School Scholarship Fund [4528]
Senator Carl O. Koella, Jr. Memorial Scholarships [3233]
George Koeppel Scholarships/All School [10321]
Herb Kohl Educational Foundation Excellence Scholarships [5857]
Herb Kohl Educational Foundation **[5856]**
Herb Kohl Educational Foundation Initiative Scholarships [5858]
Herb Kohl Educational Foundation Teacher Fellowships [5859]
Bob and Linda Kohlhepp Scholarships [3005]
Friends and Family of Christopher J. Kohlmeier Scholarships [8489]
James P. Kohn Memorial Scholarships [1418]
DSRSD James B. Kohnen Scholarships [3697]
Michael Koizumi APWA Scholarships [7263]
George Kokociński Memorial Scholarships [8581]
P. Johnson and C. Kolb Memorial Scholarships [8752]
Gwin J. and Ruth Kolb Research Travel Fellowships [1294]
Anna and John Kolesay Memorial Scholarships [275]
Carl Koller Memorial Research Grants [1404]
Bernie Kom Memorial Awards [10746]
Susan G. Komen for the Cure College Scholarship Awards [5861]
Susan G. Komen for the Cure Post-doctoral Fellowships - Clinical Research Grants [5862]
Susan G. Komen for the Cure **[5860]**
Vivian M. Kommer Scholarships [4603]
KON/GEICO LeaderShape Undergraduate Scholarship [5789]
KON National Alumni Chapter Grant [5783]

KON New Initiatives Grant [5784]
Koniag Education Foundation (KEF) **[5863]**
Emily Day Koppell Memorial Adelphe Scholarship [5743]
Elizabeth Munsterberg Koppitz Child Psychology Graduate Fellowships [1147]
Herman P. Kopplemann Scholarships [4761]
Kor Memorial Scholarships [5842]
The Korea Society (TKS) **[5869]**
Korean American Scholarship Foundation (KASF) **[5872]**
Korean Language Study Awards [5871]
Korean Studies Dissertation Workshop Funds [9056]
AIST Willy Korf Memorial Fund [2000]
Robert W. Korn Scholarships [10025]
Henriette and Marcel Korner Scholarships [5582]
Kosciuszko Foundation (KF) **[5876]**
Kosciuszko Foundation Graduate Study and Research in Poland Scholarships [5877]
Kosciuszko Foundation Tuition Scholarships [5878]
Kosciuszko Foundation Year Abroad Scholarships [5879]
Marcia J. Koslov Scholarship [533]
Eugene and Elinor Kotur Scholarship Trust Fund [10443]
Kovaluk Scholarship Fund [9984]
Marjorie Kovler Research Fellowships [5602]
ONLA Phil Kozel Memorial Scholarship [7585]
KPMG Foundation **[5884]**
KPMG Foundation Minority Accounting Doctoral Scholarships [5885]
KPMG Point Scholarship [8181]
Eve Kraft Education and College Scholarships [9975]
William D. Krahling Excellence in Journalism Scholarships [361]
Norman Kramer Scholarship Awards [6499]
Schmidt Kramer Scholarships for Academic Excellence [8792]
Melvin Kranzberg Dissertation Fellowships [9143]
Michael Kraus Research Grants [854]
Krawczyk-Krane Family Scholarships [8582]
Sharon Kreikemeier Memorial Scholarships [7242]
Krell Institute **[5886]**
Robert Krembil Scholarships of Merit [10747]
Kress/AAR Fellowships [1855]
Kress Conservation Fellowships [5889]
Kress Fellowships in Art History at Foreign Institutions [5890]
Samuel H. Kress Foundation Dissertation Fellowships [9084]
Samuel H. Kress Foundation **[5888]**
Samuel H. Kress Grants for Research and Publication in Classical Art and Architecture [1609]
Mathilde Krim Fellowships in Basic Biomedical Research [1536]
Central Indiana ASSE Jim Kriner Memorial Scholarships [1419]
Krist-Reavley Minority Scholarships [7987]
David A. Kronick Travelling Fellowships [6387]
Canadian Zionist Federation - Dr. Leon Aryeh Kronitz Scholarships [2640]
Eugene S. Kropf Scholarships [10105]
Kristin Bjurstrom Krueger Student Scholarship Program [6404]
Melvin Kruger Endowed Scholarship Program [7122]
Melvin Kruger Endowed Scholarships [8644]
Samuel Krugliak Legal Scholarship Fund [9517]
Judith Keller Marx Krumholz Scholarships [8713]
Michael B. Kruse Scholarships [3234]
Leo J. Krysa Family Undergraduate Scholarships [2674]
KTA Chapter Adviser Research Grant Award [5794]
George F. Kugler, Jr. Scholarships [2512]
Don Kuhn Memorial Scholarship Fund [6291]
Heloise Werthan Kuhn Scholarships [3235]
Irene Corbally Kuhn Scholarships [7774]
Arlene Kuhner Memorial Scholarship [10066]
Eldon E. and JoAnn C. Kuhns Family Scholarships [6584]
Kumin Scholars Program [8953]
Jan Kuropas Memorial Scholarships [8583]
Liela Klinger Kurtzman Memorial Scholarships [5583]
Chris Kurzweil Scholarship [3329]

Sam and Florice Kuwahara Memorial Scholarship [5553]
Henry and Chiyo Kuwahara Memorial Scholarships [5554]
Julia Kwan Endowed Scholarships [7988]
Anne Emery Kyllo Professional Scholarships [1014]
L-3 Communications Avionics Systems Scholarships [166]
La Fondation Superkutz **[5891]**
La Raza Lawyers Association of Santa Clara County **[5893]**
LA Tutors 123 **[5895]**
LA Tutors Innovation in Education Scholarships [5896]
La Voz Latina Scholarships [3290]
Roger and Jacquelyn Vander Laan Family Scholarships [4604]
Gretchen Laatsch Scholarships [1926]
Ladah Law Firm, PLLC **[5897]**
Ladah Law Firm, PLLC Injury Scholarships [5898]
Ladies Literary Club Scholarships [4605]
LAEF Scholarships [5937]
LAF Landscape Forms Design for People Scholarships [5915]
Jeffery P. LaFage Graduate Student Research Award [3882]
Lafarge Community Leaders Scholarships [2184]
Ken LaFountaine First Nations Scholarships [8876]
Ron LaFreniere Business Administration Scholarship [8877]
LAFS - Cal State University San Marcos General Scholarships [2212]
The LAGRANT Foundation **[5899]**
The Lagrant Foundation - Graduate Students Scholarships [5900]
The Lagrant Foundation - Undergraduate Students Scholarships [5901]
Ray and Kathy LaHood Scholarships for the Study of American Government [3627]
Lavina Laible Scholarships [4606]
Alexander Fraser Laidlaw Fellowships [2576]
Canadian Association for Studies in Co-operation Scholarships - Alexander Fraser Laidlaw Fellowships [2613]
Casey Laine Armed Forces Scholarships [3101]
Lake Dollars for Scholars Endowment Fund [9518]
Douglas Lake Improvement Association Scholarships [10184]
Lakselaget **[5902]**
Lakselaget Foundation Scholarships [5903]
Lalor Foundation **[5904]**
Lalor Foundation Merit Awards [9307]
Lalor Foundation Post-Doctoral Fellowships [5905]
LAM Foundation **[5906]**
Paul C. K. Lam Memorial Scholarship at The University of Akron [7593]
LAM Pilot Project Awards [5907]
Lamar University College of Engineering Scholarships [6928]
Lamaze International **[5908]**
Lambda Project 2000 Scholarship [5744]
Allen T. Lambert Scholarships [10748]
John and Lois Lamont Graduate Scholarship [2627]
Elaine Johnson Lampert Journalism Memorial Adelphe Scholarship [5745]
Lance Surety Bond Associates, Inc. **[5910]**
Lance Surety College Scholarships [5911]
Harold Lancour Scholarship for Foreign Study [2240]
Frank S. Land Scholarships [3598]
Robert S. Landauer, Sr. Memorial Fellowships [4810]
Landscape Architecture Foundation (LAF) **[5912]**
Lane Powell P.C. **[5919]**
The Lanford Family Highway Worker Memorial Scholarship Program [1219]
James D. Lang Memorial Scholarships [2563]
Frank H. Lang Merit Scholarships [5922]
Lang, Richert & Patch **[5921]**
Jason Lang Scholarships [276]
The Langfitt-Ambrose Trust Scholarship [7846]
Language Teacher Bursary Program Awards [277]
Languages In Teacher Education Scholarships [278]
Lanier Technical College **[5923]**
Paul J. Laninga Memorial Scholarship Fund [4529]
Stephen Lankester Scholarships [4607]

Lansdale Public Policy Fellowship [1245]
Lapeer County Medical Scholarship Fund [5932]
The Otis and Florence Lapham Memorial Scholarships [5508]
Lapides Fellowships in Pre-1865 Juvenile Literature and Ephemera [439]
Katherine Roberts LaPorte Memorial Adelphe Scholarship [5746]
Lapper County Community Foundation (LCCF) **[5927]**
Christian Larew Memorial Scholarships [6071]
Peter and Jody Larkin Legacy Scholarships [2455]
Arnold "Les" Larsen, FAIA, Memorial Scholarships [896]
Larson Aquatic Research Support Scholarships (LARS) [1490]
David B. Larson Fellowships in Health and Spirituality [5847]
Las Vegas Chinatown Scholarships [8352]
Laser Technology, Engineering and Applications Scholarships [9469]
Daniel Lasky Scholarship Fund [7081]
Jay and Deborah Last Fellowships [440]
Latham Diversity Scholars [5935]
Latham and Watkins L.L.P. **[5934]**
Austin E. Lathrop Scholarships [10026]
Latin American Educational Foundation (LAEF) **[5936]**
Latina Leadership Network (LLN) **[5938]**
Latinos for Dental Careers Scholarships [2830]
Karen E. Latt Memorial Scholarships [5584]
Rick and Beverly Lattin Education Scholarship Fund [4530]
Estée Lauder Point Scholarships [8182]
Candia Baker Laughlin Certification Scholarships [389]
Kenneth Laundy Entrance Scholarships [10749]
Mandel and Lauretta Abrahamer Scholarships [9573]
Robert J. Lavidge Nonprofit Marketing Research Scholarships [982]
Law Enforcement Memorial Scholarship Fund [4202]
Law Fellows Program [6710]
Law Foundation of British Columbia **[5940]**
Law Foundation of British Columbia Graduate Fellowships [5941]
Law Foundation of Newfoundland and Labrador **[5942]**
Law Foundation of Newfoundland and Labrador Law School Scholarships [5943]
Law Foundation of Ontario (LFO) **[5944]**
Law Foundation of Ontario Community Leadership in Justice Fellowships [5945]
Law Office of David D. White, PLLC [5946]
The Law Office of David P. Shapiro **[5948]**
Law Office of John J. Sheehan **[5950]**
Law Office of Matthew Shrum **[5952]**
The Law Office of Steven A. Leahy, P.C. **[5954]**
The Law Offices of David A. Black **[5956]**
Law Offices of James C. Dezao **[5958]**
The Law Offices of Judd S. Nemiro, PLLC **[5960]**
Law Offices of Michael A. DeMayo L.L.P. **[5962]**
The Law Offices of Tad Nelson & Associates **[5964]**
Law School Admission Council (LSAC) **[5966]**
Law Society of Alberta **[5968]**
Law and Society Association (LSA) **[5970]**
Law and Society Association Article Prize [5972]
Law and Society Association Dissertation Prize [5973]
Law and Society Association International Prize [5974]
Law and Society Association Undergraduate Student Paper Prize [5975]
Law Society of British Columbia **[5977]**
Law Society of British Columbia Scholarships [5978]
Law Society of Prince Edward Island (LSPEI) **[5979]**
Robert G. Lawrence Prize [1902]
Willie D. Lawson, Jr. Memorial Scholarships [6819]
Dr. James L. Lawson Memorial Scholarships [1745]
Lawsuit Legal **[5981]**
Lawsuit Legal American Nursing Support Scholarships [5983]
Verne Lawyer Scholarship [3682]

Lawyers' Committee for Civil Rights Under Law (LC-CRUL) **[5984]**
Sue Kay Lay Memorial Scholarships [3102]
Lazarian Graduate Scholarships [1678]
LCRF Grants [6141]
LCSC Presidential Out-of-State Tuition Scholarships [6035]
LCSC Welding Club Scholarships [6036]
Danny T. Le Memorial Scholarships [10385]
Franklin M. Leach Scholarships [10027]
Betsy B. and Garold A. Leach Scholarships for Museum Studies [3589]
Queenie Leader Memorial Scholarships [10793]
The Leaders of Tomorrow Scholarships [3765]
Leadership Conference Scholarship [6835]
Leadership Development Online Course Scholarships [7617]
LEAGUE Foundation Scholarships [8660]
League of Latin American Citizens General Electric Scholarships [5987]
League of United Latin American Citizens (LULAC) **[5986]**
Steven A. Leahy Law Office Marine Service/Law School Scholarships [5955]
Leakey Foundation **[5990]**
Leakey Foundation Research Grants [5992]
Learning Disabilities Association of Alberta (LDAA) **[5993]**
Learning Disabilities Association of Kingston (LDAK) **[5995]**
Learning Disabilities Association of Ontario (LDAO) **[5997]**
William C. Leary Memorial Emergency Services Scholarships [9822]
Jack W. Leatherman Family Scholarship Fund [4531]
LeClairRyan **[5999]**
LeClairRyan Diversity Scholarships [6000]
Patrick Ledden Honorary Scholarships [8714]
Hwain Chang Lee scholarships [7386]
Albert J. and Mae Lee Memorial Scholarships [7989]
William K. Lee Scholarships [7387]
Lee Womack Scholarship Fund [6570]
The Leesfield/AAJ Law Student Scholarships [517]
Robert E. Leet and Clara Guthrie Patterson Trust Awards Program in Clinical Research [4819]
Judge William B. Leffler Scholarships [10167]
The Legacy Fellowships [441]
Legacy, Inc. **[6001]**
Legacy Inc. College Undergraduate and Graduate Scholarships [6002]
Legal Aid of North Carolina, Inc. (LANC) **[6003]**
Doreen Legg Memorial Scholarships [8490]
Jay C. and B. Nadine Leggett Charitable Scholarship Fund [9519]
Herbert Lehman Education Scholarships [6646]
Lehman Family Scholarships [8715]
PCH Architects/Steven J. Lehnhof Memorial Architectural Scholarships [8491]
Gilder Lehrman Institute of American History **[6006]**
Gilder Lehrman Short-Term Fellowships [6007]
Leiber and Stoller Music Scholarships [1274]
Colonel Theodore A. Leisen Memorial and Training Endowment Funds [7249]
Lemaire Co-operative Studies Awards [2577]
Imelda "Mel" and Ralph LeMar Scholarship [3330]
Lemelson Center Fellowships [9025]
Lemelson Center Travel to Collections Awards [9026]
Lemelson Student Fellowships [9282]
The Lemon Grove Education Foundation Scholarships [8716]
Stan Lencki Scholarships [6356]
Franklin A. Lenfesty Memorial Scholarship [7537]
John Lennon Scholarships [2319]
Craig Lensch Memorial Scholarships [2378]
V.A. Leonard Scholarships [356]
Leopold Education Project Scholarships [3291]
Sherman L. and Mabel C. Lepard Scholarships [4608]
Lerner-Scott Prize [7717]
Irwin S. Lerner Student Scholarships [7168]
Les Dames d'Escoffier New York (LDNY) **[6008]**
Les Dames D'Escoffier New York Scholarships [6009]

Carol Anne Letheren Entrance Awards [10750]
Leukemia Research Foundation (LRF) **[6010]**
LEVEL **[6012]**
Brigid Leventhal Special Merit Award [3379]
Myra Levick Scholarships [449]
Jack A. and Louise S. Levine Memorial Scholarships [8492]
Saul Levine Memorial Scholarships [1037]
Harry and Miriam Levinson Scholarship [1148]
Herbert Levy Memorial Scholarship [9255]
William J. Levy Point Scholarship [8183]
Lewis-Clark Coin Club Endowed Scholarships [6037]
Lewis and Clark Fund for Exploration and Field Research [1082]
Lewis-Clark State College **[6014]**
Lewis-Clark State College Foundation Scholars Scholarships [6038]
Lewis-Clark State College Governor's Cup Scholarships [6039]
Lewis-Clark State College In-State Non-Traditional Student Scholarships [6040]
Lewis-Clark State College Library **[6056]**
Lewis-Clark State College - Military Order of the Purple Heart Scholarships [6041]
Lewis-Clark State College Provost Scholarships [6042]
Lewis-Clark State College Transfer Scholarships [6058]
Marvin Lewis Community Fund (MLCF) **[6059]**
Lloyd Lewis Fellowships in American History [7413]
George T. Lewis, Jr. Academic Scholarship Fund [4203]
Frederick D. Lewis Jr. Scholarships [3683]
Ted Lewis Memorial Scholarship [213]
Flora Lewis Memorial Scholarships [7775]
S. Evelyn Lewis Memorial Scholarships in Medical Health Sciences [10818]
Jonathan D. Lewis Point Scholarships [8184]
Lewis-Reynolds-Smith Founders Fellowship [4857]
Marvin Lewis Scholarships [6060]
Lewiston Service League Memorial Scholarships [6043]
Lexington Alumni Scholarships [6062]
Lexington Community Foundation (LCF) **[6061]**
Lexington Community Foundation Annual Scholarships [6063]
Lexington Community Foundation/CCC Scholarships [6064]
Ta Liang Memorial Awards [1806]
Liberty Mutual Scholarships [1420]
Library and Information Technology Association (LITA) **[6070]**
Richard T. Liddicoat Scholarships [4340]
Irene Brand Lieberman Memorial Scholarships [5585]
Dolores Zohrab Liebmann Fund **[6074]**
Dolores Zohrab Liebmann Fund - Graduate School Fellowships [6075]
Dolores Zohrab Liebmann Fund - Independent Research/Study Grants [6076]
Dolores Zohrab Liebmann Fund - Publication Grants [6077]
The Floyd Lietz Memorial Scholarship [8323]
Life Happens **[6078]**
LIFE Lessons Scholarship Program [6079]
Life Sciences Research Foundation (LSRF) **[6080]**
Life Sciences Research Foundation Postdoctoral Fellowship Program [6081]
Lighthouse International **[6082]**
Lighthouse International Scholarships - College-bound Awards [6083]
Lighthouse International Scholarships - Graduate Awards [6084]
Lighthouse International Scholarships - Undergraduate Awards [6085]
Roy W. Likins Scholarships [1494]
Frank R. Lillie Fellowships and Scholarships [6251]
Lilly Endocrine Scholars Fellowship Awards [3865]
Lilly Scholarships in Religion for Journalists [8549]
Esther Lim Memorial Scholarships [2918]
Lim, Ruger & Kim Scholarships [6704]
Lime Connect, Inc. **[6086]**
Tecla Lin & Nelia Laroza Memorial Scholarships [2704]
Lincoln Forum **[6090]**

AIST Ronald E. Lincoln Memorial Scholarships [2001]
John C. Lincoln Memorial Scholarships [1519]
Donald A.B. Lindberg Research Fellowships [6388]
Lindenwood University Scouting Scholarships [6929]
Carl H. Lindner Family Scholarships [3006]
George N. Lindsay Civil Rights Legal Fellowships [5985]
Margaret B. Lindsey Award for Distinguished Research in Teacher Education [487]
Johnny Lineberry Memorial Scholarships [10588]
Obrzut Ling Scholarships [8255]
Link Foundation/Smithsonian Graduate Fellowships in Marine Science [9033]
Richard Linn American Inn of Court **[6092]**
Ronald B. Linsky Fellowships for Outstanding Water Research [7213]
Linsley Scholarship Fund [2913]
LionsDeal Scholarships [6095]
Lionsdeal.com **[6094]**
F. Maynard Lipe Scholarship Award [683]
Lawrence Lipking Fellowships at the Newberry Library [7414]
Hushy Lipton Memorial Scholarship Funds [2641]
LITA/LSSI Minority Scholarships [6072]
LITA/OCLC Minority Scholarships [6073]
Literary Arts **[6096]**
Litherland/FTEE Scholarships [5438]
Ian Lithgow Memorial Awards [10751]
Littleton-Griswold Research Grants [855]
Ruth Liu Memorial Scholarships [2919]
LiveCareer **[6098]**
LiveCareer Scholarships [6099]
Lawrence Livermore National Laboratory Fellowships [9905]
Grant Livingston Memorial Scholarships [10794]
Davis Levin Livingston Public Interest Law Scholarships [3531]
David C. Lizárraga Graduate Fellowships [9660]
LLN Student Scholarships [5939]
E.C. Lloyd and J.C.U. Johnson Scholarship Fund [3266]
Patricia Lloyd Scholarship Concert Association (PLSCA) **[6100]**
Loan Forgiveness Scholarships [9463]
Virgil K. Lobring Scholarship [3331]
Local 564 Scholarship Award [5454]
Local Internet Service Scholarships [6103]
LocalInternetService.com **[6102]**
Leon I. Lock and Barbara R. Lock Scholarship Fund [4246]
Miriam "Doc" Locke Memorial Adelphe Scholarships [5747]
Mary Elizabeth Lockwood Beneventi MBA Scholarship [7153]
Loewenstein-Wiener Fellowship Award [947]
Audrey Loftus Memorial Scholarships [10099]
Stephen Logan Memorial Scholarships [4330]
Abram D. and Maxine H. Londa Scholarships [7334]
London Goodenough Association of Canada (LGAC) **[6104]**
London Goodenough Association of Canada Scholarships [6105]
Lone Star GIA Associate and Alumni Scholarships [4341]
Lawrence A. Long Memorial Law Scholarships [362]
James E. Long Memorial Post Doctoral Fellowships [5311]
L.D. and Elsie Long Memorial Scholarships [10589]
Long-term International Fellowships [3380]
Kay Longcope Scholarships [7050]
Megan Nicole Longwell Scholarships [7847]
Louise Loomis Memorial Adelphe Scholarships [5748]
L'Oreal USA Inc. **[6106]**
Lilly Lorenzen Scholarships [1470]
Suzanne and Caleb Loring Research Fellowships [6329]
Los Abogados Hispanic Bar Association **[6109]**
Barbara Lotze Scholarships for Future Teachers [562]
Lou Hochberg Awards - University Thesis/Dissertation Research Improvement and Implementation Grants [7749]
CH2M - Willie T. Loud Scholarships [6959]
Sir James Lougheed Awards of Distinction [279]

Louisiana Agricultural Consultants Association (LACA) **[6111]**
Louisiana Agricultural Consultants Association Scholarships [6112]
Louisiana Association of Criminal Defense Lawyers (LACDL) **[6113]**
Louisiana Environmental Health Association (LEHA) **[6115]**
Louisiana Library Association (LLA) **[6118]**
Louisiana Library Association Scholarships [6119]
Louisiana Public Health Association (LPHA) **[6121]**
Louisiana State Paralegal Association (LSPA) **[6123]**
Louisiana State University Health Sciences Center New Orleans - School of Medicine - Department of Ophthalmology - Eye Center **[6125]**
Louisville Institute **[6127]**
Louisville Institute Dissertation Fellowships [6128]
Louisville Institute First Book Grants for Minority Scholars [6129]
Louisville Institute Project Grant for Researchers [6130]
Louisville Institute Sabbatical Grants for Researchers [6131]
Louthian Law Firm, P.A. **[6132]**
Louthian Law School Scholarships [6133]
Love of Bonita Empowerment Scholarships [9440]
First Lieutenant Scott McClean Love Memorial Scholarship - Children of Soldiers [1714]
First Lieutenant Scott McClean Love Memorial Scholarship - Spouses of Soldiers [1715]
John Allen Love Scholarships [10304]
Loveland Archaeological Society (LAS) **[6134]**
D.J. Lovell Scholarships [9470]
Lowe Family First Summer Student Scholarships [10185]
Diane G. Lowe and John Gomez, IV Scholarships [3236]
Gertie S. Lowe Nursing Scholarship Awards [3267]
Lowry Awards for Women of Excellence [3789]
LPHA Scholarships [6122]
LSAC Research Grant Program [5967]
LSU Eye Center Clinical Retina Fellowships [6126]
Henry Luce Foundation/ACLS Dissertation Fellowships in American Art [742]
Elsa Ludeke Graduate Scholarships [3590]
David F. Ludovici Scholarships [4091]
Lugonia Alumni/Harrison Lightfoot Scholarships [8493]
Mollie Lukken Memorial Scholarships [5633]
LULAC GM Scholarships [5988]
LULAC National Scholarship Fund (LNSF) [5989]
Audrey Lumsden-Kouvel Fellowships [7415]
Juan and Esperanza Luna Scholarship [1583]
Lunenfeld-Tanenbaum Research Institute - Research Training Centre **[6137]**
Lung Cancer Research Foundation **[6140]**
Lung Health Dissertation Grants [977]
Ann and Robert H. Lurie Children's Hospital of Chicago **[6142]**
Ann & Robert H. Lurie Children's Memorial Hospital Postgraduate Administrative Fellowships [6143]
Luso-American Education Foundation (LAEF) **[6144]**
Luso-American Education Foundation C-1 General Scholarships [6145]
Luso-American Education Foundation G-1 Grants [6146]
Luso-American Education Foundation G-2 Grants [6147]
Luso-American Education Foundation G-3 Grants [6148]
Luso-American Fraternal Federation B-2 Scholarships [6149]
Luso-American Fraternal Federation B-3 Scholarships [6150]
Luso-American Fraternal Federation B-4 Scholarships [6151]
Lutheran Student Scholastic and Service Scholarships - College and University Students [2248]
Charles Luttman Scholarship [2536]
Lycoming County Medical Society Scholarships (LCMS) [4277]
Lymphatic Research Foundation Additional Support for NIH-funded F32 Postdoctoral Fellows Awards [4820]
Lymphatic Research Foundation Postdoctoral Fellowship Awards Program [4821]
Lymphoma Research Foundation (LRF) **[6155]**
Margaret Lynch Religious Study Fellowships [7634]
Boyd N. Lyon Scholarships [6162]
Boyd Lyon Sea Turtle Fund **[6161]**
The C. Lyons Fellowship Program [7047]
Verne LaMarr Lyons Memorial Scholarships [6790]
Carie and George Lyter Scholarship Fund [4247]
Margaret Smith Maase Scholarships [7388]
MABF Scholarships [6442]
John Mabry Forestry Scholarships [8423]
MAC Emeritus Scholarships for First-Time Meeting Attendees [6516]
Bill MacAloney Legacy Scholarships [2456]
MacArthur Fellows Program [6164]
MacArthur Foundation **[6163]**
Catharine Macaulay Prize [1295]
MACC Scholarships [6444]
Katie MacDonald Memorial Scholarships [9865]
Burton MacDonald and Rosemarie Sampson Fellowships [659]
Dr. Sally Macdonald Scholarships [10795]
Dr. Arlene MacIntyre Medical Student Bursaries [7640]
Nate Mack/Cindi Turner Scholarships [8353]
Robert Mack Scholarship Foundation **[6165]**
Warren Mack Scholarship [5622]
Robert Mack Scholarships [6166]
CEMF Claudette MacKay-Lassonde Graduate Scholarships [2624]
Thermoset Division/James I. Mackenzie and James H. Cunningham Scholarships [9264]
Mackenzie Municipal Services Agency **[6167]**
Mackey-Byars Scholarships for Communication Excellence [10237]
Macomb County Bar Foundation (MCBF) **[6169]**
MACPA Scholarships [6298]
Carol E. Macpherson Memorial Scholarship [10203]
Andrew Macrina Scholarships [761]
Pat and John MacTavish Scholarship Fund [4532]
Eileen C. Maddex Fellowships [5785]
Dorothy L. Maddy Workshop/Seminar Scholarship [9489]
Lawrence Madeiros Scholarships [6992]
James Madison Foundation - Junior Fellowships [6174]
James Madison Foundation - Senior Fellowships [6175]
James Madison Graduate Fellowships [6176]
James Madison Memorial Fellowship Foundation **[6173]**
Madson Graduate Scholarships [8899]
Gordon and Delores Madson Scholarship [3684]
MAES Founders Scholarships [6178]
MAES General Scholarships [6179]
MAES Graduate Scholarships [6180]
MAES: Latinos in Science and Engineering **[6177]**
MAES Padrino/Madrina Scholarships [6181]
MAES Pipeline Scholarships [6182]
MAES Presidential Scholarships [6183]
MAF Canada Scholarship Fund [6560]
Keith Maffioli Scholarships [3292]
Brandon Magalassi Memorial Scholarship Foundation **[6184]**
The Brandon Magalassi Memorial Scholarship Foundation Scholarships [6185]
John T. and Frances J. Maghielse Scholarships [4609]
Dr. Edward May Magruder Medical Scholarships [677]
Sonia S. Maguire Outstanding Scholastic Achievement Awards [9618]
Lillian Grace Mahan Scholarship Fund [9520]
Dan and Rachel Mahi Educational Scholarships [7914]
Rick Mahoney Scholarships [6357]
Maiman Student Paper Competition [7674]
Mary Main Memorial Scholarships [4762]
Maine Association of Physician Assistants (MEAPA) **[6186]**
Maine Chapter of the International Association of Arson Investigators (IAAI) **[6188]**
Maine Community College Scholarships [6222]
Maine Community Foundation **[6190]**
Maine Community Foundation - Rice Scholarships [6203]
Maine Graphic Arts Association (MGAA) **[6214]**
Maine Graphic Arts Association Scholarships [6215]
Maine Landscape and Nursery Association (MeLNA) **[6216]**
Maine Nutrition Council (MNC) **[6218]**
Maine Nutrition Council Scholarships [6219]
Maine State Employees Association (MSEA) **[6220]**
Maine Vietnam Veterans Scholarships [6204]
Maintenance Technical Reward and Career Scholarships [6836]
The Make It Move Scholarships [1594]
Make Us Proud Scholarships [4793]
Malayalee Engineers Association (MEA) **[6224]**
Malayalee Engineers Association Scholarships [6225]
MALDEF Dream Act Student Activist Scholarships [6446]
Maley/FTE Scholarships [5439]
Maley/FTEE Teacher Scholarships [5440]
Margaret Mallett Nursing Scholarship [8878]
NBCFAE Mamie W. Mallory National Scholarship Program [6813]
Ann M. Mallouk Scholarships [7389]
Malmberg Scholarships [1471]
Joseph J. Malone Fellowships in Arab and Islamic Studies [6895]
Reba Malone Scholarships [1167]
Sue A. Malone Scholarships [5662]
David C. Maloney Scholarships [7079]
Optimist Club Of Redlands - Ralph Maloof Scholarships [8494]
MALSCE Memorial Scholarships [6306]
Dr. Julianne Malveaux Scholarships [6762]
Malyon-Smith Scholarship Award [9285]
Lyle Mamer Fellowships [10661]
MANAA Media Scholarships [6382]
Manchester Scholarship Foundation - Adult Learners Scholarships [4763]
Mangasar M. Mangasarian Scholarship Fund [1702]
Manhattan Street Capital Annual National Scholarships [6227]
Manhattan Street Capital, LLC **[6226]**
Norm Manly Maritime Educational Scholarships [10768]
Mann Law Firm Scholarships [3529]
Raleigh Mann Scholarships [10238]
Mansfield Soccer Association (MSA) **[6228]**
Mansfield Soccer Association Scholarships [6229]
Honorable Carol Los Mansmann Memorial Scholarships [327]
Paul Mansur Scholarships [5345]
Mantle Cell Lymphoma Research Grants [6160]
Manufacturing Jewelers and Association of America (MJSA) **[6230]**
Many Voices Fellowships [8153]
Manzer-Keener-Wefler Scholarships [9521]
March of Dimes Foundation **[6232]**
March of Dimes General Research Grants [6233]
March of Dimes Graduate Nursing Scholarships [6234]
Stephen T. Marchello Scholarship Foundation **[6236]**
Stephen T. Marchello Scholarships [6237]
Harold and Inge Marcus Scholarships [5191]
American Turkish Society Arif Mardin Music Fellowships [9811]
Margaret Mead Award [9081]
The Margarian Law Firm **[6238]**
The Margarian Scholarships [6239]
Art Margosian Scholarship [5623]
Aurella Varallo Mariani Scholarship Program [6665]
Marine Aquarium Societies of North America (MASNA) **[6240]**
Marine Biological Laboratory (MBL) **[6242]**
Marine Biological Laboratory Pioneers Fund [6252]
Marine Corps Engineer Association (MCEA) **[6266]**
Marine Corps League Foundation **[6268]**
Marine Corps League National Scholarships [6269]
Marine Technology Society (MTS) **[6270]**
Marine Technology Society ROV Scholarships (MTS ROV) [6272]
Marines Memorial Association (MMA) **[6277]**
Shirley Stone Marinkovich Memorial Scholarships [5749]

Dr. Frank and Florence Marino Scholarships [4764]
Marion Community Foundation **[6279]**
Mariposa Elementary School PTA Scholarships [8495]
Marisol Scholarship [5750]
Marketing EDGE **[6286]**
Howard T. Markey Memorial Scholarship [3985]
Markham-Colegrave International Scholarships [805]
Markley Family Scholarship Fund [9522]
Markley Scholarships [6724]
Kaia Lynn Markwalter Endowed Scholarships [6044]
Abby Marlatt Scholarship [10322]
Marliave Scholarship Fund [1948]
Abraham Lincoln Marovitz Public Interest Law Scholarships [2897]
Olivia M. Marquart Scholarships [9828]
George Perkins Marsh Prize [1313]
Marsh Risk Consulting Scholarships [1421]
Marsh Writing/Research Scholarship Awards [5677]
Marshall-Baruch Fellowships [6295]
George C. Marshall Foundation (GCMF) **[6294]**
Marshall Memorial Fellowships [4399]
Ray and Gertrude Marshall Scholarships [762]
Ron Marshall Scholarships [1192]
Sarah Shinn Marshall Scholarships [3554]
Marshall Undergraduate Scholars Program [6296]
E.H. Marth Food and Environmental Scholarships [10615]
Martha Weston Grant [9097]
Eleanor Jean Martin Award [2705]
William B. Martin East Carolina University Scholarships [5678]
Susan B. Martin Memorial Scholarships [5038]
Bryce-Lietzke Martin Scholarships [7848]
Dick Martin Scholarships [2609]
Edna L. Martin Scholarships [3237]
Right Honourable Paul Martin Sr. Scholarships [5150]
Martin Sisters Scholarships [3555]
Dottie Martin Teacher Scholarships [7464]
John S. Martinez and Family Scholarship Fund [3200]
Eric Martinez Memorial Scholarships [9866]
Corporal Joseph Martinez U.S. Army/Durango High School AFJROTC [8354]
Anthony A. Martino Memorial Scholarships [4462]
Maryland Association of Certified Public Accountants (MACPA) **[6297]**
Maryland Poison Center (MPC) **[6299]**
Maryland Poison Center Clinical Toxicology Fellowships [6300]
Maryland Speech-Language-Hearing Association (MSHA) **[6301]**
Maryland Speech Language Hearing Association Graduate Scholarships [6302]
Jorge Mas Canosa Freedom Foundation **[6303]**
Mas Family Scholarships [6304]
The Maschhoffs Pork Production Scholarships [7037]
Beverley Mascoll Scholarships [2288]
MASNA Student Scholarships [6241]
Margaret Edwards Mason Adelphe Scholarship [5751]
Val Mason Scholarships [2746]
Masonic-Range Science Scholarships [9298]
Massachusetts Association of Land Surveyors and Civil Engineers (MALSCE) **[6305]**
Massachusetts Association of Women Lawyers (MAWL) **[6307]**
Massachusetts Bar Foundation (MBF) **[6309]**
Massachusetts Bar Foundation Legal Intern Fellowship Program (LIFP) [6310]
Massachusetts Chapter of the International Association of Arson Investigators, Inc. (MAIAAI) **[6311]**
Massachusetts Educational Financing Authority (MEFA) **[6313]**
Massachusetts Federation of Polish Women's Clubs Scholarships [5880]
Massachusetts General Hospital - Center for Engineering in Medicine (CEM) **[6315]**
Massachusetts General Hospital Clinical Translational Fellowships at Pfizer [6318]
Massachusetts General Hospital Department of Psychiatry **[6317]**
Massachusetts General Hospital/Harvard Medical School Internships [6319]

Massachusetts Historical Society (MHS) **[6325]**
Massachusetts LGBTQ Bar Association (MLGBA) **[6339]**
Massachusetts Office of Student Financial Assistance **[6341]**
Massachusetts State Automobile Dealers Association (MSADA) **[6343]**
Elizabeth Massey Award [2631]
S.O. Mast Founder's Scholarships [6253]
Master Municipal Clerks Academy Scholarships [5351]
Master's Degree with a Major in Nursing Academic Scholarships [6657]
Matanuska-Susitna College Regent's Scholarships [10089]
Ruth G. and Joseph D. Matarazzo Scholarship [1149]
Norman Matechuk Memorial Scholarships [10796]
Material Handling Education Foundation Scholarships [6346]
Material Handling Industry (MHI) **[6345]**
Larry Matfay Cultural Heritage Scholarships [5868]
Mathematics Mentoring Travel Grants for Women [2099]
Katharine & Bryant Mather Scholarship [708]
AILA Virginia Mathews Memorial Scholarships [885]
Noel D. Matkin Awards [3798]
Rene Matos Memorial Scholarships [6996]
The Renardo A. Matteucci Scholarship Fund [3206]
Greg Matthews Memorial Scholarships [7990]
Randall Matthis for Environmental Studies Scholarships [1649]
Antonio Mattos Memorial Scholarships [6152]
Mature Student Scholarship [3912]
Donald Mauer Scholarships [10239]
Al Maurer Awards [3790]
Elizabeth M. Mauro Reimbursement Awards [63]
Edmund F. Maxwell Foundation **[6347]**
Maxwell Graduate Scholarships in Medical Journalism [10240]
Edmund F. Maxwell Scholarships [6348]
Juliann and Joe Maxwell Scholarships [3238]
Juliann King Maxwell Scholarships for Riverview High School [3239]
May-Cassioppi Scholarships [3293]
Howard Mayer Brown Fellowship [1021]
John E. Mayfield ABLE Scholarships [3240]
John E. Mayfield Scholarship Fund for Cheatham County Central High School [3241]
John E. Mayfield Scholarship Fund for Harpeth High School [3242]
John E. Mayfield Scholarship Fund for Pleasant View Christian High School [3243]
John E. Mayfield Scholarship Fund for Sycamore High School [3244]
Bill Maynes Fellowships [3929]
Joseph W. Mayo ALS Scholarships [6205]
Clara Mayo Grants Program [9290]
Tadeusz Maziarz Scholarships [8584]
John Mazurek Memorial-Morgex Insurance Scholarship [296]
Giuliano Mazzetti Scholarships [9188]
Charles "Chuck" McAdams Memorial Scholarships [9644]
Walter Samuel McAfee Scholarships in Space Physics [7143]
Durwood McAlister Scholarships [4387]
McAllister Fellowships [1867]
MCBA Scholarship [6465]
McBurney General Scholarships [10323]
Robert R. McCain Memorial Scholarships [7283]
Heather McCallum Scholarships [1903]
Rev. Richard S. McCarroll and Mrs. E. Allison McCarroll Scholarships [7390]
Doreen McMullan McCarthy Memorial Academic Scholarship for Women with Bleeding Disorders [6993]
Bill McCarthy Scout Scholarship Fund [9523]
McCaughan Heritage Scholarships [1064]
McClatchy Minority Scholarship and Fellowship [9369]
McCleary Law Fellows Program [4992]
Dave McCloud Aviation Memorial Scholarships [10028]
McCloy Fellowships in Agriculture [727]
McCloy Fellowships in Environmental Policy [728]

McCloy Fellowships in Journalism [729]
McCloy Fellowships in Urban Affairs [730]
Anne O'Hare McCormick Scholarship Fund [7429]
Hans McCorriston Motive Power Machinist Grant Programs [2132]
Niqui McCown Honor and Memorial Scholarship Fund [10505]
Joseph McCulley Educational Scholarships [10292]
McDaniel College Eagle Scout Scholarships [6930]
Fred R. McDaniel Memorial Scholarships [1746]
J. McDonald and Judy Williams School of Law Scholarships [7991]
Michele L. McDonald Scholarships [3801]
Richard D. McDonough Golf Scholarship Foundation **[6349]**
Bodie McDowell Scholarships [7770]
MCEA Financial Assistance Award [6267]
McFarffels Scholarships [8256]
William H. McGannon Foundation Scholarships [6364]
William H. McGannon Foundation **[6363]**
Foster G. McGaw Graduate Student Scholarships [688]
Foster G. McGaw Scholarships [2086]
Nancy B. Woolridge McGee Graduate Fellowships [10819]
Senator Patricia K. McGee Nursing Faculty Scholarships [7365]
Lucille E. McGee Scholarships [5509]
Thomas R. McGetchin Memorial Scholarship Awards [9997]
McGill University **[6365]**
Richard McGrath Memorial Fund Awards [755]
Linda and Vincent McGrath Scholarship [5679]
Lee Kimche McGrath Worldwide Fellowships [2067]
William P. McHugh Memorial Fund Award [1197]
Mary Bowles McInnis Adelphe Scholarship [5752]
McJulien Minority Graduate Scholarships [1944]
Molly McKay Scholarships [10241]
Robert V. McKenna Scholarships [9654]
R. Tait Mckenzie Awards [8118]
J.B. and Marilyn McKenzie Graduate Student Fellowships [10186]
AIST Midwest Member Chapter - Betty McKern Scholarships [2002]
John J. McKetta Undergraduate Scholarships [905]
Arthur Patch McKinlay Scholarships [680]
McKinley Elementary School PTA Scholarships [8496]
John L. and Eleanore I. Mckinley Scholarships [3591]
Louise McKinney Post-secondary Scholarships [280]
McKinney Sisters Undergraduate Scholarships [3556]
Elizabeth McKissick Memorial Scholarships [6045]
McKnight Advancement Grants [8154]
H. H. McKnight Memorial Scholarships [10168]
C.A. "Pete" McKnight Scholarships [10242]
McKnight Theater Artist Fellowships [8155]
Paul R. McLaughlin Fellowship [8436]
McLean Scholarships [1978]
John Alexander McLean Scholarships [9731]
John McLendon Memorial Minority Postgraduate Scholarships [6738]
Ruth McMillan Student Grants [2482]
R. Roy McMurtry Fellowships in Legal History [7760]
Ronald E. McNair Scholarships in Space and Optical Physics [7144]
McNeely Stephenson Attorneys at Law **[6369]**
McNeely Stephenson of New Albany **[6371]**
McNeely Stephenson of New Albany Community Involvement Scholarships [6372]
National Association of Pediatric Nurse Practitioners McNeil Annual Scholarships [6773]
National Association of Pediatric Nurse Practitioners McNeil Rural and Underserved Scholarships [6774]
Joan Reagin McNeill Scholarships - Alpha Theta [8931]
Joan Reagin McNeill Scholarships - Theta Phi [8932]
G. William McQuade Memorial Scholarships [7284]
O. Ruth McQuown Scholarship - Graduate Award for Current Students [10135]

MCRD Museum Foundation **[6373]**
Douglas McRorie Memorial Scholarships [114]
MCRTA Book Scholarships [6449]
MDA Development Grants [6622]
MDA Research Grants [6623]
MDF Post-Doctoral Fellowships [6643]
MDI Biological Laboratory High school Student Summer Research Fellowships [6606]
David Meador Foundation - Club Management Student Scholarships [7295]
Ben Meadows Natural Resource Scholarships - Academic Achievement Scholarships [2221]
Ben Meadows Natural Resource Scholarships - Leadership Scholarships [2222]
Med Technology and Clinical Lab Science Scholarships [104]
The Medalist Club **[6375]**
The Medalist Club Post Graduate Scholarships [6376]
The Medallion Fund Scholarships [7302]
Medex Biocare Pharmacy L.L.C. **[6377]**
Medford Rogue Rotary Club **[6379]**
Medford Rogue Rotary Scholarship [6380]
Media Action Network for Asian Americans (MANAA) **[6381]**
Medical Group Management Association (MGMA) **[6383]**
Medical Library Association (MLA) **[6385]**
Medical Library Association Scholarships for Minority Students [6389]
Medical Student Rotation for Underrepresented Populations [3381]
Medicus Student Exchange Scholarships [9619]
Medieval Academy of America (MAA) **[6394]**
Medieval Academy Dissertation Grants [6396]
Rixio Medina and Associates Hispanics in Safety Scholarships [1422]
Medina County Retired Teachers Association **[6399]**
Medina County Retired Teachers Association Scholarship [6400]
Meeting Professionals International Connecticut River Valley Chapter (MPI CRV) **[6401]**
Meeting Professionals International - Wisconsin Chapter **[6403]**
MEFA Graduate Loans [6314]
Edward Heywood Megson Scholarships [10243]
Dr. Ernest and Minnie Mehl Scholarships [281]
Karl Mehlmann Scholarships [3138]
Kumar Mehta Scholarship [709]
Fred & Lena Meijer Scholarships [4610]
Susan R. Meisinger Fellowship for Graduate Study in HR [9146]
Dr. Roger E. Meisner Veterinary Medicine Educational Scholarship Fund [7501]
Carl J. Mejel Scholarship [794]
Melanoma Foundation of New England **[6406]**
Philip H. Melanson Memorial Scholarships [10154]
Frederic G. Melcher Scholarships [2018]
The Melissa Institute for Violence Prevention and Treatment **[6408]**
Ilse Hanfmann, George Hanfmann and Machteld Mellink Fellowships [1206]
Mellon/ACLS Dissertation Completion Fellowships [743]
Mellon-CES Dissertation Completion Fellowships [3440]
Mellon Fellowships for Dissertation Research in the Humanities [3450]
Mellon Fellowships for Dissertation Research in Original Sources [3451]
MHS Andrew W. Mellon Fellowships [6330]
Mellon Fellowships in Urban Landscape Studies [3739]
Andrew W. Mellon Foundation Fellowships [7740]
Institute Andrew W. Mellon Postdoctoral Research Fellowships [7614]
Richard Mellon Scholarships [10029]
Terry Mellor Continuing Education Grant [9480]
MELNA Scholarship [6217]
E.V. and Nancy Melosi Travel Grants [1314]
Memorial Foundation for Jewish Culture (MFJC) **[6410]**
Memphis Access and Diversity Scholarships [10169]
The Tatiana Mendez Future Resources Scholarships [8234]

Joseph C. Menezes Scholarship [6189]
Mennonite Central Committee Canada (MCCC) **[6415]**
Menominee Indian Tribe of Wisconsin (MITW) **[6417]**
Menominee Tribal Scholarships [6418]
Mensa Canada **[6419]**
Mensa Canada General Scholarships [6421]
Mensa Education and Research Foundation **[6423]**
Mensa Education and Research Foundation U.S. Scholarships [6424]
Mentored Clinical Scientist Development Awards [9915]
Mentored Research Scholar Grant in Applied and Clinical Research [646]
CAG Donald Menzies Bursary Awards [2554]
Benchwarmers of Redlands-Jess Mercado Football Scholarships [8497]
Merck Company Foundation **[6425]**
Merck Frosst Canada Ltd. Postgraduate Pharmacy Fellowships [1957]
Al Mercury Scholarships [10293]
Erickson Merkel Foundation Scholarships [3925]
John Merrick Law Scholarships [7992]
Gary Merrill Memorial Scholarships [6206]
MESA Student Travel Fund [6511]
Scott Mesh Honorary Grant for Research in Psychology [1134]
Christopher Mesi Memorial Music Scholarships [2803]
Mesothelioma Memorial Scholarships [9594]
Mesquite Club Evening Chapter Inc. Scholarships [8355]
Ruth Messmer Memorial Scholarships [9441]
Sanders J. Mestel Legal Scholarship Fund [9524]
Harry Mestel Memorial Accounting Scholarship Fund [9525]
Metcalf Innovation Fellowships [4366]
Nicholas Metropolis Award for Outstanding Doctoral Thesis Work in Computational Physics [1091]
Metropolitan Museum of Art **[6428]**
Metropolitan Museum of Art Bothmer Fellowship [6432]
Metropolitan Museum of Art Conservation and Scientific Research Fellowships [6433]
Metropolitan Museum of Art Research Scholarship in Photograph Conservation [6434]
Edmond A. Metzger Scholarships [1747]
Mexican American Alumni Association Scholarships [10356]
Mexican American Bar Foundation **[6441]**
Mexican American Catholic College (MACC) **[6443]**
Mexican American Legal Defense and Educational Fund (MALDEF) **[6445]**
Mexican American Legal Defense and Educational Fund Law School Scholarships [6447]
Theodore Meyer Scholarships [1015]
MFJC International Fellowships in Jewish Studies [6414]
MGH Department of Psychiatry Behavioral Neurology and Neuropsychiatry Fellowships [6320]
MGH Department of Psychiatry Eating Disorders Summer Research Fellowships [6321]
MGH Department of Psychiatry Forensic Psychiatry Fellowships [6322]
MGH Department of Psychiatry Global Psychiatric Clinical Research Training Program [6323]
MHS African American Studies Fellowships [6331]
MHS/Cushing Academy Fellowships on Environmental History [6332]
MHS Long-Term Research Fellowships [6333]
MHS/Massachusetts Society of the Cincinnati Fellowships [6334]
Miami County Retired Teachers Association **[6448]**
The Miami Foundation **[6450]**
MICA Scholarships [6532]
Michael Oykhman Criminal Defense Law **[6454]**
Bernard Michel Scholarships [2526]
Michener-Deacon Fellowship for Journalism Education [4121]
Michigan Accountancy Foundation Final Year Accounting Scholarship [6457]
Michigan Association of Certified Public Accountants (MICPA) **[6456]**
Michigan Association of Fire Fighters (MAFF) **[6458]**

Michigan Association of Realtors (MAR) **[6460]**
Michigan Auto Law **[6462]**
Michigan Auto Law Student Diversity Scholarships [6463]
Michigan Competing Band Association (MCBA) **[6464]**
Michigan Council of Women in Technology (MCWT) **[6466]**
Michigan Council of Women in Technology High School Scholarship Program [6467]
Michigan Council of Women in Technology Undergraduate Scholarship Program [6468]
Michigan Education Association (MEA) **[6469]**
Michigan Education Association Scholarships [6470]
Michigan League for Nursing (MLN) **[6471]**
Michigan League for Nursing Scholarships [6472]
Michigan Nursery and Landscape Association (MNLA) **[6473]**
Michigan Nurses Foundation (MNF) **[6475]**
Michigan Nurses Foundation Scholarships [6477]
Michigan Parkinson Foundation (MPF) **[6478]**
Michigan Realtors Scholarship Trust [6461]
Michigan Society of Fellows **[6480]**
Michigan Society of Fellows Three-Year Fellowships [6481]
Michigan Society of Professional Engineers (MSPE) **[6482]**
Michigan Society of Professional Engineers Scholarships [6483]
Michigan Space Grant Consortium (MSGC) **[6484]**
Michigan State Horticultural Society (MSHS) **[6486]**
Michigan State University - Gender, Development and Globalization Program (GDG) **[6489]**
Michigan Stormwater-Floodplain Association (MSFA) **[6491]**
Michigan Stormwater-Floodplain Association Scholarships [6492]
Michigan Sugar Co. **[6493]**
Michigan Sugar Company Hotel Restaurant/Resort Management Scholarships [6495]
Michigan Sugar Queen Scholarships [6496]
Michigan Turfgrass Foundation (MTF) **[6497]**
Michigan Water Environment Association (MWEA) **[6501]**
Bronislaw Michno Memorial Scholarships [8585]
John G. and Betty J. Mick Scholarship Fund [9526]
Microsoft Research **[6505]**
Microsoft Research Graduate Women's Scholarships [6506]
Microsoft Research PhD Fellowships [6507]
Mid-Continent Instrument Scholarships [167]
Mid-Ohio District Nurses Association (MODNA) **[6508]**
Middle East Studies Association of North America (MESA) **[6510]**
Beth Middleton Memorial Scholarships [3961]
Midlothian Rotary Club **[6512]**
Midlothian Rotary Club "Service Above Self" Scholarship [6513]
Ella and Harold Midtbo Scholarships [7391]
Midwest Archives Conference (MAC) **[6514]**
Midwest Dairy Association (MDA) **[6518]**
Midwest Food Processors Association, Inc. (MWFPA) **[6526]**
Midwest Modern Language Association Fellowships [7416]
Albert and Eloise Midyette Memorial Scholarship Fund [4204]
Migrant Health Scholarships [6846]
Mihaly Russin Scholarship Awards [8656]
Mikimoto Scholarships [4342]
Mary Ann Mikulic Scholarships [2052]
Ruth Milan-Altrusa Scholarships [6207]
Milan Getting Scholarships [9335]
Milbank Diversity Scholars Program [6530]
Milbank, Tweed, Hadley & McCloy LLP **[6529]**
Mildred Colodny Diversity Scholarships for Graduate Study in Historic Preservation [7202]
Eunice Miles Scholarships [4343]
William F. Miles Scholarships [4702]
Military Intelligence Corps Association (MICA) **[6531]**
Military Nurses Association Scholarships [2706]
Military Officers Association of America (MOAA) **[6533]**
Military Service Scholarships [8900]

Mill Creek Business Association (MCBA) [6536]
Mill Creek Business Association Scholarships [6537]
Cheryl Allyn Miller Award [9332]
Miller Electric International WorldSkills Competition Scholarships [1520]
Warren E. Miller Fellowship in Electoral Politics [1122]
Ruth R. and Alyson R. Miller Fellowships [6335]
Brian and Colleen Miller Math and Science Scholarships [3103]
Robbie Miller Memorial Scholarships [6046]
Raymond W. Miller, PE and Alice E. Miller Scholarships [4092]
Raymond W. Miller, PE Scholarships [4093]
MillerCoors Engineering and Sciences Scholarships [68]
MillerCoors National Scholarships [69]
Dolphus E. Milligan Graduate Fellowships [7087]
Carolina Panthers Players Sam Mills Memorial Scholarship Fund [4205]
Carolina Panthers Players Sam Mills Memorial Scholarships [4206]
Quincy Sharpe Mills Memorial Scholarships [10244]
George Hi'ilani Mills Perpetual Fellowships [7915]
J. Clawson Mills Scholarships [6435]
Abby and Howard Milstein Innovation Award in Reproductive Medicine [5618]
Abby and Howard Milstein Reproductive Medicine Research Award [5619]
Milton Postgraduate Fellowships [5080]
Mineral & Metallurgical Processing Division Scholarships and Richard Klimpel Memorial Scholarships [9211]
Mineralogical Association of Canada Scholarships [2022]
Minerva Scholarships [2289]
John J. Mingenback Memorial Scholarships [4468]
Mary Minglen Scholarship Program [1047]
Minneapolis Jewish Federation [6538]
Minneapolis Jewish Federation Camp Scholarships [6539]
Minnesota Association of County Probation Officers (MACPO) [6540]
Minnesota Association County Probation Officers Scholarships [6541]
Minnesota Association of Public Accountant Scholarships [6543]
Minnesota Association of Public Accountants (MAPA) [6542]
Minnesota Association of Township Scholarships [6545]
Minnesota Association of Townships (MAT) [6544]
Minnesota Division Scholarships [6522]
Minnesota GLBT Educational Fund [8661]
Minnesota Health Information Management Association (MHIMA) [6546]
Minnesota Health Information Management Association Scholarships [6547]
Minnesota Minority Junior Golf Association (MMJGA) [6548]
Minnesota Power Community Involvement Scholarships [3717]
Minnesota State Archery Association (MSAA) [6550]
Minnesota State Archery Association Scholarships Program [6551]
Jacque I. Minnotte Health Reporting Fellowships [8406]
Minority Corporate Counsel Association (MCCA) [6552]
Minority-Serving Institution Faculty Scholar Awards [474]
Minority Teacher Loans [9554]
Minority Teachers of Illinois Scholarships (MTI) [5078]
Minority Visiting Students Awards [9011]
Minton-Spidell Point Scholarship [8185]
Christine Mirzayan Science and Technology Policy Graduate Fellowships [6679]
Molly Ann Mishler Memorial Scholarships [10030]
Miss America Community Service Scholarship [6557]
Miss America Organization [6554]
Miss America Quality of Life Awards [6558]
Joseph and Catherine Missigman Memorial Nursing Scholarships [4051]

Missigman Scholarship Fund [4052]
Mission Aviation Fellowship of Canada [6559]
Mission Bay Hospital Auxiliary Scholarships [8717]
Mississippi Society of Certified Public Accountants (MSCPA) [6561]
Missouri Department of Health and Senior Services [6564]
Joshua Esch Mitchell Aviation Scholarships [4611]
Monte R. Mitchell Global Scholarships [168]
George J. Mitchell Postgraduate Scholarships [6749]
Dorothy Mitchell Scholarships [8498]
George J. Mitchell Scholarships [10349]
Mary Moore Mitchell Scholarships [6120]
Robert L. and Hilda Treasure Mitchell Scholarships [4612]
Sam Mizrahi Memorial Scholarships [4248]
MJSA Education Foundation Scholarship Fund [6231]
MKC/Preuss Scholarship Fund [8718]
MLA Continuing Education Awards (CE) [6390]
MLA Financial Assistance [6567]
MLA/NLM Spectrum Scholarship Program [6391]
MLA Research, Development, and Demonstration Project Grants [6392]
MMJGA Scholarships [6549]
MMRF Research Fellow Awards [6612]
MMUF Dissertation Grants [10679]
MMUF Travel and Research Grants [10680]
MNLA Academic Scholarships [6474]
MOAA American Patriot Scholarships [6534]
Modern Language Association of America (MLA) [6566]
Ralph Modjeski Scholarships [8198]
MODNA Nursing Education Scholarships [6509]
Francis H. Moffitt Memorial Scholarships [1807]
Molecular Evolution Fellowships [9012]
Antoinette M. Molinari Memorial Scholarships [417]
Moline Foundation [6568]
Momeni Foundation Scholastic Achievement Scholarships [7021]
Monadnock Folklore Society (MFS) [6571]
Monaghan/Trudell Fellowships for Aerosol Technique Development [1212]
Nell I. Mondy Fellowships [8905]
Mongan Commonwealth Fund Fellowship in Minority Health Policy [3161]
Monsanto Commitment To Agriculture Scholarships [6574]
Monsanto Co. [6573]
Murray Montague Memorial Scholarships [4571]
Montana Broadcasters Association (MBA) [6575]
Montana Broadcasters Association Broadcast Engineering Scholarships [6578]
Montana Health Care Association (MHCA) [6579]
Montana Society of Certified Public Accountants Helena Chapter [6581]
Montgomery County Medical Society Scholarships (MCMS) [4278]
Hugh and Elizabeth Montgomery Scholarships [6208]
ARTC Glenn Moon Scholarships [4765]
Pearl Moore Career Development Awards [7618]
Letitia Moore Charitable Trust Scholarship [10739]
Moore Middle School PTA Scholarships [8499]
Annabelle Moore Scholarship [2408]
Farmers Union Industries Foundation Stanley Moore Scholarships [7488]
NFU Foundation Stanley Moore Scholarships [7489]
Willie Hobbs Moore Scholarships [7145]
Dr. Blanca Moore-Velez Woman of Substance Scholarships [6763]
Dan Mordecai Educational Scholarships [7265]
Robert E. and Judy More Scholarship Fund [4053]
Jake S. More Scholarship [3685]
Thomas More Scholarships [4487]
Kyle R. Moreland Memorial Scholarships [4533]
Lt. Colonel Robert G. Moreland Vocational/Technical Fund [9527]
Morgan, Lewis and Bockius L.L.P. [6588]
Morgan Library & Museum [6590]
Thomas S. Morgan Memorial Scholarship [8044]
Sonia Morgan Scholarships [7335]
Morgan Stanley Pediatrics Fellowships [618]
Morgan Stanley Tribal Scholars Program [870]

John P. and Tashia F. Morgridge Scholarships [10324]
Robert L. Morlan Redlands Area Interfaith Council Scholarships [8500]
Leo F. Moro Baseball Memorial Scholarships [4249]
Frank Morrell Endowed Memorial Scholarships [6254]
Morris County Bar Association (MCBA) [6592]
Harry J. Morris, Jr. Emergency Services Scholarships [4613]
The Morris Law Firm [6595]
Morris Newspaper Corp. Scholarships [4388]
James B. Morris Scholarship Fund [6597]
James B. Morris Scholarships [6598]
June Morrison Scholarship Fund [10538]
Harry L. Morrison Scholarships [7146]
Dorothy Morrison Undergraduate Scholarships [1260]
Chapter 63 - Portland James E. Morrow Scholarships [9189]
Mortar Board National College Senior Honor Society [6599]
Mortar Board National Foundation Fellowships [6600]
Morton Cure Paralysis Fund [6601]
Morton Cure Paralysis Fund Research Grants [6602]
William Howard Morton Scholarships [7392]
Dwight Mosley Scholarships [9976]
John H. Moss Scholarships [10294]
Wilma Motley Memorial California Merit Scholarships [777]
Archie Motley Memorial Scholarships for Minority Students [6517]
Motorola Solutions Point Scholarship [8186]
John R. Mott Scholarship Foundation [6603]
John R. Mott Scholarships [6604]
Jack D. Motteler Scholarships [8257]
Mount Desert Island Biological Laboratory (MDIBL) [6605]
Mt. Hood Chapter Scholarship Awards [7697]
Mountain Memorial Funds [6255]
Dorothy Mountain Memorial Scholarships [6135]
Mountain Plains Adult Education Association (MPAEA) [6607]
Movember Clinical Trials [8304]
Movember Discovery Grants [8305]
Movember Rising Star in Prostate Cancer Research Awards [8306]
Movember Team Grants [8307]
Burton J. Moyer Memorial Fellowships [4811]
David J. Moynihan Scholarships [7373]
MPAC-DC Graduate Policy Fellowships [6630]
MPI CRV Scholarships [6402]
MPI-WI Founders Grant Program [6405]
MSCPA Scholarship - Montana Tech [6585]
MSCPA Scholarship - MSU Bozeman [6586]
MSCPA Scholarship - University of Montana [6587]
MSCPA Undergraduate Scholarships [6562]
MSEA/SEIU Part-time Student Members Scholarships [6223]
MSFHR Scholar Awards [8994]
MSFHR Trainee Awards [8995]
MSGC Undergraduate-Under-Represented Minority Fellowship Program [6485]
The MTS Student Scholarship for Graduate Students [6273]
The MTS Student Scholarship for Graduating High School Seniors [6274]
The MTS Student Scholarship for Two-Year, Technical, Engineering and Community College Students [6275]
Mu Alpha Theta [6609]
Mu Alpha Theta Summer Grants [6610]
Muddy Waters Scholarships [2316]
Mueller Undergraduate Scholarships [10618]
H.M. Muffly Memorial Scholarships [3143]
Dudley Mullins/Cabot Corporation Scholarships [7849]
Multi-Country Research Fellowships [3431]
Multicultural Work-in-Progress Grant [9098]
Multiple Myeloma Research Foundation (MMRF) [6611]
Multiple Sclerosis Society of Canada (MSSC) [6613]
Muncy Rotary Club Scholarship Fund [4054]

Muncy Scholars Award Fund [4055]
Marvin Mundel Memorial Scholarships [5192]
Anthony Munoz Foundation **[6617]**
Harry Munoz Memorial Scholarships [8501]
Rick Munoz Memorial Scholarships [8502]
Anthony Munoz Scholarships [6618]
Margaret Munro Award [2707]
Kiwanis Club of Redlands Foundation - Martin and Dorothy Munz Scholarships [8503]
Jack K. and Gertrude Murphy Fellowships [8748]
Daniel Murphy Scholarship Fund (DMSF) **[6619]**
Daniel Murphy Scholarships [6620]
Linda J. Murphy Scholarships [10644]
NACCED Annual John C. Murphy Scholarships [6742]
Muscle Shoals Kiwanis/Wal-Mart Scholarship [7538]
Muscular Dystrophy Association (MDA) **[6621]**
Music Library Association (MLA) **[6624]**
Muslim Public Affairs Council (MPAC) **[6629]**
Dr. Helen K. Mussallem Fellowships [2708]
Mustard Seed Foundation **[6631]**
Mutual of Omaha Finance Careers Scholarships [105]
Mutual of Omaha Sales and Marketing Student Scholarships [106]
MWH Scholarships [1491]
My Life As A Lawyer Scholarships [3425]
MyApartmentMap **[6633]**
MyApartmentMap Housing Scholarships [6634]
Sam A. Myar Jr. Law Scholarship [10170]
Myasthenia Gravis Foundation of America, Inc. (MGFA) **[6635]**
Myasthenia Gravis Foundation of America Nursing Research Fellowships [6636]
Myasthenia Gravis Foundation of America Student Research Fellowships [6637]
Mary Fran Myers Scholarships [10129]
Clarence & Josephine Myers Undergraduate Scholarships [9190]
MyMozaic.com **[6638]**
MyMozaic.com Annual Scholarships [6639]
The Myositis Association (TMA) **[6640]**
Myotonic Dystrophy Foundation (MDF) **[6642]**
NAACP Legal Defense and Educational Fund (LDF) **[6644]**
NAACP Legal Defense and Educational Fund, Inc. **[6647]**
NAAE Upper Division Scholarships [6712]
NAAMA Scholarships [6701]
NABA National Scholarship Program [6716]
NACA Foundation Graduate Scholarships [6725]
NACA Mid Atlantic Graduate Student Scholarships [6726]
NACA Mid Atlantic Higher Education Research Scholarships [6727]
NACA Mid Atlantic Undergraduate Scholarships for Student Leaders [6728]
NACA Multicultural Professional Development Grant [6729]
NACA Northern Plains Regional Student Leadership Scholarships [6730]
NACA South Student Leadership Scholarships [6731]
NACADA Scholarships [6673]
NACDS Foundation Merit-Based Scholarships [6736]
James B. Nachman ASCO Junior Faculty Award in Pediatric Oncology [3382]
Albert and Alice Nacinovich Music Scholarships [4056]
Irwin Allen Nadal Entrance Awards [10752]
Miles Spencer Nadal Entrance Awards [10753]
NAED/Spencer Dissertation Fellowship Program [6681]
NAFA Corporate Aviation Business Scholarship [6692]
NAFA International Dissertation Research Fellowships [6750]
NAFA Scholarship Programs [6690]
NAGAP Graduate Student Enrollment Management Research Grants [6752]
Jack Nagasaka Memorial Scholarships [8504]
NAIFA West Michigan Scholarships [4614]
NAJA Scholarships [6760]
IADR Toshio Nakao Fellowship [5252]
NALS of Arizona (NTSA) **[6649]**

NALS of Michigan **[6651]**
NALS of Michigan Scholarships [6652]
NAMM, the International Music Products Association **[6653]**
NANBPWC National Scholarships [6764]
Robyn Nance Memorial Scholarships [8505]
NAON Foundation **[6655]**
NAPABA Law Foundation Scholarships [6705]
NAPC FORUM Scholarships [6694]
NAPRHSW Scholarships [6776]
NARAL Pro-Choice America **[6658]**
NARAL Pro-Choice America Development Internships [6659]
NARAL Pro-Choice America Policy Internships [6660]
NARAL Pro-Choice America Political Internships [6661]
Chereddi NarayanaRao and Radhamanohari Scholarships [9668]
NARFE-FEEA Scholarship Awards Program [6686]
NASA RISGC Graduate Fellowships [8613]
NASA WVSGC Undergraduate Research Fellowship [10527]
NASCOE Scholarships [6744]
NASE Future Entrepreneur [6784]
Kermit B. Nash Academic Scholarships [8891]
Elizabeth Nash Foundation **[6662]**
Elizabeth Nash Foundation Scholarships [6663]
Archie Hartwell Nash Memorial Scholarships [3245]
Nashville Catholic Business Women's League (NCBWL) **[6664]**
Nashville Unit Scholarships [4863]
NASLR Mined Land Reclamation Educational Grant [6792]
NASP-ERT Minority Scholarships for Graduate Training in School Psychology [6780]
NASSCO **[6667]**
NASSLEO Scholarships - Region I [6782]
National 4th Infantry Ivy Division Association **[6669]**
National AAHAM Scholarships [504]
National Academic Advising Association (NACADA) **[6671]**
The National Academies **[6674]**
National Academy of Education (NAEd) **[6680]**
National Action Council for Minorities in Engineering (NACME) **[6682]**
National Active and Retired Federal Employees Association (NARFE) **[6685]**
National Administrative Law Judiciary Foundation (NALJF) **[6687]**
National Air Filtration Association (NAFA) **[6689]**
National Aircraft Finance Association (NAFA) **[6691]**
National Alliance of Preservation Commissions (NAPC) **[6693]**
National Alpha Lambda Delta **[6695]**
National American Arab Nurses Association (NAANA) **[6698]**
National American Arab Nurses Association Scholarships [6699]
National Arab American Medical Association (NAAMA) **[6700]**
National Asian Pacific American Bar Association (NAPABA) **[6702]**
National Association of Abandoned Mine Land Programs (NAAMLP) **[6707]**
National Association of Abandoned Mine Land Programs Scholarships [6708]
National Association for the Advancement of Colored People (NAACP) **[6709]**
National Association of Agricultural Educators (NAAE) **[6711]**
National Association for Armenian Studies and Research Scholarships [1703]
National Association of Biology Teachers (NABT) **[6713]**
National Association of Biology Teachers BioClub Student Awards [6714]
National Association of Black Accountants, Inc. (NABA) **[6715]**
National Association of Black Social Workers (NABSW) **[6717]**
National Association for Campus Activities (NACA) **[6722]**
National Association of Campus Activities Scholarships for Student Leaders [6732]

National Association of Chain Drug Stores Foundation **[6735]**
National Association of Collegiate Directors of Athletics (NACDA) **[6737]**
National Association of Container Distributors (NACD) **[6739]**
National Association for County Community and Economic Development (NACCED) **[6741]**
National Association of Farm Service Agency County Office Employees (NASCOE) **[6743]**
National Association of Fellowships Advisors (NAFA) **[6745]**
National Association of Graduate Admissions Professionals (NAGAP) **[6751]**
National Association of Health Services Executives (NAHSE) **[6753]**
National Association of Hispanic Nurses (NAHN) **[6757]**
National Association of Junior Auxiliaries, Inc. (NAJA) **[6759]**
National Association of Negro Business and Professional Women's Clubs, Inc. (NANBPWC) **[6761]**
National Association of Oil and Energy Service Professionals (OESP) **[6765]**
National Association of Pastoral Musicians (NPM) **[6767]**
National Association of Pediatric Nurse Practitioners (NAPNAP) **[6770]**
National Association of Puerto Rican Hispanic Social Workers (NAPRHSW) **[6775]**
National Association for Pupil Transportation (NAPT) **[6777]**
National Association of School Psychologists (NASP) **[6779]**
National Association of School Safety and Law Enforcement Officials (NASSLEO) **[6781]**
National Association for the Self-Employed (NASE) **[6783]**
National Association for the Self-Employed Scholarships [6785]
National Association of Social Workers (NASW) **[6786]**
National Association of State Land Reclamationists (NASLR) **[6791]**
National Association of Student Anthropologists (NASA) **[6793]**
National Association for Surface Finishing (NASF) **[6795]**
National Association of Teacher Educators for Family and Consumer Sciences (NATEFACS) **[6797]**
National Association of Women in Construction (NAWIC) **[6799]**
National Association of Women in Construction Construction Trades Scholarships [6800]
National Association of Women in Construction Founders Undergraduate Scholarships [6801]
National Association of Women Judges (NAWJ) **[6802]**
National Ataxia Foundation (NAF) **[6805]**
National Ataxia Foundation Research Fellowships [6806]
National Ataxia Foundation Research Grants [6807]
National Beta Club **[6808]**
National Beta Club Scholarships [6809]
National Biosafety and Biocontainment Training Program (NBBTP) **[6810]**
National Biosafety and Biocontainment Training Program Fellowships [6811]
National Black Coalition of Federal Aviation Employees (NBCFAE) **[6812]**
National Black Deaf Advocate Scholarships [6816]
National Black Deaf Advocates (NBDA) **[6814]**
National Black Graduate Student Association (NBGSA) **[6818]**
National Black MBA Association (NBMBAA) **[6820]**
National Black Nurses Association (NBNA) **[6822]**
National Black Nurses Association Scholarships [6823]
National Black Police Association (NBPA) **[6824]**
National Board of Boiler and Pressure Vessel Inspectors (NBBI) **[6826]**
National Board Technical Scholarships [6827]
National Business Aviation Association (NBAA) **[6828]**
National Cattlemen's Foundation (NCF) **[6840]**
National Center for American Indian Enterprise De-

velopment (NCAIED) **[6843]**
National Center for Farmworker Health (NCFH) **[6845]**
National Center for Health Statistics Postdoctoral Research Awards [9920]
National Center for Law and Economic Justice (NCLEJ) **[6847]**
National Center for Learning Disabilities (NCLD) **[6849]**
National Chapter of Canada IODE **[6851]**
National Child Support Enforcement Association (NCSEA) **[6857]**
National Collegiate Athletic Association (NCAA) **[6860]**
National Collegiate Athletic Association Postgraduate Scholarships [6863]
National Collegiate Cancer Foundation (NCCF) **[6864]**
National Community Pharmacists Association (NCPA) **[6866]**
National Community Pharmacists Association Summer Internship Programs [6868]
National Conference of Bar Examiners (NCBE) **[6872]**
National Conservation District Employees Association (NCDEA) **[6874]**
National Costumers Association (NCA) **[6876]**
National Costumers Association Scholarships [6877]
National Council on Education for the Ceramic Arts (NCECA) **[6878]**
National Council on Public History (NCPH) **[6881]**
National Council on Public History Graduate Student Travel Awards [6882]
National Council on Public History Student Project Awards [6883]
National Council of Teachers of English (NCTE) **[6884]**
National Council of Teachers of Mathematics (NCTM) **[6887]**
National Council on U.S.-Arab Relations (NCUSAR) **[6894]**
National Court Reporters Association (NCRA) **[6896]**
National Court Reporters Association Student Intern Scholarship [6897]
National Cowboy and Western Heritage Museum **[6900]**
National Dairy Herd Information Association (NDHIA) **[6902]**
National Dairy Herd Information Association Scholarship Program [6903]
National Dairy Shrine (NDS) **[6904]**
National Defense Industrial Association - Iowa-Illinois Chapter **[6906]**
National Defense Industrial Association - Picatinny Chapter **[6908]**
National Defense Science and Engineering Graduate Fellowship (NDSEG) **[6910]**
National Defense Transportation Association (NDTA) **[6912]**
National Dental Hygienists' Association (NDHA) **[6915]**
National Dental Hygienists' Association Scholarships [6916]
National Eagle Scout Association (NESA) **[6917]**
National Eating Disorders Association (NEDA) **[6937]**
National Electrical Manufacturers Representatives Association (NEMRA) **[6940]**
The National Endowment for the Humanities Fellowships [1198]
National Endowment for the Humanities Research Fellowships [660]
National Environmental Health Association (NEHA) **[6942]**
National Estuarine Research Reserve System (NERRS) **[6944]**
National Federation of the Blind (NFB) **[6946]**
National Federation of Paralegal Associations (NFPA) **[6950]**
National Federation of Republican Women (NFRW) **[6953]**
National Forum for Black Public Administrators (NFBPA) **[6956]**
National Foster Parent Association (NFPA) **[6960]**
National Gallery of Art **[6962]**

National Garden Clubs **[6964]**
National GEM Consortium **[6966]**
National GEM Consortium - MS Engineering Fellowships [6967]
National GEM Consortium - PhD Engineering Fellowships [6968]
National GEM Consortium - PhD Science Fellowships [6969]
National Geographic Conservation Trust Grants [6971]
National Geographic Expedition Council Grants [6972]
National Geographic Society **[6970]**
National Geographic Society/Waitt Grants [6973]
National Geographic Young Explorers Grants [6974]
National Greenhouse Manufacturers Association Scholarships [806]
National Ground Water Association (NGWA) **[6975]**
National Guard Association of Rhode Island **[6977]**
National Guard Association of Rhode Island Scholarship [6978]
National Guard Association of Texas (NGAT) **[6979]**
National Hartford Centers of Gerontological Nursing Excellence **[6981]**
National Hemophilia Foundation (NHF) **[6984]**
National High School Oratorical Contest Scholarship [956]
National Hispanic Coalition of Federal Aviation Employees (NHCFAE) **[6995]**
National Hispanic Foundation for the Arts (NHFA) **[6997]**
National Honor Society (NHS) **[6999]**
National Housing Endowment **[7002]**
National Huguenot Society (NHS) **[7005]**
National Huguenot Society College and Postgraduate Student Scholarships [7006]
National Humanities Center (NHC) **[7007]**
National Humanities Center Fellowships [7008]
National Industrial Belting Association (NIBA) **[7009]**
National Institute of Health Undergraduate Scholarship Program (NIH UGSP) [9930]
National Institute of Justice (NIJ) **[7011]**
National Institute of Nursing Research (NINR) **[7014]**
National Investment Company Service Association (NICSA) **[7018]**
National Iranian American Council (NIAC) **[7020]**
National Iranian American Council Fellowships [7022]
National Italian American Bar Association (NIABA) **[7024]**
National Italian American Foundation (NIAF) **[7026]**
National Judges Association (NJA) **[7029]**
National Judges Association Scholarships [7030]
National Junior Angus Association (NJAA) **[7031]**
National Junior Horticultural Association Alumni Scholarships [7034]
National Junior Horticultural Association (NJHA) **[7033]**
National Junior Swine Association (NJSA) **[7035]**
National Junior Swine Association Outstanding Member Scholarships [7038]
National Kindergarten Alliance (NKA) **[7042]**
National Law Enforcement and Firefighters Children's Foundation (NLEAFCF) **[7044]**
National Legal Aid and Defender Association (NLADA) **[7046]**
National Lesbian and Gay Journalists Association (NLGJA) **[7048]**
National LGBT Bar Association (NLGLA) **[7051]**
National Little Britches Rodeo Association (NLBRA) **[7053]**
National Medical Fellowships (NMF) **[7060]**
National Medical Fellowships Need-Based Scholarships [7061]
National Merit Harris Corporation Scholarship Program [4729]
National Merit Scholarship Corporation (NMSC) **[7062]**
National Merit Scholarship Program [7063]
National Military Family Association (NMFA) **[7068]**
National Military Intelligence Association (NMIA) **[7070]**
National Milk Producers Federation (NMPF) **[7072]**
National MS Society New Jersey Metro Chapter Scholarship Program [7075]
National Multiple Sclerosis Society - New Jersey Metro Chapter **[7074]**
National Oceanic and Atmospheric Administration - NOAA Center for Atmospheric Sciences (NCAS) **[7076]**
National Organization for Human Services (NOHS) **[7078]**
National Organization of Industrial Trade Unions (NOITU) **[7080]**
National Organization of Italian-American Women (NOIAW) **[7082]**
National Organization of Italian-American Women Scholarships [7083]
National Organization for the Professional Advancement of Black Chemists and Chemical Engineers (NOBCChE) **[7084]**
National Orientation Directors Association (NODA) **[7091]**
National Parking Association (NPA) **[7093]**
National Pathfinder Scholarships [6954]
National Pest Management Association (NPMA) **[7095]**
National Physical Science Consortium (NPSC) **[7097]**
National Potato Council (NPC) **[7099]**
National Poultry and Food Distributors Association (NPFDA) **[7101]**
National Poultry and Food Distributors Association Scholarships [7102]
National Preservation Institute (NPI) **[7103]**
National Preservation Institute Scholarships [7104]
National Press Photographers Association (NPPA) **[7105]**
National Private Truck Council (NPTC) **[7112]**
National Public Employer Labor Relations Association (NPELRA) **[7114]**
National Recreation and Park Association (NRPA) **[7117]**
National Recreation and Park Association Diversity Scholarships [7118]
National Restaurant Association Educational Foundation (NRAEF) **[7119]**
National Roofing Contractors Association (NRCA) **[7121]**
National Science Foundation (NSF) **[7123]**
National Science Foundation Graduate Research Fellowship Program (NSF-GRFP) [7125]
National Sculpture Society (NSS) **[7126]**
National Sculpture Society Scholarships [7128]
National Security Education Program - David L. Boren Fellowships [10137]
National Security Technologies Engineering and Science Scholarships [8356]
National Sheriffs' Association (NSA) **[7129]**
National Sheriffs' Association Scholarship Program [7130]
National Slovak Society Senior Scholarships [7132]
National Slovak Society of the United States of America (NSS) **[7131]**
National Society of Accountants (NSA) **[7133]**
National Society of Accountants Scholarship Program [7134]
National Society of Black Physicists (NSBP) **[7136]**
National Society, Daughters of the American Revolution (DAR) **[7148]**
National Society of Genetic Counselors (NSGC) **[7155]**
National Society of High School Scholars (NSHSS) **[7157]**
National Society of Hispanic MBAs (NSHMBA) **[7163]**
National Society for HistoTechnology (NSH) **[7165]**
National Society of Professional Surveyors (NSPS) **[7174]**
National Space Biomedical Research Institute (NSBRI) **[7176]**
National Space Biomedical Research Institute Postdoctoral Fellowships [7177]
National Space Club and Foundation **[7178]**
National Speleological Society (NSS) **[7180]**
National Sporting Clays Association (NSCA) **[7185]**
National Stone, Sand and Gravel Association (NSGA) **[7187]**
National Student Nurses' Association (NSNA) **[7189]**

National Swimming Pool Foundation (NSPF) **[7191]**
National Swimming Pool Foundation Scholarship Awards [7193]
National Taxidermists Association (NTA) **[7194]**
National Technical Honor Society (NTHS) **[7196]**
National Technical Honor Society Scholarships, [2424], [3962]
National Trust for Canada **[7198]**
National Trust for Historic Preservation **[7201]**
National Union of Public and General Employees (NUPGE) **[7203]**
National Urban Fellows (NUF) **[7208]**
National Volunteer Fire Council (NVFC) **[7210]**
National Water Research Institute (NWRI) **[7212]**
National Wildlife Federation (NWF) **[7215]**
National Women's Studies Association (NWSA) **[7217]**
National Women's Studies Association Lesbian Caucus Award [7218]
Native American Community Scholars Awards [9013]
Native American Education Grants [877]
Native American Visiting Student Awards [9014]
Native Hawaiian Chamber of Commerce Scholarships [7916]
Native Hawaiian Visual Arts Scholarships [7917]
Native Women's Association of Canada (NWAC) **[7220]**
Natural Sciences and Engineering Research Council Postgraduate Scholarships [3404]
Naval Helicopter Association Scholarship Fund **[7222]**
Naval Helicopter Association Scholarships [7223]
Naval Research Enterprise Internship Program (NREIP) [1304]
Naval Weather Service Association (NWSA) **[7224]**
Naval Weather Service Association Scholarships [7225]
Navy, Army or Air Force ROTC Scholarship Program [3502]
Navy League of the United States (NLUS) **[7226]**
Navy-Marine Corps Relief Society (NMCRS) **[7233]**
NAWJ Equal Access to Justice Scholarships [6803]
Marek Nawrot Memorial Scholarships [8586]
Nazareth Association **[7237]**
The Nazareth Scholarships [7238]
NB College of Physicians and Surgeons Medical Education Scholarships [7285]
NBCUniversal Point Scholarship [8187]
NBCUniversal Tony Coelho Media Scholarships [555]
NBHRF/ASRP Doctoral Training Awards, [372], [7267]
NBHRF Bridge Grants [7268]
NBHRF Doctoral Studentships [7269]
NBHRF Establishment Grants [7270]
NBHRF Health Research Strategic Initiative Grants [7271]
NBHRF Master's Studentships [7272]
NBHRF Postdoctoral Fellowships [7273]
NBMBAA Graduate Scholarships Program [6821]
NBRC/AMP H. Frederic Helmholz, Jr., MD Educational Research Funds [1213]
NC Hospitality Education Foundation Scholarships - Four Year College or University [7473]
NC Hospitality Education Foundation Scholarships - Graduate [7474]
NC Hospitality Education Foundation Scholarships - High School [7475]
NC Hospitality Education Foundation Scholarships - Two Year Community or Junior College [7476]
NCACPA Outstanding Minority Accounting Student Scholarships [7451]
NCBWL Scholarships [6666]
NCCF Survivor Scholarships [6865]
NCCT Postdoctoral Research Program [9941]
NCEA Postdoctoral Research Program [9943]
NCECA Graduate Student Fellowships [6880]
NCLEJ Law School Graduate Fellows and Volunteers [6848]
NCNJ-AWMA Undergraduate Scholarship [152]
NCPA Foundation Presidential Scholarships [6869]
NCRF New Professional Reporter Grant [6898]
NCRLA Golden Corral Scholarships [7477]
NCSEA Judge Ross Leadership Scholarships [6858]
NCSEA New Leader Scholarships [6859]

NCSGC Undergraduate Research Scholarships [7484]
NCSGC Undergraduate Scholarships [7485]
NCTE Research Foundation Grants [6885]
NCTM Emerging Teacher-Leaders in Elementary School Mathematics Grants for Grades K-5 Teachers [6889]
NCTM Prospective 7-12 Secondary Teacher Course Work Scholarships [6890]
NCTM School In-Service Training Grants for Grades 6-8 Teachers [6891]
NCTM School In-Service Training Grants for Grades 9-12 Teachers [6892]
NCTM School In-Service Training Grants for Grades K-5 Teachers [6893]
NDIA Picatinny Chapter Scholarships [6909]
NDSEG Fellowships [6911]
NDSGC American Indian Scholarships [7494]
NDSGC Graduate Fellowships [7495]
NDSGC Summer Faculty Fellowships [7496]
NDSGC Undergraduate Fellowships [7497]
NDSGC Undergraduate Scholarships [7498]
NDTA Academic Scholarship Program A [6913]
NDTA Academic Scholarship Program B [6914]
Nebraska Farm Bureau **[7239]**
Nebraska Farm Bureau Greater Horizon Scholarships [7240]
Nebraska High School Rodeo Association **[7241]**
Nebraska Library Association (NLA) **[7244]**
Nebraska Paralegal Association (NePA) **[7246]**
Nebraska Paralegal Association Student Scholarships [7247]
Nebraska Section American Water Works Association **[7248]**
Nebraska Society of Certified Public Accountants (NSCPA) **[7250]**
NEDA Eating Recovery Center Foundation Early Career Investigator Grants [6938]
NEDA Feeding Hope Fund for Clinical Research Grants [6939]
Nedien Hoganson Memorial Scholarships [10797]
Need-Based Scholarships [3986]
J.W. "Bill" Neese Scholarships [5300]
NEH Fellowships for Senior Scholars [2853]
NEHA/AAS Scholarship [6943]
Paul and Ruth Neidhold Business Scholarships [3294]
Craig H. Neilsen Foundation **[7253]**
Neilsen Psychosocial Research Grants - Pilot Psychosocial Research Grants [7254]
Neilsen Psychosocial Research Grants - Postdoctoral Psychosocial Fellowships [7255]
Neilsen Psychosocial Research Grants - Proof of Concept Research Grants [7256]
NELA Conference Scholarships [7297]
Edward J. Nell Memorial Scholarships in Journalism [8397]
Dave Nelsen Scholarships [6766]
Charles I. Nelson Endowed Scholarships [7993]
Tad Nelson Law Firm Scholarships [5965]
Carol Nelson Scholarship [5753]
Bill Nelson Scholarship Endowment (BNSE) [7768]
AIST Midwest Member Chapter - Don Nelson Scholarships [2003]
Hubert A. Nelson Scholarships [3718]
Judge William J. Nelson Scholarships [9442]
Law Offices of Judd S. Nemiro Dyslexia Scholarships [5961]
NEMLA Summer Fellowships [7511]
NEMRA Educational Scholarship Foundation [6941]
NERL Postdoctoral Research Program [9935]
Andrew Nerland Scholarships [10031]
NERRS Graduate Research Fellowships (GRF) [6945]
Dr. Ezra Nesbeth Scholarships [5526]
NESCPA Fifth-Year Scholarships [7251]
NESCPA General Scholarships [7252]
Amelia and Emanuel Nessell Scholarships [3719]
Netfloor USA Access Flooring **[7260]**
Netfloor USA Access Flooring College Scholarships [7261]
Reverend John S. Nettles Scholarships [3268]
Elizabeth Neuffer Fellowships [5458]
Neuroscience Certification Bursary Awards [1889]
Nevada Chapter American Public Works Association **[7262]**

Nevada Organization of Nurse Leaders (NONL) **[7264]**
Alan H. Neville Memorial Scholarships [335]
New Brunswick Health Research Foundation **[7266]**
New Brunswick Medical Education Foundation, Inc. (NBMEFI) **[7274]**
New Brunswick Nurses Association Scholarships [2709]
New England Club Managers Association (NECMA) **[7293]**
New England FEMARA Scholarships [1748]
New England Library Association (NELA) **[7296]**
New Hampshire Association of Educational Office Professionals (NHAEOP) **[7298]**
New Hampshire Automotive Dealers Association (NHADA) **[7301]**
New Hampshire Charitable Foundation (NHCF) **[7303]**
New Hampshire Higher Education Loan Corp. **[7308]**
New Hampshire Sheep and Wool Growers Association (NHSWGA) **[7310]**
New Hampshire Snowmobile Association (NHSA) **[7312]**
New Hampshire Snowmobile Association Book Scholarships [7313]
New Investigator Research Grant, [374], [393]
New Jersey Association of Osteopathic Physicians and Surgeons (NJAOPS) **[7314]**
New Jersey Broadcasters Association (NJBA) **[7316]**
New Jersey Hospital Association (NJHA) **[7318]**
New Jersey Library Association (NJLA) **[7320]**
New Jersey Performing Arts Center (NJPAC) **[7322]**
New Jersey Press Foundation (NJPF) **[7325]**
New Jersey Psychological Association (NJPA) **[7328]**
New Jersey Society of Certified Public Accountants (NJCPA) **[7330]**
New Jersey State Bar Foundation (NJSBF) **[7333]**
New Mexico Association for Bilingual Education (NMABE) **[7338]**
New Mexico Association for Bilingual Education Scholarships [7339]
New Mexico Manufactured Housing Association Scholarship Program [303]
New Museum Bogliasco Fellowship in Visual Art [2330]
New Orleans Ghost Tours **[7340]**
New Orleans Ghost Tours Scholarships [7341]
New York City Bar Association (NYCB) **[7342]**
The New York Community Trust **[7346]**
New York Financial Writers' Association (NYFWA) **[7353]**
New York Financial Writers' Associations Scholarships [7354]
New York Library Association (NYLA) **[7356]**
New York Point Honors Point Scholarship [8188]
New York School Nutrition Association (NYSNA) **[7358]**
New York State Association of Agricultural Fairs (NYSAAF) **[7360]**
New York State Association of Agricultural Fairs Scholarships [7361]
New York State Government Finance Officers' Association **[7362]**
New York State Higher Education Services Corporation **[7364]**
New York State Senate **[7366]**
New York State Senate - Legislative Fellowships [7368]
New York State Society of Certified Public Accountants (NYSSCPA) **[7372]**
New York Theological Seminary (NYTS) **[7374]**
The New York Times College Scholarships [7396]
The New York Times Co. **[7395]**
New York University School of Law - Center for Human Rights and Global Justice (CHRGJ) **[7397]**
New York Water Environment Association, Inc. (NY-WEA) **[7402]**
New York Water Environment Association Scholarships [7404]
New York Women in Communications Foundation (NYWICIF) **[7405]**

New York Women in Communications, Inc. Foundation Scholarships [7406]
Ted and Ruth Neward Scholarships [9265]
Newberry Consortium on American Indian Studies Faculty Fellowships [7417]
Newberry Consortium on American Indian Studies Graduate Student Fellowships [7418]
Newberry Library ACM/GLCA Faculty Fellowships [7419]
Newberry Library [7407]
Newberry Library/Ecole Nationale des Chartes Exchange Fellowships [7420]
Newberry Library National Endowment for the Humanities Fellowships [7421]
Newberry Library Short-Term Resident Fellowships for Individual Research [7422]
The Shanon Newberry Physical Therapy Scholarship Endowment [9584]
Newcomer Supply Student Scholarships [7169]
Caroline H. Newhouse Scholarship Fund [2793]
Newkirk Center for Science and Society [7426]
Newkirk Center for Science and Society Graduate Student Fellowships [7427]
Newman Civic Fellows Awards [2530]
Edsel Newman Scholarships [6065]
Newman University Scouting Scholarships [6931]
Jerry Newson Scholarships [3246]
The Newswomen's Club of New York (NCNY) [7428]
Alwin B. Newton Scholarships [1332]
Next Generation Social Sciences in Africa: Doctoral Dissertation Completion Fellowships [9057]
Next Generation Social Sciences in Africa: Doctoral Dissertation Proposal Fellowships [9058]
Next Generation Social Sciences in Africa: Doctoral Dissertation Research Fellowship [9059]
NFDA Professional Women's Conference Scholarships [4314]
NFPA/PACE Scholarships [6951]
NFPA Youth Scholarships [6961]
NGA Conservation Fellowships [6963]
NGAT Educational Scholarships [6980]
NGC College Scholarships [6965]
Le Hoang Nguyen College Scholarships (LHN) [10386]
The Thuy Nguyen Scholarships [10387]
NHAEOP Member Scholarships [7299]
NHEERL Postdoctoral Research Program [9937]
NHFA Scholarships [6998]
NHPGA Apprentice Scholarships [6358]
NHS National Scholarships [7000]
NHS Regional Scholarships [7001]
NIABA/NIAF Scholarships [7025]
NIAC Iranian-American Scholarship Fund [7023]
NIAF Scholarships - General Category I [7027]
NIAF Scholarships - General Category II [7028]
NIBA Presidential Scholarships [7010]
Donald E. Nichols Scholarships [1333]
George E. Nichols Undergradute Scholarships [10187]
Gunnar Nicholson Endowed Scholarships [7994]
Norman Nicholson Scholarships [2607]
AIST Midwest Member Chapter - Mel Nickel Scholarships [2004]
Nickels for Notes Music Scholarship [4354]
Herbert W. Nickens Medical Student Scholarships [1840]
Sharon Nield Memorial Scholarships [2710]
Erik Nielsen Memorial Scholarships [10798]
Mike Niemeyer Memorial Football Scholarships [8506]
Eva Nieminski Honorary Graduate Science and Engineering Scholarships [5240]
Eric Niemitalo Scholarships in Earth and Environmental Science [8879]
Helen W. Nies Memorial Scholarship [3987]
Nigerian Women Association of Georgia (NWAG) [7430]
NIJ Visiting Fellowships [7012]
Nikko Cosmetic Surgery Center [7433]
Nikko Cosmetic Surgery Center Annual Breast Cancer Survivor Scholarships [7434]
Ninety Nines, Inc. International Organization of Women Pilots [7435]
NINR Mentored Patient-Oriented Research Career Development Award [7015]

NINR Midcareer Investigator Award in Patient-Oriented Research [7016]
NINR Pathway to Independence Award [7017]
Evelyn S. Nish Scholarships [8933]
Anderson Niskanen Scholarships [3720]
Nissan North America, Inc. Scholarships [871]
NIU-CSEAS Foreign Language and Area Studies (FLAS) Fellowships [7518]
Nixon Family Scholarship Fund [10506]
Corwin Nixon Scholarships [3007]
Louise A. Nixon Scholarships [7245]
NJCBIR Individual Research Grants [9549]
NJCBIR Pilot Research Grants [9550]
NJCBIR Postdoctoral and Graduate Student Fellowships [9551]
NJCBIR Programmatic Multi-Investigator Project Grants [9552]
NJLA Scholarships [7321]
NJOEF Scholarships [7315]
NJPA Foundation Scholarship for Research on Diversity Issues [7329]
NJSA Visionary Leader Scholarships [7039]
NJSBF Labor Law Scholarships [7336]
NJSCPA College Scholarships [7331]
NJSCPA High School Scholarships [7332]
NLBRA National Royalty Scholarships [7054]
NLBRA Rainwater Scholarships [7055]
NLBRA World All Around Scholarships [7056]
NLBRA World Event Scholarships [7057]
NLBRA/Wrangler Academic Scholarships [7058]
NLBRA Youth Board Officer Scholarships [7059]
NLM Associate Fellowships [9928]
NMCRS Gold Star Scholarship Program [7235]
NMIA Scholarship Program [7071]
NMNH American Indian Program Fellowships [9034]
NMPF National Dairy Leadership Scholarships [7073]
NMSC College and University Sponsorship of Merit Scholarship Awards [7064]
NMSC Corporate-Sponsored Achievement Scholarship Awards [7065]
NMSC National Achievement Scholarship Program [7066]
NMSC Special Scholarships [7067]
NOAA EPP Undergraduate Scholarships (USP) [9891]
NOAA Graduate Sciences Scholarships [9892]
NOBCChE Procter and Gamble Fellowships [7088]
Leonard Noble Educational Scholarships [7170]
Charles S. Noble Scholarships for Study at Harvard [282]
Edna A. Noblin Dawsonville Lions Club Scholarships [5926]
Stuart L. Noderer Memorial Scholarships [8719]
George H. Nofer Scholarships for Law and Public Policy [316]
NOHIMSS Student Scholarship Program [7523]
Maureen E. Nolan-Cahill Memorial Scholarships [10032]
Alfred H. Nolle Scholarships [342]
Helen Woodruff Nolop Scholarships in Audiology and Allied Fields [3592]
Non Commissioned Officers Association Scholarships [7441]
Non Commissioned Officers Association of the United States of America (NCOA) [7440]
Deborah Munroe Noonan Memorial Research Awards [4822]
Nor' Easters Scholarships - Four-year Program [4915]
Nor' Easters Scholarships - Two-year Program [4916]
Norall Scholarship Trust [6066]
Arthur L. Norberg Travel Fund [10200]
Marian Norby Scholarships [9310]
Nordic Ski Association of Anchorage Scholarships [221]
Norfolk Southern Foundation Scholarships [1188]
North Alabama Dietetic Association Scholarships [197]
North American Conference on British Studies (NACBS) [7442]
North American Conference on British Studies Dissertation Year Fellowships [7443]
North American Conference on British Studies-Huntington Library Fellowships [7444]

North American Serials Interest Group (NASIG) [7445]
North American Society Fellowships [8119]
North American Van Lines Inc. [7448]
North American Van Lines Military Scholarship Competition [7449]
North Carolina Association of Certified Public Accountants (NCACPA) [7450]
North Carolina Association of Health Care Recruiters (NCAHCR) [7453]
North Carolina Association of Health Care Recruiters Scholarships [7454]
North Carolina Commercial Flower Growers Association (NCCFGA) [7455]
North Carolina Commercial Flower Growers Association Floriculture Scholarships [7456]
North Carolina Council of Epsilon Sigma Alpha [7457]
North Carolina Council of Epsilon Sigma Alpha Scholarships [7458]
North Carolina CPA Foundation Scholarships [7452]
North Carolina Economic Developers Association (NCEDA) [7459]
North Carolina Federation of Republican Women (NCFRW) [7463]
North Carolina Heroes Financial Hardship Grant [7466]
North Carolina Heroes Fund [7465]
North Carolina League for Nursing Academic Scholarships [4207]
North Carolina Nursery and Landscape Association Horticulture Scholarships [7468]
North Carolina Nursery and Landscape Association Inc. (NCNLA) [7467]
North Carolina Restaurant and Lodging Association (NCRLA) [7469]
North Carolina Section of the American Water Works Association (NC AWWA) [7478]
North Carolina Simmental Association (NCSA) [7481]
North Carolina Space Grant Consortium (NCSGC) [7483]
North Central, Region 9 Scholarships [9191]
North Dakota Division Scholarships [6523]
North Dakota Farmers Union (NDFU) [7486]
North Dakota Farmers Union Co-op House Scholarships [7490]
North Dakota Farmers Union Scholarships [7491]
North Dakota Space Grant Consortium (NDSGC) [7493]
North Dakota Veterinary Medical Association (NDVMA) [7500]
North Dakota Veterinary Medical Association Scholarships [7502]
North Florida Chapter Safety Education Scholarships [1423]
North Mecklenburg Teachers' Memorial Scholarships [4208]
North Ottawa Hospital Auxiliary Scholarship Fund [4534]
Michelle North Scholarships for Safety [4840]
North Texas GIA Alumni Association Scholarships [4344]
North Texas Relocation Professionals (NTRP) [7504]
North Texas Relocation Professionals Scholarships [7505]
Northampton County Medical Society Alliance (NCMSA) [7506]
Northampton County Medical Society Alliance Scholarships [7507]
NorthCoast Medical Scholarship Program [1048]
Northeast Alabama District Dietetic Association Scholarships [198]
Northeast Conference on the Teaching of Foreign Languages (NECTFL) [7508]
Northeast Modern Language Association (NeMLA) [7510]
Northeast Spa and Pool Association (NESPA) [7512]
Northeastern Illinois Chapter Scholarships [1424]
Northern Alberta Development Council Bursary Awards [283]
Northern Alberta Development Council Bursary Partnership Program [284]

The Northern Arizona Native-American Foundation (TNANAF) **[7515]**
Northern Arizona Native-American Foundation Scholarships [7516]
Northern California Chapter of HIMSS Scholarships [4832]
Northern California DX Foundation Scholarships [1749]
Northern Illinois University - Center for Southeast Asian Studies **[7517]**
Northern Indiana Community Foundation (NICF) **[7519]**
Northern Ohio Chapter of Healthcare Information Management Systems Society (NOHIMSS) **[7522]**
Northern Resident Scholarships [1935]
Northern Tier Hardwood Association (NTHA) **[7524]**
Northern Trust Point Scholarship [8189]
Cedric Northrop Fellowships [4035]
Northrop Grumman Corp. **[7526]**
Northrop Grumman Engineering Scholarships [7527]
Eugene Northrup Scholarships [6047]
Northwest Community Center Scholarships [3295]
Northwest-Shoals Community College Academic Scholarships [7539]
Northwest-Shoals Community College (NW-SCC) **[7528]**
Northwest-Shoals Community College Applied Technology Scholarships [7540]
Northwest-Shoals Community College Athletic Scholarships [7541]
Northwest-Shoals Community College Bank Independent Scholarships [7542]
Northwest-Shoals Community College Fine Arts Scholarships - Art [7543]
Northwest-Shoals Community College Fine Arts Scholarships - Drama [7544]
Northwest-Shoals Community College Fine Arts Scholarships - Music [7545]
Northwest-Shoals Community College High School Academic Scholarships [7546]
Northwest-Shoals Community College Independent Computer Scholarships [7547]
Northwest-Shoals Community College Student Activities Scholarships [7548]
Northwest Territories Law Foundation **[7553]**
Northwestern Mutual Financial Network Scholarships [8077]
Vessa Notchev Fellowships [8906]
Notre Dame Club of Canton Scholarships [9528]
NOVA Foundation Scholarships [7560]
Nova Scotia Salmon Association (NSSA) **[7555]**
Nova Scotia Salmon Association Scholarships [7556]
Novak Awards [58]
Peggy Kommer Novosad Scholarships [4615]
Mike and Flo Novovesky Scholarships [807]
Noyce Scholarships for Secondary Math and Science Education [5123]
Nicholas H. Noyes, Jr. Scholarship [5680]
NPC Scholarships [7100]
NPM Academic Scholarships [6768]
NPM Program Scholarships [6769]
NPPF Still and Multimedia Scholarships [7110]
NPPF TV News Scholarships [7111]
NPSC Fellowships [7098]
NRL-ASEE Postdoctoral Fellowships [9966]
NRMRL Postdoctoral Research Program [9939]
NSA Electrical Engineering Student Scholarships [107]
NSA Mathematics and Computer Science Student Scholarships [108]
NSHMBA Scholarships [7164]
NSHSS Academic Paper Awards [7160]
NSHSS National Scholar Awards [7161]
NSPS Scholarships [7175]
NSS Conservation Grants [7182]
NSS Education Grants [7183]
NSSA/NSCA Collegiate Scholarships [7186]
NTHA Forest Resources Scholarships for College Students [7525]
NTHS/HOSA Scholarships [7197]
Nuclear Criticality Safety Pioneers Scholarships [1038]
NUF Fellowships [7209]
Nuffield Canada **[7557]**

Nuffield Canada Farming Scholarships [7558]
NURSE Corps Scholarship Program [9924]
Nurseries Foundation Scholarship Awards [7698]
Nurseries Memorial Scholarship Awards [7699]
Nurses Organization of Veterans Affairs (NOVA) **[7559]**
Nursing Student Loans [9555]
Nuts, Bolts and Thingamajigs Scholarships [7562]
Nuts, Bolts & Thingamajigs, The Foundation of the Fabricators & Manufacturers Association, International **[7561]**
Nuts.com **[7563]**
The Nuts.com Healthy Eating Scholarships [7564]
NVIDIA Corp. **[7565]**
NVIDIA Graduate Fellowships [7566]
NWAG Georgia, USA Scholarships [7431]
NWAG Nigeria Scholarships [7432]
NWF Campus Ecology Fellowships [7216]
NWRI Fellowships [7214]
NWSA Graduate Scholarships [7219]
NYCT Paid Graduate Student Philanthropy Fellowships - Arts and Historic Preservation [7349]
NYCT Paid Graduate Student Philanthropy Fellowships - Children, Youth, Families, Education, Human Justice and Workforce [7350]
NYCT Paid Graduate Student Philanthropy Fellowships - Community Development and the Environment [7351]
NYCT Paid Graduate Student Philanthropy Fellowships - Health and People with Special Needs [7352]
NYFWA Scholarships [7355]
NYLA-Dewey Scholarship [7357]
NYU Langone Medical Center Science Student Scholarships [109]
NYU School of Law Fellowships at HRW [4999]
OAH-IEHS Huggins-Quarles Dissertation Awards [7718]
OAIA Scholarships [7690]
AEBC Rick Oakes Scholarships for the Arts [336]
OAS Academic Scholarship for Undergraduate Studies [7721]
OAS Academic Scholarships - Graduate [7722]
OAS Scholarships for Professional Development - Disaster Communications Management [7723]
OAS Scholarships for Professional Development - Radio Spectrum Monitoring Techniques and Procedures [7724]
OAS Scholarships for Professional Development - Satellite Communications [7725]
OAS Scholarships for Professional Development - The ABC of Telecommunications [7726]
WillEtta Long Oates, Gamma Nu, Memorial Scholarship [5754]
The O'Brien Foundation **[7567]**
O'Brien Foundation Fellowships [7568]
Dennis J. O'Brien USAEE/IAEE Best Student Paper Award [9884]
Obuchi Student Scholarships [3762]
Ocean Industries Student Research Awards [8557]
Oceanic Research Group (ORG) **[7569]**
Oceanic Research Group Scholarships [7570]
Edward A. O'Connor Founder's Scholarships [83]
Justice Sandra Day O'Connor Scholarship [6804]
Basil O'Connor Starter Scholar Research Awards [6235]
Odd Fellows Lodge No. 8 Endowed Scholarships [6048]
Captain Jennifer Shafer Odom Memorial Scholarships - Children of Soldiers [1716]
Captain Jennifer Shafer Odom Memorial Scholarships - Spouses of Soldiers [1717]
Don and Jan O'Dowd/SAA Statewide Scholarships [10033]
Office of Science Graduate Fellowships [9912]
Ohio Association of Broadcasters (OAB) **[7571]**
Ohio Association of Broadcaster's Kids Scholarships [7572]
Ohio Farm Bureau Federation (OFBF) **[7573]**
Ohio Newspaper Association (ONA) **[7575]**
Ohio Newspaper Association Minority Scholarships [7577]
Ohio Newspaper Association University Journalism Scholarships [7578]
Ohio Nursery and Landscape Association (ONLA) **[7580]**

Ohio Rural Electric Cooperatives Inc. **[7587]**
Ohio School Counselor Association (OSCA) **[7589]**
Ohio Space Grant Consortium (OSGC) **[7591]**
Ohio Space Grant Consortium Graduate Fellowships [7594]
Ohio Space Grant Consortium Special Minority Fellowships [7595]
Ohio State University - Kiplinger Program in Public Affairs Journalism **[7598]**
Ohio War Orphan Scholarships [10723]
Lawrence "Bud" Ohlman Memorial Scholarships [808]
OHTN Postdoctoral Fellowships [7637]
Oil & Gas, Trades & Technology (OGTT) Bursary and Scholarship Awards (OGTT) [5134]
O'Jays Scholarship Fund [9529]
The Seth Okin Good Deeds Scholarships [8235]
Oklahoma City University Full-Time Merit Scholarships [7601]
Oklahoma City University School of Law **[7600]**
Oklahoma Restaurant Association (ORA) **[7603]**
Oklahoma Restaurant Association Scholarships [7604]
Oklahoma Speech-Language-Hearing Association (OSHA) **[7605]**
Rhonda J.B. O'Leary Memorial Scholarship [3802]
Olin/Searle Fellows in Law [3995]
Jeff Oliphant Memorial Post-Graduate Scholarships [10619]
Robert B. Oliver ASNT Scholarships [1385]
MHS Andrew Oliver Research Fellowships [6336]
Frank del Olmo Memorial Scholarships [2826]
Diane Olsen Memorial Scholarship [10067]
Roy C. and Dorothy Jean Olson Memorial Scholarships [5361]
Olympia Tumwater Foundation (OTF) **[7607]**
Olympia Tumwater Foundation Traditional Scholarships [7608]
Olympia Tumwater Foundation Transitional (non-traditional) Scholarships [7609]
Omatsu FACL Scholarships [4001]
Charlie O'Meilia Scholarships [5301]
OMHF Postdoctoral Fellowships [7648]
Omicron Delta Kappa **[7610]**
Omicron Delta Kappa Foundation Scholarships [7611]
Omicron Nu Research Fellowships [5790]
Omohundro Institute of Early American History and Culture (OIEAHC) **[7612]**
Eloise Pitts O'More Scholarships [3247]
OMSBF Burlington Medical Student Bursaries [7641]
OMSBF District Four - Physician Care Bursaries [7642]
OMSBF Durham Medical Society Medical Student Bursaries [7643]
OMSBF Sun Life Financial Medical Student Bursaries [7644]
Oncology Nursing Society Foundation **[7615]**
Oncology Nursing Society Foundation - Bachelor's Scholarships [7619]
Oncology Nursing Society Foundation - Doctoral Scholarships [7620]
Oncology Nursing Society Foundation - Master's Scholarships [7621]
Oncology Trainee Travel Awards [3383]
Faith E. O'Neal Scholarships [8392]
ONECA Four Directions Scholarship [7658]
ONLA President's Scholarship [7586]
ONS Foundation Congress Scholarships [7622]
ONS Foundation Dissertation Research Grants [7623]
ONS Foundation Research Grants [7624]
Ontario Centres of Excellence (OCE) **[7626]**
Ontario English Catholic Teachers Association **[7628]**
Ontario HIV Treatment Network (OHTN) **[7636]**
Ontario Medical Association **[7638]**
Ontario Mental Health Foundation (OMHF) **[7647]**
Ontario Ministry of Children and Youth Services **[7649]**
Ontario Native Education Counselling Association (ONECA) **[7657]**
Ontario Women's Institute Scholarships [3997]
ONWA Annual Scholarships [7579]
OOBS Student Leadership Scholarships [7766]

Open Society Baltimore Community Fellowships [7661]
Open Society Fellowships [7662]
Open Society Foundations [7660]
Open Society Presidential Fellowships [7663]
Opera Foundation (OF) [7668]
Opera Foundation Scholarships [7669]
Operation JumpStart Scholarships [458]
OPERF/ABC Resident Travel Award [7755]
OPERF Educator and Student Awards [7756]
OPERF Fellowships [7757]
OPERF Small Grants [7758]
Frank Oppenheimer Scholarship Program [1049]
Dwight D. Opperman Scholarships [3686]
Optical Design and Engineering Scholarships [9471]
Optical Society of America Foundation (OSAF) [7670]
Order of Omega [7677]
Order of Omega Doctoral Fellowships [7680]
Order Sons of Italy in America (OSIA) [7681]
Order Sons of Italy Foundation General Scholarships [7683]
Order of United Commercial Travelers of America (UCT) [7685]
L'Oreal USA Fellowships for Women in Science [6107]
Oregon Association of Broadcasters (OAB) [7687]
Oregon Association of Broadcasters Scholarships [7688]
Oregon Association of Independent Accountants (OAIA) [7689]
Oregon Association of Nurseries (OAN) [7691]
Oregon Association of Nurseries Scholarship Program [7700]
Oregon Farm Bureau (OFB) [7704]
Oregon Farm Bureau Memorial Scholarships [7706]
Oregon Literary Fellowships [6097]
Oregon Medical Association (OMA) [7708]
Oregon Society of Certified Public Accountants (OSCPA) [7710]
Carl Orff Canada - Music for Children (COCMC) [7713]
Organization of American Historians (OAH) [7715]
Organization of American States (OAS) [7720]
Organization of American States AOS-Placed Scholarships [7727]
Organization of American States Graduate Scholarships [7728]
Organization of American States Self-Placed Scholarships [7729]
Organization of Black Aerospace Professionals (OBAP) [7731]
Organization of Black Aerospace Professionals General Scholarships [7733]
Organization of Chinese Americans Scholarships [1784]
Organization for Tropical Studies (OTS) [7734]
Orgone Biophysical Research Laboratory [7746]
Louisa Anne Oriente Scholarships [5681]
Original Tax Credit Scholarship [1627]
Orlando Central Florida Chapter of the Society for Technical Communication [7750]
Oronzio de Nora Industrial Electrochemistry Fellowships [3850]
Orthopaedic Foot and Ankle Fellowships [1061]
Orthopaedic Specialists Nursing Scholarships [10590]
Orthopaedic Trauma Association (OTA) [7752]
Orthopaedic Trauma Association Research Grants [7753]
Orthotic and Prosthetic Education and Research Foundation (OPERF) [7754]
Mary Reiko Osaka Memorial Scholarships [5555]
The Kenneth J. Osborn Memorial Scholarships [1808]
Royce Osborn Minority Scholarship [1398]
OSCA Graduate Student Scholarship Program [7590]
OSCPA Educational Foundation College Scholarships [7711]
OSCPA Educational Foundation High School Scholarships [7712]
OSGC Community College Scholarships [7596]
OSGC Education Scholarships [7597]
Osgoode Society for Canadian Legal History [7759]

OSHA Graduate Scholarships [7606]
Osram Sylvania Scholastic Achievement Awards [3838]
M. Dick Osumi Civil Rights and Public Interest Scholarship [5543]
The OTA Guide [7761]
Donald F. and Mildred Topp Othmer National Scholarship Awards [906]
Alvin G. Ott Fish and Wildlife Scholarships [10034]
Ellis R. Ott Scholarships [1390]
Ottawa Police 150th Anniversary Scholarships [2347]
Patricia and Armen Oumedian Scholarships [4616]
Our World-Underwater Scholarship Society (OWUSS) [7763]
Our World Underwater Scholarship Society North American Rolex Scholarships [7764]
Ted H. Ousley Scholarship Fund [4209]
Out on Bay Street [7765]
Outdoor Power Equipment Aftermarket Association (OPEAA) [7767]
Outdoor Writers Association of America (OWAA) [7769]
Outlaw Student's Medical Professions Scholarships [9595]
Outlaw Student's Minority Scholarships [9596]
Outlaw Student's Nursing School Scholarships [9597]
Outlaw Student's Teacher Scholarships [9598]
Outstanding Doctoral Thesis in Astrophysics [1092]
Overflow/PLUS Tax Credit Scholarships [1628]
Helene M. Overly Memorial Scholarships [10675]
Overseas Press Club Foundation [7771]
Overseas Press Club Foundation Harper's Magazine Scholarships [7776]
Overseas Press Club Foundation Reuters Scholarships [7777]
Victoria Ovis Memorial Scholarships [7045]
Elvina Jane Owen Awards [9855]
Charles and Melva T. Owen Memorial Scholarships [6948]
Owner-Operator Independent Drivers Association (OOIDA) [7784]
Abraham A. Oyedeji Scholarships [7393]
Michael Oykhman Criminal Law and Evidence Scholarships [6455]
Ozarks Division Scholarships [6524]
The Pac-10 Postgraduate Scholarships [7787]
Pacific 12 Conference (Pac-12) [7786]
Pacific Aviation Museum - Pearl Harbor [7788]
Pacific Institute for the Mathematical Sciences (PIMS) [7790]
Packard Fellowships for Science and Engineering [7793]
David and Lucile Packard Foundation [7792]
The Arthur J. Packard Memorial Scholarship Competition [862]
Barbara L. Packer Fellowships [442]
Dr. Nicholas Padis Memorial Graduate Scholarships [4849]
Casilda Pagan Educational/Vocational Scholarships [4964]
Laurie Page-Peck Scholarship Fund [2103]
The Pain Special Merit Award [3384]
Painting and Decorating Contractors of America (PDCA) [7794]
Ben Palacio Scholarships [9962]
Paleontological Society Student Research Grants [17]
Robert R. Palmer Research Travel Fellowships [1296]
Palo Verde High School Faculty Follies Scholarships [8357]
Pan Pacific Law Enforcement Scholarships [8745]
PanHellenic Scholarship Foundation [7796]
The PanHellenic Scholarships [7797]
ACI Charles Pankow Foundation ACI Student Fellowships [710]
Panther Cafe Scholarships [8358]
Katharine Pantzer Fellowships in the British Book Trades [2256]
Arthur and Barbara Pape Endowments [10269]
Paper-Check.Com [7798]
Paper Stock Industries (PSI) [7800]
Paper Stock Industries Chapter ISRI RRF Scholarship [7801]

Pappaioanou Veterinary Public Health and Applied Epidemiology Fellowships [2833]
Paralyzed Veterans of America (PVA) [7802]
Parapsychological Association (PA) [7804]
Parapsychological Association Research Endowments [7805]
Pardee Community Building Scholarships [8359]
Parent Cooperative Preschools International (PCPI) [7806]
Joseph M. Parish Memorial Grants [1253]
Park Law Enforcement Association (PLEA) [7808]
Cissy McDaniel Parker Scholarships [3557]
E.U. and Gene Parker Scholarships [6949]
Parkersburg Area Community Foundation [7810]
Parking Industry Institute Scholarship Program [7094]
Parkinson Canada [7875]
Parkinson Canada Basic Research Fellowships [7876]
Parkinson Canada Clinical Movement Disorder Fellowships [7877]
Parkinson Canada Clinical Research Fellowships [7878]
Parkinson Canada Graduate Student Awards [7879]
Parkinson Canada New Investigator Award Grants [7880]
Parkinson Canada Pilot Project Grants [7881]
Sylvia Parkinson Scholarships [4766]
Parkinson's Disease Foundation (PDF) [7882]
Parkinson's Disease Foundation International Research Grants Program [7884]
PARMA Scholarships [8325]
Ted Parnell Scholarship [10772]
The Paros-Digiquartz Scholarships [6276]
William E. Parrish Scholarships [8045]
Carl Parsell Scholarship Fund [6459]
Elisabeth M. and Winchell M. Parsons Scholarships [1798]
Part the Cloud Translational Research Funds [375]
Partners HealthCare Geriatric Psychiatry Fellowships [6324]
Partnership for Public Service (PPS) [7889]
Pasteur Foundation [7898]
Pasteur Foundation Postdoctoral Fellowships [7899]
Pat Tillman Foundation [7900]
PATCH [7902]
PATCH Early Childhood Education Scholarships [7903]
Senator Norman Paterson Fellowships [2711]
Patient Advocate Scholarship Program [3385]
James H. Patrenos Memorial Scholarships [8969]
Gail Patrick Charitable Trust Scholarships [3593]
Q. O. (Quint) Patrick Scholarships [10548]
Patriot Education Scholarships [6209]
Patterson, Belknap, Webb and Tyler L.L.P. [7904]
Patterson Belknap Webb & Tyler LLP Diversity Fellowships [7905]
Marvin R. and Pearl E. Patterson Family Scholarships Fund [4535]
Alice Conger Patterson Scholarships [10591]
Walter S. Patterson Scholarships [2370]
Joanne Holbrook Patton Military Spouse Scholarships [7069]
Pauahi Foundation [7906]
Paul and Inger Friend 4-H Scholarships [9574]
Arthur Paulin Automotive Aftermarket Scholarship Awards [2133]
Colorado Nurses Association: Virginia Paulson Memorial Scholarships [3144]
Ray, NORP and Katie, WOKTE Pautz Scholarships [1750]
Kenyon T. Payne Outstanding Student Awards [6500]
PBR Forces Veterans Association (PBR-FVA) [7921]
PCCE Scholarship [6952]
PCF Challenge Awards [8312]
PCF Young Investigator Awards [8313]
PDC Scholarships [1425]
PDF-APDA Summer Student Fellowships [7885]
PDF-PSG Mentored Clinical Research Awards [7886]
PDF Student Travel Award [7887]
PEA Bursaries [8290]
PEA Scholarships [8291]
Peace Frogs Fellowships [7741]

Sponsor and Scholarship Index

Chuck Peacock Memorial Scholarships [169]
Peale Scholarship Grant [8058]
Scott Pearlman Field Awards for Science and Exploration [3946]
Pearman Family Scholarships [8720]
James B. Pearson Fellowships [5659]
Martha Mitchell Pearson Memorial Scholarship [5755]
Robert L. Peaslee-Detroit Brazing and Soldiering Division Scholarships [1521]
Laura Ann Peck Memorial Endowed Scholarships [6049]
Pediatric Brain Tumor Foundation - Georgia **[7923]**
Pediatric Endocrinology Nursing Society Academic Education Scholarships [7926]
Pediatric Endocrinology Nursing Society (PENS) **[7925]**
Pediatric Endocrinology Nursing Society Convention Reimbursement Awards [7927]
Pediatric Infectious Diseases Society (PIDS) **[7928]**
Pedrozzi Scholarship Foundation **[7930]**
Mario Pedrozzi Scholarships [7931]
Peermusic Latin Scholarship [2320]
Melissa Pellegrin Memorial Scholarships [7751]
Pellegrini Scholarships [9620]
Louis Pelzer Memorial Awards [7719]
Margaret Pemberton Scholarships [2299]
Pembroke Center Faculty Fellowships [2389]
Pembroke Center Faculty Seed Grants [2390]
Pembroke Center Graduate Fellowships [2391]
Pembroke Center for Teaching and Research on Women Postdoctoral Fellowships [2392]
Dorothy E. Hofmann Pembroke Scholarships [4767]
Robert B. and Dorothy Pence Scholarships [9443]
Pennies for Art Scholarships [4355]
Pennsboro Alumni Scholarship Fund [7850]
Pennsylvania Association on Probation, Parole and Corrections (PAPPC) **[7932]**
Pennsylvania Dental Hygienists' Association (PDHA) **[7934]**
Pennsylvania Engineering Foundation Undergradaute Scholarships [7943]
Pennsylvania Heartland Unit Scholarships [4864]
Pennsylvania Land Surveyors Foundation Scholarships [7941]
Pennsylvania Library Association (PaLA) **[7936]**
Pennsylvania Library Association MLS Scholarships [7937]
Pennsylvania Music Educators Association (PMEA) **[7938]**
Pennsylvania Society of Land Surveyors (PSLS) **[7940]**
Pennsylvania Society of Professional Engineers (PSPE) **[7942]**
Pennsylvania Space Grant Consortium (PSGC) **[7944]**
Pennsylvania State System of Higher Education Foundation **[7946]**
The Penny Hoarder **[7949]**
Pension Real Estate Association (PREA) **[7951]**
Pension Real Estate Association Scholarships [7952]
P.E.O. Chapter DS Scholarships [4536]
PEO Educational Loan Funds [7954]
PEO International **[7953]**
PEO International Peace Scholarships [7955]
PEO Scholars Awards [7956]
People for the Ethical Treatment of Animals (PETA) **[7957]**
People to People International (PTPI) **[7959]**
Peoria Area Amateur Radio Club Scholarships [1751]
Pepperdine University **[7961]**
Pepperdine University Diversity Scholarships [7995]
Pepperdine University School of Law **[7963]**
Pepperdine University School of Law Armenian Student Scholarships [7996]
Pepperdine University School of Law Dean's Merit Scholarships [7997]
Pepperdine University School of Law Faculty Scholars Award [7998]
Pepperdine University School of Law JD/MBA Endowed Scholarships [7999]
Pepperdine University School of Law Special Law School Scholarships [8000]
Pepsi Scholarships [863]

Pepsi Wood County Technical/Caperton Center Scholarship Fund [7851]
Joe Perdue Scholarships [3063]
Joaquim Pereira Memorial Scholarships [6153]
Nalini Perera Little Lotus Bud Master's Scholarships [2689]
Rudy Perez Songwriting Scholarships [1275]
Perkins Coie 1L Diversity Fellowships [8011]
Perkins Coie 1L Patent Litigation and Patent Fellowships [8012]
Perkins Coie 1L Political Law Fellowships [8013]
Perkins Coie L.L.P. **[8010]**
Eleanor Perry Memorial Endowed Scholarships [6050]
Chet and Jannett Perry Rotary Club of Fort Myers Scholarship Fund [9444]
Perry Township School Memorial Scholarship Fund [9530]
Jim Perry Vocational Scholarships [809]
Persons Case Scholarships [285]
Gilberto and Lennetta Pesquera Medical School Scholarships [4453]
Pet Insurance U **[8014]**
PETA Foundation Law Internships [7958]
Pete Wilson Graduate Scholarships [8407]
Pete Wilson Journalism Scholarships [8408]
Jerome Peters Family Scholarships [6210]
Paul Evan Peters Fellowship [3073]
Kate B. and Hall J. Peterson Fellowships [443]
Lizette Peterson Homer Injury Prevention Grant Awards [1571]
Captain James H. Peterson Memorial Scholarships [4715]
Charles E. Peterson Senior Fellowships [2107]
Steve Petix Journalism Scholarships [8721]
William H. and Lena M. Petree Scholarships [10592]
Silvio and Eugenia Petrini Grants [4711]
Petroleum Engineering Scholarships [9250]
Petroleum History Society (PHS) **[8016]**
Petroleum History Society Graduate Scholarships [8017]
Petroleum Packaging Council (PPC) **[8018]**
Petroleum Packaging Council Scholarships [8019]
Pew Charitable Trusts **[8020]**
Pew Latin American Fellows Program in the Biomedical Sciences [8021]
Chuck Pezzano Scholarships [5286]
Pfafftown Jaycees/Lynn Canada Memorial Scholarships [10593]
William R. Pfalzgraf Scholarships [7852]
Dr. Harry V. Pfautz Memorial Scholarship Fund [4250]
Ruth Cook Pfautz Memorial Scholarship Fund [4251]
L. Gordon, Jr. and June D. Pfefferkorn Scholarships [10594]
Pfizer Inc. **[8022]**
Pfizer Scholarship Funds [6256]
PFLAG Columbia/Howard County **[8024]**
PFLAG Columbia-Howard County Scholarship [8025]
Carl J. Pforzheimer, Jr. Research Grants [5800]
PGSF Scholarships [8284]
Pharmaceutical Research and Manufacturers of America Foundation **[8026]**
Pharmaceutics Post Doctoral Fellowships [8030]
Pharmaceutics Research Starter Grants [8031]
Pharmaceutics Sabbatical Fellowships [8032]
Pharmacology/Toxicology Pre Doctoral Fellowships [8033]
PHE Canada National Award for Teaching Excellence in Physical Education [8120]
PHE Canada Student Awards [8121]
Marshall Phelps Athletic Memorial Scholarships [8507]
Phi Alpha Theta **[8043]**
Phi Alpha Theta Doctoral Scholarships [8046]
Phi Alpha Theta Faculty Advisor Research Grant [8047]
The Phi Beta Kappa Society **[8051]**
Phi Chi Theta **[8054]**
Phi Delta Gamma Academic Achievement Awards [8059]
Phi Delta Gamma **[8057]**
Phi Eta Sigma Distinguished Member Scholarships - Graduate or Professional [8062]
Phi Eta Sigma Distinguished Member Scholarships - Undergraduate [8063]
Phi Eta Sigma National Honor Society, Inc. **[8060]**
Phi Eta Sigma Undergraduate Scholarship Awards [8064]
Phi Kappa Phi **[8065]**
Phi Kappa Phi Fellowships [8066]
Phi Kappa Sigma (PKS) **[8067]**
Phi Kappa Sigma Foundation Scholarship [8068]
Phi Kappa Sigma Need-Based Scholarships [8069]
Phi Kappa Sigma Participation-Based Scholarships [8070]
Phi Sigma Epsilon **[8071]**
Phi Sigma Epsilon Past National President Scholarships [8078]
Phi Sigma Pi National Honor Fraternity **[8081]**
Phi Theta Kappa Scholarships [5124]
Phi Upsilon Omicron Candle Fellowships [8098]
Phi Upsilon Omicron Challenge Scholarships [8099]
Phi Upsilon Omicron Diamond Anniversary Fellowships [8100]
Phi Upsilon Omicron Founders Fellowships [8101]
Phi Upsilon Omicron Golden Anniversary Scholarships [8102]
Phi Upsilon Omicron, Inc. (Phi U) **[8084]**
Phi Upsilon Omicron Past Presidents Scholarships [8103]
Phi Upsilon Omicron Presidents Research Fellowships [8104]
Philadelphia Bar Association **[8110]**
Philadelphia Public Interest Fellowships [8111]
Catherine E. Philbin Scholarships [4356]
Shoshana Philipp (Kirshenblatt) R.N. Memorial Scholarships [9752]
Philippine Nurses Association of America (PNAA) **[8112]**
Walter T. Philippy Scholarships [6359]
Philips Lighting Continuing Education Awards [3839]
Philips Respironics Fellowships in Mechanical Ventilation [1214]
Philips Respironics Fellowships in Non-Invasive Respiratory Care [1215]
Jamie Phillips Endowed Scholarships [8001]
Phillips Fund Grants for Native American Research [1083]
CSF Charles and Claire Phillips Scholarships [3008]
Lowell Phillips Scholarships [3313]
Margaret E. Phillips Scholarships [10305]
William Philpott Scholarships [2269]
Ed Phinney Commemorative Scholarships [681]
PhRMA Foundation Health Outcomes Post Doctoral Fellowships [8034]
PhRMA Foundation Health Outcomes Pre Doctoral Fellowships [8035]
PhRMA Foundation Health Outcomes Research Starter Grants [8036]
PhRMA Foundation Health Outcomes Sabbatical Fellowships [8037]
PhRMA Foundation Informatics Research Starter Grants [8038]
PhRMA Foundation Pharmaceutics Pre Doctoral Fellowships [8039]
PhRMA Foundation Pharmacology/Toxicology Research Starter Grants [8040]
PhRMA Foundation Pharmacology/Toxicology Sabbatical Fellowships [8041]
PhRMA Foundation Pharmacology/Toxicology Post Doctoral Fellowships [8042]
PHS Commissioned Officers Foundation **[8114]**
Physical and Health Education Canada (PHE Canada) **[8116]**
The Physical Therapy Faculty Scholarship Endowment [9585]
Physicians' Services Incorporated Foundation **[8122]**
Physics of Accelerators and Related Technology for International Students [9902]
Physiotherapy Foundation of Canada **[8127]**
Physiotherapy Foundation of Canada Research Grant [8129]
Pi Gamma Mu (PGM) **[8132]**
Pi Gamma Mu Scholarships [8133]
Pi Lambda Theta Scholarships [10325]
Pi Project 2000 Tali James Memorial Scholarships [5756]

Thomas R. Pickering Graduate Foreign Affairs Fellowships [10681]
Mary Pickford Scholarships [2026]
Peter L. Picknelly Honorary Scholarships [640]
Eleonora Pidperyhora Scholarship [8587]
Ronald C. and Joyce Pierce - Mobile Section Named Scholarships [1522]
Nicholas J. Piergrossi Scholarships [4768]
Pierre Elliott Trudeau Foundation [8134]
Herschel Pifer Memorial Scholarships [7853]
Pignalberi Public Policy Scholarship [10068]
William Pigott Memorial Scholarships [3296]
David Pilon Scholarships for Training in Professional Psychology [1135]
Pilot Project Award [9239]
PIMS Postdoctoral Fellowships [7791]
John Pine Memorial Scholarships [8048]
Julia T. Pingree Student Scholarship [7300]
Pinnacle West Capital Corp. [8138]
Dr. Adolph Piotrowski Memorial Art Scholarships [8588]
Pipe Line Contractors Association of Canada [8141]
Pipe Line Contractors Association of Canada Student Bursary [8142]
Piscataqua Region Artist Advancement Grants [7305]
Stephen D. Pisinski Memorial Scholarships [8376]
Christopher Mark Pitkin Memorial Scholarships [6994]
Day Pitney LLP Scholarships [4769]
Pitsenbarger Awards [125]
Dr. Aura-Lee A. and James Hobbs Pittenger American History Scholarships [7154]
Robert Pittman Scholarships-Internships [10245]
Carter Pitts Scholarships [5474]
Donald E. Pizzini Memorial Nurse Scholarships [6580]
PKD Foundation [8143]
PKD Foundation Fellowships [8144]
A Place for Mom [8145]
Wayne F. Placek Grants [1150]
James L. Plafkin Memorial Scholarships [10188]
Al Plamann Legacy Scholarships [2457]
TFC Edward A. Plank, Jr. Memorial Scholarships [3182]
Betsy Plank/PRSSA Scholarships [8377]
PlasticPlace [8147]
PlasticPlace Young Entrepreneurs Scholarships [8148]
Plastics Pioneers Association Scholarships [9266]
Platform Support Grants [2357]
Platinum Educational Group [8149]
Katherine Barton Platt Excavation Fellowships [1237]
Platt Family Scholarship Prize Essay Contest [6091]
Playwrights' Center [8151]
Pleasantview Public Schools Fund [4564]
D.F. Plett Graduate Fellowships [8158]
D.F. Plett Historical Research Foundation, Inc. [8157]
PLSCA Scholarships [6101]
Harold and Harriet Plum Memorial Scholarships [2513]
Plumbing-Heating-Cooling Contractors Association (PHCC) [8159]
Plumbing-Heating-Cooling Contractors Association Educational Foundation Massachusetts Auxiliary Scholarships [8161]
Plumbing-Heating-Cooling Contractors Association Educational Foundation Need-Based Scholarships [8162]
Plumbing-Heating-Cooling Contractors Association Educational Foundation Scholarships [8163]
Plus Foundation [8166]
PLUS Foundation Financial Aid Scholarships [8168]
Henry DeWitt Plyler Scholarship Fund [4210]
PMCA/Penn State Fellowship in Confectionery Research [8293]
PNAA Nursing Scholarship Award [8113]
David Pohl Scholarships [9836]
Point Foundation (PF) [8169]
Point Foundation Scholarships [8662]
Daniel H. Pokorny Memorial Scholarship Awards [8543]
Pokross/Curhan Family Fund Prize [950]

Donald and Susie Polden Dean's Scholarships [10171]
Tibor T. Polgar Fellowships [4981]
Police Explorer Scholarships Program [4106]
Polish American Club of North Jersey Scholarships [5881]
Polish-American Engineers Association [8197]
Polish Falcons of America (PFA) [8199]
Polish National Alliance of Brooklyn, USA Scholarships [5882]
Polish Women's Alliance of America (PWAA) [8203]
Roy H. Pollack Scholarships [9837]
Pollard-Bailey Scholarships [8722]
A. H. Pollard Travelling PhD Scholarships [5163]
Harvey M. Pollicove Memorial Scholarships [7675]
David J. Pollini Scholarships [6360]
Justice Stewart G. Pollock Felloswships [6594]
Harold F. Polston Scholarships [1426]
Polymer Modifiers and Additives Division Scholarships [9267]
Harriet and Leon Pomerance Fellowships [1610]
Edward C. Pomeroy Awards for Outstanding Contributions to Teacher Education [488]
PON Graduate Student Grants [4789]
PON Next Generation Grants [4790]
PON Summer Fellowships [4791]
Buster Pool Memorial Scholarships [3248]
Jim Poore Memorial Scholarships [5044]
Pope Scholarship Awards [6361]
Portable Sanitation Association International (PSAI) [8206]
Portable Sanitation Association International Scholarship Fund [8207]
Louis C. Portella Memorial Scholarships [2514]
Karin Riley Porter Good Works Scholarships [8236]
Porter Physiology Development Fellowship Awards [1100]
AFT Robert Porter Scholarship Program [795]
Thomas W. Porter, W8KYZ Scholarships Honoring Michael Daugherty, W8LSE [1752]
Robert Porterfield Graduate Scholarships [9389]
Portland Area Business Association Scholarships [3921]
Portland Cement Association Scholarships [3980]
Portuguese American Leadership Council of the United States (PALCUS) [8208]
Portuguese-American Police Association of Massachusetts, Lodge II (PAPA) [8210]
Portuguese American Police Association Scholarships [8211]
Portuguese-American Scholarship Foundation [8209]
Gail Posluns Fellowships in Hematology [6139]
Postdoctoral Fellowships for Clinical Neurologists [7888]
Postdoctoral Fellowships at the Fields Institute [4020]
Poteet Strawberry Festival Association (PSFA) [8212]
Poteet Strawberry Festival Association Scholarships [8213]
Terry Linda Potter Scholarship Fund [4537]
Barbara Potter Scholarships [1055]
Erwin Potts Scholarships [10246]
Poundmaker Memorial Scholarships [10272]
George V. Powell Diversity Scholarships [5920]
Gerald Powell Scholarships [3269]
Susan Kelly Power and Helen Hornbeck Tanner Fellowships [7423]
J.R. (Joe) Power National Scholarships [8383]
Powers-Knapp Scholarships [10326]
Practising Law Institute (PLI) [8214]
Practising Law Institute Law Student Scholarships [8215]
Prairie Baseball Academy Scholarships [286]
Gerald Pratley Award [1884]
Lou and Carole Prato Sports Reporting Scholarships [8409]
Praxair International Scholarships [1523]
Presbyterian Association of Musicians (PAM) [8216]
Presbyterian Association of Musicians Scholarships [8217]
Presbyterian Church [8218]
Prescott Center for the Arts (PCA) [8220]

Prescott Fine Arts Association Scholarship Program [8221]
President's Commission on White House Fellowships [8222]
Prevent Cancer Foundation (PCF) [8224]
Prevent Cancer Foundation Fellowships [8225]
Price Benowitz LLP [8226]
Peridian International, Inc./Rae L. Price, FASLA Scholarship [1347]
Peridian International, Inc./Rae L. Price, FASLA Scholarships [5916]
Jim and Dee Price Scholarships [4565]
Judith McManus Price Scholarships [1106]
Pride Foundation [8240]
Pride Foundation Political Leadership Scholarships [8258]
Pride Foundation Regional Scholarships [8259]
Pride Foundation Scholarships [8663]
Pride Foundation Social Work Scholarships [8260]
Pride Law Fund (PLF) [8273]
Pride of the Rose Scholarship Fund [3922]
Lendon N. Pridgen, GlaxoSmithKline - NOBCChE Fellowships [7089]
Diana M. Priestly Memorial Scholarships [2564]
Dean Prim Scholarships [10595]
Primate Conservation Grants [8276]
Primate Conservation, Inc. [8275]
Eric Primavera Memorial Scholarships [4094]
Josef Princ Memorial Scholarships [8360]
R.M. Princ Scholarships [8361]
Prince Edward Island Law Student Scholarships [5980]
Prince Henry Society - New Bedford Chapter [8277]
Prince Henry Society Scholarships [8278]
Pringle Chivers Sparks Teskey [8279]
Alexander Pringle Criminal Law Scholarships [8280]
Prins Foundation Fellowship for Senior Scholars [2854]
Prins Foundation Post-Doctoral and Early Career Fellowship for Emigrating Scholars [2855]
Print and Graphics Scholarship Foundation [8281]
Print and Graphics Scholarship Foundation Awards (PGSF-GATF) [8282]
Printing Industries of America - Center for Technology and Research [8283]
Miguel Pro Scholarships [10724]
Procter & Gamble Professional Oral Health/HDA Foundation Scholarships [4893]
Professional Beauty Association (PBA) [8285]
Professional Construction Estimators Association of America, Inc. (PCEA) [8287]
Professional Development and Education Fund (PDEF) Professional Development Scholarships [9223]
Professional Employees Association [8289]
Professional Manufacturing Confectioners Association (PMCA) [8292]
Professional Research Grants [1399]
Professional Women in Pest Management Scholarships [7096]
Professional Women of Redlands, PoWeR to Continue Learning Scholarships [8508]
Progress Lane Scholarships [3183]
Progressive Dairy Producer Awards [6905]
Project Management Association of Canada (PMAC) [8294]
Property and Environment Research Center (PERC) [8296]
Property and Environment Research Center Graduate Fellowships [8297]
Property and Environment Research Center Lone Mountain Fellowships [8298]
Property and Environment Research Center Media Fellowships [8299]
ProQuest L.L.C. [8301]
Prostate Cancer Canada (PCC) [8303]
Prostate Cancer Canada Clinical Research Fellowships [8308]
Prostate Cancer Canada Graduate Studentships [8309]
Prostate Cancer Canada Postdoctoral Research Fellowships [8310]
Prostate Cancer Foundation [8311]
Proven Data Recovery [8314]

Proven Data Recovery Technology Scholarships [8315]
Provincial and Regional 4-H Scholarships [9]
Barbara F. Prowant Nursing Research Grants [1028]
PRSA Diversity Multicultural Scholarships [8378]
Peter DeWitt Pruden and Phyliss Harrill Pruden Scholarships [10247]
Prudential 1L Summer Internships [6706]
Neil Pruitt, Sr. Memorial Scholarships [6870]
Joseph E. Pryor Graduate Fellowships [343]
Cheryl White Pryor Memorial Scholarships [3558]
Phillis Brinton Pryor Panhellenic Scholarship [5757]
PSAC-AGR National Scholarships [8384]
PSAC - Coughlin National Scholarships [8385]
PSAC Regional Scholarships [8386]
PSGC/NASA Space Grant Fellowships at the PSGC Affiliate Institutions [7945]
PSHF Good Idea Grants [8381]
Psi Chi, The International Honor Society in Psychology **[8316]**
PSI Healthcare Research by Community Physicians Grants [8125]
Psychology Association of Saskatchewan **[8319]**
Psychology Association of Saskatchewan Student Scholarships - Academic Achievement [8320]
Psychology Association of Saskatchewan Student Scholarships - Research Based [8321]
Pt. Lay Memorial Scholarships [10035]
Public Accountants Association of Kansas (PAAK) **[8322]**
Public Agency Risk Managers Association (PARMA) **[8324]**
Public Education Foundation **[8326]**
Public Interest Environmental Law Fellowships [3898]
Public Interest Fellowships for Law Students of Color [4491]
Public Library Association (PLA) **[8371]**
Public Relations Society of America Maryland (PRSAMD) **[8373]**
Public Relations Student Society of America (PRSSA) **[8375]**
Public Schools of Hawaii Foundation (PSHF) **[8380]**
Public Service Alliance of Canada **[8382]**
Public Service Fellows Internship Program - Center for Government Leadership [7890]
Public Service Fellows Internship Program - Communications [7891]
Public Service Fellows Internship Program - Development [7892]
Public Service Fellows Internship Program - Education and Outreach [7893]
Public Service Fellows Internship Program - Government Affairs [7894]
Public Service Fellows Internship Program - Government Transformation and Agency Partnerships [7895]
Public Service Fellows Internship Program - Human Resources [7896]
Public Service Fellows Internship Program - Research [7897]
Duane V. Puerde Memorial Scholarships [3184]
Eugene C. Pulliam Fellowships for Editorial Writing [8902]
Pulliam/Kilgore Freedom of Information Internships [9279]
Morris M. Pulver Scholarship Funds [2642]
Harry B. Pulver Scholarships [4454]
Paul Pumpian Scholarship [1584]
Purdue University School of Mechanical Engineering - Ray W. Herrick Laboratories **[8387]**
John Purfield Endowed Scholarships [8002]
Doug Purvis Prize [2546]
Elizabeth Pusey Scholarships [3185]
A.O. Putnam Memorial Scholarships [5193]
PVA Research Foundation Fellowships [7803]
PWC Internships [8156]
Harry V. Quadracci Memorial Scholarships [4649]
Qualcomm San Diego Science, Technology, Engineering and Mathematics Scholarships [8723]
Quarter Century Wireless Association (QCWA) **[8389]**
Quarter Century Wireless Association Scholarships [8390]

Queen Elizabeth II Graduate Scholarship Program [287]
Queens County Women's Bar Association (QCWBA) **[8391]**
Queer Foundation **[8393]**
Queer Foundation Effective Writing and Scholarships [8394]
Rosa Quezeda Memorial Education Scholarships [3361]
Michael J. Quill Scholarships [9766]
Quill and Scroll International Honorary Society (QSS) **[8395]**
Bob Quincy Scholarships [10248]
AIST Judith A. Quinn Detroit Member Chapter Scholarship [2005]
Diamond & James Quong Memorial Scholarships [10799]
RAB Design Lighting Award of Excellence [3840]
Dr. J. Glenn Radcliffe Memorial Scholarships [9575]
Radio-Television Digital News Association (RTDNA) **[8398]**
Radio and Television News Directors Association and Foundation (RTNDA) - Association of Electronic Journalists (RTNDF) **[8401]**
Radio-Television News Directors Foundation Canada (RTDNF) **[8413]**
Radiological Society of North America (RSNA) **[8415]**
Dr. Sidney Rafal Memorial Scholarships [4770]
The Raffin-Gathercole Scholarships [4331]
Marjorie Usher Ragan Scholarships [10249]
Railroad and Mine Workers Memorial Scholarships [5556]
Railway Tie Association (RTA) **[8422]**
Rain Bird Intelligent Use of Water Scholarships [5917]
Rainbow Business and Professional Association (RBPA) **[8424]**
J.J. Rains Memorial Scholarships [3104]
Frederick Rakestraw Law Scholarships [7520]
Tom D. Ralls Memorial Scholarship [4285]
The NASSCO Jeffrey D. Ralston Memorial Scholarship [6668]
Rama Scholarships for the American Dream [864]
Guthikonda Ramabrahmam and Balamani [9669]
RAMEF/NRAEF Co-Branded Scholarships [8565]
Marvin Rammelsberg Scholarships [3009]
Rancho Bernardo/Smith Scholarships [8724]
A. Stanley Rand Fellowships Program [9037]
Herbert W. Rand Fellowships and Scholarships [6257]
Commander Newell S. Rand Jr. Scholarship Program [7809]
Helen F. "Jerri" Rand Memorial Scholarships [3323]
R&E Foundation Education Scholarships [8416]
James Randi Educational Foundation (JREF) **[8426]**
James Randi Educational Foundation Scholarships [8427]
Jennings Randolph Peace Scholarship Dissertation Program [9990]
United States Institute of Peace Jennings Randolph Senior Fellowship Program [9991]
Rangel Graduate Fellowship [8429]
Charles B. Rangel International Affairs Program **[8428]**
Jeannette Rankin Scholarships [8431]
Jeannette Rankin Women's Scholarship Fund **[8430]**
Rappaport Center for Law and Public Policy **[8432]**
Rappaport Fellows Program in Law and Public Policy [8437]
Marie Mathew Rask-Gamma Omicron Educational Endowment [5758]
Geeta Rastogi Memorial Scholarships [10338]
General John Paul Ratay Educational Grants [6535]
Dr. Mark Rathke Family Scholarships [3721]
James K. Rathmell Jr. Memorial Scholarships [810]
Ratner and Sugarmon Scholarship [10172]
Dennis Raveling Scholarships [2488]
Lenny Ravich "Shalom" Scholarships [1851]
Rawley Silver Awards for Excellence [450]
Rawley Silver Research Award [451]
Mary C. Rawlins Scholarships [4771]
William C. Ray, CIH, CSP Arizona Scholarships [1427]

W.B. Ray HS Class of '56 Averill Johnson Scholarships [3105]
Raytheon Co. **[8439]**
Raytheon Scholarship Program [8440]
RBC Medical Education Scholarships [7286]
RBPA Scholarships [8425]
Reach for Your Goal Scholarships [4617]
Robert H. Reakirt Scholarships [3010]
William Reaser Scholarships [7854]
Carl C. and Abbie Rebman Trust Scholarships [4566]
Redlands Baseball/Softball for Youth Scholarship [8509]
Redlands Community Scholarship Foundation **[8441]**
Redlands Community Scholarship Foundation Awards [8510]
Redlands High School Academic Decathlon Scholarships [8511]
Redlands High School Boy's Varsity Volleyball Scholarships [8512]
Redlands High School Girls' Volleyball Boosters Scholarship Awards [8513]
Redlands High School Mock Trial Scholarships [8514]
Redlands High School-PTSA Scholarships [8515]
Redlands High School Softball Booster Scholarship Awards [8516]
Redlands High School Spiritleaders Scholarships [8517]
Redlands High School Terrier Band Boosters Club Scholarships [8518]
Redlands High School Vocal Music Boosters Scholarship Awards [8519]
Redlands Morning Kiwanis Club Foundation Scholarships [8520]
Redlands Rotary Club Foundation Discretionary Scholarships [8521]
Redlands Teachers Association Scholarships [8522]
The Reese Fellowships [444]
Bob Reeve Aviation Management Scholarships [217]
Reflex Sympathetic Dystrophy Syndrome Association (RSDSA) **[8531]**
REFORMA: National Association to Promote Library and Information Services to Latinos and the Spanish-Speaking **[8533]**
REFORMA Scholarship Program [8534]
Region II Scholarships [1428]
Regional Development Corporation Scholarships [7287]
Regions Financial Corp. **[8535]**
Regions Riding Forward Scholarships Essay Contest [8536]
Registered Apprenticeship Program/CTS Scholarships (RAP) [288]
Registered Psychiatric Nurses Association of Saskatchewan (RPNAS) **[8537]**
Registry of Interpreters for the Deaf, Inc. (RID) **[8541]**
Rehabmart.com **[8544]**
Rehabmart.com Scholarships [8545]
Dan M. Reichard, Jr. Scholarships [1168]
Reid Hospital Graduate Student Scholarships [10507]
J.H. Stewart Reid Memorial Fellowship Trust, [8547], **[8546]**
Mark A. Reid Memorial Scholarship Grants [3297]
Siobhan Isabella Reid Memorial Scholarships [5994]
Jacob L. Reinecke Memorial Scholarship Fund [4538]
George Reinke Scholarships [1442]
Daniel L. Reiss Memorial Scholarship Fund [4539]
Religion Newswriters Association (RNA) **[8548]**
April Relyea Scholarship [10069]
Remkus-Sochaki Academmic Achievement Scholarships [8205]
REMSA Scholarships [1189]
Betty Rendel Scholarships [6955]
Don Renschler Scholarships [8261]
Rentec Direct **[8550]**
James Renwick Fellowship in American Craft [9004]
Bertha and Byron L. Reppert Scholarship Fund [4252]
Research Career Development Awards [7625]

RESEARCH

Research Center for Alcoholic Liver and Pancreatic Diseases **[8552]**
Research Corporation for Science Advancement (RCSA) **[8554]**
Research and Development Corporation, Newfoundland and Labrador **[8556]**
Research Resident/Fellow Grants [8417]
Reservation Counter College Scholarships [8559]
ReservationCounter.com **[8558]**
Resident Research Grants [8126]
Resident Travel Award for Underrepresented Populations [3386]
Resilience Action Fund Scholarships [3981]
Resistance Welder Manufacturers' Association Scholarships [1524]
Resources for the Future (RFF) **[8560]**
Restaurant Association of Maryland Education Foundation (RAMEF) **[8562]**
Resume Template Design Scholarships [10369]
Retail Chapter Scholarship Awards [7701]
Retail Print Music Dealers Association (RPMDA) **[8566]**
Retired League Postmasters of the National League of Postmasters (RLP) **[8568]**
Retired League Postmasters Scholarship Program [8569]
Reuters Institute Visiting Fellowships [10265]
Thomson Reuters/MLA Doctoral Fellowships [6393]
The W. Reymont Foundation **[8570]**
W. Reymont Scholarships [8589]
Mike Reynolds Journalism Scholarships [8410]
Reynoldsburg-Pickerington Rotary Club **[8594]**
Reynoldsburg-Pickerington Rotary Club High School Scholarship [8595]
Janet Reynoldson Memorial Scholarship [3687]
RFDF MBA Preparation Fellowships [8619]
RFDF Pre-MBA Fellowships [8620]
Lori Rhett Memorial Scholarships [6733]
Rho Chi, AFPE First Year Graduate Fellowships [8597]
The Rho Chi Society **[8596]**
Rho Chi Society Clinical Research Scholarships [8598]
Rhode Island Association of Former Legislators Scholarships [8608]
Rhode Island Bar Association **[8599]**
Rhode Island Foundation **[8601]**
Rhode Island Space Grant Consortium **[8612]**
Rhode Island Student Loan Authority **[8614]**
Rice-Cullimore Scholarships [1799]
Haynes Rice Scholarships [6756]
Barbara Hagan Richards Scholarships [3249]
James Edward "Bill" Richards Scholarships [3250]
Ellen Swallow Richards Travel Grants [1315]
William S. Richardson Commemorative Scholarships [7918]
Phillip Guy Richardson Memorial Scholarships [5510]
Henry and Sylvia Richardson Research Grant [3883]
J. Milton Richardson Theological Fellowships [363]
Frank J. Richter Scholarships [570]
John Riddick Student Grants [7446]
John S. and Jacqueline P. Rider Scholarships [10596]
Honorable Joseph H. Ridge Memorial Scholarships [328]
Jasper Ridge Restoration Fellowships Jasper Ridge Biological Preserve [3777]
ANN Ingrid Josefin Ridky Academic Scholarships [45]
Donald Riebhoff Memorial Scholarships [1753]
William J. Rielly/MCURC Scholarships [3011]
Bryon Riesch Paralysis Foundation (BRPF) **[8616]**
Bryon Riesch Paralysis Foundation Research Grants [8617]
Rieser Fellowships [2406]
Dan Rigel Memorial Educational Grants [1843]
Riggs Cove Foundation Scholarships [4369]
Benjamin Riggs Scholarships [4370]
Ameen Rihani Scholarship Program [1599]
Rim-Freeman Point Scholarship [8190]
Rimington Trophy Scholarships [2340]
Lois McDonald Rinehart Adelphe Scholarship [5759]
Lana K. Rinehart Scholarships [3186]
Harold and Eleanor Ringelberg Scholarships [4540]

Josephine Ringold Scholarships [4618]
Fauneil J. Rinn Scholarships [8954]
John T. Riordan Professional Education Scholarships [5307]
Rising Farmworker Dream Fund (RFDF) **[8618]**
Risk Management and Insurance Scholarships [8767]
Risk Management and Insurance Scholarships - University of Calgary [8768]
RISLA Student Loans [8615]
Ritchie-Jennings Memorial Scholarships [1923]
Paul H. Rittle Sr. Professional Development Grants [5217]
Thomas and Ruth River International Scholarships [10704]
Riverside Sheriffs Association (RSA) **[8621]**
Riverside Sheriffs Association Member Scholarship Program [8622]
Anthony Rizzo Scholarship Award [7514]
RJT Criminal Defense **[8623]**
RMNP Research Fellowship [8635]
Roanoke Bar Association (RBA) **[8625]**
Jerry Robbins Scholarship [5682]
Lawrence and Louise Robbins Scholarships [6211]
Robert Browning Scholarships [8262]
Robert J. McNamara Student Paper Awards [2072]
Robert S. McNamara Fellowships Program (RSMFP) [10698]
Robert Wood Johnson Clinical Scholarships [8630]
Robert Wood Johnson Foundation (RWJF) **[8628]**
Paul V. Roberts/AEESP Outstanding Doctoral Dissertation Award [1953]
James H. Roberts Athletic Scholarships [7855]
Faye Lynn Roberts Educational Scholarships [9445]
Clifford Roberts Graduate Fellowships [4415]
Eugene L. Roberts Jr. Prize [10250]
Marion Roberts Memorial Scholarships [2134]
Smiley Elementary School PTA - Beverly Roberts Memorial Scholarships [8523]
Elliott C. Roberts Scholarships [5168]
Mary Roberts Scholarships [3012]
Thomas Warren Roberts Scholarships [7856]
Actuary of Tomorrow - Stuart A. Robertson Memorial Scholarship [64]
A.D. Al and Maxine Robertson Memorial Scholarship [10036]
Lola Ellis Robertson Scholarships [6258]
Ben Robinette Scholarship Endowment Fund [4211]
Robinhood Marine Center Scholarships [4371]
David G. Robinson Arts Scholarships [9446]
Samuel Robinson Awards [8219]
Gertrude J. Robinson Book Prize [2616]
Helen M. Robinson Grants [5357]
NKA Dr. Violet B. Robinson Memorial Graduate Scholarship [7043]
James Robinson Memorial Scholarship - Ripley Rotary [7857]
Claude Robinson Scholarships [7040]
Nell Bryant Robinson Scholarships [8105]
Paul S. Robinson Scholarships [9115]
Sara Roby Fellowship in Twentieth-Century American Realism [9005]
August M. Rocco Scholarship Fund [9531]
Rochelle Scholarship [6124]
James and Marilyn Rockefeller Scholarships [6212]
Rockford Area Habitat for Humanity College Scholarships [3298]
Rockwell Collins Scholarships [170]
Rocky Mountain Coal Mining Institute (RMCMI) **[8631]**
Rocky Mountain Coal Mining Institute Engineering/Geology Scholarships [8632]
Rocky Mountain Coal Mining Institute Technical Scholarships [8633]
Rocky Mountain Conservancy **[8634]**
Rocky Mountain Mineral Law Foundation (RMMLF) **[8636]**
Paul W. Rodgers Scholarship [5261]
R.O.E.A. Dumitru Golea Goldy-Gemu Scholarships [1227]
Roy Seymour Rogers and Geraldine Ruth Rogers Scholarships [9732]
Kimberly Marie Rogers Memorial Scholarship Fund [4057]
Mister Rogers Memorial Scholarship [47]
Joseph Wood Rogers Memorial Scholarships [8880]

Kenneth Rogers Memorial Scholarships [6051]
Red Rogers Memorial Scholarships [10800]
Pat and Cliff Rogers Nursing Scholarships [10090]
Mary Stuart Rogers Scholarships [10561]
William C. Rogers Scholarships [4389]
Sandra Journey Rolf Scholarship Fund [5760]
Rome Prize [424]
Ronald McDonald House Charities African American Future Achievers Scholarships [8639]
Ronald McDonald House Charities (RMHC) **[8638]**
Ronald McDonald House Charities/HACER Scholarships [8640]
Ronald McDonald House Charities Scholarships [8641]
Ronald McDonald House Charities Scholarships in Asia [8642]
Dr. Orrin Rongstad Wildlife Scholarship [10091]
Charles and Ruth Ronin Memorial Scholarships [8524]
Dorothy Worden Ronken Scholarships [3594]
Roofing Industry Alliance for Progress **[8643]**
Susanna Stover Root Memorial Scholarship [5761]
Roothbert Fund **[8645]**
Roothbert Fund Scholarships [8646]
Barnes W. Rose, Jr. and Eva Rose Nichol Scholarship Fund [304]
Carl Rose Memorial Scholarships [7858]
Florence C. Rose and S. Meryl Rose Scholarships [6259]
Dr. Wayne F. Rose Scholarship Fund [4058]
Betty Rose Scholarships [1276]
Clarence J. Rosecrans Scholarship [1151]
Rosemary Quigley Memorial Scholarships [2341]
Esther Katz Rosen Fund Grants [1152]
Jack Rosen Scholarship [5683]
Ollie Rosenberg Educational Trust [4253]
Rosenberg-Ibarra Scholarships [8263]
Mandell and Lester Rosenblatt Undergraduate Scholarships [9217]
Walter A. Rosenblith New Investigator Award [4806]
Barbara Rosenblum Cancer Dissertation Scholarships [9333]
Marshall N. Rosenbluth Outstanding Doctoral Thesis Award [1093]
ASPPH/CDC Allan Rosenfield Global Health Fellowship Program [2065]
Rosenthal Bar Exam Scholarship Fund [2444]
Harold W. Rosenthal Fellowships in International Relations [2043]
Jean and Tom Rosenthal Scholarship Program [3332]
Marty Rosness Student Scholarships [1623]
IADR Norton Ross Fellowship [5253]
S. Byrl Ross Memorial Scholarship Fund [7859]
Ross/Nickey Scholarships [6563]
Colonel Jerry W. Ross Scholarships [1585]
The Bea and Harry Ross Scholarship Endowment [9586]
Ross Trust Future School Counselors Essay Competition [750]
Hon. Rudolph J. Rossetti Memorial Scholarships [2515]
Rotary Club of Annapolis Scholarship [1561]
The Rotary Club of Cape Coral Goldcoast Scholarship Fund [2784]
Rotary Club of Corpus Christi Scholarships [3106]
The Rotary Club of Rancho Bernardo Sunrise Community Service Scholarships [8725]
The Rotary Foundation **[8647]**
Rotary Foundation Global Grant Scholarships [8648]
Rotary Peace Fellowship Program [3701]
Rotary Public Safety Scholarships [4212]
Richard J. Roth Journalism Fellowships [7369]
Edward S. Roth Manufacturing Engineering Scholarships [9192]
Rothberg International School Graduate Merit Scholarships [2643]
Marjorie Roy Rothermel Scholarships [1800]
Hal Rothman Dissertation Fellowships [1316]
Theodore Rousseau Fellowships [6436]
Marion and Donald Routh Student Research Grants [1572]
Rove Pest Control **[8649]**
Rove Pest Control Scholarships [8650]
Rovelstad Scholarship in International Librarianship [3452]

Cecilia Rowan Religious Study Fellowships [7635]
Roy Rowan Scholarships [7778]
Rowe Family Fellowships [7742]
Leo S. Rowe Pan American Fund [7730]
Ellis W. Rowe Scholarships [4703]
Robert Roy Awards [1897]
Travis Roy Foundation Individual Grants [8652]
Travis Roy Foundation **[8651]**
Royal Bank Scholarships [2290]
Lucille and Edward R. Roybal Foundation **[8653]**
Lucille and Edward R. Roybal Foundation Public Health Scholarships [8654]
RPNAS Baccalaureate Level Program Scholarships [8538]
RPNAS Doctorate Level Program Scholarship [8539]
RPNAS Master's Level Program Scholarship [8540]
RSDSA Research Grants [8532]
RSNA/AAPM Fellowships for Graduate Study in Medical Physics [560]
RSNA/AUR/APDR/SCARD Radiology Education Research Development Grant [8418]
RSNA Education Scholar Grant [8419]
RSNA Research Scholar Grants [8420]
RSNA Research Seed Grants [8421]
RTDNA Presidents Scholarships [8411]
RTDNF Scholarships [8414]
The Viking Voices - Mike Ruben Honorarium and John Rice Memorial Scholarship [7860]
IPMI Richard Rubin Memorial Scholarship Award [5374]
IRARC Memorial Joseph P. Rubino WA4MMD Scholarships [1754]
Glen Ruby Memorial Scholarships [2754]
Paul and Ellen Ruckes Scholarships [823]
Lawrence E. and Mabel Jackson Rudberg Scholarships [3722]
Joe Rudd Scholarships [8637]
Lim Ruger Foundation Scholarships [5544]
Damon Runyon Clinical Investigator Awards [3518]
Ruppert Educational Grant Program [8955]
Hermann G. Rusch Scholarships [763]
Russell Athletics Scholarships [2109]
Dave & Laurie Russell Family Scholarships for Habitat for Humanity of Kent County Families [4619]
Liane B. Russell Fellowships [9908]
Kenneth W. Russell Memorial Fellowships [661]
Norman K. Russell Scholarships [7092]
Russian Brotherhood Organization of the U.S.A. (RBOUSA) **[8655]**
Russian/Central Asian Student Scholarships [10092]
Michael A. Russo Memorial Scholarships [8525]
The Anthony C. Russo Scholarships [7115]
NPELRA Foundation - Anthony C. Russo Scholarships [7116]
Lucile Rust Scholarships [8106]
Rutherford Scholars [289]
Alexander Rutherford Scholarships for High School Achievement [290]
IOIA Andrew Rutherford Scholarships [5370]
Ralph and Clara Rutledge Memorial Scholarships [4149]
Charles and Eleanor Rycenga Education Scholarship Fund [4541]
Deborah Jean Rydberg Memorial Scholarships [3299]
Ryerson Scholarships [5527]
Charles A. Ryskamp Research Fellowships [744]
SAA Native American Scholarships [9079]
SABA NC - Organizational Fellowships [9352]
SABA NC - Pro Bono Fellowships [9353]
SABA NC - Public Interest Fellowships [9354]
SAC Scholarships for Higher Education [9558]
Sacks For CF Scholarships [2342]
Chester & Maria Sadowski Memorial Scholarships [8590]
SAEMS Environmental Scholarships [9396]
Safe Schools Coalition (SSC) **[8658]**
Safelink Internet **[8665]**
Safelink Internet Scholarships [8666]
Safer Athletic Field Environments Scholarships (SAFE) [9481]
Russell Sage Foundation (RSF) **[8667]**
Russell Sage Foundation Visiting Scholars [8668]
Ruth Sager Scholarships [6260]

SAH Study Tour Fellowships [9085]
Don Sahli-Kathy Woodall Graduate Scholarships [9677]
Sons and Daughters Don Sahli-Kathy Woodall Scholarships [9678]
Saint Andrews Scholarships [8670]
Saint Andrew's Society of the State of New York **[8669]**
St. Francis Xavier Scholarships [10725]
St. James Armenian Church Memorial Scholarships [1704]
St. Joseph's Hospital School of Nursing Alumnae Scholarship [7861]
St. Louis Paralegal Association (SPA) **[8671]**
St. Louis Paralegal Association Student Scholarships [8673]
Saint Paul University Canada **[8674]**
Saint Paul University Excellence Scholarships [8675]
Saint Paul University Financial Aid Bursaries [8676]
Saints Cyril and Methodius Scholarships [8657]
SAJA Journalism Scholarships [9356]
Joseph and Amelia Saks Scholarship Fund [3270]
SALEF Health Career Scholarships [8680]
The Bill, W2ONV, and Ann Salerno Memorial Scholarship [1755]
Eugene Gene Sallee, W4YFR Memorial Scholarships [1756]
Sally Beauty Scholarships for High School Graduates [8286]
Salon Supply Store **[8677]**
Salon Supply Store Cosmetology Scholarships [8678]
Ann S. Salsberg Scholarship Awards [2516]
Salvadoran American Leadership and Education Fund (SALEF) **[8679]**
Salvatori Fellowships [5234]
Henry Salvatori Scholarships [7684]
The Walter Samek III Memorial Scholarship Fund [3207]
SAMFund **[8681]**
SAMFund Grants [8682]
Margaret Jerome Sampson Scholarships [8107]
Ray and Pearl Sams Scholarships [10597]
AIST David H. Samson Canadian Scholarships [2006]
Samsung American Legion Scholarships [957]
San Angelo Area Foundation (SAAF) **[8683]**
San Angelo Area Foundation Scholarships [8684]
San Diego Foundation **[8685]**
The San Diego Foundation Community Scholarships I [8726]
The San Diego Foundation Community Scholarships II [8727]
San Diego Pan-Pacific Law Enforcement Association (PANPAC) **[8744]**
San Francisco Foundation **[8746]**
San Francisco State University Disability Programs and Resource Center **[8749]**
San Jose American GI Forum **[8755]**
San Pasqual Academy Scholarships [8728]
Leo and Trinidad Sanchez Scholarships [8956]
Sand Hill Scholars Program [8957]
Bill Sanderson Aviation Maintenance Technician Scholarships [4841]
Leonard H. Sandler Fellowships [5000]
The Amato Sanita Brighter Future Scholarships [379]
Sanofi Pasteur Scholarships [2712]
SANS Inc./Mead Leadership Fellows Program [7509]
Santa Clara La Raza Lawyers Scholarships [5894]
SAO (Smithsonian Astrophysical Observatory) Predoctoral Fellowships [4782]
Bert Saperstein Communication Scholarships [8758]
Bert Saperstein Communications Scholarship Fund **[8757]**
Saratoga County Bar Association **[8759]**
Saratoga County Bar Association Law Student Scholarships [8760]
Frank Sarli Memorial Scholarship [6899]
SARP Education Assistance Grants [8762]
SARP Professional Development Grants [8763]
Saskatchewan Association of Recreation Professionals **[8761]**
Saskatchewan Government Insurance Actuarial Science Scholarships [8769]
Saskatchewan Government Insurance Anniversary Scholarships [8770]
Saskatchewan Government Insurance (SGI) **[8764]**
Saskatchewan Government Insurance Corporate Scholarships [8771]
Saskatchewan Hockey Association **[8774]**
Saskatchewan Hockey Association Scholarships [8775]
Saskatchewan Pulse Growers (SPG) **[8776]**
Saskatchewan Pulse Growers Undergraduate Scholarships [8778]
Saskatchewan School Boards Association **[8780]**
Saskatchewan School Boards Association Education Scholarships [8781]
Saskatchewan School Boards Association Graduate Student Awards [8782]
Saskatchewan Trucking Association **[8783]**
Saskatchewan Trucking Association Scholarships [8784]
Roger C. Sathre Memorial Scholarship Fund [5045]
Malini E. Sathyadev Memorial Scholarships [8729]
Sho Sato Memorial Scholarships [5557]
Satter Human Rights Fellowships [4787]
François J. Saucier Prize in Applied Oceanography [2685]
Dave Sauer Memorial College Scholarships [150]
James A. Sauer Memorial Fellowships [662]
Curtis M. Saulsbury Scholarship Fund [3201]
Kevin Saunders Wheelchair Success Scholarships [3107]
Dr. William A. and Marceleine J. Sautter Hanover-Horton High School Youth of Promise Scholarships [5511]
Save Mart Legacy Scholarships [2458]
Savoy Foundation Postdoctoral and Clinical Research Scholarships [4123]
John A. Savoy Scholarship Fund [4059]
Meta M. Sawyer Bursary Fund [7645]
Bill Sawyer Memorial Scholarships [6052]
Herbert M. Saylor Memorial Scholarship [9341]
SBE/Ennes Youth Scholarships [9094]
S.C. Johnson, A Family Company Scholarships [3013]
SC and R Foundation Scholarships [9460]
Leslie and Mary Ella Scales Memorial Scholarships [3271]
Scandinavian Society of Cincinnati (SSOC) **[8785]**
SC&R Foundation Grant Program [9461]
SCBWI Student Illustrator Scholarship [9099]
SCBWI Student Writer Scholarship [9100]
SCBWI Work-in-Progress Awards [9101]
SCCLA Fellowships [9398]
SCCLA Scholarships [9399]
SCDAA Post-Doctoral Research Fellowships [8892]
Mary Turnbull Schacht Memorial Scholarships [8934]
David W. Schacht Native American Student Scholarships [2231]
Millicent M. Schaffner Endowed Memorial Scholarships [4542]
Schallek Awards [6397]
Schallek Fellowships [6398]
Schatz Energy Fellowships for Graduate Studies [5004]
Abe Schechter Graduate Scholarships [8400]
Schedulers and Dispatchers Monetary Scholarships [6837]
Leopold Schepp Foundation **[8787]**
Leopold Schepp Foundation Scholarships [8788]
Robert C. and Margaret A. Schikora Scholarships [9447]
Justin G. Schiller Fellowships [445]
Schlegel-UW RIA Scholarships [2555]
Arthur M. Schlesinger, Jr. Fellowships [5603]
Harold W. Schloss Memorial Scholarship Fund [2810]
Esther Schlundt Memorial Scholarships [5112]
Schmeelk Canada Foundation **[8789]**
Richard J. Schmeelk Fellowships [8790]
Henry L.P. Schmelzer College Transitions Scholarships [6213]
Julie Schmid Research Scholarship [2033]
CSF Charlotte R. Schmidlapp Scholarships [3014]
Schmidt Kramer Injury Lawyers **[8791]**
Ronald L. Schmied Scholarships [4686]

Bernadotte E. Schmitt Grants [856]
Schneider Electric Student Merit Awards [3841]
Prof. George Schneider, Jr. Manufacturing Technology Education Scholarships [9193]
Richard J. Schnell Memorial Scholarships [3300]
B.E. Schnurr Memorial Fund Research Grants [8130]
Stanley M. Schoenfeld Memorial Scholarship [7363]
Brown Schoenheit Memorial Scholarship [10070]
Lillian P. Schoephoerster Scholarships [8108]
Dale M. Schoettler Scholarships [8753]
Scholarship Award of the Bell Aliant Pioneer Volunteers [2690]
Scholarship Foundation of the Pacific **[8793]**
The Scholarship Foundation of St. Louis **[8795]**
The Scholarship Foundation of St. Louis Scholarships [8796]
Scholarship Foundation of Santa Barbara Art Scholarship Program [8798]
Scholarship Foundation of Santa Barbara **[8797]**
Scholarship Foundation of Santa Barbara General Undergraduate, Vocational and Graduate/Medical Scholarships and Loans Program [8799]
The Scholarship Foundation of Wakefield **[8801]**
The Scholarship Foundation of Wakefield Scholarships [8802]
Scholarship for Junior PHS Commissioned Officers [8115]
Scholarships for an Education Towards Law [3812]
Scholarships for a Higher Education in Law [2361]
Scholarships of the Morris Radio Club of New Jersey [1757]
Scholarships for the Next Generation of Scientists [2777]
Scholarships for Veterans with Post-Traumatic Stress Disorder [8624]
School Library Paraprofessional Scholarships - Southern Region [2474]
School Nutrition Association (SNA) **[8803]**
School Nutrition Association of Kansas (SNA-KS) **[8809]**
School Nutrition Association of Kansas Education Scholarship [8810]
Schoolsfirst Federal Credit Union Scholarships [8526]
Schrank Family Scholarships [10189]
Susan P. Schroeder Memorial Scholarships [6053]
Kurt H. and Donna M. Schuler Cash Grants [1254]
Tanna H. Schulich MBA Entrance Scholarships [10754]
Alice Southworth Schulman, Class of 1954, Simmons Scholarships for Unitarian Universalist Women [9838]
Richard E. Schultes Research Awards [9113]
David and Jinny Schultz Family Scholarship [4543]
Al Schuman/Ecolab Undergraduate Entrepreneurial Scholarships [7120]
James F. Schumar Scholarships [1039]
Jeptha Wade Schureman Scholarship Program [3333]
Schurgin Family Foundation Scholarships [5308]
Eveline Schuster Memorial Award/Scholarship [10071]
Galvanize the Future: Edgar K. Schutz Scholarships [838]
Karen Schuvie Scholarships [5663]
Nelson Schwab Jr. Scholarships [3015]
AIST William E. Schwabe Memorial Scholarships [2007]
Schwan's Food Service Scholarships [8806]
Marla Schwartz Education Grant [534]
Marla Schwartz Grants [535]
Stephen Schwartz Musical Theatre Scholarships [4988]
Abba P. Schwartz Research Fellowships [5604]
Judge Benjamin Schwartz Scholarships [3016]
Musia and Leon Schwartz Scholarships [5586]
Fritz Schwartz Serials Education Scholarships [7447]
Evalee C. Schwarz Charitable Trust for Education **[8811]**
Evalee C. Schwarz Educational Loans [8812]
David R. Schweisberg Memorial Scholarships [7779]
Science Foundation Arizona (SFAz) **[8813]**
Science Foundation Arizona Graduate Research Fellowships (GRF) [8814]
Science, Mathematics And Research for Transformation Scholarship for Service Program (SMART) [1305]
SCIRTS (Spinal Cord Injury Research on the Translational Spectrum) Pilot Research Grants [7257]
SCIRTS (Spinal Cord Injury Research on the Translational Spectrum) Postdoctoral Fellowships [7258]
SCIRTS (Spinal Cord Injury Research on the Translational Spectrum) Senior Research Grants [7259]
SCLEOA Scholarships [9361]
Scleroderma Foundation (SF) **[8815]**
Scleroderma Foundation Established Investigator Grants [8816]
Scleroderma Foundation New Investigator Grants [8817]
Scleroderma Research Foundation (SRF) **[8818]**
SCLMA Medical Student Scholarships [9401]
Scotiabank Medical Education Scholarships [7288]
Scotiabank Scholarships [2291]
Carl A. Scott Book Scholarships [3456]
IADR David B. Scott Fellowship [5254]
Scottish Rite Foundation of Colorado **[8820]**
Scouts Canada (SC) **[8822]**
Herbert Scoville Jr. Peace Fellowship **[8824]**
Herbert Scoville Jr. Peace Fellowships [8825]
Screen Actors Guild - American Federation of Television and Radio Artists (SAG-AFTRA) **[8826]**
A.J. and Lynda Hare Scribante Scholarship Fund [5762]
CSF E.W. Scripps Foundation Scholarship Fund [3017]
Bonnie Sorenson Scudder Scholarships [3301]
Seabee Memorial Scholarship Association Scholarships [9043]
Glenn T. Seaborg Congressional Science and Engineering Fellowships [1040]
Seaman Family Scholarships [3108]
Lewis L. Seaman Junior Enlisted Awards for Outstanding Operational Support [1541]
David and Sharon Seaver Family Scholarship Fund [4544]
SEE Education Foundation Scholarships [5418]
Seed Companies Scholarships [811]
Margery J. Seeger Scholarships [4620]
Aaron Seesan Memorial Scholarship Fund [9532]
Dr. Eugene M. Seidner Student Scholarship Program [35]
Seldovia Native Association Achievement Scholarships [8829]
Seldovia Native Association **[8828]**
Seldovia Native Association General Scholarships [8830]
D. Mitchell Self Memorial Scholarship [7549]
Walter and Rita Selvy Scholarship [3688]
SEMA Memorial Scholarships [9464]
Semiconductor Research Corporation (SRC) - Global Research Collaboration (GRC) **[8831]**
Semiconductor Research Corp. (SRC) - Nanoelectronics Research Initiative (NRI) **[8837]**
Senior Innovation Scholarships [8146]
SeniorAdvice **[8839]**
SeniorAdvice Caregiver Scholarships [8840]
SeniorAdvice Volunteer Scholarships [8841]
Sentinels of Freedom **[8842]**
Sentinels of Freedom Scholarships [8843]
William "Buddy" Sentner Scholarship Awards [566]
Senyk Memorial Scholarships [10801]
SEO Optimizers **[8844]**
SEO Optimizers Scholarships [8845]
Felix R. Sepulveda Memorial Scholarships - Northside Booster Club [8527]
Sequoyah Graduate Scholarships [1834]
Serbian Bar Association of America (SBAA) **[8846]**
Serbian Bar Association of America Scholarships [8847]
Charles W. Serby COPD Research Fellowships [1216]
Sertoma Communicative Disorders Scholarship [8849]
Sertoma Hard of Hearing and Deaf Scholarships [8850]
Sertoma Inc. **[8848]**
Service League Volunteer Scholarships [10447]
Servus Credit Union 4-H Scholarships [10]
Frank B. Sessa Scholarship [2241]
Roger Sessions Memorial Bogliasco Fellowships in Music [2331]
Seton Hall Law Merit Scholarships [8855]
Seton Hall University College of Arts and Sciences - Center for Public Service **[8851]**
Seton Hall University School of Law **[8854]**
Margaret B. Ševčenko Prize in Islamic Art and Culture [4909]
John R. Sevier Memorial Scholarship Award [9998]
Hubert K. and JoAnn Seymour Scholarships [7492]
SFP Junior Investigator's Career Development Awards [9119]
SFP Mid-Career/Mentor Awards for Family Planning [9120]
SFP Student Research Grants [9121]
SFP Undergraduate Scholarships [8794]
SGI Business Insurance Diploma Scholarships [8772]
SGI Research Grants [8773]
Al Shackleford and Dan Martin Professional Scholarships [2193]
Barbara A. Shacochis Scholarships [8003]
Albert R. and Alma Shadle Fellowships [1361]
Charles Shafae Scholarships [7799]
Elizabeth Shafer Memorial Scholarships [8362]
SHAFR Dissertation Completion Fellowships [9140]
Saleem Shah Early Career Award [1158]
Josephine Hooker Shain Scholarships [4372]
Shamberg Scholarships [10431]
Judge Terry Shamsie Scholarships [3109]
The Ivan Shandor Memorial Ukrainian American Bar Association Scholarships [10444]
Albert F. Shanker Scholarship [796]
John M. and Mary A. Shanley Memorial Scholarships [9448]
William H. Shannon Fellowships [5445]
Law Office of David P. Shapiro Annual Leukemia Scholarships [5949]
Ken and Sandy Sharkey Family Scholarship Fund [4545]
Shastri L'Institut Indo-Canadien **[8856]**
Shastri Scholar Travel Subsidy Grants (SSTSG) [8857]
W.L. Shattuck Scholarships [5046]
Benjamin G. Shatz Scholarships [8004]
Luci Shaw Fellowship [5081]
Anne Shaw Fellowships [9727]
Josephine Kerbey Shaw Memorial Undergraduate Scholarship [5763]
Donna Gail Shaw Scholarship for Chapter Service [5684]
Dr. Robert and Anna Shaw Scholarships [291]
Dr. Robert Norman Shaw Scholarships [292]
Shaw-Worth Memorial Scholarship [5002]
Shear-Miles Agricultural Fellowship [10205]
Shear-Miles Agricultural Scholarship [10206]
Regina B. Shearn Scholarships [357]
Jim Sheerin Scholarships [6362]
Sheet Metal and Air Conditioning Contractors' National Association (SMACNA) **[8858]**
Sheet Metal And Air Conditioning Contractors' National Association College of Fellows Scholarships [8859]
Nettie and Edward Shelah Scholarships [9576]
Shell Incentive Scholarship Fund [8861]
Shell Oil Co. **[8860]**
Shell Oil Company Technical Scholarships [8862]
Shell Process Technology Scholarships [8863]
Susan Goldsmith Shelley Scholarship [5764]
Bruce Shelton Scholarships [10598]
Bill and Ann Sheperd Legal Scholarship Fund [3923]
Joseph Henry Shepherd Scholarship [10173]
Robert P. Sheppard Leadership Awards [7162]
David S. Sheridan Canadian Research Awards [2542]
Sheriff's Law Enforcement Association of McLennan County (SLEAMC) **[8864]**
Marion A. and Ruth Sherwood Family Fund Education Scholarships [4546]
Marion A. and Ruth K. Sherwood Family Fund Engineering Scholarships [4547]
Miller G. Sherwood Family Scholarship Fund [4548]
Morgan and Jeanie Sherwood Travel Grants [1317]
Shields-Gillespie Scholarships [1056]

Jacqueline Shields Memorial Scholarships [142]
Milton L. Shifman Endowed Scholarships [6261]
Chiyoko and Thomas Shimazaki Scholarships [5558]
Everett Oscar Shimp Memorial Scholarships [7862]
Pat Shimp Memorial Scholarships [7863]
The Shincho Graduate Fellowships for Study in Japan [5802]
Shinn Family Scholarships [6054]
Joseph Shinoda Memorial Scholarship Foundation, Inc. **[8866]**
Joseph Shinoda Memorial Scholarships [8867]
Jason Shipley Memorial Scholarships [7041]
Clair Shirey Scholarships [10037]
Shohet Scholars Program [5290]
Lynn Brower Shonk Memorial Scholarship [5765]
S. David Shor Scholarships [3018]
Shoreline Community College Foundation **[8868]**
Shoreline Community College Full-Time Continuing Students Scholarships [8881]
Shoreline Community College Part-Time Students Scholarships [8882]
Shoreline - Lake Forest Park High School Scholarship [8883]
Justice Janie L. Shores Scholarships [207]
Short-term Senior Fellowships in Iranian Studies [914]
SHOT-NASA Fellowships [9144]
Thomas E. Shown, M.D. Memorial Scholarships [10599]
SHPE Dissertation Scholarship [9130]
SHPE Foundation **[8886]**
SHPE Professional Scholarship [9131]
Ralph W. Shrader Diversity Scholarship [91]
SHRM Certification Scholarships - Individual [9147]
SHRM Foundation Academic Scholarships [9148]
Law Office of Matthew Shrum Annual Scholarships for Single Mothers [5953]
Clifford G. Shull Fellowships [9909]
Phil Shykes Memorial Scholarships [3723]
Mary Isabel Sibley Fellowships [8053]
SICB Fellowships of Graduate Student Travel (FGST) [9157]
SICB Grants-in-Aid of Research Program (GIAR) [9158]
Don and Madalyn Sickafoose Educational Trust [9533]
Sickle Cell Disease Association of America (SCDAA) **[8890]**
Sidley Austin LLP - North America **[8893]**
Sidley Diversity and Inclusion Scholarships [8894]
Sidley Prelaw Scholars Initiative [8895]
Norman Siegel Research Scholar Grants [1382]
Jeff Siegel Scholarships [7359]
Myrtle Siegfried, MD and Michael Vigilante, MD Scholarships [4279]
Siemens-ASCP Scholarship [1263]
Siemens Canada Academic Awards [3842]
Siemens Clinical Advancement Scholarship [1400]
E.J. Sierleja Memorial Fellowships [5194]
The Sigma Chi Foundation **[8896]**
Sigma Delta Chi Foundation (SDX) **[8901]**
Sigma Delta Epsilon Fellowships [8907]
Sigma Delta Epsilon, Graduate Women in Science (SDE/GWIS) **[8903]**
Sigma Diagnostics Student Scholarships [7171]
Sigma Kappa Foundation Alumnae Continuing Education Scholarships [8935]
Sigma Kappa Foundation Alzheimer's/Gerontology Scholarships [8936]
Sigma Kappa Foundation **[8908]**
Sigma Kappa Foundation Founders' Scholarships [8937]
Sigma Kappa Foundation Gerontology Scholarships [8938]
Sigma Kappa Foundation Michigan Scholarships [8939]
Sigma Theta Tau International Scholarships [2713]
Silicon Valley Community Foundation **[8946]**
APSAIL's Ralph Silverman Memorial Scholarships [2126]
Meyer D. and Dorothy C. Silverman Scholarship [3251]
Stuart Silverman Scholarships [8005]
Harvey L. Simmons Memorial Scholarships [8730]
Linda Simmons Memorial Scholarships [219]

Willard B. Simmons Sr. Memorial Scholarships [6871]
Hazel Simms Nursing Scholarships [5933]
Julian Simon Fellowships [8300]
Simon Youth Foundation (SYF) **[8958]**
Simon Youth Foundation Community Scholarships [8959]
The Simons Foundation **[8960]**
Simonton Windows Scholarships [7864]
DW Simpson Actuarial Science Scholarship Program [8963]
DW Simpson Global Actuarial Recruitment **[8962]**
Carole Simpson Scholarships [8412]
Lowe Simpson Scholarships [3019]
Ward Sims Memorial Scholarships [10038]
Sindhi Association of North America (SANA) **[8964]**
SINFONIA Educational Foundation (SEF) **[8966]**
Aaron B. Singleton Memorial Scholarship [7550]
Sino-American Pharmaceutical Professionals Association (SAPA) **[8970]**
Sino-American Pharmaceutical Professionals Association Scholarships [8971]
Helen J. Sioussat/Fay Wells Scholarships [2371]
Gadde Sitaramamma and Tirupataiah Scholarships [9670]
Bill Six Memorial Scholarship Fund [7865]
Six Meter Club of Chicago Scholarships [1758]
Sixt Rent a car **[8972]**
Sixt Rent a Car Scholarships [8973]
Leif and Inger Sjöberg Awards [1235]
Sjogren's Syndrome Foundation (SSF) **[8974]**
Skadden Fellowship Foundation **[8977]**
Skadden Fellowships [8978]
Ruth Skeeles Memorial Scholarship Fund [9534]
Skidmore, Owings and Merrill Foundation **[8979]**
Frank Foster Skillman Scholarships [3020]
Francelene Skinner Memorial Scholarships [6067]
Rand Skolnick Point Scholarship [8191]
Skooblie **[8983]**
Skooblie Scholarships [8984]
Allogan Slagle Memorial Scholarships [1835]
Lillian and Murray Slatkin Fellowships [7743]
SLEAMC Scholarships [8865]
Robert W. Sledge Fellowships [344]
Sleeping Angels Co. **[8985]**
Sleeping Angels Co. Scholarships [8986]
J. Ward Sleichter and Frances F. Sleichter Memorial Scholarship Fund [4254]
Slifka Foundation Interdisciplinary Fellowships [6437]
Dr. Alfred E. Slinkard Scholarships [8779]
Alfred P. Sloan Foundation **[8987]**
Alfred P. Sloan Foundation Graduate Scholarships - Sloan Indigenous Graduate Partnership [6683]
Alfred P. Sloan Foundation Graduate Scholarships - Sloan Minority Ph.D. Program [6684]
Sloan Northwood University Heavy-Duty Scholarships [2127]
Sloan Research Fellowships [8988]
Thomas J. Slocum Memorial Scholarships to Redstone College [171]
The Aaron and Rita Slom Scholarships [9762]
Ann Kelsay Small Scholarship [5766]
SME Coal and Energy Division Scholarships [9212]
SME Directors Scholarships [9194]
SME Education Foundation Family Scholarships [9195]
SME Environmental Division Scholarships [9213]
Dr. George M. Smerk Scholarships [1169]
SMFM/AAOGF Scholarship Awards [9206]
SmileMarketing **[8989]**
SmileMarketing Dental Scholarships [8990]
Donald Smiley Prize [1908]
James I. Smith, III Notre Dame Law School Scholarship Fund [329]
Eva Smith Bursary [5528]
The Smith Companies **[8991]**
David H. Smith Conservation Research Fellowships [9109]
Hy Smith Endowment Fund [4704]
Ryan and Jamie Smith Essay Contest [8992]
Smith Family Awards Program for Excellence in Biomedical Research [4823]
Ronald T. Smith Family Scholarships [4621]
Michael Smith Foundation for Health Research **[8993]**

Henry DeWitt Smith Graduate Scholarships [9214]
Gladys Ann Smith Greater Los Angeles Women's Council Scholarships [7230]
Stanley Smith Horticultural Fellowships [7744]
Robert H. Smith International Center for Jefferson Studies (ICJS) **[8996]**
Florence L. Smith Medical Scholarships [4705]
Brian and Cathy Smith Memorial Fund [1016]
Brian Smith Memorial Scholarships [2348]
Colonel Nate Smith Memorial Scholarships [6374]
Drew Smith Memorial Scholarships [3187]
Tacy Anna Smith Memorial Scholarships [4213]
Mary K. Smith Rector Scholarships [7866]
The Eileen J. Smith, R.N. Memorial Scholarships [5512]
Smith Scholarship Foundation **[8998]**
Ralph and Josephine Smith Scholarship Fund [4060]
Lillian Smith Scholarship for Teaching Students [10072]
A.O. Smith Scholarships [8164]
C. Bainbridge Smith Scholarships [7344]
Chapter 63 - Portland Uncle Bud Smith Scholarships [9196]
Esther M. Smith Scholarships [3188]
Helen J. and Harold Gilman Smith Scholarships [2232]
Herman J. Smith Scholarships [7004]
Joseph Sumner Smith Scholarships [9839]
Marian A. Smith Scholarships [9390]
Richard S. Smith Scholarships [9858]
William E. Smith Scholarships [199]
Drue Smith/Society of Professional Journalists Scholarships [3252]
Nadine Barrie Smith Student Awards [5433]
Smith's Personal Best Scholarships [8363]
Smithsonian American Art Museum **[9000]**
Smithsonian Institution - Archives of American Art **[9010]**
Smithsonian Institution Graduate Student Fellowships [9015]
Smithsonian Institution - National Air and Space Museum **[9020]**
Smithsonian Institution - National Museum of American History **[9024]**
Smithsonian Institution - National Museum of the American Indian **[9027]**
Smithsonian Institution - National Museum of Natural History **[9029]**
Smithsonian Institution Postdoctoral Fellowships [9016]
Smithsonian Institution Predoctoral Fellowships [9017]
Smithsonian Institution Senior Fellowships [9018]
Smithsonian Postgraduate Fellowships in Conservation of Museum Collection Program [9019]
Smithsonian Tropical Research Institute **[9035]**
Smithsonian Tropical Research Institute (STRI) - Center for Tropical Forest Science - ForestGEO (CTFS-ForestGEO) **[9040]**
Eric E. Smoker Memorial Scholarships [7521]
SMSA Scholarship **[9042]**
Virginia M. Smyth Scholarships [4382]
Gladys Snauble Scholarships [4622]
SNF Professional Growth Scholarships [8807]
SNMMI-TS Advanced Practitioner Program Scholarship [9224]
SNMMI-TS Bachelor's Degree Completion Scholarships [9225]
SNNMI Predoctoral Molecular Imaging Scholar Program [9226]
Snodgrass Scholarships [10039]
William Brewster Snow Award [1954]
A.C. Snow and Katherine Snow Smith Scholarship [10251]
Helen D. Snow Memorial Scholarships [8056]
Snowmobile Association of Massachusetts (SAM) **[9044]**
Snowmobile Association of Massachusetts Scholarships [9045]
SNRS Dissertation Research Grants [9406]
SNRS Research Grants [9407]
SNRS/STTI Research Grants [9408]
SOAP/Kybele International Outreach Grant [9231]
Boleslaw & Irena Sobczak Scholarships [8591]
Arnold Sobel Scholarships [3081]

Frank H. Sobey Awards for Excellence in Business Studies [9048]
Sobeys & Empire Work Experience & Scholarship Program - Future Leaders Awards [9049]
Sobeys Inc. **[9046]**
SOBP Travel Fellowship Award-Early Career Investigator(International) [9090]
Social Science Research Council (SSRC) **[9050]**
Sociedad Interamericana de Prensa (SIP) **[9060]**
Societe des designers graphiques du Canada **[9062]**
Société Canadienne pour l'Étude de l'Éducation **[9066]**
Société canadienne des études classiques **[9070]**
Société canadienne de recherches cliniques (SCRC) **[9072]**
Society of Allied Weight Engineers (SAWE) **[9075]**
Society of Allied Weight Engineers Scholarships **[9077]**
Society for American Archaeology (SAA) **[9078]**
Society for Applied Anthropology (SfAA) **[9080]**
Society of Architectural Historians (SAH) **[9082]**
Society for the Arts in Healthcare (SAH) **[9087]**
Society for the Arts in Healthcare Student Scholarships [9088]
Society of Biological Psychiatry (SOBP) **[9089]**
Society of Broadcast Engineers (SBE) **[9091]**
Society of Children's Book Writers and Illustrators (SCBWI) **[9095]**
Society for Cinema and Media Studies (SCMS) **[9103]**
Society for Classical Studies (SCS) **[9105]**
Society for Conservation Biology (SCB) **[9108]**
Society of Dance History Scholars (SDHS) **[9110]**
Society for Economic Botany [9112]
Society of Emergency Medicine Physician Assistants (SEMPA) **[9114]**
Society of Exploration Geophysicists (SEG) **[9116]**
Society of Exploration Geophysicists Foundation Scholarships [9117]
Society of Family Planning (SFP) **[9118]**
Society of Georgia Archivists (SGA) **[9122]**
Society of Graphic Designers of Canada Adobe Scholarships [9063]
Society of Graphic Designers of Canada Applied Arts Scholarships [9064]
Society of Graphic Designers of Canada Veer Scholarships [9065]
Society of Health and Physical Educators (SHAPE) **[9127]**
Society of Hispanic Professional Engineers (SHPE) **[9129]**
Society for Historians of American Foreign Relations (SHAFR) **[9132]**
Society for the History of Technology (SHOT) **[9141]**
Society for Human Resource Management (SHRM) **[9145]**
Society for Imaging Science and Technology **[9149]**
Society for Industrial and Organizational Psychology (SIOP) **[9151]**
Society for Integrative and Comparative Biology (SICB) **[9155]**
Society for Judgment and Decision Making (SJDM) **[9159]**
Society for Linguistic Anthropology (SLA) **[9162]**
Society for Linguistic Anthropology Student Essay Prize [9163]
Society of Louisiana Certified Public Accountants (LCPA) **[9164]**
Society of Louisiana Certified Public Accountants Scholarships [9165]
Society of Manufacturing Engineers Education Foundation (SME) **[9166]**
Society of Manufacturing Engineers Ford PAS Scholarships (SME) [9197]
The Society of Marine Port Engineers of New York (SMPE) **[9203]**
Society of Marine Port Engineers Scholarship Loans [9204]
Society for Maternal-Fetal Medicine (SMFM) **[9205]**
Society for Military History (SMH) **[9207]**
Society for Mining, Metallurgy, and Exploration (SME) **[9209]**
Society of Naval Architects and Marine Engineers (SNAME) **[9215]**

Society of Nuclear Medicine and Molecular Imaging (SNMMI) **[9219]**
Society for Obstetric Anesthesia and Perinatology (SOAP) **[9230]**
Society of Otorhinolaryngology and Head-Neck Nurses (SOHN) **[9232]**
Society of Outdoor Recreation Professionals (SORP) **[9236]**
Society for Pediatric Dermatology (SPD) **[9238]**
Society of Pediatric Nurses (SPN) **[9240]**
Society of Pediatric Nurses Educational Scholarships [9241]
The Society for Pediatric Radiology (SPR) **[9242]**
Society for Pediatric Radiology Research Fellows [9243]
Society for Pediatric Radiology Seed Grants [9244]
The Society for Pediatric Urology (SPU) **[9245]**
Society for Pediatric Urology Research Grant Program [9247]
Society of Petroleum Engineers - Evangeline Section (SPE) **[9248]**
Society for Photographic Education (SPE) **[9251]**
Society of Physics Students **[9253]**
Society of Plastics Engineers (SPE) **[9258]**
Society for the Preservation of Old Mills (SPOOM) **[9276]**
Society of Professional Journalists (SPJ) **[9278]**
Society for Psychological Anthropology (SPA) **[9280]**
Society for the Psychological Study of Lesbian, Gay, Bisexual and Transgender Issues (SPSLGBTI) **[9283]**
Society for the Psychological Study for Social Issues (SPSSE) **[9286]**
Society for the Psychological Study of Social Issues (SPSSI) **[9288]**
Society for Public Health Education (SOPHE) **[9291]**
Society of Punjabi Engineers and Technologists of British Columbia (SPEATBC) **[9295]**
Society for Range Management (SRM) **[9297]**
Society of Satellite Professionals International (SSPI) **[9299]**
Society for the Scientific Study of Sexuality (SSSS) **[9301]**
Society for the Scientific Study of Sexuality Student Research Grants [9302]
Society for the Study of Reproduction (SSR) **[9303]**
Society for Technical Communication (STC) **[9309]**
Society for Technical Communication Lone Star Community (STC LSC) **[9312]**
Society for Technical Communication Puget Sound Chapter (STC-PSC) **[9314]**
Society for Underwater Technology Houston **[9316]**
Society of University Surgeons (SUS) **[9319]**
Society of Vacuum Coaters Foundation **[9322]**
Society of Vacuum Coaters Foundation Scholarships [9323]
Society for Vascular Surgery (SVS) **[9324]**
Society of Women Engineers (SWE) **[9328]**
Sociologists for Women in Society (SWS) **[9330]**
Dr. Paul and Gayle Sohi Medical Education Scholarships [7289]
SOHN Allied Health to BSN Degree Scholarship [9233]
Louis B. Sohn Fellowships in Human Rights and Environment [2849]
SOHN Graduate Degree Scholarship [9234]
SOHN RN to BSN Degree Scholarship [9235]
SOKOL U.S.A. **[9334]**
Dale and Betty George Sola Scholarships [3724]
The Thomas Soldan Healthy Communities Scholarships [8237]
Solid Waste Association of North America (SWANA) **[9336]**
Carrie Fox Solin Blow Molding Division Memorial Scholarships [9268]
SOM Foundation Architecture, Design and Urban Design Prize [8980]
SOM Foundation Structural Engineering Travel Fellowships [8981]
SOM Foundation Travel Fellowships in Architecture, Design and Urban Design [8982]
SOMA Student Research Fellowships [9601]
Carin Alma E. Somers Scholarship Trust [2118]
Sonepar Canada Scholarship Awards [3843]

Dr. Kiyoshi Sonoda Memorial Scholarships [5559]
Sonoma County Mycological Association (SOMA) **[9340]**
Sons of Confederate Veterans (SCV) **[9342]**
Sons of Norway Foundation (SOFN) **[9344]**
Sons of Norway Foundation Scholarships to Oslo International Summer School [9346]
Sons of Union Veterans of the Civil War (SUVCW) **[9347]**
Sons of Union Veterans of the Civil War Scholarships [9348]
Sony Pictures Scholarships [2027]
Christine Soper Scholarships [4623]
SOPHE/ATSDR Student Fellowships in Environmental Health or Emergency Preparedness [9292]
SOPHE/CDC Student Fellowships in Child, Adolescent and School Health [9293]
SOPHE/CDC Student Fellowships in Injury Prevention [9294]
Theodore C. Sorensen Research Fellowships [5605]
Soroptimist International of Chambersburg Scholarship Fund [4255]
Soroptimist International of Redlands Scholarships [8528]
Paul and Daisy Soros Fellowships for New Americans **[9349]**
Paul & Daisy Soros Fellowships [9350]
Soros Justice Advocacy Fellowships - Track I [7664]
Soros Justice Advocacy Fellowships - Track II [7665]
Soros Justice Media Fellowships - Track I [7666]
Soros Justice Media Fellowships - Track II [7667]
SORP Student Conference Scholarship [9237]
Eastman Kodak Dr. Theophilus Sorrell Fellowships [7090]
Lily and Catello Sorrentino Memorial Scholarships [8609]
John Soto Scholarships [3362]
Sourdough Reunion Memorial Endowment Scholarships [10040]
South Asian Bar Association of Northern California (SABA-NC) **[9351]**
South Asian Journalists Association (SAJA) **[9355]**
South Carolina Association for Financial Professionals (SCAFP) **[9357]**
South Carolina Association for Financial Professionals Certified Treasury Professional Scholarships [9358]
South Carolina Association for Financial Professionals College Education Scholarships [9359]
South Carolina Law Enforcement Officers Association (SCLEOA) **[9360]**
South Carolina Public Health Association (SCPHA) **[9362]**
South Carolina Public Health Association Scholarships [9364]
South Carolina Restaurant and Lodging Association (SCRLA) **[9365]**
South Carolina Scholastic Press Association (SCSPA) **[9368]**
South Carolina Scholastic Press Association Scholarships [9370]
South Carolina Scholastic Press Association Yearbook Scholarships [9371]
South Carolina Tourism and Hospitality Educational Foundation Scholarships [9366]
South Carolina Undergraduate Scholarships [9367]
South Central Modern Language Association Fellowships [7424]
South Central Power Co. **[9372]**
South Central Power Scholarships [9373]
South Coast Area High School Senior Honors Scholarship Program [8800]
South Dakota Division Scholarships [6525]
South Dakota Nurses Association (SDNA) **[9374]**
South Dakota Retailers Association (SDRA) **[9376]**
South Jersey Golf Association (SJGA) **[9378]**
South Jersey Golf Association Scholarships [9379]
South Kentucky RECC High School Senior Scholarships [9382]
South Kentucky Rural Electric Cooperative Corporation (SKRECC) **[9380]**
South Texas Unit Scholarships [4865]
Southeast Alabama Dietetic Association Scholarships [200]
Southeast Asian Ministers of Education

Organization-Vietnam Scholarship Program [3763]
Southeastern Library Association (SELA) **[9384]**
Southeastern Theatre Conference **[9386]**
Southeastern Theatre Conference Secondary School Scholarships [9391]
Southern Alberta Curling Association (SACA) **[9393]**
Southern Arizona Environmental Management Society (SAEMS) **[9395]**
Southern California Chinese Lawyers Association (SCCLA) **[9397]**
Southern California Lambda Medical Association (SCLMA) **[9400]**
Southern Maine Women's Golf Association (SMWGA) **[9402]**
Southern Maine Women's Golf Association Scholarships [9403]
Southern Nevada Sports Hall of Fame Scholarships [8364]
Southern Nursing Research Society **[9404]**
Southern Regional Education Board (SREB) **[9409]**
Southern Scholarship Foundation (SSF) **[9412]**
Southern Scholarship Foundation Scholarships [9413]
Southern Section Air and Waste Management Association (SSAWMA) **[9414]**
Southwest Florida Community Foundation **[9416]**
Southwest Florida Community Foundation College Assistance Scholarships [9449]
Southwest Florida Deputy Sheriffs Association Fund Scholarships [9450]
Southwest Movers Association (SMA) **[9453]**
Southwest Movers Association Scholarships [9454]
Sovereign Nations Scholarships [872]
Iwalani Carpenter Sowa Scholarships [7919]
Master Sergeant William Sowers Memorial Scholarships [133]
Michael P. Spadafora Medical Toxicology Travel Awards [690]
Kathy Spadoni Memorial Scholarships [8264]
Amy E. Spain Memorial Scholarships [10174]
Spangenberg Shibley & Liber LLP **[9455]**
Spangenberg Shibley & Liber Video PSA Scholarship Awards [9456]
SpanishDict **[9457]**
Nathan Sparks Memorial Scholarships [3272]
Spartan Staff Scholarships [8365]
SPE Foundation General Scholarships [9269]
SPE Gulf Coast Hurricane Scholarships [9270]
SPE Injection Molding Division Scholarships [9271]
SPE Student Awards for Innovations in Imaging [9252]
SPE Thermoforming Division Memorial Scholarships [9272]
SPE Thermoplastic Elastomers Special Interest Group Scholarship [9273]
SPE Thermoplastic Materials and Foams Division Scholarships [9274]
SPE Vinyl Plastics Division Educational Grants [9275]
SPEATBC Scholarships [9296]
Special Events Internships - Los Angeles [4438]
Special Events Internships - New York [4439]
Special Fund for the Study of Women and Politics [1123]
Specialized Carriers and Rigging Association (SC&RA) **[9459]**
Specialty Equipment Market Association (SEMA) **[9462]**
Specialty Equipment Market Association Scholarships [9465]
Specialty Nursing Scholarships [4270]
Faith Speckhard Scholarships [5513]
Beatrice Drinnan Spence Scholarships [3766]
Spice Box Grants [764]
SPIE **[9466]**
SPIE Student Author Travel Grants [9472]
Phillip A. Spiegel IASP Congress Trainee Scholarship [5276]
Lawrence Alan Spiegel Remembrance Scholarships [4920]
Charles and Carol Spielberger Scholarships [1153]
Enid W. and Bernard B. Spigel Architectural Scholarships [4706]
Spina Bifida and Hydrocephalus Association of Ontario (SB&H) **[9473]**

Spinal Cord Injury BC **[9475]**
Jean and Manny Spinner Scholarships [5587]
Spirit of Anne Frank Outstanding Scholarship Award [1563]
The Spirit Square Center for Arts and Education Scholarship Fund [4214]
Spokeo **[9477]**
Spokeo Connections Scholarships [9478]
SPOOM Research Grants [9277]
Sports Internships - Los Angeles [4440]
Sports Turf Managers Association (STMA) **[9479]**
Sporty's/Cincinnati Avionics Scholarships [172]
Spotlight on Nursing **[9483]**
Spotlight on Nursing Graduate Nursing Student Scholarships [9484]
Spouse Tuition Aid Loan Program (STAP) [7236]
Dr. William E. and Norma Sprague Scholarships [4624]
Jim Springer Memorial Scholarships [3110]
The Springfield Family Scholarships [10175]
SPS Future Teacher Scholarships [9256]
SPS Leadership Scholarships [9257]
SPSmedical CS Scholarships [5264]
SPSSI Grants-In-Aid Program [9287]
SRC Master's Scholarships Program (MSP) [8835]
SREB-State Doctoral Scholars Program - Dissertation Awards [9410]
SREB-State Doctoral Scholars Program - Doctoral Awards [9411]
SRF Post-doctoral Fellowships [8819]
SSAWMA Scholarships [9415]
SSF Research Grants [8975]
SSF Student Fellowships [8976]
SSHRC Doctoral Fellowship Program [3396]
SSOC Scholarships [8786]
The SSPI Mid-Atlantic Chapter Scholarships [9300]
John F. and Anna Lee Stacey Scholarships [6901]
Ernest and Charlene Stachowiak Memorial Scholarships [3302]
Stafford Loan for Graduate Students - Unsubsidized Stafford Loans [9486]
StaffordLoan.com **[9485]**
Matt Stager Memorial Scholarship Fund [10482]
Steven A. Stahl Research Grants [5358]
Stained Glass Association of America (SGAA) **[9487]**
Standard and Poor's Award for Economic and Business Reporting - S&P Scholarships [7780]
Standard Recognition of Excellence Awards [3844]
Marion Barr Stanfield Art Scholarships [9840]
Otto M. Stanfield Law Scholarships [9841]
Lasek Stanisław and Aniela Scholarship [8592]
A.R.O.Y. Stanitz Scholarships [1228]
J. Newell Stannard Fellowships [4812]
Thomas J. Stanton, Jr. Scholarships [8853]
Star-Ledger Scholarships for the Performing Arts [7324]
Stark Community Foundation **[9490]**
Stark County Bar Association Fund [9535]
Stark County Dairy Promoters Scholarships [9536]
Kenneth and Barbara Starks Plant Resistance to Insects Graduate Student Research Awards [3884]
Peggy P. Starks Scholarship [9702]
State of Idaho Board of Education **[9546]**
State of New Jersey Department of Health - New Jersey Commission on Brain Injury Research (NJCBIR) **[9548]**
State of Wisconsin Higher Educational Aids Board (HEAB) **[9553]**
Robert W. and Bernice Ingalls Staton Scholarships [10259]
Taylor Statten Memorial Fellowships [10295]
Minnie Patton Stayman Scholarships [7948]
STC-Lone Star Chapter Traditional Education Scholarships [9313]
STC-PSC Scholarships [9315]
STC Scholarships [9311]
The Stanley H. Stearman Awards [7135]
Robert P. Stearns/SCS Engineers Scholarships [9339]
Sheri Stears Education Scholarship [10073]
Tom Steel Post-Graduate Fellowships [8274]
Harry Steele Entrance Awards [10755]
Evelyn Steele Memorial Scholarships [10802]

Joseph L. and Vivian E. Steele Music Scholarship Fund [4256]
Joseph S. Steinberg Emerging Jewish Filmmaker Fellowships [2856]
Cecilia Steinfeldt Fellowships for Research in the Arts and Material Culture [9717]
Peter T. Steinwedell Scholarships [4772]
Stelpro Scholarships 360: Energizing Potential [3845]
Elin J. Stene/Xi Scholarships [8940]
Marianne M. Stenvig Scholarships [9375]
Step Up Scholarships [8731]
Gabe Stepetin Business Scholarship Awards [312]
Stephens Anderson & Cummings **[9557]**
Mike Stephenson Legal Scholarships [6370]
Elizabeth Coulter Stephenson Scholarships [3595]
H.H. Stern Grant Awards [1898]
Joseph S. Stern, Jr. Scholarships [3021]
Charles Sternberg Scholarship [1844]
Richard Stessel Memorial Scholarships [143]
AGWT Thomas M. Stetson Scholarships [841]
Raymond H. Stetson Scholarships in Phonetics and Speech Science [54]
Steuben County Community Foundation **[9560]**
Christine K. Stevens Development Scholarships [1017]
Stevens Doctoral Awards [5312]
Benjamin F. Stevens Fellowships [6337]
Zachary Taylor Stevens Memorial Scholarships [1759]
H.L. Stevenson Scholarships [7781]
Richie Stevenson Scholarships [3253]
Allegheny Branch of Mid-America Chapter - Nancy Stewart Professional Development Scholarships [1443]
Dan Stewart Scholarships [7462]
Mary Stewart and William T. Covington, Jr. Scholarship Fund [4215]
Stickler Involved People (SIP) **[9577]**
Dr. Gunnar B. Stickler Scholarships [9578]
Dell Chenoweth Stifel Scholarship [5767]
The Richard Stockton College of New Jersey Foundation Alumni Association Graduate Awards [9587]
The Richard Stockton College of New Jersey Foundation, Inc. **[9579]**
David Stockwood Memorial Prize [81]
Louis Stokes Health Scholars Program [3349]
Louis Stokes Urban Health Policy Fellows Program [3350]
Ralph W. Stone Graduate Fellowships [7184]
Charles H. Stone Scholarships [2081]
Stonewall Community Foundation **[9588]**
Stop Hunger Scholarships [573]
Stop-Painting.com Scholarships [5147]
Martin L. Stout Scholarships [1949]
StraightForward Media **[9592]**
George A. Strait Minority Scholarship [536]
Bonnie Strangio Education Scholarships [2343]
Jay A. Strassberg Memorial Scholarships [2517]
Carole J. Streeter, KB9JBR Scholarships [1760]
John Streiff Memorial Scholarships [6055]
Marlene Streit Golf Scholarships [4481]
Stanley W. Strew Educational Fund Scholarships [2438]
STRI Short-Term Fellowships [9038]
George and Pearl Strickland Scholarships [3195]
Norman E. Strohmeier, W2VRS Memorial Scholarships [1761]
Robby Strong Cancer Survivor Scholarships [6596]
Mark and Karla Stuart Family Scholarship [8732]
Student Investigator Research Grant - General Audiology/Hearing Science [394]
Student Investigator Research Grant - Hearing Aids, Clinical Protocols and Patient Outcomes [395]
Student Investigator Research Grant - Vestibular [396]
Student Osteopathic Medical Association (SOMA) **[9599]**
Student Research Awards from the Behavioral Gerontology SIG [1861]
Student Summer Research Fellowship [397]
Student Training and Research in Tumor Immunology Grants [2775]
Students of Georgetown Inc. **[9603]**
Study Scholarships for Artists or Musicians [3610]

Stultz Scholarships [10600]
Horace W. Stunkard Scholarships [6262]
Sturgulewski Family Scholarship [10074]
Anne Sturrock Nursing Scholarships [9451]
AIST Southeast Member Chapter Gene Suave Scholarships [2008]
Subic Bay-Cubi Point Scholarships [7231]
Edward P. Suchecki Family Scholarship Fund [4549]
Caroline tum Suden/Frances Hellebrandt Professional Opportunity Awards [1101]
Suffolk Public Interest Law Group Summer Fellowships (SPILG) [8438]
Vallabhaneni Sukundamma and Lakshmaiah Scholarships [9671]
Jerome M. Sullivan Research Funds [1217]
John A. and Jean Quinn Sullivan Scholarship Funds [3725]
Phil Sullivan Scholarships [8265]
VPPPA William Sullivan Scholarships [10418]
William A. Sullivan Scholarships [7232]
Lee Summer Student Fellowship [8553]
Summerside-Natick International Friendship Hockey Scholarships [3314]
Roger K. Summit Scholarships for North America [8302]
Hatton W. Sumners Endowed Law Schools Scholarships [9608]
Hatton W. Sumners Endowed Undergraduate School Scholarships [9609]
Hatton W. Sumners Foundation, Inc. **[9607]**
Hatton W. Sumners Non-Endowed Undergraduate and Graduate Scholarships [9610]
Hatton W. Sumners Scholarships [7602]
Sun Country Amateur Golf Association (SCAGA) **[9611]**
Bruce and Marjorie Sundlun Scholarships [8610]
Superior District Legislative Mentoring Student Grants [2483]
Superior District Legislative Mentoring Student Grants RT to DC [2484]
SuperKutz Scholarships [5892]
Surety & Fidelity Association of America (SFAA) **[9613]**
Surety and Fidelity Industry Intern and Scholarship Program for Minority Students [9614]
Surface Officers' Spouses of Norfolk **[9615]**
SUS Foundation Junior Faculty Grants [9320]
Sussman-Miller Educational Assistance Award Program [305]
SUT Houston Graduate Scholarships [9317]
SUT Houston Undergraduate Scholarships [9318]
Sutherland/Purdy Scholarships [8109]
Kirk Sutlive Scholarships [4390]
Margaret Svec Scholarships [8884]
Lorraine E. Swain Scholarships [8941]
Swede Swanson Memorial Scholarships [7243]
Daniel Swarovski and Company Scholarships [4345]
Henry D. and Ruth G. Swartz Family Scholarship Fund [4550]
Hanns Swarzenski and Brigitte Horney Swarzenski Fellowship [6438]
SWE Scholarships [9329]
Jeffrey Tyler Sweitzer Wrestling Memorial Scholarship Fund [9537]
Swensrud Teacher Fellowships at MHS (Massachusetts Historical Society) [6338]
Timothy S. Sweterlitsch Memorial Scholarship Fund [9538]
Stan Swinton Scholarships [7782]
Swiss Benevolent Society of New York (SBS) **[9617]**
Switzer Environmental Fellowships [9623]
Robert and Patricia Switzer Foundation **[9622]**
Mary Switzer Research Fellowships - Distinguished Fellowships [9896]
Mary Switzer Research Fellowships - Merit Fellowships [9897]
IRFI Dr. Mubin I. Syed Scholarship and Mohtarama Afshan J. Syed Scholarship [5482]
Symantec Corp. **[9624]**
Symantec Research Labs Graduate Fellowships [9625]
Syncrude/Athabasca University Aboriginal Scholarships [9627]
Syncrude Canada Ltd. **[9626]**
Harry Taback 9/11 Memorial Scholarships [1429]

Hazaros Tabakoglu Scholarship Fund [1705]
The Tabat Scholarship Fund [4005]
TAC Foundation-3M Canada Company Scholarships [9768]
TAC Foundation-407 ETR Scholarships [9769]
TAC Foundation-Amec Foster Wheeler Scholarships [9770]
TAC Foundation-ATS Traffic Group of Companies Scholarships [9771]
TAC Foundation-Canadian Council of Independent Laboratories Graduate Student Scholarships [9772]
TAC Foundation-CCMTA Road Safety Scholarships [9773]
TAC Foundation-Cement Association of Canada Scholarships [9774]
TAC Foundation-Dillon Consulting Scholarships [9775]
TAC Foundation-Dr. Ralph Haas Graduate Student Scholarships [9776]
TAC Foundation-EllisDon Community College/CEGEP Scholarships [9777]
TAC Foundation-exp Scholarships [9778]
TAC Foundation-Golder Associates Ltd. Scholarships [9779]
TAC Foundation-HDR Corporation Graduate Student Scholarships [9780]
TAC Foundation-IBI Group Scholarships [9781]
TAC Foundation-ISL Engineering Scholarships [9782]
TAC Foundation-LEA Consulting Ltd. Scholarships [9783]
TAC Foundation-MMM Group Limited Scholarships [9784]
TAC Foundation-Municipalities Scholarships [9785]
TAC Foundation-Parsons Scholarships [9786]
TAC Foundation-Peto MacCallum Undergraduate & College Scholarships [9787]
TAC Foundation-Provinces and Territories Scholarships [9788]
TAC Foundation-SNC Lavalin Scholarships [9789]
TAC Foundation-Stantec Consulting Scholarships [9790]
TAC Foundation-Tetra Tech EBA Inc. Scholarships [9791]
TACS/Texas Tech University ISD Scholarships [9687]
John I. and Madeleine R. Taeni Scholarships [9452]
Tag and Label Manufacturers Institute (TLMI) **[9628]**
Tag and Label Manufacturers Institute Scholarships - Four-Year Colleges [9629]
Tag and Label Manufacturers Institute Scholarships - Two-Year Colleges [9630]
Tailhook Association (TA) **[9631]**
Tailhook Educational Foundation Scholarship Program [9632]
Taiwanese American Citizens League (TACL) **[9633]**
Taiwanese American Community Scholarships [9634]
Robert M. Takasugi Public Interest Fellowship **[9635]**
Robert M. Takasugi Public Interest Fellowship [9636]
Kei Takemoto Memorial Scholarships [173]
Talbert Family Memorial Scholarships [3111]
Tall Awareness Scholarships [8366]
Tall Clubs International (TCI) **[9637]**
Tall Clubs International Student Scholarships [9638]
Tall Ships America **[9639]**
Justice Stephen K. Tamura Scholarships [5545]
TANA Foundation Graduate Scholarships [9672]
Mitsuyoshi Tanaka Dissertation Award in Experimental Particle Physics [1094]
Janet Cullen Tanaka Scholarships [2096]
Alexander M. Tanger Scholarships [2372]
William J. Tangye Scholarships [5302]
Martha W. Tanner Memorial Scholarships [3022]
Hal Tanner Sr. Scholarships [10252]
Alex Tanous Foundation **[9641]**
Alex Tanous Scholarship Award [9642]
Frederick A. Tarantino Memorial Scholarship Award [9999]
Lee Tarbox Memorial Scholarships [174]

Targeted Research Initiative for Health Outcomes [3909]
Tarkanian Teacher Education Academy at Clark High School Scholarships [8367]
Tarkio College Alumni Association **[9643]**
Sheila Tarr-Smith Memorial Scholarships [8368]
Bud and Linda Tarrson Fellowships [422]
Bernard Michael Tarshis Memorial Scholarships for Jewish Studies [5588]
TaskEasy, Inc **[9645]**
TaskEasy Scholarships for Future Entrepreneurs [9646]
Jack Tate/ThinkCOLLEGE Scholarship Fund [4216]
Jordan B. Tatter Scholarships [6488]
Taylor/Blakeslee University Fellowships [3429]
Katharine Whiteside Taylor Bursary [7807]
Joshua C. Taylor Fellowships [9006]
Ryan "Munchie" Taylor Memorial Scholarships [6154]
Tom Taylor Memorial Scholarships to Spartan College of Aeronautics and Technology [175]
Charles "Buck" and Dora Taylor Scholarship [3689]
Betty & Charles Taylor Scholarships [10803]
RABC William Taylor Scholarships [3846]
The Ed Tayter Outstanding Citizen Scholarships [8238]
TCA-ACBH Scholarships [9812]
TCA Outstanding Graduate Student Awards [9695]
TCA Scholarship [9800]
TCA-UMD Scholarships [9813]
TCAdvance Scholarships [9814]
TCATA College Scholarship Program [9721]
TCDA Abbott IPCO Professional Scholarships [671]
TCDA Gandy Ink Professional Scholarships [672]
TCDA General Fund Scholarships [673]
TCDA Past Presidents Student Scholarships [674]
TD Bank Medical Education Scholarships [7290]
TD Meloche-Monnex Scholarships [2714]
Teacher Education Scholarships [1008]
Teacher Librarian Scholarships [2475]
Teacher of the Visually Impaired Loans [9556]
Teacher.org **[9647]**
Teammates Mentoring Scholarship Program [4567]
Tech Mastery Scholarships [8551]
TechChecks **[9649]**
TechChecks Business Leadership Scholarships [9650]
Technical Women's Organization Education Scholarships (TWO) [9652]
Technical Women's Organization (TWO) **[9651]**
Technology First **[9653]**
Technology Student Association (TSA) **[9655]**
Dwight Teed Scholarships [9612]
Marvin H. and Kathleen G. Teget Leadership Scholarships [9602]
Paul Tejada Memorial Scholarships [5514]
TELACU **[9658]**
Telecommunications Association of Michigan (TAM) **[9662]**
Telecommunications Association of Michigan Scholarship Fund [9663]
Telford Scholarships [40]
Tell Us Your Story Scholarships [10495]
Telluride Association (TA) **[9664]**
Telluride Association Summer Program Scholarships [9665]
Telugu Association of North America (TANA) **[9666]**
Temecula Valley Wine Society (TVWS) **[9674]**
Lee Teng Undergraduate Fellowships in Accelerator Science and Engineering [9903]
Tennessee Bar Foundation IOLTA Law School Scholarships [10176]
Tennessee Education Association (TEA) **[9676]**
Tennessee Trucking Foundation Scholarships [3254]
Mary L. Tenopyr Graduate Student Scholarships [9154]
Terra Foundation for American Art **[9679]**
The Terra Foundation Fellowships in American Art [9007]
Terra Foundation Fellowships at the Smithsonian American Art Museum [9680]
Terra Foundation Postdoctoral Teaching Fellowships at the Courtauld Institute of Art, London [9681]
Terra Foundation Postdoctoral Teaching Fellowships at the Institut National d'Histoire de l'Art, Paris [9682]

Terra Foundation Research Travel Grants [9683]
Terra Summer Residency Fellowships [9684]
Marc Tetalman, MD, Memorial Award [9227]
Steven M. Teutsch Prevention Effectiveness Fellowships [9921]
TEVA Canada Scholarship [2904]
Texas Association of Community Schools (TACS) **[9685]**
Texas Association of Developing Colleges (TADC) **[9688]**
Texas Computer Education Association (TCEA) **[9690]**
Texas Computer Education Association Professional Educator Grants [9693]
Texas Counseling Association (TCA) **[9694]**
Texas Elks State Association (TESA) **[9696]**
Texas Elks State Association Eagle Scout Scholarships [9697]
Texas Elks State Association Girl Scout Gold Award Scholarships [9698]
Texas Elks State Association Scholarships [9699]
Texas Health Information Management Association (TxHIMA) **[9700]**
Texas Music Educators Association (TMEA) **[9705]**
Texas Music Educators Association Past-Presidents Memorial Scholarships [9707]
Texas Mutual Insurance Co. **[9708]**
Texas Mutual Scholarship Program [9709]
Texas Scholarships of Academic Excellence [9559]
Texas Society of Professional Engineers (TSPE) **[9710]**
Texas Society of Professional Engineers Scholarships [9711]
Texas State Historical Association (TSHA) **[9712]**
Texas State Technical College Scholarships [176]
Texas Telephone Association (TTA) **[9718]**
Texas Telephone Association Foundation Scholarships [9719]
Textile Care Allied Trades Association (TCATA) **[9720]**
TFAS Congressional Scholarship Awards [4309]
TFI Latin America Media Arts Fund [9796]
Jim and Pat Thacker Sports Communication Internships [10253]
Anil and Neema Thakrar Family Fund No. 1 [4257]
ThanksUSA **[9722]**
ThanksUSA Scholarships [9723]
The Cover Guy Annual Scholarships [3463]
Theatre Guild Scholarship [9725]
Theatre Guild of Simsbury (TGS) **[9724]**
Theatre for Young Audiences USA (TYA/USA) **[9726]**
Dr. Peter A. Theodos Memorial Graduate Scholarships [4850]
Thermo Scientific Educational Scholarships [7172]
Thesaurus Linguae Latinae Fellowships (TTL) [9107]
THFC Medical Research Grants [4834]
Elizabeth R. Thomas Alumni Nursing Scholarship [8885]
Thomas & Betts Scholarship Awards [3847]
Barbara Thomas Bursary [5529]
Nadene M. Thomas Graduate Research Scholarships [297]
Charles C. Thomas Scholarship [1586]
Barber Owen Thomas Scholarships [8942]
C.R. Thomas Scholarships [7867]
Dorothy B. and Charles E. Thomas Scholarships [4625]
Rev. Chuck and Nancy Thomas Scholarships [9842]
Thome Foundation Awards Program in Age-Related Macular Degeneration Research [4824]
Thome Foundation Awards Program in Alzheimer's Disease Drug Discovery Research [4825]
The Honorable Raymond Thompson Endowed Scholarships [8006]
F. Christian and Betty Thompson Fellowships [7745]
Matilda B. Thompson Scholarship [4929]
Barbara and Howard Thompson Scholarships [5515]
Thompson Scholarships for Women in Safety [1430]
Dr. Andrew Thomson Prize in Applied Meteorology [2686]
Ken Thomson Scholarships [1906]
Thornberg/Havens Scholarships [3596]
Thomas P. Thornton Scholarships [5089]
Thunder Bay Community Foundation **[9728]**

Thurgood Marshall College Fund (TMCF) **[9734]**
Thurgood Marshall Fellowships Program [7345]
Dorothy J. Thurston Graduate Scholarships [4626]
TIAA **[9736]**
TIAC / Parks Canada Sustainable Tourism Scholarships [9760]
Raymond A. Tice Scholarships I [8733]
Raymond A. Tice Scholarships II [8734]
Tidewater Builders Association (TBA) **[9738]**
Tidewater Builders Association Scholarships [9739]
Tiftickjian Law Firm, P.C. **[9740]**
Tiftickjian Law Firm, P.C. Juvenile Justice Law School Scholarships [9741]
Tikvah Center for Law and Jewish Civilization **[9742]**
Tikvah Fellowships [9745]
Tikvah Fund **[9744]**
The AIWF/Patricia Tillinghast Memorial Scholarships [939]
Tillman Scholars Program [7901]
Louise Tillotson Teaching Fellowships [7306]
Louise Tillotson Teaching Professional Development Scholarships [7307]
Jack E. Tillson Scholarships [5470]
Eben Tisdale Fellowships [4310]
TMA Research Fellowships [6641]
TMCF Scholarships [9735]
Mario J. Tocco Hydrocephalus Foundation Scholarships [5028]
Richard Cecil Todd and Clauda Pennock Todd Tripod Scholarships [8082]
CSF Christopher Todd Grant Memorial Scholarships [3023]
Robert Toigo Foundation Fellowships [9747]
Robert Toigo Foundation (RTF) **[9746]**
Daniel B. Toll Memorial Scholarships [2518]
William Tomar Memorial Scholarships [2519]
The Adelle and Erwin Tomash Fellowship in the History of Information Technology [10201]
John L. Tomasovic, Sr. Scholarships [812]
Dr. Henrik and Wanda Tonning Memorial Scholarships [7291]
Took Trust Point Scholarship [8192]
George Torkildsen Literary Awards [10705]
Evald Torokvei Foundation Scholarships [10296]
Toronto and Region Conservation Authority (TRCA) **[9748]**
Toronto Rehab Scholarships in Rehabilitation-Related Research [9753]
Toronto Rehabilitation Institute **[9750]**
Toronto Rehabilitation Institute Graduate Student Scholarships - Ontario Student Opportunities Trust Fund (OSOTF) [9754]
Aram Torossian Memorial Scholarships [1706]
Ferdinand Torres Scholarships [824]
Tortuga Backpacks **[9755]**
Tortuga Backpacks Study Abroad Scholarships [9756]
Touchstone Special Achievement Scholarships [7588]
Tourette Association of America **[9757]**
Tourette Association of America Research Grant Awards [9758]
Tourism Industry Association of Canada (TIAC) **[9759]**
Touro Synagogue Foundation (TSF) **[9761]**
Town and County Club Scholarships [4773]
Charles A. Townsend Scholarships [7868]
Toyota Earth Day Scholarship Program **[9763]**
Toyota Earth Day Scholarships [9764]
Toyota Financial Services Point Scholarship [8193]
Toyota/TELACU Scholarships [9661]
The Joyce Tracy Fellowships [446]
Marie Trahan/Susman Godfrey Scholarships [9820]
TRALA Industry Scholarship Awards [9798]
Vera Tran Memorial Scholarships [10388]
Reuben Trane Scholarships [1334]
Trans Issues Internships - New York [4441]
Transamerica Retirement Solutions Leaders in Health Care Scholarships [5169]
Transatlantic Fellows Program [4400]
Translational Research Professorship [3387]
Transoft Solutions, Inc. Ahead of the Curve Scholarships (AOTC) [5221]
Transport Workers Union of America (TWU) **[9765]**
Transportation Association of Canada (TAC) **[9767]**

Transportation Association of Canada Foundation Scholarships [9792]
Traub-Dicker Rainbow Scholarships [9590]
Morton M. Traum Surface Science Student Awards [2157]
Edward Traurig Scholarships [10484]
Trelut Family Legacy Scholarships [2459]
Marie Tremaine Fellowships [2259]
Tri Delta Alpha Eta Scholarships [3559]
Tri Delta Alpha Rho Leadership Scholarships [3560]
Tri Delta Atlanta Alumnae Achievement Scholarships [3561]
Tri Delta Beta Gamma Memorial Scholarships [3562]
Tri Delta Houston Alumnae Chapter Graduate Fellowships [3563]
Tri Delta Northern Virginia Alumnae Chapter Scholarships [3564]
Triangle Coalition for STEM Education **[9793]**
Tribeca Film Institute **[9795]**
Tribute Fund Community Grant [9102]
Thomas and Glenna Trimble Endowed Scholarships [8007]
Tim Triner Letter Carriers Scholarship Fund [9539]
J.P. and Madeline Trinkaus Endowed Scholarships in Embryology [6263]
Tristin Memorial Scholarships [5996]
Johnny Trombly Scholarships [6572]
Mildred E. Troske Music Scholarships [4627]
Vincent Trotter Health Care Scholarships [8735]
Charlie Trotters's Culinary Education Foundation Scholarships [765]
Jo Anne J. Trow Scholarships [6697]
Truck Renting and Leasing Association (TRLA) **[9797]**
Truckload Carriers Association (TCA) **[9799]**
Truckload Carriers Association Scholarships [9801]
Trudeau Fellowships - Regular [8135]
Trudeau Fellowships - Visiting [8136]
Trudeau Foundation Doctoral Scholarships [8137]
William H. Truettner Fellowships [9008]
Harry S. Truman Scholarship Foundation (HSTSF) **[9802]**
TrustedPros Inc. **[9804]**
TrustedPros Scholarships [9805]
Trustees College Scholarships [6171]
Trustees Law School Scholarships [6172]
Norman J. Tschantz/Walter C. Deuble Scholarships [9540]
Tschudy Family Scholarships [5050]
TSHP R&E Foundation Scholarship Program [9807]
TSHP Research and Education Foundation **[9806]**
Tucker Family Scholarships [10254]
Jacki Tuckfield Memorial Graduate Business Scholarship Fund [6453]
Barry Tuckwell Scholarships [5346]
Richard R. Tufenkian Memorial Scholarships [1671]
Sam Tughan Scholarships [2739]
Edward Tuinier Memorial Scholarships [813]
Graydon A. Tunstall Undergraduate Student Scholarships [8049]
Earl S. Tupper 3-year Postdoctoral Fellowships in Tropical Biology [9039]
Turf and Ornamental Communicators Association (TOCA) **[9808]**
Turf and Ornamental Communicators Association Scholarship Program [9809]
Turkish Coalition of America (TCA) **[9810]**
Hans Turley Prize in Queer Eighteenth-Century Studies [1297]
Turner Family Scholarships [4217]
Jeff Turner-Forsyth Audubon Society Scholarships [10601]
James A. Turner, Jr. Memorial Scholarships [1525]
J.L. Turner Legal Association (JLTLA) **[9815]**
Mark and Vera Turner Memorial Scholarships [6068]
Emmett H. Turner Scholarships [3255]
Ira G. Turpin Scholars Fund [9541]
Tuscumbia Kiwanis Scholarship [7551]
Lydia Donaldson Tutt-Jones Memorial Research Grant [93]
Two Year/Community Broadcast Education Association Scholarship Awards [2373]
TxHIMA HIA-HIT Scholarship [9703]
TxHIMA Outstanding Student Scholarship [9704]
William R. Tyler Fellowships [3740]

Florence Tyson Grants to Study Music Pyschotherapy [1018]
U-M Alumnae Club (University of Michigan) Scholarships [4628]
UAA Accounting Club Scholarship [10075]
UAA Alaska Kidney Foundation Scholarship [10076]
UAA Alumni Association Scholarship [10077]
UAA College of Business and Public Policy Scholarships [10078]
UAA Friends of the Performing Arts Scholarship [10079]
UAA GCI, Inc. Scholarship [10080]
UAA Janice K. Barden Aviation Scholarships [6838]
UAA Kimura Scholarship Fund for Illustration [10081]
UAA Kimura Scholarship Fund for Photography [10082]
UAA Quanterra Scholarship [10083]
UAA RRANN Program Scholarships [10084]
UAB Health Policy Fellowship [10002]
UAF Alumni Association Scholarships [10100]
UAF College of Liberal Arts - Anchorage Daily News Journalism Awards [10094]
UAF Community and Technical College **[9821]**
UAF Community and Technical College Culinary Arts Scholarships [9823]
UC MEXUS-CICESE Graduate Student Short-Term Research and Training Program [10110]
UC MEXUS-CICESE Short-term Research & Training Program [10115]
UC MEXUS-CONACYT Collaborative Grants [10116]
UC MEXUS-CONACYT Doctoral Fellowships [10117]
UC MEXUS-CONACYT Postdoctoral Research Fellowships [10118]
UC MEXUS Dissertation Research Grants [10119]
UC MEXUS Grants for Dissertation Research [10111]
UC MEXUS Scholars in Residence Program - Graduate [10120]
UC MEXUS Scholars in Residence Program - Recent University Graduates [10121]
UC MEXUS Scholars in Residence Program - Visiting Faculty [10122]
UC MEXUS Small Grants for UC Faculty [10123]
UC MEXUS Small Grants for UC Postdocs [10124]
UC MEXUS Small Grants for UC Students [10125]
The UCSD Black Alumni Scholarship for Arts and Humanities [8736]
The UCSD Black Alumni Scholarships for Engineering, Mathematics and Science [8737]
UCT Scholarships [7686]
Morris K. Udall Foundation **[9824]**
Morris K. Udall Scholarships [9825]
UF Center for Latin American Studies FLAS Summer Fellowships [10133]
UFCW Local Union Scholarships [9847]
UH Manoa Starr Foundation Graduate Fellowships in Asian Studies [10138]
Ukrainian Canadian Professional and Business Club Scholarships in Education [2675]
Sandy Ulm Scholarships [4081]
The Ulman Cancer Fund for Young Adults **[9826]**
Ric Ulrich and Chuck Pischke Scholarships [8266]
UMBS Istock Family Scholarships [10190]
UMBS Returning Student Award [10191]
UMDF Clinical Research Fellowship Training Awards [9860]
Umialik Scholarships [10041]
UNC-CGI C.V. Starr Scholarships [2847]
UNCF/Merck Graduate Science Research Dissertation Fellowships, [6426], [9862]
UNCF/Merck Postdoctoral Science Research Fellowships, [6427], [9863]
Undergraduate/Graduate Scholarships [5315]
Undergraduate Session Assistants Program [7370]
Bettie Underwood Dental Assisting Scholarships [2831]
UNESCO-L'Oreal for Women in Science International Fellowships [6108]
UNH Alumni Association Legacy Scholarships [10209]
UNH Parents Association Endowment Scholarship Fund [10210]
Union of Marash Armenian Scholarships [1707]

Union Plus Scholarship Program [5451]
Unitarian Universalist Association (UUA) **[9830]**
United Engineering Foundation (UEF) **[9844]**
United Engineering Foundation Grants [9845]
United Food and Commercial Workers International Union (UFCW) **[9846]**
United Health Foundation National Association of Hispanic Nurses Scholarships [6758]
United Methodist Church General Board of Higher Education and Ministry (GBHEM) **[9848]**
United Methodist General Scholarships [9856]
United Methodist Youth Organization **[9857]**
United Mitochondrial Disease Foundation (UMDF) **[9859]**
United Negro College Fund (UNCF) **[9861]**
United Parcel Service Scholarships for Female Students [5195]
United Parcel Service Scholarships for Minority Students [5196]
United Parent Support for Down Syndrome **[9864]**
United South and Eastern Tribes, Inc. (USET) **[9867]**
United South and Eastern Tribes Scholarship Fund [9868]
U.S. Air Force ROTC **[9869]**
U.S. Air Force ROTC Express Scholarships [9872]
U.S. Air Force ROTC High School Scholarships [9873]
U.S. Air Force ROTC In-College Scholarships [9874]
U.S. Aircraft Insurance Group Professional Development Program (USAIG PDP) Scholarships [6839]
United States Army (U.S. Army) - Center of Miltary History (CMH) **[9875]**
U.S. Army Health Care **[9877]**
United States Army Warrant Officers Association (USAWOA) **[9879]**
United States Association for Energy Economics (USAEE) **[9882]**
U.S. Bank Scholarships [8738]
U.S. Bates Scholarship Program [5452]
U.S. BIA Indian Higher Education Grants [878]
U.S. Capitol Historical Society (USCHS) **[9885]**
United States Capitol Historical Society Fellowships [9886]
United States Department of Agriculture Animal and Plant Health Inspection Service (USDA APHIS) **[9887]**
U.S. Department of Commerce - National Oceanic and Atmospheric Administration (NOAA) **[9889]**
U.S. Department of Education - Office of Postsecondary Education **[9893]**
U.S. Department of Education - Office of Special Education and Rehabilitative Services - National Institute on Disability and Rehabilitation Research (NIDRR) **[9895]**
U.S. Department of Energy - Fermi National Accelerator Laboratory **[9898]**
U.S. Department of Energy - Lawrence Livermore National Laboratory (LLNL) **[9904]**
U.S. Department of Energy - Oak Ridge National Laboratory (ORNL) **[9906]**
U.S. Department of Energy - Office of Science **[9911]**
U.S. Department of Health and Human Services - Agency for Healthcare Research and Quality (AHRQ) **[9913]**
U.S. Department of Health and Human Services - Centers for Disease Control and Prevention (CDC) **[9916]**
U.S. Department of Health and Human Services - Health Resources and Services Administration (HRSA) **[9922]**
U.S. Department of Health and Human Services - National Heart, Lung, and Blood Institute (NHLBI) **[9925]**
U.S. Department of Health and Human Services - National Institutes of Health - National Library of Medicine (NLM) **[9927]**
U.S. Department of Health and Human Services - U.S. Public Health Service - National Institutes of Health (NIH) **[9929]**
The United States Department of State, Bureau of Educational & Cultural Affairs Fellowships [1199]
U.S. Environmental Protection Agency (EPA) **[9931]**

U.S. Environmental Protection Agency - National Exposure Research Laboratory (NERL) **[9934]**
U.S. Environmental Protection Agency - National Health and Environmental Effects Research Laboratory (NHEERL) **[9936]**
U.S. Environmental Protection Agency - National Risk Management Research Laboratory (NRMRL) **[9938]**
U.S. Environmental Protection Agency - Office of Research and Development - National Center for Computational Toxicology (NCCT) **[9940]**
U.S. Environmental Protection Agency - Office of Research and Development - National Center for Environmental Assessment (NCEA) **[9942]**
United States Geospatial Intelligence Foundation (USGIF) **[9944]**
United States Geospatial Intelligence Foundation Graduate Scholarships [9945]
United States Geospatial Intelligence Foundation High School Scholarships [9946]
United States Geospatial Intelligence Foundation Undergraduate Scholarships [9947]
U.S. Global Leadership Coalition **[9948]**
United States Golf Association (USGA) **[9953]**
United States Hunter Jumper Association (USHJA) **[9955]**
United States Judo Federation (USJF) **[9957]**
U.S. Medical Supplies **[9963]**
U.S. Medical Supplies' Medical Professionals of Tomorrow Scholarships [9964]
United States Naval Research Laboratory **[9965]**
U.S. Pan Asian American Chamber of Commerce (USPAACC) **[9967]**
United States Society on Dams (USSD) **[9970]**
United States Society on Dams Scholarships [9971]
United States Tennis Association Foundation **[9972]**
U.S.-U.K. Young Investigator Exchange Fellowship [376]
U.S. Ukraine Foundation (USUF) **[9983]**
U.S.-Ukraine Foundation (USUF) **[9979]**
United Student Aid Funds Inc. **[9985]**
UnitedAg **[9987]**
UnitedAg Scholarship Program [9988]
Unites States Institute of Peace (USIP) **[9989]**
Universal Studios Preservation Scholarships [2028]
Université de Montréal - Centre de Recherches Mathematiques (CRM) **[9992]**
Universités Canada **[9994]**
Universities Space Research Association (USRA) **[9996]**
University of Alabama at Birmingham School of Public Health - Lister Hill Center for Health Policy **[10001]**
University of Alaska Anchorage **[10048]**
University of Alaska Anchorage - Matanuska-Susitna College **[10087]**
University of Alaska **[10003]**
University of Alaska Fairbanks Alumni Association (UAFAA) **[10095]**
University of Alaska Fairbanks **[10093]**
University at Alaska Scholars Program [10042]
University at Albany, State University of New York - Center for Women in Government and Civil Society **[10101]**
University Aviation Association (UAA) **[10103]**
University of California, Berkeley - Institute of Governmental Studies (IGS) **[10107]**
University of California Institute for Mexico and the United States **[10109]**
University of California, Riverside - Bourns College of Engineering - Center for Environmental Research and Technology (CE-CERT) **[10112]**
University of California, Riverside - Institute for Mexico and the United States **[10114]**
University of California, Santa Barbara - Institute for Social, Behavioral, and Economic Research - Center for Nanotechnology in Society (CNS) **[10126]**
University of Colorado at Boulder - Natural Hazards Center **[10128]**
University Film and Video Association (UFVA) **[10130]**
University of Florida - Center for Latin American Studies **[10132]**
University of Florida College of Liberal Arts and Sci-

ences - Center for Women's Studies and Gender Research **[10134]**
University of Hawaii at Manoa **[10136]**
University of Hawaii at Manoa East-West Center Graduate Fellowships [10139]
University of Hawaii at Manoa Graduate Assistantship Awards [10140]
University of Hawaii at Manoa Graduate Student Organization Travel Funds [10141]
University of Hawaii at Manoa Japan Travel Bureau Scholarships [10142]
University of Louisville Alumni Association **[10143]**
University of Louisville Eagle Scout Scholarships [6932]
University of Maryland at College Park - Journalism Center on Children and Families (JCCF) **[10151]**
University of Massachusetts Dartmouth - College of Arts and Sciences - Center for Policy Analysis **[10153]**
University of Memphis **[10155]**
University of Michigan - Biological Station (UMBS) **[10178]**
University of Michigan - Center for the Education of Women **[10194]**
University of Michigan - Dearborn - Armenian Research Center (ARC) **[10197]**
University of Minnesota - Charles Babbage Institute Center for the History of Information Technology **[10199]**
University of Minnesota Office for Equity and Diversity - Women's Center **[10202]**
University of Nebraska-Lincoln - Institute of Agriculture and Natural Resources - Agricultural Research Division (ARD) **[10204]**
University of New Hampshire (UNH) **[10207]**
University of North Carolina School of Media and Journalism **[10211]**
University of Oregon (UO) **[10258]**
University of Oregon Dean's Scholarships [10260]
University of Oregon Diversity Excellence Scholarships [10261]
University of Oregon General University Scholarships [10262]
University of Oregon Presidential Scholarships [10263]
University of Oxford Department of Politics and International Relations - Reuters Institute for the Study of Journalism **[10264]**
University of Pennsylvania - School of Nursing - Center for Health Outcomes and Policy Research (CHOPR) **[10266]**
University of Pittsburgh Department of Biological Sciences - Pymatuning Laboratory of Ecology **[10268]**
University of Puget Sound LGBT Leadership Scholarships Fund [8664]
University of Saskatchewan - Native Law Centre of Canada **[10270]**
University Senior and Master's Program Scholarships [1644]
University of Southern Mississippi Eagle Scout/Gold Award Scholarship [6933]
University of Tennessee at Knoxville College of Arts & Sciences - Center for the Study of War and Society **[10273]**
University of Texas at Austin - Office of the Vice President for Research **[10275]**
University of Texas at Austin Special Research Grants [10276]
University of Toronto Accenture Scholarships [10297]
University of Toronto (U of T) **[10277]**
University of Toronto Nortel Institute Undergraduate Scholarships [10298]
University of Toronto SAC Undergraduate Grants [10299]
University of Virginia **[10300]**
University of Virginia - Institute for Advanced Studies in Culture (IASC) **[10307]**
University of Wisconsin--Madison **[10314]**
University of Wisconsin-Madison/CALS Minority Scholarships [10327]
University of Wisconsin-Madison Chancellor's Scholarships [10328]
University of Wisconsin-Madison National Merit Scholarships [10329]

University of Wisconsin-Madison Single Parent Scholarships [10330]
Upakar Indian-American Scholarship Foundation **[10337]**
UPE Scholarship Awards [10342]
Upper Left, Inc. **[10339]**
Upper Midwest Human Rights Fellowship Program [4996]
UPS Diversity Scholarships [1431]
Upsilon Pi Epsilon Association **[10341]**
Claudette Upton Scholarships [3787]
Urban Affairs Association (UAA) **[10343]**
Urban and Regional Policy (Comparative Domestic Policy) Fellowships [4401]
The Urban Scholarship Fund [9689]
CASFM-Ben Urbonas Scholarships [3132]
Urology Care Foundation/Astellas Rising Star in Urology Research Awards [10347]
Urology Care Foundation **[10345]**
US-Ireland Alliance **[10348]**
USA Freestyle Martial Arts Scholarships [8739]
USA Funds Access to Education Scholarships [9986]
USA/USA-Ukramerazha Scholarships [9982]
USA Water Ski Foundation **[10350]**
USAttorneys.com **[10352]**
USAttorneys.com Immigration Scholarships Essay Contest [10353]
USAttorneys.com National Scholarships Essay Contest [10354]
USAWOASF/Grantham University On-Line Scholarships [9880]
USAWOASF Regular Scholarships [9881]
USC Latino Alumni Association **[10355]**
USDA-NIFA-AFRI Merit Awards [9308]
USGA/Chevron STEM Scholarship Program [9954]
USGLC Internships - Communications [9949]
USGLC Internships - Government Relations [9950]
USGLC Internships - Outreach [9951]
USGLC Internships - Policy [9952]
USHJA General Scholarships [9956]
USPAACC Ampcus Hallmark Scholarships [9968]
USPAACC Denny's Hungry for Education Scholarship [9969]
USS Coral Sea CVA-43 Association **[10357]**
USS Coral Sea Remembrance Scholarships [10358]
USTA Serves College Education Scholarships [9977]
USTA Serves College Textbook Scholarship [9978]
Utility Workers Union of America (UWUA) **[10359]**
Utility Workers Union of America Scholarship Program [10360]
John D. Utterback Scholarship Program [322]
U.V.A. Faculty Fellowships [10313]
UW-Madison Engineering Diversity Scholarships [10331]
UW-Madison GLBT Alumni Council Scholarships [10332]
UW-Madison Reserve Officers Training Corps Scholarships [10333]
UW-Madison School of Education Minority Scholarships [10334]
VA AWWA Graduate Student Scholarships [1498]
VABANC Scholarships [10383]
Wallace Vail Scholarships [7337]
Vale Manitoba Operations Scholarships [9995]
Vale Master's in Engineering Scholarships [2625]
Marta Vallin Memorial Scholarships [3363]
ValuePenguin **[10361]**
ValuePenguin Scholarships [10362]
Valuing Diversity PhD Scholarships [983]
H. Wayne Van Agtmael Cosmetology Scholarship Fund [4551]
Winifred Van Hagen/Rosalind Cassidy Scholarship Award [2436]
Patricia Van Kirk Scholarships [8267]
Jacob and Rita Van Namen Marketing Scholarships [814]
Adolph Van Pelt Special Fund for Indians Scholarships [1836]
William P. Van Wagenen Fellowships [543]
Gary Vanden Berg Internship Grant [9482]
The Vander Putten Family Scholarships [3082]
Keith C. Vanderhyde Scholarships [4629]
John Vanderlee Award [2715]
René M. Vandervelde Research Grants [1845]

Vanier Canada Graduate Scholarships [3405]
Jacob R. and Mary M. VanLoo and Lenore K. VanLoo Scholarships [4630]
Dr. Csaba Oliver Vargha Medical Student Bursaries [7646]
Russell and Sigurd Varian Award [2158]
Varian Radiation Therapy Advancement Scholarship [1401]
Vascular Surgery Trainee Advocacy Travel Scholarship [9326]
Vector Marketing Canadian Scholarship Awards [10365]
Vector Marketing Corp. **[10363]**
Vector Marketing Scholarships [8079]
Vectorworks Design Scholarships [10367]
Vectorworks Inc. **[10366]**
Kodali Veeraiah and Sarojini Scholarships [9673]
VEF Fellowship Program [10380]
VEF Visiting Scholars Program [10381]
VelvetJobs **[10368]**
Ventana Medical Systems In Situ Hybridization Awards [7173]
Helen Veress-Mitchell Scholarship Fund [2788]
Graduate Fellowship Program - Peter Verhofstadt Fellowships [8836]
Vermont Paralegal Organization (VPO) **[10370]**
Vermont Paralegal Organization Scholarships [10371]
Vern Parish [964]
Chester M. Vernon Memorial Eagle Scout Scholarships [6934]
Dimitri J. Ververelli Memorial Scholarship for Architecture and/or Engineering [4851]
A. Verville Fellowships [9023]
Vesalius Trust (VT) **[10372]**
Vesalius Trust Student Research Scholarships [10374]
Veterans of Foreign Wars Scout of the Year [6935]
Veterans Health Administration - Office of Research and Development - Health Services Research and Development Service - Center for Organization, Leadership, and Management Research (COLMR) **[10375]**
Veterinary Orthopedic Society (VOS) **[10377]**
Veterinary and Pre-Veterinary Academic Scholarships [3647]
Zelda Walling Vicha Memorial Scholarships [1387]
Jill Vickers Prize [1909]
Vietnam Education Foundation (VEF) **[10379]**
Vietnamese American Bar Association of Northern California (VABANC) **[10382]**
Vietnamese American Scholarship Foundation **[10384]**
William F. Vilas Scholarships [10335]
Dr. Juan D. Villarreal/HDA Foundation Scholarships [4894]
Villers Fellowships for Health Care Justice [3958]
Susan Vincent Memorial Scholarship [6187]
Philip F. Vineberg Travelling Fellowships in the Humanities [6368]
Violin Society of America (VSA) **[10389]**
Violin Society of America Scholarships [10390]
Virgin Islands Bar Association **[10391]**
Virginia Dental Hygienist's Association Foundation **[10393]**
Virginia Historical Society (VHS) **[10395]**
Virginia Lakes and Watershed Association (VLWA) **[10397]**
Virginia Museum of Fine Arts (VMFA) **[10399]**
Virginia Museum of Fine Arts Visual Arts Fellowships [10400]
Virginia Society of Certified Public Accountants (VSCPA) **[10401]**
Virginia Tech Doctoral Scholarship [10406]
Virginia Tech Student Travel Award [1955]
Viscount Bennett Scholarships [5969]
Visible Minorities Scholarship [7207]
Vision Zero Auto Accident Prevention Scholarships [5951]
Vista Health Solutions **[10412]**
Vista Health Solutions' Scholarships [10413]
John D. Voelker Foundation **[10414]**
John D. Voelker Foundation Native American Scholarships [10415]
Von Ogden Vogt Scholarships [9843]

Miki Vohryzek-Bolden Student Paper Competition [10539]
Voices On Point Scholarship [8194]
Irma E. Voigt Memorial Scholarships [8943]
Paul A. Volcker Endowment for Public Service Research and Education [1116]
Chad Vollmer Scholarships [4631]
Voluntary Protection Programs Participants' Association (VPPPA) **[10416]**
The Sybil Jennings Vorheis Memorial Undergraduate Scholarships [4218]
Vorobek Point Scholarship [8195]
Abe Voron Scholarships [2374]
Dr. Edward G. Voss Memorial Scholarships [10192]
VPPPA June Brothers Scholarships [10419]
VSCPA Educational Foundation Graduate Scholarships [10407]
VSCPA Educational Foundation Minority Scholarships [10408]
VSCPA Educational Foundation Undergraduate Scholarships [10409]
VSCPA PhD Accounting Scholarships [10410]
W. Garfield Weston Foundation **[10420]**
WACE National Co-op Scholarship Program [10693]
Chapter 4 - Lawrence A. Wacker Memorial Scholarships [9198]
Dee Wacksman Scholarships [3024]
Jane and Gregg Waddill Memorial Adelphe Scholarship [5768]
Robert & Barbara Wade Scholarships [6069]
Percy W. Wadman, M.D. Scholarship [4291]
Wadsworth African Fellowships [10518]
Wadsworth International Fellowships [10519]
WAEPA Scholarship Program [10711]
Covington-Cincinnati/Northern Kentucky Alumni Club - Dane Wagge Scholarships [10149]
Nell and Spencer Waggoner Scholarships [10602]
Gary Wagner, K3OMI Scholarships [1762]
Jack H. Wagner Scholarships [6504]
Wagner-Torizuka Fellowships [9228]
Selman A. Waksman Endowed Scholarships in Microbial Diversity [6264]
Wal-Mart Foundation, Inc. **[10424]**
Jane C. Waldbaum Archaeological Field School Scholarships [1611]
Laramie Walden Memorial Fund [4219]
Margaret E. Waldron Scholarship Fund [4061]
Sue Walicki Nursing Scholarships [5516]
Helen Zick Walker Adelphe Scholarship [5769]
Gary Walker Memorial Scholarships [4266]
Arthur BC Walker Scholarships [7147]
Myrtle & Earl Walker Scholarships [9199]
Bruce A. Wallace Memorial Scholarships [2520]
Walmart Associate Scholarships [10425]
Martin Walmsley Fellowships for Technological Entrepreneurship [7627]
WALPA Lake Student Scholarships [10466]
Flis Walter and Anna Memorial Scholarship [8593]
Robert E. Walter Memorial Scholarship [6168]
Patty Walter Memorial Scholarships [3145]
Lynn McNabb Walton Adelphe Scholarhship [5770]
Harry Walts Memorial Graduate Scholarships [6136]
Dr. Frank and Audrey Wanamaker Medical Scholarships [7292]
War Memorial Doctoral Scholarships [6856]
Imogene Ward Nursing Scholarships [4079]
Judith Warner Memorial Scholarships [8369]
Warner Norcross and Judd L.L.P. (WNJ) **[10426]**
Warner Norcross & Judd Minority Scholarships [10427]
Earl Warren Scholarships [6648]
Colin Wasacase Scholarship [7659]
Washburn University School of Law **[10428]**
Washburn University School of Law Business and Transactional Law Center Scholarships [10432]
Washburn University School of Law Child and Family Advocacy Fellowships [10433]
Washington Association of School Business Officials (WASBO) **[10435]**
Washington City/County Management Association (WCMA) **[10437]**
Washington City/County Management Association Scholarships [10438]
Washington College Bound Scholarships [10471]
Washington CPA Foundation Scholarships [10452]
The Washington Group (TWG) **[10439]**

Washington Higher Education Coordinating Board - State Need Grants (SNG) [10472]
Washington Hospital Healthcare System (WHHS) **[10446]**
Washington Indian Gaming Association (WIGA) **[10449]**
Washington Society of Certified Public Accountants (WSCPA) **[10451]**
Washington Space Grant Consortium (WSGC) **[10454]**
Washington State Association for Justice (WSAJ) **[10457]**
Washington State Business Education Association **[10462]**
Washington State Lake Protection Association (WALPA) **[10465]**
Washington State Nurses Association (WSNA) **[10467]**
Washington State Nurses Association Foundation Scholarships (WSNF) [10468]
Washington Student Achievement Council **[10469]**
Washington University Law School Chancellor's Graduate Fellowships [10476]
Washington University Law School Olin Fellowships for Women [10477]
Washington University School of Law (WashULaw) **[10473]**
Vincent T. Wasilewski Scholarships [2375]
Water Environment Federation (WEF) **[10479]**
Water and Sewer Distributors of America (WASDA) **[10481]**
Waterbury Bar Association **[10483]**
Waterbury Bar Association Scholarships [10485]
George Waterman Memorial Scholarships [10453]
Stand Watie Scholarships [9343]
ASM Robert D. Watkins Graduate Research Fellowships [1373]
Watson-Brown Foundation **[10488]**
Watson-Brown Scholarships [10489]
Dr. James Watson Fellowship Program [4485]
Jeannette K. Watson Fellowships [10491]
Jeannette K. Watson Fellowships (JKW) **[10490]**
Thomas J. Watson Fellowships [10493]
Thomas J. Watson Foundation (TJW) **[10492]**
Glenn Watson Scholarships [9394]
George Watt Prize [26]
Wattpad **[10494]**
Wayne County Bank Scholarships [7552]
Wayne County Foundation Anonymous Scholarship Fund [10508]
Wayne County Foundation, Inc. **[10496]**
Wayne-Meador-Elliott Scholarships [7869]
Kurt Wayne Scholarships [4346]
WBA Bar President's Scholarships [10486]
WBA Paralegal/Legal Assistant Scholarships [10487]
WDHOF Undergraduate Scholarships in Marine Conservation [10640]
Richard M. Weaver Fellowships [5235]
Monica M. Weaver Memorial Fund [4062]
W.E.B. Du Bois Fellowships [7013]
John W. Webb Lecture Awards [1324]
Faye and Rendell Webb Scholarships [3112]
TCDA Cloys Webb Student Scholarships [675]
Allen and Loureena Weber Scholarships [9200]
Art and Dannie Weber Scholarships [10603]
Lester and Eleanor Webster Foundation Scholarships [9542]
Webster Society Scholarships [10478]
Sheldon Wechsler and George Mertz Contact Lens Residency Awards [418]
Kenneth G. Weckel Scholarships [6528]
WEDA Scholarship Program [10529]
WEF Canham Graduate Studies Scholarships [10480]
John V. Wehausen Graduate Scholarships for Advanced Study in Ship Hydrodynamics and Wave Theory [9218]
J.L. Weigand, Jr. Legal Education Trust Scholarships [10434]
Frank L. Weil Memorial Eagle Scout Scholarships [6936]
Arthur and Lila Weinberg Fellowship for Independent Scholars and Researchers [7425]
Alvin M. Weinberg Fellowships [9910]
Bertold E. Weinberg Scholarship [711]

Edith Weingarten Scholarship Program [1050]
Joel A. Weinstein Memorial Scholarships [5594]
The Bee Winkler Weinstein Scholarship Fund [9591]
William E. Weisel Scholarships [9201]
Susan C. Weiss Clinical Advancement Scholarships [9229]
Weissbuch Family Scholarships [8740]
Polaire Weissman Funds [6439]
Edward Kent Welch Memorial Scholarships [10604]
Welch Scholars Grants [1065]
James R. Welch Scholarship [1846]
Welder Wildlife Foundation Fellowships [10510]
Rob and Bessie Welder Wildlife Foundation **[10509]**
Sue Marsh Weller Memorial Scholarships [5113]
Dorothy Wellnitz Canadian Scholarships [1193]
Wells Fargo American Indian Scholarships - Graduate [883]
Wells Fargo Career Scholarship [10085]
Wells Fargo & Co. **[10511]**
Wells Fargo Point Scholarship [8196]
Wells Fargo Scholarships [8268]
Wells Fargo Veterans Scholarships Program [10512]
Jean Hess Wells Memorial Adelphe Graduate Scholarship [5771]
Jean Hess Wells Memorial Adelphe Scholarship [5772]
Donald M. Wells Scholarships [4632]
Wellstone Fellowships for Social Justice [3959]
Peter R. Weitz Prize [4402]
Francis X. Weninger Scholarships [10726]
Wenner-Gren Foundation **[10513]**
Wenner-Gren Foundation Dissertation Fieldwork Grants [10520]
Wenner-Gren Foundation Post-PhD Research Grants [10521]
John R. and Joan F. Werren Scholarships Fund [9543]
WESCO Student Achievement Awards [3848]
West Michigan Nursery and Landscape Association Scholarship Fund [4552]
West Virginia Coal Association (WVCA) **[10522]**
West Virginia Nurses Association District No. 3 Scholarships [7870]
West Virginia PTA (WV PTA) **[10524]**
West Virginia PTA Scholarships [10525]
West Virginia Space Grant Consortium (WVSGC) **[10526]**
Redlands Evening Lions Club - Barbara Westen Memorial Scholarships [8529]
Western Equipment Dealers Association (WEDA) **[10528]**
Western Golf Association (WGA) **[10530]**
Western Michigan Society of Health-System Pharmacists (WMSHP) **[10532]**
Western Michigan Society of Health-System Pharmacists Scholarships [10533]
Western Reserve Herb Society Scholarships [4866]
Western Social Science Association (WSSA) **[10534]**
Western Society of Criminology (WSC) **[10536]**
Western Society of Weed Science (WSWS) **[10540]**
Western Society of Weed Science Outstanding Student Scholarship Program [10541]
Western Washington University Alumni Association **[10542]**
W. Garfield Weston Awards for Northern Research [10421]
Weston Brain Institute International Fellowships in Neuroscience Program [10422]
Weston Brain Institute Rapid Response Program [10423]
Robert B. Westover Scholarships [4347]
Mary Elizabeth Westpheling - Long Beach Alumnae Association Memorial Scholarhips [5773]
Wexner Foundation **[10544]**
Wexner Graduate Fellowships/Davidson Scholars [10545]
Weyburn Credit Union **[10546]**
Frederick K. Weyerhaeuser Forest History Fellowships [4138]
WFI International Fellowships [10702]
Dr. William "Tim" Whalen Memorial Scholarships [7503]
Whan Memorial Scholarships [8080]

Edwyna Wheadon Postgraduate Training Scholarship Fund [6886]
Haemer Wheatcraft Scholarship [3690]
Stan Wheeler Mentorship Awards [5976]
Jerry Wheeler Scholarships [9377]
Paul A. Whelan Aviation Scholarships [10106]
Nellie Yeoh Whetten Award [2159]
WHHS Medical Staff Scholarships [10448]
Whidbey Island Giving Circle Scholarships [8269]
WHIMA Established Professional Scholarship [10623]
Whitaker-Minard Memorial Scholarships [7871]
Law Office of David D. White Annual Traumatic Brain Injury Scholarships [5947]
Wayne F. White and Bob Evans Legacy Scholarships [4170]
White Collar Defense Diversity Scholarships [8239]
Bradford White Corporation Scholarships [8165]
The Brian J. White Endowed Law Scholarships [8008]
Howard A. White Endowed Scholarships [8009]
Richard S. White Fellowships [4853]
White House Fellows [8223]
Mary Kean White Memorial Scholarship Fund [9544]
Paul D. White Scholarship [2173]
Portia White Scholarships [2292]
ACI Richard N. White Student Fellowships [712]
Whitehorse Shotokan Karate Club Scholarships [10804]
Robert B. and Sophia Whiteside Scholarships [3726]
Ann Cook Whitman Scholarships for Perry High School [4416]
Ann Cook Whitman Washington, DC Scholarships [4417]
Ann Collins Whitmore Memorial Scholarship (ACWMS) [8131]
Jane and Morgan Whitney Fellowships [6440]
Helen Hay Whitney Foundation Fellowships [10551]
Helen Hay Whitney Foundation **[10550]**
Why Get Your Blue On? Video Scholarship [10543]
Wi-Hi Class of '55 Scholarship [3189]
David Julian Wichard Scholarships [10255]
Alice Hersey Wick Scholarships [8944]
The L. Phil and Alice J. Wicker Scholarship [1763]
Tom Wicker Scholarships [10256]
Larry B. Wickham Memorial Scholarship for Graduate Studies [6608]
Louise Wachter Wickham Scholarships [4553]
Lois Widley Student Scholarships [5365]
WIEA Scholarships [10625]
Richard A. Wiebe Public Service Fellowships [7371]
Ethyl and Armin Wiebke Memorial Scholarships [10652]
Barbara Wiedner and Dorothy Vandercook Memorial Peace Scholarships [4639]
Edwin F. Wiegand Science and Technology Scholarships [8370]
Elmo Wierenga Alumni Scholarships [4633]
Timothy Wiese Memorial Scholarships [8754]
Elie Wiesel Foundation for Humanity **[10552]**
Fred Wiesner Educational Excellence Scholarships [2079]
WIFLE Regular Scholarship Program [10642]
WIGA Scholarships [10450]
Fred C. Wikoff, Jr. Scholarships [4220]
Teddy Wilburn Scholarships [3256]
Wild Felid Legacy Scholarships [10555]
Wild Felid Research and Management Association (WFA) **[10554]**
Wilder Dimension Scholarships for Advanced Study in Theatre Arts [3693]
The Wilderness Society (TWS) **[10556]**
Wilkinson & Company L.L.P. **[10558]**
Wilkinson and Company LLP Scholarships [10559]
Samuel S. Wilks Awards [1466]
Andrea Will Memorial Scholarships [8945]
Willamette Chapter Scholarship Awards [7702]
Willamette University **[10560]**
Willard & Spackman Scholarship Program [1051]
James B. Willett Educational Memorial Scholarship Award [10000]
M. William and Frances J. Tilghman Scholarships [3190]
S. William and Martha R. Goff Educational Scholarships [7872]

William Randolph Hearst Educational Endowments [6265]
The Williams Chorale **[10562]**
Williams Chorale Bacardi Fallon Performing Arts Scholarships [10563]
John G. Williams Foundation **[10564]**
Sidney B. Williams, Jr. Scholarships [942]
Rodney Williams Legacy Scholarships [10150]
BM1 James Elliott Williams Memorial Scholarship Fund [7922]
Alice Hinchcliffe Williams, RDH, MS Graduate Scholarships [10394]
E. E. Williams Research Grants [4873]
T. Franklin Williams Research Scholars Award Program [4804]
Aubrey L. Williams Research Travel Fellowships [1298]
John G. Williams Scholarship Fund [10565]
CSM Virgil R. Williams Scholarships [3871]
Dr. Dana Williams Scholarships [3113]
Gary and Gussie Williams Scholarships [10193]
Leon Williams Scholarships [8741]
Maxine Williams Scholarships [540]
Randy Williams Scholarships [8742]
Redlands Footlighters, Inc. - Merle and Peggy Williams Scholarships [8530]
Cenie Jomo Williams Tuition Scholarships [6721]
Lippincott Williams and Wilkins Scholarships [3058]
RS Williamson and Eliford Mott Memorial Scholarships [10549]
Edwin H. and Louise N. Williamson Endowed Scholarships [10605]
Mary Katherine "Kathy" Williamson Scholarship Fund [3273]
Beverly Willis Architecture Foundation Travel Fellowship [9086]
Gary S. Wilmer/RAMI Music Scholarships [3303]
Harriet Glen Wilmore Scholarship [4221]
Dr. Alice E. Wilson Awards [2632]
Glenn Wilson Broadcast Journalism Scholarships [7873]
The Edgar C. Wilson Fellowship [10274]
Woodrow Wilson International Center for Scholars **[10566]**
Saul T. Wilson, Jr. Scholarships [9888]
Bob Wilson Legacy Scholarships [2460]
Arthur N. Wilson, MD, Scholarships [991]
Ted G. Wilson Memorial Scholarships [8288]
William S. Wilson Memorial Scholarships [10043]
John Charles Wilson and Robert Doran Sr. Scholarships [5246]
Michael Wilson Scholarships [126]
Theo Wilson Scholarships [7783]
William E. Wilson Scholarships [9392]
Ross A. Wilson Science Scholarships [9733]
Walter C. Winchester Scholarships [4634]
Amos and Marilyn Winsand - Detroit Section Named Scholarships [1526]
Winston Build Your Future Scholarship [8808]
David A. Winston Health Policy Scholarship [2087]
Winston-Salem Foundation **[10568]**
Winston-Salem Foundation Scholarships [10606]
Winterhoff Scholarships [1774]
Winterthur Museum, Garden and Library **[10608]**
Winterthur Research Fellowships [10609]
Wire Reinforcement Institute (WRI) **[10610]**
John D. Wirth Travel Grants for International Scholars [1318]
Albert E. Wischmeyer Memorial Scholarships [9202]
Wisconsin Association for Food Protection (WAFP) **[10614]**
Wisconsin Athletic Trainers' Association (WATA) **[10616]**
Wisconsin Broadcasters Association (WBA) **[10620]**
Wisconsin Broadcasters Association Foundation Student Scholarships [10621]
Wisconsin Health Information Management Association (WHIMA) **[10622]**
Wisconsin Indian Education Association (WIEA) **[10624]**
Wisconsin Laboratory Association (WLA) **[10626]**
Wisconsin Laboratory Association Graduate Student Scholarships [10627]
Wisconsin Laboratory Association Technical Student Scholarships [10628]

Wisconsin Laboratory Association Undergraduate University Student Scholarships [10629]
Wisconsin Lawton Minority Retention Grants [10336]
William B. Wisdom Grant in Aid of Research [10634]
HCRTA/Glen O. and Wyllabeth Wise Scholarships [3025]
WLALA Scholarships [10647]
WNBA Eastman Grants [10668]
WOCN Accredited Nursing Education Scholarships [10715]
WOCN Advanced Education Scholarships [10716]
Woksape Oyate: "Wisdom of the People" Distinguished Scholars Awards [873]
Paul R. Wolf Memorial Scholarships [1809]
Emil Wolf Outstanding Student Paper Competition [7676]
Melissa J. Wolf Scholarship [10086]
Michael J. Wolf Scholarships [4635]
Wolf Trap Foundation for the Performing Arts (WTFPA) **[10630]**
Wolf Trap Grants for High School Performing Arts Teachers [10631]
The Wolf Trap Internship Program [10632]
Deborah Partridge Wolfe International Fellowships [10820]
Nona Hobbs Wolfe Memorial Scholarship [5774]
Thomas Wolfe Society (TWS) **[10633]**
Eleanor M. Wolfson Memorial Scholarship Fund [4063]
Wendy Y. Wolfson Memorial Scholarship Fund [4064]
Abel Wolman Fellowships [1492]
Woman In Rural Electrification Scholarships [9383]
The Woman's Club of Nashville Scholarship Endowment Fund [3257]
Women in Cancer Research Scholar Awards [475]
Women in Coaching National Coaching Institute Scholarships [3069]
Women in Defense, a National Security Organization (WID) **[10635]**
Women Divers Hall of Fame (WDHOF) **[10637]**
Women in Federal Law Enforcement, Inc. (WIFLE) **[10641]**
Women In Defense HORIZONS Scholarships [10636]
Women Lawyers' Association of Greater St. Louis (WLA) **[10643]**
Women Lawyers Association of Los Angeles (WLALA) **[10645]**
Women Marines Association (WMA) **[10648]**
Women on Par Scholarships [3938]
Women of Today's Manufacturing Scholarships [3304]
Women of WSAJ Bar Preparation Scholarships [10458]
Women's Army Corps Veterans' Association (WACVA) **[10653]**
Women's Army Corps Veterans Association Scholarships [10654]
Women's Business Enterprise National Council (WBENC) **[10655]**
Women's Club of Grand Haven Scholarships [4554]
Women's Health Research Foundation of Canada (WHRFC) **[10657]**
Women's Health Research Foundation of Canada Scholarship Program [10658]
Women's International Network of Utility Professionals (WiNUP) **[10659]**
Women's Italian Club of Boston Scholarships [4357]
Women's Jewelry Association (WJA) **[10662]**
Women's Jewelry Association Member Grants [10663]
Women's Leadership in Agriculture Scholarship Program [7574]
Women's Leadership Training Grant [9327]
Women's Missionary Council of the Christian Methodist Episcopal Church **[10664]**
Women's National Book Association (WNBA) **[10667]**
Women's Overseas Service League (WOSL) **[10669]**
Women's Overseas and Service League Scholarships for Women [10670]

Women's Research and Education Institute (WREI) [10671]
Women's Transportation Seminar (WTS) [10673]
Violet Wondergem Health Science Scholarships [4636]
Carolyn Wones Recruitment Scholarship Grants [3305]
Denis Wong and Associates Scholarships [7920]
Charles Fred Wonson Scholarships [10306]
Dr. Harold S. Wood Awards for Excellence [4349]
Wood County Bar Association Memorial Scholarships [7874]
Mary and Elliot Wood Foundation Graduate Scholarship Fund [4222]
Mary and Elliot Wood Foundation Undergraduate Scholarship Fund [4223]
Wood Fruitticher Grocery Company, Inc. Scholarships [201]
Rolla F. Wood Graduate Scholarships [8083]
Ed Wood Memorial Scholarship Awards [7703]
Hugh and Helen Wood Nepales Scholarships [2233]
Geoffrey H. Wood Scholarships [2740]
Irene Woodall Graduate Scholarships [778]
Woodcock Family Education Scholarship Program [306]
Woodex Bearing Company Scholarships [4373]
Frank and Betty Woodhams Memorial Scholarships [6422]
Guy A. Woodings Scholarships [10044]
Woodrow Wilson International Center for Scholars Fellowships [10567]
Woodrow Wilson National Fellowship Foundation (WWNFF) [10676]
Woodrow Wilson-Rockefeller Brothers Fund Fellowships for Aspiring Teachers of Color [10682]
Helen M. Woodruff Fellowships [1612]
Carter G. Woodson Institute for African-American and African Studies [10683]
Carter G. Woodson Institute Post-doctoral Residential Research and Teaching Fellowships [10684]
Carter G. Woodson Institute Pre-doctoral Residential Research Fellowships [10685]
Betsy B. Woodward Scholarships [1966]
Woody Guthrie Fellowship [2321]
Woodyard Family Scholarships [4568]
Marilynne Graboys Wool Scholarships [8611]
L and T Woolfolk Memorial Scholarships [3026]
Blanche E. Woolls Scholarships [2242]
Hawaii Chapter/David T. Woolsey Scholarships [5918]
Patty Wooten Scholarships [1852]
Worcester County Conservation District Annual Scholarships Program [10687]
Worcester County Conservation District (WCCD) [10686]
Worcester District Medical Society (WDMS) [10688]
Worcester District Medical Society Scholarship Fund [10689]
John W. Work III Memorial Foundation Scholarships [3258]
Working for Farmers' Success (WFS) [10690]
Working for Farmers' Success Scholarships [10691]
Workshops, Inc. and Stark MRDD Fostering Diversity Through Special Needs Scholarship Fund [9545]
World Association for Cooperative Education (WACE) [10692]
World Bank Group (WBG) [10694]
World Book Graduate Scholarships in Library and Information Science [2680]
World Council of Credit Unions (WOCCU) [10699]
World Forest Institute (WFI) [10701]
World Leisure Organization (WLO) [10703]
World Wildlife Fund (WWF) [10706]
Worldstudio AIGA Scholarships [10709]
Worldstudio Foundation [10708]
Worldwide Assurance for Employees of Public Agencies (WAEPA) [10710]
Donald Worster Travel Grants [1319]
Worthy Gemological Scholarships [10713]
Worthy Inc. [10712]
Wound, Ostomy and Continence Nurses Society (WOCN) [10714]
Wozumi Family Scholarships [8270]
WRI Education Foundation Scholarships - Graduate [10611]
WRI Education Foundation Scholarships - High School Seniors [10612]
WRI Education Foundation Scholarships - Undergraduate [10613]
Jean Wright-Elson Scholarships [8743]
Audrey L. Wright Scholarships [4637]
Davis Wright Tremaine 1L Diversity Scholarships [3535]
WSAJ American Justice Essay Scholarships [10459]
WSAJ Diversity Bar Preparation Scholarships [10460]
WSAJ Presidents' Scholarships [10461]
WSGC Community College Transfer Scholarships [10455]
WSGC Scholarships for Incoming Freshmen [10456]
WSSA Student Paper Competition [10535]
WTVD Endowment Scholarships [10257]
Wyatt, Tarrant & Combs, LLP, Dr. Benjamin L. Hooks Scholarship [10177]
WYCUP Scholarships [10700]
Wyeth Foundation Predoctoral Fellowship [9009]
Margaret Wyeth Scholarships [3306]
Wyeth-SUS Clinical Scholar Awards [9321]
Xavier Community-Engaged Fellowships [10727]
Xavier University [10717]
Xavier University Chancellor Scholarships [10728]
Xavier University Departmental Scholarships [10729]
Xavier University Honors Bachelor of Arts Scholarships [10730]
Xavier University Legacy Scholarships [10731]
Xavier University Presidential Scholarships [10732]
Xavier University ROTC Scholarships - Air Force ROTC [10733]
Xavier University ROTC Scholarships - Army ROTC [10734]
Xavier University Williams Scholarships [10735]
Xerox Corp. [10736]
Xerox Technical Minority Scholarships [10737]
Pang Xiaoyan Scholarships [2926]
Yale Graduate and Professional Students Research Fellowships [2215]
Yamhill County Farm Bureau Scholarships [7707]
Yankee Clipper Contest Club, Inc. Youth Scholarships [1764]
William J. Yankee Memorial Scholarships [1125]
Gwen Yarnell Theatre Scholarships [4028]
Yasme Foundation Scholarships [1765]
Minoru Yasui Memorial Scholarships [5560]
Marusia Yaworska Entrance Scholarships [10445]
Willa Yeck Memorial Scholarship Fund [6292]
Ralph Yetka Memorial Scholarships [10045]
Marilyn Yetso Memorial Scholarships [9829]
The YFU Americas Scholarships [10770]
YMF Scholarships [10762]
Joan C. Yoder Memorial Nursing Scholarships [10046]
York Art Association (YAA) [10738]
York Graduate Scholarships [10756]
York Regional Police Scholarships [5530]
York University - Schulich School of Business [10740]
Gary Yoshimura Scholarships [8379]
Jack and Edna May Yost Scholarships [4258]
Yottabyte [10757]
You Go Girl! Scholarships [8271]
Jessie Young Bursary Awards [1890]
Young Christian Leaders Scholarship Porgram [10759]
Young Christian Leaders Scholarships [10760]
Alma H. Young Emerging Scholar Awards [10344]
Young Investigators Achievement Award [5620]
Jeff Young Memorial Scholarships [10805]
Young Musicians Foundation (YMF) [10761]
Young People For (YP4) [10763]
Young People For Fellowships [10764]
Donnell B. Young Scholarships [308]
Pearl I. Young Scholarships [7499]
Elmer Cooke Young - Taylor Young Scholarships [4774]
Young Women's Alliance (YWA) [10765]
George D. Younger Scholarships [7394]
Yount, Hyde & Barbour Scholarships [10411]
Your Skin Is In College Ambassador Scholarships [6407]
Youth Affairs Committee Rising Star Scholarships [5531]
Youth Empowerment Summit Scholarships [6817]
Youth or the Environment Scholarships [2185]
Youth Leadership Scholarships [2469]
Youth Maritime Training Association (YMTA) [10767]
Youth Partners Accessing Capital (PAC) [354]
The Youth Scholarship Program [2871]
Youth for Understanding (YFU) [10769]
The Frank Der Yuen Aviation Scholarship [7789]
Yukon Conservation Society (YCS) [10771]
Yukon Delta Fisheries Development Association Scholarships [10047]
The Yukon Foundation [10773]
The Yukon Foundation Medical Laboratory Scholarships [10806]
Yukon Law Foundation [10807]
Yukon Law Foundation Scholarships [10808]
YWA Foundation Scholarships [10766]
Z/I Imaging Scholarships [1810]
Zagunis Student Leader Scholarships [6734]
Lisa Zaken Awards For Excellence [5197]
Dr. Marie E. Zakrzewski Medical Scholarships [5883]
Dr. Steven S. Zalcman Memorial Scholarships [5589]
James and Joy Zana Memorial Scholarships [4569]
Louis B. Zapoleon Memorial Scholarships [3027]
Zarley, McKee, Thomte, Voorhees, Sease Law Scholarship [3691]
The Zebra [10809]
The Zebra Safe Driver Scholarships [10810]
Zelle Hofmann, Voelbel and Mason, LLP [10811]
Urashi Zen Scholarships [8272]
The Zenith Fellows Award Program (Zenith) [377]
Zenko Family Scholarship Fund [4555]
Harry and Angel Zerigian Scholarships [1708]
Zeta Chapter Memorial Scholarship Awards [3307]
Zeta Phi Beta Sorority General Graduate Scholarships [10821]
Zeta Phi Beta Sorority General Undergraduate Scholarships [10822]
Zeta Phi Beta Sorority, Inc. [10813]
Zeta Sigma Project 2000 Scholarships [5775]
A.F. Zimmermann Scholarships [8050]
Blanche Raper Zimmerman Scholarships [10607]
Zimmermann Scholarships [9621]
Jacob Ziskind Memorial Fund for Upperclassmen [5104]
Morris L. and Rebecca Ziskind Memorial Scholarships [5029]
Lorraine Zitone Memorial Scholarship Fund [6293]
Amelia Zollner IPPR/UCL Internship Award [5210]
Zonta Club of Hilo [10823]
Zonta International Foundation (ZIF) [10825]
Ruth and Sherman Zudekoff Scholarships [3202]
Leo Zupin Memorial Scholarship Fund [4556]
Francis Sylvia Zverina Scholarships [4867]

WITHDRAWN

FOR REFERENCE
not to be taken from this building

CPSIA information can be obtained
at www.ICGtesting.com
Printed in the USA
FFOW04n0017211016
28683FF